FOREWORD

I am delighted to have been given this opportunity to write the foreword for the new edition of the Non League Club Directory and to welcome you to a new season of football, our national game.

The National Game Board (NGB) was formed as part of the Football Association's re-structuring a little over 3 years ago. Our remit is to develop football from the grass roots upwards, covering all players, referees, clubs and leagues below the Football League.

The NGB and everyone in the National Game Division at the F.A. has the core purpose of increasing the participation, quality and enjoyment of football.

"Participation" does not just mean playing the game, although we concentrate most of our efforts in encouraging more people to play. It applies to everyone in the game, including referees, volunteer officials, coaches and spectators.

The majority of NGB members are representatives of County Associations to which every league, club and referee is affiliated. Indeed, in most counties, their own council is dominated by league representatives, making a very strong link between leagues and the National Game Board.

We are all aware that the F.A.'s income from television will decline over the next few years but, importantly, the new contract does give the F.A. a secure income for 4 years. The National Game Board will be working to ensure that funds are available to develop the game across the country.

Although reduced income is leading to reduced distributions for prize money and facilities, 2003-2004 is likely to see 5 times the investment into non-league and schools football compared with just 5 years ago.

Through the F.A.Charter Standard programme we are striving to put qualified coaches into clubs and schools. Considerable success has already been achieved with over 18,500 coaches going through the F.A.level 1 qualification.

We remain determined, as do the Premier League and the Government, to put £60 million into the Football Foundation. With the full support of the National Game Board, the majority of this money goes straight into projects delivering huge improvements in facilities for players, officials and spectators.

We have come a long way in little more than 3 years but there is still much to do. The Board is committed to build on this early success. We need to do more to improve understanding in areas such as equality and child protection and we need to ensure that the facilities that are being built now are well maintained so that they are enjoyed, not just by the participants in football today, but also by those who will follow in increasing numbers in the years ahead.

I am sure that you will find the directory to be a valuable companion over the next 9 months. On behalf of all my colleagues on the National Game Board, I wish you a very enjoyable season.

Roger Burden

Chairman, F.A. National Game Board

ACKNOWLEDGEMENTS

When things looked bleak last year following the collapse of the Non-League Media, the support and general encouragement given to us by our readers and the old subscribers to Team Talk gave us the much appreciated confidence to concentrate once again on our original aims to promote all that's good within the 'family' of non-league football.

Obviously, we have appreciated Ladbrokes' magnificent enthusiastic support which has been channelled by Dave Greenwood.

Forbes Chapman, the well known A.F.A. ex player, coach and administrator (a legend in his own lunchtime), has looked after marketing and advertising matters, while the web site development has been enthusiastically re-organised by Andy Mullen with Steve Whitney calling on his outstanding knowledge of non-league clubs and players to provide the best possible flow of inside knowledge.

Despite a year of non-stop political manoeuvring and re-structural ideas, the leagues, clubs and county officials have been most co-operative as usual with help for this year's book.

The photographers have kept their enthusiasm and interest despite the lack of a monthly magazine to encourage their efforts, and I'm glad to say that the lads have managed to enjoy a few excellent 'relaxing' moments together during the year! My thanks go to them all: Peter Barnes, Graham Brown, Paul Carter, Andrew Chitty, Keith Clayton, Alan Coomes, Graham Cotterill, Paul Dennis, Tim Edwards, Keith Gillard, Ken Gregory, Tim Lancaster, Garry Letts, Peter Lirettoc, Eric Marsh, Dennis Nicholson, Francis Short, Colin Stevens, Neil Thaler, Darren Thomas, Roger Thomas, Roger Turner, Alan Watson, Bill Wheatcroft, Gordon Whittington, Mark Wood and Martin Wray.

Long serving readers will remember many excellent photos of Enfield and Barnet in their glory days, taken by John B Vass, Well, John retired to Scotland many years ago and has for some time supplied the photos for our Scottish section without receiving a mention in the annual acknowledgements. My apologies, and also my thanks to John for another super collection in this year's book.

Individual contributions to the Directory have again been supplied by John Anderson (Trophy & Vase Stats), Stewart Davison (Editor of The Scottish Non-League Review - contact 0141 5662 57210), John Harman (Conference), Arthur Evans (Match reports and photos), Mike Ford (Counties), Wally Goss and Mike Brown (A.F.A.), Keith Masters (Middlesex Wanderers), Mike Simmonds (Schools), Jen O'Neill (Womens Football), Dave Phillips (Isle of Man), A.J.Sarnecki (Pecking Order), Mike Wilson (General Stats and Ryman Football) and James Wright (Club stats, whose own Newsdesk and annual round-up of all the season's leagues and stats in his Newsdesk Annual are immensely popular. To all these enthusiasts, my sincere thanks for their valued contributions and general help.

It's obviously a special bonus for me to have my eldest son Michael back sharing with George Brown the House Editor's duties after a few years experience in Coventry and London, and we also welcome Robbie Hale who has taken over from Jenny in charge of office administration.

We have exciting targets for the year ahead and I'm sure with our excellent 'team' we can achieve most of them.

At the same time, we should be thoroughly enjoying ourselves within the very happy atmosphere of the non-league game. How lucky we all are!

CONTENTS

MATCH REPORTS, BREAKING NEWS AND RESULTS ACROSS THE PYRAMID.

FA Competitions	**09066 555 888**	**Dr Martens League ClubCall**	**09068 121 151**
Ryman League Newsline	**09066 555 777**	**Non-League Fixture Line**	**09066 555 950**
Unibond League Newsline	**09066 555 800**	**Womens Football Line**	**09066 555 871**

NATIONWIDE CONFERENCE

Aldershot Town	09066 555 855
Barnet	09068 121 544
Burton Albion	09066 555 883
Chester City	09068 121 633
Dagenham & Redbridge	09066 555 840
Exeter City	09068 121 634
Farnborough Town	09068 440 088
Gravesend & Northfleet	09066 555 844
Hereford United	09068 121 645
Margate	09068 800 665
Morecambe	09066 555 966
Stevenage Borough	09066 555 959
Shrewsbury Town	09068 121 194
Telford United	09066 555 982
Tamworth	09066 555 842
Woking	09066 555 070

DR MARTENS LEAGUE

Ashford Town	09066 555 854
Atherstone United	09066 555 905
Banbury United	09066 555 906
Bromsgrove Rovers	09066 555 860
Chippenham Town	09066 555 919
Clevedon Town	09066 555 942
Corby Town	09066 555 899
Crawley Town	09066 555 984
Dartford	09066 555 846
Dover	09066 555 801
Eastbourne Borough	09066 555 894
Evesham United	09066 555 863
Grantham Town	09066 555 975
Gresley Rovers	09066 555 978
Halesowen Town	09066 555 818
Hastings Town	09066 555 879
Hednesford Town	09066 555 880
Ilkeston Town	09066 555 980
King's Lynn	09066 555 802
Moor Green	09066 555 962
Newport IOW	09066 555 890
Nuneaton Borough	09066 555 848
Rothwell Town	09066 555 829
Rugby United	09066 555 971
Salisbury	09066 555 864
Stafford Rangers	09066 555 976
Stamford	09066 555 989
Taunton Town	09066 555 849
Tiverton Town	09066 555 876
Welling United	09068 800 654
Weymouth	09066 555 830
Worcester City	09066 555 810

RYMAN LEAGUE

Aylesbury United	09066 555 811
Basingstoke Town	09066 555 828
Bedford Town	09066 555 843
Billericay Town	09066 555 949
Bishops Stortford	09066 555 873
Braintree Town	09066 555 887
Bromley	09066 555 838
Canvey Island	09066 555 886
Carshalton Athletic	09066 555 877
Chesham United	09068 335 505
Croydon Athletic	09066 555 789
Croydon F.C.	09066 555 024
Egham Town	09066 555 946
Enfield	09066 555 845
Hampton	09066 555 814
Harlow Town	09066 555 889
Hayes	09066 555 968
Hendon	09066 555 836
Hitchin Town	09066 555 817
Kingstonian	09066 555 965
Kettering Town	09068 101 567
Leatherhead	09066 555 861
Leyton FC	09066 555 892
Leyton Pennant	09066 555 819
Maidenhead United	09066 555 813
Purfleet	09066 555 895
Romford	09066 555 841
Slough Town	09066 555 956
St Albans City	09066 555 822
Staines Town	09066 555 907
Sutton United	09068 121 537
Wingate & Finchley	09066 555 778

UNIBOND LEAGUE

Altrincham	09066 555 902
Barrow	09066 555 820
Bradford Park Avenue	09066 555 852
Gainsborough Trinity	09066 555 901
Guiseley	09066 555 839
Hyde United	09066 555 787
Runcorn	09066 555 972
Spennymoor United	09066 555 941
Southport	09066 555 875
Workington	09066 555 851

Eagle Bitter United Counties League

Buckingham Town	09066 555 974
St. Neots Town	09066 555 917

Hampshire League

Poole Town	09066 555 884

Foresters Essex Senior League

Enfield Town	09066 555 908

Rich City Sussex County League

East Grinstead	09066 555 823

Jewson Eastern Counties League

Wisbech Town	09066 555 865

Jewson Wessex League

Brockenhurst	09066 555 937
Fareham Town	09066 555 874
Lymington & New Milton	09066 555 943

North West Counties League

Clitheroe	09066 555 979
Warrington Town	09066 555 779

OTHER LEAGUES & ASSOCIATIONS

Bexley & District League	09066 555 781
Camberley Sunday League	09066 555 809
Coronation League	09066 555 859
Croydon Sunday League	09066 555 862
Gravesend Boys League	09066 555 869
Kent Schools FA	09066 555 928
Sutton Coldfield & District League	09066 555 784
Tandridge Junior League	09066 555 795

A Quote Insurance Reading Football League	09066 555 868
Albany Northern League	09068 121 542
Banks Brewery League	09066 555 872
Bass Brewers Kent League	09066 555 856
Cherry Red Records Hellenic League	09066 555 812
Eagle Bitter United Counties League	09066 555 885
Essex & Herts Border Combination	09066 555 903
Herts Senior County League	09066 555 832
Jewson Eastern Counties League	09068 121 543
Jewson Wessex League	09066 555 870
Midland Combination	09066 555 882
Midland Football Alliance	09066 555 866
Minerva Spartan South Midlands League	09066 555 881
North West Counties League	09066 555 944
Screwfix Direct League	09066 555 825
West Lancashire League	09066 555 831

GENERATE REVENUE FOR YOUR CLUB, LEAGUE OR ASSOCIATION WITH YOUR OWN PREMIUM RATE LINE. CALL DAVE BODDY ON 01386 550 204 NOW!

On ITV p524

Sportslines ClubCall, Avalon House,
57-63 Scrutton Street, London EC2A 4PF.
Calls cost 60p per min.

Yeovil Town outstanding and Play -Offs a Great Success

THE first season in which two clubs were programmed to leave the Conference in place of two relegated Division Three clubs put the pressure well and truly on the Chairmen and Managers of all Conference outfits with any sort of ambitions, from the very start of the campaign.

The possibility of a play-off place would surely keep the competition lively right up to the last day. And possibly all end of season games could turn into vital promotion or even relegation battles, as there were still three clubs, who would lose their Conference places as well as the four play off places to claim.

With all to play for, the season started with an enthusiastic fanfare. But it wasn't long before it became very clear that Yeovil Town were in a class of their own at the top and,as luck would have it, the thrilling fight for the next four places fizzled out completely as Morecambe, Doncaster Rovers, Chester City and, thanks to a wonderful new year run, Dagenham & Redbridge qualified for the history making play offs three weeks before the end of the season.

If qualification was a little flat, then the games themselves were absolutely thrilling. The semi-finals were not decided until penalty shoot outs at the end of the second tie and after extra time had been played. The Daggers edged out Morecambe and Doncaster Rovers just pipped Chester City. In the final Dagenham pulled back to equalise and force extra time having trailed by two goals and, after missing chances for a golden goal themselves, they suffered terrible disappointment for the second successive year as Rovers sent their fans home deliriously happy with a vital goal that returned them to the Football League.

The Yorkshire club had been relegated in a terrible state, with their share of thoroughly unpleasant supporters who were not a welcome sight around the Conference grounds. But, as the club slowly recovered, it was good to see their fans also adapting to the better manners and general attitudes of non-league culture, and Doncaster Rovers seemed to be enjoying themselves on and off the field as they recovered and built up their strength to challenge for a return to the Football League. Well, they are back and deservedly so. Hopefully, the return of the followers who did Rovers no favours at the play off final, will not be a handicap to the club in the future, as the side's' recovery and triumph is a wonderful example of how the promotion and relegation system can be used successfully.

The season however belonged to Yeovil Town, whose young squad had benefited from two seasons of fighting it out at the top of the Conference and, of course, the confidence boosting F.A.Trophy triumph at the end of the previous season at Villa Park. A squad originally brought together by David Webb, and developed by Colin Addison, had been lovingly nurtured by a dedicated, understanding manager and father figure in Gary Johnson. If all three managers had added their own vital characteristics to the squad, one man who remained all through was Steve Thompson, the permanent right hand man who is probably the non-league game's most experienced and successful player/coach.

Gary Johnson had added the final touches to complete one of the very best non-league squads ever brought together. But the fact that he had big money to use and the renowned Huish Park pitch was completely relaid to give a perfect playing surface was thanks to the club's owner, Jon Goddard-Watts. With a small, fast, ball playing mid field the opposition was regularly out passed and out-skilled on a perfect pitch and it was no surprise that Yeovil remained unbeaten in the Conference at home all season, and of course the team achieved a record points total and scored 100 goals in their 42 games.

Gary also helped to educate the home supporters to have patience, especially when the visiting opposition put ten men behind the ball and goals proved difficult to get. The Yeovil fans grew to love their manager and by the end of season you could even see the older followers joining in to sing Gary's special song.

The future looks good providing Mr Goddard-Watts, the ex Screwfix millionaire, remains to look after financial matters. The last two years trading figures shows that a deficit of over £400,000 was recorded for each campaign, so the owner, who only discovered his love for the game in his seventies and previously knew nothing about football has proved that generous loans have been vital and can bring success provided the right managers are in charge of football matters. In Yeovil's case this is exactly what has happened and, hopefully, the owner will be happy to allow Yeovil Town to owe him over a million as they settle down to recoup finances through the Football League.

The season closed with Yeovil's total of England 'capped' players reaching nine with Gavin Williams a Welsh International and fellow countryman Kevin Gall injured, while Michael McIndoe from Scotland, the Conference Player of the Year, was not considered by his country as he wasn't playing in the Highland or East of Scotland Leagues! All these players are signed on and ready for the big adventure in the Football League.

New structure for 'Pyramid of Non-League Football'

The National Game structure has caused all sorts of arguments and stress for the officials of the senior leagues and the Football Association responsible for finalising the new pyramid for football below the Nationwide Third Division. The main points of contention were the number of divisions in the levels below the proposed Conference Division Ones North and South and who would be in charge of their administration.

Even the viability of the Two Conference regional First Divisions causes a few worries as the balance of qualifying clubs was so biased towards the South that outfits such as Worcester City and Bedford Town could be facing journeys to Spennymoor United and Lancaster City.

The Football Association's summer A.G.M. passed the idea for a 1-2-3-4 structure above twelve to fourteen regional leagues. This appeared to confirm that the four competitions feeding the original three Premier divisions of the Dr Martens, Ryman and Unibond will be covering the North (Unibond), Midlands (Dr Martens), South West (Dr Martens) and South Eastern (Ryman).

As there are many more southern based clubs in the Dr Martens and the Ryman League worthy of Conference Division One status (compared with the northern sides) it will take some deep thinking to prevent many southern outfits from appearing to be going backwards, possibly after many seasons of efforts to improve their clubs both on and off the field.

In principle the idea of more regional competitions is sensible but is this the right answer? I hope so for the sake of non-league football that it is, but I sense there will be some tinkering with the plans before they are fully accepted.

Paul Fairclough takes over as England Manager

After five successful seasons in charge, John Owens stood down as England's National Game squad manager and was replaced by Paul Fairclough, who had enjoyed such a successful time when originally manager of Stevenage Borough. His reign got off to a very awkward start as once again Conference clubs did not find themselves in a position to release England's first choice players, despite the fixtures being arranged originally in the allocated 'international weeks' in the season's calender. So the squads selected for the Belgium trip comprised Under 23 players and those from the Dr Martens, Ryman and Unibond Leagues were picked to visit Italy. These games were lost, but our unbeaten record against Holland was retained thanks to a 0-0 away draw with a stronger squad, which still wasn't a first choice selection.

The Four Nations tournament was hosted by the holders Wales, and the week turned out to be a great success. Paul Fairclough was able to pick a very strong squad and only lost three from his original selection. Five of the confident Yeovil club gave the side a special presence and a Kirk Jackson hat trick in the first game against a weakened Irish team set the standard for the week. A battling 2-1 victory was achieved against Wales and for the last game Fairclough kept his promise to the squad by ensuring every member started at least one game. A 1-1 draw secured a comfortable championship win and left everyone looking forward to next year's week in Scotland, who improved with every match.

Unique F.A.Trophy Competition

The 2002-2003 F.A.Trophy competition was unique, as no Conference club featured in the semi-finals. Obviously, a number were eliminated by their colleagues as Yeovil Town beat Hereford United, Morecambe and Northwich Victoria, Halifax Town achieved a spectacular 4-1 victory over Yorkshire rivals Doncaster Rovers, consistent Trophy battlers Forest Green Rovers beat Barnet 4-2 and Southport eliminated Dagenham & Redbridge after a replay and penalties. However, if standards in the Conference are improving then so too are they in the three premier feeder leagues.

Tamworth inspired by skipper Mark Cooper and exciting young striker Scott Rickards produced consistent form to knock out Accrington Stanley (now in the Conference) 4-1 (H), Nuneaton Borough 3-0 (H), Stevenage Borough 3-0 (H), Margate 2-0 (A) and Farnborough Town 2--1 (A) before eliminating Havant & Waterloovile in the semi-finals, 1-0 & 1-1.

Not surprisingly, the Lambs from just up the road from Villa Park were red hot favourites. Burscough were having a poor season in the Unibond League, but they had beaten Yeovil Town 2-0 at Huish Park. So surely they could play! On the day they did just that and, inspired by manager Shaun Teale and goalpoacher Gary Martindale, they produced a wonderful display to deserve their famous victory and help create one of the Trophy's best ever occasions.

If Burscough, Gloucester City and Aylesbury United performed well above expectations in the Trophy, then the two finalists at Upton Park in the Vase Final were probably two of the competition favourites. Brigg Town had won at Wembley and A.F.C. Sudbury had reached the semi-final in the previous campaign. An early goal lifted the occasion and everyone enjoyed the match and the excellent way in which West Ham United presented the occasion with style and efficiency .

Favourites reach Vase Final

It was a great pity that two of non-league football's big events; (the Vase Final and the Conference play offs) should both have to be played on the same afternoon. We have few enough special days as it is and these events are two of the real highlights of the season. Another disappointment was the way that in last season's F.A.Vase Third Round (usually an open draw halved on a north and south basis) was split into three to the detriment of the twelve poor South West Clubs who were forced to eliminate each other in six all western ties. For an area which had produced five finalists in the last six years, this new system didn't even reward their third round clubs with the chance of meeting new opposition and travelling to fresh areas of the country, which is the thrill of the Vase and the fun enjoyed by sides reaching the later rounds. Some of those clubs beaten by their neighbours, but possibly strong enough to have survived against opposition from other geographical areas, may have lost their previous exemptions.

The good news for non-league clubs is the increase in prize money in the F.A.Trophy and F.A.Vase. A lot of fuss has been made about the loss of possible revenue from the early rounds of the F.A.Cup, but anyone closely involved with smaller outfits realised that the amazing win bonuses for early F.A.Cup victories bordered on the obscene. The new prize money is much more realistic, and the Vase and Trophy increases are very welcomed as sensible rewards for successful clubs in those competitions.

The F.A.Cup produced some excellent headlines with Vauxhall Motors' victory over Q.P.R., Team Bath's qualification for their First Round battle with Mansfield Town and Harrogate Railway taking on Bristol City, being the pick of the minnows.

Two F.A.Cup Fourth Roundrepresentatives

Conference clubs to enhance their reputations were Dagenham & Redbridge for the third year running, as they surpassed their previous two seasons efforts by reaching the Fourth Round and only losing 0-1 in injury time. Junior MacDougald scored in the Third Round for the third consecutive year, which must be a record for a non-league player. Farnborough Town drew Arsenal at home in the second round, but played the game at Highbury in a non-event which was a disappointment to all concerned except manager/chairman Graham Westley, who was able to recoup some of his investment before taking half the squad with him to struggling Stevenage Borough.

The Football Association has endured a much publicised year of great difficulties. A change of Chief Executive and the loss of many staff in drastic cuts lowered morale on a grand scale and the constant worry of the Wembley project costs created a dismal atmosphere at the game s headquarters. So, while finance is the main worry at Soho Square, it is good to hear that new Chief Executive Mark Palios will find the time to deal with the problems and needs of the non-league game,which after all makes up 96 per cent of this country s football F.A.staff running the day to day departmental work have grown up with the job and know the problems inside out as they have all been seen before. But hopefully the trend in recent years to introduce an influx of marketing and financial executives from well known agencies and companies on huge salaries to sort out football matters they just do not understand, will now disappear.

Some executives also found it very difficult and uncomfortable to request help from people who do know the game, preferring to turn to expensive agencies whose staff probably knew even less than they did. I am sure the present leaders at the Football Association will have different ideas..

It appears that the Conference has never been more vibrant, the three feeder leagues near the top of the pyramid are better on and off the field and their clubs have shown excellent quality and character. The Vase level outfits are improving fast and their new inter league competition will be a great addition to the season s fixture list.

Where are the knowledgeable personalities who genuinely love the non-league game and have the experience to set an example and show the leadership that we look for from the Football Association ?

The Directory Survives and Ladbrokes support greatly appreciated

I m pleased to say that The F.A.Non League Club Directory 2003 (the 25th Edition) did come out, albeit a bit late and was well received.

Greenway Media plc, who took over from the defunct Non League Media plc as publishers of The Non-League Newspaper, have seen it go from strength to strength, giving our level of the game an excellent Sunday read as it covers all areas of the country.

This Diary has been published earlier this year and you will see that it covers the months of August 2003 to December 2004. A new edition will appear at the start of every season and hopefully, if you find it useful and enjoyable, you will ensure you do not miss a year!

With new structuring of our leagues our new pyramid poster will be of particular interest and like our Directory and Diary Ladbrokes have helped us with the production of all our ideas. Ladbrokes Fair play awards are proving very popular and their all round support for football at non league level is greatly appreciated.

Our Ladbrokes Fair Play Non-League Club has been an immediate success and we hope we will be getting to know many of the members at regional functions during the year. Look out for the members ties - they are a bit special! The members magazine will be out early in the 2003-2004 season; it will be called The Ladbrokes Fairplay Magazine featuring The Non--League Knowledge . It will not be recording news, transfers and results but will include all types of features with plenty of photos from our special team of photographers, who did so well with Team Talk and still supply the Directory.

Another very popular Ladbrokes innovation last season was a National Non-League Quiz.Every club was sent an attractive poster which gave teams of four a chance to qualify for the special Ladbrokes Quiz and F.A.Trophy Final week-end in the West Midlands. The successful eight clubs were Altrincham, Barnet, Guiseley, Hertford Town, Ilfracombe Town, Rugby United, Winchester City and winners Forest Green Rovers who beat Altrincham by one point in a thrilling final.

The planned series of regional league histories covering the last 25years have been put back to ensure sufficient advertising and sponsorship revenue is obtained to cover publishing costs. But one book you must look out for at Christmas is You Have to Love It, an amusing pictorial record of a typical matchday at a non league club. It will include about 200 photos supplied by our team of stars. I am sure you will recognise the many funny situations and, of course, you will also know many of the personalities featured from all over the country. If any book sums up the fun, the hard work, the pressures and the enthusiasm of our football then it is You have to Love It .

So, it s been a difficult year but an enjoyable one. Ladbrokes support for the Directory, The Non-League Club, The DIary , The Pyramid Poster and the National Non-League Quiz has been uplifting and very satisfying and we hope the new magazine will prove an enjoyable and different read alongside the excellent Non-League Paper.

It has always been my aim to promote non-league football as thoroughly as possible, in many different and enjoyable ways. Hopefully, we are succeeding, but suggestions and new ideas are always welcome.

TONY WILLIAMS

get all the latest news on the

COMPETITIONS NEWSLINE

Updated daily with Draws, Match Dates, Venue Changes, Kick-off Times and Results for The Seven FA Competitions.

- Weekend results on Newsline after 6.30pm
- Midweek results on Newsline after 10.00pm
- Monday Cup draws on Newsline after 1.00pm.

09066 555 888

Presented by Tony Incenzo

Marketed by Sportslines, Scrutton Street, London EC2A 4PJ
01386 550204

Calls cost 60p per minute at all times.

Call costing correct at time of going to press (June 2003).

NON-LEAGUE PUBLICATIONS GET BETTER & BETTER

WEEKLY:

FOOTBALL TRAVELLER
Twenty pages (ALL the Weekly Fixtures) £1.25 reach - (01386 853288) - Bill Berry, Top O' The Bank, Evesham Road, Broadway, Worcs., WR12 7DG.

THE NON-LEAGUE PAPER
Sunday Paper giving all results and news regarding non-League football - All newsagents - Price - £1.20 - David Emery - Editor, The Non-League Paper, 2nd Floor, Hill House, Highgate Hill, London, N19 5NA. (0207 6877678).

BRISTOL SOCCERWORLD
All the results, league tables and fixtures for your league every week - 50p - M. B. Brown - Editor, Bristol Soccerworld, P.O. Box 72, Patchway, Bristol, BS34 8HT - 0117 969 5487 (T) - 0117 969 4544 (F) e-m: www.bristol-soccerworld.com

MONTHLY:

EVERYTHING FOOTBALL
Two smart magazines Sunday Only and Park Life have featured Sunday football and junior Saturday competitions respectively. So, as there are over 500 different leagues and F.A. Competitions, the hard working publisher, Mark Kettlety decided to merge the two and successfully brought out a 96 page magazine called `EVERYTHING FOOT-BALL' costing £2.50.
Any queries regarding subscriptions should be sent to Mark at 23 Lancer Way, Billericay, Essex, CM12 0XA.

BUREAU OF NON-LEAGUE FOOTBALL
Monthly update of league tables and non-league cup competitions. Mike Ford, B.N.L.F., 173 Leytonstone Road, London, E15 1LH (0208 534 0423 P/F). Annual Subscription (UK) £21.95 (EC) £22.95 (International) £25.50

WELSH FOOTBALL
Edited by Dave Collins, Welsh Football, 57 Thornhill Road, Cardiff, CF14 6PE - £2.00 each - (029 2075 3179) email welshfootball@lineone.net

EVERY SIX WEEKS:

NORTHERN VENTURES NORTHERN GAINS
The Northern League Magazine - Price - 30p - Subscriptions £3.50 for six issues including postage. Available from Peter Lax, 21 Carlton Avenue, Billingham, Cleveland.

QUARTERLY:

GROUNDTASTIC
The excellent Football Grounds Magazine - Vince Taylor, 21 Tiptree Grove, Wickford, SS12 9AL - (01268 730076) - email: vtbrooklands@btinternet.com - Price £4.20 each (including postage) - cheques made payable to Groundtastic

YEARLY:

THE CHERRY RED NON-LEAGUE NEWSDESK ANNUAL - (Usually available in May)
Compiled by: James Wright, Non-League Newsdesk email james@nlnewsdesk.co.uk - Price £4.00 + £2.00 P&P (Normal Price - £6.95 + P&P) Cheques/PO made payable to Non-League Newsdesk Annual and sent to James Wright, 6 Harp Chase, Shoreditch Road, Taunton, TA1 3RY. (01823 324938)

PYRAMID FOOTBALL GUIDE TO NON-LEAGUE (August)Edited by Martin Whybrow. Contains lively reviews and features on non-league topics and special sections on all Conference and Premier Feeder clubs. Also contains well presented ground photos, club colours and previews for the coming season. An excellent new addition to the non-league library. 190 pages £12.95. IBS Publishing: Tel No: 01303 262636 Fax: 01303 262646

The supporters guide to NON-LEAGUE FOOTBALL GROUNDS 2004.
Featuring all clubs in the four senior competitions with comprehensive ground stats and photos.Full details from: John Robinson, Soccer Books Ltd.,72 St Peters Avenue, Cleethorpes,N.E.Lincolnshire.
Tel : 01472 696226 Fax: 01472 698546. WEb site: www.soccer-books.co.uk e-mail: info@soccer-books.co.uk

F.A. NON-LEAGUE CLUB DIRECTORY - (Normally available in September)
Over 1,000 pages of information, statistics, 700 photos, club details and much much more. Cost £19.95 (including postage). Can be purchased from Tony Williams Publishing, Helland, North Curry, Taunton, Somerset, TA3 6DU. (01823 490684 or 01823490080) Discounts are available for multiple books - email: tonywilliams2812@aol.com
Also available from your local bookshop.

Tony Williams

Educated at Malvern College, one of the country's best football schools in the late sixties, he represented England Under 18 against Scotland at Celtic Park before serving as an administrative officer in the Royal Air Force for five years.

He was on Reading's books from the age of 16-22, but also represented F.A. Amateur XI's and the R.A.F. while playing mainly in the old Isthmian League for Corinthian Casuals, Dulwich Hamlet and Kingstonian joining Hereford United and Grantham during R.A.F. postings.

After taking an F.A. Coaching badge he coached at Harrow Borough, Epsom & Ewell and Hungerford Town and was asked to edit Jimmy Hill's Football Weekly after initial experience with the Amateur Footballer. Monthly Soccer and Sportsweek followed before he had the idea for a football Wisdens and was helped by The Bagnall Harvey Agency to find a suitable sponsor in Rothmans.

After launching the Rothmans Football Yearbook in 1970 as its founder and co-compiler with Roy Peskett, he was asked to join Rothmans (although a non-smoker!) in the company's public relations department and was soon able to persuade the Marketing Director that Rothmans should become the first ever sponsor of a football league.

After a season's trial sponsoring the Hellenic and Isthmian Leagues, it was decided to go national with the Northern and Western Leagues and for four years he looked after the football department at Rothmans, with Jimmy Hill and Doug Insole presenting a brilliant sponsorship package which amongst many other innovations included three points for a win and goal difference.

So Non-League football led the way with sponsorship and two, now well accepted, innovations.

Sportsmanship and goals were also rewarded in a sponsorship that proved a great success for football and for Rothmans.

After the cigarette company pulled out of their sports sponsorship Tony produced the first Non-League Annual and later The Football League Club Directory, launching 'Non-League Football' magazine with The Mail on Sunday and then Team Talk.

After his ten years with Hungerford Town, he moved West and served Yeovil Town as a Director for seven years but was thrilled when David Emery's plans for the exciting Non-League Media emerged and came into reality, thus giving the Non-League game the publicity and promotion that he and his team had been attempting to set up since the Annual (now Directory) was launched in 1978.

Sadly Non-League Media Plc is no more, although the excellent Non-League Newspaper has continued to flourish. Tony Williams Publications has been brought back into action, and last season, greatly helped by Ladbrokes' support, has published the Directory, a Non-League Diary, the Non-League Pyramid Poster and organised a national non-league quiz. A club for non-league enthusiasts has been formed and for the coming 2003-2004 season, another programme of non-league publications and promotions is planned.

The

NON-LEAGUE CLUB DIRECTORY

sponsored by

at the heart of non-league football

at the heart of non-league football

Thank You Ladbrokes

For the last two years Ladbrokes have given prizes and awards to clubs who prove themselves the most sporting amongst the senior non-league competitions.
I have understood the enthusiasm and appreciation shown to sponsors by grateful football administrators at this level since my days in charge of the first ever football sponsorship by Rothmans in the seventies. Happily, Ladbrokes have also been impressed by the spirit within our level of the game, and they have generously backed exciting ideas with enthusiastic administration and marketing.
This is their second year of sponsorship for the Directory and now with their popular Fair Play Awards established they have encouraged the introduction of the Fair Play Non-League Club which gives a chance for real non-league enthusiasts to get together and forge new friendships at matches, forums, dinners and book launches.
To keep everyone up to date with the Ladbrokes promotion, and indeed give club members a different type of magazine to enjoy, it is hoped that Ladbrokes Fair Play Magazine featuring Non-League Knowledge, published fortnightly, will gradually develop and be able to expand its circulation thanks to advertising revenue.
The Diary and the Poster showing the re-structuring of the non-league pyramid are two other popular and useful additions to the all round service available to non-league enthusiasts.
This year hundreds of wonderful photos from our team of photographers have enabled us to prepare a very special Christmas Book entitled You have to Love It . This is a light hearted photographic record of all that goes on at a club on a typical match day. Volume one will be published in the autumn and will contain over 200 photos and I m sure will make an amusing and enjoyable Christmas present for those involved with football in any capacity.
As you can see, Ladbrokes encouragement and enthusiasm have been very important in a difficult year, so hopefully, if you do fancy a little flutter on any sporting occasion, then you will use Ladbrokes, our very special sponsors, who have given the game such good support.

Ladbrokes - "A Breath of Fresh Air"

The vast majority of real football lovers hate to see cheats within the sport they love.

So when television pundits and some managers suggest that a player HAD to bring him down, HAD to dive for a penalty, HAD to pull his shirt to stop his opponent or HAD to feign injury to get an opponent into trouble, I wonder whether we really want our youngsters to grow up thinking that cheating is fine providing it pays off. After all you may not get caught!

From my experiences in business in the last three years and indeed those of my son making his way earlier in his career and of course the regular incredible performances of our politicians, I have to say that standards of integrity and honesty seem to be depressingly low. The attitude seems to be why not encourage children to grow up cheating at everything they do?

So it is particularly refreshing when a big company chooses to back a Fair Play Award scheme and to publicise and reward those who play their sport in the right spirit, within the letter of the law. It is quite possible to be successful and sporting and you will certainly feel a lot more satisfaction.

Ladbrokes Fair Play Awards have been well accepted and the company s efforts on behalf of non-league football are a breath of fresh air at a time when sport in this country is crying out for moral leadership.

Tony Williams.

LADBROKES' FAIRPLAY LEAGUE 2002/03

CLUB	LEAGUE	P	YC	RC	PTS	AVE
Stotfold	United Counties	40	14	1	17	0.43
Hassocks	Sussex County	38	21	0	21	0.55
Horsham	Ryman Div.1 South	46	25	1	28	0.61
V.C.D. Athletic	Kent League	30	16	1	19	0.63
Tuffley Rovers	Hellenic League	40	25	1	28	0.70
Prescot Cables	North West Counties	42	29	1	32	0.76
Dunston Fed. B.	Northern League	40	28	1	31	0.78
Granthan Town	Dr Marten's Prem.	42	30	1	33	0.79
Vauxhall Motors	Unibind Premier	44	36	0	36	0.82
Chipstead	Combined Counties	46	35	1	38	0.83
Berkhamstead T.	Ryman Div.1 North	46	36	1	39	0.85
Guiseley	Unibond Div.1	42	33	1	36	0.86
Sutton United	Ryman Premier	46	40	0	40	0.87
Eastbourne B.	Dr Marten's Eastern	42	41	1	44	1.05
Rugby United	Dr Marten's Western	42	36	4	48	1.14
Hereford United	Conference	42	59	3	68	1.62

Points: Yellow - 1pt Red - 3pts
Table calculated on average points per game.

at the heart of non-league football

Non League Football's Pan-Asian Partnership 2004

Many football people's idea of a perfect Saturday evening after a great victory in a thrilling match and a couple of drinks, is a relaxing curry at their favourite Indian Restaurant.

A selection of senior non-league clubs have nominated their favourite Indian Restaurants and menu2menu.com, the worlds foremost ethnic food and drink website, will distribute posters to football clubs and their chosen restaurants to highlight the link between football and the popular eastern cuisine

Club	Restaurant	Address	Telephone No
Alfreton Town	Sanam	50 King Street, Alfreton, Derbyshire	01773 830 690
Altrincham	Hale Barnes Tandoori	14 The Square, Hale Barnes, Altrincham.	01619 049 909
Arlesey Town	Raj Villa	27 High Street,Arlesey, Beds.	01462 834 962
Barking & East Ham	New Spice	Cinema Complex, Jenkins Lane, Barking	0208 591 5313
Barrow	Mithali Restaurant	252 Dalton Road, Barrow-in-Furness	01229 432 166
Beckenham Town	Raj Monet	10 Plaistow Lane, Bromley, Kent	07774 728 758
Bedworth United	Spicy Nights	King Street, Bedworth, Warwicks	02476 310 008
Bemerton Heath H.	Raj Poot	Fisherton Street, Salisbury Wilts.	01722 321 369
Billericay Town	Gandhi	3,Holly Court, High Street, Billericay, Essex	01277 652 141
Blackstones	Raj of India	2, All Saints Road, Stamford, Lincs.	01780 753 556
Boldmere St. Michaels	Jahed Tandori	425 Birmingham Road, Sutton Coldfield	0121 382 1691
Bromley	Mintoos (Take Away)	6 Baston Road, Hayes, Kent	0208 462 7788
Bromsgrove Rovers	Shimla Peppers	1 George Street, Bromsgrove.	01527 872 010
Carterton Town	Shamiana Restaurant	7 Falkland House, Blackbourton Rd Carterton, Oxon.	01993 844 230
Cheshunt	Indian Delight	63 High Street,Waltham Cross, Herts	01992 717 546
Dartford	Green Spice	Green St.,Darenth,Dartford,Kent	01474 708 885
Dover Athletic	Light of India	Burlington Complex,Townwall Street, Dover.	01304 210 666
Eastboune Borough	The Balti House	Susans Road, Eastbourne, East Sussex	01323 412 833
Epsom & Ewell	India Garden	132 High Street, Epsom, Surrey	01372 722 617
Esh Winning	Memories of India	Prospect House, 3 Pelaw Bank,Chester-le St.	0191 388 7777
Farnborough Town	Cove Tandoori	328 Fernhill Road, Cove, Farnborough	01276 31091

Club	Restaurant	Address	Telephone No
Flackwell Heath	Empire of India	3A The Straight Bit, Flackwell Heath,Bucks	01628 530 392
Folkestone Invicta	Vinodhon Tandoori	74 High Street, Hythe, Kent	01303 230 797
Garforth Town	Aagrah	Aberford Road, Garforth, Leeds	0113 287 6606
Gateshead	Rupali Restaurant	6 Bigg Market, Newcastle upon Tyne	0191 232 8629
Glossop North End	Bulls Head	102 Church Street, Glossop, Derbyshire	01457 853 291
Gornal Athletic	Le Raj Indian Cuisine	31-35 Louise Street, Lower Gornal, Dudley	01384 251 222
Gravesend & Northfleet	The Raj	28 Minton Road, Gravesend, Kent	01474 334 473
Hampton & Richmond B.	Monaf's	119 Station Road, Hampton, Middlesex	0208 979 6021
Harpenden Town	New Taj Mahal	12 Station Road, Harpendon, Herts	01582 764 188
Harrow Borough	Curry Mahal	372 Northolt Road, South Harrow	0208 422 7976
Kennek Ryhope	Motiraj Tandoori	Church Lane, Sunderland, Tyne & Wear	0191 565 6916
Lancing	Naaz Indian Restaurant	18 North Road, Lancing, West Sussex	01903 851 555
Langford	Biggles Tandoori	4-6 Shortmead Street, Biggleswade,Beds.	01767 600 122
Ledbury Town	Tandori Night	Bye Street,Ledbury, Herefordshire	01531 635 047
Leek Town	Pabna	Ashbourne Road, Leek, Staffs.	01538 281 156
Matlock Town	Bombay Nights	Crown Square Matlock, Derbyshire.	01629 56500
Merstham	Mersthall Tandoori	Portland Drive, Merstham	01737 644 670
Newport Coun ty	The Kohinoor	164 Chepstow Road, Newport,South Wales	01633 258 615
Northampton Spencer	Balti King	76 Earl Street, Upper Mounts, Northampton	01604 637 747
Oadby Town	NUha's	13 The Parade,Oadby, Leics.	0116 292 2808
Penrith	Cagney's Tandoori	17-18 King Street,Penrith, Cumbria	01768 867 721
Pickering Town	Jahangir Miah	41 Hangate, Pickering, N.Yorks.	01751 473 334
Ramsbottom United	Eastern Eye	Bolton Street,Ramsbottom	01706 823 268
Retford United	Everest	Grove Street, Retford, Notts.	01777 704 000
Salisbury City	The Golden Curry	7 Minster Street, Salisbury, Wiltshire	01722 326 454
Shortwood United	Passage to India	Market Street, Nailsworth, Nr. Stroud	01433 834 063
Southwick	Rajah	163 Od Shoreham Road, Southwick Sussex	01273 593 636
Stalybridge Celtic	Herb & Spice	Foundry Street, Dukinfield, Cheshire	0161 343 5961
Stone Dominoes	Evening Spice Restaurant	Poolside, Madeley, Nea. Crene, Cheshire	01782 750 088
Stourbridge	Ruchi Indian Restaurant	47 High Street, Lye, Stourbridge	01384 422 286
Tonbridge Angels	Ruposhi BanglaRestaurant	41 Quarry Hill Rd,Tonbridge, Kent	01732 350 308
Whitley Bay	Takdir Tandoori	11 East Parade, Whitley Bay	0191 253 0236
Winchester City	Palash Tandoori	70 Parchmant Street, Winchester, Hants.	01962 844 409
Winsford United	Balti Cottage	3 Over Square, Winsford, Cheshire	01606 557 785
Wisbech Town	Alishan Tandoori	42 Bedford Street, Wisbech, Cambs	01945 466 265
Witham Town	Mustafs Restaurant.	101 Newland Street,Witham, Essex	01376 517 330

The Non-League Club Directory

2002-2003 AWARDS

· ROLL OF HONOUR ·

FOOTBALLER OF THE YEAR
Darren Way (Yeovil Town)

MANAGER OF THE YEAR
Gary Johnson (Yeovil Town)

ENGLAND PLAYER OF THE YEAR
John Kennedy (Canvey Island)

REGIONAL AWARDS

Bridlington Town
Accrington Stanley
A.F.C. Sudbury
Tamworth
Dagenham & Redbridge
Aldershot
Eastbourne Borough
Dorchester Town
Yeovil Town

INDIVIDUAL MERIT AWARDS

Alan Robinson
Jim Harvey
Stan Strickland
Terry Brown
Brian Robinson

F.A. CUP
Dagenham & Redbridge

• REGIONAL CLUB AWARDS 2002-03 •

North East

Bridlington Town had been re-formed as a sunday league club in 1994 and worked their way through the Driffield and East Riding Leagues before joining the Northern Counties East Division One in 2000. Just two years later they had won a place in the Premier Division, and at the first attempt, they won the championship by a magnificent twenty points.This new club is obviously on a 'charge' and who's to say that they won't be challenging for further honours next season.

North West

Accrington Stanley is a name most football fans will be pleased to see back amongst the sporting headlines for all the right reasons. Last season 'Stanley' never looked in danger of missing out on the Unibond championship and promotion back to just one level below Division Three. With goals, points and spectators happily in abundance, there will be high hopes for a return to The Football League in the near future.

East Midlands

A.F.C.Sudbury

The merger of 'United' and 'Town' has enabled Sudury to boast one of the most powerful football clubs in the eastern counties. So although last season's success was probably expected, the memories of the shock semi-final defeat of 2002 was erased by their F.A.Vase Final appearance at West Ham and of course another Eastern Counties league championship was celebrated.

West Midlands

Tamworth

The disappointment of missing out on promotion on the last day of the previous season was well and truly forgotten as Tamworth enjoyed a superb campaign in which the championship soon became a formality, and an exciting F.A..Trophy run took them to Villa Park as favourites.The dream season wasn't quite complete as Burscough pulled of a surprise victory, but promotion to the Conference and a Trophy Final appearance constituted a magnificent and satisfying season.

Home Counties East & F.A. Cup Team of the Year

Dagenham & Redbridge

The hearts of the neutrals went out to 'The Daggers' when, for the second consecutive year they just missed promotion to The Football League.Their fans had enjoyed watching another great F.A.Cup run and after a slow Conference start had seen a record run of victories place their club safely in the play off positions.Perhaps the exertions in the second half of the season caught up with the only part time squad in the final quartet. But it was only a golden goal in extra time of the play off final that beat them. So close but so far from the perfect season!

· REGIONAL CLUB AWARDS 2002-03 ·

Home Counties South

Aldershot Town

Like Accrington and Tamworth, Aldershot were never really troubled at the top of their premier division. With a terrific fan base, 'The Shots' had long been favourites to move up to the Conference and closer to their ambition - a return to the Football League.Terry Brown's first full season in charge had seen a steady improvement ,with a little less flare and a lot more consistency producing that treasured promotion at last.

South East

Eastbourne Borough

Having become the third senior football club to represent Eastbourne, a town not renowned for success in the football world , 'Borough' continued with their outstanding progress by winning promotion to the Dr Martens Premier Division last season. The club has progressed steadily on and off the field by improving facilities and playing standards. Their fans have only known success in recent years and the club's excellent foundations should enable this progress to continue.

South West

Dorchester Town

With one of the most structurally beautiful stadiums, Dorchester Town have long been highly admired within the football world and with last season they bounced back to their rightful Dr Martens Premier League place with the league's Charity Shield ,won against Kettering Town, the Dorset Senior Cup won against Weymouth and the Eastern Division championship.It could hardly have been a better season for 'The Magpies'.

West Country & Wales

Yeovil Town

Having always been associated with cup successes, it was strange to see 'The Glovers' fail in sudden death competitions during a record breaking season in the Conference.Their results underlined the fact that they were just too good for the rest of the competition, and they were actually able to enjoy their title triumph in style, without the desperate end of season pressures endured by all the clubs involved in recent seasons. Yeovil were simply in a class of their own!

NON LEAGUE FOOTBALLER OF THE YEAR

DARREN WAY

(Yeovil Town)

When three separate Player of the Year awards at a club all find one name emerging as the unanimous winner, and when that player has represented by far the best non-league club in the country, then there is absolutely no doubt that he deserves to be the country's Non-League Footballer of the Year.

When you watch Darren Way in action you realise he is as near to perpetual motion as you will ever see on the football pitch. As the game develops Darren seems to be working harder and harder, and his tackling, heading, passing, closing down and general attitude made him an automatic choice for England in the Four Nations Tournament. In fact he finished his season in style with a glorious goal against Wales and a winners medal.

Darren will be the first to say he's grateful for a superb team around him but the rest of team will say his example has been equally inspirational.

PAST WINNERS

2001-02 Daryl Clare (Boston United)
2000-01 Ray Warburton (Rushden & Dia)
1999-00 Gary Abbott (Aldershot Town)
1998-99 Neil Grayson (Cheltenham Town)
1997-98 Phil Everett (Tiverton Town)
1996-97 Howard Forinton (Yeovil Town)
1995-96 Barry Hayles (Stevenage Boro)
1994-95 Kevan Brown (Woking)
1993-94 Chris Brindley (Kidderminster H.)
1992-93 Steve Guppy (Wycombe Wndrs)
1991-92 Tommy Killick (Wimborne Town)
1990-91 Mark West (Wycombe Wndrs)
1989-90 Phil Gridelet (Barnet)
1988-89 Steve Butler (Maidstone Utd)
1987-88 David Howell (Enfield)
1986-87 Mark Carter (Runcorn)
1985-86 Jeff Johnson (Altrincham)
1984-85 Alan Cordice (Wealdstone)
1983-84 Brian Thompson (Maidstone Utd)

NON LEAGUE MANAGER OF THE YEAR

Gary Johnson

(Yeovil Town)

Modern English football managers don't have to shout, scream, throw cups of tea or threaten players any more. Their image has changed thanks to the introduction as such gentlemen as Gerard Houllier and Arsene Wenger at the top. So Yeovil Town's Gary Johnson didn't look out of place as he quietly and thoughtfully re-adjusted his squad. He gently tightened up the tactics and installed a special belief and confidence throughout the club on and off the field.

He gently guided his young squad as they confidently moved up a gear, taking advantage of the near misses and the valuable experience gained from their developing seasons. It is not surprising that Gary is worshiped by the Yeovil supporters, who sing his special song at every game in return for an appreciative wave.

Yeovil Town won't be taking Division Three by surprise as their reputation has gone before them, but the quality of the lads' football will have the Johnson stamp all over it, both in style and character. Gary has proved himself to be a special manager worthy of a special award.

PAST WINNERS

2001-02 Nigel Clough (Burton Albion)
2000-01 Jeff King (Canvey Island)
1999-00 Jan Molby (Kidderminster Harr.)
1998-99 Brendan Phillips (Nuneaton Boro)
1997-98 Steve Cotterill (Cheltenham Town)
1996-97 Paul Futcher (Southport)
1995-96 Paul Fairclough (Stevenage Boro)
1994-95 Sammy McIlroy (Macclesfield T)
1993-94 Bill Punton (Diss Town)
1992-93 Martin O'Neill (Wycombe Wndrs)

ENGLAND PLAYER OF THE YEAR
JOHN KENNEDY
(Canvey Island)

Photo: Roger Turner

England's emphatic Four Nations Tournament success reflected well on Paul Fairclough's selections and one of the ' ever presents' in the vital games was John Kennedy, who was one of just two players picked from clubs outside the Conference.

John's excellent attitude and consistency impressed his manager and as he had already featured in representative squads before Fairclough took responsibility, his participation at the highest nonleague level was an inspiration to all ambitious players in the feeder leagues within the pyramid.

As the Four Nations Tournament develops in reputation and quality, the manager will be hoping to build on the experience gained by players of quality and reliabilty like Joihn Kennedy.

• INDIVIDUAL MERIT AWARDS 2002-03 •

ALAN ROBINSON

Eight years ago when Leigh R.M.I. had been relegated to Unibond Division One and were struggling at the foot of the division, Alan Robinson watched new manager Steve Waywell's second match and has been at the centre of a football fairytale ever since. Having served the club in just about every administrative position, Alan and his colleagues, have been rewarded by promotion through the Unibond Premier to the Conference, and despite poor support and the majority of Conference clubs becoming full time professionals, the "Railwaymen' achieved fifth place in their first season (2000-01) at the top level.Alan Robinson has been one of the main driving forces as Leigh R.M.I.have survived against the odds since then. He has also seen the social facilities greatly improved while always maintaining a cheerful atmosphere throughout the club.

JIM HARVEY

Now in his tenth year as manager of Morecambe, Jim Harvey has taken his club from the Unibond Premier Division in 1994-95, to the exciting Conference play offs last season. During this time he has insisted his teams always attempt to play quality football and this policy has brought three top four finishes and only two outside the top ten. Regular F.A.Cup runs have also thrilled the Shrimps supporters, as the ground 's facilities have improved along with the playing standards. Jim Harvey is one of Northern Ireland's most famous full Internationals but he has been able to bring his top level knowledge to a non-league club with great success on and off the field.

STAN STRICKLAND

Last season's Burscough triumph brought great headlines for manager Shaun Teale and long serving chairman Frank Parr, but another character who had a great deal to do with the little club's success was long serving secretary and workaholic Stan Strickland.. Taking over the job in 1983-84, Stan has seen the club rise from The North West Counties League, through the Unibond Divisor One, and now established as a solid Premier Division club, who last season was good enough to beat Yeovil Town 2-0 away during their trip to Villa Park and F.A.Trophy success. Stan is a great enthusiast for the game and his club, and is typical of the the great characters who can be found at the heart of non-league football.

TERRY BROWN

After a long and successful playing career, mainly within the upper reaches of the Isthmian League, striker Terry Brown tried a little coaching at Wokingham and took over as manager at Hayes in November 1993. By the time he left he had taken the club into the Conference, seen the ground developed in style thanks to some useful transfer fees for the likes of Jason Roberts, and proudly presented his Hayes squad as one of the most difficult to beat in non-league football. Having achieved all he could do, and finding that familiarity sometimes breeds contempt, Terry resigned and was soon appointed manager of Aldershot, one of the game's regular under achieves. In his first full season he took the Shots into the Conference and this popular football character now has the chance to lead his club back to The Football League in the near future.

BRIAN ROBINSON

Many years ago in the seventies when I was helping Hungerford Town, I can remember being impressed with the enthusiasm and obvious talent of the Bicester Town manager Brian Robinson. Well, I noticed in Banbury United's club details for this book, that a gentleman of the same name was among their management team and it transpired that having helped Brackley Town , Buckingham Town and Worecster City during his football life span, he is now with Banbury and has been involved with the game since playing at the age of nine. Since then he hasn't missed a season's involvement for the last sixty two years, and Brian is another example of someone dedicated to, and in love with, our wonderful game.

PECKING ORDER 2002-2003 by A J Sarnecki

Position in Season 99-00	00-01	01-02	02-03	Code	League	FA Cup ent	FA Cup xmt	FA Cup won	FA Trophy ent	FA Trophy xmt	FA Trophy won	FA Vase ent	FA Vase xmt	FA Vase won	C pts	T pts	V pts	Total pts
						1	4/8	1	4	2/4/6	1	1	4/6	1				
1	1	1	1	fc	FOOTBALL CONFERENCE	22	176	26	22	132	22	0	0	0	224	242	0	466
4	3	3	2	isa	ISTHMIAN Premier	24	96	28	24	68	27	0	0	0	148	191	0	339
2	2	2	3	npa	NORTHERN PREMIER Premier	23	92	29	23	66	33	0	0	0	144	191	0	335
3	4	4	4	soa	SOUTHERN Premier	22	88	37	22	64	26	0	0	0	147	178	0	325
(5	5	5)	5	isbs	ISTHMIAN First South	24	0	35	24	0	23	0	0	0	59	119	0	178
(8	8	9)	6	isbn	ISTHMIAN First North	24	0	31	24	0	17	0	0	0	55	113	0	168
9	7	7	7	sow	SOUTHERN Western	22	0	33	22	0	19	0	0	0	55	107	0	162
7	6	6	8	npb	NORTHERN PREMIER First	22	0	35	22	0	16	0	0	0	57	104	0	161
6	9	8	9	soe	SOUTHERN Eastern	22	0	21	22	0	21	0	0	0	43	109	0	152
11	10	10	10	nora	NORTHERN First	20	0	28	0	0	0	21	50	25	48	0	96	144
12	12	12=	11	ecoa	EASTERN COUNTIES Premier	21	0	17	0	0	0	22	34	48	38	0	104	142
14	14	14	12	wsx	WESSEX	21	0	24	0	0	0	21	30	29	45	0	80	125
13	15	12=	13	ncea	NORTHERN COUNTIES EAST Premier	20	0	22	0	0	0	20	26	36	42	0	82	124
10	11	11	14	nwca	NORTH WEST COUNTIES First	21	0	13	0	0	0	22	30	34	34	0	86	120
16=	13	16	15	mda	MIDLAND ALLIANCE	21	0	10	0	0	0	22	28	33	31	0	83	114
21	18	17	16	ucoa	UNITED COUNTIES Premier	18	0	13	0	0	0	19	28	22	31	0	69	100
16=	16	19	17	wesa	WESTERN Premier	17	0	15	0	0	0	17	12	21	32	0	50	82
15	17	15	18	isd	ISTHMIAN Second	16	0	13	0	0	0	16	16	16	29	0	48	77
23	22	22	19	coc	COMBINED COUNTIES	16	0	12	0	0	0	20	10	18	28	0	48	76
19	19	18	20	ssxa	SUSSEX COUNTY First	17	0	10	0	0	0	19	10	18	27	0	47	74
20	20	20	21	ssma	SPARTAN SOUTH MIDLANDS Premier	18	0	11	0	0	0	20	6	17	29	0	43	72
18	21	21	22	ken	KENT	15	0	14	0	0	0	15	10	10	29	0	35	64
22	23	23	23	hela	HELLENIC Premier	12	0	8	0	0	0	21	4	15	20	0	40	60
24	24	24	24	nceb	NORTHERN COUNTIES EAST First	15	0	6	0	0	0	17	0	19	21	0	36	57
25=	26	25	25	norb	NORTHERN Second	15	0	9	0	0	0	19	0	13	24	0	32	56
29	28	27	26	wesb	WESTERN First	13	0	4	0	0	0	15	6	14	17	0	35	52
25=	27	28	27	esxs	ESSEX SENIOR	11	0	6	0	0	0	15	0	6	17	0	21	38
27	25	26	28	nwcb	NORTH WEST COUNTIES Second	12	0	3	0	0	0	16	0	5	15	0	21	36
31	31=	29	29	swe	SOUTH WESTERN	3	0	3	0	0	0	5	10	8	6	0	23	29
28	29	32	30	ecob	EASTERN COUNTIES First	0	0	0	0	0	0	14	0	10	0	0	24	24
33=	31=	30	31	wmda	WEST MIDLAND REGIONAL Premier	0	0	0	0	0	0	14	0	8	0	0	22	22
32	33=	31	32=	cmda	CENTRAL MIDLANDS Supreme	0	0	0	0	0	0	9	6	7	0	0	22	22
36	33=	34	32=	mdca	MIDLAND COMBINATION Premier	0	0	0	0	0	0	13	0	8	0	0	21	21
33=	36	36	34	ssxb	SUSSEX COUNTY Second	4	0	0	0	0	0	7	0	3	4	0	10	14
30	30	33	35	lesa	LEICESTERSHIRE SENIOR Premier	0	0	0	0	0	0	12	0	1	0	0	13	13
37=		38	36	hama	HAMPSHIRE Premier	0	0	0	0	0	0	5	0	7	0	0	12	12
33=	33=	35	37	ssmb	SPARTAN SOUTH MIDLANDS Senior	0	0	0	0	0	0	8	0	2	0	0	10	10
40=	40=	39=	38	wcha	WEST CHESHIRE First	0	0	0	0	0	0	2	0	5	0	0	7	7
		37	39	ucob	UNITED COUNTIES First	0	0	0	0	0	0	5	0	1	0	0	6	6
37=	37=	41=	40	nala	NORTHERN ALLIANCE Premier	0	0	0	0	0	0	2	0	2	0	0	4	4
40=	37=	41=	41=	smsa	SOMERSET SENIOR Premier	0	0	0	0	0	0	1	0	2	0	0	3	3
37=	39	43=	41=	dvc	DEVON COUNTY LEAGUE	0	0	0	0	0	0	2	0	1	0	0	3	3
40=	40=	43=	43	hebw	HELLENIC First West	0	0	0	0	0	0	2	0	0	0	0	2	2
40=	40=	39=	44=	ntaa	NOTTS ALLIANCE Senior	0	0	0	0	0	0	1	0	0	0	0	1	1
		43=	44=	hebe	HELLENIC First East	0	0	0	0	0	0	1	0	0	0	0	1	1
		43=	44=	wea	WEARSIDE	0	0	0	0	0	0	1	0	0	0	0	1	1
40=			44=	mana	MANCHESTER Premier	0	0	0	0	0	0	1	0	0	0	0	1	1
			44=	cmdb	CENTRAL MIDLANDS Premier	0	0	0	0	0	0	1	0	0	0	0	1	1
			44=	dspr	DORSET PREMIER	0	0	0	0	0	0	1	0	0	0	0	1	1
					others (accepted but did not play)	1	0	0	0	0	0	1	4	0	1	0	5	6

Points are given for status (acceptance into each of the three competitions), for prestige (exemption from early rounds) and performance (number of wins, however achieved, even by walkover). Entry to the Vase is valued at one point, that to the Trophy at 4. Cup entry gives a further bonus of one point. The number of entries from each league is shown in the appropriate column. Points for exemptions are valued at two for each round missed. The entry in the table is of the total points so gained by the given league, not the number of teams given exemptions. Finally, all wins are valued at one point, regardless of opposition: giving extra points for defeating 'stronger' opponents would be too arbitrary. After all, if they lost then they were not stronger on the day!

F.A. CHALLENGE CUP 2002 - 2003 REVIEW

Last season we had the pleasure of seeing Dagenham & Redbridge and Farnborough Town feature in the Fourth Round Proper and, although Farnborough's ground switching did not please everyone, the players and officials at least had the thrill of facing the double winners and Town actually scored a goal through Rocky Baptiste.

The Daggers on the other hand received nothing but praise from everyone for their display at Norwich City, as they matched the Division One club in all departments of the game for 90 minutes before missing out on a deserved replay when The Canaries scored an injury time goal.

The F.A.'s generous prize money had encouraged 624 original entries and it certainly proved a worthwhile exercise for the little clubs whose adventure started in the early qualifying rounds-

£120,000	Dagenham & Redbridge and Farnborough Town (Conference)
£70,000	Morecambe (Conference)
£66,000	Barrow (N.P.L.), Harrogate Railway (N.Counties East)
£57,500	Crawley Town (S.P.L.), Vauxhall Motors (N.P.L.)
£46,000	Havant & Waterlooville (S.P.L.),Team Bath (Western)
£40,000	Chester City, Margate, Southport, Stevenage Borough (Conference)
£37,500	Boreham Wood, Heybridge Swifts, St Albans City (I.P.L.), Slough Town (I.Div 1N) Dover Athletic, Hastings United, Moor Green, Stafford Rangers,Tiverton Town (S.P.L.) Harrogate Town, Runcorn F.C.Halton (N.P.L.) Guiseley (N.Div 1)
£26,500	Bridlington Town (N.Counties East)
£26,000	Radcliffe Borough, Spennymoor United (N.Div 1), A.F.C.Sudbury , Wisbech Town (Eastern) Arlesey Town (I.Div1.N), Horsham (I.Div1S), Flackwell Heath (I Div 2), Arnold Town (N,Co E) Bideford (Western)

Of the above prize winners, only Bridlington Town started out in the Extra Preliminary Round, but two F.A.Vase level clubs, Harrogate Railway and Team Bath enjoyed outstanding success and of course both teams were thrilled that their First Round Cup ties were featured live on Sky T.V. For this they each received a fee of £100,000.

EXTRA PRELIMINARY ROUND

SATURDAY 24 AUGUST 2002 | **WINNING CLUBS TO RECEIVE £500**

Home		Away	Score	Att
Flixton	v	Goole	1-1	150
Comley-Excel		Ward		
R(27/8)Goole	v	Flixton	0-0*	202
(Goole won 5-4 on kicks from the penalty mark)				
Holker Old Boys	v	Bridlington Town	0-2	86
West Auckland Town	v	Winsford United	2-1	66
Allen, Pitt		Shaughnessy		
Penrith	v	Brandon United	3-2	90
Hodgson, Wright		Patterson, Robson		
Marske United	v	Salford City	1-4	131
Ward		Gardner, Giggs (2)		
Maltby Main	v	Billingham Synthonia	0-6	63
		Bridge,Walker,Wells(2),Wilkshire(2)		
Consett	v	Pontefract Collieries	4-1	76
Brown,Davidson,McLeod(2)		Wilson		
Chester-Le-Street Town	v	Northallerton Town	3-1	38
Elrington, Severn, Turner		Trainer		
Morpeth Town	v	Curzon Ashton	3-2	98
Atwell, Leach, McCabe		Humphries, Sherlock		
Nelson	v	Norton & Stockton Ancients	0-0*	80
R(27/8)Norton & S.A.	v	Nelson	1-2	70
Gallagher		Coldridge, Pates		
Ramsbottom United	v	Thackley	1-0	150
Brierley				
Horden CW	v	Armthorpe Welfare	2-1	52
Cowley, Pearson		Clegg		
Bridgnorth Town	v	Gedling Town	4-2	50
Ashley, Smith, Tanter(2)		Maddison, Newton		
Stratford Town	v	Stourbridge	4-1	188
Amos, Darroch, Sheward Spacey		Lee		
Mickleover Sports	v	Shirebrook Town	3-1	128
Cunningham (2), Payne		Johnson		
(25/8)Leek CSOB	v	Nantwich Town	0-3	184
		Hackney (2), McVey		
Grosvenor Park	v	Stafford Town	2-0	71
Daniels, Smith				
Newmarket Town	v	Ely City	2-3	111
Bruges, Stokes		Foster		
(tie awarded to Newmarket Town – Ely City removed from the Competition for playing an ineligible player)				
Dereham Town	v	AFC Wallingford	1-3	166
Hillier		Bryan (2), Ward		
Saffron Walden Town	v	Hullbridge Sports	0-1	81
		Woolf		
Bedford United & Valerio	v	Brook House	0-1	38
		Stocking		
Potters Bar Town	v	Milton Keynes City	1-2	73
Welch		Hill ,Lyon		
Sawbridgeworth Town	v	Harwich & Parkeston	2-0	69
Horne, Wheeler				
Raunds Town	v	Ruislip Manor	1-0	88
Webb				
Stotfold	v	Broxbourne Borough V&E	0-0	36
R(27/8)Broxbourne B.V&E	v	Stotfold	1-5	34
Scripps		Garrett (3), Saunders (2)		
Tiptree United	v	Ipswich Wanderers	1-1	92
Rochester		Baker		
R(27/8)Ipswich W.	v	Tiptree United	3-3*	142
Coote, Herewood		Barefield, Rochester (2)		
(Ipswich Wanderers won 7-6 on kicks from the penalty mark)				
Ilford	v	Kempston Rovers	3-0	54
Fanibuyan, March, Simpson				

Home		Away	Score	Att
Walton Casuals	v	Whitehawk	0-4	82
		Pattenden, Rowlands (2), Stevens		
(25/8)Littlehampton T.	v	Godalming & Guildford	0-6	141
		Bridger (3), Lydon, Munro, Ray		
Greenwich Borough	v	Three Bridges	1-4	30
Smith		Campbell, Massaro (2), Punt		
Deal Town	v	Chichester City Utd	2-2	231
Bartholomew		Laidlaw, Stevens		
R(27/8)Chichester City Utd	v	Deal Town	2-3	109
Hitchman, Thomas		Hayes, Jones, Pollard		
Lymington & New Milton	v	East Preston	2-2	138
Gill (2)		Huckett, Yelling		
R(27/8)East Preston	v	Lymington & New Milton	1-2	131
Clayton		Phillips, Richardson		
Moneyfields	v	Burgess Hill Town	1-0	120
Edwards				
Alton Town	v	Didcot Town	1-1	213
Edwards		McNamara		
R(28/8)Didcot Town	v	Alton Town	1-0	164
Kelly				
Horsham YMCA	v	Eastleigh	1-3	105
Durrant		Matthews (2), Rusher		
AFC Totton	v	Southwick	3-2	115
Osman (2), White		Funnell, Holden		
Ramsgate	v	Maidstone United	1-1	747
Schulz		Kempster		
R(27/8)Maidstone Utd	v	Ramsgate	1-0	432
Foley				
Chessington United	v	Ringmer	0-1	48
		Costello		
Reading Town	v	Farnham Town	3-1	74
Boylan, Clarke, Mills		Evans		
(at Farnham Town FC)				
Paulton Rovers	v	Downton	5-1	40
Catley,Colbourne(2),Woon(2)		Guy		
Highworth Town	v	Fairford Town	2-2	216
Cleverly, Miller		Gregory		
R(28/8)Fairford Town	v	Highworth Town	1-4	227
Stevenson		Cleverly, Hill, Miller(2)		
Street	v	Keynsham Town	3-1	85
Hayter, Lomax		Cummings		
Portland United	v	Welton Rovers	6-2	247
Cornick, Heath, Reader (3)		Cordy, Lewis		
Bishop Sutton	v	Melksham Town	2-1	48
Adams, Ewyther		Clayton		
Christchurch	v	Willand Rovers	3-0	96
Manning (2), Woolner				
(at Wimborne Town FC)				

*AET

ROUND STATISTICS

No.Games: 45+9 **Home Win:** 26 **Away Win:** 19

Draws: 9 Home Goals: 91 **Away Goals:** 92 **Hatricks:** 4

Total Attend: 6,796 **Av Attend:** 126

Best Home Wins

Paulton Rovers v Downton 5-1

- Portland United v Welton Rovers 6-2

Best Away Wins

Maltby Main v Billingham Synthonia 0-6

Littlehampton Town v Godalming & Guildford 0-6

Best Attendance

Ramsgate v Maidstone United 747

Where goalscorers are missing we presume 'own goals' were scored but not listed on the match details returned by the clubs.

Grosvenor Park (Midland Alliance) attack the Stafford Town (Midland Alliance) end during their first ever FA Cup tie, which was quickly followed by their first victory in the competition, beating Stafford 2-0 on the day. Photo: Steve Ayre.

PRELIMINARY ROUND

SATURDAY 31 AUGUST 2002 **WINNING CLUBS TO RECEIVE £1000**

Home		Away	Score	Att
Shildon	v	Salford City	2-4	205
Bayles, Fairhurst		Hughes (3)		
Morpeth Town	v	Woodley Sports	1-0	70
Lanton				
Hatfield Main	v	Shotton Comrades	0-1	68
		Brassell		
Selby Town	v	Newcastle Blue Star	0-0	84
(3/9)Newcastle Blue Star	v	Selby Town	2-4	100
Greenhill (2)		Barnett, Carter, Cygan, Mitchell		
Fleetwood Town	v	Workington	1-1	214
Catlow		Potts		
R(3/9)Workington	v	Fleetwood Town	1-0	325
Ennis				
Skelmersdale United	v	Penrith	1-3	128
Dugdale		Henderson (2), Lea		
Brigg Town	v	Kendal Town	2-4	186
Sherlock, Stones		Hayton (2), Sheppard (2)		
Whitley Bay	v	Harrogate Railway	2-2	303
Hay (2)		Davey, Smith		
R(2/9)Harrogate Railway	v	Whitley Bay	5-4	187
Davey, Gore, McLean Sunley, Watkinson		Chandler (2), Locker, O'Donovan		
Guisborough Town	v	Blackpool Mechanics	2-0	120
Outhwaite (2)				
Farsley Celtic	v	Seaham Red Star	4-4	94
Beech, Blackstone, Midwood, Newton		Dibie (2), Matthew, Moss		
R(3/9)Seaham Red S.	v	Farlsey Celtic	1-6	93
Matthews		Lamey (3), Midwood (2), Spence		
Glasshoughton Welfare	v	Jarrow Roofing Boldon CA	1-3	85
Stack		Nelson (3)		
Goole	v	Mossley	0-3	246
		Wolstenholm, Wosahlo (2)		
Nelson	v	Bishop Auckland	2-3	148
Grey, Haworth		Wilkinson (2)		
Ossett Town	v	Worsbrough Bridge MW	0-2	153
Shaw		Hunt, Needham		
Great Harwood Town	v	Winterton Rangers	0-0	61
R(4/9)Winterton R.	v	Great Harwood Tn	0-0*	96
(Great Harwood Town won 5-3 on kicks from the penalty mark)				
Horden CW	v	Trafford	2-1	60
I'Anson, Martin		Collins		

Home		Away	Score	Att
Evenwood Town	v	Durham City	1-4	104
Hinds		Dunwell (2), Gray, Halliday		
Prescot Cables	v	Witton Albion	3-6	289
Ellis, Garforth (2)		Burton,Clegg(2),Crompton,Lillis,Moseley		
Parkgate	v	St Helens Town	2-2	94
Cusworth, Robshaw		Poland		
R(3/9)St Helens Town	v	Parkgate	3-1	99
Cooper, Dunn, Poland		Cusworth		
Squires Gate	v	Lincoln United	1-2	89
Paynter		Walters, Williams		
Tow Law Town	v	Tadcaster Albion	2-1	167
Jones, Nicholson		Dickinson		
Abbey Hey	v	Bamber Bridge	0-0	75
R(3/9)Bamber Bridge	v	Abbey Hey	2-2*	160
Robinson, Sutch		Metz (2)		
(Abbey Hey won 4-2 on kicks from the penalty mark)				
Louth United	v	Cheadle Town	4-1	42
Creer, Hall, King, Peck		Wardle		
Ramsbottom United	v	Chadderton	3-0	242
Fielding, Lomax				
Matlock Town	v	Pickering Town	2-2	224
Holland, Williams		Wash, Wood		
R(3/9)Pickering Town	v	Matlock Town	0-1	125
		Brown		
Maine Road	v	Guiseley	1-2	64
Ingles		Cooke, Stuart		
Spennymoor United	v	Consett	4-0	161
Brunskill, Jones, Shan (2)				
Chester-Le-Street Town	v	Hall Road Rangers	2-0	52
Elrington, Leadbitter				
Atherton LR	v	Rossington Main	0-2	64
		Bingham, Henderson		
Ashington	v	Colne	7-0	245
Drysdale (2), Hepple, Livermore, Sinclair, Woodhouse (2)				
Willington	v	Atherton Collieries	0-0	57
R(2/9)Atherton Collieries	v	Willington	5-1	56
Gallagher (2), Mackenzie, Vandenberg, Wynne		Berry		
Chorley	v	Liversedge	5-0	231
Barker,Emmett,Wilkinson(3)				

F.A. CUP - PRELIMINARY ROUND

Home		Away	Score	Att
Warrington Town	v	Esh Winning	2-2	100
Holden (2)		Howe, Messer		
R(4/9)Esh Winning	v	Warrington Town	3-1*	120
Connelly, Messer (2)		Latham		
(1/9)Bacup Borough	v	Bridlington Town	1-2	110
Richards		Harper, Thacker		
(at Rossendale United FC)				
Bedlington Terriers	v	Brodsworth MW	3-0	198
Milner (3)				
Alnwick Town	v	Crook Town	1-2	112
Swordy		Burgess (2)		
Garforth Town	v	Yorkshire Amateur	3-1	168
Amos (2), Taylor		Bingley		
Stocksbridge Park Steels	v	Oldham Town	17-1	110
Beckett (2),Illingworth, Ingledow(2),Jackson(10), Tivendale (2)		Hession		
Rossendale United	v	Ossett Albion	0-1	201
Thornaby	v	Dunston Federation Brewery	1-1	67
Leach		Forbes		
R(3/9)Dunston Federation B.	v	Thornaby	2-1	104
Thompson (2)		Boyce		
Clitheroe	v	Radcliffe Borough	1-3	229
Cryer		Banim, Elliot, Wilson		
Sheffield	v	West Auckland Town	0-4	302
		McGuire, Pitt, Stout (2)		
South Shields	v	Hallam	1-2	103
Steadman		Bailey, Tesk		
Easington Colliery	v	Hebburn Town	1-3	51
Dixon		Donaghy (2), Laidler		
Washington	v	North Ferriby United	0-2	71
		Lowthorpe, Sheldon		
Peterlee Newtown	v	Billingham Synthonia	2-1	67
Conlon, Fitzgerald		Fawcett		
Billingham Town	v	Gretna		
(walkover for Billingham Town – Gretna withdrawn)				
Darwen	v	Eccleshill United	1-3	64
Hill		Buchan, Burnham (2)		
Stourport Swifts	v	Alfreton Town	1-4	128
Mulders		France, Godber (2), Highfield		
Rocester	v	Congleton Town	3-0	106
Morris, Oldaker, Wade				
Kidsgrove Athletic	v	Buxton	4-1	192
McDonald,Tobin(2),Worthington		Axcell		
Rushall Olympic	v	Sutton Coldfield Town	1-4	115
Long		Baler, Massingham (2), Tucker		
Staveley MW	v	Boston Town	0-1	88
		Dunn		
Halesowen Harriers	v	Shepshed Dynamo	1-3	113
Burns		Lawrence, Master		
Newcastle Town	v	Leek Town	0-1	223
		Whittaker		
Belper Town	v	Gresley Rovers	0-1	319
		Crawford		
(1/9)Mickleover Sports	v	Cradley Town	2-1	197
Holness, Payne		Perry		
Redditch United	v	Grosvenor Park	2-1	184
Cowley, Sutton		Anifowose		
Bourne Town	v	Eastwood Town	1-1	102
Thorpe		White		
R(3/9)Eastwood Town	v	Bourne Town	3-1	162
Kennerdale,Morgan,Stubley		Edwards		
Bedworth United	v	Causeway United	1-1	159
Partridge		Harris		
R(4/9)Causeway Utd	v	Bedworth United	1-2*	165
Dixon		Goodman, Steane		

Home		Away	Score	Att
Histon	v	Quorn	2-3	107
Coburn, Munns		Keast (2), Noble		
Oadby Town	v	Rugby United	2-2	249
Miller (2)		Hall (2)		
R(3/9)Rugby United	v	Oadby Town	2-3	207
Beard, Hall		Miller, Taft, Warner		
Atherstone United	v	Studley	3-0	180
Cammock, Leeson, Lenton				
Stratford Town	v	Ludlow Town	3-1	133
Moore,Sheward,Stephenson		Moore		
(1/9)Biddulph Victoria	v	Bridgnorth Town	2-0	174
Baker, Marron				
Nantwich Town	v	Holbeach United	4-0	83
Gleghorn,Hackney,Wilkinson(2)				
Chasetown	v	Spalding United	0-1	95
		Lawrence		
Corby Town	v	Stamford	0-6	168
		Ashby,Ndekwe,Pritchard(3),Steadman		
Arnold Town	v	Racing Club Warwick	1-0	161
Shepherd				
Kings Lynn	v	Deeping Rangers	1-0	690
Stephenson				
Willenhall Town	v	Glapwell	1-0	118
Moseley				
Pelsall Villa	v	Borrowash Victoria	1-1	52
Bishop		Hutchings		
R(3/9)Borrowash V.	v	Pelsall Villa (3/9)	1-4	59
Shuttleworth		Bishop, Morgan, Perry, Tolley		
Shifnal Town	v	Blackstones	1-4	73
MacKenzie		Cobb, Epps, Preston, Williams		
Glossop North End	v	Boldmere St Michaels	1-0	89
Henniker				
Solihull Borough	v	Oldbury United	2-0	188
Hamilton, Titterton				
Barwell	v	Bromsgrove Rovers	1-1	168
Watkins		Southwick		
R(3/9)Bromsgrove R.	v	Barwell	4-3	309
Banner,Dyson,Ford,Palmer		Lucas (2), Thornhill		
Long Buckby	v	Marlow	0-2	74
		Ryder, Wilkins		
Newmarket Town	v	Ilford	1-3	123
Rhodes		Emmanuel, Nicholls, Stirling		
Barking & East Ham United	v	Soham Town Rangers	4-3	159
Ramsey,Read(2),Thomas		Kingston, Reed (2)		
Hullbridge Sports	v	Edgware Town	2-5	53
Boothe, Woolf		Maharjan, Thomas (2), Yoki (2)		
Great Yarmouth Town	v	Holmer Green	2-1	138
Thompson (2)		Gardner		
Desborough Town	v	Romford	1-2	91
Drain		King, Leslie		
Southall Town	v	Wroxham	1-6	68
Lewinson		Edridge,Fox,Horton(2),Howes,terrington		
Northampton Spencer	v	Yaxley	1-1	93
Stratford		Acton		
R(3/9)Yaxley	v	Northampton Sp.r	5-1*	95
Chapman,Clarke,Hailstone(3)		Hanill		
Banbury United	v	Berkhamsted Town	1-1	292
Taylor		Lowe		
R(3/9)Berkhamsted T.	v	Banbury United	1-4	162
Palmer		Sylla (4)		
Hoddesdon town	v	AFC Sudbury	0-2	110
(at Hertford Town FC)		Claydon, Spearing		
Cheshunt	v	Wembley	3-0	62
Adams, Beattie, Cox				
Maldon Town	v	Flackwell Heath	1-1	85
Witney		Catlin		
R(3/9)Flackwell Heath	v	Maldon Town	1-0	93
Anson				

F.A. CUP - PRELIMINARY ROUND

Home		Away	Score	Att
Leighton Town	v	Royston Town	2-2	120
Boad, Chesters		Smith (2)		
R(4/9)Royston Town	v	Leighton Town	3-0	110
Emmett, Smith, Thorne				
Chalfont St Peter	v	Hemel Hempstead Town	0-3	112
		Hammett (2), McDonagh		
Clacton Town	v	Sawbridgeworth Town	3-1	116
Brown, Gove, Howell		Campbell		
Wealdstone	v	Leyton	1-3	268
Mapes		Fenton, Gregoiou, Tucker		
Cogenhoe United	v	Diss Town	0-2	92
		Key, White		
Bowers United	v	Arlesey Town	1-4	88
Deakin		Samuel (3), Tekell		
Wivenoe Town	v	Yeading	0-3	74
		Brown, Miller, Telemaque		
Stotfold	v	Hornchurch	1-1	68
Garrett		Elder		
R(3/9)Hornchurch	v	Stotfold	4-4*	384
Benstock,Nathan,Risley(2)		Cottenden,Garrett,Hayes,Wiseman		
(Stotfold won 5-4 on kicks from the penalty mark)				
St Neots Town	v	Stansted	6-0	106
Bloss,Byrne,Finney,Kuhne(3)				
Bury Town	v	Barton Rovers	2-3	191
Harrison, Tatham		Carey (2), Lochhead		
Lowestoft Town	v	Uxbridge	0-2	282
		Gill, Tunnell		
Raunds Town	v	Burnham Ramblers	5-1	74
Anderson (2), Bunting, Koriya, Richardson		Down		
Wootton Blue Cross	v	Brackley Town	3-1	78
Bartley, Joswiak (2)		Baird		
Stewarts & Lloyds	v	Ford Sports Daventry	1-0	32
Morrow				
Harlow Town	v	Aveley	0-1	115
		Curran		
Stowmarket Town	v	Southall	1-6	109
Pannell		Elliott (2), Olwemy, O'Sullivan (3)		
Wisbech Town	v	Woodbridge Town	3-1	312
Furnell (2), McManus		Calver		
Brook House	v	Burnham	2-3	62
Cannon, Vargas		Martin (2), Walkington		
Hanwell Town	v	Great Wakering Rovers	0-3	79
		Trenkel (3)		
Mildenhall Town	v	London Colney	0-0	138
R(4/9)London Colney	v	Mildenhall Town	1-0	75
Hewing				
Tilbury	v	Gorleston	4-3	57
Downs, Ray, Stubbs (2)		Harvey, Ingram, Pillar		
(at Aveley FC)				
Concord Rangers	v	Hertford Town	2-3	60
Greaves (2)		Cooper, Moore, Parratt		
Ware	v	Milton Keynes City	5-1	132
Field(2),Hunt,Kearney,McAter		Bevis		
Haringey Borough	v	Northwood	0-1	62
		Carter		
Ipswich Wanderers	v	Leyton Pennant	2-3	140
Bell, Coote		Matthews, Stevens		
Letchworth	v	Staines Town	1-1	67
Thomas		Reed		
R(4/9)Staines Town	v	Letchworth	1-0	161
Reilly				
(at Egham Town FC)				
Clapton	v	Beaconsfield SYCOB	0-3	40
		Jones, Sears (2)		
Witham Town	v	Wingate & Finchley	0-5	75
		Boateng,Harrold,Moules,Taylor,Williams		

Home		Away	Score	Att
(4/9)St Margaretsbury	v	Dunstable Town	2-0	68
Porter, Ulatowski				
(at Dunstable Town FC)				
East Thurrock United	v	Harefield United	1-2	116
		Dunne, Ursell		
Buckingham Town	v	Tring Town	3-0	103
Abdi, Cole, Primus				
Rothwell Town	v	Kingsbury Town	3-1	109
Kearns, Mintus, Turner		Acquah		
Brentwood	v	AFC Wallingford	2-2	52
Hobden (2)		Simpson, Ward		
R(3/9)AFC Wallingford	v	Brentwood	4-1	114
Antonowicz, Shildrick (3)		Ashby		
Fakenham Town	v	Southend Manor	1-3	96
Coe		Coleman, Cox (2)		
Wick	v	Abingdon United	1-4	66
Price		Fontaine, Marriott, Parsons, Ridley		
Merstham	v	St Leonards	3-4	60
Burridge, Malik, Traynor		Lovell (3), Ray		
Three Bridges	v	Didcot Town	3-1	80
Gregg, Massaro, Punt		Concannon		
Erith Town	v	Ringmer	0-3	90
		Henry, Montgomory (2)		
North Leigh	v	Cowes Sports	0-5	82
		Butler, Hart, McDonald (3)		
Bromley	v	Abingdon Town	3-2	255
Bartley, Drewett (2)				
Lymington & New Milton	v	Dulwich Hamlet	1-1	171
Gill		Kadi		
R(3/9)Dulwich Hamlet	v	Lymington & New Milton	1-3	153
Coleman		Gill, Green		
Redhill	v	Peacehaven & Telscombe	1-3	99
Lippett		Brown, Lockhart (2)		
Gosport Borough	v	Wantage Town	2-1	122
Hensman, Lindsey		Newport		
Oxford City	v	Cray Wanderers	0-1	129
		Watkins		
Deal Town	v	Hythe Town	4-2	248
James, Jones, Pollard		Porter (2)		
Eastleigh	v	Erith & Belvedere	5-0	189
Beck (3), Kenna, Matthews				
Fisher Athletic	v	Wokingham Town	7-0	108
Dolby (2) Huggins (4)				
Whyteleafe	v	Reading Town	1-0	170
Nicholas				
Whitstable Town	v	Chipstead	1-2	137
Jackson		Berry, Jenns		
Croydon Athletic	v	Eastbourne Borough	0-0	185
R(3/9)Eastbourne B.	v	Croydon Athletic	4-1	412
Allen,Crabb,Pearce,Smart		Jackson		
AFC Totton	v	Thamesmead Town	2-0	139
Egerton, Shaw				
Molesey	v	Hassocks	3-0	80
Alighieri, Wright (2)				
Bedfont	v	Whitehawk	3-1	79
Gardner, Griffith, Postins		Rowlands		
Saltdean United	v	VCD Athletic	0-3	73
		Collins, Dimmock,Ward		
Beckenham Town	v	Croydon	1-2	97
Clews		Cecil, Hall		
Brockenhurst	v	Fleet Town	3-2	96
Bailey-Pearce,Marwood(2)		Moore, Pearson		
Newport (IW)	v	Blackfield & Langley	1-1	181
Quarmby		Wheatland		
R(3/9)Blackfield & Langley	v	Newport (IW)	0-3	159
		Gibbons (2), Perry		
Moneyfields	v	BAT Sports	0-2	104
		Gregory, Willes		

Home		Away	Score	Att
Chertsey Town	v	Arundel	4-1	142
Beasant,Burton(2),Vercesi		Ansley		
Tunbridge Wells	v	Ashford Town(Middx)	2-1	87
Hickmott (2)		Lawrence-Jones		
Fareham Town	v	Tooting & Mitcham United	1-1	249
Manneh		Dack		
R(3/9)Tooting & M.	v	Fareham Town	1-0	319
Nwanze				
(30/8)Eastbourne Tn	v	Windsor & Eton	1-1	208
Brockwell		Walsh		
R(4/9)Windsor & Eton	v	Eastbourne Town	4-2	92
Adams(2),Dyke,O'Connor		Barden (2)		
Godalming & Guildford	v	Whitchurch United	3-0	82
Bridger, Harrison, Ray				
Thame United	v	Slough Town	1-2	258
Gardner		Browne, Spencer		
(1/9)Pagham	v	Bracknell Town	3-2	180
McIntosh, Stevens (2)		Harte, Smith		
Sandhurst Town	v	Herne Bay	2-6	82
Hutchings, Mulvaney		Hearn (2), Jones (3), Whittaker		
Sittingbourne	v	Slade Green	2-2	162
Campbell, Drury		Laming, Prett		
R(3/9)Slade Green	v	Sittingbourne	3-1	156
Eldridge, Laming, Prett		Drury		
Metropolitan Police	v	Lancing	4-0	78
Dunn, Tomlinson (3)				
Camberley Town	v	Cove	0-1	99
		Anderson		
Horsham	v	Lordswood	2-2	234
Collins, Geddes		Weeks		
R(3/9)Lordswood	v	Horsham	1-2	147
Clout		French, Payne		
Lewes	v	Thatcham Town	1-0	344
Curnon				
Chatham Town	v	Egham Town	0-0	150
R(3/9)Egham Town	v	Chatham Town	0-1	122
		Mitchell		
Bognor Regis Town	v	Worthing	1-0	706
Russell				
Banstead Athletic	v	Leatherhead	1-4	133
Nolan		Chabaan (2), Inglethorpe (2)		
Westfield	v	Dorking	1-2	70
Wildins		Duffell, White		
Tonbridge Angels	v	Maidstone United	2-3	1027
Portway, Royston		Butler (3)		
Hillingdon Borough	v	Chessington & Hook United	2-2	103
Gallagher, McGinty		Justice, Wicks		
R(3/9)Chessington & H.	v	Hillingdon Borough	1-3	192
Justice		McGinty (2), Morrissey		
Corinthian Casuals	v	Epsom & Ewell	1-1	105
Raishbrook		Huckle		
R(3/9)Epsom & Ewell	v	Corinthian Casuals	1-2	118
Morris		Georgiou, Lyward		
Walton & Hersham	v	Andover	2-1	147
Harkness, O'Donnell		Bennett		
Ashford Town	v	Carshalton Athletic	1-3	344
Hassett		Dublin, Hampsher, Todd		
AFC Newbury	v	Hailsham Town	2-1	107
Watt (2)		Southwood		
Selsey	v	Ash United	3-0	146
Lowery, Stillman, Vanson				
Eastbourne United	v	Cobham	0-3	102
		Mesher (2), Weekes		
(1/9)Dartford	v	Carterton Town	2-2	279
Eagle, Tutton		Lewis, Threlfall		
R(3/9)Carterton Town	v	Dartford	1-0	103
Hamill				

Home		Away	Score	Att
Chard Town	v	Swindon Supermarine	2-0	79
Ritchie, Wilson				
Frome Town	v	Shortwood United	0-1	187
		Scarlett		
Bishop Sutton	v	Cinderford Town	1-3	72
Adams		Addis, Bale, Griffin		
Torrington	v	Westbury United	2-1	105
Stevens (2)		Perkins		
Odd Down	v	Paulton Rovers	0-2	91
		Colbourne (2)		
Clevedon Town	v	Bitton	2-2	193
Lester, Wyatt		Branch, Cole		
R(2/9)Bitton	v	Clevedon Town	1-2	316
Branch		Lester, Wickerman		
Highworth Town	v	Cirencester Town	3-0	228
Jack, Joyce, Saye				
Hungerford Town	v	Shepton Mallet	2-0	95
Green, Mildenhall				
Bridport	v	Taunton Town	2-3	235
Gale, Hitchcock		Baston, Laight, Myers		
Elmore	v	Backwell United	1-2	44
Robinson		Ayre, Patch		
Bashley	v	Mangotsfield United	2-2	216
Davis, Wakefield		Davis, Edwards		
R(3/9)Mangotsfield U.	v	Bashley	0-1	243
		Anstey		
Salisbury City	v	Bideford	1-2	482
King		Parker, Pickard		
Barnstaple Town	v	Team Bath	0-4	148
		Kamara-Taylor (3), Lewis		
Corsham Town	v	Portland United	3-1	120
Coleman, Kilmurry, Price		Reader		
Devizes Town	v	Ilfracombe Town	5-2	61
Godley, Lisle, Mooney Richardson (2)		Shell, Varley		
Bournemouth	v	Bridgwater Town	3-0	115
Dancer, Lucas, Till				
Falmouth Town	v	Bristol Manor Farm	2-0	146
Ashburn, Stevens				
Merthyr Tydfil	v	Christchurch	5-0	353
Belle,Dorrian,Price,Regan(2)				
Porthleven	v	Dorchester Town	0-5	284
		Harris,Keeler,Oldbury,Shepherd (2)		
Tuffley Rovers	v	St Blazey	0-1	92
		Street		
Minehead Town	v	Gloucester City	0-2	144
		Howard, Thompson		
Weston Super Mare	v	Calne Town	4-0	160
Bevan (2),Lee, Mehew				
Yate Town	v	Hallen	4-2	215
Casey, Metheringham (3)		Pritchard, Westlake		
Dawlish Town	v	Wimborne Town	0-3	122
		Cannie (2), Roast		
Brislington	v	Evesham United	2-2	144
Cook, Rosslee		Bullock, May		
R(3/9)Evesham Utd	v	Brislington	3-2	147
Bullock, Jukes, May		Claridge (2)		
Street	v	Bemerton Heath Harlequins	1-3	87
Hayter		Cole, Palmer, Richardson		

ROUND STATISTICS

No.Games: 197*+38 **Home Win:** 93 **Away Win:** 104
Draws: 38 **Home Goals:** 418 **Away Goals:** 405
Hatricks: 25 **Total Attend:** 35 **Av Attend:** 150
* Walkover
Best Home Win: Stocksbridge PSteels v Oldham T. 17-1
Best Away Win: Corby Town v Stamford 0-6
Best Att: Tonbridge Angels v Maidstone Utd 1027

Brackley Town (Hellenic) clear the danger during their 3-1 away defeat against Wootton Blue Star (U.Co. Prem). Photo: Steve Ayre.

Corby Town (Dr Martens Eastern) 'keeper Darren Horrigan, makes a fine save this time round, however, visitors Stamford (Dr Martens Eastern) cruised through to the next round winning 6-0. Photo: Peter Barnes.

Mark Highfield seals a fine Alfreton Town (Unibond Prem Div. 1) win with the sides fourth goal to progress through to the First Qualifying round at the expense of home side Stourport Swifts (Dr Martens Western). Photo: Bill Wheatcroft.

FIRST QUALIFYING ROUND

SATURDAY 14 SEPTEMBER 2002 **WINNING CLUBS TO RECEIVE £7500**

Home		Away	Score	Att
Eccleshill United	v	St Helens Town	3-2	89
Gelder, Jones, Verity		Molloy, Poland		
Bedlington Terriers	v	Ossett Albion	1-0	314
Milner				
Radcliffe Borough	v	Abbey Hey	4-1	213
Banim (2), Elliott, Kay		Evans		
Esh Winning	v	Harrogate Railway	1-2	111
Burns		Davey (2)		
Horden CW	v	Shotton Comrades	4-1	93
Davine (3), I'Anson		Buck		
Dunston FB	v	Selby Town	2-0	101
Adamson, Hamil				
Kendal Town	v	North Ferriby United	2-1	267
Sheppard (2)		Powell		
Workington	v	Mossley	2-1	289
Dickinson, Wilson		Taylor		
(15/9)Hallam	v	Stocksbridge Park Steels	2-3	388
Bates		Beckett, Beggs, Ingledow		
Bishop Auckland	v	Rossington Main	3-3	118
Edgcumbe,Skedd,Wilkinson		Debenham, Henderson, Walker		
R(17/9)Rossington Main	v	Bishop Auckland	1-1*	136
Black		Wilkinson		
(Rossington Main won 4-1 on kicks from the penalty mark)				
Jarrow Roofing Boldon CA	v	Billingham Town	2-4	65
Chow (2)		Rowntree, Turner (3)		
Morpeth Town	v	Guisborough Town	0-1	77
		Outhwaite		
West Auckland Town	v	Chorley	6-3	104
Allen (2), Carter, Raitt, Rose, Stout		Mason, Weston, Wilkinson		
Chester -Le-Street T.	v	Penrith	2-0	68
Guggy, Turner				
Great Harwood Town	v	Crook Town	1-1	103
Bursnell				
R(18/9)Crook Town	v	Great Harwood Town	1-1*	158
Dalton		Eastham		
(Great Harwood Town won 8-7 on kicks from the penalty mark)				
Bridlington Town	v	Garforth Town	1-0	213
Harper				
Tow Law Town	v	Matlock Town	5-4	191
McKenna(3),Nicholson,Vasey		Brown, Clarke, Handbury, Taylor		
Witton Albion	v	Ramsbottom United	1-1	303
Rednell		Brierley		
R(17/9)Ramsbottom	v	Witton Albion	2-3	272
Lomax (2)		Burton, Moseley (2)		
Farsley Celtic	v	Lincoln United	3-1	107
Ball, Midwood (2)		Williams		
Durham City	v	Worsbrough Bridge MW	5-1	143
Douglas, Halliday, Healer Irvine (2)		Turner		
Guiseley	v	Hebburn Town	3-0	220
Flower, Stuart, Thackwray				
Peterlee Newtown	v	Louth United	4-0	58
Crosby, Hinton, Jewson (2)				
Spennymoor United	v	Ashington	1-1	236
Lynch		Drysdale		
R(17/9)Ashington	v	Spennymoor United	1-2	283
Herron		Ainsley, Grant		
Atherton Collieries	v	Salford City	1-0	99
Trewhitt				
Alfreton Town	v	Kidsgrove Athletic	0-1	315
		Twigg		
Nantwich Town	v	Rocester	2-0	174
O'Leary				

Home		Away	Score	Att
Eastwood Town	v	Redditch United	1-2	162
Kennerdale		Sutton		
Stamford	v	Oadby Town	3-1	236
Green,Pritchard,Steadman		Miller		
Boston Town	v	Sutton Coldfield Town	1-1	94
Lovelace		Tucker		
R(17/9)Sutton C.	v	Boston Town	2-0	72
Baker, Tucker				
Kings Lynn	v	Quorn	4-1	699
Bacon,Staff,Stephenson(2)		Noble		
Blackstones	v	Pelsall Villa	2-2	67
Harrold (2)		Allen, Tolly		
R(17/9)Pelsall Villa	v	Blackstones	3-2	70
Allen, Howell, Perry		Farrington, Harrold		
Bromsgrove Rovers	v	Gresley Rovers	5-0	794
Banner, Becketts, Burgess Danks, Frost				
Solihull Borough	v	Glossop North End	9-0	221
Amos (2), Hamilton, Hewitt Lovelock, Shepherd, Smith (3)				
Willenhall Town	v	Atherstone United	0-2	167
		Cammock, Charley		
Mickleover Sports	v	Shepshed Dynamo	0-1	244
		Peck		
Arnold Town	v	Biddulph Victoria	1-1	176
Shepherd		Baker		
R(17/9)Biddulph V.	v	Arnold Town	1-2	131
Marron		Brown, Shepherd		
Leek Town	v	Spalding United	2-1	287
Freestone, Hassell		Lawrence		
Stratford Town	v	Bedworth United	1-2	305
Amos		Partridge, Steane		
Stewarts & Lloyds	v	Burnham	0-1	25
		Howell		
Rothwell Town	v	Southend Manor	3-2	142
Smith, Turner (2)		Cox, Curtis		
Cheshunt	v	Edgware Town	4-0	69
Cox, Parry (2), Wales				
Hertford Town	v	AFC Wallingford	1-4	115
Williams		Shildrick,Small-King,Stevens,Wood		
Royston Town	v	London Colney	3-2	98
Easley, Thorne, Ward		Ross (2)		
Hemel Hempstead Town	v	St Neots Town	7-1	165
Hammett (2), Highton (2) Moore, Watters		Kuhne		
Ilford	v	Clacton Town	2-3	138
Emmanuel, March		Brown, Hillier, Howell		
Wootton Blue Cross	v	Wroxham	2-1	110
Griggs, Joswiak		Fox		
Raunds Town	v	AFC Sudbury	1-3	165
Anderson		Betson, Claydon (2)		
Barking & East Ham United	v	Banbury United	1-0	168
Nickle				
Leyton Pennant	v	Great Yarmouth Town	3-3	96
Barnes, Johnston, Jones		Bilham, Howes, Thompson		
R(17/9)Great Yarmouth T.	v	Leyton Pennant	5-1	182
Adcock, Bilham (2), George, Thompson		Field		
Staines Town	v	Uxbridge	1-2	176
		Cleary, Tunnell		
(at Egham Town FC)				
Harefield United	v	Barton Rovers	2-1	104
Dunne (2)		Donnelly		
Tilbury	v	Yeading	0-2	53
(at East Thurrock United FC)		Miller, Telemaque		

Home		Away	Score	Att
Beaconsfield SYCOB	v	Great Wakering Rovers	5-0	76
Dell, Hughes, Jones, Markman, Paris				
Northwood	v	Wisbech Town	1-2	214
Moore		Hill, Sedlan		
Aveley	v	Stotfold	2-2	94
Danny, Keith				
R(17/9)Stotfold	v	Aveley	0-2	93
		Martin (2)		
Diss Town	v	Romford	3-0	265
Gilman, Key, Lindsey				
St Margaretsbury	v	Arlesey Town	1-2	136
Stock		Richards, Samuel		
Southall	v	Yaxley	2-3	41
Kadi, Robinson		Hailstone (2), Harrison		
Flackwell Heath	v	Buckingham Town	2-1	78
Jefferies, Mernagh		Cole		
Leyton	v	Marlow	0-1	92
		Evans		
Wingate & Finchley	v	Ware	2-0	142
Harrold, Shafer				
Bromley	v	BAT Sports	2-1	303
Langley, Luckett		Ferguson		
Herne Bay	v	Cowes Sports	3-2	192
Collins, Denly, Jones		McDonald (2)		
Peacehaven & Telscombe	v	Carterton Town	1-2	71
Lockhart				
Walton & Hersham	v	Cove	3-0	107
Edgar, O'Donnell, Pickett				
Horsham	v	Slade Green	3-0	273
Carney, Charman, Collins				
Lewes	v	Brockenhurst	2-1	243
Newman		Glenister		
Eastleigh	v	Croydon	2-0	209
Hughes, Matthews				
Abingdon United	v	Leatherhead	2-3	178
Curtin, Peirson		Chabaan (2), Inglethorpe		
Chatham Town	v	Godalming & Guildford	2-3	207
Austin, Tilley		Bridger, Lydon, Newman		
Molesey	v	Fisher Athletic	3-0	88
Panter (3)				
Bognor Regis Town	v	Windsor & Eton	4-1	351
Birmingham (2), Hudson Rutherfors		O'Connor		
VCD Athletic	v	Bedfont	2-1	70
Hodgkinson		Williams		
Tunbridge Wells	v	Selsey	2-2	134
Clark, Millins		Dewey, Lee		
R(18/9)Selsey	v	Tunbridge Wells	2-1	164
Chester, Vanson		Millins		
Newport (IW)	v	Maidstone United	0-4	455
		Marshall (3), Webster		
Metropolitan Police	v	Corinthian Casuals	1-0	75
Tomlinson				
Hillingdon Borough	v	Lymington & New Milton	2-3	80
Gallagher, McGinty		Phillips (2), Sims		
Gosport Borough	v	Deal Town	2-1	212
Lindsey, Lis		Hayes		
Eastbourne Borough	v	AFC Newbury	6-2	397
Adams (2), Austin, Price Ramsey, Westcott		Caswell, Romeo		
St Leonards	v	Slough Town	1-2	244
		Gilkes (2)		
Tooting & Mitcham United	v	Cobham	0-0	353
R(17/9)Cobham	v	Tooting & Mitcham	0-3	105
		Endersby, Onochie (2)		

Home		Away	Score	Att
AFC Totton	v	Pagham	3-1	162
James, Sherrington (2)		Miles		
Carshalton Athletic	v	Dorking	4-0	235
Darlington (2), Tagro, York				
Cray Wanderers	v	Whyteleafe (15/9)	1-0	265
Tompkins				
Ringmer	v	Chertsey Town	1-2	120
Johnson				
Chipstead	v	Three Bridges	1-3	84
Mitchell		Langridge, Massaro, Pullen		
St Blazey	v	Bournemouth	1-0	201
Harrington				
Team Bath	v	Backwell United	3-1	62
Cozic (2), Prince		Hewitt		
Torrington	v	Hungerford Town	0-1	149
		Howell		
Yate Town	v	Bideford	0-4	260
		Gough, Pickard, Southgate (2)		
Bemerton Heath Harlequins	v	Shortwood United	2-1	172
Cole, Richardson		Green		
Merthyr Tydfil	v	Chard Town	2-0	461
Price (2)				
Weston Super Mare	v	Wimborne Town	3-1	243
Birkby, Cross, Mehew		Turner		
Clevedon Town	v	Dorchester Town	2-0	195
Vickerman, Watts				
Gloucester City	v	Bashley	3-0	305
Cox, Harris, Thompson				
Devizes Town	v	Taunton Town	0-1	160
		Laight		
Falmouth Town	v	Evesham United	1-2	191
Ashburn		Pratt, Wolsey		
Highworth Town	v	Cinderford Town	2-3	251
Hulbert, Mills		Griffin, Hopkins		
Paulton Rovers	v	Corsham Town	2-1	132
Woods, Woon		Price		

ROUND STATISTICS

No.Games: 99+11 **Home Win:** 61 **Away Win:** 38
Draws: 11 **Home Goals:** 230 **Away Goals:** 149
Hatricks: 6 **Total Attend:** 20,229 **Av Attend:** 184

Best Home Win

Solihull Borough v Glossop North End 9-0

Best Away Wins

Newport (IW) v Maidstone United 0-4

Yate Town v Bideford 0-4

Best Attendance

Bromsgrove Rovers v Gresley Rovers 794

Kings Lynn v Quorn 699

Alfreton Town's (Unibond Prem. Div1) Darren Twigg (No.10) scores the only goal of the game to knock visitors Kidsgrove Athletic (Unibond Prem. Div1) out of the Cup. Photo: Bill Wheatcroft.

Kevin Hughes raps up the scoring for Beaconsfield SYCOB (South Midlands) in the final moments of the game to give the home side a comfortable 5-0 victory over Great Wakering Rovers (Isthmian DivN1). Photo: Gordon Whittingham

Stocksbridge Park Steels' (Unibond Prem. Div.1) substitute Duane Beckett (No.12) scores the visitors equaliser to set his side up for a 3-2 win over Hallam (Northern Counties East Prem.) Photo: Bill Wheatcroft.

SECOND QUALIFYING ROUND

SATURDAY 28 SEPTEMBER 2002 **WINNING CLUBS TO RECEIVE £7500**

Home		Away	Score	Att.
Chester-Le-Street Town	v	Harrogate Railway	5-5	109
Andison, Blower (2) Leadbitter, Turner		Danby, Gore, McDaid, Smith		
R(30/9)Harrogate R.	v	Chester-Le-Street	7-2*	278
Constable, McLean (2) Smith (2), Stansfield, Sunley		Elrington, Grute		
Colwyn Bay	v	West Auckland Town	4-0	235
Graham (3), Limbert				
Hyde United	v	Tow Law Town	7-3	307
Ashwell, Evans (2), Eyre Foster (3)		Innes, Nicholson (2)		
Guisborough Town	v	Guiseley	3-3	190
Mowbray (3)		Cooke, Stuart, Watson		
R(30/9)Guiseley	v	Guisborough Town	1-0	199
Henry				
Stocksbridge Park Steels	v	Ashton United	0-2	270
		Connor, Dormer		
Stalybridge Celtic	v	Workington	2-2	421
Denham, Potts		Murray (2)		
R(1/10)Workington	v	Stalybridge Celtic	3-1	378
Ennis, Goulding, Murray		Hallows		
Bedlington Terriers	v	Vauxhall Motors	1-2	280
Fletcher		Aspinall, Fearns		
Durham City	v	Peterlee Newtown	3-0	217
Brightwell, Dunwell, Irvine				
Gainsborough Trinity	v	Frickley Athletic	3-2	351
Ellington, Nicholson, Stant		Hemstock, Morris		
Whitby Town	v	Bradford (Park Avenue)	0-4	517
		Martin,Maxwell,Prendergast,Stansfield		
Harrogate Town	v	Great Harwood Town	2-0	342
Jackson, Turley				
Marine	v	Eccleshill United	2-2	248
Hussin (2)		Gelder, Harrison		
R(1/10)Eccleshill Utd	v	Marine	2-3*	176
Jones		McNally (2), Taylor		
Runcorn FC Halton	v	Wakefield & Emley	2-0	245
McNeil, Parle				
Bridlington Town	v	Witton Albion	3-1	323
Burdick, Palmer, Thacker		Moseley		
Droylsden	v	Farsley Celtic	4-3	210
Burke, Salmon, Wright (2)		Blackstone, Henderson, Midwood		
Altrincham	v	Kendal Town	1-0	513
Young				
Accrington Stanley	v	Billingham Town	2-0	737
James, Mullin				
Spennymoor United	v	Atherton Collieries	5-0	226
Bell, Brunskill (2), Lee (2)				
Horden CW	v	Worksop Town	0-4	269
		Roberts (2), Townsend (2)		
Rossington Main	v	Radcliffe Borough	0-7	160
		Banim(3),Diggle,Hardy(2),Keeling		
Lancaster City	v	Blyth Spartans	2-4	357
Atkinson, Whittaker		McManhon (2), Robson		
Dunston FB	v	Burscough	2-0	131
Adamson, Hogg				
Gateshead	v	Barrow	3-4	292
Dixon, Goodchild, Preen		Hall, Housham, Necovic (2)		
Shepshed Dynamo	v	Stafford Rangers	0-2	315
		Edwards (2)		
Bedford Town	v	Pelsall Villa	6-1	461
Harrison (2), Lawley, Miller Paul, Smeathers				
Kings Lynn	v	Cambridge City	1-0	1041
Holmes				

Home		Away	Score	Att.
Bromsgrove Rovers	v	Tamworth	1-2	1115
Palmer		Rickards (2)		
Bedworth United	v	Moor Green	1-4	270
McGregor		Lamey (2), Robinson, Walker		
Ilkeston Town	v	Atherstone United	7-0	435
Kelly (5), Mitchell, Nwadike				
Sutton Coldfield Town	v	Halesowen Town	0-2	269
		Ashby, Leadbeater		
Hednesford Town	v	Hucknall Town	0-0	506
R(1/10)Hucknall Town	v	Hednesford Town	3-3*	411
Cooke, Huckerby, Nangle		Jones, Rae, Simkin		
(Hucknall Town won 6-5 on kicks from the penalty mark)				
Redditch United	v	Leek Town	1-1	309
Field		MacPherson		
R(1/10)Leek Town	v	Redditch United	1-2	303
Whittaker		Arshad, Booth		
Nantwich Town	v	Arnold Town	0-3	243
		Shepherd (2), Wilkins		
Solihull Borough	v	Grantham Town	0-2	349
		Clarice (2)		
Worcester City	v	Stamford	3-3	810
Jackson,Lyons,Middleton		Bailey, Ndekwe (2)		
R(1/10)Stamford	v	Worcester City	1-2	365
Bailey		Heeley, Owen		
Hinckley United	v	Kidsgrove Athletic	3-0	283
Jenkins, Sadler (2)				
Walton & Hersham	v	Chesham United	1-0	228
Harkness				
Harefield United	v	AFC Sudbury	4-4	192
Dunne, Keen, Ursell (2)		Bennett (2), Howlett, Norfolk		
R(1/10)AFC Sudbury	v	Harefield Town	5-0	302
Bennett, Betson, Claydon, Norfolk, Owen				
Grays Athletic	v	Marlow	1-0	237
Hayzelden				
Molesey	v	Hitchin Town	3-1	140
Ahmad, Ekoku (2)		Fontenelle		
Hendon	v	Tooting & Mitcham United	3-0	249
Haworth (2), Yates				
Leatherhead	v	Bromley	1-1	321
Webb		Amoako		
R(1/10)Bromley	v	Leatherhead	2-4	415
Watts (2)		Chadban, Ruggles (3)		
Godalming & Guildford	v	Hampton & Richmond Borough	0-1	201
		Sestanovich		
AFC Wallingford	v	Eastbourne Borough	0-1	238
		Goodwin		
Clacton Town	v	Kingstonian	2-3	465
Gove, Pack		Clarke, Sills		
Billericay Town	v	Yeading	3-1	448
Graham (2), Williams		Newby		
Hayes	v	Bognor Regis Town	6-0	311
Cochrane, Hodge (2), Jaruis, Jolly, Molesley				
AFC Totton	v	Slough Town	2-2	342
Bundy, Osman		Palmer, Winston		
R(1/10)Slough Town	v	AFC Totton	2-0	360
Browne, Spencer				
Rothwell Town	v	Barking & East Ham United	1-0	221
Turner				
Maidenhead United	v	Welling United	1-2	285
Allen		Nade, Sodje		
Lewes	v	Eastleigh	0-0	437
R(2/10)Eastleigh	v	Lewes	2-4*	357
Kenna, Matthews		Clark, Driscoll, Reid, Venables		

Crawley's (Dr Martens Prem.) Ernie Cooksey (3) fires in a spectacular volley against visitors Great Yarmouth Town (Dr Martens East). Photo: Alan Coomes.

Rothwell (Dr Martens East) midfielder Jamie Kearns puts an Barking & East Ham United (Isthmian Div.N1) striker under pressure, during his sides' 1-0 home win. Photo: Peter Barnes.

Aveley (Isthmian Div.1N) skipper Wes Faulkner heads powerfully away from the challenge of Three Bridges' (Sussex Div.1) Sean Gilby. Photo: Franics Short.

Home		Away	Score	Att
Horsham	v	Yaxley	2-0	320
Charrman (2)				
Havant & Waterlooville	v	Harrow Borough	2-1	210
Taylor (2)		Fitzsimon		
Diss Town	v	Chertsey Town	2-3	321
Key, Miller		Bere, Pomroy, Taylor		
Canvey Island	v	Folkestone Invicta	2-1	429
Forbes, Gregory		Ayling		
Carshalton Athletic	v	Chelmsford City	1-1	577
Oueifio		Gray		
R(2/10)Chelmsford C.	v	Carshalton Athletic	1-0*	537
Samuels				
(29/5)Maidstone Utd	v	Boreham Wood	2-5	937
Butler, Ribbens		Dixon (2), Forrester,Meah (2)		
Heybridge Swifts	v	Sutton United	1-1	58
Hunter		Watson		
R(1/10)Sutton United	v	Heybridge Swifts	1-2	385
Fowler		Abrahams, Rainford		
Uxbridge	v	Braintree Town	1-2	130
Frape		Cousins, Cowan		
Hastings United	v	Selsey	4-1	400
Flanagan (2), Playford, Webb		Selsey		
Flackwell Heath	v	Royston Town	2-2	84
Bowler, Franklin		Howard, Smith		
R(2/10)Royston Town	v	Flackwell Heath	0-0*	152
(Flackwell Heath won 5-3 on kicks from the penalty mark)				
Hemel Hempstead Town	v	Cray Wanderers	3-1	181
Bruce, Hammett, Nartey		Tompkins		
Enfield	v	Bishop's Stortford	1-5	161
Coppard		Hyatt, Paul (2), Southam, Sugrue		
Beaconsfield SYCOB	v	Gosport Borough	1-2	80
Markman		Hensman (2)		
Burnham	v	Herne Bay	0-1	65
		Collins		
Aldershot Town	v	Aylesbury United	3-1	1681
Moody (2), Taylor		Williams		
Dover Athletic	v	Basingstoke Town	2-0	824
Dent, Glover				
Lymington & New Milton	v	Cheshunt	3-1	175
		Parry		
Carterton Town	v	Arlesey Town	0-6	173
		Cort (3), Reynolds, Samuel, Tekell		
Crawley Town	v	Great Yarmouth Town	3-0	723
Hockton,McDonnell,Stevens				
Wisbech Town	v	VCD Athletic	6-1	426
Flanz(2),Furnell,Jimson(2),Sedlan		Penny		
Wootton Blue Cross	v	Purfleet	0-4	121
		Akurang,Bowes,Georgiou,Simpson		

Home		Away	Score	Att
Three Bridges	v	Aveley	1-3	149
McKenzie		Blunden (2), Mosely		
Ford United	v	Metropolitan Police	4-2	59
Allen,Boffong,Hacket,Poole		Tomlinson (2)		
St Albans City	v	Wingate & Finchley	2-0	532
Crawshaw, De Souza				
Tiverton Town	v	Taunton Town	1-1	1380
Chenoweth		Laight		
R(2/10)Taunton Town	v	Tiverton Town	0-2	1365
		Ovens (2)		
Bath City	v	Merthyr Tydfil	5-0	744
Foster(2), Rollo(2), Thorne				
Weston Super Mare	v	Clevedon Town	2-0	552
Bevan, Mehew				
Gloucester City	v	Newport County	1-1	774
Hoskins		Davis		
R(30/9)Newport Co.	v	Gloucester City	4-0	619
Davis (2), Walker				
Team Bath	v	Bemerton Heath Harlequins	6-1	385
Cozic, Lavety (3), Lewis Sobara		Cole		
Bideford	v	St Blazey	3-1	715
Gough, Pickard, Southgate		Richardson		
Hungerford Town	v	Paulton Rovers	2-1	113
Hopkins (2)		Perry		
Evesham United	v	Cinderford Town	1-1	187
Pratt		Donovan		
R(1/10)Cinderford Tn	v	Evesham United	0-5	171
		Bullock, Jukes (2), Pinkney, Pratt		
Chippenham Town	v	Weymouth	1-4	917
Paul		Dean, Jones, Phillips (2)		

ROUND STATISTICS

No.Games: 84+17 **Home Win:** 48 **Away Win:** 36
Draws: 17 **Home Goals:** 212 **Away Goals:** 168
Hatricks: 8 **Total Attend:** 39,027 **Av Attend:** 386

Best Home Wins
Ilkeston Town v Atherstone United 7-0
Hayes v Bognor Regis Town 6-0

Best Away Wins
Rossington Main v Radcliffe Borough 0-7
Carterton Town v Arlesey Town 0-6

Best Attendance
Aldershot Town v Aylesbury United 1681

Purfleet (Isthmian Prem) take an early lead with this George Georgiou's penalty, and never looked back from there going on to beat Wooton Blue-Cross (U.Co Prem) 4-0. Photo: Gordon Whittingham.

Left: Purfleet's Steve Pashley in an aerial challenge with Flackwell Heath's match-winner Gavin Mernagh. Photo: Francis Short.

Right: James Body, Hastings, looks set to make on challenge on Hendon's Iain Duncan. Photo: Roger Turner.

Marvin Samuel heads Arlesey Town into the lead during their 2-1 away win against Isthmian Division One North rivals Hemel Hempstead. Photo: Steve Ayre.

Adam Miller, of Grays Athletic, gets in a timely challenge to block fellow Isthmian Premier League side Hayes' Justin Cochran from getting in a shot on goal, in Grays 2-1 home win. Photo: Alan Coomes.

THIRD QUALIFYING ROUND

SATURDAY 12 OCTOBER 2002 **WINNING CLUBS TO RECEIVE £10,000**

Home		Away	Score	Att
Harrogate Railway	v	Workington	4-0	402
Ames (2), Smith (2)				
Droylsden	v	Spennymoor United	0-0	342
R(15/10)Spennymoor	v	Droylsden	3-2	342
Ainsley, Lee, Lynch		Porter, Salmon		
Accrington Stanley	v	Harrogate Town	0-0	1112
(15/10)Harrogate Town	v	Accrinton Stanley	3-2	602
Bonsall, McNaughton (2)		Halford, Smith		
Bradford (Park Avenue)	v	Bridlington Town	3-5	425
Maxwell (2), Stansfield				
Burdick,Harrison(2),Palmer,Thacker				
Vauxhall Motors	v	Gainsborough Trinity	6-1	226
Cumiskey (2), Fearns, Haddrell (2), Lawton		Stant		
Durham City	v	Blyth Spartans	1-1	713
Mudd		Baker		
R(17/10)Blyth Spartans	v	Durham City	3-1	832
Brumwell, Emerson, Pepper				
Barrow	v	Hyde United	3-1	1074
Bullimore, Hume		Hargreaves		
Ashton United	v	Runcorn FC Halton	0-3	347
		Lightfoot, McNeil, Price		
Dunston FB	v	Marine	0-1	297
		Black		
Colwyn Bay	v	Radcliffe Borough	1-2	425
Limbert		Banim (2)		
Guiseley	v	Altrincham	2-1	428
Senior, Stuart		Band		
Ilkeston Town	v	Kings Lynn	6-1	694
Kielt (3), Mitchell, Whitehead, Woolley				
Redditch United	v	Arnold Town	0-1	465
		Hudson		
Hinckley United	v	Tamworth	1-3	1139
Mitchell		Cooper, Follett, Hatton		
Moor Green	v	Halesowen Town	3-1	649
Lamey (2), Scheppel		Ashby		
Wisbech Town	v	Bedford Town	1-0	833
Petty				
Hucknall Town	v	Worcester City	1-0	697
Mayman				
Grantham Town	v	Worksop Town	1-0	915
Neil				
Stafford Rangers	v	Rothwell Town	3-0	849
Davidson, Gibson, Lovatt				
Canvey Island	v	Aveley	2-0	423
Boylan, Protheroe				
Billericay Town	v	Braintree Town	4-0	715
Campbell,Essandoh,Graham(2)				
Heybridge Swifts	v	Herne Bay	1-0	270
Budge				
Hemel Hempstead T.	v	Arlesey Town	1-2	337
Bruce		Reynolds, Samuel		
Dover Athletic	v	Welling United	2-2	1302
Dent, Glover		Nade, Riviere		
R(15/10)Welling Utd	v	Dover Athletic	1-3	735
Powell		Day, Nicky, Spiller		

Home		Away	Score	Att
Molesey	v	Chertsey Town	3-1	287
Brandy (2), Sheffield		Burton		
Bishop's Stortford	v	Eastbourne Borough	1-0	452
Southam				
Flackwell Heath	v	Purfleet	1-0	204
Mernagh				
Grays Athletic	v	Hayes	2-1	315
McLean, Vaughan		Hastings		
AFC Sudbury	v	Walton & Hersham	2-0	374
Bishop, Claydon				
Hastings United	v	Hendon	2-1	795
Simmonds, Webb		Forbes		
Slough Town	v	Hampton & Richmond Borough	4-2	537
Boot (3), Howard		Ocquaye, Riddell		
St Albans City	v	Chelmsford City	1-0	839
De Souza				
Boreham Wood	v	Kingstonian	2-0	498
Honeyball				
Leatherhead	v	Ford United	1-2	333
Inglethorpe		Bejada, Willis		
Horsham	v	Hungerford Town	1-0	607
Charman				
Havant & Waterlooville	v	Evesham United	4-0	329
Hambley, Haughton, Taylor, Wood				
Weston Super Mare	v	Bath City	0-5	1029
		Eaton (3), Kemp, Rollo		
Bideford	v	Gosport Borough	3-1	916
Gough, Pickard, Southgate		Scammell		
Aldershot Town	v	Lewes	2-0	1870
Moody (2)				
Newport County	v	Team Bath	0-3	736
		Kamara-Taylor, Lewis, Sorbara		
Lymington & New Milton	v	Crawley Town	0-2	480
		Fear, Hockton		
Tiverton Town	v	Weymouth	4-2	1191
Nancekivell, Peters (2)		Ashford, Whiteman		

ROUND STATISTICS

No.Games: 42+4 **Home Win:** 30 **Away Win:** 12
Draws: 4 **Home Goals:** 89 **Away Goals:** 53
Hatricks: 3 **Total Attend:** 29,382 **Av Attend:** 639

Best Home Wins

Vauxhall Motors v Gainsborough Trinity 6-1

Ilkeston Town v Kings lynn 6-1

Best Away Win

Weston Super Mare v Bath City 0-5

Best Attendance

Aldershot Town v Lewes 1870

Carl Shutt, Kettering Town (Conference), climbs above a Hastings Town (Dr Martens Prem.) defender to head towards goal. Photo: Roger Turner.

Guiseley (Unibond Div1) 'keeper James Shutt manages to turn round the post a shot from Tamworth's (Dr Martens Prem.) Mark Cooper, during their 3-3 draw. Photo: Darren C Thomas.

Luke Prince, Team Bath (Western Lge) holds off Horsham's (Isthmian Div1S) Andy Salako. Photo: Franics Short.

FOURTH QUALIFYING ROUND

SATURDAY 26 OCTOBER 2002 **WINNING CLUBS TO RECEIVE £20,000**

Home		Away	Score	Att
Wisbech Town	v	Harrogate Town	0-2	1061
		Bonsall, Whellans		
Blyth Spartans	v	Runcorn FC Halton	1-3	851
Pery		Leadbitter, Lunt, McNeil		
Morecambe	v	Grantham Town	3-1	1055
Drummond, Rogan (2)		Clarke		
(27/10)Telford United	v	Doncaster Rovers	0-2	1012
		Barnes (2)		
Ilkeston Town	v	Stafford Rangers	0-5	903
		Bailey, Davidson (2), Heath, Lovatt		
Burton Albion	v	Halifax Town	2-1	1990
Dudley, Kirkwood		Quailey		
Moor Green	v	Leigh RMI	2-1	525
Gayle (2)		Maamria		
Harrogate Railway	v	Marine	4-2	703
Davey (2), Smith (2)		Bainbridge, Black		
Arnold Town	v	Scarborough	0-2	910
Northwich Victoria	v	Spennymoor United	3-1	713
Norris, Quinn, Woodward		Shan		
Hucknall Town	v	Vauxhall Motors	1-1	593
Prindiville		Young		
R(29/10)Vauxhall M.	v	Hucknall Town	5-1	401
Cumiskey, Fearns, Hadrell (2), Young		Mayman		
Guiseley	v	Tamworth	3-3	724
Senior (2), Trevitt		Follett, Hallam, Warner		
R(29/10)Tamworth	v	Guiseley	2-3	1124
Hallam, Hemmings		Senior, Summer		
Southport	v	Bridlington Town	4-1	1004
Lloyd,Whitehall(2),Winstanley		Brunton		
Radcliffe Borough	v	Chester City*	2-4	1138
Banim, Hardy		Cameron, Sugden (3)		
Nuneaton Borough	v	Barrow	1-1	1623
Love		Tarrant		
R(29/10)Barrow	v	Nuneaton Borough	4-3	1919
Anthony (2), Tarrant (2)		McGregor, Quayle		
AFC Sudbury	v	St Albans City	1-2	702
Claydon		De Souza, Moran		
Bishop's Stortford	v	Boreham Wood	1-1	969
Williamson		Boyle-Renner		
R(28/10)Boreham W.	v	Bishop's Stortford	4-1	903
Boyle-Renner, Browne, Dixon, Grime		Joun		
Heybridge Swifts	v	Bideford	2-0	516
Budge, Cobb				
Bath City	v	Yeovil Town (27/10)	1-1	3470
Cleverley		Lockwood		
R(29/10)Yeovil Town	v	Bath City	3-1	4393
Demba (2), McIndoe		Foster		
Slough Town	v	Canvey Island	3-2	875
Boot (2)		Brayley, Forbes		
Aldershot Town	v	Dagenham & Redbridge	0-4	2491
		Bruce, Hill, Matthews, McDougald		
Hastings United	v	Kettering Town	0-0	1538
R(29/10)Kettering Tn	v	Hastings United	0-5	1144
		Playford,Remy,Yates,Zahana-Oni(2)		
Havant & Waterlooville	v	Billericay Town	3-1	631
Blake, Haughton, Taylor		Wallace		
Hereford United	v	Arlesey Town	1-0	1718
Parry				
Horsham	v	Team Bath	0-0	1543
R(28/10)Team Bath	v	Horsham	1-1*	1581
Lewis		Charman		
(Team Bath won 4-2 on kicks from the penalty mark)				
Gravesend & Northfleet	v	Margate	1-2	1827
Stadmart		Collins, Keister		
Forest Green Rovers	v	Ford United	2-1	601
Odejayi, Richardson		Kimble		
Flackwell Heath	v	Crawley Town	1-4	567
Mernagh		Cooksey, Harkin, Holmes, Hooper		
Dover Athletic	v	Woking	1-1	1636
Dent		Simpemba		
R(29/10)Woking	v	Dover Athletic	1-2	1806
Abbey		Day, Tyne		
Barnet	v	Tiverton Town	0-2	1390
		Mudge (2)		
Grays Athletic	v	Stevenage Borough	1-2	757
Vaughan		Jackson, Trott		
Molesey	v	Farnborough Town	0-6	514
		Baptiste (3), Butterworth, Holloway Piper		

ROUND STATISTICS

No.Games: 32+8 **Home Win:** 16 **Away Win:** 16
Draws: 8 **Home Goals:** 64 **Away Goals:** 76
Hatricks: 2 **Total Attend:** 49,821 **Av Attend:** 1,246

Best Home Win
Vauxhall Motors v Hucknall Town 5-1
Best Away Win
Molesey v Farnborough Town 0-6
Best Attendance
Yeovil Town v Bath City 4393

Gravesend's Akpo Sodje gets in a downward header before Margate's Paul Lamb (3) can get in a challenge, during this all Conference affair, which Margate won 2-1.

Photo: Alan Coomes

Jamie Window goes past Bristol City's Lee Peacock during the Isthmian Premier sides 0-7 defeat....

....it could have been so different though had this strike, from the same player, not have come back off the post in the first minute of the match.

More action from the Heybridge Swifts v Bristol City match, here we Swifts' David Rainsford shielding the ball from City's Joe Burnell. Photos: Roger Turner.

FIRST ROUND PROPER

SATURDAY 16 NOVEMBER 2002 **WINNING CLUBS TO RECEIVE £20,000**

Farnborough Town (5) 5 Harrogate Town (1) 1

Baptiste 2, 35, Taggart 6 Hunter 11

Charlery 13, Lenny Piper 21 Att: 1,090

Farnborough: Pennock,Warner,Bunce,Laker,Gregory,Chris Piper,Lenny Piper (Butterworth 74),Taggart (Annon78), Carroll, Charlery (Green 65),Baptiste

Subs not used: Osborn, Patterson,

Harrogate Town: Connor ,Richardson ,McNaughton ,Merris (Turley ,25) ,Sykes (Aspin ,45) ,David Donaldson (Kerr ,45) ,Bonsall ,Sturpy ,Hunter ,Marcelle ,Whellans

Subs not used Jackson, Mitchell,

Tiverton Town (1) 1 Crawley Town (1) 1

Pears 18 McDonnell 36 Att: 1840

Tiverton Town: Edwards, Winter, Rudge, Peters, Haines, Rogers, Rees, Cousins, Holloway (Nancekivell 59), Mudge (Ovens 68), Pears (Everett 68).

Subs not used: Lynch, Steele

Crawley T: Little, Judge, Cooksey, Hooper, Pullan, Fear (Hemsley 89), Holmes, Harkin, Le Bihan, Stevens, McDonnell.

Subs not used Hockton, Bagnall, Payne, Brake.

(26/11)Crawley Town(0) 3 TivertonTown (1) 2

McDonnell 66, 80, Bagnall 87 Pears 8, 64 Att: 3,907

Crawley T: Little, Judge,Cooksey ,Hooper (Bagnall 73), Pullan, Fear, Holmes, Harkin (Hemsley 89), Le Bihan,McDonnell, Stevens.

Subs not used: Hockton, Payne, Patterson.

Tiverton Town: Edwards,Peters,Rudge,Cousins,Winter (Mudge 89),Haines (Steele 89),Nancekivell,Rees,Rogers,Everett,Pears.

Subs not used Ovens, Lynch, Holloway.

Dover Athletic (0) 0 Oxford United (1) 1

Oldfield 22 Att: 4,302

Dover: Hyde,Browne,Readings, Arnott,Norman,Day,Chapman, Spiller,Dyer (Glover 69),Tyne,Dent.

Subs not used: Davies, James, Sykes, Williams.

Northwich Victoria (0) 0 Scunthorpe United (1) 3

Torpey 38, 48, 72 (p)

Att: 1,680

Northwich: Parry,Came,Ingram,Walsh (Quinn 56),Sedgemore, Devlin, Val Owen,Norris,Street, Allan (Garvey 62),Blundell.

Subs not used: Connett, Taylor, Davis.

Yeovil Town (0) 0 Cheltenham Town (1) 2

Alsop 8, Devaney 64

Att: 6,455

Yeovil: Weale, Skiverton, Pluck (Grant 57), O'Brien, Lindegaard (Demba 83),Way, Crittenden, McIndoe, El Kholti, Giles, Forinton (Alford 66).

Subs not used: Sheffield, Thompson.

Chesterfield (0) 1 Morecambe (1) 2

Davies 74 Elam 43, Thompson 90

Att: 3,703

Morecambe: Mawson, Swan, McKearney, Bentley,Hill, Colkin, Stringfellow, Drummond, Rigoglioso (Thompson 77), Elam (Black 83), Carlton (Perkins 83).

Subs not used Gouck, Ubershar.

AFC Bournemouth (1) 2 Doncaster Rovers (0) 1

Thomas 38, Elliott 73 Gill 71 Att: 5,371

Doncaster: Warrington,Marples, Ryan, Morley, Price,Hudson, Gareth Owen (Watson 77), Albrighton (Barrick 83), Paterson (Gill 59), Barnes, Jackson (sent off 54).

Subs not used Nelson, Foster.

Dagenham & Redbridge (3) 3 Havant & Waterlooville (2) 2

McDougald 14, Shipp 18,24 Haughton 21, 27 Att: 1,546

Dag & Red: Roberts, Smith, Heffer, Matthews, Potts (Vickers 65) Janney,Terry(Hill 65), Shipp,Bruce, McDougald, West(Perkins 86)

Subs not used: Gothard, Chambers.

Havant & W: Kerr,Masson,Ferrett,Hale,Hall,Hanson,Paul Wood,Hambley,Howe,Taylor,Haughton.

Subs not used Gayle, Davis, Ford, Craig Leworthy, Sparshatt.

Team Bath (0) 2 Mansfield Town (3) 4

Heiniger 71, Kamara-Taylor 83 Lawrence 19,36, Tisdale 43 (og), Christie 56

Att: 5,469

Team Bath: Northmore,Watson,Wisson,Ball,Tisdale,Nichols,Matt Lewis (Fulham 66),Cozic (Heiniger 38),Prince,Sorbara (Kamara-Taylor 45),Lavety.

Subs not used: Gibson, Chris Lewis.

Bristol Rovers (0) 0 Runcorn FC Halton(0) 0

Att: 4135

Runcorn: McMillan,Parle,Lightfoot,Tomlinson,Ellis,Ness,Lunt (Gamble 72),Morley,Leadbetter,McNeil (Watson 46),Kinney.

Subs not used Winstanley, Baines, McGinn.

(26/11) Runcorn FCH(1) 1 Bristol Rovers (1) 3

Barrett 19 (og) Grazioli 17, Carlisle 108, Gilroy 119 Att: 2,434

Runcorn: McMillan,Carragher,Ellis,Tomlinson,Ness,Parle (sent off 102),Lunt,Morley,Gamble,Leadbetter,McNeil (Watson 22)

Subs not used: Baines, Dacey, McGinn, Winstanley.

Leyton Orient (1) 1 Margate (1) 1

Martin 25 Keister 42 Att: 3,605

Margate: Mitten, Oates, Lamb, Edwards, Shearer, Porter, Keister (Munday 86), Saunders, McFlynn, Sodje, Collins.

Subs not used Smith, Perry, Turner, Griffiths.

(26/11) Margate (0) 1 Leyton Orient (0) 0

Keister 51 (pen) Att: 2,048

at Dover Athletic FC

Margate: Mitten, Shearer, Edwards, Porter, Oates, Lamb, Saunders (Munday 83), Sodje, McFlynn, Collins, Keister

Subs not used: Smith, Beard, Turner, Griffiths.

Oldham Athletic (1) 2 Burton Albion (1) 2

Low 18, Hall 90 Webster 42 (p), Dudley 59

Att: 5,806

Burton: Duke, Henshaw, Reddington, Hoyle (sent off 23), Talbot, Dudley (Kavanagh 75), Clough, Kirkwood, Glasser, Webster, Moore (Anderson 81).

Subs not used Blount, Robinson, Glover.

(27/11) Burton Albion(0) 2 Oldham Athletic (0) 2

Moore 84, 110 Wijnhard 50, Eyres 116

Att: 3,416

(Oldham Athletic won 5-4 on kicks from the penalty mark)

Burton: Duke,Henshaw,Reddington,Hoyle,Talbot (Sinton 83),Kirkwood (Anderson 58),Glasser,Clough,Stride,Webster,Moore (Blount 111)

Subs not used: Robinson, Kavanagh.

Barrow (1) 2 Moor Green (0) 0

Holt 16, Salmon 49 Att: 2,650

Barrow: Bishop, Shaw, Salmon, Hume, Maxfield, Anthony (sent off 74), Housham,Rogers, Warren, Arnold (Dawson 68), Holt

Subs not used: Hall, Tearney, Bullimore, Liddicott.

Moor Green: Rachel, Hughes, Gillard, Sanders, Robinson, Stanley (Faulds 52), Woodley (Evans 75) ,Lamey, Gayle (Blake 84), Martin, Myers. Subs not used Walker, Scheppel.

Shrewsbury Town (2) 4 Stafford Rangers (0) 0

Jemson 32, Wilding 39,74 Att: 5,114
Tolley 89
Stafford Rangers: Price, Alex Gibson, Carter, Barrow, Daniel, Lovatt, Robinson (McAughtrie 81), Robert Heath (Downes 80), Edwards (Bailey 55), Davidson,Robin Gibson.
Subs not used Beale, Ward.

Hereford United (0) 0 Wigan Athletic (0) 1

Green 90 Att: 4,086
Hereford: Baker, Clarke, Tretton, James, Rose, Galloway, Parry, Williams, Pitman (Wright 89), Guinan, Eribenne.
Subs not used: Griffiths, Purdey, Teesdale, Smith.

Forest Green Rovers (0) 0 Exeter City (0) 0

(17/11) Att: 2147
Forest Green: Perrin, Coupe, Jones, Richardson, Lee Russell, Matthew Russell (Grayson 69), Owers (Allen 88), Foster, Sykes, Meechan, Odejayi.
Subs not used: Shuttlewood, McLoughlin, Futcher.

(26/11) Exeter City (1) 2 Forest Green Rovers (1) 1

Sheldon 25, Moore 85 Richardson 20 Att: 2,951
Forest Green: Perrin, Lee Russell, Jones, Richardson, Jenkins, Matthew Russell, Owers, Foster, Sykes (Grayson 82), Odejayi, Meechan.
Subs not used Shuttlewood, Allen, Coupe, Langan.

Scarborough (0) 0 Cambridge United (0) 0

Att: 2084
Scarborough: Woods, Shepherd, Holdsworth, Hotte, Ormerod, Henry (Sillah 78), Stoker, Pounder, Keith Scott, Raw (Fatokun 70), Campbell (Blunt 75).
Subs not used: Walker, Dryden.

(26/11) Cambridge U.(1) 2 Scarborough (0) 1

Wanless 31, Hotte 97 (og) Jordan 90 Att: 3,373
Scarborough: Woods, Hotte, Holdsworth, Shepherd, Ormerod, Stoker, Jordan, Pounder (Blunt 63), Campbell (Rose 63), Keith Scott, Raw (Fatokun 45).
Subs not used Dryden, Walker.

Stevenage Borough (1) 1 Hastings United (0) 0

Howell 6 Att: 1,821
Stevenage: Westhead, Trott, Gary MacDonald, Stirling, Travis (Wormull 45), Howell, Blackwood, Scott (Jamie Campbell 66), Fraser, Midson (MacDonald 71), Jackson.
Subs not used: Sigere, Wilson.
Hastings Utd: King, Burt, Osborne, Adam Flanagan (sent off 87), Yates, McArthur, Playford, Simmonds (Ruddy 80), Hegley, Honey (Webb 80), Zahana-oni (sent off 90).
Subs not used Body, Cornwall, Brown.

Colchester United (0) 0 Chester City (0) 1

Tate 83 Att: 2,901
Chester: Brown, Brady (Michael Brown 66), Guyett, Bolland, Hatswell, McIntyre, Carey, Carden, Davies, Clare (Blackburn 88), Tate (Ruffer 89).
Subs not used Sugden, Beesley.

Torquay United (2) 5 Boreham Wood (0) 0

Russell 6 (p), Gritton 43,62
Kyffour 76, Fowler 89 Att: 2,739
Boreham W: Imber, Wotton, Lee Harvey, Howard (Wall 71), Grime, Meah (Raymond 62), Browne, Boyle-Renner, Honeyball (sent off 29), Forrester, Kodra (Walker 45).
Subs not used Sappleton, Addai.

Vauxhall Motors (0) 0 Q.P.R. (0) 0

(at Chester City FC) Att: 3507
Vauxhall Motors: Ralph, Collins, McDermott, Brazier, Haddrell, Lawton, Aspinall, Nesbitt (Lynch 87), Young, Fearns, Cumiskey.
Subs not used: Thompson, Hogg, Derek Ward, Welton.

(26/11) Q.P.R. (1) 1 Vauxhal Motors (1) 1

Thomson 18 Brazier 22 Att: 5,336
(Vauxhall Motors won 4-3 on kicks from the penalty mark)
Vauxhall Motors: Ralph, Lawton (Thompson 119), Brazier, Collins, McDermott, Nesbitt, Aspinall (Lynch 71), Haddrell, Cumiskey, Fearns, Young (Welton 81).
Subs not used Hogg, Derek Ward.

Slough Town (1) 1 Harrogate Railway (0) 2

Bubb 30 Smith 53, Davey 68
Att: 1,687
Slough T: McCann, Howard, Barrowcliff, Palmer, Brown, Bryon Bubb, Spencer, Metcalfe, Alvin Bubb (Wilkinson 77), Winston, Boot (Deaner 73).
Subs not used: Gyoury, Briach, Jean-Zepherin.
Harrogate Railway: Neale, Ames, Danby, Wilson, Watkinson, Walker, Stansfield, Gore, McLean (Constable 87), Smith (Hart 73), Flynn (Davey 50).
Subs not used McDade, Phillpott.

Heybridge Swifts (0) 0 Bristol City (4) 7

Att: 2,046 Roberts 16, 40, Tinnion 40 (pen)
Murray 45, 61, Lita 66, 82
Heybridge: Banks, Blackwell,John Pollard, Culverhouse, Barber, Abrahams, Tomlinson (Gough 60), Baillie, Rainford, Budge, Windows (Hunter 68).
Subs not used: Payne, Cobb, Bruce.

Luton Town (2) 4 Guiseley (0) 0

Spring 3, Brkovic 45, 65,
Thorpe 45 Att: 5,248
Guiseley: Hill, Peter Atkinson, Freeman, Trevitt, Shaw, James Nettleton (Reilly 67), Henry, Sumner, Stuart (Chattoe 79), Senior (Newhouse 63), Cooke.
Subs not used Shutt, Hey.

Southport (1) 4 Notts County (2) 2

Pickford 43, 60, Allsopp 8, 41
Thomson 75, Lane 90 Att: 3,519
Southport: Welsby, Barry Jones, Clark, Winstanley, Lane, Pickford, Soley, Gibson, Howell (Steve Jones 74), Lloyd-Williams (Thomson 50), Whitehall.
Subs not used: Dickinson, Sullivan, Scott.

Stockport County (2) 4 St Albans City (0) 1

Beckett 24, Fradin 42 Browne 68
Burgess 57 (p), 80 Att: 3,303
St Albans C: Wilmot, Smith, Campbell (Moran 69), Derek Browne, Gould (sent off 54), Kean (Mackail-Smith 75), Castle, Challinor, Oakes, De Souza (Crawshaw 65), Stafford Browne.
Subs not used Roberts, Naylor.

ROUND STATISTICS

No.Games: 40+10 **Home Win:** 21 **Away Win:** 19
Draws: 10 **Home Goals:** 79 **Away Goals:** 77
Hatricks: 1 **Total Attend:** 189,660 **Av Attend:** 3,793

Best Home Win
Torquay United v Boreham Wood 5-0
Best Away Win
Heybridge Swifts v Bristol City 0-7
Best Attendance
Hull City v Macclesfield Town 8003

St Alban's City's Stafford Browne chellenges for the ball during his side's 1-4 defeat at Second Division Stockport County.

Miguel De Souza takes on the Stockport defence during the same match.

Photos: Bill Wheatcroft.

Stevenage Borough (Conference) 'keeper, Mark Westhead, makes a fine save from Third Division Darlington's Ashley Nicholls. Photo: Bill Wheatcroft.

Simon Travis on the attack for Stevenage during their 1-4 defeat at Darlington.

Photo: Bill Wheatcroft.

Boro's Richard Howell meets the ball first to make the scores level after just four minutes.

Photo: Bill Wheatcroft.

SECOND ROUND

Harrogate Railway (0) 1 - (1) 3 Bristol City
Davey 78 | 3,500 | Walker 20 (og), Murray 53, Roberts 90

Harrogate Railway: Neale, Walker, Danby, Wilson, Watkinson (Constable 69), McLean, Ames, Gore, Stansfield (Hart ,77), Flynn (Davey 56),Smith. Subs not used: Sunley, McDade.

Crawley Town (1) 1 - (1) 2 Dagenham & Redbridge
McDonnell 3 | 4,516 | McDougald 26, Janney 88

Crawley T: Little, Judge, Cooksey, Hooper (sent off 79), Pullan, Fear, Holmes (Hemsley 70), Harkin (Payne 80), Le Bihan, McDonnell (Hockton 88), Stevens. Subs not used: Bagnall, Brake.
Dag & Red: Roberts, Matthews, Potts, Smith (Vickers 45), Shipp, McGrath, Terry, Janney, Heffer, McDougald, West (Stein 76). Subs not used Gothard, Hill, Pitcher,

---

Darlington (2) 4 - (1) 1 Stevenage Borough
Hodgson 2, Offiong 38,63, Conlon 46 | 2661 | Howell 4

Stevenage: Westhead, Trott (Stirling 53), Jamie Campbell, Gary MacDonald, Wormull, Howell (Midson 54), Scott, Louis Riddle, Travis, MacDonald, Sigere (McMahon 62). Subs not used Wilson, Boyd.

Macclesfield Town (0) 2 - (0) 0 Vauxhall Motors
Lightbourne 82, Tipton 90 | 2,972

Vauxhall Motors: Ralph, Lawton, McDermott, Brazier, Haddrell, Collins, Aspinall, Nesbitt (Lynch 84), Cumiskey (Welton 85), Young, Fearns. Subs not used Thompson, Hogg, Derek Ward.

Margate Town (0) 0 - (2) 3 Cardiff City
1,362 | Thorne 28, Boland 34, Fortune-West 88

Margate: Mitten, Edwards, Shearer, Porter (Munday 85), Oates, Saunders, Sodje, McFlynn (Beard 73), Lamb (Clarke 58), Keister, Collins. Subs not used: Smith, Turner.

Morecambe (2) 3 - (2) 2 Chester City
Bently 28, 45, Rigoglioso 57 | 4,293 | Bolland 25, Clare 42

Morecambe: Mawson, McKearney, Bentley, Swan, Colkin, Rigoglioso, Stringfellow, Drummond, Elam (Murphy 87), Thompson (Black 74), Carlton (Curtis 65). Subs not used: Talbot, Ubershar.
Chester: Brown, Brady (Ruffer 52), Guyett, Hatswell, Bolland, McIntyre, Carey (Kelly 52), Carden, Davies (Michael Brown 66), Sugden (sent off 45), Clare. Subs not used Twiss, Beesley.

Shrewsbury Town (2) 3 - (0) 1 Barrow
Van Blerk 7, Jemson 19, 76 | 3232 | Housham 60

Barrow: Bishop, Shaw, Maxfield, Salmon, Hume, Warren, Housham (Tearney 89), Gaughan, Arnold (Robinson 83),Bullimore, Holt. Subs not used Hall, Rogers, Liddicott.

Southport (0) 0 - (2) 3 Farnborough Town
2,534 | Lenny Piper 26, Carroll 39, Green 76

Southport: Dickinson, Barry Jones, Clark, Winstanley, Lane (sent off 90), Soley, Steve Jones, Gibson, Howell (Sullivan 69), Thomson, Whitehall. Subs not used: Lloyd-Williams, Scott, Bauress, Welsby.
Farnborough: Pennock, Warner, Bunce, Laker, Gregory, Carroll, Watson, Lenny Piper (Holloway 70), Chris Piper, Charlery, Baptiste (Green 76). Subs not used Taggart, Osborn, Annon.

THIRD ROUND

	Plymouth Argyle	(1) 2	-	(1) 2	Dagenham & Redbridge
	Stonebridge 44, Wotton 61		11,885		Terry 13, McDougald 67

Dag & Red: Roberts, Heffer, Smith, Matthews, Vickers, Janney, Terry, Shipp, McGrath, West (Hill 85), McDougald (Rooney 89). Subs not used Gothard, Potts, Stein.

Replay	Dagenham & Redbridge	(1) 2	-	(0) 0	Plymouth Argyle
	Shipp 20, McDougald 85		4,530		

Dag & Red: Roberts, Smith, Matthews, Vickers, Janney, Terry, Heffer, Shipp, McGrath, McDougald, West(Rooney77). Subs not used: Gothard, Stein, Hill, Potts.

	Darlington	(2) 2	-	(2) 3	Farnborough Town
	Nicholls 13, Clark 37		4,260		Baptiste 10, Carroll 19, 60

Farnborough: Pennock, Warner, Bunce, Laker, Gregory, Butterworth (Annon 89), Watson, Carroll, Holloway, Charlery (Vansittart 88), Baptiste. Subs not used Taggart, Green, Benstead.

	Ipswich Town	(1) 4	-	(0) 0	Morecambe
	Clapham 2, Darren Bent 65, 77, Ambrose 75		18,529		

Morecambe: Mawson, Thompson (Murphy 22), McKearney, Bentley (sent off 20), Swan, Colkin (Ubershar 23), Rigoglioso (Talbot 68), Drummond, Stringfellow, Elam, Carlton. Subs not used Black, Curtis.

FOURTH ROUND

Norwich City 1 (0) - (0) 0 Dagenham & Red.

Abbey 90

Att: 21,164

THE TEAM			THE TEAM
Green			Roberts
Drury			Smith
Mackay			Heffer
Fleming			Matthews
Russell			Vickers
Mulryne			Shipp
Holt			Janney
McVeigh			Terry
Rivers		S70	McGrath
Roberts		S89	West
Nielson	S77		McDougald
SUBS			**SUBS**
Abbey	(77)		Cole
Crichton			Hill
Henderson			Gothard
Kenton		(70)	Rooney
Llewellyn		(89)	Stein

Farnborough 1 (0) - (2) 5 Arsenal

Baptiste 71

Campbell 19
Jeffers 23, 68
Bergkamp 74
Lauren 79

Att: 35,108 at Highbury

THE TEAM			THE TEAM
Pennock			Taylor
Warner			Lauren
Gregory			Campbell
Bunce			Cycan
Annon			van Bronckhorst
Watson			Vieira
Lee	SO28	S56	Pires
Carroll	S86		Parlour
Holloway	S76	S66	Toure
Charlery	S80		Jeffers
Baptiste		S76	Kanu
SUBS			**SUBS**
Butterworth	(80)	(56)	Bergkamp
Chris Piper	(76)	(76)	Edu
Lenny Piper	(86)		Luzhny
Taggart			Seaman
Vansittart		(66)	Wiltord

Above: Norwich City 'keeper, Robert Green, is put under pressure by Dagenham's Paul Terry.

Right: Dagenham's Junior McDougald is closed down by Darel Russell.

Below: The Cannaries' goalkeeper, Robert Green, shows a 'safe pair of hands' from this Paul Terry corner. Photos: Peter Barnes.

Action from Farnborough's dream tie at Highbury. Top: Danny Carroll challenges Puscul Cygan, whilst Wiltord controls the ball under pressure from Justin Gregory. Photos Stuart MacFarlane. Inset: Tony Pennock safely catches an Arsenal corner. Photo: Eric Marsh.

F.A. CUP
PRIZE MONEY

	EP	P	1Q	2Q	3Q	4Q	1P	2P	3P	TOTAL
Dagenham & Redbridge						20000	20000	30000	50000	120000
Farnborough Town						20000	20000	30000	50000	120000
Morecambe						20000	20000	30000		70000
Harrowgate Railway		1000	7500	7500	10000	20000	20000			66000
Barrow				7500	10000	20000	20000			57500
Crawley Town				7500	10000	20000	20000			57500
Vauxhall Motors				7500	10000	20000	20000			57500
Guiseley		1000	7500	7500	10000	20000				46000
Slough Town		1000	7500	7500	10000	20000				46000
Spennymoor United		1000	7500	7500	10000	20000				46000
Team Bath		1000	7500	7500	10000	20000				46000
Chester City						20000	20000			40000
Southport						20000	20000			40000
Stevenage Borough						20000	20000			40000
Boreham Wood				7500	10000	20000				37500
Dover Athletic				7500	10000	20000				37500
Harrogate Town				7500	10000	20000				37500
Hastings Town				7500	10000	20000				37500
Havant & Waterlooville				7500	10000	20000				37500
Heybridge Swifts				7500	10000	20000				37500
Moor Green				7500	10000	20000				37500
Runcorn FC Halton				7500	10000	20000				37500
St Albans City				7500	10000	20000				37500
Stafford Rangers				7500	10000	20000				37500
Tiverton Town				7500	10000	20000				37500
Bridlington Town	500	1000	7500	7500	10000					26500
AFC Sudbury		1000	7500	7500	10000					26000
Arlesey Town		1000	7500	7500	10000					26000
Arnold Town		1000	7500	7500	10000					26000
Bideford		1000	7500	7500	10000					26000
Flackwell Heath		1000	7500	7500	10000					26000
Horsham		1000	7500	7500	10000					26000
Molesey		1000	7500	7500	10000					26000
Radcliffe Borough		1000	7500	7500	10000					26000
Wisbech Town		1000	7500	7500	10000					26000

F.A. CUP
TOP GOAL SCORERS

10 GOALS

P. Jackson	Stocksbridge PS

9 GOALS

K. Smith	Harrogate Railway
J. Banim	Radcliffe Borough

8 GOALS

S. Davey	Harrogate Railway

7 GOALS

R. Baptiste	Farnborough Town

6 GOALS

A. Claydon	AFC Sudbury
M. Samuel	Arlesey Town
M. Midwood	Farsley Celtic
E. Tomlinson	Met. Police

5 GOALS

R. Shepherd	Arnold Town
P. McDonald	Cowes Sports
N. McDonnell	Crawley Town
J. McDougald	Dagenham & Red.
R. Matthews	Eastleigh
D. Bridger	Godalming & G.
B. Hammett	Hemel Hempstead
G. Charman	Horsham
A. Chabaan	Leatherhead
T. Boot	Slough Town
P. Garrett	Stotfold
C. Kamara-Taylor	Team Bath
R. Hailstone	Yaxley

4 GOALS

A. Shildrick	AFC Wallingford
P. Moody	Aldershot Town
N. Sylla	Banbury United
J. Milner	Bedlington Terriers
O. Pickard	Bideford
M. Southgate	Bideford
K. Wilkinson	Bishop Auckland
L. Wilkinson	Chorley
L. Huggins	Fisher Athletic
S. Malbranque	Fulham
N. Thompson	Gt Yarmouth Town
R. Senior	Guiseley
M. Stuart	Guiseley
B. Dunne	Harefield United
W. Haughton	Havant & W'looville
J. Taylor	Havant & W'looville

4 goals continued....

L. Jones	Herene Bay
M. McGinty	Hillingdon Borough
L. Kelly	Ilkeston Town
P. Kiely	Ilkeston Town
J. Sheppard	Kendal Town
A. Inglethorpe	Leatherhead
K. Gill	Lymington & N.M.
S. Butler	Maidstone United
R Van Nistelroy	Manchester United
N. Lamey	Moor Green
J. Miller	Oadby Town
G. Coulbourne	Paulton RoversC.
Reader	Portland United
J. Turner	Rothwell Town
M. Smith	Royston Town
S. Kuhne	St Neots Town
G. Pritchard	Stamford
P. Massaro	Three Bridges
S. Nicholson	Tow Law Town
M. Haddrell	Vauxhall Motors
M. Moseley	Witton Albion
G. Ndah	Wolverhampton W.

Junior McDougald, scorer of five FA Cup goals, was unlucky not to add to his tally during Dagenham's 1-0 defeat by Norwich City in teh Fourth Round.

Photo: Peter Barnes.

F.A. CUP ATTENDANCE COMPARISON
Seasons 2000-01 - 2002-03
PRELIMINARY & QUALIFYING ROUNDS

Season	Round	Games	Total Attendance	Average Attendance	Ave. +/- (%)
2000-01	Extra Preliminary	19	2,515	132	-
2001-02		15	2,135	142	8%
2002-03		54	6,796	126	-11%
2000-01	Preliminary	240	32,688	136	-
2001-02		230	28,444	124	-9%
2002-03		235	35,195	150	21%
2000-01	1st Qualifying	119	19,319	162	-
2001-02		123	20,979	171	6%
2002-03		110	20.229	184	8%
2000-01	2nd Qualifying	106	37,523	354	-
2001-02		103	40,971	398	12%
2002-03		101	39,027	386	-3%
2000-01	3rd Qualifying	52	23,180	446	-
2001-02		50	30,801	616	38%
2002-03		46	29,382	639	4%
2000-01	4th Qualifying	42	43,431	1,034	-
2001-02		43	55,619	1,293	25%
2002-03		40	49,821	1,246	-4%
2000-01	Totals	578	158,656	274	-
2001-02		564	178,949	317	16%
2002-03		586	180,450	310	-2%

COMPETITION PROPER

Season	Round	Games	Total Attendance	Average Attendance	Ave. +/- (%)
2000-01	1st Round	48	171,399	3,571	-
2001-02		52	198,937	3,825	8%
2002-03		50	189,660	3,793	-0.8%
2000-01	2nd Round	26	123,420	4,747	-
2001-02		24	120,358	5,015	6%
2002-03		24	104,601	4,358	-13%
2000-01	3rd Round	40	575,052	14,376	-
2001-02		38	564,855	14,865	3%
2002-03		39	573,961	14,717	-1%
2000-01	4th Round	19	398,241	20,960	-
2001-02		17	330,365	19,433	-7%
2002-03		20	403,950	20,198	4%
2000-01	5th Round	11	250,899	22,809	-
2001-02		9	244,356	27,151	19%
2002-03		9	241,427	26,825	-1%
2000-01	6th Round	4	100,663	25,165	-
2001-02		5	173,492	34,698	38%
2002-03		5	153,658	30,732	-11%
2000-01	Semi-Final	2	103,578	51,789	-
2001-02		2	97,315	48,658	-6%
2002-03		2	99,772	49,886	3%
2000-01	Final	1	72,500		
2001-02		1	73,963		
2002-03		1	73,726		
2000-01	Totals	151	1,795,752	11,892	-
2001-02		148	1,803,641	12,187	3%
2002-03		150	1,840,755	12,272	0.7%

F.A.CUP WINNERS PRIZE MONEY FOR SEASON 2003-2004 AND DATES OF ROUNDS

Extra Preliminary Round	£500	Saturday 23 August
Preliminary Round	£1,000	Saturday 30 August
First Qualifying Round	£2,250	Saturday 13 September
Second Qualifying Round	£3,750	Saturday 27 September
Third Qualifying Round	£5,000	Saturday 11 October
Fourth Qualifying Round	£10,000	Saturday 25 October
First Round Proper	£12,500	Saturday 8 November
Second Round Proper	£15,000	Saturday 6 December
Third Round Proper	£50,000	Saturday 3 January
Fourth Round Proper	£75,000	Saturday 24 January

TELEVISION FEES

Live Broadcasts	
First & Second Rounds Proper	£50,000 per club.
Third to Sixth Rounds Proper	£265,000 per club.
Highlights Broadcast	
First & Second Rounds Proper	£9,000 per club
Third to Sixth Rounds Proper	£30,000 per club

RADIO FEES

Full match commentary	£9,000 per club
Half Match commentary	£4,500 per club
20-45 minutes	£2,250 per club
0-19 minutes	No Fee.

F.A. UMBRO TROPHY

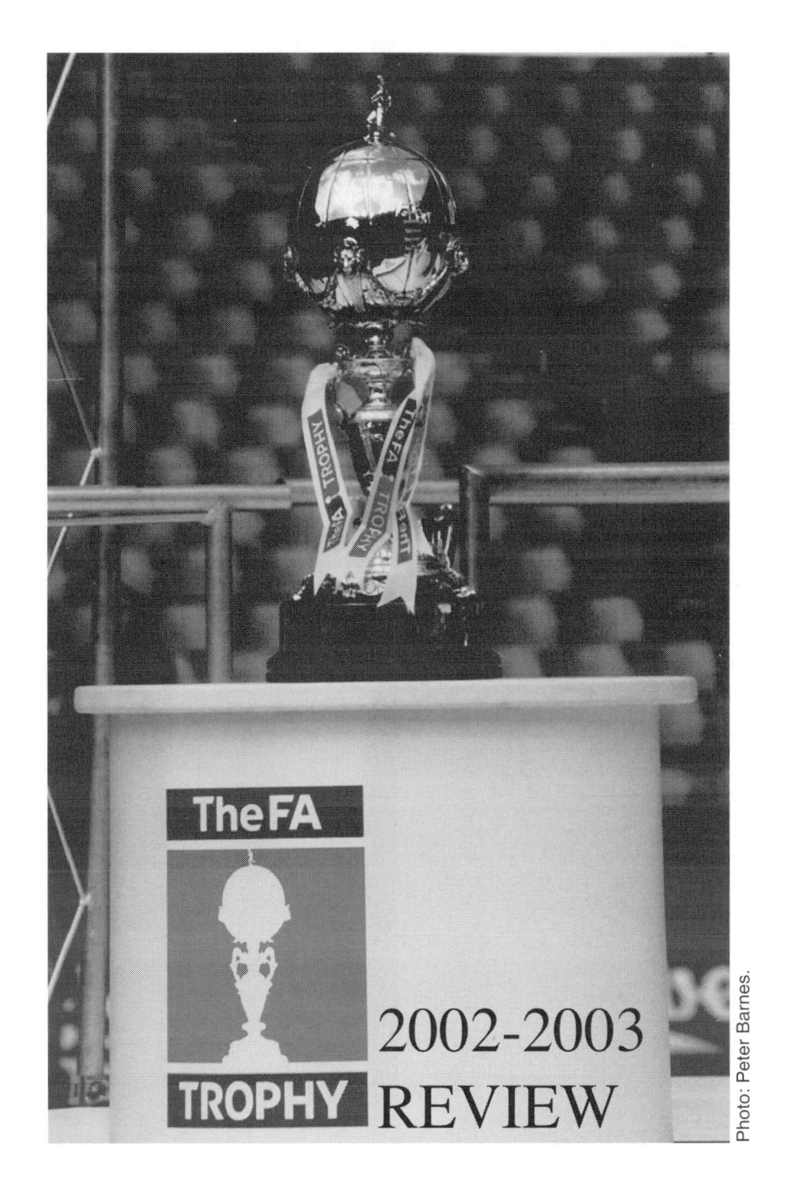

Photo: Peter Barnes.

PRELIMINARY ROUND

SATURDAY 5 OCTOBER 2002 **WINNING CLUBS TO RECEIVE £600**

Home		Away	Score	Att
Chorley	v	Stocksbridge Park S.	1-1	238
Eatock		Green		
R(8/10)Stocksbridge	v	Chorley	1-0	134
Green				
Alfreton Town	v	Guiseley	5-0	248
Bettney, Godber (2) Knapper				
Rocester	v	Workington	2-2	92
Ede, Wade		Murray (2)		
R(8/10)Workington	v	Rocester	2-2*	350
Goulding, Murray		Alexander, Seward		
(Rocester won 4-3 on kicks from the penalty mark)				
Rossendale United	v	Witton Albion	2-2	232
Brooks (2)		Furnival, Pritchard		
R(8/10)Witton Albion	v	Rossendale United	2-0	203
Burton, Moseley				
Farsley Celtic	v	Ossett Town	1-0	140
Smithard				
Trafford	v	Belper Town	2-0	123
Cowley, McAllister				
Lincoln United	v	Bishop Auckland	4-3	114
Panson,Smith (2),Williams		Dixon, Edgcumbe, Lake		
Bamber Bridge	v	Leek Town	2-2	201
Leaver, Shepherd		MacPherson, Sucharewycz		
R(8/10)Leek Town	v	Bamber Bridge	3-1*	203
MacPherson,Martin,Whittaker				
North Ferriby United	v	Matlock Town	3-0	181
Fisher, Lowthorpe, Wood				
Radcliffe Borough	v	Eastwood Town	0-1	160
		Kennerdale		
Shepshed Dynamo	v	Taunton Town	2-2	133
Mackay, Morris		Laight, Redwood		
R(8/10)Taunton Town	v	Shepshed Dynamo	3-0	251
Gammon, Laight				
Atherstone United	v	Gloucester City	0-1	170
		Hoskins		
Rothwell Town	v	Cinderford Town	4-0	125
Kearns (2),McIluain,Turner				
Racing Club Warwick	v	Clevedon Town	0-1	100
		Jefferies		
Bromsgrove Rovers	v	Banbury United	0-1	607
		Sylla		
Solihull Borough	v	Sutton Coldfield T.	2-0	237
Lovelock, Smith				
Mangotsfield United	v	Stourport Swifts	4-2	280
Campbell,Edwards,Elsey,Seal		Bayliss, Shirley		
Merthyr Tydfil	v	Evesham United	2-0	391
Dorrian, Mainharing				
Bedworth United	v	Corby Town	0-1	148
		Foreman		
Croydon Athletic	v	Tonbridge Angels	0-3	198
		Barnes, Cass, Portway		
Histon	v	Wingate & Finchley	3-0	98
Andrews, Cambridge (2)				
Leyton Pennant	v	Oxford City	0-2	63
		Whitehead, Wimble		
East Thurrock United	v	Sittingbourne	2-0	157
Bauckham, Cartlidge				

Home		Away	Score	Att
Fleet Town	v	Epsom & Ewell	1-1	142
Haddow		Rogers		
R(9/10)Epsom & E.	v	Fleet Town	2-0	83
Hall, Huckle				
Dorchester Town	v	Yeading	4-1	316
Groves (2), Jermyn (2)		Miller		
Aveley	v	Newport (IW)	2-0	83
Curran, Mosely				
Spalding United	v	Barton Rovers	3-0	189
Goodhand, Lewsam (2)				
Harlow Town	v	Uxbridge	2-2	113
McNally, Southgate		Bamford, Tunnell		
R(8/10)Uxbridge	v	Harlow Town	1-2*	122
Bamford		Blaney, Cowley		
Bracknell Town	v	Fisher Athletic	2-2	122
Hammonds, Williams		Ponsford, Powell		
R(7/11)Fisher Athletic	v	Bracknell Town	4-7*	111
Barr(2), Fletcher, Powell		Crittenden(4),Osgood,Smith,Teague		
Corinthian Casuals	v	Barking & East Ham U.	4-3	82
Georgiou, Goodwin, Raishbrook, Waghorn		Dormer, Regis (2)		
Burnham	v	Arlesey Town	3-1	103
Bartley,Walkington,Wordsworth		Cort		
(6/10)Wealdstone	v	Banstead Athletic	0-0	236
R(8/10)Banstead Ath.	v	Wealdstone	0-1*	101
		Beckford		
Erith & Belvedere	v	St Leonards	2-0	102
Billenness, Neufville				
Hornchurch	v	Walton & Hersham	2-6	263
Fox, Jones		Dolan(2),Edgar(2),O'Donnell,Whelan		
Metropolitan Police	v	Dulwich Hamlet	1-1	112
Prins		Perkins		
R(8/10)Dulwich Hamlet	v	Metropolitan Police	3-1	119
Coleman, Kadi, Side		Tomlinson		
Hertford Town	v	Molesey	1-0	109
Williams				
Northwood	v	Tooting & Mitcham U.	0-2	172
		Forbes, Onochie		
Windsor & Eton	v	Ashford Tn. (Middx)	2-1	147
Adams, Manuel		Jolly		
Kings Lynn	v	Chertsey Town	4-0	601
Holmes(2),Stephenson,Watts				
Salisbury City	v	Dartford	2-0	410
Funnell, King				
Berkhamsted Town	v	Leatherhead	6-0	137
Aldridge, Hall, Nightingale Pedder, Smith, Webb				
Slough Town	v	Wembley	2-0	341
Boot (2)				
Bashley	v	Marlow	1-2	187
		Ryder, Wilkins		
Bognor Regis Town	v	Wivenhoe Town	5-2	303
Murphy, Russell (2), Wyatt 92)		Carmichael, Henson		
Horsham	v	Tilbury	4-0	302
Carney, Castrechino, Charman, Geddes				

Right: Cinderford Town's (Dr Martens West) player/manager is put under pressure by Rothwell Town (Dr Martens East) striker Jason Turner, scorer of one of Rothwell's four goals, in their home victory over Cinderford.
Photo: Peter Barnes.

Below: Chris Whelan scores with his head during Walton & Hersham's (Isthmian 1S) 6-2 win away to Hornchurch (Isthmian 1N).
Photo: Gordon Whittingham.

Bottom: Jamie Goodwin scores Corinthian Casuals' (Isthmian 1S) winner, in the home side's 4-3 victory over Barking & East Ham United (Isthmian 1N).
Photo: Francis Short.

FIRST ROUND

SATURDAY 2 NOVEMBER 2002 **WINNING CLUBS TO RECEIVE £750**

Home		Away	Score	Att
Spennymoor United	v	Witton Albion	4-3	248
Beasley,Cullen,Jones,Shan		Johnson, Moseley, Rendell		
Blyth Spartans	v	North Ferriby United	5-3	432
Forster,Hutton,McMahon(2)		Knight, Powell (2)		
Burscough	v	Marine	0-0	242
R(4/11)Marine	v	Burscough	1-3*	224
Bainbridge		Lawless, Martindale (2)		
Gresley Rovers	v	Harrogate Town	0-0	302
R(5/11)Harrogate T.	v	Gresley Rovers	3-0	276
Hunter, Whellans (2)				
Droylsden	v	Ashton United	2-1	327
Burke, Wright		Miller		
Lincoln United	v	Alfreton Town	2-3	168
Smith, Williams		Goddard, Heath, Hindley		
Stocksbridge P.S.	v	Whitby Town	0-1	182
		Gildea		
Gateshead	v	Hyde United	0-2	122
		Foster (2)		
Leek Town	v	Eastwood Town	4-1	226
Danylyk, Hassell, MacPherson,Suchwarewycz		Butler		
Farsley Celtic	v	Trafford	7-2	113
Beech, Freeman, Iqbal, Midwood (2),Smithard,Stevenson		Collins (2)		
Rocester	v	Colwyn Bay	0-2	108
		Furlong (2)		
Kidsgrove Athletic	v	Frickley Athletic	1-1	100
Morgan		Evans		
R(5/11)Frickley Ath.	v	Kidsgrove Athletic	2-1*	92
Bernard, Jackson		Nolan		
Gainsborough Trinity	v	Kendal Town	3-1	345
Ellington, Eshelby, Stant		Walmaley		
Mangotsfield United	v	Redditch United	3-1	216
Davis, Hallett,Seal		Arshad		
Corby Town	v	Rothwell Town	0-5	184
		Foley, Garside, Kearns, Mitus		
Halesowen Town	v	Bath City	4-3	403
Ashby (2), Colwell, Elmes		Eaton (2), Thorne		
Grantham Town	v	Hinckley United	3-2	413
Clarke (2), Minett		Dakin, March		
Banbury United	v	Gloucester City	1-1	478
Sylla		Bayliss		
R(5/11)Gloucester C.	v	Banbury United	2-1	326
Hoskins, Wilkinson		Redknap		
(5/11)Weston S.M.	v	Cirencester Town	2-2	125
Bevan, O'Hagan		McCabe, Reasoh		
R(7/11)Cirencester T.	v	Weston Super Mare	3-2*	120
Hunt, McCabe, Robinson		Bevan, O'Hagan		
(after abandoned tie on 2/11, 1-1 45 mins, waterlogged pitch)				
Solihull Borough	v	Swindon Supermarine	7-1	148
Cooper,Corbett,Shepherd(3) Thomas, Titterton		Bennett		
Clevedon Town	v	Hednesford Town	2-4	172
Dew, Price		Airdrie, Francis, Piearce (2)		
Rugby United	v	Hucknall Town	2-1	218
Hall (2)		Williams		
Taunton Town	v	Merthyr Tydfil	1-2	346
Redwood		Belle, Pritchard		
Thame United	v	Bromley	3-2	120
Stewart, West (2)		Amaning, Harris		
Great Wakering Rovers	v	Ford United	2-2	145
Ewers, Pilkington		Fiddes, Whyte		
R(5/11)Ford United	v	Great Wakering R.	6-1*	88
Bajada, Fiddes, Kimble O'Sullivan, Poole, Whyte		Hampshire		
Burnham	v	Aylesbury United	0-2	200
		Baker, Manuella		

Home		Away	Score	Att
Oxford City	v	Egham Town	4-2	108
Charles,Craker,Dark,Simms		Deluca, Edwards		
Corinthian Casuals	v	Croydon	1-0	53
Waghorn				
Hastings United	v	Chelmsford City	1-0	599
Zahana-Oni				
Hitchin Town	v	Chatham Town	3-1	256
Bone (2), Brennan		Neal		
Lewes	v	Slough Town	6-4	320
Amanoel, Curnow, Green, Hack, Reid		Bubb (2), Giles		
East Thurrock United	v	Kingstonian	1-3	293
Mallon		Jones, Tomlinson, Wingfield		
Tooting & Mitcham U.	v	Dulwich Hamlet	2-3	421
Dowling (2)		Adeniyi, Perkins (2)		
Aveley	v	Weymouth	1-4	74
Curran		Charles, Phillips, Rawlinson (2)		
Harlow Town	v	Wealdstone	2-0	221
Ansell, Blaney				
Horsham	v	Ashford Town	2-0	301
Butcher, Flemming				
Whyteleafe	v	Walton & Hersham	1-5	148
Hynes		Dolan, Edgar(3), Wimble		
Worthing	v	Cambridge City	1-4	256
Knee		Dooding,Hayes,Nightingale,Wardley		
Staines Town	v	Epsom & Ewell	1-2	126
Butler		Hall, Ingham		
Carshalton Athletic	v	Folkestone Invicta	2-1	347
Johnson, Todd		Tait		
Bracknell Town	v	Heybridge Swifts	0-2	136
		Budge, Hunter		
Windsor & Eton	v	Welling United	2-2	174
Adams, Brady		Seabury, Standen		
R(5/11)Welling United	v	Windsor & Eton	3-5	247
Hogg, Nade (2)		Manuel, O'Connor (4)		
Sutton United	v	Harrow Borough	2-1	332
Bolt, Corbett		Gavin		
Hemel Hempstead T.	v	Histon	2-3	109
Watters, West		Andrews, Rowe (2)		
Salisbury City	v	Erith & Belvedere	2-2	431
Brown, Thomas		Adams, Gowler		
R(12/11)Erith & Bel.	v	Salisbury City	2-0	93
Benetts, Davy				
Berkhamsted Town	v	Bishop's Stortford	2-2	191
Richardson, Yates		Joun, Southam		
R(5/11)Bishops Stort.	v	Berkhamsted Town	2-0	221
Paul (2)				
Eastbourne Borough	v	Hertford Town	4-1	355
Ducille,Ramsey (2),Smart		Cooper		
Bognor Regis Town	v	Boreham Wood	2-0	306
Hudson, Leigh				
Chippenham Town	v	Dorchester Town	4-1	534
Griffin,Horgan,Mings,Paul		Hann		
Spalding United	v	Hampton & Rich. Boro.	2-1	199
Goodhand, Greentham		Cory		
Marlow	v	Bedford Town	1-1	226
Shepherd		Slinn		
R(5/11)Bedford Town	v	Marlow	1-2	368
Slinn		Gibson, Ryder		
Tonbridge Angels	v	Maidenhead United	3-2	448
Barnes (2), Pavey		O'Connor, Yakk		
Kings Lynn	v	Stamford	1-2	637
Holmes		Ndekwe (2)		
Enfield	v	Basingstoke Town	1-2	91
Armstrong		Ewin, McAllister		

Above: Opportunity missed, as Bedford (Isthmian Premier) watch this effort go over the bar during their 1-2 replay defeat at home to Marlow (Isthmian 1N).
Below: Basingstoke's (Isthmian Premier) Craig McAllister fails to add to his early goal as he fires this shot over the goal, however, his side progress through to the next round, beating Enfield (Isthmian Premier) 2-1 on the day.
Photos: Gordon Whittington.

SECOND ROUND

SATURDAY 30 NOVEMBER 2002 **WINNING CLUBS TO RECEIVE £1000**

Home		Away	Score	Att
Droylsden	v	Colwyn Bay	1-2	221
Haarhoff		Graham, Limbert		
Stafford Rangers	v	Alfreton Town	0-2	782
		Bradshaw, Knapper		
Moor Green	v	Blyth Spartans	2-3	285
Blake, Sanders		Brumwell, McMahon, Williams		
Spennymoor United	v	Halesowen Town	1-1	268
Lee		Stone		
R(3/12)Halesowen T.	v	Spennymoor United	4-1	391
Ashby (2),Hines,Leadbitter		Woodhouse		
Tamworth	v	Accrington Stanley	4-1	951
Hallam, Hemmings (3)		James		
Worksop Town	v	Solihull Borough	4-2	555
Kotylo, Smith, Todd (2)		Campbell (2)		
Runcorn FC Halton	v	Rugby United	0-3	263
		Hall, Pearson (2)		
Histon	v	Farsley Celtic	3-4	141
Andrews, Rowe (2)		Bairston,Blackstone,Iqbal,Stevenson		
Harrogate Town	v	Burscough	2-2	291
Hunter, Whellans		Taylor, Teale		
R(3/12)Burscough	v	Harrogate Town	3-2	160
Lawless, Norman, Wright		McNaughton, Mohan		
Vauxhall Motors	v	Frickley Athletic	4-2	185
Cumiskey, Fearns, Welton		Morris (2)		
Stalybridge Celtic	v	Rothwell Town	2-0	473
Davis, Eastwood				
Wakefield & Emley	v	Spalding United	5-0	227
Bambrook(3),Gomersal,Ryan				
Leek Town	v	Hyde United	3-1	303
MacPherson,Whittaker(2)		Ferguson		
Ilkeston Town	v	Hednesford Town	3-1	436
Freestone (2), Kelly		Maguire		
Lancaster City	v	Stamford	6-1	181
Atkinson, Brown, Love, Welch (2), Yates		Pritchard		
Grantham Town	v	Gainsborough Trinity	0-1	525
		Eshelby		
Barrow	v	Whitby Town	4-2	853
Bullimore, Holt, Hume (2)		Dixon, Dunning		
Bradford Park Avenue	v	Altrincham	0-1	437
		Thornley		
Chippenham Town	v	Aylesbury United	0-1	580
		McGrath		
Hastings United	v	Eastbourne Borough	0-2	906
		Ducille, Ramsey		
Heybridge Swifts	v	Weymouth	2-1	314
Sodje		Hutchinson		
Dover Athletic	v	Ford United	2-0	804
Glover, Spiller				
Canvey Island	v	Carshalton Athletic	2-0	385
Minton, Parmenter				
Windsor & Eton	v	Hitchin Town	3-1	195
Brady, Carroll, Rosier		Nolan		

Home		Away	Score	Att
Oxford City	v	Braintree Town	1-0	146
Wise				
Gloucester City	v	Merthyr Tydfil	0-0	417
R(3/12)Merthyr Tydfil	v	Gloucester City	0-1	340
		Cox		
St Albans City	v	Hayes	0-1	468
		Case		
Havant & Waterlooville	v	Billericay Town	1-1	277
Hambley		Wallacef		
R(3/12)Billericay Town	v	Havant & Waterlooville	1-2*	327
Wallace		Taylor (2)		
Basingstoke Town	v	Sutton United	0-2	528
		Fowler (2)		
Horsham	v	Thame United	1-2	327
Geddes		Avery, Freeman		
Kingstonian	v	Erith & Belvedere	5-1	372
Pinnock, Sills, Thurgood Wingfield (2)		Adams		
Grays Athletic	v	Tiverton Town	3-1	334
Burnett, Cooper, Douglas		Mudge		
Purfleet	v	Tonbridge Angels	3-2	244
Bowes, Keeling		Greatorex (2)		
Harlow Town	v	Lewes	0-3	178
		Allen, Green, Reid		
Bishop's Stortford	v	Marlow	2-2	349
Brauam, Uyatt		Evans, Pritchard		
R(3/12)Marlow	v	Bishop's Stortfprd	2-3	145
Pritchard		Brauam (2), Trevor		
(tie awarded to Marlow – Bishop's Stortford removed for playing an ineligible player)				
Newport County	v	Epsom & Ewell	2-1	489
Cowe, Shephard		Stevens		
Chesham United	v	Walton & Hersham	0-0	243
R(3/12)Walton & H.	v	Chesham United	0-1	133
		Hay		
Bognor Regis Town	v	Hendon	1-4	266
Russell		Crace, Ofori, Randall, Towler		
Mangotsfield United	v	Dulwich Hamlet	0-1	297
		Allen		
Cambridge City	v	Crawley Town	0-1	327
		McDonnell		
Worcester City	v	Aldershot Town	1-0	1562
Wilde				
Corinthian Casuals	v	Cirencester Town	0-4	103
		Hopkins (2), Knight (2)		

Top left: Purfleet's (Isthmian Premier) fires in a shot past the visitor's Danny Tingley, during the home side's 3-2 win over Tonbridge (Dr Martens East).
Photo: Alan Coomes.

Top right: Bradford Park Avenue's (Unibond Premier) Jason Maxwell looks to take the ball off Altrincham's (Unibond Premier) Gary Talbot, during Altrincham's 1-0 away win.
Photo: Darren C Thomas.

Left: Steve Yates and Danny Simmonds combine to set up another attack for Hastings (Dr Martens Premier)in their 0-2 defeat at home to Eastbourne Borough (Dr Martens East).
Photo: Roger Turner.

Below: Stafford Rangers' (Dr Martens Premier) Craig McAughtrie (stripes) clears this Alfreton (NPL 1) attack but the away side claim a 0-2 victory to progress through to the next round.
Photo: Bill Wheatcroft.

THIRD ROUND

SATURDAY 11 JANUARY 2003 | **WINNING CLUBS TO RECEIVE £1100**

Home		Away	Score	Att
(14/1)Farsley Celtic	v	Gainsborough Trinity	1-1	217
Smithard		Ellinston		
R(21/1)Gainsborough	v	Farsley Celtic	2-1	336
Stant, Timons		Beech		
Kettering Town	v	Altrincham (14/1)	1-1	1072
Shutt		Adams		
R(14/1)Altrincham	v	Kettering Town	3-3*	436
Murphy,Shuttleworth,Smith		Asombang, Murphy, Norman		
(Altrincham won 5-3 on kicks from the penalty mark)				
(15/1)Chester City	v	Worksop Town	1-2	1393
Twiss		Smith, Townsend		
(14/1)Leek Town	v	Southport	1-2	428
Danylyk		Jones, Lane		
Alfreton Town	v	Halesowen Town	2-1	681
Hobson, Johnson		Collins		
(14/1)Leigh RMI	v	Vauxhall Motors	1-2	229
Robertson		Fearns (2)		
(14/1)Rugby United	v	Telford United	0-2	404
		Brown, Moore		
(14/1)Stalybridge Celtic	v	Scarborough	0-3	613
(14/1)Northwich Victoria	v	Barrow	3-1	543
Blundell, Quinn		Shaw		
Wakefield & Emley	v	Burton Albion	1-0	802
Senior				
(14/1) Ilkeston Town	v	Burscough	0-3	248
		Bowen, Hyland, Norman		
Tamworth	v	Nuneaton Borough	3-0	2045
Cooper, Hallam, Jephcott				
(14/1)Lancaster City	v	Morecambe	0-1	2257
		Elam		
Colwyn Bay	v	Blyth Spartans	1-0	321
Furlong				
(14/1)Halifax Town	v	Doncaster Rovers	4-1	1770
Fitzpatrick, Killeen (2), Quailey		Green		
(14/1)Woking	v	Chesham United	3-0	1284
Abbey, Patmore (2)				
(14/1)Dover Athletic	v	Gravesend & N'fleet	1-0	814
Spiller				
(14/1)Stevenage Bor.	v	Oxford City	2-1	846
Campbell		Craker		
(14/1)Forest Green R.	v	Barnet	4-2	552
Grayson(2),Odejayi,Owers		Midgley, Purser		
Windsor & Eton	v	Thame United	3-2	307
Brady, Hill (2)		Jones, West		
(14/1)Aylesbury Utd	v	Kingstonian	1-0	431
Baker				
Eastbourne Borough	v	Farnborough Town	0-1	1576
		Bunce		
(14/1)Gloucester City	v	Lewes	3-2	338
Cox, Griffiths, Smith		Kamara, Kennett		
Dagenham & Redbridge	v	Marlow	5-2	1055
Cole,Fletcher,Stein(2),West		Gibson, Ryder		
(14/1)Hayes	v	Crawley Town	2-1	296
Clark, Warner		McDonnell		
Dulwich Hamlet	v	Margate	0-2	553
		Leberl, Sigere		
Canvey Island	v	Cirencester Town	5-1	349
Boylan(2), Duffy, Gregory Protheroe		Corbett		
(14/1)Heybridge Swifts	v	Hendon	0-0	210
R(28/1)Hendon	v	Heybridge Swifts	2-1	177
Crace, Gallagher		Abrahams		
(13/1)Worcester City	v	Newport County	3-2	1128
Middleton, Webster (2)		Plant, Walker		
(14/1)Purfleet	v	Grays Athletic	1-2	325
Lee		Leaburn, Miller		
(14/1)Hereford United	v	Yeovil Town	1-2	2425
Smith		Lockwood, Pluck		
Sutton United	v	Havant & Waterlooville	1-3	645
Watson		Hambley, Haughton, Howe		

Cirencester (Dr Martens West) goalkeeper Sean Purcell saves at the feet of Canvey Island's (Isthmian Premier) Lee Boylan (No.10), during Canvey's 5-1 home victory.
Photo: Alan Coomes.

Below: Margate (Conference) 'keeper, Charlie Mitten, clears the ball to maintain his side's clean sheet in their 2-0 win away to Dulwich Hamlet (Isthmian 1S).
Photo: Steve Ayre.

Bottom: Nathan Bunce fires in the only goal of the match to give Farnborough Town (Conference) a tight passage through to the next round at the expense of Eastbourne Borough (Dr Martens East).
Photo: Roger Turner.

FOURTH ROUND

SATURDAY 1 FEBRUARY 2003 **WINNING CLUBS TO RECEIVE £1500**

Home		Away	Score	Att.
Colwyn Bay	v	Havant & Waterlooville	0-2	351
		Hambley (2)		
(11/2)Scarborough	v	Dover Athletic	1-1	899
Pounder		Dent		
R(17/2)Dover Athletic	v	Scarborough	2-1*	801
Halifax Town	v	Grays Athletic	3-2	1653
Clarkson, Midgeley, Quailey		Fayenuwo, Vaughan		
(4/2)Windsor & Eton	v	Vauxhall Motors	1-1	351
Sanders		Fearns		
R(11/2)Vauxhall M.	v	Windsor & Eton	0-3	268
		Dyke, Townley, Adams		
(31/1)Northwich Victoria	v	Canvey Island	2-1	708
Garvey, Teather		Protheroe		
Altrincham	v	Aylesbury United	0-1	732
		Manuella		
(11/2)Worksop Town	v	Hayes	2-3	1064
Todd, Townsend		Case, Hastings (2)		
Yeovil Town	v	Morecambe	2-1	3984
Jackson, Skiverton		Black		
Alfreton Town	v	Burscough	1-1	602
Robshaw		Bowen		
R(4/2)Burscough	v	Alfreton Town	2-0	190
McHale (2)				
Gainsborough Trinity	v	Forest Green Rovers	0-2	710
		Grayson, Owers		
Worcester City	v	Margate	0-2	1364
		Beard, Braithwaite		
Dagenham & Redbridge	v	Southport	0-0	1307
R(4/2)Southport	v	Dagenham & Red.	2-2*	569
Pickford, Soley		Matthews, Terry		
(Southport won 4-3 on kicks from the penalty mark)				
Gloucester City	v	Woking	0-0	1073
R(4/2)Woking	v	Gloucester City	0-2	976
		Webb, Harris		
Wakefield & Emley	v	Hendon	0-0	529
R(4/2)Hendon	v	Wakefield & Emley	0-1*	245
		Wilson		
Tamworth	v	Stevenage Borough	3-0	1452
Colley, Cooper, Jephcott				
Telford United	v	Farnborough Town	2-3	928
Barlow, Foran				

Southport (Conference) 'keeper Steve Dickenson and defender Steve Soley can only watch as Lee Matthews hits the post during their goalless draw with Dagenham & Redbridge (Conference).

Photo: Alan Coomes.

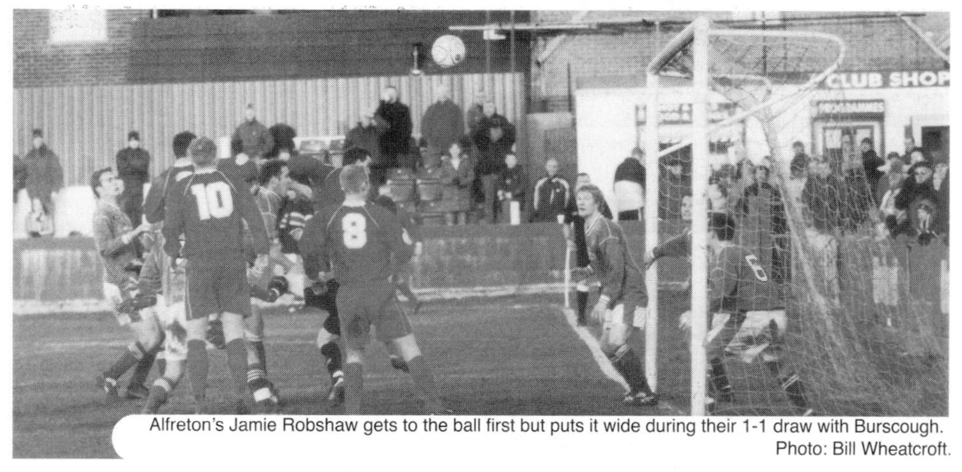

Alfreton's Jamie Robshaw gets to the ball first but puts it wide during their 1-1 draw with Burscough.
Photo: Bill Wheatcroft.

This time Southport 'keeper Steve Dickinson makes a fine save against Dagenham in the 0-0 draw.
Photo: Alan Coomes.

Ryan Fance runs at the Burscough defence but the home side stand firm to win this replay 2-0.
Photo: Bill Wheatcroft.

FIFTH ROUND

SATURDAY 22 FEBRUARY 2003 — **WINNING CLUBS TO RECEIVE £2500**

DOVER ATLETIC . . 0	FOREST GREEN R 3
	Foster, Odejayi, Grayson
	Att: 932

MARGATE 0	TAMWORTH. 2
	Sale, Hallam
	Att: 971

FARNBOROUGH . . 2	HALIFAX TOWN 0
Baptiste, Vansittart	
	Att: 863

YEOVIL TOWN. . . . 2	NORTHWICH V 1
Lockwood, Gall	Blundell
	Att: 4469

BURSCOUGH. 5	WAKEFIELD & E.....0
McHale (2), Norman (2)	
Lawless (og)	Att: 437

AYLESBURY 2	WINDSOR & E 2
Williams, Maskell	O'Connor, Townley
	Att: 847

WINDSOR & E 1	AYLESBURY.........1*
Carroll	Baker
Aylesbury won 4-3 on pens	Att: 476

GLOUCESTER CITY . 1	SOUTHPORT 1
Cox	Scott
	Att: 1237

SOUTHPORT 1	GLOUCESTER C 3
Thomson	Cox (3)
	Att: 835

HAVANT & W'LOOVILLE 3	HAYES....................0
Davis, Blake, Taylor	
	Att: 437

The Ups and Downs of a Penalty kick!

Above: Having gone the wrong way the Hayes (Isthmian P) 'keeper can only sit and count his lucky stars that this penalty kick hits the post, however, Havant's (Dr Martens P) Dean Blake proves that following up brings rewards by scoring from the rebound. Photo: Roger Turner.

Whilst below: Burscough's (Northern Premier P) Peter Wright has his penalty saved by Wakefield & Emley (Northern Premier P) 'keeper Paul Cuss, however, the eventual Trophy winners knocked five past the visitors with no reply. Photo: Bill Wheatcroft.

Gloucester City's (Dr Martens West) Jimmy Cox cooly slots past the oncoming Southport (Conference) 'keeper to give his side the lead in his sides 1-1 draw. Inset: Gloucester supporters dress for the part in their club's efforts to progress to the next round. Photos: Peter Barnes.

John Norman scores goal number two in Burscough's 5-0 win over Wakefield & Emley. Photo: Bill Wheatcroft.

Aylesbury (Isthmian P)defend their goal during their 2-2 draw with Windsor & Eton (Isthmian 1S). Photo: Steve Ayre.

QUARTER-FINALS

SATURDAY 22 FEBRUARY 2003 **WINNING CLUBS TO RECEIVE £2500**

FOREST GREEN R 1 HAVENT & W'LOOVILLE . 2

Grayson 10 Wood 62, Hambley 76

Att: 1016

FOREST GREEN ROVERS: Perrin, Jenkins, Langan (Cleverley 75), Foster, Grayson, Meechan, Owers (Futcher 80), Richardson, Russell, Jones, Odejayi.
Subs not used: Adams, Giannangelo, Tweddle.

HAVENT & WATERLOOVILLE: Kerr, Masson, Poate, Davis, Hall, Hanson, Blake, Hambley, Howe (Gayle 90), Taylor, Wood§.
Subs not used: Haughton, Leworthy, Chambers, May.

Havant's Bobby Howe tries to outwit Forest Green's Martin Foster.

YEOVIL TOWN.... 0 BURSCOUGH 2

Wright 8, 78

Att: 4934

YEOVIL TOWN: Weale, Lockwood (Crittenden 71), Skiverton, Pluck, way, Johnson (Lindegaard 83), Gall, McIndoe, Williams, El Kholti, Jackson (Grant 83).
Subs not used: O'Brien, Collis

BURSCOUGH: M Taylor, Underwood, Bluck, Teale, J Taylor, MacAuley, Lawless, Byrne (Molineux 65), wright (Bowen 81), Norman, Martindale.
Subs not used: Maguire, McHale.

Forest Green Rovers put more pressure on the Havant & Waterlooville defence in their efforts to increase their 1-0 lead. Here we see Forest Green's Jon Richardson meeting the ball first.

Having gone down to an early first half goal, Havant & Waterlooville's squad celebrate their second half revival, which saw them net two to progress to the semi-finals.

Both Havant's Tim Hambley (No.8) and Forest Green's Kevin Langan keep their eyes on the ball.

All Photos: Peter Barnes.

AYLESBURY 2	GLOUCESTER C. . . 1
Ibe 4, Hunter 15	Burns 35 (Pen)
	Att: 1435

AYLESBURY: Worgan, Williams, Stanley, Gordon, McGrath, Plumber, Hunter, Manuella, Ibe, Maskell, Baker.
Subs not used: Bangura, Dicker, Corbould, Wiffin, Pritchard.

GLOUCESTER: Bath, Thompson, Harris, Griffiths, Steadman§, Bayliss, Burns, Cox, webb, Hoskins, Wilkinson.
Subs not used: Smith, Radcliffe, Marshall, Chipps, Barrett.

§ - Sent-off.

FARNBOROUGH . . 1	TAMWORTH 2
L Piper 70	Colley 51, Hatton 84
	Att: 1312

FARNBOROUGH: Pennock, C Piper, Taggart, Annon, Charley, L Piper, Pitcher, Green (Vansittart 88), Butterworth, Baptiste, Rodwell. **Subs not used:** Osborn, Patterson, Potter, Ayres.

TAMWORTH: Acton, Warner,Follett, Robinson, walsh, Hatton, Colley, Evans, Sale (Hallam 50), Rickards, Hannie (McGorry 90).
Subs not used: Barnes, Grocutt, Johnson.

1st Leg

AYLESBURY . . . . . 1 BURSCOUGH 1

Maskel 60 | Martindale 69

Att: 1523

AYLESBURY UNITED: Worgan, Williams, Stanley, Gordon, Ifura, Plumber, Campion, Manuella, Ibe, Maskell, Hunter.
Subs: Bangura, Baker, McGrath, Joe, Heeps.

BURSCOUGH: M Taylor, Underwood, Bluck, Teale, J Taylor, MacAuley, Lawless, Bowen, Wright, Norman, Martindale.
Subs: Burns, Maguire, White, Molineux, McHale.

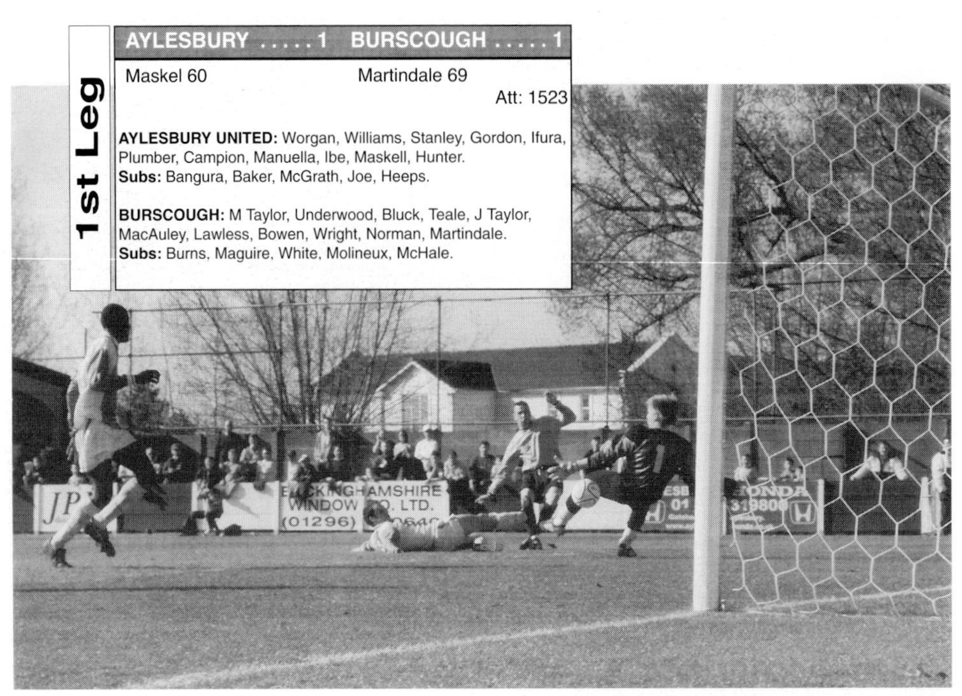

Gary Martindale scores Burscough's all important equaliser nine minutes after home side Aylesbury United had taken the lead in the first leg draw (1-1). Photo: Eric Marsh.

Aylesbury's Craig Maskell shapes up to cross the ball as Burscough defender Joe Taylor closes in.
Photo: Roger Turner.

The Aylesbury goalkeeper, Worgan, wins this ariel duel despite the close attention of Burscough's goalscorer Martindale, in the clubs' 1st leg match.
Photo: Eric Marsh.

Below: Craig Maskell strikes teh ball from outside the box to leave Burscough goalkeeper, Matthw Taylor, rooted to the spot and to give the home side a 1-0 lead in this Semi-Final 1st leg tie.
Photos: Roger Tuner

2nd Leg

BURSCOUGH. . . . . 1 AYLESBURY 0

Teale 90 (pen)

Att: 1773

BURSCOUGH: M Taylor, Underwood, Bluck, Teale, J Taylor, MacAuley, Lawless, Bowen, Wright, Norman, Martindale.
Subs: McHale, Maguire, Molineux, White, Burns.

AYLESBURY UNITED: Worgan, Williams, Stanley, Gordon, Ifura, Plummer, Baker, Manuella, Bangura, Maskell, McGrath.
Subs: Ibe, Campion, Dicker, Joe, Heeps.

Left: Havant's Brett Poate is put under pressure by Tamworth's Scott Rickards.

Below: Tamworth put late pressure on the Havant goal in their 1-0 1st leg victory.

Bottom: Havant's defence comes under attack again, this time it's Tamworth captain Mark Cooper who leaps to meet the ball.

Photos: Peter Barnes.

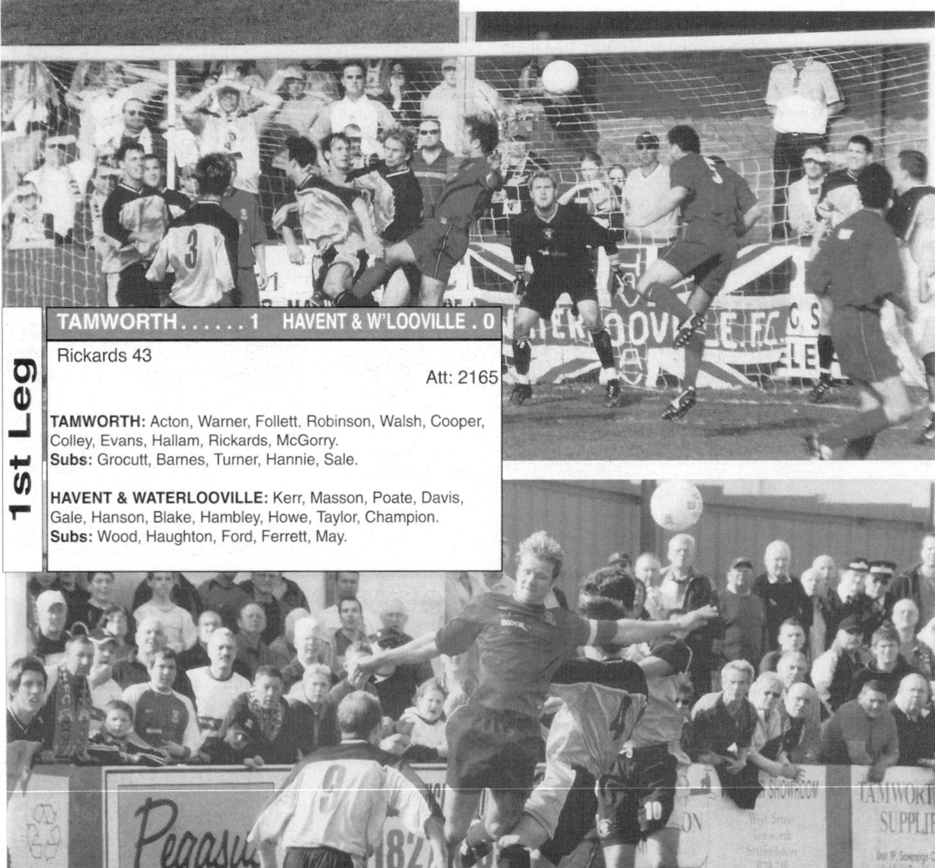

1st Leg

TAMWORTH . . . . . . 1 HAVENT & W'LOOVILLE . 0

Rickards 43

Att: 2165

TAMWORTH: Acton, Warner, Follett, Robinson, Walsh, Cooper, Colley, Evans, Hallam, Rickards, McGorry.
Subs: Grocutt, Barnes, Turner, Hannie, Sale.

HAVENT & WATERLOOVILLE: Kerr, Masson, Poate, Davis, Gale, Hanson, Blake, Hambley, Howe, Taylor, Champion.
Subs: Wood, Haughton, Ford, Ferrett, May.

2nd Leg

HAVENT & W'LOOVILLE 1	TAMWORTH 1
Taylor 42	Rickards 111
	Att: 1331

HAVENT & WATERLOOVILLE: Kerr, Champion, Poate, Haughton, Masson, Hanson, Blake, Hambley, Howe, Taylor, Wood. **Subs:** Ferrett, May, Leworthy, Turner, Gale.

TAMWORTH: Acton, Warner, Follett, Robinson, Walsh, Cooper, Colley, Evans, Hallam, Rockards, McGorry.
Subs: Grocutt, Barnes, Turner, Hatton, Sale.

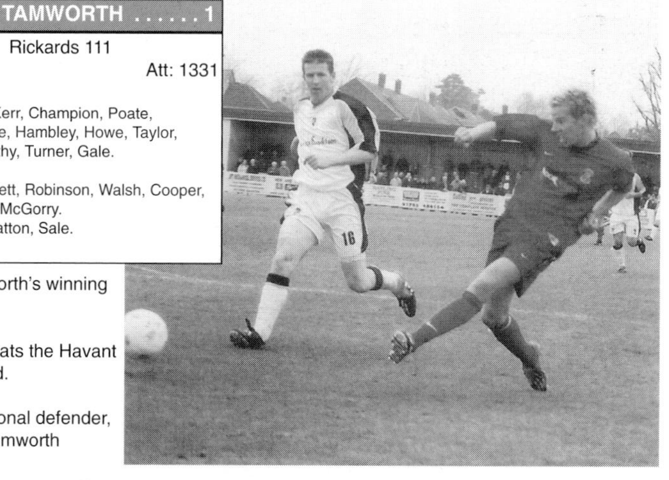

Right: Scott Rickards fires in Tamworth's winning goal in extra-time.

Below: Tamworth's Mark Hallam beats the Havant defence to send the ball goal bound.

Bottom: Havant's England International defender, James Taylor, clears yet another Tamworth attack.

Photos: Roger Turner.

F.A. CARLSBERG TROPHY - AT A GLANCE

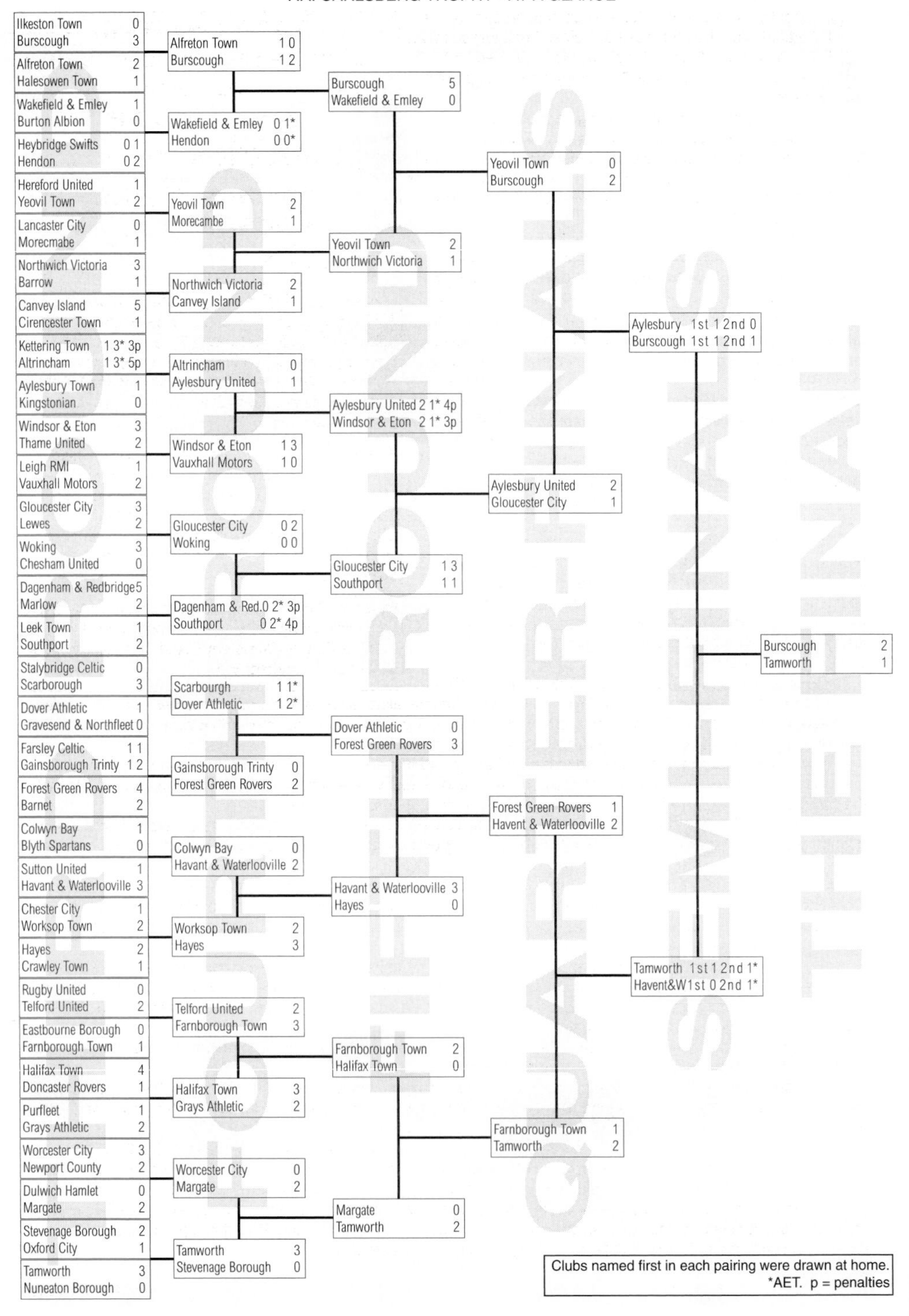

Ilkeston Town 0
Burscough 3
Alfreton Town 2
Halesowen Town 1
Wakefield & Emley 1
Burton Albion 0
Heybridge Swifts 0 1
Hendon 0 2
Hereford United 1
Yeovil Town 2
Lancaster City 0
Morecmabe 1
Northwich Victoria 3
Barrow 1
Canvey Island 5
Cirencester Town 1
Kettering Town 1 3* 3p
Altrincham 1 3* 5p
Aylesbury Town 1
Kingstonian 0
Windsor & Eton 3
Thame United 2
Leigh RMI 1
Vauxhall Motors 2
Gloucester City 3
Lewes 2
Woking 3
Chesham United 0
Dagenham & Redbridge 5
Marlow 2
Leek Town 1
Southport 2
Stalybridge Celtic 0
Scarborough 3
Dover Athletic 1
Gravesend & Northfleet 0
Farsley Celtic 1 1
Gainsborough Trinty 1 2
Forest Green Rovers 4
Barnet 2
Colwyn Bay 1
Blyth Spartans 0
Sutton United 1
Havant & Waterlooville 3
Chester City 1
Worksop Town 2
Hayes 2
Crawley Town 1
Rugby United 0
Telford United 2
Eastbourne Borough 0
Farnborough Town 1
Halifax Town 4
Doncaster Rovers 1
Purfleet 1
Grays Athletic 2
Worcester City 3
Newport County 2
Dulwich Hamlet 0
Margate 2
Stevenage Borough 2
Oxford City 1
Tamworth 3
Nuneaton Borough 0
Alfreton Town 1 0
Burscough 1 2
Wakefield & Emley 0 1*
Hendon 0 0*
Yeovil Town 2
Morecambe 1
Northwich Victoria 2
Canvey Island 1
Altrincham 0
Aylesbury United 1
Windsor & Eton 1 3
Vauxhall Motors 1 0
Gloucester City 0 2
Woking 0 0
Dagenham & Red. 0 2* 3p
Southport 0 2* 4p
Scarbough 1 1*
Dover Athletic 1 2*
Gainsborough Trinty 0
Forest Green Rovers 2
Colwyn Bay 0
Havant & Waterlooville 2
Worksop Town 2
Hayes 3
Telford United 2
Farnborough Town 3
Halifax Town 3
Grays Athletic 2
Worcester City 0
Margate 2
Tamworth 3
Stevenage Borough 0
Burscough 5
Wakefield & Emley 0
Yeovil Town 2
Northwich Victoria 1
Aylesbury United 2 1* 4p
Windsor & Eton 2 1* 3p
Gloucester City 1 3
Southport 1 1
Dover Athletic 0
Forest Green Rovers 3
Havant & Waterlooville 3
Hayes 0
Farnborough Town 2
Halifax Town 0
Margate 0
Tamworth 2
QUARTER-FINALS
Yeovil Town 0
Burscough 2
Aylesbury United 2
Gloucester City 1
Forest Green Rovers 1
Havant & Waterlooville 2
Farnborough Town 1
Tamworth 2
SEMI-FINALS
Aylesbury 1st 1 2nd 0
Burscough 1st 1 2nd 1
Tamworth 1st 1 2nd 1*
Havent&W 1st 0 2nd 1*
THE FINAL
Burscough 2
Tamworth 1
Clubs named first in each pairing were drawn at home.
*AET. p = penalties

A Trophy final without a Conference side present was a dream come true for these two sides but it turned into a nightmare for Tamworth as they were outsped, out-skilled and outscored by their zippy and spirited opponents.

By virtue of their league winning promotion to the Conference and the experience of most of their squad the Midland side were overwhelming favourites. Their supporters outnumbered Burscough's by five to one and all seemed set for a red and white victory as the teams lined up to be introduced to chief guest Martin Peters.

Before Uriah Rennie could signal for the start we had a pitch incursion by a streaker from the Tamworth end. Annoying and unwelcome as such distractions are this one did bring a sense of decorum to his seconds of notoriety in that he was wearing tights and red suspenders. As he was whisked away, deservedly to miss the match, the proper field action began.

Smart work by Steve Evans and the lanky Mark Sales led to Burscough's giving away a corner which Scott Rickards headed over when, on another day, he would have scored a first minute opener. Sale's height again caused problems, making a chance for Richard Follett who shot wide. Next Dave Robinson burst through from his defensive role, closed in on Matthew Taylor on the near post, and attempted a nutmeg. Luckily for Burscough the ball deflected just wide with Rickards screaming for the square pass and a certain Tamworth opener.

Mark Byrne's dribbling and John Lawless' shot just over brought the Greens into the attacking picture before, in the 25th minute, a Lawless run put Gary Martindale clear. The experienced striker, profiting from a defence which had been led astray by Peter Wright's run, waited just a second for the advancing Darren Acton before coolly pushing the ball into the corner. 1-0 to the B's.

Immediately Tamworth skipper Mark Cooper retaliated with a fierce free kick which Matthew Taylor fisted over. With the alert Taylor in goal and his brother, Joe, accompanying player manager Shaun Teale at the heart of the defence, Burscough kept the Tamworth forwards pretty quiet after their opening minutes to go in with a deserved half time lead.

F A TROPHY FINAL
IN PARTNERSHIP WITH CARLSBERG
AT VILLA PARK.
ATTENDANCE 14,265.

BURSCOUGH 2

Martindale 25, 55

TAMWORTH 1

Cooper 78

Burscough:- Matthew Taylor, Shaun Teale, Joe Taylor, Carl Macauley (sub Michael White 77th min), John Lawless, Ryan Bowen, Peter Wright, John Norman, Gary Martindale (sub Kris McHale 80th min), Mark Byrne (sub John Bluck 84th min), Paul Burns. Subs not used- Gary McGuire (g/k) and Marvin Molyneux.

Tamworth:- Darren Acton, Rob Warner, Richard Follett, Dave Robinson, Steve Walsh, Mark Cooper, Nick Colley, Steve Evans (sub Mark Turner 64th min), Scott Rickards (sub Paul Hatton 88th min), Brian McGorry, Mark Sale (sub Mark Hallam 54th min). Subs not used- Darren Grocutt and Neil Barnes(g/k).

Referee:- Mr U D Rennie (Sheffield and Hallamshire F A) assisted by Messrs R L Lewis (Shropshire F A) and S J Tanner (Somerset F A). Fourth official Mr M Clattenburg (Durham F A).

A well watered pitch found some of the swifter forward players, such as Rickards and Byrne, slipping on the greasier parts as the sun went down. Burscough kept up the pace whereas the disappointing Lambs seemed to lack the same urgency, edge and desire in addition to lacking their opponents' speed.

Just after Rickards' promising run had ended by coming up against three doughty defenders the Lancastrians doubled their lead. Lawless' scuffed shot, following a mazy dribble, saw Acton diving to his left but failing to hold on. Martindale, on the follow up, hooked the rebound home to double his team's lead.

Thirty five minutes still to go and plenty of time for Tamworth to strike back. On came the previously prolific Mark Hallam. In due course he was followed to the front line by an increasingly irritated Steve Walsh as the pressure mounted. The Taylor brothers were stalwarts, Joe tackling and heading away, Matthew defending his six yard area, often via his trademark punching and palming.

Twelve minutes left and pressure paid. Cooper was able to flick the ball from the left over the keeper's head at the near post and Tamworth were in with a chance. Two subs immediately followed and Burscough were pushed back. They defended desperately, their previous supremacy cast aside although Wright, in a breakout, found himself in a one on one with Acton but shot into the side netting.

At the other end Burscough's fans' hearts missed a beat as keeper Taylor miscued a clearance but relief and joy came with the final whistle and the underdogs were victors.

There were no protests from the vanquished, or their supporters who applauded Burscough warmly as they paraded their prize. "Yes, we're disappointed," confessed manager Darren Gee, "we lacked a cutting edge and didn't get enough pressure from wide areas. We seriously under performed."

An elated Shaun Teale, looking a little shell shocked, declared, "It takes a bit of sinking in. But 23 clean sheets this season speaks for itself. I reminded the lads it would be a waste of the Yeovil result if we didn't win. It's a wonderful place," he added as the romance of a national victory at his beloved Villa Park sank in.

The wandering Teale had returned, via a greengrocer's business, to his castle and carried off the Trophy, a fitting end to a competitive final, one which had lived up to its occasion and setting. Well done, players and supporters of both contestants. Thanks for the exemplary behaviour and entertainment.

Arthur Evans.

BURSCOUGH F.C.

(Unibond Northern Premier League)

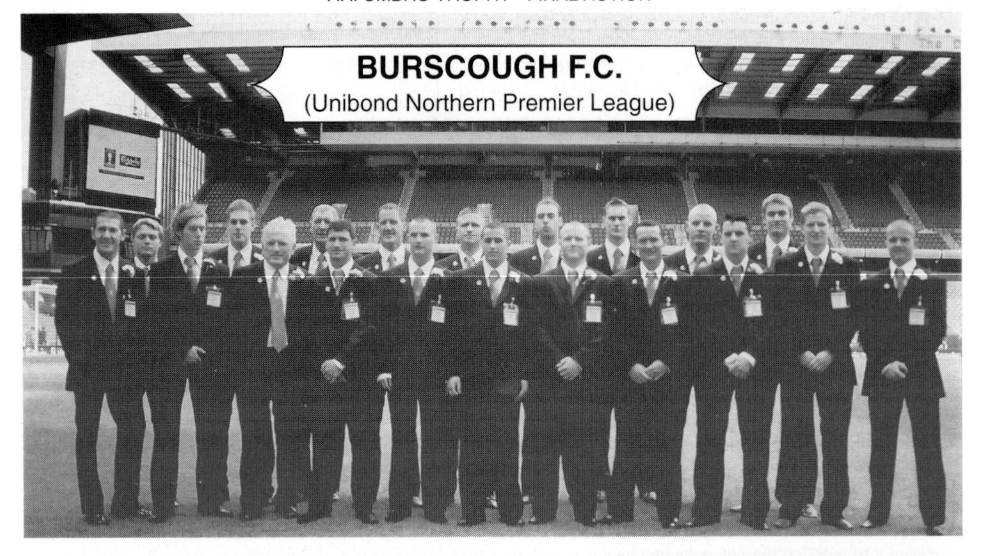

Above the Burscough squad proudly line up before the final at Aston Villa's, Villa Park. Photo: Roger Turner.

Right: Shaun Teale leads his defence in clearing this ariel attack. Photo: Bill Wheatcroft.

Left: Burscough's wing-back, Mark Byrne, takes on Tamworth defender Richard Follett. Photo: Peter Barnes.

Bottom left: Gary Martindale opens the scoring for Burscough. Photo: Peter Barnes.

Bottom Right: Burscough captain, Carl MacCauley runs at Tamworth's Mark Sale. Photo: Peter Barnes.

TAMWORTH F.C.

(Dr Martens Premier League)

The Tamworth squad enjoying the photo call prior to their big match. Photo Peter Barnes.

Mark Cooper gives his Tamworth team mates some hope with his 78th minute goal. Photo: Bill Wheatcroft.

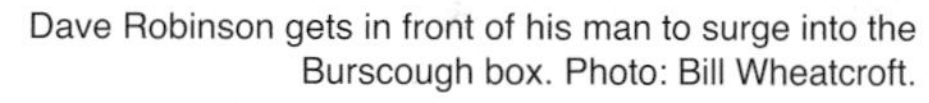

Dave Robinson gets in front of his man to surge into the Burscough box. Photo: Bill Wheatcroft.

Tamworth's Mark Sale attempts to shield the ball from Burscough's John Bluck. Photo: Roger Turner.

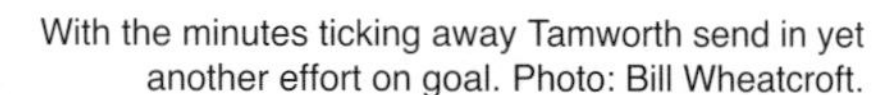

With the minutes ticking away Tamworth send in yet another effort on goal. Photo: Bill Wheatcroft.

Photo: Peter Barnes.

Photo: Eric Marsh.

Photo: Roger Turner.

Man of the Match
GARY MARTINDALE

Photo: Peter Barnes.

PAST F.A. TROPHY FINALS

1970 MACCLESFIELD TOWN 2 (Lyond, B Fidler) — Northern Premier League
TELFORD UNITED 0 — Southern League
Att: 28,000
Macclesfield: Cooke, Sievwright, Bennett, Beaumont, Collins, Roberts, Lyons, B Fidler,Young, Corfield, D Fidler.
Telford: Irvine, Harris, Croft, Flowers, Coton, Ray,Fudge, Hart, Bentley, Murray, Jagger. Ref: K Walker

1971 TELFORD UTD 3 (Owen, Bentley, Fudge) — Southern League
HILLINGDON BORO. 2 (Reeve, Bishop) — Southern League
Att: 29,500
Telford: Irvine, Harris, Croft, Ray, Coton, Carr, Fudge, Owen, Bentley, Jagger ,Murray.
Hillingdon B.: Lowe, Batt, Langley, Higginson, Newcombe, Moore, Fairchild,Bishop, Reeve, Carter, Knox. Ref: D Smith

1972 STAFFORD RANGERS 3 (Williams 2, Cullerton) — Northern Premier League
BARNET 0 — Southern League
Att: 24,000
Stafford R.: Aleksic, Chadwick, Clayton, Sargeant, Aston, Machin, Cullerton, Chapman,Williams, Bayley, Jones.
Barnet: McClelland, Lye, Jenkins, Ward, Embrey, King, Powell, Ferry, Flatt, Easton, Plume . Ref: P Partridge

1973 SCARBOROUGH 2 (Leask, Thompson) — Northern Premier League
WIGAN ATHLETIC 1 (Rogers) aet — Northern Premier League
Att:23,000
Scarborough: Garrow, Appleton, Shoulder, Dunn, Siddle, Fagan, Donoghue, Franks,Leask (Barmby), Thompson, Hewitt.
Wigan: Reeves, Morris, Sutherland, Taylor,Jackson, Gillibrand, Clements, Oats (McCunnell), Rogers, King, Worswick. Ref: H Hackney

1974 MORECAMBE 2 (Richmond, Sutton) — Northern Premier League
DARTFORD 1 (Cunningham) — Southern League
Att: 19,000
Morecambe: Coates, Pearson, Bennett, Sutton, Street, Baldwin, Done, Webber,Roberts (Galley), Kershaw, Richmond.
Dartford: Morton, Read, Payne, Carr, Burns,Binks, Light, Glozier, Robinson (Hearne), Cunningham, Halleday. Ref: B Homewood

1975 **1** MATLOCK TOWN 4 (Oxley, Dawson, T Fenoughty, N Fenoughy) — Northern Premier League
SCARBOROUGH 0 — Northern Premier League
Att: 21,000
Matlock: Fell, McKay, Smith, Stuart, Dawson, Swan, Oxley, N Fenoughy, Scott, T Fenoughty, M Fenoughty.
Scarborough: Williams, Hewitt, Rettitt, Dunn, Marshall, Todd, Houghton, Woodall, Davidson, Barnby, Aveyard. Ref: K Styles

1976 SCARBOROUGH 3 (Woodall, Abbey, Marshall(p)) — Northern Premier League
STAFFORD R. 2 (Jones 2) aet — Northern Premier League
Att: 21,000
Scarborough: Barnard, Jackson, Marshall, H Dunn, Ayre (Donoghue), HA Dunn, Dale,Barmby, Woodall, Abbey, Hilley.
Stafford: Arnold, Ritchie, Richards, Sargeant,Seddon, Morris, Chapman, Lowe, Jones, Hutchinson, Chadwick. Ref: R Challis

Former West Ham player, Eddie Presland, shows off the Trophy after Dagenham & Redbridge, under his management, beat Mossley 2-1 in the 1980 final.

1977 Att: 21,500
SCARBOROUGH 2 (Dunn(p), Abbey) Northern Premier League
DAGENHAM 1 (Harris) Ishthmian League
Scarborough: Chapman, Smith, Marshall (Barmby), Dunn, Ayre, Deere, Aveyard,Donoghue, Woodall, Abbey, Dunn.
Dagenham: Hutley, Wellman, P Currie, Dunwell,Moore, W Currie, Harkins, Saul, Fox, Harris, Holder. Ref: G Courtney

1978 Att: 20,000
ALTRINCHAM 3 (King, Johnson, Rogers) Northern Premier League
LEATHERHEAD 1 (Cook) Isthmian League
Altrincham: Eales, Allan, Crossley, Bailey, Owens, King, Morris, Heathcote,Johnson, Rogers, Davidson (Flaherty).
Leatherhead: Swannell, Cooper, Eaton, Davies,Reid, Malley, Cook, Salkeld, Baker, Boyle (Bailey). Ref: A Grey

1979 Att: 32,000
STAFFORD RANGERS 2 (A Wood 2) Northern Premier League
KETTERING TOWN 0 Isthmian League
Stafford: Arnold, F Wood, Willis, Sargeant, Seddon, Ritchie, Secker, Chapman, A Wood, Cullerton, Chadwick (Jones).
Kettering: Lane, Ashby, Lee, Eastell, Dixey,Suddards, Flannagan, Kellock, Phipps, Clayton, Evans (Hughes). Ref: D Richardson

1980 **2** Att : 26,000
DAGENHAM 2 (Duck, Maycock) Isthmian League
MOSSLEY 1 (Smith) Northern Premier League
Dagenham: Huttley, Wellman, Scales, Dunwell, Mooore, Durrell, Maycock, Horan,Duck, Kidd, Jones (Holder).
Mossley: Fitton, Brown, Vaughan, Gorman, Salter, Polliot, Smith, Moore, Skeete, O'Connor, Keelan (Wilson). Ref: K Baker

Notes:

1 The only occasion three members of the same family played in the same FA Trophy Final team.

2 The first of the Amateurs from the Isthmian League to win the FA Trophy

3 Goalkeeper Terry Moore had also won an Amateur Cup Winners Medal with Bishop's Stortford in 1974

Wycombe Wanderers' Paul Hyde makes a perfect full length dive to keep Runcorn out, during the 1993 final, which Wycombe won 4-1.

Photo: Roger Turner.

1981 **3** Att:22,578
BISHOP'S STORTFORD 1 (Sullivan)
Isthmian League
SUTTON UNITED 0
Isthmian League
Bishop's Stortford: Moore, Blackman, Brame, Smith (Worrell), Bradford, Abery, Sullivan,Knapman, Radford, Simmonds, Mitchell.
Sutton Utd.: Collyer, Rogers, Green, J Rains,T Rains, Stephens (Sunnucks), Waldon, Pritchard, Cornwell, Parsons, Dennis. Ref: J Worrall

1982 Att:18.678
ENFIELD 1 (Taylor) Isthmian League
ALTRINCHAM 0 Alliance Premier League
Enfield: Jacobs, Barrett, Tone, Jennings, Waite, Ironton, Ashford, Taylor,Holmes, Oliver (Flint), King. Ref: B Stevens
Altrincham: Connaughton, Crossley, Davison, Bailey, Cuddy, King (Whitbread), Allan, Heathcote, Johnson, Rogers, Howard.

1983 Att: 22,071
TELFORD UTD 2 (Mather 2) NORTHWICH VICTORIA 1 (Bennett)
Alliance Premier League Alliance Premier League
Telford: Charlton, Lewis, Turner, Mayman (Joseph), Walker, Easton, Barnett,Williams, Mather, Hogan, Alcock.
Northwich: Ryan, Fretwell, Murphy, Jones, Forshaw, Ward, Anderson, Abel (Bennett), Reid, Chesters, Wilson. Ref: B Hill

1984 NORTHWICH VICTORIA 1 (Chester) BANGOR CITY 1 (Whelan) Att: 14,200
Replay NORTHWICH VICTORIA 2 (Chesters(p), Anderson) BANGOR CITY 1 (Lunn) Att: 5,805 (at Stoke)
Alliance Premier League Alliance Premier League
Northwich: Ryan, Fretwell, Dean, Jones, Forshaw (Power 65), Bennett, Anderson,Abel, Reid, Chesters, Wilson. Ref: J Martin
Bangor: Letheren, Cavanagh, Gray, Whelan, Banks,Lunn, Urqhart, Morris, Carter, Howat, Sutcliffe (Westwood 105) . Same in replay.

1985 WEALDSTONE 2 (Graham, Holmes) BOSTON UNITED 1 (Cook) Att: 20,775
Alliance Premier League Alliance Premier League
Wealdstone: Iles, Perkins, Bowgett, Byatt, Davies, Greenaway, Holmes, Wainwright,Donnellan, Graham (N Cordice 89), A Cordice.
Boston: Blackwell, Casey, Ladd,Creane, O'Brien, Thommson, Laverick (Mallender 78), Simpsom, Gilbert, Lee, Cook. Ref: J Bray

1986 ALTRINCHAM 1 (Farrelly) RUNCORN 0 Att: 15,700
Gola League Gola League
Altrincham: Wealands, Gardner, Densmore, Johnson, Farrelly, Conning, Cuddy,Davison, Reid, Ellis, Anderson. Sub: Newton.
Runcorn: McBride, Lee, Roberts,Jones, Fraser, Smith, S Crompton (A Crompton), Imrie, Carter, Mather, Carrodus. Ref: A Ward

1987 KIDDERMINSTER HARRIERS 0 BURTON ALBION 0 Att: 23,617
Replay KIDDERMINSTER HARRIERS 2 (Davies 2) BURTON ALBION 1 (Groves) Att: 15,685 (at West Brom)
Conference Southern League
Kidderminster: Arnold, Barton, Boxall, Brazier (sub Hazlewood in rep), Collins (subPearson 90 at Wembley), Woodall, McKenzie, O'Dowd, Tuohy, Casey, Davies. sub:Jones.
Burton: New, Essex, Kamara, Vaughan, Simms, Groves, Bancroft, Land, Dorsett, Redfern, (sub Wood in replay), Gauden.
Sub: Patterson. Ref: D Shaw

1988 ENFIELD 0 TELFORD UNITED 0 Att: 20,161, Ref: L Dilkes
Replay ENFIELD 3 (Furlong 2, Howell) TELFORD 2 (Biggins, Norris(p)) Att: 6,912 (at W Brom)
Conference Conference
Enfield: Pape, Cottington, Howell, Keen (sub Edmonds in rep), Sparrow (sub Hayzleden at Wembley), Lewis (sub Edmonds at Wembley), Harding, Cooper, King,Furlong, Francis.
Telford: Charlton, McGinty, Storton, Nelson, Wiggins, Mayman (sub Cunningham in rep (sub Hancock)), Sankey, Joseph, Stringer (sub Griffiths at Wembley, Griffiths in replay), Biggins, Norris.

1989 TELFORD UNITED 1 (Crawley) MACCLESFIELD TOWN 0 Att: 18,102
Conference Conference
Telford: Charlton, Lee, Brindley, Hancock, Wiggins, Mayman, Grainger, Joseph, Nelson, Lloyd, Stringer. Subs: Crawley, Griffiths.
Macclesfield: Zelem, Roberts, Tobin, Edwards, Hardman, Askey, Lake, Hanton, Imrie, Burr, Timmons. Subs: Devomshire, Kendall.
Ref: T Holbrook

1990 BARROW 3 (Gordon 2, Cowperthwaite) LEEK TOWN 0 Att: 19,011
Conference Northern Premier League
Barrow: McDonnell, Higgins, Chilton, Skivington, Gordon, Proctor, Doherty (Burgess), Farrell (Gilmore), Cowperthwaite, Lowe, Ferris.
Leek: Simpson, Elsby (Smith), Pearce, McMullen, Clowes, Coleman (Russell),Mellor, Somerville, Sutton, Millington, Norris Ref: T Simpson

1991 WYCOMBE W. 2 (Scott, West) — KIDDERMINSTER H. 1 (Hadley) — Att: 34,842
Conference — Conference
Wycombe: Granville, Crossley, Cash, Kerr, Creaser, Carroll, Ryan, Stapleton,West, Scott, Guppy (Hutchinson). Ref: J Watson
Kidderminster: Jones, Kurila, McGrath, Weir, Barnett, Forsyth, Joseph (Wilcox), Howell (Whitehouse), Hadley, Lilwall, Humphries

1992 COLCHESTER UTD* 3 (Masters, Smith, McGavin) — WITTON ALBION 1 (Lutkevitch) — Att: 27,806
Conference — Conference
Colchester: Barrett, Donald, Roberts, Knsella, English, Martin, Cook, Masters,McDonough (Bennett 65), McGavin, Smith. Ref: K P Barratt
Witton: Mason, Halliday, Coathup, McNeilis, Jim Connor, Anderson, Thomas, Rose, Alford, Grimshaw (Joe Connor), Lutkevitch (McCluskie)

1993 WYCOMBE W*. 4 (Cousins, Kerr, Thompson, Carroll) — RUNCORN 1 (Shaughnessy) — Att: 32,968
Conference — Conference
Wycombe: Hyde, Cousins, Cooper, Kerr, Crossley, Thompson (Hayrettin 65),Carroll, Ryan, Hutchinson, Scott, Guppy. Sub: Casey.
Runcorn: Williams, Bates, Robertson, Hill, Harold (Connor 62), Anderson, Brady (Parker 72), Brown, Shaughnessy, McKenna, Brabin
Ref: I J Borritt

1994 WOKING 2 (D Brown, Hay) — RUNCORN 1 (Shaw (pen)) — Att: 15,818
Conference — Conference
Woking: Batty, Tucker, L Wye, Berry, Brown, Clement, Brown (Rattray 32), Fielder, Steele, Hay (Puckett 46), Walker. Ref: Paul Durkin
Runcorn: Williams, Bates, Robertson, Shaw, Lee, Anderson, Thomas, Connor, Mclnerney (Hill 71), McKenna, Brabin. Sub: Parker

1995 WOKING 2 (Steele, Fielder) — KIDDERMINSTER H. 1 aet (Davies) — Att: 17,815
Conference — Conference
Woking: Batty, Tucker, L Wye, Fielder, Brown, Crumplin (Rattray 42), S Wye, Ellis, Steele, Hay (Newberry 112), Walker. (Sub: Read(gk)
Kidderminster: Rose, Hodson, Bancroft, Webb, Brindley (Cartwright 94), Forsyth, Deakin, Yates, Humphreys (Hughes 105), Davies, Purdie. Sub: Dearlove (gk) Ref: D J Gallagher

1996 MACCLESFIELD TOWN 3 (Payne, OG, Hemmings) — NORTHWICH VICTORIA 1 (Williams) — Att: 8,672
Conference — Conference
Macclesfield: Price, Edey, Gardiner, Payne, Howarth(C), Sorvel, Lyons, Wood (Hulme 83), Coates, Power, Hemmings (Cavell 88).
Northwich: Greygoose, Ward, Duffy, Burgess (Simpson 87), Abel (Steele), Walters, Williams, Butler (C), Cooke, Humphries, Vicary.
Ref: M Reed

1997 WOKING 1 (Hay 112) — DAGENHAM & REDBRIDGE 0 — Att: 24,376
Conference — Isthmian League
Woking: Batty, Brown, Howard, Foster, Taylor, S Wye, Thompson (sub Jones 115), Ellis, Steele (L Wye 108), Walker, Jackson (Hay 77).
Dagenham: Gothard, Culverhouse, Connor, Creaser, Jacques (sub Double 75), Davidson, Pratt (Naylor 81), Parratt, Broom, Rogers, Stimson (John 65). Ref: J Winter

1998 CHELTENHAM TOWN 1 (Eaton 74) — SOUTHPORT 0 — Att: 26,387
Conference — Conference
Cheltenham: Book, Duff, Freeman, Banks, Victory, Knight (Smith 78), Howells, Bloomer, Walker (sub Milton 78), Eaton, Watkins. Sub: Wright.
Southport: Stewart, Horner, Futcher, Ryan, Farley, Kielty, Butler, Gamble, Formby (sub Whittaker 80), Thompson (sub Bollard 88), Ross. Sub: Mitten. Ref: G S Willard

1999 KINGSTONIAN 1 (Mustafa 49) — FOREST GREEN ROVERS 0 — Att: 20,037
Conference — Conference
Kingstonian: Farrelly, Mustafa, Luckett, Crossley, Stewart, Harris, Patterson, Pitcher, Rattray, Leworthy (Francis 87), Akuamoah. Subs (not used): John, Corbett, Brown, Tranter
Forest Green Rovers: Shuttlewood, Hedges, Forbes, Bailey (Smart 76), Kilgour, Wigg (Cook 58), Honor (Winter 58), Drysdale, McGregor, Mehew, Sykes. Subs (not used): Perrin, Coupe Ref: A B Wilkie

2000 KINGSTONIAN 3 (Akuamoah 40, 69, Simba 75) — KETTERING TOWN 2 (Vowden 55, Norman 64p) — Att: 20,034
Conference — Conference
Kingstonian: Farelly, Mustafa, Luckett, Crossley, Stewart (Saunders 77), Harris, Kadi (Leworthy 83), Pitcher, Green (Basford 86), Smiba, Akuamoah. Subs (not used): Hurst, Allan
Kettering Town: Sollit, McNamara, Adams, Perkins, Vowden, Norman (Duik 76), Fisher, Brown, Shutt, Watkins (Hudson 46), Setchell (Hopkins 81). Subs (not used): Ridgway, Wilson Ref: S W Dunn

2001 CANVEY ISLAND 1 (Chenery) — FOREST GREEN ROVERS 0 — at Villa Park Att: 10,007
Isthmian League — Conference
Forest Green Rovers: Perrin, Cousins, Lockwood, Foster, Clark, Burns, Daley, Drysdale (Bennett 46), Foster (Hunt 75), Meecham, Slater. Subs (not used): Hedges, Prince, Ghent
Canvey Island: Harrison, Duffy, Chenery, Bodley, Ward, Tilson, Stimson (Tanner 83), Gregory, Vaughan (Jones 76), Parmenter. Subs (not used): Bennett, Miller, Thompson. Ref: A G Wiley

2002 YEOVIL TOWN 2 (Alford, Stansfield) — STEVENAGE BOROUGH 0 — at Villa Park Att: 18,809
Conference — Conference
Yeovil Town: Weale, Lockwood, Tonkin, Skiverton, Pluck (White 51), Way, Stansfield, Johnson, Alford (Giles 86), Crittenden (Lindegaard 83), Mclndoe. Subs (not used): O'Brien, Sheffield
Stevenage Borough: Wilkerson, Hamsher, Goodliffe, Trott, Fraser, Fisher, Wormull (Stirling 71), Evers (Williams 56), Jackson, Sigere (Campbell 74), Clarke. Subs (not used): Campbell, Greygoose Ref: N S Barry

TOP GOAL SCORERS 2002 - 2003

Player	Club	No. goals	Round reach	No. hatrick	Hatrick details
G Martindale	Burscough	5	Winners	-	
N Grayson	Forest Green Rovers	5	Quarter Finals		
J Cox	Gloucester City	5	Quarter Finals		
T Hambley	Havant & waterlooville	5	Semi Finals		
S Edgar	Walton & Hersham	5	2nd Round	1	1st Round
C O'Connor	Windsor & Eton	5	5th Round	1	1st Round
A Crittenden	Bracknell Town	4	1st Round	1	Preliminary Rd Replay
K McHale	Burscough	4	Winners		
J Norman	Burscough	4	Winners		
J Ashby	Halesowen Town	4	3rd Round		
J Taylor	Havant & Waterlooville	4	Semi Finals		
McPherson	Leek Town	4	3rd Round		
T Fearns	Vauxhall Motors	4	4th Round		
C O'Connor	Windsor & Eton	4	5th Round	1	1st Round Replay
J Baker	Aylesbury United	3	Semi Finals		
T Brauam	Bishop's Stortford	3	2nd Round		
D McMahon	Blyth Spartans	3	3rd Round		
M Russell	Bognor Regis Town	3	2nd Round		
J Lawless	Burscough	3	Winners		
P Wright	Burscough	3	Winners		
C Furlong	Colwyn Bay	3	4th Round		
D Perkins	Dulwich Hamlet	3	3rd Round		
S Ramsey	Eastbourne Borough	3	3rd Round		
L Piper	Farnborough Town	3	Quarter Finals		
M Smithard	Farsley Celtic	3	3rd Round		
R Whellans	Harrogate Town	3	2nd Round		
C Holmes	Kings Lynn	3	1st Round		
P Wingfield	Kingstonian	3	3rd Round		
D Whittaker	Leek Town	3	3rd Round		
D Smith	Lincoln United	3	1st Round		
N Ryder	Marlow	3	3rd Round		
J Kearns	Rothwell Town	3	2nd Round		
D Hall	Rugby United	3	3rd Round		
M Shepherd	Solihull Borough	3	2nd Round	1	1st Round
M Cooper	Tamworth	3	Runners-up		
M Hallam	Tamworth	3	Runners-up		
A Hemmings	Tamworth	3	Runners-up	1	2nd Round
M West	Thame United	3	3rd round		
N Barnes	Tonbridge Angels	3	2nd Round		
S Bambrook	Wakefield & Emley	3	5th Round	1	2nd Round
F Dolan	Walton & Hersham	3	2nd Round		
K Adams	Windsor & Eton	3	5th Round		
M Brady	Windsor & Eton	3	5th Round		
G Murray	Workington	3	Preliminary Round		
A Todd	Worksop Town	3	4th Round		

HIGHEST SCORING CLUBS 2002 - 2003

25 Goals
Burscough
22 Goals
Windsor & Eton
17 Goals
Tamworth
15 Goals
Gloucester City

14 Goals
Farsley Celtic
Havant & Waterlooville
13 Goals
Leek Town
12 Goals
Alfreton Town

11 Goals
Aylesbury United
Solihull Borough
Walton & Hersham
10 Goals
Cirencester Town
Forest Green Rovers
Halesowen Town
Lewes
Marlow

F.A. CARLSBERG VASE

Photo: D.Nicholson

2002-2003 REVIEW

FIRST ROUND QUALIFYING

SATURDAY 7 SEPTEMBER 2002 — **WINNING CLUBS TO RECEIVE £150**

Home		Away	Score	Att
Blackpool Mechanics	v	Sheffield	0-0*	37
R(10/9)Sheffield	v	Blackpool Mech.	3-1	70
Bray (3)		Blaney		
Chester-Le-Street Town	v	Eccleshill United	0-1	70
		Burnham		
Nelson	v	Curzon Ashton	2-0	87
Gray (2)				
South Shields	v	Holker Old Boys	0-2	83
		Murphy (2)		
Thackley	v	Retford United		
(walkover for Thackley – Retford United removed from the Competition for not having floodlights)				
West Allotment Celtic	v	Goole	2-1	101
Malone, Potts				
Selby Town	v	Louth United	0-1	85
		Creer		
New Mills	v	Northallerton Town	1-5	215
Land		Boyle, Onions (3), Osborne		
Crook Town	v	Guisborough Town	1-3	80
Dawson		Outhwaite		
Marske United	v	Prudhoe Town	1-2	119
Ward		MacDonald (2)		
Winsford United	v	Great Harwood Town	3-0	
Davis, Lamb, Miranda				
Brodsworth MW	v	Jarrow Roofing Boldon CA	3-2	59
Humphries, Pugh, Taylor		Chow, Welson		
Poulton Victoria	v	Hebburn Town	2-0	74
Bates, Fry				
Easington Colliery	v	Warrington Town	0-1*	45
		Webster		
Hatfield Main	v	Penrith	1-2*	58
Bradley		Henderson, Hodgson		
Chadderton	v	Glasshoughton Welfare	2-2*	68
Doyle, Kelly		Bradley, Fox		
R(10/9)Glasshoughton W.	v	Chadderton	6-0	53
Bradley (2), Fox, Haigh, Parker (2)				
Norton & Stockton Ancients	v	Washington	0-2	13
		Donnelly, Feasey		
Oldham Town	v	Parkgate	0-6	39
		Cusworth(3),McKenzie,Robshaw (2)		
Malvern Town	v	Rainworth MW	5-0	63
Cox (2), Hooper (3)				
Causeway United	v	Bolehall Swifts (8/9)	6-0	131
Coates,Dixon,Hall,Hancox, Richards,Young				
(at Halesowen Town FC)				
Willenhall Town	v	Marconi	6-0	77
Bullimore,Hay(3),Moseley,Quilt				
Bourne Town	v	Bromyard Town	3-3*	55
Edwards, Munton, Notley		Hobbs, Mogford, Willetts		
(Bourne Town won 4-3 on kicks from the penalty mark)				
Kimberley Town	v	Carlton Town	3-4	43
George		Bignall, Heverin, Holmes, Korol		
Oldbury United	v	Dunkirk	5-2	25
Campbell,Ross(2),Wood(2)		Chulan, Silcock		
Nettleham	v	Shawbury United	2-8	16
Beesley (2)		Davies (4), Giles (3)		
(at Brigg Town FC)				
Handrahan Timbers	v	Congleton Town	0-3	56
		Jones, Scully (2)		
Lye Town	v	Anstey Nomads	5-0	63
Bagley, Bedi, Burgess, Taylor, Wilkes				

Home		Away	Score	Att
Heath Hayes	v	Tividale	2-0	50
Baker, Tucker				
Glapwell	v	Westfields	3-1	70
Ashley, Clarke, Kingsley		Craddock		
Quorn	v	Blackstones	4-2*	102
Dawson, Noble, Turner(2)		Challnor, Tiley		
Biddulph Victoria	v	Kirby Muxloe (8/9)	2-1	151
Baker, Burge		Smith		
Blackwell MW	v	Lincoln Moorlands	1-0	47
Millward				
Staveley MW	v	Cradley Town	0-1	45
		Perry		
Rolls Royce Leisure	v	Pegasus Juniors	3-1	30
Farmery, Taylor (2)		Stone		
Ledbury Town	v	Coventry Sphinx	3-2	86
Colwell (3)		McSheffrey, Stevenson		
Greenacres (Hemel Hemp.)	v	Downham Town		
(walkover for Greenacres (Hemel Hempstead) – Downham Town withdrawn)				
Ware	v	Hullbridge Sports	3-1	97
Field, Moy (2)		Saveall		
Whitton United	v	Enfield Town	1-3	198
Layton		Brotherton (2), Snowden		
Great Yarmouth Town	v	Clacton Town	1-3	105
Thompson		Hillier, Howell (2)		
Hoddesdon Town	v	Ruislip Manor	5-2*	33
Conner, Redford, Roberts, Wood (2)		Richardson, White		
(at Hertford Town FC)				
Fakenham Town	v	Ely City	1-3	91
White		Moye (2), Smith		
Felixtowe & Walton Utd	v	Letchworth	2-0	56
Leyton	v	Brimsdown Rovers	1-0	101
Williams				
Welwyn Garden City	v	Henley Town	2-1*	64
Dickson, Omatato		Arden		
Holmer Green	v	Bugbrooke St Michaels	3-1*	54
Keeley, Scholes, Stottor		Cotton		
Chalfont St Peter	v	Norwich United	0-2	35
		Hunton, Romano		
Beaconsfield SYCOB	v	Harwich & Parkeston	3-2	38
Markman, Paris, Sears		Hearn, Neale		
Halstead Town	v	Thetford Town	2-0	112
Chatters, Owers				
Stowmarket Town	v	Harpenden Town	4-2	92
Jopling,Mayes(2),Whatlings		Bound, Price		
Brook House	v	Leighton Town	0-2	45
		Walters, Welling		
Brackley Town	v	Buckingham Town	1-4	125
Eldridge		Abdi, Cole, Julius, Max-Grant		
Gorleston	v	Romford	4-1	120
Bishop, Harvey, Pillar		Riley		
Bury Town	v	Haringey Borough	2-1	94
North (2)		Amadi		
Brightlingsea United	v	Clapton		
(walkover for Clapton – Brightlingsea United withdrawn)				
Lowestoft Town	v	Edgware Town	4-3	145
Godbold, King, McGee (2)		Maharjan, Thomas		
Biggleswade Town	v	Cornard United	1-2	34
Drummond		Cook, Ford		
Long Buckby	v	Wootton Blue Cross	1-5	39
Fretwell		Bartley (3), Joswiak (2)		

Home		Away	Score	Att
Westfield	v	Eastbourne Town	3-4	30
Classey, Flynn, Wetherall		Brockwell (3), Walsh		
Horsham YMCA	v	Chipstead	1-1*	66
Flint		Jenns		
R(10/9)Chipstead	v	Horsham YMCA	3-2	78
Berry (2), Brett		Flint, Francis		
Wantage Town	v	Carterton Town	1-0	56
Spiero				
Merstham	v	Hartley Wintney	6-0	41
Burridge, Jupp, Watts (4)				
Lordswood	v	Redhill	1-2	62
Crust		Hobbs, Umberto		
Whitstable Town	v	Raynes Park Vale	2-4*	116
Brown, Jackson		Denny, Morrow		
Godalming & Guildford	v	Three Bridges	1-0	67
Ray				
Abingdon United	v	Chessington United	3-0	65
Beckett, Brandon, Hooper				
Ringmer	v	Eastbourne United	2-0	80
Brown, Johnson				
Farnham Town	v	Whitehawk	0-4	60
		Pattenden (3), Rowlands		
Ramsgate	v	Deal Town	1-2	175
Takalobigashi		Hayes, Jones		
Hungerford Town	v	Petersfield Town	4-0	68
Hopkins(2),Howell,Philpott				
East Preston	v	AFC Totton	0-3	98
		Hurst, Sherrington, Whiddett		
Gosport Borough	v	Chichester City Utd	3-0	142
Camfield,Hensman,Scammell				
Eastleigh	v	Peacehaven & Telscombe	6-0	119
Hughes, Lawes(3), Matthews, Thorpe				
Pagham	v	Greenwich Borough	0-3	59
		Matthias, Sinclair, Smith		
Frome Town	v	Downton	4-2	177
Peters (3), Salter		Guy, White		
Poole Town	v	Christchurch	0-0*	156
R(10/9)Christchurch	v	Poole Town	2-0	140
Johnson, Manning				
Elmore	v	Harrow Hill	4-0	45
Chaplin,Harvey,Rowland(2)				
Paulton Rovers	v	Barnstaple Town	3-0	58
Russell, Woon (2)				
Wellington Town	v	Devizes Town	1-2	48
Burne		Godley, Richardson		
Clevedon United	v	Almondsbury Town	1-1*	78
White		Mizon		
R(10/9)Almondsbury Town	v	Clevedon United	2-4	95
Watts (2)		Cheesman (2), Lowis, White		
Falmouth Town	v	Bristol Manor Farm	4-2	120
Ashburn(3), Turner		Beale, Williams		
Portland United	v	Ilfracombe Town	0-1	99
		Squire		

***Above:** Brackley's (Hellenic Prem) Vinney Byfield puts in a strong challenge against local rivals Buckingham Town (U.Co Prem). Photo: Peter Barnes.*
***Above right:** Peter Montgomery puts the pressure on the Eastbourne United's (Sussex D2) defence during Ringmer's (Sussex D1) 2-0 victory. Photo: Roger Turner.*
***Right:** Sheffield's (N.Co.E Prem) Duncan Bray complete's his hat-trick against Blackpool Mechanics (N.W.Co D2). Photo: Bill Wheatcroft.*

SECOND ROUND QUALIFYING

SATURDAY 21 SEPTEMBER 2002 **WINNING CLUBS TO RECEIVE £200**

Home		Away	Score	Att
Guisborough Town	v	Darwen	2-1	110
Kasonali, Outhwaite		Webb		
Woodley Sports	v	Horden CW	2-2*	67
Jones, Norton		Cowley, Huntley		
R(24/9)Horden CW	v	Woodley Sports	2-1	83
Cowley, Devine		Norton		
Atherton Collieries	v	Cheadle Town	2-1	40
Gallagher, Wynne		Morgardo		
West Allotment Celtic	v	Warrington Town	1-1*	96
Malone		Naylor		
R(24/9)Warrington T.	v	West Allotment Celtic	3-1	68
Latham (2), Moores		Chilton		
(22/9)Bacup Borough	v	Cammell Laird	0-4	100
		Hoy, Nezianya, Reay, Robinson		
(at Rossendale United FC)				
Squires Gate	v	Brandon United	2-4*	81
Archer, Blundell		Cuthbertson, Marsden, Patterson		
Atherton LR	v	Sheffield	4-5*	56
Andrews,Kelly(2),Roach		Bagshaw (2) Bray (2), Pickess		
Thornaby	v	Willington	4-0	45
Arnold, Clarke (2), Reeve				
Kennek Ryhope CA	v	Northallerton Town	1-3	32
Andrews		Boyle, Onions, Shardha		
Esh Winning	v	Whickham	4-0	58
Burns,Gawthorpe,Mawson, Messer				
Penrith	v	Stand Athletic	3-0	86
Henderson,Williams,Wright				
Bridlington Town	v	North Shields	8-0	178
Bowsley,Burdick(2),Harper, Harrison,Palmer(2),Richards				
(20/9)Newcastle Blue Star	v	Newcastle Benfield Saints	3-5*	169
Crawford, Thompson		Bond, Leavey, Scope, Young (2)		
Louth United	v	Armthorpe Welfare	1-3	34
Hall		Johnson, Riley		
Fleetwood Town	v	Alsager Town	2-0	142
Catlow, Riches				
Harrogate Railway	v	Skelmersdale United	2-0	88
Stansfield, Walker				
Alnwick Town	v	Ashington	0-7	70
		Atkinson, Campbell, Drysdale, Hepple, Sinclair, Woodhouse (2)		
Winsford United	v	Thackley	1-1*	110
Stott		Patterson		
R(24/9)Thackley	v	Winsford United	3-2	87
Howley, Patterson (2)		Anderson, Davis		
Abbey Hey	v	Maltby Main	8-1	65
Evans,Gibson,Johnson, Levendis(3),Morrison(2)		Watkinson		
Nelson	v	Evenwood Town*	2-1	113
Howarth, Smith		Dinsley		
Morpeth Town	v	Washington	3-1	42
Asiaman, Beavers, WalkerHood				
Peterlee Newtown	v	Maine Road	3-1	50
Crosby, Dobell (2)		Chappell		
Poulton Victoria	v	Seaham Red Star	2-1	90
Bates, Riley		Dibie		
Liversedge	v	Prudhoe Town	4-1	89
Gomersall,Meehan,Morris(2)		Maddison		
Washington Nissan	v	Flixton	0-1	36
		Jones		
Winterton Rangers	v	Parkgate	3-2*	65
McDonald,Neal,Shrimpton		Cusworth, McKenzie		
Tadcaster Albion	v	Eccleshill United	0-7	54
		Dyson(2), Harrison, Jones(3), Price		
Shildon	v	Glasshoughton Welfare	6-3	143
Bolton, Ellison, Rutter (3)		Henderson, Parker, Smith		
Murton	v	Rossington Main	3-0	25
Helens, Hill, Price				
Brodsworth MW	v	Shotton Comrades	2-0	61
Collinson, Humphries				
Pontefract Collieries	v	Holker Old Boys	5-1	32
Britten, Edmond, Leigh, Twitchen, Whitehouse		John		
Colne	v	Hall Road Rangers	1-3	55
Craddock		Barnwell (3)		
Mossley	v	Ramsbottom United	3-1	240
Carroll, Hevicon, Phillips		Lomax		
Garforth Town	v	Formby	4-1	100
Allison, Amos, Traore		Bourne		
Worsbrough Bridge MW	v	Yorkshire Amateur	0-1	50
		Wales		
Lye Town	v	Dudley Town	3-1	61
Bedi, Burgess, Taylor		Cooksey		
West Midlands Police	v	Holbeach United	1-4	36
Speed				
Boston Town	v	Deeping Rangers	1-2*	116
Price		Korkmaz		
Oldbury United	v	Blackwell MW	6-1	45
Hampson,Ross(2), Rowe (2), Wood		Brooks		
Buxton	v	Daventry Town	1-0	193
Cheetham				
St Andrews	v	Chasetown	0-1	56
		Ball		
Brierley & Hagley	v	Malvern Town	1-2*	28
Yapp		Hooper, Whittal-William		
Stratford Town	v	Wednesfield	13-0	125
Allen, Darroch(3), Gallagher, Halford, Niblett(4), Spacey (2), Stephenson				
Holwell Sports	v	Congleton Town	1-2	110
Keast		Scully, Shaw		
Fernhill County Sports	v	Tipton Town	2-0	28
Fairhurst, Nesbitt				
Cradley Town	v	Stafford Town	0-1	39
		Rawlinson		
Coalville Town	v	Mickleover Sports	0-1	77
		Payne		
(22/9)Meir KA	v	Ludlow Town	1-0	71
Moran				
Shawbury United	v	Boldmere St Michaels	0-1	41
		Russell		
Gedling Town	v	Blaby & Whetstone Athletic	5-1	63
Howarth, Jepson, Newton Maddison (2)		Elliott		
Highfield Rangers	v	South Normanton Athletic	2-5	50
Fernandes, Jonas		Brocklehurst, Coleman(2), Hutchinson(2)		
Birstall United	v	Borrowash Victoria	1-2	59
Cain		Powell, Strzyzewski		
Glapwell	v	Carlton Town	0-3	92
		Bignall (2), Heverin		
Barrow Town	v	Leamington	0-1	220
		Shearsby		
Willenhall Town	v	Friar Lane OB	1-0	79
Hay				
Leek CSOB	v	Ledbury Town	1-5	80
Heler		Colwell (2), Preedy (3)		
Norton United	v	Kings Heath	3-0	63
Hubbard (2), Loton				

Home		Away	Score	Att
Biddulph Victoria	v	Rugby Town	0-1	61
		Pulford		
Ibstock Welfare	v	Heath Hayes	8-0	82
Eagling, Emery, Nicholson(2) Smith, Turville (3)				
Sutton Town	v	Glossop North End	5-6*	106
Booth,Short(2),Thorpe(2)		Grant, Hamilton (3), Press (2)		
Wellington	v	Alvechurch	2-4	89
Morgan, Thomas		Fitzpatrick (3), Rostill		
Stone Dominoes	v	Causeway United	1-2	130
Cartwright		Harris, Simpson		
Shifnal Town	v	Rolls Royce Leisure	0-1	56
		Burrows		
Long Eaton United	v	Pershore Town	2-1	95
Briscoe (2)		Wood		
Quorn	v	Shirebrook Town	1-2	141
Varney		Johnson, Orton		
Nuneaton Griff	v	Bourne Town	4-1	55
Rathbone,Smith(2),Williams		Morton		
(22/9)Downes Sports	v	Halesowen Harriers	0-5	95
		Chatwin (2), Hughes, Webb (2)		
(at Halesowen Harriers FC)				
Little Drayton Rangers	v	Pelsall Villa	1-4	104
		Howell, King, Tolley (2)		
Grosvenor Park	v	Gornal Athletic	4-0	51
Anifowose (2), James				
Stansted	v	Bedford United & Valerio	2-1	43
Mercer, Thomas		Smith		
Eton Manor	v	Buckingham Town	0-3	40
		Cole, Grant, Whittiker		
St Margaretsbury	v	Beaconsfield SYCOB	4-3*	37
Porter, Winger (2)		Gumbs, Hughes		
Ipswich Wanderers	v	Concord Rangers	1-1*	97
Goldfinch		Greaves		
R(24/9)Concord R.	v	Ipswich Wanderers	2-3*	38
Greaves, Shuttleworth		Bell, Burman, Lowe		
Harefield United	v	Northampton Spencer	3-1	77
McCullough(2), Ursell		Anger		
Warboys Town	v	Needham Market	1-5	55
Young		Pitt, Rickwood (2), Saker, Wake		
Burnham Ramblers	v	Somersham Town	2-1	46
Down, Hull		Osbourn		
Greenacres (Hemel H.)	v	Stowmarket Town	3-1	68
Berry, Bourne, Perrin		Jopling		
Potters Bar Town	v	Bicester Town	6-1	78
Dickie,Doolan,Ferguson(3) Smart		Please		
Broxbourne Borough V&E	v	Tring Town	3-2	39
Alhadi, Langston, Reade		Hall, Woolfrey		
March Town United	v	Lowestoft Town	0-5	62
		Godbold, McGee (4)		
Eynesbury Rovers	v	Maldon Town	0-4	86
		Docking,Prudance,Warwick,Witney		
Basildon United	v	Enfield Town	0-2*	178
		Riley (2)		
Cheshunt	v	Leighton Town	2-0*	61
Parry (2)				
Biggleswade United	v	London Colney	1-2*	52
Luhman		Jahumpa, Walshe		
Leverstock Green	v	Cockfosters	1-0	53
Starbrook				
Wootton Blue Cross	v	Holmer Green	2-0	71
Bartley, Matthews				
Felixstowe & Walton Utd	v	Colney Heath	3-1	90
Andrews, Fuller (2)		Lacey		
Welwyn Garden City	v	Rothwell Corinthians	1-2	52
Franklin		Harding, Wood		

Home		Away	Score	Att
Kempston Rovers	v	Norwich United	0-2	53
		Bugdale, Prior		
Woodbridge Town	v	Haverhill Rovers	0-5	75
		Cowling (2), Green, Miles		
Dunstable Town	v	Halstead Town	2-3*	43
Carney, Christie		Chinnery, Metson, Owers		
Stanway Rovers	v	Royston Town	5-1	60
Curtis,Driver,Grice(2)		Hash		
Clacton Town	v	Potton United	3-1	124
Hillier, Simba (2)		Davidson		
Hanwell Town	v	Ely City	5-2	56
Asombang(2),Rowlands(2) Sroka		Randle, Styles		
Leyton	v	Hoddesdon Town	5-1	69
Fenton,Gregoriou(2),Williams		Redford		
Gorleston	v	Saffron Walden Town	2-1*	143
Cockrill, Wooldridge		Barker		
(match abandoned in 113th minute – Saffron Walden Town having insufficient number of players – FA decided that the score would stand)				
St Ives Town	v	Southall Town	3-4	63
Ewles (2), Thrale		Lewinson, Morris, Newing (2)		
Newmarket Town	v	Ilford	2-1	120
Rhodes (2)		Hammick		
Bury Town	v	Brentwood	4-0	139
Harrison(2),Tatham,Throgood				
Witham Town	v	Yaxley	1-3	40
Farmer		Hailstone, Harrison (2)		
Southall	v	Flackwell Heath	0-1	63
		Bowler		
Diss Town	v	Sawbridgeworth Town	2-0	189
Gilman, Key				
Hadleigh United	v	Southend Manor	2-2*	82
Cracknell, Godbold		Nicks, Rolfe		
R(24/9)Southend M.	v	Hadleigh United	4-0	40
Curtis,Dawson,Nicks,Smith				
Cornard United	v	Desborough Town	3-1	40
Bethall (2), Evason		Rielly		
(22/9)Woodford Town	v	Soham Town Rangers	1-4	92
Forde		Bugg, Kingston (2), Rutter		
Ware	v	Bowers United	4-3*	91
		Dirnett, Smith		
Clapton	v	Langford	2-1	22
Whiteman,		Rowley		
East Grinstead Town	v	Herne Bay	4-3	160
Arrow(2),Burns,Thompson		Denly, Peachey, Thompson		
Bedfont	v	Hungerford Town	2-2*	37
Abdel Rahman, King				
R(24/9)Hungerford T.	v	Bedfont	2-5	61
Mildenhall		Harris, Postins, Shannon, Williams, Willis		

Herne Bay's (Kent Lge) Justin Smale fires in a shot against East Grinstead (Sussex D2) during his side's 3-4 defeat. Photo: Roger Turner.

Home		Away	Score	Att
Wantage Town	v	Saltdean United	1-0	64
Whitworth				
(22/9)Cray Wanderers	v	Godalming & Guildford	2-1	126
Bennett, Tompkins		Newman		
Alton Town	v	Erith Town	2-3*	75
Healey, Larven		Ademosu, Hackett, Summers		
Hythe Town	v	Deal Town	1-1*	103
Brazier		Jones		
R(24/9)Deal Town	v	Hythe Town	6-4*	120
Goodban, James, Jones(3) Smith		Brazier, Heath (2), Light		
Sidlesham	v	Redhill	7-0	45
Davies(4),Tipper(2),Williams				
VCD Athletic	v	Littlehampton Town	2-1	52
Norris, Ward		Gibbs		
Whitehawk	v	Reading Town	2-0	92
Cooper, Pattenden				
Oakwood	v	Lymington Town	1-3	18
Christensen		Marden, Matcalf (2)		
Chessington & Hook United	v	Beckenham Town	4-3	82
Martin, Wicks (3)		Barnett, Cooney, Kane		
Greenwich Borough	v	Wokingham Town	4-0	15
Ani-Okoye(2),Garrett,Sinclair				
Cobham	v	Hillingdon Borough	3-1*	43
Mesher		McGinty		
Raynes Park Vale	v	BAT Sports	1-2	39
Kendall		Gregory (2)		
Camberley Town	v	Withdean 2000	0-2	77
		Francis (2)		
Arundel	v	Hassocks	3-1	70
Norgate (2), Scerri		Burnham		
Gosport Borough	v	Ringmer	3-0	132
Hensman,Lindsey,Thompson				
Slade Green	v	Viking Greenford	6-1	51
Bowey, Carr, Laming, O'Boyle, Prett (2)		Wharton		
Sandhurst Town	v	Southwick	1-0	67
Lymington & New Milton	v	Wick	11-1	130
Gill(3), Keeping, Phillips(6), Richardson		Simeon		
Blackfield & Langley	v	Eastleigh	1-7	121
Wheatland		Carter, Kenna, Laws(3), Rusher(2)		
Eastbourne Town	v	Winchester City	2-5	191
Barden, Fuller		Bicknell(2), Forbes, Waite		
Fareham Town	v	Walton Casuals	0-1	140
		D'Rozario		
Lancing	v	Hailsham Town	0-1	79
		Spencer		

Goal number four for Maldon (E.Co.Prem)as Terry Warwick slips the ball past the advancing Eynesbury (U.Co.D1) 'keeper. Photo: Gordon Whittington.

Home		Away	Score	Att
Chipstead	v	AFC Newbury	1-3	74
		Neville, Roberts, Romeo		
AFC Totton	v	Sidley United	2-1	126
James, Whiddett		Tate		
Abingdon United	v	Milton United	2-0	162
Fontaine, Peirson				
Cove	v	Merstham	1-5	32
Mercer		Burridge (2), Davis, Hulls, King		
Tunbridge Wells	v	Didcot Town	0-2	101
		Cooper		
Whitchurch United	v	Broadbridge Heath	0-7	47
		Gallagher, Harwood, Jarvand, Liddell (2), McCall, Sweatman		
Corsham Town	v	Brislington	2-0	120
Lodge, Price				
Falmouth Town	v	Gloucester United	2-1*	151
Burchell, Stevens		Harris		
Westbury United	v	Elmore	2-1	104
Colbourne, Seals		Thomas		
Calne Town	v	Shepton Mallet	2-0	60
Davis (2)				
Bridport	v	Fairford Town	0-1	132
		Chessell		
Ilfracombe Town	v	Torrington	1-2	102
Squire		Langhead, Robinson		
Christchurch	v	Odd Down	2-0	78
Taylor (2)				
Frome Town	v	Liskeard Athletic	0-1	161
		Harvey		
Backwell United	v	Dawlish Town	6-1	43
Ayres, Byrne, Gready (2) Hewitt, Patch		Vicary		
Tuffley Rovers	v	Cullompton Rangers	3-1	55
Cooper, Keveren, Wilson		Jee		
Minehead Town	v	Chipping Norton Town	3-1	47
Perkins, Watson (2)		Odom		
Hamworthy United	v	Bitton	2-3	175
Bedward, Orchard		Branch, Warren, Williams		
Shortwood United	v	Wootton Bassett Town	5-1	55
Cole,Evans(2),Green,King		Tooley		
Welton Rovers	v	Keynsham Town	3-2	65
		Bloomfield, Silverthorne		
Chard Town	v	Highworth Town	0-4	74
		Hill, Mills		
Paulton Rovers	v	Launceston	2-1	153
Colbourne, Woon		Tilley		
Cirencester Academy	v	Willand Rovers		
(walkover for Willand Rovers – Cirencester Academy withdrawn)				
Street	v	Yate Town	1-2	74
Hayter		Bennett, Metheringham		
Exmouth Town	v	Bournemouth	0-1	80
		Blythe		
Bridgwater Town	v	Pewsey Vale	9-1	184
Forward,Heywood(3),Kirk, Smith,Sokol,Young(2)		Flippance		
Newton Abbot	v	Amesbury Town	3-3*	70
Cambray, Hancox, Mason		Clark, Hughes, Matthews		
R(25/9)Amesbury T.	v	Newton Abbott	1-4	65
Matthews		Le Huray, Mason, Palmer, Prowse		
Devizes Town	v	Bishop Sutton	5-1	60
Godley, Grange, Grifin, Richardson, Slattery		Maggs		
Clevedon United	v	Hook Norton	3-2	77
Jenkins, Tudor, White		Farley, Wilkins		

FIRST ROUND PROPER

SATURDAY 19 OCTOBER 2002 **WINNING CLUBS TO RECEIVE £250**

Home		Away	Score	Att
Brandon United	v	Murton	3-0	54
Robson (3)				
Armthorpe Welfare	v	Bridlington Town	1-1*	70
Roden		Palmer		
R(22/10)Bridlinton T.	v	Armthorpe Welfare	3-3*	263
Brunton,Harrison,Jackson		Batchelor, Rankine, Sanderson		
(Bridlington Town won 6-5 on kicks from the penalty mark)				
Eccleshill United	v	Poulton Victoria	1-3	82
Morgan		Bates (2), Riley		
Pontefract Collieries	v	Penrith	5-0	60
Britten,Leigh(2),Twitchen(2)				
Abbey Hey	v	Liversedge	3-0	65
Carven,Robinson,Williams				
Esh Winning	v	Mossley	0-2	152
		Pickering (2)		
Salford City	v	Thackley	2-1	73
Willcock (2)		Sugden		
Warrington Town	v	Flixton	1-2	72
Latham		Comley-Excel (2)		
Nelson	v	Dunston Federation Brewery	0-1	123
		Sankey		
Garforth Town	v	Northallerton Town	0-1	95
		Bishop		
Horden CW	v	Ashington	1-0*	65
Jewson				
Peterlee Newtown	v	Ossett Albion	2-5	59
Dobell, Hall		Bradley(2),Horne,Torunczak,Watts		
Hall Road Rangers	v	Hallam	4-3	65
Barnwell,Cockin(2),Underwood		Bates, Maybury		
Newcastle Benfield Saints	v	Morpeth Town	1-2	84
Bond		Asiamath, Beavers		
Nantwich Town	v	Fleetwood Town	0-3	94
		Barnes, Catlow (2)		
Brodsworth MW	v	Billingham Synthonia	2-6	70
Taylor (2)		McGhee (2), Wilson (2), Wood (2)		
Cammell Laird	v	Shildon	4-1	111
Fofana, Nazianya, Reay Robinson		Key		
Sheffield	v	Winterton Rangers	3-2*	122
Beaumont, Bray, Pickess		Alderson, Doyle		
Yorkshire Amateur	v	Guisborough Town	1-2	136
Ibbetson		Jameson, Walker		
Atherton Collieries	v	Harrogate Railway	4-6*	52
Fisher (2), Swailes		Gore, Hart (2), McClean, McDaid		
Borrowash Victoria	v	Stafford Town	2-0	57
Freeman, Widdison				
Rolls Royce Leisure	v	Long Eaton United	0-2	79
		Brady, Heath		
Stratford Town	v	Stourbridge	0-1	171
		Baker		
Malvern Town	v	Norton United	0-2	76
		Hubbard, Powell		
Congleton Town	v	Oldbury United	4-1	143
Booth, Shaw, Smith (2)		Wood		
Pelsall Villa	v	Studley	1-3	73
Nicholls		Coppin, Grubb, Mitchell		
Glossop North End	v	Ford Sports Daventry	1-2	128
Radcliffe		Thomas, Williams		
Barwell	v	Ledbury Town	4-1	82
Clamp, Lucas(2), Puttnam		Preedy		
Nuneaton Griff	v	Grosvenor Park	0-1	40
		Ferguson		
Carlton Town	v	Lye Town	4-2*	43
Bignall(2), Dickinson,		Burgess, Wilkes		

Home		Away	Score	Att
Boldmere St Michaels	v	Halesowen Harriers	2-1*	92
Burgess, Busby		Chatwin		
Newcastle Town	v	Buxton	2-0	101
Harris (2)				
Stewarts & Lloyds	v	Deeping Rangers	3-0	51
Farr, Torrance (2)				
Alvechurch	v	Rugby Town	0-3	113
		Lavery, Pulford (2)		
Holbeach United	v	Fernhill County Sports	6-0	105
Appleby, Keeble(4), Nuttle				
Meir KA	v	Causeway United	2-3	55
Hope, Wilsham		Hall, Williams, Young		
Gedling Town	v	Cogenhoe United	2-0	53
Jepson, Maddison				
Wisbech Town	v	Chasetown	2-1	335
Petty, Thackray		Ball		
Willenhall Town	v	South Normanton Athletic	2-0	95
Bullimore, Hay				
Bridgnorth Town	v	Shirebrook Town	0-2	72
		Burdett, Johnson		
Mickleover Sports	v	Leamington	2-0	275
Holnes, Mays				
Ibstock Welfare	v	Raunds Town	0-1	92
		Freeman		
Burnham Ramblers	v	Bury Town	1-4	75
Beale		Harrison (2), Tatham (2)		
Hanwell Town	v	Greenacres (Hemel H.)	8-3	52
Asombang(2),Brown,Mundy, Rowlands(2), Tucker(2)		Armstrong, Downey, Perrin		
Kingsbury Town	v	Cornard United	4-2	43
Elliott (2), Jones (2)		Bethell, Ford		
Southend Manor	v	Norwich United	2-3*	67
Smith, Wilson		Hunton (2), Murphy		
Gorleston	v	Newmarket Town	3-2	132
Cockrill,Ingram,Wooldridge		Rhodes, Stokes		
Leverstock Green	v	Potters Bar Town	1-2*	130
Burfoot		Jordan, Martin		
Buckingham Town	v	Clapton	4-1	96
Cole, McGillycuddy (2)		Hope		
Lowestoft Town	v	Ipswich Wanderers	5-1	140
Head,King(2),Poppy,Stokeld		Hehir		
London Colney	v	Broxbourne Borough V&E	2-0	40
Jones, Tipper				
Diss Town	v	Rothwell Corinthians	3-3*	186
Gilman, Hardy, Miller		Briffa, Chong (2)		
R(22/10)Rothwell C.	v	Diss Town	0-5	79
		Key (2), Miller, White		
St Margaretsbury	v	Stansted	8-0	58
Barker, Howard(2), Stock, Ulatowski(3), Winger				
Ware	v	Needham Market	3-0	110
Field (2), Moy				
Halstead Town	v	Stanway Rovers	2-3	210
Chatters, Johnston		Curtis, Driver (2)		
Haverhill Rovers	v	Soham Town Rangers	0-3	131
		Bugg, Chatters, Rutter		
Felixstowe & Walton United	v	Leyton	0-5	85
		Emery,Gregoriou,Lewis,Williams,Wood		
Enfield Town	v	North Leigh	3-1	309
Brotherton,Bunn,Riley		Pearman		
Clacton Town	v	Southall Town	0-1	98
		Christie		
Wootton Blue Cross	v	Cheshunt	0-0*	85
R(22/10)Cheshunt	v	Wootton Blue Cross	0-2	68
		Bartley, Stupple		

Home		Away	Score	Att	Home scorers	Away scorers
Maldon Town	v	Harefield United	2-0	92	Reinelt (2)	
Yaxley	v	Flackwell Heath	5-1	60	Acton,Bate,Harrison,Stevens(2)	Jefferies
Lymington & New Milton	v	Walton Casuals	5-2	104	Gill, Phillips (3), Town	D'Rozario, Hunter
Cowes Sports	v	Greenwich Borough	2-1	92	Burrows, Johnston	Garrett
Whitehawk	v	Broadbridge Heath	3-0	60	Pattenden, Rowland (2)	
Sandhurst Town	v	Gosport Borough	1-0	88	Mulvaney	
Lymington Town	v	Selsey	0-3	82		Ford (2), Morey
Chessington & Hook United	v	Abingdon United	2-1	104	Justice, Wood	Moss
Merstham	v	Withdean 2000	0-5	60		Francis (2), Pook, Rowland (2)
Maidstone United	v	Sidlesham	2-4	295	Foley, Sinden	Brown, Davies, Tipper, Williams
Winchester City	v	Cray Wanderers	5-2	231	Forbes (3), Smith (2)	Bennett, Cirillo
Wantage Town	v	East Grinstead Town	5-2*	80	Newport (3), Roche (2)	Burns, Horner
Cobham	v	BAT Sports	5-3	35	Marriott, Parker, Shea, Petrvzziello (2)	Gregory (3)
Andover	v	AFC Newbury	3-1	207	Bennett (2), Butler	Romeo
AFC Wallingford	v	Arundel	0-1	108		Blake
Slade Green	v	Erith Town	0-2*	74		Hackett, Summers
Hailsham Town	v	Brockenhurst	1-2*	93	Smith	Lynn, Msauo
Eastleigh	v	Deal Town	4-0	300	Beck, Hughes (2), Kenna	
VCD Athletic	v	AFC Totton	1-5	45	Penny	Bundy, James(2), Shaw, Whiddett
Thatcham Town	v	Moneyfields	2-3	84	Cook, Perry	Eastman (2), Mould
Bedfont	v	Didcot Town	1-3	82	Postins	Concannon, Heapy, Ogslbey
St Blazey	v	Yate Town	3-2	193	Daly, Hooper, Richardson	Metheringham (2)
Falmouth Town	v	Devizes Town	2-3*	199	Massie (2)	Godley, Richardson, Slattery
Newton Abbott	v	Willand Rovers	0-1	90		Ebdy
Clevedon United	v	Bournemouth	1-2	141	White	Antel, Blyth
Bridgwater Town	v	Bitton	0-1	223		Lee
Shortwood United	v	Calne Town	1-0	60	Evans	
Christchurch	v	Tuffley Rovers	4-2	95	Manning, Rideout, Taylor Wells	Cooper (2)
Fairford Town	v	Team Bath	0-0*	76		
R(21/10)Team Bath	v	Fairford Town	5-2*	46	Cozic, Lavety, Lewis, Sorbaro, Stocco	Stoddart, Webb
Wimborne Town	v	Minehead Town	4-0	194	Barnes,Cannie,Honeybun,Turner	
Welton Rovers	v	Highworth Town	5-0	105	Bidwell,Chambers,Davis,Lewis	
Liskeard Athletic	v	Bideford	0-2	221		Gough (2)
Corsham Town	v	Backwell United	1-0*	93	Kilmurray	
Melksham Town	v	Paulton Rovers	1-4	131	Bown	Colbourne, Miller (2), Woon
Torrington	v	Westbury United	3-2	80	Pickard, Stevens (2)	Colbourne, Wheeler

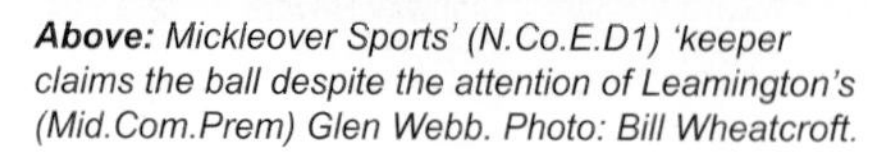

***Above:** Mickleover Sports' (N.Co.E.D1) 'keeper claims the ball despite the attention of Leamington's (Mid.Com.Prem) Glen Webb. Photo: Bill Wheatcroft.*

***Above right:** Craig Maddison's spot kick gives Gedling Town (N.Co.E.D1) the lead over Cogenhoe United (U.Co.Prem). Photo: Gordon Whittington.*

***Right:** Carlton Town (Cen.Mids.SP) on the attack against Lye Town (W.Mids.Prem). Photo: Gordon Whittington.*

SECOND ROUND PROPER

SATURDAY 9 NOVEMBER 2002 | **WINNING CLUBS TO RECEIVE £400**

Home		Away	Score	Att
(19/11)Sheffield	v	Guisborough Town	1-2	122
Pickess		Mowbray, Walker		
Cammell Laird	v	Harrogate Railway	3-4	115
Hanna,Nazinaya,Robinson		Davey(2),Smith,Watkinson,McDaid		
Pontefract Collieries	v	Northallerton Town	1-2	93
Britten		Cook, Onions		
Billingham Synthonia	v	Whitley Bay	0-1	151
		Chandler		
Consett	v	Billingham Town	1-4	76
Halliday		Chillingsworth, Skelton(2), Turner		
Dunston Federation Brewery	v	Tow Law Town	3-2	177
Foster, Sankey, Thompson		Innes, Nicholson		
Ossett Albion	v	Durham City	0-4	165
		Douglas (3), Dunwell		
Brigg Town	v	Horden CW	2-1	179
Drayton (2)		Martin		
Abbey Hey	v	Hall Road Rangers	2-0	53
Hancock (2)				
Morpeth Town	v	Brandon United	2-1	68
Lawton, Leach		Alderson		
Thornaby	v	Fleetwood Town	1-1*	57
Clarke		Riches		
R(12/11)Fleetwood T.	v	Thornaby	4-1	91
Catlow,Cygal,Flynn,Mainds		Banks		
Bridlington Town	v	Poulton Victoria	2-1	191
Richards (2)		Riley		
Salford City	v	Mossley	1-2	150
Giggs		Matthews, Phillips		
Clitheroe	v	Bedlington Terriers	3-1	485
Cryer (2), Whittingham		Chapman		
Prescot Cables	v	West Auckland Town	2-1	199
Clark, Todd		Allen		
Flixton	v	St Helens Town	2-1	74
Matthews, Turner		Molloy		
Mickleover Sports	v	Raunds Town	2-1	107
Wood		Anderson		
Borrowash Victoria	v	Rugby Town	0-3	70
		McBain, Poole, Thompson		
Carlton Town	v	Oadby Town	1-2	79
Bignall		Blockley, Miller		
Shirebrook Town	v	Congleton Town	5-4	170
Burdett, Carter, Johnson(2) Orton		Bickerstaffe, Park, Scully, Smith		
St Neots Town	v	Newcastle Town	0-3	89
		Bott (2), Harris		
Boldmere St Michaels	v	Rushall Olympic	1-2*	92
Roberts		Brown, Evans		
Stewarts & Lloyds	v	Ford Sports Daventry	2-3	43
McCann, Torrance		Evans (2), Giles		
Norton United	v	Gedling Town	1-2	68
Hubbard		Mabon, Scoffham		
Causeway United	v	Long Eaton United	2-1	138
Dixon, Young		Briscoe		
Willenhall Town	v	Arnold Town	4-0*	164
Bullimore,Hay(2),Whitcombe				
Wisbech Town	v	Holbeach United	2-2*	504
Furnell, Hill		Hudson, Nuttall		
R(12/11)Holbeach Utd	v	Wisbech Town	3-0	456
Hudson, Keeble, Nuttall				
Barwell	v	Grosvenor Park	0-3	87
		Ferguson, Merchant, Salmon		
Heanor Town	v	Studley	0-2	110
		Crisp, Neath		
Pickering Town	v	Stourbridge	3-2	139
Dale, Ibbotson,		Eccleston, Lee		
(20/11)Withdean 2000	v	St Margaretsbury	2-2*	87
Francis, Pook		Howard, Winger		
R(3/12)St Margaretsbury	v	Withdean 2000	0-1	59
		Simmons		
Cobham	v	Gorleston	0-1	44
		White		
Lowestoft Town	v	Sidlesham	5-0	174
Durrant,Godbold,Head, Poppy, Stokeld				
Diss Town	v	Tiptree United	3-2	216
Key, Miller, Wright		Cogger, Houghton		
Sandhurst Town	v	Dorking	3-3*	74
Mulvaney (3)		Ahmet, Lunn		
R(19/11)Dorking	v	Sandhurst Town	4-1	95
Lunn (2), White (2)		Mulvaney		
Soham Town Rangers	v	Selsey	2-3	152
Bugg, Rutter		Hinshlewood, More, Reed		
Potters Bar Town	v	Yaxley	0-1	79
		Sanderson		
Mildenhall Town	v	Maldon Town	2-4*	129
Allis, Ogilvie		Gray, Smith, Warwick (2)		
Didcot Town	v	Wootton Blue Cross	1-2	154
McNamara		Seaman (2)		
Thamesmead Town	v	Leyton	3-1	80
Burns, Merridan, Springett		Fenton		
Wroxham	v	Enfield Town	2-0	287
Fox, Lewis				
Chessington & Hook United	v	Ware	2-4*	95
Smith, Wood		McArdle, Moy, Wingrove (2)		
Norwich United	v	Stotfold	1-1*	56
Hunton		Wiseman		
R(19/11)Stotfold	v	Norwich United	1-2*	88
Cottenden		Hunton, Nicholls		
London Colney	v	Milton Keynes City	2-2*	39
Ross, Tipper		Bevis, Hyde		
R(12/11)Milton Keynes C.	v	London Colney	1-0	38
Hart				
Arundel	v	Erith Town	1-0	103
McCaughlin				
Burgess Hill Town	v	Stanway Rovers	2-1	202
Andrews (2)		Bate		
AFC Sudbury	v	Southall Town	1-0	267
Bennett				
Ash United	v	Kingsbury Town	4-1	87
Horton,Mitchell,Short(2)		Moran		
Whitehawk	v	Abingdon Town	2-0	75
Pattenden, Venton				
Buckingham Town	v	Bury Town	2-0	145
Cole, McGillyciddy				
Hanwell Town	v	Dereham Town	2-1	72
Holmes, Rowlands		Parr		
Bitton	v	Wimborne Town	2-1	152
Cole, King		Honeybun		
Devizes Town	v	Wantage Town	3-2	71
Dix, Godley (2)		Bedwell, Roche		
(19/11)Christchurch	v	Torrington	3-2	95
Rideout, Wells		Langmead, Yeo		

Home		Away	Score	Att
Brockenhurst	v	Bemerton Heath Harlequins	1-0	60
Winchester City	v	Shortwood United	3-2	211
Forbes (3)		Cole, Evans		
St Blazey	v	Hallen	1-0	196
Parsons				
Welton Rovers	v	Bournemouth	2-1	67
Cordy, Lewis		Drew		
Moneyfields	v	Paulton Rovers	1-0	102
Jones				
Eastleigh	v	Porthleven	1-3	176
Lawes		Hodge, Miller (2)		
Bideford	v	Cowes Sports	5-0	225
Gough(3),Powell,Southgate				
AFC Totton	v	Andover	2-0	158
Richie, Whiddett				
Team Bath	v	Lymington & New Milton	2-3*	56
Sobora, Wisson		Gill, Phillips, Strong		
Willand Rovers	v	Corsham Town	1-0	105
Jones				

***Above:** Thamesmead's (Kent Prem) Paul Springett heads clear in a crowded golamouth, whilst Leyton's (Isthmian D2) Des Thomas is outjumped by the same player **right**. Photos: Alan Coomes.*

***Below:** This Stotfold (U.Co.Prem) effort skimmed over the bar in their 2-1 replay defeat by Norwich United (E.Co.Prem). Photo: Gordon Whittington.*

THIRD ROUND PROPER

SATURDAY 7 DECEMBER 2002 **WINNING CLUBS TO RECEIVE £600**

Home		Away	Score	Att
Prescot Cables	v	Flixton	6-2	177
Flood, O'Donnell, Todd(2) Torpy (2)		Richards (2)		
Rugby Town	v	Bridlington Town	1-2*	213
Pulford		Palmer, Suddaby		
Fleetwood Town	v	Abbey Hey	3-1	101
Catlow (3)		Stanton		
Grosvenor Park	v	Billingham Town	0-3	76
		Skelton, Woodhouse (2)		
(14/12)Pickering Town	v	Causeway United	2-2*	107
Conner (2)		Barnes (2)		
R(21/12)Causeway U.	v	Pickering Town	1-2*	204
Dixon		Drinkall, Wood		
(11/12)Dunston Federation B.	v	Whitley Bay	0-2	140
		Ludlow, Taylor		
Oadby Town	v	Mickleover Sports	2-2*	149
Stevenson, Warner		Middleditch, Payne		
R(10/12)Mickleover S.	v	Oadby Town	2-3	101
Middleditch, Payne		Warner (3)		
Clitheroe	v	Studley	4-1	352
Cryer(2),Stewart,Whittingham		Crisp		
(14/12)Morpeth Town	v	Willenhall Town	3-2	75
Lawton, McGwie, Nesbitt		Hay, Quilt		
Brigg Town	v	Rushall Olympic	2-1	207
Drayton, Roach		Homer		
Guisborough Town	v	Mossley	0-1	173
		Carroll		
Northallerton Town	v	Shirebrook Town	6-3	182
Cook,Diamond,Foreman, Onions (2),Osborne		Johnson, Orton, Widdowson		
Durham City	v	Gedling Town	7-3*	152
Dunwell (3), Halliday, Healer (2), Kitchen		Elliott, Mabon, Scoffman		
(14/12)Newcastle Town	v	Harrogate Railway	3-1	142
Bott, Dundas (2)				
AFC Sudbury	v	Hanwell Town	6-0	301
Bennett(2),Claydon(3),Rayner				
Buckingham Town	v	Ash United	4-2	162
Max-Grant(3),McGillycuddy		Calvert, Short		

Home		Away	Score	Att
Moneyfields	v	Gorleston	0-4	142
		Cockrill,Harvey,Ingram,Wooldridge		
Yaxley	v	Wroxham	0-1	120
		Fox		
Dorking	v	Ware	0-1	136
		Cooper		
Holbeach Utd	v	Burgess Hill Town	1-4	218
Keeble		Carr (2), Chruchill, Harper		
Milton Keynes City	v	Diss Town	0-2	105
		Barzey, Miller		
Wootton Blue Cross	v	Thamesmead Town	2-1	167
Joswiak, Slinn		Tuley		
Ford Sports Daventry	v	Withdean 2000	1-2*	60
Pearce		Francis (2)		
Maldon Town	v	Selsey	3-0	97
Reinelt, Warwick (2)				
Lowestoft Town	v	Norwich United	3-0	204
McGee (2), Stokeld				
Whitehawk	v	Arundel	2-5*	87
Pattenden, Southwell		Blake, Scerri, Webb, Wimbleton		
St Blazey	v	AFC Totton	5-1	338
Daly, Hooper, Penry Richardson (2)		James		
Welton Rovers	v	Christchurch	0-5	67
		Manning (2), Rideout,Wells (2)		
Devizes Town	v	Bitton	2-2*	75
Godley, Slattery		Bryant, King		
R(10/12)Bitton	v	Devizes Town	0-2	89
		Drewitt (2)		
Willand Rovers	v	Lymington & New Milton	4-5	152
Ebdy, Murray (3)		Phillips, Strong (2), Turner (2)		
Bideford	v	Porthleven	3-2	353
Gough,Hawkings,Southgate		Hodge (2)		
Brockenhurst	v	Winchester City	0-7	213
		Brewster, Forbes, Jackson(3), Mancey, Smith		

Kevin Slinn gives Wotton Blue Cross (U.Co.Prem) the lead against Thamesmead Town (Kent Lge), in their 2-1 3rd Round victory. Photo: Gordon Whittingham.

FOURTH ROUND PROPER

SATURDAY 18 JANUARY 2003 **WINNING CLUBS TO RECEIVE £800**

Home		Away	Score	Att
Lymington & New Milton	v	Mossley	2-3	291
Phillips (2)		Headley, Howard, Matthews		
Newcastle Town	v	Winchester City	0-1	231
		Manley		
Northallerton Town	v	Burgess Hill Town	0-3	255
		Day, Edwards, Harper		
Wroxham	v	Prescot Cables	0-2	307
		Clark, Torpy		
Ware	v	Clitheroe	0-1	568
		Jackson		
Oadby Town	v	Bideford	4-2	435
Mintus,Towers,Warner(2)		Chapman, Gough		
Wootton Blue Cross	v	Whitley Bay	1-2*	416
Griggs		Ludlow (2)		
Maldon Town	v	Morpeth Town	3-0	261
Huttley, Rienelt, Witney				
Gorleston	v	Billingham Town	3-1	304
Ingram (3)		Swalwell		
Durham City	v	AFC Sudbury	0-4	375
		Banya, Bennett (3)		
Devizes Town	v	Christchurch	3-1	162
Dix (2), Hopkins		Taylor		
Bridlington Town	v	Arundel	3-0	360
Harper, Palmer, Thacker				
Withdean 2000	v	Diss Town	2-2*	325
Lamont, Pook		Gilman, Hardy		
R(21/1)Diss Town	v	Withdean 2000	3-1	452
Hardy (2), Johnson		Francis		
Lowestoft Town	v	Buckingham Town	2-0	421
McGee, Stokeld				
Brigg Town	v	Fleetwood Town	3-1	332
Borman, Carter, Stead		Catlow		
Pickering Town	v	St Blazey	2-3	218
Willgrass, Wood		Daly, Harrington, Watkins		

Morpeth (Northern D1) 'keeper Neil Fairbain and Maldon's (East. Co. Prem) Terry Warwick (9) can only watch as Maldon Town's Craig Huttley sends his free kick straight into the back of the net. Photo: Alan Coomes.

Whitley Bay's (Northern D1) Danny Anderson wins the ball in the air away to Wootton Blue Cross: Photo: Steve Ayre.

Above: Morpeth's Carr goes close with this effort in his side's 0-3 defeat by Maldon Town. Photo: Roger Turner.

Whitley Bay 'keeper, Terry Burke, fails to stop Wootton Blue Cross taking an early lead. Photo: Steve Ayre.

FIFTH ROUND PROPER

SATURDAY 8 FEBRUARY 2003 **WINNING CLUBS TO RECEIVE £1000**

BRIGG TOWN 4	DISS TOWN 1
Carter (3), Daryton	Key
	Att: 476

WHITLEY BAY 1	OADBY TOWN 2
Scroggins	Julian, Warner
(AET)	Att: 684

GORLESTON 1	BRIDLINGTON Tn . . 2
Wooldridge	Harper, Palmer
	Att: 450

ST BLAZEY 1	AFC SUDBURY 1
Band	Bennett
(AET)	Att: 944

REPLAY (15/2)

AFC SUDBURY . . . 7	ST BLAZEY 1
Banya, Bennett, Claydon (3), Rayner (2)	Daly
	Att: 725

LOWESTOFT Tn . . 2	MALDON TOWN. . . . 3
Durrant, Payne	Cow, Reinelt, Warwick
(AET)	Att: 668

MOSSLEY. 2	PRESCOT CABLES . 1
Coyne, Kilheeney	Baker
	Att: 665

BURGESS HILL . . . 1	WINCHESTER CITY . 2
Carr	Smith
	Att: 476

CLITHEROE 1	DIVIZES TOWN 3
Garner	Godley (3)
(AET)	Att: 563

Burgess Hill Town's (Sussex Lge) Steve Harper makes a determined effort to get to the ball ahead of the Winchester City (Hampshire Lge) defender.
Photo: D.Nicholson.

Gary Jackson fires in the only goal of the game to take Clitheroe (N.W.Co) through to the next round at the expense of Ware (Isthmian D2).
Photo:Gordon Whittington.

Burgess Hill Town's Phil Churchill takes off towards the Winchester City goal.

Winchester's Ian Mancey shields the ball from Jay Head.

Ashley Carr nets Burgess Hill's only goal of the game in the first minute, during his side's 1-2 defeat at home to Winchester City.

Photos: Roger Turner.

QUARTER-FINALS

SATURDAY 1 MARCH 2003 **WINNING CLUBS TO RECEIVE £2000**

BRIGG TOWN . . . . 2 BRIDLINGTON Tn . . 1

Carter 13, 85 (Pen) Harper 18

Att: 942

BRIGG TOWN: Steer, Roach, Nevis, Thompson, Hope, Rowland, Stones, Wilby, Borman, Drayton, Carter.
Subs: Sherlock, Raspin, Blanchard, Stead, Gawthorpe.
BRIDLINGTON: Kelly, Thompson, Robinson, Baker, Harper, Suddaby, Burdick, Thacker, P Palmer, Harrison, Lewis.
Subs: Taylor, Jackson, Houghton, C Palmer, Bramley.

OADBY TOWN . . . . 1 WINCHESTER CITY. 0

Blake 68 (og)

Att: 888

OADBY TOWN: Maruna, Horner, fenton, Mintus, Julian, Blockley, Brennan, Orton, A warner, C Warner, Poultney.
Subs: Wright, Bacon, Adam, Swingler, Barber.
WINCHESTER: Crowfoot, Waite, Bicknell, Smith, Lang, Blake, Webber, green, Mancy, Forbes, Birks.
Subs: Rodgers, Brewster, Piper, Goss, Kirby.

DEVIZES TOWN. . . 0 MALDON TOWN. . . . 3

Reinelt 18, Smith 70, Warwick 72

Att: 491

DEVIZES: Swan, Mooney, Drewitt, Hopkins, coombes, Campbell, Hardman, Ludgrove, Dix, Hunt, Griffin.
Subs: Godley, Lyal, Mason, Bryan, Jackson.
MALDON: Stanbridge, Warwick, Coe, Huttley, Adams, Gray, Bailey, Shade, Witney, Smith, Granfield.
Subs: Emerson, Docking, Rienelt, Streetley, Leeke.

MOSSLEY. . . . . 0 AFC SUDBURY 2

Bennett 12, 45

Att: 1065

MOSSLEY: Hackney, Trees, Cross, Phillips, Taylor, Howard, Matthews, Calligan, Welton, Kilheeney, Headley.
Subs: Pointon, Heaton, Lewis, Coyne, Carroll.
SUDBURY: Greygoose, Head, Spearing, Tracey, Bishop, Anderson, Rayner, Gardiner, Bennett, Claydon, Betson.
Subs: Banya, Norfolk, Howlett, Taylor, Cheetam.

Winchester City (Hampshire Lge) desperately look to equalise against Oadby Town (Mid.Comb). Photo: Steve Ayre.

Oadby Town's Glynn Morner sets off on an attack, whilst Winchester's Lloyd Webber gets set to make a challenge. Photo: Steve Ayre

SEMI-FINALS

1st Leg
Maldon Town 0
AFC Sudbury 1
Wall 74 (og) .... Att: 1,163

MALDON SQUAD
Stanbridge, Cranfield, Coe, Emerson, Goodacre, Rienelt, Thompson, Gray, Warwick, Bailey, Huttley, Witney, Docking, Wall, Streetley, Younan.

AFC SUDBURY SQUAD
Greygoose, Head, Spearing, Tracey, Bishop, Anderson, Rayner, Gardiner, Bennett, Claydon, Betson, Banya, Hyde, Howlett, Norfolk, Owen.

2nd Leg
AFC Sudbury 2
Claydon 67, 80
Maldon Town 0
.... Att: 1,407

AFC SUDBURY SQUAD
Greygoose, Head, Spearing, Tracey, Bishop, Anderson, Rayner, Gardiner, Bennett, Claydon, Betson, Banya, Hyde, Howlett, Norfolk, Owen.

MALDON SQUAD
Stanbridge, Cranfield, Coe, Emerson, Goodacre, Rienelt, Thompson, Gray, Warwick, Bailey, Huttley, Witney, Docking, Wall, Streetley, Younan.

A Maldon defender clears the danger during the 1st Leg.
Photo: Eric Marsh

Sudbury Town players celebrate after they take the lead in the 1st Leg, thanks to a Maldon own goal.
Photo: Roger Turner.

A packed stand watch on as the home club fire in a free kick in the second half.

Photo: Eric Marsh.

The Maldon Town 'keeper manages to hold on to the ball in this goal mouth scamble. Photo: Eric Marsh.

Whilst it's Maldon Town's turn to put the Sudbury defence under pressure below. Photo: Roger Turner

Maldon Town's Terry Warwick fails to score from the penalty spot.

Photo: Roger Turner.

SEMI-FINALS

1st Leg

Oadby Town 0

Brigg Town 2

Drayton 61, Roach 73 . . . . . . Att: 1,231

OADBY SQUAD

Maruna, Horner, Julian, Mintus, Towers, Blockley, Fenton, Orton, C Warner, A Warner, Poultney, Bacon, Swingler, Wright, Adam, Miller.

BRIGG SQUAD

Steer, Raspin, Rowland, Thompson, Hope, Blanchard, Stead, Stones, Borman, Roach, Carter, Sherlock, Drayton, Wilby, Henson, Gawthorpe.

2nd Leg

Brigg Town 1

Carter 15 (Pen)

Oadby Town 1

Horner 7 . . . . Att: 1,179

BRIGG SQUAD

Steer, Raspin, Rowland, Thompson, Hope, Blanchard, Stead, Stones, Borman, Roach, Carter, Sherlock, Drayton, Wilby, Henson, Gawthorpe.

OADBY SQUAD

Maruna, Horner, Julian, Mintus, Towers, Blockley, Fenton, Orton, C Warner, A Warner, Poultney, Bacon, Swingler, Wright, Adam, Miller.

Simon Roach holds off Oadby Town's Tyrone Mintus during the 1st Leg of their Vase Semi-final.
Photo: Peter Barnes.

This time it's Tyrone Mintus who has the upper hand as he wins this aerial challenge with Brigg striker Craig Stones.
Photo: Peter Barnes.

Oadby Town's Curtis Warner looks to break away from Brigg's Danny Hope.
Photo: Peter Barnes.

Top:
Oadby Town midfielder, Ross Blockley, sets up an early attack in his side's 0-2 home defeat against Brigg Town.
Photo: Peter Barnes.

Above:
Brigg Town goalkeeper, Damien Steer, punches clear in the second half at Topps Park.
Photo: Peter Barnes.

Inset:
Marc Orton sets up another Oadby attack, despite the close attention of Brigg Town's Steve Carter.
Photo: Peter Barnes.

F.A. CARLSBERG VASE - AT A GLANCE

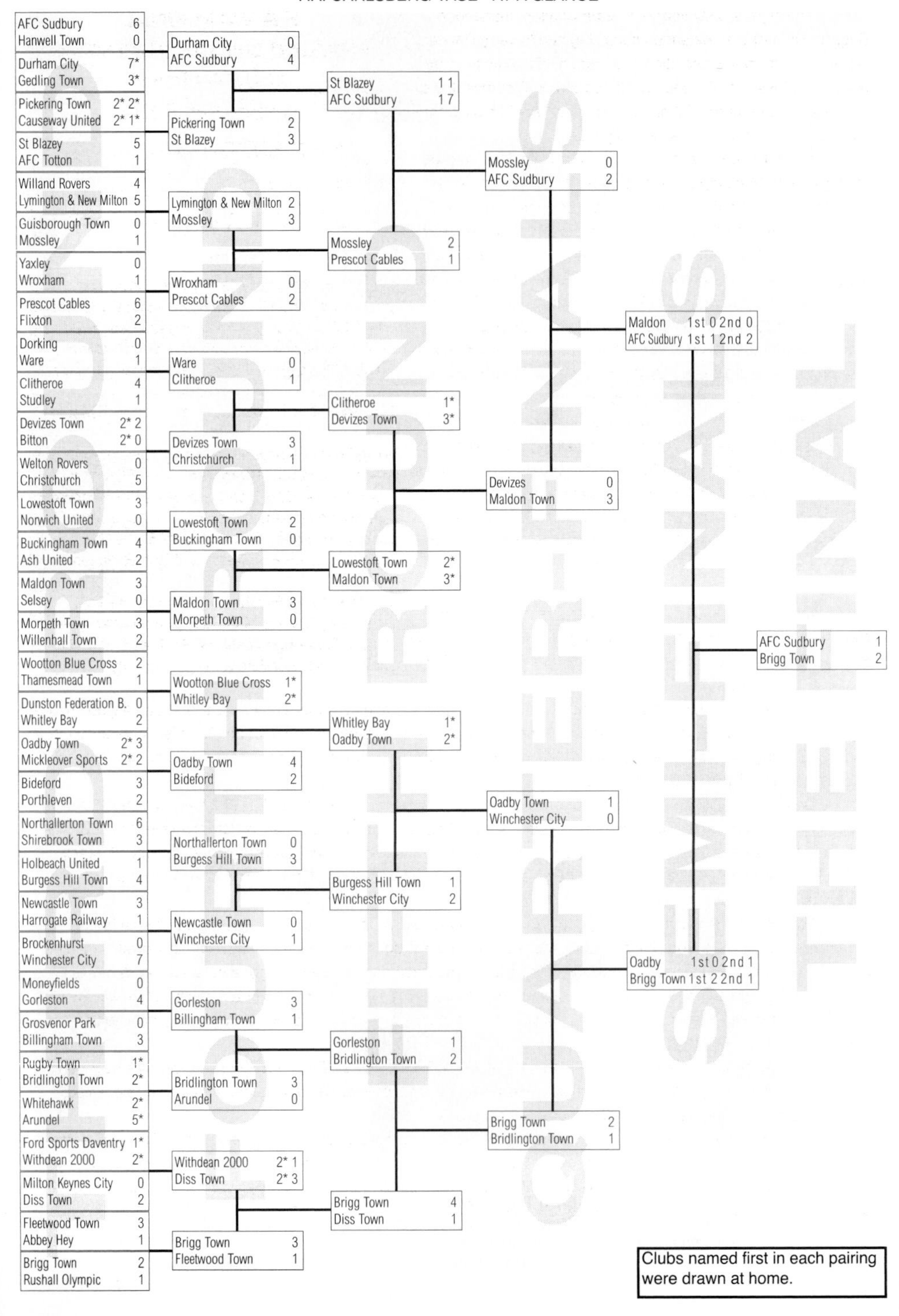
FOURTH ROUND
FIFTH ROUND
QUARTER-FINALS
SEMI-FINALS
THE FINAL
AFC Sudbury 6
Hanwell Town 0
Durham City 7*
Gedling Town 3*
Pickering Town 2* 2*
Causeway United 2* 1*
St Blazey 5
AFC Totton 1
Willand Rovers 4
Lymington & New Milton 5
Guisborough Town 0
Mossley 1
Yaxley 0
Wroxham 1
Prescot Cables 6
Flixton 2
Dorking 0
Ware 1
Clitheroe 4
Studley 1
Devizes Town 2* 2
Bitton 2* 0
Welton Rovers 0
Christchurch 5
Lowestoft Town 3
Norwich United 0
Buckingham Town 4
Ash United 2
Maldon Town 3
Selsey 0
Morpeth Town 3
Willenhall Town 2
Wootton Blue Cross 2
Thamesmead Town 1
Dunston Federation B. 0
Whitley Bay 2
Oadby Town 2* 3
Mickleover Sports 2* 2
Bideford 3
Porthleven 2
Northallerton Town 6
Shirebrook Town 3
Holbeach United 1
Burgess Hill Town 4
Newcastle Town 3
Harrogate Railway 1
Brockenhurst 0
Winchester City 7
Moneyfields 0
Gorleston 4
Grosvenor Park 0
Billingham Town 3
Rugby Town 1*
Bridlington Town 2*
Whitehawk 2*
Arundel 5*
Ford Sports Daventry 1*
Withdean 2000 2*
Milton Keynes City 0
Diss Town 2
Fleetwood Town 3
Abbey Hey 1
Brigg Town 2
Rushall Olympic 1
Durham City 0
AFC Sudbury 4
Pickering Town 2
St Blazey 3
Lymington & New Milton 2
Mossley 3
Wroxham 0
Prescot Cables 2
Ware 0
Clitheroe 1
Devizes Town 3
Christchurch 1
Lowestoft Town 2
Buckingham Town 0
Maldon Town 3
Morpeth Town 0
Wootton Blue Cross 1*
Whitley Bay 2*
Oadby Town 4
Bideford 2
Northallerton Town 0
Burgess Hill Town 3
Newcastle Town 0
Winchester City 1
Gorleston 3
Billingham Town 1
Bridlington Town 3
Arundel 0
Withdean 2000 2* 1
Diss Town 2* 3
Brigg Town 3
Fleetwood Town 1
St Blazey 1 1
AFC Sudbury 1 7
Mossley 2
Prescot Cables 1
Clitheroe 1*
Devizes Town 3*
Lowestoft Town 2*
Maldon Town 3*
Whitley Bay 1*
Oadby Town 2*
Burgess Hill Town 1
Winchester City 2
Gorleston 1
Bridlington Town 2
Brigg Town 4
Diss Town 1
Mossley 0
AFC Sudbury 2
Devizes 0
Maldon Town 3
Oadby Town 1
Winchester City 0
Brigg Town 2
Bridlington Town 1
Maldon 1st 0 2nd 0
AFC Sudbury 1st 1 2nd 2
Oadby 1st 0 2nd 1
Brigg Town 1st 2 2nd 1
AFC Sudbury 1
Brigg Town 2
Clubs named first in each pairing were drawn at home.

F A VASE FINAL
IN PARTNERSHIP WITH CARLSBERG AT UPTON PARK.
ATTENDANCE 6,634.

A.F.C SUDBURY 1

Raynor 30

BRIGG TOWN 2

Housham 2, Carter 68

AFC Sudbury:- Dean Greygoose, David Head (sub Lee Norfolk 63rd min), Tony Spearing, Chris Tracey, John Bishop, Wayne Anderson (sub Lee Owen 73rd min), Terry Rayner, Aaron Gardiner (sub Sam Banya 79th min), Gary Bennett, Andrew Claydon, Paul Betson.
Subs (not used) Ross Taylor and Simon Hyde.

Brigg Town:- Damien Steer, Roy Raspin, Phil Rowland, Graham Thompson, Dave Blanchard, Craig Stones, Carl Stead (sub Ross Thompson 41st min), Steve Housham, Lee Borman (sub Simon Drayton 87th min), Simon Roach, Steve Carter. Subs (not used) Rob Nevis and Rob Gawthorpe

Referee:- Mr M Fletcher (Worcestershire F A), assisted by Messrs M G Robinson (Durham F A0 and J T Taylor (Lancashire F A). Fourth official Mr B Curson (Leicestershire and Rutland F A)

The sight of sixty year old Ralph Clayton, manager of Brigg Town, giving an extended consoling hug to Terry Rayner, scorer of Sudbury's consolation goal, emphasised the tremendous friendliness of this most warm hearted of all competitions. "He told me to be proud. I'd played well and I would have another chance," said Rayner, "it was a really nice touch."

It was Clayton's second victory in a Vase final, having managed a 1996 triumph over Clitheroe. "We played better in '96," he recalled. Setting aside any suggestion he might retire, Raz commented, "I still get a tremendous kick out of being with these fellows." His counterpart, Keith Martin, on the contrary, stuck firmly to his previously publicised retirement decision, even though he would "miss the crack in the dressing room."

Brigg secretary and West Ham United fan, Bob Taylor, was delighted the final was being played at the Hammers' stadium where the pitch looked in first, not last, game of the season order. There was not a bare patch to be seen.

Prior to kick off both teams huddled in their bonding circles, Brigg rather as an afterthought on viewing Sudbury's grouping. However, it was the Lincolnshire side who found the net first. With not even the second minute completed Craig Stones headed down and Steve Housham hit a left foot volley, from outside the box, the net bulging before Dean Greygoose had reached full stretch. Howsham was playing his first Vase match of the season, helping out Brigg in their injury crisis as he had done a dozen times during the season. Howsham has been a Barrow stalwart for three seasons but is encouraged to play midweek for Brigg as Barrow's players live too far away for a home training session to be feasible.

Sudbury were stunned by the goal but almost straightaway had an equalising chance, Andrew Claydon heading wide an opening provided by a corner. Full back David Head then profited from a defensive misunderstanding but could only deflect the ball for a goal kick. A Head cross provided Raynor with a second chance but he failed to make contact from the vicinity of the penalty spot.

Come the 30th minute and Raynor did equalise. Brigg failed to clear a loose ball and Raynor's shot, from just inside the penalty area, found the target through a group of players. Claydon's pace was troubling the Brigg defenders, Gary Bennett nearly profiting from one run and keeper Damien Steer, under pressure, dropping one high ball, luckily for a corner. Sudbury custodian, Greygoose, tipped over a dangerous cross from Simon Roach as half time closed in.

For most of the second half Brigg had the upper hand. Greygoose saved well at the foot of a post from Dave Blanchard. Steer's long drop kick saw Greygoose charging out to palm out of Roach's path, and the forward then put a chance on the net roof. Just over twenty minutes to go and Brigg became delirious for a second time. A free kick way out on the right seemed to spell no danger. Steve Carter, as he admitted, sent over a cross with the sole intention of beating the first defender. Instead it sailed over Greygoose's frantically flailing backpedalling limbs to find the back of the net.

Sudbury charged back. Claydon's shot was blocked. Substitute Lee Owen brought a brilliant flick over from Steer but Brigg substitute Simon Drayton, put clear by Roach, hesitated as the goal gaped and then found himself beating the same defender three times before losing the ball.

A last minute penalty plea looked to have gone Sudbury's way but referee Fletcher overruled his assistant's flag before signalling time had expired and waving away a surge of furiously protesting Suffolk folk. Sportingly they soon put their protest to bed, manager Martin acknowledging honestly that his side had not done themselves justice and could therefore not complain about Brigg's victory.

Arthur Evans.

AFC Sudbury and Brigg Town make their way out on to the pitch. Photo: Roger Turner.

Below: Terry Rayner's equaliser for Sudbury.
Bottom: Steve Carter's free-kick floats in despite the efforts of Sudbury's Tony Spearings, to give Brigg a 2-1 lead.
Photos: Steve Ayre

With less than two minutes on teh clock Brigg Town's Steve Housham scores.

Photo: Peter Barnes.

BRIGG TOWN

(Northern Counties East - Premier Division)

PAST F.A. VASE FINALS

1975 HODDESDON TOWN 2 (Spartan Sth Mids) EPSOM & EWELL 1 (Surrey Senior) Att: 9,500
Sedgwick 2 Wales Ref: Mr R Toseland
Hoddesdon: Galvin, Green, Hickey, Maybury, Stevenson, Wilson, Bishop, Picking, Sedgwick, Nathan, Schofield
Epsom & Ewell: Page, Bennett, Webb, Wales, Worby, Jones, O'Connell, Walker, Tuite, Eales, Lee

1976 BILLERICAY TOWN 1 (Essex Senior) STAMFORD 0 (aet) (United Counties) Att: 11,848
Aslett Ref: Mr A Robinson
Billericay: Griffiths, Payne, Foreman, Pullin, Bone, Coughlan, Geddes, Aslett, Clayden, Scott, Smith
Stamford: Johnson, Kwiatowski, Marchant, Crawford, Downs, Hird, Barnes, Walpole, Smith, Russell, Broadbent

1977 BILLERICAY TOWN 1 (Essex Senior) SHEFFIELD 1 (aet) (Yorkshire) Att: 14,000
Clayden Coughlan og Ref: Mr J Worrall
Billericay: Griffiths, Payne, Bone, Coughlan, Pullin, Scott, Wakefield, Aslett, Clayden,Woodhouse, McQueen. Sub: Whettell
Sheffield: Wing, Gilbody, Lodge, Hardisty, Watts, Skelton, Kay, Travis, Pugh, Thornhill,Haynes. Sub: Strutt
Replay BILLERICAY TOWN 2 SHEFFIELD 1 Att: 3,482
Aslett, Woodhouse Thornhill at Nottingham Forest
Billericay: Griffiths, Payne, Pullin, Whettell, Bone, McQueen, Woodhouse, Aslett, Clayden, Scott, Wakefield
Sheffield: Wing, Gilbody, Lodge, Strutt, Watts, Skelton, Kay, Travis, Pugh, Thornhill, Haynes

1978 NEWCASTLE BLUE STAR 2 (Wearside) BARTON ROVERS 1 (South Midlands) Att: 16,858
Dunn, Crumplin Smith Ref: Mr T Morris
Newcastle: Halbert, Feenan, Thompson, Davidson, S Dixon, Beynon, Storey, P Dixon, Crumplin, Callaghan, Dunn. Sub: Diamond
Barton Rovers: Blackwell, Stephens, Crossley, Evans, Harris, Dollimore, Dunn, Harnaman, Fossey, Turner, Smith. Sub: Cox

1979 BILLERICAY TOWN 4 (Athenian) ALMONDSBURY GREENWAY 1 (Glos. Co) Att: 17,500
Young 3, Clayden Price Ref: Mr C Steel
Billericay: Norris, Blackaller, Bingham, Whettell, Bone, Reeves, Pullin, Scott, Clayden,Young, Groom. Sub: Carrigan
Almondsbury: Hamilton, Bowers, Scarrett, Sulllivan, Tudor, Wookey, Bowers, Shehean, Kerr,Butt, Price. Sub: Kilbaine

1980 STAMFORD 2 (United Counties) GUISBOROUGH TOWN 0 (Northern) Att: 11,500
Alexander, McGowan Ref: Neil Midgeley
Stamford: Johnson, Kwiatkowski, Ladd, McGowan, Bliszczak I, Mackin, Broadhurst, Hall,Czarnecki, Potter, Alexander. Sub: Bliszczak S
Guisborough: Cutter, Scott, Thornton, Angus, Maltby, Percy, Skelton, Coleman, McElvaney,Sills, Dilworth. Sub: Harrison

1981 WHICKHAM 3 (Wearside) WILLENHALL 2 (aet) (West Midlands) Att: 12,000
Scott, Williamson, Peck og Smith, Stringer Ref: Mr R Lewis
Whickham: Thompson, Scott, Knox, Williamson, Cook, Ward, Carroll, Diamond, Cawthra,Robertson, Turnbull. Sub: Alton
Willenhall: Newton, White, Darris, Woodall, Heath, Fox, Peck, Price, Matthews, Smith,Stringer. Sub: Trevor

1982 FOREST GREEN ROVERS 3 (Hellenic) RAINWORTH M.W 0 (Notts Alliance) Att: 12,500
Leitch 2, Norman Ref: Mr K Walmsey
Forest Green: Moss, Norman, Day, Turner, Higgins, Jenkins, Guest, Burns, Millard, Leitch, Doughty. Sub: Dangerfield
Rainworth M.W: Watson, Hallam, Hodgson, Slater, Sterland, Oliver, Knowles, Raine, Radzi, Reah, Comerford. Sub: Robinson

1983 V.S. RUGBY 1 (West Midlands) HALESOWEN TOWN 0 (West Midlands) Att: 13,700
Crawley Ref: Mr B Daniels
VS Rugby: Burton, McGinty, Harrison, Preston, Knox, Evans, ingram, Setchell, Owen,Beecham, Crawley. Sub: Haskins
Halesowen Town: Coldicott, Penn, Edmonds, Lacey, Randall, Shilvock, Hazelwood, Moss, Woodhouse,P Joinson, L Joinson. Sub: Smith

1984 STANSTED 3 (Essex Senior) STAMFORD 2 (United Counties) Att: 8,125
Holt, Gillard, Reading Waddicore, Allen Ref: Mr T Bune
Stanstead: Coe, Williams, Hilton, Simpson, □Cooper, Reading, □Callanan, Holt, Reevs,Doyle, Gillard. Sub: Williams
Stamford: Parslow, Smitheringate, Blades, McIlwain, Lyon, Mackin, Genovese, Waddicore,Allen, Robson, Beech. Sub: Chapman

1985 HALESOWEN TOWN 3 (West Midlands) FLEETWOOD TOWN 1 (N W Counties) Att: 16,715
L Joinson 2, Moss Moran Ref: Mr C Downey
Halesowen: Coldicott, Penn, Sherwood, Warner, Randle, Heath, Hazlewood, Moss (Smith),Woodhouse, P Joinson, L Joinson
Fleetwood Town: Dobson, Moran, Hadgraft, Strachan, Robinson, Milligan, Hall, Trainor, Taylor(Whitehouse), Cain, Kennerley

1986 HALESOWEN TOWN 3 (West Midlands) SOUTHALL 0 (Isthmian 2 South) Att: 18,340
Moss 2, L Joinson Ref: Mr D Scott
Halesowen: Pemberton, Moore, Lacey, Randle (Rhodes), Sherwood, Heath, Penn, Woodhouse, PJoinson, L Joinson, Moss
Southall: Mackenzie, James, McGovern, Croad, Holland, Powell (Richmond), Pierre,Richardson, Sweales, Ferdinand, Rowe

1987 ST. HELENS 3 (N W Counties) WARRINGTON TOWN 2 (N W Counties) Att: 4,254
Layhe 2, Rigby Reid, Cook Ref: Mr T Mills
St Helens: Johnson, Benson, Lowe, Bendon, Wilson, McComb, Collins (Gledhill), O'Neill,Cummins, Lay, Rigby. Sub: Deakin
Warrington: O'Brien. Copeland, Hunter, Gratton, Whalley, Reid, Brownville (Woodyer), Cook,Kinsey, Looker (Hill), Hughes

1988 COLNE DYNAMOES 1 (N W Counties) EMLEY 0 (Northern Counties East) Att: 15,000
Anderson Ref: Mr A Seville
Colne Dynamoes: Mason, McFafyen, Westwell, Bentley, Dunn, Roscoe, Rodaway, Whitehead (Burke),Diamond, Anderson, Wood (Coates)
Emley: Dennis, Fielding, Mellor, Codd, Hirst (Burrows), Gartland (Cook), Carmody,Green, Bramald, Devine, Francis

1989 TAMWORTH 1 (West Midlands) SUDBURY TOWN 1 (aet) (Eastern) Att: 26,487
Devaney Hubbick Ref: Mr C Downey
Tamworth: Bedford, Lockett, Atkins, Cartwright, McCormack, Myers, Finn, Devaney, Moores,Gordon, Stanton. Subs: Rathbone, Heaton
Sudbury Town: Garnham, Henry, G Barker, Boyland, Thorpe, Klug, D Barker, Barton, Oldfield,Smith, Hubbick. Subs: Money, Hunt
REPLAY TAMWORTH 3 SUDBURY TOWN 0 Att: 11,201
Stanton 2, Moores at Peterborough
Tamworth: Bedford, Lockett, Atkins, Cartwright, Finn, Myers, George, Devaney, Moores,Gordon, Stanton. Sub: Heaton
Sudbury Town: Garnham, Henry, G Barker, Boyland, Thorpe, Klug, D Barker, Barton, Oldfield,Smith, Hubbick. Subs: Money, Hunt

1990 YEADING 0 (Isthmian 2 South) BRIDLINGTON TOWN 0 (aet) (N Co East) Att: 7,932
Ref: Mr R Groves
Yeading: Mackenzie, Wickens, Turner, Whiskey (McCarthy), Croad, Denton, Matthews, James(Charles), Sweates, Impey, Cordery
Bridlington: Taylor, Pugh, Freeman, McNeill, Warburton, Brentano, Wilkes (Hall), Noteman,Gauden, Whiteman, Brattan (Brown)

Replay YEADING 1 BRIDLINGTON TOWN 0 Att: 5,000
Sweales at Leeds Utd FC
Yeading: Mackenzie, Wickens, Turner, Whiskey, Croad (McCarthy), Schwartz, Matthews,James, Sweates, Impey (Welsh), Cordery
Bridlington: Taylor, Pugh, Freeman, McNeill, Warburton, Brentano, Wilkes (Brown), Noteman,Gauden (Downing), Whiteman, Brattan

1991 GRESLEY ROVERS 4 (West Midlands) GUISELEY 4 (aet) (Northern Co East) Att: 11,314
Rathbone, Smith 2, Stokes Tennison 2, Walling, A Roberts Ref: Mr C Trussell
Gresley: Aston, Barry, Elliott (Adcock), Denby, Land, Astley, Stokes, K Smith, Acklam,Rathbone, Lovell (Weston)
Guiseley: Maxted, Bottomley, Hogarth, Tetley, Morgan, McKenzie, Atkinson (Annan),Tennison, Walling, A Roberts, B Roberts

Replay GUISELEY 3 GRESLEY ROVERS 1 Att: 7,585
Tennison, Walling, Atkinson Astley at Bramall Lane
Guiseley: Maxted, Annan, Hogarth, Tetley, Morgan, McKenzie (Bottomley), Atkinson,Tennison (Noteman), Walling, A Roberts, B Roberts
Gresley: Aston, Barry, Elliott, Denby, Land, Astley, Stokes (Weston), K Smith, Acklam, Rathbone, Lovell (Adcock)

1992 WIMBORNE TOWN 5 (Wessex) GUISELEY 3 (Northern Premier Div 1) Att: 10,772
Richardson, Sturgess 2, Killick 2 Noteman 2, Colville Ref: Mr M J Bodenham
Wimborne: Leonard, Langdown, Wilkins, Beacham, Allan, Taplin, Ames, Richardson, Bridle,Killick, Sturgess (Lovell), Lynn
Guiseley: Maxted, Atkinson, Hogarth, Tetley (Wilson), Morgan, Brockie, A Roberts,Tennison, Noteman (Colville), Annan, W Roberts

1993 BRIDLINGTON TOWN 1 (NPL Div 1) TIVERTON TOWN 0 (Western) Att: 9,061
Radford Ref: Mr R A Hart
Bridlington: Taylor, Brentano, McKenzie, Harvey, Bottomley, Woodcock, Grocock, A Roberts, Jones, Radford (Tyrell), Parkinson. Sub: Swailes
Tiverton Town: Nott, J Smith, N Saunders, M Saunders, Short (Scott), Steele, Annunziata, KSmith, Everett, Daly, Hynds (Rogers)

1994 DISS TOWN 2 (Eastern) TAUNTON TOWN 1 (Western) Att: 13,450
Gibbs (p), Mendham Fowler Ref: Mr K. Morton
Diss Town: Woodcock, Carter, Wolsey (Musgrave), Casey (Bugg), Hartle, Smith, Barth, Mendham, Miles, Warne, Gibbs
Taunton Town: Maloy, Morris, Walsh, Ewens, Graddon, Palfrey, West (Hendry), Fowler, Durham, Perrett (Ward), Jarvis

1995 ARLESEY TOWN 2 (South Midlands) OXFORD CITY 1 (Ryman 2) Att: 13,670
Palma, Gyalog S Fontaine Ref: Mr G S Willard
Arlesey: Young, Cardines, Bambrick, Palma (Ward), Hull, Gonsalves, Gyalog, Cox, Kane,O'Keefe, Marshall (Nicholls). Sub: Dodwell
Oxford: Fleet, Brown (Fisher), Hume, Shepherd, Muttock, Hamilton (Kemp), Thomas, Spittle, Sherwood, S Fontaine, C Fontaine. Sub: Torres

1996 BRIGG TOWN 3 (N Co East) CLITHEROE 0 (N W Counties) Att: 7,340
Stead 2, Roach Ref: Mr S J Lodge
Brigg: Gawthorpe, Thompson, Rogers, Greaves (Clay), Buckley (Mail), Elston, C Stead, McLean, N Stead (McNally), Flounders, Roach
Clitheroe: Nash, Lampkin, Rowbotham (Otley), Baron, Westwell, Rovine, Butcher, Taylor (Smith), Grimshaw, Darbyshire, Hill (Dunn)

1997 WHITBY TOWN 3 (Northern) NORTH FERRIBY UTD. 0 (N Co East) Att: 11,098
Williams, Logan, Toman Ref: Graham Poll
North Ferriby: Sharp, Deacey, Smith, Brentano, Walmsley, M Smith, Harrison (Horne), Phillips (Milner), France (Newman), Flounders, Tennison
Whitby Town: Campbell, Williams, Logan, Goodchild, Pearson, Cook, Goodrick (Borthwick), Hodgson, Robinson, Toman (Pyle), Pitman (Hall)

1998 TIVERTON TOWN 1 (Western) TOW LAW TOWN 0 (Northern) Att: 13,139
Varley Ref: M A Riley
Tiverton: Edwards, Felton, Saunders, Tatterton, Smith J, Conning, Nancekivell (Rogers), Smith K (Varley), Everett, Daly, Leonard (Waters)
Tow Law: Dawson, Pickering, Darwent, Bailey, Hague, Moan, Johnson, Nelson, Suddick, Laidler (Bennett), Robinson.

1999 TIVERTON TOWN 1 (Western) BEDLINGTON TERRIERS 0 (Northern) Att: 13, 878
Rogers 88 Ref: W. C. Burns
Bedlington Terriers: O'Connor, Bowes, Pike, Boon (Renforth), Melrose, Teasdale, Cross, Middleton (Ludlow), Gibb, Milner, Bond. Subs: Pearson, Cameron, Gowans
Tiverton Town: Edwards, Fallon, Saunders, Tatterton, Tallon, Conning (Rogers), Nancekivell (Pears), Varley, Everett, Daly, Leonard. Subs: Tucker, Hynds, Grimshaw

2000 DEAL TOWN 1 (Kent) CHIPPENHAM TOWN 0 (Western) Att: 20,000
Graham 87 Ref: E. K. Wolstenholme
Deal Town: Tucker, Kempster, Best, Ash, Martin, Seager, Monteith, Graham, Lovell, Marshall, Ribbens. Subs: Roberts, Warden, Turner
Chippenham Town: Jones, James, Andrews, Murphy, Burns, Woods, Brown, Charity, Tweddle, Collier, Godley. Subs: Tiley, Cutler

2001 TAUNTON TOWN 2 (Western) BERKHAMPSTED TOWN 1 (Isthmian 2) (at Villa Park) Att: 8,439
Fields 41, Laight 45 Lowe 71 Ref: E. K. Wolstenholme
Taunton Town: Draper, Down, Chapman, West, Hawkings, Kelly, Fields (Groves), Laight, Cann (Tallon), Bastow, Lynch (Hapgood). Subs: Ayres, Parker
Berkhampsted Town: O'Connor, Mullins, Lowe, Aldridge, Coleman, Brockett, Yates, Adebowale, Richardson, Smith, Nightingale. Subs: Ringsell, Hall, Knight, Franklin, Osborne

2002 WHITLEY BAY 1 (Northern) TIPTREE UNITED 0 (Eastern) (at Villa Park) Att: 4742
Whitley Bay: Caffrey, Sunderland, Walmsley, Dixon (Neil), Chandler, Walton, Fenwick (Cuggy). Subs: Cook, Livermore
Tiptree United: Haygreen, Battell, Wall, Houghton, Fish, Streetley (Gillespie), Wareham (Snow), Daly, Barefield, Aransibia (Parnell), Brady. Subs: Powell, Ford. Ref: A Kaye

All Finals at Wembley unless otherwise shown

TOP GOAL SCORERS 2002 - 2003

Player	Club	No. goals	Round reach	No. hatrick	Hatrick details
L Phillips	Lymington & New Milton	13	4th Rnd Proper	3	2nd Q (2), 1st Rnd P
G Bennett	AFC Sudbury	10	Runners-up	1	4th Rnd Proper
D Godley	Devizes Town	9	Quarter-finals	1	4th Rnd Proper
G McGee	Lowestoft Town	9	5th Rnd Proper	1	2nd Qualifying Rnd
A Claydon	AFC Sudbury	8	Runners-up	2	3rd & 5th Rnd P.
S Carter	Brigg Town	8	Winners	1	4th Rnd Proper
L Catlow	Fleetwood Town	8	4th Rnd Proper	1	3rd Rnd Proper
G Hay	Willenhall Town	8	3rd Rnd Proper	1	1st Qualifying Rnd
A Forbes	Winchester City	8	Quarter-finals	2	1st & 2nd Rnd P.
S Francis	Withdean 2000	8	4th Rnd Proper		
R Gough	Bideford	7	4th Rnd Proper	1	2nd Rnd Proper
D Laws	Eastleigh	7	2nd Rnd Proper	2	1st Qual. & 2nd Qual.
T Warwick	Maldon Town	7	Semi-finals		
D Onions	Northallerton Town	7	4th Rnd Proper	1	1st Qualifying Rnd
T Pattenden	Whitehawk	7	3rd Rnd Proper		
P Palmer	Bridlington Town	6	Quarter-finals		
P Bignall	Carlton Town	6	2nd Rnd Proper		
R Reinelt	Maldon Town	6	Semi-finals		
D Bray	Sheffield	6	2nd Rnd Proper		
R Gregory	BAT Sports	5	1st Rnd Proper	1	1st Round Proper
S Drayton	Brigg Town	5	Winners		
S Jones	Deal Town	5	1st Rnd Proper	1	2nd Qual. Replay
A Key	Diss Town	5	5th Rnd Proper		
G Ingram	Gorleston	5	5th Rnd Proper		
K Rowlands	Hanwell Town	5	3rd Rnd Proper		
R Colwell	Ledbury Town	5	1st Rnd Proper	1	1st Qualifying Rnd
K Gill	Lymington & New Milton	5	4th Rnd Proper	1	2nd Qualifying Rnd
J Hunton	Norwich United	5	3rd Rnd Proper		
C Warner	Oadby Town	5	Semi-finals		
P Mulvaney	Sandhurst Town	5	2nd Rnd Proper	1	2nd Rnd Proper
S Johnson	Shirebrook Town	5	3rd Rnd Proper		
R Davies	Sidlesham	5	2nd Rnd Proper	1	2nd Qualifying Rnd
D Bartley	Wotton Blue Cross	5	4th Rnd Proper	1	1st Qualifying Rnd

HIGHEST SCORING CLUBS 2002 - 2003

26 Goals

Lymington & New Milton

Lowestoft Town

25 Goals

AFC Sudbury

23 Goals

Devizes Town

Maldon Town

22 Goals

Bridlington Town

Winchester City

20 Goals

Diss Town

18 Goals

Brigg Town

Eastleigh

17 Goals

Northallerton Town

Gorleston

16 Goals

Buckingham Town

Causeway United

Christchurch

ENGLAND SEMI-PROFESSIONAL REPRESENTATIVE FOOTBALL

Following a very disappointing Four Nations Home International Tournament at the end of the 2001-2002 season, when the England manager John Owens received very little co-operation from the Conference clubs, and was unable to benefit from any real political muscle from the Football Association, new boss Paul Fairclough was at least able to call upon most of his first choice selections for the week in Wales.

Half the confident Yeovil Town championship winning squad were included and although two of the early season representative games were for the under 23s and one 'England' team was selected from the three feeder leagues - Dr Martens, Rymans and Unibond- at least a wider selection of players had enjoyed representative game experience.

The successes of the week were the mid field 'engine room' of Darren Way, Lee Johnson and Stuart Drummond, with Kirk Jackson and Roscoe D'Sane outstanding up front and giant keeper Chris Weale in magnificent form. The Irish were certainly handicapped as their football season is now contested throughout the summer, so their first choices were unavailable.

As holders and hosts, the pressure was on Wales but they couldn't recapture the form of 2002, and after a close victory over the Scots they lost to England and surprisingly, to the Irish. Scotland insist on selection from the Highland and East of Scotland leagues only, but their officials were pleased with their squad's improvement and look forward to a championship success at home next year.

This tournament is developing and all four countries should really concentrate on selecting their very best players. If they do, the standard of competition would be magnificent and a wonderful advert for our level of football and should attract bigger and bigger support.

England squad before their Four Nations match against Ireland at Merthyr Tydfil.

Photo: Roger Turner.

INTERNATIONAL FRIENDLIES

ITALY 3 - 2 ENGLAND

Kennedy 47, Boardman 89

Wednesday 20th November 2002 at AC Cremonese - Att: 1500

ENGLAND

1. Matt Baker . . . . Hereford United
2. Adam Lockwood . . . . Yeovil Town
3. Michael Rose . . . . . . Hereford United
4. Lee Johnson (capt) . . . . . Yeovil Town
5. Jonathon Boardman . . . . Woking
6. Wayne Payton . . . Nuneaton Borough
7. John Kennedy . . . . Canvey Island
8. Wayne Purser . . . . Barnet
9. Gary Thompson . . . . Morecambe
10. Ryan Sugden . . . . Chester City
11. Aaron Webster . . . . Burton Albion

Subs:

12. Dale Anderson . . . . Burton Albion
13. Chris Weale (GK) . . . . . . Yeovil Town
14. Martin Lancaster . . . . . . Chester City
15. Chris Blackburn . . . . Chester City
16. Darren Way . . . . Yeovil Town

All capped.

Referee

Mr M Mazzoleni (Bergamo)

BELGIUM 3 - 1 ENGLAND

D'Sane 79

Tuesday 11th February 2003 at KV Ostend - Att: 870

ENGLAND

1. Lance Key . . . . Kingstonian
2. John Kennedy . . . . Canvey Island
3. Steve Ward (capt) . . . . Canvey Island
4. Marc Pullan . . . . Crawley Town
5. Chris Duffy . . . . Canvey Island
6. Anthony Rivierre . . . . . Welling United
7. Ian Craney . . . . Altrincham
8. Fiston Manuella . . . Aylesbury United
9. Adam Wilde . . . . Worcester City
10. Craig McAllister . . Basingstoke Town
11. Scott Rickards . . . . Tamworth

Subs:

12. Mike Tomlinson . . . . Runcorn
13. Nikki Bull (GK) . . . . . . Aldershot Town
14. Roscoe D'Sane . . . . . Aldershot Town
15. John Keeling . . . . Purfleet
16. Ton Sills . . . . Kingstonian

All capped.

Referee

Mr R Cooleman (Belgium)

HOLLAND 0 - 0 ENGLAND

Tuesday 25th March at BV Sparta - Att: 950

ENGLAND

1. Wayne Brown. . . . . Chester City
2. John Kennedy. . . . . Canvey Island
3. Scott Guyett (capt). . . . . Chester City
4. Danny Collins. . . . . Chester City
5. Michael Rose . . . . . . Hereford United
6. Mark Janney . . Dagenham & Redbridge
7. Richard Norris. . . . Northwich Victoria
8. Stewart Drummond. . . . . Morecambe
9. Lee Elam . . . . Morecambe
10. Gregg Blundell . . . Northwich Victoria
11. Junior Agogo. . . . . Barnet

Subs:

12. Lee Johnson . . . . Yeovil Town
13. Chris Weale (GK) . . . . . . Yeovil Town
14. Jimmy Jackson . . Gravesend & N'fleet
15. Roscoe D'Sane. . . . . Aldershot Town
16. Adrinano Rigoglioso . . . . Morecambe

All capped.

Referee

Mr H J M C Jaspers (Holland)

Scott Guyett, who captained England during their 0-0 draw with Holland, is seen here shaking hands with the Republic of Ireland skipper before their opening match in the Four Nations Tournament at Merthyr Tydfil.

Photo: Roger Turner.

FOUR NATIONS TOURNAMENT

ENGLAND 4 - 0 REP. OF IRELAND

D'Sane 15, Jackson 22, 37, 49

Tuesday 20th May 2003 at Merthyr Tydfil

ENGLAND

1. Chris Weale .... Yeovil Town
2. John Kennedy(72) ..... Canvey Island
3. Scott Guyett (capt)..... Chester City
4. Terry Skiverton .... Yeovil Town
7. Michael Rose ...... Hereford United
9. Lee Johnson(75) .... Yeovil Town
10. Darren Way.......... Yeovil Town
11. Stewart Drummond..... Morecambe
14. Lee Elam............ Halifax Town
15. Kirk Jackson(80) .... Yeovil Town
16. Roscoe D'Sane..... Aldershot Town

Subs:

5. Jon Boardman............ Woking
6. Wayne Hatswell(72) ..... Chester City
8. Tristram Whitman ... Doncaster Rov.
12. Paul Terry(75) .... Dagenham
13. Matt Baker (GK) .... Hereford United
17. Junior Agogo(80) .... Barnet
18. Richard Norris.... Northwich Victoria

Referee

Mr M Whitby (Wales)

OTHER RESULTS

WALES	**2 - 1**	**SCOTLAND**
SCOTLAND	**4 - 3**	**REP. OF IRELAND**
REPUBLIC OF IRELAND	**2 - 0**	**WALES**

ENGLAND 2 - 0 WALES

Way 16, D'Sane 73 (pen)

Thursday 22nd May 2003 at Merthyr Tydfil

ENGLAND

1. Chris Weale .... Yeovil Town
2. John Kennedy....... Canvey Island
3. Scott Guyett (capt)..... Chester City
4. Terry Skiverton(70)....... Yeovil Town
7. Michael Rose ...... Hereford United
9. Lee Johnson.......... Yeovil Town
10. Darren Way(82) .... Yeovil Town
11. Stewart Drummond..... Morecambe
14. Lee Elam............ Halifax Town
15. Kirk Jackson.......... Yeovil Town
16. Roscoe D'Sane(86) ... Aldershot Town

Subs:

5. Jon Boardman............ Woking
6. Wayne Hatswell (70)..... Chester City
8. Tristram Whitman(86).. Doncaster Rov.
12. Paul Terry (82)........... Dagenham
13. Matt Baker (GK) .... Hereford United
17. Junior Agogo.............. Barnet
18. Richard Norris.... Northwich Victoria

Referee

Mr S Duff (Scotland)

Yeovil's Darren Way puts England one up, after firing past Wales goalkeeper Tony Pennock.

Photo: Roger Turner.

ENGLAND 1 - 1 SCOTLAND

D'Sane 59

Saturday 24th May 2003 at Carmarthen Town

ENGLAND

13. Matt Baker (GK) . . . . Hereford United
2. John Kennedy. . . . . . . Canvey Island
3. Scott Guyett (capt). . . . . Chester City
5. Jon Boardman . . . . Woking
7. Michael Rose . . . . . . Hereford United
9. Lee Johnson . . . . Yeovil Town
8. Tristram Whitman . . . Doncaster Rov.
12. Paul Terry (70). . . . . Dagenham
18. Richard Norris(62) . . Northwich Victoria
17. Junior Agogo(77) . . . . Barnet
16. Roscoe D'Sane . . . . . Aldershot Town

Subs:

1. Chris Weale . . . . Yeovil Town
4. Terry Skiverton . . . . Yeovil Town
6. Wayne Hatswell . . . . Chester City
10. Darren Way. . . . . Yeovil Town
11. Stewart Drummond (70) . . Morecambe
14. Lee Elam(62) . . . . Halifax Town
15. Kirk Jackson(77) . . . . Yeovil Town

Referee

Mr P Tuitte (Republic of Ireland)

FINAL TABLE	P	W	D	L	F	A	Pts	GD
ENGLAND	3	2	1	0	7	1	7	6
SCOTLAND	3	1	1	1	6	6	4	0
REPUBLIC OF IRELAND	3	1	0	2	5	8	3	-3
WALES	3	1	0	2	2	5	3	-3

England's Four Nations Tournament goalscorers.....

Roscoe D'Sane	3
Kirk Jackson	3
Darren Way	1

Left:
Junior Agogo challenges for the ball during England's match against Scotland.

Below:
Tristram Witman is closed down by Scotland's Ross Archiebald.

Below:
Yeovil Town's Lee Johnson ways up his options whilst Doncaster Rovers' Tristram Witman sets off on a run.

Photos: Roger Turner.

Aldershot Town striker Roscoe D'Sane makes clean contact with the ball to score England's equaliser against Scotland.

Not this time, Wales goalkeeper, Tony Pennock, makes a fine save from England's Kirk Jackson, during the home nation's 2-0 defeat.

D'Sane adds to his tournament goal tally with this penalty, to put England 2-0 up against Wales.

Photos: Roger Turner.

ENGLAND'S RESULTS 1979 - 2003

BELGIUM

11.02.03	KV Ostend	1 - 3

FINLAND UNDER-21

14.04.93	Woking	1 - 3
30.05.94	Aanekoski	0 - 2

GIBRALTAR

27.04.82	Gibraltar	3 - 2
31.05.95	Gibraltar	3 - 2

HOLLAND

03.06.79	Stafford	1 - 0
07.06.80	Zeist	2 - 1
09.06.81	Lucca	2 - 0
03.06.82	Aberdeen	1 - 0
02.06.83	Scarborough	6 - 0
05.06.84	Palma	3 - 3
13.06.85	Vleuten	3 - 0
20.05.87	Kircaldy	4 - 0
11.04.95	Aalsmeer	0 - 0
02.04.96	Irthlingborough	3 - 1
18.04.97	Appingedam	0 - 0
03.03.98	Crawley	2 - 1
30.03.99	Genemuiden	1 - 1
21.03.00	Northwich	1 - 0
22.03.01	Wihemina FC	3 - 0
24.04.02	Yeovil Town	1 - 0
25.03.03	BV Sparta 25	0 - 0

ITALY

03.06.80	Zeist	2 - 0
13.06.81	Montecatini	1 - 1
01.06.82	Aberdeen	0 - 0
31.05.83	Scarborough	2 - 0
09.06.84	Reggio Emilia	0 - 1
11.06.85	Houten	2 - 2
18.05.87	Dunfermline	1 - 2
29.01.89	La Spezia	1 - 1
25.02.90	Solerno	0 - 2
05.03.91	Kettering	0 - 0
01.03.99	Hayes	4 - 1
01.03.00	Padova	1 - 1
20.11.02	AC Cremonese	3 - 2

NORWAY UNDER-21

01.06.94	Slemmestad	1 - 2

REPUBLIC OF IRELAND

24.05.86	Kidderminster	2 - 1
26.05.86	Nuneaton	2 - 1
25.05.90	Dublin	2 - 1
27.05.90	Cork	3 - 0
27.02.96	Kidderminster	4 - 0
25.02.97	Dublin	0 - 2
16.05.02	Boston	1 - 2
20.05.03	Merthyr Tydfil	4 - 0

SCOTLAND

31.05.79	Stafford	5 - 1
05.06.80	Zeist	2 - 4
11.06.81	Empoli	0 - 0
05.06.82	Aberdeen	1 - 1
04.06.83	Scarborough	2 - 1
07.06.84	Modena	2 - 0
15.06.85	Harderwijk	1 - 3
23.05.87	Dunfermline	2 - 1
18.05.02	Kettering	2 - 0
24.05.03	Carmarthen Town	0 - 0

USA

20.03.02	Stevenage Boro.	2 - 1

WALES

27.03.84	Newtown	1 - 2
26.03.85	Telford	1 - 0
18.03.86	Merthyr Tydfil	1 - 3
17.03.87	Gloucester	2 - 2
15.03.88	Rhyl	2 - 0
21.03.89	Kidderminster	2 - 0
06.03.90	Merthyr Tydfil	0 - 0
17.05.91	Stafford	1 - 2
03.03.92	Aberystwyth	1 - 0
02.03.93	Cheltenham	2 - 1
22.02.94	Bangor	2 - 1
28.02.95	Yeovil Town	1 - 0
23.05.99	St Albans	2 - 1
16.05.00	Llanelli	1 - 1
13.02.01	Rushden & Dia.	0 - 0
14.05.02	Boston	1 - 1
22.05.03	Merthyr Tydfil	2 - 0

RESULTS SUMMARY	P	W	D	L	F	A
Belgium	1	0	0	1	1	3
Finland Under-21	2	0	0	2	1	5
Gibraltar	2	2	0	0	6	4
Holland	17	12	5	0	33	7
Italy	13	3	6	3	16	14
Norway Under-21	1	0	0	1	1	2
Republic of Ireland	8	6	0	2	18	7
Scotland	10	5	3	2	18	12
USA	1	1	0	0	2	1
Wales	17	9	5	3	22	14
TOTAL RECORD	**72**	**38**	**19**	**15**	**118**	**69**

MANAGERS 1979 - 2003

1979	Howard Wilkinson
P 2 W 2 D 0	L 0 F 6 A 1
1980 - 1984	Keith Wright
P 17 W 9 D 5	L 3 F 30 A 16
1985 - 1988	Kevin Verity
P 12 W 7 D 2	L 3 F 23 A 15
1989 - 1996	Tony Jennings
P 19 W 10 D 4	L 5 F 27 A 18
1997	Ron Reid
P 2 W 0 D 1	L 1 F 0 A 2
1998 - 2002	John Owens
P 14 W 8 D 5	L 1 F 22 A 10
2002 -	Paul Fairclough
P 6 W 2 D 2	L 2 F 10 A 7

GOALSCORERS 1979 - 2003

13 GOALS...
Carter

6 GOALS...
Ashford

5 GOALS...
Davison
C. Williams

4 GOALS...
Culpin
D'Sane,
Roscoe
Johnson

3 GOALS...
Adamson
Grayson
Kirk Jackson
Opponents
Watkins

2 GOALS...
Alford, Carl
Barrett
Casey
Cordice
Hayles
Hill
Howell
Mutrie
Patmore
J. Watson
Weatherstone
Whitbread

1 GOAL...
Agana
Anderson, Dale
Boardman, Jon
Bolton
Bradshaw
Browne
Cavell
Charles
Charley, Ken
Crittenden, Nick
Davies
Drummond, Stewart
Furlong, Paul
Hines
Humphreys
Kennedy, John
Kimmins
Leworthy
McDougald
Mayes
Moore, Neil
O'Keefe
Pitcher
Robbins
Robinson
Roddis
Rogers
Ryan, Tim
Sellars
I. Smith
O. Smith
Stephens
Stott
S. Taylor
Venables
Way, Darren
Webb
Wilcox

ENGLAND SEMI-PRO CAPS 1979 - 2003

KEY TO COUNTRY CODES:

E - Eire	**I - Italy**	**F - Finland**
G - Gibraltar	**H - Holland**	**N - Norway**
S - Scotland	**W - Wales.**	**US - U.S.A.**

Players capped for the first time during season 2001-02 are shown in bold.

Gary Abbott (Welling) 87 v I(s), S(s), 92 W(s) 3

David Adamson (Boston Utd) 79 v S, H 80 v I,S, H 5

Tony Agana (Weymouth) 86 v E 1

Junior Agogo (Barnet) 03 v H, i (s), S 3

Carl Alford (Kettering T. & Rushden & Ds) 96 v E,H 2

Dale Anderson (Burton Albion) 02 v H 03 v I 2

Mark Angel (Boston United) 02 v W(s), E, S 3

Ian Arnold (Kettering Town) 95 v W(s), H 2

Jim Arnold (Stafford Rangers) 79 v S, H 2

Nick Ashby (Kettering & Rushden & Diamonds) 94 v F, N, 95 v G 96 v E, H 5

Noel Ashford (Enfield & Redbridge Forest.) 82 v G,H,S. 83 v I,H,S, 84 W,H,S,I, 85 W,I(s), 86 E,E, 87 W(s), I,H,S. 90 v W,E 91 I(s) 21

John Askey (Macclesfield) 90 v W 1

Matt Baker (Hereford United) 03 v I, S 2

Paul Bancroft (Kidderminster H.) 89 v I,W 90 I,W.E, 91 v W 6

Chris Banks (Cheltenham T.) 98 v H, 99 W 2

Keith Barrett (Enfield) 81 v H,S,I 82 v G,I,H,S 83 v I,H,S 84 v W(s), H, S 85 I,H,S 16

Laurence Batty (Woking) 93 v F(s), 95 v W,H,G 4

Mark Beeney (Maidstone) 89 v I(s) 1

Paul Beesley (Chester C.) 01 v H(s) 1

Dean Bennett (Kidderminster H) 00 v W(s) 1

Graham Benstead (Kettering) 94 v W,F,N(s) 3

Kevin Betsy (Woking) 98 v H(s) 1

Marcus Bignot (Kidderminster H) 97 v H 1

Chris Blackman (Chester City) 03 v I 1

Greg Blundell (Northwich Victoria) 03 v H 1

Jon Boardman (Woking) 03 v I, S 2

Jimmy Bolton (Kingstonian) 95 v G 1

Steve Book (Cheltenham Town) 99 v I,H,W 3

Gary Brabin (Runcorn) 94 v W,F,N 3

Mark Bradshaw (Halifax T.) 98 v H 1

Leon Braithwaite (Margate) 02 v US 1

Colin Brazier (Kidderminster) 87 v W 1

Stewart Brighton (Bromsgrove) 94 v W 1

Steve Brooks (Cheltenham) 88 v W(s) 90 v W,E 3

Derek Brown (Woking) 94 v F(s,N 2

Kevan Brown (Woking) 95 v W,H,G 96 v H 97 v E 5

Wayne Brown (Chester C.) 01 v W, H(s), 02 v US, H(s),W,S. 03 v H 7

Corey Browne (Dover) 94 v F(s),N(s), 95 v H(s) 3

David Buchanan (Blyth) 86 v E(s,E 2

Nicki Bull (Aldershot Town) 03 v B

Brian Butler (Northwich) 93 v F 1

Steve Butler (Maidstone) 88 v W, 89 v I,W 3

Gary Butterworth (Rushden & Diamonds) 97 v E,H 98 v H 99 v I,H,W 00 v I 7

Chris Byrne (Macclesfield T.) 97 v H 1

Mark Carter (Runcorn & Barnet) v 87 v W,I,H,S 88 v W, 89 v I,W, 90 v I,E, 91 v I,W(s) 11

Kim Casey (Kidderminster) 86 v W,E,E(s), 87 v W,I 5

Paul Cavell (Redbridge) 92 v W 93 v F 2

Lee Charles (Hayes) 99 v I(s), H(s), W(s) 3

Kevin Charlton (Telford) 85 v W,I 2

Ken Charlery (Boston U) 01 vH(s) 1

Andrew Clarke (Barnet) 90 v E,E 2

David Clarke (Blyth Spartans) 80 v I,S(s),H, 81 v H,S,I 82 v I,H,S 83 v H,S 84 v H,S,I 14

Gary Clayton (Burton) 86 v E 1

Robert Codner (Barnet) 88 v W 1

John Coleman (Morecambe) 93 v F(s) 1

Darren Collins (Enfield) 93 v F(s), 94 v W,F,N 4

Andy Comyn (Hednesford T.) 98 v H(s), 99 v I(s),H(s),W(s) 4

Steve Conner (Dartford, Redbridge & Dagenham & R) 90 v I 91 v I,W 92 v W 93 v F 5

David Constantine (Altrincham) 85 v I,H,S 86 v W 4

Robbie Cooke (Kettering) 89 v W(s), 90 v I 2

Scott Cooksey (Hednesford T.) 97 v E, 98 vH(s) 01 v W(s),H 4

Alan Cordice(Wealdstone)83 v I,H,S 84 vW,S(s), I(s),85 I,H,S 9

Rob Cousins (Yeovil Town) 00 I v I(s),H,W 3

Ken Cramman (Gateshead & Rushden & Diamonds) 96 v E 97 v E,H 3

Ian Craney Altrincham) 03 v B 1

Nick Crittendon (Yeovil Town) 02 v US (s) 1

Paul Cuddy (Altrincham) 87 v I,H,S 3

Paul Culpin (Nuneaton B) 84 v W, 85 v W(s) ,I,H,S 5

Michael Danzey (Woking) 99 v I,H 2

Paul Davies (Kidderminster H.) 86 v W, 87 v W,I,S, 88 v W 89 v W 6

John Davison (Altrincham) 79 v S,H 80 v I,S, 81 v H,S ,I 82 v G,I,H,S 83 I,H,S 84 W,H,I,S 85 v I,H,S 86 v W,E,E 24

John Denham (Northwich Victoria) 80 v H 1

Peter Densmore (Runcorn) 88 v W 89 v I 2

Phil Derbyshire (Mossley) 83 v H(s) S(s) 2

Mick Doherty (Weymouth) 86 v W(s) 1

Neil Doherty (Kidderminster H.) 97 v E 1

Stuart Drummond (Morecambe) 00 v I(s),H ,W 01 v W ,H 02 v US, W,E(s), S 03 v H, I, W, S (s) 13

Roscoe D'Sane (Aldershot Town) 03 v B(s),H(s),E,W,S 5

Chris Duffy (Canvey Island) 03 v B

Neil Durkin (Leigh RMI) 02 v H(s) 1

Lee Elam (Morecambe) 03 v H,E,W,S)s) 4

Paul Ellender (Scarborough) 01 v W(s) 1

Lee Endersby (Harrow Bor.) 96 v H 1

Mick Farrelly (Altrincham) 87 v I,H,S 3

Steve Farrelly (Macclesfield & Kingstonian) 95 v H(s),G(s), 00 v I,H,W(s) 5

Trevor Finnegan (Weymouth) 81 v H,S 2

Murray Fishlock (Yeovil Town) 99 v H(s) 1

Richard Forsyth (Kidderminster) 95 v W,H,G 3

Ian Foster (Kidderminster H) 00 v W(s) 1

Paul Furlong (Enfield) 90 v I,E,E 91 v I,W 5

Mark Gardiner (Macclesfield T.) 97 v E 1

CLUB REPRESENTATION 2002 - 2003

CLUB	LEAGUE	PLAYER(S)	FRIENDLIES		FOUR NATIONS		TOTAL	
			Apps	Gls	Apps	Gls	Apps	Gls
Aldershot Town	Ryman Premier	Nikki Bull	0+1	0	0	0	0+1	0
		Roscoe D'Sane	0+2	1	3	3	3+2	4
Altrincham	Unibond Premier	Ian Craney	1	0	0	0	1	0
Aylesbury United	Ryman Premier	Fiston Manuella	1	0	0	0	1	0
Barnet	Conference	Junior Agogo	1	0	1	0	2	0
		Wayne Purser	1	0	0	0	1	0
Basingstoke Town	Ryman Premier	Craig McAllister	1	0	0	0	1	0
Burton Albion	Conference	Aaron Webster	1	0	0	0	1	0
		Dale Anderson	0+1	0	0	0	0+1	0
Canvey Island	Ryman Premier	Chris Duffy	1	0	0	0	1	0
		John Kennedy	3	1	3	0	6	1
		Steve Ward	1	0	0	0	1	0
Crawley Town	Dr Martens Premier	Marc Pullan	1	0	0	0	1	0
Chester City	Conference	Chris Blackburn	0+1	0	0	0	0+1	0
		Wayne Brown (GK)	1	0	0	0	1	0
		Danny Collins	1	0	0	0	1	0
		Scott Guyett	1	0	3	0	4	0
		Wayne Hatswell	0	0	0+2	0	0+2	0
		MartinLancaster	0+1	0	0	0	0+1	0
		Ryan Sugden	1	0	0	0	1	0
Dagenham & Redbr.	Conference	Mark Janney	1	0	0	0	1	0
		Paul Terry	0	0	1+2	0	1+2	0
Doncaster Rovers	Conference	Tristram Whitman	0	0	1+2	0	1+2	0
Gravesend & N'fleet	Conference	Jimmy Jackson	0+1	0	0	0	0+1	0
Hereford United	Conference	Matt Baker (GK)	1	0	1	0	2	0
		Michael Rose	2	0	3	0	5	0
Kingstonian	Ryman Premier	Lance Key (GK)	1	0	0	0	1	0
		Tim Sills	0+1	0	0	0	0+1	0
Morecambe	Conference	Stewart Drummond	1	0	2+1	0	3+1	0
Morecambe/Halifax	Conference	Lee Elam	1	0	2+1	0	3+1	0
		Adrinano Rigoglioso	0+1	0	0	0	0+1	0
		Garry Thompson	1	0	0	0	1	0
Northwich Victoria	Conference	Gregg Blundell	1	0	0	0	1	0
		Richard Norris	1	0	1	0	2	0
Nuneaton Borough	Conference	Warren Peyton	1	0	0	0	1	0
Purfleet	Ryman Premier	John Keeling	0+1	0	0	0	0+1	0
Runcorn	Unibond Premier	Mike Tomlinson	0+1	0	0	0	0+1	0
Tamworth	Dr Martens Premier	Scott Rickards	1	0	0	0	1	0
Welling United	Dr Martens Premier	Anthony Rivierre	1	0	0	0	1	0
Woking	Conference	Jonathan Boardman	1	1	1	0	2	1
Worcester City	Dr Martens Premier	Adam Wilde	1	0	0	0	1	0
Yeovil Town	Conference	Adam Lockwood	1	0	0	0	1	0
		Lee Johnson	1+1	0	3	0	4+1	0
		Darren Way	0+1	0	2	1	2+1	1
		Chris Weale (GK)	0+2	0	2	0	2+2	0
		Terry Skiverton	0	0	2	0	2	0
		Kirk Jackson	0	0	2+1	3	2+1	3

Jerry Gill (Yeovil T.) **97** v E 1
John Glover (Maidstone Utd) **85** v W,I,H,S 4
Mark Golley (Sutton Utd.)
87 v H(s),S, **88** v W, **89** v I,W, **92** v W 6
Jason Goodliffe (Hayes) **00** v I, H,W, **01** W **02** US, W,E,S. 8
Paul Gothard (Dagenham & Redb.)
97 v E(s), **99** v I(s),W(s) 3
Mark Gower (Barnet) **02** v H, W, E, S(s) 4
Neil Grayson (Cheltenham T.) **98** v H **99** v I,H,W 4
Phil Gridelet (Hendon & Barnet) **89** v I,W, **90** v W,E,E 5
Steve Guppy (Wycombe W.) **93** v W 1
Scott Guyett (Southport) **01** v H, **03** v H,I,W,S. 5
Tim Hambley (Havant & Waterlooville) **02** v H 1
Steve Hanlon (Macclesfield) **90** v W 1
David Harlow (Farnborough T.) **97 v** E(s),H 2
Wayne Hatswell (Chester City) **03** v E(s),W(s),
Barry Hayles (Stevenage Bor.) **96** v E,H 2
Greg Heald (Barnet) **02** v H 1
Brian Healy (Morecambe) **98** v H 1
Tony Hemmings (Northwich) **93** v F 1
Andy Hessenthaler (Dartford) **90** v I 1
Kenny Hill (Maidstone Utd) **80** v I,S,H 3
Mark Hine (Gateshead) **95** v W(s),H 2
Simeon Hodson (Kidderminster) **94** v W,F,N 3
Colin Hogarth (Guiseley) **95 v** W,H 2
Steven Holden (Kettering) **94** v W,F,N(s) **95** v H,G 5
Mark Hone (Welling United) **90** v I **93** v F, **94** vW(s),F(s),N 5
Gary Hooley (Frickley) **85** v W 1
Dean Hooper (Kingstonian) **98** v H 1
Keith Houghton (Blyth Spartans) **79** v S 1
Barry Howard (Altrincham) **81** v H,S,I **82** v G,I,H,S 7
Neil Howarth (Macclesfield) **95** v H(s) **97** v E 2
David Howell (Enfield) **85** v H(s),S(s) **86** v W,E **87** v W,IH,S
88 v W, **89** v I,W **90** v I,E,E 14
Lee Howells (Cheltenham T.) **98** v H **99 v** W 2
Lee Hughes (Kidderminster Harriers) **96** v E,H **97** v E,H 4
Delwyn Humphreys (Kidderminster H.)
91 v W(s) **92** v W **94** v W,F,N **95** v W,H 7
Steve Humphries (Barnet) **87** v H(s) 1
Nicky Ironton (Enfield) **83** H(s) **84** v W 2
Jimmy Jacksion (Gravesend & Northfleet) 03 v H(s) 1
Justin Jackson (Morecambe & Rushden & Diamonds)
00 v W **01** v W 2
Kirk Jackson (Stevenage Borough) **02** v US, E,S,(Yeovil Town)
03 v E,W,S(s) 6
Mark Janney (Dagenham & Redbridge) **03** v H 1
Tony Jennings (Enfield)
79 v S,H **80** v I,S,H **81 v** H,S,I **82** v G,I,H,S 12
Jeff Johnson (Altrincham) **81** v S,I **82** v G,I,H,S **83** v I,H,S
84 v H,S,I **84 v** I,H,S **86** v W(s),E,E 18
Lee Johnson (Yeovil Town) **03** v I, H(s), E, W, S 5
Steve Jones (Leigh RMI) **01** v H 1
Tom Jones (Weymouth) **87** v W 1
Antone Joseph(Telford U. & Kidderm'terH.)**84** v S(s), **85** v W,I,
H,S **86** v W(s), **87** W,I(s),H, **88** v W **89** v I,W **90 v** I,E,E 15
John Keeling (Purfleet) **03** v B(s) 1
John Kennedy (Canvey Island) **03** v I, B, H, E, W, S 6
Andy Kerr (Wycombe) **93** v W 1
Lance Key (Kingstonian) 03 v B 1
Ged Kimmins (Hyde Utd.) **96** v E(s),H(s) **97 v** E(s) 3
Mike Lake (Macclesfield) **89** v I 1
Martin Lancaster (Chester City) **03** vI (s)
Andy Lee (Telford U. & Witton A.) **89** I(s), **91** v I,W 3
David Leworthy (Farnborough & Rushden & Diamonds)
93 v W, **94** v W **97** v E,H 4
Adam Lockwood (Yeovil Town) **02** v E **03** v I 2
,Kenny Lowe (Barnet) **91 v** I,W 2
Craig McAllister (Basingstoke Town) **03** v B 1
Martin McDonald (Macclesfield) **95** v G(s) 1
Junior MacDougald (Dagenham & Redbridge) 01 v H(s) 1
02 W, E(s), S(s) 4
Mark McGregor (Forest Green Rovers & Nuneaton Borough)
00 v I(s),H(s) **01** v W(s) 3
Kevin McIntyre (Doncaster Rovers) **00 v** H(s)W, **01 v** W(s)H 4
John McKenna (Boston Utd)
88 v W(s), **90** v I,E,E **91 v** I,W, **92** vW 7
Fiston Manuella (Aylesbury United) **03** v B 1
John Margerrison (Barnet) **87 v** W 1
Simon Marples (Doncaster Rovers) **00 v** I,H 2
Leroy May (Stafford R.) **95 v** G(s) 1
Bobby Mayes (Redbridge) **92 v** W
Paul Mayman (Northwich Vic) **80 v** I,S 2
Stewart Mell (Burton) **85v** W 1
Neil Merrick (Weymouth) **80** v I(s),S 2
Russell Milton (Dover) 94 v F,N 2
Trevor Morley (Nuneaton) **84 v** W,H,S,I **85 v** W,S(s) 6
Neil Moore (Telford United) **02** v US (s),H, W, E,S 5
Tarkan Mustafa (Rushden & Diamonds) **01** v W,H 2
Les Mutrie (Blyth Spartans) **79 v** S,H, **80** v I,S,H
Mark Newson (Maidstone U) **84 v** W,H,S,I, **85 v** W 5
Doug Newton (Burton) **85** v W,H,S 3
Paul Nicol (Kettering T) **91 v** I,W, **92** v W 3
Richard Norris (Northwich Victoria) **03** v H, S, 2
Steve Norris (Telford) **88** v W(s) 1
Joe O'Connor (Hednesford T.) **97 v** E,H(s) 2
Eamon O'Keefe (Mossley) **79 v** S,H 2
Frank Ovard (Maidstone) **81** v H(s),S(s),I(s) 3
Andy Pape (Harrow Bor. & Enfield) **85** v W(s,)H,S,
86 v W(s),E, **87** v W,I,H,S **88** v W, **89 I**W, **90** I,W,E 15
Brian Parker (Yeovil Town) **80** v S 1
Warren Patmore (Yeovil Town) **99** v I,H,W, **00 v** I,H, **01** W,H 7
Gary Patterson (Kingstonian) **99** v I,H, **00** v H,W, **01 v** W,H 7
Steve Payne (Macclesfield T.) **97 v** H 1
Trevor Peake (Nuneaton Bor) **79 v** S,H 2
David Pearce (Harrow Bor) **84 v** I(s) 1
Warren Peyton (Nuneaton Borough) **02** v H(s) **03** v I 2
Brendan Phillips (Nuneaton Bor. & Kettering T.),
79 v S,H, **80 v** S(s),H 4
Gary Philips (Barnet) **82 v** G 1
Owen Pickard (Yeovil T.) **98** v H(s) 1
Geoff Pitcher (Kingstonian) **99 v** W, **00 v** I,H,W, **01** v W,H 6
Phil Power (Macclesfield T.) **96** v E(s),H(s) 2
Ryan Price (Stafford R. & Macclesfield)
92 v W(s) **93** v W,F **96** v E,H **97 v** H 6
Steve Prindiville **98 v** H(s) 1
Marc Pullan (Crawley Town) **03** v B 1
Wayne Purser (Barnet) **03** v I 1
Mark Quayle (Telford United) **02** v H 1
Simon Read (Farnborough) **92** v W(s) 1
Andy Reid (Altrincham) **95 v** W 1
Carl Richards (Enfield) **86 v** E 1
Derek Richardson (Maidstone U) **83 v** I, **84 v** W, **86** v E 4
Ian Richardson (Dagenham & Red) **95 v** G 1
Kevin Richardson (Bromsgrove) **94** v W,F,N 3
Paul Richardson (Redbridge) **92** v W, **93 v** W, F 3
Scott Rickards (Tamworth) **03** v B 1
Adriano Rigoglioso (Morecambe) **03** v H(s) 1

Anthony Rivierre (Welling United) **03** v B 1

Terry Robbins (Welling) **92 v** W, **93** v W,F, **94** v W,F,N 6

Peter Robinson (Blyth S) **83 v** I,H,S **84** W,I 85 v W 6

Nick Roddis (Woking) **01** v H **02** US,H,W,E(s),S 6

John Rogers (Altrincham) **81 v** H,S,I **82 v** I(s),S 5

Paul Rogers (Sutton) **89** v W, **90** v I, E(2), **91** I,W 6

Colin Rose (Witton Alb.) **96 v** E(s), H 2

Kevin Rose (Kidderminster) **94 v** F(s),N 2

Michael Rose (Hereford United) **03** v I, H, E, S 4

Brian Ross (Marine) **93 v** W(s),F(s), **94** v W(s) **95 v** W,H 5

Carl Ruffer (Chester City) **01** v H(s) 1

Tim Ryan (Southport & Doncaster Rovers)
98 v H, **99 v** I,H,W, **00 v** I,H,W **01** v W,H
02 v US,H,W,I,S 14

Neil Sellars (Scarboro) **81** v H,S,I **82** v G,H(s),S, **83 v** I,H,S 9

Mark Shail (Yeovil T.) **93** v W 1

Simon Shaw (Doncaster Rovers) **99** v I,H 2

Peter Shearer (Cheltenham) **89 v** I(s) 1

Paul Shirtliff (Frickley A. & Boston U.) **86** vE,E **87** v W,I,H
88 v W **89 v** I, W, **90 v** I,W,E,E, **92 v** W **93** v W,F 15

Paul Showler (Altrincham) **91** v I(s),W 2

Tim Sills (Kingstonian) **03** v B 1

Gordon Simmonite (Boston United) **79** v S(s,)H(s), **80** v I,S,H 5

Gary Simpson(Stafford R.) **86** v E,E, **87** v I,H,S,**90** v I,W,E,E 9

Wayne Simpson (Stafford) **94** v F,N(s) 2

Terry Skiverton (Yeovil Town) **01 v** W **02 v** US **03** v !,W, 4

Glenn Skivington (Barrow) **90** v I,W,E **91** v I,W 5

Adrian Smith (Kidderminster H) **00** v I(s),H(s),W 3

Alan Smith (Alvechurch) **82** v G,I,S 3

Ian Smith (Mossley) **80** v I,S,H(s) 3

Mark Smith (Stevenage Bor.)
96 v E,H **98** v H **99** v I,H,W **00 v** I,H,W(s) 9

Ossie Smith (Runcorn) **84** v W 1

Tim Smithers (Nuneaton) **85** v W(s),I **86** v W 3

Adam Sollitt (Kettering Town) **00** v I(s),H(s),W 3

Adam Stansfield (Yeovil Town) **02** v W (s), I, S 3

Simon Stapleton (Wycombe) **93** v W 1

Mickey Stephens (Sutton), **82** v G,S(s) **86 v** W,E,E(s) 5

Billy Stewart (Southport) **98** v H 1

Mark Stimson (Canvey Island) **02** v US 1

Bob Stockley (Nuneaton Borough) **80** v H 1

Darren Stride (Burton Albion) **02** v H 1

Steve Stott (Kettering T., Rushden & Ds & Yeovil T.)
95 v W,H(s),G **96** v E,H **99** v H,W(s) 7

Ryan Sugden (Chester City) 03 v I 1

James Taylor (Havant & Waterlooville) **02** v H,W, E(s),S(s) 4

Peter Taylor (Maidstone) **84** v HSI 3

Steve Taylor (Bromsgrove R.) **95** v G 1

Shaun Teale (Weymouth) **88** v W 1

Paul Terry (Dagenham & Redbridge) **03** vE (s), W(s), S 3

Stuart Terry (Altrincham) **95** v W 1

Brian Thompson(Yeovil & Maidstone) **79** v S,H **81** v H,S,I
82 v I,H,S **83 v** I,H,S **84** v W,H,S,I 15,

Neil Thompson (Scarborough) **87** v W,I,H,S 4

Garry Thompson (Morecambe) **03** v I 1

Steve Thompson (Wycombe) **93** v W 1

Kevin Todd (Berwick Rangers) **91** v W 1

Mike Tomlinson (Runcorn F.C.Halton) **03** v B (s) 1

Anthony Tonkin (Yeovil Town) **02** v US 1

Simon Travis (Forest Green Rovers) **02 v** US, H. 2

Mark Tucker (Woking) **96** v E 1

Tony Turner (Telford) **85 v** W 1

Paul Underwood (Rushden & D) **99** v I,H **00 v I01** v W 4

David Venables(Stevenage B)**94 v** W(s)**95 v** H,G**96 v** E,H(s) 5

Jamie Victory (Cheltenham T.) **98** vH(s) 1

David Waite (Enfield) **82** v G 1

Paul Walker (Blyth) **86 v** W,E,E(s), **87 v** S(s) 4

Steve Walters (Northwich Victoria) **97** v H 1

Mark Ward (Northwich Victoria) **83** v S(s) 1

Steve Ward (Canvey Island) **03** v B 1

Dale Watkins (Cheltenham T.) **98** v H **99** v I(s), **00** v I,H,W 5

John Watson (Wealdstone, Scarborough & Maidstone)
79 v S(s),H **80** v I,S,H **81** v H,S,I **82** v I,H,S **83** v I,H,S
84 v W(s),H,S,I 18

Steve Watson (Farnborough Town) **02** v US(s), W(s), S 3,

Liam Watson (Marine) **95** v W,H(s) 2

Paul Watts (Redbridge Forest) **89** v W **90** v I,E,E **91** v I
92 v W **93** v W,F 8

Darren Way (Yeovil Town) **03** vI (s), E, W 3

Chris Weale (Yeovil Town) 03 v I (s), H (s), E, W. 4

Simon Weatherstone (Boston United) **02** v W(s),E,S(s) 3

Paul Webb (Bromsgrove R & Kidderminster H)
93 v F **94** v W,F,N(s) **95** v W,H,G **96** v E,H **97** v E,H 11

Aaron Webster (Burton Albion) **02 v** H(s),W,S(s) **03** v I 3

Mark West (Wycombe W) **91** v W 1

Steve West (Woking) **01** v W(s) 1

Barry Whitbread (Runcorn & Altrincham) **79 v** S,H
80 v I,S,H, **81 v** I 6

Tristram Whitman (Doncaster Rovers) **03** v W(s), S 2

Russ Wilcox (Frickley) **86** v W,E 2

Adam Wilde (Worcester City) **03** v B 1

Barry Williams (Nuneaton Borough) **99** v H(s),W 2

Colin Williams (Scarborough & Telford Utd.)
81 v H, S **82** v I,H,S 5

Roger Willis (Barnet) **91** v I(s) 1

Paul Wilson (Frickley Athletic) **86** v W 1

Andy Woods (Scarborough) **02** v US,H(s),W,S. 4

Simon Wormull (Dover Athletic) **99** v I(s),W **02 v** W,E,S. 5

Mark Yates (Cheltenham Town) **99** v I, W 2

THE NATIONWIDE CONFERENCE

FOOTBALL CONFERENCE

Founded 1979

President: J C Thompson MBIM, Minst.M

Chairman: W J King **Chief Executive:** J A Moules

Secretary: Kellie Discipline
Riverside House, 14B High Street, Crayford, Kent DA1 4HG
Tel: 01322 411021 Fax: 01322 550965

The 2002-2003 Conference season was notable for the fact that the competition's high standards had at last -but we hope not finally- been acknowledged with the incentive of promotion to the Football League being increased from one place to two. One club has to ascend automatically and another through a play - off for the next four teams.

The outcome was that Yeovil Town went through with some comfort as the Champions and thrilling play-offs saw Doncaster Rovers eliminate Chester City (both ex league clubs) on penalties after two legs had each ended with a brace of goals shared, while Dagenham + Redbridge became the other finalist by eliminating Morecambe after each club had scored the odd goal in three in their home legs, so again it needed penalties to decide the issue.

This left the crucial final, which was initially dominated at the Britannia Stadium, Stoke, by the former Football League outfit before the Daggers retrieved a two goal deficit to take the game into extra-time, but on this occasion penalties were not required as Francis Tierney scored a golden goal to restore Doncaster Rovers' status of yesteryear, which also encourages teams with former traditions not to abandon hope.

Elsewhere, the relegation issue was not finally decided until the the last day of the campaign, when with Kettering Town already down Southport and Nuneaton Borough lost their final matches - and thereby safety - to be replaced by three league champions in Accrington Stanley (Unibond), Aldershot Town (Ryman) and Tamworth (Dr.Martens), the former pair being ex Football League outfits with colourful histories, while Tamworth are on their way up despite the disappointment of their surprise defeat in the F.A.Trophy Final.

Down from 'the big time' come Shrewsbury Town and Exeter City and the strength of the Conference can be assessed by the fact that neither can realistically be described as overwhelming favourites for a speedy return.

Hereford United finished one place below the play-offs and will have something to say about that, as will the likes of Chester City, Morecambe and Dagenham & Redbridge, all of whom will look to the progress of Rushden & Diamonds and Wycombe Wanderers in the elite as an example of what can be achieved.

Bill Mitchell

FINAL LEAGUE TABLE 2002-03

		HOME					AWAY						
	P	W	D	L	F	A	W	D	L	F	A	Pts	GD
1. Yeovil town	42	16	5	0	54	13	12	6	3	46	24	95	63
2. Morecambe	42	17	3	1	52	13	6	6	9	34	29	78	44
3. Doncaster rovers	42	11	6	4	28	17	11	6	4	45	30	78	26
4. Chester City	42	10	6	5	36	21	11	6	4	23	10	75	28
5. Dagenham & Redbridge	42	12	5	4	38	23	9	4	8	33	36	72	12
6. Hereford United	42	9	5	7	36	22	10	2	9	28	29	64	13
7. Scarborough	42	12	3	6	41	28	6	7	8	22	26	64	9
8. Halifax Town	42	11	5	5	34	28	7	5	9	16	23	64	-1
9. Forest Green Rovers	42	12	3	6	41	29	5	5	11	20	33	59	-1
10. Margate	42	8	9	4	32	24	7	2	12	28	42	56	-6
11. Barnet	42	9	4	8	32	28	4	10	7	33	40	53	-3
12. Stevenage Borough	42	7	6	8	31	25	7	4	10	30	30	52	6
13. Farnborough Town	42	8	6	7	37	29	5	6	10	20	27	51	1
14. Northwich Victoria	42	6	5	10	26	34	7	7	7	40	38	51	-6
15. Telford United	42	7	2	12	20	33	7	5	9	34	36	49	-15
16. Burton Albion	42	6	6	9	25	31	7	4	10	27	46	49	-25
17. Gravesend & Northfleet	42	8	5	8	37	35	4	7	10	25	38	48	-11
18. Leigh RMI	42	8	5	8	26	34	6	1	14	18	37	48	-27
19. Woking	42	8	7	6	30	35	3	7	11	22	46	47	-29
20. Nuneaton Borough	42	9	4	8	27	32	4	3	14	24	46	46	-27
21. Southport	42	6	8	7	31	32	5	4	12	23	37	45	-15
22. Kettering Town	42	4	3	14	23	39	4	4	13	14	34	31	-36

LEADING GOALSCORERS 2002-03

PLAYER	CLUB	TOTAL	CONF	FAT	FAC
Paul Barnes	Doncaster Rovers	27	25	0	2
Kirk Jackson	Yeovil Town	26	24	1	1
Gregg Blundell	Doncaster Rovers	22	20	2	0
Junior Agogo	Barnet	20	20	0	0
Neil Grayson	Forest Green Rovers	20	15	5	0
Rocky Baptisite	Farnborough Town	20	11	2	7
Wayne Curtis	Morecambe	18	18	0	0
Dino Maamria	Stevenage Borough	18	17	0	1
Daryl Clare	Chester City	18	17	0	1
Mark Stein	Dagenham & Red.	18	16	2	0
Christian Moore	Burton Albion	18	16	0	2
Steve West	Dagenham & Red.	17	16	1	0
Paul Moore	Telford United	17	16	1	0

ATTENDANCES 2002-03

		Highest	Lowest	Average	01-02 Ave.	Diff
1	Yeovil	8111	2126	4741	2871	1870
2	Doncaster Rovers	5344	2783	3540	2408	1132
3	Chester City	3821	1745	2405	1274	1131
4	Hereford United	3271	1400	2037	1551	486
5	Woking	3332	1426	1986	1891	95
6	Stevenage Borough	2801	1272	1897	1715	182
7	Halifax	3082	1299	1752	NA	
8	Burton Albion	2523	1393	1746	NA	
9	Dagenham & Redbridge	2588	1219	1599	1915	-316
10	Morecambe	2239	869	1462	1288	174
11	Scarborough	3435	824	1381	1194	187
12	Kettering Town	2068	422	1360	NA	
13	Barnet	1909	769	1342	1456	-114
14	Nuneaton Borough	2337	718	1257	1277	-20
15	Gravesend & Northfleet	2036	876	1228	NA	
16	Southport	2447	768	1160	1048	112
17	Telford United	2047	720	985	1002	-17
18	Farnborough Town	2114	500	881	837	44
19	Forest Green Rovers	1836	576	857	840	17
20	Northwich Victoria	2305	459	751	885	-134
21	Margate	1415	385	684	1218	-534
22	Leigh RMI	864	305	483	493	-10

RESULTS CHART 20002-03

		1	2	3	4	5	6	7	8	9	10	11	12	13	14	15	16	17	18	19	20	21	22
1	Barnet		2-2	0-3	2-1	1-2	1-2	2-0	1-4	0-0	2-1	0-2	4-0	0-1	1-1	3-4	2-1	3-0	3-1	0-2	3-0	0-0	2-1
2	Burton Albion	0-3		2-0	0-0	1-2	2-0	2-3	1-1	2-2	2-0	2-0	0-1	0-1	1-4	1-1	1-0	1-1	1-0	1-2	4-7	0-2	1-1
3	Chester City	1-1	2-1		5-2	1-0	0-2	0-1	1-1	2-0	0-1	0-0	2-1	5-0	2-1	2-3	1-2	0-0	2-0	2-0	4-1	2-2	2-2
4	Dagenham & Redbridge	5-1	1-2	1-0		3-3	1-0	3-1	4-0	0-0	1-0	3-1	3-1	3-0	1-1	2-0	1-2	1-0	0-3	3-2	1-1	1-1	0-4
5	Doncaster Rovers	2-1	1-0	0-0	5-1		1-0	1-0	4-1	0-0	2-0	1-0	1-0	3-1	1-1	1-2	1-1	0-1	0-0	0-0	1-3	3-1	0-4
6	Farnborough Town	2-2	5-1	1-2	1-0	0-0		0-3	1-1	3-0	2-2	0-1	1-0	4-1	2-3	3-2	0-2	1-1	2-1	0-1	2-2	5-0	2-4
7	Forest Green Rovers	4-4	2-0	0-2	5-2	1-2	3-1		2-1	0-2	1-3	1-0	4-1	4-1	1-0	1-0	6-1	0-0	0-2	0-3	1-1	3-2	2-1
8	Gravesend & Northfleet	2-2	3-2	0-1	1-2	2-2	0-0	1-1		1-0	3-0	0-2	1-3	1-2	3-2	1-1	4-1	5-2	1-3	2-1	0-2	4-2	2-4
9	Halifax Town	2-4	0-1	0-0	3-3	2-1	1-0	1-1	2-1		1-0	4-0	1-0	2-2	1-0	0-5	3-1	2-1	3-4	1-0	2-0	1-1	2-3
10	Hereford United	4-0	4-0	0-0	2-1	2-4	2-1	1-1	3-0	1-1		2-0	0-1	2-3	1-2	1-2	2-1	0-1	0-2	2-2	2-0	5-0	0-0
11	Kettering Town	1-2	1-2	0-1	1-3	0-2	1-4	2-3	1-1	0-1	2-3		0-1	1-1	3-2	2-2	3-0	1-3	1-0	1-0	2-4	0-3	0-1
12	Leigh RMI	4-2	4-2	0-4	1-3	0-2	3-2	1-0	0-0	0-2	0-2	2-2		2-0	1-0	1-1	1-1	0-2	1-1	2-1	0-3	1-0	2-4
13	Margate Town	2-2	0-0	0-1	0-1	2-1	0-0	3-0	4-2	2-1	0-2	2-2	2-0		1-1	4-4	1-1	3-1	1-0	1-1	1-1	2-1	1-2
14	Morecambe Town	1-1	5-0	1-1	2-1	3-0	1-1	4-0	2-0	2-0	3-1	1-0	2-1	2-0		3-1	3-2	3-1	3-0	3-1	1-0	5-0	1-2
15	Northwich Victoria	1-1	1-3	1-1	0-2	1-2	2-2	2-1	1-2	0-2	2-2	1-2	0-1	1-0	3-2		3-1	0-2	2-1	1-1	2-1	1-3	1-2
16	Nuneaton Borough	3-2	1-2	1-0	1-3	0-3	0-2	3-2	0-1	2-0	0-3	1-0	0-2	3-2	1-1	1-4		1-1	3-2	3-0	1-0	1-1	1-1
17	Scarborough Town	1-1	4-1	0-1	0-1	2-5	1-0	3-0	3-2	0-1	2-1	4-1	2-0	3-2	1-0	4-1	4-1		2-2	1-2	1-4	1-1	2-1
18	Southport	2-1	2-2	1-3	2-3	0-4	0-0	2-2	1-1	2-0	1-2	0-0	4-2	0-2	2-3	1-1	1-0	1-1		3-2	1-1	5-1	0-1
19	Stevenage Borough	1-2	0-1	0-1	2-0	2-3	5-0	0-0	1-0	0-1	0-2	2-0	3-1	1-3	1-1	2-2	3-1	1-1	3-0		1-3	1-1	2-2
20	Telford United	2-1	0-2	0-1	1-2	4-4	0-2	0-1	2-1	1-2	0-1	2-0	1-1	0-0	0-3	1-0	1-2	0-2	2-0	1-3		1-0	0-5
21	Woking	0-0	2-2	1-0	0-0	2-2	1-0	1-0	2-3	2-1	1-2	2-1	3-0	1-5	0-6	2-3	2-1	2-1	1-1	1-5	3-0		1-1
22	Yeovil Town	0-0	6-1	1-1	2-2	1-1	2-0	1-0	2-2	3-0	4-0	4-0	3-1	2-1	2-0	2-1	3-2	1-0	6-0	2-1	3-0	4-0	

Nationwide Conference Awards 2002-2003

MONTH	MANAGER	CLUB	GOALSCORER	CLUB
August	Dave Penney	Doncaster Rovers	Wayne Curtis	Morecambe
			Gregg Blundell	Northwich Victoria
			Jamie Pitman	Hereford United
			Mark Quayle	Nuneaton Borough
			Christian Moore	Burton Albion
			Novreddine Maamria	Leigh RMI
September	Gary Johnson	Yeovil Town	Ryan Sugden	Chester City
October	Dave Penney	Doncaster Rovers	Christian Moore	Burton Albion
			Ryan Mallon	Halifax Town
			Abdoulai Demba	Yeovil Town
November	Mark Wright	Chester City	Daryl Clare	Chester City
December	Graham Turner	Hereford United	Daryl Clare	Chester City
			Stephen West	Dagenham & Redbridge
			Paul Barnes	Doncaster Rovers
			Robert Gill	Doncaster Rovers
January	Chris Wilder	Halifax Town	Daryl Clare	Chester City
February	Colin Addison	Forest Green Rovers	Paul Barnes	Doncaster Rovers
March	Gary Johnson	Yeovil Town	Kirk Jackson	Yeovil Town
April	Jim Harvey	Morecambe	Kevin Gall	Yeovil Town
	Gary Johnson	Yeovil Town		

MANAGER OF THE YEAR AWARD

Gary Johnson — Yeovil Town

GOALSCORER OF THE YEAR AWARD

Paul Barnes — Doncaster Rovers

PERFORMANCE OF THE MONTH AWARDS

August	Telford United
September	Gravesend & Northfleet
October	Nuneaton Borough
November	Morecambe
December	Scarborough
January	Telford United
February	Telford United
March	Stevenage Borough
April	Woking

PROGRAMME OF THE YEAR AWARD

Dagenham & Redbridge

FAIR PLAY AWARD

Hereford United

2002 -2003 CONFERENCE MANAGER & TEAM OF THE YEAR

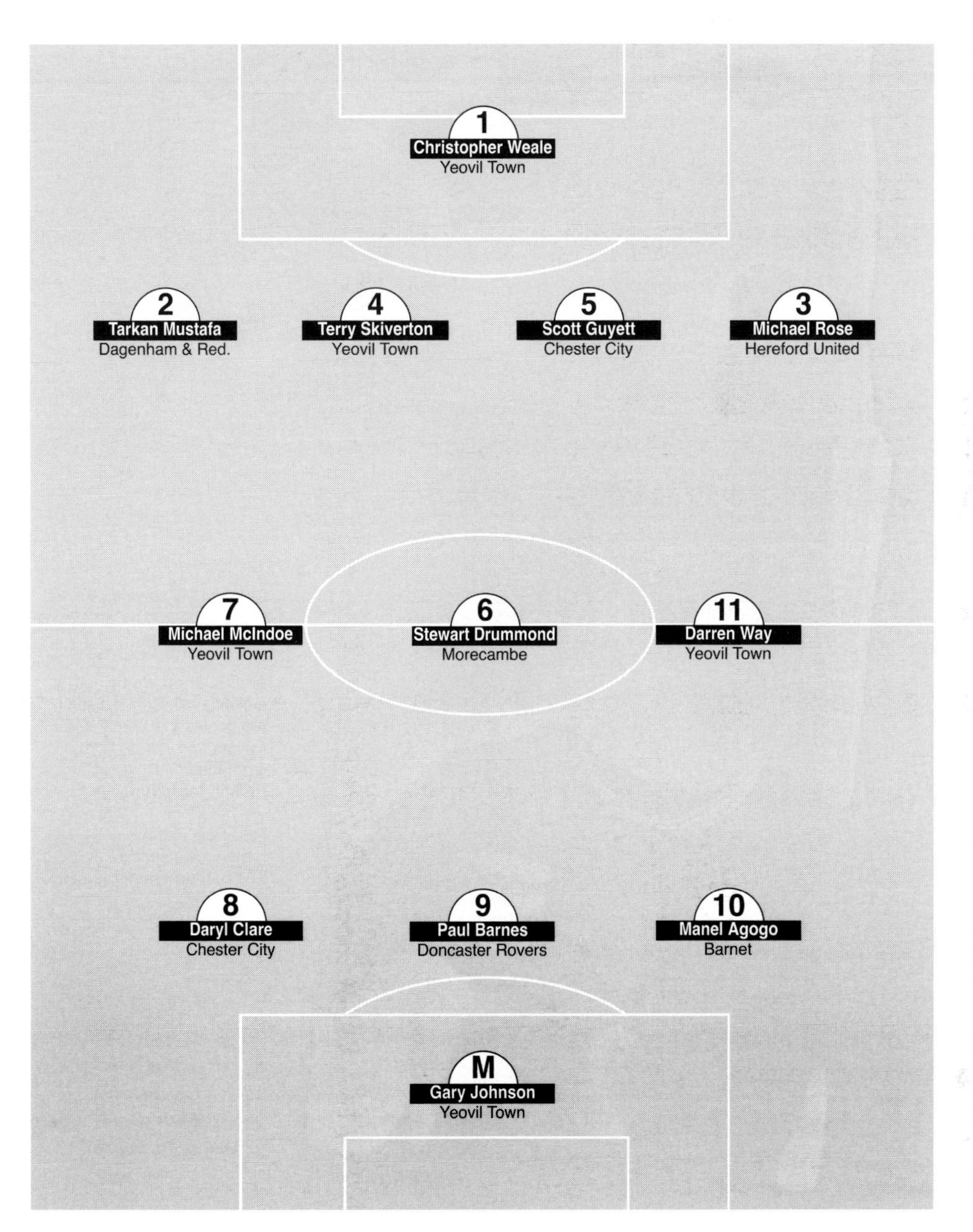

CONFERENCE TEAM OF THE YEAR 2002 -2003

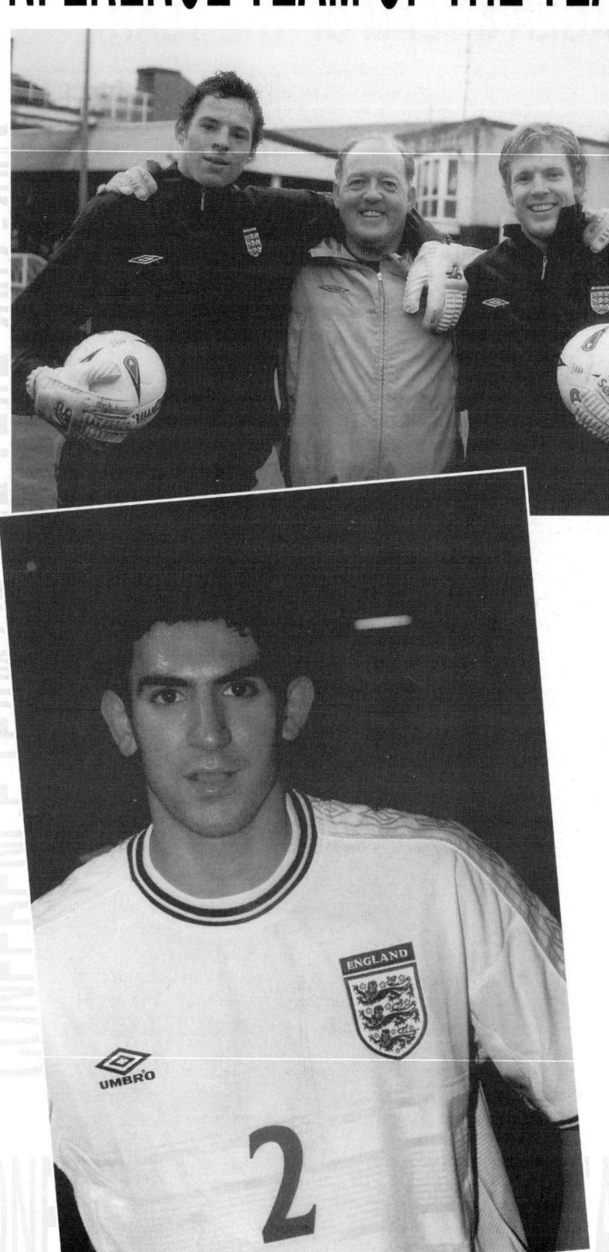

Some of the players selected in the 2002-2003 Conference Team of the Year.

Above: **Chris Weale** (left) is pictured with England semi-pro goalkeeper coach, Mick Payne, and international team-mate Matt Baker. Photo: Roger Turner.

Left: Dagenham & Redbridge's **Tarkan Mustafa**. Photo: Peter Barnes.

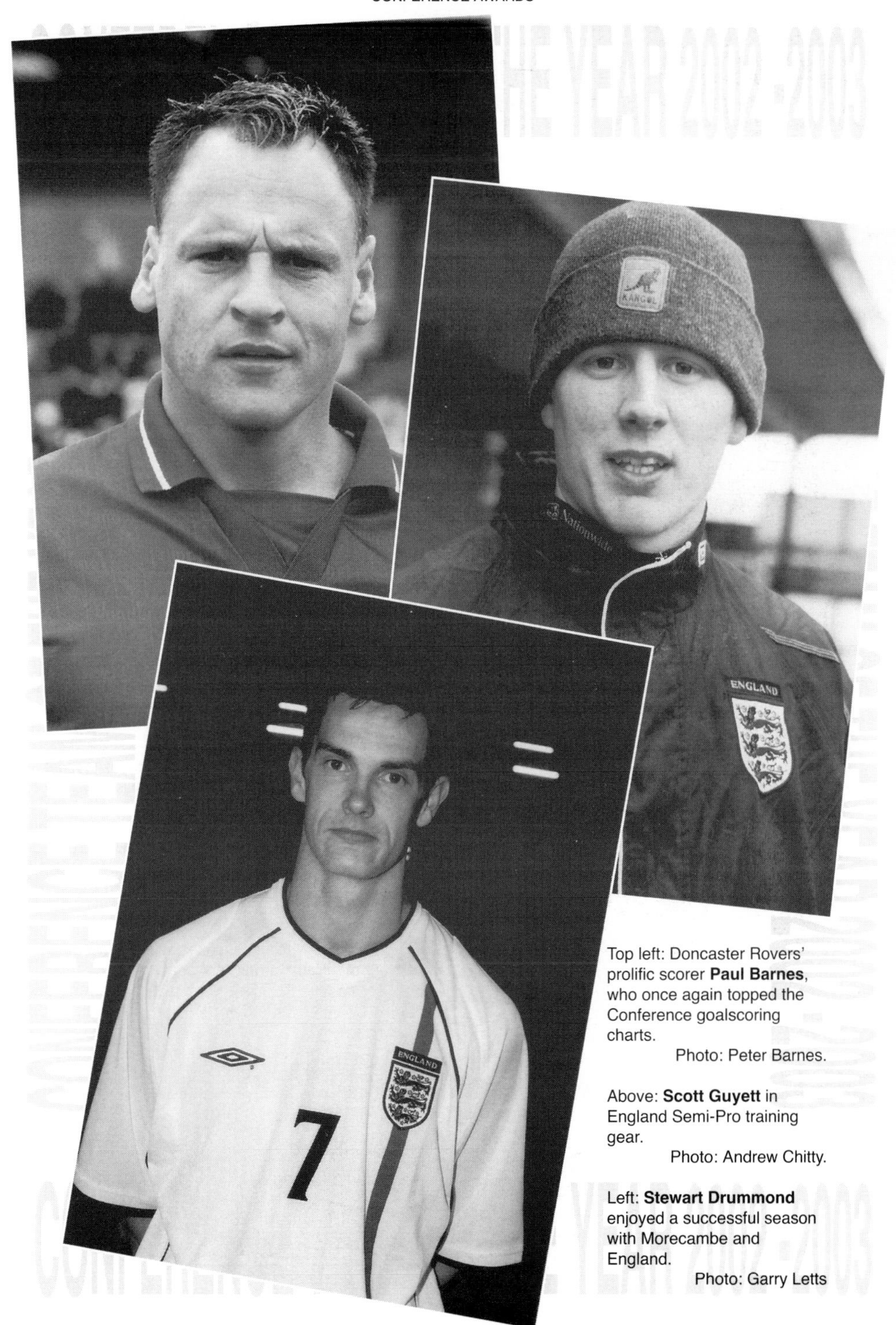

Top left: Doncaster Rovers' prolific scorer **Paul Barnes**, who once again topped the Conference goalscoring charts.
Photo: Peter Barnes.

Above: **Scott Guyett** in England Semi-Pro training gear.
Photo: Andrew Chitty.

Left: **Stewart Drummond** enjoyed a successful season with Morecambe and England.
Photo: Garry Letts

All photos by Keith Clayton.

Above: Paul Barnes, Doncaster Rovers' top goalscorer, turns provider as he gets his cross in during the Conference Play off final.

Left: Mark Stein desperately stretches to meet the ball but sees his effort go agonisingly wide.

Opposite (top): Doncaster's Steve Foster gets set to clear the ball before Dagenham & Redbridge's Mark Stein can get to the ball.

Right: Tony Roberts makes an important save from a Paul Barnes shot.

SEMI FINAL - FIRST LEG

Dagenham & Redbridge	**(1)**	**2**	**Morecambe**	**(1)**	**1**
Stein 7, 66 (pen)			Goodwin 29 (og)	Att: 3,447	
Doncaster Rovers	**(0)**	**1**	**Chester City**	**(1)**	**1**
Whitman 90			McIntyre 37	Att: 6,857	

Promotion Play offs

SEMI FINAL - SECOND LEG

Morecambe	**(0)**	**2**	**Dagenham & Redbridge**	**(0)**	**1**
West 50 (og), Rigoglioso 86			Terry 89		Att: 5,405

Aggregate Score 3-3. Dagenham & Redbridge won 3-2 on penalties.

Chester City	**(1)**	**1**	**Doncaster Rovers**	**(0)**	**1**
Hatswell 31			Barnes 57		Att: 5,702

Aggregate Score 2-2. Doncaster Rovers won 4-3 on penalties.

Conference Play off final 'Man of the Match', Paul Green, tries to give Dagenham and England Semi Professional defender, Tarkan Mustafa, the slip.

PLAY OFF FINAL

Dagenham & Redbridge	**(0)**	**2**	**Doncaster Rovers**	**(1)**	**3**
Stein 63, Mustafa 78			Green 39, Morley 55 tierney 110		Att: 13,092

Score after 90 mins 2-2. Doncaster Rovers won on 'Promotion Goal' in extra time

Promotion Play offs

Above: Danny Shipp meets the ball first but puts his header wide of the Doncaster goal, whilst below John McGrath goes even closer only to see his chance deflect off the crossbar.

Doncaster's Dave Morley directs his header into the top right hand corner of the Dagenham goal to increase Rovers' lead to two goals after 55 minutes.

Doncaster Rovers celebrate their promotion to Division Three after defeating Dagenham & Redbridge in the inaugural Conference 'Promotion Play Off' final played at Stoke City's Britannia Stadium.

The Doncaster fans celebrate with their heros after the Play off final.

ACCRINGTON STANLEY

One of football's best known clubs has achieved another stage in a remarkable recovery.

Accrington Stanley had disappeared in some disarray in 1962, when financial problems saw them drop out of the Football League. But a national advertising campaign for milk brought the club's name into every household, so their resurgance will be meaningful to more than just the Stanley supporters.

Last season was a dream for all involved at The Crown Ground and manager John Coleman took the advice of many senior bossesand didn't let cup competitions interfere with the club's concentration on promotion. Harrogate Town beat Stanley aftyer a replay in the F.A.Cup and an early 4-1 F.A.Trophy hammering by finalists Tamworth cleared theminds for a safe run in!

What a run it was! Only four defeats, all of them away from home, and a fifteen game unbeaten start to the season was followed by a little relaxation over the Christmas period - as you do - and then came another tremendous seventeen game unbeaten run, to claim the championship and promotion to the Conference.

Goalscorers are always heroes, so Paul Mullin and Lutel James, with 66 goals between them, enjoyed cult status. The club just missed the 'ton' by three goals but did claim 100 points.

A wonderful team achievement means Accrington Stanley are just one step from regaining their treasured Football League status and, hopefully, John Coleman can build a team good enough to consolidate before pushing to achieve their ambition.

L-R - Back row - Steve Hacker, Gordon Armstrong, Steve Flitcroft, Paul Cook, Jamie Speare, Jonathon Smith, Paul Howarth, Robbie Williams, Steve Hollis, Andy Proctor
Front row - Andy Gouck, Brian Welch, Andy Waine, Lutel James, Peter Cavanagh, Darren Connell, Dean Calcutt, Rory Prendergast

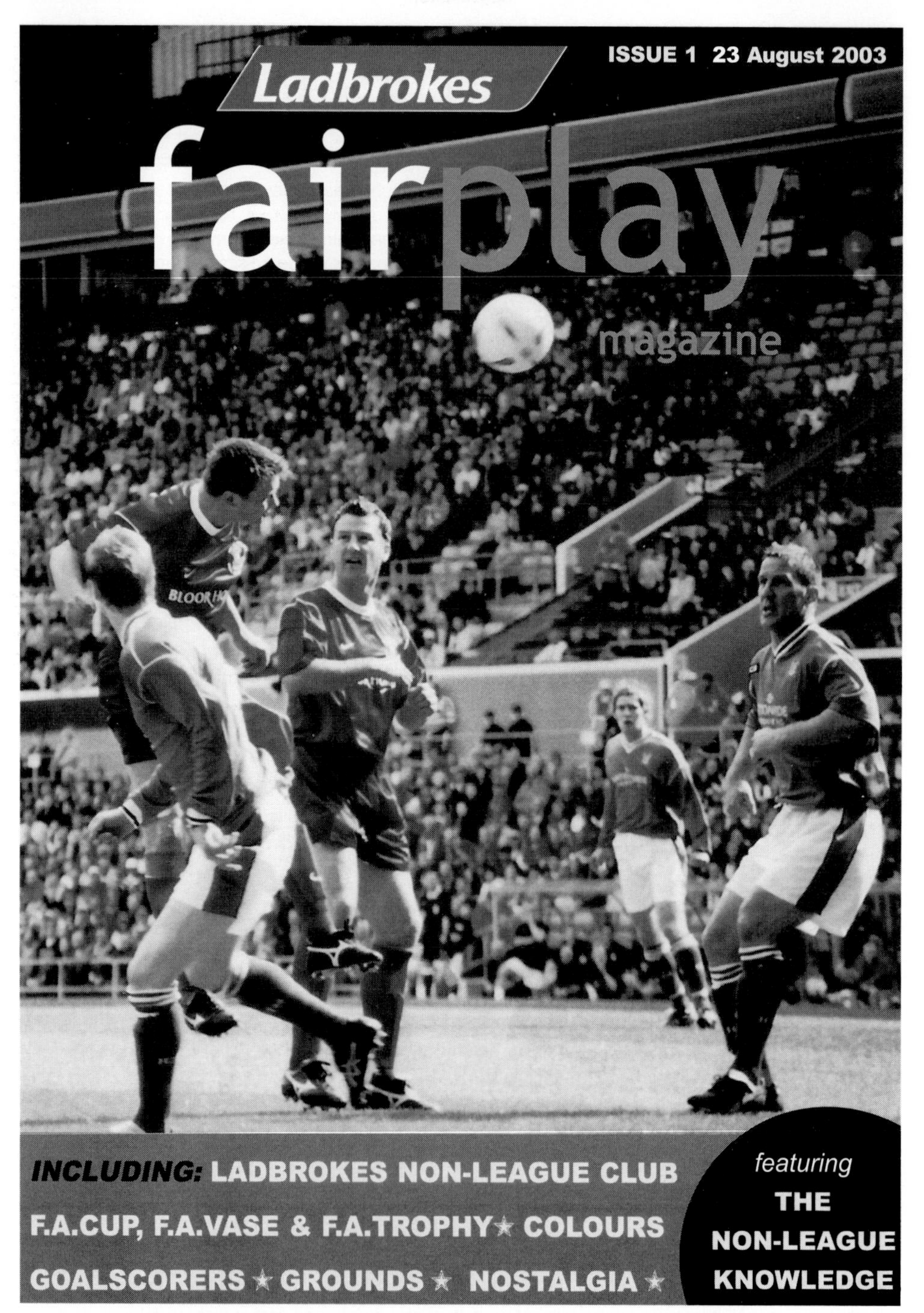

A fortnightly magazine for Ladbrokes' Fair Play Non-League Club members
For more information phone 01823 490080/490684

Date	Comp.	Opponents	Att.	Score	Goalscorers
17/08	Unib. P	RUNCORN HALTON	602	2 - 1	Payne 8, Mullin 44
20/08	Unib. P	Colwyn Bay	450	2 - 1	Mullin 73, Carden 85
24/08	Unib. P	Marine	361	3 - 0	Williams 40, Smith 56, James 70
26/08	Unib. P	FRICKLEY ATHLETIC	936	2 - 1	Calcutt 4 34
31/08	Unib. P	Harrogate Town	706	2 - 0	Mullin 78, Smith 84
04/09	Unib. P	VAUXHALL MOTORS	1032	2 - 1	James 60 71
07/09	Unib. P	Stalybridge Celtic	790	4 - 1	Williams 12, Mullin 43, Cavanagh 70 82
11/09	Unib. P	BARROW	1334	2 - 1	Mullin 45, Carden 49
14/09	Unib. P	DROYLSDEN	1195	2 - 1	Carden 17, James 25[p]
21/09	Unib. P	WAKEFIELD & EMLEY	1455	1 - 1	James 78[p]
24/09	Unib. P	Ashton United	409	2 - 2	Mullin 55 60
28/09	FA Cup Q2	BILLINGHAM TOWN	747	2 - 0	Mullin 40, James 72[p]
02/10	Unib. P	BURSCOUGH	1488	4 - 2	Calcutt 56, Carden 61 72 90
05/10	Unib. P	Bradford Park Avenue	760	1 - 1	Mullin 76
09/10	Unib. P	COLWYN BAY	1367	2 - 0	Sampson 35, Mullin 51
12/10	FA Cup Q3	HARROGATE TOWN	1112	0 - 0	
15/10	FA Cup Q3 rep	Harrogate Town	602	2 - 3	Smith 50, Halford 54
19/10	Unib. P	WORKSOP TOWN	1134	1 - 1	Calcutt 45
26/10	Unib. P	Frickley Athletic	290	1 - 2	Cavanagh 45[p]
02/11	Unib. P	Barrow	1442	0 - 1	
06/11	Unib. P	GATESHEAD	606	2 - 1	Cavanagh 32, Sertori 37
13/11	Unib. P	STALYBRIDGE CELTIC	892	4 - 1	Mullin 42, James 48 90, Knowles 58
16/11	Unib. P	HUCKNALL TOWN	942	2 - 0	Cavanagh 25, Mullin 52
19/11	Lge Cup 2	Barrow	524	2 - 3	Mullin 10 36
24/11	Unib. P	Hyde United	652	3 - 3	Mullin 20, James 56 90[p]
30/11	FA Trophy 2	Tamworth	951	1 - 4	Mullin 80
04/12	Unib. P	ASHTON UNITED	665	4 - 1	Gouck 23, James 49 74[p], Procter 86
07/12	Unib. P	Wakefield & Emley	452	0 - 0	
14/12	Unib. P	BRADFORD PARK AVENUE	873	3 - 1	James 45[p] 75[p], Mullin 79
17/12	Pres. Cup 1	Ashton United	101	2 - 4	Black 26, Smith 56
21/12	Unib. P	Hucknall Town	332	1 - 2	Mullin 28
28/12	Unib. P	GAINSBOROUGH TRINITY	1068	3 - 0	Mullin 7, James 84 89
11/01	Unib. P	Gateshead	273	1 - 5	James 27
18/01	Unib. P	MARINE	925	5 - 0	Smith 7, Proctor 19 89, James 33 44[p]
22/01	Lancs MT 2	SOUTHPORT	324	2 - 0	Halford 68, Carden 85
25/01	Unib. P	Burscough	576	1 - 0	Halford 17
29/01	Lancs MT QF	LANCASTER CITY	360	3 - 1	James 42, Mullin 50 81
01/02	Unib. P	Runcorn Halton	421	2 - 0	James 19[p] 36[p]
08/02	Unib. P	HARROGATE TOWN	1074	3 - 2	Payne 6, Smith 65, Mullin 81
22/02	Unib. P	Worksop Town	1063	4 - 1	James 16 38[p], Mullen 50 55
26/02	Lancs MT SF	KENDAL TOWN	580	1 - 2	James 55[p]
01/03	Unib. P	BLYTH SPARTANS	1116	3 - 2	James 8, Proctor 20, Mullin 46
11/03	Unib. P	Altrincham	600	1 - 1	Prendergast 25
15/03	Unib. P	Lancaster City	677	2 - 1	James 24[p], Mullin 64
22/03	Unib. P	WHITBY TOWN	1355	1 - 1	Smith 86
01/04	Unib. P	Blyth Spartans	418	3 - 0	Mullin 2, Prendergast 76, Proctor 83
05/04	Unib. P	Droylsden	539	2 - 2	James 35[p] 90
06/04	Unib. P	Whitby Town	566	3 - 0	James 45 70, Mullin 58
12/04	Unib. P	ALTRINCHAM	2263	3 - 1	James 45[p] 89, Halford 80
15/04	Unib. P	Vauxhall Motors	396	1 - 0	Prendergast 34
19/04	Unib. P	Gainsborough Trinity	420	5 - 1	Prendergast 28, James 44 78[p] 90, Mullin 85
21/04	Unib. P	LANCASTER CITY	1318	1 - 1	James 25
26/04	Unib. P	HYDE UNITED	1290	1 - 0	Calcutt 14
03/05	Ptr Swales Chall. Shl	MARINE	552	2 - 0	Mullin 37 63

ACCRINGTON STANLEY

GROUND DETAILS

Crown Ground, Livingstone Road,
Accrington, Lancs. BB5 5BX
Tel: 01254 383235
Office: 01254 397869
Website: www.accrington stanley.co.uk
email Address: info@accringtonstanley.co.uk

Directions: Arriving on A680 from Clayton-le-Moors Livingstone Rd is on left 50 yds past Crown Hotel. From M62/M66, through town centre on A680 -Livingstone Rd 500 yds on right after Victoria Hospital.
1 1/2 miles from Accrington(BR).

Capacity: 5,000
Cover: 2,000
Seats: 1,200

Clubhouse: Open five nights and matchdays. Private functions. Well stocked tea-bar in ground.

Club Shop: Sells replica kits, sweaters,etc
Contact: Liz Rackstraw (01254 397869)

MATCHDAY PROGRAMME

Programme - Pages: 44 Price: £1.20
Editor: P Terry. (01282 866768)

Local Press:
Accrington Observer, Lancashire Evening Telegraph.
Local Radio:
Radio Lancashire, Red Rose Radio.

Formed: 1968
Nickname: Reds
Sponsors: Hyndburn Borough Council
Colours: Red/red/red
Change colours: All White
Midweek home matchday: Tuesday
Youth Lge: Lancs Youth Floodlit League.
Reserves: Lancashire League

CLUB OFFICIALS

Chairman: Eric Whalley

President: J C Prescott/J Hudson

Secretary: Philip Terry
8 Princess Street, Colne, Lancs BB8 9AN.
Tel: 01286 866768 (H), 01282 864000 (B).

e-mail: philipterry@tiscal.co.uk

Commercial Director: John de Maine

FOOTBALL MANAGEMENT TEAM

MANAGER: **JOHN COLEMAN**

Date of Appointment	July 1999
Date of Birth:	12 Oct. 1962
Place of Birth:	Kirby

PREVIOUS CLUBS

As manager	Ashton United
As player	Kirby, Burscough, Marine, Southport, Runcorn, Macclesfield, Rhyl, Morecambe, Lancaster C.

HONOURS

As Manager:	N.P.L. Div. 1, NPL Lge Cup

* * *

Asst Manager:	Jimmy Bell
Chief Scout:	Mike Carter
Osteopath:	Martin Dixon D.O.
Physio:	Paul Jones

Season	League	Div.	Pos.	Home						Away						
				P	W	D	L	F	A	W	D	L	F	A	Pts	Manager
02-03	NPL	Prem	1	44	18	4	0	53	20	12	6	4	44	24	100	John Coleman
01-02	NPL	Prem	6	44	10	7	5	47	27	11	2	9	42	37	72	John Coleman
00-01	NPL	Prem	9	44	12	4	6	44	34	6	6	10	28	33	63	John Coleman
99-00	NPL	Div 1	1	42	14	5	2	55	19	11	4	6	41	24	84	John Coleman
98-99	NPL	Prem	22	42	5	5	11	24	37	4	4	13	23	40	36	Bill Rodaway
97-98	NPL	Prem	20	42	5	9	7	28	30	3	5	13	21	38	38	Tony Greenwood
96-97	NPL	Prem.	11	44	11	4	7	45	36	7	8	7	32	34	66	Stan Allen
				P	W	D	L	F	A	Pts						
95-96	NPL	Prem.	7	42	17	14	11	62	54	*62						Stan Allen
94-95	NPL	Prem	15	42	12	13	17	55	77	49						Eric Whalley
93-94	NPL	Prem	16	42	14	7	21	63	85	49						Phil Staley
92-93	NPL	Prem	6	42	20	13	9	79	45	73						Phil Staley

HONOURS

NPL Challenge Cup 01-02,
NPL Challenge Shield 01-02,
N West Counties Lg R-up 86-87;
Cheshire County Lg Div 2 80-81 (R-up 79-80);
Lancs Comb 73-74 77-78 (R-up 71-72 75-76),
Lg Cup 71-72 72-73 73-74 76-77;
George Watson Trophy 71-72 73-74;
John Duckworth Trophy 85-86;
Lancs Jun. Cup (now MarsdenTrophy) 01-02, R-up 83-84 96-97;
Lancs U18 Cup 89-90;
N.W.All Div Cup 94-95; Anglo-Barbados Cup 95.,
IVW Alliance Cuo Finalists 95-96,
Lancs Floodlit Youth Lge 2001-02.

PREVIOUS

Leagues:
Lancs Combination 70-78;
Cheshire County 78-82;
North West Counties 82-87.

Names: None
Grounds:, None

Past Players who progressed to the Football League

David Hargreaves (Blackburn R. 77),
Ian Blackstone (York C.),
Gus Wilson (Crewe),
Glen Johnstone (Preston),
DarrenLyons (Bury),
Martin Clark (Crewe 92-93),
Mark Wright (Wigan 93-94),
Paul Collings (Bury 93-94),
Brett Ormerod (Blackpool 96-97),
Harvey Cunningham (Doncaster R.),
Gareth Seddon (Bury)

CLUB RECORDS

Attendance: 2,465
v Farsley Celtic 06.05.01 Unibond Div. 1.
(10,081 v Crewe Alexandra, F.A. C. 2nd Rd 5/12/92
- played at Ewood Park,Blackburn).
Career Goalscorer: David Hargreaves 328.
Career Appearances: Chris Grimshaw 362.
Win: 10-0
v Lincoln United 99-00
Fee Paid : £15,000
Paul Mullin from Radcliffe Borough 00-01
Fee Received: £60,000
for Gary Williams from Doncaster R

BEST SEASON

FA Trophy: 2nd Rd 99-00

F.A.Cup: 2nd Rd 92-93
1-6 v Crewe Alexandra (H)
League clubs defeated: None

League: 2002-03
Northern Premier League Champions

LAST SEASON

F.A. Cup: 3rd Qual Rd.
F.A. Trophy: 2nd Round
League: N.P.L. Champions
Top Goalscorer: Lutel James
Player of the Year: Jonathon Smith
Captain: Peter Cavanagh

	Birthplace	D.O.B.	Previous Clubs
			Bold print denotes England semi-professional international.
GOALKEEPERS			
Jon Kennedy			Blackpool, Gateshead (L), Sunderlamd, Worksop Town
Jamie Speare	Liverpool	95.11.76	Bury, Cwmbran Town, Sligo Rovers, Darlington, Everton
DEFENDERS			
Gordon Armstrong	Newcastle	15.07.67	Burnley, Bury, Sunderland, Bristol C. (L), Northampton T. (L)
Peter Cavanagh	Liverpool	14.10.81	Liverpool
Steve Halford	Bury	21.09.80	Bury, Chester City
Steve Hollis	Liverpool	22.08.72	Ashton United, Fleetwood, Hyde United (L), Wigan Athletic, Liverpool.
Paul Howarth	Lancashire		Rossendale Utd., Accrington Stanley, Shrewsbury T.
Jonathon Smith	Lancashire		Great Harwood, Darwen.
MIDFIELD			
Dean Calcutt	Yorkshire		Bradford P.A., Emley, Brackenhall United
Paul Cook	Liverpool	22.02.67	Burnley, Wigan Ath. (L), Stockport Co., Tranmere Rov., Coventry C., Wolves, Norwich C, Wigan Ath., Marine.
Steve Flitcroft			Blackburn Rovers, Hyde United (L)
Andy Gouck	BLackpool	08.06.72	Morecambe, Rochdale, Blackpool
Michael Knowles	Morecambe	03.0374	Morecambe
Rory Prendergast	Pontefract	06.04.78	Bradford P.A.,Frickley Athletic, Emley, Nuneaton Bor. (L), Northwich Vic. (L), York City, Barnsley
Andy Procter	Lancashire		Great Harwood T.
Andrew Waine	Manchester	24.02.83	Burnley
FORWARDS			
Darren Connell	Blackpool	03.02.83	Scarborough, Gainsborough T, Hucknall T & Barrow (L), Macclesfield Town, Blackpool.
Lutel James	Manchester	02.06.72	Bury, Hyde United, Guiseley, Scarborough, Selby Town, Yorkshire Amateurs
Paul Mullin	Lancashire		Radcliffe Borough, Clitheroe Town, Trafford, Darwen, Accrington Stanley (Juniors)
Brian Welch	South Shields	17.07.73	Lancaster City, Clitheroe T, Accrington S., Netherfiield, Droylsden, Accrington S, Barrow, Burnley, Hebburn

ALDERSHOT TOWN

In similar fashion to their promotion colleagues from Accrington, Aldershot Town enjoyed a supreme season in the League.

They did not appear to be bothered by progress in the national cups although they did beat Bashley in the Hampshire competition. To lose to Cheshunt in the League Cup was a 'suspect' result, but defeat by Dagenham & Redbridge in the F.A.Cup and Worcester City away in the F.A.Trophy might have been expected.

The experience of manager Terry Brown was probably the key factor in seeing this club finally achieve its ambition and reach the top of the non league pyramid. His signings were timed correctly and all played their part in keeping The Shots out in front despite a late challenge from Canvey Island and a mid season loss of fire power.

Roscoe D'Sane proved to be a great asset and his goals, vital penalty kicks and general mobility saw him force his way into the England team and become a regular in the white shirt. Paul Moody, Karl Ready and Ray Warburton were older players whose experience proved vital and, of course, the faithful supporters, who had roared them up the pyramid since their reformation, relished the run in as it became clear they would join Accrington Stanley in a great reunion just one step away from renewing rivalry with old colleagues now in Divisions Two and Three.

A lot of peolpe had worked hard for the 'new' Aldershot since 1992 and all their planning, endeavour, money and true support has been rewarded. One more big push is needed, but at least that Football League place is now in sight.

L-R - Back Row: Lee Charles, John Notter, Tim Sills, Mark Kleboe, Richard Barnard, Ben Lauder-Dyke, Anthony Charles, Ray Warburton, Dominic Sterling, Jason Chewins. **Middle**: Simon Pullen (Reserve/Youth manager), Martin Kuhl, Dean Hooper, Jamie Taylor, Stuart Tanfield, Roscoe D'Sane, Nick Roddis, Aaron McLean, Michael Harper, Luke Gedling, Jon Challinor, Paul Priddy (GK Coach), Alan McCreeney (Physio). **Front**: Luke Walker, Brett Cooper, Lee Champion, Terry Brown (Manager), Stuart Cash (Asst. Manager), Tyrone Smith, Rob Westall, Steve Valandia. Missing: Nikki Bull, James Rodwell. **Photo**: Eric Marsh

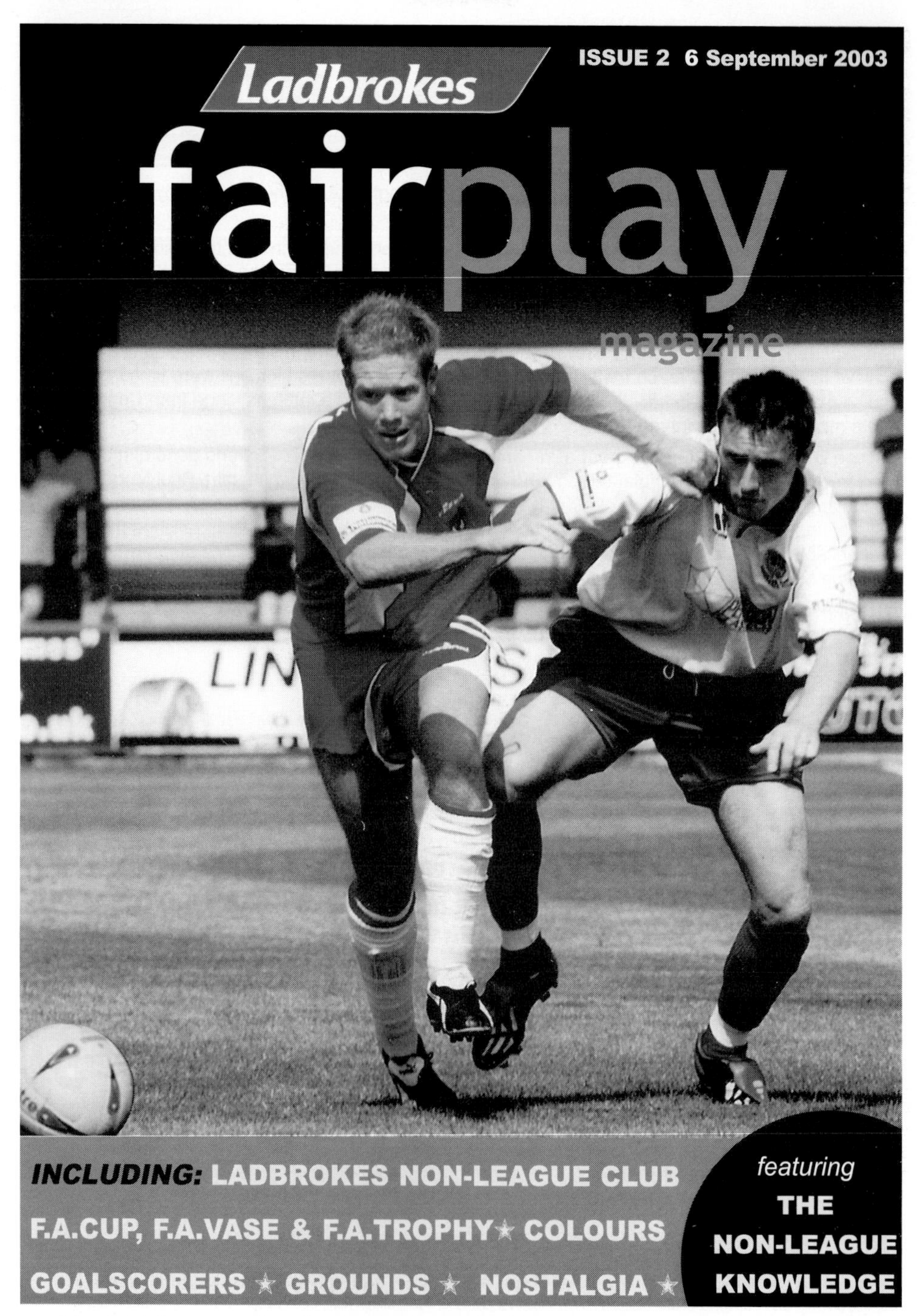

A fortnightly magazine for Ladbrokes' Fair Play Non-League Club members
For more information phone 01823 490080/490684

Date	Comp.	Opponents	Att.	Score	Goalscorers
17/08	Ryman P	Hitchin Town	974	3 - 1	Charles 17, Chewins 38, Taylor 87
20/08	Ryman P	BASINGSTOKE TOWN	2289	0 - 3	
24/08	Ryman P	BRAINTREE TOWN	1694	3 - 0	Harper 57 61, Nutter 84
26/08	Ryman P	Bishop's Stortford	894	1 - 1	Nutter 33
04/09	Ryman P	Enfield	395	2 - 1	L Charles 80, Nutter 86
07/09	Ryman P	GRAYS ATHLETIC	1875	2 - 1	Moody 1[p], L Charles 66
10/09	Ryman P	Maidenhead United	847	2 - 1	Moody 33, D'Sane 78
14/09	Ryman P	Ford United	426	3 - 2	Moody 7 47[p], Carroll 29
17/09	Ryman P	CANVEY ISLAND	2058	1 - 0	Cousins 13
21/09	Ryman P	HEYBRIDGE SWIFTS	1813	2 - 0	L Charles 21, Taylor 78
24/09	Ryman P	Bedford Town	693	2 - 1	D'Sane 15 64[p]
28/09	FA Cup Q2	AYLESBURY UNITED	1815	3 - 1	Taylor 28, Moody 73 76
01/10	Ryman P	HARROW BOROUGH	1704	0 - 1	
05/10	Ryman P	Aylesbury United	905	2 - 3	Taylor 62, Moody 78
12/10	FA Cup Q3	LEWES	1870	2 - 0	
15/10	Hants SC 2	FARNBOROUGH TOWN	1244	2 - 1	D'Sane, Ready
19/10	Ryman P	CHESHAM UNITED	1770	1 - 2	Roddis 75
22/10	Ryman P	Hampton & Richmond Borough	705	3 - 1	Kuhl 21, Taylor 38, Parker 82
26/10	FA Cup Q4	DAGENHAM & REDBRIDGE	2549	0 - 4	
02/11	Ryman P	Chesham United	671	3 - 1	D'Sane 24 31, Moody 41
04/11	Ryman P	Boreham Wood	439	1 - 0	D'Sane 89[p]
09/11	Ryman P	BILLERICAY TOWN	2288	0 - 0	
12/11	Ryman P	HAYES	1774	1 - 0	Chewins 29
19/11	Lge Cup 2	Cheshunt	n/k	0 - 1	
26/11	Ryman P	KINGSTONIAN	1956	2 - 1	L Charles 26, Sterling 84
30/11	FA Trophy 2	Worcester City	1562	0 - 1	
03/12	Hants SC 3	BOURNEMOUTH	657	3 - 2	A Charles, Taylor(2)
07/12	Ryman P	PURFLEET	2018	1 - 0	Langston 5
14/12	Ryman P	HITCHIN TOWN	1989	1 - 0	Browne 62
21/12	Ryman P	St Albans City	1538	0 - 2	
26/12	Ryman P	SUTTON UNITED	2564	3 - 2	D'Sane 6 83, Brooker 24[og]
28/12	Ryman P	Braintree Town	757	1 - 2	Browne 24
04/01	Ryman P	BISHOP'S STORTFORD	1964	0 - 0	
18/01	Ryman P	Grays Athletic	675	0 - 0	
24/01	Ryman P	FORD UNITED	1848	2 - 1	D'Sane 1, Hooper 37
28/01	Hants SC QF	EASTLEIGH	839	2 - 1	L Charles(2)
01/02	Ryman P	BOREHAM WOOD	1748	1 - 0	Roddis 19
04/02	Aldershot QF	Fleet Town	170	2 - 3	Warner 26, Moody 73
08/02	Ryman P	BEDFORD TOWN	2078	2 - 1	D'Sane 5[p] 35[p]
15/02	Ryman P	Heybridge Swifts	503	4 - 0	Charles 11, Warburton 39, Barber 78[og], Holsgrove 90
01/03	Ryman P	Harrow Borough	731	2 - 0	Buckle 11, Browne 70
04/03	Ryman P	MAIDENHEAD UNITED	2018	1 - 1	Browne 22
08/03	Ryman P	HAMPTON & RICHMOND BOR.	2012	4 - 0	D'Sane 68 90[p], A Charles 72, L Charles 82
11/03	Hants SC SF(1)	ANDOVER	1010	2 - 0	Hammond, Harper
15/03	Ryman P	Billericay Town	1089	1 - 0	D'Sane 8
25/03	Hants SC SF(2)	Andover	802	2 - 2	
29/03	Ryman P	Hayes	1305	0 - 1	
01/04	Ryman P	AYLESBURY UNITED	1835	1 - 0	Browne 80
05/04	Ryman P	ENFIELD	2049	2 - 0	D'Sane 39[p], Buckle 45
08/04	Ryman P	Basingstoke Town	1617	1 - 0	Buckle 64
12/04	Ryman P	Kingstonian	1220	2 - 0	Buckle 36, Holsgrove 45
15/04	Ryman P	Canvey Island	3553	1 - 0	D'Sane 28[p]
19/04	Ryman P	ST ALBANS CITY	2883	5 - 1	Holsgrove 28, McLean 45 78 88, Childs 85
21/04	Ryman P	Sutton United	2002	1 - 1	D'Sane 60
26/04	Ryman P	HENDON	3419	6 - 2	Buckle 19, D'Sane 75, Holsgrove 79, Bull 82, McLean 84, Browne 86
01/05	Ryman P	Hendon	511	3 - 1	Roddis 4, Browne 38, Hammond 51
03/05	Ryman P	Purfleet	728	2 - 1	Akurang 40[og], Charles 78
08/05	Hants SC F	Bashley	n/k	2 - 1	McLean 23 69 (at Southampton)

ALDERSHOT TOWN

GROUND DETAILS

Recreation Ground,
High Street,
Aldershot,
Hants GU11 1TW
Tel: 0870 112 4112
Fax: 0870 112 5112
Club Newsline: 09066 55585
Official Website: www.theshots.net
Unofficial Website: www.shotsweb.co.uk

Formed: 1992

Nickname: The Shots

Sponsors: Hi-Speed Services Ltd

Colours: Red /Blue Trim

Change Colours: White/Red Trim

Midweek matchday: Tuesday

Reserves League: Capital League

Directions: Ground situated on eastern end of High Street next to large multi-storey B.T. building. From M3 (jct 4) take A325 to Aldershot. After five miles at r'bout take 1st exit marked town centre (A323) into Wellington Ave. At Burger King r'bout take 2nd exit into High Street - ground on left, large carpark adjacent. 5 mins walk from Aldershot (BR)
Capacity: 7,500
Cover: 6,850
Seats: 1,800
Clubhouse:
Open on matchdays and for special functions
Steward: Wally Clarke 01252 320211 x212
Club Shop:
Range of souvenirs, programmes, replica kits.
Open matchdays or
contact Janet Guess (01252-528007) for mail order

CLUB OFFICIALS

Chairman: Karl Prentice

Vice Chairman: John McGinty

Company Secretary: tba

Press Officer: Nick Fryer Tel:01252 32011

MATCHDAY PROGRAMME

Pages: 44 Price: £2.00
Editors: Karl Prentice, Rachel Pearce
Tel: 01256 471630

Local Press: Aldershot News, Farnham Herald
Local Radio: County Sound (96.4, 1476 khz), BBC Southern Counties (104.6 fm)

FOOTBALL MANAGEMENT TEAM

MANAGER:	**TERRY BROWN**
Date of Appointment	
Date of Birth	5th August 1952
Place of Birth	Hillingdon

PREVIOUS CLUBS

As manager	Hayes (93-02)
As coach	Wokingham Town
As player	Hayes, Slough Town, Hayes, Wokingham Town

HONOURS

as manager	Isthmian League Championship 95-96, 02-03
As player	None

Asst Man.: Stuart Cash
Chief Scout:
Physio: Alan McCreanney

Season	League	Div.	Pos.	Home P	W	D	L	F	A	Away W	D	L	F	A	Pts	Manager
02-03	Isthmian	P	1	44	17	3	3	41	19	16	3	4	40	20	105	Terry Brown
01-02	Isthmian	P	3	42	12	4	5	44	23	10	3	8	32	28	73	George Borg
00-01	Isthmian	P	4	41	15	4	1	41	11	6	7	8	32	28	74	George Borg
99-00	Isthmian	P	2	42	13	2	6	39	23	11	3	7	32	28	77	George Borg
98-99	Isthmian	P	7	42	11	4	6	53	21	5	10	6	30	27	62	George Borg
97-98	Isthmian	1	1	42	16	3	2	48	12	12	5	4	41	24	92	Steve Wigley
96-97	Isthmian	1	7	42	10	7	4	32	21	9	7	5	35	24	71	Steve Wigley

Season	League	Div.	Pos.	P	W	D	L	F	A	Pts	Manager
95-96	Isthmian	1	5	42	21	9	12	81	46	72	Steve Wigley
94-95	Isthmian	1	4	42	23	5	14	80	53	74	Steve Wignall
93-94	Isthmian	2	3	42	30	7	5	78	27	97	Steve Wignall

HONOURS

Isthmian Premier Division 02 - 03, R-up: 99 - 00
Division 1 97 - 98
Division 3 92 - 93
Isthmian League Cup: 98 - 99
Isthmian Charity Shield: 99 - 00

Hampshire Senior Cup 98 - 99, 99 - 00, 01 - 02
Suburban West Division 94 - 95
Allied Counties (West) 93 - 94
Suburban Shield 95 - 96
Hampshire Floodlit Cup 97 - 98, 98 - 99, 01 - 02
Southern Youth League 99 - 00, 01 - 02
Southern Youth League Cup 98 - 99

PREVIOUS

Name None

Ground None

Leagues Isthmian Div.3 92-3, Div 2 93-94, Div 1 94-98, Prem.98-03

Past Players who progressed to the Football League

CLUB RECORDS

Attendance: 7,500
v Brighton & Hove Albion FA Cup 1st Rd 18.11.00
"Ground" record: 19,138
Aldershot FC v Carlisle Utd, FA Cup 4th Rd replay 28/1/70

Win: 8-0
v Bishop's Stortford (a) League 5.9.98
9-1
v Andover (n) Hants Senior Cup Final 99-00

Defeat: 0-6
v Worthing (a) Puma Cup 2.3.99

Career Goalscorer: Mark Butler 155. (92-98)

Career Appearances: Jason Chewins 400 (93 – Present)

Transfer Fee Paid: £20,000
to Woking for Grant Payne (11.99)

Transfer Fee Received: £6,000
for Leon Gutzmore from Bedford Town (11.99)

BEST SEASON

FA Cup: Second Round 99-00 v Exeter City

FA Trophy: Fourth Rd Replay 99-00

FA Vase: Quarter Final 93-94

LAST SEASON

F.A. Cup: 4th Qual. Rd.
F.A. Trophy: 2nd Round
League: Isthmian Champions
Top Goalscorer: Roscoe D'Sane
Player of the Year: Nikki Bull
Captain: Ray Warburton

ALDERSHOT TOWN PLAYING SQUAD

Bold print denotes England semi-professional international.

	Birthplace	D.O.B.	Previous Clubs
GOALKEEPERS			
Richard Barnard	Frimley	27.12.80	Maidenhead United, Millwall
Nikki Bull	Hastings	02.10.81	Q.P.R., Aston Villa (Trainee)
DEFENDERS			
Anthony Charles	Isleworth	11.03.81	Hayes, Crewe Alex (£5,000), Brook House
Jason Chewins	Hants		Wealdstone, Basingstoke Town, Alton Town
John Nutter	Hants	13.06.82	Wycombe W, Blackburn R (Trainee)
Dominic Sterling	London		Hayes, Wealdstone,Wimbledon
Ray Warburton NC	Rotherham	07.10.67	Boston United, Rushden & Diamonds, Northampton Town, York City, Rotherham U
MIDFIELD			
Dean Hooper ESP	Harefield	13.04.71	Peterborough Utd, Kingstonian, Swindon T., Hayes, Chalfont St Peter, Yeading, Marlow, Brentford (Jnr)
Steve Perkins ESP	Southport	05. 11.75	Dagenham & Redbridge, Woking, Stevenage Borough, Plymouth Argyle, Crediton Town, Burscough
Nick Roddis ESP	Rotherham	18.02.73	Margate, Woking, Hayes, Yeading, Boston U, Boston T, Nott'm Forest (Juniors)
FORWARDS			
Nana Achamfuur			Egham Town
Lee Charles ESP	Hillingdon	20.08.71	Nuneaton Borough, Hayes, Barnet, Q.P.R.,Chertsey T.
Roscoe D'Sane ESP RP	London		Woking, Slough Town, Southend, Crystal Palace
Mark Hammond	Sidcup	03.10.78	Cray Wanderers, Bromley, Welling United, Dover A Millwall
Aaron McLean	Hammersmith	25.05.83	Leyton Orient
Tim Sills ESP	Surrey	10.09.79	Kingstonian, Basingstoke T., Camberley T., Millwall
Stuart Tansfield	Berks		Wokingham Town
Jamie Taylor	Crawley	16.12.82	Horsham, Broadbridge Heath

BARNET

The early season news that Underhill did not meet Football League standards was disappointing and strange, as the club had played happily in Division Three in season 2000-2001.

So there was no LDV Trophy involvement and manager Peter Shreeves knew from the start that finances were tight and players were more likely to be sold than bought.

Four points taken off the champions elect Yeovil Town showed what could be done and although the Bees seemed able to raise their game for the better opposition they were unable to achie any kind of real consistency.

Over the course of the campaign such senior players as Greg Heald, Wayne Purser and John Doolan moved on and attacking stars Junior Agogo and Mark Gower followed them at the end of the season. Before the final weeks, Shreeves decided he had had enough and Martin Allen moved up to take responsibilty as a number one for the first time at this level.

League inconsistencies could have been tolerated a little easier if there had been some excitement in the cups, but a deserved F.A.Cup home defeat at the hands of Tiverton Town and defeat at Forest Green in the F.A.Trophy were. to say the least, disappointing. The law of averages surely should give Barnet a Trophy run soon!

The enthusiasm of manager Allen and the signing of Juliano Grazioli, a natural goalscorer who will relish conference football, could see Barnet spirits lifting this season, although the big black cloud of doubt still hangs over Underhill Stadium.

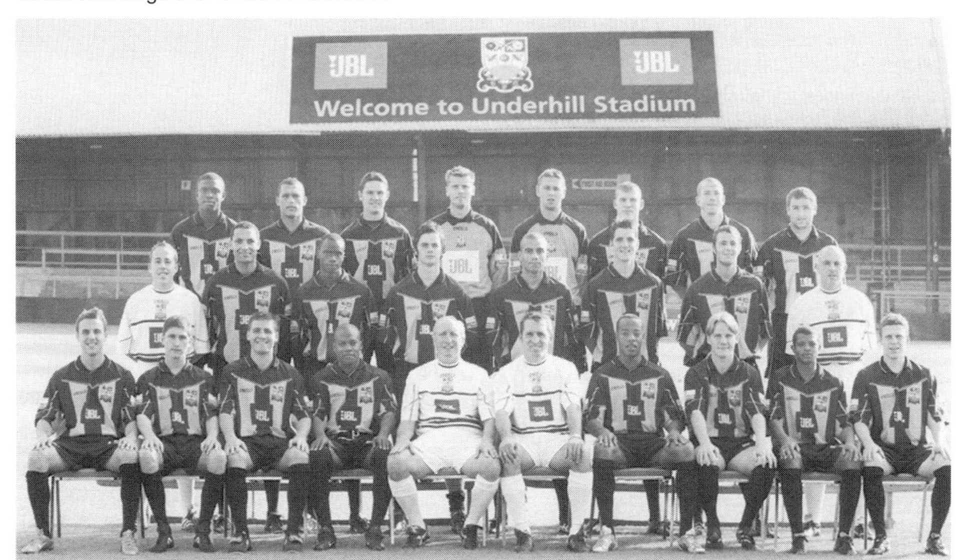

2002-03 Squad - L-R - Back Row: Ismail Yakubu, Danny Brown, Mark Arber, Lee Harrison, Danny Naisbitt, Lee Pluck, Greg Heald, John Doolan. **Middle Row:** Lee Taylor (Physio), Jason Soloman, Ade Olayinka, Stuart Niven, Neil Midgley, Ben Strevens, Frazer Toms, Paul Wilson (Coach). **Front Row**: Wayne Purser, Craig Pope, Lee Gledhill, Toby Oshitola, Peter Shreeves (Manager), Martin Allen (1st XI Coach), Junior Agogo, Mark Gower, Leon Bell, Lee Flynn

BARNET

Match Facts 2002-03

The number shown directly below the player's name is his squad number.
Where a number is shown instead of an "X" in the columns this represents a substitute appearance and the number indicates the player replaced.

Comp.	Date	Opponents	Venue.	Score	Goalscorers	Att.
						SQUAD NUMBER
Conf 1	Aug-17	Doncaster R	A	L 1-2	Strevens	3023
Conf 2	Aug-20	Yeovil T	H	W 2-1	Gower Strevens	1668
Conf 3	Aug-24	Chester C	H	L 0-3		1347
Conf 4	Aug-26	Burton A	A	W 3-0	Arber Agogo Gower	1984
Conf 5	Aug-31	Halifax T	H	D 0-0		1316
Conf 6	Sep-03	Margate	A	D 2-2	Gower Midgley	735
Conf 7	Sep-07	Telford U	H	W 3-0	Gower Strevens Oshitola	1067
Conf 8	Sep-14	Leigh RMI	A	L 2-4	Strevens(p) Agogo	405
Conf 9	Sep-17	Farnborough T	H	L 1-2	Agogo	1069
Conf 10	Sep-21	Scarborough	A	D 1-1	Agogo	1266
Conf 11	Sep-23	Stevenage B	A	W 2-1	Agogo(p) Strevens	2130
Conf 12	Sep-28	Morecambe	H	D 1-1	Doolan	1250
Conf 13	Oct-05	Forest Green R	A	D 4-4	Soloman Agogo Strevens Gower	871
Conf 14	Oct-08	Gravesend & N	H	L 1-4	Strevens	1360
Conf 15	Oct-12	Nuneaton B	H	W 2-1	Agogo(p) Purser	1421
Conf 16	Oct-19	Kettering T	A	W 2-1	Agogo Purser	1704
FAC 4q	Oct-26	Tiverton Town	H	L 0-2		1390
Conf 17	Nov-02	Northwich V	H	L 3-4	Agogo(2) Strevens	1093
Conf 18	Nov-09	Woking	A	D 0-0		1761
Conf 19	Nov-16	Leigh RMI	H	W 4-0	Agogo(2) Gower Strevens	1021
Conf 20	Nov-23	Forest Green R	H	W 2-0	Gower Agogo	1144
Conf 21	Nov-30	Hereford U	A	L 0-4		1471
Conf 22	Dec-07	Nuneaton B	A	L 2-3	Toms Agogo(p)	866
Conf 23	Dec-14	Telford U	A	L 1-2	Gower	779
Conf 24	Dec-26	Dagenham & R	H	W 2-1	Heald Agogo	1727
Conf 25	Dec-28	Yeovil T	A	D 0-0		4850
Conf 26	Jan-04	Doncaster R	H	L 1-2	Hendon	1859
FAT 3	Jan-14	Forest Green R	A	L 2-4	Purser Midgley	552
Conf 27	Jan-18	Chester C	A	D 1-1	Heald	1944
Conf 28	Jan-25	Burton A	H	D 2-2	Brown Doolan	1555
Conf 29	Jan-28	Dagenham & R	A	L 1-5	Agogo	1414
Conf 30	Feb-08	Halifax T	A	W 4-2	Agogo(2) Brown Heald	2119
Conf 31	Feb-15	Margate	H	L 0-1		1160
Conf 32	Feb-22	Scarborough	H	W 3-0	Soloman Doolan Oshitola	1056
Conf 33	Mar-01	Farnborough T	A	D 2-2	Yakubu Wiper	886
Conf 34	Mar-08	Stevenage B	H	L 0-2		1909
Conf 35	Mar-15	Morecambe	A	D 1-1	Purser	1667
Conf 36	Mar-18	Southport	H	W 3-1	Midgley(2) Purser	769
Conf 37	Mar-22	Hereford U	H	W 2-1	Midgley Agogo	1588
Conf 38	Mar-29	Southport	A	L 1-2	Gower	906
Conf 39	Apr-12	Kettering T	H	L 0-2		1198
Conf 40	Apr-19	Gravesend & N	A	D 2-2	Midgley Pope	1358
Conf 41	Apr-21	Woking	H	D 0-0		1617
Conf 42	Apr-26	Northwich V	A	D 1-1	Agogo	523

Lee HARRISON	Lee GLEDHILL	Lee FLYNN	Mark GOWER	Greg HEALD	Mark ARBER	John DOOLAN	Ben STREVENS	Junior AGOGO	Wayne PURSER	Danny BROWN	Stuart NIVEN	Danny NAISBITT	Neil MIDGLEY	Fraser TOMS	Bai Mass LETTE JALLOW	Ismael YAKUBU	Lee PLUCK	Leon BELL	Craig POPE	Toby OSHITOLA	David HILLIER	Ben WIPER	Jason SOLOMAN	Ricky MILLARD	Chris CASHMAN	Michael PRICE	Ian HENDON	Guy LOPEZ	Keith ROWLAND	Guy BUTTERS	Matt LANGSTON
1	**2**	**3**	**4**	**5**	**6**	**7**	**8**	**9**	**10**	**11**	**12**	**13**	**14**	**15**	**16**	**17**	**18**	**19**	**20**	**22**	**23**	**24**	**25**	**26**	**27**	**28**	**30**	**32**	**34**	**37**	**38**
x	x	x	x		x		x	x					x		8		x	x	19	9	x										
x	x		x		x		x	x					x			19	x	x	x		x		9								
x	x		x		x		x	x					x		18	23	x	x	x	14	x										
x	x	x	x		x	x	x	x					x			25	x	8		7			x								
x		x	x		x	x	x	x					x			7	x	14	x	3			x								
x			x		x	x	x	x					x		7	25	x		x	9	x		x								
x			x		x	x	x	4					7		25	x	x		x	x	x		x								
x	20		x		x	x	x	14		18			x			x	x		x	x	x										
x	x		x		x	x	x	x		x			x			x	x			11			7								
x	x		x		x	x	x	x		x			x			x	x	14		11											
x	x		x			x	x	x	14	x			x			x	x			9			x								
x	x		x			x	x	x	x	x						x	x	11	17	10			x								
x			x			x	x	x	x	x			x			10	x		x				x								
x	x		x	x		x	x	x	x	x			x				5	7		14			x								
	11		x	x		x	x	x	x	x		x	10			x	x		x	9											
			x	x		x		x	x		25	x	x	14		x	x	7	x				x								
			x	x		x	x	x	x		x	x	20	12		x	x		x				17								
			x	x		x	x	x	x			x	x	14		x	x		x												
	x		x	x		x	x	x	15			x		x		25	x		x				x								
			x	x	x	x	x	x	17			x	15	x		x			x						28	x					
			x	x	x	x	x	x	17			x	9	x		x			x							x					
		7	x	x		x	x	x	20			x	15	x		x	x		x							x					
		x	x	x		x	x	x	x			x		x		x	x	15													
		x	x	x		x		x	x			x		10		x	x			28			x			x					
		x	x	x		x		x	x			x	15	x		x	x										x				
		x	x	x		x		x	x			x	x	9		x	x			10			4				x				
		x	x	x		x		x	x			x	x	18		x	x			9							x				
		x	x	x		x			x				x	x		x	x			15			17	x			x				
		x	x	x		x		x	x			x	x			x				10			x				x				
		x	x	x		x		x		x		x	x	11		x	x						x								
		x	x	x				x	20	15		x	x	x		x	x		x	18			x								
		x	x	x		x		x	x	x		x	x	11		x							x								
			x	x		x		x	x	x		x	x	10		x	x			25			x								
		x		x		x		x	x			x		x		x	x		17	x			x								
		x	x	x		x		x	x			x		x		x	x		25			10	x								
		x	x	x		x		x	x			x	x	x	15	x	x												9		
		x	x	x					x			x	x	x	32		x		x									x	x		
		x	x			x			x			x	x	x	7		x		x						15				x	x	
		x	x	x				10	x			x	x	x			x		x										x	x	15
		x	x				20	x				x	x	x			x		x									18	x	x	x
		x	x					x				x	x	x		x	x		34	18									x	x	x
		x	x					15				x	x	x		x	38		x					13				x	x	x	x
		x	x				14	x		x			x			x	x		x	9				x				x		x	
		x	x					x		x			x			x	x		x	14				x				x	11	x	17

BARNET

GROUND DETAILS

Underhill Stadium,
Westcombe Drive,Herts.EN5 2BE

TEL: 020 8441 6932(office)
020 8449 6325 (ticket office)
Fax: 020 8447 0655
email: info@barnetfc.com
Club Call: 09068 121 544

Directions: Take junction 23 off the M25, follow signs for Barnet (A100), the ground is located at the foot of Barnet Hill. Tube :High Barnet (Northern Line), 400 yds
Train: New Barnet (1.5 miles)

Capacity: 4,057

Match Tickets:
From £8 - £15. (£10/£12 for away fans)

Club Shop:
Contact: Melvyn Beresford 0208440 0725

Refreshments:
Bar for all post match and five tea-bars

Founded: 1888

Nickname: The Bees

Sponsors: J.B.L.

Colours: Black & amber shirts, black shorts & socks

Change colours: All white

Midweek matchday: Tuesday 7.45

Newsline: 09068 12 15 44 (calls charged at premium rate)

Reserve League: None

CLUB OFFICIALS

Chairman: Tony Kleanthous

Directors: A.Adie,G. Slyper, C.Bean

Chief Executive / Secretary Andrew Adie
Tel Nos:01707 872518 (H) 0208441 6932 X204 (W)
07719 287453 (M) 0208447 0655 Fax)
Email: aadie@barnetfc.com

Company Secrrtary: Christopher Bean

P.R.Consultant to the Board: Dennis Signy OBE

Commercial Manager: Ben Keogh
Marketing Manager: Kevin Mullen

MATCHDAY PROGRAMME

Pages: 48 Price: £2.00
Editor: Kevin Mullen
Tel Nos: 020 84416932 (H) 07774132066 (M)
WEBSITE: www.barnetfc.com
Club call: 09068 121 544

FOOTBALL MANAGEMENT TEAM

HEAD COACH	**MARTIN ALLEN**
Date of Appointment	April 2003
Date of Birth:	14 August 1965
Place of Birth:	Reading
PREVIOUS CLUBS	
As manager:	
As asst. manager/coach	Barnet, Reading
As player	Q.P.R., West Ham, Portsmouth

First Team Coach:	Adrian Whitbread
Physiotherapist:	Damien Doyle
Club Playing Status:	Full Time

Season	League	Div.	Pos.	P	Home W	Home D	Home L	Home F	Home A	Away W	Away D	Away L	Away F	Away A	Pts	Manager
02-03	Conference	-	11	42	9	4	8	32	28	4	10	7	33	40	53	Peter Shreeves
01-02	Conference	-	5	42	10	4	7	30	19	9	6	6	34	29	67	John Still / Peter Shreeves
00-01	Football Lge	3	24	46	9	8	6	44	29	3	1	19	23	52	45	John Still/Tony Cottee/John Still
99-00	Football Lge	3	6	46	12	6	5	36	24	9	6	8	23	29	75	John Still
98-99	Football Lge	3	16	46	10	5	8	30	31	4	8	11	24	40	55	John Still
97-98	Football Lge	3	7	46	10	8	5	35	22	9	5	9	26	29	70	John Still
96-97	Football Lge	3	15	46	9	9	5	32	23	5	7	11	14	28	58	Terry Bullivant
95-96	Football Lge	3	8	46	13	6	4	40	19	5	10	8	25	26	70	Ray Clemence
94-95	Football Lge	3	12	42	8	7	6	37	27	7	4	10	19	36	56	Ray Clemence
93-94	Football Lge	2	24	46	4	6	13	22	32	1	7	15	19	54	28	Gary Phillips

HONOURS

FA Amateur Cup 1945-46. Runners-up 1947-48, 1958-59.
FA Trophy runners-up 1971-72.
Athenian League x 5. Athenian Premier Div. x 2.
Southern League Div.1 1965-66. Div. 1 South 1976-77.
Southern League Cup 1976-77.
London League 1897, 1906, 1907.
London Senior Cup x 3. London Charity Cup x 2.
Middlesex Senior Cup x 2. Middlesex Charity Cup x 2.
Herts Senior Cup x 12. Herts Charity Cup x 25.
Wendy Fair Capital League 1988-89.
Clubcall Cup 1988-89.
Football Conference Winners 1990-91.
Football Conference runners-up 1986-87, 1987-88, 1989-90.

CLUB RECORDS

Attendance: 11,026
v Wycombe W., FA Amateur Cup 4th Rnd, 1951-52.

Career Goalscorer: Arthur Morris, 400, 1927-34.

Career Appearances: Les Eason, 648, 1965-74, 1977-78.

Transfer Fee Paid: £130,000
to Peterborough Utd for Greg Heald.

Transfer Fee Received: £800,000
from Crystal Palace for Dougie Freedman.

PREVIOUS

Leagues: Olympian League, London League, Athenian League, Southern League, Alliance Premier*, Gola League*, Vauxhall Conference*, Football League.

Names: Barnet Alston.

Grounds: Queens Road, Totteridge Lane.

* Same competetion different title.

BEST SEASON

FA Cup: 3rd Round
1964-65, 1970-71, 1972-73, 1981-82, 1990-91, 1991-92, 1993-94.

League Clubs Defeated (as a non-league club) Newport County (1970-71, a Northampton Town1990-91

FA Trophy: Finalists 1971-72.

League: Conference Champions 1990-91.

Past Players who progressed to the Football League

Colin Powell (Charlton Ath), Gary Borthwick (AFC Bournemouth), Graham Pearce (Brighton & H.A), Russell Townsend (Northampton Tn), Colin Barnes (Torquay Utd), Gary Phillips (Brentford), Keith Alexander (Grimsby Town), Nicky Bissett (Brighton & H.A.), Robert Codner (Brighton & H.A.), Lee Payne (Newcastle Utd), Phil Gridelet (Barnsley), david Regis & Paul Harding (Notts County).

LAST SEASON

F.A. Cup: 4th Qual. Round
F.A. Trophy: 3rd Round
Conference: 11th
Top Goalscorer: Junior Agogo
Captain: Greg Heald
Player(s) of the Year: Junior Agogo

BARNET PLAYING SQUAD

	Birthplace	D.O.B.	Previous Clubs

Bold print denotes England semi-professional international.

GOALKEEPERS

Ricky Millard	London	03.05.84	Youth Team
Danny Naisbitt	Bishop Auckland	25.11.78	Walsall

DEFENDERS

Ian Hendon E.u21,Y	Ilford	05.12.71.	Sheffield Wednesday, Tottenham Hotspur (Trainee)
Simon King	Oxford	11.04.83	Oxford United
Danny Maddix Wednesday	Ashford	11.10.67	Tottenham Hotspur (Trainee), Q.P.R., Sheffield
Chris Plummer E u21	Isleworth	12.10.76	Q.P.R.
Lee Pluck	London		From Trainee
Mark Rooney	Lambeth	19.05.78	Dagenham& Red, St.Albans City, Aylesbury Utd., Watford (juniors)
Jamie Smith			From Trainee
Tony Taggart	London		Farnborough Town, Brentford (junior)

MIDFIELD

Mark Cumberbatch			Protec Youth Academy
Soloman Henry	London		Protec Youth Academy
Bai Mass Lette 'Max' Jallow	London		Youth Team
Guy Lopez	Calais		Local Football
Mark Williams	London	19.10.81	Brentford
Ismail Yakubu	London		Barnet School of Excellence

FORWARDS

Giuliano Grazioli	Marylebone	23.03.75	Wembley, Yeovil Town(L), Woking (L), Peterborough U. Stevenage B (L), Swindon Town, Bristol Rovers.
Liam Hatch RP	Kent		Gravesend & Northfleet, Herne Bay £25,000
Lee Roach			Protec Youth Academy
Ben Strevens	Edgware	24.05.80	Wingate & Finchley

BURTON ALBION

Reaching the Conference in style from the Unibond League and having enjoyed a run to the F.A.Trophy semi-finals by defeating three Conference clubs all bode well for Albion in the senior competition. So it wasn't surprising that player manager Nigel Clough showed faith in most of the squad that had won him promotion.

Just like many promoted clubs before them, however, Albion found the standard week in and week out just a little tougher than they expected. Strangely, it was at home that the main difficulty lay and, if it hadn't been for their stirling away form in the first half of the season Clough's men would have been in real trouble. As it was, the pressure remained until the last weeks of the campaign when the defeat of luckless Kettering Town ensured safety, and the whole club could take stock of their Conference experience and plan for a more stable future.

The squad has been strengthened substantially and much of this has been achieved by careful 'housekeeping'. But a good cup run with an attractive tie with Oldham Athletic brought them a large television fee plus their winning bonus, so
with a solid home following, the club appears to be on a much sounder financial basis than most. They will start the season with five Internationals including new signings midfielder Barry Williams from Nuneaton and Ryan Sugden from Scarborough, so with Robbie Talbot joining Moore, Ducros and Anderson up front there will be plenty of competition for first team places and Albion can reasonably expect to be keeping well away from the danger zones at the foot of the Conference this season.

Back Row (L-R): Ray Hudson, Matt Brown, Glenn Kirkwood, Darren Stride, Colin Hoyle, Aaron Webster, Dan Robinson, Matt Duke, Barry Williams, Ian Wright,Lee Colkin, Ryan Sugden, Steve Booth, Andy Garner
Front Row (L-R): Dale Anderson, Andy Sinton, Robbie Talbot, Andy Ducros, Nigel Clough, Gary Crosby, Christian Moore, Terry Henshaw, Darren Wassall, Jon Howard

BURTON ALBION

Match Facts 2002-03

The number shown directly below the player's name is his squad number.
Where a number is shown instead of an "X' in the columns this represents a substitute appearance and the number indicates the player replaced.

Comp.	Date	Opponents	Venue.	Score	Goalscorers	Att.
						SQUAD NUMBER
Conf 1	Aug-17	Scarborough	H	D 1-1	Evans	1821
Conf 2	Aug-20	Northwich V	A	W 3-1	Moore(2) Anderson	893
Conf 3	Aug-24	Leigh RMI	A	L 2-4	Evans Moore	503
Conf 4	Aug-26	Barnet	H	L 0-3		1984
Conf 5	Aug-31	Telford U	A	W 2-0	Moore Anderson	1311
Conf 6	Sep-03	Forest Green R	H	L 2-3	Kavanagh(p) Moore	1598
Conf 7	Sep-07	Halifax T	H	D 2-2	Moore Kavanagh(p)	1636
Conf 8	Sep-14	Dagenham & R	A	W 2-1	Clough Webster	1527
Conf 9	Sep-17	Gravesend & N	H	D 1-1	Glover	1412
Conf 10	Sep-21	Southport	A	D 2-2	Stride Farrell	1331
Conf 11	Sep-24	Chester C	A	L 1-2	Glover	2440
Conf 12	Sep-28	Margate	H	L 0-1		1640
Conf 13	Oct-05	Woking	A	D 2-2	Webster Reddington	1426
Conf 14	Oct-08	Yeovil T	H	D 1-1	Moore	1989
Conf 15	Oct-11	Hereford U	H	W 2-0	Moore(2) Anderson	2149
Conf 16	Oct-19	Stevenage B	A	W 1-0	Moore	1770
FAC 4q	Oct-26	Halifax T	H	W 2-1	Dudley Kirkwood	1990
Conf 17	Nov-02	Morecambe	H	L 1-4	Anderson(p)	1688
Conf 18	Nov-09	Kettering T	A	W 2-1	Anderson Webster	1743
FAC 1	Nov-16	Oldham Athletic	A	D 2-2	Webster(p) Dudley	5802
Conf 19	Nov-23	Woking	H	L 0-2		1558
FAC 1r	Nov-27	Oldham Athletic	H	D 2-2 *	Moore(2)	3416
Conf 20	Nov-30	Farnborough T	A	L 1-5	Moore	934
Conf 21	Dec-06	Doncaster R	H	L 1-2	Kavanagh(p)	2341
Conf 22	Dec-14	Halifax T	A	W 1-0	Talbot	1469
Conf 23	Dec-21	Dagenham & R	H	D 0-0		1447
Conf 24	Dec-26	Nuneaton B	A	W 2-1	Stride O'Halloran	2337
Conf 25	Dec-28	Northwich V	H	D 1-1	Kirkwood	1833
Conf 26	Jan-01	Nuneaton B	H	W 1-0	Reddington	2523
Conf 27	Jan-04	Scarborough	A	L 1-4	Kirkwood	1428
FAT 3	Jan-11	Wakefield & Emley	A	L 0-1		802
Conf 28	Jan-18	Leigh RMI	H	L 0-1		1393
Conf 29	Jan-25	Barnet	A	D 2-2	Stride Moore	1555
Conf 30	Feb-08	Telford U	H	L 4-7	Moore(2) Stride Dudley(p)	1516
Conf 31	Feb-15	Forest Green R	A	L 0-2		986
Conf 32	Feb-22	Doncaster R	A	L 0-1		3026
Conf 33	Mar-01	Gravesend & N	A	L 2-3	Reddington Stride	1140
Conf 34	Mar-08	Chester C	H	W 2-0	Ducros Sinton	2183
Conf 35	Mar-15	Margate	A	D 0-0		577
Conf 36	Mar-22	Farnborough T	H	W 2-0	Moore Howard	1548
Conf 37	Mar-25	Southport	H	W 1-0	Moore	1402
Conf 38	Apr-05	Hereford U	A	L 0-4		1780
Conf 39	Apr-12	Stevenage B	H	L 1-2	Webster	1523
Conf 40	Apr-19	Yeovil T	A	L 1-6	Gummer	5691
Conf 41	Apr-21	Kettering T	H	W 2-0	Howard Anderson	1570
Conf 42	Apr-26	Morecambe	A	L 0-5		2239

Matt DUKE	Tony HENSHAW	Paul TALBOT	Neil GLASSER	Mark BLOUNT	Darren WASSELL	Darren STRIDE	Dale ANDERSON	Steve FARRELL	Christian MOORE	Aaron WEBSTER	Colin HOYLE	Dan ROBINSON	Steve EVANS	Glen KIRKWOOD	Jason KAVANAGH	Craig DUDLEY	Paul WRAITH	Nigel CLOUGH	Craig SWINSLOE	Sean GUMMER	Aaron JOHNSON	Matthew O'HALLORAN	Andy DUCROS	Andy SINTON	Lee GLOVER	Jon HOWARD	John BURNS	Ben PETTY	Stuart REDDINGTON	Steve GOUGH	Lee CAMP
1	**2**	**3**	**4**	**5**	**6**	**7**	**8**	**9**	**10**	**11**	**12**	**13**	**14**	**15**	**16**	**17**	**19**	**20**	**21**	**22**	**23**	**23**	**23**	**24**	**25**	**25**	**26**	**26**	**27**	**28**	**30**
x	x	x	x	x			3		x	x	x		x	x				x						14							
x	x	x	x	x			x		x	8	x		x	x	14			x						20							
x	x	x	x	x		15	x	24	14		x		x	x	x									x							
x	x		x	x		x	9	x	x	x	x			7	5			x						x							
x	5	x		x		x	10		x	x	x			x	x	15		x						x							
x	x	x				x		15	x	x	x			x	x	11		x						x							
x	x	x	15			x		17	x	24	x			x	x	x		x						x							
x		x	x	x		x		17	x	3	x		x	20	x	x		x													
x				x		x			x	x	x		x	14	x	x		x						x	10						
x		24		x		x		17		x	x			x	x	x	7	x						x	x						
x				x				5	x	x	x		17	x	x	x		x			16			x	x						
x	x		x					25	x	x	x		15	x	x	24		x						x	x						
x	15	11	x			25			x	x	x			x	x	x		x							x				x		
x	4	x	x			16			x	x	x		17	x	x	x		x											x		
x	x	x				x			x	x	x		25			x		x							x				x	17	
x	x	x	x			x	10		x	x				x		x		x						17					x		
x	x	x	x			x	10		x	x	x			x		x		x						20	17						
x	x	x				x	10		x	8	x			x		x		x						x	17				x		
x	x	x	x			x	x	8		x	x					24		25						x	x				x		
x	x	x	x				10		x	x	x			x	17	x		x											x		
x	x	x	x				x			x	x		16	x	x			x							4				x	15	
x	x	x	x	10		x	15		x	x	x			x				x						3					x		
x	x	x		x		15	3		x	x				x	2			x						x			x		x		
x		24	x	x		x	11		x	x					x	x		x						x			20		x		
x	x	x	x	x		x	17		x	x				x		x		10									x				
x	x	x	x	27		x	17		x	x				x		x											x		x		
x	x		x			x	x		17	x				x		x		26				x		23			x		x		
x	x	x			x	x	3		x				x	7				x				x		14			x		x		
x	x		x				x	24	x	x				x		x		26				x		17			x		x		
	x	15			x		x	23	x	x	6	x		x				x				x					x		x		
	x		x		x		x	23	x	x	6							x				x					x		x	26	x
	x		x		x	x	x			x	x					4		x				x		x						23	x
	x	24	x		x	x			x	x	x					x		x				6		x							x
	x	x	x			x	20		x	24	x					x		x						x					x	4	x
	x	x			x	x	24		x	20						x		x					x	x					x		x
	x				x	x		23	x	x	x					x		x					x	x				24			x
x	x			x	x	x		15	x	x	x			6						24				x				x	x		
x				x		x			x	x	x					x		23					x	x		x		12	x		
x	x	24		x		x			x	x						x		23					x	x		x			x		
x	x	24		x		x			x	x	27					x							x	x		x		23	x		
x	x	24		x		x	17		x	x						x							x	x		x		23	x		
x	x	17		x		x	x			x	x					x							x	x		x		23			
x	x	24				x	x		x	x	x					26							12	x		x		x	x		
x	x	x		x			x			x							x	8	23	x			x					x	x		
x	x					x	23		x	x	x							x					x	x		x			x		
x	x	x		27			x		x	x	x									8			x	x		x		24	x		

BURTON ALBION

GROUND DETAILS

Eton Park,Princess Way,Burton-on-Trent
DE14 2RU
Tel: 01283 565938

Directions: No1. From M1 South: Take Jct 23 (A50 Derby).Join A38 south at Toyota factory(A38 B'ham & Lichfield) .Leave A38 at Burton North Clay Mills (A5121), over first roumdabout, past Pirelli factory and turn right at next r'bout . Ground on left past Metro supermarket.**No.2 From M! North:Jct 28** (A38 Derby) , Follow A38 through Derby until A5121(Burton North Clay Mills) then as No 1.**No.3 From South M5:** M40 join M42 North. Leave at Jct 9, A446 (Lichfield & Belfry Golf). Join A38 North sign posted Burton. Leave A38 at second turn for Burton (Clay Mills) A5121 then as No.1 **No.4 From M6 North:** Leave at Jct 15 (A500 to Stoke) join A50 (to Uttoxeter& Burton), follow A50 until junction with A38 at Toyota factory. Then as No.1

Parking: Large Car Park at the ground.

Capacity: 4,500
Cover: 2,500
Seats: 464

Clubhouse: `The Football Tavern' - open normal pub hours. Full hot & cold menu.
Steward: T.B.A

Club Shop: Yes
Match Tickets:

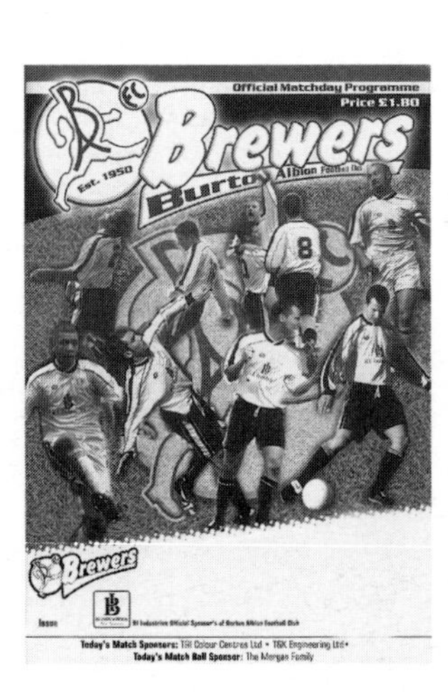

MATCHDAY PROGRAMME

Pages: 48 Price: £1
Editor: Fleur Robinson(01283 537272)
Clubcall:09066 555 883

Local Press: Burton Daily Mail (01283 43311)
Local Radio: Radio Derby,Centra F.M.,Ram F.M.

Founded:	1950
Nickname:	Brewers
Sponsors:	Knott & Bison
Colours:	Yellow with black trim
Change colours:	Blue
Midweek matchday:	Tuesday
Reserve League:	
Club Websites	www.burtonalbionfc.co.uk www.brewerstreet.com

CLUB OFFICIALS

Chairman: C B Robinson
01283 537272W)

President:

Vice-Chairman:

Directors: C.B.Robinson, Spiers,C.Brodie,R.Bowering,C.Simpson,T.Whyman ansd P.Brown

Secretary: Tony A Kirkland
40 Hurst Drive, Stretton, Burton-on-Trent DE13 0ED
07774 102485 (Mobile)

Commercial Manager: Fleur Robinson

Press Officer: Ben Robinson(01283 537272)

FOOTBALL MANAGEMENT TEAM

MANAGER **NIGEL CLOUGH**

Date of Appointment: March1999
Date of Birth: 19th March 1966
Place of Birth: Sunderland

PREVIOUS CLUBS
As manager
As asst. manager/coach
As player Heanor Town, Nottm. Forest, Liverpool

HONOURS
As manager: N.P.L. Champions 2001-02
F.A. Trophy Semi-Finalists 01-02

As player England - Full & u21 caps

Assistant Manager: Gary Crosby
Physiotherapist: Matthew Brown
Scout: Steve Booth
Club's Playing Status: Part-time.

Season	League	Div.	Pos.	Home P	Home W	Home D	Home L	Home F	Home A	Away W	Away D	Away L	Away F	Away A	Pts	Manager
02-03	Conference	-	16	42	6	6	9	25	31	7	4	10	25	47	49	Nigel Clough
01-02	N.P.L.	Prem	1	44	17	5	0	59	12	14	6	2	47	18	104	Nigel Clough
00-01	Southern	Prem.	2	42	14	6	1	36	13	11	7	3	40	23	88	Nigel Clough
99-00	Southern	Prem.	2	42	15	3	3	47	15	8	6	7	26	28	78	Nigel Clough
98-99	Southern	Prem.	13	42	7	2	12	29	27	10	5	6	29	25	58	John Barton
97-98	Southern	Prem.	3	42	12	4	5	39	19	9	4	8	25	24	71	John Barton
96-97	Southern	Prem.	6	42	10	7	4	37	32	8	5	8	33	31	66	John Barton

Season	League	Div.	Pos.	P	W	D	L	F	A	Pts	Manager
95-96	Southern	Prem.	16	42	13	12	17	55	56	51	John Barton
94-95	Southern	Prem.	3	42	20	15	7	55	39	75	John Barton
93-94	Southern	Prem.	11	42	15	11	16	57	49	56	Brian Kenning

HONOURS

Southern League
Lg Cup 63-64 96-97, 99-00 (R-up 88-89),
Div 1 (Nth) R-up 71-72 73-74;

Northern Premier Champions 2001-02
Lg Chall Cup 82-83 (R-up 86-87),
Presidents Cup R-up 85-86 (SF 86-87);

FA Trophy R-up 86-87;

Birmingham Snr Cup 53-54 70-71 (R-up 86-87);
GMAC Cup SF 86-87;
Bass Charity Vase 81-82 85-86,
Challenge Cup 84-85;
West Mids Lg R-up 53-54;
Staffs Sen Cup 55-56

PREVIOUS

Leagues: West Midlands 1950-58
Southern 58-79, 80-2001
Northern Premier 79-80, 01-02

Grounds: Wellington Street 50-57

Names: None

Past Players who progressed to the Football League

L Green & T Parry & S Aston (Hartlepool65/66),
G Hunter (Lincoln 65), D Jones (Newport 68),
R Barker & J Bourne & T Bailey (Derby 67/69/70),
M Pollock & S Buckley (Luton 74),
P Ward (Brighton75), Tony Moore (Sheffield Utd 79),
C Swan & G Clayton (Doncaster 80 & 86),
RJobson (Watford 82), P Haycock (Rotherham 86),
A Kamara (Scarborough 87),
P Groves (Leicester City 88),
S Cotterill & J Gayle (Wimbledon 89),
D Carr(Crystal Pal. 89),
D Smith & D Roberts (Wolves 90 & 92)

CLUB RECORDS

Attendance: **5,860**
v Weymouth, Southern Lg Cup Final 2nd leg, 1964
(22,500 v Leicester City, F.A. Cup 3rd Rd 1984
- played at Derby County F.C.)

Goalscorer: Ritchie Barker, 157

Appearances: Phil Annable, 567

Win:

Fee Paid: **£21,000**
to Kidderminster H.for R Jones and J Pearson

Fee Received: **£60,000**
for Darren Carr to Crystal Palace 1989

BEST SEASON

FA Trophy: R-up 86-87 (SF 74-75)

FA Cup: 3rd Rd Prop 55-56, 84-85. 1st Rd 9 times

League: Champions Northern Prem. 01-02

LAST SEASON

F.A. Cup: 1st Round Proper
F.A. Trophy: 1st Round Proper
Conference: 16th
Top Goalscorer: Christian Moore
Players of the Year Christian Moore & Matt Duke
Caotain: Darren Stride

Bold print denotes England semi-professional international.

	Birthplace	D.O.B.	Previous Clubs
GOALKEEPERS			
Matt Duke UP	Derby	16.07.77	Sheffield Utd, Alfreton T, Matlock T
Dan Robinson	Derby	01.09.82	Blackpool, Derby County (Junior)
DEFENDERS			
Steve Chettle	Nottingham	27.09.68	Nottingham Forest,Barnsley ,Walsall (L),Grimsby T.
Lee Colkin	Nuneaton	15.07.74	Hednesford Town, Northampton Tow.
Colin Hoyle DMP, UP	Derby	15.01.72	Boston Utd, King's Lynn, Mansfield, Notts Co., Bradford C, Barnsley, Arsenal
Darren Wassall UP	Edgbaston	27.06.68	Birmingham, Derby Co., Nottingham Forest
Ian Wright	Lichfield	10.03.72	Hereford United, Hull City, Bristol Rovers, Stoke City,
MIDFIELD			
Nigel Clough Eu-21, E 'B', E-Full Int., UP	Sunderland	19.03.66	Manchester C, Liverpool, Nottingham Forest, AC Hunters
Sean Gummer		14.04.81	Belper Town, Mandal F.C.(Norway), Belper T., Derby Co
Jon Howard	Sheffield	7.10.71	Chesterfield, Shefield United.
Andy Sinton ES, E'B', E-Full Int	Newcastle	19.03.66	Wolves, Tottenham Hotspur, Sheffield Wed., QPR, Brentford, Cambridge Utd
Darren Stride ESP, UP	Burton-on-Trent	28.09.75	From Youth team
Aaron Webster ESP, UP	Burton-on-Trent	19.12.80	From Youth team
Barry Williams	Birmingham	19.12.80	Alvechurch,Ely City,Redditch United
ESP,DMP			
FORWARDS			
Dale Anderson ESP UP	Birmingham	10.11.79	Bromsgrove R, Hednesford T, WBA, Nottingham Forest
Andy Ducros	Nuneaton	16.09.77	Nuneaton Boro , Kidderminster H(£100,000),Nuneaton B
Glenn Kirkwood	Chesterfield	03.12.76	Ilkeston T, Doncaster R, Eastwood T
Christian Moore UP	Derby	04.11.72	Ilkeston T (£17,000), Forest Green R, Leicester Utd, Belper, Gresley R, Nuneaton B, Stockport, Leicester C
Ryan Sugden ESP	Bradford	26.12.80	Scarborough, Oldham Athletic
Robbie Talbot	Liverpool	31.10.79	Burscough (£10,000), Marine, Rochdale

CHESTER CITY

Finishing the season with a rock hard defence and some splendid play off performances, Chester City became most people's favourites for promotion this season.

Ace striker Daryl Clare joined when City were enjoying a wonderful start to the campaign but gradually the pressure seemed to affect them and the nerves really set in at home and vital defeats were suffered at The Deva Stadium against clubs far below them in the league.

The lifeline of the play offs was a bonus that kept spirits up as it became clear that a challenge for automatic promotion had died and their defence became stronger as the campaign developed. The Cups brought a victory over Colchester United, but was followed by an exit from the competition at Morecambe and their first F.A.Trophy tie was lost at home to Worksop Town.

The thrilling play off semi-final against Doncaster Rovers held everyone in suspense until the penalty shoot out decided cruelly against Mark Wright's boys.The manager has had stormy managerial experiences since his illustrious playing

career. So, with a chairman who has also hit the headlines for a variety of reasons over the years, Chester City are always liable to find themselves in turmoil, which doesn't help settle the squad down to concentrate on actually winning football matches.

This Conference club will start the season with five international defenders plus Daryl Clare to threaten opposition rearguards,so Chester City will remain a strong favourite for promotion, but have they the stability?

Back row, left to right: Ryan Sugden, Scott Guyett, Wayne Hatswell, Martyn Lancaster, Carl Ruffer, David Cameron,John Worsnop. Phil Bolland, Wayne Brown, Daniel Collins, Mark Beesley, Michael Brown, Kevin McIntyre, James Kelly and Michael Twiss.**Front row:** Chris Blackburn, James Haarhoff, Stuart Whittaker, Steve Brodie, Joe Hinnigan (Physio), Mark Wright (Manager),Steve Bleasdale (Ass.Man), Alan Cottrell (Chief Scout), Shaun Carey, Ben Davies, Lee Woodyatt and Paul Carden,l

CHESTER CITY

Match Facts 2002-03

The number shown directly below the player's name is his squad number.
Where a number is shown instead of an "X' in the columns this represents a substitute appearance and the number indicates the player replaced.

Comp.	Date	Opponents	Venue.	Score	Goalscorers	Att.
						SQUAD NUMBER
Conf 1	Aug-17	Kettering T	H	D 0-0		2367
Conf 2	Aug-19	Telford U	A	W 1-0	Sugden	1409
Conf 3	Aug-24	Barnet	A	W 3-0	Sugden Twiss Beesley	1347
Conf 4	Aug-26	Scarborough	H	D 0-0		2292
Conf 5	Aug-31	Forest Green R	A	W 2-0	Beesley(2,1p)	812
Conf 6	Sep-03	Morecambe	H	W 2-1	Twiss Sugden	2039
Conf 7	Sep-06	Leigh RMI	H	W 2-1	Sugden Beesley	2273
Conf 8	Sep-14	Hereford U	A	D 0-0		2289
Conf 9	Sep-17	Halifax T	A	D 0-0		2178
Conf 10	Sep-21	Dagenham & R	H	W 5-2	Sugden(2) Kelly(p) Bolland Guyett	2231
Conf 11	Sep-24	Burton A	H	W 2-1	Sugden(2)	2440
Conf 12	Sep-28	Doncaster R	A	D 0-0		4867
Conf 13	Oct-05	Margate	A	W 1-0	Cameron	925
Conf 14	Oct-08	Nuneaton B	H	L 1-2	Sugden	2564
Conf 15	Oct-13	Gravesend & N	H	D 1-1	Sugden	2210
Conf 16	Oct-19	Woking	A	L 0-1		2019
LDV 1	Oct-22	Plymouth Argyle	H	L 1-2	Guyett	1126
FAC 4q	Oct-26	Radcliffe Borough	A	W 4-2	Sugden(3) Cameron	1138
Conf 17	Nov-02	Yeovil T	H	D 2-2	Clare(2)	3821
Conf 18	Nov-09	Stevenage B	A	W 1-0	Clare	1716
FAC 1	Nov-16	Colchester United	A	W 1-0	Tate	2901
Conf 19	Nov-23	Margate	H	W 5-0	Clare(3) Sugden Hatswell	1930
Conf 20	Nov-30	Southport	A	W 3-1	Carey Carden Rufer	2447
FAC 2	Dec-07	Morecambe	A	L 2-3	Bolland Clare	4293
Conf 21	Dec-14	Leigh RMI	A	W 4-0	Clare(2) Guyett Sugden	851
Conf 22	Dec-20	Hereford U	H	L 0-1		2507
Conf 23	Dec-26	Northwich V	A	D 1-1	Twiss	2305
Conf 24	Dec-28	Telford U	H	W 4-1	Clare(2,1p) Davies Beesley	2594
Conf 25	Jan-01	Northwich V	H	L 2-3	Clare(2)	3151
Conf 26	Jan-04	Kettering T	A	W 1-0	Clare	1788
FAT 3	Jan-15	Worksop Town	H	L 1-2	Twiss	1393
Conf 27	Jan-18	Barnet	H	D 1-1	Clare	1944
Conf 28	Jan-25	Scarborough	A	W 1-0	Clare	1938
Conf 29	Feb-08	Forest Green R	H	L 0-1		2245
Conf 30	Feb-15	Morecambe	A	D 1-1	Twiss	2012
Conf 31	Feb-22	Dagenham & R	A	L 0-1		1870
Conf 32	Mar-01	Halifax T	H	W 2-0	Clare Quayle	2928
Conf 33	Mar-08	Burton A	A	L 0-2		2183
Conf 34	Mar-17	Doncaster R	H	W 1-0	Twiss	2928
Conf 35	Mar-22	Southport	H	W 2-0	Carden Lane(og)	2292
Conf 36	Mar-29	Farnborough T	A	W 2-1	Davies Cameron(p)	1050
Conf 37	Apr-05	Gravesend & N	A	W 1-0	Beasley	1273
Conf 38	Apr-12	Woking	H	D 2-2	Ruffer Twiss	2165
Conf 39	Apr-15	Farnborough T	H	L 0-2		1869
Conf 40	Apr-19	Nuneaton B	A	L 0-1		1371
Conf 41	Apr-21	Stevenage B	H	W 2-0	Clare(p) Brady	1745
Conf 42	Apr-26	Yeovil T	A	D 1-1	McIntyre	8111
PSF 1	May-01	Doncaster R	A	D 1-1	McIntyre	6857
PSF 2	May-05	Doncaster R	H	D 1-1	Hatswell	5702

Wayne BROWN 1	Steve HARKNESS 2	Mark CLIFFORD 2	Danny BYRNE 2	Kevin McINTYRE 3	Shaun CAREY 4	Phil BOLLAND 5	Wayne HATSWELL 6	Chris BLACKBURN 7	Jimmy KELLY 8	Michael TWISS 9	Mark BEESLEY 10	Steve BRODIE 11	Micky BROWN 12	Ian JOY 13	Paul CARDEN 14	Ryan SUGDEN 15	Martyn LANCASTER 16	Adam GRIFFIN 16	Carl RUFFER 17	John WORSNOP 18	David CAMERON 19	Ben DAVIES 20	Lee WOODYATT 22	Danny COLLINS 24	Scott GUYETT 25	Jon BRADY 26	Daryl CLARE 27	Chris TATE 28	Mark QUAYLE 28	Ian McCALDON 30
x				x			x	x	x	x	x					10			x		22	x	x		x					
x	x			x	x		x	x	x	x			15			x			4		x				x					
x	x			x			x	x	x	x	19					x			15		x		x		x					
x	x			x			x	x	x	x	15		x			x			x				12		x					
x	x			x			x	x	x	x	x	x				9			x			11			x					
x	x			x			x	x	x	x	x		10		x	x			2			15			x					
x				x			x	x	x	x	15		x		x	x			x						x					
x				x			x	x	x	x	x	10	x		x	12			x						x					
x	x			x		x			x	x	15	x	11			x			x				x		x					
x	x			x		x		x	x	x		x	11			x			x						x					
x	x			x		x		x	x	x			7		x	x	25		x		9				x					
x	x			x		x		x	x	x	9		7			x			x				x		x					
	x			x		x		2	x	x			13		x	x	x		x		9					x				x
x				x		x	x	x	x	15			26		x	x			x		x	14				x				
				x	x	x	x		x	12			x			x			x		x					x				x
x				x	x	x	x	x		19	15		x			x	x				x	12				x				
				x		x	x	x		x	x		2		x	10						x	26		x	x				x
x				x		x	x	x					26		x	x			15		28	x			x	x		x		
x						x		x					15		x	x			x			x	x		x	x	x	26		
x				x	x	x	x								x	x			4			x			x	x	x	15		
x				x	x	x	x	27					26		x				28			x			x	x	x	x		
x				x	x	x	x			27	15		26		x	x						x			x	x	x			
x				x	x	x	x						15		x	x			4			x	26		x	x	x			
x				x	x	x	x		4				20		x	x			26			x			x	x	x			
x				x	x	x	x		26	15					x	x						x			x	x	x			
x				x	x	x	x						26		x	x					15	x			x	x	x			
x				x	x	x	x		4	x			26		x				9			x			x	x	x			
x				x	x	x	x			x	x		25		x				4			x			x		x			
x				x		x	x		9	x	x		x		x				x		10	x				12	x			
x						x	x		x	x					x	x			x			x	x				x			
x			15	x	x				x	x			x			x	x		x		12		x		x	22				
x		x		x					x	15			2		x	x		3	x			x		x	x		x			
x				x			x		x				27		x	x			x			x		x	x		x			
x				x	x	x	x		x	8	15		20		x	x			x			x					x			
x				x		x	x		x	15					x	x						x		x	x		x			
x				x		x	x		x	28					x	27						x		x	x	20	x		x	
x				x	x	x	28			x					x						28		x	x	x		x		x	
x				x		x			x	x	22				x	28			x				x	x		9	x		x	
x				x	8				x	22					x				x		28	x	x	x	x		x		x	
x				x	9				x	x	x				x				x			x		x			x		10	
x				x	17	x			x	10	x				x				x			x		x	x				x	
x				x	x	x	4		x	10	x				x				x			x		x					x	
x				x		x	x		x	6	x				x				x			x			x	14	x		10	
x				x	x	x		22		13				x		x						x	x		x	x	x		15	
				x		x		13	x	26				x	x	19				x	x	x			x	x	x			
x				x	x	x	x	20		27					x	x					15	x			x	x	x			
x				9		x	x	x	x	x				x	x	19					x	14	x			x				
x				x		x	x							15	x	x					27	x		x	x	x	x			
x				x		x	x							26	x	x					15	x		x	x	x	x			

CHESTER CITY

GROUND DETAILS

Deva Stadium,Bumpers Lane, Chester CH1 4LT

Tel: 01244 371376 or 371809
Admin. Office Fax: 01244 390265
emails: mike_CCFC@Hotmail.com
Nicki_CCFC@Hotmail,com
Web site: http://www.chesterfc.co.uk

SIMPLE DIRECTIONS:
Follow signs to Chester, into Town Centre, then follow signs to Queensferry (A548) to Sealand Road. Turn into Bumpers Lane, signed ChesterCity F.C.Two miles to Town centre and British Rail,Chester (01244 340170). Car Parking at ground

MATCH TICKETS: Adults £10-£12 concessions £7-£9
Child £5 standing £6 sitting

CAPACITY:	5,814
SEATED:	3,094
COVERED TERRACING:	2,640

Refreshments: Six tea bars
Clubhouse: Open matchdays & for private bookings
Contact: The club office on 01244 371376
Function/Banqueting facilities: Yes
Limited guests on match day at #1,50 each
CLUB SHOP: Yes

MATCHDAY PROGRAMME

Pages: 36 Price: £2.00
Editor: Rob Ashcroft
Email: alyndalerob@yahoo.co.uk
Tel Nos: 01244 602 111 (H) 01244 680801(H)
Club call: 09068 121 633

Local Press: Chester Chronicle, Evening Leader
Local Radio: Radio Merseyside, Marcher Sound

Founded:	1885
Nickname:	The Blues
Club Sponsors:	Pentagon Glass-Tech.
Club colours:	Royal Blue & White Royal Blue Shorts and Socks
Change colours:	All White
Midweek home matchday:	Tuesday
Reserves' League:	Avon Insurance Division One
Clubcall	0906 8121633

CLUB OFFICIALS

President	T.B.A.
Honory Vice Presidents	J Kane, L Lloyd, M Swallow
Chairman	Stephen Vaughan
Vice Chairman	Fred Williams
Directors	D.Liversage, Richard Lynes
Secretary	Michael Beech
Commercial Manager	Jim Jones

FOOTBALL MANAGEMENT TEAM

MANAGER: MARK WRIGHT

Date of Appointment
Date of Birth: 1st August 1963
Place of Birth: Dorchester (Ox.)

PREVIOUS CLUBS
As manager Southport, Oxford Utd.
As player Oxford Utd., Southampton, Derby Co., Liverpool

HONOURS
As manager
As player England: u21: 4; E: 45
FAC '92

* *

Assistant Manager:	Ted McMinn
Physiotherapist:	Joe Hinnigan
Youth development:	Chas Osula
Community Officer	David James
Club's Playing Status:	Full Time

Season

	League	Div.	Pos.	Home P	W	D	L	F	A	Away W	D	L	F	A	Pts	Manager
02-03	Conference	-	4	42	10	6	5	36	21	11	6	4	23	10	75	Mark Wright
01-02	Conference	-	14	42	7	7	7	26	23	8	2	11	28	28	54	G.Hiill, S.Mungall &Mark Wright
00-01	Conference	-	8	42	9	8	4	29	19	7	6	8	20	24	62	Graham Barrow
99-00	Football Lge	3	24	46	5	5	13	20	36	5	4	14	24	43	39	Kevin Ratcliffe/Terry Smith/Ian Atkins
98-99	Football Lge	3	14	46	6	12	5	28	30	7	6	10	29	36	57	Kevin Ratcliffe
97-98	Football Lge	3	14	46	12	7	4	34	15	5	3	15	26	46	61	Kevin Ratcliffe
96-97	Football Lge	3	6	46	11	8	4	30	16	7	8	8	25	27	70	Kevin Ratcliffe
95-96	Football Lge	3	8	46	11	9	3	45	22	7	7	9	27	31	70	Kevin Ratcliffe
94-95	Football Lge	2	23	46	5	6	12	23	42	1	5	17	14	42	29	Mike Pejic/Derek Mann*/Kevin Ratcliffe*
93-94	Football Lge	3	2	42	13	5	3	35	18	8	6	7	34	28	74	Graham Barrow

HONOURS

League Division 3N Cup 35-36 36-37; R-up 45-46
Debenhams Cup 77
Welsh Cup Winners 07-08 32-33 46-47
R-up 08-09 09-10 34-35 35-36
52-53 53-54 54-55 57-58 65-66 69-70
Combination 1908-09 R-up 1903-1908 (5 times)
Cheshire County Lge 21-22 25-26 26-27 R-up 30-31
Cheshire Senior Cup 1894-95 96-97 1903-04
07-08 08-09 30-31 31-32
R-up 1887-88 92-93 93-94 1904-05 10-11 28-29
Lancashire League Runners -Up 2001-02

PREVIOUS

Leagues: The Combination 1890-1899, 1901-1910
Lancashire Combination 1910-1914
Cheshire County League 1919-1931
Football League 1931-2000

Grounds: Faulkner St. 1885-98; Old Showground 1898-99
Whipcord Lane 1901-06; Sealand Road. 1906-1990
Moss Rose, Macclesfield (ground share) 90-92

Names: Chester F.C. until 1983

Past Players who progressed to the Football League

not yet applicable

CLUB RECORDS

Attendance: 5,638
v Preston N.E., Div. 3, 2.4.1994
(Sealand Rd.) 20,500 v Chelsea, FAC 16.1.52

Record win: 12-0
v York City, Div. 3N, 1.2.1936

Record defeat: 2-11
v Oldham Ath. (A), Div. 3N, 19.1.1952

Career goalscorer: Stuart Rimmer 135 (84-88 & 91-98)

Career appearances: Ray Gill 406 League Apps. 51-62

Transfer fee paid: £94,000
for Stuart Rimmer, to Barnsley, Aug. 1991

Transfer fee received: £300,000
for Ian Rush from Liverpool, May 1980

BEST SEASON

FA Trophy: Semi Finalists, 2000-01

FA Cup: 5th Round
1890-91, 1976-77, 79-80

As Conference club: 3rd Rd, 2000-01
League Clubs Defeated Oxford United & Plymouth A
(as non-league club) 0-2001-02
Conference 8th

Nationwide Trophy (Lg Cup) Winners 2000-01

LAST SEASON

F.A. Cup: Second Round
FA Trophy: 3rd Round
Conference: 4th
Top Goalscorer:
Player of the Year:
Captain:

CHESTER CITY PLAYING SQUAD

	Birthplace	D.O.B.	Previous Clubs	Bold print denotes England semi-professional international.
GOALKEEPERS				
Wayne Brown ESP	Southampton	14.01.77	Weston-Super-Mare, Bristol C	
Michael Jago			Liverpool (Trainee)	
DEFENDERS				
Phil Bolland	Liverpool	26.08.76	Oxford Utd (£15,000), Southport, Altrincham, Knowsley U., Trafford, Salford C, Altrincham	
Scott Guyett	Ascot	20.01.76	Oxford Utd, Southport, Gresley R, Brisbane C. (Aust)	
Steve Harkness EY	Carlisle	27.08.71	Sheff.Wed., Blackburn, Benfica (Port), Liverpool, Carlisle	
Andy Harris	Springs	26.02.77	Leyton Orient, Southend United, Liverpool	
Wayne Hatswell	Swindon	08.02.75	Oxford Utd, Forest Green R, Witney T, Cinderford T	
Iain Jenkins	Prescot	24.11.72	Shrewsbury Town, Dundee United, Chester City, Everton	
Ian Joy			U.S.A., Kidderminster Harriers, Montrose, Stirling Albion	
Carl Ruffer ESP	Manchester	-	Runcorn, Woodley Sports	
Mark Williams	Liverpool	10.11.78	Hereford Utd, Rotherham, Rochdale	
MIDFIELD				
Jon Brady	Australia	14.01.75	Woking, Rushden & Diamonds, Hayes, Wycombe W	
			Brentford, Swansea City, Australia	
Paul Carden	Liverpool	29.03.79	Doncaster R, Chester C, Rochdale, Blackpool	
Shaun Carey NC	Kettering	13.05.76	Rushden & Diamonds, Norwich C.	
Ben Davies	Birmingham	27.05.81	Kiderminster H., Walsall	
Jimmy Kelly	Liverpool	14.02.73	Doncaster R, Hednesford T, Wolves, Wrexham	
Kevin McIntyre ESP	Liverpool	23.12.77	Doncaster R, Tranmere R.	
Michael O'Brien	Liverpool	25.09.79	Droylsden.Torquay United, Everton	
Michael Twiss	Salford	26.12.77	Leigh RMI, Port Vale, Sheffield Utd, Manchester Utd	
FORWARDS				
Mark Beesley	Lancaster	10.01.81	Preston	
Steve Brodie	Sunderland	14.01.73	Swansea, Scarborough, Sunderland	
Daryl Clare Eire U21	Jersey	01.08.78	Boston United, Grimsby	
Ian Foster	Liverpool	11.11.76	Kidderminster Harriers, Barrow, Hereford Utd., Liverpool	
Stuart Whittaker	Liverpool	02.01.75	Southport, Macclesfield, Wigan, Bolton, Liverpool	

DAGENHAM & REDBRIDGE

'The Daggers' are one of the most popular senior non-league clubs in the country, probably through their exciting televised F.A.Cup exploits against Football League and Premier League opponents in recent seasons. They also caught the imagination of the neutrals in their unsuccessful season long battle with Boston United when manager Gary Hill kept his cool under severe pressure two years ago.

The East End outfit has steadily strengthened on and off the field thanks to development masterminded by a sensible board with experienced staff. Last season saw the club react badly to the disappointment of just missing promotion and it wasn't until the second half of the campaign that a record eleven consecutive victories took them safely into the play offs.

After a penalty shoot out success against Morecambe, the Daggers came back from 0-2 to force extra time and only then did they succumb to a Doncaster Rovers golden goal. So close, but so far!. Once again everyone at the club showed great sportsmanship and dignity.

If Conference matters were getting a bit heavy, then F.A.Cup games have been a breath of fresh air. For the third season in succession Dagenham & Redbridge featured in the Third Round Proper and Junior MacDugald scored third round goals in all three competitions. Last season of course Hill's boys reached the Fourth Round and lost in injury time at Norwich City. Strangely the F.A.Trophy hasn't brought the same success recently but they are probably due a return to the final very soon.

The club is now working on a full time basis, but the pain of consistent disappointments has probably taken its toll. So another championship challenge may be too much to expect - but a cup run ? That's a different matter altogether.

Back Row (left to right): Tim Cole, Danny Shipp, Mark Bentley, Paul Bruce, Ashley Vickers, Danny Hill
Middle Row: Alan Kimble, Mark Smith, Tarkan Mustafa, James Pullen, Tony Roberts, Leon Braithwaite, Jimmy Jackson, Tom McGowan
Front Row: Alex Meechan, Chris Piper, Lenny Piper, Lee Matthews, Lee Goodwin, Tony Scully, Mark Stein

DAGENHAM & REDBRIDGE

Match Facts 2002-03

The number shown directly below the player's name is his squad number.
Where a number is shown instead of an "X' in the columns this represents a substitute appearance and the number indicates the player replaced.

Comp.	Date	Opponents	Venue.	Score	Goalscorers	Att.
						SQUAD NUMBER
Conf 1	Aug-17	Leigh RMI	H	W 3-1	Stein(2) McGavin	1305
Conf 2	Aug-20	Gravesend & N	A	W 2-1	Stein Shipp	2036
Conf 3	Aug-24	Scarborough	A	W 1-0	Hotte(og)	1192
Conf 4	Aug-26	Telford U	H	D 1-1	Hill	1711
Conf 5	Aug-31	Farnborough T	A	L 0-1		998
Conf 6	Sep-03	Nuneaton B	H	L 1-2	Stein	1549
Conf 7	Sep-07	Doncaster R	A	L 1-5	Shipp	4294
Conf 8	Sep-14	Burton A	H	L 1-2	Stein	1527
Conf 9	Sep-17	Kettering T	H	W 3-1	Terry Stein McDougald(p)	1235
Conf 10	Sep-21	Chester C	A	L 2-5	Terry Bruce	2231
Conf 11	Sep-24	Margate	A	W 1-0	Stein	686
Conf 12	Sep-28	Southport	H	L 0-3		1341
Conf 13	Oct-05	Hereford U	A	L 1-2	West	1761
Conf 14	Oct-08	Woking	H	D 1-1	Janney	1348
Conf 15	Oct-12	Morecambe	H	D 1-1	West	1219
Conf 16	Oct-19	Northwich V	A	W 2-0	McDougald(2,1p)	720
LDV 1	Oct-22	Kidderminster H	H	L 1-3	Janney	742
FAC 4q	Oct-26	Aldershot Town	A	W 4-0	McDougald(p) Hill Bruce Matthews	2549
Conf 17	Nov-02	Forest Green R	H	W 3-1	West Shipp Mayo	1277
Conf 18	Nov-09	Yeovil T	A	D 2-2	McDougald(p) Fletcher	4289
FAC 1	Nov-16	Havant & W	H	W 3-2	Shipp(2) McDougald	1546
Conf 19	Nov-23	Hereford U	H	W 1-0	West	1444
Conf 20	Nov-30	Halifax T	A	D 3-3	McDougald(2) West	1630
FAC 2	Dec-07	Crawley Town	A	W 2-1	McDougald Janney	4516
Conf 21	Dec-14	Doncaster R	H	D 3-3	West(2) McGrath	1739
Conf 22	Dec-21	Burton A	A	D 0-0		1447
Conf 23	Dec-26	Barnet	A	L 1-2	Terry	1727
Conf 24	Dec-28	Gravesend & N	H	W 4-0	West(2) McGrath(p) Stein	1849
FAC 3	Jan-04	Plymouth Argyle	A	D 2-2	Terry McDougald	11885
FAT 3	Jan-11	Marlow	H	W 5-2	Stein(2) Fletcher Cole West	1055
FAC 3r	Jan-14	Plymouth Argyle	H	W 2-0	Shipp McDougald	4530
Conf 25	Jan-18	Scarborough	H	W 1-0	West	1566
FAC 4	Jan-25	Norwich City	A	L 0-1		21164
Conf 26	Jan-28	Barnet	H	W 5-1	Stein(2) McDougald Shipp West	1414
FAT 4	Feb-01	Southport	H	D 0-0		1307
FAT 4r	Feb-04	Southport	A	D 2-2*	Matthews Terry ** Lost 3-4 on pens.*	569
Conf 27	Feb-08	Farnborough T	H	W 1-0	McDougald(p)	1542
Conf 28	Feb-11	Telford U	A	W 2-1	Shipp McDougald	877
Conf 29	Feb-15	Nuneaton B	A	W 3-1	Watts Shipp McDougald	1105
Conf 30	Feb-22	Chester C	H	W 1-0	Watts	1870
Conf 31	Mar-01	Kettering T	A	W 3-1	Stein(3)	1392
Conf 32	Mar-04	Stevenage B	H	W 3-2	Stein(2) McDougald	1905
Conf 33	Mar-08	Margate	H	W 3-0	Hill Janney West	1901
Conf 34	Mar-15	Southport	A	W 3-2	Matthews Hill Mustafa	1002
Conf 35	Mar-22	Halifax T	H	D 0-0		1766
Conf 36	Mar-29	Stevenage B	A	L 0-2		2408
Conf 37	Apr-05	Morecambe	A	L 1-2	Shipp	2069
Conf 38	Apr-07	Leigh RMI	A	W 3-1	West(3)	403
Conf 39	Apr-12	Northwich V	H	W 2-0	Shipp Stein	1494
Conf 40	Apr-19	Woking	A	D 0-0		2159
Conf 41	Apr-21	Yeovil T	H	L 0-4		2588
Conf 42	Apr-26	Forest Green R	A	L 2-5	West Terry	1020
PSF 1	May-01	Morecambe	H	W 2-1	Stein(2,1p)	3447
PSF 2	May-05	Morecambe	A	L 1-2	Terry *Agg: 3-3, won 3-2 after pens.*	5405
PF	May-10	Doncaster R	N	L 2-3	Stein Mustafa *@ Stoke City*	13092

Tony ROBERTS	Tim COLE	Ashley VICKERS	Lee GOODWIN	Mark SMITH	Steve HEFFER	Mark JANNEY	Paul TERRY	Danny SHIPP	Mark STEIN	Paul BRUCE	Steve PERKINS	Junior McDOUGALD	Danny HILL	Steve WEST	Steve McGAVIN	John KEELING	Jamie MURAT	Yohance LEWIS	Lee MATTHEWS	Paul GOTHARD	Danny HAYZELDEN	Gary FLETCHER	Tarkan MUSTAFA	Mark ROONEY	Steve VAUGHAN	Ross JOHNSON	Paul MAYO	Kelechi OPARA	Jason BROOM	Steve POTTS	Geoff PITCHER	Steve WATTS	John McGRATH
1	**2**	**3**	**4**	**5**	**6**	**7**	**8**	**9**	**10**	**11**	**12**	**13**	**14**	**15**	**16**	**16**	**16**	**16**	**17**	**18**	**19**	**19**	**19**	**20**	**21**	**23**	**23**	**23**	**23**	**24**	**25**	**25**	**26**
x		x	x				x	x	x	x	x	14	x	10	x						16					x							
x		x	x		x		x	x	x	x	x	12	10	4	x											x							
x		x			x		x	x	x	x	x	x	12	x	10						11					x							
x		x			x		x	x	x	x	8	x	x	x	9					1						x							
		x			x	11	x	14	x	x	x	x	x	x	12					x						x							
x		x	15		x			x	x		x	16	x	x	x						x			23		x							
x		x	x		x	16	x	x	x		x	19	12	x	x						x												
x		x	x		11	x	x	14	x	x		x	x	7												x				x			
x		x			x	x	x	8	x	x		x	x	17					x		11									x			
x	17	x			x	x	x	8	x	x	6	x		x					x					x									
x		x		24			x	14	x	x	x	x	x	10					x					x						x			
x		x				14	x	11	x	x	x	x	x	12					x					x						x			
x				x		16	x	14	x		x	12	x	x		x			x					x						x			
x				x		x	x	8	x	16	x	14	x	x		x			x											x			
x				x	x	x		x			6	15	x	x					x			x					x			x			
x				x	x		x	x				x		19					x			x		x			x			x			
	x	x		x		x		x			x	x		19			12	2		x		x		x			x						
x				x	x	x	x	x	x	x		x	10	13					x											x			
x		11		x	x	x	x	x		x		x		x					x					6			15			x			
x		19		x	x	x	x	x	11	x		x		13					x			x								x			
x		24		x	x	x	x	x		x	15	x	8	x					x											x			
x		11		x		x	x	x		x		x	x	x					x					14						x			
x		24		x		x	x	x				x	15	x					x					7						x	x		x
x		5		x	x	x	x	x	15			x		x					x											x			x
x		x		26	x	x	x	x				x		x					x			6								x			x
x		x		x			x	x				x							x			x		x						x			x
x	17	x			x	20	x	x				x		19					x			x		x						x			x
x	x	x				x	x	x	19				x	x					x			x		8						14			x
x		x		x	x	x	x	x				x	15	x					x					13									x
	x		x		x	x			x				x	7				26		x		x		x	6					x			x
x		x		x	x	x	x	x				x		x					x					15									x
	24	x			x			x	x			19	x	26					x	x		x		x						x			x
x		x		x	x	x	x	x	15			x		x					x					26									x
x	x	x		x	15		x	x	x			x	8	x					x	1													x
	x			x	x			x	x			x	15	x					x	x				26						x			x
	x			x	x		x	x	x			x	26	10					x	x				x	8								x
x	x	x			x		x	x	x			x	2						x				x	10									x
x		x			x		x	x	x			x	26						x				x	10				25				x	x
x		x			x		x	x	x			x	26	25					x				x	10								x	x
x	19	x			x	13	x	x	x			x		25					x				x									x	x
x		x			x	25	x	x	x			x	26	13					x				x									x	x
x		x		x	x	8	x	x	x			x	3						x				x									10	x
x				x	x	19		x				x	x	25					x				x	13						x		x	x
x	x		14	x	x			x				x	x	x					x				x	26									x
x	x	x	x			19		x	14	26		x	x	x					x				x										x
x	x	x	x			14		x	x			15	x	x					x				x						26				x
x		x	x	x	x	x		x	x			x		13					x				4						x				7
x	x	x	x		7	x	9	x	x					x					x				x						26				x
x	x	x	x		x		6	x	x				9	x					x				x						26				x
			x	x	x		x	10	x				x	x						x			6	x	14				x	x			
	x		x		x		x	x	x				9	x					x	x			x						26	8			x
	x		x	15	x	x	x						x	x						x			7	14					x	x			x
x	x		x			x	x	x	x					x					x				x						26				x
x	x		x	15	7	x	x	x	x					x					x				x						26				x
x	x	26	x	4	8	x	x	x	x					x					x				x										x

DAGENHAM & REDBRIDGE

GROUND DETAILS

Victoria Road, Dagenham,RM10 7XL

Tel: 0208 592 1549 Fax: 0208 593 7227

Clubcall: 09066 555 840

email: info@daggers.co.uk

web site:www.daggers.co.uk

DIRECTIONS: On A112 between A12 & A13. Buses 103 & 174, Dagenham East tube station, turn left and after approximately 500 yards take 5th turning left into Victoria Road.

MATCH TICKETS: Adults £9-£12 concessions £5-£6
No concessions in Carling Stand unless Season Ticket holders
Family(I adult with up to two children) £19 in the family stand

CAPACITY: 6,090
SEATS: 1,028
COVERED: 3,000

CLUBHOUSE: Open 7 days 11am-11pm.
Refreshnments: Hot & cold food available plus three tea bars
Two bars and sponsors bar
Available for Functions: Tony Manhood 0208 592 7194
Shop Contact: SteveThompson 0208 5927194

CLUB SHOP: Open on matchdays
for enquiries on other days contact Steve, above.

MATCHDAY PROGRAMME

Pages: 48 **Price:** £2.00
Editor: Dave Simpson Tel: 07860 119430 (M)

Local Press: Dagenham Post, Ilford Courier,Yellow Advertiser, Walthamstow Guardian, Barking & Dagenham Recorder

Local Radio: BBC Radio Essex, Capital Gold, GLR London Live

Formed: 1992
Nickname: Daggers
Colours: Red shirts, white shorts, red socks
Change strip: Blue & white stripes,black shorts and socks.
Midweek matchday: Tuesday
Reserves Lge: Capital League
Sponsors Main: Compass Plumbing Supplies
Kit: Vandanell
Programme: Recorder Group Newspapers
Match Reports: 0930 555840

CLUB OFFICERS

Chairman: Dave Andrews

Joint Presidents: John & Brian East

Vice Chairman: David Ward

Secretary: Derek Almond,
149 Kings Head Hill, Chingford,
London E4 7JG
Tel: 0181 524 2689

Commercial Manager: Steve Thompson c/o Club

Press Officer: Dave Simpson
Tel: 07860 119430

FOOTBALL MANAGEMENT TEAM

MANAGER: GARRY HILL

Date of appointment: 7th May 1999
Date of Birth: 15th October 1959
Place of Birth: Essex

PREVIOUS CLUBS
As manager: St. Albans, Heybridge Swifts
As player: None
HONOURS
As manager: Conference R-Up 2001-02
Play-Off R-Up 2002-3
Isthmian Prem. League 99-00
As player: N.A.

Asst Manager: Terry Harris

Chief Scout: Mick Loughton

Safety Officer: Phil Milchard

Physio: Richard Harper

Playing Status: Part-t ime

Season	League	Div.	Pos.	P	Home W	Home D	Home L	Home F	Home A	Away W	Away D	Away L	Away F	Away A	Pts	Manager
02-03	Conference	-	5	42	12	5	4	38	23	9	4	8	33	36	72	Garry Hill
01-02	Conference	-	2	42	13	6	2	35	20	11	6	4	35	27	84	Garry Hill
00-01	Conference	-	3	42	13	4	4	39	19	10	4	7	32	35	77	Garry Hill
99-00	Isthmian	Prem.	1	42	20	1	0	58	13	12	4	5	39	22	101	Garry Hill
98-99	Isthmian	Prem.	3	42	10	8	3	40	15	10	5	6	31	29	73	Ted Hardy
97-98	Isthmian	Prem.	4	42	11	6	4	43	25	10	4	7	30	25	73	Ted Hardy
96-97	Isthmian	Prem.	4	42	11	3	7	32	21	7	8	6	25	22	65	Ted Hardy

Season	League	Div.	Pos.	P	W	D	L	F	A	Pts	Manager
95-96	Conference	-	21	42	7	12	23	43	73	33	Graham Carr
94-95	Conference	-	15	42	13	13	16	56	69	52	Dave Cusack
93-94	Conference	-	6	42	15	14	13	62	54	59	John Still

HONOURS

(Ryman) Isthmian League Prem. Div. 99-00

(Ryman) Isthmian one2one Charity Shield 2000-01

F.A. Trophy Runners-up 96-97

Essex Senior 97-98

PREVIOUS

Names:
Ilford FC (1881) & Leytonstone (1886) merged in 1979 to form Leytonstone-Ilford.
They & Walthamstow Avenue (1900) merged in 1988 to form Redbridge Forest
who in turn merged with Dagenham (1949) in 1992 to form Dagenham & Redbridge.

Grounds: None

Leagues: GMV Conference 92-96; Isthmian Lge 96-2000

Past Players who progressed to the Football League

Warren Barton (via Maidstone Utd '89 to Wimbledon '90)
Andy Hessenthaler (Watford '91)
Juan Mequel DeSouza (Birmingham C. '94)
Ian Richardson (Birmingham City '95)

CLUB RECORDS

Attendance: 5,500 v Leyton Orient - FA Cup 1st Rnd - 14.11.92
5,492 v Charlton A - F.A.Cup 3rd Rd Replay- 27.01.01
5,949 v Ipswich Town F.A.Cup 3rd Rd -03-01-02

Career goalscorer (all competitions): Paul Cobb 84 (97-01)
Danny Shipp 98 (95-03)

Career appearances (all competitions): Jason Broom - 338
(Steve Corner - 257. Paul Watts - 174)

Win: 8-1 v Woking (A)
GMV Conference 19/4/94
7-0 v Oxford (H) Isthmian Lge1/11/97

Defeat: 0-5
v Stalybridge Celtic (A) GMV Conference 31/4/94
v Northwich Victoria, GMV Conference 3/9/94
v Hyde Utd (H) FA Trophy 2nd Rd.
v Croydon ,Isthmian Lg.Cup(A) 99/00

Transfer fee paid as Dagenham & Redbridge F.C. £15,000
to Purfleet for Paul Cobb in August 1997

Transfer fee received as Dagenham & Redbridge F.C. £65.00
from Birmingham City for Ian Richardson in May 1995

BEST SEASON

FA Cup: Fourth Round v Norwich City (A) 0-12002-03
League clubs defeated Lincoln City 00-01,Exeter C01-02
Plymouth Argyle 02-03

FA Trophy: Runners-up 96-97

League: Conference Runners-up 01-02

LAST SEASON

F.A. Cup: 4th Round

F.A. Trophy: 4th Round

Conference: 5th & Runners Up in Play Offs

Top Goalscorer: Mark Stein 24

Player of the Year: Tony Roberts

Captain: Lee Matthews

DAGENHAM & REDBRIDGE PLAYING SQUAD

	Birthplace	D.O.B.	Previous Clubs
			Bold print denotes England semi-professional international.
GOALKEEPERS			
Tony Roberts Wales: Full & SP.	Holyhead	04.08.69	QPR, Millwall, St.Albans C
DEFENDERS			
Tim Cole RP	London		Walthamstow Pennant, Leyton Pennant
Lee Goodwin RP	Stepney	05.09.78	West Ham
Lee Matthews RP	Southend		Southend, Purfleet, £3,000 to Dag & Red
Tarkan Mustafa ESP,NC	London	28.08.73	Kingstonian, Kettering Town, Wimbledon, Clapton
Mark Smith ESP, NC	Luton	-	Stevenage B, Hitchin, Woking, Hitchin, Letchworth, Hitchin
Ashley Vickers RP	Sheffield	14.06.72	Sheffield U, Worcester C, Malvern T, 61 Club, Heybridge S
MIDFIELD			
Mark Bentley	London	07.01.78	Gravesend & N, Aldershot T, Enfield, Aveley, Enfield.
Paul Bruce	London	18.02.78	QPR
Danny Hazelden	Essex		Grays Ath., Hornchurch, Aveley, Wimbledon (Junior)
Danny Hill Eu-21	Enfield	01.01.74	Cardiff, Oxford Utd, Tottenham
Jimmy Jackson	Kent		Charlton
Mark Janney RP	Romford	02.12.77	Spurs
Lenny Piper	London	08.08.77	Kingstonian,St.Albans C,Welling U, Gillingham,Wimbledon.
Steve Vaughan			Youth Team
FORWARDS			
Leon Braithwaite DMP	London	17.12.72	Margate, Welling United, St Patricks Athletic, Charlton Athletic, Exeter City, Bishops Stortford
Neale Fenn	Edmonton	18.01.77	Peterborough United, Tottenham Hotspur.
Junior McDougald ESP, RP	Big Spring	12.01.75	Spurs, Brighton, Rotherham, FC Toulon, Camb.C., Millwall, Camb.C., Leyton O
Alex Meechan	Plymouth	29.01.80	Forest Green Rovers, Bristol City, Swindon.
Chris Piper	London	20.10.81	Farnborough Town, St Albans City, Charlton Athletic
RP			
Keith Scott	Westminster	10.06.67	Leigh RMI, Scarborough, Dover Ath., Colchester Utd, Reading, Wycombe W., Watford, Bournemouth, Norwich C, Stoke C., Swindon T, Wycombe W, Lincoln City.
Danny Shipp RP	Romford	25.09.76	West Ham, Coleraine
Mark Stein EY	Cape Town	29.01.66	Luton, Bournemouth, Chelsea, Stoke, Oxford Utd, QPR, Luton

EXETER CITY

Supporters of the Grecians must have felt their club was being taken away from them by outside invaders, as personalities in football, who had questionable football reputations at best, seemed to be bringing their favourites to their knees.

Amidst threats of closure, loss of points and general disarray, the club sunk to the bottom of Division Three and despite a flutter at the end disappeared into the Conference.

But out of darkness...

The atmosphere at the ground and amongst all the real supporters, who have rallied together to pull the club through in its centenary season, is now magnificent. The real people have got their outfit back and true supporters have taken responsibility with the guidance and experience of Ivor Doble. Leading this campaign are Ian Huxham, Terry Pavey and Julian Tagg with Steve Perryman using all his experience to help young manager Eamonn Dolan.

The club admin team led by a very cool and well organised Sally Cooke gives visitors the impression of a happy and relieved outfit, working hard to create a new and positive atmosphere. The supporters have certainly responded with great emotion as they too feel they have their treasured Grecians back on the right tracks.

During all the bad times the club programme always kept its amazing standards under the guidance and editorship of club statistician supreme, Mike Blackstone. Mike has helped us over the years with many publications and his knowledge and love for Exeter City cannot by surpassed.

The players at St James Park are still a little shell shocked by all that has happened in the last eighteen months but they are responding well and must be inspired by their supporters and the club spirit all around them. A substantial sponsor 'Flybe' has been welcomed just at the right time and the whole city now seems to be behind their team.

Survival will not be easy, but Exeter City Football Club is a very emotional and special football centre at present.

TW.

Back Row (L-R): Dixie Dean (Physio), Gareth Sheldon, Alex Stanley, Alex Jeannin, Barry McConnell, Olivier Brassart, Lewis Reed, Leslie Afful, Judith Ansell (Physio). Middle Row: John Wills (Fitness adviser) Reinier Moor, Sean Canham, Steve Flack, James Bittner, Chris Todd, Martin Rice, Santos Gaia, Kwame Ampadu, Martin Thomas, Dick Bedford (Matchday staff). Front Row: Tiv Lowe (Centre of excellence manager), Sean Devine, Julian Tagg (Director), Scott Hiley (player-coach), Eamonn Dolan (manager), Steve Perryman (Director of Football), Glenn Cronin, Ian Huxham (Director), James Coppinger, Mike Redford (Youth Development).

EXETER CITY

GROUND DETAILS

St James' Park, Exeter EX4 6PX

Office Opening Hours:
Mon-Fri: 9.00am-5.00pm.
Sat Matchdays: 9.30am-until end of match

General Enquiries: 01392 411243
Fax: 01392 413959
Commercial Dept: 01392 413954
Centre of Excellence: 01395 233883

Official Web Sites:
www.exetercityfc.co.uk
www.ecfst.org.uk

Independent Web Sites:
www.exeterexiles.co.uk
www.ecfc.co.uk
Gnet@domeus.co.uk
http://thegrecian.homestead.com

SIMPLE DIRECTIONS:

By Road:
Take the M5 exiting at junction 30, follow signs for Exeter City Centre, along Sidmouth Road and onto Heavitree Road, at the roundabout take the 4th exit into Western Way and then the second exit onto Tiverton road, then take the next left into St. James Road. On-street car parking, otherwise city centre car parks and walk to ground.

By Rail:
Nearest station: St James' Park. served by Exmouth branch line trains. Half hourly throughout the day.
Nearest main line stations, Exeter Central or Exeter St Davids.

MATCH TICKETS:
Adults £10 upwards. Concessions available.
Ticket office: Tel: 01392 411243.

CAPACITY: 9,036

Refreshments:
Centre Spot Social Club in adjacent St James' Centre; Corporate Hospitality rooms; Kiosks around the ground.

Club Shop:
At ground in St James' Centre; In city centre at Bedford street, Exeter (manned voluntarily by members of Exeter City Supporters Trust).

Founded: 1904
Nickname: Grecians
Team Sponsors: Flybe
Club Colours: Red & White striped shirts; white shorts
Change Colours: Blue shirts, blue shorts
Midweek Home Matchday: Tuesday
Reserves' League: None - Only friendlies played.

CLUB OFFICIALS

Honorary Life President: Clifford Hill
Honorary President: Ivor Doble
Board of Directors:
Ian Huxham; Terry Pavey; Julian Tagg
Associate Directors:
Dave Bennett, Paul Dobson, Keith Hartshorn, Dave Newbery, Steve Perryman MBE, Malcolm Shelbourne, Norman Warne
Football Administrator: Sally Cooke
Commercial Director: Annie Bassett
Shop Manager: Kelly Ingleson
Club Chaplain: Richard Chewter
Head Groundsman: Martin Vaughan
Groundstaff: Dave Richards
St James' Centre Manager: Sally Anne Fenwick
Ground Safety Officer: Malcolm Thompson

FOOTBALL MANAGEMENT TEAM

Director of Football: Steve Perryman MBE
Date of Appointment: June 2003
Date of Birth: 21st December 1951
Place of Birth: Ealing
Previous Clubs
as manager: Managed Clubs in Japan's J-League; Brentford
as a player: Tottenham Hotspur; Oxford United; Brentford

Team Manager: Eamonn Dolan
Date of Appointment: June 2003
Date of Birth: 20th September 1967
Place of Birth: Dagenham
Previous Clubs
as manager: None
as player: West Ham U.; Bristol C.; Birmingham C.; Exeter City

Player-Assistant Manager: Scott Hiley
Centre of Excellence Manager: Tiv Lowe
Youth Development Officer: Mike Radford
Football in the Community Officer: Jamie Vittles
Club Doctor: Dr. David Kernick
Consultant Orthopaedic Surgeon: Peter Schranz FRCS

Season	League	Div.	Pos.	Home P	W	D	L	F	A	Away W	D	L	F	A	Pts	Manager
02-03	Football Lge	3	23rd	46	7	7	9	24	31	4	8	11	26	33	48	John Cornforth/Neil McNab/Gary
01-02	Peters															
00-01	Football Lge	3	16th	46	7	9	7	25	32	7	4	12	23	41	55	John Cornforth
99-00	Football Lge	3	19th	46	8	9	6	22	20	4	5	14	18	38	50	Noel Blake
98-99	Football Lge	3	21st	46	8	6	8	27	30	3	5	15	19	42	44	Peter Fox
97-98	Football Lge	3	12th	46	13	6	5	32	18	4	7	12	15	32	63	Peter Fox
96-97	Football Lge	3	15th	46	10	8	5	39	25	5	7	11	29	38	60	Peter Fox
95-96	Football Lge	3	22nd	46	6	9	8	25	30	6	3	14	23	43	48	Peter Fox
94-95	Football Lge	3	14th	46	9	9	5	25	22	4	9	10	21	31	57	Peter Fox
93-94	Football Lge	3	22nd	42	5	5	11	25	36	3	6	13	11	34	34	Terry Cooper
	Football Lge	2	22nd	46	8	7	8	38	37	3	5	15	14	46	45	Alan Ball

HONOURS

Fourth Division Champions 1990
Promoted Fourth to Third Division: 1964; 1977
Division Three South Runners-Up 1932-33
Third Division South Cup winners 1934

PREVIOUS

Leagues: East Devon Senior League 1904-05
Plymouth & District League 1905-08
Southern League 1908-20
Football League 1920-2003

Past Players who progressed to the Football League

Not applicable

MATCHDAY PROGRAMME

Pages: 48 Price: £2.00
Editor: Mike Blackstone
email: MJ.blackstone@virgin.net
Printers: Kingfisher Print & Design, Totnes
Tel: 01803 867087

Local Press: Express & Echo; Western Morning News
Local radio: BBC Radio Devon; Gemini Radio

CLUB RECORDS

Attendance: 21,018
v Sunderland, FA Cup quarter-final replay, 1931

Football League victory: 8-1
v Coventry City, Div 3 South 1926
v Aldershot, Div 3 South 1935

Cup victory: 14-0
v Weymouth, FA Cup, 1908

Football League Defeat: 0-9
v Notts County, Div 3 South 1948
v Northampton Town, Div 3 South 1958

Career league goalscorer: Tony Kellow
129, 1976-78, 1980-83, 1985-88.

Career league appearances: Arnold Mitchell
495, 1952-66

Transfer fee paid: £65,000
to Blackpool for Tony Kellow, March 1980

Transfer fee received: £500,000
from Manchester City for Martin Phillips, November 1995

BEST SEASON

Football League:
8th Division Three (now Div 2), 1979-80

FA Cup: Quarter-Final 1931; 1981

Football League Cup: Never beyond 4th round

FA Trophy: n/a

LAST SEASON

FA Cup: 3rd round
Football League Cup: 1st round
Top Goalscorer: Steve Flack 14
Player of year: Kevin Miller
Captain: Chris Curran

EXETER CITY PLAYING SQUAD

	Birthplace	D.O.B.	Previous Clubs	Bold print denotes England semi-professional international.
GOALKEEPERS				
James Bittner		1978	Chippenham Town, Salisbury City, Chippenham Town, Fulham	
DEFENDERS				
Santos Gaia Brazil u18	Brazil	1980	Corinthians of Brazil	
Scott Hiley	Plymouth		Portsmouth, Southampton, Manchester City, Birmingham City (£1090,000), Exeter C	
Alexandre Jeannin	France	30.12.80	Lens, Racing club Paris, Darlington, Troy	
Lewis Reed	Plymouth	15.09.84	Youth Team	
Chris Todd	Swansea	22.08.81	Drogheda United, Swansea City	
MIDFIELD				
Kwame Ampadu Eire u21	Bradford	20.12.70	Leyton O, Swansea C, W. B. A.(£50k), Plymouth Argyle (L), Arsenal	
Glenn Cronin Eire u18	Dublin	14.09.81	Youth Team	
Barry McConnell	Exeter	01.01.77	Weston-super-Mare (L), Youth Team	
Martin Thomas	Lymington	12.09.73	Oxford United,Swansea City, Fulham, Leyton Orient, Southampton	
FORWARDS				
Les Afful	Liverpool	04.02.84	Youth Team	
Scot Canham	Exeter	26.09.84	Youth Team	
James Coppinger E.Youth	Middlesbrough	10.01.81	Hartlepool United (L), Newcastle United, Darlington	
Sean Devine	Lewisham	06.09.72	Wycombe W, Barnet, Millwall (YTS), Bromley, Erith & Belvedere, Fisher Athletic	
Steve Flack	Cambridge	29.05.71	Cardiff City, Cambridge City, Foxton £10,000	
Reinier Moor Eire u20	Holland	12.06.83	Youth Team	
Gareth Sheldon	Birmingham	31.0180	Scunthorpe United	

FARNBOROUGH TOWN

To an outsider it appeared that Farnborough Town had had its heart ripped out in a very strange and selfish act by its previous owner.

But as no one outside the club can really understand the financial workings or contractuial agreements, it would not be fair to comment.

However, after a good cup run which ended in the wonderful luck of landing a tie with Arsenal, it was agreed that the game should be played at Highbury much to most outsiders' disgust. The game itself, although a thrill for the players and club supoporters, really proved to be a football non event.

Manager-owner-chairman Graham Westley saw that his investment in the club, that he had grown to accept could not be developed on or off the field, could be repaid through the cup tie income. He was also aware that the ambitious chairman of Stevenage Borough would welcome him as manager at Broadhall Way, especially with the cream of his Farnborough squad.

So another sad chapter of the topsy turvy Farnborough story was written, and Ian McDonald helped the remains of his squad to reach the quarter finals of the F.A.Trophy while struggling to survive in the Conference for another year.

This was achieved, but a new owner has brought in a new manager and many new players.

Thank you and good bye Mr McDonald and skipper Tony Pennock.

Once again the club is set for another season of rebuilding a new squad capable of consolidating for a few sound and steady years that the poor 'Boro' supporters can quietly appreciate.

Left to Right - Top: Adie Hayes, Paul Harkness, Dean Green, Matt Pattison, Marc Thompson, Carl Hutchings, Jay Lovett
Middle: Dominic Reece, Barrington Belgrave, Tom Neill, Mark Osborn, Will Packham, Nick Burton, Dalvinder Pardesi, Ali Chaaban
Front: John Martin, Ross Weatherstone, Billy Beall, Ken Charlery, Sasha Opinel, Richard Hodgson

FARNBOROUGH TOWN

Match Facts 2002-03

The number shown directly below the player's name is his squad number.
Where a number is shown instead of an "X' in the columns this represents a substitute appearance and the number indicates the player replaced.

Comp.	Date	Opponents	Venue.	Score	Goalscorers	Att.
					SQUAD NUMBER	
Conf 1	Aug-17	Hereford U	A	L 1-2	Lee	1910
Conf 2	Aug-20	Stevenage B	H	L 0-1		799
Conf 3	Aug-24	Halifax T	H	W 3-0	L Piper Green Charlery	626
Conf 4	Aug-26	Doncaster R	A	L 0-1		3436
Conf 5	Aug-31	Dagenham & R	H	W 1-0	Taggart	998
Conf 6	Sep-03	Yeovil T	A	L 0-2	*@Dorchester Town*	2231
Conf 7	Sep-07	Southport	A	D 0-0		1080
Conf 8	Sep-14	Scarborough	H	D 1-1	Rodwell	629
Conf 9	Sep-17	Barnet	A	W 2-1	Green(2)	1069
Conf 10	Sep-21	Leigh RMI	H	W 1-0	Holloway	595
Conf 11	Sep-24	Forest Green R	H	L 0-3		500
Conf 12	Sep-28	Telford U	A	W 2-0	L Piper Charlery	762
Conf 13	Oct-05	Northwich V	A	D 2-2	L Piper Charlery	658
Conf 14	Oct-08	Margate	H	W 4-1	Carroll(2) Charlery L Piper	741
Conf 15	Oct-12	Kettering T	H	L 0-1		794
Conf 16	Oct-19	Morecambe	A	D 1-1	Watson	1024
FAC 4q	Oct-26	Molesey	A	W 6-0	Baptiste(3) Butterworth Holloway C Piper	514
Conf 17	Nov-02	Nuneaton B	H	L 0-2		644
Conf 18	Nov-09	Gravesend & N	A	D 0-0		1070
FAC 1	Nov-16	Harrogate Town	H	W 5-1	Baptiste(2) Taggart Charlery L Piper	1090
Conf 19	Nov-23	Northwich V	H	W 3-2	Baptiste(2) L Piper	641
Conf 20	Nov-30	Burton A	H	W 5-1	Charlery(3) Baptiste L Piper(p)	934
FAC 2	Dec-07	Southport	A	W 3-0	L Piper Carroll Green	2534
Conf 21	Dec-14	Southport	H	W 2-1	Vansittart Baptiste	591
Conf 22	Dec-21	Scarborough	A	L 0-1		1403
Conf 23	Dec-26	Woking	H	W 5-0	Baptiste(2) Charlery(2) Laker	1639
Conf 24	Dec-28	Stevenage B	A	L 0-5		1803
FAC 3	Jan-04	Darlington	A	W 3-2	Carroll(2) Baptiste	4260
FAT 3	Jan-11	Eastbourne Borough	A	W 1-0	Bunce	1576
Conf 25	Jan-18	Halifax T	A	L 0-1		1894
FAC 4	Jan-25	Arsenal	H *	L 1-5	Baptiste *@ Highbury*	35108
FAT 4	Feb-01	Telford U	A	W 3-2	L Piper(2) Baptiste	928
Conf 26	Feb-04	Hereford U	H	D 2-2	Baptiste Patterson	1030
Conf 27	Feb-08	Dagenham & R	A	L 0-1		1542
Conf 28	Feb-15	Yeovil T	H	L 2-4	Butterworth Vansittart	2114
FAT 5	Feb-22	Halifax T	H	W 2-0	Baptiste Vansittart	863
Conf 29	Feb-25	Doncaster R	H	D 0-0		947
Conf 30	Mar-01	Barnet	H	D 2-2	Pitcher Baptiste	886
Conf 31	Mar-04	Leigh RMI	A	L 2-3	Pitcher C Piper	305
Conf 32	Mar-08	Forest Green R	A	L 1-3	Harkness	825
Conf 33	Mar-11	Woking	A	D 1-1	Pitcher	1889
FAT 6	Mar-15	Tamworth	H	L 1-2	L Piper	1312
Conf 34	Mar-22	Burton A	A	L 0-2		1548
Conf 35	Mar-25	Telford U	H	D 2-2	L Piper Vansittart	529
Conf 36	Mar-29	Chester C	H	L 1-2	Vansittart	1050
Conf 37	Apr-05	Kettering T	A	W 4-1	L Piper(2) Baptiste Charlery	877
Conf 38	Apr-12	Morecambe	H	L 2-3	Vansittart Charlery	803
Conf 39	Apr-15	Chester C	A	W 2-0	Baptiste(2)	1869
Conf 40	Apr-19	Margate	A	D 0-0		635
Conf 41	Apr-21	Gravesend & N	H	D 1-1	Charlery	1015
Conf 42	Apr-26	Nuneaton B	A	W 2-0	L Piper Pitcher	1710

Tony PENNOCK 1	Michael WARNER 2	Justin GREGORY 3	Tim O'SHEA 4	Nathan BUNCE 5	Barry LAKER 6	Steve WATSON 7	Lenny PIPER 8	Joff VANSITTART 9	Christian LEE 10	Tony TAGGART 11	Danny POTTER 12	Mark OSBORN 13	Chris PIPER 14	Dean GREEN 15	Danny CARROLL 16	Gary PATTERSON 17	Ken CHARLERY 18	Gary BUTTERWORTH 19	Gary HOLLOWAY 20	Gareth GWILLEM 21	Rocky BAPTISTE 22	Darren ANNON 24	Leroy GRIFFITHS 25	Geoff PITCHER 26	Stuart REEKS 27	Paul HARKNESS 29	Mark AYRES 31	Jim RODWELL 33
x	x	x	x		x		x	19	18	x				x			x	x	x		11							
x	x	x			x		x	11	x	x			x	x			10		x									x
x	x	x			x		x	8	x	x			x	x			14	11	x									x
x	x	x	6		x		x	x	x	9			x	x			10		x									x
x	x	x	x				x			x			x		20		x	x	x			3	8					x
x	x		x			4	x			x			x		19		x	x	x			x	8					x
x	x					x			x	19			x		14		x	x	x		25	x	x					x
x	x					x	15		x	19			22	x			x	x	x		x	x						x
x	x	x				x	18			x			11	x	20		x	x	x			x						x
x	x	x			3	x				x				x	11		x	x	x			x	10					x
x		x			x	x	20			x			15	x			x	x	x			x	24					x
x				x	x	x	x			x			x	33	x		x		x	8		14						x
x	x	x		x	x		x	19	18					24	x		x	x	x			x						
x	x	x		x	x	x	x		18					24	x		x		x			x						
x	x	x		x	x	x	x		20	18			7	x	x		x		x									
x	x	x		x	x	x	x						19	22	x			x	16		x							x
x		x		x	x	x	7		x				x		x			x	16		x	5						x
x		x		x			19		x				x	33	x	16		x	x		x	x						x
x	x	x		x	x		x			x			x		x		x		x		16	11						
x	x	x		x	x		x			x			x	18	x		x	8			x	11						
x	x			x	x	x	x			14			x	16	x		x		7		x	x						
x	x	x		x	x	x	x					1	x	8	x		x		16		x							
x	x	x		x	x	x	x						x	22	x		x		8		x							
x	x	x			x		x	18	20	14			x		x		x		x		x	x						
x	x	x		x	x	x	x		20	14			x				x		x		x							
x	x	x		x	x	x	x	18					x		x		x		8		x	3						
x		x		x	x	x	x	14		18			x		x		x		24		x	x						
x	x	x		x	x	x		18							x		x	x	x		x	19						
x	x			x	x		22	x	9	x			x		x			x	x		x							
x	x	x		x	x	x		18		5				19	x		x	x	x		x							
x	x	x		x		x	16		x				20		x		x	18	x		x	x						
x							x	16	x	x	22		x	x	x	15	x	x			x	x						
x							x	x	x	x	9		x			x	x	x			x	x						
x							x	18		x			x			x	x	x			x	x		x	x			
x							x	15		x	22			x		x	x	x			x	x		x	x	8		
x							x	x	x	x			x	19		x	x	x			x	x						
x							x		x	x			x			x	x	x			x	x		x				
x							x	x	x	x			10			x	9	x			x	x		x	x			
x							x			x	8		x	x		x		x			x	x		x	x	19		
x							x		17	x			x	x		x		x			x			x	x	x		
x							x		x	x	10		x	x				x			x	x		x		x		
x							x	15		x	26		x	x			x	x			x	x		x				x
x							x	18		x	15		x	x			x	x			x	x				x	33	x
x							x	x		x			x	17		x	x	x			x	x						x
x							x	x	x	x			x	17		x	22	x			x	x						x
x							x	x	x	x			x			26	22	x			x	x		x		11		x
x							x	x	x	x			x	26		19	9	x			x	x		x				x
x							x	x	x	x	15		x	x		x	x				x					x		
x							x	x	x	x			x	x		x	x				x	x						
x							x		x	x	29	1	x	x		x	x				x	x				x		15
							x	x		x	x	x	x			x	x	8				x		x		x		

FARNBOROUGH TOWN

GROUND DETAILS

Cherrywood Road,
Farnborough, Hampshire GU14 8UD

Telephone:	01252 541469
Fax:	01252 372640

Directions: From M3 exit 4, take A325 towards Farnborough, right into Prospect Ave. (club signposted), 2nd right into Cherrywood Rd, ground on right.
20-30 min walk from Farnborough Main, Farnborough North , Frimley BR stations and town centre.
Whippet mini-bus 19 No 12 Bus passes ground.
Parking: 200 spaces at club at £1.00 plus local streets
Match Tickets: Adults £9-10 concessions £6-7

Capacity:	4,163
Seated:	627
Covered Terracing:	1,350

Clubhouse:	OpenThur/Fri/Sat/Sun. Bar
Refreshments:	Two tea bars

Club Shop:
Boro' Leisurewear shop - all types of club leisurewear and matchballs (contact Gaye Hoyle 01252 691129)
Supporters Club shop:
Old programmes, scarves, badges etc (contact Paul Doe).

MATCHDAY PROGRAMME

Pages: 32 Price: £2
Editor: Michael O'Connor
Clubcall: 09068 440 088
Local Press: Farnborough News
Local Radio: BBC Southern Counties
County Sound

Founded:	1967
Nickname:	The "Boro" or "Town"
Club Sponsor:	T.B.A.
Club Colours:	Red & white shirts,
Change colours:	Yellow & Blue
Midweek matchday:	Tuesday
Reserves' League:	Capital League
Club Website:	www.ftfc.co.uk

CLUB OFFICIALS

President:	**Charles Mortimer**
Chairman:	Vic Searle
Non Executive Directors:	**T.B.A/**
Football Secretary:	**Vince Williams** Tel: 01252 541469
Commercial Consultant:	**David Hughes** Tel No: 01252 541469
Press Officer:	**Claire Percy**

Tel No: 01252 370990

FOOTBALL MANAGEMENT TEAM

MANAGER:	**Tommy Taylor**
Date of Appointment:	29.04.03
Date of Birth:	26.09.51
Place of Birth:	Hornchurch

PREVIOUS CLUBS

As manager	Cambridge U, Leyton O, Darlington
As player	Leyton O, West Ham United

HONOURS

As manager	Play Offs twive with LeytonO
As player	FA.Cup &Cup Winners Cup Final with W.H.U.

* * *

Asst. Manager/Coach:	Ian McDonald
Reserve Team Manager:	Tony Milstead
Physio:	Dave Spratt
Club Playing Status:	Part Time

Season	League	Div.	Pos.		Home					Away						Manager
				P	W	D	L	F	A	W	D	L	F	A	Pts	
02-03	Conference	-	13	42	8	6	7	37	29	5	6	10	20	27	51	Graham Westley/ Tommy Taylor
01-02	Conference	-	7	42	11	3	7	38	23	7	4	10	28	31	61	Graham Westley / Ian McDonald
00-01	Isthmian	P	1	42	14	5	2	43	13	17	1	3	43	14	99	Graham Westley
99-00	Isthmian	P	12	42	8	5	8	25	19	6	6	9	27	36	53	Graham Westley
98-99	Conference	-	22	42	6	5	10	29	48	1	6	14	12	41	32	Alan Taylor
97-98	Conference	-	18	42	10	3	8	37	27	2	5	14	19	43	44	Alan Taylor
96-97	Conference	-	7	42	9	6	6	35	29	7	7	7	23	24	61	Alan Taylor
95-96	Conference	-	10	42	8	6	7	29	23	7	8	6	34	35	59	Alan Taylor
94-95	Conference	-	14	42	8	5	8	23	31	7	5	9	22	33	55	Alan Taylor
93-94	Southern	P	1	42	15	4	2	43	18	10	3	8	31	26	82	Alan Taylor

HONOURS

Southern League — Prem. Div. 90-91 93-94,

Isthmian League — Prem. Div. 00-01, R-up 88-89, Div 1 84-85, Div 2 78-79, Lge Cup 99-00,

Athenian Lg — Div 2 78-79,

Spartan Lge — 72-73 73-74 74-75 (Lg Cup 74-75),

London Spartan Lge — 75-76 (Lg Cup 75-76),

Hants Senior Cup — 74-75 81-82 83-84 85-86 90-91 (R-up 93-94)

PREVIOUS

Leagues: Surrey Senior 68-72; Spartan 72-76; Athenian 76-77; Isthmian 77-89 99-01; Alliance Premier (Conference) 89-90 91-93 94-99; Southern 90-91 93-94.

Grounds: Queens Road, Farnborough (1969-1976)

Past Players who progressed to the Football League

Dennis Bailey (Crystal Palace),
Paul Mortimer (Charlton Athletic),
Tommy Jones (Aberdeen),
Allan Cockram (Brentford),
Paul Holsgrove (Millwall),
Maik Taylor (Barnet),
Martin Rowlands (Brentford)

CLUB RECORDS

Attendance: 3,581
v Brentford 22/11/95 (FA Cup)

Win: 11-0
v Chertsey Town (H), Spartan League 72-73

Defeat: 2-10
v Worplesdon (H), Surrey Senior Lge Div. 1 68-69

Career Goalscorer: Simon Read 209, 1986-1994

Career Appearances: Brian Broome 529, 1980-1994

Season Goalscorer: Simon Read 53, 1988-89

Transfer Fee Paid: Undisclosed

Transfer Fee Received: £50,000
from Dover Athletic for David Leworthy, August1993

BEST SEASON

FA Cup: 4th Rd Proper 2002-2003
1-5 v Arsenal(H) but played at Highbury

League club defeated: Torquay Utd 91-92
Darlington 2002-03

FA Trophy: Quarter Final 92-93,02-03

FA Vase: Semi-Final 75-76 76-77

League: 5th Conference 91-92

LAST SEASON

F.A. Cup: 4th Round
F.A. Trophy: 6th Round
League: 13th Conference
Top Goalscorer: Rocky Baptiste
Player of the Year: Tony Pennock
Captain: Steve Watson/Tony Pennock

FARNBOROUGH TOWN PLAYING SQUAD

	Birthplace	D.O.B.	Previous Clubs

Bold print denotes England semi-professional international.

GOALKEEPERS

Name	Birthplace	D.O.B.	Previous Clubs
Mark Osborne	Bletchley	19.06.81	Wycombe Wanderers
Will Packham	Brighton	13.01.81	Brighton & Hove Albion

DEFENDERS

Name	Birthplace	D.O.B.	Previous Clubs
Nick Burton RP	Norfolk	02.10.75	Gravesend & Northfleet, Hampton & Richmond B., Aldershot T., Yeovil T., Torquay U., Portsmouth
Jay Lovett	Plymouth	22.01.78	Brentford (£75k), Hereford Utd (L), Gravesend & N'fleet (L), Crawley Town, Saltdean United, Plymouth Argyle
Tom Neill			Chesham United, Watford
Sasha Opinel			Casteinau-le-Cres,France
Marc Thompson			Harrogate Town, York City
Ross Weatherstone	Reading	16.05.81	Boston United,Oxford United

MIDFIELD

Name	Birthplace	D.O.B.	Previous Clubs
Matthew Beall	Enfield	04.12.77	Dover A (L),.Leyton Orient, Cambridge United
Dean Green	London	-	Hampton & Richmond, Leyton Pennant, Dulwich Hamlet, Crawley T, Dulwich Hamlet, Waltham Abbey, Fulham
Adie Hayes	Norwich	22.05.78	Cambridge City, Kings Lynn, Boston Utd, Diss Town, Kettering T., Cambridge U.
Richard Hodgson			Darlington
Carl Hutchings			Leyton Orient, Southend Utd., Exeter C (L), Brentford (L), Bristol City, Brentford
Matt Pattison			Camberley Town.
Dominic Reece			Halesowen T., Woking, Sutton Coldfield T., Atherstone Utd , Redditch Utd, Hednesford T., Aston Villa (App).

FORWARDS

Name	Birthplace	D.O.B.	Previous Clubs
Barrington Belgrave	Bedford	16,09,80	Southend Utd, Yeovil Town, Plymouth Argyle, Norwich C.
Ali Chaaban			Leratherhead, Dorking
Ken Charlery ESP, NC	Stepney	28.11.64	Dag & Red, Boston Utd, Barnet, Stockport, Peterborough Utd, Birmingham C, Peterborough U, Watford, Peterborough U, Maidstone U, Fisher Ath., Basildon Utd, Beckton Utd
Leroy Griffiths	Surrey		Q.P.R., Hampton & Richmond Bor., Corinthian-Casuals, Banstead Athletic, Sutton United
Paul Harkness			Walton & Hersham, Leatherhead, Basingstoke Town, Camberley T. North Shore Utd. (N.Z.), Walton & Hersham, Camberley, Brighton (Juniors).
Dalvinder Pardesi			Bournemouth, Southampton

FOREST GREEN ROVERS

After a poor start and a consequent change of manager, the experienced Colin Addison took over from Nigel Spink and
the batle was on. Results didn't immediately improve and a replay defeat was suffered in the F.A.Cup at Exeter City while gradual team strengthening and morale boosting was underway.
The Addison touch became apparent in the new year, when a sudden burst of goals against Leigh RMI proved it could be done and belief seeped into the squad with extra confidence being enjoyed by the powerful young striker Kayode Odejayi and his old partners Alex Meecham and Neil Grayson. Rovers only just lost to Yeovil Town away and this turned out to be the only defeat between the beginning of December and the end of March. During this time a position away from the troubled areas was achieved and the club must have felt very strange indeed.
The play off places were settled well before the end of the season, but at times Rovers were heading the group below the top five and the old joke about altitude nose bleeds seemed to be popular around the Cotswold villages. This was a tremendous managerial achievement of a real professional and Colin Addison also had eyes on the club's favourite competition - the F.A.Trophy. Conference teams were falling like flies and a quarter final draw with Havant & Waterlooville was surely within the side's capabilities. Football has a way of bringing you down to earth, however, and instead of the Trophy being relief from Conference survival battles, it was just another game for a successful side, who possibly eased off a bit after taking the lead and then couldn't get their rhythm back. So the season ended quietly, but they did achieve their best ever Conference position of ninth.
Sadly the loss of Meecham and Odejayi has left mature top scorer Grayson (a splendid 20 goals at the age of 38) needing extra help. Manager Addison may have to rebuild and it could take time, but he's done it before and who would bet against another difficult to beat Forest Green Rovers squad developing this season?

Back Row: Scott Rogers, Adie Adams, Steve Jones, Steve Perrin, Chris Giannangelo, Gary Owers, Steve Jenkins, James Pike (No longer at club)
Middle Row: Steve Lock (Physio) Tim Harris (Coach) Danny Allen, Rob Cook (Emigrated to Australia) Martin Foster, John Cant, Neil Grayson, Kevin Langan, Luke Jones, Paddy Mullen (Coach) Dave Tyrrell (Kit Manager)
Front Row: Matthew Russell, Steve Cowe, Jon Richardson, Paul Birch (Coach - now with Birmingham City), Colin Addision (Manager), Gareth Stoker, Denny Ingram, Alex Sykes.

FOREST GREEN ROVERS

Match Facts 2002-03

The number shown directly below the player's name is his squad number.
Where a number is shown instead of an "X' in the columns this represents a substitute appearance and the number indicates the player replaced.

Comp.	Date	Opponents	Venue.	Score	Goalscorers	Att.
						SQUAD NUMBER
Lg 1	Aug-17	Woking	A	L 0-1		1717
Lg 2	Aug-20	Hereford U	H	L 1-3	Grayson	1514
Lg 3	Aug-24	Southport	H	L 0-2		602
Lg 4	Aug-26	Margate	A	L 0-3		410
Lg 5	Aug-31	Chester C	H	L 0-2		812
Lg 6	Sep-03	Burton A	A	W 3-2	Heggs Odejayi Meechan	1598
Lg 7	Sep-07	Morecambe	A	L 0-4		1041
Lg 8	Sep-14	Gravesend & N	H	W 2-1	Odejayi Grayson(p)	711
Lg 9	Sep-17	Stevenage B	H	L 0-3		645
Lg 10	Sep-21	Nuneaton B	A	L 2-3	Grayson(p) Cooper(og)	1136
Lg 11	Sep-24	Farnborough T	A	W 3-0	Grayson(p) Sykes Odejayi	500
Lg 12	Sep-28	Kettering T	H	W 1-0	Odejayi	685
Lg 13	Oct-05	Barnet	H	D 4-4	Meechan(2) Richardson Odejayi	871
Lg 14	Oct-07	Telford U	A	W 1-0	Odejayi	720
Lg 15	Oct-11	Doncaster R	A	L 0-1		3508
Lg 16	Oct-19	Scarborough	H	D 0-0		751
FAC 4q	Oct-26	Ford United	H	W 2-1	Richardson Odejayi	601
Lg 17	Nov-02	Dagenham & R	A	L 1-3	Meechan	1277
Lg 18	Nov-09	Halifax T	H	L 0-2		753
FAC 1	Nov-17	Exeter City	H	D 0-0		2147
Lg 19	Nov-23	Barnet	A	L 0-2		1144
FAC 1r	Nov-26	Exeter City	A	L 1-2	Richardson	2951
Lg 20	Nov-30	Northwich V	A	L 1-2	Grayson	460
Lg 21	Dec-07	Leigh RMI	H	W 4-1	Odejayi(2) Sykes Meechan	576
Lg 22	Dec-14	Morecambe	H	W 1-0	Sykes	623
Lg 23	Dec-21	Gravesend & N	A	D 1-1	Grayson	876
Lg 24	Dec-26	Yeovil T	H	W 2-1	Odejayi Skiverton(og)	1836
Lg 25	Dec-28	Hereford U	A	D 1-1	Grayson	3271
Lg 26	Jan-01	Yeovil T	A	L 0-1		4692
Lg 27	Jan-04	Woking	H	W 3-2	Richardson Grayson Sykes	901
FAT 3	Jan-14	Barnet	H	W 4-2	Grayson(2,1p) Owers Odejayi	552
Lg 28	Jan-18	Southport	A	D 2-2	D Jones(2)	880
Lg 29	Jan-25	Margate	H	W 4-1	Grayson Odejayi Foster Edwards(og)	763
FAT 4	Feb-01	Gainsborough Tr	A	W 2-0	Owers Grayson	710
Lg 30	Feb-08	Chester C	A	W 1-0	Meechan	2245
Lg 31	Feb-15	Burton A	H	W 2-0	Cook Tweddle	986
FAT 5	Feb-22	Dover Athletic	A	W 3-0	Foster Odejayi Grayson(p)	963
Lg 32	Mar-01	Stevenage B	A	D 0-0		1834
Lg 33	Mar-08	Farnborough T	H	W 3-1	Odejayi(2) Richardson	825
FAT 6	Mar-15	Havant & W	H	L 1-2	Grayson	1016
Lg 34	Mar-22	Northwich V	H	W 1-0	Meechan	676
Lg 35	Mar-25	Nuneaton B	H	W 6-1	Meechan(3) Grayson(2,1p) Sykes	679
Lg 36	Mar-29	Leigh RMI	A	L 0-1		445
Lg 37	Apr-05	Doncaster R	H	L 1-2	Grayson	986
Lg 38	Apr-08	Kettering T	A	W 3-2	Cowe(2) Meechan(p)	422
Lg 39	Apr-12	Scarborough	A	L 0-3		1146
Lg 40	Apr-19	Telford U	H	D 1-1	Grayson	801
Lg 41	Apr-21	Halifax T	A	D 1-1	Meechan	1366
Lg 42	Apr-26	Dagenham & R	H	W 5-2	Grayson(2) Richardson Odejayi Cowe	1020

Steve PERRIN 1	Matthew COUPE 2	Steve JENKINS 3	Alan McLOUGHLIN 4	Jamie IMPEY 5	Lee RUSSELL 6	Kevin LANGAN 7	Martyn FOSTER 8	Neil GRAYSON 9	Alex MEECHAN 10	Carl HEGGS 11	Alex SYKES 12	Ellis GLASSUP 13	Simon FUTCHER 14	Trevor TEARNEY 16	Danny ALLEN 17	Adrian ADAMS 18	Luke JONES 19	Gary OWERS 20	Rob COOK 21	Steve COWE 24	Jon RICHARDSON 25	Matthew RUSSELL 27	Darren JONES 28	Kayode ODEJAYI 29	Lee PRITCHARD 30	Justin SHUTTLEWOOD 33	Ben CLEVERLEY 34	Steve TWEDDLE 39
x	x	x	x	x		x	x	x	x	14			x					x										
x	x	x	x	x		x	x	x	x		x			2				x										
x	x	x	x		x	x	x	x	x	4	x			2				x	7									
x	x	x	x	x	x		x	x	x	5	x		10	9				x										
x	x	x	x		x		x	x	x	9	x			x	4						x			16				
x	x		x		x		x	29	x	x	x		17		x						x			x				
x	x	x	x		x		x	11	x	x	x		12						2		x			x				
x	x	x	x		x	x	x	11		x	x				12				4		x			x				
x	x	x	x		x	x	x	11	2	x	x								4		x			x				
x	x	x	x		x	x	x	x	2		x				x			4	17					x				
x	x	x			x	x	x	x	9		x							x					x	x				
x		x			x	x	x	x			x							x			9	x	x	x				
x		x			x	x		x	7		x							x	6		x	x	x	x				
x		x					x	10	x		x				x			x			x	x	x	x				
x	x	x				17	x	x			x				x			x			x		x	x				
x	x	x				x		x		9	x				x		7	x			x		x	x				
x	x	x				x	x	x		9	x				x			x	17		x			x				
x	x	x				x	x	7	x		x		12						x		x	x		x				
x	x	x					x	2	x		x	1			20			x			x	x	x	x				
x	x				x		x	27	x		x				20			x			x	x	x	x				
	x		20		x		x	2	x		x				12			x			x	x	x	x		x		
x		x			x		x	12	x		x							x			x	x	x	x				
		x			x	6	x	x	x		29							x	10		x	x	x	x		x		
x		x				25	x	x	24		x							x	9	x	x	x	x	x				
x	9	x				x	x	x			x							x		x	x		x	x				
x		x				x	x	x	8									x	24	x	x	x	x	x				
x		x				x	x	x			x							x			x	x	x	x			12	
x	x	x				x	x	x										x	29	27	x	x	x	x				
x	x	x				x	x	x	9		x							x	7	12	x		x	x				
x		x				x	x	x	9		x							x	20	x	x	x		x				
x		x				x	x	x	x									x			x	x	x	x			6	
x		x			x	x	x		x									x		27		x	x	x			x	
x		x				x	x	x	x		29							x		7	x	x	x	x			9	
x		x			28	x	x	x	x									x			x	x	x	x				9
x		x				x	x	x	x									x			x	x		x			x	9
x		x				x	x		x									x	20		x	x	x	x			x	34
x						x	x	x	x				27					x		7	x	x	x	x			x	
x						x		x	x				x			14		x	x		x		x	x			x	
x		x				x		x	x									x	20		x	x	x	x			x	29
x		x				x	x	x	x				20					x			x	x	x	x			7	
x						x	x	x	x									x		29	x	x	x	x			x	
x		7				x	x	x	x		x		12					x		10	x	x	x	x				
x						x	x	x	x		x							x		27	x	x	x	x				
x		x				x	x	x	x		x							x		9	x		x	x				
x		x				x	x		x		x		7			24		x		x	x		x	x				
x		x					x		x		x				x	x		x		x	x			x	12			
x		x					x	x	x		x				12	29		x	x	x	x			x				
x		x					x	x	x		x				20	12		x	10	x	x		x	x				
x		x					x	x	x		x					10		x	20	x	x		x	x				

FOREST GREEN ROVERS

GROUND DETAILS

'The Lawn',
Nympsfield Road,
Forest Green,
Nailsworth,
Glos. GL6 0ET

TELEPHONE NUMBERS:

01453 834860
(Matchday & Club AdministrationCentre)
Fax: 01453 835291
Lawnside Fitness Suite: 01453 832268
Social Club: 01453 833295

SIMPLE DIRECTIONS:
About 4 miles south of Stroud on the A46 towards Bath. InNailsworth turn into Spring Hill from the mini roundabout and the ground is approx. half a mile up the hill on the left. The nearest BR station is Stroud

CAPACITY:	5,141
COVERED TERRACING:	2500
SEATED:	526

SOCIAL FACILITIES: Clubhouse open every evening. Bar and lounge. Open before and after Saturday matches.

CLUB SHOP: Open only on matchdays selling souvenirs and programmes. Contact Andy Whiting.

MATCHDAY PROGRAMME

Pages: 52 Price: £2.00
Editor: Clive White clivewhite@aol.com

Local Press: Stroud News & Journal
Gloucester Citizen

Local Radio: Star FM
BBC Radio Gloucestershire

Founded:	1890
Nickname:	Rovers
Sponsors:	Sheffield Insulations & Smiths (Gloucester) Ltd
Club Colours:	Black & white striped shirts, black shorts, red socks.
Change Colours:	Green & White
Midweek matchday:	Tuesday
Reserves' League:	College Academy
Youth League:	Glos. CountyYouth Lge
Club's Playing Status:	Part Time

CLUB OFFICIALS

President	Peter Vick
Vice President	John Duff
Chairman	Ken Boulton (acting)
Secretary	Colin Peake (acting)

c/o The Lawn, Nympsfield Road,
Forest Green, Nailsworth, Glos. GL6 0ET
Tel: 01453 834860 Fax: 01453 835291

Press Off. Heather Cook(daytime in club office)
Tel: 01453 823281 Mobile 07775 603287

Marketing & Operations Colin Peake

FOOTBALL MANAGEMENT TEAM

MANAGER:	**COLIN ADDISON**
Date of appointment	4th September.2002
Date of Birth:	18th May 1940
Place of Birth:	Taunton

PREVIOUS CLUBS

As manager	**Swansea City, Yeovil Town, Scarborough**
As Asst. Man/Coach	
As player	**York City, Nottm. Forest,**
Arsenal,	
	Sheff. Utd., Hereford Utd.

HONOURS

As manager	**Conference R-up 00-01**
As player	

Coach:	Paul Birch
Physio:	Steve Lock
Youth Academy:	Darren Perrin

TO BE CHECKED

Season	League	Div.	Pos.	Home P	W	D	L	F	A	Away W	D	L	F	A	Pts	Manager
02-03	Conference	-	9	42	12	3	6	41	28	5	5	11	20	33	59	N Spink/ Colin Addison
01-02	Conference	-	18	42	7	7	7	28	32	5	8	8	26	44	51	Nigel Spink
00-01	Conference	-	16	42	6	9	6	28	28	5	6	10	15	26	48	F Gregan/ N. Spink & D. Norton
99-00	Conference	-	19	42	11	2	8	35	23	2	6	13	19	40	47	Frank Gregan
98-99	Conference	-	12	42	9	5	7	28	22	6	8	7	27	28	58	Frank Gregan
97-98	Southern	Prem	1	42	16	3	2	51	20	11	5	5	42	35	89	Frank Gregan

Season	League	Div.	Pos.	P	W	D	L	F	A	Pts	Manager
96-97	Southern	Southern	1	42	27	10	5	87	40	91	Frank Gregan
95-96	Southern	Southern	8	42	22	8	12	85	55	74	Frank Gregan
94-95	Southern	Midland	18	42	11	13	18	56	76	46	Frank Gregan
93-94	Southern	Midland	15	42	12	12	18	61	84	48	Pat Casey

HONOURS

FA Trophy R-up 98-99,00-01
FA Vase 81-82,
Southern League - Premier Div . 97-98,
Southern Div . 96-97;
Hellenic Lg 81-82,
Gloucs Nthn Sen Lg 37-38 49-50 50-51,
Gloucs Sen Cup 84-85 85-86 86-87,
Gloucs Sen Amat Cup (N) 26-27 45-46 71-72 75-76 77-78,
Gloucs Sen Prof Cup 84-85 85-86 86-87.

PREVIOUS

Leagues: Stroud & Dist. 1890-1921, Glos Northern Snr 22-67, Glos Co. 67-73, Hellenic 73-82, Southern League 82-98, Conference 98-.

Name: Stroud FC, 1989-92

Ground: None

Past Players who progressed to the Football League

G Rogers (Newport Co. 85)
K Gill (Newport Co. 85),
M England (Bristol Rov 85).
Wayne Hatswell (Oxford Utd. 00)

CLUB RECORDS (since 1998)

Attendance: 3,002
v St. Albans City, FA Umbro Trophy 18.04.99

Win: 8-0
v Fareham Town Southern Lge. Southern Div. 96-97

Defeat: 0-7
v Moor Green, Southern Lge. Midland Div. 85-86.

Career Goalscorer: Karl Bayliss

Career Appearances: Alex Sykes

Transfer Fee paid: £20,000
for Adrian Randall from Salisbury City

Transfer Fee Received: £35,000
for Marc McGregor to Nuneaton Borough (July 2000)
for Wayne Hatswell to Oxford United (Dec. 2000)

BEST SEASON

FA Cup: 2nd Round 99-00
0-3 v Torquay Utd. (H)

FA Trophy: Runners-up 98-99, 00-01

FA Vase: Winners 81-82.

League: 12th Conference 98-99

LAST SEASON

F.A. Cup: 1st Round
F.A. Trophy: 6th Round
Conference: 9 th (Best Position)
Top Goalscorer: Neil Graysobn 20
Player of the Year: Jon Richardson
Captain: Jon Richardson

FOREST GREEN ROVERS PLAYING SQUAD

Bold print denotes England semi-professional international.

	Birthplace	D.O.B.	Previous Clubs
GOALKEEPERS			
Chris Giannangeo	Australia		
Ellis Glassup	Cornwall		St.Austell
Steve Perrin	Wiltshire	27.10.70	Melksham T, Trowbridge T
DEFENDERS			
Denny Ingram	Sunderland	27.06.76	Northwich Victoria, Scarborough, Hartlepool United
Steve Jenkins Wales Int.	Bristol	02.01.80	Brentford, Southampton (Acadamy).
Steve Jones	Bristol	25.12.70	Cheltenham T, Swansea C., Cheltenham T., Forest Green R.
Kevin Langan British Univ.	Jersey	07.04.78	Team Bath, Bristol C
Scott Morgan	Colchester	22.03.75	Barry Town, Galway Utd., Dorchester Town, West Ham U, Brentford, Bournemouth (YT)
Jon Richardson	Nottingham	29.08.75	Oxford United, Exeter City
MIDFIELD			
Daniel Allen	Swindon	09.09.83	From Youth team
Rob Cook DMP	Stroud	28.03.70	Basingstoke T, Forest Green R, Cinderford T, Forest Green R, Shortwood Utd
Martin Foster	Rotherham	29.10.77	Doncaster R, Greenock Morton, Leeds
Gary Owers	Newcastle	03.10.68	Notts Co., Bristol C, Sunderland
Scott Rogers	Bath	23.05.79	Tiverton Town
Matthew Russell	Dewsbury	17.01.78	Exeter City, Scarborough, Halifax Town, Doncaster Rovers Scarborough.
Gareth Stoker	Bishop Auckland	22.02.73	Scarborough, Cardiff City, Hereford United, Bishop Auckland Hull City, Leeds United (YT)
Alex Sykes British Univ., DMP	Newcastle-u-Lyme	02.04.74	Nuneaton B, Forest Green R, Endsleigh, Cheltenham T, Mansfield T., Westfields
FORWARDS			
Adi Adams	Rinteln, Germany	12.06.84	Youth Team
John Cant			Melksham Town (L),From Youth Team
Steve Cowe	Gloucester	29.09.74	Newport County, Hererford Utd., Swindon Town (£100,000), Aston Villa (YT)
Luke Jones			YouthTeam
Neil Grayson ESP, NC	York	01.11.64	Cheltenham T, Hereford Utd, Northampton, Boston Utd, Gateshead, Chesterfield, York, Doncaster R, Rowntrees.

GRAVESEND & NORTHFLEET

It is a big step from playing Ryman Premier Division fixtures each week to the regularl facing of Conference quality opposition.

'Fleet' visited Yeovil on the first day of the season and played the favourites at Dorchester, led by two goals but drew 3-3 and at one stage of the seasonthey had reached an exciting seventh position in the table. So the quality was there.

However, once the pressure of regularly meeting top opposition dug in, points became difficult to grind out and by the end of the season the Kent club needed a victory to preserve their membership within the senior competition.

As often happens the squad found it easier to lift their game against top opposition, but struggled against the lower clubs. Despite the loss of previous season's heroes Francis Duku and Steve McKimm for long periods of the campaign, Andy Ford's squad never featured in the Conference relegation positions. (But then neither did poor Nuneaton Borough nor Southport until the last day !)

The manager has made wholesale changes to his squad, but there is little doubt it will be a long tough struggle, as so many conference rivals have now turned full time and appear to have money to invest.

Perhaps a cup run would be an inspiration as a Third Round defeat by Dover Athletic halted F.A.Trophy hopes last season and a home defeat in the Fourth Qualifying Round of the F.A.Cup by Margate certainly didn't lift morale earlier in the campaign.

Back Row (L-R): Anthony Hogg, Andrew Drury, Kevin Budge, Lee Shearer, Jimmy Strouts, Robin Trott, Louie Evans. Middle Row: Neil Withington, James Bent, Rob Owen, Jake Slade, Perry Spackman, Terry Penfold, Robbie Grace, Eddie McClements, Ron Hilyard. Front Row: Dave Lawson, Matt Lee, Justin Skinner, Steve McKimm, Andy Ford, Patrick Gradley, James Pinnock, Gary Farr.

GRAVESEND & NORTHFLEET

Match Facts 2002-03

The number shown directly below the player's name is his squad number.
Where a number is shown instead of an "X" in the columns this represents a substitute appearance and the number indicates the player replaced.

Comp.	Date	Opponents	Venue.	Score	Goalscorers	Att.
						SQUAD NUMBER
Conf 1	Aug-17	Yeovil T	A*	D 2-2	Bentley Jackson	2948
Conf 2	Aug-20	Dagenham & R	H	L 1-2	Booth(p)	2036
Conf 3	Aug-24	Hereford U	H	W 3-0	Burton(2) Kwashi	1130
Conf 4	Aug-26	Stevenage B	A	L 0-1		1849
Conf 5	Aug-31	Southport	H	L 1-3	Stadhart	1054
Conf 6	Sep-03	Woking	A	W 3-2	Stadhart(3)	2721
Conf 7	Sep-07	Nuneaton B	H	W 4-1	Stadhart(2) Sodje Kwashi	1044
Conf 8	Sep-14	Forest Green R	A	L 1-2	Sodje	711
Conf 9	Sep-17	Burton A	A	D 1-1	Strouts	1412
Conf 10	Sep-21	Telford U	H	L 0-2		1096
Conf 11	Sep-24	Doncaster R	H	D 2-2	Strouts Kwashi	1326
Conf 12	Sep-28	Northwich V	A	W 2-1	Hatch Cole	760
Conf 13	Oct-05	Scarborough	H	W 5-2	Hatch(2) Stadhart(p) Jackson Hotte(og)	1259
Conf 14	Oct-08	Barnet	A	W 4-1	Kwashi Jackson Stadhart Hatch	1360
Conf 15	Oct-13	Chester C	A	D 1-1	Booth	2210
Conf 16	Oct-19	Leigh RMI	H	L 1-3	Stadhart(p)	1246
FAC 4q	Oct-26	Margate	H	L 1-2	Stadhart(p)	1850
Conf 17	Nov-02	Halifax T	A	L 1-2	Jackson	1529
Conf 18	Nov-09	Farnborough T	H	D 0-0		1070
Conf 19	Nov-23	Scarborough	A	L 2-3	Strouts Bentley	1205
Conf 20	Nov-30	Morecambe	A	L 0-2		1062
Conf 21	Dec-07	Kettering T	H	L 0-2		954
Conf 22	Dec-14	Nuneaton B	A	W 1-0	Lye	969
Conf 23	Dec-21	Forest Green R	H	D 1-1	Giles	876
Conf 24	Dec-28	Dagenham & R	A	L 0-4		1849
Conf 25	Jan-01	Margate	A	L 2-4	Wilkins Barnett	1415
Conf 26	Jan-04	Yeovil T	H	L 2-4	Jackson Budge	1404
FAT 3	Jan-14	Dover Athletic	A	L 0-1		814
Conf 27	Jan-18	Hereford U	A	L 0-3		1814
Conf 28	Jan-21	Margate	H	L 1-2	Giles	1041
Conf 29	Jan-25	Stevenage B	H	W 2-1	Bentley Goodliffe(og)	1323
Conf 30	Feb-08	Southport	A	D 1-1	Jackson	1003
Conf 31	Feb-15	Woking	H	W 4-2	Stadhart(2) Burton Bentley	1163
Conf 32	Feb-22	Telford U	A	L 1-2	Wilkins Barnett	834
Conf 33	Mar-01	Burton A	H	W 3-2	Bentley(2) Jackson	1140
Conf 34	Mar-08	Doncaster R	A	L 1-4	Stadhart	3156
Conf 35	Mar-15	Northwich V	H	D 1-1	Duku	1017
Conf 36	Mar-22	Morecambe	H	W 3-2	Bentley McKimm Kwashi	1040
Conf 37	Mar-29	Kettering T	A	D 1-1	Evans	1070
Conf 38	Apr-05	Chester C	H	L 0-1		1273
Conf 39	Apr-12	Leigh RMI	A	D 0-0		385
Conf 40	Apr-19	Barnet	H	D 2-2	Hatch Duku	1358
Conf 41	Apr-21	Farnborough T	A	D 1-1	Hatch	1015
Conf 42	Apr-26	Halifax T	H	W 1-0	Hatch	1950

Jamie TURNER	Matt LEE	Justin SKINNER	Nick BURTON	Aaron BARNETT	Francis DUKU	Robbie GRACE	Robert OWEN	Craig WILKINS	Che STADHART	Jimmy JACKSON	Paul WILKERSON	Steve McKIMM	Danny LYE	Len WATTS	Adrian PENNOCK	Jimmy STROUTS	Liam HATCH	Mark BENTLEY	Austin BERKELEY	Gary ABBOTT	Jay LOVETT	Jamie COYLE	Paul BOOTH	Luke GEDLING	Paul STURGESS	Tostao KWASHI	John NUTTER	Louie EVANS	Akpo SODJE	Kevin BUDGE	Simon PARKER	Chris GILES	Tim COLE	Ben WHITE	Hamid BARR	Dwayne PLUMMER	Jamie CARTER
1	2	3	4	5	6	7	8	9	10	11	12	14	15	16	16	17	18	19	20	20	20	21	22	22	23	24	25	25	26	26	27	27	28	28	29	29	30
x		x	x			14		x	x	x	x				x	x	x					10		x	18												
x		x	x			x		22	x	x					x	x	x	11				x		x	23												
x		x	x					22	x	x	x		2		x	x	x	24				x			x												
x		x	x			2		24	x	x	x		5		x	x	x					x			x												
	x	x				19	18	x	x	x	x		x		x	x	x	3							x												
	x	x				x	x	x	x	x	x		x		x							x			22												
	x					x	x	x	x	x	x		x		x							x		x	23			22									
	x	x				x	x	x	x	x	x		x		x										8			x		3							
x		x				x		x	x	x	x		x		x	26									x			x		8							
x		x						x	x	x	x		x		x	26						23		x	x			x		24							
x								x	x	x	x		x		x	x								x	x					24		x					
x								x	x	x	x		x		x	x						14		x	x					18		x					
x		28			24			x	x	x	x		x		x	x								x	x							x					
x		x			23			x	x	x	x		x		x	x						4		x	x												
x					18			x	x	x	x		x		x	x						11			x			24				x		x			
x						14	29	x	x	x	x		x		x							x			x			22				x		x			
x						29	x	x	x	x			x		x		23					x		x	x			22						x			
x			19				x	x	x	x			x				x				x	x						x						x		22	
x		x	x				x	x	x	x							x				x	21				x								x			
x		x	x				x		x	x					x		x		x							x								x		29	
x	x	x	x		15		10	x	x	x		x					x		x							x											
x	x	x	x				5		x	x					x		x		x				29		x	20								x			
	x						x	x	x	x		x			x		x		x		x				20						x						
x	x						x	x	x	x		x			x		x								15		10		x		x						
x	x	x					x		x	x		x			x		x								15		26		x		x						
x	x	x	x				x		x	x					x		x										4		x		x						
x	x	x	x				x		x	x		x			x	x					4				2		x		15								
x x			x				x	x	x			x			x	x	x								x		10										
x x			9			24	x	25	x						x	x	x								x		x				x		x				
x	x					x	x	x	x					x		x	x										3		18		x		x		11		
x	x		9			x	x	x		x				x		x	x														x		x				
	x	x				x		x	x	x				x	28		x								27		26		x		x		x				
	x	x				x	x	x	x	x				x	8		x								28						x		x				
		x				x	x	x	x	x				x	x		x								17		28			8	x		x				
		x					x	x	x	x	28			x	x		x								x		10			x			x				
	x						x	x	x	x	x			x	28		x								15		14			x	x		x				
	16	x		x				x	x	x	28			x	x	24	x								x		x						x				
	x	x		x		x		x	x	x	x					10	x			x					14		x										
	x	x		x		x		x	x	x	x						x			x					10		x										
	x	x				x	x	3	x	x	x					8	x			x					x		x										
	x	x		x		x		x	x	x	x				x	10				x					14		x		25								
	x	x		x		x			x	x					x	x				x					x				x								
	x	x		x		26	18		x	x	x			x	x	x									x				x	24							
	x	x		x			26		x	x	x			x	x	x	x												x								

GRAVESEND & NORTHFLEET

GROUND DETAILS

Stonebridge Road,
Northfleet,
Kent
DA11 9GN
Tel: 01474 533796

Directions: From A2 take Northfleet/Southfleet exit (B262), follow toNorthfleet then B2175 (Springhead Rd) to junc A226, turn left (The Hill, Northfleet), road becomes Stonebridge Rd, grd on right at bottom of steep hill after 1 mile - car parking for 400-500. 2 mins from Northfleet BR station

Capacity:	4,184
Cover:	3,000
Seats:	500

Clubhouse: Fleet Social Centre. Hot and cold food available at tea bars on matchdays

Club Shop: Sells progs, hats, scarves, badges etc, & other memorabilia. Contact: Jessica McQueen

MATCHDAY PROGRAMME

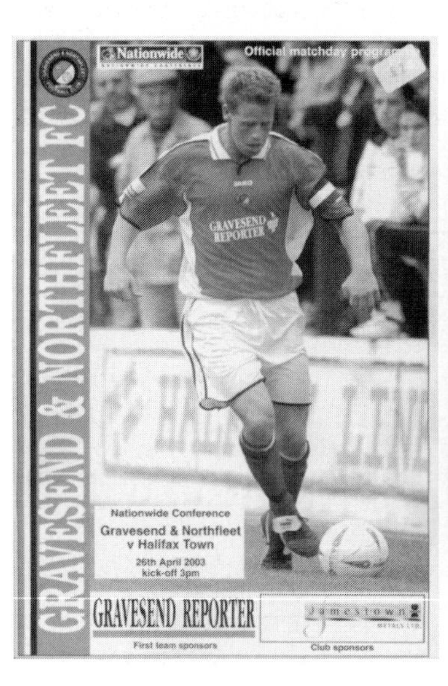

Pages: 46 Price: £2.00
Editor: T.B.A.
Clubcall: 09066 555844
Local Press: Gravesend Reporter, Kent Messenger. Gravesend Messenger The News Shopper
Local Radio: Invicta Radio, Radio Kent.

Formed:	1946
Nickname:	The Fleet
Sponsors:	Gravesend Reporter
Colours:	Red/white/red
Change colours:	Silver/black/silver
Midweek matchday:	Tuesday
Youth Team:	P.A.S.E. League
Website:	www.gnfc.co.uk
Clubcall line:	09066 555844

CLUB OFFICIALS

Chairman: Brian Kilcullen

Vice Chairman: Jason Botley

Directors: Bob Gunton, Maurice Norman,Mick Ward and Mark Lindup,Roly Edwards and Mark Lindop.

Company & Football Secretary: Roly Edwards c/o Football Club

Commercial Manager &Press Officer:T.B.A.
Tel: 01474 533796 (W)
email: fleet@stonebridgerd.freeserve.co.uk

FOOTBALL MANAGEMENT TEAM

MANAGER	**ANDY FORD**
Date of Appointment	September 1997
Date of Birth:	4th May 1954
Place of Birth:	Minehead

PREVIOUS CLUBS

As manager	
As asst. manager/coach	
As player	Minehead, AFC Bournemouth, Southend U., Swindon T., Gillingham

HONOURS

As manager	Isthmian Lge Premier Div. 01-02, Full Members Cup 00-01, Kent Senr Cup 99-00, 00-01,01-02
As player	

Assistant Manager: Phil Handford
Coach: Ron Hillyard
Physio: T.B.A.
Club's Playing Status: Part -time

Season	League	Div.	Pos.	P	Home W	D	L	F	A	Away W	D	L	F	A	Pts	Manager
02-03	Conference	-	17	42	8	5	8	37	35	4	7	10	25	38	48	Andy Ford
01-02	Isthmian	Prem.	1	42	14	4	3	43	18	17	2	2	47	15	99	Andy Ford
00-01	Isthmian	Prem.	6	42	12	3	6	32	21	10	2	9	31	25	71	Andy Ford
99-00	Isthmian	Prem.	11	42	9	6	6	36	25	6	4	11	30	42	55	Andy Ford
98-99	Isthmian	Prem.	10	42	11	2	8	31	23	7	4	10	23	30	60	Andy Ford
97-98	Isthmian	Prem.	13	42	10	5	6	41	25	5	3	13	24	42	53	Steve Lovell
96-97	Southern	Prem.	14	42	10	4	7	34	27	6	3	12	29	46	55	Chris Weller

Season	League	Div.	Pos.	P	W	D	L	F	A	Pts	Manager
95-96	Southern	Prem.	11	42	15	10	17	60	62	55	Gary Aldous
94-95	Southern	Prem.	14	42	13	13	16	38	55	52	Gary Aldous
93-94	Southern	South.	1	42	27	11	4	87	24	93	Gary Aldous

HONOURS

Isthmian League (Rymans) Champions: 2001-2002
Isthmian Lague Full Members Cup 2001-02
Southern League Southern League 57
Southern Div 94-95,
Div 1 Sth 74-75 R-up 70-71 88-89,
Lg Cup 77-78 R-up 57-58,
Champ Cup 77-78;
Kent Sen Cup 48-49 52-53 80-81, 99-00,00-01,01-02
R-up 47-48 76-77 90-91 97-98;
Kent Floodlit Cup 69-70 R-up 72-73;
Kent Sen Shield R-up 47-48 51-52;
Kent Interm Cup R-up 87-88;
Kent Midweek Lg 95-96, R-up 92-93 93-94 94-95;
Kent Youth Lg 95-96 96-97;
Lg Cup 82-83 86-87 96-97

PREVIOUS

Leagues: Kent (Gravesend Utd),
Southern 46-79, 80-96
Alliance Prem. 79-80
Isthmian 1997-2002

Names: Gravesend Utd.and Northfleet Utd
(merged 1946)

Ground: Central Avenue (Gravesend Utd)
(Northfleet always played at StonebridgeRd)

Past Players who progressed to the Football League

Several incl. most recently:
K Baron (Aldershot 60), R Dwight (Coventry 62),
R Cameron (Southend 63), R McNichol (Carlisle 65),
A Humphreys (Mansfield 64), B Thornley (Brentford 65),
P Jeavons (Lincoln 66), B Fry (Orient 66),
B Gordine (Sheffield Utd 68),
T Baldwin (Brentford 77),
L Smelt (Nottm Forest 80),
T Warrilow (Torquay 87),
J.Bullard (West Ham U.98)

CLUB RECORDS

Attendance: 12,036
v Sunderland, FA Cup 4th Rd 12.2.63.
26.081
v Aston Villa FA Cup 3rd Rd 95-96 at Villa Park
Goalscorer: Steve Portway 150+(92-94, 97-01)
Appearances: Ken Burrett 537
Win: 8-1
v Clacton Tn, Sth Lge 62-63,
(7-0 Godalming 95-96 FAC).
Defeat: 0-9
v Trowbridge Tn, Southern Lge Prem Div 91-92
Fee Paid: £8,000
for Richard Newbery (Wokingham 96),
& for Craig Williams(Tonbridge 97)
Fee Received: £35,000
for Jimmy Bullard (West Ham 1998)

BEST SEASON

FA Cup: 4th Round
Replay 1963, 2-5 v Sunderland (A), 1-1 (H)

FA Trophy: Fifth Round
01-02

League: 5th in The Alliance Premier 79-80

LAST SEASON

F.A. Cup: 4th Qualifying Round
F.A. Trophy: 3rd Round Round
League: 19th
Top Goalscorer: Che Stadhart 12
Player of the Year: Mark Bentley
Captain: Jimmy Jackson

GRAVESEND & NORTHFLEET PLAYING SQUAD

	Birthplace	D.O.B.	Previous Clubs

Bold print denotes England semi-professional international.

GOALKEEPERS

	Birthplace	D.O.B.	Previous Clubs
John Slade			Youth Team
Paul Wilkerson	Hertford	11.12.74	Stevenage B, Welling Utd, Hayes, Slough T, Watford

DEFENDERS

	Birthplace	D.O.B.	Previous Clubs
Francis Duku RP	London	-	Dulwich Hamlet, Grays Ath., Crawley T, Romford, Crawley T., Maidenhead U., Collier Row, Reading, West Ham
Matthew Lee RP	Farnborough	13.05.79	Sutton Utd, Gravesend, Charlton Ath.
Eddie McClements			Fulham (YTS)
Adrian Pennock	Ipswich	27.03.71	Gillingham, Bournemouth, Molde (Nor.), Norwich (App)
Lee Shearer	Rochford	23.10.77	Margate, Dover Athletic, Jaro FC (Finland), Leyton Orient
Justin Skinner RP	Dorking	17.09.72	Aylesbury Utd, Wimbledon
Robin Trott	Orpington	17.08.74	Grays Athletic, Stevenage Borough, Welling United, Mansion F.C. (Hong Kong), Gillingham (YTS)

MIDFIELD

	Birthplace	D.O.B.	Previous Clubs
Pat Gradley			Q.P.R., Charlton Ath.
Steve McKimm RP	London	30.07.75	Kingstonian, Hayes, Farnborough T, Dulwich Hamlet, Molesey, Hendon
Robert Owen RP	Kent	-	Sittingbourne, Tonbridge, Sittingbourne, Gillingham
Jimmy Strouts Comb. Services Rep.	Yorkshire	21.08.71	Dover Ath., Stevenage B, Dover Ath., Sittingbourne, Harrogate T, Frickley Ath., Harrogate RA

FORWARDS

	Birthplace	D.O.B.	Previous Clubs
Ben Abbey	Reading		Macclesfield T., Woking, Stevenage Bor.Southend Utd, Oxford Utd, CrawleyT., Maidenhead Utd, Osterley
Louie Evans	Peterborough		Hitchin T, Cambridge C, Kings Lynn, Peterborough U.
Robert Owen RP	Kent	-	Sittingbourne, Tonbridge, Sittingbourne, Gillingham
Tostao Kwashi			Fisher Athletic, Mjallby (Swe.),Cape United (Zimbabwe)
James Pinnock	Dartford	01.08.78	Kingstonian, Chesham Utd (L), Dover Ath. (L), Gillingham (App)

HALIFAX TOWN

Having dropped into the Conference from the Football League for a second time it will be hoped that the lessons of the first experience will have been absorbed. The club allowed the wrong people back in charge, as the glamour of the League and the stadium improvements lured characters who were possibly more interested in personal prestege than the well being of HalifaxTown Football Club.

The appointment of manager Chris Wilder to bring in local players, whom he knew to be sound, loyal and not greedy succeeded like a dream. The manager had worked wonders at Alfreton Town and once his new lads settled down they strung an excellent run of results together and a place in the play offs seemed a distinct possibillity. The fitness and availability of big striker Simon Parke was important to the side and his injuries affected their promising F.A.Trophy run, which fizzled out at Farnborough Town at the quarter final stage.

This defeat seemed to deflate morale a little and The Shaymen dropped out of the play off reckoning, but a final position of eighth would have been considered a triumph when the club was desperately trying to settle down at the beginning of the campaign.

President Robert Holmes, who had stood by the club through all its recent ups and downs, was thrilled by the resurgance of spirit developed by the reorganised board and club staff. There is no doubt that a shrewd manager and a happy backroom staff will give Halifax Town an excellent chance of promotion this season.

So let's hope they will not let the wrong type of 'helper' into the club again should they be attracted by a return to the Football League

Back Row (L-R): Adam Quinn, Simon Parke, Ryan Poole (GK), Shaun Garnett, Clint Davies (GK), Christian Lee, Mark Monington. Middle Row: Tommy Geldert (Fitness coach), Michael Senior, Kevin Sandwith, Jon Cullen, Darren Hockenhull, Andy Farrell, Ryan Hindley, Alan Jackson (Club physio). Front Row: Daniel Hudson, Craig Midgley, Lewis Killeen, Paul Stoneman (youth team manager), Chris Wilder (Manager), Sean McAuley (Asst. Manager), Steve Bushell, Lee Elam, Ryan Mallon.

HALIFAX TOWN

Match Facts 2002-03

The number shown directly below the player's name is his squad number.
Where a number is shown instead of an "X' in the columns this represents a substitute appearance and the number indicates the player replaced.

Comp.	Date	Opponents	Venue.	Score	Goalscorers	Att.
						SQUAD NUMBER
Conf 1	Aug-17	Telford U	H	W 2-0	Kerrigan Midgley(p)	1616
Conf 2	Aug-20	Morecambe	A	L 0-2		1524
Conf 3	Aug-24	Farnborough T	A	L 0-3		626
Conf 4	Aug-26	Northwich V	H	L 0-5		1491
Conf 5	Aug-31	Barnet	A	D 0-0		1316
Conf 6	Sep-03	Scarborough	H	W 2-1	Park Mallon	1557
Conf 7	Sep-07	Burton A	A	D 2-2	Mallon Stoneman	1636
Conf 8	Sep-10	Doncaster R	H	W 2-1	Clarkson Barrick(og)	3082
Conf 9	Sep-17	Chester C	H	D 0-0		2178
Conf 10	Sep-21	Yeovil T	A	L 0-3		2126
Conf 11	Sep-24	Southport	A	L 0-2		1008
Conf 12	Sep-28	Nuneaton B	H	W 3-1	Stoneman Farrell Fitzpatrick	1402
Conf 13	Oct-05	Stevenage B	A	W 1-0	Midgley	1722
Conf 14	Oct-08	Kettering T	H	W 4-0	Mallon(3,1p) Stoneman	1639
Conf 15	Oct-12	Margate	H	D 2-2	Fitzpatrick Saunders(og)	1519
Conf 16	Oct-19	Hereford U	A	D 1-1	Mallon	1699
LDV 1	Oct-22	Chesterfield	A	L 0-2		1382
FAC 4q	Oct-26	Burton A	A	L 1-2	Quailey	1990
Conf 17	Nov-02	Gravesend & N	H	W 2-1	Mallon Farrell	1529
Conf 18	Nov-09	Forest Green R	A	W 2-0	Quailey Mallon	753
Conf 19	Nov-23	Stevenage B	H	W 1-0	Hartfield	1517
Conf 20	Nov-30	Dagenham & R	H	D 3-3	Killeen Fitzpatrick Hartfield	1630
Conf 21	Dec-07	Woking	A	L 1-2	Killeen	1734
Conf 22	Dec-14	Burton A	H	L 0-1		1469
Conf 23	Dec-20	Doncaster R	A	D 0-0		3201
Conf 24	Dec-26	Leigh RMI	A	W 2-0	Fitzpatrick Parke	815
Conf 25	Dec-28	Morecambe	H	W 1-0	Farrell	2122
Conf 26	Jan-01	Leigh RMI	H	W 1-0	Clarkson	2050
Conf 27	Jan-04	Telford U	A	W 2-1	Quailey(2)	880
FAT 3	Jan-14	Doncaster R	H	W 4-1	Killeen(2) Quailey Fitzpatrick	1770
Conf 28	Jan-18	Farnborough T	H	W 1-0	Monington	1894
Conf 29	Jan-25	Northwich V	A	W 2-0	Monington Clarkson	1014
FAT 4	Feb-01	Grays Athletic	H	W 3-2	Quailey Clarkson Midgley(p)	1653
Conf 30	Feb-08	Barnet	H	L 2-4	Killeen(2)	2119
Conf 31	Feb-15	Scarborough	A	W 1-0	Sandwith	1835
FAT 5	Feb-22	Farnborough T	A	L 0-2		863
Conf 32	Mar-01	Chester C	A	L 0-2		2928
Conf 33	Mar-04	Yeovil T	H	L 2-3	Parke(2)	2222
Conf 34	Mar-08	Southport	H	L 3-4	Parke Fitzpatrick Garnett	1544
Conf 35	Mar-15	Nuneaton B	A	L 0-2		1231
Conf 36	Mar-22	Dagenham & R	A	D 0-0		1766
Conf 37	Mar-29	Woking	H	D 1-1	Midgley	1558
Conf 38	Apr-05	Margate	A	L 1-2	Midgley	509
Conf 39	Apr-12	Hereford U	H	W 1-0	Quailey	1299
Conf 40	Apr-19	Kettering T	A	W 1-0	Clarkson	713
Conf 41	Apr-21	Forest Green R	H	D 1-1	Farrell	1366
Conf 42	Apr-26	Gravesend & N	A	L 0-1		1950

Lee BUTLER	Alistair ASHER	Sean McCAULEY	Steve BUSHELL	Phil HAIGH	Paul STONEMAN	Kevin SANDWITH	Stuart ELLIOTT	Phil CLARKSON	Craig MIDGLEY	Steve KERRIGAN	Ian FITZPATRICK	Adam QUINN	Tom MORGAN	Neil GRAYSTON	Michael SENIOR	Simon PARKE	Paul GEDMAN	Leon RYAN	Brian QUAILEY	Shaun GARNETT	Robert HERBERT	Jamie INGLEDOW	Charlie HARTFIELD	John BERESFORD	Andy FARRELL	Nicky HEINEMANN	Mark MONINGTON	Ryan MALLON	Lewis KILLEEN	Neil TOLSON	Luke IBBOTSON
1	**2**	**3**	**4**	**5**	**6**	**6**	**7**	**8**	**9**	**10**	**11**	**12**	**13**	**14**	**15**	**16**	**17**	**17**	**18**	**19**	**20**	**21**	**21**	**21**	**22**	**23**	**23**	**24**	**24**	**24**	**25**
x	x	x	x	x	x		24	x	x	x	x					10									9			x			
x	x	x	x	x	x		9	x	x	x	x					10												x			
x	x	x	x	x	x		2	x	x	9	x			16		x												x			
x	9	x	x	x	x		x	x	x	x	x			8		10												x			
x	x		x	x	x		x	x			x	x		x		x									16			11			
x	x		x	x	x		x	x			x	11		x		x			16						24			x			
x	x		x	x	x		x	x		16	x			x		x			2									x			
x	x			x			x	x		16	x	11		x		x			x	x		24						x			
x	x				x		x	x	11	16	x	2		x		x			x	x								x			
x	x				x		x	x	8	12	16	x		x		x			x	x								x			
x		14	x		x		x	x	10	x	x			x			18		x	x								x			
x			x	9	x		x	x	x		x			x		x				x					24			x			
			x	x	x			x	x		x	11	x	x		x				x	22				x			16			
x		15	x		x			x	x					x	x	x	26		16	x					x			x			
x	x		x		x			x	x		18			x					x	x					x			x			
x	x	x		6	x			x	x		x	x		x				18	x						11			x			
	x			x							x		x	x	x	17		x		x	x				x	14		x			2
x	x	x	x	x				x	x		14	x		x	17	12		x	x												
x	x	18	x					x	x		x	x		x				22	x	x					11			x			
x	x					x		x	x		x	x		18	x	11			x	x								x			
	x					x			x		x		x		x	2			x	x	15		x				x		x		
	x		x			x			x		x	x	x	21		24			x	x			x		18				x		
	x		x			x			x		x		x		x			15	x	x					18		x		x		
	x		x			x		x	x		x		x			x			9	x							x		x		
x	x		x			x		x	x		x	11		8		x				x					16		x		x		
x	x		x			x		x	x		x					x			16	x					11		x		x		
x	x		x			x		x	x		x			22					11	x					x		x		x		
x	x		x			x		x	x		2			17				22	x	x					x		x		x		
x	x		x			x		x	x		x	x				24			x								x		x		
x	x		x			x			x		x	x		6	x			18	x					9			x		x		
x	x		x			x			x		x	x		11	x				x						15		x		x		
x	x		x			x		x	x		x	x			24			18	x						11		x		x		
x	x		x			x		x	x		x	x							x	x									x		
x	x		x			x		x	x		x					11			x	x					18		x		x		
x	x		x			x		x	x		x	x		18		24			x						11		x		x		
x	x		x			x		x	x		x	x		6		18			x						8		x		x		
x	x	x						x	x		3	x		x	x	8			x						x		x				
x	x							x	x		18	x		x	x	x			x	x	15				16		x				
x	x		x			x		x	x		8	x			12	x			x	x					18		x				
x			x			x		x	x		x			x	8	x			16	x					x		x				
x			x			x		x	x			x		x	x	x			16	x					x						
x	x		x					x	x		16	x		x	x	x			x	x					18					15	
x	x		x					x	x			x		x		8			x	x					x					x	
x	x	9	x					x	x		18			x		24			x	x					x					x	
x	x		x			x		x	x			x		x					x	x					x						
x	x		x			x		x	x		14	x		x	4	18			x	x					x						
x			x			x		x	x		x	x		x		22			x	x					x						

HALIFAX TOWN

GROUND DETAILS

The Shay Stadium
Halifax
West Yorks.
HX1 2YS
Tel: 01422 341222
Fax: 01422 349487
email: theshay@halifaxafc.co.uk
Website: halifaxafc.co.uk

Directions: M62, J24, head towards the city centre. The ground is on the right signposted "The Shay"
Nearest Railway station: Halifax, 1/2 mile from ground

Capacity:	**9,500**
Covered Seating:	**2,500**
Covered Standing:	**7,000**

Clubhouse: Yes, open during normal licensing hours.

Club Shop: Yes, contact club.

MATCHDAY PROGRAMME

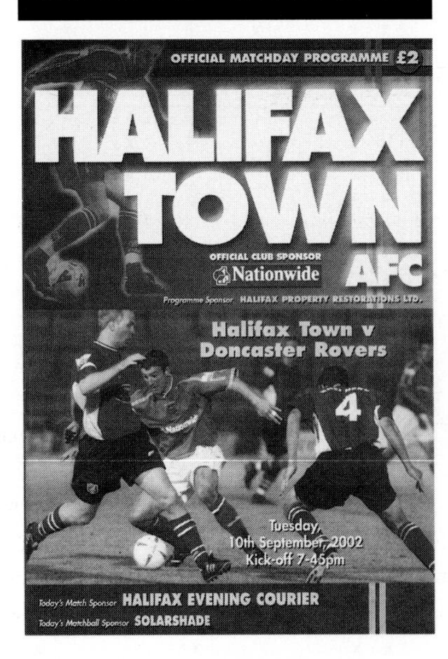

OFFICIAL MATCHDAY PROGRAMME £2
HALIFAX TOWN
OFFICIAL CLUB SPONSOR
Nationwide
AFC
Halifax Town v
Doncaster Rovers
Tuesday,
10th September, 2002
Kick-off 7-45pm
Today's Match Sponsor HALIFAX EVENING COURIER
Today's Matchball Sponsor SOLARSHADE

Price: £2 Pages: 32
Editor: Tony Charlton

Founded:	1911
Nickname:	The Shaymen
Sponsors:	Nationwide B.S.
Colours:	Blue shirts, white shorts, blue socks
Change colours:	White shirts, blue shorts, white socks
Midweek matchday:	Tuesday 7.45

CLUB OFFICIALS

President: Bob Holmes

Chairman: David Cairns

Vice-Chairman: Adrian Hall

Other Directors: Bob Bland, T Charlton, Martin Fox,Richard Harrison, Ray Moreland (HTST Representative), Phil Jewitt

Chief Executive: Tony Kniveton

Club Secretary: Richard Groves
c/o the club Tel: 0771 5254323 (M)

Commercial Manager: Gavin Butler
Tel:07966 167078
e-mail:commercial@halifaxafc.co.uk

FOOTBALL MANAGEMENT TEAM

MANAGER: CHRIS WILDER

Date of Appointment June 2002
Date of Birth: 23rd September 1967
Place of Birth: Wortley

PREVIOUS CLUBS
As player/manager Alfreton Town 01-02
As player Southampton (A), Sheffield Utd., Rotherham Utd., Notts Co., Bradford C., Sheffield Utd., Brighton & H.A., Halifax T., Alfreton T.

HONOURS
As manager NCE 01-02 - League Championship, League Cup, President's Cup

* * *

Player Coach Sean McCauley
Youth Team Coach: Paul Stoneman
Physiotherapist: Alan Jackson

Season	League	Div.	Pos.	Home (or total) P	W	D	L	F	A	Away W	D	L	F	A	Pts	Manager
02-03	Conference	-	8	42	11	5	5	34	28	7	5	9	16	23	64	Chris Wilder
01-02	League	Div.3	24	46	5	9	9	24	28	3	3	177	15	56	36	Paul Bracewell/Alan Little
00-01	League	Div.3	23	46	7	6	10	33	32	5	5	13	21	36	47	Paul Bracewell
99-00	League	Div.3	18	46	15	9	22	44	58						54	Mark Lillis
98-99	League	Div.3	10	46	10	8	5	33	25	7	7	9	25	31	66	Kieran O'Regan
97-98	Conference		1	42	17	4	0	51	15	8	8	5	23	28	87	G. Mulhall & K. O'Regan
96-97	Conference		19	42	9	5	7	39	37	3	7	11	16	37	48	J. Carroll/G. Mulhall&K. O'Regan
95-96	Conference		15	42	13	13	16	49	63						52	John Bird/John Carroll
94-95	Conference		8	42	17	12	13	68	54						63	John Bird
93-94	Conference		13	42	13	16	13	55	49						55	Peter Wragg/John Bird

CLUB RECORDS

Attendance: 36,885
v Tottenham H., FA Cup 5th Rd, 14.02.53

Win: 12-0
v West Vale Ramblers, FA Cup 1st Q. Rd. 13-14

Defeat: 0-13
v Stockport C., Div. 3 North, 33-34

Career Goalscorer: Albert Valentine

Career Appearances: John Pickering

Transfer Fee Paid: £50,000
for Ian Juryeff to Hereford Utd.

Transfer Fee Received: £250,000
for Wayne Allison from Watford

PREVIOUS

Leagues: Yorkshire Comb. 1911-12
Midland League 1912-21
Football League - Division 3 North 1-21-58
- Division 3 1958-63, 69-76, 92
Division 4 1963-69

Grounds: Sandhall Lane 1911-15, Exley 1919-21

Names: None

Chris Wilder

HONOURS

Conference Champions 1997-98
Promotion to Division 3 1968-69

Past Players who progressed to the Football League between 93-98

Geoff Horsfield (Fulham)

BEST SEASON

FA Cup: Fifth Round 1913-14, 52-53

FA Trophy: 3rd Round 93-94

Football League: 3rd, Division 3 1969-70

Conference: Champions 1997-98

LAST SEASON

F.A. Cup: 4th Qualifying Round

F.A.Trophy: 5th Round Round

Conference: 8th

Leading Goalscorer: Ryan Mallon

Captain: Shawn Garnett

Player of the Year: Craig Midgley

HALIFAX TOWN — PLAYING SQUAD

Bold print denotes England semi-professional international.

	Birthplace	D.O.B.	Previous Clubs
GOALKEEPERS			
Clint Davies			Birmingham City, Woking (L), Nuneaton Borough (L), Tamworth (L)
DEFENDERS			
Shaun Garnett	Wallesey	22.11.69	Oldham Athletic, Tranmere Rovers
Darren Hockenhull			Rochdale, Blackburn Rovers
Sean McAuley	Sheffield	23.06.72	Manchester U., St. Johnstone, Hartlepool U., Scunthorpe U., Rochdale, Portland Timbers (USA).
Mark Monington	Mansfield	21.10.70	Boston United, Rotherham United, Rochdale, Burnley
Adam Quinn	Sheffield	02.06.82	Sheffield Wednesday
Kevin Sandwith	Workington	30.04.78	Doncaster Rovers, Carlisle United, Telford United
Paul Stoneman	Whitley Bay	26.02.73	Blackpool, Colchester Utd.
MIDFIELD			
Steve Bushell	Manchester	28.12.72	York City, Blackpool, Stalybridge Celtic.
Jon Cullen			Peterborough Utd, Sheffield Utd, Hartlepool Utd, Doncaster Rov., Shrewsbury T.,Carlisle Utd, Darlington
Lee Elam ESP	Durham	10.01.73	Morecambe
Danny Hudson	Mexborough	25.06.79	Doncaster Rovers (L), Rotherham United
Ryan Mallon	Sheffield	22.03.83	Sheffield United
Craig Midgley	Bradford	24.06.76	Bradford C., Hartlepool U.
Mick Senior	Huddersfield	03.03.81	Huddersfield Town (App)
FORWARDS			
Andy Farrell	Easington	21.12.83	from trainee
Ryan Hindley	Sheffield		Alfreton Town , Worksop Town, Shefield Wednesday
Lewis Killeen	Peterborough	13.04.82	Shefield United
Christian Lee	Aylesbury	08.10.76	Eastwood T, Rushden & Diamonds, Farnborough T Bristol R, Rochdale, Northampton, Gillingham, Doncaster R
Simon Parke	Bradford		Bradford P.A., Guiseley

HEREFORD UNITED

Graham Turner's devotion to the club was clear for everyone to see as he reverted to the Chairman/Manager role and took responsibilty for just about everything. The season wasn't a spectacular success but, considering the financial background since the club was relegated in 1997, it was a very positive step in the right direction.

The Conference programme brought few highlights but a final position of sixth, top of the middle order below the play- offs, was the perfect launching pad for a concerted effort this campaign and with the manager's contacts and experience don't be surprised if the Bulls aren't one of this season's leaders.

In both national knock out competitions last season United had tough home draws. In the F.A. Cup a visit of high flying Wigan Athletic was selected as a Sky televised match and the club was thrilled that their luck with the bonus of television fees in this competition and indeed the Conference and Trophy, had continued. These funds have been the outfit's lifeblood as the struggle has gone on day to day. Wigan won, as did holders Yeovil Town in the F.A.Trophy, but the games attracted two good attendances and the young team grew in experience.

Goalscoring is all important in every club and Hererford probably think they have most departments well covered on last season's form, So an improvement in this campaign may rely on Steve Guinan, Paul Parry and Ben Smith finding their form in front of goal. One thing is certain, and that is the Bulls supporters will turn out in force and should their club be challenging, the noise will be worth a goal in every home game.

L-R Back Row: David Brown, Jordan King, Michael Rose, Paul Parry, Matthew Baker, Steve Quinn, Andrew Tretton, Richard Teesdale, Rob Sawyers
Front Row: Rob Purdie, Jamie Pitman, Richard O'Kelly (Coach), Graham Turner (Chairman / Director of Football), Tony Ford (Coach), Ben Smith, Danny Williams.

HEREFORD UNITED

Match Facts 2002-03

The number shown directly below the player's name is his squad number.
Where a number is shown instead of an "X' in the columns this represents a substitute appearance and the number indicates the player replaced.

Comp.	Date	Opponents	Venue.	Score	Goalscorers	Att.
						SQUAD NUMBER
Conf 1	Aug-17	Farnborough T	H	W 2-1	Pitman(2)	1910
Conf 2	Aug-20	Forest Green R	A	W 3-1	Parry Wright Williams	1514
Conf 3	Aug-24	Gravesend & N	A	L 0-3		1130
Conf 4	Aug-26	Morecambe	H	L 1-2	Pitman	2106
Conf 5	Aug-31	Nuneaton B	A	W 3-0	Guinan Pitman Parry	1354
Conf 6	Sep-09	Woking	A	W 2-1	Clarke Boardman(og)	2080
Conf 7	Sep-14	Chester C	H	D 0-0		2289
Conf 8	Sep-17	Yeovil T	H	D 0-0		2282
Conf 9	Sep-21	Stevenage B	A	W 2-0	Clarke Rose	1685
Conf 10	Sep-24	Kettering T	A	W 3-2	James Guinan Duik(og)	1434
Conf 11	Sep-28	Scarborough	H	L 0-1		2171
Conf 12	Oct-05	Dagenham & R	H	W 2-1	Guinan Williams	1761
Conf 13	Oct-08	Leigh RMI	A	W 2-0	Clarke Parry	425
Conf 14	Oct-11	Burton A	A	L 0-2		2149
Conf 15	Oct-15	Northwich V	H	L 1-2	Parry	1400
Conf 16	Oct-19	Halifax T	H	D 1-1	Pitman	1699
LDV 1	Oct-22	Northampton T	H	L 3-4	Eribenne(2) Parry	1047
FAC 4q	Oct-26	Arlesey Town	H	W 1-0	Parry	1718
Conf 17	Nov-02	Doncaster R	A	L 0-2		3486
Conf 18	Nov-09	Southport	H	L 0-2		1646
FAC 1	Nov-16	Wigan Athletic	H	L 0-1		4005
Conf 19	Nov-23	Dagenham & R	A	L 0-1		1444
Conf 20	Nov-30	Barnet	H	W 4-0	Guinan(3) Smith	1471
Conf 21	Dec-14	Woking	H	W 5-0	Rose(2) Smith(2) Guinan	1565
Conf 22	Dec-20	Chester C	A	W 1-0	Guinan	2507
Conf 23	Dec-26	Telford U	A	W 1-0	Guinan	2047
Conf 24	Dec-28	Forest Green R	H	D 1-1	Grant	3271
Conf 25	Jan-01	Telford U	H	W 2-0	Grant Smith	3077
FAT 3	Jan-14	Yeovil T	H	L 1-2	Smith	2425
Conf 26	Jan-18	Gravesend & N	H	W 3-0	Parry(2) Sawyers	1814
Conf 27	Jan-25	Morecambe	A	L 1-3	Guinan	1437
Conf 28	Feb-04	Farnborough T	A	D 2-2	Pitman Williams	1030
Conf 29	Feb-08	Nuneaton B	H	W 21	Grant Lovett	2071
Conf 30	Feb-11	Margate	A	W 2-0	Rose Parry	667
Conf 31	Feb-15	Northwich V	A	D 2-2	Purdie Grant	896
Conf 32	Feb-22	Stevenage B	H	D 2-2	Guinan Wright	2322
Conf 33	Mar-01	Yeovil T	A	L 0-4		6487
Conf 34	Mar-08	Kettering T	H	W 2-0	Smith Clarke	2062
Conf 35	Mar-15	Scarborough	A	L 1-2	Parry	1179
Conf 36	Mar-22	Barnet	A	L 1-2	Parry	1588
Conf 37	Mar-29	Margate	H	L 2-3	Parry Guinan	1959
Conf 38	Apr-05	Burton A	H	W 4-0	Guinan(2) Hawley Correia	1780
Conf 39	Apr-12	Halifax T	A	L 0-1		1299
Conf 40	Apr-19	Leigh RMI	H	L 0-1		1690
Conf 41	Apr-21	Southport	A	W 2-1	Williams Correia	1103
Conf 42	Apr-26	Doncaster R	H	L 2-4	Williams Correia	2449

Matt BAKER 1	Matt CLARKE 2	Michael ROSE 3	Andy TRETTON 4	Ian WRIGHT 5	Tony JAMES 6	Jamie PITMAN 7	Ben SMITH 8	Scott VOICE 9	John GRANT 10	Paul PARRY 11	Danny WILLIAMS 12	Richard TEESDALE 15	Robert SAWYERS 16	Robert PURDIE 17	Steve GUINAN 18	Andy MARTIN 20	Michael HUSBANDS 21	James FOX 22	Mike GALLOWAY 23	Chuki ERIBENNE 24	Jay LOVETT 30	Alberto CORREIA 32	Karl HAWLEY 33
x	x	x	x	x	x	x				x	x		x	11	x	2							
x	x	x	x	x	x	x				x	x		x		x								
x	x	x	x	x	x	x		12		x	x	4	x	16	x								
x	x	x		x	x	x		18	16	x	x	x	x	15	x								
x	x	x		x	x	x		18	x	x	x	x		10	x								
x	x	x	x	x	x	x			x	x	x				x								
x	x	x	x	x	x	x			x		x		17	x	x			10					
x	x	x	x	x	x	x			x		x		x	16	x								
x	x	x	x	x	x	x		10	x	x	x			11	x								
x	x	x	x	x	x	x			x	x	x			10	x								
x	x	x	x	x	x	x				x	x		12	x	x			17					
x	x	x	x		x	x				x	x	x		11	x				x				
x	x	x	x		x	x				x	x	x			x				x				
x	x	x	x	x	x	x				x	x			12	x			2	x				
x	x	x	x	x	x	x				x	x	5		12	x			18	x				
x	x	x	x		x	x				x	x	x							x	x			
x	x	x	x		x	x				x	x	x	2		11				x	x			
x		x	x	18	x	x				x	x	x			x				x	x			
x	11	x	x	x	x	x				x	x				x				x	x			
x	x	x	x	x	x		24			x	x				x				x	x			
x	x	x	x	7	x	x				x	x				x				x	x			
x	x	x	x	x	x	x	12		18	x	x			2	x				x				
x	x	x	x		x	x	x		x	x				10	x				x				
x	x	x	x		x	x	x		x	x	x	2		10	x								
x	x	x	x	10	x	x	x		x	x	x			8	x								
x	x	x	x		x	x	x		x	x	x			8	x								
x	x		x		x		x		x	x	x	2	x	x	x		17						
x	x	x	x		x	x	x		x	x	x	2			x								
x		x	x		x	x	x		x	x	x	x		10	x		12						
x		x	x		x	x	x		x	x			x	x			17				x		
x		x	x		x	x	x		x	x	x				x		18				x		
x		x		x	x	x	x		x	x	x	6			x						x		
x		x		x	x	x	x		x	x				x	x		18				x		
x		x	x	x	x	x	x		x	x				x			10				x		
x		x	x	x	x	x	x		x	x		5		x	17						x		
x		x	x	3	x	x	x		x	x	x			11	x						x		
x	30	x	x		x	x	x		x	x	x			12	x						x		
x	x	x	x		x	x	x		x	x	x			10	x						12		
x	x	x	x	x		x	x			x	x			x	x						17		
x	x	x	x	x	x	x	x			x	x			12	x								
x	x	x	x	x			x			x	x			x	12							x	x
x	x	x	x	x			x			x	18			x	x							x	x
x	x	x	x	x	4	16	x		32				x	x	x							x	x
x	x	x		x	x	x			x		x	2		x	x							17	x
x		x		x	x	x	x		x		x	x		5	x							33	x
x	x	x	15		x	x	x			x	x	x		7	x							x	18

HEREFORD UNITED

GROUND DETAILS

Edgar Street,
Hereford.
HR4 9JU

Telephone Tel: 01432 276666
Fax 01432 341359
Club Call 09068 121645

E-mail HUFCbulls@hotmail.com
Website: http://www.herefordunited.co.uk

SIMPLE DIRECTIONS: From Hereford city centre follow signs to Leominster (A49) into Edgar Street.
Car parking for 600 near the ground(60p Sats,free mid week).
Nearest railway station Hereford

Match Tickets: Adults £8-£10
concessions £3-£7 plus family combinations.

CAPACITY: 8,843
SEATED: 2,761
COVERED TERRACING: 6,082

SOCIAL FACILITIES: Clubhouse open on matchdays
REFRESHMENTS: Three Tea Bars
CLUB SHOP: Yes

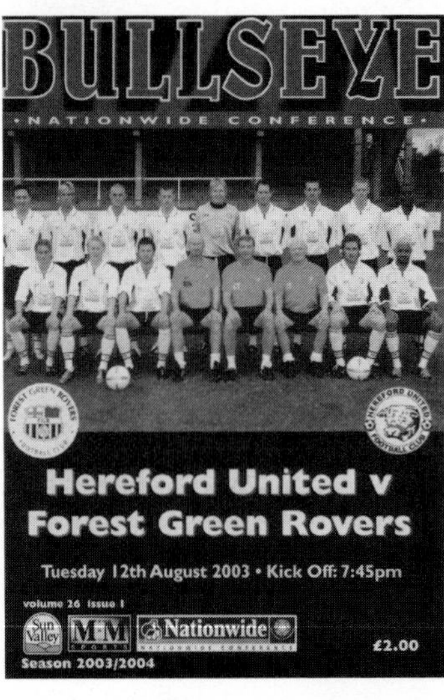

BULLSEYE
NATIONWIDE CONFERENCE
Hereford United v
Forest Green Rovers
Tuesday 12th August 2003 • Kick Off: 7:45pm
volume 26 issue 1
Nationwide
£2.00
Season 2003/2004

MATCHDAY PROGRAMME

Pages: 32 Price: £2.00
Editor: Lee Symonds
Clubcall: 09068 121 645

Other club publications: None

Local Press: Hereford Journal; Hereford Times; Worcester Evening News
Local Radio: BBC Hereford & Worcester

Founded: 1924

Nickname: The Bulls

Sponsors: Sun Valley

Club Colours: White & black shirts, black shorts, white trim; white socks.

Change Colours: Red shirts; red shorts; red socks

Midweek matchday: Tuesday

CLUB OFFICIALS

Chairman/Director of Football Graham Turner

Company Secretary Joan Fennessy

Directors George Hyde Ron Jukes, Grenville Smith, Hugh Brookes, Aidan McGivern.

Club Secretary Joan Fennessy
c/o the club
Tel: 01432 276666 Fax: 01432 341359

FOOTBALL MANAGEMENT TEAM

MANAGER: **GRAHAM TURNER**

Date of Appointment August 1995
Date of Birth: 5th October 1947
Place of Birth: Ellesmere Port

PREVIOUS CLUBS
As manager Shrewsbury T., Aston Villa, Wolverhampton W.
As player Wrexham, Chester City, Shrewsbury T.
HONOURS
As manager League: Div.3 78-79 (Shrewsbury), Div.4 87-88, Div.3 88-89; S.V.T. 87-88 (Wolves)
As player England - Youth cap.

* * *

Coaches:
Chief Scout: Ron Jukes

Physio: Richard O'Kelly
Club Playing Status: Full Time

Season	League	Div.	Pos.	P	Home W	Home D	Home L	Home F	Home A	Away W	Away D	Away L	Away F	Away A	Pts	Manager
02-03	Conference	-	6	42	9	5	7	36	22	10	2	9	28	29	64	Graham Turner
01-02	Conference	-	17	42	9	6	6	28	15	5	4	12	22	38	52	Graham Turner/Phil Robinson
00-01	Conference	-	11	42	6	12	3	27	19	8	3	10	33	27	57	Graham Turner
99-00	Conference	-	8	42	9	6	6	43	31	6	8	7	18	21	59	Graham Turner
98-99	Conference	-	13	42	9	5	7	25	17	6	5	10	24	29	55	Graham Turner
97-98	Conference	-	6	42	11	7	3	30	19	7	6	8	26	30	67	Graham Turner

Season	League	Div.	Pos.	P	W	D	L	F	A	Pts	Manager
96-97	F. League	3	24	46	11	14	21	50	65	47	Graham Turner
95-96	F. League	3	6	46	20	14	12	65	47	74	Graham Turner
94-95	F. League	3	16	42	12	13	17	45	62	49	Graham Turner
93-94	F. League	3	20	42	12	6	24	60	79	42	Greg Downs & John Layton

HONOURS

Football League Div. 3 75-76, Div. 4 R-up 72-73;

Southern League R-up 45-46 50-51 71-72
NW Championship 58-59
Div. 1 58-59,
Cup Winners 52 57 59

Welsh Cup Winners 89-90,
R-up 3 times;

PREVIOUS

Leagues: Birmingham League;
Birmingham Combination;
Southern League 39-72;
Football League 72-97

Names: None

Ground: None

Past Players who progressed to the Football League

Since joining the Conference: Gavin Mahon (Brentford)

CLUB RECORDS

Attendance: 18,114
v Sheffield Wed., FA Cup 3rd Rd, 4.1.58

Career Goalscorer: Unknown
Career Appearances: unknown

Win: 6-0 v Burnley (A), Div. 4 24.1.87

Defeat: 0-6 v Rotherham Utd (A), Div. 4 29.4.89

Transfer Fee Paid: £75,000
to Walsall for Dean Smith, 7.94
Transfer Fee Received: £250,000
for Darren Peacock from Q.P.R., 3.91
+ a further £240,000
when he moved to Newcastle Utd. 3.91

BEST SEASON

FA Trophy: Semi-Finals 00-01

FA Cup: 4th Rd 71-72 (as Southern League side),
76-77, 81-82, 89-90, 91-92
League Clubs Defeated (as a non-league club): Exeter C 53-54,Aldershot 56-57,Q.P.R. 57-58,Millwall 65-66,North"ton T 70-71, Northampton T,Newcastle U71-72,Colchester United & Brighton & H 97-98,Hartlep'l U&YorkC 99-00 Wrexham01-2

League: 22nd Football League Div.ision 2 1976-77

LAST SEASON

F.A. Cup: First Round
F.A. Trophy: 3rd Round
Conference: 6th
Top Goalscorer: Steve Guinan
Player of the Year: Tony James
Captain: Ian Wright

HEREFORD UNITED PLAYING SQUAD

Bold print denotes England semi-professional international.

Player	*Birthplace*	*D.O.B.*	*Previous Clubs*
GOALKEEPERS			
Matt Baker ESP	Harrogate	18.12.79	Hull
Kenny Griffiths	Devon	-	Torquay
DEFENDERS			
Ryan Green Wales Full			Wolves,Torquay U, Millwall, Cardiff C. Sheffield W
Tony James Wales SP	Birmingham		W.B.A.
Jordan King			Telford United
Michael Rose ESP	Salford	28.07.82	Chester City, Manchester United
Richard Teesdale	Birmingham	-	Walsall
Andy Tretton	Derby	09.10.76	Shrewsbury Town, Derby County
MIDFIELD			
Dean Craven			Bridgnorth Town, Shrewsbiry T, W.B.A.
Paul Parry Wales SP	Hereford		Youth team
Jamie Pitman FA XI	Trowbridge	06.01.76	Woking, Yeovil T, Hereford Utd, Swindon Town
Robert Purdie	Leicester	-	Leicester
Ian Rodgerson	Hereford	09.04.66	Pegasus Jun., Hereford U., Cardiff C., Birmingham C., Sunderland, Cardiff C.
Rob Sawyers			Barnet, Wolverhampton Wanderers
Ben Smith	Chelmsford	23.11.78	Southend, Yeovil T, Reading, Arsenal
Danny Williams	Sheffield	02.03.81	Chesterfield
FORWARDS			
David Brown			Telford United, Manchester United
Scott Voice	Birmingham	12.08.74	Bilston T, Stourbridge, Bilston T, Stourbridge, Wolves
John Grant	Manchester	09.08.81	Crewe
Neil Gough	Harlow	01.09.81	Hampton & Richmond, Leyton Orient
Steve Guinan	Birmingham	24.12.75	Shrewsbury, Plymouth, Camb Utd., Crewe A, Halifax T, Burnley, Darlington, Nottingham F
Robert Purdie			Leicester City

LEIGH R.M.I.

It may be an advantage to be among everyone's favourites for relegation each season from the Conference. Being underdogs, determined to prove a point, can keep a squad fired up each week.

Last season Steve Waywell, who had given seven years of tremendous service, finally called it a day after a seven game run without a point at the end of the year. Mark Patterson took over and a wonderful battling finish to the season was highlighted by their last four results bringing eight points from two wins and two draws.

This remarkable recovery helped to shatter the hopes of Southport and Nuneaton Borough and once again the Railwaymen had proved the doubters wrong.

The club hopes to move into a purpose built stadium to share with their present neighbours Leigh Rugby League club in the very near future. New chairman Bill Taylor will be masterminding the move, but it is very important that Pattterson's squad can continue to survive while off field developments are accomplished.

England internationals Neil Durkin and Warren Peyton will be influential in mid field while Martyn Lancaster should be a stalwart at the back, but it will be most important that the new strike force of David McNiven, Ged Kielty and Marcus Hallows produce the goals. Hopefully for local fans, the Railwaymen will stay in the Conference long enough to enjoy the new stadium.

Back Row, left to right: Arthur Molyneux (Kitman), Gerry Harrison, Neil Durkin, Wyane Maden, Stuart Coburn, Andy Heald, Ian Martin, Martin Lancaster (Capt), Nicky Hill, Marcus Hallows, Alan Bent (Physio).
Front Row: Ian Pendlebury, David McNiven, Ged Courtney, Warren Peyton, Mark Patterson (Manager), Phil Starbuck (Asst. Manager), Ged Kielty, Neil Robinson, Ian Monk, Guy Heffernan.

LEIGH R.M.I.

Match Facts 2002-03

The number shown directly below the player's name is his squad number.
Where a number is shown instead of an "X' in the columns this represents a substitute appearance and the number indicates the player replaced.

Comp.	Date	Opponents	Venue.	Score	Goalscorers	Att.
						SQUAD NUMBER
Conf 1	Aug-17	Dagenham & R	A	L 1-3	Black	1305
Conf 2	Aug-20	Doncaster R	H	L 0-2		867
Conf 3	Aug-24	Burton A	H	W 4-2	Maamria(3) Kielty	503
Conf 4	Aug-26	Woking	A	L 0-3		2160
Conf 5	Aug-31	Margate	H	W 2-0	Monk Maamria	327
Conf 6	Sep-03	Southport	A	L 2-4	Harrison Salt	1097
Conf 7	Sep-06	Chester C	A	L 1-2	Guyett(og)	2273
Conf 8	Sep-14	Barnet	H	W 4-2	Maamria(3) Heald	405
Conf 9	Sep-17	Nuneaton B	H	D 1-1	Whittaker	401
Conf 10	Sep-21	Farnborough T	A	L 0-1		595
Conf 11	Sep-24	Scarborough	A	L 0-2		950
Conf 12	Sep-28	Yeovil T	H	L 2-4	Kielty Whittaker	415
Conf 13	Oct-05	Morecambe	A	L 1-2	Kielty	1258
Conf 14	Oct-08	Hereford U	H	L 0-2		425
Conf 15	Oct-11	Stevenage B	H	W 2-1	Kielty CWard	335
Conf 16	Oct-19	Gravesend & N	A	W 3-1	Maamria(2,1p) Monk	1246
LDV 1	Oct-22	Southport	A	W 4-3	Kielty Salt Tolson Howell(og)	481
FAC 4q	Oct-26	Moor Gren	A	L 1-2	Maamria	680
Conf 17	Nov-02	Kettering T	H	D 2-2	Courtney Tolson	402
Conf 18	Nov-09	Northwich V	A	W 1-0	Maamria	608
LDV 2	Nov-12	Wrexham	H	L 3-4	Kielty(2) Maamria	703
Conf 19	Nov-16	Barnet	A	L 0-4		1021
Conf 20	Nov-23	Morecambe	H	W 1-0	Maamria	506
Conf 21	Nov-30	Telford U	H	L 0-3		406
Conf 22	Dec-07	Forest Green R	A	L 1-4	Heald(p)	576
Conf 23	Dec-14	Chester C	H	L 0-4		851
Conf 24	Dec-26	Halifax T	H	L 0-2		815
Conf 25	Dec-28	Doncaster R	A	L 0-1		3719
Conf 26	Jan-01	Halifax T	H	L 0-1		2050
FAT 3	Jan-14	Vauxhall Motors	H	L 1-2	Robertson	229
Conf 27	Jan-18	Burton A	A	W 1-0	Maamria	1393
Conf 28	Jan-25	Woking	H	W 1-0	Courtney	435
Conf 29	Feb-08	Margate	A	L 0-2		535
Conf 30	Feb-15	Southport	H	D 1-1	Monk	565
Conf 31	Mar-01	Nuneaton B	A	W 2-0	Heald(2)	1187
Conf 32	Mar-04	Farnborough T	H	W 3-2	Scott Maden Salt	305
Conf 33	Mar-08	Scarborough	H	L 0-2		525
Conf 34	Mar-11	Yeovil T	A	L 1-3	Scott	5330
Conf 35	Mar-22	Telford U	A	D 1-1	Monk	802
Conf 36	Mar-29	Forest Green R	H	W 1-0	Lancaster	445
Conf 37	Apr-05	Stevenage B	A	L 1-3	Maden	2130
Conf 38	Apr-07	Dagenham & R	H	L 1-3	Monk	403
Conf 39	Apr-12	Gravesend & N	H	D 0-0		385
Conf 40	Apr-19	Hereford U	A	W 1-0	Salt	1690
Conf 41	Apr-21	Northwich V	H	D 1-1	Monk	439
Conf 42	Apr-26	Kettering T	A	W 1-0	Scott	768

Stuart COBURN 1	Gerry HARRISON 2	Paul WILLIAMS 3	Neil DURKIN 4	Wayne MADEN 5	Neil FITZHENRY 6	Ian MONK 7	Ged KIELTY 8	Dino MAAMRIA 9	Neil CAMPBELL 9	Tony BLACK 10	Paddy WILSON 10	Mark PATTERSON 10	Damien WHITEHEAD 11	Mark WARD 12	Neil PRINCE 12	Andy HEALD 14	Phil SALT 15	Nicky SPOONER 16	Liam BLAKEMAN 16	Keith SCOTT 16	Martyn LANCASTER 17	John McGILL 18	Neil FISHER 19	Daniel BENT 19	Ian PENDLEBURY 19	Dominic LUDDEN 20	Ged COURTNEY 21	Chris CORNELLY 32	Neil TOLSON 32	Guy HEFFERNAN 32	Stuart WHITTAKER 33	John ROBERTSON 34	Nicky HILL 34	Chris WARD 34	Mark FORD 34
x	x		x	x	x	x		x		x			x			11	x	4								x									
x	x		x	x	x	x	x	x		x			4			2	x									x									
x			x	x	x	x	x	x		x						x	x					10				x									
x	x		x	x	4	x	x	x		x			14			x	x									x		10							
x	x	20	x	x		x	x	x		x						x	x									x									
x	x	32	x	x		x	x	x		x						x	x					8						x							
x		x	x	x	x	x	x	x		x			10			x	x						6					3							
x		10	x	x	x	x	x	x		x						x	x														x				
x		10	x	x	x	x	x	x		x			8			x	x						8								x				
x		6	x	x	x	x	x	x								x	x														x			x	
x			x	x	x	x	x	x								x	x					34	6								x			x	
x		14	x	x	x	x	x	x								x	x						4				34				x			x	
x		x	x	x	x	x	x	x									x						x				33				x			19	
x		x	x	x	x	x	x	x									x						x				19				x				
x	19	x	x	x	x	x	x	x									x						x				x							21	
x	x		x	x	x	x	x	x						8			x						x				x		21						
x		x	x	x	x	3	x	x								x	x						x				x		21						
x	x	8	x	x	x	x	x	x								19	x						x				x		21						
x	x	x	x		x	x	x										x		3								x		x			x			
x	x		x	x	x	x	x	x									x		34								33		9		x	x			
x	x	x	x	x	x		x	x									x						x								x				
x	x	x		x	x	x	x	x									x		19				x						7		x				
x	x	19	x	x	x	x	x	x									x						x						33		x				
x	x	33	x	x		x	x	x								8	x						x				15		x		x				
x	x		x	x	x	x	x									6	x						34				8		x		x	x			
x			x	x	x	x	x	x								x	x						34				9		14		x	x			
x	x	19	x	x	x		x				x					8							x				10		x		x		x		
x	x	x	x		x		15				21					x	x						33				x		x		x		x		
x	x	x	x	34	x		6				21					x	x							x			x				x		x		
x		x		x	x			x				15				x	x										x		x		x	x			
x	x	x	x		x		x	x									x				x			x			19				x				
x	x	x	x		x		x	x								33	x				x			x			19				x				
x	x	x	x	2	x	x	3	x					21			x	x				x						x								
x	x		x	x	x	x	15	x									x				x						x								x
x		x	x	6	x	x			x				16			x	x			x	x														x
x	3	x	x	x		x			x				9			x	x			x	x						16								x
x	11		x		x	x			x				x			x	x			x	x										6				x
x	3	x	x	x	x	x			x							7	x			x	x						16								x
x	x		x		x	x			x						x	2	6			x	x				x		16								x
x	x		x			x			x							x	x			x	x				x		9			16					x
x	x		x	x	9	x			x						x	12	x			19	x				x										x
x			x	x	19	x			x						x		34			x	x				x		32			x					x
x	x		x	x	x	x			14						x	x				x	x						x								2
x	x		x	x	x	x			x						x	12	x								x					19					x
x	x		x	x	x	x			x						x		x			6					x		9		2						x
x	x		x	x	x	x			x							x	x			x					14		9								x

LEIGH R.M.I.

GROUND DETAILS

Hilton Park,
Kirkhall Lane,
Leigh WN7 1RN
Tel: 01942 743743 (Office)
Fax: 01942 768856
Web site: http://www.leigh-rmi.co.uk

DIRECTIONS:
From M61 junction 5, follow the Westhoughton sign to r'about, then follow signs to Leigh. Keep on main road to the traffic lights, left into Leigh Road, carry on about 3 miles to the traffic lights. Turn left and first right to the next set of lights. Right onto Atherleigh Way, A579 at the first set of traffic lights, turn left (B & Q on right), at the next set of lights turn right into Kirkhall Lane (Leigh town centre), at the 2nd opening on right turn into Prescott St., carry on to top, turn right, ground on left.

CAPACITY:	8000
COVER:	4,000
SEATS:	2,000

CLUBHOUSE: Open matchdays with food available.
Pre-match meals can be arranged.
2 separate function facilities for 200 and 100.

CLUB SHOP: At the ground & open most days. Contact club.

MATCHDAY PROGRAMME

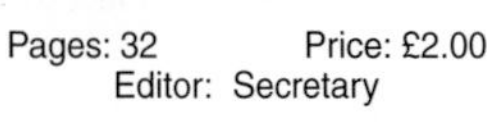

Pages: 32 Price: £2.00
Editor: Secretary

Local Press: Bolton Evening News

Local Radio: Radio Lancs, Red Rose Radio, G.M.R.

Formed:	1896
Nickname:	Railwaymen
Sponsors:	Widdows Mason
Colours:	Red & white striped shirts black shorts and white socks
Change colours:	All Yellow
Midweek home matchday:	Tuesday
Reserve Team	None

CLUB OFFICIALS

Chairman:	T.B.A.
Vice Chairman:	Alan Leach
Directors:	L Berry, K Freer, W Taylor, G Culshaw
President:	T.B.A.
Secretary:	Alan Robinson 55 Janice Drive, Fulwood, Preston, Lancs. PR2 9TY. Tel: 01772 719266 (H) 01942 743743 (Club) 07974 651231 (M)
Press Officer:	Secretary

FOOTBALL MANAGEMENT TEAM

MANAGER:	**MARK PATTERSON**
Asst Manager	Mark Ward
First Team Coach:	Gary Thompson
Physiotherapist:	Dave Pover
Chief Scout:	TBA
Club's Playing Status:	Part - time

Season	League	Div.	Pos.	P	Home W	D	L	F	A	Away W	D	L	F	A	Pts	Manager
02-03	Conference	-	18	42	8	5	8	26	34	6	1	14	18	37	48	Steve Waywell / Mark Patterson
01-02	Conference	-	16	42	6	4	11	29	29	9	4	8	27	29	53	Steve Waywell
00-01	Conference	-	5	42	11	5	5	38	24	8	6	7	25	33	68	Steve Waywell
99-00	N.P.L.	Premier	1	44	15	3	4	42	17	13	5	4	49	28	92	Steve Waywell
98-99	N.P.L.	Premier	8	42	6	10	5	30	26	10	5	6	33	28	63	Steve Waywell
97-98	N.P.L.	Premier	3	42	12	6	3	32	15	9	7	5	31	26	76	Steve Waywell

Season	League	Div.	Pos.	P	W	D	L	F	A	Pts	Manager
96-97	N.P.L.	One	2	42	24	11	7	65	33	83	Steve Waywell
95-96	N.P.L.	One	14	40	14	7	19	53	59	49	Steve Waywell
94-95	N.P.L.	Premier	22	42	9	4	29	49	94	31	Mick Holgate
93-94	N.P.L.	Premier	20	42	8	12	22	50	75	*35	Mick Holgate

HONOURS

Northern Premier League Champions 1999-2000
NPL League Cup 99-00, Division 1 R-up 96-97;
Premier Inter League (GMAC) Cup 87-88;
Cheshire County Lg 78-79,
Challenge Shield 78-79;
Lancs Combination 57-58
R-up 29-30 55-56 66-67,
Lg Cup 28-29 53-54 56-57 65-66,
Div 2 R-up 48-49 50-51;
West Lancs League 10-11 11-12;
Lancs Junior Cup 24-25 29-30 (R-up x 4);
Lancs Floodlit Trophy 84-85 (R-up 83-84);
Lancs FA Cup 84-85

PREVIOUS

Leagues: Lancashire Alliance 1891-97;
Lancashire League 1897-1900;
Lancashire Combination 17-18, 19-39, 46-68;
Cheshire County League 68-82;
North West Counties League 82-83;
Northern Premier League 83-2000

Name: Horwich R.M.I. until 1995

Ground: Grundy Hill, Horwich until 1994

PastPlayers who progressed to the Football League

Harold Lea (Stockport 58),
David Holland (Stockport 59),
Jim Cunliffe (Stockport 60),
Frank Wignall (Everton 58),
Gary Cooper (Rochdale73),
Tony Caldwell (Bolton 83),
Raymond Redshaw (Wigan 84),
Tony Ellis (Oldham 86),
Paul Jones (Oldham , Nov. 99),
SteveJones (Crewe Alex 01).

CLUB RECORDS

Attendance:
(at Horwich) 8,500 v Wigan Ath Lancs Jnr Cup 54
(at Leigh) 7,125 v Fulham, FAC 98-99

Win: Unknown

Career Appearances: Neil McLachlan

Career Goalscorer: Neil McLachlan

Defeat: 2-9 v Brandon Utd (H)
FA Cup 1998-99

Transfer fee paid: £6,000
to Prescot Cables for Peter Cumiskey 99-00

Transfer fee received: £75,000
from Crewe A. for Steve Jones 2001

BEST SEASON

FA Trophy: Quarter Final 90-91

FA Cup: First Round
28-29, 1-2 v Scarborough (H),
82-83, 0-3 v Blackpool (A)
98-99 (replay), 0-2 v Fulham (H) after 1-1,
00-01, 0-3 v Millwall (H - played away)

FA Vase: N/A

League: 00-01 5th Conference

LAST SEASON

F.A. Cup: 4th Qual.Round
F.A. Trophy: 3rd Round
Conference: 18th
Top Goalscorer: Dino Maamria
Player of the Year: Stuart Colby
Captain: Gerry Harrison

LEIGH R.M.I. PLAYING SQUAD

Player	*Birthplace*	*D.O.B.*	*Previous Clubs*

Bold print denotes England semi-professional international.

GOALKEEPERS

Player	Birthplace	D.O.B.	Previous Clubs
Stuart Coburn	Manchester	05.05.75	Altrincham, Trafford, Irlam T, Maine Road

DEFENDERS

Player	Birthplace	D.O.B.	Previous Clubs
Gerry Harrison	Lambeth	15.04.72	Prestwich Heys, Halifax Town, Sunderland, Burnley, Huddersfield T (L), Hereford United (L), Cardiff City (L), Bristol City,Watford
Martyn Lancaster	Wigan	10.11.08	Chester City
Wayne Maden	Preston	17,04.83	Blackpool
Paul Shepherd			Oldham Athletic, Luton Town, Ayr United, Leeds United

MIDFIELD

Player	Birthplace	D.O.B.	Previous Clubs
Ged Courtney	Liverpool		Accrington Stanley, Marine, Stalybridge Celtic
Neil Durkin ENP	Blackburn	01.07.76	Darwen, Padiham, Feniscowles
Ged Kielty UP	Manchester	01.09.76	Manchester C, Cobh Ramblers, Southport, Barrow, Altrincham
Andy Heald	Manchester	26.07.80	Morecambe
Warren Peyton ESP, NC	Bury		Doncaster Rovers, Nuneaton Borough, Bury, Rochdale

FORWARDS

Player	Birthplace	D.O.B.	Previous Clubs
Marcus Hallows	Bolton	07.07.75	Stalybridge Celtic,Leigh RMI,Bolton Wanderers,Horwich RMI
David McNiven	Leeds	27.05.78	Northwich Victoria,Oldham Athletic, York City
Ian Monk GMVC, UP	Burnley	30.06.68	Clitheroe, Ashton U, Macclesfield, Morecambe
Damien Whitehead	Whiston	24.04.79	Macclesfield Town, Drogheda (L), Warrington Town
Noureddine Maamria Tunisia u-21	Tunisia	18.02.74	Southport, Doncaster R, Ayr Utd, Glentoran
Tony Ellis	Salford	20.10.64	Burnley, Rochdale, Stockport, Bury, Blackpool, Preston, Stoke, Preston, Oldham, Nothwich V, Horwich RMI

Departures: Andy Farrell, Jamie Udall, Alistair Lindsay, Dominic Ludden, Neil Fitzhenry, Paul Williams,Tony Black, Neil Fisher, Darren Callard, Peter Connelly, Craig Gilligan, Noureddine Maamria and Tony Ellis.

MARGATE

A second season in the Conference often seems to be an anti climax for players and fans alike, but in Margate's case, although they were playing home games at Dover, the campaign proved to be a success.

Consolidation was the aim as their Hartsdown Park ground was receiving its facelift and this was achieved with some style. The front runners including Leon Braithwaite, Phil Collins and later on Jean-Michel Sigere who all impressed but the squad was well balanced and on their day they could take on the best.

The Kent Senior Cup was won against Welling United, and, although their F.A.Trophy exit to Tamworth was disappointing, the victory over Leyton Orient in a replay at Brisbane Road was the highlight of the season. This win brought a visit from Cardiff City, one of the glamour teams of Division Two and the extra income more than made up for the 0-3 defeat against a very good side.

Manager Chris Kinnear is extremely experienced at non-league level and it will be intertesting to see how his close season rebuilding has left his squad . Adrian Clarke, Che Stadhart and Warren Patmore have joined Sigere in the atttack so there will be plenty of choice and it is very important that Conference form can be retained until the new ground welcomes "The Gate' back home.

(Left to Right) Back Row: Paul Lamb, Eddie Youds, Charlie Mitten, Phil Smith, Warren Patmore, Iain O'Connell **Middle Row:** Jay Saunders, Che Stadhart, Adrian Clarke, Simon Beard, Jake Leberl, Graham Porter, Greg Oates, John Michel Sigere. **Front Row:** Bill Edwards, Paul Abbott, Ian Pulman, Chris Kinnear (Manager), Kevin Raine (Asst. Manager), Terry McFlynn, Darren Annon, John Keister

MARGATE

Match Facts 2002-03

The number shown directly below the player's name is his squad number.
Where a number is shown instead of an "X' in the columns this represents a substitute appearance and the number indicates the player replaced.

Comp.	Date	Opponents	Venue.	Score	Goalscorers	Att.
						SQUAD NUMBER
Conf 1	Aug-17	Morecambe	H	D 1-1	Sodje	413
Conf 2	Aug-20	Kettering T	A	D 1-1	Oates	1602
Conf 3	Aug-24	Northwich V	A	L 0-1		474
Conf 4	Aug-26	Forest Green R	H	W 3-0	McDonald Braithwaite Munday	410
Conf 5	Aug-31	Leigh RMI	A	L 0-2		327
Conf 6	Sep-03	Barnet	H	D 2-2	Braithwaite(2)	735
Conf 7	Sep-07	Stevenage B	H	D 1-1	Braithwaite	520
Conf 8	Sep-14	Nuneaton B	A	L 2-3	Watts Love(og)	918
Conf 9	Sep-17	Woking	A	W 5-1	Braithwaite(3) Watts(2,1p)	1485
Conf 10	Sep-21	Doncaster R	H	W 2-1	Watts Lamb	1002
Conf 11	Sep-24	Dagenham & R	H	L 0-1		686
Conf 12	Sep-28	Burton A	A	W 1-0	Braithwaite(p)	1640
Conf 13	Oct-05	Chester C	H	L 0-1		925
Conf 14	Oct-08	Farnborough T	A	L 1-4	Saunders	741
Conf 15	Oct-12	Halifax T	A	D 2-2	Sodje Stoneman(og)	1519
Conf 16	Oct-19	Southport	H	W 1-0	Collins	565
FAC 4q	Oct-26	Gravesend & N	A	W 2-1	Keister Collins	1850
Conf 17	Nov-02	Scarborough	A	L 2-3	Sodje McFlynn	1134
Conf 18	Nov-09	Telford U	H	D 1-1	Keister	385
FAC 1	Nov-16	Leyton Orient	A	D 1-1	Keister	3605
Conf 19	Nov-23	Chester C	A	L 0-5		1930
FAC 1r	Nov-26	Leyton Orient	H	W 1-0	Keister(p)	2048
Conf 20	Nov-30	Yeovil T	A	L 1-2	Shearer	4147
FAC 2	Dec-07	Cardiff City	H	L 0-3		1362
Conf 21	Dec-14	Stevenage B	A	W 3-1	Collins McFlynn Oates	1272
Conf 22	Dec-21	Nuneaton B	H	D 1-1	Beard	504
Conf 23 X	Dec-28	Kettering T	H	D 2-2	Keister Saunders	1004
Conf 24 X	Jan-01	Gravesend & N	H	W 4-2	Collins Porter Keister Beard	1415
FAT 3	Jan-11	Dulwich Hamlet	A	W 2-0	Sigere Leberl	553
Conf 25 X	Jan-18	Northwich V	H	D 4-4	Collins Braithwaite Beard McFlynn	758
Conf 26	Jan-21	Gravesend & N	A	W 2-1	Sodje Owen(og)	1041
Conf 27	Jan-25	Forest Green R	A	L 1-4	Beard	763
FAT 4	Feb-01	Worcester City	A	W 2-0	Beard Braithwaite(p)	1304
Conf 28	Feb-08	Leigh RMI	H	W 2-0	Collins Saunders	535
Conf 29 X	Feb-11	Hereford U	H	L 0-2		667
Conf 30	Feb-15	Barnet	A	W 1-0	Sodje	1160
FAT 5 X	Feb-22	Tamworth	H	L 0-2		1100
Conf 31	Mar-01	Woking	H	W 2-1	Braithwaite Oates	527
Conf 32	Mar-08	Dagenham & R	A	L 0-3		1901
Conf 33	Mar-11	Morecambe	A	L 0-3		1252
Conf 34	Mar-15	Burton A	H	D 0-0		577
Conf 35	Mar-22	Yeovil T	H	L 1-2	Sigere	1083
Conf 36	Mar-25	Doncaster R	A	L 1-3	Sigere	2888
Conf 37	Mar-29	Hereford U	A	W 3-2	Sigere(2) Collins	1959
Conf 38	Apr-05	Halifax T	H	W 2-1	Saunders Leberl	509
Conf 39	Apr-12	Southport	A	W 2-0	Saunders Keister	768
Conf 40	Apr-19	Farnborough T	H	D 0-0		635
Conf 41	Apr-21	Telford U	A	L 0-1		1016
Conf 42	Apr-26	Scarborough	H	W 3-1	Sodje Sigere Braithwaite	525

Phil SMITH 1	Greg OATES 2	Paul LAMB 3	Bill EDWARDS 4	Lee SHEARER 5	Graham PORTER 6	John KEISTER 7	Leon BRAITHWAITE 9	Simon BEARD 10	Jay SAUNDERS 11	Mark MUNDAY 12	Terry McFLYNN 15	Iain O'CONNELL 16	Phil COLLINS 18	Jake LEBERL 19	Sam SODJE 21	Charlie McDONALD 23	Jean-Michel SIGERE 23	Charlie MITTEN 24	Adrian WEBSTER 25	Adrian CLARKE 25	Steve WATTS 26	Leroy GRIFFITHS 26	Ian PULLMAN 26
x	x	x	x			x	x		x		x	x		x	x				7				
x	x	x	x			x	x		x		19	x		x	x	x							
x	x	16	x		x	x	x		x	15	x	x			x	x							
x	x	x	x	23	11	x	x		x	x	7	x			x	x							
x	x	x	x	23	3	x	x			x	7	x		x	x	x							
	x	x		16	x	x	x		x	7	23	x		x	x	x		x					
	x	x	x	x	x		x		x	4	x		15	x	x			x					
	x	x		x	x	x	x		x		7			x	x			x			x		
	x	x		x	x	x	x		x				9	x	x			x			x		
	x	x		x	x	x	x		x					x	x			x			x		
	x	x		x	x	x	x		x				7	x	x			x			x		
	x	x	2	x	x	x	x		x					x	x			x			x		
		x	x	x	x	x	x		x				26	x	x			x			x		
		x	x	x	x		x	26	x				x	x	x			x			x		
		x	x	x	x		x	x	x				x	x	x			x					
	x	x	x	18	x	x	x		x				x	x	x			x					
	x	x	x	x		x	x	x	x				x	x				x					
	x	x	x	x	3	x	x		x		7		x	x	x			x					
	x	x	x	18	x	x			x		26		x	x	x			x				x	
	x	x	x	x	x	x			x	7	x		x		x			x					
	x	x	x	x	x	x			x	11	x		x		x			x				18	
	x	x	x	x	x	x			x	11	x		x		x			x					
	x	x	x	x	x	x			x	21	x		x		x			x		3		11	
	x	x	x	x	x	x		15	x	5	x		x		x			x		3			
	x		x	x		x		x	x		x		x		x			x		x			
	x		x	x		x		x	x		x		x		x		7	x		x			
	x	25	x		x	x		x	x		x		x		x		7	x		x			
	x		x		x	x		x	x		18		x		x		x	x		x			
	x		x		x	x	23	x	x				x	7	x		x	x		x			
	x				x	x	7	x	x		2		x	x	x		x	x		x			
x	x		x		x		23	x	x		x		x	15	x		x			x			
x	x		x		x	18	15	x	x		x		x	21	x		x			x			
x	x		x		x	x	x	x	x		7		x	10	x					x			
x	x		x			x	x	x	x				x	x	x		18			x			
x	x		x			x	x	x	x				x	x	x		18			x			
x	x		x	2	x		x		x		x		x	x	x		18			x			
x	x		x		x		x	18	x		x		x	x	x		15			x			
x	x		x	x	x	15	x		x		x		x	x			18			x			
x	x	x	x	x		16	x		x		x	x	x	x			9						
x	x	x	x	x		5	x		x		x		x	x	x		18			3			
x	x		x			x	x		x		x			x	x		x			x			
x	x	25	x		23	x	x		x		x			x	x		x			x			
x	x	x	x	21	x		x		x				25	x	x		x			x			
x	x	x	x	18	x		x		x			9	x	x	x		x			5			
x	x	x	x		x				x		x			x	x		x			x			15
x	x	x	x		x	15			x		x	11		x	x		x			x			23
x	x	x	x		x	x	18						x	x	x		x			x			
x	x	x	x		x	x	18				7		x	x	x		x			x			3
x	x	x	x		x	x	x		21		7	6		x	x		x			x			

MARGATE

GROUND DETAILS

Hartsdown Park,
Hartsdown Road,
Margate CT9 5QZ

Telelpone:	01843 221769
Fax:	01843 221769
Email:	office@margatefc.com
Web site:	www.margatefc.com

Directions:
A28 into Margate, turn right opposite Dog & Duck P.H. into Hartsdown Road, proceed over crossroads and ground is on left.
Ten mins walk from Margate (BR)

Capacity:	6,000
Cover:	6,000
Seats:	1000

Clubhouse:
Flexible hours, private functions, matchday facilities.

Club Shop:
Contacts: Dave and Debra Canham (01843 221769)

Hartsdown Park is being completely re-deveolped

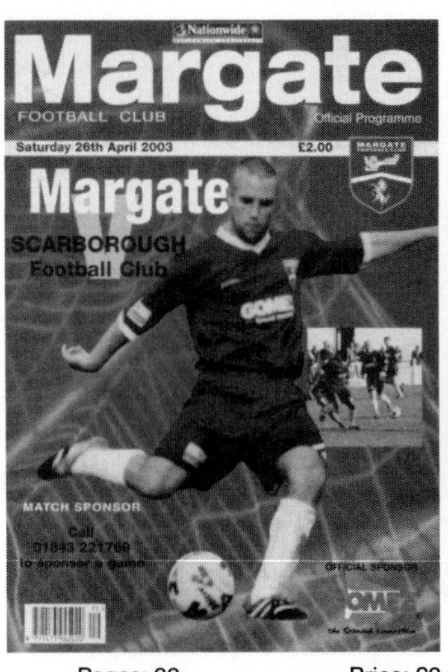

MATCHDAY PROGRAMME

Pages: 32 Price: £2.00
Editor:Keith Smith (07766 232071)
Clubcall: 09068 800 665
Local Press:
Isle of Thanet Gazette, Thanet Times, Thanet Extra
Local Radio:
Radio Kent, Invicta Radio, TLR

Formed:	1896
Nickname:	The Gate
Sponsors:	A Gomez Ltd.
Newsline:	09068 800 665
Colours:	Royal Blue shirts & shorts, white socks
Change colours:	Red shirts withred shorts and black socks
Midweek matchday:	Tuesday

CLUB OFFICIALS

Chairman:	Jim Parmenter
President:	Gordon Wallis
Vice Chairman:	Keith Piperr
Directors:	K Piper & J Parmenter
Secretary:	Ken Tomlinson 65 Nash Road, Margate , Kent CT9 4BT Tel & Fax: 01843 291040 (M) 07710033566
Executive Operations Manager:	David Canham Tel: 01843 299734
Press Officer:	Jim Parmenter 01227 832121(W) 07980 016916 (M)

FOOTBALL MANAGEMENT TEAM

MANAGER	**CHRIS KINNEAR**
Date of Appointment	August 1996
Date of Birth:	10th July 1954
Place of Birth:	Dagenham

PREVIOUS CLUBS

As manager	Dover Athletic
As player	West Ham, Leyton Orient, Wealdstone, Maidstone U., Barnet, Dagenham, Dover A.

HONOURS

As manager Southern Lge: Prem Div. x 3, R-up x1; Southern Div. x1, R-up x1; Lge. Cup x2, R-up x1 Kent Senior Cup: x 3 R-up x 1

* * *

Asst. Manager:	Kevin Hales
Physio:	Joihn Griffin
Chief Scout:	Kevin Raine
Club's Playing Status:	Part-time

Season	League	Div.	Pos.	Home P	W	D	L	F	A	Away W	D	L	F	A	Pts	Manager
02-03	Conference	-	10	42	8	9	4	32	24	7	2	12	28	42	56	Chris Kinnear
01-02	Conference	-	8	42	7	9	5	33	22	7	7	7	26	31	58	Chris Kinnear
00-01	Southern	P	1	42	17	2	2	47	14	11	5	5	28	13	91	Chris Kinnear
99-00	Southern	P	3	42	13	4	4	33	16	10	4	7	31	27	77	Chris Kinnear
98-99	Southern	S	2	42	13	5	3	44	16	14	3	4	40	17	89	Chris Kinnear
97-98	Southern	S	6	42	14	3	4	37	16	9	5	7	34	26	77	Chris Kinnear
96-97	Southern	S	5	42	11	2	8	36	29	10	7	4	34	18	72	Chris Kinnear
95-96	Southern	S	11	42	11	5	5	36	22	7	0	14	32	40	59	Karl Elsey
94-95	Southern	S	13	42	9	2	10	36	37	6	5	10	24	35	52	Mark Weatherley & Andy Woolford
93-94	Southern	S	9	42	13	2	6	44	25	7	6	8	32	33	68	Mark Weatherley & Andy Woolford

HONOURS

HONOURS

Southern Lge 35-36, 00-01
Lge Cp 67-68,97-98, R-up 61-62 74-75,
Div 1 62-63, R-up 66-67, Div 1 Sth 77-78,
East Div R-up 33-34,
Southern Div. R-up: 98-99
Merit Cup 66-67 77-78, Midweek Sect. 36-37,
Kent Lge (4), R-up (5), Div 2 (4), Lge Cp 5),
Kent Senior Cup (6),
Kent Senior Shield (8),
Kent F'lit Cp 62-63 66-67 75-76

PREVIOUS

Leagues: Kent 11-23 24-28 29-33 37-38 46-59; Southern 33-37, 59-2001

Grounds: Margate College;
Dreamland, Northdown Rd; Garlinge

Name: Thanet Utd 1981-89

Past Players who progressed to the Football League

Over 40 including

J Yeomanson (West Ham 47),
D Bing & G Wright (West Ham 51), T Bing (Spurs 56),
S Foster (C Palace 61), J Fraser (Watford 62),
R Walker (Bournemouth 65), K Bracewell (Bury 66),
T Jenkins & R Flannigan (Reading 69-70),
M Blyth (Millwall 78), M Buglione (St Johnstone 92)

CLUB RECORDS

Attendance: 14,500
v Spurs, FA Cup 3rd Rd 73

Goalscorer: Dennis Randall 66 (season 66-67)

CareerAppearances: Bob Harrop

Win: 8-0
v Stalybridge Celtic(H) 01-02, v Tunbridge Wells (H) 66-67,
& v Chatham Town (H) 87-88

Defeat: 11-0
v AFC Bournemouth (A), FAC 1st Rd. 20.11.71

Fee paid: £5,000
for Steve Cuggy (Dover Athletic 93)

Fee received: Undisclosed
for Martin Buglione (St Johnstone 92-93)

BEST SEASON

FA Trophy: 6th Round 2001-2002
FA Cup: Third Round
72-73 0-6 v Spurs (H),
36-37 1-3 v Blackpool (A)
League clubs defeated: Gillingham 29-30,
Q. P.R., Crystal Palace 35-36,
Bournemouth & Boscombe Ath. 61-62, Swansea 72-73
Leyton Orient 2002-03

LAST SEASON

F.A. Cup: 2nd Rd Proper
F.A. Trophy: 5th Round
Conference: 10th
Top Goalscorer: Leon Braithwaite 12
Player of the Year: sam Sodje
Captain: Graham Porter

MARGATE PLAYING SQUAD

Player	*Birthplace*	*D.O.B.*	*Previous Clubs*
GOALKEEPERS			
Charlie Mitten	Woolwich	09.10.74	Dover Athletic, Thamesmead, Gillingham
Phil Smith	Harrow	14.12.79	Dover Athletic, Folkestone Invicta, Millwall
Lee Turner DMP	London	04.03.65	Gravesend, Bury T, Corinthian, Sittingbourne, Corinthian, Leyton Orient
DEFENDERS			
Billy Edwards DMP	12.05.75		Sutton Utd, Tooting & Mitcham, Sutton Utd, Fisher Ath
Paul Lamb DMP	Kent	19.04.73	Gravesend, Ramsgate, Margate, Dartford, Ramsgate
Jake Leberl	Manchester	02.04.77	Dover Athletic,Crewe Alexandra
Greg Oates			
Iain O'Connell DMP	Southend	09.10.70	Dover Ath (£3,000), Southend
Graham Porter DMP		29.10.74	Ashford T, Erith & Belvedere, Horsham, Maidstone Utd
Jay Saunders DMP	Kent	15.01.79	Gravesend, Gillingham
Sam Sodje	Nigeria		Stevenage Borough
MIDFIELD			
Darron Annon RL	London	17.02.72	Enfield, Kingstonian, Brentford, Carshalton Ath
Simon Beard	Bromley	08.09.72	Dover Ath, Hastings T, Sittingbourne, West Ham
John Keister Sierra Leone Int.	Manchester	11.11.70	Stevenage B, Shrewsbury, Chester C, Walsall, Tigres (Sierra Leone)
Terry McFlynn	Magherafelt	27.03.81	Woking, QPR, Manchester Utd
FORWARDS			
Adrian Clarke ES	Cambridge	28.09.74	Southend United, Arsenal,
Wesley Hammond			YouthTeam
Warren Patmore ESP, RP	Kingsbury	14.08.71	Rushden & Diamonds, Yeovil T,, Northwood Ards, Northampton, Millwall,Cambridge Utd, Northwood
Aaron Perry			Youth Team
Jean-Michel Sigere	France	26.01.77	Rushden & Diamonds, Bordeaux (France)
Akpo Sodje	Nigeria	-	Hayes, Stevenage Borough
Che Stadhart RP	London	-	Hampton & Richmond Bor., Chalfont St Peter Leyton Pennant, Stevenage B, Leyton Pennant

Bold print denotes England semi-professional international.

MORECAMBE

Accepted as one of the best footballing sides in the division, Morecambe recovered from hesitant early season form to impress everyone with the quality and consistency of their play. Only the outstanding class of Yeovil Town prevented the Shrimps from challenging for automatic promotion.

England regular Stewart Drummond ruled in mid field and chipped in with eleven goals to go with the power striking of Wayne Curtis and Lee Elam, who also won an England place. Morecambe only lost once at home and Jim Harvey's squad were a confident outfit ready for anyone.Their F.A.Cup run to the Third Round and a second meeting with Ipswich Town proved this. Although they lost, this time at Portman Road, and didn't progress far in the F.A.Trophy, losing to the top club at Yeovil in the Fourth Round, the season was really a considerable success until the dreaded play offs.

In their last twelve Conference games Morecambe won seven, and entered the challenge for the second promotion place as the club who had timed their run to perfection. On the other hand Dagenham & Redbridge, their opponents in the semi-final had lost the plot in the last weeks of the season and looked uncomfortable.

The record books will show that the Essex club won a thrilling two legged tie after penalties and no club really deserved to lose. Morecambe's excellent season had ended in frustration and a very empty feeling. Where was the fairness to it all?

This season will be a real test of character as the squad should be just as good and they know they can hold their own with the best. As we have been told on many occasions the championship isn't a sprint, it's a marathon, so Morecambe will have time to regain their confidence, their style and their determination and who's to say they cannot win promotion outright this time.?

Back Row: Dean Howell, Jim Bentley, Stewart Drummond, Michael Stringfellow, Iain Swan, Adriano Rigoglioso, Wayne Curtis.
Middle Row: Nik Rogan, Chris Lane, Gary Thompson, Craig Mawson, Keiron Walmsley, Danny Carlton, Dale Gordon.
Front Row: Gary Hunter, Paul Osborne, Jim Harvey (manager) Andy Mutch (assistant manager) Lee Dodgson, David Perkins

MORECAMBE

Match Facts 2002-03

The number shown directly below the player's name is his squad number.
Where a number is shown instead of an "X' in the columns this represents a substitute appearance and the number indicates the player replaced.

Comp.	Date	Opponents	Venue.	Score	Goalscorers	Att.
						SQUAD NUMBER
Conf 1	Aug-17	Margate	A	D 1-1	Gouck	413
Conf 2	Aug-20	Halifax T	H	W 2-0	Elam(2)	1524
Conf 3	Aug-24	Yeovil T	H	L 1-2	Swan	1343
Conf 4	Aug-26	Hereford U	A	W 2-1	Curtis(2)	2106
Conf 5	Aug-31	Stevenage B	H	W 3-1	Curtis(2) Carlton	1015
Conf 6	Sep-03	Chester C	A	L 1-2	Drummond	2039
Conf 7	Sep-07	Forest Green R	H	W 4-0	Curtis(2) Elam Drummond	1041
Conf 8	Sep-14	Kettering T	A	L 2-3	Curtis Elam	1353
Conf 9	Sep-18	Northwich V	A	L 2-3	Curtis(p) Black	645
Conf 10	Sep-21	Woking	H	W 5-0	Drummond(3) Rigoglioso Stringfellow	1007
Conf 11	Sep-24	Telford U	H	W 1-0	Curtis	869
Conf 12	Sep-28	Barnet	A	D 1-1	Elam	1250
Conf 13	Oct-05	Leigh RMI	H	W 2-1	Thompson Murphy	1258
Conf 14	Oct-08	Scarborough	A	L 0-1		1179
Conf 15	Oct-12	Dagenham & R	A	D 1-1	Rigoglioso	12198
Conf 16	Oct-19	Farnborough T	H	D 1-1	Rigoglioso	1024
LDV 1	Oct-22	Shrewsbury Town	A	L 0-3		1602
FAC 4q	Oct-26	Grantham Town	H	W 3-1	Rogan(2) Drummond	1055
Conf 17	Nov-02	Burton A	A	W 4-1	Carlton(2) Elam McKearney	1688
Conf 18	Nov-09	Doncaster R	H	W 3-0	Drummond Thompson Carlton	1971
FAC 1	Nov-16	Chesterfield	A	W 2-1	Elam Thompson	3703
Conf 19	Nov-23	Leigh RMI	A	L 0-1		506
Conf 20	Nov-30	Gravesend & N	H	W 2-0	Thompson Elam	1067
FAC 2	Dec-07	Chester C	H	W 3-2	Bentley(2) Rigoglioso	4293
Conf 21	Dec-14	Forest Green R	A	L 0-1		623
Conf 22	Dec-21	Kettering T	H	W 1-0	Curtis	1094
Conf 23	Dec-26	Southport	H	W 3-0	Rigoglioso(2) Curtis	1954
Conf 24	Dec-28	Halifax T	A	L 0-1		2122
Conf 25	Jan-01	Southport	A	W 3-2	Carlton Drummond(p) Rigoglioso	1375
FAC 3	Jan-04	Ipswich Town	A	L 0-4		18529
FAT 3	Jan-14	Lancaster City	A	W 1-0	Elam	2279
Conf 26	Jan-18	Yeovil T	A	L 0-2		4353
Conf 27	Jan-21	Nuneaton B	A	D 1-1	Curtis	718
Conf 28	Jan-25	Hereford U	H	W 3-1	Elam Curtis Tretton(og)	1437
FAT 4	Feb-01	Yeovil T	A	L 1-2	Black	3984
Conf 29	Feb-08	Stevenage B	A	D 1-1	Stringfellow	1809
Conf 30	Feb-15	Chester C	H	D 1-1	Rigoglioso	2012
Conf 31	Feb-22	Woking	A	W 6-0	Carlton(2) Talbot Rigoglioso Thompson Drummond	1491
Conf 32	Mar-01	Northwich V	H	W 3-1	Talbot(2) Rigoglioso	1332
Conf 33	Mar-08	Telford U	A	W 3-0	Elam Curtis Davies(og)	1040
Conf 34	Mar-11	Margate	H	W 3-0	Bentley Elam Black	1252
Conf 35	Mar-15	Barnet	H	D 1-1	Elam	1667
Conf 36	Mar-22	Gravesend & N	A	L 2-3	Curtis Drummond	1040
Conf 37	Mar-29	Nuneaton B	H	W 3-2	Drummond (2p) Mansell(og)	1604
Conf 38	Apr-05	Dagenham & R	H	W 2-1	Rigoglioso Curtis	2069
Conf 39	Apr-12	Farnborough T	A	W 3-2	Black(2) Rodwell(og)	803
Conf 40	Apr-19	Scarborough	H	W 3-1	Bentley Elam Price(og)	1957
Conf 41	Apr-21	Doncaster R	A	D 1-1	Curtis	2783
Conf 42	Apr-26	Burton A	H	W 5-0	Elam Curtis Bentley Thompson Black(p)	2239
PSF 1	May-01	Dagenham & R	A	L 1-2	Goodwin(og)	3447
PSF 2	May-05	Dagenham & R	H	W 2-1	Rigoglioso West(og)	5405

1 Craig MAWSON	2 Dave McKEARNEY	3 Lee COLKIN	4 Jamie MURPHY	5 Jim BENTLEY	6 Stewart DRUMMOND	7 Adriano RIGOGLIOSO	8 Andy GOUCK	9 Robbie TALBOT	11 Gary THOMPSON	12 Neil UBERSCHAR	14 Iain SWAN	15 Alan MORGAN	16 Dave PERKINS	17 Danny CARLTON	18 Mike STRINGFELLOW	19 Ryan BLACK	20 Nick ROGAN	21 Wayne CURTIS	22 Michael KNOWLES	23 Lee ELAM	24 Keith HILL	25 Perry TAYLOR	28 Tony HALLAM	29 Lee COLLINS
x	x	x			x	x	x		x	x	x			11		8	21	x			x			
x	x	x			x	x	x		x	x	x			21				x	11	8	x			
x	x	x			x	x	x		x	x	x				8	12		x		7	x			
x	x	x			x	18			x	11	x			21	x			x	x	x	x			
x	x	x			x	3			x		x			21	x	11		x	x	x	x			
x	x	x			x	11			x		x			2	x	22		x	x	x	x			
x	22	x			x	x				7	x			19	x	x		x	x	x	x			
x		x			x	x	7			22	x			19	x	x		x	x	x	x			
x	x	x			x	12	18			x	x			23	x	x		x		x	x			
x	x	x			x	x	18			24	x			21	x	x		x		x	x			
x	x	x			x	x	9				x			23	x	x	19	x		x	x			
x	x	x	x		x		4			x	x				x	x	19	x		x		21		
x	x	x	11		x	x			18		x				x	x	19	x		x	x			
x	x				x	x	x		x		x			20			7	x	x	x	x			
x	x	x			x	x	24		x	x	x			21			11	x		x	x			
x	x	x			x	x	19		x		x			14		x		x		x	x			
x	x	x		x	x	x					x			21		x	5	x		x	x			
x	x	x		x	x	x	19				x		17	x		x	x				x			
x	x	x		x	x	x	18		x		5		23	x	x					x	x			
x	x	x		x	x	x	7		x		x		14	x		11				x	x			
x	x	x		x	x	x			7		x		17	x	x	23				x	x			
x	x	x		x	x	x	7		14		x		17	x	x					x	x			
x	x	x		x	x	x			x		x		3	x	x	11		23		x				
x	x	x	23	x	x	x			x		x			x	x	11		17		x				
x	x	x	x	x	x			21	x		x				x	4	23	x		x				
x	x	x		x	x				2	19	x				x	x	21	x		x	x			
x	x	x	19	x	x	x			21		x				x	x		x		x	5			
x		x	23	x	x	x		21		x	x			19	x	x		x		x				
x	x	x	15	x	x	x		17	x		x	11		x	x					x				
x	x	x	3	x	x	x		7	x	11	x			x	x					x				
x			x	x	x	x		21	x	x		12	x	7	x			x		x				
x	x		x		x	x		7	x		x	2	x	x	x			17		x				
x			x	x	x	x			x		x	x	x	21	x	7		x		11				
x	x		x	x	x	x			x		5		x		x	18	11	x		x				
x	x	x	x	21					x	x	x	x	x	22		12		x		x				
x			28	x	x	x		17	x		x	x	x	x	x					x			15	
x	x		9	x	x	x		x	x		x		x		x			23		x				
x	x		x		x	x		x	x		x		x	18	x	11		9		x				
x	x			x	x	x		x	x		x	16	x	9	x	21		x						
x	x		11	x	x	x		x	x		x		x		x	23		9		x				
x	x			x	x	x		x	x		x		x		x	9		23		x				
x	x		9	x	x	x		x	x		x		x		x		11	18		x				
x	x		11	x	x	x		7	x		x		x	21	x			x		x				
x	x	28	5	x	x	x		11	x		x		x					x		x				x
x	x		x		x	x		7	x		x		x		29	21		x		x				x
x	x			x	x	x		21	x		x		x		7	29		x		x				x
x	x		14	x	x			21	x		x		x		19	x		x		x				x
x	x		x	x	x			21	x	29			x		x	11		x		x				x
x	x			x	x				x		x	2	x	21	11	x		x		x				x
x	x		14	x	x	x			x		x		x	7	29			x		x				x
x	x		x	x	x	x		7	x	16			x	21	x			x		x				

MORECAMBE

GROUND DETAILS

Christie Park,
Lancaster Road,
Morecambe,
Lancashire LA4 5TJ

TELEPHONE 01524 411797
Fax: 01524 411797

email: neil@morecambefc.com
Web site: http://www.morecambefc.com

DIRECTIONS:
From south leave M6 motorway at junction 34. Follow signs for Morecambe through Lancaster, on A589, go straight across the first 2roundabouts, and at the third (with the Shrimp pub on your left), follow thesigns for Town Centre - Christie Park is approx. 600 metres on your left

CAPACITY: 6,300
SEATED: 1,200
COVERED TERRACING: 4,300

CLUB SHOP: On ground and open on matchdays. Also commercial office open Monday to Friday 9.00 - 5.00 selling the same goods

SOCIAL FACILITIES: J B's open normal licensing hours

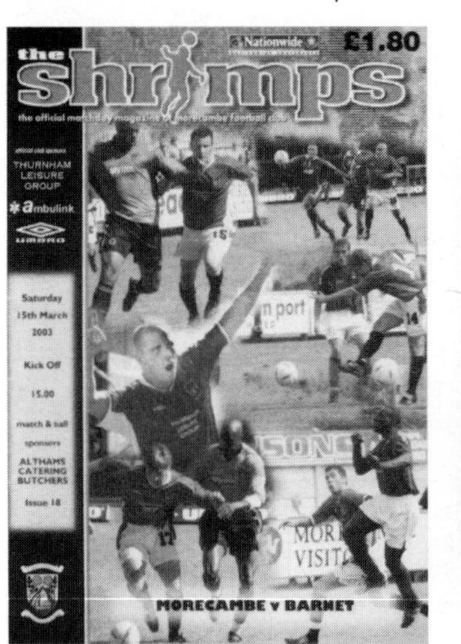

MATCHDAY PROGRAMME

Pages: 48 Price: £2,00
Editor: Sean O'Connor
Other club publications: "Gazetta de la Shrimpa"
Clubcall: 09066 555966

Local Press: Morecambe Visitor; Morecambe Guardian; Lancashire Evening Post; The Citizen
Local Radio: Radio Lancashire; Red Rose Radio; Bay Radio

Founded: 1920

Nickname: The Shrimps

Club sponsor: Thurnham Leisure Group & UMBRO

Club colours: Red shirts, white shorts, black socks

Change colours: Yellow shirts, blue shorts and yellow socks.

Midweek home matchday: Tuesdays, 7.45pm kick-off

Reserve Team's League: Lancashire Lge Div. 1 & North West All. Yth Div.

CLUB OFFICIALS

Honorary President Jim Bowen

Chairman Peter McGuigan

Vice Chairman Graham Hodgson

Directors Peter Cross, Stuart Forrest, Mark Hallam, Rod Taylor

Company & Club Secretary Neil Marsdin

Commercial Manager Peter Howard

FOOTBALL MANAGEMENT TEAM

MANAGER JIM HARVEY

Date of Appointment June 1994
Date & Place of Birth: 2nd May 1958,Lurgan N.Ireland
PREVIOUS CLUBS
As manager None
As asst. manager Morecambe (Jan - June 1994)
As player Glenavon, Arsenal, Hereford Utd., Bristol C., Tranmere Rov., Crewe Alex.
HONOURS
As manager Spalding Cup 97-98; NPL R-up 94-95
Conference Runners-Up 2002-2003
As player N. Ireland - u23.,
Leyland Daf Cup, Mercantile Trophy
Promotion from Division 4 & Division 3

Assistant Manager Andy Mutch
Second Team Manager Jeff Udall
2nd Team Asst. Manager Tony Gribbins
Football in the Community Derek Quinn
Sports Therapist David Edge

Club's Playing Staus: Some full time players

Season

Season	League	Div.	Pos.	P	W	D	L	F	A	W	D	L	F	A	Pts	Manager
					Home					Away						
02-03	Conference	-	2	42	17	3	1	52	13	6	6	9	34	29	78	Jim Harvey
01-02	Conference	-	6	42	12	5	4	30	27	5	6	10	33	40	62	Jim Harvey
00-01	Conference	-	19	42	8	5	8	35	29	3	7	11	29	37	45	Jim Harvey
99-00	Conference	-	3	42	10	7	4	46	29	8	9	4	24	19	70	Jim Harvey
98-99	Conference	-	14	42	9	5	7	31	29	6	3	12	29	47	53	Jim Harvey
97-98	Conference	-	5	42	11	4	6	35	30	10	6	5	42	34	73	Jim Harvey
96-97	Conference	-	4	42	10	5	6	34	23	9	4	8	35	33	66	Jim Harvey

Season	League	Div.	Pos.	P	W	D	L	F	A	Pts	Manager
95-96	Conferece	-	9	42	17	8	17	78	72	59	Jim Harvey
94-95	N.P.L.	Premier	2	42	28	10	4	99	34	94	Jim Harvey
93-94	N.P.L.	Premier	7	42	20	7	15	90	56	67	Bryan Griffiths

HONOURS

F.A. Trophy 73-74,
Spalding Cup 97-98,
Conference Runners-up 2002-2003
Northern Premier Lge R-up 91-92 94-95,
Presidents Cup 91-92,
Lancs Combination 24-25 61-62 62-63 66-67 67-68
R-up 1923-24, 25-26,
Lg Cup 26-27 45-46 64-65 66-68;
Lancashire Junior Cup (now ATS Trophy) x8
25-27 61-63 68-69 85-87 92-93, 95-96;
Lancashire Senior Cup 67-68,

PREVIOUS

Leagues: Lancs Combination 1920-68, Northern Premier 1968-1995

Grounds: Woodhill Lane 1920-25, shared with cricket club who still play there

Past Players who progressed to the Football League

Fred Blondel (Bury 1946),
Herbert Harrison (Accrington 1947),
Gordon Milne (Preston 1956),
Ray Charnley (Blackpool 1957),
Geoff Slack (Stockport 1958),
Ron Mitchell (Leeds 1958), Derek Armstrong (Carlisle 1961),
Alan Taylor(Rochdale 1973),
John Coates (Southport via Burscough & Skelmersdale 1975),
Keith Galley (Southport 1975),
Brian Thompson (West Ham 1977),
Malcolm Darling (Bury 1978)
David Eyres (Blackpool), Kenny Lowe (Barnet via Barrow),
Steve Gardner (Bradford City), Dave Lancaster (Chesterfield)

CLUB RECORDS

Attendance: 9,324 v Weymouth FA Cup 4.1.62

Win: 14-0 v Rossendale Utd, Lancs Combination Sept 1967 (Arnold Timmins scored 8)

Defeat: 0-14 v Chorley(A), 19th April 1946

Transfer fee paid: £25,000 to Northwich V. for Steve Walters, July 2000

Transfer fee received: £175,000 from Rushden & Diamonds for Justin Jackson, July 2000

Career Goalscorer: Keith Borrowdale 289 1956-68, 78-79 Lancashire Combination
John Coleman 130 1990-1995 (Northern Premier League)

Career Appearances: Steve Done 523 + 7 sub 1968-78

BEST SEASON

FA Cup: 3rd Round 1961-62 v Weymouth (H) 0-1
2000-01 v Ipswich T (H) 0-3

League clubs defeated: Chester City 1961-62, Cambridge Utd.(2000-01)

FA Trophy: Winners 73-74,
S-Final: 2001-02
Quarter Final: 72-73, 77-78, 93-94

League: 3rd Conference 1999-2000

LAST SEASON

F.A. Cup: 3rd Round

F.A. Trophy: 4th Round

Conference: 2nd

Top Goalscorer: Wayne Curtis

Player of the Year: Craig Mawson

Club Captain: Stewart Drummond

Semi-Professional Capped Players

John Coleman, Mike Bignall, Brian Healy, Stewart Drummond, Justin Jackson, Lee Elam, Adriano Rigoglioso and Gary Thompson (U23)

Bold print denotes England semi-professional international.

Player	*Birthplace*	*D.O.B.*	*Previous Clubs*
GOALKEEPERS			
Craig Mawson	Keighley	16.05.79	Halifax T, Burnley
DEFENDERS			
Jim Bentley	Liverpool	11.06.76	Telford Utd, Manchester C
Chris Lane	Liverpool	25.05.79	Southport (£12,500), Hereford United, Everton (YTS)
David McKearney	Liverpool	20.06.68	Prescot Cables, Bolton, Northwich V, Crewe, Wigan, Chorley
Jamie Murphy	Manchester	25.02.73	Halifax, Cambridge Utd, Doncaster R, Blackpool
David Perkins	Blackpool		From Youth team
Iain Swan	Glasgow	16.10.79	Leigh RMI, Partick Thistle, Oldham
MIDFIELD			
Ryan-Zico Black NI Y	Manchester	04.08.81.	Youth team
Stuart Drummond ESP	Preston	11.12.75	Youth team
Dean Howell	Burton on Trent	29.11.80	Southport,Stoke City, Notts Co., Crewe Alexandra
Mike Stringfellow	Lancaster	09.10.81	From Youth team
FORWARDS			
Danny Carlton	Leeds	22.12.83	Youth Team
Wayne Curtis	Barrow	06.03.80	Holker OB
Adriano Rigoglioso	Liverpool	28.05.79	Liverpool, Marine
Nick Rogan	Blackpool	15.1083	Kendal Town
Gary Thompson	Kendal	24.11.80	Youth team

Departures: Greg Brown, Mark Wright, Nick Coyle,Colin Woodthorpe,Keith Hill, Lee Colkin, Neil Uberschar, Andy Gouck,Michael Knowles, Lee Elam, Ian Arnold and Robbie Talbot

NORTHWICH VICTORIA

Probably the most important news for Northwich Victoria has been the fact that funds seem to be available for their new ground.

To outsiders it seems very strange that such a renowned club with such a famous ground should be allowed to be split up at all.

But it's happened and while the Vics are playing at Witton Albion's Wincham Park (also a comparatively new ground), they must improve their home form.

Last season the Vics were a middle of the table team in results and ambition. You felt they were happy to be away from the danger zone, but realistic enough to realise they were not going to challenge for honours.

They were probably expecting to lose away to Yeovil Town in the F.A.Trophy and were pleased to get through to lose 0-3 to Scunthorpe United in the F.A.Cup.

This isn't to say the club had lost its way, but it had lost its home and, as the only outfit to have qualified to contest every Conference season (Telford United were spared relegation when the club due promotion failed a ground grading), they deserved to be able to pace themselves as they re-grouped away from their historic Drill Field.

Manager Jimmy Quinn still helped the lads on the field and scored a few goals, while Gregg Blundell did well enough to gain a transfer to Doncaster Rovers and into the Football League. Quinn has moved on and the club will be hoping to improve on fourteenth position, but realistically it may be difficult to lift the players and supporters without a home of their own.

NORTHWICH VICTORIA

Match Facts 2002-03

The number shown directly below the player's name is his squad number.
Where a number is shown instead of an "X" in the columns this represents a substitute appearance and the number indicates the player replaced.

Comp.	Date	Opponents	Venue.	Score	Goalscorers	Att.
						SQUAD NUMBER
Conf 1	Aug-17	Stevenage B	A	D 2-2	Garvey Norris	1636
Conf 2	Aug-20	Burton A	H	L 1-3	Rioch	893
Conf 3	Aug-24	Margate	H	W 1-0	Blundell(p)	474
Conf 4	Aug-26	Halifax T	A	W 5-0	Blundell(3) Devlin McNiven	1491
Conf 5	Aug-31	Doncaster R	H	L 1-2	Allan	1160
Conf 6	Sep-07	Yeovil T	A	L 1-2	Allan	2154
Conf 7	Sep-14	Woking	A	W 3-2	Street(2) Blundell	1649
Conf 8	Sep-18	Morecambe	H	W 3-2	Blundell Street Allan	645
Conf 9	Sep-21	Kettering T	A	D 2-2	Norris Norman(og)	1286
Conf 10	Sep-24	Nuneaton B	A	W 4-1	Blundell(2,1p) Street Allan	1012
Conf 11	Sep-28	Gravesend & N	H	L 1-2	Blundell	760
Conf 12	Oct-05	Farnborough T	H	D 2-2	Taylor Allan	658
Conf 13	Oct-08	Southport	A	D 1-1	Owen	984
Conf 14	Oct-13	Scarborough	H	L 1-4	Blundell	1156
Conf 15	Oct-15	Hereford U	H	W 2-1	Street(2)	1400
Conf 16	Oct-19	Dagenham & R	A	L 0-2		720
FAC 4q	Oct-26	Spennymoor United	H	W 3-1	Norris Woodward Quinn	713
Conf 17	Nov-02	Barnet	A	W 4-3	Allan(2) Blundell Doolan(og)	1093
Conf 18	Nov-09	Leigh RMI	H	L 0-1		608
FAC 1	Nov-16	Scunthorpe United	H	L 0-3		1724
Conf 19	Nov-23	Farnborough T	A	L 2-3	Allan Blundell	641
Conf 20	Nov-30	Forest Green R	H	W 2-1	Garvey Blundell	460
Conf 21	Dec-07	Telford U	A	L 0-1		726
Conf 22	Dec-14	Yeovil T	H	L 1-2	Devlin	691
Conf 23	Dec-21	Woking	H	L 1-3	Owen	506
Conf 24	Dec-26	Chester C	H	D 1-1	Devlin	2305
Conf 25	Dec-28	Burton A	A	D 1-1	Quinn	1833
Conf 26	Jan-01	Chester C	A	W 3-2	Devlin Quinn(p) Blundell	3151
Conf 27	Jan-04	Stevenage B	H	D 1-1	McNiven	690
FAT 3	Jan-14	Barrow	H	W 3-1	Blundell Quinn Maxfield(og)	543
Conf 28	Jan-18	Margate	A	D 4-4	Norris Devlin Blundell Mitten(og)	758
Conf 29	Jan-25	Halifax T	H	L 0-2		1014
FAT 4	Jan-31	Canvey Island	H	W 2-1	Garvey Teather	708
Conf 30	Feb-08	Doncaster R	A	W 2-1	McNiven(p) Blundell	2941
Conf 31	Feb-15	Hereford U	H	D 2-2	McNiven Teather	896
FAT 5	Feb-22	Yeovil T	A	L 1-2	Blundell	4469
Conf 32	Mar-01	Morecambe	A	L 1-3	Blundell(p)	1332
Conf 33	Mar-08	Nuneaton B	H	W 3-1	Blundell Devlin McNiven	582
Conf 34	Mar-15	Gravesend & N	A	D 1-1	Blundell	1017
Conf 35	Mar-18	Kettering T	H	L 1-2	Turner	459
Conf 36	Mar-22	Forest Green R	A	L 0-1		676
Conf 37	Mar-28	Telford U	H	W 2-1	Garvey McNiven	530
Conf 38	Apr-05	Scarborough	H	L 0-2		503
Conf 39	Apr-12	Dagenham & R	A	L 0-2		1494
Conf 40	Apr-19	Southport	H	W 2-1	Allan Garvey	700
Conf 41	Apr-21	Leigh RMI	A	D 1-1	Allan	439
Conf 42	Apr-26	Barnet	H	D 1-1	Norris	523

Paul GIBSON	Gary KELLY	Chris ROYLE	Greg RIOCH	Rob MATTHEWS	Andy TURNER	Denny INGRAM	Steve DAVIS	Steve GARVEY	Val OWEN	Gregg BLUNDELL	David McNIVEN	Mark DEVLIN	Andy TAYLOR	Jake SEDGEMORE	Richard NORRIS	Andy WOODWARD	Danny GRIGGS	Steve WALSH	Mark McGUIRE	Jimmy QUINN	Kevin STREET	Jamie McGUIRE	Jon ALLAN	Ben CONNETT	Paul TEATHER	Danny JARRETT	Matthew PARRY	Shaun CAME	Gareth SEDDON	Damien WHITEHEAD	Gareth OWEN
1	**2**	**3**	**4**	**4**	**5**	**6**	**7**	**8**	**9**	**10**	**11**	**12**	**14**	**15**	**16**	**17**	**18**	**19**	**20**	**21**	**21**	**23**	**24**	**25**	**28**	**29**	**30**	**31**	**31**	**32**	
x		x	x	x			x	x		x	4	x	14	x	x	x															
x		x	x	x			x	x		x	4	x	x		x	x	6			12											
x		x	x	x		x		x		x	x	x	4	15	x	x				10											
x		x	x			x		x	x	x	x	x	15		x	x			16	8											
x		x	x	15		x		x	x	x	x	x	7		x	x							10								
x		x	x			x		x	x	x		x	11		x			x			15		x								
x		x	x			x		12	x	x		x	x		21		23	x			x		x								
x		x	x			x		11	x	x		x	x	8				x			x		x								
x		x	x			x		x		x		x	x		23		12	x			x		x			5					
		x	x			x		12		x		x	x	x	11	18		x			x		x				x				
		x	x			x		x		x		x	x	x	14	x							x				x				
x			x	12				17	x	x	9	x	x	x			x	x			x		x								
x		x	x			x		12	x			x	x	x			x			23	x		x								
x		x				x		17	x	x	x	x	18	x			x	x		10	x										
		x	x			x		21	x	x		x	x	x	23						x		x				x				
		x	x	15		x		12	x	x		x	x	x	x					11	x						x				
		x	x			x		2		x		x		x	11	x		x		23	x		x				x				
		x				x				x		x		x	x	x		x			x		x				x				
						x		11		x		x	x	x	x			x		12	x		x				x	x			
						x		23	x	x		x		x	x			x		18	x		x				x	x			
			x			x		8	x	x		x		18	x			x			x		x	x				x			
			x			x		x	x	x		x	7	x	x					23			x				x	x			
		x	x			x		x	x	x		x	2	x	x		8			x					3		x				
		x	x						x	x		x	18	x	x		23	x		x			x				x				
		x	x			x			x	x		x		x	x		20			x			x		11		x				
		x	x			x		15	x	x		x	17	x	x		x			23			x				x				
			x			x		8	x			x	17	x	x		x			x			x				x	x			
			x			x		18		x	20	x	x	x	x		9	x		x							x	x			
						x		x		x	18	x	x	x	x		12	x		31							x	x	x		
						x	x	x		x	x	x	25	x	x		10	6		x					x		x				
		x				x		x		x	x	x	25	x	x			10		x					x		x				
		x	x			x		x		x	x	x		x	x		7			x							x				
		x	x			x		x		x	x	x		x	x		3			9			10		x		x				
	x	x				x	x	x		x	x	x		x	x		23						x		11						
	x	x				x	x	x		x	x			x			30			17			x		x			x			
	x	x	x			x	x	x		x	x	x			x					20			x		23						
	x	x	x			x	x	x		x	7	x		x	x								x		15						
	x	x	x			x		x		x	x	x	23	x	x								x								
	x	x	x		7	x		x		x	x	x		x	x								x					23			
	x	x	x		23	x		x		x	x	x	15	x	x								x					2			
	x	x	x			x		x		x	x	x		x	25					10			3		x			x			
		x	x			x		x			x	x		x	10												x	x		x	x
		x	x			x		x			x	x	14	x	32								3				x	x		x	x
		x				x	x	x			31	x	11	x	x					x		x					x			x	
		x	x				x	x			x	x		x	x							x	x	x						23	
		x	x				x				x	x	x	x	x							x	x	x							15
		x	x				x	x			x	x	x	x	11								x	x						12	x

NORTHWICH VICTORIA

GROUND DETAILS

Wincham Park,Wincham,Northwich, Cheshire
Tl/Fax:01606 43008

Directions: At.Jct 19 M6 take A556 towards Northwich for 3 miles, then right at dual carriageway into A539 for half a mile to lights.. Turn right and after 3/4 mile, turn left opposite BlackGreyhound Inn. Ground is half a mile on left after canal bridge.

CAPACITY	4,000
SEATED	800
COVERED TERRACING	1,500
CLUB SHOP	Located outside ground.Open match days

CLUBHOUSE:
Large social club with members lounge and seperate function room-both available for hire. Bass Beer, Pool, Darts, TV etc. Witton Albion Social Club at Wincham Park welcomes all away supporters.

Correspondancr to:
Northwich Victoria F.C., Leftwich House, Queen Street,Northwich, Cheshire. CW9 5JN

MATCHDAY PROGRAMME

Editor: Brian Edge

Pages: 48 Price: £2.00

Other club publications: 'Distant Vics'
(a bi-monthly magazine for exiled Vics' fans)

Local Press: Northwich Guardian (Wed.); Northwich Chronicle (Wed.); Daily Post; Manchester Evening News Pink (Sat.)
Local Radio: GMR (BBC Manchester); Piccadilly Radio; Signal Radio

Founded:	1874
Nickname:	Vics,Greens or Trickies.
Club Sponsors:	Britannia Carpets
Club colours:	Green shirts, white shorts and white socks
Change colours:	Sky Blue / navy /navy
Midweek home matchday:	Tuesday
Reserve Team's league:	Lancashire League

CLUB OFFICIALS

Chairman Dave Stone

Company Secretary Graham Cookson

Directors Derek Nuttall, Jim Rafferty

Associate Directors
Graham Cookson (Co.Sec), Dave Edgeley, Ted Carthy(Gen Man), Peter Garret, Dave Thomas.

President &
Football Secretary Derek Nuttall c/o the club
Tel: 01606 41450 Fax: 01606 330577

Commercial Manager: Brian Edge Tel : 01606 41450 or 07711 505414

FOOTBALL MANAGEMENT TEAM

MANAGER: Steve Davis

Assistant Manager:	Brendan O'Connell
First Team Coach:	Steve Davis
Physio:	Phil Lea
Res& YouthTeam Manager:	Ted Carthy
Club's Playing Status:	Part-time

Season	League	Div.	Pos.	P	Home W	D	L	F	A	Away W	D	L	F	A	Pts	Manager
02-03	Conference	-	14	42	6	5	10	26	34	7	7	7	40	38	51	Jimmy Quinn
01-02	Conference	-	13	42	9	4	8	32	34	7	3	11	25	36	55	Jimmy Quinn
00-01	Conference	-	17	42	8	7	6	31	24	3	6	12	18	43	46	Mark Gardiner/Keith Alexander
99-00	Conference	-	18	42	10	8	3	33	25	3	4	14	20	53	51	Mark Gardiner
98-99	Conference	-	7	42	11	3	7	29	21	8	6	7	31	30	66	Phil Wilson/Mark Gardiner
97-98	Conference	-	9	42	8	9	4	34	24	7	6	8	29	35	60	Phil Wilson
96-97	Conference	-	6	42	11	5	5	31	20	6	7	8	30	34	63	Mark Hancock/ Phil Wilson

Season	League	Div.	Pos.	P	W	D	L	F	A	Pts	Manager
95-96	Conference	-	8	42	16	12	14	72	64	60	Brian Kettle
94-95	Conference	-	10	42	14	15	13	77	66	57	John Williams
93-94	Conference	-	15	42	11	19	12	44	45	52	John Williams

HONOURS

Welsh Cup R-up 1881/82,1888-89; FA Trophy 1983/84, R-up 1982/83 & 1995/96; Bob Lord Trophy 1979/80, 92/93; Northern Premier Lge R-up 1976/77; Northern Premier Lge Cup 1972/73, R-up 1978/79; Cheshire County Lge 1956/57, R-up 1924/25, 47/48; Cheshire County Lge Cup 1925/35; Manchester Lge 1902/03, R-up 1900/01, 03/04, 07/08, 08/09, 11/12; The Combination R-up 1890/91; Cheshire Senior Cup 1880-81, 81/82, 82/83, 83/84, 84/85, 85/86,1928/29, 36/37, 49/50, 54/55, 71/72, 76/77, 78/79, 83/84, 93/94. R-up 1891/92,96/97, 1905/06, 08/09, 47/48, 50/51, 63/64, 65/66, 69/70, 70/71, 77/78, 85/86; 98/99 Staffordshire Senior Cup 1978/79, 79/80, 89/90, R-up 1986/87, 90/91; CheshireAmateur Cup 1901/02, R-up 1898/99, 02/93, Northwich Senior Cup 1948/49, 58/59,59/60, 63/64, 64/65, 65/66, 67/68, 68/69, 69/70, 71/72, 74/75, R-up x7; Mid Chesh Sen Cup 1984/85, 85/86, 87/88, 89/90, 00-01 91/92, 93/94, 94/95, 96/97,98/99,01-02, R-up 1982/83, 83/84, 90/91, 92/93;02-03; North-West Floodlit Lge 1966/67, 75/76; Cheshire Lge Lancs. Comb. Inter-Lge Cup 1961/62; Guardian Charity Shield 1985/86, 86/87, 87/88

PREVIOUS

Leagues: The Combination 1890-1892, Football League Div.2 1892-94, The Combination 1894-1898, The Cheshire League 1898-1900, Manchester League 1900-12, Lancashire 1912-19, Cheshire County League 1919-68, Northern Premier League 1968-79

Grounds: The Drill Field

Past Players who progressed to the Football League

Tony Hemmings (Wycombe W), Tony Bullock (Barnsley), Darren Tinson (Macclesfield T) Lee Steele (Shrewsbury) Paul Tait (Crewe Alex),Shaun Teale (Tranmere R & Aston Villa) , Mark Birch (Carlisle U),Mark Birch (Carlisle U) and Gary Fletcher (Leyton O,Mark Bailey &Adie Mike (LincolnC) Kevin Street (Bristol R) and Greg Blundell (Doncaster R)

CLUB RECORDS

Attendance: 11,290 v Witton Albion, Cheshire League, Good Friday 1949

Win: 17-0 v Marple Ass. 15.12.1883
Defeat: 3-10 v Port Vale 7.2.1931

Career Goalscorer: Peter Burns 160 - 1955-65
Career Appearances: 970 by Ken Jones 1969-85

Transfer Fee paid: £12,000 to Hyde United for Malcolm O'Connor - August 1988
Transfer Fee received: £50,000 from Leyton Orient for Gary Fletcher - June 2001 from Chester City for Neil Morton -October 2001

BEST SEASON

FA Cup: Quarter Finals 1883-84
League clubs defeated: Rochdale,Peterborough,Watford (all 76-7),Chester C (82-3).,Crewe A(84-5) & Bury (00-1)

FA Trophy: Winners 83-84 R-up 82-83 95-96

League: 4th Conference 80-81

LAST SEASON

F.A. Cup: 1st Round
F.A. Trophy: 5th Rd Round
Conference: 14th
Top Goalscorer: Greg Blundell 19
Player of the Year: Jake Sedgemore
Captain: Val Owen

NORTHWICH VICTORIA PLAYING SQUAD

Player	*Birthplace*	*D.O.B.*	*Previous Clubs*	Bold print denotes England semi-professional international.
GOALKEEPERS				
Ben Connett			Liverpool	
Andy Woods	Colchester Rovers, Barrow		Scarborough, Halifax Town, Doncaster	ESP
DEFENDERS				
Phil Brazier			Vauxhall Motors, Liverpool	
Lee Brough British Univ.			Youth Team	
Shaun Came	Crewe	15.06.83	Macclesfield Town	
Keiron Charnock			Wigan Athletic	
Mark Foran	Aldershot	30.10.73	Telford United, Bristol Rovers 75,000),Crewe Alexandra, Peterborough United, Sheffield United, Millwall.	
Chris Royle	Manchester	-	Winsford Utd, Congleton T, Witton Alb., Northwich V, Reading	
Lee Woodyatt	Chester		Chester City	
Steve Walsh	Warrington		Reserve Team	
MIDFIELD				
Chris Blackburn	Chester	02.08.82	Chester City	
Mark Devlin	Irvine	08.01.73	Stoke, Exeter	
Steve Garvey	Stalybridge	22.11.73	Blackpool, Crewe Alexandra	
Richard Norris	Birkenhead	05.01.78	Marine, Crewe	
Val Owen	Manchester	-	Southport, Hednesford T, Northwich V, Hyde Utd	
FORWARDS				
Jonathon Allen	Carlisle		Carlisle United	
Dean Butterworth			Chorley, Trafford,Abbey Hey	
Chris Thompson	Liverpool		Grimsby Town	
Chris Ward			Birmingham City(£70,000), Lincoln City (L), Lancaster City	

Departures:
Paul Gibson, Jamie Bates, Steve Capper, Andy Woodward, Denny Ingram, Greg Rioch, Jake Sedgemore, Andy Taylor, Craig Skinner, Rob Matthews, Gregg Blundell, Jimmy Quinn, Danny griggs, David McNiven, Kevin Street and Michael Holt.

SCARBOROUGH

Only a Scarborough supporter really knows how horrific the situation was at the McCain Stadium last season.

We read about financial troubles and can only sympathise with all those who were just attempting to follow their favourite football club as it lurched from one frightening heading to another.

Chairman Malcolm Reynolds must have wondered what he had taken on when he realised the club had to go into administration, a player had to serve a term 'inside', the club secretary resigned during the season and the ground capacity was slashed by the council. Poor discipline from a previous campaign raised the threat of suspension and a director was jailed for offences away from the football club.

Considering these incredible situations how the outfit managed to complete the campaign in a more than respectable position is a great credit to manager Russell Slade.

Hopefully, a tranquil summer break has given the staff a chance to boost the squad and concentrate on a solid pre-season and perhaps a quieter campaign ahead.

The knock out cups gave some relief from the pain with a reasonable run to the Fourth Round in the F.A.Trophy before a disappointing defeat at the hands of Dover Athletic, while the F.A.Cup brought a tie with Cambridge United and Boro only went out after a replay.

In the early days of the F.A.Trophy, Scarborough built a terrific reputation for themselves and how good it would be to see them pull away from the squalid off field schemings and once again demand the headings for the right reason - a Trophy Final.

Their supporters certainly deserve it !

Left to Right - Back row: Karl Rose, Keith Gilroy, Shaun Rennison, Gareth Downey, Leigh Walker, James Dudgeon, Glenn Downey, Mark Quayle
Front row: Ashley Lyth, Jacques Williams, Tommy Raw, David Pounder, Nick Henry (player-coach), Russell Slade (manager), Brian Hodgson (kit manager), Michael Price, Mark Hotte, Scott Kerr, Steve Baker.

SCARBOROUGH

Match Facts 2002-03

The number shown directly below the player's name is his squad number.
Where a number is shown instead of an "X' in the columns this represents a substitute appearance and the number indicates the player replaced.

Comp.	Date	Opponents	Venue.	Score	Goalscorers	Att.
						SQUAD NUMBER
Lg 1	Aug-17	Burton A	A	D 1-1	Rose	1821
Lg 2	Aug-20	Southport	H	D 2-2	Shepherd Scott	1346
Lg 3	Aug-24	Dagenham & R	H	L 0-1		1192
Lg 4	Aug-26	Chester C	A	D 0-0		2292
Lg 5	Aug-31	Woking	H	D 1-1	Scott	1192
Lg 6	Sep-03	Halifax T	A	L 1-2	Shepherd(p)	1557
Lg 7	Sep-07	Kettering T	H	W 4-1	Fatokun(2) Shepherd(p) Dryden	1078
Lg 8	Sep-14	Farnborough T	A	D 1-1	Fatokun	629
Lg 9	Sep-16	Telford U	A	W 2-0	Pounder G Brown(og)	756
Lg 10	Sep-21	Barnet	H	D 1-1	Scott	1266
Lg 11	Sep-24	Leigh RMI	H	W 2-0	Fatokun Sillah	950
Lg 12	Sep-28	Hereford U	A	W 1-0	Pounder	2171
Lg 13	Oct-05	Gravesend & N	A	L 2-5	Scott(2)	1259
Lg 14	Oct-08	Morecambe	H	W 1-0	Fatokun	1179
Lg 15	Oct-13	Northwich V	H	W 4-1	Campbell(2) Scott Pounder	1156
Lg 16	Oct-19	Forest Green R	A	D 0-0		751
LDV 1	Oct-22	Doncaster R	H	L 1-2	Scott	1206
FAC 4q	Oct-26	Arnold Town	A	W 2-0	Scott(2)	910
Lg 17	Nov-02	Margate	H	W 3-2	Ormerod Pounder Raw	1134
Lg 18	Nov-09	Nuneaton B	A	D 1-1	Scott	1237
FAC 1	Nov-16	Cambridge United	H	D 0-0		2084
Lg 19	Nov-23	Gravesend & N	H	W 3-2	Mallon Campbell Scott	1205
FAC 1r	Nov-26	Cambridge United	A	L 1-2	Jordan	3373
Lg 20	Nov-30	Stevenage B	A	D 1-1	Campbell	1629
Lg 21	Dec-07	Yeovil T	H	W 2-1	Fatokun O'Brien(og)	1470
Lg 22	Dec-14	Kettering T	A	W 3-1	Scott Holdsworth Ormerod	1372
Lg 23	Dec-21	Farnborough T	H	W 1-0	Bunce(og)	1403
Lg 24	Dec-26	Doncaster R	H	L 2-5	Shepherd(p) Henry	3435
Lg 25	Dec-28	Southport	A	D 1-1	Brassart	1049
Lg 26	Jan-04	Burton A	H	W 4-1	Blunt(2) Shepherd Fatokun	1428
FAT 3	Jan-14	Stalybridge Celtic	A	W 3-0	Raw Sillah Bowman(og)	613
Lg 27	Jan-18	Dagenham & R	A	L 0-1		1566
Lg 28	Jan-25	Chester C	H	L 0-1		1938
Lg 29	Feb-08	Woking	A	L 1-2	Rose	1631
FAT 4	Feb-11	Dover Athletic	H	D 1-1	Pounder	965
Lg 30	Feb-15	Halifax T	H	L 0-1		1835
FAT 4r	Feb-17	Dover Athletic	A	L 1-2	Dempsey	801
Lg 31	Feb-22	Barnet	A	L 0-3		1056
Lg 32	Mar-01	Telford U	H	L 1-4	Sillah	824
Lg 33	Mar-08	Leigh RMI	A	W 2-0	Cohen Taylor	525
Lg 34	Mar-15	Hereford U	H	W 2-1	Pounder Taylor	1179
Lg 35	Mar-22	Stevenage B	H	L 1-2	Shepherd(p)	1193
Lg 36	Mar-28	Yeovil T	A	L 0-1		7008
Lg 37	Apr-01	Doncaster R	A	W 1-0	Sillah	4155
Lg 38	Apr-05	Northwich V	A	W 2-0	Pounder(2)	503
Lg 39	Apr-12	Forest Green R	H	W 3-0	Pounder(2) Taylor	1146
Lg 40	Apr-19	Morecambe	A	L 1-3	Fatokun	1957
Lg 41	Apr-21	Nuneaton B	H	W 4-1	Sillah Gilroy(p) Taylor Weatherstone(og)	1451
Lg 42	Apr-26	Margate	A	L 1-3	Cohen	525

Andy WOODS	Scott JORDAN	Mark HOTTE	Paul SHEPHERD	Shaun RENNISON	Steve BAKER	Jason BLUNT	Gareth STOKER	Neil CAMPBELL	Karl ROSE	David POUNDER	Anthony ORMEROD	Darren CONNELL	Gary COHEN	Cleveland TAYLOR	Leigh WALKER	David HENDERSON	Michael PRICE	Gary BRADSHAW	Danny HALL	Keith GILROY	Scott KERR	Olivier BRASSART	Bimbo FATOKUN	Mohammed SILLAH	Mark PATTERSON	Richard CRAWFORD	Colin CRYAN	Ryan MALLON	Paul DEMPSEY	Richard DRYDEN	Nick HENRY	Keith SCOTT	David RIDLER	Tom RAW	David HOLDSWORTH
1	2	3	4	5	6	7	8	9	10	11	12	14	15	16	17	18	18	19	19	19	20	21	22	23	24	25	25	25	25	26	27	28	28	29	30
x		11	x	x	x		x	x	x	21	9											x								x	x	x			
x	21		x	x	x		x		x	12	x											x								x	x	x			
x		x	x	x	x	12	x	10	x	x	x																				x	x			
x		x	x	x			x	12	x	x	x																			x	x	x			
x		x	x	x			x	10	x	x	x											x								x		x			
x		x	x	x			x	10	x	x	x											x	12							x		x			
x	x	x	x	x			24	x	22		9											x	x		x					x		x			
x		x	x	x			x		12	3	x											x	x		22					x	x	x			
x		x	x	x			24		22	x												x	x		x					x	x	x			
x		x	x	x		26	24		x	x												x			x					x	x	x			
x	x	x	x	x			27	22		x	28											x	x	x							x	x			
x	x	x	x	x			x	28	22	x												5	x	x						x		x			
x	x	x	x				x	x	21	x	4											x	9	x						x		x			
x		x	x				x	28	x	x	x											x	x			26				x		x			
x	28	x	x				x	10	x	x	x											x	x				x			22		x			
x	4	x	x			22	x	x		x	x											x	x				x			x					
		x	x			28	x	x		x	x				x							x	x				x				21	x		22	
		x	x			12	x	x	28	x	x				x								29							x	x	x		x	
		x	x			11	x		x	x	x				x																x	x		x	x
		x				21	x	x		9	x				x							x								x	x	x		x	x
x		x	x			9	x	x		x	x												29	27							x	x		x	x
x	12		x			x	x	x	28	x	x																	x		x		x			x
x	x	x	x			11	x	x	9	x	x												29									x		x	x
x	x	x	x			x	x	x		12	x											25	28					x				x			x
x	x	x	x			x	x	x		25	x												9					x				x			x
x	x	x	x			x			x	7	x											x	10					x		28		x			x
x	x	x	x			x	x	x	12	9	x											2						x				x			x
x		x	x			x	x	x		25	x											x						x			4	x			x
x		x	x			12	x	x	9	x	x											x						27		x	x	x			
x		x	x			10	x	28	x	x	x											x	x									x			x
		x	x				x		x	x	x				x	8						x	x	27						x	x			22	
x		x				x	x		x	x												x	x							x	x			22	x
		x	x			9	x	x	x	27	x				x							x								x	x	3			x
x			x				x	29	x	x	x				28							x							11	x		x		x	x
x		x	x				x	10	x	x	x											x							29	x		x		x	
x		x	x				x	28		x	x							x					8						x	x		x			x
x		x	x				x	x		x	11					3						x							x	x		x			x
		x	x				x			x	x		x	x	x				x					19					x						x
x		x	x				x			x	19	15	x	x				x					16	x					x						x
x		x	x				x			x			x	x							x	x		x					15						x
x			x				x			x		15	x	x			x				x	x		x					x						
x			x							x	x		x	x			x				x	x	12	x					x						
x		15	x							x			x	x						x	x	x	25	x					x				x		
x							x			x			x	15			x			x	x		x	x					x				x		
x					25		x			x	16			x			x			x	x	22	x	x					x				x		
x		18	21				x			x		22		x			x			x		x	x	x					x				x		
x			x				x			x		16		x			x			x	x		x	x									x		
x							x			x		22		x			x			x	x		x	x					x				x		
x		25					x						16	x			x			x	x	x	x	x					x				x		

SCARBOROUGH

GROUND DETAILS

McCain Stadium
Seamer Road
Scarborough
N. Yorkshire YO12 4HF

TELEPHONE
Tel: 01723 375094
Fax: 01723 366211
Newsline: 0891 121650

SIMPLE DIRECTIONS The ground is situated on the main Scarborough to York road (A64), about half a mile beyond B&Q on the left as you go into Scarborough. Scarborough central (BR) about 2 miles. Car Parking: Ample in streets around the ground.

CAPACITY	5,900
SEATING	3,500
COVERED TERRACING	1,000

CLUB SHOP: Open matchdays

SOCIAL FACILITIES: Clubhouse - open matchdays only

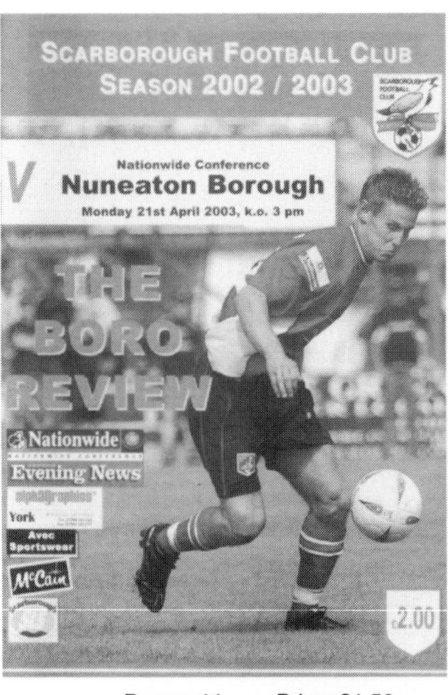

MATCHDAY PROGRAMME

Pages: 44 Price: £1.50
Editor: Dereck Meginson
Other club publications: None

Local Press:
Scarborough Evening News; The Mercury

Local Radio: Radio York; Y.C.R. Radio

Founded:	1879
Nickname:	The Seadogs
Club Sponsors:	OCM Ltd
Colours	All Red.
Change colours:	Black/blue/black
Midweek Matchday:	Tuesday

CLUB OFFICIALS

Chairman Malcolm Reynolds

President John R Birley

Company Secretary Philip Webster

Directors : M.Reynolds, J Birley & I.Scobbie

Secretary,Press Off.& Commercial Manager

Stephen GrahamTel Nos: 01723 375094 (W)
07798 538318 (M) 01723 366211 (Fax)
Email:infoscarboroughfc@yahoo.co.uk.
Correspondance to club.

FOOTBALL MANAGEMENT TEAM

MANAGER: RUSSELL SLADE

Date of Appointment:	November 2001
Date of Birth:	10.10.60
Place of Birth:	Wokingham

PREVIOUS CLUBS

As manager:	Notts County, Jt Manager Sheff.Utd
As coach:	Northampton T, Notts C,Sheff U.
As player:	Notts County

Firts Team Coach	N.Henry
Physiotherapist	Kevin Farley
Centre of Excellence Director	Mitch Cook
Youth Team Manager	Ian Kerr
Kit Man:	Brian Hogson

Season	League	Div.	Pos.	P	Home W	Home D	Home L	Home F	Home A	Away W	Away D	Away L	Away F	Away A	Pts	Manager
02-03	Conference	-	7	42	12	3	6	41	28	6	7	8	22	26	64	RussSlade
01-02	Conference	-	12	42	9	6	6	27	22	5	8	8	28	41	*55	Neil Thompson
00-01	Conference	-	10	42	7	9	5	29	25	7	7	7	27	29	58	C. Addison/ Neil Thompson
99-00	Conference	-	4	42	10	6	5	36	14	9	6	6	24	21	69	Colin Addison
98-99	F. League	3	24	46	8	3	12	30	39	6	3	14	20	38	48	Mike Wadsworth

Season	League	Div.	Pos.	P	W	D	L	F	A	Pts	Manager
97-98	F. League	3	6	46	19	15	12	67	58	72	Mike Wadsworth
96-97	F. League	3	12	46	16	15	15	65	68	63	Mike Wadsworth
95-96	F. League	3	23	46	8	16	22	39	69	40	Ray McHale
94-95	F. League	3	21	42	8	10	24	49	70	34	Philip Chambers
93-94	F. League	3	14	42	15	8	19	55	61	53	Philip Chambers

HONOURS

FA Trophy 72-73 75-76 76-77
Vauxhall Conference 86-87
Bob Lord Trophy 83-84
NPL Lge Cup 76-77
North Eastern Cos Lge 62-63, Lge Cup 62-63
Midland Lge 29-30
Scarborough & Dist. Lge 45-46
E. Riding Cup x 8; N. Riding Sen. Cup x 17

PREVIOUS

Leagues: Northern 1898-1910 14-26
Yorkshire Combination 10-14; Yorkshire 26-27;
Midland 27-40 46-60 63-68
Scarborough & Dist. 45-46
Northern Counties 60-62; North Eastern 62-63;
Northern Premier 68-79
Alliance Premier 79-87 99-
Football League 87-99

Name: None

Past Players who progressed to the Football League

when Scarborough was a Non-League club.

CLUB RECORDS

Attendance: 11,162
v Luton Town, FAC 3rd Rd, 1938

Victory: 6-0 v Rhyl Athletic, FA Cup 29.11.30

Defeat: 0-8 v Mansfield Town (H), FA Cup 22.11.52

Career Goalscorer: Unknown

Career Appearances: 196 Steve Richards 87-91

Transfer Fee Paid: £100,000
for Martin Russell to Leicester C., Feb. 87

Transfer Fee Received: £350,000
for Craig Short from Notts Co. (£150K 7/89 + £250K9/92)

BEST SEASON

FA Cup: 3rd Round 30-31 37-38 75-76 77-78

League Clubs Defeated (as non-league club):LincolnC(30-1) York C (32-3), Darlington (37-8), Bradford C(64-5),Oldham A (72-3),Crewe A(73-4), P.N.E(75-6),Crewe A & Rochdale (77-8)

FA Trophy: Winners 72-73 75-76 76-77

Football League: 5th in Division 4, 88-89

League Cup: 4th Round 92-93

LAST SEASON

F.A. Cup: 1st Round
F.A. Trophy: 4th Round
Conference: 7th
Top Goalscorer: Keith Scott
Player of the Year: David Pounder
Captain: Gareth Stoker
Highest League Attendance: 3,435 v Doncaster R

SCARBOROUGH PLAYING SQUAD

Player	*Birthplace*	*D.O.B.*	*Previous Clubs*
			Bold print denotes England semi-professional international.
GOALKEEPERS			
Gareth Downey	Sunderland	08.02.81	Hartlepool United
Adam Sollitt ESP	Sheffield	22.06.77	Rushden & Diamonds, Northampton Town, Kettering Town, Gainsborough Trinity, Barnlsey
Leigh Walker	Sheffield	27.02.81	Stalbridge Celtic, Emley, South Normanton Ath., Barnsley, Sheffield Utd
DEFENDERS			
Steve Baker Ire u21	Pontefract	08.09.78	Middlesbrough, Huddersfield Town (L), Darlington (L), Hartlepool (L)
Steve Capper	Ireland		Sunderland
James Dudgeon S u20	Newcastle	19.03.81	Barnsley, Lincoln City
Mark Hotte	Bradford	27.09.78	Oldham
Michael Price W U21	Wrexham	29.04.82	North Ferriby United, Hull City, Everton
Matthew Redmile	Nottingham	12.11.76	Notts Co., ShrewsburyTown, North Ferriby United
Shaun Rennison	Northallerton	23.11.80	From Trainee
MIDFIELD			
Glen Downey	Newcastle	20.09.78	Bishop Auckland, Hartlepool United (YTS)
Wayne Gill	Chorlley	28.11.75	Oldham Athletic, Blackburn R(L), Dundee United (L), Tranmere Rovers, Blackpool,
Ashley Lyth	Whitby		Leicester City, Scarborough
Nick Henry Div 2	Liverpool	21.02.69	Tranmere, Walsall, Sheffield Utd, Oldham
Jamie Sherlock (NC)			Brigg Town, North Ferriby United
Jacques Williams	Liverpool	25.04.83	Birmingham City, Bordeaux (trainee)
FORWARDS			
Keith Gilroy Eire u21	Sligo	08.07.83	Middlesbrough, Sligo Rovers
David Pounder	Newcastle	03.02.80	From Trainee
Mark Quayle ESP	Liverpool	02.10.78	Telford United, Morecambe, Altrincham, Ilkeston Town,Leigh RMI, Halifax Town, Notts Co., Rverton
Tommy Raw	Whitby		Middlesbrough
Karl Rose	Barnsley	12.10.78	Barnsley
Chris Senior	Huddersfield	03.03.81	Huddersfield Town

Departures:
Andy Woods, Richard Dryden, Steve Baker,Gareth Stoker, Jason Blunt, Scott Jordon, Anthony Ormorod, Andy Wright, Oliver Brassart,David Henderson, Keith Scott, Neil Cambell and Paul Shepherd

SHREWSBURY TOWN

After 53 years in the Football League the thought of life 'below' may have been frightening for Shrewsbury Town supporters and even the club staff.

However, from our experience at the Directory we have had the utmost co-operation with our requests, and the club secretary Judith Shone and their programme editor Ian Whitfield have been most enthusiastic. It will obviously help the club to have a manager who has experienced life in the Conference and it appears that everyone at the Gay Meadow is looking positively forward and is working towards a quick return.

The two up and two down arrangement, although frightening from a Division Three perspective, is an encouraging lifeline for those actually in the Conference and the Shrews squad is certainly strong enough to achieve their immediate ambition.

Although obviously disappointing for Shrewsbury fans for its final outcome, last season will probably be remembered by the neutral football followers as the year Shrewsbury Town achieved a splendid F.A.Cup victory over a strong Everton side. Players like Luke Rodgers and Nigel Jemson became household names overnight and the Third Division heroes were given terrific media coverage and a wonderful second home cup tie against Chelsea.

The Shropshire lads couldn't do it again, but the televison money and cup bonuses were banked and surely the club could strengthen and survive to build again. Sadly, it all went wrong and the slide couldn't be halted.

However, the squad looks strong enough to challenge throughout the season and by April I'm sure atttendances will be impressive, hopes will be high and - who knows? - it could be a quick return to Divison Three.

Left to Right - Back Row: Darren Tinson, Jamie Tolley, Darren Moss, Mark Cartwright, Colin Cramb, Ian Dunbavin, Steve Watts, Sam Aiston, Martin O'Connor.
Middle Row: Dave Timmins (GK Coach), Chic Bates (1st XI Coach), Chris Packer, Dave Edwards, Jake Sedgemore, Danny March, Neville Thompson, Karl Murray, Steve jagielka, Alan Rivers (Kit Manager), Rachael Greenley (Physio).
Front Row: Ross Stephens, Dave Ridler, Leon Drysdale, Luke Rodgers, Jimmy Quinn (Manager), Save Cooke (asst. Manager), Ryan Lowe, Ian Fitzpatrick, Gregor Rioch, Glenn Tolley

SHREWSBURY TOWN

GROUND DETAILS

Shrewsbury Town Football Club
Gay Meadow,
Shrewsbury SY2 6AB

Office: 01743 36011
Commercial: 01743 356316
Email: info@shrewsburytown.co.uk
Website: www.shrewsburytown.com

WHO'S WHO?

President:
K.R.Woodhouse

Directors:
R.E.Wycherley (Chairman), K.J.Sayfritz, M.R.Whitrick, Judith Shone (Company Sec.)

Associate Directors:
M. Ashton, H. J. Wilson, A. T Jones, A. Hopkins, M. J. Starkey, T J.Allen, R. Edwards

Club Patrons:
Mr R Brown, Mrs G Brown, Mr J Fellows, Williams and Picken

Life Vice-Presidents:
Dr. J. Millard-Bryson, G. W. Nelson

Life Members:
C. Smith

Secretary:
Mrs Judy Shone BA (Hons)

Marketing Manager:
Mike Thomas

Resources Manager:
Chris Jarrett

Media Manager:
Ian Whitfield

Operations Manager:
Mike Ashton

Stadium Manager:
Brian Perry

Matchday Safety Officer:
Clive Parry

Chaplain:
Rev.Tim Welch

Community Officer:
Brian Williams

HONOURS

Division III Champions
1993-94
1978-79

Division IV Runners-up
1974-75

Welsh Cup Winners
6 times

Auto Windscreen Shield
Finalists 1996

MEDICAL TEAM

Hon. Consultant Physician:
Dr Robert Wilson

Club Doctor:
Dr Chris Tomlinson

Hon. Consultant Orthopaedic Surgeon:
Mr Dai Rees, M.Ch.Orth., FCRS.

Senior Physiotherapist:
Rachael Greenley BSc (Hons), MCSP, SRP

FOOTBALL MANAGEMENT TEAM

Manager:
Jimmy Quinn

Assistant Manager:
Dave Cooke

First Team Coach:
Chic Bates

Kit Manager:
Alan Rivers

Youth Coach:
Nigel Vaughan

MATCHDAY PROGRAMME

Pages:
48 + cover
Price:
£2.00

Editorial:
Kevin Davies, Andy Davies
and a whole host more.

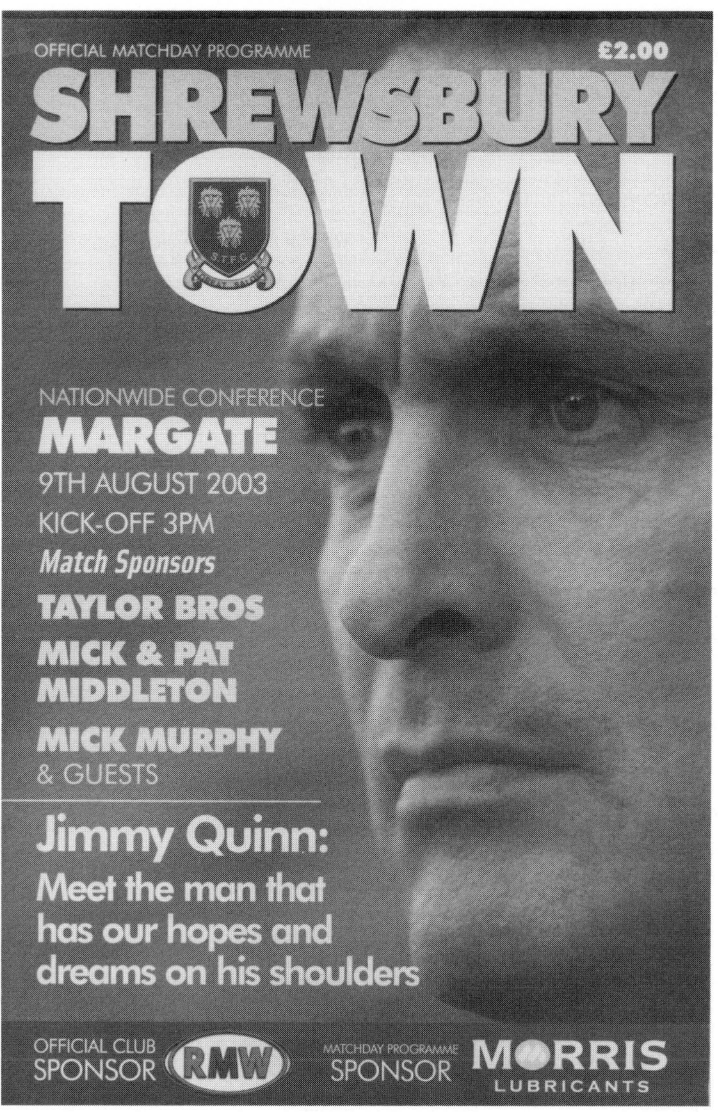

Season	League	Div.	Pos.		Home					Away					
				P	W	D	L	F	A	W	D	L	F	A	Pts
02-03	Football Lge	3	24	46	5	6	12	34	39	4	8	11	28	53	41
01-02	Football Lge	3	9	46	13	4	6	36	19	7	6	10	28	34	70
00-01	Football Lge	3	15	46	12	5	6	30	26	3	5	15	19	39	55
99-00	Football Lge	3	22	46	5	6	12	20	27	4	7	12	20	40	40
98-99	Football Lge	3	15	46	11	6	6	36	29	3	8	12	16	34	56
97-98	Football Lge	3	13	46	16	13	17	61	62	61					
96-97	Football Lge	2	22	46	8	6	9	27	32	3	7	13	22	42	46
95-96	Football Lge	2	18	46	13	14	19	58	70	53					
94-95	Football Lge	2	18	46	9	9	5	34	27	4	5	14	20	35	53
93-94	Football Lge	3	1	42	10	8	3	28	17	12	5	4	35	22	79

SHREWSBURY TOWN PLAYING SQUAD

	Birthplace	D.O.B.	Previous Clubs
			Bold print denotes England semi-professional international.
GOALKEEPERS			
Mark Cartwright			Wrexham, Brighton
Ian Dunbavin	Huyton		Liverpool
Joe Hart			Youth Team
DEFENDERS			
Leon Drysdale	Walsall		Youth Team
Darren Moss Wales Youth	Wrexham	24.05.81	Chester City
Dave Riddler	Liverpool		Scarborough, Macclesfield Town, Wrexham
Gregor Rioch			Macclesfield T,Hull City, Peterborough T., Barnet (L), Luton T
Darren Tinson			Macclesfield Town.
MIDFIELD			
Sam Aiston	Newcastle		Sunderland, Chester C (L), Stoke City (L)
Ian Fitzpatrick	Manchester		Halifax Town, Manchester United
Steve Jagielka	Manchester		Stoke City
Karl Murray	Highbury		Youth Team
Chris Packer			Youth Team
Jake Sedgmore	Wolverhampton		Northwich Victoria, Hereford Utd, Hednesford T, W.B.A.
Glenn Tolley			Youth Team
Jamie Tolley Wales u21	Ludlow		Youth Team
FORWARDS			
Colin Cramb			Bristol Rovers, Crewe Alexandra
Ryan Lowe	Liverpool		Burscough
Luke Rodgers	Birmingham		Youth Team
Steve Watts			Leyton Orient, with Welling U, Margate, Lincoln C and Dagenham & Redbridge all on loan
Neville Thompson			Youth Team

STEVENAGE BOROUGH

Having originally being one of the favourites for last season's championship , Borough failed to play to their potential and soon life became difficult for manager Wayne Turner. By Christmas time the rot had really set in and assistant manager John Dreyer took over temporary control as Turner stood down. An F.A.Cup tie at Darlington gave some relief from chasing points, but also brought a heavy defeat and the transfer of Kirk Jackson, whom apparently hadn't been rated by the heirarchy, provided cash for new signings. After a defeat by Tamworth in the F.A.Trophy the club was ready for something spectacular to happen, and along trotted a white horse with a knight bearing gifts from Farnborough via Highbury!

Graham Westley felt he had done all that was possible at Farnborough Town, as he had taken the club as far as he could. Their cup tie against Arsenal had given him the chance to recoupe some of his financial investment so he was happy to take on the Stevenage manager's role and bring seven of his players with him.

The manager and chairman at Stevenage are two very strong characters, so while all is going well it could be the perfect partnership to drive the club forward and challenge to achieve their ambition of Football League status. They certainly have a squad of quality including four internationals, so I am quite sure Stevenage Borough will be featuring in the play offs this season providing there is harmony behind the scenes.

T.W.

L-R - Back: Jamie Cook, Lee Flynn, Justin Richards, Sam McMahon, Simon Travis, Simon Wormull, Micky Warner.
Middle: Anthony Elding, Tony Battersby, Peter Costello, Mark Westhead, Lionel Perez, Barry Laker, Rocky Baptiste, Jamie Gould
Front: Graham Pearce (Asst. Manager), Danny Carroll, Jason Goodliffe, Graham Westley (Manager), Steve Watson, Gary Holloway, Graham Benstead.

STEVENAGE BOROUGH

Match Facts 2002-03

The number shown directly below the player's name is his squad number.
Where a number is shown instead of an "X' in the columns this represents a substitute appearance and the number indicates the player replaced.

	Comp.	Date	Opponents	Venue.	Score	Goalscorers	Att.
							SQUAD NUMBER
1	Conf 1	Aug-17	Northwich V	H	D 2-2	Sigere Jackson	1636
2	Conf 2	Aug-20	Farnborough T	A	W 1-0	Houghton(p)	799
3	Conf 3	Aug-24	Nuneaton B	A	L 0-3		1206
4	Conf 4	Aug-26	Gravesend & N	H	W 1-0	Sigere	1849
5	Conf 5	Aug-31	Morecambe	A	L 1-3	Goodliffe	1015
6	Conf 6	Sep-02	Telford U	H	L 1-3	J Campbell	1458
7	Conf 7	Sep-07	Margate	A	D 1-1	McMahon	520
8	Conf 8	Sep-14	Yeovil T	H	D 2-2	Jackson(2)	1879
9	Conf 9	Sep-17	Forest Green R	A	W 3-0	McMahon Goodliffe(p) Jackson	645
10	Conf 10	Sep-21	Hereford U	H	L 0-2		1685
11	Conf 11	Sep-23	Barnet	H	L 1-2	Goodliffe(p)	2130
12	Conf 12	Sep-28	Woking	A	W 5-1	C McDonald(2) Williams Blackwood Jackson	1768
13	Conf 13	Oct-05	Halifax T	H	L 0-1		1722
14	Conf 14	Oct-08	Doncaster R	A	D 0-0		3477
15	Conf 15	Oct-12	Leigh RMI	A	L 1-2	C McDonald	335
16	Conf 16	Oct-19	Burton A	H	L 0-1		1770
17	LDV 1	Oct-22	Swansea City	H	W 2-1	Jackson Pacquette	746
18	FAC 4q	Oct-26	Grays Athletic	A	W 2-1	Trott Jackson	760
19	Conf 17	Nov-02	Southport	A	L 2-3	Pacquette Midson	966
20	Conf 18	Nov-09	Chester C	H	L 0-1		1716
21	LDV 2	Nov-12	Luton Town	H	L 3-4	Pacquette Scott Nicholls(og)	2601
22	FAC 1	Nov-16	Hastings United	H	W 1-0	Howell	1821
23	Conf 19	Nov-23	Halifax T	A	L 0-1		1517
24	Conf 20	Nov-30	Scarborough	H	D 1-1	Pacquette	1629
25	FAC 2	Dec-07	Darlington	A	L 1-4	Howell	3351
26	Conf 21	Dec-14	Margate	H	L 1-3	Sigere	1272
27	Conf 22	Dec-21	Yeovil T	A	L 1-2	Williams	4940
28	Conf 23	Dec-26	Kettering T	A	L 0-1		2068
29	Conf 24	Dec-28	Farnborough T	H	W 5-0	Richards(3,1p) Blackwood Wormull	1803
30	Conf 25	Jan-04	Northwich V	A	D 1-1	Goodliffe	690
31	FAT 3	Jan-14	Oxford City	H	W 2-1	J Campbell Craker(og)	846
32	Conf 26	Jan-18	Nuneaton B	H	W 3-1	Fraser Trott Richards	1651
33	Conf 27	Jan-25	Gravesend & N	A	L 1-2	Wormull	1323
34	FAT 4	Feb-01	Tamworth	A	L 0-3		1432
35	Conf 28	Feb-08	Morecambe	H	D 1-1	Richards	1809
36	Conf 29	Feb-22	Hereford U	A	D 2-2	Laker Pitman(og)	2322
37	Conf 30	Mar-01	Forest Green R	H	D 0-0		1834
38	Conf 31	Mar-04	Dagenham & R	A	L 2-3	Elding Wormull	1905
39	Conf 32	Mar-08	Barnet	A	W 2-0	Maamria(2)	1909
40	Conf 33	Mar-15	Woking	H	D 1-1	Richards	2801
41	Conf 34	Mar-22	Scarborough	A	W 2-1	Maamria Carroll	1193
42	Conf 35	Mar-24	Kettering T	H	W 2-0	Battersby(p) Elding	1865
43	Conf 36	Mar-29	Dagenham & R	H	W 2-0	Carroll Elding	2408
44	Conf 37	Apr-05	Leigh RMI	H	W 3-1	Elding(3)	2130
45	Conf 38	Apr-07	Telford U	A	W 3-1	Battersby Cook Elding	721
46	Conf 39	Apr-12	Burton A	A	W 2-1	Battersby Carroll	1523
47	Conf 40	Apr-19	Doncaster R	H	L 2-3	Maamria Wormull	2424
48	Conf 41	Apr-21	Chester C	A	L 0-2		1745
49	Conf 42	Apr-26	Southport	H	W 3-0	Bunce Carroll Maamria	2382

Squad Number in brackets following player name; M? shows match number played in and if a substitute "rep" shows player replaced.

ALSO PLAYED:

Joe Flack (11) M28 rep 22; Dudley Campbell (18) M1 rep 10, M27 rep 17; John Dreyer (19) M1, M5; George Boyd (21) M26;

Mark WESTHEAD 1	Simon TRAVIS 2	Stuart FRASER 3	Matt FISHER 4	Jason GOODLIFFE 5	Robin TROTT 6	Simon WORMULL 7	Sam McMAHON 8	Kirk JACKSON 9	Justin RICHARDS 9	Jean-Michel SIGERE 10	Gary HOLLOWAY 10	Adrian CLARKE 11	Richard HOWELL 12	Phil WILSON 12	Martin WILLIAMS 14	Jamie COOK 14	Scott HOUGHTON 15	Louis RIDDLE 15	Jamie CAMPBELL 16	Leonel PEREZ 16	Jude STERLING 17	Danny CARROLL 18	Jack MIDSON 20	Neil SMITH 21	Graeme TOMLINSON 22	Richard PACQUETTE 22	Tony BATTERSBY 22	Michael BLACKWOOD 24	Charlie McDONALD 25	Richard SCOTT 27	Dino MAAMRIA 27	Gary McDONALD 28	Michael WARNER 32	Justin GREGORY 33	Steve WATSON 34	Nathan BUNCE 35	Barry LAKER 36	Anthony ELDING 37
x	x		x			x		x		x		15					x		x		x			x	7													
x	x	7	x	x		x		x		x							x		x		x			x														
x	x		x	x		x		x		x			7				x		x		x			x	15													
x	x		x	x	x	x	x	x		x		x					11		x				10		7													
x	x	x		x		x		x		x					x		7		x		x		17		10													
x	x	x		x		11		x		x		x	x		x		12		x		x				9													
x	x		x	x	x		x	x				x			x				x					8	x													
x	x		x	x	x		x	x						1	x				x					25				x	x									
x	x		x	x	x		x	x							x				x					24				x	x									
	x		x	x	x	24	x	x		14				x	x				x						25			x	x									
x	x		x	x	x		x	x		9									x					x	x			x										
x	x	16	x	x	x		x	x		9					x				x						25			x	x									
x	x	16	x	x	x		x	x		14					x				x						4			x	x									
x	x		x	x	x		x	x		9					x			24	x									x	x									
x	x		x	x	x	15	x	10		x					x			x	x					6					x									
x	x		x	x	x	4	x	24		22					x				x							x		x	x									
x	x	x			x	x		x					x	1				x			x					x		x										
x	x	x		x	x	x		x					x					x	7		5					x		x										
x	x	x			x			x					x					x			x		9			x		x		24								
x	x	x			x			x		24			x					x			x		9			x		x				x						
x	x	x				x		7		20			x					x			x		x			x		12		x		x						
x	x	x			x	2		x					x						27		x		x					x	20	x		x						
x	x	x			x	x		24					7					x	x				25			x		x	x	x								
x	x				x	x				25			24					x	x				22			x		x	x	x		x						
x	x				x	x	10			x			x					x	x		6		12						x	x		x						
x						x	x		x	21			26						x		x								x	x		x						
x	x	x		28			x		x						x				x		x							26		x		x						
x	x	x		x		x	x		x									x	x		7					x		x	15									
x	x	x		x	x	x	x		x					1	x				x							14		x										
x	x	x	x	x	x	x			x						x				x									x	9			4						
	x	x	x	x	x	x			x					x	x			24	2									x				x						
x	x	x		x	x	x	x		x						x				x									x										
x	x	x		x	x	x	x		x										x									x	x			16						
	x	x	7		x	x	x		x					x	x				x									x	24			x						
	10					x	7		x		x									x		x							x				x	x	x	x	x	
	10					x			x		x									x		x							32		9		x	x	x	x	x	x
				27		x			37		x					10				x		x									x		x	x	x	x	x	x
	33			7		x			x		x					35				x		x											x	x	x	x	x	x
x	x			x		x	7		37		x					10						x									x		x		x		x	x
x	x			x		x			22		18					x						x									x		x		x		x	x
x	x			x			x		x							35						x					27				x		x		x	x	x	9
x	x			x			x		x							35						x					27				x		x		x	x	x	9
x	x			x		14	x		37							x						x					x						x		x	x		x
x	x	34		x		14	x		37							x						x					x								x	x	x	x
x	x	14		x		x										x						x					x				22	37			x	x	x	x
x	x			x		x										x						x					x				37		14		x	x	x	x
x	x			x		x			27		14					x						x									x		x		x		x	x
x	x	x		x		10					x					28						x									x	x			x		x	x
x	x			x		x			27		7					x				1		x									x				x	x	x	x

ALSO PLAYED:

Louis Opara (22) M31 rep 3, M33 rep 25; Adam Furness (23) M11 rep 21; Roger Willis (26) M19;
Leon Bell (26) M26, M27, M29 rep 7, M30 rep 24; Neil Mustoe (27) M32 rep 7, M33 rep 24; Phil Gray (29) M32 rep 14, M35 rep 25

STEVENAGE BOROUGH

GROUND DETAILS

Stevenage Stadium,
Broadhall Way,
Stevenage,
Herts SG2 8RH

Tel: 01438 223223
Fax: 01438 743666
email:roger@stevenageborofc.com
Web site: http://www.stevenageborofc.com

SIMPLE DIRECTIONS:
Stevenage South exit off A1(M) - ground on right at second roundabout.Spectators are however advised to go straight on at this roundabout and park inthe Showground opposite the stadium. The stadium is one mile from Stevenage BRstation. Buses SB4 and SB5

CAPACITY: 7,107

SEATED: 3,404

(included away stand all seater)

COVERED TERRACING: 3,703

Groundsman: Ken Watters

CLUB SHOP: Mon - Sat 9-5.30. Broadhall Way, Stevenage. 01438 218061. Sells a complete range of club merchandise including a customising service. Mail Order, credit cards accepted, contact Tracey Levy (01438 218061)

SOCIAL FACILITIES:
Tel.: 01438 218079. Clubhouse at ground open Monday to Friday 7 - 11pm,Saturday noon - 2.00 & 4.30 - 11pm, Sunday: All day from noon. Contact: Jenny Cairns

Clubcall: 09066 555982

FOOTBALL MANAGEMENT TEAM

MANAGER: **GRAHAM WESTLEY**

Date of Appointment: 2003
Date of Birth: 4th March 1968
Place of Birth: Isleworth

PREVIOUS CLUBS
As manager: Enfield, Kingstonian, Farnborough T.
As player: QPR, Gillingham, Walton & Hersham

HONOURS
As manager: Ryman Lge Champs. 2000-01
Ryman Lge Cup 99-00

* * *

Assistant Manager Graham Pearce
1st Team Coach Graham Benstead
Physiotherapist Karl Jones
Chief Scout Alan Carrington
Scouts Paul Tippins and Gary Isott

Nickname: Boro'
Club Sponsors: Sun Banking Corporation
Club colours: Red/red/white
Change colours: All Yellow
Midweek home matchday: Tuesday
Reserve Team's League: Capital League
Club's Playing Status: Some Full time players

CLUB OFFICIALS

Chairman: Phillip Wallace

Club Administrator: Roger Austin
01438 218072

Commercial Manager: Clive Abrey
01438 218073

Press Officer: Steve Watkins
Tel Nos: 01438 218072 (W) 07771 523661 (M)

PROGRAMME
Pages: 36 Price: £2.00
Editor: Stuart Govier Tel: 01438 210895

Other club publications: The Borough Yearbook

Local Press: Stevenage Gazette; Comet; Stevenage Mercury; Herald
Local Radio: Chiltern Radio; BBC Three Counties Radio and Hertbeat

Season	League	Div.	Pos.	Home P	Home W	Home D	Home L	Home F	Home A	Away W	Away D	Away L	Away F	Away A	Pts	Manager
02-03	Conference	-	12	42	7	6	8	31	25	7	4	10	30	30	52	W. Turner / Graham Westley
01-02	Conference	-	11	42	10	4	7	36	30	5	6	10	21	30	55	P. Fairclough / Wayne Turner
00-01	Conference	-	7	42	8	7	6	36	33	7	11	3	35	28	63	Paul Fairclough
99-00	Conference	-	10	42	8	5	8	26	20	8	4	9	34	34	57	R./ Steve Wignall /P Fairclough
98-99	Conference	-	6	42	9	9	3	37	23	8	8	5	25	22	68	Paul Fairclough / Richard Hill
97-98	Conference	-	15	42	8	8	5	35	27	5	4	12	24	36	51	Paul Fairclough
96-97	Conference	-	3	42	15	4	2	53	23	9	6	6	34	30	82	Paul Fairclough

Season	League	Div.	Pos.	P	W	D	L	F	A	Pts	Manager
95-96	Conference	-	1	42	27	10	5	101	44	91	Paul Fairclough
94-95	Conference	-	5	42	20	7	15	68	49	67	Paul Fairclough
93-94	Isthmian	Prem.	1	42	31	4	7	88	39	97	Paul Fairclough

HONOURS

GM Vauxhall Conference 95-96,
Isthmian Lge Prem 93-94,
Div 1 91-92, Div 2 (North) 85-86 90-91;
Utd Counties Lg Div 1 80-81 (Div 1 Cup 80-81),
Herts SnrCup R-up 85-86, 93/94;
Herts Charity Cup R-up 93-94,
Herts Charity Shield R-up83-84,
Televised Sports Snr Floodlit Cup 89-90,
Eastern Professional F'lit Cup Group winner
81-82 85-86 86-87 88-89 90-91 91-92,
South Co's Comb. Cup 91-92;
Essex & Herts Border Comb.(Reserves) 94/95
Essex & Herts (Western Div) 95-96

PREVIOUS

Leagues: Chiltern Youth 76-79;
Wallspan South Combination 79-80;
United Counties 80-84;
Isthmian 84-94

Grounds: King George V Playing Field 1976-80

Past Players who progressed to the Football League

Richard Wilmot & NeilTrebble (Scunthorpe Utd) 1993,
Simon Clark (Peterborough United) 1994,
Leo Fortune West (Gillingham) 1995,
Phil Simpson (Barnet) 1995,
Barry Hayles (Bristol Rovers) 1997)

CLUB RECORDS

Attendance: 6,489 v Kidderminster H.,
GM Vauxhall Conference 25.1.97

Win: 11-1 v British Timken Athletic (H),
United Counties League Div.1, 1980-81

Defeat: 0-7 v Southwick (H),
Isthmian League Div. 1, 1987-88

Career goalscorer: Barry Hayles

Career appearances: Martin Gittings

Transfer fee paid: £20,000
for Richard Leadbetter to Hereford United 1999

Transfer fee received: £300,000
for Barry Hayles (Bristol R.) July 97

BEST SEASON

FA Cup: Fourth Round replay 97-98.
1-2 v Newcastle Utd. (A) after 1-1
also 3rd Round 1996-97.
0-2 v Birmingham City (A)

League clubs defeated: Leyton Orient 96-97;
Cambridge Utd., Swindon Town 97-98

FA Trophy: Runners-up 01-02

League: Conference Champions 95-96

LAST SEASON

F.A. Cup: 2nd Round
F.A. Trophy: 4th Round
Conference: 12th
Top Goalscorer: Dino Maamria 17
Player of the Year: Jason Goodliffe
Captain: Steve Watson
Highest League Attendance: 2,801 v Woking

STEVENAGE BOROUGH PLAYING SQUAD

Player	*Birthplace*	*D.O.B.*	*Previous Clubs*
GOALKEEPERS			
Mark Westhead	Blackpool	19.07.75	Leigh RMI, Wycombe, Kidderminser, Telford Utd, Bolton W., Blackpool Mechs
Lionel Perez	France	24.04.67	Cambridge United,Newcastle United,Sunderland\
DEFENDERS			
Nathan Bunce RP	Hillingdon	02.05.75	Stevenage B, Hayes, Yeading, Brentford
Jason Goodliffe ESP	Hillingdon	07.03.74	Hayes, Brentford
Lee Flynn	London	04.09.73	Barnet, Hayes,Hendon, Boreham Wood, Romford
Barry Laker RL	London		Sutton Utd, Banstead Ath., Wimbledon (Junior)
Geoff Pitcher ESP, FATx2	Sutton	15,08,75	Brighton, Colchester United (NC), Woking, Farnborough Town,KingstonianWatford ,Millwall (YTAS)
Simon Travis ESP, British Univ.	Preston	22.03.77	Forest Green R, Telford Utd, Stockport, Holywell T, Torquay
Michael Warner RL	Harrogate	17.01.74	Northampton, Tamworth, Redditch Utd
MIDFIELD			
Jamie Cook	Oxford	02.08.79	Boston United, Oxford United
Peter Costello	Halifax	31.10.68.	Boston United, Hong Kong,Kettering T Lincoln City(L), Peterborough United, Rochdale, Bradford City
Jamie Gould	Northampton	15.01.82	Boston United, Northampton (YTS)
Gary Holloway	Surrey		Farnborough T, Hampton & Richmond Borough, Walton & Hersham.
Sam McMahon	Newark	10.02.76	Leicester, Camb.U
Steve Watson ESP; RL	London		Sutton Utd, Croydon, Whyteleafe, Crystal Palace (Junior)
Simon Wormull ESP, NC	Crawley	01.12.76	Rushden & Diamonds, Dover Ath., Brentford, Tottenham
FORWARDS			
Rocky Baptiste	London		Luton, Hayes, Wealdstone, Willesden Hawkeye, Chelsea (Junior)
Danny Carroll	Surrey	-	Crawley T, Dulwich Hamlet, Bromley, Whyteleafe, Chipstead, Whyteleafe
Anthony Elding	Boston	16.04.82	Boston United, Lincoln C (Jnrs), Grimsby T (Jnrs)
Howard Forinton RP	Oxford	18.09.75	Oxford City, Yeovil Town,Torquay United, Peterborough United(£250,000), Birmingham City (£50,000), Yeovil Town, Oxford City, Abingdon Town, Oxford United
Justin Richards			Bristol Rovers (£75,000) W.B.A.

Bold print denotes England semi-professional international.

Departures: D.J.Cmpbell, Jamie Campbell, Adrian Clarke, John Dreyer, Matt Fisher, Stuart Fraser, Scott Houghton, Richard Howells, Kirk Jackson, Jean-Mchel Sigere, Neil Smith, Jude Stirling, Paul Sturgess, Graeme Tomlinson, Robin Trott,Martin Williams.

TAMWORTH

Having just missed out on promotion on the final day of the previous season, the Lambs were determined to go one step better and,although they didn't start the campaign too well, Darren Gee's men settled down and an amazing run of 38 points from a possible 42 took them into a strong position at Christmas and they never really looked back.

As their position became more secure they were also able to use the F.A.Trophy as a relaxing tournament away from the pressure of chasing points. They started by beating Accrington Stanley, their counterparts from the Unibond League, by a creditable 4-1 scoreline and then followed this with defeats of four Conference clubs - Nuneaton Borough, Stevenage Borough, Margate and Farnborough Town.

With those scalps captured and a strong position in the league, Tamworth cruised happily towards the end of the campiagn with a two legged defeat of Havant & Waterlooville in the Trophy semi-final and were confidently presented as favourites for the final against Burscough.

Unfortunately for them, the short trip to Villa Park didn't produce a glorious end of season celebration, although their free scoring skipper Mark Cooper did round off his excellent campaign by scoring their goal in a 1-2 defeat.

The wonderful Tamworth fans weren't going to grumble, as they had enjoyed a superb season and they couldn't wait to tour the Conference grounds with their beloved Lambs in the season ahead.

T.W.

Tamworth in action against Burscough in the Trophy Final played at West Ham United. Photo: Peter Lirettoc.

Date	Comp.	Opponents	Att.	Score	Goalscorers	
17/08	D.M. P	Havant & Waterlooville	582	3 - 0	Follett 45, Rickards 76, Colley 90	
20/08	D.M. P	MOOR GREEN	1012	2 - 2	Cooper 24 54	
24/08	D.M. P	CRAWLEY TOWN	758	1 - 1	Rickards 58	
26/08	D.M. P	Hinckley United	791	1 - 1	Rickards 45	
31/08	D.M. P	CHIPPENHAM TOWN	805	0 - 1		
03/09	D.M. P	Halesowen Town	656	0 - 0		
07/09	D.M. P	CHELMSFORD CITY	649	3 - 1	Hallam 8, Walsh 57, Rickards 63[p]	
09/09	D.M. P	Worcester City	1530	0 - 0		
14/09	D.M. P	WELLING UNITED	740	2 - 0	Hemmings 40 65[p]	
17/09	D.M. P	Grantham Town	534	1 - 2	Hemmings 72[p]	
21/09	D.M. P	Hastings United	521	3 - 2	Cooper 14 85, Walsh 47	
28/09	FA Cup Q2	Bromsgrove Rovers	1115	2 - 1	Rickards 49 79	
05/10	D.M. P	BATH CITY	831	6 - 1	Rickards 8 89, McGorry 27, Sale 51, Cooper 55, Turner	
08/10	D.M. P	HEDNESFORD TOWN	1078	1 - 0	Hatton 83	
12/10	FA Cup Q3	Hinckley United	1139	3 - 1	Cooper 74 78, Follett 88	
19/10	D.M. P	Folkestone Invicta	413	3 - 2	Walsh 44, Cooper 60, McGorry 85	
26/10	FA Cup Q4	Guiseley	724	3 - 3	Warner 25, Hollis 72, Hallam 90	
29/10	FA Cup Q4 rep	GUISELEY	1124	2 - 3	Hallam 6, Hemmings 11	
02/11	D.M. P	Dover Athletic	1127	3 - 0	Hallam 45, Cooper 78, Hemmings 86	
06/11	Lge Cup 1	SUTTON COLDFIELD TOWN	329	1 - 3	Rickards 71	
09/11	D.M. P	CAMBRIDGE CITY	785	3 - 1	Hallam 13, Rickards 39, Cooper 56	
13/11	Birm SC 2	Grosvenor Park	103	5 - 2	Sale 33 54 90[p], Cooper 40[p], Turner 86	
19/11	Staffs SC 2	RUSHALL OLYMPIC	233	1 - 1	Swan 75	
23/11	D.M. P	Welling United	651	1 - 1	Cooper 50	
30/11	FA Trophy 2	ACCRINGTON STANLEY	951	4 - 1	Hemmings 27 33[p] 62, Hallam 50	
07/12	D.M. P	HASTINGS UNITED	744	2 - 0	Burt 5[og], McGorry 45	
10/12	D.M. P	STAFFORD RANGERS	844	2 - 1	Rickards 47, Sale 90	
14/12	D.M. P	Chelmsford City	627	4 - 0	A Turner 14, Rickards 25, Colley 48, Hallam 71	
17/12	Staffs SC 2 rep	Rushall Olympic	131	1 - 3	Swan 70	
21/12	D.M. P	GRANTHAM TOWN	868	3 - 1	Cooper 49 63, Rickards 90	
26/12	D.M. P	HINCKLEY UNITED	1208	2 - 0	Cooper 24, Rickards 82	
28/12	D.M. P	Chippenham Town	1209	0 - 3		
04/01	D.M. P	WORCESTER CITY	1610	1 - 2	Jephcott 51	
11/01	FA Trophy 3	NUNEATON BOROUGH	2045	3 - 0	Jephcott 5, Hallam 25, Cooper 50	
14/01	D.M. P	TIVERTON TOWN	799	1 - 1	Jephcott 72	
18/01	D.M. P	Weymouth	753	1 - 0	Evans 17	
25/01	D.M. P	HALESOWEN TOWN	1150	3 - 1	Collins 52 76, Hallam 55	
01/02	FA Trophy 4	STEVENAGE BOROUGH	1452	3 - 0	Jephcott 18, Cooper 70, Colley 90	
08/02	D.M. P	Tiverton Town	981	1 - 0	Jephcott 71	
11/02	Birm SC 3	WEST BROMWICH ALBION	474	1 - 1	Sale 20	Won 4 3 after pens.
15/02	D.M. P	Newport County	804	1 - 0	Atkinson 24	
18/02	D.M. P	WEYMOUTH	895	3 - 0	Follett 7, Colley 88 90	
22/02	FA Trophy 5	Margate	971	2 - 0	Sale 10, Hallam 74	
25/02	D.M. P	Ilkeston Town	691	1 - 0	Collins 45	
01/03	D.M. P	Moor Green	1007	2 - 0	Atkinson 68, Collins 90	
08/03	D.M. P	FOLKESTONE INVICTA	1395	2 - 0	Munden 60[og], Hallam 88	
11/03	Birm SC QF	Moor Green	213	3 - 1	Walsh 41, Swan 49 55	
15/03	FA Trophy QF	Farnborough Town	1312	2 - 1	Colley 51, Hatton 84	
22/03	D.M. P	DOVER ATHLETIC	1529	1 - 2	Fisher 83	
29/03	D.M. P	Hednesford Town	1182	1 - 0	Evans 2	
05/04	FA Trophy SF(1)	HAVANT & WATERLOOVILLE	2165	1 - 0	Rickards 43	
12/04	FA Trophy SF(2)	Havant & Waterlooville	1331	1 - 1	Rickards 111	
15/04	D.M. P	Stafford Rangers	1884	2 - 1	Cooper 52, Fisher 71	
19/04	D.M. P	Cambridge City	825	1 - 0	Evans 80	
21/04	D.M. P	ILKESTON TOWN	1583	1 - 1	Rickards 66	
23/04	D.M. P	HAVANT & WATERLOOVILLE	408	3 - 3	Hatton 21, Evans 42, Grocott 62	
26/04	D.M. P	NEWPORT COUNTY	1396	0 - 0		
01/05	D.M. P	Crawley Town	411	0 - 1		
03/05	D.M. P	Bath City	1116	2 - 0	Grocott 57, Turner 65	
18/05	FA Trophy F	BURSCOUGH	n/k	0 - 0		@ Aston Villa

TAMWORTH

GROUND DETAILS

The Lamb Ground, Kettlebrook,
Tamworth, Staffs B77 1AA

Tel: 01827 65798
Fax: 0182762236
website: www.thelambs.co.uk
email: russell@thelambs.co.uk

Directions: Follow the signs for Town Centre/Snowdome, then for Kettlebrook. The entrance to the ground &car parks is in Kettlebrook Road, 50yards from the traffic island by the railway viaduct (B5000)

Capacity: 4,100
Cover: 1,191
Seats: 518

Clubhouse: Club on ground - open matchdays, training nights and tote night only

Clubshop: Yes

MATCHDAY PROGRAMME

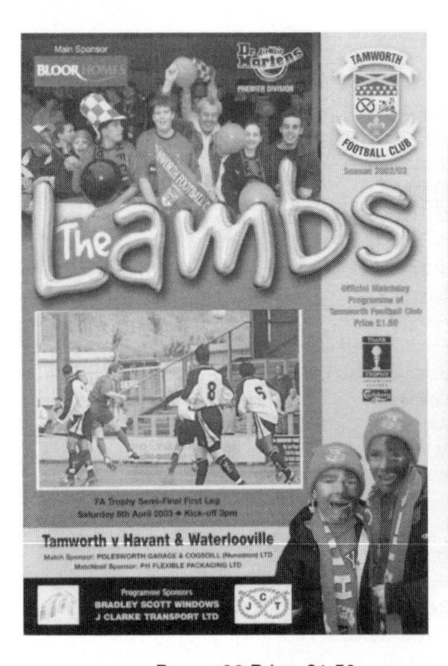

Pages: 36 Price: £1.50
Editor: Dave Clayton & Mark Lane
email:manonthemoon@ntlworld.com

Press: Tamworth Herald,Tamworth Times
Radio: Centre FM,Captal Gold/Radio WM

Formed: 1933

Sponsors: Bloor Homes

Nickname: Lambs or Town

Colours: All Red

Change colours: White,black,black

Midweek home matchday: Tuesday

Reserves' League: Mid. Comb. Reserve Div.

CLUB OFFICIALS

Chairman: Bob Andrews

President: Len Gendle

Secretary: Russell Moore,
97 Honeybourne, Belgrave, Tamworth,
Staffs B77 2JG
Tel: 01827 706538 (H) 07811 267304 (M)

Press Officer: Dave Clayton

07815 046899 (M)

Commercial Manager: Russell Moore

Safety Officer: Tony Reeves

FOOTBALL MANAGEMENT TEAM

MANAGER: DARRON GEE

Date of Appointment: May 2002
Date of Birth: 3rd August 1962
Place of Birth: Nottingham

PREVIOUS CLUBS
As manager: Dunkirk
As asst. man.: Grantham Town, King's Lynn, Tamworth
As player
HONOURS
As Manager: Southern Lge. Prem Div. 02-03
FA Trophy R-up 02-03
As Player:

* * *

Asst Manager: T.B.A.
Chief Scout: T.B.A.
Youth Development: Ian Wilson
Physio: Peter Denham

Season	League	Div.	Pos.		Home					Away						Manager
				P	W	D	L	F	A	W	D	L	F	A	Pts	
02-03	Southern	P	1	42	12	6	3			14	4	3			88	Darron Gee (73-32)
01-02	Southern	P	2	42	16	5	0	46	14	8	8	5	28	36	75	Gary Mills
00-01	Southern	P	12	42	11	4	6	38	24	6	4	11	20	31	59	Paul Hendrie
99-00	Southern	P	6	42	12	4	5	50	26	8	6	7	30	41	70	Paul Hendrie
98-99	Southern	P	9	42	10	5	6	37	30	9	0	12	25	37	62	Paul Hendrie
97-98	Southern	P	15	42	10	4	7	43	30	4	7	10	25	35	53	Paul Hendrie
				P	W	D	L	F	A						Pts	
96-97	Southern	M	1	40	30	7	3	90	28						97	Paul Hendrie
95-96	Southern	M	6	42	22	3	17	97	64						69	Paul Hendrie
94-95	Southern	M	3	42	24	8	10	98	70						80	Les Green
93-94	Southern	M	7	42	19	7	16	82	68						64	Paul Wood

HONOURS

F.A.Trophy Finalists 02-03, FA VaseWinners 88-89;
West Mids Lge
63-64 65-66 71-72 87-88, R-upx2 67-69, Div 2 55-56, Lg Cupx5 64-66 71-72 85-86 87-88, R-up 70-71;
Birmingham Senior Cup
60-61 65-66 68-69, R-up 36-37 63-64;00-01
Staffs Senior Cup
58-59 63-64 65-66 01-02, R-up 55-56 66-67 70-71;
Midland F'lit Cup R-up 71-72 72-73;
Camkin Cup 71-72 (R-up 70-71);
Southern Lge.Prem. Div 2002-03 Midland Div 96-97
Premier Div. 02-03, R-up 01-02

PREVIOUS

Leagues:
Birmingham Combination 33-54,
West Midlands (initially Birmingham Lg) 54-72, 84-88
Southern 72-79 83-84 89-03
Northern Premier 79-83

Grounds: Jolly Sailor Ground 33-34

Past Players who progressed to the Football League

P Hilton (WBA 49),
A Godridge (Swansea 50),
W Ealing (Doncaster),
Higgins (Fulham),
P Weir (Cardiff),
S Fox (Wrexham),
S Cartwright (Colchester 88),
S Ryder (Walsall),
D Williams (Brentford)

CLUB RECORDS

Attendance: 4,920
v Atherstone Tn, Birm Comb 48

Season Goalscorer: Percy Vials 64 (36-37)
Career Appearances: Dave Seedhouse 869
Career Goalscorer: Graham Jessop 195

Defeat: 0-11
v Solihull (A), Birmingham Comb. '40
Win: 14-4
v Holbrook Institute (H), Bass Vase '34

Transfer Fee paid: £7,500
for Tony Hemmings (Ilkeston Town) Dec 2001
Transfer Fee received: £7,500
for Martin Myers (Telford Utd, 90)

BEST SEASON

FA Cup: 2nd Rd 69-70 (0-6 at Gillingham)

FA Trophy: Runners-up 02-03

FA Vase: Winners 88-89

LAST SEASON

F.A. Cup: 4th Qualifying Round.
F.A. Trophy: Runners-up
League: Southern League Champions
Top Goalscorer: Mark Cooper 18
Player of the Year: Richard Follett
Captain: Mark Cooper

TAMWORTH

	Birthplace	D.O.B.	Previous Clubs	Bold print denotes England semi-professional international.
GOALKEEPERS				
James Lindley	Sutton in Ashfield	23.07.81	Notts County, Gresley Rovers	
Philip Whitehead	Halifax	17.12.69	Reading, W.B.A., Oxford United, Halifax T (L) Scunthorpe (L) Halifax T (L), Barnsley, Halifax T.	
DEFENDERS				
Mark Barnard	Sheffield	27.11.75	Worksop, Northwich Victoria	
Richard Follett	Leamington Nottingham Forest	29.08.79	R.C.Warwick, Kings Lynn (L),Scunthorpe(L), British Univ	
Tom Jordon			Bristol City, Southend United	
Paul Hatton	Kidderminster	02.11.78	Hednesford U , Birmingham City	
Dave Robinson	Nottingham	14.07.75	KIngs Lynn, Grantham T, Gresley R, IlkestonT., HeanorT	
Gary Setchell	Kings Lynn	08.05.75	Rushden & D,Kettering Town, Kings Lynn	
Joe Taylor	Ormskirk	06.04.80	Burscough	
MIDFIELD				
Mark Cooper	Wakefield	18.12.69	Forest Green R,Hednesford T, Rushden &Diamonds Leyton O,Hartlep'l U,Exeter C,Wycombe W, Fulham, Birmingham C, Exeter C,BristolCity	
Matt Fisher Army		29.04.76	Stevenage B, Kettering T,Gedling T, Ashfield U.	
Karl Johnson	Birmingham	12.09.81	Reserves	
Joe Hanney	Leicester	25.04.83	Reserves	
Phil Trainer	Wolv'hampton	03.07.81	Halesowen T,Kidsgrove A,Northwich V, Crewe A	
Mark Turner	Bebington	04.10.72	Kings Lynn, Telford United	
Robert Warner	Stratford	20.04.77	Hereford United (YTS)	
FORWARDS				
Darren Collins ESP	Winchester	24.05.67	Cambridge C,Kettering T,Rushden & D, Enfield, Aylesbury U, Northampton Town, Petersfield United	
Brett Darby	Leicester	10.11.83	Southend United, Leicester City	
Marc McGregor	Southend Oxford United	30.04.78	Nuneaton B, Forest Green R, Endsleigh, ESP	
Scott Rickards ESP	Sutton Coldf'ld	03.11.81	Derby County, Oldham A (L), Mansfield (L), Walsall (L)	
Mark Sale	Burton on Trent	27.02.72	Doncaster R, Rushden & D, Stoke C, Cambridge U, Birmingham C., Torquay U, Preston N.E., Mansfield T, Colchester U	

TELFORD UNITED

With a new ground developing around them, the Telford United squad found it hard work last season as a quiet start left them with nowhere to go. They were never really in touch with the leaders, but nor were they seriously threatened with relegation.

The cups didn't bring any relief from the tedium either, as home defeats by Doncaster Rovers in the F.A.Cup and Farnborough Town in the F.A.Trophy were extremely disappointing.

Perhaps the highlights of the campaign were a freak game at Burton, where The Bucks returned with a 7-4 victory, and the home fixture against Doncaster, when the Rovers raced into a 4-0 lead only for Telford to fight back for a point!

Jake King had done well to hold the club together in a difficult stage of its development and to ensure United would be able to keep their record of competing in the Conference for every year since the competition's inauguration. But pressures of work and probably a natural weariness persuaded him to stand down and the club has appointed Mick Jones to take up the reigns.

A huge change of personnel in the summer has brought many interesting names to the New Bucks Stadium and for those supporters who remember the days of great F.A.Trophy runs to Wembley and fabulous F.A.Cup giant killing exploits, maybe the pendulum is swinging and it will soon be their day once again.

TELFORD UNITED FC 2002-03

Back row L-R: Gary Fitzpatrick, Matthew Bloomer, Peter Smith, Grant Brown, Paul Edwards, Craig Jones, Tony Lormor, Mark Foran, Richard Scott.

Front Row: David Brown, Gareth Hanmer, Paul Moore, Kevin Jobling, Jake King, Steve Palmer, Ashley Wooliscroft, Jordan King, Kevin Davies

TELFORD UNITED

Match Facts 2002-03

The number shown directly below the player's name is his squad number.
Where a number is shown instead of an "X' in the columns this represents a substitute appearance and the number indicates the player replaced.

Comp.	Date	Opponents	Venue.	Score	Goalscorers	Att.
					SQUAD NUMBER	
Conf 1	Aug-17	Halifax T	A	L 0-2		1616
Conf 2	Aug-19	Chester C	H	L 0-1		1409
Conf 3	Aug-24	Doncaster R	H	D 4-4	Moore Foran Smith D Brown	1170
Conf 4	Aug-26	Dagenham & R	A	D 1-1	Foran	1711
Conf 5	Aug-31	Burton A	H	L 0-2		1311
Conf 6	Sep-02	Stevenage B	A	W 3-1	D Brown(2) Moore	1458
Conf 7	Sep-07	Barnet	A	L 0-3		1067
Conf 8	Sep-14	Southport	H	W 2-0	Moore D Brown	812
Conf 9	Sep-16	Scarborough	H	L 0-2		756
Conf 10	Sep-21	Gravesend & N	A	W 2-0	D Brown Fitzpatrick	1096
Conf 11	Sep-24	Morecambe	A	L 0-1		869
Conf 12	Sep-28	Farnborough T	H	L 0-2		762
Conf 13	Oct-05	Kettering T	A	W 4-2	Smith(2) D Brown Moore	1481
Conf 14	Oct-07	Forest Green R	H	L 0-1		720
Conf 15	Oct-13	Yeovil T	H	L 0-5		1509
Conf 16	Oct-19	Nuneaton B	A	L 0-1		1007
FAC 4q	Oct-27	Doncaster R	H	L 0-2		1012
Conf 17	Nov-02	Woking	H	W 1-0	Barlow	743
Conf 18	Nov-09	Margate	A	D 1-1	Jobling	385
Conf 19	Nov-23	Kettering T	H	W 2-0	Moore Smith	793
Conf 20	Nov-30	Leigh RMI	A	W 3-0	Moore(2) D Brown	406
Conf 21	Dec-07	Northwich V	H	W 1-0	Smith	726
Conf 22	Dec-14	Barnet	H	W 2-1	D Brown Moore	779
Conf 23	Dec-21	Southport	A	D 1-1	D Brown	853
Conf 24	Dec-26	Hereford U	H	L 0-1		2047
Conf 25	Dec-28	Chester C	A	L 1-4	D Brown	2594
Conf 26	Jan-01	Hereford U	A	L 0-2		3077
Conf 27	Jan-04	Halifax T	H	L 1-2	D Brown	880
FAT 3	Jan-14	Rugby United	A	W 2-0	D Brown Moore	404
Conf 28	Jan-18	Doncaster R	A	W 3-1	Smith Sayer Moore	3333
FAT 4	Feb-01	Farnborough T	H	L 2-3	Foran Barlow	928
Conf 29	Feb-08	Burton A	A	W 7-4	Moore(2) Davies Barlow Foran Hanmer King	1516
Conf 30	Feb-11	Dagenham & R	H	L 1-2	Foran	877
Conf 31	Feb-22	Gravesend & N	H	W 2-1	D Brown Fitzpatrick	834
Conf 32	Mar-01	Scarborough	A	W 4-1	D Brown(2,1p) Foran Moore	824
Conf 33	Mar-08	Morecambe	H	L 0-3		1040
Conf 34	Mar-22	Leigh RMI	H	D 1-1	Moore	802
Conf 35	Mar-25	Farnborough T	A	D 2-2	D Brown Fitzpatrick	529
Conf 36	Mar-29	Northwich V	A	L 1-2	Smith	530
Conf 37	Apr-05	Yeovil T	A	L 0-3		7558
Conf 38	Apr-07	Stevenage B	H	L 1-3	D Brown	721
Conf 39	Apr-12	Nuneaton B	H	L 1-2	Palmer	987
Conf 40	Apr-19	Forest Green R	A	D 1-1	Moore	801
Conf 41	Apr-21	Margate	H	W 1-0	King	1016
Conf 42	Apr-26	Woking	A	L 0-3		3045

Phil EDWARDS	Ashley WOOLISCROFT	Gareth HANMER	Kevin DAVIES	Mark FORAN	Grant BROWN	Gary FITZPATRICK	Kevin JOBLING	Peter SMITH	Paul MOORE	Steve PALMER	Richard SCOTT	Jordan KING	Dean SPINK	Matt BLOOMER	Tony LORMOR	David BROWN	Ben MORLEY	Craig JONES	Martin BARLOW	Steve KERRIGAN	Ronnie SAYER	Paul PETTINGER	David CAMERON
1	**2**	**3**	**4**	**5**	**6**	**7**	**8**	**9**	**10**	**11**	**12**	**14**	**15**	**16**	**18**	**19**	**20**	**21**	**22**	**23**	**24**	**25**	**26**
x	x	x	8	x	x		x	x	18	x	x	11		x	x								
x		x		x	x	x	x	12	x	x	x	8		x	x								
x	8	x		x	x	x	x	x	x	x		11		x	x	18							
x	x		x	x	x		x	x		x	14	x		x		x							
x	x	4	x	x	x	x	x	x	6	x				x		x							
x	x	11	x	x	x	x		10	x	x		x		x	19	x							
x	x	7	x	x	x	x	x	11	x	x				x		x							
x		x	14	x	x	x		10	x			x		x		x	x		x				
x		x		x	x	x		10	x			x	x		15	x	x		x				
x		x		x	x	x		10	x			x		x		x	x		x				
x		x		x	x	x		10	x	7		x		x		x	x		x				
x		x		x	x	x		16	x	x				x		x	x		x				
x	x	x		x	x	x		x	23	x		7				x			x	x			
x	x	x		x	x	x		x	x	x						x			x				
x	x	x	11	x	x	x		x		x		2		x		x		16	x				
x		x	5	x	x	x	11	22		x		x		x		x			x	x			
		x			x	x		x	19	x		x	x			x		x	x	x			
x		x	x		x	x	15	x		x			x	x		23			x	x			
x		x	x		x	x	11	x	23	x			x			x			x	x			
x		x	x	x	x	x		x	x	x						x			x				
x		x	x	x	x	x		x	x	x						x			x				
x		x	x	x	x	x		x	x	x						x			x				
x		x	x	x	x	x		x	x	x						x			x				
x	x	x	x	x		x		x	x	x						x			x				
x	x	x	x	x		x		x	x	x		11				x			x				
x	x	x	x	x			x	x	x			x				x		1			x		
	x	x	x	x		x	11	x	x	x						x			x			x	
	x	x	x	x		x		x	x	x		11				x			x			x	
	x	x	x		x	x	2	x	x	x						x			x			x	
		x	x	x	x	x		x	x			x							x		7	x	x
x		x	x	x	x	x	11	x	x	x						x			x				
x		x	x	x	x	x			x			x				x			x				x
x		x	x	x	x	x		19	x	14		x				x			x				x
x		x	x	x	x	x	11	26	x	x		x				x							x
x		x	x	x	x	x		14	x	x		x				x							x
x		x	x	x	x	x		26	x	x		11				x			x				x
x		x	x	x	x	x		x	x	x		9				x			x				
x		x	x	x	x	x		x	x	x		10				x			x				
x		x	x	x	x	x		x	x	x		9				x			x				
x		x	x	x	x	x		x	x	x		9				x			x		11		
x		x	x	x	x	x	5		x			x				x			x		x		
x	x	x	x		x	x	x		x	x		22							x		x		
x	x	x	x	x	x	x	9	x	x	x									x				
x	x	x	x	x	x	x	x	x	x	x		11									9		
x	x	x	2	x	x	x		x	x			x				x			x		9		

TELFORD UNITED

GROUND DETAILS

New Bucks Head Stadium
The Bucks Way,
Telford,
Shropshire TF1 2TU

Tel: 01952 640064
Fax: 01952 640021
email: officialtelfordunited.com
web site: www.telford.united-fc.co.uk

SIMPLE DIRECTIONS:
Leave M54 Junction 6.and takeA518.At second island take second exit,then left at third island and turn right immediately after railway bridge.

CAPACITY:	6,315
SEATED:	2,152
COVERED TERRACING:	2,856

SOCIAL FACILITIESI
In concourses and main complex

CLUB SHOP:
Telephone 01952 640064for details

MATCHDAY PROGRAMME

Pages: 32 Price: £2.00
Editor: Mike Ferriday/Robin Eaves

Clubcall: 09066 555 982

Local Press: Shropshire Star; Telford Journal,Telford News,Local Radio: BBC Radio Shropshire;Beacon Radio; Telford FM; WABC

Founded:	1876
Nickname:	The Bucks
Club Sponsors:	T.B.A.
Club colours:	All White
Change colours:	Claret
Midweek home matchday:	Monday

CLUB OFFICIALS

President	Gerald Smith
Chairman	Andy Shaw
Directors:	Andy Shaw, Rob Cave, Mike Ferriday and Paul Booth
Football Secretary	Mike Ferriday c/o the club 01952 640064
Commercial Manager	Robin Eaves
Press Officer	Robert Cave 0771 0227337

FOOTBALL MANAGEMENT TEAM

MANAGER: Mick Jones

Assistant Manager:	Kevin Jobling
Coach:	Roger Preece
Physio:	Brin May
Club's Playing Status:	Some full time players

Season

Season	League	Div.	Pos.	P	Home W	Home D	Home L	Home F	Home A	Away W	Away D	Away L	Away F	Away A	Pts	Manager
02-03	Conference	-	15	42	7	2	12	20	33	7	5	9	34	36	49	Jake King
01-02	Conference	-	9	42	8	6	7	34	31	6	9	6	29	27	57	Jake King
00-01	Conference	-	6	42	13	1	7	33	23	6	7	8	18	28	65	Jake King
99-00	Conference	-	16	42	12	4	5	34	21	2	5	14	22	45	51	Alan Lewer / Jake King
98-99	Conference	-	17	42	7	8	6	24	24	3	8	10	20	36	46	Jimmy Mullen / Alan Lewer
97-98	Conference	-	20	42	6	7	8	25	31	4	5	12	28	45	42	Steve Daly / Jimmy Mullen
96-97	Conference	-	9	42	6	7	8	21	30	10	3	8	25	26	58	Wayne Clarke

Season	League	Div.	Pos.	P	W	D	L	F	A	Pts	Manager
95-96	Conference	-	13	42	15	10	17	51	56	55	Wayne Clarke
94-95	Conference	-	19	42	10	16	16	53	62	46	Gerry Daly / George Foster
93-94	Conference	-	17	42	13	12	17	41	49	51	Gerry Daly

HONOURS

FA Trophy Winners 71-72, 82-83, 88-89.
R-up 69-70, 87-88;
Birmingham League1920-21, 1934-35, 1935-36;
Cheshire League 1945-46, 1946-47, 1951-52;
Edward Case Cup 1952-53, 1954-55;
Welsh Cup 1901-02, 1905-06, 1939-40;
BirminghamSenior Cup 1946-47;
Walsall Senior Cup 1946-47;
Birmingham League Challenge Cup 1946-47;
Shropshire Senior Cup (30);
Southern League Cup 1970-71;
Midland Floodlit Cup 1970-71, 1982-83, 1988-89,
Runners-up 1969-70, 1987-88

PREVIOUS

Leagues: Southern League, Cheshire League, Birmingham League

Name: Wellington Town (prior to 1969)

Grounds: None

Past Players who progressed to the Football League

A.Walker (Lincoln City),G.French (Luton Town),
K.McKenna (Tranmere Rovers), S.Norris (Scarborough),
David Pritchard (Bristol Rovers) 1994,
Sean Parrish (Doncaster Rovers) 1994,
Steve Foster (Bristol R.);
Peter Wilding, Roger Preece, Mark Williams & Martyn Naylor
- all to Shrewsbury 1997
Neil Moore (Mansfield Town)

CLUB RECORDS

Attendance: 13,000 v Shrewsbury Town
Birmingham League - 1936

Win: **Unknown**
Defeat: **Unknown**

Career appearances: **Unknown**
Career goalscorer: Jack Bentley

Transfer fee paid: £20,000
to Wrexham for Jake Edwards

Transfer fee received: £50,000
from Scarborough for Stephen Norris

BEST SEASON

FA Cup: 5th Round 84-85, 0-3 v Everton (A), 47,402.
Also 4th Rd. 83-84, 3rd Rd.86-87,2nd Rd. 82-83,85-86,91-92

League clubs defeated: Wigan (82-3), Rochdale, Stockport C.& Northampton T(83-4)Bradford C, Darlington,Lincoln C.& P.N.E. (84-85),Stockport C (85-6),Burnley (86-7) and Stoke City (91-92)

FA Trophy: Winners 70-71, 82-83, 88-89.
R-up 69-70, 87-88

League: 3rd Conference 81-82

LAST SEASON

F.A. Cup: 4th Qualifying Round
F.A. Trophy: 4th Round
Conference: 15
Top Goalscorer: Paul Moore & David Brown
Player of the Year: Kevin Davies
(Club) Captain: Steve Palmer
Highest League Attendance: 2.047

TELFORD UNITED PLAYING SQUAD

Player	*Birthplace*	*D.O.B.*	*Previous Clubs*

Bold print denotes England semi-professional international.

GOALKEEPERS

Craig Jones	Birmingham	-	Walsall
Chris McKenzie	Northampton	14.05.72	Nuneaton Borough, Corby Town, Hereford United, LeytonOrient
Martin Taylor	Tamworth	09.12.66	Wycombe W,Crewe A (L).Scunthorpe U(L),Carlisle U(L), Derby County, Mile Oak Rovers

DEFENDERS

Trevor Challis	Paddington	23.10.75	Bristol Rovers,Q.P.R.
Matthew Clarke			Hereford U,Kidderminsterr H,HalesowenT Wolverhampton W.
Scott Eustace Leicester C.	Leicester	13.06.75	Hinckley Utd,Stevenage B, Cambridge U, Mansfield T,
Scott Green	Walsall	15.01.70	Wrexham, Wigan Athletic,Bolton Wanderers, Derby County
Neil Howarth ESP	Farnworth	15.11.71	Cheltenham Town,Macclesffield T,Burnley
Nick Porter	Newport	-	Youth Team
Sam Ricketts			Oxford United
Ashley Wolliscroft	Stoke	28.12.79	Stoke
Stuart Whitehead			Darlington,Carlisle U,Bolton W, Bromsgrove Rovers

MIDFIELD

Martin Barlow	Barnstaple	25.06.71	Weymouth,Exeter City, Plymouth Argyle
Richard Lavery			Nuneaton Borough,Hinckley United,Tamworth,Atherstone U, Sotton Coldfield T,Massey Ferguson,Nuneaton B,Hinckley U, Bedworth U
Fitzroy Simpson	Bradford on Avon	26.02.70 Swindon Town.	Walsall, Hearts, Portsmouth, Bristol C (L), Manchester C,
Lee Williams			Cheltenham Town,Mansfield Town,Shamrock Rovers
Paul Moore	Birmingham	-	Bromsgrove R, Stourport Swifts, Paget R, Redditch Utd, Bromsgrove R, Stourbridge, Bromsgrove R, Kidderminster, Walsall

FORWARDS

Michael Blackwood		30.09.79	Halesowen Town,Stevenage Borough,Worcester City,Wrexham,
			Aston Villa
Lee Mills	Mexborough	10.07.70	Stoke C,Coventry C, Portsmouth, Bradford C, Port Vale, Derby County Wolves, Stocksbridge Park Steels
Paul Moore	Birmingham		Bromsgrove R, Stourport Swifts,Paget Rangers,Redditch United Bromsgrove R, Stourbridge,Bromsgrove Rovers,Kidderminster H, Walsall.
Chris Murphy			Shrewsbury Town
Justin Rowe			Hereford United, Grosvenor Park, Contintal Star

WOKING

In a season when one kept reading of goals flying past Woking at an embarrassing rate (and their defence certainly were no longer a laughing matter), it is a tremendous compliment to someone that The Cards stayed up!

Geoff Chapple started off with a run of victories that took Woking to the top of the table and I dare say supporters thought he was back in the old routine. So what went wrong as the defence began to cave in and result after result gave the impression their defence hadn't turned up? Conceding four goals was sometimes considered an improvement!

Poor Geoff had never suffered like this and not surprisingly he stood down to be replaced by Glenn Cockerill.

How does a club, which regularly concedes five, suddenly produce a 1-0 victory over quality opposition for a new manager. Had everybody been trying?

Woking's reputation in the knockout cups had been second to none in recent seasons, so their fans hoped, without any luck, for some cup relief after the grind of the league. Excellent draws were gained in the F.A.Cup at Dover and in the F.A.Trophy at Gloucester, but having done the hard work disappointing defeats at home gave the impression the lads were nervous in front of their own fans. Confidence had to be regained somehow. Relegation stared everyone at Woking very firmly in the face, as their poor away form counteracted any slight improvments at Kingfield Stadium. Then a quite staggeringly dreadful 0-6 home defeat against Morecambe brought in a new policy of very serious defending. This inspired the club's famous run of nine consecutive draws and gave everyone a very pleasant unbeaten period to boost morale. So, when it came to the real crunch on the last day of the season, Cockerill's men were ready!

If there was dancing in the streets of Old Woking that night, you can imagine how they felt in Nuneaton and Southport as their clubs sunk into the bottom three places for the first time in the campaign and promptly fell straight through the trapdoor.The results that will remain in every Woking fan's memory for some time were: Nuneaton Borough 0 Farnborough Town 2, Stevenage Borough 3 Southport 0 and WOKING 3 Telford United 0

Fancy saying thank you to old 'friends' from Stevenage !

Left to right - Back Row: Nixon Ajoge, Raphael Nade, Jefferson Louis, Davis Haule

Middle Row: Ron Rawlings - Kit Manager, Joe McNab, Jamie Campbell, Chris Sharpling, Liam Cockerill, Ben Townsend, Ashley Bayes, Jon Boardman, Ryan Northmore, Dean Clark, Gary MacDonald, Phil Parsons, Steve Ferguson, Neil Sharp, Steve Snelling - Physio

Front Row: Amos Foyewa, Ian Proctor, Ian Selley, Matt Crossley - Assistant Manager, Glenn Cockerill, Peter Johnson - Reserve & Youth Team Manager, Neil Smith - Club Captain, Scott Canham, Narada Bernard.

WOKING

Match Facts 2002-03

The number shown directly below the player's name is his squad number.
Where a number is shown instead of an "X' in the columns this represents a substitute appearance and the number indicates the player replaced.

Comp.	Date	Opponents	Venue.	Score	Goalscorers	Att.
						SQUAD NUMBER
Conf 1	Aug-17	Forest Green R	H	W 1-0	Abbey	1717
Conf 2	Aug-20	Nuneaton B	A	D 1-1	Abbey	1241
Conf 3	Aug-24	Kettering T	A	W 3-0	Banger(2) Patmore	1608
Conf 4	Aug-26	Leigh RMI	H	W 3-0	Payne Abbey Patmore	2160
Conf 5	Aug-31	Scarborough	A	D 1-1	Brady	1192
Conf 6	Sep-03	Gravesend & N	H	L 2-3	Patmore Abbey(p)	2721
Conf 7	Sep-09	Hereford U	H	L 1-2	Sharpling	2080
Conf 8	sep`4	Northwich V	H	L 2-3	Patmore Sharpling	1649
Conf 9	Sep-17	Margate	H	L 1-5	Abbey	1485
Conf 10	Sep-21	Morecambe	A	L 0-5		1007
Conf 11	Sep-24	Yeovil T	A	L 0-4		4003
Conf 12	Sep-28	Stevenage B	H	L 1-5	Payne Abbey Patmore	1768
Conf 13	Oct-05	Burton A	H	D 2-2	Moore Banger	1426
Conf 14	Oct-08	Dagenham & R	A	D 1-1	Moore	1348
Conf 15	Oct-12	Southport	A	L 1-5	Abbey	1023
Conf 16	Oct-19	Chester C	H	W 1-0	Abbey(p)	2019
LDV 1	Oct-22	Luton Town	H	L 0-2		1216
FAC 4q	Oct-26	Dover Athletic	A	D 1-1	Simpemba	1636
FAC 4qr	Oct-29	Dover Athletic	H	L 1-2	Abbey	1806
Conf 17	Nov-02	Telford U	A	L 0-1		743
Conf 18	Nov-09	Barnet	H	D 0-0		1761
Conf 19	Nov-23	Burton A	A	W 2-0	Patmore(2,1p)	1558
Conf 20	Dec-01	Doncaster R	A	L 1-3	Patmore	3051
Conf 21	Dec-07	Halifax T	H	W 2-1	Patmore Kember	1734
Conf 22	Dec-14	Hereford U	A	L 0-5		1565
Conf 23	Dec-21	Northwich V	A	W 3-1	Nade Sharpling Patmore(p)	506
Conf 24	Dec-26	Farnborough T	A	L 0-5		1639
Conf 25	Dec-28	Nuneaton B	H	W 2-1	Patmore Cooper(og)	2067
Conf 26	Jan-04	Forest Green R	A	L 2-3	Patmore Banger	901
FAT 3	Jan-14	Chesham United	H	W 3-0	Patmore(2,1p) Abbey	1336
Conf 27	Jan-18	Kettering T	H	W 2-1	Patmore(2p)	2031
Conf 28	Jan-25	Leigh RMI	A	L 0-1		435
FAT 4	Feb-01	Gloucester City	A	D 0-0		1073
FAT 4r	Feb-04	Gloucester City	H	L 0-2		1007
Conf 29	Feb-08	Scarborough	H	W 2-1	Austin(p) Sharpling	1631
Conf 30	Feb-15	Gravesend & N	A	L 2-4	Patmore Collins	1163
Conf 31	Feb-22	Morecambe	H	L 0-6		1491
Conf 32	Mar-01	Margate	A	L 1-2	Sharpling	527
Conf 33	Mar-08	Yeovil T	H	D 1-1	Boardman	3332
Conf 34	Mar-11	Farnborough T	H	D 1-1	Coates	1889
Conf 35	Mar-15	Stevenage B	A	D 1-1	Austin(p)	2801
Conf 36	Mar-22	Doncaster R	H	D 2-2	Williams Nade	2007
Conf 37	Mar-29	Halifax T	A	D 1-1	Canham	1558
Conf 38	Apr-05	Southport	H	D 1-1	Nade	1815
Conf 39	Apr-12	Chester C	A	D 2-2	Foyewa(2)	2165
Conf 40	Apr-19	Dagenham & R	H	D 0-0		2159
Conf 41	Apr-21	Barnet	A	D 0-0		1617
Conf 42	Apr-26	Telford U	H	W 3-0	Townsend Foyewa Canham	3045

Also Played: Squad Number in brackets following player name; M? shows match number played in and if a substitute "rep" shows player replaced.

Steve FARRELLY 1	Clint DAVIES 1	David PIPER 2	Anthony ALLMAN 3	Scott SMITH 4	Jon BOARDMAN 5	Scott CANHAM 6	Jon BRADY 7	Ben TOWNSEND 7	Barry MOORE 8	Dean AUSTIN 8	Warren PATMORE 9	Chris SHARPLING 10	Nicky BANGER 11	Robert BURCH 11	Grant PAYNE 12	Scott STEELE 14	Chris COLLINS 15	Wayne BURNETT 16	Robert KEMBER 17	Tony TUCKER 18	Stuart REEKS 19	Ben ABBEY 20	Paul STEELE 21	Lee SANDFORD 22	Tom WHITE 22	Dean CLARK 22	Jamie CAMPBELL 23	Sean EVERS 24	Martin WILLIAMS 24	Ian SIMPEMBA 26	Amos FOYEWA 26	Raphael NADE 27	Jamal DA COSTA 28	Ian HAMILTON 30	Shwan JALAL 31	Neil SMITH 32	Jonathan COATES 33	Ashley BAYES 40
x		x	x	11	x		x		x		x		x						x			x		x														
x		x	x	2	x		x		x		x	9	x		11				x			x		x														
x		x	x		x		x		x		x	20	x		9	8			x			x		x														
x		x	x		x		x		x		x	9	x		11	x						x		x														
x		x	x	20	x		x		x		x				9	x			x			x		x														
x		x	x	2	x		x		x		x	8			x	3			x			x		x														
x		x	x		x		x		x			x			2	3		x	x			x		x														
x		x			x		x		x		x	x				17		x	x			x		x				2										
x		x	x		x		x				x	x	x		3		2	x				11		x				x										
x			x	x	x		x		x		15	x	3			17	x		x			x		x														
x		x	x	x	x		x		25				2		x							x		x				x										
				x	x		x		x		x		x		9					x	x	x		x				x										
		x	x	x	x				x		20		x		11				x			x						x		x					x			
		x	x		x				x		x				9		x		x		3	x						x		x					x			
		x			x						x		19		29	x	x		x		x	x								x					x			
		3	x	x	x						26	x	32				x		x			x								x				x	x	x		
		x	26	x	x						x	30	x		x				x		4									x				x	x	x		
			x	x	x				x			x	10		20		x				3	x								x				x	x	x		
		32		x	x				x		8		x		20		x		x			x								x				x	x	x		
		15	x	x	x						x		x		20		x		x		3	x								x				x	x			
		26		x	x						x		x				x		x		x		5							x		x		x	x			
			4	x							x	11	x				x		x		x									x		x		x	x		x	
					15					x	x						x		x		x									x		x	17	x	x	x	x	
					x					x	x	27							x		x									x		x		x	x	x	x	
			19		x					x	x	17							x		x	30								x		x		x	x	x	x	
					x					x	x	x	10						x			27								x		x		x	x	x	x	
		8			x					x	x	x	9						x			30								x		x		x	x	x	x	
31					x					x	x	x	30						x			17								x		x		x	x	x	x	
					x					x	x	x	10						x	x		17								x		x		x		x	x	
		20		21	x					x	x	x	x								30	x	x											x	x	x	x	
		10			x			x		x	x	x	x								8	11	x									x		x	x		x	
					x			x			x	x	9								x	21	x									x		x	x	x	x	
				x	x			x				x			20		x		x			x												x	x	x	x	
				x	x			x		x		x	20		x				x		8	x												x	x	30	x	
				x				x		x		x							x			27			x		x					x			x	x	x	
			x					x		x	x	x		x			x		x						x							x	15	x			3	
			4	x	x			x		x	x	x		x					x								x		32			x				x	17	
			32	x	x			x		x	x	27		x			x										x		15			x				x	x	
				30	x	x		x			x	x		x			x										x		9			x		x			x	
				6	x	x		x			x	x		x			x					9					x		33			x		x			x	
					x	x		x		x		x		x			x		10							x	x		x					23		x		
	x				x	x		x		x	10	x					x									32	x		x		15	x				x		
	x				x	x		x		x	x	x															x		x		10	x				x		
					x	x		x			x	x									x					32	x		x		19	x				x		x
					x	x		x			27						x									30	x		x		x	x		x		x		x
					x	x		x			26	x					x									30	x				x	x		x		x		x
					x	x		x		x	x	x					x									x	x		22		8	x				23		x
					x	x		x		x	27	x					x		32								x		26		x	x				x		x

ALSO PLAYED: Simon Rodger (25) Conf 11; Glenn Cockerill (29) Conf 15

WOKING

GROUND DETAILS

Kingfield Stadium,
Kingfield Road,
Woking,
Surrey. GU22 9AA.

Tel: 01483 772470
Fax: 01483 888423
Football Office Fax: 01483729230
Web site: http://www.wokingfc.co.uk

Simple Directions:
M25 J10 or 11, signposted from outskirts of Town. Ground 1 mile. Woking B.R. Station & buses from Woking.

Capacity:		6,000
Seated:		2,500
Terracing -	**Covered:**	1,400
	Uncovered:	2,100

SOCIAL FACILITIES:
Clubhouse open on matchdays. Food available.

CLUB SHOP: Phone 01483 772470 for details.

Founded: 1889

Nickname: The Cards

Club colours: Red & white halved shirts, & white shorts and red & white socks.

Change colours: All Yellow

Midweek home matchday: Tuesday 7.45pm.

Club Sponsors: T.B.A.

Newsline 09066 555070

CLUB OFFICIALS

Chairman: Chris Ingram
Directors: Chris Ingram,Phil Ledger JP, Bob Drennan,John Buchanan,Julian Golding and Mike Bidmead (Company Secretary)

Managing Director Brian Blower
Tel No: 01483 772470

Football Director Phil J Ledger J.P.
19 Ainsdale Way, Woking, Surrey. GU21 3PP.
Tel: 01483 725295 (H), 07831 271369 (M)

Press Officers Phil Ledger & Brian Blower
Club Administrator Sue Day

MATCHDAY PROGRAMME

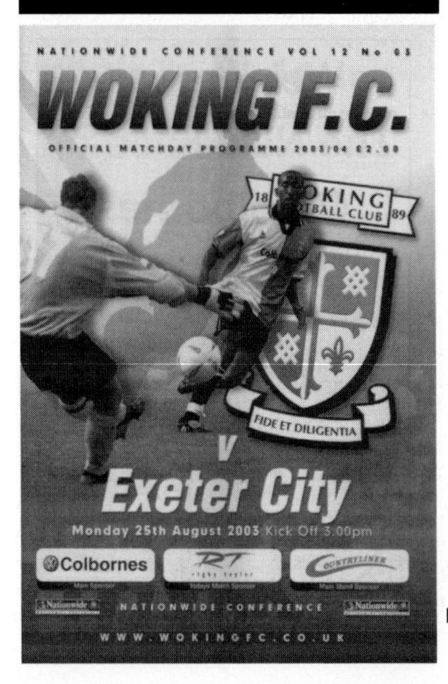

FOOTBALL MANAGEMENT TEAM

MANAGER: GLEN COCKERILL

Assistant Manager: Matt Crossley
Reserve & Youth Team Manager: Peter Johnson
Physio: Barry Kimber
Club's Playing Status: Part time

Pages: 48 **Price:** £2.00
Editor: Paul Beard 01344 482018
Clubcall: 09066 555 070

Other club publications:
"Winning isn't Everything" (fanzine)
Local Press: Woking News & Mail; Woking Herald; Surrey Advertiser
Local Radio: BBC Surrey Sussex; County Sound; BBC Southern Counties

Season	League	Div.	Pos.	Home P	W	D	L	F	A	Away W	D	L	F	A	Pts	Manager
02-03	Conference	-	19	42	8	7	6	30	35	3	7	11	22	46	47	Geoff Chapple / Glenn Cockerill
01-02	Conference	-	19	42	7	5	9	28	29	6	4	11	31	41	48	Colin Lippiatt/Geoff Chapple
00-01	Conference	-	14	42	5	10	6	30	30	8	5	8	22	27	54	Colin Lippiatt
99-00	Conference	-	14	42	5	6	10	17	27	8	7	6	28	26	52	Brian McDermott/Colin Lippiatt
98-99	Conference	-	9	42	9	5	7	27	20	9	4	8	24	25	63	John McGovern/Brian McDermott
97-98	Conference	-	3	42	14	3	4	47	22	8	5	8	25	24	74	John McGovern
96-97	Conference	-	5	42	10	5	6	41	29	8	5	8	30	34	64	Geoff Chapple

Season	League	Div.	Pos.	P	W	D	L	F	A	Pts	Manager
95-96	Conference	-	2	42	25	8	9	83	54	83	Geoff Chapple
94-95	Conference	-	2	42	21	12	9	76	54	75	Geoff Chapple
93-94	Conference	-	3	42	18	13	11	58	58	67	Geoff Chapple

HONOURS

FA Trophy 93-94, 94-95, 96-97
FA Amateur Cup 57-58
GM VauxhallConference R-up 94-95, 95-96
Isthmian League: 91-92, R-up 56-57
Div.2 South 86-87
Isthmian Lge Cup: 90-91, R-up 89-90
Surrey Senior Cup: 12-13, 26-27, 55-56, 56-57, 71-72, 90-91, 93-94, 95-96, 99-00;
London Senior Cup R-up 82-83
Isthmian League Charity Shield 91-92, 92-93
Vauxhall Championship Shield 94-95, R-up 95-96.

PREVIOUS

Leagues: Isthmian 1911-92

Grounds: Wheatsheaf, Ivy Lane (pre 1923)

Past Players who progressed to the Football League

Ray Elliott (M'wall 46), Charlie Mortimore (A'shot 49), Robert Edwards (Chelsea 51), Ron Newman (Portsmouth 55), Mervyn Gill (Southampton 56),John Mortimore (Chelsea 51), Reg Stratton (Fulham 59), George Harris (Newport Co. 61), Norman Cashmore (A'shot 63), Alan Morton (C. Palace 67), William Holmes (Millwall 70), Richard Forbes (Exeter 79), Kevin Rattray (Gillingham 95), Steve Foster (Bristol Rov. 97), Justin Jackson (Notts Co. 98), Kevin Betsy (Fulham 98).

CLUB RECORDS

Attendance: 6,000
v Swansea, FA Cup - 1978/79
v Coventry C., FA Cup - 1996-97

Win: 17-4 v Farnham, 1912-13

Defeat: 0-16 v New Crusaders, 1905-06

Career Goalscorer: C Mortimore 331, 1953-65

Career Appearances: B Finn 564, 1962-74

Transfer Fees

Paid: £60,000 for Cris Sharpling (C.Palace) - 2001

Received: £150,000 for Steve Foster (Bristol Rovers) - May 1997
£150,000 for Kevin Betsy (Fulham)

BEST SEASON

FA Cup: 4th Round 90-91,0-1 v Everton (A) Att 34,724
League clubs defeated: West Bromwich Albion (90-91)
Cambridge United & Millwall (96-97)

FA Trophy: Winners 93-94, 94-95, 96-97.

FA Amateur Cup: Winners 75-58

League Conference Runners-up 94-95, 95-96

LAST SEASON

F.A. Cup: 4th Qual. Round
F.A. Trophy: 4th Round replay
Conference: 19th
Top Goalscorer: Warren Patmore
Player of the Year: Warren Patmore
Captain: John Boardman & others
Highest League Attendance: 3,045 v Telford Utd

WOKING — PLAYING SQUAD

Player	*Birthplace*	*D.O.B.*	*Previous Clubs*
			Bold print denotes England semi-professional international.
GOALKEEPERS			
Ashley Bayes	Lincoln	19.04.72	Bohemians (Dublin), Leyton O, Exeter City, Torquay United Brentford
Ryan Northmore			Team Bath, Torquay United
DEFENDERS			
Nixon Ajoge			Coventry City
Narada Bernard			Bournemouth,Arsenal,Tottenham Hotspur
Jonathan Boardman	Reading	27.01.81	Crystal Palace
Jamie Campbell	Birmingham	21.10.72	Exeter City, Brighton, Cambridge U, Barnet , Cambridge U (L), Mansfield T(L),Luton Town
Gary McDonald			Stevenage Bor.,Peterborough United,Havant & Waterlooville, Portsmouth
Ian Proctor			Youth Team
Neil Sharp	Hemel Hempstead	19.01.78	Swansea City, Merthyr Tydfil, Barry Town
Scott Smith New Zealand Int.	Christchurch	06.03.75	Rotherham United, Kettering Town
Ben Townsend			Wycombe Wanderers
MIDFIELD			
Scottt Canham	Newham	05.11.74	Leyton Orient,Brentford,Torquay United(L),West Ham United
Dean Clark			Hayes, Uxbridge,Brentford
Liam Cockerill			Youth Team
Sean Evers	Hitchin	10.10.77	Plymouth Argyle, St.Johnstone, Reading, Luton Town
Joe McNab	Brighton	29.1080	Utah Blitz (U.S.A.),Newport IOW,Utah Blitz (U.S.A.) Portsmouth,Manchester City.
Phil Parsons			Youth Team
Ian Selley	Chertsey	14.06.74	Wimbledon, Fulham, Arsenal
Neil Smith	Lambeth	30.09.71	Stevenage B, Reading, Fulham, Gillingham, Spurs(YTS)
FORWARDS			
Amos Foyewa			Bournemouth,West Ham United
Steve Ferguson	Scotland		Tottenham Hotspur, East Fife
Davis Haule	Tanzania		Harrow Borough, Hendon,Wembley,U.S.A., Finland, Wimbledon, Birmingham City
Raphael Nade	Paris		Welling United, Hampton & Richmond B,Troyes (France), Le Havre (France)
Chris Sharpling	Bromley	21.04.81	Crystal Palace (£60,000)

You Have to Love It!

Anyone who becomes involved with a football club, at any level,
finds their life, and those of all around them, seriously affected by their duties -
whether as a player, member of coaching staff, administrator or loyal supporter.

The full-time professional game attracts career minded football people,
on and off the field, but to be fully involved with non-League football

"You Have to Love It!"

Over the last twenty five years a team of eccentric ground hopping photographers have
toured the football grounds of England
and supplied photos for The FA Non-League Club Directory
and Team Talk magazine on a purely honorary basis.

They have always kept an eye open for an amusing situation as well as a good action
shot or a spectacular goal. In this book their photos will illustrate
all the effort that goes into the week-end's football matches on and off the field,
as three million enthusiasts contribute their own little bit to
the world's most popular game.

This is a very special Christmas book of amusing and enlightening photos illustrating all
that happens at a non-league club on an average matchday.

I'm sure it will bring a great deal of enjoyment to everyone involved with the world of
football outside the Football League

The book is planned for publication in November
and further details are available by contacting us on 01823 490080

Tony Williams

The followowing three pages show what bits of the book will look like

Preparing the ground needs expertise & experience

We compare our playing surface to a bowling green

but not necessarily favourably

Clear unambiguous signs are important

Supporters and press need to know where everything is to be found

18

You Have to Love It!

although the players show they are capable of producing some sophisticated mid-field play

NORTHERN PREMIER LEAGUE

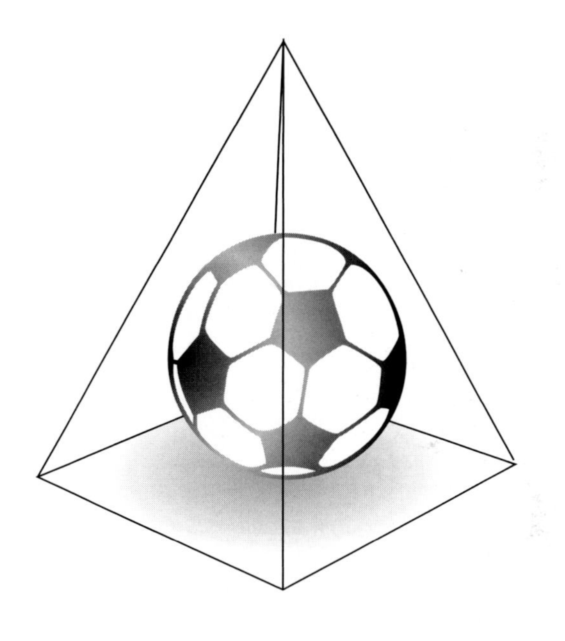

PYRAMID SECTION

UniBond
NORTHERN PREMIER

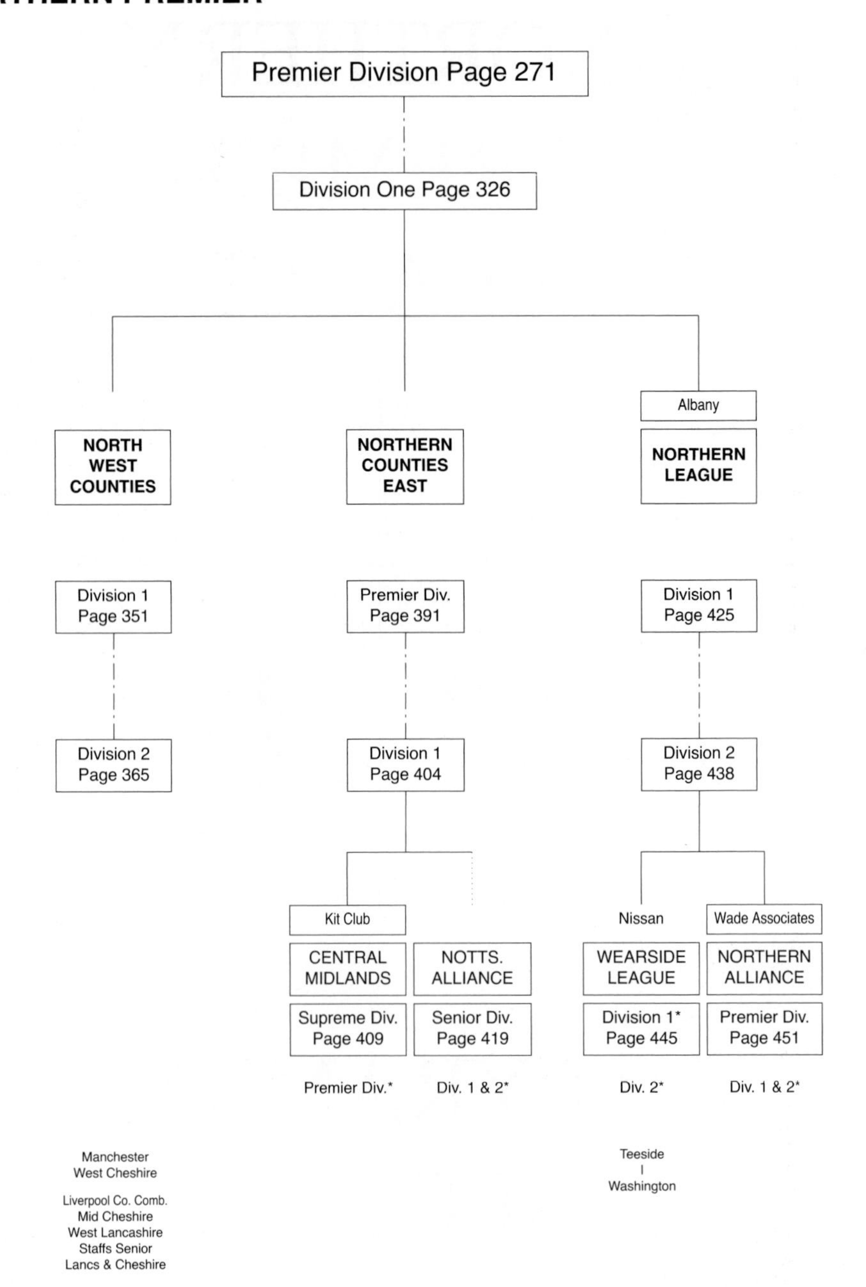

Premier Division Page 271
Division One Page 326
Albany
NORTH WEST COUNTIES
NORTHERN COUNTIES EAST
NORTHERN LEAGUE
Division 1 Page 351
Division 2 Page 365
Premier Div. Page 391
Division 1 Page 404
Division 1 Page 425
Division 2 Page 438
Kit Club
CENTRAL MIDLANDS
Supreme Div. Page 409
Premier Div.*
NOTTS. ALLIANCE
Senior Div. Page 419
Div. 1 & 2*
Nissan
WEARSIDE LEAGUE
Division 1* Page 445
Div. 2*
Wade Associates
NORTHERN ALLIANCE
Premier Div. Page 451
Div. 1 & 2*
Manchester
West Cheshire
Liverpool Co. Comb.
Mid Cheshire
West Lancashire
Staffs Senior
Lancs & Cheshire
Teeside
Washington

UniBond League

President: N White F.S.C.A.
Chairman: Peter Maude
Vice Chairman: Tom Culshaw
Chief Executive: Duncan Bayley
Secretary & Treasurer: R D Bayley
22 Woburn Drive, Hale, Altrincham, Cheshire WA15 8LZ
Tel: 0161 980 7007 Fax: 0161 904 8850
Press Secretary: P Bradley
7 Guest Road, Prestwich, Manchester M25 7DJ
Tel: 0161 798 5198 Fax: 0161 773 0930

This was a season where the Unibond League saved the best until the last. Some two weeks after the domestic campaign finished the small village side of Burscough triumphed against all odds to become the first Unibond League outfit to win the FA trophy since Stafford Rangers in 1979. Indeed, only Leek Town in 1990 had even made the final since Stafford's success. For a village with a population of just 8,000, a quarter of whom travelled to Villa Park for the Trophy Final, the achievement was all the more remarkable. Burscough were 400-1 outsiders when the competition began and still rank outsiders at 11/4 in the final despite having caused the sensation of the non-League campaign by dismissing Trophy holders, and eventual Conference champions, Yeovil Town from the competition on their own Huish Park home. In addition, the 'Linnets' had never previously ventured further than the first round proper.

Throw in the fact that for player-manager Sean Teale in his first season at Burscough it was a nostalgic return to Villa Park where he had enjoyed such a distinguished full time career and the story had all the makings of a 'Boys Own' serial. The heartache was provided by Jeff Underwood who was the only Burscough player to be dismissed in the entire season and he paid a penalty out of all proportion to his offence by missing the final against Dr Martens Premier League champions Tamworth. Surely Burscough, with half of their team hand reared through their excellent youth system, couldn't take the 'Lambs' to the slaughter? But they did and after two clinical strikes from 'Man of the Match' Gary Martindale, who could begrudge chairman Frank Parr his tears and immense pride at Burscough's success after 57 years of involvement with the club.

Back on the domestic scene it was a season dominated from start to finish by one of the best known names in football as former Football League founders Accrington Stanley led the Premier Division. Their mid-season away form gave the chasing pack a glimmer of hope but once that problem was sorted out Stanley went on to win the title with a massive sixteen point advantage over runners-up Barrow. The latter were then shocked immediately after the final whistle of the season when manager Kenny Lowe resigned due to work and family commitments. Accrington will surely grace the Conference but the Unibond League, having lost one former Football League outfit, received another in return when Southport were relegated on the final day of the season to end a decade of top flight non-League football.

At the opposite end of the table both Colwyn Bay and Hyde United experienced dreadful seasons and both were relegated some way before the season ended. For many months it seemed Frickley Athletic would be involved in the relegation play-offs but, not for the first time in recent campaigns, the South Yorkshire club built an amazing late escape route and suddenly cup finalists Gateshead found themselves staring relegation in the face. The North East club's poor run of form at the wrong time saw them lose both the league challenge cup final against Marine and their battle against the drop.

The first division title race emulated the higher tier with Alfreton Town also leading from start to finish. Unlike Accrington, however, the Derbyshire outfit were extremely grateful to hang on to their lead in a photo-finish with Spennymoor United, with only goal difference eventually separating the two teams. The 'Moors' made up ground hand over fist in the final month but couldn't quite overtake the leaders although they did finish with the consolation of regaining their premier division status, relinquished a couple of seasons ago. The introduction of play-offs in the Unibond League has been a resounding success and, in addition to the two automatically promoted clubs, no fewer than six other first division clubs entered the final day's fixtures with hope of promotion. Two of them, Matlock Town and Belper Town fought out a goalless draw that eliminated them both from the equation, whilst Witton Albion's failure to stop Spennymoor's charge saw the former Conference club consigned to another season of first division football.

That left Radcliffe Borough, North Ferriby United and Chorley to battle it out in the play-offs with premier division third from bottom club Gateshead. A goal from Borough's 45 goal hot shot Jody Banim saw off Ferriby's challenge and Chorley's five goal blast against Gateshead set up a play-off final that attracted almost a four figure gate and was intriguing to say the least. Borough went two up and only some terrific saves from Lee Bracey prevented a rout before Chorley shocked their hosts with two late goals that levelled matters. Extra-time failed to separate the two teams and after forty four games the third promotion spot came down to penalties. Radcliffe's nerve held and they clinched premier division action next term with victory by four goals to two in the shoot-out.

As mentioned Marine took the league challenge cup but failed to double up when they lost in the annual Peter Swales Memorial Shield (cup winners v league champions) as Accrington Stanley retained the prize they had won twelve months earlier against Burton Albion. The president's cup witnessed an all Tameside final with Stalybridge Celtic running out 6-3 winners over the two legs against neighbours Ashton United whilst Hucknall Town beat Droylsden to lift the chairman's cup with the only goal of the game coming in stoppage time of extra-time!

The Unibond League made a big impact on the FA Cup as early as the Preliminary Round with Stocksbridge PS striker Paul Jackson equalling the all time Cup goalscoring record as he popped in 10 against unfortunate Oldham Town, who went down 17-1. Later in the competition it was Vauxhall Motors and Runcorn FC Halton who made the headlines against Football League opposition. The 'Motormen' first held 1982 finalists, Queen's Park Rangers, to a draw before defeating them in a penalty shoot-out after a second stalemate. They then made life extremely difficult for Macclesfield Town before bowing out bravely in a match televised live on Sky. Runcorn also took Football League opponents Bristol Rovers to a replay and extra time but couldn't quite emulate Vauxhall. Other clubs to reach the First Round Proper were Barrow, Guiseley and Harrogate Town but only the former progressed to join Vauxhall in the Second Round, losing out to Shrewsbury Town, conquerors of Everton in the following round.

Phil Bradley.

FINAL LEAGUE TABLE 2002-03

			HOME					AWAY						
		P	W	D	L	F	A	W	D	L	F	A	Pts	GD
1.	Accrington Stanley	44	18	4	0	53	20	12	6	4	44	24	100	53
2.	Barrow	44	14	5	3	41	21	10	7	5	43	31	84	32
3.	Vauxhall Motors	44	14	3	5	46	19	8	7	7	35	27	76	35
4.	Stalybridge Celtic	44	14	5	3	52	26	7	8	7	25	25	76	26
5.	Worksop Town	44	9	6	7	42	35	12	3	7	40	32	72	15
6.	Harrogate Town	44	10	4	8	38	31	11	4	7	37	32	71	12
7.	Bradford Park Avenue	44	12	6	4	42	27	8	4	10	31	43	70	3
8.	Hucknall Town	44	8	8	6	32	28	9	7	6	40	34	66	10
9.	Droylsden	44	11	4	7	31	21	7	6	9	31	31	64	10
10.	Whitby Town	44	8	4	10	38	38	9	8	5	42	31	63	11
11.	Marine	44	10	5	7	39	31	7	5	10	24	29	61	3
12.	Wakefield & Emley	44	8	12	2	22	17	6	6	10	24	32	60	-3
13.	Runcorn F.C Halton	44	9	6	7	33	37	6	9	7	36	37	60	-5
14.	Altrincham	44	9	7	6	34	27	8	2	12	24	36	60	-5
15.	Gainsborough Trinity	44	9	5	8	35	35	7	6	9	32	31	59	1
16.	Ashton United	44	9	8	5	42	39	7	4	11	29	40	58	-8
17.	Lancaster City	44	8	1	13	33	39	8	8	6	38	36	57	-4
18.	Burscough	44	9	6	7	26	24	5	3	14	18	27	51	-12
19.	Blyth Spartans	44	9	3	10	34	40	5	6	11	33	47	51	-20
20.	Frickley Athletic	44	7	5	10	18	33	6	3	13	27	45	47	-33
21.	Gateshead	44	5	7	10	34	39	5	4	13	26	42	41	-21
22.	Colwyn Bay	44	3	5	14	28	47	2	4	16	24	52	24	-47
23.	Hyde United	44	3	4	15	22	47	2	4	16	18	51	23	-58

PROMOTION/RELEGATION PLAY-OFFS
SEMI FINALS

Chorley 5 - 2 Gateshead   Radcliffe Borough 1 - 0 North Ferriby United

FINAL

Radcliffe Borough 2 - 2 Chorley
(AET - Radcliffe Borough won 4-2 on penalties)

LEADING GOALSCORERS

Lge	Cup	Tot		Lge	Cup	Tot	
33	3	36	Lutel JAMES (Accrington S)	22	6	28	Lee ELLINGTON (Gainsboro' T)
31	2	33	Andy WHITTAKER (Lancaster C)	21	1	22	Aaron WILFORD (Whitby Town)
29	9	38	Terry FEARNS (Vauxhall Motors)	19	8	27	Andy TODD (Worksop Town)
24	6	30	Phil EASTWOOD (Stalybridge C)	17	1	18	Andy HAYWARD (Bradford PA)
24	8	30	Paul MULLIN (Accrington Stanley)				

(In order of League Goals)

HIGHEST ATTENDANCES

2263	AccringtonStan v Altrincham	12/04/03	1355	Accrington Stan v Whitby Town	22/03/03
1520	Barrow v Lancaster City	26/12/02	1334	Accrington Stan v Barrow	11/09/02
1501	Barrow v Blyth Spartans	26/08/02	1318	Accrington Stan v Lancaster City	21/04/03
1488	Accrington Stan v Burscough	02/10/02	1302	Barrow v Hucknall T	17/08/02
1455	Accrington Stan v W & Emley	21/09/02	1290	Accrington Stan v Hyde United	26/04/03
1442	Barrow v Accrington Stan	02/11/02	1240	Gainsborough T v Worksop Town	26/12/02
1367	Accrington Stan v Colwyn Bay	09/10/02			

MONTHLY SPONSORSHIP AWARDS

	CLUB OF MONTH	GOALSCORING
Aug	Accrington Stanley	Accrington Stanley
Sep	Ashton United	Blyth Spartans
Oct	Vauxhall Motors	Vauxhall Motors
Nov	Vauxhall Motors	Worksop Town
Dec	Stalybridge Celtic	Harrogate Town
Jan	Wakefield & Emley	Stalybridge Celtic
Feb	Hucknall town	Droylsdon
Mar	Marine	Barrow
Apr/May	Accrington Stanley	Hucknall Town

PREMIER DIVISION 02-03		1	2	3	4	5	6	7	8	9	10	11	12	13	14	15	16	17	18	19	20	21	22	23
1	ACCRINGTON STANLEY		3-1	4-1	2-1	3-2	3-1	4-2	2-0	2-1	2-1	3-0	2-1	3-2	2-0	1-0	1-1	5-0	2-1	4-1	2-1	1-1	1-1	1-1
2	ALTRINCHAM	1-1		1-0	1-2	3-2	0-0	0-0	4-2	3-1	1-0	1-1	4-0	0-4	0-0	4-1	3-0	0-1	1-1	3-3	0-2	0-1	2-1	2-4
3	ASHTON UNITED	2-2	1-0		2-2	2-1	1-4	0-0	2-2	2-1	3-2	1-3	3-1	5-0	2-3	2-1	2-2	2-3	3-3	1-1	2-1	2-2	1-1	1-4
4	BARROW	1-0	4-0	0-3		2-1	3-2	3-0	2-1	0-0	2-1	3-2	2-0	1-2	1-1	3-0	2-2	1-0	3-0	1-0	1-2	1-1	2-2	3-1
5	BLYTH SPARTANS	0-3	0-2	4-0	1-1		1-2	2-1	1-1	0-1	4-2	2-1	3-2	0-3	1-2	1-3	1-0	1-1	3-1	1-4	2-5	2-1	2-3	2-1
6	BRADFORD P.A.	1-1	1-1	1-1	2-2	5-1		3-2	4-2	3-1	2-2	1-0	2-0	1-0	0-3	5-1	0-1	2-1	3-2	2-1	1-0	1-1	2-3	0-1
7	BURSCOUGH	0-1	0-3	3-2	2-0	1-3	0-1		3-0	0-0	1-0	4-4	1-0	0-1	2-0	0-0	0-0	2-1	3-3	0-1	0-0	1-0	0-2	3-2
8	COLWYN BAY	1-2	2-3	1-1	3-4	1-2	2-0	1-3		0-3	2-3	0-3	2-3	0-1	3-6	2-0	1-1	0-2	1-3	1-1	1-1	3-2	1-1	0-2
9	DROYLSDEN	2-2	1-0	0-1	0-2	7-0	2-0	1-0	2-1		3-1	3-0	0-2	2-1	0-0	0-1	1-5	0-1	2-0	1-1	1-1	1-0	2-1	0-1
10	FRICKLEY ATHLETIC	2-1	0-3	1-0	1-2	1-0	0-3	0-0	3-0	0-2		2-2	1-0	0-1	0-0	0-0	0-1	1-3	2-2	1-0	1-0	0-3	1-7	1-3
11	GAINSBOROUGH TRINITY	1-5	2-1	1-2	0-2	3-2	2-2	0-1	2-1	1-4	2-0		0-1	1-2	2-2	4-2	2-1	0-0	1-1	1-1	2-1	4-1	0-1	4-2
12	GATESHEAD	5-1	0-0	0-1	2-2	3-0	1-1	1-0	2-2	0-2	2-2	1-1		2-3	1-5	2-1	3-3	1-2	2-3	0-1	3-2	0-1	1-3	2-3
13	HARROGATE TOWN	0-2	3-0	0-1	3-2	3-1	5-2	2-1	4-1	0-0	1-2	0-2	1-3		2-0	3-1	1-3	1-1	3-1	1-0	2-2	1-2	0-2	2-2
14	HUCKNALL TOWN	2-1	4-1	2-3	0-3	0-2	1-2	3-1	2-1	2-0	1-0	0-0	1-1	1-1		2-0	1-1	2-1	3-3	2-2	1-2	1-1	1-2	0-0
15	HYDE UNITED	3-3	0-2	1-1	1-3	1-1	3-1	1-0	0-2	1-3	2-3	1-5	0-1	1-5	0-1		2-3	0-2	0-2	0-1	1-0	0-1	3-3	1-4
16	LANCASTER CITY	1-2	3-0	1-3	1-5	1-4	2-3	2-1	1-0	0-3	4-0	0-1	2-1	1-2	1-2	4-1		1-0	1-1	0-1	1-2	5-2	0-1	1-4
17	MARINE	0-3	0-1	1-0	3-1	2-1	4-2	1-0	0-0	2-2	0-1	0-0	4-2	2-2	2-1	4-1	4-0		0-2	1-2	1-2	2-1	5-5	1-2
18	RUNCORN F.C. HALTON	0-2	3-2	3-2	1-1	2-2	2-0	0-2	6-2	0-0	0-1	0-5	1-1	2-1	0-3	1-1	1-4	2-1		1-0	0-5	4-1	1-1	3-0
19	STALYBRIDGE CELTIC	1-4	2-0	4-1	4-3	1-1	2-2	1-0	3-1	2-1	3-1	3-0	4-4	4-1	1-2	6-0	1-0	2-1	0-1		2-2	0-0	2-0	4-1
20	VAUXHALL MOTORS	0-1	4-0	5-1	1-1	0-1	0-1	1-0	2-3	2-1	5-0	1-0	3-0	1-1	5-1	1-0	6-2	1-1	2-1	2-1		1-0	3-2	0-1
21	WAKEFIELD & EMLEY	0-0	2-1	1-1	0-1	1-1	2-1	1-0	2-1	2-2	0-0	2-1	2-1	1-0	1-1	1-1	1-4	1-1	0-0	0-0	1-1		1-0	1-0
22	WHITBYT OWN	0-3	0-1	3-2	1-1	4-4	0-1	0-2	1-0	5-2	3-1	3-0	2-2	4-2	3-3	3-2	2-3	2-0	0-3	1-2	1-2	0-1		0-1
23	WORKSOP TOWN	1-4	1-2	3-2	0-2	1-1	7-1	0-2	4-1	4-1	2-4	0-1	2-0	1-2	5-4	2-1	1-1	2-1	2-2	1-1	1-1	2-1	0-0	

UNIBOND LEAGUE CHALLENGE CUP FINAL

QUARTER-FINALS (4TH ROUND)

Gateshead	5	-	4	Alfreton Town (AET)
Marine	1	-	0	Worksop Town
Radcliffe Borough	3	-	4	Ossett Town
Vauxhall Motors	0	-	1	Rossendale United

SEMI-FINALS

Gateshead	4	-	0	Rossendale United
Ossett Town	0	-	1	Marine

THE FINAL

Gateshead	0	-	1	Marine
Marine	2	-	0	Marine

Marine win 3-0 on aggregate

UNIBOND LEAGUE PRESIDENTS CUP FINAL

QUARTER-FINALS (2ND ROUND)

Ashton United	1	-	0	North ferriby United
Runcorn FC Halton	3	-	1	Spennymoor United
Stalybridge Celtic	3	-	0	Colwyn Bay
Wakefield & Emley	5	-	1	Kidsgrove Atheltic

SEMI-FINALS

Ashton United	1	-	0	Wakefield & Emley
Runcorn FC Halton	2	-	4	Stalybridge Celtic

THE FINAL

Stalybridge Celtic	4	-	2	Ashton United
Ashton United	1	-	2	Stalybridge Celtic

Stalybridge Celtic win 6-3 on aggregate

UNIBOND LEAGUE CHAIRMANS CUP FINAL

QUARTER-FINALS (2ND ROUND)

Bamber Bridge	8	-	2	Kendal Town
Blyth Spartans	3	-	0	Frickley Athletic
Droylsden	4	-	2	Witton Albion (AET)
Lincoln United	0	-	2	Hucknall Town

SEMI-FINALS

Droylsden	1	-	1	Bamber Bridge

AET - Droylsden won 7-6 on penalties

Hucknall Town	4	-	1	Blyth Spartans

THE FINAL

Droylsden	0	-	1	Hucknall Town (AET)

PETER SWALES UNIBOND LEAGUE CHALLENGE SHIELD

Accrington Stanley	2	-	0	Marine

ALFRETON TOWN

PROGRAMME - Pages: 32 Price: £1.50
Editor: Chris Tacey (01302 722415)

Newsline: 01773 830277
Local Radio: Radio Derby
Local Press: Derbyshire Times; Derby Evening Telegraph; Chad, Ripley & Heanor News

CLUB OFFICIALS

Chairman: Wayne Bradley **V- C**: Sam Egan

Secretary: Tom Hill, 4 Westwood Drive,Swanpool,Lincoln LN6 0HJ

Tel Nos 01522 683630 (H) 07885020797(M)

Match Day Sec: Roger Taylor 9 Priory Rd, Alfreton, Derbys. DE55 7J T(01773 835121)

FOOTBALL MANAGEMENT TEAM

Manager:David Lloyd
Assistant Manager: Charlie Wiliamson
Physio: Mick Jenkins

FACT FILE

Formed: 1959
Nickname: The Reds
Sponsors: Impact Marketing & Publicity Ltd
Colours: all red Change colours: all white
Midweek home matchday: Tuesday
Res League: Mid Regional Alliance + Under 19s,18s, 16s, 15s, 13s, & 12s

2002-2003

Captains: Steve Heath & Darren Brookes
Top Scorer: Mick Goodber
Player of the Year: John Knapper

GROUND: Town Ground, North St., Alfreton, Derbys Tel: 01773 521734 Admin.
Club Website: alfretontownfc.com
Directions: M1 junction 28 and follow A38 towards Derby for 1 mile,left onto B600, right at main road to town centre and left after1/2 mile down North St.- ground on right. Half mile from Alfreton (BR) station.Buses:91,92,93 from Derby and Mansfield.Rainbow 1 from Nott'ingham
Capacity: 5,000 Cover: 1,000 Seats:1,600
Clubhouse: H & C food & drinks on ground.Exclusive Bar open on ground matchdays Supporters Club bar outside ground open every day.
Club Shop: Programmes & club souvenirs. Contact Brian Thorpe Tel: 01773 836251

PREVIOUS **Leagues:** Central All.(pre-reformation 21-25) 59-61; Midland (Counties) 25-27 61-82; N.C.E. 82-87; Northern Premier 87-99

BEST SEASON **FA Trophy:** 1st Rd Proper 94-95. **FA Vase:** 5th Round 99-00
FA Cup: 1st Rd 3rd replay 69-70. Also 1st Rd 73-74. - League clubs defeated: Lincoln 24-25

RECORDS **Attendance:** 5,023 v Matlock Tn, Central All 60.
Scorer: J Harrison 303 **Win:** 15-0 v Loughborough, Midland Lge. 69-70
Appearances: J Harrison 560 **Defeat:** 1-9 v Solihull FAT 97, 0-8 v Bridlington 92.
Fees - Paid: £2,000 for Mick Goddard (Worksop Town)) **Received:** £7,000 for Paul Eshelby (Ilkeston Tn 96-97)

HONOURS: N.C.E. Lg 84-85,2001-02 (Lg Cup 84-85,01-02); Midland Co. Lg 69-70 73-74 76-77 (R-up 71-72 80-81 81-82), Lg Cup 71-72 72-73 73-74; Derbyshire Sen Cup (7) and Runners -up (8) Div Cup (N) 64-65; Evans Halshaw Floodlit Cup 87-88 95-96; Cent All Lg.R-Up 63-64; NPL Div 1 R-Up 95-96 NCE Presidents Cup Winners 2001-02 Unibond Div 1 Champions 2002-03

Players progressing: M Wright (68), A Kowalski (73), A Henson (81), Philip Greaves (86) (All Chesterfield), A Woodward (Grimsby T. 70), A Taylor (Chelsea72), R Greenhough (Chester C. 85), K Smith (Exeter C. 89) M Duke (Sheff.Utd 99)

Date	Comp.	Opponents	Att.	Score	Goalscorers
17/08	Unib. 1	FARSLEY CELTIC	257	2 - 0	Brookes 45, Godber 85
20/08	Unib. 1	Trafford	143	2 - 2	Godber 37 49[p]
24/08	Unib. 1	Workington	332	3 - 0	Jules 11, Godber 20, Goddard 52
26/08	Unib. 1	MATLOCK TOWN	563	2 - 0	Robshaw 61, Godber 77
31/08	**F.A.C.** P	Stourport Swifts	128	4 - 1	France 15, Godber 30 44[p], Knapper 90
03/09	Unib. 1	KIDSGROVE ATHLETIC	285	2 - 0	Godber 19, Hobson 45
07/09	Unib. 1	Chorley	299	4 - 2	Bradshaw 14, Goddard 19, Knapper 33[p], Godber 61
10/09	Unib. 1	Leek Town	304	2 - 3	Goddard 33, Bettney 57
14/09	**F.A.C.** Q1	KIDSGROVE ATHLETIC	315	0 - 1	
21/09	Unib. 1	WITTON ALBION	325	1 - 1	Johnson 40
24/09	Unib. 1	Rossendale United	136	4 - 3	Godber 35, France 47 73, Bettney 48
28/09	Unib. 1	BISHOP AUCKLAND	260	4 - 1	Knapper 16[p], Goddard 61, Godber 80, Hogg 89
05/10	**F.A.T.** P	GUISELEY	248	5 - 0	Godber 8 90, Shaw 31[og], Bettney 38, Knapper 80[p]
08/10	Unib. 1	Belper Town	608	5 - 2	Godber 5 43, Goddard 17, France 35 40
12/10	Unib. 1	Farsley Celtic	136	3 - 0	Goddard 10, France 21, Godber 74
15/10	Unib. 1	ROSSENDALE UNITED	195	3 - 0	Johnson 33, Godber 62 64
19/10	Unib. 1	Spennymoor United	262	2 - 1	Hindley 46, Godber 76
29/10	Unib. 1	OSSETT TOWN	268	5 - 1	Bradshaw 10, Bettney 57, Robshaw 70, Circuit 80, Dolby 89
02/11	**F.A.T.** 1	Lincoln United	168	3 - 2	Heath 4, Hindley 17, Goddard 57
05/11	Unib. 1	Lincoln United	156	3 - 1	Goddard 53 66, Godber 60
09/11	Unib. 1	KENDAL TOWN	347	4 - 3	Robshaw 3, Hindley 21, Godber 33, Heath 89
12/11	Unib. 1	TRAFFORD	271	6 - 1	Godber 23 31, Dolby 52, Robshaw 64, Hindley 71, Bettney 90
19/11	Derbys SC 3	RIPLEY TOWN	n/k	3 - 0	
23/11	Unib. 1	WORKINGTON	364	3 - 0	Godber 40, Johnson 53, Bettney 63
26/11	Lge Cup 2	Stocksbridge Park Steels	191	4 - 1	Dolby 40, Robshaw 45, Godber 73, Knapper 84[p]
30/11	**F.A.T.** 2	Stafford Rangers	782	2 - 0	Bradshaw 31, Knapper 75
07/12	Unib. 1	Stocksbridge Park Steels	215	3 - 2	Knapper 55, Bradshaw 57, Flynn 65[og]
14/12	Unib. 1	North Ferriby United	210	2 - 2	Godber 15, Bettney 44
17/12	Derbys SC QF	GLOSSOP NORTH END	143	3 - 0	Godber 18 36, Hogg 60
26/12	Unib. 1	STOCKSBRIDGE PARK STEELS	372	1 - 1	Robshaw 53
28/12	Unib. 1	Bamber Bridge	271	2 - 0	France 55, Robshaw 71
04/01	Unib. 1	EASTWOOD TOWN	505	4 - 1	France 42 52 81, Johnson 75
11/01	**F.A.T.** 3	HALESOWEN TOWN	681	2 - 1	Hobson 58, Johnson 88
14/01	Lge Cup 3	EASTWOOD TOWN	222	4 - 1	Robshaw 11, Bradshaw 47, Knapper 85[p], Hindley 90
18/01	Unib. 1	Guiseley	362	2 - 2	Johnson 17 47
25/01	Unib. 1	BELPER TOWN	715	1 - 2	Johnson 77
01/02	**F.A.T.** 4	BURSCOUGH	602	1 - 1	Robshaw 50
04/02	**F.A.T.** 4 rep	Burscough	190	0 - 2	
08/02	Unib. 1	GUISELEY	393	1 - 3	Johnson 45
12/02	Lge Cup QF	Gateshead	127	4 - 5	Highfield 37, Knapper 50 90, Dolby 57
22/02	Unib. 1	Bishop Auckland	185	0 - 0	
25/02	Derbys SC SF	Belper Town	331	1 - 0	Bradshaw 39
01/03	Unib. 1	LINCOLN UNITED	421	2 - 2	Askey 57, Knapper 61
04/03	Unib. 1	Radcliffe Borough	355	4 - 2	Godber 51, Dolby 53, Whealing 58[og], Circuit 64
08/03	Unib. 1	Kidsgrove Athletic	194	1 - 0	Askey 15
15/03	Unib. 1	Kendal Town	272	1 - 4	Hindley 90
18/03	Unib. 1	RADCLIFFE BOROUGH	329	3 - 2	Goddard 23, Knapper 42, Askey 80
22/03	Unib. 1	Eastwood Town	360	4 - 0	Goddard 7 24, Hobson 67 70
29/03	Unib. 1	CHORLEY	478	1 - 3	Bradshaw 74
01/04	Unib. 1	Matlock Town	908	4 - 2	France 5, Johnson 62, Knapper 74[p] 90[p]
05/04	Unib. 1	LEEK TOWN	565	1 - 2	Knapper 57[p]
08/04	Unib. 1	SPENNYMOOR UNITED	360	1 - 1	Johnson 45
12/04	Unib. 1	Witton Albion	330	2 - 1	Godber 52 66
15/04	Derbys SC F(1)	Mickleover Sports	n/k	5 - 0	Hindley 40 50, Dolby 59 86, Robshaw 89
19/04	Unib. 1	NORTH FERRIBY UNITED	382	3 - 4	Godber 15, Knapper 44[p], Goddard 76
21/04	Unib. 1	Ossett Town	281	2 - 1	Goddard 22, France 63
26/04	Unib. 1	BAMBER BRIDGE	500	1 - 1	Johnson 64
29/04	Derbys SC F(2)	MICKLEOVER SPORTS	172	2 - 1	Hobson 6, Knapper 25

PLAYING SQUAD

Goalkeepers: Lee Butler (Halifax T.), Stuart Ford (Ilkeston T.), Gavin Saxby (Clipstone Welfare), Paul Varney (Hallam).

Defenders: Mark Blount (Burton A), Carl Bardshaw (Scunthorpe U), Darren Brookes (Worksop T.), Grant Brown (Telford U), James Elliott (Emley), Neil Grayston (Halifax T.), John Haydon (Forest Green R.), Lee Hobson (Hallam), Mark Jules (Halifax T.), Darren Schofield (Denaby U)

Midfield: Ian Askey (Stocksbridge P.S.), Steve Circuit (Gainsborough T.), Chris Dolby (Harrogate T.), Mick Goddard (Worksop T.), Mark Highfield (Hallam), Steve Johnson (Eastwood), Nathan Kerry (Denaby Utd), John Knapper (Ilkeston T.), Chris Marks (Gresley R.), Emeka Nwadiki (Ilkeston T.), Ian Robinson (Ilkeston T.), Gary Thorpe (Worksop T.).

Forwards: Chris Bettney (Stavely MW), Ryan France (Local Football), Mick Godber (Ossett T.), Matt Hogg (Club Academy), Craig Housley (Notts County), James Robshaw (Ossett Albion).

ALTRINCHAM

CLUB OFFICIALS

Chairman: Geoffrey Goodwin
President: Noel White
Directors
Grahame Rowley, Andrew Shaw,
Geoff Goodwin
Secretary: Graham Heathcote
Press Officer: John Pollit
Match Secretary: George Heslop

FOOTBALL MANAGEMENT TEAM

Manager: Graham Heathcote
Assistant manager: Dalton Steele
Physiotherapist: Gary Thompson

FACT FILE

Formed: 1903
Nickname: The Robins
Sponsor: Go Goodwins Coaches
Colours: Red & white stripes/black/red&white
Change colours: Blue/black/black
Midweek matchday: Tuesday
Youth League: North West Youth Alliance

2002-2003

Captain & Top Scorer: Rod Thornley
P.O.Y. x3 : Ian Craney

Pages: 40 Price: £1.50
Editor: Graham/Terry Rowley 0161 928 1045
Local Radio: GMR (BBC);
Signal Radio; Piccadilly Radio
Local Press: Sale & Altrincham Messenger;
Manchester Evening News

GROUND: Moss Lane, Altrincham, Cheshire WA15 8AP. **e.mail** www.altyfc.u-net.com
Tel: 0161 928 1045(Office) 0161 9228 1045 (Club) Fax: 0161 926 9934
Directions: M6 junction 19; A556/M56 (Manchester Airport) to junction 7; signs Hale and Altrincham; through 1st traffic lights then 3rd right into Westminster Road and continue into Moss Lane. Ground on right.
CAPACITY: 6,085 **COVER:** Yes **SEATS:** 1,154
Clubhouse: Bar under the stand open on match days only. Two snack bars on ground for pies, crisps, soft drinks etc **Club Shop:** Yes (Contact: Jenny Heslop 0161 928 1045

PREVIOUS **Leagues:** Manchester 03-11, Lancashire Comb. 11-19, Cheshire County 19-68, Northern Premier 68-79, 97-99; Conference 79-97 99-00 **Grounds:** Pollitts Field -1903-1910 **Names:** None

RECORDS **Attendance:**10,275 Altrincham Boys v Sunderland Boys,English Schools Shield 3rd Round 28.02.25
Goalscorer: Jack Swindells 252 - 1965-71 **Appearances:** JohnDavison 677 - 1971-86
Win: 9-2 v Merthyr Tydfil,Vauxhall Conference, Feb 1991 **Defeat:** Unknown
Fee Paid: £15,000 to Blackpool for Keith Russell
Fee Received: From Scarborough for Kevin Ellison £45,000

BEST SEASON **FA Trophy:** Winners 77-78, 85-86 **League:** Conference Champions 1979-80, 80-81
FA Cup: 85-86 4th Round, 0-2 v York City (A) League clubs defeated:15

HONOURS FA Trophy 77-78, 85- 86; Alliance Premier League 79-80, 80-81; Bob Lord Trophy 80-81; Northern Prem. Lge: Champions 98-99; Lge.Cup 69-70 97-98; N.P.L. Shield 79-80; Cheshire County League: Champions 65-66, 66-67; Lge Cup 50-51, 52-53, 63-64; Cheshire Senior Cup 04-05, 33-34, 66-67,81-82; Manchester League 04-05; Cheshire Amateur Cup 03-04.

Players Progressing: Several, most recent being G Barrow (Wigan Ath. 81), J Rogers(Wigan Ath., 82), P Conning (Rochdale, 86), E Bishop (Tranmere R. 88), P Edwards (Crewe, 88), A Kilner (Stockport C. 90), P Showler (Barnet, 91), S Johnson & A Reid (Bury 92), C Freeman (Doncaster R. 93), T Carke (Shrewsbury T. 93),Nicky Daws (Bury), Kevin Ellison (Leicester City), Danny Adams (Macclesfield Town)

Back row, left to right: Neil Ryan, Peter Band, Jason Gallagher, Simon Woodford, Andy Mooore, StephenRose, Andy Macdonald Mark Maddox.
Front: Alex Frost, Shaun Smith, Geoff Goodwin(Chairman), Rod Thornley, Ian Craney, Andy Tinnicliffe and Gary Scott

Match Facts 2002-03

Date	Comp.	Opponents	Att.	Score	oalscorers
17/08	Unib. P	HARROGATE TOWN	552	0 - 4	
20/08	Unib. P	Vauxhall Motors	315	0 - 4	
24/08	Unib. P	Hucknall Town	302	1 - 4	Talbot 61
26/08	Unib. P	GATESHEAD	540	4 - 0	Thornley 21[p] 56 62, Band 89
31/08	Unib. P	Blyth Spartans	528	2 - 0	Thornley 52 90
03/09	Unib. P	BURSCOUGH	494	0 - 0	
07/09	Unib. P	HYDE UNITED	696	4 - 1	Band 60, McDonald 69, Ryan 89[p], Young 90
10/09	Unib. P	Wakefield & Emley	318	1 - 2	Band 34
14/09	Unib. P	Ashton United	443	0 - 1	
18/09	Ches. SC 1	Crewe Alexandra	482	2 - 3	Thornley 20 27
24/09	Unib. P	MARINE	477	0 - 1	
28/09	**F.A.C.** Q2	KENDAL TOWN	513	1 - 0	Young 74
01/10	Unib. P	Lancaster City	325	0 - 3	
05/10	Unib. P	STALYBRIDGE CELTIC	897	3 - 3	Thornley 11[p], Young 47, McDonald 64
08/10	Unib. P	VAUXHALL MOTORS	455	0 - 2	
12/10	**F.A.C.** Q3	Guiseley	428	1 - 2	Band 69
15/10	Unib. P	Burscough	294	3 - 0	Gallagher 14, Craney 83 87
19/10	Unib. P	WHITBY TOWN	620	2 - 1	Thornley 45[p], Band 66
26/10	Unib. P	WAKEFIELD & EMLEY	602	0 - 1	
02/11	Unib. P	Worksop Town	754	2 - 1	Thornley 40 42[p]
05/11	Unib. P	BARROW	574	1 - 2	Craney 48
09/11	Unib. P	Gainsborough Trinity	467	1 - 2	Thornley 55
12/11	Unib. P	BRADFORD PARK AVENUE	495	0 - 0	
16/11	Unib. P	GAINSBOROUGH TRINITY	576	1 - 1	Band 43
18/11	Lge Cup 2	HYDE UNITED	206	1 - 2	Lunt 10
23/11	Unib. P	FRICKLEY ATHLETIC	582	1 - 0	Thornley 33
30/11	**F.A.T.** 2	Bradford Park Avenue	437	1 - 0	Thornley 6
02/12	Unib. P	Marine	231	1 - 0	Band 87
10/12	Pres. Cup 1	Colwyn Bay	115	1 - 2	Webster 83[og]
14/12	Unib. P	Stalybridge Celtic	857	0 - 2	
26/12	Unib. P	DROYLSDEN	715	3 - 1	Craney 24 59, Gardner 45
28/12	Unib. P	Colwyn Bay	447	3 - 2	Band 31, Craney 61, McDonald 86
04/01	Unib. P	LANCASTER CITY	604	3 - 0	Gardner 86 90, Adams 89
14/01	**F.A.T.** 3	Kettering Town	1072	1 - 1	Adams 61
18/01	Unib. P	RUNCORN HALTON	628	1 - 1	Craney 66
22/01	**F.A.T.** 3 rep	KETTERING TOWN	436	3 - 3	Shuttleworth 35[p], Smith 39, Murphy 43 Won 5 4 after pens.
01/02	**F.A.T.** 4	AYLESBURY UNITED	732	0 - 1	
08/02	Unib. P	BLYTH SPARTANS	548	3 - 2	Sullivan 19, Maddox 50, Lunt 83
15/02	Unib. P	Gateshead	264	0 - 0	
22/02	Unib. P	Whitby Town	402	1 - 0	Gardner 67[p]
01/03	Unib. P	WORKSOP TOWN	738	2 - 4	Craney 13, Shuttleworth 67[p]
04/03	Unib. P	Barrow	881	0 - 4	
11/03	Unib. P	ACCRINGTON STANLEY	600	1 - 1	Craney 56
15/03	Unib. P	Hyde United	485	2 - 0	Robertson 10, Band 69
18/03	Unib. P	Harrogate Town	368	0 - 3	
22/03	Unib. P	HUCKNALL TOWN	557	0 - 0	
29/03	Unib. P	Bradford Park Avenue	440	1 - 1	Shuttleworth 34
31/03	Unib. P	Droylsden	316	0 - 1	
05/04	Unib. P	ASHTON UNITED	595	1 - 0	Hughes 62
12/04	Unib. P	Accrington Stanley	2263	1 - 3	Shuttleworth 67[p]
19/04	Unib. P	COLWYN BAY	560	4 - 2	Thornley 25 30, Craney 44, Scott 61
21/04	Unib. P	Runcorn Halton	334	2 - 3	Band 27, Craney 55
26/04	Unib. P	Frickley Athletic	215	3 - 0	Band 5 52, Lunt 90

PLAYING SQUAD

Goalkeeper:

Defenders: Chris Adams (Ashton Utd), Steve Aspinall (Runcorn F.C.Halton), Mark Maddox (Barrow), Stephen Rose (Chester City), Neil Ryan (Portland Timbers USA), Gary Scott (Leigh RMI), Barry Shuttleworth (Accrington Stanley), Gary Talbot (Northwich V.), Paul Robertson (Kidsgrove Ath.), Paul Taylor (Hyde Utd).

Midfielders: Ian Craney (Runcorn), Tony Cullen (Salford City), Jason Gallagher (Hyde Utd), Kevin Mairs (Youth Team), Danny Murphy (Mossley), Marc Whiteman (Bury).

Forwards: Pater Band (Hyde Utd), Ian Duerdan (Hucknall T.), Dave Gardner (Salford City), Rod Thornley (Congleton T.), Andy Tunnicliffe (Trafford), Chris Young (Hyde Utd).

ASHTON UNITED

CLUB OFFICIALS

Acting Chairman:David Wright
President: R.Thomasson
Vice Chairman: J Milne
Directors: David Wright, Mike Cummings, Dickie Day, Kevin O'Carroll,Arthur Mycroft, Jim Pinder,Jim Sutherland, Stuart Jones, Eric Stafford and Terry Hollis.
Secretary: Graham O'Neill,5 Lydgate Drive, Oldham, Lanvcs.OL4 5HH
Tel Nos: 0161 652 0939 (H) 07769 795104
Press Officer: M.Crabtree
Match Sec Neil Harding (07754 090126)

FACT FILE

Formed: 1878 Nickname: Robins
Club Sponsors: Wheelbrook Services
Colours: Red & white halves/black/red
Change colours: Amber & Blue/blue/amber & blue
Midweek matchday: Tuesday
Website: www.aufc4.freeserve.co.uk

FOOTBALL MANAGEMENT TEAM

Manager: Gerry Quinn
Physio: Martin Grose

GROUND Surrey Street, Hurst Cross, Ashton-u-Lyne OL6 8DY.
Tel: 0161339 4158. (office) 01613 301511 (Social Club). Fax 0161 339 4158
Directions: M62 jct 20, A627(M) to Oldham, keep in right hand 2 lanes, leave at Ashton sign after 2 miles passing Belgrade Hotel, take A627 at next island,keep in left lane and take slip road signed Ashton-under-Lyme, at island follow Stalybridge/Park Road sign, go straight ahead for 3 miles to ground at Hurst Cross. BR to Charles Street (Ashton), or Stalybridge. Buses 331, 332, 337, 408(Ashton-Stalybridge) all pass ground
Capacity: 4,500 Seats: 250 Cover: 750
Clubhouse: Open 11am-11pm. Refreshment bar open matchdays
Club Shop: Yes - contact Ken or Steve Lee (0161 330 9800)

PROGRAMME
Pages: 22 Price: £1
Editor:Ken Lee (0161 330 9800)
Local Press: Ashton Reporter, Ashton Advertiser Local Radio: GMR

PREVIOUS **Leagues:** Manchester; Lancs Comb 12-23, 48-64, 66-68; Midland 64-66; Cheshire Co. 23-48, 68-82; Nth West Count 82-92.
Name: Hurst 1878-1947. Ground: Rose Hill 1878-1912

CLUB RECORDS **Attendance:** 11,000 v Halifax Town, FA Cup First Round 1952.
Scorer: Mark Edwards, 37 **Appearances:** Micky Boyle, 462.
Win: 11-3 v Staylbridge Manchester Interm Cup 55 **Defeat:** 11-1 v Wellington Town Cheshire Lge 46-47.
Fee Paid: £9,000 for Andy Whittaker (Netherfield, 1994) **Fee Received:** £15,000 for Karl Marginson (Rotherham, Mar. 1993)

BEST SEASON **FA Trophy**: Qtr Final v Dagenham (0-1) (A0 96-97
FA Cup: 1st Rd replay 52-53, 1-2 v Halifax T (A), after 1-1. Also 1st Rd 55-56, 1-6 v Southport (A)

HONOURS Northern Prem Lge Div 1 Cup 94-95; Manchester Sen Cup 1884-85 13-14 75-76 77-78; Manchester Lge 11-12; Lancs Comb. Div 2 60-61 (Lge Cup 62-63); Manchester Prem. Cup 79-80 82-83 92-93 00-01 01-02; N.W.C. Lge 91-92;Challenge Cup 91-92, Div 2 87-88; F' lit League 90-91; Challenge Shield 92-93; Manchester Chall Shield 35-36 38-39 49-50 53-54 R-up 34-35 39-40, Manchester Interm Cup 58-59 62-63 65-66, R-up 60-61 64-65; Manchester Jnr Cup 1894-95 10-12 32-33; Unifilla Div 1 Cup 96-97,98-99

Players progressing: A Ball (Blackpool), J Mahoney (Stoke C.), B Daniels(Manchester C.), R Jones (Rotherham U.), A Arrowsmith (Liverpool), N Stiffle(Crystal Palace), K Marginson (Rotherham U), P Wilson (Plymouth Argyle)

Back row left to right: Greg Challender,Darren Royle, James Riordan, Andy Johnson, Phil Denney, Alex Green, Jason Dormer, Lee Blackshaw, Gareth Hamlet and Gareth Morris.
Front row: Gerry Quinn (Manager), Peter Carty, Fredrick Maiomi, Chris Connelly, Lee Calvert, Paul Garvey and Martin Grose (physio)

Date	Comp.	Opponents	Att.	Score	Goalscorers
20/08	Unib. P	WHITBY TOWN	275	1 - 1	Connor 20
24/08	Unib. P	STALYBRIDGE CELTIC	702	1 - 1	Miller 62
26/08	Unib. P	Gainsborough Trinity	493	2 - 1	Dormer 58 90
31/08	Unib. P	BRADFORD PARK AVENUE	280	1 - 4	Miller 26
03/09	Unib. P	Wakefield & Emley	308	1 - 1	Miller 18
07/09	Unib. P	Gateshead	187	1 - 0	Baylis 71
10/09	Unib. P	WORKSOP TOWN	255	1 - 4	Denney 31[p]
14/09	Unib. P	ALTRINCHAM	443	1 - 0	Morris 44
17/09	Unib. P	Barrow	841	3 - 0	Cornelly 83 89, Marrass 90
21/09	Unib. P	Droylsden	503	1 - 0	Blackshaw 84
24/09	Unib. P	ACCRINGTON STANLEY	409	2 - 2	Challender 62, Miller 84
28/09	**F.A.C.** Q2	Stocksbridge Park Steels	270	2 - 0	Connor 62[p], Fleury 90
01/10	Unib. P	Vauxhall Motors	207	1 - 5	Wolstenholme 11
05/10	Unib. P	BLYTH SPARTANS	253	2 - 1	Miller 52, Connor 90[p]
08/10	Unib. P	Whitby Town	274	2 - 3	Cornelly 6, Fleury 54
12/10	**F.A.C.** Q3	RUNCORN HALTON	347	0 - 3	
15/10	Unib. P	WAKEFIELD & EMLEY	185	2 - 2	Miller 60, Calvert 62
19/10	Unib. P	Hucknall Town	227	3 - 2	Miller 7, Connor 54, Wolstenholme 68
26/10	Unib. P	GATESHEAD	205	3 - 1	Miller 32 48, Denney 68
29/10	Manc PC 1	TRAFFORD	138	3 - 2	Riorden 34 51, Carty 90
02/11	**F.A.T.** 1	Droylsden	327	1 - 2	Miller 28
05/11	Unib. P	Runcorn Halton	202	2 - 3	Miller 14, Cornelly 69
09/11	Unib. P	BURSCOUGH	202	0 - 0	
12/11	Unib. P	Colwyn Bay	148	1 - 1	Morris 61
16/11	Unib. P	HYDE UNITED	353	2 - 1	Royle 28, Morris 61
19/11	Lge Cup 2	VAUXHALL MOTORS	169	1 - 2	Morris 16
23/11	Unib. P	Lancaster City	279	3 - 1	Denney 21, Carty 77 84
30/11	Unib. P	MARINE	213	2 - 3	Carty 33, Royle 85
04/12	Unib. P	Accrington Stanley	665	1 - 4	Cornelly 80
14/12	Unib. P	Blyth Spartans	349	0 - 4	
17/12	Pres. Cup 1	ACCRINGTON STANLEY	101	4 - 2	Connor 25, Morris 61 82, Denny 90
21/12	Unib. P	FRICKLEY ATHLETIC	225	3 - 2	Garvey 46, Connor 57[p], Rowe 59
26/12	Unib. P	COLWYN BAY	186	2 - 2	Smith 89, Connor 90[p]
14/01	Manc PC QF	Maine Road	82	4 - 0	Rush 41, Rowe 55 77, Carty 64
18/01	Unib. P	Stalybridge Celtic	826	1 - 4	Rowe 61
25/01	Pres. Cup QF	NORTH FERRIBY UNITED	163	1 - 0	Royle 88
28/01	Unib. P	VAUXHALL MOTORS	180	2 - 1	Connor 49 64[p]
01/02	Unib. P	Harrogate Town	466	1 - 0	Rowe 74
08/02	Unib. P	Bradford Park Avenue	271	1 - 1	Smith 38
15/02	Unib. P	GAINSBOROUGH TRINITY	242	1 - 3	White 18
22/02	Unib. P	HUCKNALL TOWN	213	2 - 3	Garvey 13, Morris 51
25/02	Manc PC SF	FLIXTON	102	6 - 1	Denney 2 15[p], Morris 9, Rowe 32, S Smith 61, Murphy 88
01/03	Unib. P	Marine	254	0 - 1	
11/03	Unib. P	DROYLSDEN	208	2 - 1	Fleury 23 59
18/03	Pres. Cup SF	WAKEFIELD & EMLEY	182	1 - 0	Dormer 45
22/03	Unib. P	Worksop Town	478	2 - 3	Royle 57, Denney 65
25/03	Unib. P	HARROGATE TOWN	234	5 - 0	Miller 16, Smith 19, Denney 20 79, Carty 25
29/03	Pres. Cup F(1)	Stalybridge Celtic	634	2 - 4	Denney 6 69
01/04	Unib. P	Frickley Athletic	158	0 - 1	
05/04	Unib. P	Altrincham	595	0 - 1	
08/04	Unib. P	Burscough	125	2 - 3	Royle 60, Rowe 90
12/04	Unib. P	BARROW	337	2 - 2	Denney 36, Miller 51
16/04	Manc PC F	DROYLSDEN	n/k	2 - 0	Denney 7, Fleury 61 (at Oldham Athletic)
19/04	Unib. P	RUNCORN HALTON	190	3 - 3	Morris 38, Miller 45, Royle 55
21/04	Unib. P	Hyde United	325	1 - 1	Morris 48
24/04	Pres. Cup F(2)	STALYBRIDGE CELTIC	610	1 - 2	Miller 50
26/04	Unib. P	LANCASTER CITY	195	2 - 2	Miller 14, Denney 65

PLAYING SQUAD

Goalkeepers: Andy Johnston (Great Harwood).

Defenders: Lee Connor (Farsley Celtic), Paul France (Stalybridge Celtic), Mike Jeffermen (Youth Team), Gareth Morris (Youth Team), Darren Royle (Flixton), Andy Thackeray (Nuneaton Bor.), Danny White Buxton).

Midfield: Lee Calvert (Ossett Albion), Mike Carmody (Altrincham), Chris Grose (Youth Team), Dean Johnson (Ossett Albion), Ashley Partington (Youth Team), Arren Sutcliffe (Youth Team).

Forwards: Peter Carty (Curzon Ashton), Phil Denney (Bradford P.A.), Jason Dormer (Hyde Utd), Craig Fleur (Curzon Ashton), Paul Garvey (Flixton), Jamie Miller (Liversedge), Rodney Rowe (Wakefield & Emley)

BARROW

CLUB OFFICIALS

President: Alan Dunn
Chairman: Brian Keen
Football Secretary; Russell Dodd,
9 Keswick Avenue,Barrow in Furness,
Cumbria.LA14 4LL
Tel: 01229 827286(H) 07778 700137 (M)
Press Officer: Phil Yelland
83 Camus Drive, Edinburgh EH10 6QY
Tel: 0131 445 1010 (H)
0131 476 8131 (W) 0776 1235538(M)
Barrow Soccer Hotline: 09066 555820
Manager: Lee Turnbull

FACT FILE

Founded: 1901
Nickname: Bluebirds
Sponsors: T.B.A.
Colours: White/blue/white
Change: Red/red/white
Midweek matchday: Tuesday

2002-2003

Captain: Mark Hume
Top Scorer: Grant Holt
Player of the Year: Grant Holt

Pages: 44 Price: £1.50
Editor: Russell Dodd (01229 827286)

Local Press: North West Evening Mail,
Barrow & West Cumberland Advertiser
Local Radio: BBC Radio Cumbria, Bay Radio

GROUND: Holker Street Stadium, Wilkie Road, Barrow-in-Furness, CumbriaLA14 5UW
Tel: 01229 820346 e-mail: directors@barrowfc.com
Directions: M6 to junction 36, A590 to Barrow, enter Barrow on Park Road and after about 2 miles turn left into Wilkie Rd - ground on right. B.R.1/4 mile
Capacity: 4,500 **Seated:** 1000 **Covered Terracing:** 1,200

Clubhouse: Barrow F.C. Cross Bar next to ground. Open matchdays and Functions only. Snack bars on ground **Club Shop:** Situated on the ground.(Paul Akred (01229 824308)

PREVIOUS **Leagues:** Lancs Comb 01-21; Football League 21-72; Northern Premier 72-79, 83-84, 86-89, 92-98; 99- GM Vauxhall Conference 79-83, 84-86, 89-92, 98-99 **Grounds:** The Strawberry & Little Park, Roose **Names:**None

RECORDS **Attendance:** 16,854 v Swansea Town, FA Cup 3rd Rd. 1954
Career Appearances: Colin Cowperthwaite 704 **Career Goalscorer:** Colin Cowperthwaite 282 (Dec '77-Dec '92).
Defeat: 1-10 v Hartlepool Utd, Football Lge Div 4, 1959 **Win:** 12-0 v Cleator, FA Cup 1920.
Transfer Fee Paid: £9,000 for Andy Whittaker (Ashton Utd, July 94).
Transfer Fee Received: £40,000 for Kenny Lowe (Barnet, Jan 91)

BEST SEASON **FA Trophy:** Winners 1989-90, Semi-Final 87-88
FA Cup: Third Round Proper 9 times including once as a non-League club 90-91, 0-1 v Bolton Wanderers (A)

HONOURS F.A. Trophy Winners 89-90, Northern Premier League 97-98, 88-89, 83-84; R-up 2002-03. Lge Cup R-up 87-88, Lge Shield 84-85 R-up 89-90 98-99; Bob Lord Trophy R-up 90-91, Cumbrian Cup 82-8383-84 (R-up 84-85), Lancs Floodlit Cup R-up 86-87, Lancs Sen Cup 54-55 (R-up 51-52 65-66 66-67 69-70), Lancs Challenge Trophy 80-81 (R-up 81-82 84-85 01-02), Lancs Comb 20-21, R-up 13-14, Div 2 R-up 04-05 10-11. Unibond Chairman's Cup (00-01)President's Cup 01-02

Players progressing: I McDonald, N McDonald, J Laisby, B Diamond, F Gamble, B Knowles, G Skivington, P Byron, L Edwards, K Lowe, M Dobie, T Rigby, N Doherty.

Date	Comp.	Opponents	Att.	Score	Goalscorers
17/08	Unib. P	HUCKNALL TOWN	1302	1 - 1	Bullimore 86
20/08	Unib. P	Runcorn Halton	343	1 - 1	Ward 43
24/08	Unib. P	Colwyn Bay	346	4 - 3	Hume 21, Tarrant 25, Ward 33, Stannard 54[og]
26/08	Unib. P	BLYTH SPARTANS	1501	2 - 1	Nesovic 81, Gaughan 90[p]
31/08	Unib. P	Frickley Athletic	208	2 - 1	Hume 63, Gaughan 90[p]
07/09	Unib. P	WHITBY TOWN	1012	2 - 2	Hall 49, Hume 81
11/09	Unib. P	Accrington Stanley	1334	1 - 2	Ward 22
14/09	Unib. P	Bradford Park Avenue	368	2 - 2	Tarrant 8, Nesovic 90
17/09	Unib. P	ASHTON UNITED	841	0 - 3	
21/09	Unib. P	Worksop Town	739	2 - 0	Maxfield 39, Nesovic 90
24/09	Unib. P	STALYBRIDGE CELTIC	870	1 - 0	Hume 80
28/09	**F.A.C.** Q2	Gateshead	295	4 - 3	Nesovic 36 84, Hall 49, Housham 74
05/10	Unib. P	VAUXHALL MOTORS	977	1 - 2	Gaughan 90[p]
08/10	Unib. P	RUNCORN HALTON	757	3 - 0	Hume 42 82, Tierney 54
12/10	**F.A.C.** Q3	HYDE UNITED	1074	3 - 1	Bullimore 15, Crookes 23[og], Hume 46
14/10	Unib. P	Hyde United	363	3 - 1	Holt 12 20 88
19/10	Unib. P	Vauxhall Motors	250	1 - 1	Holt 45
26/10	**F.A.C.** Q4	Nuneaton Borough	1678	1 - 1	Tarrant 30
29/10	**F.A.C.** Q4 rep	NUNEATON BOROUGH	1919	4 - 3	Tarrant 36 90, Anthony 78 88
02/11	Unib. P	ACCRINGTON STANLEY	1442	1 - 0	Hume 18
05/11	Unib. P	Altrincham	574	2 - 1	Gaughan 65[p], Housham 84
09/11	Unib. P	WAKEFIELD & EMLEY	1211	1 - 1	Anthony 68
12/11	Unib. P	Harrogate Town	402	2 - 3	Housham 59, Arnold 90
16/11	**F.A.C.** 1	MOOR GREEN	2650	2 - 0	Holt 16, Salmon 49
19/11	Lge Cup 2	ACCRINGTON STANLEY	524	3 - 2	Bee 13, Swarbrick 45, Dawson 49
23/11	Unib. P	Gateshead	254	2 - 2	Anthony 2, Gaughan 30
26/11	Unib. P	Burscough	189	0 - 2	
30/11	**F.A.T.** 2	WHITBY TOWN	853	4 - 2	Holt 8, Hume 25 60, Bullimore 90
03/12	Unib. P	Stalybridge Celtic	511	3 - 4	Connell 28 77, Bullimore 50
07/12	**F.A.C.** 2	Shrewsbury Town	4210	1 - 3	Housham 60
10/12	Lge Cup 3	Radcliffe Borough	92	1 - 2	Housham 84
21/12	Unib. P	GAINSBOROUGH TRINITY	1004	3 - 2	Holt 21 52, Arnold 29
26/12	Unib. P	LANCASTER CITY	1520	2 - 2	Holt 42, Arnold 74
28/12	Unib. P	Droylsden	269	2 - 0	Holt 60, Tarrant 90
01/01	Unib. P	Lancaster City	888	5 - 1	Arnold 5 48 75[p], Holt 11, Tarrant 90
04/01	Unib. P	MARINE	1218	1 - 0	Holt 62
14/01	**F.A.T.** 3	Northwich Victoria	543	1 - 3	Shaw 90
18/01	Unib. P	HYDE UNITED	1036	3 - 0	Connell 30 42, Housham 82
21/01	Lancs MT 2	KENDAL TOWN	293	0 - 1	
25/01	Unib. P	Gainsborough Trinity	494	2 - 0	Connell 47, Holt 54
08/02	Unib. P	FRICKLEY ATHLETIC	1038	2 - 1	Salmon 44, Shaw 48
25/02	Unib. P	Blyth Spartans	345	1 - 1	Ridley 85
01/03	Unib. P	BURSCOUGH	942	3 - 0	Holt 18 71, Arnold 60
04/03	Unib. P	ALTRINCHAM	881	4 - 0	Housham 25 65, Hume 31, Gaughan 84[p]
08/03	Unib. P	Whitby Town	357	1 - 1	Arnold 84
15/03	Unib. P	HARROGATE TOWN	1013	1 - 2	Salmon 90
22/03	Unib. P	COLWYN BAY	854	2 - 1	Gaughan 39[p], Holt 90
25/03	Unib. P	Hucknall Town	199	3 - 0	Gaughan 23[p], Holt 29, Hume 82
29/03	Unib. P	Wakefield & Emley	243	1 - 0	Warren 90[p]
05/04	Unib. P	BRADFORD PARK AVENUE	1022	3 - 2	Anderson 20, Gaughan 76[p], Salmon 90
12/04	Unib. P	Ashton United	337	2 - 2	Dormer 14[og], Kewley 90
15/04	Unib. P	WORKSOP TOWN	788	3 - 1	Hill 1, Hume 86, Brough 90
19/04	Unib. P	DROYLSDEN	911	0 - 0	
21/04	Unib. P	Marine	252	1 - 3	Ridley 88
26/04	Unib. P	GATESHEAD	877	2 - 0	Arnold 6, Hume 78

PLAYING SQUAD

Goalkeepers: Neil Bennett (Airdrie), Simon Bishop (Dunstion Federation Brewery), Stevbe Jones (Thornaby).

Defenders: Anthony Hall (Gateshead), Andy Hill (Vickers SC), Mark Hume (Doncaster R.), Ian Mc Guckin (Oxford Utd), Lee Rogers (Grantham T.), **Simon Shaw** (Doncaster R.), Stuart Thomas (Scunthorpe U), Lee Turnbull (Halifax T.), Lee Warren (Doncaster R.)

Midfield: Graham Anthony (Carlisle U), Troy Bennett (Gainsborough T.), Scott Brough (Scunthorpe U), Wayne Bullimore (Grantham T.), Steve Gaughan (Halifax T.), Steve Housham (Scunthorpe Utd), Scott Maxfield (Doncaster R.),Nigel Pepper (Scunthorpe Utd), Steve Ridley (Scunthorpe Utd).

Forwards: **Ian Arnold** (Morecambe), Neil Campbell (Scarborough), Brian Dawson (Bootle), Steve Gill (Barrow Rangers), Grant Holt (Singapore), Gavin Knight (North Ferriby Utd), Nicky Peverell (Blyth Spartans), Carl Waters (Holker OB)

BLYTH SPARTANS

CLUB OFFICIALS

Chairman: Tommy Hedley

Secretary: Joe Hobin, c/o Croft Park, Plessey Road, Blyth NE24 3 JE, NE24 2HJ. Tel: 01670 360820.

Press Officer: Brian Grey

FOOTBALL MANAGEMENT TEAM

Manager: Paul Baker
Assistant Manager: Tom Wade

FACT FILE

Formed: 1899 Nickname: Spartans
Sponsors: Federation Brewery.
Colours: Green & white stripes/black
Change colours: Yellow
Midweek Matches: Tuesday
Local Press: Newcastle Journal & Evening Chronicle.

2002-2003

Captain : Richard Forster
Leading Goalscorer: Glen Robson

Pages: 64 Price: £1
Editor: Brian Grey Tel: 0191 2650119

GROUND: Croft Park, Blyth, Northumberland. Tel: 01670 354818 FAX: 01670 545592
Website: www.spartans.freeserve.co.uk

Directions: Through Tyne tunnel heading north on A19, take Cramlington turn A1061, follow signs for Newsham/Blyth. Right fork at railway gates in Newsham, down Plessey Rd, ground can be seen on left. Buses X24, X25, X26, X1 from Newcastle.

Capacity: 6,000 Seats: 300 Cover: 1,000

Clubhouse: Open every night plus Saturday & Sunday lunch & matchdays. Available for wedding functions. Pies & sandwiches available.

Souvenir Shop: Large selection. Contact: Bob Bell (01670 369144)

PREVIOUS Leagues: Northumberland 01-07; Northern Alliance 07-13, 46-47; North Eastern13-14 19-39 47-58 62-64; Northern Combination 45-46; Midland 58-60; Northern Counties 60-62; Northern 62-94. Names: None Grounds: None

CLUB RECORDS Fee Received: £30,000 for Les Mutrie (Hull City) 1979. Fee Paid:

BEST SEASON **FA Trophy:** Quarter-Final replay 79-80 82-83. **FA Amateur Cup:** Semi-Final 71-72.
FA Cup: 5th Rd replay 77-78 (lost to Wrexham). 1-1 (A) 1-2 (H) at Newcastle United

League clubs defeated Gillingham 22-23, Crewe Alexandra, Stockport County 71-72, Chesterfield, Stoke City 77-78, Bury 95-96.

HONOURS Nth Lg(10) 72-73 74-76 79-84 86-88 94-95, (R-up 71-72 73-74 77-78 84-85 94-95), Lg Cup(5) 72-73 77-79 81-82 91-92 94-95, Presidents Cup 96-97; Nth Eastern Lg35-36 (R-up 22-23, Lg Cup 49-50 54-55); Northumberland Lg 03-04; Northern All.08-09 12-13 (R-up 46-47); Northumberland Snr Cup (19); Shields Gazette Cup 95-96.

Players Progressing: William McGlen (Manchester Utd 46), Joe Roddom (Chesterfield 48), Henry Mills (Huddersfield 48), John Allison (Reading 49), James Kelly (Watford 49), Robert Millard (Reading 49), Jim Kerr (Lincoln 52), James Milner (Burnley 52), John Hogg (Portsmouth 54), John Allison(Chesterfield 55), John Inglis (Gateshead 57), John Longland (Hartlepool 58), Alan Shoulder (Newcastle 79), Les Mutrie (Hull City 79), Steve Carney(Newcastle 80), Craig Liddle (Middlesbrough 94), Paul O'Connor (Hartlepool 95). Gustavo Di Lella (Hartlepool 98)

Date	Comp.	Opponents	Att.	Score	Goalscorers
17/08	Unib. P	Lancaster City	282	4 - 1	Robson 12[p] 16, Pepper 80, Little 90
24/08	Unib. P	GAINSBOROUGH TRINITY	426	2 - 1	Brumwell 11, Robson 77
26/08	Unib. P	Barrow	1501	1 - 2	Robson 13
31/08	Unib. P	ALTRINCHAM	528	0 - 2	
03/09	Unib. P	Worksop Town	738	1 - 1	Martin 49
07/09	Unib. P	FRICKLEY ATHLETIC	326	4 - 2	Hutton 20, McMahon 45, Pepper 71, Brumwell 84
10/09	Unib. P	Whitby Town	326	4 - 4	Williams 28, Robson 33, Little 45, Emerson 90
14/09	Unib. P	Marine	265	1 - 2	McMahon 75
18/09	Unib. P	BRADFORD PARK AVENUE	286	1 - 2	Hutton 90
21/09	Unib. P	RUNCORN HALTON	344	3 - 1	Pepper 14, Lightfoot 31[og], Emerson 84
24/09	Unib. P	Wakefield & Emley	211	1 - 1	Hutton 45
28/09	**F.A.C.** Q2	Lancaster City	357	4 - 2	Kilbane 18[og], McMahon 45 53, Robson 90
05/10	Unib. P	Ashton United	253	1 - 2	Perry 22
12/10	**F.A.C.** Q3	Durham City	702	1 - 1	Baker 67
17/10	**F.A.C.** Q3 rep	DURHAM CITY	832	3 - 1	Brumwell 32, Emerson 61, C Pepper 68
19/10	Unib. P	Colwyn Bay	195	2 - 1	Stewart 22, Hutton 61
26/10	**F.A.C.** Q4	RUNCORN HALTON	851	1 - 3	Perry 54
30/10	N'humbs SC 1	West Allotment Celtic	202	2 - 1	Emerson 81, Anderson 88[og]
02/11	**F.A.T.** 1	NORTH FERRIBY UNITED	432	5 - 3	Fisher 11[og], Hutton 28, Foster 40[p], McMahon 49 90
06/11	Lge Cup 1	BISHOP AUCKLAND	250	2 - 3	Williams 44, McMahon 78
09/11	Unib. P	VAUXHALL MOTORS	318	2 - 5	Robson 70[p] 81
11/11	Unib. P	Droylsden	185	0 - 7	
16/11	Unib. P	Burscough	193	3 - 1	McMahon 28, Stewart 66, Robson 75
23/11	Unib. P	STALYBRIDGE CELTIC	317	1 - 4	Robson 51[p]
26/11	N'humbs SC QF	ASHINGTON	277	2 - 1	C Pepper 10 15
30/11	**F.A.T.** 2	Moor Green	323	3 - 2	Williams 23, Brumwell 45, McMahon 55
04/12	Unib. P	WAKEFIELD & EMLEY	291	2 - 1	Perry 53, Myhill 60
07/12	Unib. P	Runcorn Halton	202	2 - 2	Brumwell 49 90
14/12	Unib. P	ASHTON UNITED	349	4 - 0	McMahon 24, Perry 44 84, Robson 65
26/12	Unib. P	Gateshead	495	0 - 3	
28/12	Unib. P	HYDE UNITED	421	1 - 3	Brumwell 38
11/01	**F.A.T.** 3	Colwyn Bay	321	0 - 1	
18/01	Unib. P	Gainsborough Trinity	338	2 - 3	Robson 41[p], Emerson 68
25/01	Chair. Cup QF	FRICKLEY ATHLETIC	277	3 - 0	Williams 9, Emerson 33, Robson 40[p]
01/02	Unib. P	LANCASTER CITY	347	1 - 0	Pepper 74
08/02	Unib. P	Altrincham	548	2 - 3	Emerson 21, Hutton 82
11/02	Unib. P	WHITBY TOWN	328	2 - 3	Perry 86, Robson 88
22/02	Unib. P	COLWYN BAY	337	1 - 1	Emerson 70
25/02	Unib. P	BARROW	345	1 - 1	Emerson 63[p]
01/03	Unib. P	Accrington Stanley	1116	2 - 3	McMahon 45 59
04/03	Unib. P	HARROGATE TOWN	309	0 - 3	
08/03	Chair. Cup SF	Hucknall Town	152	1 - 4	Robson 37
12/03	Unib. P	Hucknall Town	142	2 - 0	Emerson 9, Williams 45
15/03	Unib. P	DROYLSDEN	339	0 - 1	
19/03	Unib. P	Bradford Park Avenue	188	1 - 5	Williams 72
22/03	Unib. P	BURSCOUGH	276	2 - 1	Stewart 5 75
25/03	Unib. P	WORKSOP TOWN	324	2 - 1	Little 45, Williams 60
29/03	Unib. P	Frickley Athletic	212	0 - 1	
01/04	Unib. P	ACCRINGTON STANLEY	418	0 - 3	
05/04	Unib. P	MARINE	366	1 - 1	Forster 79[p]
08/04	Unib. P	Harrogate Town	280	1 - 3	Martin 50
12/04	Unib. P	Vauxhall Motors	153	1 - 0	McMahon 31
15/04	Unib. P	HUCKNALL TOWN	376	1 - 2	McMahon 80
18/04	Unib. P	Hyde United	255	1 - 1	Robson 63
21/04	Unib. P	GATESHEAD	676	3 - 2	Perry 19, Robson 61 65
23/04	N'humbs SC SF	NEWCASTLE UNITED RES.	523	1 - 3	Emerson 42
26/04	Unib. P	Stalybridge Celtic	525	1 - 1	Hunter 13

PLAYING SQUAD

Goalkeepers Craig Cotterill (Youth Team), Stuart Dawson (Spennymoor Utd), Phil Naisbett (Whitley Bay).

Defenders: Richard Foster (Hartlepool Utd), Ian Irving (Morpeth), Michael Laws (Whitley Bay), Paddy Little (Jarrow Roofing), Colin Morton (Hibernian).

Midfield:

Forwards: Paul Baker (Durham City), Scott Emerson (York City), Craig Perry (Billingham T.), Tony Woodhouse (Spennymoor Utd).

BRADFORD PARK AVENUE

CLUB OFFICIALS

Chairman: Frank Thornton

President: Charlie Atkinson

Secretary: Steven Burnett
21 Edward Turner Close, Low Moor,
Bradford BD12 0AS
Tel: 01274 608344(H) 07866 076220 (M)

Press Officer: Tim Clapham

Commercial Manager: C Higgins

FOOTBALL MANAGEMENT TEAM

Manager: Trevor Storton

Asst Manager: Ian Thompson

Physio: Ray Killick

FACT FILE

Formed: 1907
Reformed: 1988
Nickname: Avenue
Club Sponsor: Bakes & Lord
Colours: White & green/green/ white
Change colours Yellow
Midweek Matches: Wednesday
Reserves' league: Lancashire League
Local Press: Telegraph & Argus
Local Radio: Radio Leeds

PROGRAMME

Pages: 36 Price: £1.20
Editor: Martin Worthy Tel: 08700 110485

GROUND Horsfall Stadium, Cemetery Rd., Bradford, West Yorks BD6 2NG (01274 604578)

Directions: M62 J 26. Along M606 to the end. At roundabout take A6036 (signed Halifax) and pass Odsal Stadium on left hand side. At next r'about take 3rd exit A6036 (Halifax), in approx. 1 mile turn left into Cemetery Rd (by Kings Head Pub). Ground 150 yards on left

Capacity: 5,000 Cover: 2,000 Seats: 1,247

Club Shop: Yes - contact Russell Foulds (c/o Ground) or 01924 440901 **Clubhouse:** Yes

PREVIOUS
Leagues: Southern 07-08; Football League 08-70; Northern Premier 70-74; West Riding County Amtr 88-89; Central Mids 89-90; N. W. Counties 90-95
Grounds: Park Avenue 07-73; Valley Parade 73-74; Manningham Mills 88-89; Bramley R.L.F.C., McLaren Field 89-93; Batley 93-96

CLUB RECORDS
Attendance: 1,007 v Bradford City 97 (Centenary Chall). 32,810 v Blackpool, War Cup 1944
Win: 11-0 v Denby Dale FAC 1908 **Defeat:** 0-7 v Barnsley 1911
Scorer: Len Shackleton 171 1940-46 **Appearances:** Tommy Farr 542 1934-50
Fee Received: £34,000 for K Hector (Derby County 1966)
Fee Paid: £24,500 for L Leuty (Derby County 1950)

BEST SEASON
FA Vase: 2nd Rd Prop 94-95 **FA Trophy:** 3rd Rd 98-99
FA Cup: Qtr finals 1912-13 v Aston Villa (0-5), 19-20 v Bristol City (A) 0-2, 45-46 v Birmingham City 2-2 (H) 0-6 (A) Agg 2-8

HONOURS
Football Lge Div 2 R-up 1914; 3rd Div N 28; Yorkshire Lge 21, 23; Midland Lge 32; West Riding Snr Cup 11,13, 25, 27, 32,36, 51, 53, 63; West Riding County Cup 28-29, 90-91; N.W.C. Lg 94-95, Challenge Trophy 94-95. N.P.L. (Unibond) Division One Champions 2000-01

L-R - Back Row: D Wilson (Kit Man), Simon Collins, Andy Hayward, Richard Tracey, Matthew Boswell, Jason Maxwell, Ryan Crossley, Nicky Wood Andy Wright. **Front Row:** Martin James, Andy Quinn, Wayne Benn (Captain), Danny Walsh, Craig Smith, Stephen Olekseywcz, Carl Serrant

Date	Comp.	Opponents	Att.	Score	Goalscorers
17/08	Unib. P	GATESHEAD	323	2 - 0	Hayward 23, Lindley 86
19/08	Unib. P	Hyde United	436	1 - 3	Hayward 9
24/08	Unib. P	Runcorn Halton	265	0 - 2	
26/08	Unib. P	MARINE	332	2 - 1	Hayward 35, Daly 51
31/08	Unib. P	Ashton United	280	4 - 1	Tracey 50, Stansfield 53, Painter 89 90
04/09	Unib. P	HUCKNALL TOWN	341	0 - 3	
11/09	Unib. P	GAINSBOROUGH TRINITY	261	1 - 0	Mitchell 36[p]
14/09	Unib. P	BARROW	368	2 - 2	Mitchell 23 75[p]
18/09	Unib. P	Blyth Spartans	286	2 - 1	Maxwell 66, Prendergast 77
21/09	Unib. P	Lancaster City	352	3 - 2	Hayward 24 85, Prendergast 45
25/09	Unib. P	WORKSOP TOWN	402	0 - 1	
28/09	**F.A.C.** Q2	Whitby Town	517	4 - 0	Marlin 36, Maxwell 52, Stansfield 70, Prendergast 83
01/10	Unib. P	Frickley Athletic	286	3 - 0	Hayward 41 51, Prendergast 75
05/10	Unib. P	ACCRINGTON STANLEY	760	1 - 1	Lindley 58
09/10	Unib. P	HYDE UNITED	301	5 - 1	Hayward 32, Prendergast 58 74, Maxwell 61 81
12/10	**F.A.C.** Q3	BRIDLINGTON TOWN	425	3 - 5	Stansfield 19, Maxwell 63 78
15/10	Unib. P	Hucknall Town	150	2 - 1	Hayward 44, Martin 46
19/10	Unib. P	Wakefield & Emley	449	0 - 2	
26/10	Unib. P	Gainsborough Trinity	404	2 - 2	Maxwell 7 30
30/10	Unib. P	COLWYN BAY	234	4 - 2	Prendergast 4 48, Stansfield 33, Hayward 37
02/11	Unib. P	RUNCORN HALTON	345	3 - 2	Mitchell 48[p], Painter 71, Prendergast 80
09/11	Unib. P	DROYLSDEN	314	3 - 1	Farley 13[og], Welsh 68, Painter 81
12/11	Unib. P	Altrincham	495	0 - 0	
20/11	Lge Cup 2	SPENNYMOOR UNITED	165	2 - 2	Hayward 90, Tracey 107 5 4
23/11	Unib. P	WHITBY TOWN	340	2 - 3	Prendergast 54, Hayward 84
30/11	**F.A.T.** 2	ALTRINCHAM	437	0 - 1	
03/12	Unib. P	Worksop Town	571	1 - 7	Whitehead 45[og]
07/12	Unib. P	LANCASTER CITY	257	0 - 1	
10/12	West RCC 2	Yorkshire Amateur	56	4 - 1	Painter 3, Bingham 55, Mitchell 67[p], Prendergast 70
14/12	Unib. P	Accrington Stanley	873	1 - 3	Daly 2
28/12	Unib. P	Stalybridge Celtic	847	2 - 2	Painter 27, Hooper 45[og]
22/01	Lge Cup 3	OSSETT TOWN	134	4 - 5	Lindley 18 108, Vickerage 62, Mitchell 104[p]
29/01	Unib. P	HARROGATE TOWN	437	1 - 0	Mitchell 61[p]
01/02	Unib. P	Gateshead	266	1 - 1	Hayward 24
08/02	Unib. P	ASHTON UNITED	271	1 - 1	Wright 11
12/02	West RCC QF	ECCLESHILL UNITED	130	1 - 0	Collins 14
15/02	Unib. P	Marine	288	2 - 4	Mitchell 48[p], Hayward 85
22/02	Unib. P	VAUXHALL MOTORS	253	1 - 0	Wright 69
25/02	Unib. P	Burscough	145	1 - 0	Collins 10
11/03	West RCC SF	Harrogate Town	312	0 - 2	
19/03	Unib. P	BLYTH SPARTANS	188	5 - 1	Maxwell 6, Little 16[og], Collins 25 60, Foster 74[og]
22/03	Unib. P	Vauxhall Motors	251	1 - 0	Tracey 33
24/03	Unib. P	FRICKLEY ATHLETIC	294	2 - 2	Collins 56, Hayward 73
27/03	Unib. P	Droylsden	176	0 - 2	
29/03	Unib. P	ALTRINCHAM	440	1 - 1	Stansfield 84
05/04	Unib. P	Barrow	1022	2 - 3	Walsh 7, Collins 34
09/04	Unib. P	WAKEFIELD & EMLEY	288	1 - 1	Walsh 76
15/04	Unib. P	Colwyn Bay	118	0 - 2	
19/04	Unib. P	STALYBRIDGE CELTIC	329	2 - 1	Hayward 20, Collins 87
21/04	Unib. P	Harrogate Town	607	2 - 5	Stansfield 18, Maxwell 65
23/04	Unib. P	BURSCOUGH	168	3 - 2	Maxwell 3, Hayward 15, Painter 75
26/04	Unib. P	Whitby Town	332	1 - 0	Hayward 59

PLAYING SQUAD

Goalkeepers: Jamie Holmshaw (Stocksbridge PS), Chris Howe (Belper T.), Robert Montgomery (Vauxhall M.), Lutz Pfannenstiel (Singapore)

Defenders: Neil Bagshaw (Rotherham Utd), Ryan Crossley (Wakefield & Emley), Martin James (Winsford Utd), Graham Mitchell (Halifax T.), Mike Thompson (Frickley Ath.).

Midfield: Wayne Benn (Halifax T.), Simon Collins (Belper T.), Phil Lindley (Local Football), Michael Quigley (Northwich V), Andy Quinn (Gainsborough T.), Gary Reece (Belper T.), Craig Smith (Halifax T.), Danny Walsh (Kettering T.), Andy Wright (Whitby T.).

Forwards: Anthony Bingham (Youth Team), Andy Hayward (Frickley Ath.), Jason Maxwell (Gainsborough T.), MIchael Nunn Army), Robbie Painter (Gateshead), Richard Tracey (Scarborough), Mark Vickerage (Brodsworth Welfare)

BURSCOUGH

CLUB OFFICIALS

Chairman: **Frank Parr**
Vice Chairman: **Stuart Heaps**
President: **Rod Cottam**
Secretary/Press Off.Keith Maguire,218
Bescar Lane, Scarisbrick, Lancs. L40 9QT
TelNo: 01704 880587(H)
07970 030588 (M)
Email sstrick@109redgate.freeserve.co.uk

FOOTBALL MANAGEMENT TEAM

Manager: Mike Marsh
Asst Manager:Ian Bishop
Physio: Mel Singleton

FACT FILE

Founded: 1946
Nickname: Linnets
Sponsors: Nationwide Produce plc.
Colours: Green/white/green
Change colours:Sky blue /navy blue
.Midweek Matches: Tuesday
Reserves: Lancashire League

2002-2003

Captain: Carl Macauley
Top Scorer: Gary Martindale
Player of the Year: Jore Taylor

Pages:44 Price £1.50
Editor: Eric & Sue Berry

Local Radio: Radio Lancs,Red Rose.

GROUND: Victoria Park, Bobby Langton Way, Mart Lane, Burscough, Ormskirk, Lancs L40 0SD Tel: 01704 893237 Website: www.burscoughfc.co.uk
Directions: M6 Jct 27, follow signs thru Parbold A5209, right into Junction Lane (signed Burscough & Martin Mere) to lights, right onto A59 to Burscough Village, 2nd left over canal bridge into Mart Lane to ground. 200 yards from Burscough Bridge BR station (Wigan-Southport line). Half mile from Burscough Junction (Ormskirk Preston line)
Capacity: 2,500 **Seats:** 270 **Cover:**1,000 **Club Shop:** Yes: Margaret Manuel (01704893166)
Clubhouse: `Barons Club' (privately owned, access outside grd). Mon-Thurs 7-11pm, Fri 4-11pm, Sat 1-11pm, Sun noon-3 & 7-10.30pm. No food

PREVIOUS **Leagues:** Liverpool Co Comb. 46-53, Lancs Comb. 53-70, Cheshire Co.70-82, North West Cos 82-98, Unibond NPL98-01

CLUB RECORDS **Attendance:** 4,798 v Wigan Athletic,F.A.Cup 3rd Qual.Rd.1950-51
Goalscorer: Johnny Vincent 60 53-54. Most Goals in Game: Louis Bimpson 7. In Career: Wes Bridge 188
Win: 10-0 v Cromptons Recreation 1947 & v Nelson 1948-49, both Lancs. Comb.
Defeat: 0-9 v Earlstown, Liverpool County Comb.1948-49
Fee paid: £2,500 Stuart Rudd (Skelmersdale Utd 00-01)
Fee Received: £20,000 from Rochdale for Lee McEvilly 2001-02

BEST SEASON **FA Cup:** 1st Rd 59-60 77-78 79-80 80-81
FA Trophy: Winners 2002-2003 **FA Vase:** 1994-95 (Last 16)

HONOURS Liverpool Chall. Cup 47-48 50-51,54-55; George Mahon Cup 47-48; Liverpool County Comb Div 1, 49-50 (Div 2 53-54, 67-68); Lancs Comb.Div 2 53-54; Lancs Comb Div 1 55-56 69-70; Lord Wavertree Cup 67-68; Cheshire Co. Lge R-up 70-71, Lge Cup 74-75 R-up 73-74; Lancs Jnr Cup 47-4849-50 66-67; Liverpool Non-Lg Snr Cup 55/56, 71-72; N.W.C. Lge 82-83, Lge Cup 92-93 95-96 R-up 91-92, Chall. Shield 82-83, 95-96; Liverpool Sen. Cup R-up 92-93,95-96, 99-00., Liverpool Jun. Cup 00-01.

Players progressing: L Bimpson, B Parker (Liverpool 53), B Pilson (Stoke 53-54), A Green (Huddersfield), K Waterhouse (Preston), F Gamble (Derby 80), Tony Rigby (Bury), S Teale (Aston Villa), L Watson (Preston), K Formby A Russell (Rochdale 94),G Martindale (Bolton 94), S Perkins (Plymouth A. 97), M.Yates (Dundee 99), L. Trundle (Wrexham), R. Lowe (Shrewsbury T.), L McEvilly (Rochdale 02)

Date	Comp.	Opponents	Att.	Score	Goalscorers
17/08	Unib. P	Worksop Town	523	2 - 0	Taylor 9, Wright 76
20/08	Unib. P	LANCASTER CITY	237	0 - 0	
24/08	Unib. P	WAKEFIELD & EMLEY	701	1 - 0	Norman 53
31/08	Unib. P	Whitby Town	298	2 - 0	Martindale 48[p], McHale 65
03/09	Unib. P	Altrincham	494	0 - 0	
07/09	Unib. P	HUCKNALL TOWN	207	2 - 0	Norman 62, Martindale 90
10/09	Unib. P	Runcorn Halton	256	2 - 0	Norman 59, Martindale 90[p]
14/09	Unib. P	Hyde United	257	0 - 1	
17/09	Unib. P	MARINE	250	2 - 1	McHale 22, Martindale 90
21/09	Unib. P	Frickley Athletic	162	0 - 0	
24/09	Unib. P	COLWYN BAY	167	3 - 0	Madin 21, Martindale 52, McHale 88
28/09	**F.A.C.** Q2	Dunston Federation Brewery	131	0 - 2	
02/10	Unib. P	Accrington Stanley	1488	2 - 4	Wright 48 50
05/10	Unib. P	DROYLSDEN	304	0 - 0	
12/10	Unib. P	Gateshead	167	0 - 1	
15/10	Unib. P	ALTRINCHAM	294	0 - 3	
19/10	Unib. P	GAINSBOROUGH TRINITY	171	4 - 4	Molyneux 21, Martindale 26 31, Lawless 54
22/10	Lge Cup 1	COLWYN BAY	123	1 - 3	Martindale 2
26/10	Unib. P	Lancaster City	297	1 - 2	Martindale 16[p]
29/10	Live SC 1	ST HELENS TOWN	157	3 - 2	McHale 41, Teale 76, Wright 106
02/11	**F.A.T.** 1	MARINE	242	0 - 0	
04/11	**F.A.T.** 1 rep	Marine	224	3 - 1	Molyneaux 88, Lawless 102, Wright 118
09/11	Unib. P	Ashton United	202	0 - 0	
16/11	Unib. P	BLYTH SPARTANS	193	1 - 3	Martindale 20
26/11	Unib. P	BARROW	189	2 - 0	Norman 8, Lawless 90
30/11	**F.A.T.** 2	Harrogate Town	291	2 - 2	Teale 78[p], Taylor 90
03/12	**F.A.T.** 2 rep	HARROGATE TOWN	160	3 - 2	Wright 5, Norman 12, Lawless 54
07/12	Unib. P	FRICKLEY ATHLETIC	132	1 - 0	McCauley 81
10/12	Chair. Cup 1	Bamber Bridge	73	2 - 4	Hyland 37, Lawless 62
14/12	Unib. P	Droylsden	143	0 - 1	
17/12	Lancs MT 1	BLACKPOOL MECHANICS	52	0 - 1	
26/12	Unib. P	VAUXHALL MOTORS	234	0 - 0	
28/12	Unib. P	Harrogate Town	409	1 - 2	Hyland 33
14/01	**F.A.T.** 3	Ilkeston Town	248	3 - 0	Hyland 22, Bowen 41, Norman 68
18/01	Unib. P	Wakefield & Emley	223	0 - 1	
20/01	Live SC QF	LIVERPOOL	413	0 - 5	
25/01	Unib. P	ACCRINGTON STANLEY	576	0 - 1	
01/02	**F.A.T.** 4	Alfreton Town	602	1 - 1	Bowen 58
04/02	**F.A.T.** 4 rep	ALFRETON TOWN	190	2 - 0	McHale 73 75
08/02	Unib. P	Stalybridge Celtic	530	0 - 1	
18/02	Unib. P	Vauxhall Motors	208	0 - 1	
22/02	**F.A.T.** 5	WAKEFIELD & EMLEY	437	5 - 0	McHale 11 74, Norman 23 77, Lawless 80
25/02	Unib. P	BRADFORD PARK AVENUE	145	0 - 1	
01/03	Unib. P	Barrow	942	0 - 3	
08/03	Unib. P	Gainsborough Trinity	301	1 - 0	Lawless 53
11/03	Unib. P	Colwyn Bay	145	3 - 1	Martindale 60, Lawless 86, Wright 90
15/03	**F.A.T.** QF	Yeovil Town	4934	2 - 0	Wright 8 77
18/03	Unib. P	WORKSOP TOWN	204	3 - 2	Wright 9 40 55
22/03	Unib. P	Blyth Spartans	276	1 - 2	Wright 33
25/03	Unib. P	GATESHEAD	165	1 - 0	Wright 90
29/03	Unib. P	HYDE UNITED	170	0 - 0	
01/04	Unib. P	Hucknall Town	135	1 - 3	Byrne 11
05/04	**F.A.T.** S.F. (1)	Aylesbury United	1546	1 - 1	Martindale 68
08/04	Unib. P	ASHTON UNITED	125	3 - 2	McHale 58, Hyland 73, Teale 84
12/04	**F.A.T.** S.F. (2)	AYLESBURY UNITED	1773	1 - 0	Teale 90
14/04	Unib. P	Marine	302	0 - 1	
16/04	Unib. P	STALYBRIDGE CELTIC	164	0 - 1	
19/04	Unib. P	HARROGATE TOWN	186	0 - 1	
21/04	Unib. P	WHITBY TOWN	132	0 - 2	
23/04	Unib. P	Bradford Park Avenue	168	2 - 3	Wright 11, Norman 58
26/04	Unib. P	RUNCORN HALTON	187	3 - 3	Martindale 55, Wright 82[p], Hyland 83
18/05	**F.A.Trophy Final**	Tamworth	14,265	**2 - 1**	at Aston Villa

PLAYING SQUAD

Goalkeepers: John Bagnall (Bashley), Gary Maguire (Stockport County), Matty Taylor (P.N.E.)

Defenders: Ryan Bowen (Youth Team), Neil Hanson (Bootle), Carl Macauley (Southpport), Tommy Molloy (Youth Team), Jeff Underwood (Southport),

Midfield: Ray Birch (CongletonT.), Paul Burns (Accrington Stanley), Steve Hussey (Everton), Marvin Molyneux (Youth Team), Peter Wright (Halifax T.).

Forwards: Kris McHale (Marine), John Lawless (Youth Team), Gary Martindale (Telford Utd), John Norman (Morecambe)

DROYLSDEN

CLUB OFFICIALS

Chairman: **David Pace**

Secretary: **Alan Slater**
83 King Edward Rd.,Hyde,
Cheshire SK14 5JJ
Tel & Fax: 0161 368 3687

FOOTBALL MANAGEMENT TEAM
Manager: David Pace
Asst Manager: Aeon Lattie
Physio Alan Cross

FACT FILE
Formed: 1892
Nickname: The Bloods
Sponsors:Alpha Court Windows
Colours: Red /black/black
Change: Sky & navy/navy/Sky & Navy
Midweek matchday: Monday
Club Website: wwwdroylsdenfc.fsnet.co.uk

2002-2003
Captain: Garry Burke
Top Scorer: Garry Burke
Player of the Year: Danny Winter

GROUND The Butchers Arms Ground, Market Street, Droylsden, Manchester M43 7AY
Tel: 0161 370 1426/8341 FAX: 0161 370 8341

Directions: Jct 23 M60 signed .A635 to Manchester fromOldham direction and A6140 Ashton under Lyme from Stockpoort direction. Join A635 towards Manchester (1.5 miles from ground).Rt at lights onto A662 to Droylsden.Turn right into Market Street after half a mile.Over lights ground on left.

Capacity: 3,500 Cover: 2,000 Seats:500

Clubhouse: Pub hours except matchdays. Pool and darts **Shop:** Yes Metal Badges

Pages: 24 Price: £1.00
Editor: T.B.A
Local Press:
Tameside Reporter, Tameside Advertiser
Local Radio: BBC Manchester

PREVIOUS **Leagues:** Manchester; Lancs Com 36-39, 50-68; Cheshire County 39-50, 68-82; NW Counties 82-87

CLUB RECORDS **Attendance:** 4,250 v Grimsby, **FA Cup** 1st rd 1976
Scorer: E Gillibrand 78 (1931-32) **Win:** 13-2 v Lucas Sports Club
Fee Received: £11,000 for Tony Naylor (Crewe)

BEST SEASON **FA Cup:** 2nd Rd 78-79 v Altrincham (H) 0-2. League clubs defeated: Rochdale 78-79
FA Vase: **FA Trophy:**

HONOURS Northern Prem Lge Div 1 98-99, R-up 89-90, Div 1 Cup 87-88, R-up 88-9, 98-9 NPL President's Cup 98-99 Chairmans Cup R-up: 01-0202-03; NW Counties Lge Div 2 86-87; Cheshire County Lge R-up 39-40 45-46, Lge Cup 77-78 (R-up 76-77); Lancs Comb Div 2 R-up 55-56 58-59 62-63; Manchester Lge 30-31 32-33 (Lge Cup 23-24 33-34); Manchester Prem Cup 80-81 (R-up 83-84 90-91 93-94 02-03); Man Sen Cup 72-73 75-76 78-79 (R-up 72-73 75-76 78-79); Manchester Interm Cup 59-60 64-65 69-70; Manchester Chall Shield 46-47

Players progressing: Albert Butterworth & F Letchford (Blackpool 1931), William Davies & Maurice Randall (Crewe 1947), William Mellor (Accrington 1950), Geoff Tonge (Bury 1960), David Campbell (WBA 1962), Kevin Randall (Bury 1965), Peter Litchfield (Preston 1979), Tony Naylor (Crewe 1990)

Back row, left to right: Aeori Lattie, Nigel Evans, Harvey Cunningham, James Glendenning, Robert Pell, Adam Farley, Robert Trees, Mark Bradshaw, David Kerr, Iain Brunskill and Alan Cross (Physio).
Front row: Neil Hall, Darren Wright, Danny Warner, Paul Phillips, Steve Porter, Scott Willis and Steve Quinn

Date	Comp.	Opponents	Att.	Score	Goalscorers
17/08	Unib. P	FRICKLEY ATHLETIC	221	3 - 1	Hall 38[p], Wright 60, Nazha 90
19/08	Unib. P	Marine	263	2 - 2	Salmon 51, Nazha 55
24/08	Unib. P	Harrogate Town	461	0 - 0	
26/08	Unib. P	VAUXHALL MOTORS	311	1 - 1	Wright 67
31/08	Unib. P	Colwyn Bay	306	3 - 0	Murphy 46, Salmon 52, Burke 58
02/09	Unib. P	RUNCORN HALTON	257	2 - 0	Locke 27, Nazha 65
07/09	Unib. P	LANCASTER CITY	312	1 - 5	Nazha 60
09/09	Unib. P	Hyde United	371	3 - 1	Rush 55, Wright 81, Salmon 90
14/09	Unib. P	Accrington Stanley	1195	1 - 2	Salmon 78
16/09	Unib. P	HUCKNALL TOWN	246	0 - 0	
21/09	Unib. P	ASHTON UNITED	503	0 - 1	
25/09	Unib. P	Gateshead	173	2 - 0	Hall 4, Haarhoff 18
28/09	**F.A.C.** Q2	FARSLEY CELTIC	210	4 - 3	Wright 7 90, Salmon 25, Burke 52
30/09	Unib. P	GAINSBOROUGH TRINITY	201	3 - 0	Wright 8 44, Hall 89[p]
05/10	Unib. P	Burscough	304	0 - 0	
07/10	Unib. P	MARINE	167	0 - 1	
12/10	**F.A.C.** Q3	SPENNYMOOR UNITED	342	0 - 0	
15/10	**F.A.C.** Q3 rep	Spennymoor United	342	2 - 3	Salmon 28, Porter 53
22/10	Lge Cup 1	Rossendale United	111	1 - 2	Haarhoff 18
26/10	Unib. P	Worksop Town	639	1 - 4	Nazha 90
02/11	**F.A.T.** 1	ASHTON UNITED	327	2 - 1	Burke 32 66
09/11	Unib. P	Bradford Park Avenue	314	1 - 3	Haarhoff 33
11/11	Unib. P	BLYTH SPARTANS	185	7 - 0	Haarhoff 25, Burke 40, Salmon 55 74 87, Wilson 56, Wright 79
16/11	Unib. P	Stalybridge Celtic	690	1 - 2	Haarhoff 4
23/11	Unib. P	WAKEFIELD & EMLEY	261	1 - 0	Cameron 21[p]
30/11	**F.A.T.** 2	COLWYN BAY	221	1 - 2	Haarhoff 3
14/12	Unib. P	BURSCOUGH	143	1 - 0	O'Brien 72
21/12	Unib. P	GATESHEAD	171	0 - 2	
26/12	Unib. P	Altrincham	715	1 - 3	Hall 65[p]
28/12	Unib. P	BARROW	269	0 - 2	
04/01	Unib. P	Gainsborough Trinity	357	4 - 1	Nazha 1, O'Brien 37, Haarhoff 48, Wright 64
11/01	Unib. P	Whitby Town	265	2 - 5	Nazha 64, Wright 90
18/01	Unib. P	HARROGATE TOWN	222	2 - 1	Porter 33[p], Haarhoff 65
25/01	Chair. Cup 1	Guiseley	204	3 - 1	Wright 5, Salmon 15, Haarhoff 43
01/02	Unib. P	Frickley Athletic	137	2 - 0	Wright 2, Salmon 83
08/02	Unib. P	COLWYN BAY	211	2 - 1	Chambers 4, Salmon 88
15/02	Unib. P	Vauxhall Motors	262	1 - 2	Salmon 65
24/02	Chair. Cup QF	WITTON ALBION	136	4 - 2	Kevan 52, Wright 84, Glendenning 94, Salmon 104
01/03	Unib. P	WHITBY TOWN	168	2 - 1	Chambers 10, Kevan 53
11/03	Unib. P	Ashton United	208	1 - 2	Wright 82
15/03	Unib. P	Blyth Spartans	339	1 - 0	Burke 1
17/03	Chair. Cup SF	BAMBER BRIDGE	152	1 - 1	Glendenning 116 7 6
22/03	Unib. P	HYDE UNITED	347	0 - 1	
25/03	Unib. P	Runcorn Halton	138	0 - 0	
27/03	Unib. P	BRADFORD PARK AVENUE	176	2 - 0	Chambers 39, O'Brien 76
29/03	Unib. P	Lancaster City	264	3 - 0	O'Brien 81, Salmon 86, Murphy 88
31/03	Unib. P	ALTRINCHAM	316	1 - 0	Hall 66[p]
05/04	Unib. P	ACCRINGTON STANLEY	539	2 - 2	Wright 33 90
07/04	Unib. P	WORKSOP TOWN	184	0 - 1	
09/04	Unib. P	Hucknall Town	138	0 - 2	
19/04	Unib. P	Barrow	911	0 - 0	
21/04	Unib. P	STALYBRIDGE CELTIC	537	1 - 1	Salmon 44[p]
26/04	Unib. P	Wakefield & Emley	176	2 - 2	Kevan 1 72
28/04	Chair. Cup Final	HUCKNALL TOWN	287	0 - 1	

Match Facts 2002-03

PLAYING SQUAD

Goalkeepers Rob Hackney (Mossley), Paul Phillips (Curzon Ashton).

Defenders: Dave Ashton (Curzon Ashton), Gary Burke (Northwich Victoria), Paul Challinor (Ilkeston T.), Darren Esdaille (Cheadle), Adam Farley (Altrincham), James Glendenning (St.Helens), Aeon Lattie (Flixton), Stuart Locke (Accrington Stanley), Ged Murphy (Stalybridge Celtic), Chris O'Brien (Chester City), Danny Warner (Curzon Ashton).

Midfield: Harvey Cunningham (Chorley), Neil Hall (Hyde Utd), Sammy Hill (Chester City), Mick Jones (Oswestry T.), David Kerr (Chester City), Alex Kevan (Lancaster City), Steve Porter (Burscough), Steve Quinn (Wooding Sports).

Forwards: Leroy Chambers (Belper T.), Nigel Evans (Stalybridge Celtic), Leon Hamilton (Curzon Ashton), Lloyd Richardson (Salford City), Darren Wright (Chester City)

FRICKLEY ATHLETIC

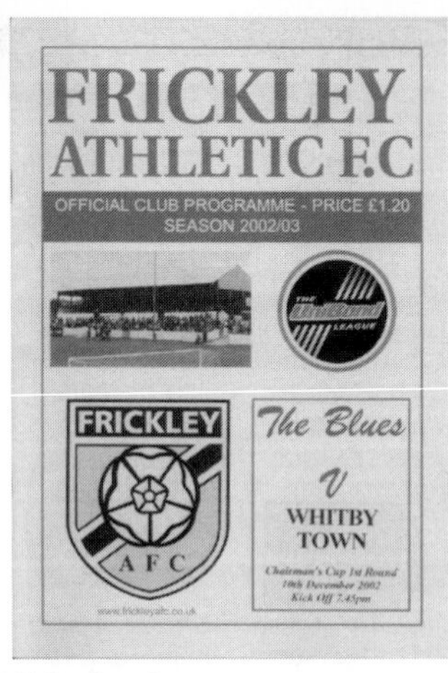

CLUB OFFICIALS

Chairman: Peter Bywater

Directors: K. Day, P. Draper, S. Pennock, T. Corke and B. Jackson

Financial Secretary: A. Steele
Tel: 0114 2460218

Secretary: Steve Pennock, 3 Kingsley Crescent, Armthorpe, Doncaster DN3 3JG
Tel: 01302 835956

FOOTBALL MANAGEMENT TEAM

Manager: Phil Sharpe

Assistant Manager: Mark Hancock

2002-2003

Captain & P.o.Y: Mark Hancock

Top goalscorer: Lee Morris

FACT FILE

Formed: 1910

Nickname: The Blues

Sponsors: T.B.A.

Colours: All blue with white stripe on shirt

Change colours: Yellow & black.

Midweek home matchday: Tuesday

Website: www.frickleyafc.co.uk

Local Press: South Yorks Times, Hemsworth & South Elmsall Express.

Local Radio: Radio Sheffield, Radio Hallam, Radio Leeds and Ridings F.M.

PROGRAMME

Pages: 40 Price: £1

Editor: Steve Pennock Tel: 01302 835956

GROUND Westfield Lane, South Elmsall, Pontefract Tel/Fax: 01977 642460 email: steve@ frickleyafc.co.uk

Directions: Follow signs for South Elmsall from A1 and A638. Left at Superdrug warehouse, right at T junction and immed. left up Westfield Lane. Left into Oxford Road (opposite Westfield Hotel) - ground at bottom on right. Two miles from South Elmsall (BR).

Capacity: 6,000 Cover: 2,500 Seats: 800

Clubhouse: On ground open matchdays, food available. **Club Shop:** Yes Contact: P.Draper (01977 642460)

PREVIOUS Leagues: Sheffield; Yorkshire 22-24; Midland Counties 24-33 34-60 70-76;Cheshire County 60-70; Northern Premier 76-80; GMV Conference (Alliance Premier) 80-87. Name: Frickley Colliery

CLUB RECORDS **Attendance:** 6,500 v Rotherham United, FA Cup First Round 1971.
Goalscorer: K Whiteley. **Defeat:** 0-12 v Worksop 2000-01 Unibond Premier **Fee Paid:** £1,800.
Fee Received: £12,500 for Paul Shirtliff (Boston Utd) & £12,500 for Russ Wilcox (Northampton)

BEST SEASON **FA Cup:** 3rd Rd 1985-86 (1-3 v Rotherham H).2nd Rd 84-85 (0-1 at Darlington). 1st Rd 36-37 57-58 63-64 71-72 73-74 83-84 86-87 88-89 00-01. League clubs defeated: Hartlepool United 85-86. **FA Trophy:** Quarter-Finals 84-85.

HONOURS Alliance Premier Lg R-up 85-86, Midland Counties Lg R-up 72-73 (Lg Cup 75-76),Yorkshire Lg R-up 23-24, Sheffield & Hallamshire Senior Cup 27-28 56-57 60-6162-63 66-67 78-79 85-86 87-88 89-90 99-00, Sheffield Assoc. Lg 20-21 (R-up 11-12).

Players Progressing: Dennis Smith & Jack Brownsword (Hull1946), Stan Scrimshaw (Halifax 1947), William Callaghan (Aldershot 1949), Leo Dickens 1950), John Ashley & Graham Caulfield (York 1950 & 67), Ron Barritt(Leeds 1951), John Pickup (Bradford PA 1955), Tom Hymers & Arthur Ashmore &Stewart Gray (Doncaster 1958 & 66 & 78), Colin Roberts (Bradford City 1959),Derek Downing (Middlesbrough 1965), Graham Reed & Russell Wilcox (Northampton1985 & 86), Will Foley (Swansea 1986), Gary Brook (Newport 1987), Wayne Scargill (Bradford City 94-95), Andy Hayward (Rotherham Utd.).

Back row, left to right: Antony Jackson, Phil Sharpe (Manager), Robert Peel, Pete Myers, Craig Marsh, Jon Wordsworth, Craig Elkin, Andy Evans, Mark Hine, Paul Marquis and Ronnie Akers (Physio). **Front row:** Lee Morris, Remo Nesa, David Jones, Mark Hancock (Assistant Manager), Ryan Williams, Chris Gowen, Mark Wilkinson and Paul Bruke.

Date	Comp.	Opponents	Att.	Score	Goalscorers
17/08	Unib. P	Droylsden	221	1 - 3	Myers 40
20/08	Unib. P	WORKSOP TOWN	394	1 - 3	Jackson 15
24/08	Unib. P	LANCASTER CITY	178	0 - 1	
26/08	Unib. P	Accrington Stanley	936	1 - 2	Hancock 38
31/08	Unib. P	BARROW	208	1 - 2	Hancock 58[p]
03/09	Unib. P	Gainsborough Trinity	332	0 - 2	
07/09	Unib. P	Blyth Spartans	326	2 - 4	Wordsworth 37, Evans 86
10/09	Unib. P	GATESHEAD	121	1 - 0	Hine 7
17/09	Unib. P	Harrogate Town	347	2 - 1	Kerr 10, Burke 44
21/09	Unib. P	BURSCOUGH	162	0 - 0	
24/09	Unib. P	Whitby Town	275	1 - 3	Burke 84
28/09	**F.A.C.** Q2	Gainsborough Trinity	351	2 - 3	Hemstock 3, Morris 87
01/10	Unib. P	BRADFORD PARK AVENUE	286	0 - 3	
05/10	Unib. P	Hyde United	281	3 - 2	Evans 53 90, Hemstock 81
09/10	Sheff SC 1	HARWORTH COLLIERY INSTITUTE	69	3 - 1	Morris 18, Gowan 33, Peel 50
12/10	Unib. P	WHITBY TOWN	157	1 - 7	Marquis 4
15/10	Unib. P	GAINSBOROUGH TRINITY	121	2 - 2	Evans 64, Jackson 87
19/10	Unib. P	Runcorn Halton	228	1 - 0	Elkin 63
22/10	Lge Cup 1	Stocksbridge Park Steels	132	0 - 2	
26/10	Unib. P	ACCRINGTON STANLEY	290	2 - 1	Bernard 32[p], Marquis 36
02/11	**F.A.T.** 1	Kidsgrove Athletic	100	1 - 1	Evans 90
05/11	**F.A.T.** 1 rep	KIDSGROVE ATHLETIC	85	2 - 1	Bernard 48, Jackson 115
09/11	Unib. P	COLWYN BAY	147	3 - 0	Hancock 33[p], Williams 48, Morris 55
12/11	Sheff SC 2	STOCKSBRIDGE PARK STEELS	106	1 - 2	Williams 32
16/11	Unib. P	MARINE	136	1 - 3	Evans 85
19/11	Unib. P	Hucknall Town	156	0 - 1	
23/11	Unib. P	Altrincham	582	0 - 1	
30/11	**F.A.T.** 2	Vauxhall Motors	185	2 - 4	Morris 3 80
07/12	Unib. P	Burscough	132	0 - 1	
10/12	Chair. Cup 1	WHITBY TOWN	70	2 - 1	Morris 82, Elkin 90
14/12	Unib. P	HYDE UNITED	119	0 - 0	
21/12	Unib. P	Ashton United	225	2 - 3	Newton 2, Morris 71[p]
26/12	Unib. P	Wakefield & Emley	360	0 - 0	
25/01	Chair. Cup QF	Blyth Spartans	277	0 - 3	
01/02	Unib. P	DROYLSDEN	137	0 - 2	
08/02	Unib. P	Barrow	1038	1 - 2	Bernard 7
15/02	Unib. P	Colwyn Bay	210	3 - 2	Lindley 20, Bernard 65, Newton 72
22/02	Unib. P	RUNCORN HALTON	182	2 - 2	Bernard 57, Morris 85
25/02	Unib. P	Lancaster City	206	0 - 4	
01/03	Unib. P	Vauxhall Motors	185	0 - 5	
04/03	Unib. P	HUCKNALL TOWN	138	0 - 0	
11/03	Unib. P	Worksop Town	483	4 - 2	Morris 40 46, Barnard 58[og], Hancock 68[p]
15/03	Unib. P	VAUXHALL MOTORS	184	1 - 0	Robinson 22
18/03	Unib. P	STALYBRIDGE CELTIC	183	1 - 0	Reece 52
22/03	Unib. P	Gateshead	202	2 - 2	Morris 40, Bernard 62
24/03	Unib. P	Bradford Park Avenue	294	2 - 2	Jackson 89, Hatto 90
29/03	Unib. P	BLYTH SPARTANS	212	1 - 0	Russell 84
01/04	Unib. P	ASHTON UNITED	158	1 - 0	Hatto 84
05/04	Unib. P	Stalybridge Celtic	415	1 - 3	Jackson 22
12/04	Unib. P	HARROGATE TOWN	234	0 - 1	
17/04	Unib. P	Marine	241	1 - 0	Robinson 42
21/04	Unib. P	WAKEFIELD & EMLEY	227	0 - 3	
26/04	Unib. P	ALTRINCHAM	215	0 - 3	

PLAYING SQUAD

Goalkeepers: Mark Samways (Glasshoughton Welfare), Richard Siddall (Gateshead).

Defenders: Mark Hancock (Bradford P.A.), Nicky Limber (Gainsborough T.), Paul Marquis (Bradford P.A), Kieron O'Brien (Ossett T.), Duncan Richards (Harrogate T.), Phil Sharpe (Ulseley), Jonathon Wordsworth (Stocksbridge Park Steels).

Midfield: Craig Elkin (South Kenley Colliery), Mark Hine (Armthorpe Welfare), Duncan Milligan (Harrogate T.), Remo Nesa (P.N.E.), Chris Newton (Farsley Celtic), Ryan Williams (Harrogate T.).

Forwards: Curtis Bernard (Harrogate T.), Paul Burke (Harrogate T.), Gary Hurlstone (Stocksbridge Park Steels), Antony Jackson (South Kenley Colliery), Lee Morris (Hallam), Martin Regan (Farsley Celtic)

GAINSBOROUGH TRINITY

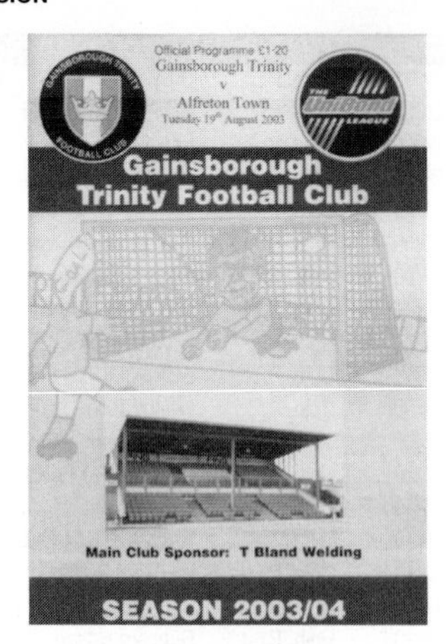

CLUB OFFICIALS
Chairman: John Reames
President : Ken Marsden
Chief Executive: Rick Knowles
Secretary/Press Officer: Frank Nicholson
9 North Street, Morton,
Gainsborough, Lincs DN213AS.
Tel. 01427 615239, Fax 01427 615239

FOOTBALL MANAGEMENT TEAM
Manager: Paul Mitchell
Asst Manager: Peter Rinckavage
Physio: Bob Bradbury

FACT FILE

Formed: 1873
Nickname: The Blues
Sponsors: T Bland Welding
Colours: Nlue/white/blue.
Change colours: All yellowMidweek home matchday: Tuesday
Youth League: Northern Youth Alliance
2002-2003
Captaiun: Darren Knowles
Top Scorer: Lee Ellington 28
Olayer of thge Year:Danny Brownn

GROUND The Northolme, Gainsborough, Lincs DN21 2QW
Tel: 01427 - 613295 (office) 679109 (club) 613295 (Fax)
Website: www.gainsboroughtrinity.co.uk email: nicholsons.northstreet@virgin.net
Directions: The Northolme is situated opposite the Texaco and Fina petrol stations on the A159 Gainsborough to Scunthorpe road. Two miles from Lea Road (BR)
Capacity: 4,000 Cover: 2,500 Seats: 504
Clubhouse: Executive `Club on the Park' (01427 613688) open Saturday matchday lunchtimes. Restaurant facilities.
Club Shop: Souvenirs - Wendy Godley (01427 611612)
Programmes - Nigel Tasker (01522 542014)

PROGRAMME
Pages: 44 Price: £1.20
Editor: John Marriott (01427 613638)

Local Press: Gainsborough News, Lincolnshire Echo.
Local Radio: BBC Radio Lincs, Lincs FM

PREVIOUS Leagues: Midland Counties 1889-96, 12-60, 61-68, Football Lge 1896-1912, Central Alliance 60-61.**Names :& Grounds** None
CLUB RECORDS **Attendance:** 9,760 v Scunthorpe Utd. Midland Lge. 1948.
Fee Paid: £3,000 for Stuart Lowe (Buxton 89-90). **Fee Received:** £30,000 for Tony James (Lincoln 1988).
Win: 7-0 v Fleetwood Town and Great Harwood Town. **Defeat:** 2-7 v Hyde Utd.

BEST SEASON **FA Cup:** 3rd Rd 1886-87 v Lincoln C (A) 0-1 after 2-2, 1st Rd on 33 occasions. **FA Trophy:** 4th Rd, 2002-2003
HONOURS Northern Prem Lge Cup 81-82 96-97 (R-up 71-72 97-98); Midland Co's Lge 1890-91,1927-28, 48-49, 66-67 (R-up 1891-92, 1895-96, 13-14, 28-29); Lincs Senior Cup 1889-90, 92-93, 94-95, 97-98, 1903-05, 06-07, 10-11, 46-49, 50-51, 57-59, 63-64,2002-2003. Unibond Chairman's Cup: R-up: 2001-2002

Players Progressing: Since 1980 - Stewart Evans (Sheffield Utd 80), Tony James, Ian Bowling & John Schofield (Lincoln 88), Dave Redfern(Stockport 91), Richard Logan (Huddersfield 93), Glenn Humphries (Hull City).

Back row, left to right: Danny Brown, Chris Hurst, Andy Brownrigg, Dan Barrett, Barry Richardson, Alex Allen, Neil Allison, Max Nicholson and John Reed. **Front row:** Lee Ellington, Luke Staton, Mark Anderson, Peter Jellett (Physio), Phil Stant (Manager), Colin Benson (Assistant Manager), Dean Walling (Player/ Coach), Darren Knowles and Neil Mann. **Photo**:Chris Etchells

Date	Comp.	Opponents	Att.	Score	Goalscorers
17/08	Unib. P	HYDE UNITED	337	4 - 2	Anderson 28, Staton 45[p], Ellington 53 69
20/08	Unib. P	Hucknall Town	319	0 - 0	
24/08	Unib. P	Blyth Spartans	426	1 - 2	Brownrigg 32
26/08	Unib. P	ASHTON UNITED	493	1 - 2	Ellington 59
31/08	Unib. P	Gateshead	182	1 - 1	Ellington 6
03/09	Unib. P	FRICKLEY ATHLETIC	332	2 - 0	Stant 15[p] 74
07/09	Unib. P	VAUXHALL MOTORS	326	2 - 1	Eshelby 51, Hunt 78
11/09	Unib. P	Bradford Park Avenue	261	0 - 1	
14/09	Unib. P	Whitby Town	308	0 - 3	
17/09	Unib. P	WAKEFIELD & EMLEY	274	4 - 1	Ellington 17, Stant 35 58 72
21/09	Unib. P	Marine	291	0 - 0	
28/09	**F.A.C.** Q2	FRICKLEY ATHLETIC	351	3 - 2	Stant 2[p], Ellington 20, Nicholson 50
30/09	Unib. P	Droylsden	201	0 - 3	
05/10	Unib. P	LANCASTER CITY	381	2 - 1	Stant 47, Ellington 80
08/10	Unib. P	HUCKNALL TOWN	386	2 - 2	Ellington 65[p], Stant 80
12/10	**F.A.C.** Q3	Vauxhall Motors	228	1 - 6	Stant 43
15/10	Unib. P	Frickley Athletic	121	2 - 2	Ellington 2 50
19/10	Unib. P	Burscough	171	4 - 4	Teale 19[og], Stant 32, Alcide 70, Ellington 82[p]
22/10	Lge Cup 1	Hucknall Town	95	3 - 0	Barrett 21, Lucas 66, Ellington 84
26/10	Unib. P	BRADFORD PARK AVENUE	404	2 - 2	Stant 44 60
29/10	Unib. P	HARROGATE TOWN	329	1 - 2	Ellington 73
02/11	**F.A.T.** 1	KENDAL TOWN	345	3 - 1	Stant 2, Ellington 30, Eshelby 47
05/11	Unib. P	Stalybridge Celtic	338	0 - 3	
09/11	Unib. P	ALTRINCHAM	467	2 - 1	Ellington 20 81
16/11	Unib. P	Altrincham	576	1 - 1	Stant 80
19/11	Lge Cup 2	North Ferriby United	105	3 - 2	Stant 2 10, Ellington 30
23/11	Unib. P	COLWYN BAY	327	2 - 1	Timmins 41, Eshelby 71
30/11	**F.A.T.** 2	Grantham Town	547	1 - 0	Eshelby 65
07/12	Unib. P	MARINE	358	0 - 0	
10/12	Lincs SC SF	LINCOLN UNITED	182	2 - 1	Callery 65, Ellison 90
14/12	Unib. P	Lancaster City	277	1 - 0	Ellington 90[p]
17/12	Lge Cup 3	Worksop Town	442	1 - 3	Mike 54
21/12	Unib. P	Barrow	1004	2 - 3	Jones 23 37
26/12	Unib. P	WORKSOP TOWN	1240	4 - 2	Stant 19, Ellington 51, Jones 64, Stones 67
28/12	Unib. P	Accrington Stanley	1068	0 - 3	
04/01	Unib. P	DROYLSDEN	357	1 - 4	Jones 10
14/01	**F.A.T.** 3	Farsley Celtic	277	1 - 1	Ellington 8
18/01	Unib. P	BLYTH SPARTANS	338	3 - 2	Callery 2 12, Jones 3
21/01	**F.A.T.** 3 rep	FARSLEY CELTIC	336	2 - 1	Timmons 8, Stant 80
25/01	Unib. P	BARROW	494	0 - 2	
01/02	**F.A.T.** 4	FOREST GREEN ROVERS	710	0 - 2	
08/02	Unib. P	GATESHEAD	353	0 - 1	
15/02	Unib. P	Ashton United	242	3 - 1	Camm 24, Ellington 33 38[p]
22/02	Unib. P	Hyde United	251	5 - 1	Grant 34 73 74, Stanton 39, Ellington 54
01/03	Unib. P	Harrogate Town	407	2 - 0	Eshelby 16, Jones 80
04/03	Unib. P	STALYBRIDGE CELTIC	317	1 - 1	Grant 13
08/03	Unib. P	BURSCOUGH	301	0 - 1	
15/03	Unib. P	RUNCORN HALTON	288	1 - 1	Ellington 31
22/03	Unib. P	Runcorn Halton	429	5 - 0	Grant 21, Brown 64, Ellington 72 86, Jones 90
29/03	Unib. P	Vauxhall Motors	175	0 - 1	
05/04	Unib. P	WHITBY TOWN	414	0 - 1	
12/04	Unib. P	Wakefield & Emley	183	1 - 2	Ellington 73
19/04	Unib. P	ACCRINGTON STANLEY	420	1 - 5	Jones 66
21/04	Unib. P	Worksop Town	523	1 - 0	Grant 25
26/04	Unib. P	Colwyn Bay	140	3 - 0	Jones 15 67, Fallows 65
29/04	Lincs SC F	GRANTHAM TOWN	390	4 - 0	Brown 55, Grant 60, Staton 82, Jones 90

PLAYING SQUAD

Goalkeepers: Christopher Noye (Retford T.)

Defenders: Alax Allen (Brodsworth Welfare), Neil Allison (Geylong Utd, New Zealand), Danny Barrett (Matlock T.), Ian Gore (Boreham Wood), Wayne Hall (York City), David Jervis (Mansfield T.), Darren Knowles (Northwich Victoria), Richard Lucas (Hednesford T.), Stuart Reddington (Burton Albion), Chris Timons (Stalybridge Celtic).

Midfield: Colin Alcide (Cambridge Utd), Neil Bray (Long Eaton Utd), Darren Holmes (Hallam), Chris Hurst (Frickley Ath.), Tom Jones (Stocksbridge Park Steels), Joh Reed (Ethnicoz Perez ,Greece), Carl Smith (Worksop T.), Luke Staton (Merthyr Tydfil).

Forwards: Mark Anderson (Scunthorpe Utd), Lee Ellington (Exeter City), Phil Stant (Hinckley Utd),Gareth Grant (Lincoln City), Gary Jones (Hucknall T.), Martin Newham (Long Eaton Utd), Max Nicholson (Woodlands & Wellington, Singapore)

HARROGATE TOWN

CLUB OFFICIALS

Chairman: Bill Fotherby

Vice Chairman: Howard Matthews

President: George Dunnington

Club/Company Secretary
Brian Russell 24 Hall Lane, Harrogate, HG13DK Tel/Fax: 01423 525341

Managing Director: Nigel Pleasants

FOOTBALL MANAGEMENT TEAM
Team Manager: John Reed
Player/Coach: Neil Aspin

FACT FILE

Formed: 1919

Nickname: Town

Colours: Yellow & Black stripes/black/black

Change colours:All claret

Midweek home matchday: Tuesday

Website:www.harrogatetownafc.co.uk

2002-2003

Captain & Top Scorer: Robbie Whelans

Player of the Year: Simon Sturdy

Pages: 40 Price: £1.50
Editor: Bob Head
01423 549153 - 07799 834918M

Local Press: Yorkshire Post Group
Harrogate Advertiser Series
Local Radio: Radio Leeds, Radio North Yorkshire ,Stray F.M.Stray FM.

GROUND: Wetherby Road, Harrogate.
Tel: 01423 880675 Office & Fax Sec.& Admin.Tel. & Fax: 01423 525341

Directions: From Leeds turn right at traffic lights (Nidd Vale Motors) into Hookstone Road, continue to Woodlands Hotel (traffic lights) turn left into Wetherby Road, ground on the right. From Harrogate (BR), turn left and left again, cross road (Odeon Cinema), proceed for about 400yds to main road, crossover to The Stray (open land) using footpath which leads to Wetherby Rd, ground 200yds on left. From A61 turn right onto southern by pass then left on to A661.Ground 400 yds on right after Sainsburys, lights and Woodlands Hotel.
From the West on A59 straight on to Wetherby Rd from Empress roundabout. ground on left.
From North: A59 exit from M1 then southern bypass to Wetherby Rd
Capacity: 3,800 Cover: 1,300 Seats: 500 Shop: Yes.Contact: Alan Williams 0781 4119378
Clubhouse: Oopen every match day, for functions & special events. Tel: 01423 883671

PREVIOUS **Names:** Harrogate FC1919-32, Harrogate Hotspurs 35-48 **Ground:** Starbeck Lane 1919-20
Leagues: West Riding 1919-20 Yorkshire 20-21, 22-31, 57-82; Midland 21-22; Northern 31-32; Harrogate & District 35-37 7 40-46 WRCAL 37-40 West Yorkshire 46-57; Northern Counties East 82-87

CLUB RECORDS **Attendance:** 4,280 v Railway Athletic, Whitworth Cup final 1950.
Win: 13-0 v Macklefield **Defeat:** 1-10 v Methley United 1956

BEST SEASON **FA Vase:** 4th Round 89-90 **FA Cup:** 1st Round Proper v Farnborough Town (a) 1-5 2002-2003
F.A.Trophy: 3rd Rd Replay v Spennymoor United 99-00 & 2001-02 v Doncaster Rovers (away) 0-2

HONOURS N.P.L. Div 1 Champions 2001-02, Div 1 Cup 89-90; N.C.E.L. Div 1(Nth) R-up 84-85 plus 3rd 85-86 & promoted.(Reserve Div 85-86, Reserve Div Cup 86-87); Yorkshire League Div 1 26-27 R-up 62-63 Div 2 81-82, Div 3 R-up 71-72 80-81; West Riding County Cup 62-63 72-73 85-86; 01-02, 02-03; West Riding Challenge Cup 24-25 26-27

Players progressing: Tony Ingham (Leeds 47), Stewart Ferebee (York C. 79),Tim Hotte (Halifax T. 85), Andy Watson (Halifax T. 88), Ian Blackstone (York C. 95) , Eric Stephenson (Leeds Utd 1932)

L-R - Back Row: Neil Aspin, Scott Bonsall, Simon Sturdy, Mark Atkins, Mick McNaughton, Liam Sutcliffe, Michael Ord, Ashley Connor, Marc Smith, James Riordan, Thomas Woollard. **Front:** Colin Hunter, James McDaid, Richard Dunning, Gary Bradshaw, Bill Fotherby, Robbie Whellans, John Reed, James Turley, Ben Sherwood, Glen Naylor. Mascot: Flynn McNaughton

Date	Comp.	Opponents	Att.	Score	Goalscorers
17/08	Unib. P	Altrincham	552	4 - 0	Whellans 23 90, Donaldson 39, Morris 81
20/08	Unib. P	STALYBRIDGE CELTIC	575	1 - 0	Merris 30
24/08	Unib. P	DROYLSDEN	461	0 - 0	
31/08	Unib. P	ACCRINGTON STANLEY	706	0 - 2	
03/09	Unib. P	Whitby Town	291	2 - 4	Hunter 59, Whellans 83
07/09	Unib. P	WAKEFIELD & EMLEY	427	1 - 2	Hunter 37
10/09	Unib. P	Marine	224	2 - 2	Marcelle 59, Williams 75[p]
14/09	Unib. P	Vauxhall Motors	265	1 - 1	McNaughton 21
17/09	Unib. P	FRICKLEY ATHLETIC	347	1 - 2	Hancock 30[og]
21/09	Unib. P	HYDE UNITED	387	3 - 1	Marcelle 41, Hunter 60, Merris 87
24/09	Unib. P	Hucknall Town	259	1 - 1	Sturdy 87
28/09	**F.A.C.** Q2	GREAT HARWOOD TOWN	342	2 - 0	Jackson 3, Turley 12
01/10	Unib. P	GATESHEAD	317	1 - 3	Kerr 28
05/10	Unib. P	Runcorn Halton	311	1 - 2	Tomlinson 72
08/10	Unib. P	Stalybridge Celtic	448	1 - 4	Mohan 40
12/10	**F.A.C.** Q3	Accrington Stanley	1112	0 - 0	
15/10	**F.A.C.** Q3 rep	ACCRINGTON STANLEY	602	3 - 2	Bonsall 40, McNaughton 45 61
19/10	Unib. P	LANCASTER CITY	408	1 - 3	Bonsall 41
26/10	**F.A.C.** Q4	Wisbech Town	1061	2 - 0	Whellans 32, Bonsall 80
29/10	Unib. P	Gainsborough Trinity	329	2 - 1	Whellans 19, Hunter 72
02/11	**F.A.T.** 1	Gresley Rovers	302	0 - 0	
05/11	**F.A.T.** 1 rep	GRESLEY ROVERS	276	3 - 0	Whellans 25 74[p], Hunter 84
09/11	Unib. P	Gateshead	343	3 - 2	Whellans 45, Merris 60, Donaldson 68
12/11	Unib. P	BARROW	402	3 - 2	Whellans 18[p] 63, C Donaldson 54,
16/11	**F.A.C.** 1	Farnborough Town	1090	1 - 5	Hunter 11
19/11	Lge Cup 2	BISHOP AUCKLAND	225	4 - 0	Kerr 17, Whellans 28, Hunter 31, Donaldson 32
23/11	Unib. P	WORKSOP TOWN	517	2 - 2	Turley 45, Whellans 49
30/11	**F.A.T.** 2	BURSCOUGH	291	2 - 2	Whellans 27[p], Hunter 58
03/12	**F.A.T.** 2 rep	Burscough	160	2 - 3	McNaughton 55, Mohan 90
07/12	Unib. P	Hyde United	268	5 - 1	Turley 47 59 73, Whellans 56 90
10/12	West RCC 2	HARROGATE RAILWAY ATHLETIC	341	3 - 1	Whellans 18, Bonsall 38, Donaldson 59
14/12	Unib. P	RUNCORN HALTON	321	3 - 1	McNaughton 37, Curtis 41, Hunter 66
21/12	Unib. P	Colwyn Bay	227	1 - 0	Sykes 1
28/12	Unib. P	BURSCOUGH	409	2 - 1	Donaldson 25, Bonsall 90
11/01	Unib. P	HUCKNALL TOWN	470	2 - 0	Hunter 16 66
18/01	Unib. P	Droylsden	222	1 - 2	Herbert 66
25/01	Lge Cup 3	Gateshead	217	0 - 1	
29/01	Unib. P	Bradford Park Avenue	437	0 - 1	
01/02	Unib. P	ASHTON UNITED	466	0 - 1	
08/02	Unib. P	Accrington Stanley	1074	2 - 3	McNaughton 16, Hunter 31
11/02	West RCC QF	Halifax Town	430	2 - 1	Whellans 58 60[p]
15/02	Unib. P	WHITBY TOWN	488	0 - 2	
22/02	Unib. P	Lancaster City	294	2 - 1	Sturdy 63, Whellans 80
01/03	Unib. P	GAINSBOROUGH TRINITY	407	0 - 2	
04/03	Unib. P	Blyth Spartans	309	3 - 0	Turvey 21 31, McDaid 44
08/03	Unib. P	COLWYN BAY	315	4 - 1	Jackson 22, Smith 29, Hunter 32, Sturdy 77
11/03	West RCC SF	BRADFORD PARK AVENUE	312	2 - 0	M Smith 11, Whellans 26
15/03	Unib. P	Barrow	1013	2 - 1	Whellans 29 45
18/03	Unib. P	ALTRINCHAM	368	3 - 0	Hunter 37, Smith 47, Jackson 89
22/03	Unib. P	MARINE	425	1 - 1	Smith 90
25/03	Unib. P	Ashton United	234	0 - 5	
02/04	Unib. P	Wakefield & Emley	147	0 - 0	
05/04	Unib. P	VAUXHALL MOTORS	355	2 - 2	Smith 11 13
08/04	Unib. P	BLYTH SPARTANS	280	3 - 1	Whellans 1, Hunter 34, McNaughton 52
12/04	Unib. P	Frickley Athletic	234	1 - 0	McNaughton 29
16/04	West RCC F	Farsley Celtic (N)	680	3 - 1	Hunter 55, Sykes 102, Whellans 109
19/04	Unib. P	Burscough	186	1 - 0	Smith 66
21/04	Unib. P	BRADFORD PARK AVENUE	607	5 - 2	Sykes 29 73 75, Hunter 31, Turley 36
26/04	Unib. P	Worksop Town	517	2 - 1	McNaughton 54, Dunn 80

PLAYING SQUAD

Goalkeepers: Ashley Connor (Rotherham Utd), Adam Mitchell (Pickering T.), Liam Sutcliffe (Farsley Celtic).

Defenders: Neil Aspin (Hartlepool Utd), Mark Bowes (Hamilton Acad.), Simon Collins (Garforth T.), Lee Cowling (Kingstonian), Lennie Curtis (Kettering T.), Stuart Elliott (Halifax T.), John Fielding (York City), Chris Hudson (Whitby T.), Dylan Kerr (Gateshead), James McDaid (Harrogate R.A.), Mike McNaughton (Frickley Ath.), Michael Nelson (Bury), Jamie Riordan (Ashton Utd), Sean Roberts (Hull City), Simon Sturdy (Pickering T.).

Midfield: Mark Atkins (Shrewsbury T.), Scott Bonsall (Hednesford T.), Scott Conlon (Canberra Cosmos, Aust.),David Donaldson (Gresley R.), Jamie Horsley (Ossettt A.),Colin Hunter (Morecambe), Danny Lowe (Northampton T.), David Merris (Guiseley), Michael Ord (Sorrento, Aust.), Ben Rhodes (York City), Marc Thompson (York C), Simon Watson (Doncaster R.), Andy Wright (Doncaster R.).

Forwards: Iain Dunn (Gainsborough T.), Scott Jackson (Ossett T.), Ross Marchant (Sunderland), Glenn Naylor (Darlington), Marc Smith (Eastwood T.), James Turley (Stalybridge C.), Robbie Whellans (Farsley C.)

HUCKNALL TOWN

CLUB OFFICIALS

Chair:Brian Holmes **V-Chair:** Glen Lathell
President: Andy Stewart
Secretary: Paul Dobson,15 Abbey Court,Beeston,Nottingham NG9 2RB
Tel No: 01158753185 (H) 07743 177649(M)
Commercial Manager: Daniel Lewis
01773 838340 (H) 07802 266268)M)
General Manager: David Green
Press Officer: Andy Donaldson

FOOTBALL MANAGEMENT TEAM

Director of Football: Steve Burr
Asst.Director of Football: Peter Wragg
Assistant Manager: Steve Prindiville
Physio: Jason Truscott

FACT FILE

Founded: 1987
Nickname: The Town
Sponsors: Doff-Portland
Colours: Yellow/black/yellow
Change colours: Allblue
Midweek matches: Tuesday
Reserves' League: Central Conference
Club Website: www.hucknalltownfc.co.uk

2002-2003

Captain: Craig Gaunt
P.o.Y .& Top Scorer:: Mark Nangle

Pages: 92 Price: £1.30
Editor: Drew Baker(07811 117789)

Local Press: Hucknall & Bulwell Dispatch; Nottm Evening Post; Nottm Football Post

GROUND Watnall Road, Hucknall, Notts NG15 6EY Tel: 0115 956 1253
Directions: M1 jct 27, A608 to lights, right onto A611 to Hucknall, right at r'bout (new by-pass), over next r'bout, right at next r'bout into Watnall Rd -grd on right.(B6009) From M1 jct 26 follow Nottm signs to lights on island, left onto A610, right at Three Ponds Pub onto B600 towards Watnall, 200 yds past Queens Head turn right signed Hucknall, follow over m'way and past Rolls Royce -ground on left. Nearest station Hucknall
Capacity: 5,000 Seats: 270 Cover: 2,200
Clubhouse: Every night and weekend lunchtimes
Club Shop: Yes, Lynne Taylor - 0115 9630206

PREVIOUS **Leagues:** Bulwell & Dist. 46-59 60-65; Central All. 59-60; Notts Spartan 65-70; Notts All. 70-89; Central Midlands 89-92 Northern Counties East 92-97, Unibond 97-
Ground: Wigwam Park 46-54 Name: Hucknall Colliery Welfare (until pit closure 1988)

CLUB RECORDS **Attendance:** 1,436 v Ilkeston Town, FA Cup 4th Qual 28/10/00 **Appearances:** Dave McCarthy 282,Paul Tomlinson 240
Goals: Maurice Palethorpe approx 400 (80s & 90s)

BEST SEASON **FA Cup:** 4th Q Rd v Ilkeston Town 00-01 lost 0-1 and 2001-02 v Cambridge City (A) 1-3 after 1-1
FA Vase: Quarter Final 85-86 **FA Trophy:** 3rd Rd v Redditch 98-99 , Leigh RMI 00-01

HONOURS Northern Counties (East) Lg Div 1 R-up 92-93 (Lg Cup 93-94 96-97 97-98) Presidents Cup 96-97;
Central Mids Lg x2 89-91 R-up 91-92, Lg Cup x3 89-92; Notts All.Sen (4) 76-78 87-89, Div 1 Div 1 72-73 80-81 86-87
Div 2 70-71; Intermediate Cup 72-73 78-81 84-84; Lge Cup 78-79; Unibond Chairmans Cup Winners 2002-2003
Notts Snr Cup 84-85 90-91 97-98 99-00,02-03 R-up 83-84 85-86 87-88 89-90 98-99 00-01 Unibond Lg.: Div 1 R-Up 98-99

L - R - Back row: Nick Taylor, Mark Nangle, Paul Mitchell, Chris Shaw, Simon Brown, Adi Brevett, James Lindlay, Stuart Nelson, Lee Soar, Alistair Asher, James Tevendale, Kelvin Mushambi, Danny Bacon. **Front row:** Carl Adams, Clint Marcelle, John Burns, Steve Burr (Director of Football), Brian Holmes (Chairman), Jason Truscott (physio), Danny Mayman, Dean Barrick, Gary Ricketts.

Date	Comp.	Opponents	Att.	Score	Goalscorers	
17/08	Unib. P	Barrow	1302	1 - 1	Huckerby 35	
20/08	Unib. P	GAINSBOROUGH TRINITY	319	0 - 0		
24/08	Unib. P	ALTRINCHAM	302	4 - 1	Nangle 4 80 89, Huckerby 22	
26/08	Unib. P	Wakefield & Emley	298	1 - 1	Starbuck 53	
31/08	Unib. P	LANCASTER CITY	262	1 - 1	Starbuck 65	
04/09	Unib. P	Bradford Park Avenue	341	3 - 0	Nangle 54 74, Huckerby 90	
07/09	Unib. P	Burscough	207	0 - 2		
10/09	Unib. P	STALYBRIDGE CELTIC	225	2 - 2	Ricketts 65, Huckerby 67	
14/09	Unib. P	COLWYN BAY	195	2 - 1	Ricketts 58, Prindiville 81[p]	
16/09	Unib. P	Droylsden	246	0 - 0		
21/09	Unib. P	Vauxhall Motors	204	1 - 5	Ricketts 68	
24/09	Unib. P	HARROGATE TOWN	259	1 - 1	Lenagh 31 F	
28/09	**F.A.C.** Q2	Hednesford Town	506	0 - 0		
01/10	**F.A.C.** Q2 rep	HEDNESFORD TOWN	355	3 - 3	Cooke 36, Nangle 48, Huckerby 114	Won 6 5 after pens.
04/10	Unib. P	WORKSOP TOWN	485	0 - 0		
08/10	Unib. P	Gainsborough Trinity	386	2 - 2	Starbuck 21[p], Brown 72	
12/10	**F.A.C.** Q3	WORCESTER CITY	652	1 - 0	Mayman 22	
15/10	Unib. P	BRADFORD PARK AVENUE	150	1 - 2	Williams 10	
19/10	Unib. P	ASHTON UNITED	227	2 - 3	Farrell 8, Mitchell 42	
22/10	Lge Cup 1	GAINSBOROUGH TRINITY	95	0 - 3		
26/10	**F.A.C.** Q4	VAUXHALL MOTORS	385	1 - 1	Prindiville 85[p]	
29/10	**F.A.C.** Q4 rep	Vauxhall Motors	401	1 - 5	Mayman 65	
02/11	**F.A.T.** 1	Rugby United	214	1 - 2	Williams 71	
09/11	Unib. P	Hyde United	267	1 - 0	Nangle 38	
12/11	Unib. P	WHITBY TOWN	196	1 - 2	Williams 68 F	
16/11	Unib. P	Accrington Stanley	942	0 - 2		
19/11	Unib. P	FRICKLEY ATHLETIC	156	1 - 0	Starbuck 71[p]	
23/11	Unib. P	RUNCORN HALTON	166	3 - 3	Nangle 15, Jones 20, Hicks 43	
30/11	Unib. P	Gateshead	163	5 - 1	Hicks 12, Cooke 17, Mayman 38, Marcelle 49, Jones 65	
13/12	Unib. P	Worksop Town	592	4 - 5	Mitchell 25, Cooke 28 76, Williams 50	
21/12	Unib. P	ACCRINGTON STANLEY	332	2 - 1	Mayman 46, Marcelle 81	
28/12	Unib. P	Marine	239	1 - 2	Huckerby 3	
11/01	Unib. P	Harrogate Town	470	0 - 2		
18/01	Unib. P	Whitby Town	301	3 - 3	Mayman 33, Cooke 70, Marcelle 89	
25/01	Chair. Cup QF	Lincoln United	160	2 - 0	Battersby 69, Nangle 73	
01/02	Notts SC 3	Boots Athletic	170	3 - 2	Adams 45, Nangle 71 90	
08/02	Unib. P	Lancaster City	289	2 - 1	Marcelle 39[p], Mitchell 65	
15/02	Unib. P	WAKEFIELD & EMLEY	233	1 - 1	Mitchell 27	
22/02	Unib. P	Ashton United	213	3 - 2	Mayman 11, Lenagh 33 79	
25/02	Unib. P	HYDE UNITED	159	2 - 0	Nangle 14, Cooke 74	
01/03	Unib. P	GATESHEAD	243	1 - 1	Lenagh 64	
04/03	Unib. P	Frickley Athletic	138	0 - 0		
08/03	Chair. Cup SF	BLYTH SPARTANS	152	4 - 1	Burns 42, Lenagh 52, Adams 54[p], Mayman 75	
12/03	Unib. P	BLYTH SPARTANS	142	0 - 2		
15/03	Unib. P	Stalybridge Celtic	593	2 - 1	Nangle 25, Adams 56[p]	
22/03	Unib. P	Altrincham	557	0 - 0		
25/03	Unib. P	BARROW	199	0 - 3		
27/03	Notts SC QF	SUTTON TOWN	204	1 - 0	Bacon 34	
01/04	Unib. P	BURSCOUGH	135	3 - 1	Mayman 38, Starbuck 51, Bacon 73	
05/04	Unib. P	Colwyn Bay	188	6 - 3	Bacon 1 20 44 59, Nangle 21, Burns 72	
09/04	Unib. P	DROYLSDEN	138	2 - 0	Marcelle 3, Bacon 32	
15/04	Unib. P	Blyth Spartans	376	2 - 1	Bacon 21, Adams 68	
19/04	Unib. P	MARINE	192	2 - 1	Bacon 47, Marcelle 70	
21/04	Unib. P	VAUXHALL MOTORS	219	1 - 2	Brown 15	
23/04	Unib. P	Runcorn Halton	169	3 - 0	Adams 61[p] 72, Cooke 70	
24/04	Notts SC F	Teversal	704	2 - 0	Bacon 25, Marcelle 26	(at Notts County)
28/04	Chair. Cup F	Droylsden	287	1 - 0	Brown 120	

PLAYING SQUAD

Goalkeepers Russell Cooke (Notts County), Stuart Nelsonn (Doncaster R.).

Defenders: Alistair Asher (Halifax T.), Jermaine Bailey (Eastwood T.), Dean Barrick (Nuneaton Bor.), Kieran Begley (Local Football), Craig Gaunt (Moor Green), Stuart Hicks (Mansfield T.), John Keegan (Rossendale Utd), Danny Mayman (Clipstone Welfare), Craig Shaw (Gainsborough T.), Lee Soar (Lincoln Utd) **Steve Prindiville** (Stafford Rangers)

Midfield: Carl Adams (Hednesford T.), Danny Bacon (Mansfield T.), John Burns (Burton Albion), Dannny Farthing (PIckering T.), Gareth Holmes (Nuneaton Bor.), Paul Mitchell (Arnold T.), **Gary Patterson** (Farnborough T.), Jamie Roberts (Eastwood T.), Steve Roebuck (South Normanton Ath.)

Forwards: Clint Marcelle (Harrogate T.), Kelvin Mushambi (Sporting Lions, Zimbabwe), Mark Nangle (Hucknell Rolls Royce) Gary Ricketts (Hinckley Utd), Mark Sale (Tamworth), James Tevendale (Stocksbridge Park Steels)

LANCASTER CITY

Lancaster City
Football Club
Official Matchday Programme
See the Vision ... Feel the Game

CLUB OFFICIALS

Chairman:Ron Moore **Pres:** M Woodhouse

Vice Chairman: Andrew Pye

Secretary: Barry Newsham
13 Kingsdale Road, Lancaster LA1 5NE
Tel No: 01524 64024
e-mail: barry,newsham@tiscali,co,uk
Match Secretary: Mike Sparks
Commercial Man.: Cora Patel
Email : mike@sparks13.freeserve.co,uk

FOOTBALL MANAGEMENT TEAM

Manager: Phil Wilson
Asst.Man.: Peter Ward
Physio: D Hughes

FACT FILE

Formed: 1905
Nickname: Dolly Blues
Sponsors: Reebok
Colours:Sky Blue& white stripes/Navy/Navy
Change colours: All white
Midweek matchday: Tuesday
Reserve League: Lancashire League
Club Website: www.lancastercityfc.com

2002-2003
Captain: AndyFensome
Andy Whittaker 31
Player of the Year: Paul; Sparrow

Pages:40 Price: £1.50
Editor:Cora Patel (07764 589500)
Local Press:
Lancaster Guardian, Morecambe Visitor, Lancashire Evening Post, Lancaster Citizen.
Local Radio:
Red Rose, Radio Lancashire, Bay Radio

GROUND Giant Axe, West Road, Lancaster LA1 5PE Tel: 01524 382238 (Office).
Capacity: 3064 Cover: 900 Seats: 513
Directions: M6 junc 33, follow into city, left at lights immediately after Waterstones bookshop, 2nd right, pass railway station on right, follow road down hill, ground 1st right. 5 mins walk from both bus & rail stations
Clubhouse: "The Dolly Blue Tavern" just outside the ground. Also a new tea bar inside ground serving food and drinks. **Club Shop:** Inside ground, selling metal badges, pennants, programmes and other souvenirs etc. Contact Eric Williams (01524 33398)

PREVIOUS
Leagues: Lancs Combination 05-70; Northern Premier 70-82; North West Counties82-87.
Name: Lancaster Town. **Ground:** Quay Meadow 05-06 (club's 1st 2 games only!)

CLUB RECORDS
Attendance: 7,500 v Carlisle, FA Cup 1936.
Goalscorer: David Barnes 130 League & cup. **Appearances:** Edgar J Parkinson, 591 league & cup.
Win: 8-0 v Leyland Motors (A), 83-84. **Defeat:** 0-10 v Matlock T, NPL Division One, 73-74

BEST SEASON
FA Vase: Second Rd 86-87 90-91. **FA Cup:** 2nd Rd 46-47 (1-4 (A) v Gateshead) 72-73 (1-2 (A) v Notts County)
FA Trophy: Third Rd 74-75 75-76. League Clubs defeated: Barrow, Stockport County 21-22

HONOURS
Northern Prem. Lg Cup R-up 79-80 (Div 1 Cup R-up 90-91), Lancs Combination 21-22 29-30 34-35 35-36 (R-up 19-20 22-23 27-28 51-52, Lg Cup 21-22, Div 2 R-up14-15), Lancs Jun. Cup (ATS Challenge Trophy) 27-28 28-29 30-31 33-34 51-52 74-75 (R-up 06-07 08-09 19-20 26-27,00-01), Lancs Yth (u18) Cup 87-88 88-89 (R-up 86-87 89-90), President's Cup 1994-95 Unibond Div 1 95-96, Div 1 Lge Cup 95-96., Lg.Challenge Cup 99-00 , 00-01

Players Progressing: J McNamee (Workington 75), B O'Callaghan (Stoke C.), I Stevens (Stockport Co. 86), G Johnstone (P.N.E. 93), M Clark & W Collins (Crewe Alex.), G Wilson (Crewe Alex.). P.Thomson (NAC Breda 99) Chris Ward (Birmingham City)

Match Facts 2002-03

Date	Comp.	Opponents	Att.	Score	Goalscorers
17/08	Unib. P	BLYTH SPARTANS	282	1 - 4	Haddow 88
20/08	Unib. P	Burscough	237	0 - 0	
24/08	Unib. P	Frickley Athletic	178	1 - 0	Whittaker 68
26/08	Unib. P	RUNCORN HALTON	364	1 - 1	Whittaker 65
31/08	Unib. P	Hucknall Town	262	1 - 1	Whitter 32
03/09	Unib. P	GATESHEAD	253	2 - 1	Whittaker 8, Atkinson 59
07/09	Unib. P	Droylsden	312	5 - 1	Whittaker 1 69 73[p] 75 84
14/09	Unib. P	WORKSOP TOWN	398	1 - 4	Atkinson 26
21/09	Unib. P	BRADFORD PARK AVENUE	352	2 - 3	Whittaker 14 68[p]
23/09	Unib. P	Hyde United	301	3 - 2	Whittaker 65, Perkins 69, Welch 90
28/09	**F.A.C.** Q2	BLYTH SPARTANS	357	2 - 4	Atkinson 32, Whittaker 75
01/10	Unib. P	ALTRINCHAM	325	3 - 0	Miller 24, Haddow 78, Butler 86
05/10	Unib. P	Gainsborough Trinity	381	1 - 2	Whittaker 87
12/10	Unib. P	Stalybridge Celtic	433	0 - 1	
16/10	Unib. P	Gateshead	125	3 - 3	Haddow 2 65, Welch 16
19/10	Unib. P	Harrogate Town	408	3 - 1	Whittaker 55[p], Welch 70, Love 87
26/10	Unib. P	BURSCOUGH	297	2 - 1	Whittaker 30, Welch 62
02/11	Unib. P	VAUXHALL MOTORS	316	1 - 2	Whittaker 30
05/11	Unib. P	Colwyn Bay	149	1 - 1	Whittaker 18
09/11	Unib. P	MARINE	303	1 - 0	Whittaker 37
12/11	Lancs MT 1	Darwen	81	4 - 1	Bennett 28, Love 44, Yates 72 89
19/11	Lge Cup 2	LEEK TOWN	170	2 - 0	Bennett 50, Mercer 73
23/11	Unib. P	ASHTON UNITED	279	1 - 3	Whittaker 6
30/11	**F.A.T.** 2	STAMFORD	181	6 - 1	Atkinson 1, Brown 50, Yates 65, Love 68, Welch 75 89
03/12	Unib. P	HYDE UNITED	244	4 - 1	Love 3, Atkinson 45, Haddow 54, Diggle 90[og]
07/12	Unib. P	Bradford Park Avenue	257	1 - 0	Brown 48
10/12	Lge Cup 3	Rossendale United	108	1 - 4	Atkinson 65
14/12	Unib. P	GAINSBOROUGH TRINITY	277	0 - 1	
26/12	Unib. P	Barrow	1520	2 - 2	Love 73, Welch 76
28/12	Unib. P	WHITBY TOWN	295	0 - 1	
01/01	Unib. P	BARROW	888	1 - 5	Haddow 87
04/01	Unib. P	Altrincham	604	0 - 3	
14/01	**F.A.T.** 3	MORECAMBE	2279	0 - 1	
21/01	Lancs MT 2	Fleetwood Town	153	1 - 0	Mercer 23
29/01	Lancs MT QF	Accrington Stanley	360	1 - 3	Whittaker 86
01/02	Unib. P	Blyth Spartans	347	0 - 1	
08/02	Unib. P	HUCKNALL TOWN	289	1 - 2	Welch 23
22/02	Unib. P	HARROGATE TOWN	294	1 - 2	McGonnell 51
25/02	Unib. P	FRICKLEY ATHLETIC	206	4 - 0	Yates 15, Whittaker 82 90, Clitheroe 83
01/03	Unib. P	WAKEFIELD & EMLEY	249	5 - 2	Yates 4 70[p], Welch 25, Haddow 58, Whittaker 78
04/03	Unib. P	COLWYN BAY	232	1 - 0	Whittaker 65
08/03	Unib. P	Vauxhall Motors	214	2 - 6	Whittaker 58 77
15/03	Unib. P	ACCRINGTON STANLEY	677	1 - 2	Welch 8
18/03	Unib. P	Runcorn Halton	164	4 - 1	Welch 7, Whittle-Williams 31, Whittaker 67 89
22/03	Unib. P	Wakefield & Emley	188	4 - 1	Whittaker 67[p] 89 90, Welch 85
29/03	Unib. P	DROYLSDEN	264	0 - 3	
31/03	Unib. P	Marine	224	0 - 4	
05/04	Unib. P	Worksop Town	444	1 - 1	Rigby 86
12/04	Unib. P	STALYBRIDGE CELTIC	299	0 - 1	
19/04	Unib. P	Whitby Town	293	3 - 2	Whittaker 78, Haddow 89, Lowe 90
21/04	Unib. P	Accrington Stanley	1318	1 - 1	Bennett 74
26/04	Unib. P	Ashton United	195	2 - 2	Bennett 48, Clitheroe 51

PLAYING SQUAD

Goalkeepers Mark Thornley (Barrow).

Defenders: Gary Bauress (Aberysthwyth T.), Stewart Clitheroe (Port Vale), Ciaran Donaghy (Cliftonville), Andy Fensome (Morecambe), Jimmy Graham (Guiseley), Farrell Kilbane (Stafford Rangers), Paul Rigby (Kendal), John Robertson (Leigh RMI), Paul Sparrow(Rochdale), Jamie Udall (Leigh RMI).

Midfield: **Brian Butler** (Leigh RMI), Phil Clarkson (Halifax T.), Lee Clitheroe (Oldham Ath.), Timmy Graham (Glenavon), Steve Jones (Southport), Richard Mercer (P.N.E.), Andy Scott (Southport).

Forwards: Junior Bent (Kettering T.), Neil Morton (Morecambe), Michael Yates (Dundee)

MARINE

CLUB OFFICIALS

Chairman: Paul Leary

President: Dennis Hargreaves

Secretary: John Wildman
4 Ashbourne Avenue, Blundellsands,
Liverpool L23 8TX Tel: 0151 924 5248

Press Off: Steve Rimmer (0151 928 9722)

Club Website: www.marinefc.com

FOOTBALL MANAGEMENT TEAM

Manager: Roly Howard
Asst Mgr/Coach: Dave Thompson
Physio: Anne Fisher

FACT FILE

Formed: 1894
Nickname: The Mariners, The Lilywhites
Sponsors: Arriva
Colours: White/black/black
Change colours: Yellow/Green/Green
Midweek matchday: Tuesday
Reserves' League: Lancs. League Div. One

2002-2003

Captain: Gary Randles
Top Scorers: Rick Bainbridge, Tommy Taylor
P.o.Y.: Peter Crookes

Pages: 40 Price: £1.20
Editor: Dave Rannard
Local Press: Crosby Herald, Liverpool Echo, Daily Post Local Radio: BBC Radio Merseyside, Radio City

GROUND Rossett Park, College Road, Crosby, Liverpool L23 3AS (Tel: 0151 924 1743)
Directions: College Road is off main Liverpool-Southport road (A565) in Crosby. Ground ten minutes walk from Crosby & Blundellsands (Mersey Rail). Bus No. 92
Capacity: 3,185 Cover: 1,400 Seats: 400

Clubhouse: Open daily. Concert Hall (250 seats), Members Lounge (100 seats).
Club Shop: Sells replica kit and range of souvenirs.Metal Badges in home and away colours. Contact: Joanne Cross (0151 929 3616)

PREVIOUS
Leagues: Liverpool Zingari; Liverpool Co. Comb.; Lancs Combination 35-39, 46-69; Cheshire County 69-79.
Name: Waterloo Melville **Ground:** Waterloo Park (1894-1903)

CLUB RECORDS
Attendance: 4,000 v Nigeria, Friendly 1949
Goalscorer: Paul Meachin 200 **Win:** 14-2 v Rossendale Utd (A), Cheshire County Lge 25/2/78
Appearances: Peter Smith 952 **Defeat:** 2-11 v Shrewsbury Town F.A.Cup 1st Rd 1995
Fee Paid: £6,000 for Jon Penman (Southport Oct. 1995) **Fee Received:** £20,000 for Richard Norris (Crewe 96)

BEST SEASON
FA Trophy: Semi Final 83-84, 91-92 **FA Amateur Cup:** Runners up 31-32 (SF 46-47)
FA Cup: 3rd Rd 92-93, 1-3 v Crewe Alex. (A) League clubs defeated: Barnsley 75-76, Halifax T. 92-93

HONOURS FA Amateur Cup R-up 31-32; Northern Prem Lg. 93-94 94-95, R-up 85-86 91-92, Lg Cup 84-85 91-92 02-03 R-up 80-81 85-86 Presidents Cup R-up 83-84 86-87; Cheshire Co. Lg73-74 75-76 77-78 R-up 72-73; Lancs Comb. R-up 46-47 Lg Cup 46-47 63-64 68-69; Liverpool Comb. 27-28 30-31 33-34 34-35 Lg Cup 30-31; Lancs Tphy 87-88 90-91 99-00; Lancs Jnr Cup 78-79; Lancs Amtr Cup (5); Liverpool Snr Cup 78-79 84-85 87-88 89-90 94-95 99-00; Liverpool Non-Lge Cup 68-69 75-76 76-77; Liverpool Chal. Cup 42-43 44-45 71-72.

Players Progressing: A Sharrock, S Brooks (Southport 73 &77), A Jones (Leeds 60), G Williams (Preston 72), J Lacy (Fulham), P Beesley (Sheffield Utd), M Kearney (Everton 81), A Finlay (Shrewsbury 81), P Cook (Norwich), P Edwards (Crewe), I Nolan (Tranmere), J McAteer(Bolton W.), R Norris (Crewe 96).

The squad celebrate after their Unibond League Cup Final triumph

L - R - Back: Roger Patience (Asst. Manager), Ann Fisher (Physio), Keith Johnson (Physio), Rick Bainbridge, Eddie Hussin, Jon Wareing, James Connelly, John Paul Stanhope, Gary Randles, Paul McNally, Peter Crookes and Roly Howard (Manager)
Front: Neil Black, Will Dolan, Dave Nolan, Tommy Taylor, Ian Gargan and PaulCulshaw. **Photo:** Rob Lovett (Crosby Herald)

Date	Comp.	Opponents	Att.	Score	Goalscorers
17/08	Unib. P	Wakefield & Emley	227	1 - 1	Bailey 49
19/08	Unib. P	DROYLSDEN	263	2 - 2	McNally 37 87
24/08	Unib. P	ACCRINGTON STANLEY	361	0 - 3	
26/08	Unib. P	Bradford Park Avenue	332	1 - 2	Hussin 50
31/08	Unib. P	WORKSOP TOWN	339	1 - 2	Morgan 84
03/09	Unib. P	Stalybridge Celtic	429	1 - 2	Townsend 76
07/09	Unib. P	Colwyn Bay	256	2 - 0	McNally 45, Taylor 83
10/09	Unib. P	HARROGATE TOWN	224	2 - 2	Keegan 69, Taylor 89
14/09	Unib. P	BLYTH SPARTANS	265	2 - 1	Taylor 17, Dolan 53
17/09	Unib. P	Burscough	250	1 - 2	Keegan 37
21/09	Unib. P	GAINSBOROUGH TRINITY	291	0 - 0	
24/09	Unib. P	Altrincham	477	1 - 0	Lally 27
28/09	**F.A.C.** Q2	ECCLESHILL UNITED	248	2 - 2	Hussin 31 56
01/10	**F.A.C.** Q2 rep	Eccleshill United	176	3 - 2	McNally 22 38, Taylor 118
05/10	Unib. P	Whitby Town	294	0 - 2	
07/10	Unib. P	Droylsden	167	1 - 0	Taylor 23
12/10	**F.A.C.** Q3	Dunston Federation Brewery	297	1 - 0	Black 32
14/10	Unib. P	STALYBRIDGE CELTIC	268	1 - 2	Taylor 88
19/10	Unib. P	HYDE UNITED	251	4 - 1	Bainbridge 27 73, Crookes 47[og], Hussin 89
22/10	Lge Cup 1	Witton Albion	157	5 - 3	Black 21, Taylor 48 92 118, Keegan 89
26/10	**F.A.C.** Q4	Harrogate Railway Athletic	703	2 - 4	Bainbridge 60, Black 85
02/11	**F.A.T.** 1	Burscough	242	0 - 0	
04/11	**F.A.T.** 1 rep	BURSCOUGH	224	1 - 3	Bainbridge 21
09/11	Unib. P	Lancaster City	303	0 - 1	
12/11	Lancs MT 1	Bamber Bridge	76	3 - 2	McNally 37, Black 71, Bainbridge 77
16/11	Unib. P	Frickley Athletic	136	3 - 1	Bainbridge 54, Black 58, Hussin 79
18/11	Lge Cup 2	STALYBRIDGE CELTIC	174	2 - 0	Keegan 70, Dolan 83
23/11	Unib. P	VAUXHALL MOTORS	324	1 - 2	Keegan 73[p]
30/11	Unib. P	Ashton United	213	3 - 2	Dolan 11 41, Bainbridge 35
02/12	Unib. P	ALTRINCHAM	231	0 - 1	
07/12	Unib. P	Gainsborough Trinity	358	0 - 0	F
09/12	Lge Cup 3	HYDE UNITED	104	1 - 0	Bainbridge 4
14/12	Unib. P	WHITBY TOWN	230	5 - 5	Hussin 13, McNally 27 36, Proctor 87, Dolan 90
26/12	Unib. P	RUNCORN HALTON	364	0 - 2	
28/12	Unib. P	HUÇKNALL TOWN	239	2 - 1	Hussin 74, McNally 90
04/01	Unib. P	Barrow	1218	0 - 1	
14/01	Lancs MT 2	Rossendale United	130	1 - 2	Taylor 87
18/01	Unib. P	Accrington Stanley	925	0 - 5	
25/01	Lge Cup QF	WORKSOP TOWN	256	1 - 0	Taylor 13
01/02	Unib. P	Hyde United	307	2 - 0	Taylor 73, Black 78
08/02	Unib. P	Worksop Town	607	1 - 2	Bainbridge 16
10/02	Live SC QF	WARRINGTON TOWN	119	1 - 0	McNally 29
15/02	Unib. P	BRADFORD PARK AVENUE	288	4 - 2	Nolan 5, Proctor 23[p] 64[p], Bainbridge 68
26/02	Unib. P	Runcorn Halton	208	1 - 2	Bainbridge 80
01/03	Unib. P	ASHTON UNITED	254	1 - 0	Bainbridge 53
10/03	Unib. P	WAKEFIELD & EMLEY	222	2 - 1	Hussin 3, McNally 70
15/03	Unib. P	Gateshead	208	2 - 1	Taylor 83, Bainbridge 90
17/03	Unib. P	COLWYN BAY	233	0 - 0	
22/03	Unib. P	Harrogate Town	425	1 - 1	Bainbridge 43
25/03	Lge Cup SF	Ossett Town	214	1 - 0	Bainbridge 20
29/03	Unib. P	GATESHEAD	252	4 - 2	Hussin 28, Stanhope 36, Taylor 89 90
31/03	Unib. P	LANCASTER CITY	224	4 - 0	Taylor 58, Nolan 60 85, Stanhope 90
05/04	Unib. P	Blyth Spartans	366	1 - 1	Dolan 47
09/04	Lge Cup F (1)	Gateshead	184	1 - 0	Nolan 4 (at South Shields)
14/04	Unib. P	BURSCOUGH	302	1 - 0	Proctor 85
17/04	Unib. P	FRICKLEY ATHLETIC	241	0 - 1	
19/04	Unib. P	Hucknall Town	192	1 - 2	Nolan 49
21/04	Unib. P	BARROW	252	3 - 1	Black 28, Nolan 34, McNally 87
24/04	Lge Cup F (2)	GATESHEAD	425	2 - 0	Bainbridge 27, McNally 31
26/04	Unib. P	Vauxhall Motors	254	1 - 1	McMullen 13[og]

PLAYING SQUAD

Goalkeepers Peter Crookes (HYde Utd), Billy Stewart (Rhyl).

Defenders: James Connelly (Southport), Kevin Formby (Southport), Jon Gautrey (Southport), Lee Mullin (Tranmere R.), Neil Murphy (Altrincham), Gary Randles (Runcorn), Steve Rimmer (Hyde Utd), Jon Wareing (Wigan Ath.).

Midfield: Ricky Bainbridge (Local Football), Anthony Bowden (Accrington Stanley), Will Dolan (Youth Team), Michael Douglas (Ashville), Eddie Hussin (Winsford Utd), Michael Keegan (Swansea City), Paul McNally (Runcorn FC Halton).

Forwards: Neil Black (Tranmere R.), Lee Furlong (Burscough), John Morgan (Southport), David Thompson (Southport), Ritchie Townsend (Cwmbran T.)

RADCLIFFE BOROUGH

CLUB OFFICIALS

Chairman: Bernard Manning (Junior)

President: Bernard Manning (Senior)

Directors: D. Murgatroyd, M Darlington, K.Glendon, Barney Hampson, B. Manning jr. G Fielding (Company Secretary)

Football Secretary: Ian Hannay

Both c/o Radcliffe Borough

FOOTBALL MANAGEMENT TEAM

Manager: Kevin Glendon
Coach: Ronnie Evans
Physio: Roy Davies

FACT FILE

Formed: 1949
Nickname: Boro'
Sponsors: T.B.A.
Colours: Blue/blue/white
Change colours: Green & white hoops
Midweek home matchday: Tuesday
Reserve Team: No
Youth Team U18: Yes

2002-2003

Captain: David Bean
Top Scorer: Jody Banim 45

Pages: 28 Price: 80p
Editor: Roy Swinbank

Local Press: Radcliffe Times, Bolton Evening News, Manchester Evening News
Local Radio: GMR, Piccadilly Tower F.M. Bolton

GROUND: Stainton Park, Pilkington Road, Radcliffe, Lancs., M26 3PE 0161 724 5937 (club) 0161 724 8346 (Office) 0161 723 3178(Fax) Website: www.radcliffeborough.co.uk
Directions: M62 junction 17 - follow signs for Whitefield and Bury . Take A665 to Radcliffe. Thro' town centre, turn right into Unsworth St. (opposite Turf Hotel). Ground on left half mile Colshaw Close East. 1/2 mile from Radcliffe(BR)
Capacity: 3,000 Cover: 1,000 Seats: 350
Clubhouse: (0161 724 5937) `The Boro' - public house on ground with food available
Club Shop: Yes

PREVIOUS — **Leagues:** South East Lancs; Manchester 53-63; Lancs Comb. 63-71; Cheshire County 71-82; North West Counties 82-87
Ground: Bright Street 1949-70.

CLUB RECORDS — **Attendance:** 2,495 v York City (F.A.C 1st Round 2000-01)
Goalscorer: Ian Lunt **Appearances:** Chris Lilley.
Fee Paid: £5,000 for Gary Walker(Buxton, 1991). **Fee Received:** £15,000 for Paul Mullin (Accrington Stanley 2000-01)

BEST SEASON — **FA Trophy:** 3rd Rd v Gateshead 1995-96
FA Cup: 1st Round Proper, 00-01 v York City 1-4)**FA Vase:** 4th Rd v Boston Town 93-94

HONOURS — Unibond Lge Div One Champ 96-97; North West Counties Lg 84-85 (Div 2 82-83); Lancs Combination Lg. Cup 69-70; Manchester Lg R-up 55-56 (Lg Cup 58-59 joint); Manchester Prem. Cup R-up 97-98

Players progressing: Jim Hayman (Bury 50), Ian Wood (Oldham Athletic 65), Robert Hutchinson (Rochdale 74), Gary Haworth (Rochdale 84), Kevin Hulme (Bury 89), Neil Hardy (Stockport County)

Back row, left to right: Roy Davies (Physio), Scot Hartford, Alan Warren, Simon Kelly, Eamon Kelly, Simon Kay, Danny Hurst, Dave Felgate, Richard Landon, David Bean, Niell Hardy, Tony Wealing, Kevan Glendon (Manager) and Ronnie Evans (asst. Man) **Front row**: Scott Wilson, Jody Banim, Barrie Keeling, Danny Grant, Scott Catterall (sponsor), Bernard Manning (Chairman), Bernard Manning (President), Wayne Bradshaw (Sponsor), Eamonn Elliott, James Price, Richard Battersby and Ian Lunt.

Date	Comp.	Opponents	Att.	Score	Goalscorers
17/08	Unib. 1	Guiseley	183	0 - 0	
20/08	Unib. 1	KENDAL TOWN	148	2 - 4	Banim 47, Whealing 51
24/08	Unib. 1	EASTWOOD TOWN	160	1 - 1	Keeling 31
31/08	**F.A.C.** P	Clitheroe	229	3 - 1	Wilson 13, Banim 48, Elliott 73
07/09	Unib. 1	Farsley Celtic	127	1 - 1	Bean 63
10/09	Unib. 1	Stocksbridge Park Steels	172	1 - 0	S Kelly 71
14/09	**F.A.C.** Q1	ABBEY HEY	213	4 - 1	Kay 62, Elliott 73[p], Banim 82 86
17/09	Unib. 1	MATLOCK TOWN	142	0 - 1	
21/09	Unib. 1	BELPER TOWN	171	1 - 1	Dempsey 82[p]
24/09	Unib. 1	LEEK TOWN	138	0 - 1	
28/09	**F.A.C.** Q2	Rossington Main	160	7 - 0	Diggle 45, Banim 48 68 71, Hardy 54 63, Keeling 82
02/10	Unib. 1	Bishop Auckland	187	3 - 1	Wilson 33, Banim 39, Battersby 74
05/10	**F.A.T.** P	EASTWOOD TOWN	160	0 - 1	
12/10	**F.A.C.** Q3	Colwyn Bay	n/k	2 - 1	Banim 41 90
15/10	Unib. 1	Leek Town	171	2 - 1	Landon 62, Banim 72
19/10	Unib. 1	CHORLEY	243	1 - 1	Southwood 33[og]
26/10	**F.A.C.** Q4	CHESTER CITY	1138	2 - 4	Banim 73, Hardy 90
29/10	Unib. 1	WORKINGTON	121	1 - 1	Hardy 90
02/11	Unib. 1	BAMBER BRIDGE	158	2 - 1	Elliott 20, Banim 74
05/11	Unib. 1	TRAFFORD	121	4 - 2	Whealing 37 58, Banim 43 50
09/11	Unib. 1	Bamber Bridge	243	1 - 0	Banim 82
16/11	Unib. 1	Trafford	233	3 - 0	Kay 24, Landon 27, Elliott 90
19/11	Lancs MT 1	Leigh RMI	n/k	0 - 1	
23/11	Unib. 1	Eastwood Town	140	1 - 0	Landon 49
26/11	Lge Cup 2	COLWYN BAY	85	3 - 2	Landon 36, Kay 88, Hardy 119
30/11	Unib. 1	GUISELEY	158	2 - 1	Landon 9, Whealing 45
07/12	Notts SC 2	RUDDINGTON UNITED	n/k	3 - 0	
07/12	Unib. 1	SPENNYMOOR UNITED	203	7 - 4	Elliott 4[p], Banim 15 80 90[p], Hardy 75[p], Whealing 85, Battersb
10/12	Lge Cup 3	BARROW	92	2 - 1	Bean 37, Battersby 45
26/12	Unib. 1	ROSSENDALE UNITED	292	2 - 1	Banim 35, Keeling 66
28/12	Unib. 1	North Ferriby United	229	2 - 4	Banim 23, Landon 35
18/01	Unib. 1	BISHOP AUCKLAND	165	1 - 0	Landon 76
21/01	Unib. 1	Witton Albion	240	2 - 2	Banim 19 27
25/01	Lge Cup QF	OSSETT TOWN	206	3 - 4	Keeling 24 45, Hardy 44
01/02	Unib. 1	Workington	582	3 - 1	Banim 12 89, Hardy 70
08/02	Unib. 1	LINCOLN UNITED	210	4 - 1	Hardy 21, Landon 33 52, Keeling 90
11/02	Unib. 1	Spennymoor United	199	2 - 0	Banim 12 83
15/02	Unib. 1	Chorley	465	2 - 2	Keeling 6, Banim 84[p]
22/02	Unib. 1	WITTON ALBION	284	4 - 2	Bean 15, Banim 16 17 72, Johnson 48[p]
01/03	Unib. 1	Ossett Town	236	4 - 0	Keeling 33, Banim 47, Carden 74, Landon 89
04/03	Unib. 1	ALFRETON TOWN	355	2 - 4	Brookes 10[og], Banim 68
08/03	Unib. 1	Matlock Town	251	1 - 2	Banim 82
15/03	Unib. 1	Kidsgrove Athletic	187	0 - 0	
18/03	Unib. 1	Alfreton Town	329	2 - 3	Banim 29, Bean 51
22/03	Unib. 1	KIDSGROVE ATHLETIC	185	5 - 1	Elliott 14 49, Banim 31, Hardy 70 87
25/03	Unib. 1	FARSLEY CELTIC	150	3 - 0	Banim 36, Battersby 51, Whealing 75
29/03	Unib. 1	Lincoln United	148	1 - 0	Hardy 38
01/04	Unib. 1	Kendal Town	192	1 - 0	Hardy 45
05/04	Unib. 1	STOCKSBRIDGE PARK STEELS	320	4 - 0	Battersby 14, Hardy 25, Banim 42 80
12/04	Unib. 1	Belper Town	341	0 - 0	
19/04	Unib. 1	OSSETT TOWN	210	7 - 1	Brown 15, Keeling 35, Banim 59 82[p] 86, Whellans 76 90
21/04	Unib. 1	Rossendale United	214	3 - 1	Banim 39, Sampson 57 60
26/04	Unib. 1	NORTH FERRIBY UNITED	390	2 - 0	Banim 21, Whealing 54
29/04	Play-off SF	NORTH FERRIBY UNITED	463	1 - 0	Banim 47
03/05	Play-off Final	CHORLEY	956	2 - 2	Banim 23, Hardy 45 Won 4 2 after pens

PLAYING SQUAD

Goalkeepers: David Felgate (Leigh RMI), Danny Hurst (Cheadle).

Defenders: Richard Battersby (Oldham Ath.), David Bean (Cheadle), Dave Brown (Salford City), Martin Diggle (Worksop T.), Simon Kay (Chorley), James Price (Chorley), Steve Spencer(Altrincham), Tony Whealing (Leigh RMI).

Midfield: Simon Carden (Accrington Stanley), Mark Dempsey (Alfreton T.), Eamnon Elliott (Ossett T.), Neil Hardy (Stockport County), Simon Kelly (Youth Team), Gary Simpson (Accrington Stanley).

Forwards: Jody Banim (Hyde Utd), Chris Denham (Stalybridge Celtic), Richard Landon (Altrincham), Lee Potter (Bradford P.A.), **Phil Power** (Altrincham)

RUNCORN F.C. HALTON

CLUB OFFICIALS

Chairman: Dr David Robertson

Vice Chairman: Ian Burgess

Secretary: Debbie Quaile,
57 The Moorings, Lydiate,
Liverpool L31 2PR
Tel: 0151 531 1296 (H)
0161 200 4925 (W)
07970 175652 (M)

FOOTBALL MANAGEMENT

Manager: Liam Watson

Assistant Manager: Neil Whalley

FACT FILE

Formed: 1918
Nickname: The Linnets
Midweek matchday: Tuesday
Colours: Yellow/&green/yellow
Change: Sky blue/dark blue/darkblue.
No Reserve team
Youth's league: Northwest Alliance
Website: www.runcornfchalton.co.uk
Local Press: Runcorn Weekly News,
Liverpool Echo, Runcorn World,
Manchester Evening News.
Local Radio:
Radio Merseyside, GMR.Wire F.M

GROUND HaltonStadium, Lowerhouse Lane, Widnes, Cheshire. WA8 7DZ
Tel No: Matchdays only 0151 5106000 Fax matchdays only 0151 510 6001
Directions: From M62 take junction 7 and follow signs to Widnes and Auto quest Stadium. Follow Widnes by -pass and then turn right onto Ashley Way. At roundabout take second exit and go straight onto the next roundabout where the Stadium ia on the right.
Capacity: 12,500 Covered Seats: 12,500
Clubhouse: Open on matchdays. Light snacks available.
Club Shop: Phone club.

PROGRAMME
Pages: 36 Price: £1.20
Editor: Secretary

PREVIOUS **Leagues:** Lancs Combination; Cheshire Co. Lg; Northern Prem. Lge. 68 -81; Alliance Premier (Conference) 81-96.
Names: Runcorn **Grounds:** Canal Street, Runcorn

CLUB RECORDS **Attendance:** 10,111 v Preston - FA Cup 1938-39.
Goalscorer: Alan Ryan (66 goals in 64 appearances 67-68).
Win: 11-1 v Congleton Town 64-65. **Defeat:** 0-9 v Wellington 46-47.
Fee Paid: £17,000 for Simon Rudge, Hyde Utd, 1989. **Fee Received:** £80,000 for Ian Woan, Nottm Forest, 1990.

BEST SEASON **FA Trophy:** Runners-up 85-86, 92-93, 93-94. **FA Cup:** Second Round Replay 85-86,0-4 v Wigan Ath. (A), after 1-1. Second Round also 47-48, 67-68, 77-78, 86-87,87-88, 88-89. League clubs defeated: Scunthorpe Utd. 1947-48, Notts. Co (1967-68), Chester City 1987-88, Wrexham 1988-89.

HONOURS Lancs Jnr Cup 1918-19; Cheshire Lg 1919-20, 36-37, 38-39, 39-40, 62-63;Cheshire Snr Cup 24-25, 35-36, 61-62, 64-65, 67-68, 73-74, 74-75, 84-89 (5times), R-up 93-94; Cheshire Co. Bowl 37-38; Northern Premier Lg 75-76, 80-81(R-up 74-75); NPL Chall Cup 74-75, 79-80, 80-81; NPL Challenge Shield 80-81,81-82; Alliance Premier Lg 81-82, Gola Lg Championship Shield 82-83, 85-86; Bob Lord Trophy 82-83, 84-85, R-up 91-92. FA Trophy R-up 85-86, 92-93, 93-94.NPL Pres.Cup 98-99

Players Progressing: Mark McCarrick, Eddie Bishop, Jim Cumbes, Graham Abel,Barry Knowles, Mark Jones, Don Page, David Pugh, Ian Woan, Gary Brabin, Paul Robertson, Mike Smith,Mark Carter

Left to right

Back row:
Mal Liptrot (Kit Manager),
John Ryder,
David Robinson,
Mark Winstanley,
Mike Tomlinson,
David Ness,
David Gamble.

Middle row:
Gary Lunt,
Michael Short,
Neil Whalley (Asst Man.),
Liam Watson (Player/Man.),
Steve Latham.

Front row:
Steve Carragher,
Alan Cowley,
Tony Ward,
John McAllister,
Chris Price

Date	Comp.	Opponents	Att.	Score	Goalscorers	
17/08	Unib. P	Accrington Stanley	602	1 - 2	Price 86	
20/08	Unib. P	BARROW	343	1 - 1	McNeil 74	
24/08	Unib. P	BRADFORD PARK AVENUE	265	2 - 0	Lightfoot 45 56	
26/08	Unib. P	Lancaster City	364	1 - 1	Lightfoot 83	
31/08	Unib. P	STALYBRIDGE CELTIC	397	1 - 0	Leadbetter 76	
02/09	Unib. P	Droylsden	257	0 - 2		
07/09	Unib. P	Worksop Town	687	2 - 2	Carragher 28, Watson 84[p]	
10/09	Unib. P	BURSCOUGH	256	0 - 2		
14/09	Unib. P	GATESHEAD	227	1 - 1	Carragher 34	
17/09	Unib. P	Colwyn Bay	223	3 - 1	Leadbeater 3, McNeil 17, Kinney 41	
21/09	Unib. P	Blyth Spartans	344	1 - 3	Lightfoot 83	
28/09	**F.A.C.** Q2	WAKEFIELD & EMLEY	245	2 - 0	McNeil 32, Parle 77	
05/10	Unib. P	HARROGATE TOWN	311	2 - 1	Parle 3, Morley 21	
08/10	Unib. P	Barrow	757	0 - 3		
12/10	**F.A.C.** Q3	Ashton United	347	3 - 0	McNeil 1, Lightfoot 57[p], Price 81	
19/10	Unib. P	FRICKLEY ATHLETIC	228	0 - 1		
26/10	**F.A.C.** Q4	Blyth Spartans	851	3 - 1	McNeil 13, Leadbeater 27, Lunt 41	
28/10	Unib. P	Hyde United	334	2 - 0	Lunt 30, Parle 74	
02/11	Unib. P	Bradford Park Avenue	345	2 - 3	Gamble 26, Kinney 47	
05/11	Unib. P	ASHTON UNITED	202	3 - 2	Price 35 59, Kinney 45	
09/11	Unib. P	Whitby Town	299	3 - 0	Kinney 38, Lunt 66, Gamble 72	
12/11	Unib. P	VAUXHALL MOTORS	401	0 - 5		
16/11	**F.A.C.** 1	Bristol Rovers	4135	0 - 0		
23/11	Unib. P	Hucknall Town	166	3 - 3	Leadbetter 5, Morley 40, Lunt 45	
26/11	**F.A.C.** 1 rep	BRISTOL ROVERS	2434	1 - 3	Barrett 19[og]	
30/11	**F.A.T.** 2	RUGBY UNITED	263	0 - 3		
03/12	Lge Cup 2	CHORLEY	128	1 - 3	Cosgrove 79	
07/12	Unib. P	BLYTH SPARTANS	202	2 - 2	Lightfoot 4, Price 27	
10/12	Pres. Cup 1	LEEK TOWN	101	2 - 1	Gamble 18, Watson 82	
14/12	Unib. P	Harrogate Town	321	1 - 3	McNeil 8	
21/12	Unib. P	WAKEFIELD & EMLEY	203	4 - 1	Gamble 25[p], Watson 52, McNeil 75 87	
26/12	Unib. P	Marine	364	2 - 0	Kinney 2, McNeil 78	
15/01	Live SC QF	TRANMERE ROVERS	201	1 - 4	Parle 90	
18/01	Unib. P	Altrincham	628	1 - 1	Parle 44	
21/01	Unib. P	Vauxhall Motors	254	1 - 2	Gamble 76[p]	
25/01	Pres. Cup QF	SPENNYMOOR UNITED	151	3 - 1	McGinn 26, Parle 35, Gamble 45	
01/02	Unib. P	ACCRINGTON STANLEY	421	0 - 2		
22/02	Unib. P	Frickley Athletic	182	2 - 2	Price 17, Leadbetter 41	
26/02	Unib. P	MARINE	208	2 - 1	Leadbetter 50 51	
01/03	Unib. P	Stalybridge Celtic	534	1 - 0	Kinney 8	
12/03	Pres. Cup SF	STALYBRIDGE CELTIC	178	2 - 4	Watson 17[p], McGinn 62	
15/03	Unib. P	Gainsborough Trinity	288	1 - 1	Lightfoot 80	
18/03	Unib. P	LANCASTER CITY	164	1 - 4	Price 88	
22/03	Unib. P	GAINSBOROUGH TRINITY	429	0 - 5		
25/03	Unib. P	DROYLSDEN	138	0 - 0		
29/03	Unib. P	WORKSOP TOWN	242	3 - 0	Carragher 2, Kinney 66, Parle 72	
02/04	Unib. P	WHITBY TOWN	102	1 - 1	Leadbetter 56	
05/04	Unib. P	Gateshead	210	3 - 2	Leadbetter 47, Lightfoot 49, McGinn 55	(at South Shields FC)
09/04	Unib. P	HYDE UNITED	112	1 - 1	McGinn 60	(at Prescot Cables)
12/04	Unib. P	COLWYN BAY	113	6 - 2	Price 26, **Lightfoot 3** (30 43 48), McGinn 59, Prescott 70[p]	(at Prescot Cables)
15/04	Unib. P	Wakefield & Emley	167	0 - 0		
19/04	Unib. P	Ashton United	190	3 - 3	Leadbeater 32 62, McGinn 75	
21/04	Unib. P	ALTRINCHAM	334	3 - 2	Carragher 44, Price 45, Prescott 45	
23/04	Unib. P	HUCKNALL TOWN	169	0 - 3		
26/04	Unib. P	Burscough	187	3 - 3	Lightfoot 2 23, Leadbetter 44	

PLAYING SQUAD

Goalkeeper: Mark Winstanley (Prescot Cables).

Defenders: Ian Baines (St.Helens), Steve Carragher (Accrington Stanley), Peter Ellis (Knowsley Utd), Chris Lightfoot (Morecambe), Anthony McMillan (Wigan Ath.), David Ness (Youth Team), Chris Price (Morecambe), Tony Ward (Chorley).

Midfield: Mike Harris (Trafford), Steve Lathom (Youth Team), Francis McMahon (Wigan Ath.), Dominic Morley (Droylsden), Andy Norris (Wigan Ath.), Lee Parle (Local Football), Neil Whalley (Droylsden).

Forwards: Wes Kinney (Droylsden), Kevin Leadbetter (Southport), Matthew McNeil (Droylsden), **Liam Watson** (Accrington Stanley)

SOUTHPORT

CLUB OFFICIALS

President: T.B.A.

Chairman: Charles Clapham

Directors
C Clapham,S Shrouder (Vice Chairman), B J Hedley, A Pope, P Abrams,T Medcroft, S Porter, G.Tait

Football Secretary: Ken Hilton
34 Mill Lane, Burscough, Ormskirk L40 5TS
Tel: 01704 894504 (H) 07802 661906 (M)

Sales & Marketing Manager:
Derek Hitchcock
Tel: 07976 555782
e-mail: derek@hitchcock98.freeserve.co.uk

Press Officer: Haydon Reece

FOOTBALL MANAGEMENT TEAM
Manager: Mike Walsh
Reserve Team Coach: Tony Murphy
Physiotherapist: Brett Harris

FACT FILE

Founded: 1881

Nickname: The Sandgrounders

Club Sponsors: V K Vodka Kick

Club colours: Old Gold / black /black

Change colours: All white

Midweek home matchday: Tuesday

Reserves' League: Lancashire League

Club's Playing Status: Part-time

2002-03

Captain: Steve Soley

P.o.Y.:Steve Pickford

Leading Scorer:Peter Thomson

Pages: 48 Price: £2.00
Editor: Derek Hitchcock (07976 555782)
Clubcall: 09066 555 875

Local Press: Southport Visiter; The Champion
Local Radio: Dune F.M.; Radio Merseyside; Radio City; Radio Lancashire

GROUND Haig Avenue, Southport, Merseyside. PR8 6JZ
Ground: 01704 533422 Fax: 01704 533455 Ticket Office: 01704 533422

DIRECTIONS: From M6 - M58 through Ormskirk (A570) to Southport. Straight on at Tesco/McDonalds roundabout. Right at the mini r'about and the ground is on the right

Capacity: 6,008 **Seated:** 1,660 **Covered Terracing:** 1,100

Clubhouse: Open 6.00-11.00 every night and match days. Tel: 01704 530182

Club Shop: Scarves, replica kits and large range of souvenirs for sale.
Contact D Hitchcock, c/o Southport F.C or e-mail: derek@hitchcock98.freeserve.co.uk

PREVIOUS
Leagues: Conference, Northern Premier League, Football League, Lancashire Combination
Grounds: Ash Lane **Names:** Southport Central; Southport Vulcan

CLUB RECORDS
Attendance: 20,010 v Newcastle United, FA Cup - 1932
Record win: 8-1 v Nelson - 01.01.31 **Record defeat:** 0-11 v Oldham - 26.12.62
Career goalscorer: Alan Spence 98 **Career appearances:** Arthur Peat 401 - 1962-72
Transfer fee paid: £20,000, for Martin McDonald from Macclesfield Town - 1995
Transfer fee received: £25,000, from Rochdale for Steve Whitehall - 1991

BEST SEASON
FA Cup: Quarter Final, 1930-31,.1-9 v Everton (A) (The first Division 3 North team to reach the Quarter Finals)
League club defeated: Mansfield Town (1998-9) (as a non-league club)
FA Trophy: Runners-up 97-98, 0-1 v Cheltenham Town **League:** Football League Div. 3 23rd 73-74

HONOURS
FA Trophy R-up 97-98; Football League Division Four 1972/73 Runners-up 1966/67; Third Division North Section Cup 1937/38; Northern Premier League 1992/93, League Cup 1990/91, League Shield 1993/94; Liverpool Senior Cup 1930/31, 1931/32, 1943/44, 1957/58 (shared), 1963/64 (shared), 1974/75, 1990/91, 1992/93, 1998/99; Lancashire Senior Cup 1904/05; Lancashire Junior Cup 1919/20, 1992/93, 1996-97, 1997-98

Players P rogressing: Shaun Teale, Andy Mutch, Steve Whitehall, Tony Rodwell

Season	League	Div.	Pos.		Home					Away						
				P	W	D	L	F	A	W	D	L	F	A	Pts	Manager
02-03	Conference	-	21	42	6	8	7	31	32	5	4	12	23	37	45	Phil Wilson
01-02	Conference	-	15	42	9	6	6	40	26	4	8	9	13	23	53	Phil Wilson
00-01	Conference	-	4	42	9	5	7	33	24	11	4	6	25	22	69	Mark Wright
99-00	Conference	-	9	42	10	5	6	31	21	5	8	8	24	35	58	Paul Futcher / Mark Wright
98-99	Conference	-	18	42	6	9	6	29	28	4	6	11	18	31	45	Paul Futcher
97-98	Conference	-	16	42	9	5	7	32	26	4	6	11	24	32	50	Paul Futcher
96-97	Conference	-	11	42	8	5	8	27	28	7	5	9	24	33	55	Steve Joel / Ronnie Moore

Season	League	Div.	Pos.	P	W	D	L	F	A	Pts	Manager
95-96	Conference	-	6	42	18	12	12	77	64	66	Billy Ayre
94-95	Conference	-	3	42	21	9	12	68	50	72	Brian Kettle/Billy Ayre
93-94	Conference	-	4	42	18	12	12	57	51	66	Brian Kettle

Match Facts 2002-03

Date	Comp.	Opponents	Att.	Score	Goalscorers
17/08	Conf.	NUNEATON BOROUGH	1311	1 - 0	Whitehall 90
20/08	Conf.	Scarborough	1346	2 - 2	Lloyd-Williams 36, Thomson 74
24/08	Conf.	Forest Green Rovers	602	2 - 0	Grayson 15[og], Bauress 89
26/08	Conf.	KETTERING TOWN	1327	0 - 0	
31/08	Conf.	Gravesend & Northfleet	1054	3 - 1	Thomson 52[p] 74, Gibson 71
03/09	Conf.	LEIGH RMI	1097	4 - 2	Thomson 44 45, Pickford 50, Connolly 90
07/09	Conf.	FARNBOROUGH TOWN	1080	0 - 0	
14/09	Conf.	Telford United	812	0 - 2	
17/09	Conf.	Doncaster Rovers	3975	0 - 0	
21/09	Conf.	BURTON ALBION	1331	2 - 2	Soley 31, Lloyd-Williams 63
24/09	Conf.	HALIFAX TOWN	1008	2 - 0	Pickford 2, Soley 61
28/09	Conf.	Dagenham & Redbridge	1341	3 - 0	Soley 45[p] 79, Thompson 84
05/10	Conf.	Yeovil Town	4727	0 - 6	
08/10	Conf.	NORTHWICH VICTORIA	984	1 - 1	Lloyd-Williams 19
12/10	Conf.	WOKING	1023	5 - 1	Sullivan, Winstanley 62, Whitehall 78 85 87
19/10	Conf.	Margate	565	0 - 1	
22/10	LDV Vans 1N	LEIGH RMI	481	3 - 4	Whitehall 9 70 77
26/10	**F.A.C.** Q4	BRIDLINGTON TOWN	1004	4 - 1	Whitehall 37 47, Winstanley 52, Lloyd-Williams 62
02/11	Conf.	STEVENAGE BOROUGH	966	3 - 2	Nolan 14, Pickford 37, Thomson 73
09/11	Conf.	Hereford United	1646	2 - 0	Soley 51, Thompson 90
16/11	**F.A.C.** 1	NOTTS COUNTY	3519	4 - 2	Pickford 43 60, Thomson 75, Lane 90
23/11	Conf.	YEOVIL TOWN	1602	0 - 1	
30/11	Conf.	CHESTER CITY	2447	1 - 3	S Jones 61
07/12	**F.A.C.** 2	FARNBOROUGH TOWN	2534	0 - 3	
14/12	Conf.	Farnborough Town	591	1 - 2	Lane 61
17/12	Lancs MT 1	GREAT HARWOOD TOWN	n/k	4 - 1	S Jones, Scott, Gibson, Mulvaney
21/12	Conf.	TELFORD UNITED	853	1 - 1	Soley 41
26/12	Conf.	Morecambe	1954	0 - 3	
28/12	Conf.	SCARBOROUGH	1049	1 - 1	Soley 24
01/01	Conf.	MORECAMBE	1375	2 - 3	Edwards 60, Thompson 85
14/01	**F.A.T.** 3	Leek Town	428	2 - 1	Howell 16, James 33
18/01	Conf.	FOREST GREEN ROVERS	880	2 - 2	Pell 1 19
22/01	Lancs MT 2	Accrington Stanley	324	0 - 2	
25/01	Conf.	Kettering Town	1200	0 - 1	
01/02	**F.A.T.** 4	Dagenham & Redbridge	1307	0 - 0	
04/02	**F.A.T.** 4 rep	DAGENHAM & REDBRIDGE	569	2 - 2	Pickford 10, Soley 90 Won 4 3 after pens.
08/02	Conf.	GRAVESEND & NORTHFLEET	1003	1 - 1	Thompson 50[p]
11/02	Live SC 1	Prescot Cables	239	3 - 1	Johnson 12, Ray 15, Mulvaney 36
15/02	Conf.	Leigh RMI	565	1 - 1	Howell 24
22/02	**F.A.T.** 5	Gloucester City	1237	1 - 1	Scott 76
25/02	**F.A.T.** 5 rep	GLOUCESTER CITY	835	1 - 3	Thomson 12
01/03	Conf.	DONCASTER ROVERS	1265	0 - 4	
04/03	Conf.	Nuneaton Borough	774	2 - 3	Thomson 47, Jones 51
08/03	Conf.	Halifax Town	1544	4 - 3	Mulvaney 17 49 53, Pell 89
15/03	Conf.	DAGENHAM & REDBRIDGE	1002	2 - 3	Ashcroft 46, Howell 54
18/03	Conf.	Barnet	769	1 - 3	Wheatcroft 56
22/03	Conf.	Chester City	2292	0 - 2	
25/03	Conf.	Burton Albion	1402	0 - 1	
29/03	Conf.	BARNET	906	2 - 1	Ashcroft 36, Mulvaney 66
05/04	Conf.	Woking	1815	1 - 1	Thomson 78
12/04	Conf.	MARGATE	768	0 - 2	
19/04	Conf.	Northwich Victoria	700	1 - 2	Howell 90
21/04	Conf.	HEREFORD UNITED	1103	1 - 2	Pickford 59
26/04	Conf.	Stevenage Borough	2382	0 - 3	

PLAYING SQUAD

Goalkeepers: Steve Dickinson (Guiseley), Kevin Welsby (Leek T.).

Defenders: Martin Clark (Crewe Alexander), Barry Jones (York City), Ian Nolan (Wigan Ath.).

Midfield: Paul Haddow (Lancaster City), Steve Pickford (Stalybridge Celtic), Steve Soley (Carklisle Utd).

Forwards: Lee Ashcroft (Lancaster City), Chris Bennett (Lancaster City), Mark Byrne (Burscough), Lee Mulvaney (Youth Team), Peter Thomson (Luton T.), Paul Wheatcroft (Scunthorpe Utd), Steve Whitehall (Nuneaton Bor.), Andy Whittaker (Lancaster City)

SPENNYMOOR UNITED

Chairman & Press Off: Barrie Hindmarch

Vice Chairman: T. Metcalfe

Football Match Secretary
Brian Boughen,141 Durham Rd,
Spennymoor, Co.Durham. DL16 6JU
Tel: 01388 811874

Commercial Man: Des Beamson

General Sec.: Tom Metcalfe
Tel: 01388 811561

FOOTBALL MANAGEMENT TEAM

Manager: Alex Mathie
Coach: Jason Ainsley
Physio: Peter Carey

FACT FILE

Founded: 1904
Nickname: The Moors
Sponsors: T.B.A.
Club colours: Black & white stripes/black/white.
Change colours: All red
Midweek home matches: Tuesday
Reserve Team: None

2002-2003
Captain & Player of the Year: Jason Ainsley
Leading Goalscorer: Danny Brunskill

Pages: 44 Price: £1
Editor: Joan Wood

Local Press: Northern Echo; The Journal

GROUND Brewery Field, Durham Road, Spennymoor, County Durham DL16 6JN Tel: 01388 811934 Directions: From South; A1(M), A167, A688,straight on at mini-r'bout, 3rd exit at next large r'bout (St Andrews church opposite), pass Asda on left, straight on at junction, pass Salvin Arms (Durham Rd), ground 200 yds on left. From A167North - leave at Croxdale (N.E.S.S. factory), right at cemetery on left - this is Durham Rd - ground half mile on right. Nearest rail stations are Durhamand Bishop Auckland (via Darlington)-buses from there.
Capacity: 7,500 **Seats:** 300 **Cover:** 2,000
Clubhouse: (01388 814100) Open eves. 7-11pm, Sat 12-11pm (matchdays only), Sun12-2 & 7-10.30pm. Bar snacks. Private functions. Tea bar in ground. **Club Shop:** Sells replica kit, memorabilia, programmes etc. Contact Mrs A. Plumer (01388 811640)

PREVIOUS **Leagues:** Northern 05-08 60-90; North Eastern 08-37 38-58; Wearside 37-38;Midland Counties 58-60; Northern Counties East 90-93. **Ground:** Wood Vue 1901-1904. **Names:** None.

CLUB RECORDS **Attendance:** 7,202 v Bishop Auckland, Durham County Challenge Cup 30/3/57.
Win: 19-0 v Eden Colliery, North Eastern Lge 6/2/37. **Defeat:** 0-16 v Sunderland`A', Durham Snr Cup 4.1.02 (H.T.: 0-10)
Goalscorer: Dougie Humble 200+ **Appearances:** Ken Banks 600+.
Fee Paid: £3,500 for Don Prattie (Gretna) **Fee Received:** £20,000 for Michael Heathcote (Sunderland, 88).

BEST SEASON **FA Trophy:** Semi Final 77-78
FA Cup: 3rd Rd 36-37, 1-7 v West Bromwich Albion(A). League clubs defeated : Hartlepool 27-28, Southport 75-76.

HONOURS Northern Premier Lg Cup 93-94 (Div 1 R-up 93-94); Northern Lg(6) 67-68 71-7273-74 76-79 (R-up(3) 74-75 79-81), Lg Cup(5) 65-66 67-68 79-81 86-87; Turney Wylde Cup 80-81; J R Cleator Cup 80-81 86-87; Northern Counties (East) Lg 92-93(Lg Cup 92-93); Durham Challenge Cup 29-30 44-45 45-46 53-54 62-63 67-68 72-7373-74 74-75 75-76 78-79 82-83 93-94 94-95 95-96 97-98; Durham Benevolent Bowl26-27 29-30 31-32 47-48 58-59 60-61; North Eastern Lg(4) 09-10 44-46 56-57 (Lg Cup 28-29).

Players Progressing: Over fifty, including: H. Hubbick (Burnley, 3.25), T .Dawson (Charlton, 3.39), T. Flockett (Charlton, 4.49), J. Smallwood(Chesterfield, 12.49), J. Oakes (Aldershot, 5.54), J. Adams (Luton Town, 53),Alan Moore (Chesterfield), Michael Heathcote (Sunderland, 5.87), Jason Ainsley(Hartlepool, 94), Richie Alderson (York City 97), Graeme Paxton (Newcastle Utd 97)

Back row, left to right: Peter Carey (Physio), Steve Bell, Michael Robson, David Goodchild, Martin Kearney, Jamie Pollock (Manager),Steve Hutt, Andy Shaw, Nicky Mohan, Leigh Grant and John Duffy (Assistant Physio). Front row: Ben Ryan, Stuart Brightwell, Jason Ainlsey (Assistant Manager), Chris Lynch, Steve Preen, Danny Brunskill, Neall Bishop and Anthony Woodhouse.

Date	Comp.	Opponents	Att.	Score	Goalscorers
31/08	**F.A.C.** P	CONSETT	161	4 - 0	Shaw 14 33, Brunskill 18, Jones 51
03/09	Unib. 1	KENDAL TOWN	181	1 - 0	Shaw 67
07/09	Unib. 1	Matlock Town	192	1 - 0	Shaw 87
10/09	Unib. 1	Farsley Celtic	79	1 - 1	Shaw 70
14/09	**F.A.C.** Q1	ASHINGTON	236	1 - 1	Lynch 68
17/09	**F.A.C.** Q1 rep	Ashington	263	2 - 1	Ainsley 43, Grant 72
21/09	Unib. 1	EASTWOOD TOWN	180	3 - 0	Lynch 26, Ainsley 75, Ryan 78
24/09	Unib. 1	WORKINGTON	148	2 - 1	Bell 37, Ainsley 39
28/09	**F.A.C.** Q2	ATHERTON COLLIERIES	226	5 - 0	Lee 41 88, Bell 45, Brunskill 60 78
02/10	Durham CC P	NORTON & STOCKTON ANCIENTS	109	6 - 4	Woodhouse 18, Brunskill 41 63, Jones 60 75, Ryan 80
05/10	Unib. 1	Kidsgrove Athletic	207	0 - 1	
08/10	Unib. 1	TRAFFORD	217	3 - 0	Woodhouses 4 72, Grant 85
12/10	**F.A.C.** Q3	Droylsden	342	0 - 0	
15/10	**F.A.C.** Q3 rep	DROYLSDEN	342	3 - 2	Ainsley 17, Lynch 76, Lee 89
19/10	Unib. 1	ALFRETON TOWN	262	1 - 2	Lynch 66
22/10	Durham CC 1	DURHAM CITY	235	3 - 2	Ainsley 65[p] 84, Woodhouse 81
26/10	**F.A.C.** Q4	Northwich Victoria	731	1 - 3	Shaw 84[p]
02/11	**F.A.T.** 1	WITTON ALBION	248	4 - 3	Beasley 26, Shan 43, Jones 56, Cullen 66
05/11	Unib. 1	Bamber Bridge	106	2 - 1	Lynch 5, Preen 22
09/11	Unib. 1	OSSETT TOWN	194	3 - 0	Shaw 6, Preen 72, Lynch 89
13/11	Durham CC 2	Sunderland Res.	447	2 - 1	Lynch 72, Lee 75[p]
16/11	Unib. 1	Leek Town	285	3 - 1	Ainsley 60, Bell 73, McPherson 83[og]
20/11	Lge Cup 2	Bradford Park Avenue	165	2 - 2	Woodhouse 47, Ainsley 119 4 5
25/11	Unib. 1	Guiseley	179	2 - 0	Lynch 31, Woodhouse 83
30/11	**F.A.T.** 2	HALESOWEN TOWN	268	1 - 1	Lee 67[p]
03/12	**F.A.T.** 2 rep	Halesowen Town	391	1 - 4	Woodhouse 12
07/12	Unib. 1	Radcliffe Borough	203	4 - 7	Bell 15, Lynch 33, Lee 69[p] 72[p]
10/12	Pres. Cup 1	BISHOP AUCKLAND	159	5 - 0	Shaw 6 80[p], Bishop 19, Brunskill 23, Brightwell 88
14/12	Unib. 1	Rossendale United	135	2 - 1	Brightwell 27, Preen 50
17/12	Unib. 1	Kendal Town	169	1 - 1	Woodhouse 83
21/12	Unib. 1	LEEK TOWN	227	2 - 1	Goodchild 44, Shaw 83
28/12	Unib. 1	Witton Albion	291	3 - 5	Johnson 7[og], Preen 34, Woodhouse 55
11/01	Unib. 1	North Ferriby United	131	2 - 2	Preen 86, Goodchild 90
14/01	Durham CC QF	Dunston Federation Brewery	n/k	0 - 3	
18/01	Unib. 1	NORTH FERRIBY UNITED	174	0 - 3	
25/01	Pres. Cup QF	Runcorn Halton	151	1 - 3	Preen 51
28/01	Unib. 1	STOCKSBRIDGE PARK STEELS	113	6 - 0	Preen 2 45, Cullen 27, Grant 46, Ainsley 50, Brunskill 70
08/02	Unib. 1	KIDSGROVE ATHLETIC	170	2 - 1	Shaw 28, Brunskill 64
11/02	Unib. 1	RADCLIFFE BOROUGH	199	0 - 2	
22/02	Unib. 1	Chorley	276	0 - 2	
25/02	Unib. 1	GUISELEY	156	2 - 1	Shaw 62 75[p]
01/03	Unib. 1	BELPER TOWN	167	3 - 0	Kennedy 3[og], Goodchild 15, Ainsley 69
04/03	Unib. 1	Trafford	86	3 - 0	Brunskill 5 19, Bishop 21
08/03	Unib. 1	BAMBER BRIDGE	178	3 - 0	Lynch 38, Ainsley 44, Brunskill 66
11/03	Unib. 1	BISHOP AUCKLAND	231	1 - 2	Bishop 27
15/03	Unib. 1	Belper Town	243	1 - 0	Woodhouse 55
18/03	Unib. 1	LINCOLN UNITED	139	3 - 1	Woodhouse 28 55 67
22/03	Unib. 1	CHORLEY	199	0 - 0	
25/03	Unib. 1	Lincoln United	101	2 - 0	Preen 12, Ainsley 88
29/03	Unib. 1	MATLOCK TOWN	209	1 - 1	Lynch 50
01/04	Unib. 1	Ossett Town	133	1 - 0	Aspinall 8[og]
05/04	Unib. 1	FARSLEY CELTIC	203	2 - 0	Mohan 9, Brunskill 33
08/04	Unib. 1	Alfreton Town	360	1 - 1	Bell 1
12/04	Unib. 1	Eastwood Town	117	1 - 0	Preen 82
15/04	Unib. 1	Workington	232	2 - 1	Preen 57[p] 85[p]
19/04	Unib. 1	ROSSENDALE UNITED	226	3 - 0	Lynch 9, Brunskill 18, Preen 89
21/04	Unib. 1	Bishop Auckland	494	2 - 3	Preen 45[p], Brunskill 61
24/04	Unib. 1	Stocksbridge Park Steels	190	3 - 0	Preen 13, Brightwell 20, Middleton 30[og]
26/04	Unib. 1	WITTON ALBION	424	3 - 0	Ainsley 24, Brunskill 30, Preen 52

PLAYING SQUAD

Goalkeeper: Martin Kearney (Frickley Ath.).

Defenders: Mark Foster (West Auckland T.), David Goodchild (Gateshead),Leigh Grant (Whitby T.), Gary Hobson (York City), Steve Hutt (Bishop Auckland), Nicky Mohan (Harrogate T.), Chyris Lynch (Gateshead).

Midfield: Graeme Atkinson (Tamworth), Steve Bell (Bishop Auckland), Neil Bishop (Gateshead), Nick Richardson (Harrogate), Michael Robson (Maske Utd), Carl Shippen (Sunderland).

Forwards: Stewart Brightwell (Durham City), Danny Brunskill (Bishop Auckland), Alex Mathie (PIckering T.), Steve Preen (Gateshead), Ben Ryan (South Shields), Andrew Shaw (Bishop Auckland), Anthony Shandran (Burnley)

STALYBRIDGE CELTIC

CLUB OFFICIALS

President: Roy Oldham
Chairman: Peter Dennerly
Vice Chairman: Dorothy Norton
Directors:
B McCallum, G Crossley, G Greenwood, J Dillon, R Gorski, P Fenton
Club Secretary: Martyn Torr
Tel: 07860 841765
Football Sec. & Commercial Man.
John Hall
Tel: 0161 4560765(H) 0161 338 2828(W)
07813 864492 (M)
Press Officer: Keith Trudgeon
Tel: 0161205 7631 (B) 0161 304 8934 (H)
07767 404642

FOOTBALL MANAGEMENT TEAM

Manager: David Miller
Assistant Manager: Gerry Luczka
Sports Therapist: David Pover
Chief Scout: Ian Senior

2002-2003

Captain: Kevin Parr
Top Scorer & P.o.Y.: Phil Eastwood 30
+ P.o.Ys.: Dave German, Darren Bowman

PROGRAMME

Pages: 40 Price: £1.50
Editor: Nick Shaw Tel: 0161 633 1117

FACT FILE

Formed: 1909
Nickname: Celtic
Sponsors: Stepan & Tameside T.M.B.C.
Club colours: Blue & white/blue/ blue
Change colours: All Gold
Midweek matchday: Tuesday
Reserves' League: None
Local Press: Manchester Evening News, Manchester Evening News Pink (Sun. a.m.), Ashton Reporter, Ashton Advertiser
Local Radio: G.M.R. (BBC Manchester), 96.2 The Revolution

GROUND Bower Fold, Mottram Road, Stalybridge, Cheshire SK15 2RT
Tel: 0161 338 2828 Fax: 0161 338 8256. Club Website: www.stalybridgeceltic.co.uk

Directions: From Stockport and South: M60,M67 to end of Motorway through large roundabout to traffic lights.Then left to mini roundabout and left again into Mottram Road.Follow signs to Stalybridge, down hill and ground is on left next to Hare & Hounds pub.

Capacity: 6,108 **Seats:** 1,200 **Cover:** 1,200

Clubhouse: Open matchdays only. Food available **Club Shop:** Contact Bob Rhodes Tel: 01457 764044 (H)

PREVIOUSLeagues: Lancashire Comb. 1911-12, Central League 12-21, Football League 21-23, Cheshire County Lge 23-82, North West Counties 82-87, Northern Premier 87-92, 98-01, Conference 92-98, 01-02

CLUB RECORDS **Attendance:** 9,753 v WBA, FA Cup replay, 22-23 **Defeat:**1-10 v Wellington Town 9.3.4
Career goalscorer: Harry Dennison 215 **Win:** 16-2; v Manchester NE 1.5.26 & v Nantwich 22/10/326
Career appearances: Kevin Booth 354 **Goalscorer (season):** Cecil Smith 77 1931-32
Fee paid: £15,000 to Kettering Town for Ian Arnold 95 **Fee received:** £16,000 for Lee Trundle from Southport

BEST SEASON **FA Cup:** Second Round 93-94, 1-3 v Carlisle Utd.(A); 99-00 1-2 v Chester City (H). League clubs defeated: None
FA Trophy: 6th Rd.v Stevenage Borough 0-1 2001 02 **League**: 12th Conference 92-93

HONOURS Northern Premier Lge Prem Div 91-92, 00-01, R-up 90-91; Div.1 R-up 87-88; Cheshire County Lg 79-80, R-up 77-78 Lg Cup 21-22 R-up 46-47, 81-82; Challenge Shield 77-78, R-up 79-80, Res Div R-up 81-82; N.W. Cos Lg 83-84, 86-87, Lge Cup R-up 83-84, Champions v Cup Winners Trophy 83-84; Lancs Comb Div 2 11-12; Cheshire Snr Cup 52-53, 00-01 R-up 54-55, 80-81; Manchester Snr Cup 22-23, Intermediate Cup 57-58, 68-69, R-up 56-57, 67-68, 69-70; Challenge Shield 54-55, 00-01 (Junior Cup 62-63); Lancs Floodlit Cup 88-89, R-up 89-90; Reporter Cup R-up 74-75; Edward Case Cup 77-78.

Players progressing: Too numerous to list. but includes recently Eamoon O'Keefe, John Anderson, Lee Trundle

Celebrating the President's Cup triumph. **L - R - Back:** Gerry Luczka (Asst.Man.), Dave Miller (Manager), Marcus Hallows, Greg Pearce, Terry Bowker, Kenny Mayers, Craig Dootson, Darren Bowman and Phil Eastwood. **Front** Dave German, Chris Denham, Danny Hooper, Colin Potts (Covered!), Kevin Parr (Capt), Nathan Wharton and Ian Senior (Chief Scout).

Date	Comp.	Opponents	Att.	Score	Goalscorers
17/08	Unib. P	VAUXHALL MOTORS	486	2 - 2	Hallows 52 56
20/08	Unib. P	Harrogate Town	575	0 - 1	
24/08	Unib. P	Ashton United	702	1 - 1	Hallows 41[p]
26/08	Unib. P	COLWYN BAY	502	3 - 1	Eastwood 73, Hallows 81, Mayers 86
31/08	Unib. P	Runcorn Halton	397	0 - 1	
03/09	Unib. P	MARINE	429	2 - 1	Denham 42 88
07/09	Unib. P	ACCRINGTON STANLEY	790	1 - 4	Mayers 45
10/09	Unib. P	Hucknall Town	225	2 - 2	Hallows 89, Parr 90
14/09	Unib. P	Wakefield & Emley	372	0 - 0	
16/09	Ches. SC 1	Northwich Victoria	197	1 - 2	Parr 4
21/09	Unib. P	WHITBY TOWN	432	2 - 0	Eastwood 40 85
24/09	Unib. P	Barrow	870	0 - 1	
28/09	**F.A.C.** Q2	WORKINGTON	421	2 - 2	Potts 88, Denham 89
01/10	**F.A.C.** Q2 rep	Workington	378	1 - 3	Hallows 65
05/10	Unib. P	Altrincham	897	3 - 3	Denham 38, Parr 65, Wharton 78
08/10	Unib. P	HARROGATE TOWN	448	4 - 1	Eastwood 20, Mayers 36, Parr 48, Fitzgerald 53
12/10	Unib. P	LANCASTER CITY	433	1 - 0	Eastwood 14[p]
14/10	Unib. P	Marine	268	2 - 1	Denham 7, Mayers 45
19/10	Unib. P	GATESHEAD	522	4 - 4	Mayers 3, Eastwood 9 60, Parr 69
26/10	Unib. P	Colwyn Bay	250	1 - 1	Mayers 2
02/11	Unib. P	WAKEFIELD & EMLEY	563	0 - 0	
05/11	Unib. P	GAINSBOROUGH TRINITY	338	3 - 0	Eastwood 17 45, Parr 53
09/11	Unib. P	Worksop Town	687	1 - 1	Mayers 37
13/11	Unib. P	Accrington Stanley	892	1 - 4	Eastwood 13
16/11	Unib. P	DROYLSDEN	690	2 - 1	Eastwood 47, Denham 78
18/11	Lge Cup 2	Marine	174	0 - 2	
23/11	Unib. P	Blyth Spartans	317	4 - 1	Eastwood 10, Potts 25 42, Mayers 88
30/11	**F.A.T.** 2	ROTHWELL TOWN	473	2 - 0	Davies 23, Eastwood 62[p]
03/12	Unib. P	BARROW	511	4 - 3	Eastwood 7 9 53, Bowman 40
07/12	Unib. P	Whitby Town	313	2 - 1	Eastwood 14, Potts 46
10/12	Pres. Cup 1	WORKINGTON	159	4 - 1	Potts 34 57, Eastwood 48, Wharton 86
14/12	Unib. P	ALTRINCHAM	857	2 - 0	Scott 18[og], Pearce 37
26/12	Unib. P	Hyde United	909	1 - 0	Eastwood 36
28/12	Unib. P	BRADFORD PARK AVENUE	847	2 - 2	Davis 1, Eastwood 37[p]
01/01	Unib. P	HYDE UNITED	968	6 - 0	Mayers 12, Eastwood 21 75, Potts 65 80, Denham 89
14/01	**F.A.T.** 3	SCARBOROUGH	613	0 - 3	
18/01	Unib. P	ASHTON UNITED	826	4 - 1	Bowman 23, Eastwood 45 51, Denham 64
25/01	Pres. Cup QF	COLWYN BAY	411	3 - 0	Denham 9 66, Eastwood 90
08/02	Unib. P	BURSCOUGH	530	1 - 0	Denham 83
22/02	Unib. P	Gateshead	224	1 - 0	Wharton 22
01/03	Unib. P	RUNCORN HALTON	534	0 - 1	
04/03	Unib. P	Gainsborough Trinity	317	1 - 1	Hallows 1
08/03	Unib. P	WORKSOP TOWN	512	4 - 1	Hallows 22 30 77 85
12/03	Pres. Cup SF	Runcorn Halton	178	4 - 2	Wharton 13, Hallows 22, Eastwood 45 90
15/03	Unib. P	HUCKNALL TOWN	593	1 - 2	Eastwood 8
18/03	Unib. P	Frickley Athletic	183	0 - 1	
29/03	Pres. Cup F(1)	ASHTON UNITED	634	4 - 2	Mayers 9 22, Eastwood 62, Potts 88
01/04	Unib. P	Vauxhall Motors	229	1 - 2	Wharton 44
05/04	Unib. P	FRICKLEY ATHLETIC	415	3 - 1	Mayers 44, Potts 46, Denham 89
12/04	Unib. P	Lancaster City	299	1 - 0	Potts 45
16/04	Unib. P	Burscough	164	1 - 0	Eastwood 15
19/04	Unib. P	Bradford Park Avenue	329	1 - 2	Potts 75
21/04	Unib. P	Droylsden	537	1 - 1	Mayers 16
24/04	Pres. Cup F(2)	Ashton United	610	2 - 1	Wharton 54, Hallows 83
26/04	Unib. P	BLYTH SPARTANS	525	1 - 1	Hallows 83

PLAYING SQUAD

Goalkeeper: Craig Dootson (Leigh RMI).

Defenders: Terry Bowker (Bamber Bridge), Danny Caldicott (Atherton Collieries), Stephen Clegg (Manchester Utd), Jerome Fitzgerald (Rossendale Utd), David German (Leigh RMI), Gary Parkinson (Blackpool).

Midfield: Darren Bowman (Rossendale Utd), Adam Douglas (P.N.E.), Matthew Edgington (Prestwich Heys), Danny Hooper (Woodley Sports), Barrie Keeling (Radcliffe Bor.), Steve Lenagh (Hucknall T.),Dean Martin (Bradfortd P.A.), Kevin Parr (Glossop), Dave Ridings (Leigh R.M.I.), Nathan Wharton (Radcliffe Bor.).

Forwards: Tony Black (Accrington Stanley), Greg Brickhill (Atherton Collieries),Phil Eastwood (Southport), Steve Foster (Hyde Utd), Andy Payton (Burnley), Colin Potts (Lancaster City)

VAUXHALL MOTORS F.C.

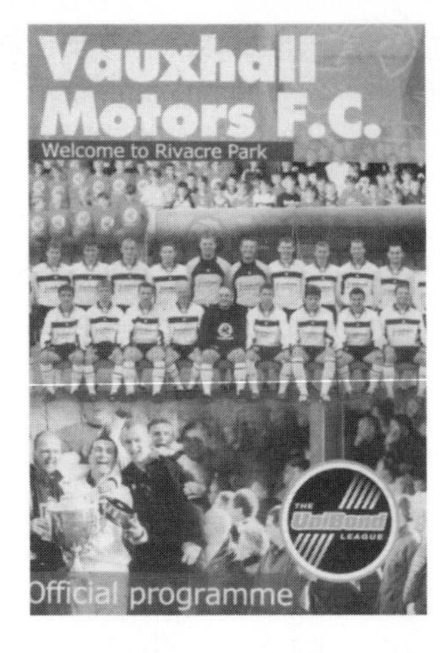

36 Pages
Programme Website Editor: Andy Wilson
Tel No; 077884 75516

CLUB OFFICIALS

President: G.White

Chairman: Len Jones

Vice Chairman: T.B.A.

Treasurer: Harry Deary

Secretary: Carole Paisey, 31 South Road, West Kirby, Wirral CH48 3HG

Tel & Fax No: 0151 625 6936

FOOTBALL MANAGEMENT TEAM

Manager: Alvin McDonald
Asst. Manager: Peter Carroll

FACT FILE

Formed: 1963
Re-formed 1995
Nickname: The Motormen
Club Sponsors: Lookers Wirral
Colours: White/navy blue/white
Midweek Matchday: Tuesday
Reserves' Lge: Wset Cheshire Lge.
Club Website:http:// www.vauxhall.co.uk

2002-2003

Captain: Phil Brazier
Leading Goalscorere: Terry Fearns
Player of the Year: Wayne McDermott

GROUNDVauxhall Sports Ground, Rivacre Road, Ellesmere Port, South Wirrall. CH66 1Nj
Tel 7 Fax: 0151 328 1114 (Ground) 0151 327 2294 (Club)
Email: admin@vauxhallfc.co.uk

Directions: M 53 junction 5, take the A41 to Chester. At the first set of lights (at Chimneys pub) turn left into Hooton Green. Follow to end and turn left at T-junction. Follow to the end and take right at the T-junction into Rivacre Rd. Ground is 250 yards on right.
Floodlights: Yes Clubhouse: Yes Club Shop: Yes Mrs J.Grimshaw (01948 860774)

HONOURS West Cheshire Lge Div 1 86, 95, 03 R-up 84, Div 2 84. W. Ches. Lge Bowl 68, Pyke Cup 2000, R-up 73, 01
N.W.C. Lge. 2nd Div 88-89 95-96; Raab Karcher Chall Cup 90-91;.NWC Challenge Cup 98-99, Division 1 99-00,
Unibond League Div 1 R-up 2001-02 Premier Division R-up 2001-2002
N.W.Co Floodlit Trophy Winners 99-00. Cheshire Amateur Cup R-up 87 ,94,2000
Wirral Senior Cup 87, R-up 83, 84, 95, 00; Wirrall Amateur Cup 86 R-up 87; Wirral Junior Cup 83

PREVIOUS **Leagues:** Ellesmer Port Lge., Wirral Combination, West Cheshire League 66-87, 92-95; North West Counties Lg 87-92, 95-00,
Names: Vauxhall Motors 63 -87, 93-95 Vauxhall GM 88-92, 95-99

BEST SEASON **FA Vase:** S-Final 99-00 v ChippenhamTown 0-1 aet (2 legs)
F.A.Trophy: 4th Round 2001-02 v Northwich Vics 0-4 & 2002-03 vWindsor & Eton (0-0 & 0-3)
F.A Cup: Second Round Proper v Macclesfield Town (0-2) after beating Q.P.R. (0-0 H, 1-1 A Won 4-3 after pens)

RECORDS **Attendance:** 1,500 v English F.A. XI, 1987

Back row left to right: Wayne McDermott, Terry Fearns, Phil Brazier (captain), Nicky Young, Liam Croxton, Steve Hilton, Chris Holmes, Matt Haddrell, Rob Lawton, Peter Cumiskey and Brad Cullen **Front row:** Carl Nesbitt, Paul Hart, Carl Spellman, Kevin Lynch, Alvin McDonald (Manager), Jon Paul Stanhope, Neil Rigby, Ian Horrigan and Kevin Thompson.

Date	Comp.	Opponents	Att.	Score	Goalscorers
17/08	Unib. P	Stalybridge Celtic	486	2 - 2	Aspinall 25, Welton 70
20/08	Unib. P	ALTRINCHAM	315	4 - 0	Haddrell 1 89, Fearns 15 19
24/08	Unib. P	WORKSOP TOWN	281	0 - 1	
26/08	Unib. P	Droylsden	311	1 - 1	Haddrell 2
04/09	Unib. P	Accrington Stanley	1032	1 - 2	Fearns 54
07/09	Unib. P	Gainsborough Trinity	326	1 - 2	Cumiskey 79
10/09	Unib. P	COLWYN BAY	247	2 - 3	Cumiskey 39, Lawton 50
14/09	Unib. P	HARROGATE TOWN	265	1 - 1	Aspinall 35
21/09	Unib. P	HUCKNALL TOWN	204	5 - 1	Fearns 7 45 89, Young 52 55
24/09	Ches. SC 1	WITTON ALBION	102	3 - 2	Welton 15 21, Thompson 87
28/09	**F.A.C.** Q2	Bedlington Terriers	280	2 - 1	Aspinall 54, Fearns 62
01/10	Unib. P	ASHTON UNITED	207	5 - 1	Young 29 79, Fearns 53 81 85
05/10	Unib. P	Barrow	977	2 - 1	Cumiskey 50 64
08/10	Unib. P	Altrincham	455	2 - 0	Fearns 4, Collins 81
12/10	**F.A.C.** Q3	GAINSBOROUGH TRINITY	228	6 - 1	Cumiskey 18[p] 89, Fearns 27, Haddrell 69 85, Lawton 75
19/10	Unib. P	BARROW	250	1 - 1	Fearns 63
26/10	**F.A.C.** Q4	Hucknall Town	385	1 - 1	Young 73
29/10	**F.A.C.** Q4 rep	HUCKNALL TOWN	401	5 - 1	Haddrell 17 44, Cumiskey 23[p], Young 40, Fearns 70
02/11	Unib. P	Lancaster City	316	2 - 1	Fearns 66 73
05/11	Unib. P	HYDE UNITED	205	1 - 0	Fearns 40
09/11	Unib. P	Blyth Spartans	318	5 - 2	Collins 17, Welton 71 80 89, Nesbitt 83
12/11	Unib. P	Runcorn Halton	401	5 - 0	Young 10, Cumiskey 39 62, Welton 58, Aspinall 90
13/11	Ches. SC QF	Crewe Alexandra	110	1 - 2	Robinson 52
16/11	**F.A.C.** 1	QUEENS PARK RANGERS	3507	0 - 0	Played at Chester City
19/11	Lge Cup 2	Ashton United	169	2 - 1	Fearns 48 72
23/11	Unib. P	Marine	324	2 - 1	Fearns 26 28
26/11	**F.A.C.** 1 rep	Queens Park Rangers	5336	1 - 1	Brazier 22 Won 4 3 after pens.
30/11	**F.A.T.** 2	FRICKLEY ATHLETIC	185	4 - 2	Morris 16[og], Cumiskey 82, Fearns 83, Welton 89
07/12	**F.A.C.** 2	Macclesfield Town	2972	0 - 2	
10/12	Lge Cup 3	CHORLEY	110	2 - 1	Cumiskey 47 75
14/12	Unib. P	GATESHEAD	222	3 - 0	Fearns 15 84, Young 87
21/12	Unib. P	WHITBY TOWN	220	3 - 2	Fearns 49 72, Cumiskey 67
26/12	Unib. P	Burscough	234	0 - 0	
28/12	Unib. P	WAKEFIELD & EMLEY	280	1 - 0	Fearns 3
14/01	**F.A.T.** 3	Leigh RMI	229	2 - 1	Fearns 2 12
18/01	Unib. P	Gateshead	204	2 - 3	Fearns 44, Haddrell 55
21/01	Unib. P	RUNCORN HALTON	254	2 - 1	Young 18 23
25/01	Lge Cup QF	ROSSENDALE UNITED	206	0 - 1	
28/01	Unib. P	Ashton United	180	1 - 2	Cumiskey 67[p]
04/02	**F.A.T.** 4	Windsor & Eton	351	1 - 1	Fearns 24
08/02	Unib. P	Whitby Town	317	2 - 1	Lynch 19, Young 86
11/02	**F.A.T.** 4 rep	WINDSOR & ETON	268	0 - 3	
15/02	Unib. P	DROYLSDEN	262	2 - 1	Cumiskey 10, Young 66
18/02	Unib. P	BURSCOUGH	208	1 - 0	Haddrell 15
22/02	Unib. P	Bradford Park Avenue	253	0 - 1	
25/02	Unib. P	Worksop Town	557	1 - 1	Brazier 54
01/03	Unib. P	FRICKLEY ATHLETIC	185	5 - 0	Fearns 8 86, Haddrell 36 84, Lynch 88
05/03	Unib. P	Hyde United	237	0 - 1	
08/03	Unib. P	LANCASTER CITY	214	6 - 2	Haddrell 5, Lawton 18, Young 49, Fearns 55 88, Cumiskey 86
15/03	Unib. P	Frickley Athletic	184	0 - 1	
22/03	Unib. P	BRADFORD PARK AVENUE	251	0 - 1	
25/03	Unib. P	Colwyn Bay	202	1 - 1	Cumiskey 14
29/03	Unib. P	GAINSBOROUGH TRINITY	175	1 - 0	Tomlinson 47
01/04	Unib. P	STALYBRIDGE CELTIC	229	2 - 1	Lynch 81, Fearns 84
05/04	Unib. P	Harrogate Town	355	2 - 2	Young 77, Lynch 87
12/04	Unib. P	BLYTH SPARTANS	153	0 - 1	
15/04	Unib. P	ACCRINGTON STANLEY	396	0 - 1	
19/04	Unib. P	Wakefield & Emley	161	1 - 1	Fearns 38
21/04	Unib. P	Hucknall Town	219	2 - 1	Fearns 31, Young 54
26/04	Unib. P	MARINE	254	1 - 1	McDermott 47

PLAYING SQUAD

Goalkeeper: Andrew Ralph (Kidsgrove Ath.).

Defenders: Phil Brazier (Rochdale), Ian Horrigan (Rhyl), Wayne McDermott (Leek T.), Andy McMullen (Burscough), Kevin Thompson (Heswall), Mike Tomlinson (Runcorn F.C.Halton), Derek Ward (Total Network Solutions).

Midfield: Danny Collins (Chester C.), Matthew Hogg (Bamber Bridge), Robbie Lawton (Caenarfon T.), Kevin Lynch (Prescot Cables), Neal McCann (Shrewsbury T.), Carl Nesbitt (Paulton R.), Jon Stanhope (Connahs Quay Nomads), Stuart Wright (Shell).

Forwards: Peter Cumiskey (Leigh RMI), Terry Fearns (St. Helens T.), Paul Hart (Altrincham), Tony Sullivan (Southport), Darren Vicary (Stalybridge Celtic), Nicky Young (Bromborough Pool)

WAKEFIELD & EMLEY

CLUB OFFICIALS

Chairman: **Peter Matthews.**
President: **Peter Maude**

Secretary/Press Officer: **T.B.A.**

FOOTBALL MANAGEMENT TEAM
Manager: Ian Banks
First Team Coach: John Peachey
Asst Manager: Jimmy Martin
Physio: Daryl Brook.

FACT FILE
Formed: 1903
Nickname: 'The Pewits
Sponsors: Eurotrail
Colours: Claret & Sky/blue/claret
Change Colours. White/navy/navy
Mid week matchday: Tuesday
Reserves' Lge: N. Co's E
Web: www.emlyyafc.free-online.co.uk
E.Mail:richard.poulain@btopenworld.com

GROUND Wakefield Wildcats RLFC., Belle Vue Stadium, Doncaster Rd., Wakefield
Tel. No: 01924 211611
Directions: Jct 39 M1 ,follow A636 to Wakefield, then A638 Doncaster Road
1 mile from town centre.
Capacity: 11,000 Cover: 5,000 Seats: 1,050
Clubhouse: (01924 848398). Members' social club open seven nights a week and Saturday & Sunday. Bingo, discos, occasional cabaret.
Club Shop: Yes .Contact Nancy Matthews

Pages: 34 Price: £1
Editor: Glyn Burns 01226292518
Local Press: Hudd'field Examiner, Hudd'field & Dist't Chronicle.,Wakefield Express
Local Radio: Radio Leeds, Radio Sheffield, Pulse FM, Huddersfield FM.,Ridings F.M.

HONOURS FA Vase Runners-up 87-88; Northern Premier Lge Div 1 R-up 90-91; Northern Counties E Lge 87-88, 88-89 (R-up 85-86); Yorkshire Lg 75-76 77-78 79-80 81-82(R-up(5) 72-74 76-77 78-79 80-81, Lg Cup 69-70 78-79 81-82, Div 2 R-up 69-0; Sheffield & Hallamshire Senior Cup 75-76 79-80 80-81 83-84 88-89 90-91 91-9297-98; Huddersfield Challenge Cup 82-83 83-84 85-86; Huddersfield Lg(4) 65-69.

PREVIOUS **Leagues:** Huddersfield; Yorkshire 69-82; Northern Counties East 82-89.
Names: Emley FC 1903-2002 **Grounds:** Emley Welfare Sports Ground

CLUB RECORDS **Attendance:** 5,134 v Barking, Amateur Cup 3rd Proper 1/2/69.
18,629 v West Ham Utd, at Upton Pk, 3rd Rd Proper 3/1/99.
Win: 12-0 v Ecclesfield Red Rose9-6-97 **Defeat:** 7-1 v Altrincham 25-4-98.
Goalscorer: Mick Pamment 305. **Appearances:** Ray Dennis 762.
Fee Received: £60,000 for Michael Reynolds (Ayr Utd 98)

BEST SEASON **FA Amateur Cup:** Third Round replay 69-70.
FA Vase: Runners-up 87-88 (Semi-Final86-87).
FA Trophy: Quarter Final 98-99
FA Cup: Third Round Proper 97-98 (1-2 v West Ham Utd) **League Club Defeated:** Lincoln City 1997-98

Players progressing: A Sweeney (Hartlepool Utd 79), G Cooper(Huddersfield Tn 84), J Francis (Sheffield Utd 88), S Smith (Crewe Alexandra1992), C Alcide (Lincoln City 95), C Hurst (Huddersfield Tn 97), G Hurst (Ayr Utd 98), M.Reynolds (Ayr United 1998)

Back row left to right: Daryl Brook (Physio), Ronnie Glavin (Manager), Paul David, Gary Hatto, Ryan Crossley, Mickey Norbury, Andy Wilson, Paul Cuss, Simeon Bambrook, Danny Day, Jimmy Martin (Assistant Manager) and John Peachey (Coach). **Front row:** Lee Ryan, Michael Reynolds, Steve Nicholson (Captain), Robert Tonks, MilesThorpe and Nicky Wood

Date	Comp.	Opponents	Att.	Score	Goalscorers	
17/08	Unib. P	MARINE	227	1 - 1	Rowe 22	
21/08	Unib. P	Gateshead	176	1 - 0	A Wilson 89	
24/08	Unib. P	Burscough	701	0 - 1		
26/08	Unib. P	HUCKNALL TOWN	298	1 - 1	Manousios 90	
31/08	Unib. P	Hyde United	333	1 - 0	David 44	
03/09	Unib. P	ASHTON UNITED	308	1 - 1	Wood 31	
07/09	Unib. P	Harrogate Town	427	2 - 1	Bambrook 41[p], Rowe 46	
10/09	Unib. P	ALTRINCHAM	318	2 - 1	Day 18, Bambrook 57	
14/09	Unib. P	STALYBRIDGE CELTIC	372	0 - 0		
17/09	Unib. P	Gainsborough Trinity	274	1 - 4	Bambrook 44	
21/09	Unib. P	Accrington Stanley	1455	1 - 1	Bambrook 86[p]	
24/09	Unib. P	BLYTH SPARTANS	211	1 - 1	Bambrook 67[p]	
28/09	**F.A.C.** Q2	Runcorn Halton	245	0 - 2		
01/10	Unib. P	Worksop Town	606	1 - 2	Rowe 70[p]	
05/10	Unib. P	COLWYN BAY	218	2 - 1	Thorpe 39, Rowe 69[p]	
08/10	Unib. P	GATESHEAD	271	2 - 1	Thorpe 60, Day 81	
15/10	Unib. P	Ashton United	185	2 - 2	Gomersall 6, M Wilson 8	
19/10	Unib. P	BRADFORD PARK AVENUE	449	2 - 0	Gomersall 16, Bambrook 43	
26/10	Unib. P	Altrincham	602	1 - 0	Tonks 58	
02/11	Unib. P	Stalybridge Celtic	563	0 - 0		
05/11	Unib. P	WHITBY TOWN	277	1 - 0	Day 89	
06/11	Sheff SC 2	SWINTON ATHLETIC	94	2 - 1	Manousios 44 49	Welfare Ground, Emley
09/11	Unib. P	Barrow	1211	1 - 1	Ryan 85	
12/11	Unib. P	HYDE UNITED	266	1 - 1	Bambrook 51[p]	
20/11	Lge Cup 2	GATESHEAD	108	1 - 3	Ryan 90	
23/11	Unib. P	Droylsden	261	0 - 1		
30/11	**F.A.T.** 2	SPALDING UNITED	230	5 - 0	Bambrook 8 59 81, Gomersall 18, Ryan 70	
04/12	Unib. P	Blyth Spartans	291	1 - 2	Day 2	
07/12	Unib. P	ACCRINGTON STANLEY	452	0 - 0		
14/12	Unib. P	Colwyn Bay	185	2 - 3	Bambrook 47[p], Gomersal 61	
21/12	Unib. P	Runcorn Halton	203	1 - 4	Thorpe 89	
26/12	Unib. P	FRICKLEY ATHLETIC	360	0 - 0		
28/12	Unib. P	Vauxhall Motors	280	0 - 1		
03/01	Unib. P	WORKSOP TOWN	442	1 - 0	Bradshaw 20[og]	
11/01	**F.A.T.** 3	BURTON ALBION	802	1 - 0	Senior 79	
18/01	Unib. P	BURSCOUGH	223	1 - 0	Senior 74	
25/01	Pres. Cup 1	FARSLEY CELTIC	176	2 - 1	Bambrook 50 85	
01/02	**F.A.T.** 4	HENDON	519	0 - 0		
04/02	**F.A.T.** 4 rep	Hendon	245	1 - 0	Wilson 113	
15/02	Unib. P	Hucknall Town	233	1 - 1	Ryan 83	
22/02	**F.A.T.** 5	Burscough	437	0 - 5		
25/02	Pres. Cup QF	KIDSGROVE ATHLETIC	68	5 - 1	Senior 68 102, Bambrook 96 110 116	
01/03	Unib. P	Lancaster City	249	2 - 5	Bambrook 66 90[p]	
05/03	Sheff SC QF	Maltby Main	n/k	3 - 5	Senior 10 41, Marton 86	
10/03	Unib. P	Marine	222	1 - 2	Senior 80	
15/03	Unib. P	Whitby Town	322	1 - 0	Wilson 76	
18/03	Pres. Cup SF	Ashton United	182	0 - 1		
22/03	Unib. P	LANCASTER CITY	188	1 - 4	Day 6	
29/03	Unib. P	BARROW	243	0 - 1		
02/04	Unib. P	HARROGATE TOWN	147	0 - 0		
09/04	Unib. P	Bradford Park Avenue	288	1 - 1	Day 7	
12/04	Unib. P	GAINSBOROUGH TRINITY	183	2 - 1	Adams 34, Thorpe 49	
15/04	Unib. P	RUNCORN HALTON	167	0 - 0		
19/04	Unib. P	VAUXHALL MOTORS	161	1 - 1	Adams 64	
21/04	Unib. P	Frickley Athletic	227	3 - 0	Bambrook 62[p] 78 83	
26/04	Unib. P	DROYLSDEN	176	2 - 2	Bambrook 59, Clarke 87	

PLAYING SQUAD

Goalkeeper: Paul Cuss (Huddersfield T.).

Defenders: Andy Brownrigg (Gainsborough T.), Steve Nicholson (Farsley Celtic), Richard Walker (Youth Team).

Midfield: Simeon Bambrook (Garforth), Paul David (Bradley Rangers), Gary Hatto (Frickley Ath.), Alex Higgins (Stalybridge Celtic), Chris Prasher (Youth Team), Phil Taylor (Brodsworth Welfare),Miles Thorpe (Frickley Ath.), Robert Tonks (Local Football), Andy Wilson (Ossett Albion), Mark Wilson (Ossett Albion).

Forwards: Danny Day (Ossett Albion), Craig Gomersall (Liversedge), Michael Reynolds (Leigh RMI), Chris Senior (Huddersfield T.), Steve Smith (Sheffield F.C.), Wael Nazha (Droysden)

WHITBY TOWN

CLUB OFFICIALS

Chairman: Graham Manser.
President: Brooks Mileson
Secretary: Charlie Woodward
6 Westlands Ave, Whitby,
North Yorks YO21 3DZ Tel: 01947 602312
Press Officer: Secretary

FOOTBALL MANAGEMENT TEAM

Manager: Harry A Dunn
Coach: Graham Robinson
Physio: Greg Henderson

FACT FILE

Formed: 1926
Nickname: Seasiders
Sponsors: Sports Net.
Colours: All Royal Blue
Change Colours: All white.
Midweek matchday: Wednesday
Reserve League: Teeside League

2002-2003
Captain: Graham Robinson
Top Scorers: Ian Ure & Aaron Wilford 22
Players of the Year: Lee Ure & Graeme Williams

Pages: 40 Price: £1.20
Editor: C Woodward (01947 602312)

Local Press: Whitby Gazette, Northern Echo.
Local Radio: Yorkshire Coast Radio

GROUND Turnbull Ground, Upgang Lane, Whitby, North Yorks
Fax: 01947 603779 Tel: 01947 604847

Directions: Take the A174 road from town centre.
Ground on offside travelling towards Sandsend.

Capacity: 3,200 Cover: 500 Seats: 300

Clubhouse: Mon-Fri 7-11pm, Sat 12-11pm, Sun 12-2 & 7-10.30.
Club Shop: Yes Contact the Secretary

PREVIOUS **Leagues:** Northern League 1926-97. **Name:** Whitby United (pre 1950). **Grounds:** None

CLUB RECORDS **Attendance:** 4,000 v Scarborough, N Riding Senior Cup 18.4.65
Win: 11-2 v Cargo Fleet Works 1950 **Defeat:** 3-13 v Willington 24.3.28
Career Goalscorer: Paul Pitman (382) **Career Appearances:** Paul Pitman (468)
Transfer Fee Paid: £2,500 for John Grady (Newcastle Blue Star 90)
Fee Received: £5,000 for Graham Robinson (Gateshead 97)

BEST SEASON **FA Vase:** Winners 97. **FA Amateur Cup:** Runner-up 1964-6 **FA Trophy:** QuarterFinals 1983-84
FA Cup: 2nd Round 83-84 v Wigan A (a) 0-1,1985-86 v York C (a) 1-3 League Clubs beaten: Halifax Town 1983-84

HONOURS : F.A Amateur Cup R-up 64-65; FA Vase 96-97; NPL Div 1 97-98; Northern Lge 92-93 96-97 (R-up 27-28 63-64 67-68 81-82 82-83), Lg Cup 28-29 63-64 69-70 76-77 84-85 95-96; Rothmans National Cup 75-76 77-78; Nth Riding SnrCup 64-65 67-68 82-83 89-90, 98-99; N Riding Bene Cup 92-93; J R Cleator Cup 84-85 92-93 95-96 96-97; Mickey Skinner Trophy [5], Unibond Presidents Cup R-up 99-00

Players Progressing: Malcolm Poskett (Hartlepool), Sammy Kemp (Huddersfield), Jimmy Mulvaney (Hartlepool, Barrow, Stockport), Bobby Veart (Hartlepool), Derek HamptonJ amie Burt, Trevor Smith, John Linacre & Phil Linacre (Hartlepool), Mark Hine (Grimsby). David Logan (Mansfield) Jamie Burt (Chesterfield).

L-R - Back Row: D Logan, M Swales, B Dixon, R Hore, B Linighan, D Campbell, M Kearney, S Nicholson, A Reed, P Campbell, T Hall, A Snills, C Woodward (Secretary), G Henderson (Physio)
Front: H A Dunn, (Manager), G Williams, A Gilzea, S Johnson, C Veart, L Ure, D McTiernan, S Swales, D Wheeler (Coach)

Match Facts 2002-03

Date	Comp.	Opponents	Att.	Score	Goalscorers
17/08	Unib. P	COLWYN BAY	317	1 - 0	Robinson 41
20/08	Unib. P	Ashton United	275	1 - 1	Robinson 45
24/08	Unib. P	Hyde United	284	3 - 3	Ure 61, Veart 69[p] 83[p]
31/08	Unib. P	BURSCOUGH	298	0 - 2	
03/09	Unib. P	HARROGATE TOWN	291	4 - 2	Ure 19, Veart 54[p], Zoll 84, Wilford 87
07/09	Unib. P	Barrow	1012	2 - 2	Ure 40, Zoll 62
10/09	Unib. P	BLYTH SPARTANS	326	4 - 4	Veart 55[p], Wilford 70, Campbell 89, Ure 90
14/09	Unib. P	GAINSBOROUGH TRINITY	308	3 - 0	Zoll 37 64 67
17/09	Unib. P	Worksop Town	672	0 - 0	
21/09	Unib. P	Stalybridge Celtic	432	0 - 2	
24/09	Unib. P	FRICKLEY ATHLETIC	275	3 - 1	Gildea 12, Wilfort 63 87
28/09	**F.A.C.** Q2	BRADFORD PARK AVENUE	517	0 - 4	
05/10	Unib. P	MARINE	294	2 - 0	Zoll 18, Campbell 70
08/10	Unib. P	ASHTON UNITED	274	3 - 2	Veart 4, Reid 52, Robinson 81
12/10	Unib. P	Frickley Athletic	157	7 - 1	Wilford 17 28 58, Veart 26, Zoll 57, Skelton 84, Ure 86
19/10	Unib. P	Altrincham	620	1 - 2	Veart 63
26/10	Unib. P	HYDE UNITED	302	3 - 2	Wilford 30 33 59
30/10	Lge Cup 1	Gateshead	132	3 - 6	Ure 28 57, Skelton 65
02/11	**F.A.T.** 1	Stocksbridge Park Steels	182	1 - 0	Gildea 44
05/11	Unib. P	Wakefield & Emley	277	0 - 1	
09/11	Unib. P	RUNCORN HALTON	299	0 - 3	
12/11	Unib. P	Hucknall Town	196	2 - 1	Gildea 1, Robinson 3
16/11	Unib. P	GATESHEAD	275	2 - 2	Wilford 45 53
23/11	Unib. P	Bradford Park Avenue	340	3 - 2	Wilford 23, Ure 29, Gildea 65
30/11	**F.A.T.** 2	Barrow	853	2 - 4	Dixon 11, Dunning 33
07/12	Unib. P	STALYBRIDGE CELTIC	313	1 - 2	Gildea 52
10/12	Chair. Cup 1	Frickley Athletic	70	1 - 2	Zoll 64
14/12	Unib. P	Marine	230	5 - 5	Wilford 1 52, Ure 5 40, Williams 86
17/12	N. Riding SC P2	Edgehill	176	4 - 0	Ure 2 13 57, Dunning 77 at Pickering Town
21/12	Unib. P	Vauxhall Motors	220	2 - 3	Ure 31 78
28/12	Unib. P	Lancaster City	295	1 - 0	Wilford 79
11/01	Unib. P	DROYLSDEN	265	5 - 2	Dixon 7 75, Zoll 49, Wilford 63 83
18/01	Unib. P	HUCKNALL TOWN	301	3 - 3	Veart 54 86[p], Wilford 81
27/01	N. Riding SC QF	YORK CITY	282	3 - 0	Reid 24, Robinson 55, Wilford 77
08/02	Unib. P	VAUXHALL MOTORS	317	1 - 2	Gildea 34
11/02	Unib. P	Blyth Spartans	328	3 - 2	Ure 27, Wilford 45, Williams 90
15/02	Unib. P	Harrogate Town	488	2 - 0	Gildea 33, Williams 90
22/02	Unib. P	ALTRINCHAM	402	0 - 1	
25/02	N. Riding SC SF	Scarborough	551	2 - 3	Ure 16 88
01/03	Unib. P	Droylsden	168	1 - 2	Ure 48
08/03	Unib. P	BARROW	357	1 - 1	Gildea 56
15/03	Unib. P	WAKEFIELD & EMLEY	322	0 - 1	
22/03	Unib. P	Accrington Stanley	1355	1 - 1	Robinson 51
29/03	Unib. P	Colwyn Bay	175	1 - 1	Ure 67
02/04	Unib. P	Runcorn Halton	102	1 - 1	Skelton 61
05/04	Unib. P	Gainsborough Trinity	414	1 - 0	Swales 89
06/04	Unib. P	ACCRINGTON STANLEY	566	0 - 3	
12/04	Unib. P	WORKSOP TOWN	326	0 - 1	
16/04	Unib. P	Gateshead	185	3 - 1	Wilford 45, Ure 51, Laws 75
19/04	Unib. P	LANCASTER CITY	293	2 - 3	Ure 23, Swales 41
21/04	Unib. P	Burscough	132	2 - 0	Robinson 23 26
26/04	Unib. P	BRADFORD PARK AVENUE	332	0 - 1	

PLAYING SQUAD

Goalkeepers: David Campbell (Gateshead), Marc Riches (Gatehead).

Defenders: Ben Dixon (Singapore), Kevin Graham (Rowntrees York), David Logan (Bishop Auckland), Scott Nicholson (Tow Law T.), Allan Price (Fishburn Park), Martin Reed (Gateshead),Tom Reid (Pickering T.), Mark Swales (Billingham Synthonia), Steve Swales (Halifax T.), Aaron Wilford (Scarborough), Graeme Williams (Guisborough T.).

Midfield: Keiran Darlow (Frickley Ath.), Ragiab Al Mgaryef (Libya), Alex Gildea (Scarborough), Martin Gray (Darlington), Adam Jewell (Scarborough), Danny Richmond (Shildon), Craig Veart (Spennymoor Utd).

Forwards: Richard Dunning (Blackburn R.), Graeme Robinson (Gateshead),Mark Salvati (York City), Glen Smith (Staithes F.C.), Lee Ure (Norton), Andrew Windross (Gainsborough T.)

WORKSOP TOWN

Pages: 28-32 Price: £1
Editor: Matt Halfpenny 01909 500491/500500

Local Press: Worksop Guardian, Worksop Star, Nottingham Football Post.
Local Radio: Radio Sheffield, Radio Hallam, Radio Lincoln,Trax FM

CLUB OFFICIALS

Chairman: Neil Hood
Club Secretary: Keith Illett, 2 Mount Ave., Worksop, Notts (01909 487934)
Company Secretary & Commercial Manager: Lisa Hamilton-Clark
Press Officer: Lisa Hamilton Clark

FOOTBALL MANAGEMENT TEAM

Team Manager: Steve Ludlam
Assistant Manager: Peter Rinkcavage
Physio: RTony Smith

FACT FILE

Formed: 1861
Nickname: The Tigers
Sponsors: D.T.H. Engineers
Colours: All Amber
Change colours: All Blue
Midweek matchday: Tuesday
Youth Teams' Lge: Central Mid.Res
U18s: Notts Imp.

2002-2003

Leading Goalscorer & Player of the Year:
Andy Todd (27 goals)

GROUND
Babbage Way, off Sandy Lane, Worksop, Notts S80 1UJ (01909 501911).
Directions: M1 jct 31 (from north) jct 30 (from south), follow Worksop signs,join A57 and follow signs for Sandy Lane Industrial Estate - ground on left. 5mins walk from station.
Capacity: 3,000 Cover: 1,000 Seats:1,000
Clubhouse: Tigers Club. Normal licensing hours. Pool, quiz nights, disco etc.
Club Shop: `The Tigershop' 30 page catalogue from S.Medlam01909 501911

PREVIOUS **Leagues:** Midland (Counties)1896-98 1900-30 49-60 61-68 69-74, Sheffield Assoc. 1898-99 1931-33, Central Comb. 33-35, Yorkshire 35-39, Central All. 47-49 60-61, Northern Premier 68-69,74-
Grounds: Netherton Road, Bridge Meadow, Central Ave. (pre 1989), The Northolme (Gainsborough Trin. - shared) 89-92.

CLUB RECORDS **Attendance:** 2,100 v Chris Waddle XI Linden Whitehead's testimonial 0 7.05.01
Goalscorer: Kenny Clark, 287 **Appearances:** Kenny Clark 347
Win: 20-0 v Staveley, 1/9/1894 **Defeat:** 1-11 v Hull City Res., 55-56. **Unibond Highest :** 12-0 v Frickley Ath.
Fee Received: £47,000 for Jon Kennedy, Sunderland May 2000 **Paid:** £5,000 for Kirk Jackson to Grantham Town, 98-99

BEST SEASON **FA Cup:** 3rd Rd: 07-08 v Chelsea (A) 1-9, 21-22 v Southend (H) 1-2, 22-23 v Spurs (A) 0-0, 0-9, 55-56 v Swindon (A) 0-1. 2nd Rd: 25-26, 1st Rd: 20-21, 26-27, 61-62, 78-79. **League Clubs defeated:** Rotherham T. 1894-95, Grimsby T. 94-95, Nelson 1921-22, Chesterfield 22-23, Coventry C. 25-26, Bradford C. 55-56. **FA Trophy**: Q,Final 1-2 v Forest Green 00-01

HONOURS N.P.L. Presidents Cup 85-86 95-96, Unibond Div One Runners-up 97-98, Unibond Premier Div. Runners-up 98-99,Unibond Chairman"s Cup:2001-02 Sheffield Assoc. Lg 1898-99, Sheffield & Hallamshire Snr Cup 23-24 52-53 54-55 65-66 69-70 72-73 81-82 84-85 96-97, Mansfield Charity Cup 22-23; Midland Cos Lg 21-22 65-66 72-73 (R-up 62-6366-67 73-74).

Players P rogressing: J Brown (Sheff Wed), G Dale (Chesterfield 48), A Daley (Doncaster 50), K Wood (Grimsby 51), H Jarvis (Notts Co. 51), B Taylor (Leeds 51), S Rhodes 51, D Gratton 52, A Hodgkinson 53, J Harrison 67 (Sheffield Utd), S Lloyd & P Marshall (Scunthorpe 54), A Rhodes (QPR 54), R Moore (Rotherham 55), H Mosby (Crewe 56), L Moore (Derby 57), H Bowery (Nottm Forest 75), T Moore (Rochdale 84), S Adams (Scarborough 87), D Moss (Doncaster 93), Jon Kennedy (Sunderland 00), K Jackson (Darlington 01).

L - R - Back Row: Andy Todd, Kevin Davies, Darren Roberts, Richard Dryden, Ian Bowling, Robert Pell, Paul Sykes, Andy Brownrigg, Mark Haran. **Front**: Steve Hawes, Richard Peacock, Matty Caudwell, Ryan Davis, Gavin Smith, Linden Whitehead, Alex Callery, Adam Muller, Gary Townsend. **Missing**: Ryan Ludlam, Darren Bradshaw, Neil Glasser.

Date	Comp.	Opponents	Att.	Score	Goalscorers
17/08	Unib. P	BURSCOUGH	523	0 - 2	
20/08	Unib. P	Frickley Athletic	394	3 - 1	Beesley 7, Roberts 28 84
24/08	Unib. P	Vauxhall Motors	281	1 - 0	Whitehead 68
26/08	Unib. P	HYDE UNITED	663	2 - 1	Smith 27, Peacock 36
31/08	Unib. P	Marine	339	2 - 1	Linighan 22, Ludlam 36[p]
03/09	Unib. P	BLYTH SPARTANS	738	1 - 1	Todd 8
07/09	Unib. P	RUNCORN HALTON	687	2 - 2	Roberts 45, Ludlam 78
10/09	Unib. P	Ashton United	255	4 - 1	Peacock 20, Roberts 27, C Smith 50, Ludlam 85
14/09	Unib. P	Lancaster City	398	4 - 1	Ludlam 43[p], Todd 49 73, Roberts 63
17/09	Unib. P	WHITBY TOWN	672	0 - 0	
21/09	Unib. P	BARROW	739	0 - 2	
25/09	Unib. P	Bradford Park Avenue	402	1 - 0	Muller 78
28/09	**F.A.C.** Q2	Horden Colliery Welfare	269	4 - 0	Roberts 58 90, Townsend 69 73
01/10	Unib. P	WAKEFIELD & EMLEY	606	2 - 1	Townsend 44, Todd 78
04/10	Unib. P	Hucknall Town	485	0 - 0	
12/10	**F.A.C.** Q3	Grantham Town	915	0 - 1	
19/10	Unib. P	Accrington Stanley	1134	1 - 1	Linighan 51
26/10	Unib. P	DROYLSDEN	639	4 - 1	Roberts 32 63, Townsend 49, G Smith 76
02/11	Unib. P	ALTRINCHAM	754	1 - 2	Todd 74[p]
06/11	Sheff SC 2	Grimethorpe Miners Welfare	n/k	4 - 1	G Smith 40, Townsend 92 102, Peacock 108
09/11	Unib. P	STALYBRIDGE CELTIC	687	1 - 1	Roberts 44
23/11	Unib. P	Harrogate Town	517	2 - 2	Townsend 41, Hawes 77
26/11	Lge Cup 2	Matlock Town	350	3 - 2	Todd 8, Muller 66 113
30/11	**F.A.T.** 2	SOLIHULL BOROUGH	555	4 - 2	Todd 39[p] 80, Smith 55, Kotylo 76
03/12	Unib. P	BRADFORD PARK AVENUE	571	7 - 1	Todd 26[p] 80, Muller 31, Hawes 33, Kotylo 38, Townsend 48, Whitehead
13/12	Unib. P	HUCKNALL TOWN	592	5 - 4	Townsend 36 72, Todd 45 48 70
17/12	Lge Cup 3	GAINSBOROUGH TRINITY	442	3 - 1	Ludlam 21, Todd 77[p] 90
26/12	Unib. P	Gainsborough Trinity	1240	2 - 4	Whitehead 76, Todd 90
28/12	Unib. P	GATESHEAD	636	2 - 0	Linighan 35, Roberts 89
03/01	Unib. P	Wakefield & Emley	442	0 - 1	
15/01	**F.A.T.** 3	Chester City	1393	2 - 1	Townsend 60, G Smith 90
18/01	Unib. P	COLWYN BAY	611	4 - 1	Roberts 7, Linighan 23, Todd 44, Whitehead 78
25/01	Lge Cup QF	Marine	256	0 - 1	
08/02	Unib. P	MARINE	607	2 - 1	Peacock 41, Todd 65
11/02	**F.A.T.** 4	HAYES	1064	2 - 3	Todd 85[p], Townsend 89
22/02	Unib. P	ACCRINGTON STANLEY	1063	1 - 4	Todd 23[p]
25/02	Unib. P	VAUXHALL MOTORS	557	1 - 1	Muller 60
01/03	Unib. P	Altrincham	738	4 - 2	Whitehead 20 36, Muller 57, Caldwell 87
05/03	Sheff SC QF	South Kirkby Colliery	n/k	5 - 1	Muller 5 37, Todd 22[p] 81, Whitehead 61
08/03	Unib. P	Stalybridge Celtic	512	1 - 4	Whitehead 67
11/03	Unib. P	FRICKLEY ATHLETIC	483	2 - 4	Todd 50, Muller 85
15/03	Unib. P	Colwyn Bay	247	2 - 0	McMahon 14[og], Caldwell 25
18/03	Unib. P	Burscough	204	2 - 3	Muller 35, Todd 62
22/03	Unib. P	ASHTON UNITED	478	3 - 2	Todd 12[p] 37, Townsend 53
25/03	Unib. P	Blyth Spartans	324	1 - 2	Little 16[og]
29/03	Unib. P	Runcorn Halton	242	0 - 3	
31/03	Unib. P	Hyde United	319	4 - 1	Muller 18 75, Hawes 31, Townsend 46
05/04	Unib. P	LANCASTER CITY	444	1 - 1	Peacock 22
07/04	Unib. P	Droylsden	184	1 - 0	Todd 82
12/04	Unib. P	Whitby Town	326	1 - 0	Barnard 42
15/04	Unib. P	Barrow	788	1 - 3	Townsend 37
19/04	Unib. P	Gateshead	178	3 - 2	Roberts 28, Caldwell 58, Townsend 74
21/04	Unib. P	GAINSBOROUGH TRINITY	523	0 - 1	
26/04	Unib. P	HARROGATE TOWN	517	1 - 2	Whitehead 22
29/04	Sheff SC SF	Stocksbridge Park Steels	400	4 - 0	Roberts 20 55, Whitehead 74, Caldwell 88
06/05	Sheff SC F	Doncaster Rovers	813	2 - 1	Barnard 24, Ludlam 87[p] (at Sheffield Wednesday)

PLAYING SQUAD

Goalkeepers: Ian Bowling (Kettering T.), Dave McCarthy (Hucknall T.), Ross Turner (Alfreton T.).

Defenders: Darren Beesley (Boston Utd), Darren Bradshaw (Stevenage Bor.), Kevin Davies (Telford Utd), Ryan Davis (Luton T.), Richard Dryden (Scarborough), Mark Haran (Kettering T.), Brian Linighan (Gainsborough T.), Ryan Ludlam (Sheffield Utd), Gavin Smith (Sheffield Wed.), Paul Sykes (Harrogate T.), Nicky Sood (Wakefield & Emley).

Midfield: Matthew Caudwell (Doncaster R.), Alex Callery (Glasshoughton Welf.), Neil Glasser (Burton A), Steve Hawes (Altrincham), Krystof Kotylo (Nuneaton Bor.), Richard Peacock (Chester City), Andy Todd (Eastwood T.), Linden Whitehead (Alfreton T.).

Forwards: Andy Gray (Grantham Town), Robert Pell (Southport), Darren Roberts (Tamworth), Gary Townsend (Youth Team), Andy Womble (Belper T.)

COLWYN BAY

Match Facts 2002-03

Date	Comp.	Opponents	Att.	Score	Goalscorers	
17/08	Unib. P	Whitby Town	317	0 - 1		
20/08	Unib. P	ACCRINGTON STANLEY	450	1 - 2	Furlong 65	
24/08	Unib. P	BARROW	346	3 - 4	Rigby 2, Jeffries 10, Moody 65	
26/08	Unib. P	Stalybridge Celtic	502	1 - 3	Jones 44	
31/08	Unib. P	DROYLSDEN	306	0 - 3		
07/09	Unib. P	MARINE	256	0 - 2		
10/09	Unib. P	Vauxhall Motors	247	3 - 2	Edge 62, Kissock 81, Stannard 89	
14/09	Unib. P	Hucknall Town	195	1 - 2	Hicks 21[og]	
17/09	Unib. P	RUNCORN HALTON	223	1 - 3	Kissock 58[p]	
21/09	Unib. P	GATESHEAD	237	2 - 3	Kissock 67, Furlong 75[p]	
24/09	Unib. P	Burscough	167	0 - 3		
28/09	FA Cup Q2	WEST AUCKLAND TOWN	235	4 - 0	Graham 13[p] 15 50, Limbert 90[p]	
01/10	Unib. P	HYDE UNITED	175	2 - 0	Kissock 45, Edge 52	
05/10	Unib. P	Wakefield & Emley	218	1 - 2	Limbert 87[p]	
09/10	Unib. P	Accrington Stanley	1367	0 - 2		
12/10	FA Cup Q3	RADCLIFFE BOROUGH	n/k	1 - 2	Limbert 14	
19/10	Unib. P	BLYTH SPARTANS	195	1 - 2	Graham 38	
22/10	Lge Cup 1	Burscough	123	3 - 1	Jeffries 14, Graham 27, Stannard 63	
26/10	Unib. P	STALYBRIDGE CELTIC	250	1 - 1	Limbert 53	
30/10	Unib. P	Bradford Park Avenue	234	2 - 4	Edge 30, Furlong 54	
02/11	FA Trophy 1	Rocester	108	2 - 0	Furlong 71 86	
05/11	Unib. P	LANCASTER CITY	149	1 - 1	Limbert 55[p]	
09/11	Unib. P	Frickley Athletic	147	0 - 3		
12/11	Unib. P	ASHTON UNITED	148	1 - 1	Limbert 47	
23/11	Unib. P	Gainsborough Trinity	327	1 - 2	Jones 78	
26/11	Lge Cup 2	Radcliffe Borough	85	2 - 3	Limbert 17, McIlvogue 60	
30/11	FA Trophy 2	Droylsden	221	2 - 1	Limbert 28, Graham 90[p]	
07/12	Unib. P	Gateshead	176	2 - 2	Caton 36, Moody 47	
10/12	Pres. Cup 1	ALTRINCHAM	115	2 - 1	Furlong 42 47	
14/12	Unib. P	WAKEFIELD & EMLEY	185	3 - 2	Furlong 23, Stannard 31, Graham 53	
21/12	Unib. P	HARROGATE TOWN	227	0 - 1		
26/12	Unib. P	Ashton United	186	2 - 2	Graham 50, Kissock 82	
28/12	Unib. P	ALTRINCHAM	447	2 - 3	Graham 25 36	
04/01	Unib. P	Hyde United	353	2 - 0	Graham 12, Lally 15	
11/01	FA Trophy 3	BLYTH SPARTANS	321	1 - 0	Furlong 81	
18/01	Unib. P	Worksop Town	611	1 - 4	Kissock 48	
25/01	Pres. Cup QF	Stalybridge Celtic	411	0 - 3		
01/02	FA Trophy 4	HAVANT & WATERLOOVILLE	351	0 - 2		
08/02	Unib. P	Droylsden	211	1 - 2	Graham 45	
15/02	Unib. P	FRICKLEY ATHLETIC	210	2 - 3	Limbert 85[p], Stannard 90	
22/02	Unib. P	Blyth Spartans	337	1 - 1	McIlvogue 11	
04/03	Unib. P	Lancaster City	232	0 - 1		
08/03	Unib. P	Harrogate Town	315	1 - 4	Furlong 34	
11/03	Unib. P	BURSCOUGH	145	1 - 3	Rogers 47	
15/03	Unib. P	WORKSOP TOWN	247	0 - 2		
17/03	Unib. P	Marine	233	0 - 0		
22/03	Unib. P	Barrow	854	1 - 2	Furlong 37	
25/03	Unib. P	VAUXHALL MOTORS	202	1 - 1	Stannard 58	
29/03	Unib. P	WHITBY TOWN	175	1 - 1	McIlvogue 49	
02/04	North WCC QF	PORTHMADOG	n/k	1 - 4	Evans 37	
05/04	Unib. P	HUCKNALL TOWN	188	3 - 6	Davies 49, Graham 80 82	
12/04	Unib. P	Runcorn Halton	113	2 - 6	Graham 78, Jones 90	(at Prescot Cables)
15/04	Unib. P	BRADFORD PARK AVENUE	118	2 - 0	Williams 48, McIlvogue 75	
19/04	Unib. P	Altrincham	560	2 - 4	Graham 68, Davies 80	
26/04	Unib. P	GAINSBOROUGH TRINITY	140	0 - 3		

HYDE UNITED

Match Facts 2002-03

Date	Comp.	Opponents	Att.	Score	Goalscorers
17/08	Unib. P	Gainsborough Trinity	337	2 - 4	Smith 10, Nolan 43
19/08	Unib. P	BRADFORD PARK AVENUE	436	3 - 1	Webster 60, Foster 67, Smith 90
24/08	Unib. P	WHITBY TOWN	284	3 - 3	Evans 13, Madin 53 63
26/08	Unib. P	Worksop Town	663	1 - 2	Foster 78[p]
31/08	Unib. P	WAKEFIELD & EMLEY	333	0 - 1	
02/09	Ches. SC P	NORTHWICH VICTORIA	211	1 - 3	Evans 25
07/09	Unib. P	Altrincham	696	1 - 4	Crookes 75
09/09	Unib. P	DROYLSDEN	371	1 - 3	Evans 28
14/09	Unib. P	BURSCOUGH	257	1 - 0	Hargreaves 70
18/09	Unib. P	Gateshead	146	1 - 2	Foster 86
21/09	Unib. P	Harrogate Town	387	1 - 3	Foster 33[p]
23/09	Unib. P	LANCASTER CITY	301	2 - 3	Foster 15, Evans 78
28/09	FA Cup Q2	TOW LAW TOWN	307	7 - 3	Foster 7 35 38, Evans 45 90, Ashwell 48, Eyre 66
01/10	Unib. P	Colwyn Bay	175	0 - 2	
05/10	Unib. P	FRICKLEY ATHLETIC	281	2 - 3	Eyre 21, Anthony 48
09/10	Unib. P	Bradford Park Avenue	301	1 - 5	Sadiq 79
12/10	FA Cup Q3	Barrow	1074	1 - 3	Hargreaves 22
14/10	Unib. P	BARROW	363	1 - 3	Evans 6
19/10	Unib. P	Marine	251	1 - 4	Foster 26
24/10	Lge Cup 1	TRAFFORD	182	2 - 1	Foster 8, Meszaros 42
26/10	Unib. P	Whitby Town	302	2 - 3	Foster 34, Hargreaves 70
28/10	Unib. P	RUNCORN HALTON	334	0 - 2	
02/11	FA Trophy1	Gateshead	122	2 - 0	Foster 29 89
05/11	Unib. P	Vauxhall Motors	205	0 - 1	
09/11	Unib. P	HUCKNALL TOWN	267	0 - 1	
12/11	Unib. P	Wakefield & Emley	266	1 - 1	Foster 34
16/11	Unib. P	Ashton United	353	1 - 2	Foster 58
18/11	Lge Cup 2	Altrincham	206	2 - 1	Hayder 3, Meszaros 11
24/11	Unib. P	ACCRINGTON STANLEY	652	3 - 3	Foster 39, Hulme 45, Hayder 64
30/11	FA Trophy 2	Leek Town	303	1 - 3	Ferguson 90
03/12	Unib. P	Lancaster City	244	1 - 4	Evans 44
07/12	Unib. P	HARROGATE TOWN	268	1 - 5	Foster 12
09/12	Lge Cup 3	Marine	104	0 - 1	
14/12	Unib. P	Frickley Athletic	119	0 - 0	
26/12	Unib. P	STALYBRIDGE CELTIC	909	0 - 1	
28/12	Unib. P	Blyth Spartans	421	3 - 1	Tee 39, Foster 62 85
01/01	Unib. P	Stalybridge Celtic	968	0 - 6	
04/01	Unib. P	COLWYN BAY	353	0 - 2	
18/01	Unib. P	Barrow	1036	0 - 3	
01/02	Unib. P	MARINE	307	0 - 2	
22/02	Unib. P	GAINSBOROUGH TRINITY	251	1 - 5	Evans 17
25/02	Unib. P	Hucknall Town	159	0 - 2	
05/03	Unib. P	VAUXHALL MOTORS	237	1 - 0	Wilson 16
15/03	Unib. P	ALTRINCHAM	485	0 - 2	
22/03	Unib. P	Droylsden	347	1 - 0	Ellis 71
29/03	Unib. P	Burscough	170	0 - 0	
31/03	Unib. P	WORKSOP TOWN	319	1 - 4	Wilson 90
09/04	Unib. P	Runcorn Halton	112	1 - 1	Coleman 3 (at Prescot Cables)
12/04	Unib. P	GATESHEAD	186	0 - 1	
18/04	Unib. P	BLYTH SPARTANS	255	1 - 1	Foster 33
21/04	Unib. P	ASHTON UNITED	325	1 - 1	Foster 3
26/04	Unib. P	Accrington Stanley	1290	0 - 1	

UniBond PVA can tackle anything.

DIVISION 1 FINAL LEAGUE TABLE 2002-03

			HOME					AWAY						
		P	W	D	L	F	A	W	D	L	F	A	Pts	GD
1.	Alfreton Town	42	11	5	5	51	29	15	4	2	55	30	87	47
2.	Spennymoor United	42	15	2	4	44	15	12	4	5	37	27	87	39
3.	Radcliffe Borough*	42	13	4	4	55	28	12	6	3	35	18	85	44
4.	North Ferriby United	42	13	5	3	40	16	10	4	7	38	29	78	33
5.	Chorley	42	13	4	4	47	21	8	6	7	33	30	73	29
6.	Belper Town	42	11	5	5	28	24	9	8	4	25	18	73	11
7.	Witton Albion	42	9	8	4	37	25	10	7	4	30	25	72	17
8.	Matlock Town	42	11	4	6	34	28	9	6	6	33	20	70	19
9.	Leek Town	42	11	4	6	33	24	9	5	7	30	22	69	17
10.	Workington	42	11	4	6	42	31	8	6	7	31	29	67	13
11.	Farsley Celtic	42	10	4	7	36	33	7	7	7	30	34	62	-1
12.	Kendal Town	42	10	5	6	34	22	8	2	11	34	36	61	10
13.	Bamber Bridge	42	9	3	9	28	24	6	6	9	27	35	54	-4
14.	Guiseley	42	6	7	8	36	30	8	4	9	32	33	53	5
15.	Bishop Auckland	42	9	8	4	36	30	4	2	15	22	53	49	-25
16.	Lincoln United	42	6	4	11	35	32	6	5	10	32	45	45	-10
17.	Stocksbridge PS	42	5	6	10	30	34	6	3	12	24	47	42	-27
18.	Rossendale United	42	8	1	12	36	46	4	4	13	22	42	41	-30
19.	Kidsgrove Athletic	42	7	4	10	27	33	2	7	12	22	38	38	-22
20.	Ossett Town	42	4	8	9	20	34	4	1	16	19	46	33	-41
21.	Eastwood Town	42	3	4	14	18	40	2	4	15	15	52	23	-59
22.	Trafford	42	5	4	12	22	39	0	2	19	12	60	21	-65

PROMOTION/RELEGATION PLAY-OFFS
SEMI FINALS

Chorley 5 - 2 Gateshead   Radcliffe Borough 1 - 0 North Ferriby United

FINAL

Radcliffe Borough 2 - 2 Chorley
(AET - Radcliffe Borough won 4-2 on penalties)

DIVISION ONE 02-03	1	2	3	4	5	6	7	8	9	10	11	12	13	14	15	16	17	18	19	20	21	22
1 Alfreton Town		1-1	1-2	4-1	1-3	4-1	2-0	1-3	4-3	2-0	1-2	2-2	2-0	3-4	5-1	3-2	3-0	1-1	1-1	6-1	1-1	3-0
2 Bamber Bridge	0-2		0-0	1-2	2-0	2-2	4-2	1-0	1-0	2-2	0-4	2-0	0-1	0-1	2-1	0-1	0-1	1-2	3-0	5-1	1-2	1-0
3 Belper Town	2-5	2-1		3-1	4-2	2-1	1-2	2-1	0-3	0-0	0-1	1-0	2-1	0-0	1-0	0-0	1-1	0-1	4-3	1-0	1-1	1-0
4 Bishop Auckland	0-0	2-2	2-2		2-1	3-0	1-1	1-1	2-0	1-0	1-1	1-1	1-5	1-3	3-1	1-3	5-3	3-2	2-1	2-0	0-0	2-3
5 Chorley	2-4	3-1	1-2	4-1		3-1	1-1	2-3	5-0	3-0	3-1	2-1	4-0	2-1	1-2	2-2	1-0	2-0	0-0	4-0	1-0	1-1
6 Eastwood Town	0-4	0-1	0-3	1-2	0-1		1-4	1-3	1-3	4-4	0-0	1-2	0-0	2-3	2-1	0-1	1-1	0-1	3-0	1-0	0-3	0-3
7 Farsley Celtic	0-3	2-1	0-1	3-0	3-3	2-1		2-2	0-1	5-4	4-3	4-1	1-5	0-1	1-0	1-1	1-0	1-1	2-0	4-3	0-1	0-1
8 Guiseley	2-2	3-3	0-0	7-0	2-1	4-0	0-1		1-2	0-0	2-2	4-0	0-3	1-2	2-6	0-0	3-1	0-2	1-2	2-0	0-1	2-2
9 KendalTown	4-1	0-1	2-1	3-0	4-1	1-0	0-1	2-1		1-1	1-0	0-3	0-0	3-3	2-0	0-1	2-0	1-1	0-1	4-1	1-2	3-3
10 Kidsgrove Athletic	0-1	2-1	0-2	3-1	1-0	0-1	1-3	1-1	3-1		0-4	2-4	2-3	2-0	1-3	0-0	1-2	1-0	2-3	2-0	2-2	1-1
11 Leek Town	3-2	0-1	4-0	3-1	2-1	2-0	1-1	1-0	1-0	1-0		2-3	1-0	2-2	1-0	1-2	2-2	1-3	3-2	1-1	1-2	0-1
12 Lincoln United	1-3	1-1	0-1	3-3	1-2	6-0	4-1	2-3	3-1	0-2	0-0		1-5	4-2	0-0	0-1	1-2	0-2	2-0	5-0	0-1	1-2
13 Matlock Town	2-4	1-0	0-0	4-2	2-2	1-0	2-2	1-2	1-5	2-0	0-1	1-2		1-0	1-0	2-1	3-3	0-1	2-0	3-1	2-0	3-2
14 North Ferriby Utd	2-2	2-0	0-0	1-0	1-1	5-0	2-0	3-1	1-0	1-0	4-1	2-1	0-0		7-1	4-2	1-0	2-2	0-1	1-0	0-1	1-1
15 Ossett Town	1-2	4-0	1-2	2-1	1-2	1-0	1-1	0-0	2-2	2-2	0-5	1-1	0-0	0-4		0-4	2-1	0-1	1-3	0-0	1-1	0-2
16 Radcliffe Borough	2-4	2-1	1-1	1-0	1-1	1-1	3-0	2-1	2-4	5-1	0-1	4-1	0-1	2-0	7-1		2-1	7-4	4-0	4-2	4-2	1-1
17 Rossendale United	3-4	1-3	0-4	3-1	0-1	2-3	4-3	1-4	1-4	1-0	1-0	3-3	1-0	2-1	0-1	1-3		1-2	6-3	3-1	1-3	1-2
18 Spenymoor United	1-2	3-0	3-0	1-2	0-0	3-0	2-0	2-1	1-0	2-1	2-1	3-1	1-1	0-3	3-0	0-2	3-0		6-0	3-0	3-0	2-1
19 Stocksbridge P.S.	2-3	1-1	0-0	3-1	1-4	2-1	1-3	2-3	1-1	3-4	0-1	1-1	1-1	1-2	2-0	0-1	5-1	0-3		2-0	1-1	1-2
20 Trafford	2-2	1-3	0-2	0-1	0-3	0-0	1-1	0-2	1-2	0-0	3-1	3-2	1-2	0-4	1-0	0-3	1-2	0-3	3-1		2-3	3-2
21 Witton Albion	1-2	1-2	1-1	1-0	1-1	1-1	2-2	5-0	3-1	1-0	0-0	1-2	0-4	1-1	2-0	2-2	2-0	5-3	1-1	4-1		2-1
22 Workington	0-3	3-3	2-1	2-2	1-1	7-2	0-1	1-0	2-1	2-1	0-1	5-1	2-1	2-1	2-1	1-3	2-1	1-2	1-2	3-0	3-3	

TOP GOALSCORERS

Lge	Cup	Tot	
36	9	43	Jody BANIM (Radcliffe Borough)
31	7	38	Gavin KNIGHT (Nth Ferriby Utd)
24	9	33	Mike MOSELEY (Witton Albion)
24	7	31	Mick GODBER (Alfreton Town)
21	1	22	Steve PREEN (Spennymoor Utd- inc 7 for Gateshead)
20	6	26	James TEVENDALE (Stocks'ge)
20	5	25	Dave WHITTAKER (Leek Town)

(In order of League Goals)

HIGHEST ATTENDANCE

908   Matlock Town v Alfreton Town   31/03/03

CLUB OF THE MONTH AWARDS

Aug	Alfreton Town	Jan	Ossett Town
Sept	Spennymoor Utd	Feb	Radcliffe Borough
Oct	Alfreton Town		
Nov	Alfreton Town	Mar	Bishop Auckland
Dec	Kidsgrove Athletic	Apr/May	Radcliffe Borough

BAMBER BRIDGE

CLUB OFFICIALS

President: **Arthur Jackson**
Chairman: **David Spencer**
Secretary : **David Rowland**
c/o B.B.F.C.
Commercial Manager: **Keith Brindle**

FOOTBALL MANAGEMENT TEAM

Manager: **Paul Byron**
Asst Manager: **Andy Farley**
Physio: **Andy Hosgood**

FACT FILE

Founded: 1952
Nickname: Brig
Sponsors: T.B.A.
Colours: White/black/black
Change Colours: Yellow/blue/yellow
Midweek Matches: Tuesday
Reserves' League: Lancashire Legue
Website: www.bamberbridge-fc,co.uk

2002-2003
Captain: Jez Baldwin Top Scorer: Mark Wane 14 P.o.Y.: Alex Porter

PROGRAMME

Pages: 36 Price: £1
Editor: Dave Rowland (01772 312987)

GROUND Irongate, Brownedge Road, Bamber Bridge, Preston, Lancs.PR5 6UX
Tel Nos: Club Office 01772-909690; Social Club 01772-909695; Fax No. 01772-909691

Directions: M6 Junct 29, A6 (Bamber Bridge Bypass) towards Walton-le-Dale, to r'bout, A6 London Road to next r'bout, 3rd exit signed Bamber Bridge (Brownedge Road) and first right. Ground 100 yds at end of road on left. Just over a mile from Bamber Bridge (BR).
Capacity: 3,000 Seats: 1008 Cover: 800 Club Shop: Yes
Clubhouse: On ground. Open all day Saturday matchdays, every evening and Sunday lunch. Refreshment cabin on ground serves hot & cold drinks & snacks etc during matches.

PREVIOUS
Leagues: Preston & District 52-90; North West Counties 90-93.
Grounds: King George V Ground, Higher Walton 1952-86. **Names:** None

CLUB RECORDS
Attendance: 2,300 v Czech Republic, Pre-Euro 96 Friendly.
Win: 8-0 v Curzon Ashton N.W.Co. 94-95. **Defeat:** Unknown
Fee Paid: £10,000 to Horwich R.M.I.for Mark Edwards.
Fee Received: £15,000 from Wigan Athletic for Tony Back, 1995.

BEST SEASON
FA Vase: Semi Final 91-92 (lost 0-2 on agg to Wimborne Tn).
FA Cup: 2nd Round Proper, 99-00, v Cambridge United (A) Lost 0-1

HONOURS
Nth West Co's Lge R-up 92-93 (Div 2 91-92, F'lit Cup R-up 91-92); Preston &Dist Lge(4) (R-up (3); Guildhall Cup 78-79 80-81 84-85 89-90, R-up 77-78 79-80 87-88; Lancs Amtr Shield 81-82, R-up 80-81 89-90; Lancastrian Brigade Cup 76-77 89-90 90-91; A.T.S.Lancs Trophy 94-95, R-Up 95-96, NPL Chall Cup 94-95; NPL 1st Div R-Up 94-95; NPL Prem Div Champ 95-96.

Back row, left to right: Billy Abbott, Stuart Shepherd, Jimmy King, Graham Bennett, David Hankin, Stuart Honor, Simon Woodward, Cyril Sharrock, Alex Porter, Andy Hosgood (physio) and Phil Brown.
Front row: Phil Robinson, Stewart Clitheroe, Mark Wane, Andy Farley (Assistant player-manager), Paul Byron (Manager), Dave Leaver, Danny Kent, Phil Miller and Jez Baldwin.

BELPER TOWN

BELPER TOWN FOOTBALL CLUB LTD.
Nailers
REVIEW
Official Matchday Programme Season 2003/04 £1.20
Main Club Sponsor
Glow-worm
Quality through design
UniBond League Division One
Chorley FC
Saturday 16th August 2003
Kick Off. 3.00 pm
Match Sponsors: Harvey's Bar, King Street, Belper

Pages: 32 Price £1.00
Editor:Dave Laughlin 01773 856556

Local Press: Belper News, Derby Evening Telegraph, Belper Express
Local Radio: BBC Radio Derby

CLUB OFFICIALS

Chairman: Phil Varney
President: T.B.A.
Secretary: Bryan Rudkin
12 Crown Terrace,Bridger Street,Belper,
Derbyshire DE96 1BD Tel: 01773 825468
(H) 07710 444195 (M)
Press Officer: Nigel Oldrini

FOOTBALL MANAGEMENT TEAM

Manager: Gary Marrow
Asst Manager/ Coach: Mark Ogley

FACT FILE

Formed: 1883
Nickname: Nailers
Colours: Yellow/black/black & yellow
Change colours: All white
Midweek home matchday: Tuesday
Reserves' League: Midlands Reg All
2002 -2003
Captain: Steve Kennedy
Top Goalscorer :Mark Ward
Players of the Year:
Dean Jones & Gary Ingham

GROUND

Address: Christchurch Meadow, Bridge Street, Belper DE56 1BA (01773825549).
Directions: From M1 North, Jnct 28 onto A38 towards Derby, turn off at A610 (Ripley/Nottingham), then 4 exit at roundabout towards Ambergate. At junction with A6 (Hurt Arms Hotel) left to Belper. Ground on right past traffic lights. 400 yards from Belper (BR)
Capacity: 2,640 Cover: 790 Seats: 350
Clubhouse: Open matchdays and for functions with bar and hot and cold food available.

PREVIOUS
Leagues: Central Alliance 57-61; Midland Co's 61-82, Northern Counies East 1982-97
Grounds: Acorn Ground prior to 1951
Names: None

CLUB RECORDS
Attendance: 3,200 v Ilkeston Town, 1955
Goalscorer: Mick Lakin 231 **Appearances:** Gil Rhodes
Fee Received: #2,000 for Craig Smith from Hinckley United **Fee Paid:** £2,000 to Ilkeston Town for Jamie Eaton. 2001
Victory: 15-2 v Nottingham Forest 'A'1956 **Defeat:** 0-12 v Goole Town 1965

BEST SEASON
FA Vase: Semi-final 94-95 **FA Amateur Cup:** Not entered
FA Trophy: 3rd Qual Rd 97-98
FA Cup: 1st Rd Prop 1887-88 v Sheff Wed. (H) 2-3 (4th Qual. Rnd 1957-58, 00-01 ,01-02)

HONOURS
Northern Counties East Lge 84-85, Midland Counties Lg 79-80; Central Alliance Lge 58-59; Derbys Snr Cup 58-59 60-61 62-63 79-80

Players progressing: None

L-R - Back Row: Dominic Crookes, Craig Ludlam, Mark Ward, Dean Jones, Gary Ingham, Micky Allsop, Andy Simpson, Andy Evans, Liam Walshe. **Front:** Neil Ashley, Sean Gummer, Lee Stratford, Steve Kennedy, David Brown (sponsor), Gary Marrow (Manager), Richie Butler, Chris Hilton, Darren Turner.

BISHOP AUCKLAND

CLUB OFFICIALS

Chairman: Terry Jackson
Vice-Chairman: T.B.A.
Secretary/Press Off.: Tony Duffy,
90 Escomb Road, Bishop Auckland,
Co. Durham, DL14 6TZ
Commercial Manager: T.B.A.

FOOTBALL MANAGEMENT TEAM
Manager: Brian Honour
Asst Mgr: Tony Boylan
Physio: T.B.A.

FACT FILE
Formed: 1886 Nickname: Bishops
SponsorsEBAC
Colours: All Sky & Navy blue
Change colours: Red & white.
Midweek home matchday: Wednesday.
Reserve Team: None.
Local Press: Northern Echo,
Evening Gazette, Newcastle Journal.
Local Radio: Radio Cleveland, Radio
Metro, Radio Newcastle, Century Radio
2002-03
Top Scorer: N.Maddison
Capt & P.o.Y.: Brian Rowe.

Pages: 28 Price: £1.20
Editor: Bobby Wake (01388 609428)

GROUND DETAILS

Address: C/o Shildon F.C. Dean Street, Shildon, Co.Durham Tel No: 01388 773877
Directions: As for Shildon F.C.
Clubhouse: Yes, B.A. Social Club 0138 8603686

PREVIOUS **Leagues**: N East Counties 1889-90/ Northern Alliance 1890-91/ Northern 1893-1988.

CLUB RECORDS **Attendance:** 17,000 v Coventry, FA Cup 2nd Rd 6/12/52. **Appearances:** Bob Hardisty.
Win: 12-3 v Kingstonian, Amateur Cup 55. **Defeat:** 0-7 v Halifax Tn FA Cup 2nd Rd 66-67.
Fee Paid: £2,000. **Fee Received:** £9,000 for David Laws from Weymouth.

BEST SEASON **FA Amateur Cup:** Winners 10 times **FA Trophy:** Quarter Finals 78-79, 88-89, 96-97, 99-00
FA Cup: 4th Rd 54-55, 1-3 v York City (H).
League clubs defeated: Crystal Palace, Ipswich 54-55, Tranmere 56-57.

HONOURS FA Amateur Cup 1895-96, 1899-1900 13-14 20-22 34-35 38-39 54-56 57-58 (R-up(8)01-02 05-06 10-11 14-15 45-46 49-51 53-54); Northern Lg(19) 1898-99 1900-02 08-10 11-12 20-21 30-31 38-39 46-47 49-52 53-5666-67 84-86, R-up (17) 78-79 86-87 96-97, Lg Cup(7) 49-51 53-55 59-60 66-67 75-76); D'ham Chall Cup 1891-92 98-99 1930-31 38-39 51-52 55-56 61-62 66-67 84-8585-86 87-88 96-97, 98-99 HFS Loans Lg Div 1 R-up 88-89. Plus tournaments in Isle of Man, Spain, Portugal etc

Players Progressing: B Paisley (Liverpool), F Richardson & S O'Connell (Chelsea 46 & 54), R Hardisty & K Williamson (Darlimgton 46 & 52), W Shergold (Newport 47), N Smith (Fulham 48), R Steel & K Murray (Darlington 50),A Adey (Doncaster 50), F Palmer & A Stalker (Gateshead 51 & 58), A Sewell(Bradford City 54), G Barker (Southend 54), J Major (Hull 55), H Sharratt(Oldham 56), F McKenna (Leeds 56), J Barnwell (Arsenal 56), D Lewis (Accrington Stanley 57), C Cresswell (Carlisle 58), W Bradley (Man Utd), L Brown(Northampton), P Baker (Southampton), M Gooding (Rotherham), K Nobbs & A Toman(Hartlepool), P Hinds (Dundee Utd), Jeff Smith (Bolton W.) 2001.Danny Mellanby (Darlington2001 M.Nelson (Bury) 2001

BRIDLINGTON TOWN

CLUB OFFICIALS

Company & Club Secretary:
Chris Bemrose, 16 North Back Lane,
Bridlington, E. Yorks. YO16 7BA
Tel: 01262 604036 (H & F) 01262 676836(B)
e-mail Admin@brudtownafc.freeserve.co.uk

President: Barrie Garton

Chairman & Man.Director:
Gary Wilkinson
Tel: 07767 402745

Directors: D. Wilkinson, C. Webb & D Brewer

Match Sec.: Jonathon Bemrose
Tel: 01262 673995 (H) 01262 408224 (B)

FACT FILE

Founded: 1994
Sponsors: Barton Engineering,
PBS Construction (N.E.) Ltd
Wilkinson Caravans
Colours: All Red
Change Colours: All White
Midweek Matchday: Tuesday
Website: www.bridtownafc.freeserve.co.uk

2002-03

Captain & P.o.Y.: Lee Harper
Top Goalscorer: Paul Palmer 30

40 pages Price £1.00
Editor: Jonathon Bemrose

GROUND Queensgate Stadium, Queensgate, Bridlington YO16 7LN
Tel: 01262 606879

Capacity: 3,000 Seats: 742 Covered Standing 250 Executive Boxes: 2 Floodlights: Yes

Directions **From south on A165** - Pass golf course, straight over lights. Turn right at r'about by B&Q. Turn left at next lights & over rlwy bridge. At r'about bear left and then straight on up Quay Road. After lights turn right into Queensgate & ground is 800yds on right.
From south & west via A614 (formerly A166) - Straight on at lights (Hosp. on right). At r'about straight on to mini-r'about & take 2nd exit rt.. Over the first lights,left at next lights into Queensgate.Ground 800yds on rt.

Clubhouse: Open every evening & all day Sat & Sun

Club Shop: open on matchdays only

FOOTBALL MANAGEMENT TEAM

Team Manager: Billy Heath
Asst Manager: Mark Carroll
Coach: Pete Smurthwaite

PREVIOUS **Leagues:** Driffield Lg.; East Riding County Lg., Northern Counties East -2003
Names: Grays Inn 1986, Greyhound F.C. 1988

CLUB RECORDS **Attendance:** 432 for an F.A. Sunday Cup Semi-Final 3.3.2000
Appearances: Neil Grimson 200+ (87-97)
Goalscorer: Neil Grimson
Win: 15-1 v Rudston (A), Driffield Lg Cup 94-95

BEST SEASON **FA Cup:** 4th Qual. Rd 02-03, 1-4 v Southport (A)
FA Vase: 6th Rd 02-03, 1-2 v Brigg Town (A)

HONOURS: E. Riding Sen. Co. Cup 96-97, 01-02. E Riding Co. Lg Div. 1 95-96, Sen. Cup 98-99; NCE Prem Div. Champions 02-03, Div1 R-up 2001-02, Presidents Cup R-up 01-02, Wilkinson Sword Trophy .01-02.

Back Row L-R: Pete Smurthwaite-Coach, Mark Carroll-Asst Manager, Tony Berry-Committee, Stuart Baldwin, Steve Heath, Kevin Smith, Jason Harris, Craig Wardale(GK), Nick Houghton, Gavin Kelly (GK), Craig Suddaby, Lee Jackson, Paul Palmer, Danny Drayton, Steve Robinson, Billy Heath-Manager, Barry Garton-President, Phil Bonnett-Committee.
Seated L-R: Joyce Norton-Committee, Peter Norton-Committee, Kirk Blake, Shaun Baker, Wayne Lewis, Lee Harper-Captain, Andy Taylor, Matt Edeson, Craig Burdick, Gary Wilkinson-Chairman/MD, Chris Webb-Director of Juniors.
Kneeling L-R: Paul Farley, Andy Thompson, Gary Wilkinson Junior (Mascot), Martin Thacker, Phil Harrison

CHORLEY

CLUB OFFICIALS

Chairman: Ken Wright

Commercial Manager: T.B.A.

Secretary / Press Officer:
Mick Wearmouth
6 Avondale Rd, Chorley, Lancs. PR7 2ED
Tel: 01257 271395

FOOTBALL MANAGEMENT TEAM

Player - Manager: Mark Molyneaux
Reserve Team Manager: Dave Tulloch

FACT FILE

Formed: 1883
Nickname: The Magpies
Sponsors: Lex - Auto
Colours:White & black stripes/black/black
Change colours: All blue
Midweek matchday: Tuesday
Reserve League: Lancashire League
Local Press: Lancs Evening Post, Chorley Guardian.
Local Radio: Radio Lancs.

2002-2003

Captain: & P.o.Y.: Ian Leather
Top Scorer: Andy Mason

PROGRAMME

Pages: 32 Price: £1.
Editor: John Newman

GROUND Victory Park, Duke Street, Chorley, Lancs Tel: 01257 263406
Directions: M61 jct 6, A6 to Chorley, going past Yarrow Bridge Hotel on Bolton Rd turn left at 1st lights into Pilling Lane, 1st right into Ashley St..,ground 2nd left. From M6; jct 27, follow signs to Chorley, left at lights,continue for 2 1/2 miles on A49, right onto B5251, on entering Chorley turn right into Duke Street 200yds after Plough Hotel. 1/4 mile from Chorley (BR).
Capacity: 4,100 Cover: 2,800 Seats: 900
Clubhouse: 01257 275662. Open every evening. Weekend entertainment, Snacks available
Club Shop: Yes.

PREVIOUS Leagues: Lancs Alliance 1890-94; Lancs 94-1903; Lancs Comb. 03-68, 69-70;Northern Premier 68-69, 70-72, 82-88; Cheshire County 72-82; GMV Conference 88-90.
Grounds: Dole Lane 1883-1901; Rangletts Park 01-05; St George's Park 05-20. Name: None

CLUB RECORDS **Attendance:** 9,679 v Darwen, 1931-32. **Goalscorer:** Peter Watson.
Fee Paid: Undisclosed to Marine for Brian Ross 1995. **Fee Received:** £22,500 for Paul Mariner (Plymouth, 1973).

BEST SEASON **FA Cup:** 2nd Rd 86-87 v P.N.E. (A) 0-5 after 2-2 at Blackburn, 90-91 v Shrewsbury Town (A) 0-1
League Clubs defeated in F.A. Cup : Wolverhampton W 1986-87 and Bury 1990-91 **FA Trophy:** Semi-Final 1995-96.

HONOURS Northern Premier Lg 87-88, Cheshire Co. Lg 75-76 76-77 81-82, Lancs Comb. 19-2022-23 27-28 28-29 32-33 33-34 45-46 59-60 60-61 63-64 (R-up 21-22 26-27 48-4962-63 64-65 65-66, Lg Cup 24-25 58-59 62-63), Lancs Lg 1896-97 98-99, Lancs Alliance 1892-93 (R-up 94-95), Lancs Jnr Cup 1894-95 1908-09 23-24 39-40 45-4657-58 58-59 60-61 63-64 64-65 75-76 79-80 81-82 82-83.

Players Progressing: Charles Ashcroft (Liverpool 1946),William Healey (Arsenal 49), Stan Howard (Huddersfield 52), Derek Hogg (Leicester 52), William Norcross (Southport 59), Micky Walsh (Blackpool 71),Paul Mariner (Plymouth 73), Graham Barrow (Wigan 76), Steve Galliers (Wimbledon77), Kevin Tully (Bury 80), Geoff Twentyman (Preston 83), Gary Buckley (Bury84), Chris Hunter (Preston 84).

Back row, left to right: Paul Eatock, Lee Wilkinson, Billy McCartney, Ian Leather and Paddy Kerr.
Middle Row: Mark Molyneaux (Manager), Phil Haslam (Kit Manager), Ian Bold, Ian Parke, Paul Varley, Anthony Hogan, Chris Patterson, Lee Southwood, Julie Anderson (Physio), Wayne Goodison (Assistant Manager) and Jack Kirkland (Chairman).
Front row: Darren Emmett, David Eatock, Brian Sneyd (Sponsor), Matt Wright and Danny Kent.

COLWYN BAY

CLUB OFFICIALS

Chairman: Henry Chapman

Directors:M.Roberts,R.Hayley,C.Chambers, Miss M Jones, Miss J.E.Jones

Commercial Manager: Carol Beard

Secretary : Mike Roberts, 18 Belgrave Road,Colwyn Bay, N.Wales
Tel Nos:01492 534724(H)
07887 782565 (M)

Press Officer: Andy Owens: 0161 4316938

FOOTBALL MANAGEMENT TEAM

Manager: Jimmy Mullen
Asst Manager: Bernard MackaY
Physio: Colin Edwards

FACT FILE

Formed: 1885
Nickname: Meredith & KirkhamSponsors: Bay View Centre
Colours: All Sky Blue.
Change colours: GoldReserve Team:
Midweek home matchday: Tuesday
Unofficial Club Website: www.cbfc.tk

2002-2003

Captain: Carl Furlong
P.o.Y.: Matthew Boswell
Top Scorer: Deinol Graham 16

Colwyn Bay
Clwb Pêl Droed Bae Colwyn

Pages: 28 Price: £1
Editor: Aled Williams(07748 788168)
Local Press: North Wales Weekly News, North Wales Pioneer.
Club Website: www.cbfc.skynow.co.uk

GROUNDLlanelian Road, Old Colwyn, N.Wales. Tel: 01492 514581
Email Address:CBFC@MIKEROBS.COMDirections: M55 North Wales Coast - approaching Colwyn Bay take 1st exit signposted Old Colwyn, left at bottom slip road, straight over r'bout into Llanelian Rd - ground half mile on right. 2 miles from Colwyn Bar BR station.
Capacity: 2,500 Seats: 250 Cover: 700
Clubhouse: Open matchdays only.
Club Shop: Yes - contact: Matthew Motram (01492 515951) Metal Badges: Yes

PREVIOUS
Leagues: Nth Wales Coast 01-21 33-35; Welsh National 21-30; Nth Wales Comb. 30-31; Welsh Lg (Nth) 45-84; North West Counties 84-91
Grounds: Eiras Park 1930-82; Llanelian Road 82-92; Northwich Victoria FC 92-93; Ellesmere Port Stadium94-95 (2 years in exile thro' dispute with FAW re League of Wales).

CLUB RECORDS
Attendance: 5,000 (at Eiras Park) v Borough United, 1964.
Goalscorer: Peter Donnelly **Appearances:** Bryn A Jones

BEST SEASON
FA Trophy: Quarter Finals 96-97.
F.A Cup: Second Round Proper 95-96 v Blackpool (A) 0-2. League club defeated: Wrexham(Welsh Cup)

HONOURS
Northern Premier Lg Div 1 91-92 (Div 1 Cup 91-92); North West Counties Lg R-up90-91 (Div 3 R-up 83-84, Lg Cup 88-89, Floodlit Cup 90-91; Welsh Cup SF 91-92;Welsh National Lg R-up 27-28 29-30; Nth Wales Comb. 30-31; Welsh Lg Nth 64-6582-83 83-84 (R-up 35-36 45-46 63-64), Lg Cup 27-28; Alves Cup 63-64; Cookson Cup 73-74 79-80 80-81 81-82 83-84; Barritt Cup 79-80 81-82 83-84; Nth Wales Coast Chal. Cup 30-31 31-32 81-82 82-83 83-84 95-96 97-98; Nth Wales Coast Jnr Cup 1898-99. North Wst Coast Cup 99-00.

Players progressing: Peter Suddaby (Blackpool), Gareth Davies (Wrexham).

Photo:
Ian Saunders,
Colwyn Bay FC
Website Administrator

FARSLEY CELTIC

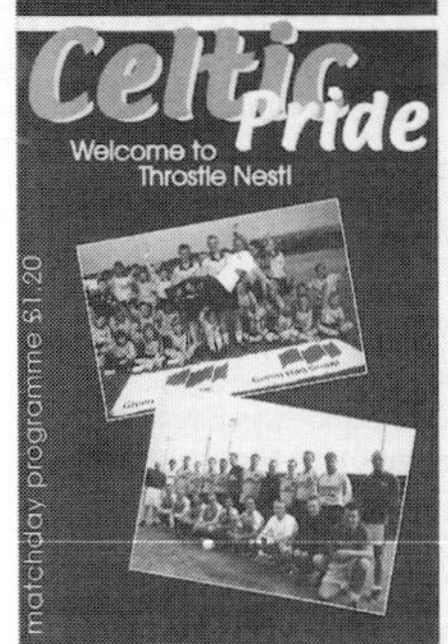

CLUB OFFICIALS

Chairman: John E. Palmer

Match Day Sec.: Nicholas Gill,
4 Victoria Gardens,Pudsey, Leeds LS28 7SP
Tel: 0113 2361633 (H) 07929 000872 (M)

FOOTBALL MANAGEMENT TEAM

Manager:Lee Sinnott

Reserves Manager: Gary Stokes

Coach: John Deacy

2002-2003

Captain: Chris Stabb

Top Scorer: Mick Midwood

FACT FILE

Formed: 1908
Nickname: Villagers
Colours: All Royal Blue
Change colours: All Yellow
Midweek home matchday: Tuesday
Reserves' League: Lancashire
Local Press: Yorkshire Evening Post, Telegraph & Argus, Pudsey Times
Local Radio: Radio Leeds, Radio Aire, Radio Pennine

PROGRAMME

Pages: 32 Price £1
Editor: Les Wood

GROUND: Throstle Nest, Newlands, Farsley, Pudsey, Leeds LS28 5BE Email: GRG LSL@aol.com
Directions: From North East: A1 south to Wetherby, A58 to Leeds, at 1st island (approx 8 miles) take 3rd exit (A6120 ring-rd), follow Bradford signs to 12th r'bout (approx 12 miles) - 1st exit (B6157 Stanningley). From M62 jct 26, M606 (Bradford) to r'bout, 4th exit (A6177) passing McDonalds on left, continue on Rooley Lane - Sticker Lane passing Morrisons store on left to lights (approx 3 miles) - right onto A647 (Leeds) to 2nd r'bout, 2nd exit (B6157 Stanningley). Continue 800yds passing Police & Fire Stations on left.Turn left down New Street at Tradex warehouse before turning right into Newlands. Ground at bottom of road. One mile from New Pudsey (BR)
Capacity: 4,000 Cover: 1,500 Seats: 300
Clubhouse: Lounge, games room and committee room Open every evening and Friday and weekend lunchtimes. New multi-purpose Leisure Centre available evenings and afternoons
Club Shop: League & non-League progs & magazines. Club badges, scarves,ties, sweaters, training suits, polo & T-shirts. Various souvenirs & photos. Contact: Brian Falkingham, 27 Rycroft Ct., Leeds LS13 4PE. 0113 255 0749 e-mail: clubshop@breathemail.net

PREVIOUS **Leagues:** West Riding County Amateur; Leeds Red Triangle; Yorkshire 49-82; Northern Counties East 82-87
Grounds: Red Lane, Farsley; Calverley Lane, Farsley (prior to 1948)

CLUB RECORDS **Attendance:** 11,000 (at Elland Road) v Tranmere Rovers, FA Cup 1st Rd 1974

BEST SEASON **FA Amateur Cup:** Third Round, 34-35
FA Cup: 1st Rd 74-75 (see above). Lost 0-2. **FA Vase:** Quarter Final 87-88

HONOURS West Riding County Cup 57-58 59-60 66-67 70-71 83-84 87-88 95-96 96-97 00-01; Yorkshire League 59-60 68-69 (R-up 57-58 58-59 70-71 71-72); Div 2 51-52;League Cup 62-63 63-64 66-67 96-97

Players progressing: Barry Smith (Leeds 1951), Paul Madeley (Leeds 1962),William Roberts (Rochdale 1988), Stuart McCall (Bradford City)

Back row left to right: Damien Place, Gary Shaw, Liam Sutcliffe, Damien Henderson, Paul Cuthbertson and Andy Lamb
Front row: Simon Brooker, Richard Hepworth, Liam Gray, Andy Shields and Chris Newton

GATESHEAD

CLUB OFFICIALS

Chairman: Mike Gulson

Vice Chairman: Bob Waggott

General Manager: John Young

Secretary: : Ray Kipling

Tel No; 07789 846333

Press Officer: Dean Ranyard

FOOTBALL MANAGEMENT TEAM

Manager : Derek Bell

Physio: Bev Dougherty

FACT FILE

Founded: 1930

Nickname: The Tynesiders

Sponsors: Logitog

Colours: White with black trim/ black/ white

Change colours: Claret & Blue

Midweek home matchday: Wednesday

Supporters' Unofficial Website:

www.gatesheadfc.co.uk

2002-2003

Captain: Gareth McAlindon

Top Scorer: David Colvin.

P.O.Y.: Rob Jones

Pages: 24 Price: £1.00

Editor: Ken Turner 07944 099280

Local Press: Gateshead Post, Newcastle Chronicle ,South Shields Gazette, Sunday Sun. Local Radio: BBC Radio Newcastle, Metro FM, Century Radio.

GROUND International Stadium, Neilson Road, Gateshead, NE10 0EF. Tel: 0191 478 3883 Fax : 0191 427 5211.

Directions: From the South follow A1(M) to Granada services (Birtley),take right hand fork marked A194(M) (Tyne Tunnel, South Shields) follow A194 to first roundabout, turn left onto A184 - then 3 miles to stadium. Turn right at traffic lights into Neilson Road. BY RAIL to Newcastle Central Station,transfer to the Metro System and then to Gateshead Stadium.

Capacity: 11,795 Seats: 11,795 Cover: 3,300

Clubhouse: Bar inside Tyne & Wear stand open before, during and after matches

Club Shop: Sells full range of souvenirs, badges, programmes & fanzines. Contact: Gerald Crowe 0191 3016265 (W)

PREVIOUS **Leagues:** Football League - Div. 3 N. 30-58, Div.4 58-60, Northern Counties League 60-62, North Regional League 1962-1968, Northern Premier 68-70, 73-83,85-86, 87-90; Wearside 70-71; Midland Lge 71-72; Alliance Premier (Conference)83-85, 86-87, 90-98. **Grounds:** Redheugh Park - 1930-1971

CLUB RECORDS **Attendance:** 11,750 v Newcastle United (Pre-Season Friendly. 7th August 95)

Win: 8-0 v Netherfield, Northern Premier League. **Defeat:** 0-9 v Sutton United, 22.09.90, GMVC.

Career goalscorer: Bob Topping **Career appearances:** Simon Smith, 450, 85-94

Fee paid: £9,000 for Paul Cavell (Dagenham &Redbridge). **Fee received:** For Kenny Cramman from Rushden & D.

BEST SEASON **FA Cup:** Quarter Final, 1952-53. v Bolton W (H) 0-1 **FA Trophy:** Quarter Final, 0-1 v Wycombe W. (A) 13.3.93

HONOURS Football League Div. 3 North R-up 31-32, 49-50; Northern Premier - Champions82-83, 85-86; Runners-up 89-90; Northern Premier League Cup R-up 89-90; 02-03Multipart Shield 85-86.

Players Progressing: Osher Williams(Southampton, Stockport, Port Vale, Preston), John McGinley (Sunderland,Lincoln), Billy Askew (Hull City, Newcastle United), Lawrie Pearson (Hull City,Port Vale), Ian Johnson (Northampton Town), Ken Davies (Stockport), Kenny Lowe(Birmingham C., Barnet, Darlington, Stoke C.), Rob Jones (Stockport Coun ty)

Back row left to right: R.Howe (Kit Manager), S. Preen, L.Ellison, R.Bowman, P.Thompson and R.Jones. **Middle Row:** T.Miller (Press Officer),A Waggott (Director), S.Bowey, J.Mohan, L.Fitzgerald, Triallist, A.Swan, C, Lynch,B. Dougherty (Physio)., T.Buckingham, M.Coulson,(Secretary) and T.Bone (Director). **Front row:** S.Johansen, G De Lella, P.Ross, S.Agnew, J.Gibson (Chairman), G.Gill (Asst Manager), R Watson,W. Edgcumbe G.McAlindon and R.Alderson

GUISELEY

CLUB OFFICIALS
Chairman: Philip Rogerson
Secretary: Bruce Speller
71 Oxford Avenue, Guiseley,
Leeds LS20 9BY
Tel: 01943 874534
Email: bruce.speller@virgin.net
Press Officer: John Martin
Tel: 01943 879473
Directors: P. Rogerson, S.Allen

FOOTBALL MANAGEMENT TEAM
Manager: Neil Parsley
Assistant Manager: Clive Freeman
Physio: Benn Gallagher

PROGRAMME
Pages: 40 Price: £1
Editor: Rachel O'Connor

FACT FILE
Formed: 1909
Colours:White/navy/white
Change Colours :Yellow/Navy
Midweek home matchday: Tuesday
Reserves' League: Lancashire League
Club Website: www.guiseleyafc.co.uk
Local Press: Yorkshire Evening Post, Bradford Telegraph & Argus, Airedale &Wharfedale Observer, Wharfe Valley Times

GROUND: Nethermoor, Otley Road, Guiseley, Leeds LS20 8BTTel: 0943 873223
Directions: Via M1 to M62 jct 28, follow Airport signs to junction of A65 at Horsforth. R-about turn left onto A65 through Rawdon to Guiseley centre. Ground 1/4 mile past traffic lights, on the right,entrance on A65 opposite Silver Cross factory. Further car parking available,frst right after ground, off Ings Crescent. 5 mins walk from Guiseley (BR/Metro) station.
Capacity: 3,000 Cover: 1,040 Seats: 427
Clubhouse: (01943 872872) Open before and after all games (closes 11pm). Snack bar within ground open before and during matches.
Club Shop: Sells programmes, various items of clothing, key rings, badges, mugs etc. Phone Jennifer Rogerson 01943 879236

PREVIOUS **Leagues:** West Riding Co. Amtr; West Yorks; Yorkshire 68-82; Northern Co's East82-91.

CLUB RECORDS **Attendance:** 2,486 v Bridlington Town, FA Vase Semi Final 1st Leg 89-90.

BEST SEASON **FA Cup:** First Round Proper 1994-95, 1-4 v Carlisle Utd. (at Valley Parade); 99-00, v Forest Green Rov. (A)
FA Vase: Winners 1990-91 (R-up 91-92, S.F. 94-95).
FA Trophy: Semi-Final 1994-95.

HONOURS FA Vase 90-91 (R-up 91-92), Northern Premier Lg Div 1 94-95 (Presidents Cup 94-95, Div 1 Cup 92-93), Northern Counties (East) Lg 90-91 (Lg Cup 90-91), West Riding County Cup(5 inc 94-95), Yorkshire Lg R-up 79-80 81-82 (Lg Cup 79-80).

Players Progressing: Keith Walwyn (York City), Frank Harrison (Halifax Town),Dean Walling (Carlisle United), Richard Annan (Crewe Alexandra). Dave Hanson (Halifax Town), Geoff Horsfield (Birmingham City)

HYDE UNITED

CLUB OFFICIALS
Chairman: Stephen Hartley
Secretary: Tony Beard,
30 Fishermans Close,Winterley, Sandbach,
Cheshire. CW11 4SW
Tel & Fax: 01270 212473
07778 792502 (M) See email below.
Commercial Manager: Paul Harrop
Tel No: 0161 368 1031

FOOTBALL MANAGEMENT TEAM
Manager: Steve Waywell
Assistant Manager: Tony Ellis
Physio: Danny Crawford
2002-2003
Captain: Mark Sertori
Leading Goalscorer: Steve Foster 21
Player of the Year: Steve Foster

PROGRAMME
Pages: 32 Price: £1.
Editor: Mark Dring 0161 336 8076

FACT FILE
Formed: 1919 Nickname: The Tigers
Club Sponsors: Allen Mills Howard Ltd
Colours: Red/white/red
Change All Sky Blue
Midweek home matchday: Monday
Website: www.hydeunited.co.uk
Local Press: Tameside Advertiser & Hyde Reporter.
Local Radio: GMR, Key 103 BBC ,GMR

GROUND Tameside Stadium, Ewen Fields, Walker Lane, Hyde SK14 5PL (0161 368 1031).
Directions: On entering Hyde follow signs for Tameside Leisure Park - in Walker Lane take 2nd car park entrance nr Leisure Pool, follow road around to the stadium. Quarter of a mile from Newton (BR). Train from Manchester (15 minutes)
Capacity: 4,130 Cover: 2,000 Seats: 660
Clubhouse: (0161 368 1621). Open most nights, 150 seats. +Sponsors Lounge for 70
Club Shop: Yes, selling normal range of products. Contact Tony Beard 07778 792502 email: beard@fishermans.fslife.co.uk

PREVIOUS **Leagues:** Lancs & Cheshire 19-21; Manchester 21-30; Cheshire County 30-68, 70-82; Northern Prem. 68-70

CLUB RECORDS **Att** 9,500 v Nelson, FA Cup 1952. **Scorer:** P O'Brien 247. **Appearances:** S Johnson 623.
Defeat: (as Hyde F.C.) 0-26 v Preston North End, F.A. Cup.
Fee Paid: £8,000 for Jim McCluskie (Mossley, 1989). **Fee Received:** £50.000 for Colin Little (Crewe Alexandra) 1995.

BEST SEASON **FA Cup:** 1st Rd 54-55(1-5 v Workington(A), 83-84 0-2 v Burnley (H), 94-95 1-3 v Darlington. (H)
FA Trophy: Semi Final 88-89 94-95 95-96

HONOURS Prem Inter-Lge Cup R-up (2) 88-90; NPL R-up(2) 87-89, 99-00 (Lg Cup 85-86 88-89 95-96(R-up 83-84 94-95), Chal. Shield 96-97, (R-up 86-87 90-91); Cheshire Co. Lg(3)54-56 81-82 (Lg Cup 33-34 52-53 54-55 72-73 81-82, Lg Chal. Shield(2) 80-82; Manchester Lg(5) 20-23 28-29 29-30 (Lg (Gilgryst) Cup(4) 27-29 49-50 70-71);Cheshire Snr Cup 45-46 62-63 69-70 80-81 89-90 96-97; Manchester Prem. Cup 93-94, 94-95, 95-96, 98-99,Snr Cup 74-75, Int Cup 55-56 56-57(jt), Jnr Cup 21-22 68-69;Lancs & Cheshire F'lit Cup(2) 54-56; Ashton Chal. Cup(6) 30-34 39-40 47-48;Hyde Chal Cup(2) 27-29; Reporter Cup(3) 72-74 75-76; Gavin Nicholson Mem Trophy79-80; Lancs F'lit Trophy(2) 86-88; Edward Case Cup(4), Unifilla Cup Winners: 99-00.
Players Progressing since 1980s: George Oghani (Bolton 1983), Kevin Glendon (Burnley 1983), Peter Coyne (Swindon 1984),Colin Little (Crewe Alex. 1995),Lutel James (Bury), Simon Yeo (Llincoln City 2002)

DIVISION ONE ACTION

ABOVE: Farsley's Amjad Iqbal holds off the challenge of Witton's Steve Cunningham. **Photo**: Darren C Thomas

BELOW: A real scramble in the Kendal goalmouth during their visit to Alfreton Town. **Photo**: Bill Wheatcroft.

KENDAL TOWN

CLUB OFFICIALS

Chairman: David Willan

President: M Macklin

Secretary: Craig Campbell, 34 High Sparrowmire,Kendal, Cumbria LA9 5PD Tel: 01539 734209 (H)

Match Sec: John Wharton 3 Vickers Hill, Kendal, Cumbria. Tel: 01539 734209

Press Officer: Peter Savage 01539 726488

FOOTBALL MANAGEMENT TEAM

Manager:Peter Smith

Asst Manager: Bruce Richardson

Physio: Stan Casey

PROGRAMME

Pages: 32 Price: £1.00

Editor: John Wharton (01539734209)

FACT FILE

F ormed: 1920

Nickname: Town

Colours: Black & white stripes/black/black

Change colours: All yellow

Midweek home matchday: Tuesday

Local Press: Westmorland Gazette Lancaster Evening Post

Local Radio: Radio Cumbria, The Bay.

GROUND Parkside Road, Kendal, Cumbria
Tel: 01539 727472

Directions: M6 junction 36, follow signs for Kendal (South), right at lights, left at r-bout to `K' Village - Parkside Rd on right opposite factory main offices - ground 400 yds. A mile & a half from Oxenholme (BR) station - bus service to `K' village, No 41 or 41A

Capacity: 2,490 Cover: 1,000 Seats: 250

Clubhouse: The Park, open all matchdays. Pies & pasties available

Club Shop: No

PREVIOUS **Leagues:** Westmorland; North Lancs; Lancs Combination 45-68; Northern Premier 68-83; North West Counties 83-87

CLUB RECORDS **Attendance:** 5,184 v Grimsby Town, FA Cup 1st Rd 1955
Goalscorer: Tom Brownlee. **Win:** 11-0 v Great Harwood 22/3/47. **Defeat:** 0-10 v Stalybridge Celtic 1/9/84
Fee Paid: Undisclosed for Tom Brownlee (Bradford C., 66). **Fee Received:** £10,250 for Andy Milner (Man. City 95)

BEST SEASON **FA Vase:** 3rd Rd 89-90 **FA Trophy:** 2nd Rd 80-81.
FA Cup: 2nd Rd replay 63-64, 1-4 v Chesterfield(A) after 1-1. 2nd Rd 49-50, 1st Rd 45-4648-49 52-53 54-55 55-56 64-65

HONOURS Lancs Comb. 48-49 64-65 (R-up 45-46 53-54 61-62 63-64, Lg Cup 55-56 60-61), Westmorland Snr Cup(12) 24-25 31-33 35-36 46-48 63-64 65-66 71-72 86-8789-89 90-91

Players progressing: John Laidlaw (Carlisle 1946), Louis Cardwell (Crewe 1947),Herbert Keen (Barrow 1953), Alec Aston (Preston 1955), Horace Langstreth(Torquay 1956), John Simpson (Lincoln 1957), Dennis Rogers (Accrington 1959),Tom Brownlee (Bradford City 1965), Peter McDonnell (Bury 1973), Keith Silken(Workington 1973), Roger Wicks (Darlington 1981), Andy Milner (Man City)

Back row, left to right: Bruce Richardson (Ass Man), Adam Tower, Lee Pennington, Richard Close (Captain), Lee Ward, Philip Hodgson, Andy Owen, Damian Corcoran, Lee Bowen, Peter Smith (Manager) and Stan Casey (Trainer). **Front row:** James Sheppard, Chris Park, Mike McKechnie, Dave Foster, Ryan Close (Mascot), Gary Prosser, Gareth Jones, Jamie Close,Ian Simpson

KIDSGROVE ATHLETIC

CLUB OFFICIALS

Chairman: Terry Hillman

Vice Chairman: Stan Brown

President: Ernie Langford

Secretary: Alan Thompson
7 Sandown Road, Crewe, Cheshire CW1 3TE
Tel: 01270 256588 (H) 07712 956400 (M)

FOOTBALL MANAGEMENT TEAM

Manager:Bernard Taylor
Physio: Graham Plant

FACT FILE

Formed: 1952
Nickname: "The Grove"
Colours: All Royal Blue with white trim
Change Colours: All yellow
Midweek Matches: Wednesday

PROGRAMME
Pages: 32 Price: £1
Editor: John Neisbett

GROUND: Clough Hall, Hollinswood Road, Kidsgrove, Stoke-on-Trent, Staffs
Tel: 01782 782412

Directions: M6 Jct 16, A500 towards Stoke, 2nd jctn onto A34 towards Manchester, turn right at 1st lights down hill,rt at lights into Cedar Rd , 2nd right into Lower Ash Rd, 3rd left into Hollinwood Rd to ground. BR Kidsgrove (5mins)
Capacity: 4,500 Seats: 400 Cover: 600 Floodlights: Yes

Clubhouse: Yes. Food matchdays. Seating 180 with Sky TV, Big Screen

HONOURS NWC Div. 1 97-98, 01-02; NWC Chall. Cup 97-98;
Mid Cheshire Lg 70-71,78-79 86-87 87-88, R-up 68-69 85-86; Lg Cup 67-68 69-70 85-86, R-up 84-85 86-87;
Staffs County Lge; Burslem & Tunstall Lge. Floodlit Trophy R-up: 1999

PREVIOUS **Leagues:** Burslem & Tunstall 1953-63, Staffordshire County 63-66, Mid Cheshire Lge. 66-90, North West Counties 90-2002.
Ground: Vickers & Goodwin 1953-60

BEST SEASON **FA Cup:** 1995, 1st Qualifying Round, 1-3 v Hinckley
FA Vase: Semi-Final 1997-98, 2-3 agg. v Tiverton Town

RECORDS **Attendance:** 1,903 v Tiverton Town, FA Vase S-F 1998.
Victory: 23-0 v Cross Heath W.M.C., Staffs Cup 1965
Transfer Fee Received: Richard Mitchell 2001-02 £3,000
Career Goalscorer: Scott Dundas 53 1997-98
Defeat: 2-7 v Glossop N.E., NWCL Div 1 93-94.

Players Progressing: Mark Bright (Crystal Palace), Ronnie Jepson (Port Vale).

L-R - Back Row: Dave Eaton, Darren Twigg, Chris Holmes, Wayne Mountford, Phil Traynor, Dale Hawtin.
Front Row: Paul Robertson, Steve Ashton, Danny Worthington, Steve Tobin, Andy Porter **Photo**: Bill Wheatcroft

LEEK TOWN

CLUB OFFICIALS

President: D.J.Bray

Chairman: Paul Burston

Directors:
Paul Burston, AlanClarke and Andy Wain

Secretary: Christine Osmond
10 Corporation St, Stoke on Trent ST44AU
Tel: 01782 847936 (H)

Commercial Manager: T.B.A.

Press Officer: Mike Cope

FOOTBALL MANAGEMENT TEAM

Manager: John Ramshaw

Assistant Manager: Mark O'Kane

Physio: Bill Allen & Dave Massey

FACT FILE

Founded: 1946
Nickname: The Blues
Club Sponsors: Kerrygold
Colours: All Blue
Change colours: All Yellow
Reserve team league: Manchester League
Midweek home matchday: Tuesday
Newsline: 0930 55 54 53
Press: Leek Post & Times, EveSentinel
Local Radio: Radio Stoke, Signal Radio

2002-2003

Captain: Wayne Johnson
Top Goalscorer: Dave Whittaker

GROUND Harrison Park, Macclesfield Road, Leek ST13 8LD
Tel: 01538 399278 Fax: 01538 399826

Directions: Opposite Courtaults chemical works on A523 Macclesfield to Buxton road half a mile out of Leek heading towards Macclesfield.

Capacity: 3,600 Seated: 625 Covered Terracing: 2,675

Club Shop: Contact Mark Graham at club on 01538 399278.

Clubhouse: `Blues' Bar openmatch days. Functions by request (01538 383734)

Programme
Pages: 40 Price: £1.00
Editors: Steve Reynolds & Tracy Cope

PREVIOUS **Leagues:** Staffs County, Manchester 51-54 57-73, West Mids (B'ham) 54-56,Cheshire County 73-82, North West Counties 82-87, Northern Premier 87-94 95-97,Southern League 94-95, Conference 97-99
Names: Abbey Green Rovers/ Leek Lowe Hamil. **Grounds:** None

CLUB RECORDS **Attendance:** 5,312 v Macclesfield Town, F.A. Cup Second Qualifying Round 73-74 **Win / Defeat:** Unknown
Transfer fee paid: £2,000 for Simon Snow (Sutton Town) **Transfer fee received:** £30,000 for Tony Bullock (Barnsley)
Career goalscorer: Dave Suttons 144 **Career appearances:** Gary Pearce 447.

BEST SEASON **FA Cup:** 2nd Rd 90-91, 0-4 v Chester (A) after 1-1 League clubs defeated: Scarborough 90-91.
FA Trophy: Runners-up 89-90, Q-F 85-86.

HONOURS FA Trophy R-up 89-90; Northern Premier Lg 96-97, R-up 93-94 (Div 1 89-90, Div 1Cup R-up 88-89, Presidents Cup R-up 93-94, Lg Shield 90-91); North West Co's LgCup 84-85 (Charity Shield 84-85); Cheshire County Lg 74-75 (Challenge Shield74-75); Manchester Lg 51-52 71-72 72-73 (Lg Cup 72-73); Staffs Snr Cup 95-96,R-up 54-55 81-82 95-96, Jnr Cup 51-52 70-71 (R-up 47-48 48-49 49-50)); StaffsCo. Lg 50-51 69-70 70-71 73-74 (R-up 47-48 49-50, Lg Cup 70-71 73-74); LeekPost Charity Shield 46-47; Leek Cup 47-48 52-53 70-71 71-72 (R-up 46-47); MayBank Cup 47-48 50-51 71-72; Hanley Cup 48-49 70-71 (R-up 49-5); Mid Cheshire LgDiv 2 87-88 (Div 2 Cup 87-88); Evans Halshaw Floodlit Cup Winners 93-94 94-95; Southern Lge Cup R-up 94-95; Unibond Lge Chall Cup R-up 95-96

Players progressing: Geoff Crosby (Stockport 52), Bill Summerscales (70), Mark Bright (81) & Martyn Smith (84) allto Port Vale, Paul Edwards (Crewe 89), Tony Bullock (Barnsley 97)

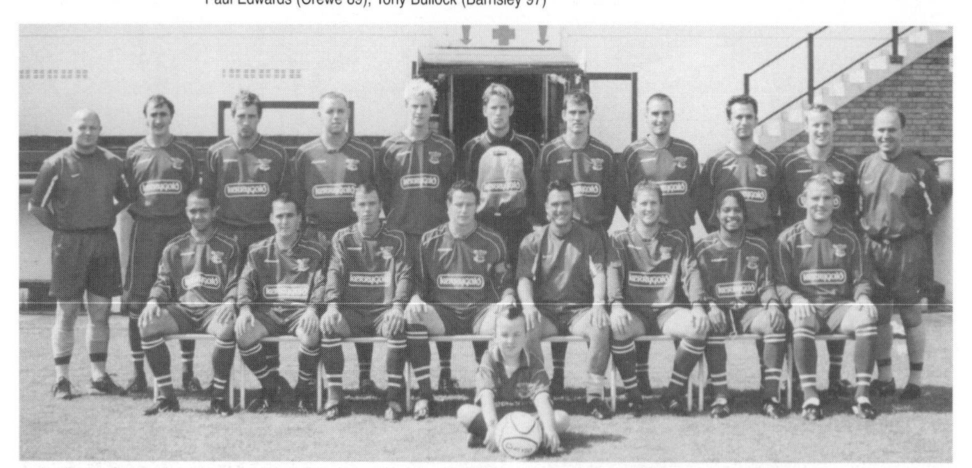

L-R - Back Row: Dave Massey (Physio), Dave Macpherson, Glyn Hancock, Gary Sucharewycz, James Byrne, Steve Hodgeson, Martin Ridey, Dave Whittaker, Danny Porter, Wayne Thornhill, Nick Cipolla (GK Coach). **Front**: Josh Ford, Colin Fletcher, Peter Wild, Wayne Johnson (Captain), John Ramshaw (Manager), John Hassall (Player/Asst. Man), Chris Bailey, Chris White. Mascot: Adrian Warnas.

LINCOLN UNITED

CLUB OFFICIALS

Chairmen: Robin Taylor & Maurice Bull
President: Phil Morley
Vice Chairman: T.B.A.
General Manager: Roy Parnham
Secretary/Press Officer: Peter Doyle
4 Roxborough Close,Lincoln LN6 0QL
Tel No: 07971 034693 (M)
e-mail: peterdoyle@arcasys.com

FOOTBALL MANAGEMENT TEAM

Managers: John Wilkinson
Physio:Mark Hicks

FACT FILE

Formed: 1938
Nickname: United
Colours: All white
Change Colours: All light blue
Midweek home matchday: Tuesday
Reserves ' League: Lincolnshire

2002-2003

Captain: Paul Miller
Top Scorer: Ian Williams
Player of the Year: Karl Horswood

£1
THE UniBond LEAGUE
UniBond
NORTHERN PREMIER LEAGUE Ltd
DIVISION ONE
LINCOLN UNITED FOOTBALL CLUB OFFICIAL PROGRAMME
Ground: Ashby Avenue Lincoln Tel: 01522 696400
LINCOLN UNITED FC

Programme
Pages: 40 Price:£1.00
Editor:G.Lines
Local Press: Lincolnshire Echo
Lincoln Standard

GROUND Ashby Avenue, Hartsholme, Lincoln Tel: 01522 690674
Directions: From Newark A46 onto Lincoln relief road (A446), right at 2nd r'bout for Birchwood (Skellingthorpe Rd), go for 1 mile passing lake and Country Park, 1st right 10yds after 30mph sign into Ashby Ave., ground entrance200 yds, opposite Old Peoples home. From north follow A57 via Saxilby until reaching A46 Lincoln Relief Road - continue on this and turn left at r'bout signed Birchwood then as above. 3 miles from Loncoln Central (BR)
Capacity: 2,714 Seats: 400 Covered: 1,084
Clubhouse: Open daily normal licensing hours. Matchday snack bar -hot &cold food & drinks
Club Shop: Yes. Contact:Secretary

PREVIOUS
Leagues: Lincs 45-48 60-67; Lincoln 48-60; Yorks 67-82; Northern Co'sEast 82-86, 92-95; Central Mids 82-92
Grounds: Skew Bridge (40s); Co-op Sports Ground (to mid 60s); Hartsholme Cricket Ground (to 82)
Name: Lincoln Amateurs (until an ex-pro signed in 1954)

CLUB RECORDS
Attendance: 2,000 v Crook Town, FA Amateur Cup 1st Rd Proper, 1968
Scorer: Tony Simmons 215 **Appearances:** Steve Carter 447
Win: 12-0 v Pontefract Colls 95. **Defeat:** 0-7 v Huddersfield Town FA Cup 1st Round Proper16-11-91
Fee Paid: £1000 for Paul Tomlinson (Hucknall Town ,Dec 2000)
Fee Received: £3,000 for Dean Dye (Charlton Ath., 7.91)

BEST SEASON
FA Cup: First Round Proper 91-92 (0-7 at Huddersfield Town), 97-98 v Walsall (0-2 Away)
FA Trophy: 3rd 3Rd **F.A.Vase:**

HONOURS
Northern Counties East - Prem Div. 94-95, Div 1 92-93, Div 1 Sth 82-83,Div 2 85-86, Presidents Cup 94-95; Yorks Lg 70-71 73-74 (Lg Cup 70-71); Lincs Lg 63-64; Lincs Snr `A' Cup 72-73 85-86 95-96, R-up 91-92 94-95, `B' Cup 63-6470-71; Central Mids Lg 91-92 (Wakefield Cup 90-91); Evans Halshaw Floodlit Cup R-up 92-93; Lincs I'mediate Cup(7) 67-73 80-81; Blankney Hunt Inter Lge 95-96,Cup 95-96 Lincs Sen Cup: R-up 97-98 Unifla Div 1 Cup R-up 97-98

Back row, left to right: R.Taylor (Chairman), G.Goddard (Manager), D. Bent, G.Lewis, G Pawson, S Cherry, L.Cooper, B.Brown, P.Watts, K.Horswood, P.Tittcomb (Asst.Manager) and P.Morley (President). **Front row:** M.Hicks (Physio), P.Muser, G Walters, I.Williams, D.Hopgreaves., G.Buckthorpe and R.Armstrong.

MATLOCK TOWN

CLUB OFFICIALS

Chairman: Darrell Holmes
Vice Chairman: Tom Wright
Chief Executive:: Keith Brown
`Barncroft', 1 Malvern Gardens
Matlock, Derbyshire DE4 3JH
01629 584231 (H)
Press Officer: Ian Richardson
Commercial Manager: Keith Brown

FOOTBALL MANAGEMENT TEAM

Manager: Ernie Moss Asst.Man: Sean O'Neil
Physio: Michael Cunningham

FACT FILE

Formed: 1885 Nickname: The Gladiators
Sponsors: T.Nutt & Sons (Carpets) Ltd.
& Westons of Wiirksworth (TV & Radio)
Colours: Blue/white/blue Change : All yellow
Midweek home matchday: Tuesday
Local Press: Matlock Mercury
Derbyshire Times, Derby Evening Telegraph,
Chesterfield Express & Sheffield Star
Local Radio: Radio Derby & Peak 107 F.M.

2002-2003

Captain: Chris James Top Scorer: Danny Holland P.o.Y.: James Lukic

GROUND Causeway Lane, Matlock, Derbyshire
Tel: 01629 583866 (& Fax)

Directions: On A615, 500 yds from town centre and Matlock (BR)
Capacity: 5,500 Cover:1,200 Seats: 560
Clubhouse: Gladiators Social Club, on ground, open matchdays only
Club Shop: Yes. Contact: Sue Tomlinson (01629 583866)

PROGRAMME
Pages 40 Price £1.00
Editor: Mike Tomlinson (01629 583866)
Website: www.matlocktownfc.co.uk

PREVIOUS **Ground:** Hall Leys (last century). **Leagues:** Midland Counties 1894-96; Matlock & District; Derbys Senior; Central Alliance 24-25 47-61; Central Combination 34-35; Chesterfield & District 46-47; Midland Counties 1961-69

CLUB RECORDS **Attendance:** 5,123 v Burton Albion, FA Trophy 1975
Win: 10 v 0 Lancaster (A) **74** **Defeat:** 0-8 v Chorley (A) 71
Career **Goalscorer:** Peter Scott. **Career** **Appearances:** Mick Fenoughty
Fee Paid: £2,000 for Kenny Clarke1996 **Fee Received:** £10,000 for Ian Helliwell (York)

BEST SEASON **FA Trophy:** Winners 1974-75
FA Cup: 3rd Rd 76-77. 1st Rd 1885-86 86-87 86-8787-88 1959-60 74-75 75-76 89-90
League clubs defeated: Mansfield Town 76-77

HONOURS Northern Prem Lge R-up 83-84, Lge Cup 77-78, Shield 78-79; Midland Counties Lge 61-62 68-69; Central All (North) 59-60 60-61, R-up 61-62 62-63,Div 1 Cup R-up 61-62, Div 2 59-60, Div 2 Cup 59-60 60-61; Derbyshire Sen Cup74-75 76-77 77 78 80-81 83-84 84-85 91-92, R-up 60-61 72-73 73-74 75-76 80-8181-82 82-83 89-90 93-94 97-98; Derbyshire Div Cup (North) 61-62 R-up 62-63;Evans Halshaw Floodlit Cup 88-89 91-92; Anglo-Italian Non-League Cup 79

Players progressing: Keith Haines (Leeds 1959), Wayne Biggins (Burnley 1984),Darren Bradshaw (Chesterfield 1987), Les McJannet (Scarborough 1987), Ian Helliwell (York 1987)

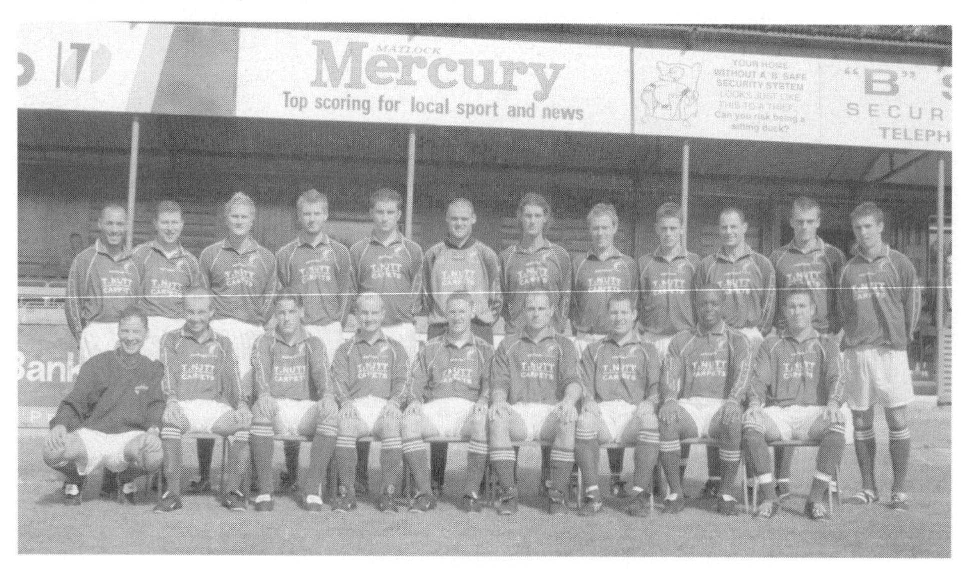

NORTH FERRIBY UNITED

CLUB OFFICIALS

President: Brian Thacker
Chairman: Les Hare
Vice Chairman: T.B.A.
Press Officer: Mike O'Brian
Secretary: Stephen Tather
16 Peasholme, Heads Lane, Hessle,
E Yorks HU13 0NY
Tel: 01482 642046 (H) Fax 01482 647244;
01482 351903 (B)

FOOTBALL MANAGEMENT TEAM

Manager: Brian France
Asst Mgr: Paul Olsson
Physio: Martin Woodmansey

FACT FILE

Founded: 1934
Nickname: United
Sponsors: Dransfield Developments
Colours: All white with green trim
Change colours: All yellow
Midweek matches: Tuesday
Reserves League: Humber Premier
Local Press: Hull Daily Mail

2002-2003

Captain & Po.Y.: Steve Fisher
Top Scorer: Gavin Knight 36

GROUND: Grange Lane, Church Road, North Ferriby HU14 3AA Tel: 01482 634601
Directions: Main Leeds-Hull road A63 or M62, North Ferriby is 8 miles west of Hull. Into North Ferriby, thru village passed the Duke of Cumberland Hotel, right down Church Rd, ground half mile on left. One mile from North Ferriby (BR)

Capacity: 3,000 Seats: 250 Cover: 1,000 Floodlights: Yes
Clubhouse: Bar, lounge, TV, pool open every night
Club Shop: Yes (Charles Hart (01482 6668550

PROGRAMME

Pages: 40 Price: £1.20
Editor: Dave Simmons Tel & Fax: 01482 632502

HONOURS FA Vase Finalist 96-97; Yorkshire Lg R-up 75-76, Lg Cup 74-75, Div 2 70-71;
N.C.E. Prem Div : Champions 99-00 R-up 97-98, Div 1 85-86 (Lg Cup R-up) 90-91 97-98,
Presidents Cup 90-91, 98-99, 99-00 Div 1 (North), R-up 82-83, Res. Div R-up 90-91;
E. Riding Snr Cup (11), E. Riding Church Lg 37-38

PREVIOUS **L eagues:** East Riding Church; East Riding Amateur; Yorks 69-82

BEST SEASON **FA Cup:** 3rd Q 97-98,98-99 **F.A.Trophy:** 4th Ropund 2001-02 **FA Vase:** R-up 96-97, SF 88-89, QF 89-90

RECORDS **Attendance:** 1,800 v Tamworth, FA Vase Semi-Final, 1989
Goalscorer: Andy Flounders 50, 98-99 **Appearances:** Richard Woomble, 74-94
Win: 9-0 v Hatfield Main, N.C.E. Lge Prem 97-98. **Defeat:** 1-7 v North Shields,N.C.E. Lge Prem 91.
Fee received: £6,000 for Dean Windass (Hull City,1988)

Players progressing: T Hotte (Hull) 88, I Ironside (Halifax) 88, D France, D Windass & M Matthews (Hull) 91.

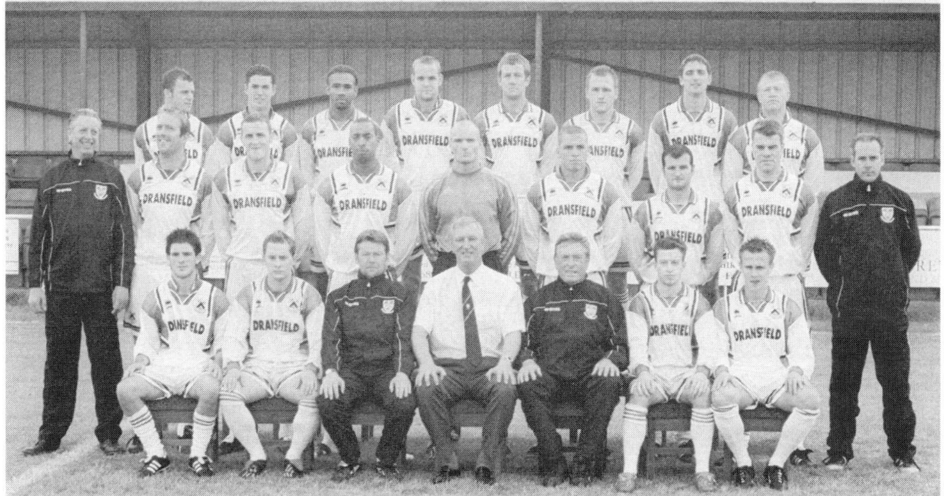

The 2003-04 North Ferriby Squad

OSSETT TOWN

CLUB OFFICIALS

President: Paul Jervis

Chairman: Graham Firth

Football Chairman: Peter Wilkinson

Commercial Manager: Graham Willis

Secretary: Bruce Saul c/o Club

FOOTBALL MANAGEMENT TEAM

Manager: Gary Brook
Asst Manager: B. Crawther
Coach:Nigel Yarrow

PROGRAMME

Pages: 56 Price: £1.00
Editor: Secretary

FACT FILE

Founded: 1936
Sponsors:: Builders Supply(Wakefield) Ltd
Colours:Red with white trim
Change colours: All sky
Midweek matches: Tuesday
Reserves' League: Lancashire League
Website: www.ossetttown.freeserve.co.uk
Local Press: Dewsbury Reporter, Wakefield Express

GROUND: Ingfield, Prospect Road, Ossett, Wakefield WF5 8AN Tel: 01924 272960

Directions: M1 jct 40, B6129 to Ossett, left into Dale Street, left again at lights opposite bus station on ring road, ground on left. Nearest stations Dewsbury or Wakefield Westgate - both three miles from. Buses 116, 117, 126 and127 from Wakefield, buses 116, 126 and 127 from Dewsbury, buses 117, 118 or 216 from Leeds

Capacity: 4,000 Seats: 360 Cover:1,000 Floodlights: Yes

Clubhouse: Open Fri & Sun lunchtimes, all day Sat and every evening. Pie & peas, chips, soup from tea bar

Club Shop: Yes (Graham Willis (h) 01924 266393)

PREVIOUS **Leagues:** Leeds 36-39; Yorkshire 45-82; N.C.E. 83-99 **Ground:** Fern House (pre-1958)

RECORDS **Attendance:** 2,600 v Manchester Utd, friendly 1988

Win: 10-1 v Harrogate RA (H), N.C.E. Lge Prem. Div. 27/4/93 **Defeat:** 0-7 v Easington Colliery, FA Vase 8/10/83

Fee received: £1,350 for Derek Blackburn (Swansea 1957)

Appearances: Steve Worsfold **Goalscorer:** Dave Leadbeater

HONOURS Northern Counties East - Lg Cup 89-90, Div 2 88-89, Res. Div 88-89, Res.Cup 87-88 88-89; West Riding County Cup 58-59 81-82.

Players progressing: Arnold Kendall (Bradford C.) 1949, Ron Liversidge(Bradford C.) 56, Derek Blackburn (Swansea) 57, Simon Lowe (Barnsley) 83, Gary Chapman (Bradford C.) 88, Mick Norbury (Scarborough) 1989, Mike Williams(Sheffield W.) 90, Dean Trott (Northampton) 98, Paul Cuss (Huddersfield Town) 98.

PRESCOT CABLES

CLUB OFFICIALS

President: Mr B F Taylor
Chairman: Ted Mercer
Vice Chairman: G.Hayward
Commercial Manager: Arthur McCumiskey
Secretary: Doug Lace
20 Cable Road, Prescott,
Merseyside L35 5AW

FOOTBALL MANAGEMENT TEAM

Manager: Tommy Lawson
Asst Manager: Andy Gray

FACT FILE

Founded: 1886
Nickname: Tigers
Colours: Gold/black/gold
Change colours: All blue
Midweek Matches: Tuesday
Pages: 30 Price: 70p
Editor: Ken Derbyshire

GROUND Valerie Park, Hope Street, Prescot. L34 6HD
Tel: 0151 430 0507 email: kenderbyshire@blueyonder.co.uk

Directions: M62 Jct 7. A57 to Prescot. Take 3rd exit at roundabout after two and a half miles. Turn right after another 1/2 mile. Right at Hope & Anchor pub, into Hope Street..

Capacity: 4,400 Seats: 200 Cover: 550 Floodlights: Yes

Clubhouse: Refreshment bar, open matchdays/evenings for hot & cold refreshments

Club Shop: No but ties & metal badges available.

PREVIOUS **Leagues:** Liverpool Co. Comb.; Lancs Comb. 1897-98 18-20 27-33 36-67; Ches. Co. 33-36 78-82; Mid Cheshire 67-78; N.W.C. 82-2003

Names: Prescot Athletic; Prescot Cables 46-65 80-90; Prescot Town 65-80.

CLUB RECORDS **Attendance:** 8,122 v Ashton National, 1932

BEST SEASON **FA Cup:** 2nd Rd 57-58 59-60 **FA Vase:** 2nd Rd 1998-99

HONOURS N.W.C. Champions 2002-03; Lancs Comb. 56-57 (Lg Cup 47-48); Ches. Lg Div 2 76-77; Mid Ches. Lg 76-77; L'pool Non-League Cup (4) 51-53 58-59 60-61; L'pool Chal. Cup (5) 28-30 48-49 61-62 77-78; George Mahon Cup 36-37.

ROSSENDALE UNITED

CLUB OFFICIALS

Chairman: Steve.Draper

V Chairmain: David White

President: David White

Press Officer: Kevin Procter

Secretary: Kevin Proctor
5 Booth Street, Waterfoot,
Rossendale, Lancs BB4 9AL
Tel: 01706 223405

FOOTBALL MANAGEMENT TEAM

Manager: Jimmy McBride
Ass. Man.Bryan Griffith
.Physio: Phil Atkinson

2002-2003

Captain: Dave Gamble
Top Scorer: Craig Sargeson & Chris Brooks
P.o.Y.: Chris Fitzsimmons

PROGRAMME

28 pages -£1.00
Editor: David Howarth

FACT FILE

Founded: 1898
Nickname: The Stags
Sponsors: Swinburne James Insurance
Colours: Blue & white stripes/blue/blue
Change colours: All Red
Midweek Matchday: Tuesday
Website: www.rosendaleunited.co.uk
Local Radio: Red Rose, Radio Lancashire.
Local Press: Lancs Evening Telegraph,
Rossendale Free Press

GROUND Dark Lane, Staghills Rd, Newchurch, Rossendale, Lancs BB4 7UA
Tel: 01706 215119 (Ground); 01706 213296 (Club) Email: rossendaleunited@zen.co.uk

Directions: M60 Junc 18, M66 north following signs for Burnley, then A682 to Rawstenstall, take 2nd exit sign Burnley A682, at 1st lights turn right into Newchurch Rd, 1.5 miles turn right into Staghills Rd, grd 800 yards right

Capacity: 2,500 Cover: Yes Seats: 500 Floodlights: Yes

Clubhouse: Evenings & matchdays. Hot snacks. Pool, satellite TV, concert room **Club Shop:** Yes (Dave Rudge 01706 213296)

PREVIOUS **Leagues:** N.E. Lancs Comb.; Lancs Comb. 1898-99 1901-70; Central Lancs 1899-1901; Cheshire County 70-82; NWC 82-89 93-01; N.P.L. 89-93. **Grounds:** None

RECORDS **Attendance:** 12,000 v Bolton Wanderers FA Cup 2nd Rd 71
Appearances: Johnny Clarke 770, 1947-65 **Goalscorer:** Bob Scott
Fee Paid: £3,000 for Jimmy Clarke (Buxton, 1992)
Fee Received: £1,500 for Dave O'Neill (Huddersfield Town, 1974)
Win: 17-0v Ashton Town, Lancs Comb.1911-12
Defeat: 0-14 v Morecambe, Lancs Comb. 67-68

BEST SEASON **FA Cup:** 2nd Rd 71-72, 1-4 v Bolton W. at Bury FC. Also 1st Rd 75-76 Also 1st Rd 75-76, 0-1 v Shrewsbury T. (H)
FA Trophy : 2nd Rd 81-82 **FA Vase:** 5th Rd 86-87,88-89

HONOURS N.W.C. Lg Div 1 88-89 00-01(R-up 87-88 93-94), Div 2 R-up 85-86, Chall Cup 93-94

Players progressing: T Lawton, G Smith (Bradford C 52), E Hartley & W O'Loughton (Oldham 56/60), C Blunt (Burnley 64), F Eyre (Bradford PA 69), D O'Neill (Huddersfield), C Parker (Rochdale 92).

DIVISION ONE ACTION

Workington 'keeper, Steve Pape, saves despite pressure from Kendal'sJamie Close in the Boxing Day derby.
Photo: Alan Watson

DIVISION ONE ACTION

ABOVE: Belper's Steve Kennedy (5) and Gary Ingham somehow manage to keep this Radcliffe Borough effort out.

Photos: Bill Wheatcroft.

BELOW: Radcliffe's Scott Wilson (on the line) tries in vain to keep Chorley's Lee Wilkinson's 90th minute equaliser out.

STOCKSBRIDGE PARK STEELS

CLUB OFFICIALS

President: J.Newton
Chairman: Alan Bethel
Vice-Chairman: M Grimmer
Secretary: Michael Grimmer
48 Hole House Lane, Stocksbridge
Sheffield S36 1BT Tel: 0114 288 6470
Press Officer: Edwin O'Sullivan
Commercial Manager: Andrew Horsley
Tel: 0114 288 3867

FOOTBALL MANAGEMENT TEAM

Manager: Wayne Biggins
Asst Manager: Graham Furness
Physio: Graham Furness

FACT FILE

Formed: 1986
Nickname: Steels
Sponsors:John Crawshaw (Butchers)
Colours: Yellow/ blue/yellow
Change colours: All blue
Midweek matches: Tuesday
Reserves' League: SheffieldCounty Senior

2002-03

Player of the Season: James tevendale
Leading Goalscorer: James Tevendale - 27
Captain: Jeremy Illingworth

Pages: 28 Price:1.00
Editor: Edwin O'Sullivan
Tel: 0114 288 4218

Local Press:
Look local, Green'un, The Star

GROUND Bracken Moor Lane, Stocksbridge, Sheffield. Tel: 0114 288 2045
Fax: 0114 288 8305 Club Website: http://members.aol.com/spsfc/

Directions: M1 jct 35a (from S), 36 (from N), A616 to Stocksbridge.
On arrival in Stocksbridge turn left into Nanny Hill under the Clock Tower and continue up the hill for about 500 yds - ground on left

Capacity: 3,500 Cover: 1,000 Seats: 450

Clubhouse: Open 7 days (lunchtime & evenings). No food. Separate foodbar for matches

Club Shop: Mrs Janet Cartledge 01226 759023 badges, mugs, shirts, progs, scarves etc .

PREVIOUS **Ground:** Stonemoor 49-51 52-53 **Names:** Stocksbridge Works, Oxley Park;clubs merged in 1986
Leagues: Sheffield Amateur/ Sheffield Association/Yorkshire 49-82

CLUB RECORDS **Attendance:** 2,000 v Sheffield Wed., Floodlight opening Oct '91
Fee Received: £15,000 for Lee Mills (Wolves, 1992) **Fee Paid:** Nil
Win: 5-0 v Warrington Town NPL 96-97 **Defeat:** 2-7 Witton Albion 2001-02
Scorer: Trevor Jones (145) **Appearances:** Not known

BEST SEASON **FA Cup:** 4th Q 50-1, 56-7 **FA Trophy:** 3rd Q 96-97 **FA Vase:** 4th Rd 95-96.

HONOURS Northern Co's East Prem Div 93-94, R-up 95-96, Div 1 91-92, Lg Cup 94-95; Sheffield Snr Cup 92-93 95-96,98-99.
Oxley Park F C: County Sen Div 1 85-86:Stocksbridge Works FC: Yorkshire Lge Div 1 51-52 54-55 55-56 56-57 57-58 61-62 62-63, Div 2 50-51 64-65, Div 3 70-71 74-75, Lge Cup 61-62 Sheffield Snr Cup 51-52

Players progressing: Peter Eustace (Sheffield Wednesday) 1960 (from Stocksbridge Works) , Lee Mills (Wolverhampton W.) 1992

L-R - Back Row: Elam, Bonser, Brookes, Siddall R, Middleton, Ring, Biggins (manager). **Front**: Siddall C, Richards, Johnson, Knox, O'Carroll

WITTON ALBION

CLUB OFFICIALS

President: T Stelfox

Chairman: M Worthington

Secretary: Phil Chadwick
29 Jack Lane, Davenham, Northwich,
Cheshire CW9 8LF Tel: 01606 44845

FOOTBALL MANAGEMENT TEAM

Manager: Benny Phillips
Physio: Steve Crompton

FACT FILE

Formed: 1887
Nickname: The Albion
Colours: Red & white stripes/ black/red
Change colours: All yellow
Midweek matchday: Tuesday
Reserve League: Altrincham U21
Website: www.wittonalbion.co.uk

Pages: 32 Price: £1
Editor: Secretary

Local Press: Northwich Guardian, Northwich Chronicle
Local Radio: BBC GMR, BBC Radio Stoke

GROUND Bargain Booze Stadium, Wincham Park, Chapel St, Wincham, Northwich.
Tel/Fax: 01606 43008 Email: bp-uh-2000@aol.com

Directions: M6 junc 19. A556 towards Northwich, after 3 miles turn onto A559 at beginning of dual carriageway, after 3/4 mile turn left opposite Black Greyhound Inn, grd 1/2 mile on left immediately after crossing Canal Bridge

Capacity: 4,500 Seated: 650 Cover: 2,300

Clubhouse: Concert room and Vice-Presidents room open matchdays, Tuesday,Thursday, Friday evenings. Food available for private functions **Club Shop:** Yes (Debbie Waterman)

PREVIOUS
Leagues: Lancs Comb.; Cheshire County -79; Northern Premier 79-91, GMV Conference 91-94
Grounds: Central Ground, Witton Street, Northwich

CLUB RECORDS
Attendance: 3,940 v Kidderminster Harriers - FA Trophy Semi-Final 13.4.91 (Wincham Road)
9,500 v Northwich Victoria - Cheshire League 7.4.50 (Central Ground)
Win: 13-0 v Middlewich (H) NS Cup .**Defeat:** 0-9 v Macclesfield Town (a) 18.9.65
Fee Paid: £12,500 to Hyde Utd for Jim McCluskie 91 **Fee Received:** £11,500 for Peter Henderson from Chester City.
Goalscorer: Frank Fidler 175 (1947-1950) **Appearances:** Alf Ashley 556 (1946-1958)

BEST SEASON
FA Trophy: Runners-up 91-92, Semi-Finals 90-91, 92-93
FA Cup: 91-92 Second Round 91-92, 1-5 v Preston North End (A). League clubs defeated: Halifax Town91-92

HONOURS
Northern Prem Lge 90-91; Cheshire County Lge 48-49 49-50 53-54 (R-up 50-51),Lge Cup 53-54 75-76; Cheshire County Sen Cup (7); FA Trophy R-up 91-92 (SF 90-91 92-93)

Players progressing: P Henderson (Chester C.), Chris Nicholl (Burnley - ex-Southampton manager), Phil Power (Crewe), Neil Parsley & Mike Whitlow (Leeds), Geoff Horsfield (Halifax Town ,Fulham), Robert Trees (Bristol Rovers).

WORKINGTON

Pages: 36 Price: £1
Press Off/ Ed: Steve Durham (01946 61380)

Local Press:
Evening News & Star, Times & Star
Local Radio: BBC Radio Cumbria, C.F.M

CLUB OFFICIALS

Chairma: Dale Brotherton
President: Minnie Thexton
Vice Chairman: Humphrey Dobie
Match Sec.: Steve Durham (01946 61380)
Secretary: Dale Brotherton
Lime House, Holm Hill, Dalston, Carlisle
CA5 7BX Tel: 07977 759903

FOOTBALL MANAGEMENT TEAM

Manager:Tommy Cassidy
Asst. Man:Kenny Brown
Physio: Les Sharkey

FACT FILE

Formed: 1884 (reformed 1921)
Nickname: Reds
Sponsors:West Cumbria Scaffolding
Colours: All Red
Change colours:All Blue.
Midweek matchday: Tuesday
Reserves' League: Cumberland County
Website: www.workingtonredsafc.co.uk

2002-2003
Captain & P.o.Y.: Will Varty
Top Scorer: Glenn Murray

GROUND: Borough Park, Workington, Cumbria CA14 2DT Tel: 01900 602871

Directions: A66 into town, right at `T' junction, follow A596 for 3/4 mile - ground is then visible and signposted. Ground is north of town centre 1/4 mile from Workington (BR) station &1/2 mile from bus station

Capacity: 2,500 Cover:1,000 Seats: 350 Floodlights: Yes

Clubhouse: Open matchdays and for private functions. Food on matchdays restricted menu

Club Shop: Sells programmes, badges, magazines, pennants, photographs, replica kit, T-shirts. etc. Contact :John Crook (01946 832710)

HONOURS Football League: 5th in Div 3 65-66, 3rd Div 4 63-64, Cumberland County Cup 1886-91(x5) 95-00(x5) 1906-08(x2) 09-10 24-25 34-35 36-38(x2) 49-50 53-54 67-68 85-86 95-96, 99-00 (R-up 1885-86 91-92 1899-1901(x2) 02-03 08-09 11-12 23-24 26-27 29-30, 46-47 68-69 78-79) Football League Cup QF 63-64 64-65; N.P.L. Presidents Cup 83-84; North Eastern Lge R-up 38-39, Lge Cup 34-35 36-37 R-up 37-38; N.W. Trains Lg Div 1 98-99

PREVIOUS **Leagues:** Cumberland Assoc. 1890-94; Cumberland Sen. Lge 94-1901, 03-04; Lancashire Lge 1901-03; Lancashire Comb. 04-10; North Eastern 10-11, 21-51; Football League 51-77
Grounds: Various 1884-1921, Lonsdale Park 21-37

BEST SEASON **FA Cup:** 4th Rd 33-34. 1st Rd - 53 occasions.
FA Trophy: Q. Final 99-00 **FA Vase:** 6th Rd, 98-99 (1st season)

RECORDS **Attendance:** 21,000 v Manchester Utd, FA Cup 3rd Rd 4/1/58
Goalscorer: Billy Charlton 193 **Win:** 17-1 v Cockermouth Crusaders, Cumb-erland Sen. Lge 19/1/01
Appearances: Bobby Brown 419 **Defeat:** 0-9 v Chorley (A), NPL Prem. Div., 10/11/87
Fee Paid: £6,000 for Ken Chisholm (Sunderland,'56) **Fee Received:** £33,000 for Ian McDonald (Liverpool, '74)

Players progressing: Numerous, the best known being John Burridge.

Back row, left to right: Kenny Brown, Ted Sharkey, Richard Prokas, Craig Lewis, Will Varty, Stuart Williamson, James Parker and Tonny Cassidy.
Front row::James Holland, Andrew Coyles, Craig Potts, Stuart Moffat, Lee Armstrong, Craig Johnston, Robert Ennis and John Wharton.
Photo: Steve Durham.

THE NORTH WEST COUNTIES FOOTBALL LEAGUE

President: W J King **Chairman:** D Tomlinson

Secretary: Geoff Wilkinson, 46 Oaklands Drive,
Penwortham, Preston PR1 0YY Tel: 01772 746312

Press Officer: Paul Lawler, 61 Cable Street,
Formby, Merseyside L37 3LU Tel/Fax: 01704 875575

FINAL LEAGUE TABLE 2002-03

DIVISION ONE		P	W	D	L	F	A	Pts
1	Prescot Cables	42	30	6	6	110	38	96
2	Clitheroe	42	28	8	6	97	38	92
3	Mossley	42	27	7	8	100	41	88
4	Newcastle Town	42	23	12	7	83	52	81
5	Skelmersdale United	42	22	8	12	91	51	74
6	Nantwich Town	42	19	11	12	90	74	68
7	St Helens Town	42	17	14	11	77	60	65
8	Congleton Town	42	19	8	15	72	62	65
9	Salford City	42	17	12	13	84	63	63
10	Fleetwood Town	42	17	9	16	73	70	60
11	Alsager Town	42	15	11	16	61	67	56
12	Squires Gate	42	13	12	17	58	71	51
13	Abbey Hey	42	12	13	17	56	73	49
14	Atherton LR	42	11	12	19	65	86	45
15	Ramsbottom United	42	11	11	20	73	83	44
16	Warrington Town	42	11	11	20	48	66	44
17	Woodley Sports	42	11	9	22	62	85	42
18	Curzon Ashton	42	11	9	22	60	87	42
19	Atherton Collieries	42	11	7	24	52	85	40
20	Glossop North End	42	10	9	23	55	104	39
21	Flixton	42	10	8	24	44	112	38
22	Winsford United	42	10	7	25	48	91	37

DIVISION TWO		P	W	D	L	F	A	Pts
1	Bacup Borough	34	25	2	7	91	32	77
2	Stone Dominoes	34	24	3	7	94	34	75
3	Maine Road	34	23	2	9	74	55	71
4	Padiham	34	20	5	9	69	42	65
5	Holker Old Boys	34	18	7	9	65	42	61
6	Great Harwood Town	34	15	7	12	64	61	52
7	Nelson	34	13	12	9	50	40	51
8	Darwen	34	14	7	13	59	64	49
9	Norton United	34	14	6	14	50	52	48
10	Colne	34	14	5	15	65	53	47
11	Ashton Town	34	12	9	13	49	53	45
12	Castleton Gabriels	34	10	8	16	43	60	38
13	Cheadle Town	34	10	8	16	39	56	38
14	Blackpool Mechanics	34	9	10	15	39	52	37
15	Leek CSOB	34	8	9	17	46	57	33
16	Daisy Hill	34	7	5	22	42	93	26
17	Oldham Town	34	4	12	18	40	86	24
18	Chadderton	34	5	5	24	33	80	20

RESULT GRIDS

DIVISION ONE 02-03	1	2	3	4	5	6	7	8	9	10	11	12	13	14	15	16	17	18	19	20	21	22
1 Abbey Hey		2-2	3-2	2-2	1-0	1-1	1-1	1-1	2-2	1-0	0-3	1-0	1-3	0-1	0-2	3-5	0-0	2-2	0-4	1-2	3-2	1-1
2 Alsager Town	1-2		2-0	0-1	1-2	2-3	3-2	4-0	3-2	3-1	1-4	1-2	0-0	1-0	0-0	1-0	2-0	2-3	0-1	0-0	4-1	0-4
3 Atherton Collieries	1-0	1-3		3-1	1-3	0-1	0-1	2-1	3-0	1-3	0-2	2-3	2-2	1-1	1-1	0-1	0-5	2-1	1-2	0-0	1-3	3-1
4 Atherton LR	4-1	1-2	4-3		2-2	1-4	3-1	3-4	2-0	1-2	0-3	0-4	2-2	2-2	0-4	1-3	1-2	0-0	2-2	1-0	1-2	1-1
5 Clitheroe	1-0	6-1	2-0	0-0		3-0	2-1	3-2	4-0	5-0	1-2	2-1	1-2	1-1	7-1	3-0	3-2	4-2	2-1	1-0	0-0	2-1
6 Congleton Town	1-0	0-0	1-2	4-2	3-0		3-0	2-1	7-0	4-1	0-1	3-1	5-2	1-3	2-0	1-6	0-1	1-0	0-1	3-0	2-1	1-0
7 Curzon Ashton	2-1	1-2	0-3	3-5	0-2	1-0		3-3	2-2	7-1	3-2	0-2	1-1	0-1	3-2	1-3	0-2	2-0	0-0	2-2	1-2	3-3
8 Fleetwood Town	1-3	0-3	3-0	3-1	1-1	3-1	3-0		7-4	5-0	1-1	3-4	3-2	2-1	0-0	1-4	2-1	0-0	1-1	2-1	1-0	4-1
9 Flixton	2-1	3-2	0-2	0-0	0-3	1-1	1-2	0-1		3-1	0-5	0-1	0-4	0-4	0-7	0-5	3-0	1-1	4-1	1-0	1-0	2-1
10 Glossop North End	1-1	4-3	1-1	2-1	0-0	1-1	2-4	0-3	2-2		2-2	4-3	0-1	0-3	1-1	2-2	2-1	4-3	1-1	3-0	0-1	0-1
11 Mosley	2-1	1-2	3-1	7-2	3-1	2-3	6-0	1-0	8-0	5-0		0-3	1-0	3-2	3-2	1-0	1-1	2-1	2-0	1-0	4-0	1-0
12 Nantwich Town	3-5	1-1	1-1	0-2	0-4	2-2	1-2	3-0	3-3	1-2	1-0		4-4	1-2	2-2	2-2	3-2	1-1	2-1	3-2	3-1	6-1
13 Newcastle Town	1-3	2-0	2-0	0-3	0-0	3-1	3-1	1-1	3-0	4-0	2-2	1-3		2-1	2-1	1-1	3-0	0-0	2-0	4-0	4-3	2-0
14 Prescot Cables	6-0	4-1	4-0	3-1	4-2	4-1	3-0	2-1	9-0	2-1	0-0	6-0	1-0		2-1	3-0	2-2	4-3	3-1	3-0	5-0	2-0
15 Ramsbottom United	0-1	1-1	1-4	1-3	0-1	1-1	1-1	0-2	1-2	3-2	2-2	0-4	2-3	2-4		4-1	2-1	1-2	1-1	4-0	5-2	1-4
16 Salford City	1-1	4-0	1-2	1-1	1-4	2-1	3-1	3-1	2-0	3-0	1-1	2-2	1-2	3-1	7-0		0-4	1-1	2-2	1-2	0-0	0-0
17 Skelmersdale Utd	1-1	4-1	5-1	1-2	0-1	3-0	4-1	3-1	4-1	5-1	1-0	2-1	2-3	1-2	2-1	6-1		8-1	0-0	2-2	3-1	0-0
18 Squires Gate	4-0	0-0	3-2	2-0	0-6	3-0	3-2	1-1	2-0	4-2	1-3	0-1	1-1	0-2	2-1	2-1	1-2		2-3	2-2	0-2	2-1
19 St Helens Town	2-1	1-1	6-1	5-3	1-1	2-1	2-2	3-0	1-1	5-2	2-1	1-1	3-4	0-3	2-3	0-5	1-2	0-0		3-1	1-1	7-0
20 Warrington Town	1-1	0-2	4-0	1-1	1-2	2-2	1-0	1-4	1-0	4-1	4-2	1-1	0-2	1-0	3-3	1-1	1-2	2-0	0-1		3-0	0-2
21 Winsford Town	0-3	2-2	2-0	2-0	1-7	2-3	0-2	2-0	0-1	1-3	0-5	0-4	1-1	1-1	1-3	2-3	1-1	2-0	1-2	1-2		3-2
22 Woodley Sports	2-4	1-1	2-2	2-2	1-2	1-1	3-1	3-0	4-2	2-0	0-2	5-6	1-2	2-3	1-5	2-1	1-3	0-2	0-4	1-0	4-1	

DIVISION TWO 02-03	1	2	3	4	5	6	7	8	9	10	11	12	13	14	15	16	17	18	19
1 Ashton Town		1-2	3-2	2-1	3-1	1-1	2-0	0-4	1-1	0-1	1-1	0-4	0-2	0-0	3-3	6-0	5-1	n/a	1-0
2 Bacup Borough	1-0		1-0	4-1	6-0	0-1	4-1	4-0	0-2	2-0	3-0	4-2	4-0	1-1	4-2	1-1	0-1	n/a	2-1
3 Blackpool Mechanics	2-2	0-7		2-3	1-0	2-0	1-2	4-1	1-1	2-2	0-0	2-0	0-2	0-0	2-1	3-1	0-2	n/a	1-2
4 Castleton Gabriels	0-0	2-1	2-1		2-0	0-4	2-1	2-1	6-0	2-2	0-2	3-2	1-4	0-0	0-2	2-2	2-3	n/a	1-2
5 Chadderton	0-1	0-1	3-3	2-1		1-5	1-2	4-1	3-5	0-0	0-2	0-2	2-5	1-1	3-2	1-2	0-2	n/a	1-0
6 Cheadle Town	0-2	1-5	0-0	2-2	1-0		0-2	1-0	3-4	4-3	0-1	1-1	0-2	1-1	0-1	1-1	1-1	n/a	0-3
7 Colne	3-1	3-4	0-1	3-0	4-0	0-0		5-0	1-2	1-1	3-1	3-3	1-2	3-3	1-2	7-1	2-0	1-0	1-3
8 Daisy Hill	1-2	1-5	0-0	4-0	2-0	1-3	2-4		1-0	0-2	1-1	2-2	2-6	3-3	0-1	1-1	1-3	1-1	0-3
9 Darwen	3-1	4-2	1-2	2-1	1-0	5-0	0-3	2-0		0-3	2-2	5-0	4-0	0-0	0-2	1-1	1-1	n/a	3-5
10 Great Harwood Town	4-1	2-7	3-1	1-1	2-0	5-1	4-2	4-0	0-3		3-0	0-0	1-2	0-3	5-2	3-0	3-1	n/a	1-2
11 Holker Old Boys	3-0	1-0	3-0	2-0	5-1	1-0	3-1	3-1	2-0	5-0		1-1	2-4	2-0	1-2	5-2	3-1	n/a	1-3
12 Leek CSOB	0-0	0-4	2-0	1-2	1-3	0-1	2-1	4-0	5-1	4-0	1-3		0-1	1-1	3-0	0-2	2-2	1-1	0-3
13 Maine Road	1-2	2-1	1-1	1-0	3-2	3-1	3-1	4-1	3-1	1-3	2-5	3-1		1-2	2-1	5-2	2-1	n/a	1-1
14 Nelson	1-1	0-1	1-2	1-0	2-0	2-0	0-1	0-2	4-1	2-3	2-2	1-0	2-1		3-1	2-1	2-1	n/a	2-0
15 Norton United	2-1	1-3	1-0	1-1	0-0	1-0	3-1	1-2	1-1	4-1	1-1	4-0	0-1	1-0		2-0	1-2	n/a	3-4
16 Oldham Town	3-4	1-4	2-1	0-0	4-4	1-2	0-0	2-5	1-2	1-1	2-0	1-1	1-2	0-7	0-0		1-3	0-3	1-1
17 Padiham	2-0	0-2	1-1	1-2	2-0	2-1	1-2	9-2	2-0	3-1	3-0	1-0	3-2	3-1	3-0	6-1		3-0	1-1
18 Stand Athletic	n/a	1-0	1-1	n/a	n/a	3-0	n/a	7-0	n/a	n/a	n/a	n/a	n/a	2-7	n/a	3-1	2-2		n/a
19 Stone Dominoes	3-2	0-1	2-1	4-1	6-0	2-3	1-0	8-0	7-1	4-0	2-1	2-1	6-0	6-0	4-1	3-1	0-1	n/a	

LEAGUE CHALLENGE TROPHY

FIRST ROUND

Cheadle Town 0 Castleton Gabriels 3
Colne 2 Stand Athletic 1
Great Harwood Town 3 Ashton Town 0
Holker Old Boys 2 Darwen 1
Leek CSOB 0 Chadderton 1
Nelson 8 Daisy Hill 1
Norton United 2 Stone Dominoes 2 (aet)
Replay: Stone Dominoes 2 Norton United 1
Oldham Town 2 Blackpool Mechanics 3
Padiham 2 Bacup Borough 1

SECOND ROUND

Abbey Hey 0 Great Harwood Town 2
Alsager Town 1 Castleton Gabriels 2
Blackpool Mechanics 0 Salford City 3
Congleton Town 5 Atherton LR 0
Curzon Ashton 1 Prescot Cables 3
Fleetwood Town 0 Skelmersdale United 3
Flixton 3 Atherton Collieries 2
Holker Old Boys 0 Maine Road 5
Nelson 2 Newcastle Town 4
Padiham 3 Glossop North End 2
Ramsbottom United 3 Colne 1
Squires Gate 1 Nantwich Town 3
Stone Dominoes 0 Mossley 5
Warrington Town 3 Chadderton 0
Winsford United 1 St Helens Town 3
Woodley Sports 2 Clitheroe 3

THIRD ROUND

Clitheroe 4 Prescot Cables 1
Flixton 1 Skelmersdale United 3
Maine Road 0 Newcastle Town 2
Mossley 4 Nantwich Town 3
Padiham 4 Castleton Gabriels 1
Ramsbottom United 1 Great Harwood Town 0
St Helens Town 2 Congleton Town 4
Warrington Town 0 Salford City 2

QUARTER-FINALS

Clitheroe 3 Skelmersdale United 1
Padiham 2 Congleton Town 1
Ramsbottom United 2 Newcastle Town 4
Salford City 2 Mossley 4

SEMI-FINALS

1st Leg: Clitheroe 4 Padiham 1
2nd Leg: Padiham 1 Clitheroe 1

1st Leg: Mossley 4 Newcastle Town 1
2nd Leg: Newcastle Town 2 Mossley 1

FINAL

Clitheroe 1 Mossley 2
(7th May at Bury)

DIVISION TWO TROPHY

FIRST ROUND

Darwen 2 Great Harwood Town 4

Castleton Gabriels 2 Chadderton 1

Holker Old Boys 2 Norton United 1

SECOND ROUND

Ashton Town 1 Holker Old Boys 0

Castleton Gabriels 0 Bacup Borough 3

Cheadle Town 5 Blackpool Mechanics 2

Daisy Hill 0 Colne 1

Great Harwood Town 3 Nelson 1

Oldham Town 4 Leek CSOB 0

Padiham 2 Stone Dominoes 4

Stand Athletic v Maine Road

(walkover for Maine Road)

QUARTER-FINALS

Ashton Town 3 Colne 1

Bacup Borough 6 Cheadle Town 1

Maine Road 0 Stone Dominoes 1

Oldham Town 2 Great Harwood Town 2

(aet Oldham won 5-4 on penalties)

SEMI-FINALS

Oldham Town 0 Ashton Town 3

Stone Dominoes 6 Bacup Borough 0

FINAL

Ashton Town 1 Stone Dominoes 2

(16th April at Congleton Town)

£1
Atherton
Laburnum
Rovers
North West Counties League - Division 1
Crilly Park
R e v i e W
Official Matchday Programme For The Season 2002/2003

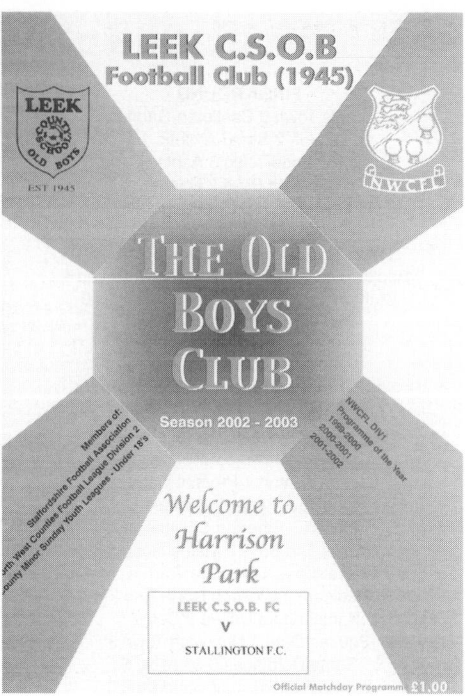
LEEK C.S.O.B
Football Club (1945)
LEEK COUNTY SCHOOLS OLD BOYS
EST 1945
NWCFL
THE OLD
BOYS
CLUB
Season 2002 - 2003
Members of:
Staffordshire Football Association
NWCFL DIV1
Programme of the Year
1999-2000
2000-2001
2001-2002
Welcome to
Harrison
Park
LEEK C.S.O.B. FC
V
STALLINGTON F.C.
Official Matchday Programme £1.00

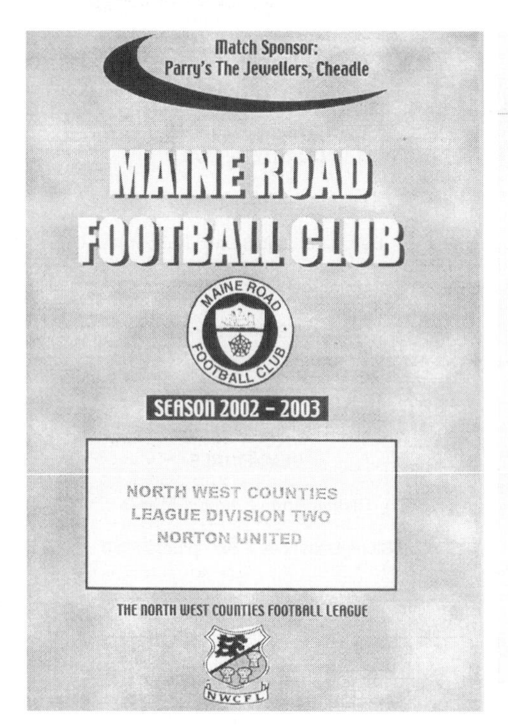
Match Sponsor:
Parry's The Jewellers, Cheadle
MAINE ROAD
FOOTBALL CLUB
MAINE ROAD FOOTBALL CLUB
SEASON 2002 - 2003
NORTH WEST COUNTIES
LEAGUE DIVISION TWO
NORTON UNITED
THE NORTH WEST COUNTIES FOOTBALL LEAGUE
NWCFL

North West Counties Football
League
V
Nantwich
Town
BLUE
Review
Monday
April 21st 2003
3.00pm
Winsford
United
Football Club

ABBEY HEY

Secretary: Gordon Lester, 6 Newhaven Avenue, Hr.Openshaw, Manchestewr M11 1HU
Tel Nos: 0161 370 0270 (H) 0161 200 4630 (W)

Ground: Abbey Stadium, Goredale Avenue, Gorton, Manchester 18
Tel: 0161 231 7147 (Club) Fax: 01823 490281

Directions: A57 towards Hyde, right into Woodland Avenue approx one & a half miles past Belle Vue junction, right again into Ryder Brow Rd, 1st left after bridge into Goredale Ave. **Nearest Railway Station:** Ryder Brow
Capacity: 1000 Seats: 100 Cover: 300 Floodlights: Yes

Honours Manchester Amat. Lge 65-66: S.E. Lancs Lge 66-67, 68-69 R-up 67-68; Div.2 68-69; Lge Shield 65-66: Manc. Co. Amat. Cup 64-65, 67-68, 68-69, R-up 63-64: Manchester Lge Prem. Div. 81-82, 88-89, 90-91, 93-94, 94-95; Div. 1 70-71; Div.2 88-89, 92-93, 93-94; Gilcryst Cup 76-77, 88-89, R-up 97-88; Open Tphy 78-79,79-80, 92-93: Manchester Chall. Tphy 82-83, 95-96, 96-97. N.W. Trains Div 2 R-up 98-99

Previous Leagues: Manchester Amateur; South East Lancs; Manchester Lge.

Record Attendance: 400 v Manchester City XI oct 99

FACT FILE

Formed: 1902
Colours:Red& white/red/red & white
Midweek matchday: Tuesday

CLUB PERSONNEL

Chairman: James Whittaker
0161 445 0036

Emergency Contact; G.Lester
0161 370 0270 or 0161 236 3311 ext 2800

ALSAGER TOWN

Secretary: Pauline Matthews, 43 Ellgreave Street, Dalehall, Stoke -0n-Trent, ST6 4DJ
Tel No: 01782 834296

Ground: The Town Ground, Wood Park, Alsager. Tel: 01270 882336

Directions: M6, Junction 16, A500 towards Stoke. Leave A500 at 2nd exit (A34 to Congleton), at 2nd set of lights turn left for Alsager. Turn right opposite Caradon/Twyfords (500 yds), into Moorhouse Ave., Woodland Court 1/2 mile on right.
Nearest Railway station: Alsager

HONOURS Joint Runners -up Mid Cheshire Div. 2, Runners-up Springbank Vending Lge.

PREVIOUS **Leagues:** Mid Cheshire Div. 2; Springbank Vending Lge.

RECORD **Attendance:** 110 v Formby Sept 99, League. 200 v Port Vale (friendly)

FACT FILE

Founded: 1968
Colours: Black & white/black/black
Change colours: Yellow & sky blue/yellow/yellow
Midweek Matches: Wednesday

CLUB PERSONNEL

Chairman: Peter Clegg
Tel: 01270 876013
1st Team Sec.: Pauline Matthews
Tel: 01782 834296H

ATHERTON COLLIERIES

Secretary: Emil Anderson, 109 Douglas St, Atherton M46 9EB Tel Nos: 01942 879209 (H) 0161 288 6355 (W) 0792 937461 (M) Email: geocities.com/ath-c-g-c

Ground: Atherton Colls Football Ground,Alder St., Atherton, Gt ManchesterTel:01942884649.

Directions: M61 Jct 5, follow sign for Westhoughton, left onto A6, right ontoA579 (Newbrook Rd/Bolton Rd) into Atherton. At first set of lights turn leftinto High Street, 2nd left into Alder St. to ground. Quarter mile from AthertonCentral (BR).
Seats: 300 Cover: 1,000 Capacity: 2,500 Floodlights: Yes

Clubhouse: Open Mon-Fri 7-11pm, Sat 11am-11pm, Sun noon-3 & 7-10.30pm. Hot &cold food on matchdays. **Club Shop:** No, but programmes & badges are available

PREVIOUS Leagues: Bolton Combination 20-50, 52-71; Lancs Combination 50-52, 71-78; Cheshire County 78-82.

HONOURS: BNWCFL 3rd Div Champ 86/87; Bridge Shield 85/86; Lancs County FA Shield19/20, 22/23, 41/42, 45/46. 56/57, 64/65; Tennents F/lit Trophy Finalist 94/95; NWCFL Div 2 R/up 95/96 Gpldline Trophy 2001-02 Worthington Challenge Trophy R-up 2001-02

RECORDS **Attendance:** 3,300 in Lancs Combination, 1920's

Players Progressing: J Parkinson (Wigan), Russell Beardsmore(Manchester Utd).

FACT FILE

Founded: 1916
Nickname: Colls
Club Sponsors: Kensite
Colours: Black & white stripes/black/black.
Change colours: Yellow/blue/yellow
Reserves' Lge: NWTL Res Div
Midweek Matches: Monday
Programme: 40 pages, £1
Editor: Secretary
Club Website:
geocities@frank35.freeserve.co.uk

CLUB PERSONNEL

Chairman: Steve Payne
Vice Chairman:
President: T.B.A.
Foster Feste
Physio: Chris Roberts

ATHERTON L.R.

Secretary: Steve Hartle,165 Bolton Road, Atherton, Gtr Manchester M46 9AD (01942 870253)

Ground: Crilly Park, Spa Road, Atherton, Greater Manchester (01942 883950).
Directions: M61 to Jct 5, follow signs for Westhoughton, left onto A6, right onto A579 (Newbrook Rd/Bolton Rd) over the railway bridge, right into Upton Rd passing Atherton Central Station, left into Springfield Rd and left again into Hillside Rd into Spa Rd and ground.
Capacity: 3,000 Seats: 250 Cover: 3 sections Floodlights: Yes
Clubhouse: Open normal licensing hours. **Club Shop:** No

PREVIOUS **Name:** Laburnum Rovers 56-80 **Grounds:** Laburnum Road 56-58 Hagfold 58-66
Leagues: Bolton Comb.; Cheshire County 80-82; NWCL 82-94; NPL 94-97.
RECORDS **Attendance:** 1,856 v Aldershot Town, FA Vase Quarter-Final replay 5/3/94.
Appearances: Jimmy Evans **Fee Paid:** £500 for Joey Dunn from Warrington T.
Scorer: Shaun Parker **Fee Received:** £1,500 for Stuart Humphries to Barrow
BEST SEASON **FA Cup:** 3rd Qual Rd 96-97, 0-2 v Bamber Bridge
FA Vase: Semi-Final rep. 94-95, 1-2 v Diss Town **FA Trophy:** 1st Qual Rd 96-97
HONOURS: North West Co Lge 92-93 93-94, Champs Trophy 92-93 93-94, F/Lit Trophy 93-94; N.P.L.Div.1 Cup R-up 95-96,Goldline Trophy 98-99, Bolton Hosp Cup: 84-85; 01-02 W.Houghton Ch C 81-82
Players progressing : Barry Butler (Chester), Lee Unsworth(Crewe).Phil Priestley(Rochdale)

FACT FILE
Formed: 1956 Nickname: The Panthers
Sponsors: VeeKay Engineering
Colours: Yellow & Navy
Change colours: Green & White
Midweek Matches: Tuesday
Reserves' League: North West Co Res Div
Prog: 48 pages £1.0 (Best in league 4th year)
Ed: Tim Lees. e-mail : lr-16@hotmail.com
website:www.intheteam.com/athertonir
Local Radio: GMR

CLUB PERSONNEL
Chairman:Alan Grundy
Financial Director: Ray Price
Manager:Tom Foster & Denis Haslam

BACUP BOROUGH

Secretary: Frank Manning, 38 Acre Avenue, Stacksteads, Bacup OL13 0HN
Tel: 01706 877460 (H)

Ground: West View, Cowtoot Lane, Blackthorn, Bacup, Lancashire
Tel: 01706 878655

Directions: From M62, M66 onto A681 through Rawtenstall to Bacup centre, leftonto A671 towards Burnley, after approx 300 yds right (immed. before the Irwell Inn) climbing Cooper Street, right into Blackthorn Lane then first left intoCowtoot Lane to ground.

Capacity: 3,000 Seats: 500 Cover: 1,000 Floodlights: Yes

Clubhouse: Open matchdays and private functions (for which buffets can be provided). Pies and sandwiches on matchdays.
Club Shop: Not yet

HONOURS Lancs Jnr Cup 10-11 (R-up 22-23 74-75); Lancs Comb. 46-47 (Lg Cup R-up46-47 80-81; NW Co's Lg Div 2 R-up 89-90.

PREVIOUS **League:** Lancs Comb. 03-82Name: Bacup FC.Grounds: None

BEST SEASON **FA Cup: FA Vase:**

RECORD **Attendance:** 4,980 v Nelson 1947 **Scorer:** Jimmy Clarke

FACT FILE
Founded: 1875
Nickname: The Boro
Club Sponsors: B & E Boys Ltd
Colours: White with black trim, black, black
Change colours: Yellow, Blue, Blue
Midweek Matches: Wednesday
Programme
22 Pages 50p
Editor: D Whatmough (0706 875041)

CLUB PERSONNEL
President: W. Shufflebottom
Chairman: Ken Peters
Vice Chairman: D. Whatmough

Manager: Brent Peters
Assistant Manager: Simon Holding

CLITHEROE

Secretary: Colin Wilson, 4 Moss Street, Clitheroe, Lancs BB7 1DP
Tel/Fax: 01200 424370 Mobile: 07714 382232

Ground: Shawbridge, Clitheroe, Lancs (01200 423344).
Directions: M6 jct 31, A59 to Clitheroe (17 miles), at 5th r'bout continue for half a mile and turn left at Pendle Road. Ground one mile, behind Bridge Inn' on the right. 11 miles from Blackburn BR station: Clitheroe
Capacity: 2,400 Seats: 300 Cover: 1200 Floodlights: Yes

Clubhouse: Open during matches. Snacks available **Club Shop:** Yes.
HONOURS FA Vase Runners-up 95-96; Lancs Comb. 79-80, Lg Cup 34-35; Lancs Challenge Tphy 84-85; NW C Lge 85-86, Div 2 84-85, Div 3 83-84; East Lancs Floodlit Trophy 94-95.N.W.Trains Floodlit Cup: 98-99

PREVIOUS **Leagues**: Blackburn & Dist.; Lancs Comb. 03-04 05-10 25-82.

BEST SEASON **FA Cup:** **FA Vase:** Runners-up 95-96

RECORDS **Attendance:** 2,000 v Mangotsfield, FA Vase Semi/F 95-96.
Goalscorer: Don Francis **Appearances**: Lindsey Wallace.

Players progressing Ray Woods (Leeds 1950), Chris Sims (Blackburn 1960), Lee Rogerson (Wigan Ath), Carlo Nash (Crystal Palace).

FACT FILE
Formed: 1877.
Nickname: The Blues
Colours: Blue & white /blue/blue
Change colours: All yellow
Midweek matchday: Tuesday
Reserves' Lge: N.W.C.L
Programme: Yes

President: T.B.A.
Chairman: David Burgess
Vice Chairman:John Robinson
Commercial Manager: T.B.A.
Manager: Lee Sculpher
Asst. Manager: Martin Eatough
Physio: Steve McCullough
2002-2003
Captain: Neil Spencer
Top Scorers: Gary Jackson & Lee Cryer 26
Player of the Year: Jason Jones

CONGLETON TOWN

Secrtary & Press Officer: Paul Kelly, 19 Melrose Drive, Crew, Cheshire CW1 3YD
Tel Nos: 01270 212599 (H) 01270 612250 (W) 07759430019 (M)
GROUND Booth Sttreet Ground, Crescent Road, Congleton, Cheshire Tel: 01260 74460
Directions: On approach to Congleton via Clayton bypass take second right after fire station, into Booth Street. Two miles from Congleton (BR)
Capacity: 5,000 Cover: 1,200 Seats: 250
Clubhouse: Open match days only **Club Shop:** Yes. Contact:Gerry Brocklehurst
PREVIOUS **Leagues:** Crewe & Dist; North Staffs; Macclesfield; Cheshire 20-39, 46-65, 78-82; Mid Cheshire 68-78; Nth West Co 82-87, N.P.L. 87-01
Name: Congleton Hornets (prior to current club's formation in 1901)
CLUB RECORDS **Attendance:** 7,000 v Macclesfield, League 53-54 **Fee Paid:** None.
Goalscorer: Mick Biddle 150+ **Fee Received:** £5,000 for D Frost (Leeds)
Appearances: Ray Clack 600+ & Graham Harrison 600+
BEST SEASON **FA Trophy:** 3rd Qual. Rd 89-90 90-91. **FA Vase:** 4th Rd 76-77 80-81
FA Cup: 1st Rd 89-90, 0-2 v Crewe A. (A) League clubs defeated: None
HONOURS North West Counties League R-up 85-86; Cheshire County League R-up 20-2121-22 (Div 2 81-82); Mid Cheshire League 73-74 75-76 77-78 (R-up 69-70 71-72 76-77, League Cup 71-72; Cheshire Senior Cup 20-21 37-38
Players progressing: Ron Broad (Crewe 55), Jack Mycock (Shrewsbury 58),Steve Davies (Port Vale 87), L Hamlet (Leeds), Jimmy Quinn (West Ham), Ian Brightwell (Man City)

FACT FILE
Formed: 1901 Nickname: Bears
Colours:White/black/black
Change colours: Yellow & Blue
Midweek home matchday: Tuesday
Website:http://members.aol.com/beartown
Programme: Pages: 48 Price: £1.00
Editor: Ken Mead c/oClub
Local Radio: Radio Stoke, Signal.Local Press: Congleton Chron, Staffs Eve Sentinel

CLUB PERSONNEL
Chair: Peter EvansV- Chair: Steve Burgess
Press Officer: Ken Mead-07710405674(M)
Manager: Kevin Langley
Ass.Managers: Mark Cox & Gary Bickerstaff
Physio: Paul Kelly
2002-2003
Captain : Adrian Reilly
Leading Goalscorer: Dave Shaw 29
Ps.o.Y.: Chris Burke & Andy Park

CURZON ASHTON

Secretary: Robert Hurst, 36 Russell Road, Partington, Manchester M31 4DZ
Tel: 0161 775 3883 Fax 0161 775 8787 Mob 0771 325 2310 Email:curzonashton@byford.co.uk
Ground: National Park, Katherine Street, Ashton-under-Lyne OL7 6DA (0161 330 6033)
Directions: M60 Jct 23 to Ashton- u -Lyme on Manchester Rd (A635) then turn into Williams Street.Ground at bottom of road.One and a half miles from Ashton-under-Lyne (BR)
Capacity: 5,000 Cover: 450 Seats: 350 Floodlights: Yes
Clubhouse: Every night. Food on matchdays. **Club Shop:** Contact Roy Howe, 0161 220 8345

PREVIOUS **Leagues:** Manchester Amat.; Manchester (-1978); Cheshire Co. 78-82; N.W C. 82-86 Northern Prem. Lge. 87-97, N.C.E. 97-98, N.W.C. 98-01

BEST SEASON **FA Cup:** 3rd Qual. Rd replay 89-90, 1-3 v Mossley (A) after 1-1
FA Vase: Semi-Final 79-80 **FA Trophy:** 2nd Qual. Rd 82-83, 84-85

HONOURS **NWC Lge Div.2 r-up 99-00;** Cheshire Co. Lge Div 2 R-up 78-79: Manchester Lge 77-78, R-up 74-75 75-76; Lge Cup 77-78, R-up 74-75 75-76; Murray Shield R-up 75-76: Manchester Amat. Lge 63-64 65-66, R-up 64-65: Manchester Prem. Cup x 5

RECORDS **Attendance:** 1,826 v Stamford, FA Vase SF 1980
Goalscorer: Alan Sykes **Appearances:** Alan Sykes 620
Win: 7-0 v Ashton United **Defeat:** 0-8 v Bamber Bridge

FACT FILE
Formed: 1963 Nickname: The Blues
Colours: All Blue Change colours: All Red
Midweek matches: Monday
Programme: 40pages £1.00
Editor: Robert Hurst (0161 775 3883)
Website: www.curzon-ashton.co.uk

CLUB PERSONNEL
Chairman: Harry Galloway
Vice Chairman: R.onnie Capstick
Chief Executive: Harry Twamley
President: Peter Mayo
Press Officer:Graham Shuttleworth
Treasurer: Sam Shuttleworth
Manager: Gary Lowe
Assistant Manager: Derek Hall
Physio: Martin Rothwell

FLEETWOOD TOWN

Secretary: Kevin Pennington, 1 Carlisle Avenue, Fleetwood, Lancs. FY7 8LP.
Tel: 01253 771602 (H); 01253 822626 (B) 07967 192843 (M)
Email Address: fleetwoodfreeportfc@btinternet .com
or:kevin@fffcfreeserve.co.uk

Ground: Highbury Stadium, Park Avenue, Fleetwood, Lancs (01253 770702)

Directions: From M55, junction 3, follow signs (A585) to Fleetwood. At Nautical College campus (onleft) traffic island take first left, at second island take 6th exit. Stadium is 3/4 mile on left.

PREVIOUS **Leagues:** None **Names:** Fleetwood Wanderers (97-98)

RECORD **Attendance:** 6,150 v Rochdale F.A.Cup 1st Round 65-66

BEST SEASON: **FA Cup:** **FA Vase:**

HONOURS NWCFL v 2 Champions: 98-99 Div 2 Trophy Winners: 98-99

FACT FILE
Founded: 1997
(amalgamation of Fleetwood F.C. and Fleetwood Town who had disbanded at the end of season 1995-96)
Colours: Red & white/black/red
Change Colours:
Midweek Matchday: Tuesday
Programme: Price: Pages:
Editor:
Club Website: www.fleetwoodfreeportfc.co.uk

CLUB PERSONNEL
Chairman: Jim Betmead

get all the latest news on the

COMPETITIONS NEWSLINE

Updated daily with Draws, Match Dates, Venue Changes, Kick-off Times and Results for The Seven FA Competitions.

- Weekend results on Newsline after 6.30pm
- Midweek results on Newsline after 10.00pm
- Monday Cup draws on Newsline after 1.00pm.

09066 555 888

Presented by Tony Incenzo

Marketed by Sportslines, Scrutton Street, London EC2A 4PJ
01386 550204
Calls cost 60p per minute at all times.

Call costing correct at time of going to press (June 2003).

GLOSSOP NORTH END

Secretary: Peter Hammond, 15 Longmoor Road, Simmondley, Glossop, Derbys SK139NH
Tel: 01457 863852(H) 01457 854411(B)

Ground: Surrey Street, Glossop, Derbys (01457 855469).
Directions: A57 to Glossop.Left at traffic lights (near Tresco sign) into Glossopbrook Road then Follow road to top of hill and ground is on right. Buses 236 and 237 from Manchesterpass ground. Railway Station: Glossop Central.
Capacity: 2,374 Seats: 209 Cover: 509 Floodlights: Yes

Clubhouse: Licensed bar. Hot & cold drinks and pies etc on matchdays. **Club Shop:** Yes

HONOURS NWC Lge Lamot Pils Tphy 90-91; Manchester Lg 27-28(Gilgryst Cup 22-23 29-30 34-35 74-75); FA Amateur Cup QF 08-09. Manchester Premier Cup 1997 and 1998. Derbyshire Senior Cup 2000-01.

PREVIOUS **Leagues:** Midland 1896-98; Football Lge 1898-1915; Manchester Lge 15-56 66-78; Lancs Combination 56-66; Cheshire County 78-82.
Names: Glossop North End 1886-1898; Glossop FC 1898-1992.

BEST SEASON **FA Cup:** Quarter Final 1909 **FA Vase:**

RECORDS **Attendance:** 10,736 v Preston North End, FA Cup 1913/14
Fee paid: £3,000 for Andy Gorton (Lincoln City, 1989).
Fee received: £3,000 for Andy Gorton (Oldham Athletic, 1990).

Players progressing: Jimmy Rollands (Rochdale), Ray Redshaw (Wigan Athletic).

FACT FILE

Founded: 1886 Re-formed 1992
Nickname: Hillmen
Sponsor: T.B.A.
Colours: All Royal Blue
Change colours: AllGold.
Midweek Matches: Tuesday
Reserves' League: N.W.Co Res Lg
Programme: 32 pages, 50p
Editor: John Hamilton (01457 866216)

CLUB PERSONNEL

Chairman: Syd White
President: C T Boak
Press Officer: Secretary
Manager: Micky Boyle
Asst Manager: Ian Boyle
Physio:Mick Parr

MOSSLEY

Secretary: David Buckley, 18 Chellow Dene, Mossley, Ashton-under-Lyne, Lancs. OL5 0NB.
Tel: 01457 835989 Email:bobbuckley@mossleyafc.fsnet.co.uk
Ground: Seel Park, Market Street, Mossley, Lancs. (Grd 01457 832369), (Club 01457 836104)
Directions: From north; M60 J.23, then A635 to Ashton-U-Lyne, A670 Mossley to town centre Grd behind market place. From south; M6 Junc 19, A556, M56 to Junc 3, A5103 to M'chester, then Mancunian Way (A57M) to A635. Follow Ashton signs 5m, the Mossley signs via A670 to town centre. Rail: Mossley BR. Buses 153 from Manchester, 343 from Oldham, 350 from Ashton
Capacity: 4,500 Cover: 1,500 Seats: 200 Floodlights: Yes
Clubhouse: Open nights and matchdays **Club Shop**: Yes

HONOURS FA Trophy Runners-up 79-80; Northern Premier League 78-79 79-80 (R-up 80-81 81-82 82-83, Chall Cup 78-79; NWC Floodlit Trophy R-up 95-96 NWTL Div 1 R-up 98-99

BEST SEASON **FA Cup:** 2nd Rd replay 49-50, also 2nd Rd 80-81 & 1st Rd 6 times.
FA Trophy: Runners-up 79-80 **FA Vase:** 6th Rd 96-97, 99-00

PREVIOUS **Leagues:** Ashton; South East Lancs; Lancs Comb. 18-19; Cheshire County 19-72; Northen Prem. **Names:** Park Villa 03-04; Mossley Juniors 04-09.

RECORDS **Attendance:** 7,000 v Stalybridge 1950 **Fee Paid:** £2,300
Fee Received: £25,000 for Eamon O'Keefe (Everton, 1979)

FACT FILE

Formed: 1903 Nickname: Lilywhites
Colours:Black & white stripes/black/black
Change: Yellow/blue/blue
Midweek matchday: Tuesday
Programme: 28 Pages £1.00
Editor: John A. Cawthorne
Local Press : Oldham Evening Chronicle/ Mossley & Saddleworth Reporter/Manchester Evening News/Tameside Advertiser/Pink Final
Local Radio: BBC GMR/Key 103/ 96.2 Revolution

CLUB PERSONNEL

Chair: Sam Rigby Pres.: J Wharmby
Manager: Benny Phillips
Website: www.welcometo/mossleyafc
www.mossley.20m.com
Email: mossleyafc@hotmail.com

NANTWICH TOWN

Secretary: Bernard Lycett, 'Rivington", Clay lane, Haslington, Crewe CW11 5SE
Tel: 01270 584066 (H) 07876320280 Email Address: blycett@aol
Ground: Jackson Avenue, off London Road, Nantwich, Cheshire. Tel: 01270 624098
Directions: M6 Jct 16, A500 for Nantwich (about 8 miles), continue on A52 over railway crossing (London Rd), second right after railway crossing into Jackson Ave.
From Chester, use the A51.
Three miles from Crewe (BR).
Capacity: 1,500 Seats: 150 Cover: 555 Floodlights: Yes

Clubhouse: Every night except Sunday 8pm-11pm. Hot pies available **Club Shop:** Yes

HONOURS Cheshire Co. Lg 80-81; Ches. Snr Cup 75-76; N.W. Co.Lg.Cup 94-95

PREVIOUS **Leagues:** Shropshire & Dist.; The Combination 1892-94; Lancs Comb. 12-15; Cheshire Combination 19-38; Manchester; Mid-Cheshire; Cheshire County 68-82.
Name: Nantwich FC (pre 1973)

RECORDS **Attendance:** 2,750 v Altrincham, Cheshire Senior Cup 66-67
Fee r eceived: £4,000 from Stafford Rangers for D.Dawson
Record Goalscorer in Season: Gerry Duffy, 42 in 61-62

FACT FILE

Founded: 1884
Nickname: Dabbers
Club Sponsors: Jim Barrie Plant Hire
Colours: Black & white/black/black
Change colours: All green
Midweek matchday: TuesdayReserves' League:Springbank Midland
Programme: 18 pages, 65
Editor: Che Kerrin (01270 624098)
Club Website: www.nantwichtownfc.co.uk

CLUB PERSONNEL

Chairman: Clive Jackson
6 Spencer Close, Crewe CW2 8DT
01270 664469 (H) 07970 546238 (B)
Manager: Nigel Cleghorn
Physio: Ivan Robertson

NEWCASTLE TOWN

Secretary: John F Cotton, 293 Weston Rd., Weston Coyney, Stoke-on-Trent, Staffs. St3 6HA
Tel: 01782 333445 (H) 07977516879(M)
Ground: Lyme Valley Parkway Stadium, Lilleshall Rd, Clayton, Newcastle-under-Lyne, Staffs (01782 662351) (Club 01782 662350 also a fax)
Directions: M6 jct 15, A500 for Stoke, left at r'bout A519 for Newcastle, rightat 2nd r'bout into Stafford Ave., 1st left into Tittensor Road to ground. 3miles from Stoke-on-Trent (BR).
Seats: 300 Cover: 1,000 Capacity: 4,000 Floodlights: Yes **Club Shop:** Yes
Clubhouse: Saturday matchdays 12-7.30pm, midweek 5-11pm. Hot & cold food available.
HONOURS: Nth West Co's Lg Div 1 R-up 95-96 96-97,99-00 Div 2 R-up 91-92, Challenge Cup 96-97, R-up 99-00 F/Lit Trophy R-up 96-97; Lamot Pils Tphy 91-92; Mid Cheshire Lg Div1 85-86, R-up 86-78, Div 2 82-83, 90-91, Lge Cup 84-85; Walsall Snr Cup 93-94 94-95 R-up 95-96; Sentinel Cup 94-95; Tennents Floodlit Trophy 92-93 95-96; Staffs Snr Cup R-up 95-96, 01-02; Staffs M/W F/Light Lge 94-95 R-up 95-96; Staffs Presidents CupWinners 2002-03
RECORDS - Attendance: 3,948 v Notts County FA Cup Nov 96 **Win:** 8-0v Skelmersdale U.
Defeat: 0-5 v Eastwood Hanley (A) **Appearances:** Neil Pesteridge 385 (Lg only)
Goalscorer: Shaun Wade 105 (NWCL only) **F.A.Vase:** S-Final 99-00
PREVIOUS - Leagues: Hanley & Dist. Sunday; North Staffs Sunday; Potteries & Dist.Sunday; Res Refuge Ass Mid; Newcastle & Dist/ Staffs Co.; Mid Cheshire.
Names: Parkway Hanley (founded 1964, later Clayton Park, ParkwayClayton); Newcastle Town (founded 1980) - clubs merged in 1986.

FACT FILE
Founded: 1964 Nickname: Castle.
Sponsors:T.B.A.
Colours: All Royal Blue/blue/white
Change colours: All yellow
Midweek Matches: Tuesday
Reserve Team: SpringbankVending.Midland
Programme: 40 pages,£1.00
Editor: Peter Tindall 01260 280983 (H)
Website: www.nitvision.net/newcastletownfc

CLUB PERSONNEL
Chairman: J W Walker
Vice-Chairman: K G Walshaw
Press Officer: Mark Barlow (07976 805875)
General Manager:Jimmy Wallace
Manager: Michael Bates
Asst Manager: Michael Bates
Physio:Lee Arnold

2002-2003
Captain: Mark Beeston
Top Scorer: Andy Bott 31
Player of The Year:John Diskin

RAMSBOTTOM UNITED

Secretary: Malcolm Holt, 23 Newcombe Road,Holcombe Brook, Ramsbotham, Lancs.
Tel Nos: 01204 883085 (H) 0776 1828487 (M)

Ground: Riverside Ground, Acre Bottom, Ramsbottom. Tel: 01706 822799(Cricket Club)
Answer Phone: 01706 822458 (for match details) **Floodlights**: Yes
Email Sddress: final.inspection@madison filter.com
Directions: M66(North) to junction 1, take A56 towards Ramsbottom. After one mile turn left into Bury New Road. Turn left after the Mondi Paper Mill along the road running parallel with the East Lancs Railway. From North: M65 jct 8- A56 Follow signs ro Ramsbottom into town centre. Railway: Bury (Metrolink to Manchester) and Ramsbottom (East Lancs Railway)

HONOURS: Bolton Comb. Div. One Champs 72-73; Bolton Comb. Prem Div. 76-77, 86-87; Manchester Lge Div. One Champs 90-91; Manchester Lge Div. 1 Cup Winners 90-91; Gilgryst Cup Winners 94-95; NWCFL Div 2 Champ 96-97, Trophy 95-96

RECORDS **Attendance:** 829 v Southport F.A.C. 3Q 98-99
PREVIOUS **Leagues:** Bury Amateur League, Bolton Combination, Manchester Lge.
BEST SEASON: F.A. Cup: 3rd Q 1998-99 **F.A. Vase:** 2nd Round 98-99, 99-00

FACT FILE
Formed: 1966
Colours: Blue with white trim/blue/white
Change Colours:
Midweek Matchday: Tuesday
Programme: Pages: 46 Price:
Editor: Chris Dunn
Website: fhttp.ramsbottom united.2ya.oom

CLUB PERSONNEL
Prtesident: John Smith
Chairman Harry Williams (01706 823029)
Vice Chairman: Ian McCool
Press Officer: Ian McCool
Managers:Andy Grimshaw & Jimmy Clarke
Asst. Manager: Chris Burke

2002-2003
Captain: Ged Walsh
Top scorer~: Glynn Barker
Player of the Year: Simon Marsh

SALFORD CITY

Secretary: Frank McCauley, 22 Beverley Road, Pendlebury, Salford M27 4HY
Tel: 0161 736 0021 E mail: mccauley@yahoo.co.uk **Ground:** Moor Lane, Kersal, Salford, Manchester. Tel: 0161 792 6287
Directions: M62 jct 17, A56 Bury New Road to Manchester, continue thro' 4 sets of lights, right into Moor Lane, ground 500 yds left. 4 miles from Manchester Victoria (BR). Buses 96, 139, 94, 95 to Moor Lane
Capacity: 8,000 Seats: 260 Cover: 600 Floodlights: Yes
Clubhouse: Open matchdays only. Hot snacks

HONOURS Lancashire Amateur Cup 72-73 74-75 76-77; Manchester Senior Cup, Manchester Challenge Cup, Manchester Lg 74-75 75-76 76-77 78-79. Reserve Division North 2000-01. Reserve Division North Cup 2000-01.

PREVIOUS **Leagues:** Manchester 63-80; Cheshire Co. 80-82.
Names: Salford Central 40-63; Salford Amateurs 1963 until merger with Anson Villa; Salford FC.
Ground: Crescent, Salford

BEST SEASON **FA Cup:** **FA Vase:**

RECORDS **Attendance:** 3,000 v Whickham FA Vase 1981

FACT FILE

Founded: 1940
Nickname: Ammies
Colours: White with blue trim/blue/blue
Change colours: Yellow and sky blue
Midweek Matches: Tuesday
Reserves' League: NWC Res. Div. S.
Programme: 24 pages, £1.00
Editor: Dave Cooper

CLUB PERSONNEL

Chairman: DavidTaylor
Manager: Andy Brown
Press Officer: Secrtary
Commercial Manager: Stevie Plant

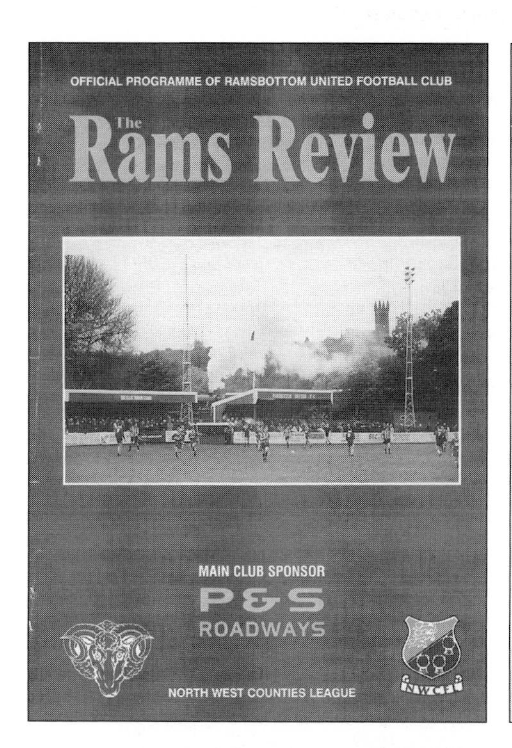
OFFICIAL PROGRAMME OF RAMSBOTTOM UNITED FOOTBALL CLUB
The
Rams Review
MAIN CLUB SPONSOR
P&S
ROADWAYS
NORTH WEST COUNTIES LEAGUE
NWCFL

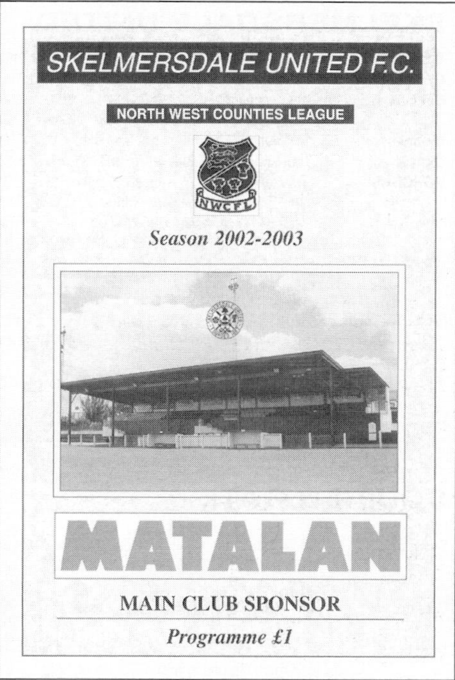
SKELMERSDALE UNITED F.C.
NORTH WEST COUNTIES LEAGUE
NWCFL
Season 2002-2003
MATALAN
MAIN CLUB SPONSOR
Programme £1

Welcome to Springbank Stadium Home of
STONE DOMINOES F.C.
Official Programme
Stone
DOMINOES
F.C.
Member of the
North Western Counties
Football League
NWCFL
www.stonedominoesfc.co.uk

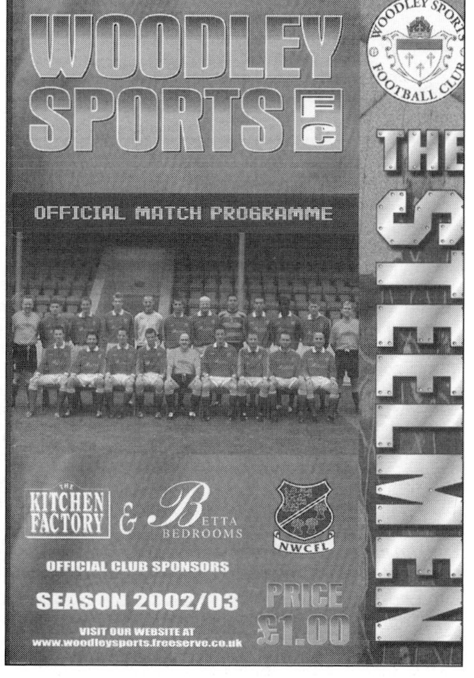
WOODLEY SPORTS FC
WOODLEY SPORTS FOOTBALL CLUB
THE STEELMEN
OFFICIAL MATCH PROGRAMME
KITCHEN FACTORY
& Betta BEDROOMS
NWCFL
OFFICIAL CLUB SPONSORS
SEASON 2002/03
PRICE £1.00
VISIT OUR WEBSITE AT
www.woodleysports.freeserve.co.uk

SKELMERSDALE UNITED

Secretary: Bryn Jones, 34 Bromilow Road, Skelmersdale, Lancs. WN8 8TU
Ground: c/o Burscough F.C.
Directions: as for BurscoughnF.C. for 2003-2004
Capacity: 10,000 Seats: 250 Cover: 1,000 Floodlights: Yes
Clubhouse: None. Matchday food bar sells hot drinks, soup, pies & pasties etc
Club Shop: No, but badges available in two colours.
HONOURS FA Amateur Cup 70-71 R-up 66-67; Ches. Co. Lg 68-69 69-70, Jubilee Cup 69-70; Lancs F'lit Cup 69-70; Lancs Jnr Cup 69-70 70-71; Ashworth Cup 70-71; Barassi Anglo-Italian Cup 70-71; Lancs Non-Lge Cup 73-74 74-75; North West Co's Lg Cup: 99-00 R-up 82-83.N.W.Co Div 2 R-Up: 97-98

PREVIOUS **Leagues:** Liverpool County Comb., Lancashire Comb. 1891-93, 03-07, 21-24 55-68, 76-78, Cheshire County 68-71 78-82, Northern Premier 71-76.

BEST SEASON **FA Cup:** 1st Rd 67-68, 0-2 v Scunthorpe(A), 68-69, 0-2 v Chesterfield(A), 71-72, 0-4 v Tranmere R. (H) **FA Amateur Cup:** Winners 70-71

RECORDS **Attendance:** 7,000 v Slough, FA Amat Cup Q-F '67

FACT FILE
Founded: 1882
Nickname: Skem
Sponsors:Matalan
Colours: Blue & white stripes/blue/blue
Change colours: Red & white stripes/red/red
Midweek Matches: Tuesday
Reserves: Liverpool Co Football Combination
Programme: 32 pages, £1
Editor: Nic Rudd)(nicrudd@ talk21 .com**CLUB PERSONNEL**
President: D.Tomlinson
Managing Director: A.Gore -
Press Officer: Secretary
Manager: Paul Gallagher
Asst Manager: Mick Buoey
Coach: CliffTalbot
Physio: Billy Leigh& Ronnie Taylor
2002-2003
Captain,Top Scorer and Player of the Year: Stuart Rudd

SQUIRES GATE

Secretary: Jeff Webster, 168 Highcross Road, Poulton-Le-Fylde, FY6 8DA. Tel/Fax: 01253 890846. Mobile 077406 44335

Ground: School Road, Marton, Blackpool, Lancs. Tel: 01253 798584

Directions: M6 to M55 jct 4, left onto A583, right at 1st lights (Whitehall Rd) follow signs for airport. Ground approx 1.5 miles on right. Nearest station Blackpool South.
Capacity: 1000 Seats: 2 new stands (100 seats) Cover: One side Floodlights: Yes
Clubhouse: Yes

HONOURS West Lancs Lg: Div 2 80-81, Richardson Cup 86-87, N.W.C.L 2nd Div Trophy winners 2000/01

PREVIOUS **Leagues:** W. Lancs (pre-1991)

RECORD **Attendance:** 600 v Everton 95

FACT FILE

Formed: 1948
Colours: Royal/black/royal
Change Colours:
Midweek Matches: Tuesday
Programme: 20 pages Price:
Editor:

CLUB PERSONNEL

Chairman: P Mack (01772 339955)
Life Vice President: Wilf Carr

Manager: Gordon Fell
Assistant Manager: Joe Dewhurst
Reserves Manager: Dean Whitehead

ST HELENS TOWN

Secretary: John McKiernan,35 Royston Gardens,Peasley Cross,St Helens WA 1RJ Tel No: 01744 635826 **Ground:** St Helens R.L.F.C. , Knowsley Road, St Helens **Directions: From South:** M62 Jct 7-5th exit (St Helens) 3rd r'about (Sherdley), follow Town Centre signs. Left at r'about to L'pool & Prescot.Rt at lights then left at Black Bull after 1 mile. Ground on right. **From North:** M6.Jct 23 take A580 to L'pool.7 mile left to A570 and 1st Rt into Bleak Hilll Road.Left at right hand bend after 1 mile into Mill Brow. At T jct left at Black Bull, turn right -ground on left.
Capacity: 19,100 **Seats:** 2,362 **Cover:** 12,408 **Floodlights:** Yes

Clubhouse: Weekdays 8-11pm, Saturday matchdays 2-6.30pm. **Club Shop:** Yes
HONOURS: FA Vase 86-87; George Mahon Cup 49-50; Lancs Comb. 71-72, Div 2 50-51, Lg Cup R-up 70-71;Liverpool Snr Non Lge Cup R-up 76-77; Lancs Jnr Cup R-up 66-67; Bass Charrington Cup 73-74; Carling Chall Cup r-up 93-94; N.W.C. Floodlit Trophy r-up 97-98.

PREVIOUS **Leagues:** Lancs Comb. 03-14 49-75; Liverpool County Comb. 49-74; Cheshire County 74-82. **Grounds:** Park Road 01-52; City Road 52-53.

BEST SEASON **FA Cup:** 4th Q Rd 85-86 **FA Vase:** Winners 86-87

RECORDS **Gate:** 4,000 v Manchester City, Bert Trautmann transfer match,April 1950.
Goalscorer: S Pennington **W in:** 10-4 v Everton `B' 1952
Appearances: Alan Wellens **Defeat** : 1-8 v Liverpool Res., L'pool Snr Cup 1950

FACT FILE
Founded: 1946
Nickname: `Town'
Colours: Red & white/white/red
Change colours: Royal blue & white/white/royal blue
Midweek Matches: Tuesday
Programme: 24 pages, 50p
Editor: John McKiernan (01744 600612)
Local Press: Reporter, Star, Echo.
CLUB PERSONNEL
Chairman/Press Officer: Jim Barrett
Public Liaison Officer: John McKiernan
01744 635826 (H) 01744 24348 (W)
Manager: John Davison
Asst Manager: G Walker
Coach: John Neary

STONE DOMINOES

Secretary: Vicky Turner,Springbank House,Station Road,Barlaston, Staffs ST12 9DE
Tel: 01782 373298 (H) 07866 096198 (M) 01782 220775 (W)

Ground: Springbank Stadium, Kings Park, Meir Heath, Stoke on Trent, Staffs.
Tel: 01785 761891

Directions: Please Phone club for details

Floodlights: Yes

Honours: Midland Lge Div. 1 99-00, Div. 2 R-up 96-97, N.W.C.: Div 2 Winners 2002-2003
Div.1 Cup 98-99, Div. 2 Cup 96-97, Charity Shield 00

Previous League: Midland League

Record Attendance: 207 v Bacup Borough 21.4.03

FACT FILE
Formed: 1987
Colours:White/red/white
Change Colours: Yellow/blue/white
Midweek Matchday: Tuesday
Programme: Price:£1.00

PERSONNEL
Chairman: Bob Bowers
Springbank House, Station Road,
Barlaston, Staffs.
Tel: 01782 373298 (H) 01785 815551 (B)

Manager: Andy O'Connor
Physios: Rob Brindley & Steve Killeen

2002-2003
Captain: Lee Lawton
Top Scorer: Dave Walker 30

TRAFFORD

GROUND: Shawe View, Pennybridge Lane, Flixton, Urmston, Manchester M41 5DL
Tel: 0161 7471727 Email: dave-murray@traffordfc.freeserve.co.uk

Directions: M60 jct 9, B5158 towards Urmston, at 1st r/about take 1st exit, 1st lights turn right into Moorside Road, at nextr/about 2nd exit into Bowfell Rd, at next lights turn sharp left, then immediately right into Pennybridge Lane next to Bird-in-Hand Pub parking on left 100yds

Capacity: 2,500 Cover: 740 Seats: 292
Clubhouse: Yes **Club Shop:** Yes
Previous - Leagues: Mid Ches. 90-92; N.W.C. 92-97; N.P.L. 97-03. **Name**: NorthTrafford 90-94.

CLUB RECORDS **Attendance:** 803 v Flixton (NPL Div 1 27/12/97)
Goalscorer: Garry Vaughan 88 **Appearances:** Garry Vaughan 293
Win: 10-0 v Haslingden St Mary's (LancsAmt Shield 91)
Defeat: 0-6 v Oldham Town (NWCL Div 2 93)
Fee Paid: Undisclosed for Jock Russell (Radcliffe Borough)
Fee Received: Undisclosed for Mike Turner (Witton A.)

BEST SEASON **FA Vase:** 5th Rd 95-96 **FA Trophy:** 3rd Round 2000-01
FACup: 2nd Rd Qual 95-96,99-00

HONOURS Lamont Pils Trophy 93-94; NWCL Div 1 96-97, Div 2 R-up 93-94, Lge ChallCup R-up 96-97; Res Div 93-94; Carling Chall Cup R-up 94-95; Manchester PremCup R-up 94-95, R-up 96-97, Res Div Champ 96-97, Cup 96-97; Manchester Amt Cup 96-97,01-02 Unifilla 1st Div Cup 97-98 Unibond Presidents Cup 99-00 Mid Cheshire Div 2 99-00

FACT FILE
Formed: 1990
Nickname: The North
Sponsors: Caffro Construction Ltd
Colours: All White
Change colours: All Yellow
Midweek Matchday: Tuesday
Reserve League: Mid Cheshire Div 2
Website: www.traffordfc.freeserve.co.uk
Programme
Pages: 44 Price: £1
Editor: David Murray (0161 775 7509)

CLUB PERSONNEL
Chairman: Tom Walmsley
President: David Roberts
Secretary: Graham Foxall
90 Grosvenor Road, Urmston M41 5AQ
Tel: 0161 747 4502

Manager: Joey Dunn
Asst Manager: Stuart Humphries

WARRINGTON TOWN

Secretary: Barry Thorpe, 46 Greenheys Road,Little Hulton,Manchester M389TP(01617901490)
Ground: Cantilever Park, Common Lane, Latchford, Warrington WA4 2RS
Tel: 01925 631932 (Club), 01925 653044 (office), 01925-653044 (FAX,only on matchdays).
Directions: M6 junction 20, then A50 towards Warrington. After 2 miles turn left immediately after swing bridge into Station Road, ground 600yds on left. From town centre travel 1 mile south on A49, left at lights into Loushers Lane, ground quarter mile on right. 2miles from Warrington Bank Quay (BR)
Capacity: 2,000 **Cover:** 650 **Seats**: 350 **Floodlights:** Yes **Club Shop:** Yes (Barry Thorpe)
Clubhouse: Weekdays 1-11pm, Sat. 12-11pm, Sun. 12-11 p.m. Bar food on matchdays

PREVIOUS **Leagues:** Warrington & Dist. 49-52; Mid-Cheshire 52-78; Cheshire Co. 78-82; N.W.C. 82-90; N.P.L 90-97. **Name:** Stockton Heath 1949-62.

RECORDS **Attendance:** 2,600 v Halesowen T., FA Vase S-F 1st leg 85-86.
Goalscorer: Steve Hughes 167
Fee Received: £60,000 for Liam Watson (Preston N. E.) 92-93

BEST SEASON **FA Cup:** 4th Qual. Rd 94-95 replay with Hyde Utd..
FA Vase: Runners-up 86-87 **FA Trophy:** Quarter-Finalists 92-93

HONOURS: FA Vase R-up 86-87; N.W.C. Lge 89-90 (Lg Cup 85-86 87-88 88-89 (R-up 89-90), Div 2 00-01R-up 86-87, Div 3 R-up 82-83; Mid-Cheshire Lg 60-61 R-up 57-58, Lg Cup 54-55 55-56 11-12 72-73, Altrincham Amat. Cup 54-55,

Players progressing recently: M Leonard (Everton), N Whalley & L Watson (P.N.E.) 92-93.

FACT FILE
Formed: 194 8 Nickname: The Town
Colours: Blue & yellow/blue/blue
Change colours: Orange/black/black
Midweek matchday: Tuesday
Reserves' League: Mid-Cheshire
Programme: 48-60 Pages £1.00
League Programme of the Year 2002-03
Editor: Paul Roach, 55 Moorcroft,
New Brighton, Mold, Flintshire CH7 6RU
Tel: 01352 752489, 07740 430190 (M))

CLUB PERSONNEL
Chairman: Harry Boden
Vice Chairman: D.J.Hughes
Press Officer: Colin Serjent
Managers: Derek Brownbill & Glenn Walker
Coach: Steve Pennington

2002-2003
Captain: Lee Webster
Top Scorer: Andy Moore
Player of the Year: Andy Moore

WOODLEY SPORTS

Secretary: Tony Whiteside, 4 Hayfield Road, Bredbury, Stockport, Cheshire SK6 1DE
0161 406 5599 (W) 077787 66382 (M)

Ground: Lambeth Grove Stadium, Lambeth Grove, Woodley, Stockport.
Tel: 0161 494 6429 Floodlights: yes

Directions: M60 Jct 25, follow signs (A560) Bredbury, take left filter at lights which brings you onto A560 Stockport Road for approx 1 mile, turn left at pub, Lowes Arms into Mill Street which goes into Mill Lane. Over bridge take 2nd right into Woodlands Avenue, then 1st left into Lambeth Grove.
Ground 200 yards ahead.
Floodlights: Yes

HONOURS NWC Div 2 99-00

RECORD **Attendance:** 1,500 v Stockport County

PREVIOUS **Leagues:** Lancashire & Cheshire, Manchester League.

BEST SEASON **FA Cup:** 99-00 **FA Vase:** 1st Round 1998-99

FACT FILE

Founded: 1970
Colours: Royal Blue & white stries/White/Red
Change Colours:White
Midweek Matchday: Tuesday
Programme: Pages: 48 Price:£1.00
Editor:Tony Whiteside

CLUB PERSONNEL

Chairman: Ian Campbell
20 Boundary Green,Denton, Manchester M34 3BYTel No: 0161 336 2745
Manager:Tony Hancock
Asst. Manager:Paul Kirkham
Physio:Darrin Whittaker

2002-2003

Captain: Andy Pavey
Top Scorer & P.o.Y.: Mike Norton

ASHTON TOWN

Secretary: Stephen Barrett, 11 Clement Avenue, Atherton M46 0PT
Tel Nos: 01942 889492 (H) 01942 529312 (W)
Ground: Edge Green Street, Ashton-in-Makerfield, Wigan WN4 8SY (01942 510677)
Directions: M6 Jct 23, A49 to Ashton-in-M. Right at lights onto A58 towards Bolton. After 3/4 mile turn right at `Rams Head' P.H. into Golbourne Rd. After 200 yds right into Edge Green Str. Ground at end.
Floodlights: No

HONOURS Warrington Lg Guardian Cup.
PREVIOUS **Leagues:** Warrington, Lancs Comb. 03-11 71-78, Ches. Co. 78-82.
BEST SEASON **FA Vase:** Prelim. Rd 84-85
RECORD **Gate:** 600 v Accrington Stanley 76-77

FACT FILE

Founded: 1962
Colours: Red with white trim/red/red
Change colours: All sky blue
Midweek Matches: Tuesday
Programme: Price: Pages:
Editor:

CLUB PERSONNEL

President: W Pomfrett
Chairman: Len Riley
Manager: Norman Hickson
Physio:

BLACKPOOL MECHANICS

Secretary: Brian Wood,7 Kendal Avenue,Blackpool FY3 7LG (01253 391079)
Ground: Jepson Way, Common Edge Rd, Blackpool, Lancs FY4 5DY (01253 761721).
Directions: M6 to M55, follow Airport signs. Left at r'bout along A583 (Preston New Rd) to lights, right into Whitehill Rd, becomes School Rd, to lights.Straight over main road & follow signs for Blackpool Mechanics F.C. to ground.Rail to Blackpool North - then bus 11c from Talbot Rd bus station (next to rail station) to Shovels Hotel, Common Edge Rd.
Capacity: 2,000 Seats: 250 Cover: 1,700 Floodlights: Yes
Clubhouse: Match days, training nights. Dancehall. Matchday, hot food.
Club Shop: Manager Andrew Sneddon (01253 729962). Ties, sweaters, old programmes, badges.
HONOURS Lancs Comb Bridge Shield 72-73; NW Co's. Lg Div 3 85-86; W Lancs Lg 60-61 62-63; Lancs County FA Shield 57-58 60-61:
PREVIOUS **Leagues:** Blackpool & Fylde Comb., West Lancs, Lancs Comb. 62-68.
Grounds: Stanley Pk 47-49
RECORD **Gate:** 1,200 v Morecambe, Lancs Comb, August 1968

FACT FILE

Founded: 1947 Nickname: Mechs
Sponsors: Bloomfield Bakery Blackpool.
Club colours: Tangerine/white/tangerine
Change colours: All blue
Midweek matchday: Wednesday
Programme: 10 pages, 50p
Editor: David Gore

CLUB PERSONN

Chairman: John Sanderson
President: Gregory Gregorio
Commercial Manager: John Sanderson
Manager: Brian Wilson
Asst Man.: Stuart Parker
Coach: William Singleton.

CASTLETON GABRIELS

Secretary: David Lord, 34 Fairway, Castleton, Rochdale OL11 3BU Tel: 01706 522719
Ground: Butterworth Park, Chadwick Lane, off Heywood Rd., Castleton, Rochdale. Tel: 01706 527103) **Directions:** M62 Jct 20, A6272M to r'bout. Left towards Castleton (A664Edinburgh Way) to next r'bout, keeping Tesco Superstore to the left, take 1st exit to next r'bout, take 2nd exit into Manchester Rd (A664), after just under mile turn right at `Top House' P.H. into Heywood Rd., to end & ground on right
Capacity: 1,500 Seats: 400 Cover: 650 Floodlights: Yes
Clubhouse: Open seven nights a night and all day Saturday. Pie & peas and sandwiches available matchdays (pie & peas only at Reserve matches) **Club Shop:** No
HONOURS Manchester Lge 86-87, Murray Shield 86-87; Res Div Cup 95-96.
PREVIOUS **Leagues:** Rochdale Alliance 24-84; Manchester 84-89.
Name: St Gabriels (pre-1960s) **Ground:** Park pitches; Springfield Pk 60-81.
RECORDS **Gate:** 640 v Rochdale, pre-season friendly 1991 **Win:** 8-0 v Squires Gate N.W.Co.Div 2 94 **Defeat:** 1-10 v Blackpool Mechanics N.W.Co.Div 2 95

FACT FILE

Founded: 1924 Nickname: Gabs
Club Sponsors: Kick Off
Colours: Sky & Navy Blue/Sky & Navy/Navy
Change colours: All red
Midweek matchday: Tuesday
Reserves ' League: N.W.C. Res. Div.
Programme: 28 pages, 50p
Editor: David Jones (01942 730220 -W)

CLUB PERSONNEL

Chairman: Rod Harling
Vice Chairman: R Butterworth
Press Officer: Secretary
Manager/Coach:David Jones
Assistant Manager:Roy Grundy
Coach: Neil Mills

CHADDERTON

Secretary: Ronald Manton,77 Denton Lane, Chadderton, Oldham OL9 9AC
Ground: Andrew Street, Chadderton, Oldham, Lancs (0161 624 9733) **Capacity:** 2,500
Directions: M62 Jct 20, A627(M) to M'chester.. M'way becomes dual carriageway. Left at 1st major traffic lights A669 Middleton Rd, then first left into Butterworth Street. Andrew Street is second right. Oldham Werneth (BR) 1 m or Mills Hill (BR) I m.Buses 24,181,182 to Middleton Rd
from Lever Street of Piccadilly Gardens. **Seats:** 200 **Cover**: 600 **Floodlights**: Yes
Clubhouse: Matchdays only. Hot & cold snack during & after games **Club Shop:** No
HONOURS M'chester Am Lg 62-63, North Div 55-56, M. Prem Cup R-up 82-83, Chall Tphy 71-72, R-up 72-73, M. Lg Div 1 66-67, Div 2 64-65, Gilgryst Cup 69-70, Murray Shield 65-66, Lancs Comb. Cup R-up 81-82, Alf Pettit & Hulme Celtic Cup 61-62, NWC F/lit Tphy R-up 92-93
Manchester Umbro International Cup Winners 2000
RECORD Gate: 1,500 v Guinness Ex'ts 1969 **Appearances:** Billy Elwell 750+ (64-90)
Players progressing: (include) David Platt (Crewe, Arsenal), John Pemberton (Crewe,Leeds U)

FACT FILE

Founded: 1947 Nickname: Chaddy
Colours:Red/White/White
Change colours: All Yellow
Midweek Matches: Tuesday
Programme: 28-32 pages
Editor: David Greaves
Previous Leagues: Oldham Am, Manchester Am, Manchester 64-80, Lancs Comb 80-82

CLUB PERSONNEL

Chairman: Harry Mayall
President: Derek Glynn
Manager: Mike Lester

2002-2003

Captain:Jamie Lester
P.o.Y.: Gary Kelly Top Scorer: Chris Cotton 7

CHEADLE TOWN

Secretary: David Busby, 9 Tatton Road, Handforth, Wilmslow, Cheshire Sk9 3QZ
Tel Nos: 01625 524116 ((H) o7932 634630 (M)
Ground: Park Road Stadium, Park Road, Cheadle, Cheshire SK8 2AN (0161 4282510).
Directions: M60 Jct 2, follow signs towards Cheadle (A560), first left after lights into Park Road, ground at end. 1 mile from Gatley (BR), buses from Stockport.
Capacity: 2,500 Seats: 300 Cover: 300 Floodlights Yes
Clubhouse: Open every night. Food available **Club Shop**: No
HONOURS Manchester Lg Div 1 79-80 (R-up 80-81 81-82); Manchester Amtr Cup 79-80;Lamot Pils R-up 90-91; NWCFL Div 2 Trophy R-up 95-96:
PREVIOUS **Leagues**: Manchester (pre 1987)
RECORD **Attendance :** 1,700 v Stockport County, August 1994.
Scorer: Peter Tilley **Appearances:** John McArdle
Players progressing: Ashley Ward (Crewe), Steve Bushell (York), Dean Crowe(Stoke).
2002-2003: **Captain**: Robert Kempton **Top Scorer:** Billy Bailey **P.o.Y.**: Lee Wakefield.

FACT FILE
Founded: 1961
Colours: White/navy/navy
Change colours: Red/white/red
Midweek Matches: Wednesday 7.45
Reserves' Lge: Mid Cheshire Div 2
Programme: 24 pages,£1.00
Editor: Stuart Crawford

CLUB PERSONNEL
President: Freddie Pye
Chairman: Chris Davies
Vice-Chairman: Clive Williams
Press Officer: Chris Davies (0161 428 2510).
Manager:Paul Cunningham
Player Coach: Tony Coyle

COLNE F C

Secretary: Ray Davies,11 Robinson Street,Colne, Lancs BB8 9PU (01282 859120)

Ground: Holt House Stadium, Holt House, Colne. (Tel: 01282 862545)
Directions: Enter Colne from M65 to roundabout, keep left follow signs for Keighley. At next roundabout turn left, continue on Harrison Drive over mini roundabout & follow road to ground. Nearest Railway station - Colne.
Capacity: 1,800 Seats: 100 Cover: 1000 Floodlights: Yes

Clubhouse: Yes,Small Lounge Bar open on matchdays **Club Shop:** No
HONOURS BEP Cup Winners 96-97
BEST SEASON **FA Cup:** **FA Vase:**
RECORDS **Attendance:** 240 v Nelson 97-98
Scorer: Geoff Payton **Appearances:** Nick Roscoe
PREVIOUS **Leagues:** East Lancashire League

FACT FILE
Formed: 1996
Colours: All red
Change colours: All yellow
Midweek Matchday: Wednesday
Programme: Yes Editor: Ray Moore

CLUB PERSONNEL
Chairman: Dave Blacklock
Press Officer: Ray Moore(01282 868857)
Manager:Denzil Hart

DAISY HILL

Secretary: Bob Naylor, 8 Bailey Fold, Westhoughton, Bolton, Lancs BL5 3HH 01942 813720
Ground: New Sirs, St James Street, Westhoughton, Bolton, Lancs. 01942 818544
Directions: M61 Jct 5, A58 (Snydale Way/Park Road) for 1.5 miles, left into Leigh Road (B5235) for 1 mile, right into village then left between Church and School into St James Street. Ground 250 yds on the left. Half mile from Daisy Hill (BR)
Capacity: 2,000 Seats: 200 Cover: 250 Floodlights: No Club Shop: No
Clubhouse: Open normal licensing hours during any football activity. Snacks on matchdays
HONOURS Bolton Comb Prem Div 62-63 72-73 75-76 77-78, Lg Cup 59-60 61-62 71-72 72-73; Lancs Shield 61-62 71-72 86-87:
PREVIOUS **Leagues:** Westhoughton; Bolton Comb.; Lancs Combination. 78-82.
Name: Westhoughton Town **Record Goals & Apps:**Alan Roscoe 300-450
BEST SEASON **FA Cup:** **FA Vase:**
RECORD **Attendance:** 2,000 v Horwich RMI,Westhoughton Charity Cup Final 79-80
Players Progressing: Barry Butler (Chester C)+ Phil Priestley (Rochdale)via Atherton LR

FACT FILE
Founded: 1894(first known records)
Reformed: 1952
Colours: All royal blue Change: All red
Midweek Matches: Tuesday
Reserves' Lge NWCL Res Div
Programme: 40 pages 80p
Editor: T.B.A.
CLUB PERSONNEL
Chairman:Tony Veitch
Manager: Joe Paladino

DARWEN

Secretary: Lynn Atkinson, 14 Prospect Gardens,Darwen, Lancs (01254 708158)
Ground: Anchor Ground, Anchor Road, Darwen, Lancs BB3 0BB, (01254 705627)
Directions: A666 Blackburn / Bolton road, 1 mile north of Darwen town centre,turn right at Anchor Hotel, ground 200 yds on left. One and a half miles from Darwen (BR), bus 51 to Anchor Hotel.From M65 Jct 4 signs to Darwen.Left at A666,1/2 mile left at anchor Hotel. ground 200 yds on left Capacity: 4,000 Seats: 250 Cover: 2,000 Floodlights: Yes
Clubhouse: Matchday only **Club Shop:** No
HONOURS Lancs Comb 31 32 73 75: Comb Cup 30 31 75; Lancs Jun Cup 73; Geo Watson Trophy 73; LFA Yth Cup 75; NWC Cup 83; Lancs F/Lit Trophy 90; NWC Res Div Cup 94; Blackburn & Dist Yth Lge 94 95 97, Cup 94 95 97; NW All Chall Cup 96.
PREVIOUS **Leagues**:Football Alliance 1889-91, Football Lg 1891-99, Lancs Lg 99-03,Lancs Comb. 03-75, Ches. Co. 75-82. **Ground:** Barley Bank
RECORD **Gate:** (Anchor Ground) 10,000 v Fleetwood Lancs Jun Cup 1920
BEST SEASON **FA Cup**: Semi Finals 1881

FACT FILE
Founded: 1875
Sponsors:
Colours: Red & white/red/red
Change colours: All blue
Midweek Matches: Tuesday
Reserves' League: NWC Res. Div.
Programme: 20 pages, £1.00 Editor: S.Hart
Local papers: Lancs Evening Telegraph
CLUB PERSONNEL
President: E Devlin
Chairwoman: Mrs K Marah
Manager: S Wilkes
Asst Manager: M Atkinson
Physio: Mick Sharples

Abbey Hey F.C. Back Row (L-R): Tony Hancock (Manager, Andy Harris, Jamie Fitzpatrick, James Stanton, David Amison, Dale Johnson, Liam Higginbottom, Callum Dempsey, Stuart Cole, Lee Darbyshire (physio), Paul Kirkham (Asst. Manager), Paul O'Grady, Alan Boswell.
Front Row: Brian Walsh, Phil McGahey, Jimmy Robinson, Darren Evans, Jason Kneen, Anthony Hargreaves, Ryan Gibson, Damian Morrison, Mattie Williams, Mark Egerton.

Photo: Bill Wheatcroft.

Blackpool Mechanics F.C. Photo: Bill Wheatcroft.

ECCLESHALL

Ground: Pershall Park, Chester Road, Eccleshall, Staffordshire Tel: 01785 851351
PREVIOUS **Leagues**: Midland League to2003

FACT FILE

CLUB PERSONNEL

FLIXTON

Secretary: Terry Langford, 56 Garstang Ave, Bolton, BL2 6JN Tel: 07939 557261 (M)
Ground: Valley Road, Flixton, Manchester M41 8RQ Tel: 0161 747 7757
Directions: Leave M60 take B5214 signed Urmston. At 2nd R'about take 3rd exit. Take right only lane on the exit into Davyhulme Rd. Follow road to Valley Rd, just after a left hand bend after 1.5 miles. Ground is at the other end of the road. Coaches as above and carry on to the next R'about take 4th exit (Woodbridge Rd). The ground is at the bottom of this road.
Capacity: 2,000 Cover: 650 Seats: 250 email: footytel@ntlworld.com
Clubhouse: Open daily 3.00pm-11pm. Sandwiches available most eves **Club Shop:** No
Previous Leagues: S. Manchester & Wythenshawe 60-63; Lancs & Cheshire 63-73; Manchester 73-86; NWC 86-96; NPL 97-00 **Best season FA Vase:** Semi-final 95-96
Record Attendance: 1,543 v Brigg Town FA Vase Semi-Final 95-96
HONOURS NWC Div I 95-96, Div 2 94-95 Lg.Cup 94-95 95-96 R-up 87-88, Div 3 R-up 86-87; Manc. Lg R-up x3, Div 1 77-78, Open Tphy 80-81; Lancs Amtr Cup 79-80 (R-up 80-81); Manc. Chal. Tphy 83-84 R-up x2; Manc. Prem. Cup R-up 86-87 91-92; Manc. Amtr Cup R-up 88-89

FACT FILE
Formed: 1960 Nickname: Valiants
Colours: Blue & white stripes/blue/blue
Change Colours: Gold/black/black
Midweek home matchday: Tuesday
Reserves' League: NWCo FL Res Div
Programme - Pages: 36 Price: £1.00
Editor: Roy Mitchell

CLUB PERSONNEL
Chairman: Richard Bibby President: F H Eadie
Manager: Paul Wright
Matchday Contact: Paul Chadwick
Tel : 0161 747 6315 (H) or 07754 416889 (M)
2002-03 Goalscorer: Michael Brandon
Captain: & P.o.Y.: Richard Bibby

FORMBY

Secretary: Dave Dickinson, 2 Seafield, Formby, Merseyside L37 4EL Tel : 01704 870944
Ground: Altcar Road, Formby, Merseyside (01704 833505) Website: www.formbfc.co.uk
Directions: Turn right at lights opposite Tesco into Altcar Road. Through mini roundabout and ground is on the rigt next to refuse tip
Capacity: 2,000 Seats: 220 Cover: 500 Floodlights: November 2002
Clubhouse: None. Matchday refreshment bar stocks hot food & drinks
Club Shop: Sells programmes, badges & souvenirs.
HONOURS Liverpool Co. Comb. 48-49, R-up 64-65; Liverpool Senior Cup 77-78, R-up 84-85; Challenge Cup 52-53 63-64 67-68, R-up 64-65; Amtr Cup 29-30 47-48 48-49; Lamot Pils Trophy 94-95; George Mahon Cup 64-65, R-up 55-56 56-57; Lancs Co FA Amt Cup 34-35, Worthington Trophy 00-01
PREVIOUS Leagues: Liverpool Co. Comb. 19-68/ Lancs Comb. 68-71, Ches. Co. 71-82.
BEST SEASON **FA Cup:** 1st Rd 73-74, 0-2 v Oldham Ath. (H) **FA Trophy:** 1st Rd 73-74, lost to Stalybridge Celtic **FA Vase:** 2nd Rd 96-97, lost to Tetley Walker

Founded: 1919 Nickname: Squirrels
Club Sponsors: DKS Packaging
Colours: Yellow/blue/yellow
Change:Green/black/black
Midweek Matches: Tuesday
Reserves : Liverpool Co.unty Comb Div 2
Prog: 36 pages, £1.00
Ed: Dave Cookson (01772 311681)

CLUB PERSONNEL
Chairman: Chris Welsh
Comm. Man.:Dave Dickinson (01704 870944)
Managers: Peter Hennerty & Mike Scott
Physio: Barry O'Connor

GREAT HARWOOD TOWN

Secretary: Mark Jones, 15 Elm Close, Rishton,Blackburn, BB1 4HN Tel: 01254 876822(H)
Ground: The Sportsmans, Wood Street, Great Harwood, Lancs Tel: 01254 883913
Directions: M66 from Manchester to Haslingden exit, A680 through Baxenden, Accrington to Clayton-le-Moors, left at the Hyndburn Bridge Hotel into Hyndburn Road and right into Wood Street to ground. 3miles from Rishton (BR), 6 miles from Blackburn (BR). Various buses from Heyes Lane & Park Road to Blackburn & Accrington
Capacity: 2,500 Cover: 700 Seats: 200 Floodlights: Yes
Clubhouse: The Sportsman just outside ground. Normal licensing hours. Full bar facilities. Squash courts and gym. Hot & cold snacks & drinks on matchdays from tea bar in ground
Club Shop: Sells programmes, badges, key rings, shirts. Contact: J McKay (c/o club)
HONOURS N.W.C. R-up 91-92, Div 2 90-91, Lamot Pils Tphy 89-90, R-up 90-91, Tennents F'lit Trophy 91-92, Lancs ATS Chall. Trophy 91-92, R-up 90-91
PREVIOUS Leagues: West Lancashire; Lancs Comb. 79-82; N.W.C. 82-92; N.P.L. 92-99
Record Gate: 5,397 v Manchester Utd, 1980. **Best Season - FA Cup:** 1st Qual. Rnd replay 92-93, 1-2 v Atherton LR (H), after 1-1 **FA Vase:** Quarter Finals 90-91, 1-2 v Littlehampton Town (A)

FACT FILE
Formed: 1965 Nickname: Robins
Club Sponsors: None
Colours: All red
Change colours: All blue
Midweek Matches: Monday
Reserves' league: West Lancs Lge
Programme: Pages: 20 Price: 20p
Editor: D Bennet

CLUB PERSONNEL
Chairman: William Holden
Press Officer: K Lambert
Commercial Manager: Mark Smith
Manager: M Crabbe
Asst Manager: Dave Sargent

HOLKER OLD BOYS

Secretary: John Adams, 20 Middlefield,Barrow in Furness, Cumbria. LA14 4AU(01229 431121)
Ground: Rakesmoor Lane, Hawcoat, Barrow-in-Furness, Cumbria (01229 828176)
Directions: M6 Jct 36, A590 to Barrow-in-Furness, on entering Barrow, continue on A590 past Kimberley Clark Paper Mill. Take Bank Lane,first lefttto Hawcoat 3/4 mile.At top of hill turn lrft into Rakesmoor Lane Ground 200yds on right.
Capacity: 2,500 Seats: 220Cover: 500 Floodlights: Yes
Clubhouse: Tue,Thur, Fri 8-11pm, Sat noon-11pm, Sun normal licensing. Pies & peas on matchdays **Club Shop:** No
HONOURS W Lancs Lg 86-87, R-up 85-86; Lancs Junior Shield 88-89 90-91.
PREVIOUS **Leagues:** North Western; Furness Premier; West Lancs 70-91.
RECORDS **Attendance:** 1240 v Barrow ATS Trophy 95-96 **Win:** 12-0
Defeat: 1-8 v Newcastle T. (H) 91-92 **Top Scorer:** Dave Conlin

FACT FILE
Founded: 1936 Nickname: Cobs
Sponsors: Schofield Construction &Specsavers
Colours:White with Jade band,jade& white
Change: Gold & Navy Blue/navy blue
Midweek Matches: Tuesday
Programme: 32pages, £1.00
CLUB PERSONNEL
President: David Ainsbury
Chairman: Allan W ilson V-Chair: Dick John
Press Officer: John Taylor
Manager: Derek Birrell Asst Man:Pete McKenna
Coach: Dick John Physio: Mark Hetherington
2002-03
Top Goalscorer: Paul Southward 26
Captain: Darren Hpyland P.o.Y.: Gareth Brunton

LEEK C.S.O.B.

Secretary: Stan Lockett, 5 Fitzherbert Close, Swynnerton, Stone, Staffs ST150PQ,
Tel: 01782 796062 (H) 07944 493106 (M)
Ground: Harrison Park, Macclesfield Road, Leek, Staffs, Tel: 01538 383734
Club Email: stan@slockett.freeserve.co.uk
Directions: M6 south Junc 17, A534 to Congleton - follow signs for Leek (A54), carry on to junction with A523, right onto A523, this road is direct to Leek, ground 8 miles on right just into Leek.
Capacity: 3,600 Seating: 625 Covered Terracing: 2,675 Floodlights: Yes
PREVIOUS **Leagues:** Leek & Moorland Lge, Staffs County North, Refuge Midland Lge.
RECORDS **Attendance:** 293 v Tamworth F.A.Cup 1998-99
BEST SEASON **FA Cup:** 3rd Q 98-99 **FA Vase:** 1st Round 2000-01
HONOURS Refuge Midland Lge 95-96. Lge Cup 94-95 95-96; Leek Cup 94-95 95-96; Midland Ref Charity Shield 95-96; Sportsline Chall Cup 95-96.
NWCL Div. 2winners - Programme of the Year 2001/02

FACT FILE
Founded: 1945
Colours: Red & white stripes/white/red
Change colours: All White
Midweek Matchday:Tuesday
Programme: Yes Editor: Stan Lockett
CLUB PERSONNEL
Chairman: K J Hill, 11 Springfield Drive, Leek, Staffs ST13 Tel: 01538 371859
Managers: Chris McMullen:& Andrew Walters
Assistant Manager: Paul Campion
Youth Football Officer: David Lacey
Physio: Keith Tatton & Dennis Lowndes
2002-03 Leading Goalscorer:Alan Nagington
Captain: & P.o.Y.: Matt Johnson

MAINE ROAD

Secretary: Derek Barber, Flat 4, Maple Court, 259 Wellington Rd., Heaton Moor, Stockport SK4 5BS (0161 431 8243) **Ground:** Manchester County FA Ground, Brantingham Rd., Chorlton-cum-Hardy, Manchester M21 0TT (0161 861 0344) **Directions:** M60 Jct 7, A56 towards City Centre, right onto A5145 Chorlton/Stockport, thro' lights, left at next lights into Wilbraham Rd (A6010) to Chorlton, thro' lights for approx 1 mile. Left into Withington Rd, first left into Brantingham Rd, ground 300 yds on left. 2 miles from Stretford (Metrolink (tram)), 3 miles from Piccadilly & Victoria , Virgin & First North Western trains. Buses16 16A 85 87 87A 168 188 275.
Clubhouse: Matchdays (Snacks on ground) **Shop:** No.
Capacity: 2,000 Seats: 200 Cover: 700 Floodlights: Yes.
HONOURS Manc. Prem. Lg(4) 82-86, Cup 82-83 83-84;98-98 Man.Co Prem. Cup 87-8 Chal. Cup(4) 82-83 84-87; NW Co's Lg Div 2 89-90 (R-up 88-89).
Previous Leagues: Rusholme Sunday 55-66; Manchester Amtr Sunday 66-72; Manchester 72-87
BEST SEASON **FA Cup:** 2nd Qual. 2nd replay 92-93 **FA Vase:** 4th Rd 94-95
RECORDS **Attendance:** 875 v Altrincham, FA Cup 2nd Qual. Rd 29/9/90

FACT FILE
Founded: 1955 Nickname: Blues
Sponsors:Parry's Jewellers
Colours: RoyalBlue/navy blue/royal blue
Change Colours: Yellow, Green,Yellow
Midweek matchday: Tuesday
Reserves ' League: NW Co's Lge Res. Div.
Programme: 48 pages £1.00
Editor: Mr P,Ramsden (0161 448 1659)
CLUB PERSONNEL
Chairman: R Meredith Presi: F G Thompson
Press Officer: P Ramsden
Manager: Chris Simms Physio: E Jenkinson
2002-2003 Captain: Steven Howe
P.o.Y.:Lee TodmanTop Scorer:Mark Mitchell 19

NELSON

Secretary: Paul Wilson, 56 Gisburn Road,Barrowford, Nelson BB9 8NG (01282 618803)
Ground: Victoria Park, Lomeshaye Way, Nelson, Lancs (01282 613820)
Directions: M65 jct 13, 1st left (A6068 Fence), 2nd left (B6249 for Nelson),2nd right sign Lomeshaye Village to grd
Capacity: 1500 Seats:150Cover: 200 Floodlights: Yes
Clubhouse: Bar open matchdays **Club Shop:** Yes

HONOURS Lancs Lge 54-55; Lancs Comb. 1949-50 51-52; Lg Cup 49-50 50-51 59-60; Bridge Shield 75-76 81-82; Lancs Jnr Cup 54-55; N.W.C. Div 2 Cup 96-97.

BEST SEASON **FA Cup:** 2nd Rd Proper 30-31(replay) **FA Vase:** 2nd Rd 2001-02

PREVIOUS **Leagues:** Lancashire 1889-98 1900-01; Football League 1898-1900; Lancashire Comb. 01-16 46-82; N.W.C. 82-88; West Lancashire 88-92.

FACT FILE
Founded: 1881
Nickname: Blues
Colours: Blue & white stripes/bluek/blue
Change colours: Gold and blue.
Midweek matchday: Wednesday
Reserve League: N.W.C. Res. Div.
Website: www.nelsonfc.co.uk

CLUB PERSONNEL
Chairman: A.Pickering
Managing Director: L.Treitl
Treasurer: S.Smith
Manager: Dave Hall
Assistant Manager:Ian Lang

NORTON UNITED

Secretary: Dennis Vicker, 86 Ford Green Road, Smallthorne, Stoke-on-Trent ST6 1NX
Tel: 01782 822727 (H) 01785 354200 (B)

Ground: Norton CC & MWI, Community Drive, Smallthorne, Stoke-on-Trent
Tel: 01782 838290

Directions: M6 J16, A500 to BUrslem/Tunstall, turn off on A527, bear right at traffic island to Burslem, through lights to Smallthorne, take 3rd exit on mini r'about, turn right by pedestrian crossing into Community Drive, ground 200 metres on left.
Nearest Station: Stoke-on-Trent (mainline) Longport (local)

PREVIOUS **League:** Midland League to 2001

RECORDS **Attendance:** 165 v Alsager Town 2002

HONOURS Midland League - Champions 00-01 98-99 96-97, League Cup 00-01 96-97 91-92; Staffs FA Senior Vase 98-99

FACT FILE
Founded: 1989
Colours: Black & white stripes/black/black
Change Cols.: Red & black stripes/white/white
Midweek Matchday: Wednesday
Programme: Pages: Price:
Editor:

CLUB PERSONNEL
Chairman
Stephen Beaumont
8 Maitland Grove, Trentham, Stoke-on-Trent.
Tel: 01782 642321 (H)
Manager:
Physio:

OLDHAM TOWN

Secretary: Billy O'Niel,WhitebankStadium, Whitebank Road,Oldham.OL8 3JH (0161 624 2689)
Ground: Whitebank Stadium, Whitebank Rd, Hollins, Oldham, Lancs OL8 3JH(0161 624 2689)
Directions: M62 jct 18, M66 to Heaton Pk, right on to A576, left at 2nd lights on to A6104, follow Victoria Ave. on to Hollinwood Ave. under bridge to roundabout take 2nd exit onto Hollins Road, follow Hollins Rd for one & a half miles to Fire Station, left on through gate leading onto Elm Rd and follow to next left, Whitebank Rd on left.
Capacity: 1,000 Seats: 101 Cover: Yes Floodlights: Yes
Clubhouse: Open evenings and matchdays
HONOURS NWC: Div 2 97-98, R-up 94-95; Div 3 R-up 85--86; Lg.Champions 97-98
Res Div R-up 94-95, Cup 94/95:

PREVIOUS **Leagues:** Manchester Amateur; Lancashire Comb. 81-82.

BEST SEASON **FA Cup:** **FA Vase:**

RECORD **Attendance:** 495 v Halifax Town, 1996.

FACT FILE
Founded: 1964
Colours: Blue,white,blue
Change Colours:
Midweek Matches: Tuesday
Programme: 16 pages, 50p
Editor: Secretary

CLUB PERSONNEL
Chairman: Ken Hughes
Manager: Len Cantello

PADIHAM

Secretary: Alan Smith,242 Burnley Road, Padiham, Lancs. BB112 8SS (01282 771963)
Ground: Arbories Memorial Sports Ground, Well Street, Padiham, Lancs. BB12 8LE
Tel: 01282 773742 e-mail: brooks@household60.freeserve.co.uk
Directions: M65, J8, then follow A6068 (signed Clitheroe & Padiham). At lights at bottom of hill, turn right into Dean Range/Blackburn Road towards Padiham. At the next junction turn into Holland street opposite church, then into Well Street at the side of the Hare & Hounds pub to the ground. Nearest rail station: Burnley
Floodlights: No
Honours: Lancs Amateur Cup R-up 66, Lancs Amateur Shield R-up 97, Burnley, Pendle & Rossendale Hosp. Cup 96, R-up 91; Lancs Comb. Trophy 81, R-up 82; NWC Div. 3 R-up 83-84; W. Lancs Div.1 99-00, Div.2 71-72 76-77 R-up 96-97, Pres. Cup R-up 79 94 97; E. Lancs Amat Lge R-up 06-07 **Best Season:** FA Cup: Third Rd., 1883-84
Previous Leagues: Lancashire Comb.; NW Counties; West Lancs.; N.E. Lancs;
NE Lancs Combination; East Lancs Amateur Lge.

FACT FILE
Formed: 1878
Colours: Royal blue & white/white/red
Change: Red & black/black/black
Midweek Matchday: Wednesday
Programme: Pages: Price:
Editor:

Chairman: Mick Muldoon
Brook Foot Farm Barn, Grove Lane,
Padiham, Lancs.
Tel: 01282 778831
Manager:
Physio:

WINSFORD UNITED

Secretary : Robert Astles, 40 Aldersey Road,Crewe,Cheshire CW2 8NR Tel: 01270 661623
Ground Address: Barton Stadium, Wharton, Winsford, Cheshire CW7 3EU (01606 593021).
Directions: From north; M6 J19, A556 towards Northwich to Davenham, then A5018 to Winsford. From south; M6 J18, A54 through Middlewich to Winsford. Ground quarter mile off main road in Wharton area of town. 1 mile from Winsford (BR).
Capacity: 6,000 Cover: 5,000 Seats: 250
Clubhouse: Mon-Sat 8-11pm, Sun 8-10.30pm **Club Shop:** Yes, contact Kay Lomas
Previous Lges: The Combination 02-04; Cheshire Co. 19-40, 47-82; N.W.C. 82-87, N.P.L 87-01.
CLUB RECORDS **Attendance:** 7,000 v Witton Albion 1947.**Goalscorer:** Graham Smith 66.
Apps: Edward Harrop 400.**Fee Paid:** Nil. **Fee Received:** £6,000 for Neville Southall from Bury.
BEST SEASON FA Cup: 2nd Rd 1887-88 1st Rd 1975-76 91-92 **FA Trophy:** Qtr Finals 77-78.
HONOURS N.P.L. R-up 92-93, Div 1 R-up 91-92, Lg Cup 92-93, Presidents Cup 92-93; Cheshire Co. Lg 20-21 76-77 (R-up 74-75 79-80),Lg Cup x 7 R-up x 3; Cheshire Snr Cup 58-59 79-80 92-93; Mid-Cheshire Snr Cup 90-91 92-93 (R-up 88-89); Cheshire Amateur Cup 00-01 02-03; Lancs Comb/Cheshire County Inter-Lg Cup 62-63.

FACT FILE
Founded: 1883 Nickname: Blues
Colours: All Royal Blue
Change colours: All Maroon
Midweek matchday: Tuesday
Programme: Pages: 24 Price: £1.00
Editor: R. Astles

CLUB PERSONNEL
Chairman: Mark Loveless President: A Bayliss
Vice Chairman: David Taylor
Manager: Alan Walker

2002-03
Leading Goalscorer:Paul Lamb 13
Captain: Scoott Fallan
Player of the Year: Lee Duckworth

You Have to Love It!

is a very special Christmas book of amusing and enlightening photos illustrating all that happens at a non-league club on an average matchday.

The photos have been taken by our team of photographers who are all in love with the game at this level, and I'm sure it will bring a great deal of enjoyment to everyone involved with the world of football outside the Football League

The book is planned for publication in November and further details are available by contacting us on 01823 490080 Tony Williams

'You have to Love it!'......Out in time for Christmas.

LIVERPOOL COUNTY FOOTBALL COMBINATION

President: Lord Pendry **Chairman:** H E Humphries
Secretary: J F Deal, 24 The Pastures, Crossens, Southport PR9 8RH Tel: 01704 211955

It was another excellent season for the County Combination and, in the opinion of many seasoned observers, the overall standard of play throughout the league was the highest in living memory. Nine of the league membership reached a cup final during the season and the domination of local football was illustrated by the complete domination of the Challenge Cup (all four semi-finalists and six of the quarter-finalists for the second season running).

For the first time since Saint Dominics heyday in the 1980s the league champions went unbeaten throughout the campaign and given the strength of the league, Speke's achievement was no less than magnificent. Their first ever championship was the culmination of the management team of Ian Campbell and Archie Lloyd's turn round of the club over the last five years. As the squad is now in it's prime, the club will be the team to beat for the foreseeable future.

Speke's nearest rivals, Waterloo Dock, led the league for most of the season and scored the most goals but could not compete with an unbeaten season. The consolation was winning the Carlsberg Tetley Cup (for the first time) in which the league's top goalscorer, Lee Battle, proved to the whole league his undoubted merit with all five goals in the final win over South Liverpool.

Lucas Sports came up on the blind side to clinch third place and took the Peter Coyne Cup for the third time with a single goal by Joe Gibiliru in a deserved win over Bootle.

The County FA's premier competition, the Challenge Cup, was again dominated by County Combination clubs, despite the fact that it only had 13 clubs represented in the 42 club strong competition. Marconi defeated the eventual I-Zingari League champions, NELTC, Cheshire Lines defeated the current I-Zingari League Champions, Aigburth People's Hall, and the league had six quarter-finalists for the second season running. Ironically, only Waterloo Dock were defeated by a non County Combination club, Marine Reserves, a defeat avenged by eventual winners, Royal Seaforth, in the quarter-final. The Kirkdale based side played superbly against Speke in the final, preventing the league champions from doing the double, as performed by Saint Aloysius the previous season.

As 2002-03 Challenge Cup winners, Saint Aloysius, represented the County FA in the Northern Counties Championships and, like Waterloo Dock the previous season, reached the final only to fall to Northbank, the Carlisle based side from the Northern Alliance. The Aly's route to the final was made with victories over the Northumberland FA, Lancashire FA and East Riding FA.

Unfortunately both Marconi and REMYCA United were unable to finish the season and the league's inability to attract enough clubs to form a second division is a major concern. The lack of another division causes severe strain to clubs at the bottom of the league and it remains high on the priority list for the County Combination.

FINAL LEAGUE TABLE 2002-03

		P	W	D	L	F	A	Pts
1.	Speke	34	26	8	0	83	25	86
2.	Waterloo Dock	34	25	6	3	105	34	81
3.	Lucas Sports	34	17	9	8	68	43	60
4.	St Dominics	34	18	5	11	81	61	59
5.	Bootle	34	18	3	13	80	56	57
6.	St Aloysius	34	16	8	10	75	68	56
7.	Ford Motors	34	15	10	9	73	51	55
8.	South Liverpool	34	13	12	9	53	44	51
9.	Formby	34	14	7	13	74	72	49
10.	Halewood Town	34	14	6	14	67	67	48
11.	Royal Seaforth (-3)	34	14	6	14	74	63	45
12.	South Sefton Borough	34	13	5	16	65	71	44
13.	Cheshire Lines	34	13	3	18	54	76	42
14.	Birchfield	34	10	5	19	71	82	35
15.	Prescot Leisure	34	10	4	20	41	69	34
16.	Tuebrook	34	8	5	21	52	90	29
17.	Mossley Hill Athletic	34	4	7	23	45	110	19
18	Earle	34	2	3	29	35	114	9

Pionts deducted for rule infringement.
Marconi & REMYCA resigned & all records have been expunged.

LEADING GOALSCORERS

		Lge	Cup	Tot.
Lee Battle	Waterloo Dock	31	11	42
Chris McGrath	Mossley Hill Athletic	20	14	34
Steve Daley	Birchfield	25	6	31
Jeff Dodd	St Dominics	21	9	30
Louis Culshaw	Ford Motors	27	1	28
Jason Broad	Royal Seaforth	23	5	28
Adam Williams	Speke	20	7	27
Keith Jones	South Liverpool	22	4	26
Darren Byers	South Sefton Borough	19	7	26
Brian Burns	Ford Motors	20	4	24
Terry Jones	St Aloysius	20	4	24
Mark Carney	St Dominics	19	5	24

RESULTS GRID 02-03	1	2	3	4	5	6	7	8	9	10	11	12	13	14	15	16	17	18	19	20
1 Birchfield		3-5	7-2	3-0	2-2	4-3	2-4	1-2	13-2	2-3	2-5	4-3	3-1	3-3	2-3	0-1	0-3	3-1	5-0	0-4
2 Bootle	6-2		2-1	3-1	3-2	1-2	3-0	3-0	5-2	9-1	3-0	3-3	3-0	1-2	1-2	1-1	2-3	1-2	3-2	2-2
3 Cheshire Lions	2-1	3-2		4-1	1-1	3-0	3-2	0-1	n/a	4-0	3-1	n/a	1-0	1-2	4-5	0-3	0-2	1-2	3-6	0-2
4 Earle	1-0	1-3	1-2		3-6	1-2	0-5	0-3	n/a	0-3	1-2	n/a	2-4	0-1	4-1	0-3	2-5	1-5	2-3	1-6
5 Ford Motors	3-0	1-2	2-2	3-1		1-1	1-1	1-1	n/a	3-1	3-1	2-1	2-2	3-0	3-0	0-2	5-1	2-2	1-2	0-1
6 Formby	1-1	3-0	4-2	4-1	0-2		3-1	1-3	3-2	3-0	0-2	n/a	5-2	2-1	2-7	1-3	1-4	2-3	5-4	4-4
7 Halewood Town	2-1	2-3	1-3	4-3	1-2	3-1		0-4	n/a	2-1	0-2	n/a	2-2	1-1	2-1	1-2	3-1	2-1	3-1	2-5
8 Lucas Sports	0-2	0-3	1-2	3-2	3-1	3-1	0-4		4-1	2-0	4-0	5-0	1-1	0-0	4-3	0-1	1-1	1-0	8-0	0-4
9 Marconi	n/a	n/a	n/a	n/a	4-8	n/a	n/a	n/a		n/a	n/a	n/a	n/a	0-4	n/a	n/a	n/a	n/a	n/a	n/a
10 Mossley Hill Athletic	1-3	1-4	0-0	3-3	2-6	2-2	2-5	2-6	n/a		3-3	n/a	0-3	2-1	1-0	0-5	4-4	3-5	1-1	0-2
11 Prescot Leisure	1-0	2-3	0-1	4-1	2-0	0-2	1-1	0-5	n/a	2-0		n/a	0-3	2-2	3-1	0-3	1-1	0-1	3-1	0-5
12 REMYCA United	n/a	n/a	n/a	4-3	n/a	n/a	n/a	n/a	2-1	2-1	n/a		n/a	n/a	0-1	n/a	n/a	n/a	n/a	n/a
13 Royal Seaforth	3-0	4-2	7-0	3-0	3-2	0-2	1-3	2-2	6-1	6-0	4-1	n/a		0-0	1-3	2-2	3-1	2-1	5-3	0-3
14 South Liverpool	3-3	3-0	3-0	0-0	2-4	1-1	2-1	2-0	2-0	3-3	2-0	1-0	3-2		2-2	0-1	3-0	0-2	1-1	3-2
15 South Sefton Boro'	2-4	2-0	3-1	3-0	1-1	1-5	1-1	1-3	n/a	3-1	3-1	n/a	1-2	2-2		0-1	6-0	2-1	3-1	1-4
16 Speke	4-2	2-1	2-0	7-0	3-1	3-2	4-2	2-2	n/a	3-2	1-0	n/a	2-0	1-0	1-0		2-2	1-1	8-0	0-0
17 St Aloysius	3-1	0-0	3-1	5-0	3-5	4-2	2-2	0-0	4-0	5-2	3-1	7-1	2-1	1-0	2-2	1-4		3-5	3-1	1-3
18 St Domincs	3-6	2-1	3-1	4-1	1-2	3-3	4-1	1-1	n/a	2-1	3-1	n/a	5-2	0-1	5-0	2-2	1-2		2-0	2-3
19 Tuebrook	2-2	1-3	1-3	1-1	1-2	1-1	0-3	0-2	5-1	3-0	1-0	n/a	3-2	1-3	2-0	1-2	3-2	2-3		0-1
20 Waterloo Dock	3-1	3-1	5-0	6-0	0-0	1-3	4-0	2-2	n/a	5-0	3-0	n/a	3-1	2-1	4-0	1-1	1-2	7-3	4-3	

Marconi and REMYCA United withdrew during the season.Their results are shown but have been expunged from the records.

LEAGUE CONSTITUTION - 2003/2004

AIGBURTH PEOPLES HALL
Cheshire Lines Ground, Southmead Road, Allerton, Liverpool L195NB
Tel: 0151 427 7176
Sec: Bobby Oldham 0151 423 0175

BIRCHFIELD
Edge Hill College, St Helens Road, Ormskirk, Merseyside L39 4QP
Tel: 01695 584 745
Sec: Terry Kelly
01695 421 106/07801 371539

BOOTLE
Edninburgh Park, Townsend Lane, Liverpool L6 0BB.
Tel: 0151 263 5267
Sec: Bill Jones
0151 428 2203/07939 912893

CHESHIRE LINES
Cheshire Lines Ground, Southmead Road, Allerton, Liverpool, Merseyside. Tel: 0151 427 7176
Sec: Paddy Cavanagh
0151 280 9317

FORD MOTORS
Ford Sports & Social Club, Cronton Lane, Widnes. Tel: 0151 424 7078
Sec: Terry Doyle 01928 568 329

HALEWOOD TOWN
Hilton Grace Recreation Ground, Hollies Road, Liverpool 26
Tel: 0151 437 7418
Sec: Steve Jones
0151 486 4557/07950 537 304

LUCAS SPORTS
Heron eccles Sports Ground, Abbotshey Avenue, Liverpool 18
Tel: 0151 724 4796
Sec: Tony Brodrick 0151 423 4615

MOSSLEY HILL ATHLETIC
Mossley Hill Athletic Club, Mossley Hill Road, Liverpool L18 8DX
Tel: 0151 724 4377
Sec: Mick Ware 0151 486 0071

PRESCOT LEISURE
Wood Lane Sports Ground, Prescot, Merseyside
Tel: 07812 911 673
Sec: Dave Hughes 01744 737 047

ROYAL SEAFORTH
William Collins Sports Ground, Commercial Road, Liverpool 5
Sec: Tony Stanton 0151 489 9980

ST ALOYSIUS
King George V Sports Ground, Longview Lane, Liverpool 36
Sec: Gary Walsh 0151 449 1131

ST DOMINICS
St Dominics School, Lordens Road, Huyton, Liverpool 14
Tel: 0151 489 2798
Sec: Mick Donohe 0151 259 9737

SKELMERSDALE UNITED RES.
Edgehill College, St Hellens Road, Ormskirk L39 4QP
Tel: 01695 584 745
Sec: Bryn Jones 01695 724 647

SOUTH LIVERPOOL
Jericho Lane, Otterspool, Liverpool L17 5AR.
Tel: 07932 347 956
Sec: Jim Stanway
0151 281 5704/07932 347 956

SOUTH SEFTON BOROUGH
Formby FC, Altcar Road, Formby
Tel: 01704 833 505
Sec: Bill Grace 0151 286 8985

SPEKE
Dunlops Sports Ground, Speke Hall Avenue, Speke, Liverpool 24
Tel: 0151 486 1588
Sec: Bill Locke 0151 486 1954

TUEBROOK
William Collins Sports Ground, Commercial Road, Liverpool 5
Sec: Steve Caples 0151 525 2380

WATERLOO DOCK
Edinburgh Park, Townsend Lane, Liverpool L6 0BB
Tel: 0151 263 5267
Sec: Jim Davies 0151 264 8179

CARLSBERG WEST CHESHIRE A.F.L.

Founded 1892
President: Ken Halsall
Chairman & Hon. Treasurer: Ray Prescott
Hon. General & Fixtures Secretary: Arthur Green, 46 Bertram Drive, Meols, Wirral CH47 0LH
Tel/fax: 0151 6324946 Email: arthurlgreen@hotmail.com www.west-cheshire.org.uk

Having lost three of their opening nine games and dropping 15 points by the halfway stage, Vauxhall Reserves appeared to be well out of the title race. However, an amazing run-in saw them forfeit just two points from 15 games to take the title. Four points adrift in second place were Poulton Victoria (their ninth consecutive top three finish), whilst Cammell Laird, who lead for most of the campaign, had to settle for third. It wasn't all disappointed for Cammell Laird however, as they lifted the Cheshire Amateur Cup for a record equalling ninth time, whilst also reaching the final of the Pyke Challenge Cup.

MANWEB, close to the top three for much of the season, finished their season in fourth and were disappointed to lose out in the Lancashire Amateur Cup final too. General Chemicals claimed the Runcorn Senior Cup whilst an impressive sixth place was achieved in the league, despite their poor goalscoring record.

The promoted teams, Castrol Social and Mallaby, finished eighth and ninth respectively with Mallaby also reaching the Wirral Senior Cup final. Mersey Royal replacements, Ashville (who joined the league just before the new season), finished 10th and having taken Mersey Royal's slot in the 1st Round of the Pyke Challenge Cup too, went on to win it.

Last season's champions, Christleton, struggled to find their league winning form of last year whilst, for once, failing to win the Chester Senior Cup. Down at the foot of the table Aintree Villa struggled to string results together, whilst Helsby failed to gain a single point.

2002-2003 HONOURS LIST

	Winners	**Runners Up**
Division One	Vauxhall Motors Reserves	Poulton Victoria
Division Two	Poulton Victoria Reserves	West Kirby
Division Three	Ashville Reserves	F.C. Pensby
Pyke Challenge Cup	Ashville	Cammell Laird
West Cheshire Bowl	Cammell Laird Reserves	Heswall Reserves
West Cheshire Shield	New Brighton Reserves	Grange
Cheshire Amateur Cup	Cammell Laird	Heswall
Lancashire Amateur Cup	St Dominics	Manweb
Chester Senior Cup	Chester Nomads	Blacon YC
Chester Challenge Cup	Upton AA Reserves	Christleton Reserves
Liverpool Junior Cup	Tuebrook	Aintree Villa Reserves
Runcorn Senior Cup	General Chemicals	
Wirral Senior Cup	West Kirby	Mallaby
Wirral Amateur Cup	Cammell Laird Reserves	Heswall Reserves
Bill Weight Memorial Cup	Cammell Laird	Mallaby

FINAL LEAGUE TABLES 2002-03

DIVISION ONE

		P	W	D	L	F	A	Pts
1	Vauxhall Motors R.	28	21	4	3	77	25	67
2	Poulton Victoria	28	20	3	5	74	32	63
3	Cammell Laird	28	18	6	4	59	25	60
4	Manweb	28	16	3	9	61	38	51
5	Newton	28	15	3	10	60	44	48
6	General Chemicals	28	12	6	10	40	38	42
7	Heswall	28	11	5	12	56	46	38
8	Castrol Social	28	11	5	12	44	43	38
9	Mallaby	28	11	4	13	52	49	37
10	Ashville	28	10	4	14	51	58	34
11	Christleton	28	8	7	13	40	47	31
12	Maghull	28	7	9	12	41	43	30
13	Shell	28	8	5	15	37	56	29
14	Aintree Villa	28	7	6	15	44	64	27
15	Helsby	28	0	0	28	12	140	0

Stork resigned - record expunged

DIVISION TWO

		P	W	D	L	F	A	Pts
1	Poulton Victoria Res.	30	21	5	4	68	38	68
2	West Kirby	30	19	5	6	72	43	62
3	Cammell Laird Res.	30	16	8	6	58	37	56
4	Pavilions	30	16	6	8	59	43	54
5	Blacon Y.C.	30	15	6	9	74	47	51
6	New Brighton	30	15	6	9	68	50	51
7	Heswall Reserves	30	15	4	11	59	55	49
8	Upton A.A.	30	13	5	12	60	54	44
9	Merseyside Police	30	12	5	13	58	52	41
10	Christleton Res.	30	12	5	13	52	52	41
11	Capenhurst Villa	30	12	3	15	55	57	39
12	Maghull Reserves	30	8	9	13	49	54	33
13	Aintree Villa Res.	30	8	4	18	45	66	28
14	Mond Rangers	30	7	5	18	39	70	26
15	Manor Athletic	30	7	4	19	48	82	25
16	Mersey Royal	30	2	4	24	40	104	10

DIVISION ONE RESULTS CHART 2002-03

		1	2	3	4	5	6	7	8	9	10	11	12	13	14	15
1	Aintree Villa		2-2	0-2	2-1	1-1	1-1	4-1	1-6	1-0	2-3	2-4	1-0	1-1	3-0	2-4
2	Ashville	5-2		1-3	6-1	3-1	1-2	2-1	0-2	1-1	0-1	2-1	3-2	0-4	1-1	1-2
3	Cammell Laird	7-0	0-0		3-0	2-1	2-0	4-0	2-2	1-1	3-1	2-2	4-1	0-2	2-1	1-4
4	Castrol Social	3-0	3-2	2-4		2-2	1-1	4-0	2-0	2-1	1-1	3-0	3-2	0-1	0-1	0-2
5	Christleton	2-0	5-1	1-1	3-1		2-0	5-0	0-0	2-0	1-2	2-0	0-3	2-3	0-0	0-1
6	General Chemicals	3-1	5-1	0-0	0-1	2-2		3-0	1-0	1-1	2-1	1-0	1-0	4-1	0-1	0-0
7	Helsby	0-8	2-3	0-4	0-7	0-1	1-4		1-3	0-1	0-4	1-6	1-2	0-7	0-3	0-7
8	Heswall	5-2	5-2	0-1	1-2	3-0	1-3	5-0		1-2	3-0	0-2	3-7	2-2	4-1	0-2
9	Maghull	2-3	0-4	2-3	1-1	2-2	3-1	8-0	2-2		0-0	0-3	0-1	1-1	3-1	0-2
10	Mallaby	1-1	5-2	1-0	0-1	4-2	1-3	8-2	1-2	0-1		1-2	4-2	2-3	0-0	2-5
11	MANWEB	2-1	1-0	0-1	4-1	2-1	2-1	6-1	3-0	2-0	4-3		2-2	0-1	5-0	2-2
12	Newton	2-0	0-1	2-1	3-1	2-1	3-0	8-0	1-3	1-1	2-0	3-2		2-1	2-1	1-1
13	Poulton Victoria	3-1	3-0	0-2	1-0	5-1	4-0	7-1	1-0	4-3	1-3	2-1	5-1		3-1	5-2
14	Shell	0-0	0-5	0-1	1-0	3-0	5-0	5-0	2-2	1-5	4-2	1-3	2-5	1-3		0-3
15	Vauxhall Motors Reserves	3-2	3-2	1-2	1-1	4-0	2-1	11-0	3-1	2-0	0-1	4-0	2-0	1-0	3-1	

PYKE CUP

FIRST ROUND

Cammell Laird 2 General Chemicals 0
Castrol Social 2 Poulton Victoria 3 aet
Ellesmere Port 1 Vauxhall Motors Res. 2
Helsby 0 Ashville 1
Maghull 1 Heswall 2
MANWEB 2 Mallaby 3
Newton 3 Aintree Villa 0
Stork v Christleton (walk over)

QUARTER-FINALS

Christleton 2 Cammell Laird 3 (aet)
Heswall 2 Poulton Victoria 2 (aet)
replay Poulton Victoria 0 Heswall 2
Newton 2 Ashville 4 (aet)
Vauxhall Motors Res. 2 Mallaby 3

SEMI-FINALS

Cammell Laird 2 Mallaby 0 (aet)
(at Poulton Victoria)
Heswall 0 Ashville 2 (at Cammell Laird)

FINAL

Cammell Laird 0 Ashville 1
(at Vauxhall Motors - 05.05.03)

WEST CHESHIRE BOWL

FIRST ROUND

Christleton Res. 0 Upton AA 2
Heswall Res. 2 Merseyside Police 0
Maghull Res. 2 Capenhurst Villa 3 aet
Manor Athletic 1 Pavilions 4
Mersey Royal 0 Aintree Villa Res. 3
Mond Rangers 0 Cammell Laird Res. 6
Poulton Victoria Res. 2 New Brighton 1 aet
West Kirby 3 Blacon Youth Club 4

QUARTER-FINALS

Blacon Youth Club 3 Upton AA 0
Cammell Laird Res. 4 Aintree Villa Res. 2
Capenhurst Villa 5 Heswall Res. 5 aet
Heswall Res. 2 Capenhurst Villa 0 replay
Poulton Victoria Res. 2 Pavilions 4

SEMI-FINALS

Blacon Youth Club 0 Cammell Laird Res. 2
(at Vauxhall Motors)
Heswall Res. 3 Pavilions 1 (at Ashville)

FINAL

Cammell Laird Res. 2 Heswall Res. 1
(at Vauxhall Motors - 30.04.03)

AINTREE VILLA

Chairman: John Gregson Formed: 1954
Secretary: Alf Shepherd, 154 Altway, Aintree, Liverpool L10 6LG
Tel: 0151 526 9287 (H)
Ground: Aintree racecourse.
Colours: Tangerine/white/white
Sponsors: Woolton Carpets/Aintree Conservative Club

ASHVILLE

Chairman: Eddie Parker **Club Formed:** 1949
Secretary: Dave Walton, 15 Wellesley Road, Wallasey, Wirral, Merseyside, L445UR Tel: 0151 639 9196
Ground: Villa Park, Cross Lane, Wallasey Village, Wallasey,
Tel: 0151 638 2127 **Colours:** White & black/black/black
Sponsors: Kelly Sports & West Wallasey Van Hire.

CAMMELL LAIRD

Chairman: Ray Steele
Secretary: Anthony R wood, 25 Prenton Park Rd,Prenton,Birkenh'd, MerseysideCh42 8JR Tel Nos: 0151 608 0591(H) 07931 761429 (M)
Ground: Kirklands, St Peters Road, Rock Ferry, Birkenhead
Tel: 0151 645 5991 **Colours:** All blue **Formed:** 1906
Sponsors: Hallmark Cleaning SAervices

CASTROL SOCIAL

Formed: 1954
Secretary: Mike Caulfield, 2 Weaver Road, Whitby, Ellesmere Port CH66 2JJ. Tel: 0151 355 5966 (H)
Ground: Castrol Sports & Social Club, Chester Road, Whitby, Ellesmere Port(0151 355 1730)
Colours: Royal & emerald/royal/white

CHRISTLETON

Chairman: Ron Mayers
Secretary: Ken Price, 35 Canadian Ave, Hoole, Chester CH2 3HQ
Tel: 01244 313513
Ground: Little Heath, Christleton Tel: 01244 332153
Colours: Red/black/red **Formed** 1897 Re-Formed: 1966
Sponsors: Allans Skip Hire

ELLESMERE PORT

Chairman: Gerry Fraser
Secretary: Steven Foden, 23 Hornbeam Avenue, Great Sutton, South Wirral Ch65 7AQ. Tel Nos: 0151 356 8837 (H) 07941 187632 (M)
Ground: Chester Road, Whitby, Ellesmere Port, South Wirral
Tel: 0151 200 7080 **Colours:** Yellow /navy/navy **Formed:** 1924
Previous Name: Shell FC

GENERAL CHEMICALS

Chairman: Dave Robinson
Secretary: Tony Riley 171 Cotton Lane, Runcorn, Cheshire WA7 5JB
Tel: 01928 565390
Ground: Picow Farm Road, Runcorn
Colours: Blue & white/blue/blue & white **Formed:** 1958
Sponsors: Maltacourt Ltd

HELSBY

Chairman: John Close
Secretary: John Evans, 35 Hill View Ave., Helsby, Ches. WA6 0ES
Tel: 01928 724817 (H)
Ground: Helsby Sports & Social Club Tel: 01928 722267
Colours: White/green/green **Formed:** 1895
Sponsors: Brand - Rex EVC. & Helsby Sports & Social Club

HESWALL

Chairman: Brian Flanagan
Secretary: Jake Horan ,13 Reedville Rd, Bebington, Wirral L63 2HS
Tel: 0151 644 0459
Ground: Gayton Pk,Brimstage Rd, Heswall, Wirral Tel:01513428172
Colours: Yellow/royal blue/yellow **Formed:** 1891
Sponsors: Pyramids Shopping Centre

MAGHULL

Chairman: Les Jacques **Secretary:** Danny Sherlock, 14 Alexander Drive, Lydiate, Merseyside L31 2NJ Tel: 0151 526 2306
Ground: Old Hall Field, Hall Lane, Maghull, Merseyside (0151 526 7320) **Directions:** M57 or M58 to end (Switch Island), A59 towards Preston (Northway)to lights at Hall Lane, right following signs for Maghull BR. then 200 yds on the left.1/2 m from Maghull (Merseyrail)
Colours: Blue & red stripes/blue/blue **Sponsors:** Soldier of Fortune

MANWEB

Chairman: James Parry Formed: 1932
John Shimmin, 54 Gonville Rd., Bootle, Merseyside L20 9LR
tel: 0151 933 5763 (H)
Ground: Manweb Sports & Social Club, Thingwall Rd., Liverpool L15 7LB Tel: 0151 281 5364 Colours: White/navy/white
Sponsors: Comasec yate Ltd

MALLABY

Formed: 1965
Chairman: G M Langan
Secretary: Tommy Kenny, 11 Seeley Ave., Claughton, Birkenhead CH41 0BX Tel: 0151 653 5925 (H)
Ground: Balaclava, Birkenhead Park.
Colours: Red & black stripes/black/red

NEWTON

Chairman: John Murray
Secretary: Alan Dabner, 79A Eleanor Road, Bidston, Wirral CH43 7RW. Tel NOs: 0151 653 2151 (H) 0151 993 2151 (B)
Ground: Millcroft, Frankby Road, Greasby, Wirral Tel: 0151 677 8382
Colours: Yellow/green/yellow **Formed:** 1933
Sponsors: Cory Brothers Shipping Ltd.

POULTON VICTORIA

Chairman: Thonas Quinn
Secretary: George Cooper,1 Foxhey Road, Wallasey, Wirral CH44 2ES. Tel Nos: 0151 201 2072 (H) 0151 638 9112 (W)
Ground: Victoria Park, Rankin Street, Wallasey Tel: 0151 638 3559
Colours: All Royal Blue **Formed:** 1935
Sponsors: Carlsberg & Bass

VAUXHALL MOTORS RESERVES

Chairman: Tony Woodley
Secretary: Carole Paisey, 26 South Road, West Kirby, Wirral L48 3HQ (0151 6256 936)
Ground: Vauxhall Sports Ground, Rivacre Road, Hooton, Ellesmere Port (0151 3281114)
Colours: White/royal blue/white **Formed:** 1963

WEST KIRBY

Formed: 1895
Secretary: Roy Williamson, 85 Wood Lane, Greasby, Wirrall CH49 2PX Tel: 0151 677 4860 (H)
Ground: Johnston Recreation Ground, Neston Road, Willaston, South Wirrall.
Colours: White/black/black

BLACON YOUTH CLUB
Formed: 1964
Chairman: Peter Barnes
Secretary: Colin Lawson,54 Adelaide Rd., Blacon, Chester CH1 5SZ Tel: 01244 375508 (H)
Ground: Cairns Crescent Playing Fields, Cairns Crescent, Blacon, Chester. Colours: Black & white stripes/black/black
Sponsors: George Starkey Painter & Decorator & McDonalds

CAPENHURST VILLA
Formed: 1952
Chairman: Brian Heyes
Secretary: Martin Williams, 157 Hope Farm Road, Great Sutton, South Wirral L662TJ Tel: 0151 339 8935
Ground: Capenhurst Sports Ground, Capenhurst Lane, Capenhurst Tel: 0151 339 4101
Colours: All maroon
Sponsors: Handbridge Decorators & Commercial Properties

FC PENSBY
Ground: Ridgewood Park, Pensby, Wirral

MANOR ATHLETIC
Formed: 1968
Chairman: Tony Bell
Secretary: Stewart Galtress, 3 Centurion Close, Meols, Wirrall CH47 7BZ Tel: 0151 632 3211 email: s-galtress@hotmail.com
Ground: Unilever Sports Ground, Bromborough
Colours: All royal blue

MERSEYSIDE POLICE
Formed: 1885
Secretary: Gary Dinsmore, 3 Chaffinch Close, West Derby, Liverpool L12 0NX Tel: 0151 220 0285 (H)
Ground: Police Club, Fairfield, Prescot Rd, Liverpool L7 0JD
Tel: 0151 228 2352
Colours: All navy blue with red trim.

MOND RANGERS
Formed:1967
Chairman: David Holland
Secretary: Steve Kinsella, 3 Bramble Way, Beechwood, Runcorn, Cheshire WA7 3HN Tel Nos: 01928 715178 (H) 07867 972919 (W)
Ground: Pavilions Club, Sandy Lane, Weston Point, Runcorn WA7 5EX Tel: 01928 590508
Colours: Blue & black stripes

NEW BRIGHTON
Formed: 1993
Secretary: Carl Gidman. 64 Ford Road, Upton, Wirrall CH49 0TG Tel: 0151 678 1858 (H/B)
Ground: Harrison Drive, Wallasey Village, Wallasey
Colours: Red & white/white/red & white

PAVILIONS
Formed: 1998
Secretary: Beverley Crilly, 26 Perrin Ave., Weston Point, Runcorn WA7 4BJ Tel: 01928 575938 (H)
Ground: Pavilions Complex, Sandy Lane, Weston Point, Runcorn
Tel: 01928 590508
Colours: Blue & white stripes/blue/blue

UPTON ATHLETIC ASSOCIATION
Formed: 1964
Secretary: Barry Gaulton, 24 St Marks Crescent, Whitby, Ellesmere Port L66 2XD (0151 339 1504)
Ground: Cheshire County Council Sports & Social Club, Plas Newton Lane, Chester (01244 318367)
Colours: All blue

plus
AINTREE VILLA RESERVES
ASHVILLE RESERVES
CAMMELL LAIRD RESERVES
CHRISTLETON RESERVES
HESWALL RESERVES
MAGHULL RESERVES
POULTON VICTORIA RESERVES

THE BASS/WPRC
MID CHESHIRE ASSOCIATION FOOTBALL LEAGUE

Founded 1948

President: R Atherton **Chairman:** J Walton
Hon. Secretary: G Edgeley, 61 Harris Road, Lostock Gralam, Northwich, Cheshire CW9 7PE Tel: 01606 352799

FINAL TABLES 2002-2003

DIVISION ONE

		P	W	D	L	F	A	Pts
1	Barnton	30	21	6	3	61	18	69
2	Middlewich Town	30	17	8	5	66	25	59
3	Poynton	30	17	6	7	62	38	57
4	Styal	30	17	5	8	60	41	56
5	Knutsford	30	15	9	6	52	29	54
6	Linotype	30	14	10	6	69	33	52
7	Rylands	30	13	8	9	52	44	47
8	Daten	30	12	9	9	59	42	45
9	Crosfields	30	11	8	11	50	59	41
10	Crewe	30	11	6	13	56	59	39
11	Pilkington	30	9	6	15	39	55	33
12	Broadheath Central	30	8	8	14	40	57	32
13	Cheadle Heath Nomads	30	7	6	17	35	63	27
14	Garswood United	30	6	7	17	36	67	25
15	Padgate St Oswalds	30	5	2	23	26	89	17
16	Chorlton Town	30	3	4	23	30	74	13

DIVISION TWO

		P	W	D	L	F	A	Pts
1	Golborne Sports	30	23	5	2	96	28	74
2	Bollington Athletic	30	20	5	5	92	39	65
3	Malpas	30	17	6	7	60	26	57
4	Linotype Res.	30	18	2	10	65	54	56
5	Trafford Res.	30	15	6	9	63	37	51
6	Warrington Borough	30	14	6	10	63	56	48
7	Middlewich Town Res.	30	14	5	11	49	48	47
8	Lostock Gralam	30	12	8	10	52	52	44
9	Whitchurch Alport	30	12	7	11	70	51	43
10	Poynton Res.	30	12	6	12	67	62	42
11	Pilkington Res.	30	11	6	13	55	51	39
12	Crewe Res.	30	8	7	15	45	72	31
13	Rylands Res.	30	7	5	18	33	73	26
14	Barnton Res.	30	4	6	20	32	74	18
15	Cheadle Heath Nomads Res.	30	4	5	21	53	102	17
16	Garswood United Res.	30	4	5	21	28	98	17

DIVISION ONE 02-03		1	2	3	4	5	6	7	8	9	10	11	12	13	14	15	16
1	Barnton		3-1	2-0	2-0	1-1	2-0	3-1	3-0	1-0	2-2	1-1	3-1	5-0	1-1	0-1	4-0
2	Broadheath Central	0-3		2-2	2-0	4-2	3-4	0-3	2-2	0-3	1-1	1-0	1-0	2-0	2-1	1-2	0-3
3	Cheadle Heath Nomads	1-2	1-1		0-4	3-2	2-5	2-0	1-0	2-5	1-3	0-3	2-0	1-1	0-1	1-4	0-1
4	Chorlton Town	0-2	1-0	1-2		0-2	0-2	1-1	1-2	1-2	2-2	0-2	2-0	1-3	0-1	1-2	0-2
5	Crewe	2-2	3-3	2-0	7-5		5-2	2-1	5-2	1-2	1-3	0-2	4-1	2-0	0-2	1-1	3-2
6	Crosfields	0-3	1-1	1-0	4-1	3-0		0-0	3-3	1-1	2-2	3-4	3-0	1-0	0-2	2-2	2-0
7	Daten	1-0	2-2	4-1	4-0	1-2	2-0		4-0	4-2	2-2	2-3	7-1	1-1	2-2	2-0	3-0
8	Garswood United	1-1	2-4	2-3	5-1	2-2	0-0	2-3		1-3	3-2	0-4	1-0	1-0	0-1	0-0	1-1
9	Knutsford	1-2	2-1	3-0	2-0	1-1	0-1	1-1	2-0		0-0	2-0	4-0	1-1	1-3	2-2	1-0
10	Linotype	3-1	5-0	0-1	4-1	4-2	9-0	2-1	3-0	1-1		0-1	8-0	0-0	1-0	4-2	1-3
11	Middlewich Town	0-2	0-1	4-1	2-2	3-0	4-1	2-0	5-0	1-1	1-1		5-0	6-0	2-1	1-2	1-1
12	Padgate St Oswalds	0-3	2-1	3-3	3-1	0-3	1-0	1-1	2-1	0-4	1-2	1-4		1-2	1-2	1-2	1-4
13	Pilkington	0-2	1-0	0-0	4-1	1-0	4-1	1-2	2-3	2-3	1-0	0-3	4-2		2-3	1-3	3-1
14	Poynton	0-2	2-2	3-3	7-1	2-0	4-2	2-1	3-1	1-1	0-3	0-0	4-0	4-1		3-1	4-5
15	Rylands	0-2	3-2	2-1	1-1	3-0	1-3	4-0	4-1	0-1	1-1	1-1	1-3	3-3	2-0		1-3
16	Styal	0-1	3-0	2-1	2-1	3-1	3-3	3-3	2-0	1-0	2-0	1-1	7-0	2-1	1-3	2-1	

DIVISION TWO 02-03	1	2	3	4	5	6	7	8	9	10	11	12	13	14	15	16
1 Barnton Reserves		2-2	4-1	1-1	1-3	1-4	1-4	1-1	0-1	0-3	1-0	4-1	3-0	0-1	0-5	0-0
2 Bollington Athletic	6-2		4-2	2-3	6-0	1-3	5-1	2-1	2-2	0-2	2-1	3-0	2-3	3-0	3-1	6-0
3 Cheadle Heath Nomads Reserves	2-2	3-5		1-2	5-0	2-3	0-2	1-3	1-1	1-5	3-3	5-4	2-2	1-3	2-4	0-5
4 Crewe Reserves	2-0	1-2	1-5		3-3	0-2	0-1	2-5	1-5	2-1	0-0	1-2	1-2	2-3	6-1	4-3
5 Garswood United Reserves	3-2	0-5	1-2	0-1		1-4	1-0	0-4	0-4	1-2	2-0	1-6	0-1	0-4	1-3	2-4
6 Golborne Sports	4-0	1-1	5-5	4-0	13-1		8-1	2-1	2-0	0-1	2-1	3-3	4-1	1-2	7-1	4-2
7 Linotype Reserves	5-0	1-4	4-1	1-1	1-0	0-1		1-2	3-2	4-2	0-1	5-1	3-1	3-1	3-1	4-3
8 Lostock Gralam	1-0	1-3	2-1	4-2	2-2	0-3	1-0		3-0	1-3	3-3	1-2	3-2	0-2	1-1	0-0
9 Malpas	3-0	1-1	4-1	3-1	4-0	1-1	6-0	3-0		1-2	3-1	0-1	3-0	1-0	2-1	0-0
10 Middlewich Town Reserves	4-1	0-5	2-1	2-2	1-1	1-5	1-1	2-2	0-1		2-0	1-0	1-2	0-0	0-1	2-1
11 Pilkington Reserves	2-0	0-3	5-2	5-0	3-2	1-2	2-3	3-3	0-1	2-1		2-1	4-0	0-4	0-0	1-2
12 Poynton Reserves	2-0	2-4	5-0	1-1	9-0	0-4	1-5	2-0	0-5	2-0	4-3		5-1	1-1	2-3	2-2
13 Rylands Reserves	3-2	0-4	3-2	3-3	1-1	0-1	0-4	1-2	1-0	0-1	2-2	0-2		1-3	1-4	0-3
14 Trafford Reserves	2-2	1-2	2-0	6-1	1-1	0-0	2-3	5-1	2-3	4-1	2-3	1-1	2-0		0-1	4-0
15 Warrington Borough	4-1	2-1	7-1	4-0	2-1	0-2	1-2	2-2	2-0	3-4	0-5	4-4	1-1	0-1		2-2
16 Whitchurch Alport	4-1	3-3	9-0	0-1	4-0	0-1	4-0	1-2	0-0	4-2	1-2	2-1	5-1	5-4	1-2	

DIVISION ONE CUP

FIRST ROUND

Cheadle Heath Nomads 5 Padgate St Oswalds 0
Crewe 1 Daten 0
Crosfields 2 Rylands 1
Garswood United 2 Chorlton Town 1
Knutsford 1 Barnton 2
Linotype 3 Styal 0
Middlewich Town 4 Pilkington 1
Poynton 5 Broadheath Central 1

QUARTER-FINALS

Crewe 4 Cheadle Heath Nomads 0
Garswood United 1 Crosfields 2
Middlewich Town 5 Barnton 7
Poynton 2 Linotype 4

SEMI-FINALS

Barnton 4 Linotype 1
Crewe 3 Crosfields 4

FINAL

Barnton 3 Crosfields 1
(at Trafford - 01.04.03)

DIVISION TWO CUP

FIRST ROUND

Cheadle Heath Nomads Res. 2 Crewe Res. 7
Garswood United Res. 0 Bollington Athletic 2
Golborne 5 Barnton Res. 0
Lostock G. 2 Rylands Res. 5
Middlewich Town Res. 0 Poynton Res. 3
Pilkington Res. 0 Malpas 5
Trafford Res. 0 Warrington Borough 1
Whitchurch Alport 2 Linotype Res. 5

QUARTER-FINALS

Bollington Athletic 0 Golborne Sports 6
Linotype Res. 1 Malpas 3
Rylands Res. 3 Poynton Res. 2
Warrington Borough 2 Crewe Res. 3

SEMI-FINALS

Malpas 1 Golborne Sports 2
Crewe Res. 2 Rylands Res. 1

FINAL

Golborne Sports 5 Crewe Res. 0
(at Trafford - 23.03.03)

PRESIDENT'S CUP

(For those teams knocked out of the first round of their Divisional Cups)

FIRST ROUND

Barnton Res. 0 Daten 4, Broadheath Central 0 Lostock Gralam 1,
Cheadle Heath Res. 0 Knutsford 6, Garswood Res. 1 Whitchurch Alport 4, Middlewich Res. 0 Chorlton Town 4,
Pilkington 0 Rylands 2, Styal 5 Padgate 1, Trafford Res. 2 Pilkington Res. 4

QUARTER-FINALS

Daten 1 Rylands 6, Lostock Gralam 1 Chorlton Town 0
Pilkington Res. 0 Knutsford 3, Styal 6 Whitchurch Alport 1

SEMI-FINALS

Knutsford 1 Styal 3, Lostock Gralam 0 Rylands 1

FINAL

Styal 3 Rylands 1
(at Trafford - 09.04.03)

DIVISION ONE CLUBS

BARNTON AFC
Chairman: William Perrin
Manager: Mark Emmerson
Secretary: Michael Webster, 92 Church Road, Barnton CW8 4JE (01606 782960)
Ground: Townfield, Townfield Lane, Barnton, Northwich
Colours: Black & White Stripes/Black
Change Colours: Blue & yellow /blue

BOLLINGTON ATHLETIC FC
Chairman: Albert Hall
Manager: Michael Quigley
Secretary: Anthony Holmes, 1 Princess Drive, Bollington, Macclesfield SK10 5ES Tel: 01625 574913
Ground: Recreation Ground, Bollington, Macclesfield.
Colours: Green & Black/Green
Change Colours: Maroon/Sky/Sky

BROADHEATH CENTRAL FC
Chairman: Ian Beresford
Manager: Peter Cavanagh
Secretary: David Murphy,113 Downs Drive,Timperley, Altrincham Wa14 5QU (0161 718 0523)
Ground: Viaduct Road, Broadheath, Altrincham
Tel: 0161 928 5849
Colours: Black & Red Stripes/Black
Change Colours: Blue & White Stripes/White

CHEADLE HEATH NOMADS
Chairman: Roy Welsh
Manager: Peter Blundell
Secretary: George Gibbons, 20A Gillbent Road,Cheadle Hulme,SK8 6NB Tel No: 0161 440 9951
Ground: The Heath, Norbreck Ave, Cheadle, Stockport
Tel: 0161 282 6574
Colours: Maroon & Sky blue,Maroom/maroon
Change Colours: Yelow & Green/Green/Green

CREWE FC
Chairman: Patrick Slack
Manager: Ian O'Reilly
Secretary: Mrs M Vickers, 59 Hall-o-Shaw St, Crewe (01270 581578)
Ground: Cumberland Sprts Grnd, Thomas St, Crewe.
Tel: 01270 537913
Colours: Sky Blue/Marooon/White
Change Colours: Yellow/Black/Blue

CROSSFIELDS FC
Chairman: Michael Hickey
Manager: Derek Evans
Secretary: Frank Whitehouse, 153 Birdwell Drive, Gt. Sankey, Warrington Tel: 01925 728710 (H) 01925 625750 (B)
Ground: Hood Lane Rec., Gt. Sankey, Warrington
Tel: 01925 411730
Colours: Primrose & blue
Change Colours: Orange & black

DATEN FC
Chairman: Trevor Farrington
Manager: Robert Jones
Secretary: Michael Henshall, 21 Upwood Rd., Lowton, Warrington WA3 2RL Tel: 01942 724471 01772 321800 (B)
Ground: Culcheth Sports Club, Charnock Rd., Culcheth
Tel: 01925 763096
Colours: Sky & royal blue
Change Colours: Blue & white stipes/navy

GARSWOOD UNITED FC
Chairman: Barry Mavers
Manager: Alan Clarke
Secretary: Tony McKeown,44 Dunsdale Drive, Ashton, Wigan WN4 8PT Tel No: 01942 724259
Ground: The Wooders, Simms Lane End, Garswood, Wigan. Tel: 01744 892258
Colours: Blue & White Halves/Blue/Blue
Change Colours: All Yellow

GOLBORNE SPORTS FC
Chairman: Bill Hiltyon
Manager: Andrew Smallman
Secretary: Stephen Whittle, 20 West Ave., Golborne, Warrington WA3 3EA Tel: 01942 715570 (H) 07979 550732 (M)
Ground: Simpson Playing Fields, Stone Cross Lane, Lowton WA3 2SL Tel: 01942 510161
Colours: All Yellow
Change Colours: All blue

KNUTSFORD FC
Chairman: Ken Harrison
Manager: Srewart Dow
Secretary: Kevin Deeley, 28 East Street, Guide Bridge, Manchester, M34 5DX (0161 320 9650)
Ground: Manchester Road, Knutsford
Colours: Red /Black/Black
Change Colours: Black & White stripes/White/White

LINOTYPE FC
Chairman: James Barry
Manager: Glyn Williams
Secretary: Brian McGuiness, 36 Barrington Road, Altrincham, Cheshire (0161 929 0021)
Ground: British Airways Club, Clay Lane, Timperley, Altrincham. Tel: 0161 980 7354
Colours: White/Black
Change Colours: Red & Black/White/red

MIDDLEWICH TOWN FC
Chairman: Steven Morris
Manager: David Twite
Secretary: Philip Hassell,1 Whitegate `Close,Middlewich,Cheshire CW10 0RF
Tel Nos: 01606 832185 (H) 01606832734 (W)
Ground: Seddon Street, Middlewich Tel: 01606 835842
Colours: Red/Black/Red
Change Colours: White/black

SPRINGBANK VENDING MIDLAND LEAGUE

President: T Myatt **Chairman:** P Savage

Secretary: M Stokes, 21 Corsican Drive,
Pye Green, Cannock, Staffs WS12 4SZ
Tel: 01543 878075 Fax: 01543 879008

FINAL LEAGUE TABLE 2002-03

		P	W	D	L	F	A	Pts
1	Eccleshall	36	22	12	2	85	24	78
2	Norton AG	36	23	4	9	79	40	73
3	Goldenhill Wanderers	36	21	7	8	83	55	70
4	Audley & District	36	18	13	5	67	38	67
5	Hanley Town	36	18	11	7	79	34	65
6	Redgate Clayton	36	18	10	8	64	46	64
7	Hanford	36	19	7	10	62	50	64
8	Stallington	36	18	8	10	67	53	62
9	Brocton	36	17	6	13	74	53	57
10	Milton Rangers	36	14	13	9	44	46	55
11	Alsager	36	14	8	14	53	42	50
12	Dominoes	36	13	11	12	51	47	50
13	Abbey Hulton United	36	9	11	16	59	62	38
14	Ball Haye Green	36	8	6	22	44	77	30
15	Foley	36	7	8	21	40	97	29
16	Newcastle Town Res.	36	5	11	20	42	79	26
17	Wolstanton United	36	4	11	21	46	110	23
18	Vale Juniors	36	4	9	23	43	78	21
19	Cheadle Town OB	36	2	10	24	18	69	16

RESULTS GRID 02-03	1	2	3	4	5	6	7	8	9	10	11	12	13	14	15	16	17	18	19
1 Abbey Hulton United		3-3	0-2	2-2	1-1	2-1	4-0	0-2	8-1	1-3	1-2	1-1	0-0	1-2	0-3	1-3	0-3	2-2	3-1
2 Alsager	1-0		1-3	4-0	3-1	4-1	1-1	2-3	0-1	0-1	0-1	0-2	2-0	1-1	0-0	3-0	1-3	3-1	1-0
3 Audley & District	1-0	1-1		2-1	2-1	1-0	3-0	1-1	4-2	0-1	1-2	2-1	4-0	1-1	1-1	1-0	2-2	2-1	5-1
4 Ball Haye Green	0-3	1-2	2-2		0-1	3-0	0-1	0-4	3-1	1-4	2-1	2-3	3-1	3-1	1-3	0-1	0-3	2-2	3-1
5 Brocton	2-0	2-1	3-1	5-1		4-0	0-1	3-5	4-0	2-2	1-2	2-0	1-4	1-0	1-2	1-0	3-3	4-2	7-1
6 Cheadle Town OB	0-2	0-2	0-2	1-1	2-4		0-1	0-0	1-1	0-3	0-1	0-3	0-0	2-2	0-3	2-2	0-2	0-0	2-2
7 Dominoes	2-2	0-2	2-1	3-2	1-1	0-0		0-4	4-0	4-0	2-3	0-0	2-2	4-1	0-2	1-2	4-0	1-0	1-1
8 Eccleshall	3-0	1-1	2-0	2-0	0-0	5-1	1-0		5-0	2-2	2-0	1-1	2-0	8-0	2-0	2-1	0-1	2-2	0-0
9 Foley	2-2	2-2	2-5	2-0	2-1	3-1	1-4	1-4		0-3	0-1	0-0	1-2	1-1	1-5	2-6	4-1	1-0	1-6
10 Goldenhill Wanderers	4-0	2-1	3-3	5-1	2-1	1-0	1-2	2-1	4-0		4-0	1-1	1-3	6-3	0-0	0-2	2-2	4-3	7-1
11 Hanford	3-3	3-2	1-1	0-1	2-1	3-0	2-1	0-3	1-1	3-2		0-3	0-0	3-0	1-3	0-1	2-2	1-1	2-1
12 Hanley Town	2-1	2-0	2-2	2-2	1-2	4-0	3-1	0-3	3-0	6-0	3-1		1-1	5-1	1-2	2-0	5-1	0-0	4-0
13 Milton Rangers	0-0	1-0	0-0	5-0	2-1	1-0	2-1	1-1	2-1	1-3	1-7	2-1		0-0	1-4	1-1	1-0	2-1	2-2
14 Newcastle Town Res.	2-2	0-1	1-1	2-1	0-3	0-0	0-0	0-2	1-1	1-3	1-2	1-3	2-1		0-3	1-1	1-2	3-1	1-2
15 Norton AG	4-2	2-1	0-4	3-2	2-0	3-1	0-2	2-3	2-0	5-1	1-2	1-1	0-1	1-0		2-3	0-1	4-2	3-2
16 Redgate Clayton	1-4	0-0	0-0	1-2	3-2	3-0	1-1	1-1	6-1	0-0	2-1	3-2	1-1	3-2	1-0		1-3	2-1	4-1
17 Stallington	3-2	3-0	2-3	1-0	1-2	1-0	3-2	1-1	1-1	3-0	1-1	1-1	1-0	4-2	0-3	1-3		0-1	2-1
18 Vale Juniors	0-1	0-3	0-2	1-0	1-3	0-1	1-1	1-1	1-2	1-2	0-4	0-3	1-2	6-5	0-4	3-4	3-2		2-2
19 Wolstanton United	0-5	0-4	1-1	2-2	3-3	0-2	1-1	0-6	3-1	1-4	2-4	0-7	1-1	0-3	2-6	1-1	1-7	3-2	

LEAGUE CUP 2002-03

SEMI FINALS: Hanley Town 2 Brocton 0; Norton AG 4 Audley & District 2.

FINAL (at Newcastle Town - 14.04.03)

Hanley Town 0 Norton AG 2

THE ASDA LOGIC
WEST LANCASHIRE FOOTBALL LEAGUE

President: D Procter Esq.

Chairman & General Secretary: W Carr Esq.

60 Selby Avenue, Blackpool FY4 2LZ Tel: 01253 348450

FINAL LEAGUE TABLE 2002-03

PREMIER DIVISION		P	W	D	L	F	A	Pts
1	Charnock Richard	30	20	6	4	64	31	66
2	Kirkham & Wesham	30	20	2	8	87	43	62
3	Burnley United	30	17	2	11	69	49	53
4	Dalton United	30	15	7	8	72	50	52
5	Blackrod Town	30	15	4	11	72	52	49
6	Wyre Villa	30	15	4	11	61	62	49
7	Freckleton	30	15	3	12	47	44	48
8	BAE Sports Barrow (-3)	30	14	5	11	50	43	44
9	Barnoldswick United	30	13	4	13	56	52	43
10	Eagley	30	10	9	11	51	55	39
11	Fulwood Amateurs	30	9	7	14	48	46	34
12	Turton	30	9	6	15	60	62	33
13	Blackpool Wren Rovers	30	10	2	18	51	75	32
14	Milnthorpe Corinthians	30	7	9	14	44	64	30
15	Norcross & Warbreck	30	5	8	17	37	71	23
16	Springfields	30	5	4	21	30	100	19

DIVISION TWO 02-03	1	2	3	4	5	6	7	8	9	10	11	12	13	14	15	16
1 BAE Barrow Sports Club		2-0	1-1	2-1	2-1	1-1	2-1	1-2	4-0	0-1	4-2	2-3	3-2	1-2	2-1	4-0
2 Barnoldswick United	3-2		4-3	3-3	3-0	1-2	2-2	2-2	2-4	1-0	0-3	1-0	3-1	5-0	0-2	0-1
3 Blackpool Wren Rovers	2-3	1-5		0-2	3-4	5-3	0-1	3-1	2-1	0-1	0-2	0-3	3-1	5-2	1-4	1-2
4 Blackrod Town	5-1	3-3	7-0		2-1	0-1	1-2	1-1	3-2	1-0	3-4	5-0	4-1	0-1	5-1	3-4
5 Burnley United	1-0	1-0	7-1	4-1		0-2	2-5	2-3	1-0	1-4	4-2	1-1	4-0	4-1	4-1	7-1
6 Charnock Richard	3-2	3-1	1-0	3-0	0-3		3-1	3-0	4-0	2-1	3-1	1-1	2-0	2-1	4-1	5-0
7 Dalton United	2-0	3-2	3-3	6-2	2-3	2-2		5-2	2-0	2-2	3-3	7-2	1-2	5-0	1-1	2-1
8 Eagley	3-2	1-0	0-1	0-2	3-1	1-1	3-2		1-2	3-2	0-4	4-1	2-2	5-0	0-1	2-2
9 Freckleton	1-0	3-2	2-0	3-1	0-1	3-2	1-2	1-0		0-0	3-2	1-2	4-1	3-0	1-2	2-2
10 Fulwood Amateurs	0-1	0-1	4-1	1-1	4-0	2-2	4-2	3-0	0-1		0-2	1-1	1-4	6-0	0-2	2-3
11 Kirkham & Wesham	1-1	2-1	2-1	1-2	4-0	2-0	0-2	3-2	5-1	4-1		4-0	3-0	3-2	3-1	1-3
12 Milnthorpe Corinthians	2-2	1-2	1-3	2-3	1-1	1-2	2-3	2-2	0-1	1-1	2-1		1-1	5-1	1-7	2-3
13 Norcross & Warbeck	0-1	2-3	2-3	1-4	0-4	0-2	3-2	1-1	2-2	2-1	0-3	0-2		2-2	1-1	2-2
14 Springfields	1-2	1-3	3-2	0-4	0-4	0-3	2-0	2-2	0-2	2-2	0-5	1-1	1-2		0-3	2-1
15 Turton	0-0	1-2	2-3	2-3	2-3	0-0	0-0	2-2	0-3	2-3	0-10	0-1	5-1	12-1		1-2
16 Wyre Villa	1-2	3-1	1-3	2-0	1-0	1-2	0-1	1-3	1-0	4-1	4-5	3-2	1-1	6-2	5-3	

FINAL LEAGUE TABLE 2002-03

DIVISION ONE		P	W	D	L	F	A	Pts
1	Coppull United	28	20	6	2	90	24	66
2	Fleetwood Hesketh	28	18	4	6	81	44	58
3	Bootle	28	18	4	6	66	41	58
4	Carnforth Rangers	28	14	7	7	61	44	49
5	Millom	28	14	1	13	75	64	43
6	Poulton Town	28	11	10	7	49	43	43
7	Hesketh Bank	28	12	4	12	48	50	40
8	Crooklands Casuals	28	10	9	9	42	53	39
9	Tempest United	28	10	8	10	61	50	38
10	Feniscowles	28	9	8	11	60	56	35
11	Garstang	28	9	6	13	47	63	33
12	Whinney Hill	28	9	5	14	45	64	32
13	Burnley Belvedere	28	8	2	18	30	78	26
14	Haslingden St Mary's	28	5	0	23	38	83	15
15	Lancs Constabulary (-3)	28	5	2	21	49	85	14

CUP FINALS

Richardson Cup: Eagley 2 Charnock Richard 1.
Tavern Cup: BAE Canberra 1 BAC/EE Preston 0.
President's Cup: Millom 1 Hesketh Bank 0.
Houston Cup: Garstang Res. 2 Charnock Richard Res. 0

PREMIER DIVISION CLUBS 2003-04

BAE BARROW SPORTS CLUB
Vickers Sports Club, Hawcoat Lane, Barrow-in-Furness, Cumbria. Tel: 01229 825296.

BARNOLDSWICK UNITED
Victory Park, West Close, Barnoldswick, Colne, Lancashire. Tel: 01282 815817

BLACKPOOL WREN ROVERS RESERVES
Bruce Park, School Road, Marton, Blackpool, Lancashire. Tel: 01253 760570

BLACKROD TOWN
Blackrod Community Centre, Vicarage Road, Blackrod, Lancashire. Tel: 01204 692614

BURNLEY UNITED
Barden Sports Ground, Barden Lane, Burnley, Lancashire.

CHARNOCK RICHARD
Charter Lane, Charnock Richard, Lancashire. Tel: 01257 794288

COPPULL UNITED
Springfield Road, Coppull, Lancashire. Tel: 01257 795190

DALTON UNITED
Railway Meadow, Beckside Road, Dalton-in-Furness, Cumbria. Tel: 01229 462799

EAGLEY
Eagley Sports Complex, Dunscar Bridge, Bolton, Lancashire. Tel: 01204 306830

FLEETWOOD HESKETH
Fylde Road, Southport, Merseyside. Tel: 01704 227968

FRECKLETON
Hodgson Memorial Ground, Bush Lane, Freckleton, Lancashire. Tel: 01772 679139

FULWOOD AMATEURS
Lightfoot Lane, Fulwood, Preston, Lancashire. Tel: 01772 861827

KIRKHAM & WESHAM
Recreation Ground, Coronation Road, Kirkham, Lancashire

MILNTHORPE CORINTHIANS
Strands Lane, Milnthorpe, Cumbria. Tel: 01539 562135

TURTON
Moorfield, Edgworth, Bolton, Lancashire. Tel: 07929 965160

WYRE VILLA
Hallgate Park, Stalmine Village, near Knott End, Lancashire. Tel: 01253 701468

DIVISION ONE CLUBS

Bootle (Cumbria) AFC
Carnforth Rangers FC
Euxton Villa FC
Garstang FC
Hesketh Bank FC
Millom FC
Poulton Town FC
Tempest United FC
Burnley Belvedere FC
Crooklands Casuals FC
Feniscowles FC
Haslingden St Mary's FC
Lytham St Annes FC
Norcross & Warbeck
Springfields
Whinney Hill FC

DIVISION TWO CLUBS

Askam United FC
BAC/EE Preston FC
Barrow Rangers FC
Furness Cavaliers FC
Lancashire Constabulary
Pennington FC
Stoneclough FC
Todmorden Borough FC
Aspull (Wigan Youth Lge)
Bae Canberra FC
Crosshills FC
GSK Ulverston Rangers FC
Mill Hill St Peters
Rivington (Lancs Amateur)
Thornton Cleveleys FC
(Previous League)

AIR MILES MANCHESTER FOOTBALL LEAGUE

Honorary President: Norman Noden
League Secretary: Phil Platt.
Press Officer: Scott White, 303 Rake Lane, Clifton, Salford, Lancashire, M27 8LJ
Tel: 0771 204 9561 (Mobile) Fax: 0161 288 9042

The AIR MILES Manchester League crowned new Champions in 2003 as Irlam Mitchell Shackleton repeated the agony of last season for Wythenshawe Amateurs when they crept up on the rails to snatch to spot of the Premier Division. Mitchells lost only two of their last fifteen league games, a fine achievement, and edged into first place in dramatic circumstances.

Irlam had despatched Wilmslow Albion 6-1 at home to overtake Wythenshawe at the top, but fellow hopefuls Atherton Town were a goal up at home to Sacred Heart, and few would have bet on an equaliser. Deep into injury time, Hearts' substitute Tony Kershaw chested the ball off to Jamie Sarsfield, who drove the ball home to deprive Atherton of the win, and ensure that Irlam could not be caught. League President Phil Morris was on hand to surprise the Mitchells players in their dressing room, and present them with the Championship trophy. The drama has not ended there however, as after the end of the season, it emerged that Irlam MS may have unwittingly played a contract player during the run-in, with a thorough investigation of the claims ongoing. Should the allegations be proven, then there is a real chance that Irlam MS will lose any points gained, which would strip them of the crown.

It is hard not to feel some sympathy for Wythenshawe Amateurs, who end as runners-up for the third season in succession, but an indifferent run of form after Christmas eventually cost the Ammies dearly. A haul of only sixteen points from a possible 36 allowed the chasing pack to catch them, and unusually, Wythenshawe were shy in front of goal. A scoreless draw at New Mills was followed by a 1-0 reverse at Sacred Heart to see Ammies' campaign end with everyone at Longley Lane biting their nails, and once again they were denied at the death.

Atherton Town will look back on 2003 with questions of what might have been, despite an excellent third place finish, as slips in the run-in cost them a top two spot. The Howe Bridge side faced a testing backlog of fixtures in April and May, and back-to-back defeats to East and Royton were major setbacks before Sacred Heart finally ended their hopes. There were some highpoints though, especially the late flourish from Danny Christie who finished the Premier Division's top marksman, and also the attacking football that epitomised Town's play throughout.

Despite a four match run without a win in mid-April, Stockport Georgians bounced back to claim fourth place, clinching a good final position in what was effectively a play-off game at Prestwich Heys. Once again, goals were never a problem for Georgians, but defensively, the Cromley Road side have to look back as far as mid-November for their last clean sheet, and it is this factor which scuppered hopes of a more determined effort to retain the crown.

Gary Leeming will be delighted with the debut season of Royton Town in the Premier Division, who in mid-March looked likely challengers after a great run of form, and defeated all top three at some time in the season. Four consecutive defeats in April cost Town their chance though, but the goals kept coming as Royton ended the season as the Division's leading scorers, and went four unbeaten at the end to claim fifth spot. Sixth spot represents a decent return for Prestwich Heys, but 2003 will be remembered for a notable cup double as the Sandgate Road side claimed the Goldline Trophy with a 3-0 win over Atherton Colls at the Reebok Stadium, and the Gilgryst Cup with a 4-1 victory over Springhead in front of a bumper crowd at Elton. Consistency in the league was to prove Heys' undoing, but they did despatch Irlam MS 3-1 to prove their potential, but their young team could not repeat this form regularly enough. An impressive second half to the campaign saw Dukinfield Town rise as high as second place after hovering in the lower reaches of mid-table before Christmas, a useful combination of youth and experience seeing the Blocksages side's stock rise. Aside from a double defeat to near-neighbours East, the only teams to beat Town between October and the end of the season were Irlam MS and Atherton, which underlines the potential at Dukinfield. Leigh Athletic eventually had to settle for eighth place, despite finishing their campaign in second spot, and they were again a thorn in the side of the leading teams. A lack of consistency was the Latics' main problem, but the season ended with only one defeat in six, and once again, Danny Wilson was a major influence at the club, despite missing part of the season through injury.

It is a similar tale over at Springhead where fortunes soared and dipped with too much regularity for the liking of Manager Craig Lawson, but 'Head entertained throughout, and once again proved a handful in the cups. It took eventual beaten finalists Barnoldswick United to end their West Riding Challenge Cup hopes in a tight game up in the hills, and Springhead contributed fully to an engaging Gilgryst Cup Final with Heys, where the final scoreline was a little cruel on the Lees side.

It is the end of an era at New Mills where Alan Peatfield steps down after guiding the Millers to their most successive period in decades. Everyone associated with the League would like to wish Alan well for the future. It was by no means a classic season at Church Lane, but the goalscoring exploits of Wes Gibbons set the imagination alight in the Autumn, as did the club's return to action in the FA Vase and Derbyshire Senior Cup. The appointment of Darren Lyons proved the catalyst for better things at East Manchester as they climbed away from the relegation mire, and also retained the Manchester Challenge Trophy. Between January and May, the only side to defeat East was the Champions Irlam MS, and on this form, they may well be one to watch next term. Once again, Elton Vale had a good, solid campaign, finishing with a very healthy fourteen point cushion with the bottom two, and only three wins away from a top five finish. To add to their decent league form, a debut Gilgryst Cup Semi-Final appearance, plus a place in the last eight of the Lancashire Amateur Shield were highlights, as was the form of Derek Watson, who was in prolific form and finished second best marksman.

A daunting end of season run-in ended with Wilmslow Albion finishing in thirteenth spot, and all this after many thought that they might just make a title bid after a bright unbeaten start. Carl Massa did a great job to steady the ship after the departure of Trevor Howard, but it was defensive frailty that was to cost Albion as they managed only one clean sheet after Christmas. It was Monton Amateurs who survived the three-way tussle to avoid the drop, and a four-match unbeaten run going into April proved the decisive period for the Granary Lane side. The goals of Graham Bragg and Dennis Hardman proved vital for Monton, and despite winning only one of their last four, it was to be the all-important one, a 2-0 victory at Springhead, which ensured survival. Rochdale Sacred Heart were another side with a lengthy end of season programme, but in collecting only one win from nine games, Hearts efforts eventually came to naught. A disjointed season, in which Hearts found it tough to convert draws into wins, was to cost them, though a gutsy 1-0 win over Wythenshawe underlined what they were capable of on their day. Willows had looked favourites to go down since Christmas, but regrouped well in March to win three games and give themselves some hope. A crucial loss to Monton Amateurs made survival all but impossible, and the Agecroft side ended the season bottom of the pile, but the spirit shown late on saw the campaign end with heads held high.

After several years of near misses, Breightmet United finally clinched the promotion they have craved for so long, collecting the First Division Championship to add the icing to the cake for the Bolton side. United had been front-runners for most of the season, and a nine match unbeaten run saw them clinch promotion with a thumping 8-1 win at Whalley Range, and the title at Whitworth Valley. After a tense battle for second place between no fewer than six teams at one point, Highfield United eventually claimed the runners-up berth and recover from a mid-season blip which saw them slip off the pace. 'Field also collected the Murray Shield for the third time following a penalties win over Avro at Springhead. Belden made a late burst for glory, losing only once in their last ten matches to finish only five points adrift in third, a run of six games without victory in the Winter costing them a Premier Division return. Joe Rae's side also reached the Manchester Challenge Trophy Final, where they put up a great show against East, but could not recover after going three down.

In his first season in charge at Hindsford AFC, Matty Wardrop guided the club to fourth spot, a Murray Shield Semi-Final, and the Third Round of the Lancashire Shield, a good debut season, and with Dave Fashou also in red-hot form in front of goal, the Tonics will be early favourites next season. After finishing their season ahead of the rest, Ashton Athletic had the agony of watching the sides below them inch upon them, but earlier crucial defeats to Hindsford and Breightmet were to end their hopes. Like the other sides just outside the promotion spots, Avro will look back on key results such as their defeat at Tintwistle as to where their hopes were dashed, but this should not take away from a great season in which the club were beaten Murray Shield finalists, and also reached the last eight of the Manchester Amateur Cup, putting out Trafford and Curzon reserve sides.

Wythenshawe Town once again lived up to their enigmatic billing with a season of ups and downs, and another certainty is the goalscoring output of Darren Mee, who again weighed in with a hatful of goals. The most improved side in the Division was undoubtedly Unsworth, who under the guidance of Nick Woods emerged as force, especially in defence, where they were particularly mean. As late as March, Whitworth Valley had an outside chance of promotion, but two wins from eleven games saw the Lancashire side slip down the table, and also lose out to Avro in the Murray Shield Semis. Whalley Range had an inbetween campaign, with wins too irregular to make much impression, but garnering enough points to steer well clear of the bottom, and they will hope to improve on this year's showing next term. Milton ended the season as one of the Division's form sides, winning five out of their last six games, drawing the other, to finish on 34 points, but throughout the campaign, the Rochdale side exhibited a resilient streak, and the question is whether a Milton revival is on the cards next season. Anthony Hodgkinson grabbed the headlines in a decent campaign for Tintwistle Villa, netting 20 goals in the second half of the season to help the Pennines side clear of re-election, and if Villa could carry their home form away, further improvement should follow.

After a great campaign last season, Hollinwood's hopes of continuing their drive forwards were beset by ground and internal problems, but 'Wood showed their character to bounce back and reach safety. Eleven games without a win in 2003 saw Warth Fold slip to fourteenth place, scoring only four times in this run, but the Bury side showed plenty of spirit throughout a difficult run and will hope to turn things around next season. Old Alts finished bottom after a much-troubled season at Crossford Bridge, and only the form of Wes Bancroft near the end could brighten things up, and with Manchester Royal having resigned, only Alts will have to apply for re-election.

In the Second Division, Wilmslow Albion retained the crown in magnificent style by a marvellous fourteen-point margin, dropping only four points all season. Albion have now lost only six league games in three season, but their hopes of collecting a league and cup double were ended by runners-up Dukinfield Town, who won 3-2 in the Open Trophy Final at New Mills. Third-placed Stockport Georgians also brought silverware to the league as they edged out Lancashire and Cheshire League outfit Mellor 2-1 in the Stockport Senior Cup, and our congratulations go to them. Wythenshawe Amateurs and Irlam Mitchell Shackleton garnered enough points to evade the bottom two places, which were occupied by Elton Vale and Breightmet United. Rochdale Sacred Heart romped to the Third Division Championship, also losing just once, and Ashton Athletic were runners-up with a late burst to secure promotion, and the Latics also won the Supplementary Cup in a very competitive Final with Whalley Range.

FINAL LEAGUE TABLE 2002-03

PREMIER DIVISION		P	W	D	L	F	A	Pts
1	Irlam Mitchell Shackleton	30	18	5	7	67	43	59
2	Wythenshawe Amateur	30	16	7	7	50	33	55
3	Atherton Town	30	16	6	8	64	39	54
4	Stockport Georgians	30	15	4	11	73	61	49
5	Royton Town	30	13	8	9	73	58	47
6	Prestwich Heys	30	13	7	10	51	47	46
7	Dukinfield Town (-3)	30	15	4	11	50	43	46
8	Leigh Athletic	30	12	8	10	70	48	44
9	Springhead	30	12	5	13	55	56	41
10	New Mills	30	11	6	13	57	60	39
11	Elton Vale	30	11	6	13	51	58	39
12	East Manchester	30	11	6	13	53	67	39
13	Wilmslow Albion	30	8	12	10	56	57	36
14	Monton Amateurs	30	7	5	18	42	78	26
15	Rochdale Sacred Heart	30	5	10	15	43	58	25
16	Willows	30	6	3	21	36	85	21

DIVISION ONE		P	W	D	L	F	A	Pts
1	Breightmet United	28	19	3	6	81	40	60
2	Highfield United	28	17	5	6	74	44	56
3	Belden	28	15	6	7	77	62	51
4	Hindsford (-3)	28	15	7	6	71	45	49
5	Ashton Athletic	28	14	7	7	68	40	49
6	Avro	28	14	6	8	67	44	48
7	Wythenshawe Town	28	11	9	8	53	47	42
8	Unsworth (-1)	28	12	7	9	52	45	42
9	Whitworth Valley	28	11	5	12	63	64	38
10	Whalley Range	28	11	1	16	60	71	34
11	Milton	28	9	7	12	40	54	34
12	Tintwistle Villa	28	9	2	17	41	70	29
13	Hollinwood (-3)	28	8	1	19	49	83	22
14	Warth Fold	28	5	5	18	38	81	20
15	Old Altrinchamians	28	4	1	23	29	73	13

(Manchester Royal withdrew during the course of the season)

PREMIER RESULTS GRID 02-03	1	2	3	4	5	6	7	8	9	10	11	12	13	14	15	16
1 Atherton Town		1-2	3-1	1-2	1-1	2-1	2-0	0-2	4-2	1-1	1-1	1-0	1-0	1-0	4-2	0-1
2 Dukinfield Town	0-3		0-3	1-3	1-2	2-2	7-1	2-1	2-0	1-1	4-2	1-0	5-1	2-1	2-1	2-0
3 East Manchester	1-0	3-2		3-3	1-3	0-3	3-1	1-3	2-2	2-1	4-2	0-4	3-5	2-2	1-3	1-4
4 Elton Vale	1-3	1-3	3-1		1-2	2-2	1-2	2-1	2-0	3-2	1-0	1-3	3-1	0-2	1-0	0-2
5 Irlam Mitchell Shackleton	1-4	2-0	3-0	3-2		1-1	2-1	2-1	2-1	3-1	3-3	4-2	1-2	1-2	6-1	2-0
6 Leigh Athletic	1-1	0-1	5-2	3-4	2-1		5-2	0-2	4-0	2-0	0-1	3-1	3-3	2-0	1-1	2-5
7 Monton Amateurs	0-6	1-0	2-2	1-1	2-4	2-7		1-2	0-0	2-2	2-1	0-2	1-4	3-0	0-2	0-1
8 New Mills	3-4	1-2	0-3	2-1	1-1	4-3	2-4		0-2	3-2	1-4	2-0	2-2	3-3	1-2	0-0
9 Prestwich Hayes	0-2	0-2	2-0	1-1	3-1	1-1	6-2	3-2		1-1	3-2	3-0	2-3	2-1	2-2	1-0
10 Rochdale Sacred Heart	3-6	1-1	1-3	1-1	0-2	2-2	1-2	3-3	0-2		0-3	1-3	1-2	4-0	3-0	1-0
11 Royton Town	2-0	1-1	1-2	2-1	5-4	2-1	2-2	6-4	3-2	1-1		1-1	1-5	4-2	2-2	2-0
12 Springhead	3-1	2-0	0-2	5-2	0-1	3-2	0-2	4-2	2-2	3-3	2-7		2-1	4-1	4-1	1-3
13 Stockport Georgians	3-1	4-1	4-1	5-2	2-3	1-4	3-0	2-3	1-2	2-1	2-1	2-1		1-2	4-4	1-2
14 Willows	1-6	1-2	3-4	1-3	0-4	0-5	2-1	0-4	4-1	0-2	1-7	2-2	1-4		2-1	1-3
15 Wilmslow Albion	3-3	2-0	1-1	3-1	2-2	1-3	5-3	1-1	0-1	0-1	3-3	4-0	2-2	5-1		0-0
16 Wythenshawe Amateur	1-1	2-1	1-1	2-2	1-0	1-0	3-2	0-1	1-4	4-2	3-1	1-1	5-1	2-0	2-2	

CUP FINALS

Gilgryst Cup: Prestwich Heys 4 Springhead 1. **Murray Shield:** Avro 1 Highfield United 1 aet (4-5p).

TOP GOALSCORERS

Prem Division: Danny Christie (Atherton Tn) 25. **Derek Watson** (Elton Vale) 24. **John Robinson** (Irlam MS) 21.

ATHERTON TOWN

Formed: 1964
Secretary: Gerald Butler, 43 Hope Fold Ave., Atherton, Lancs M29 0BW Tel: 01942 870326
Ground: Howe Bridge Spts Centre, Howe Bridge, Atherton Tel: 01942 884882
Directions: A579 Atherton to Leigh road - Sports Centre 800 yds on left
Colours: Royal/white/royal

BREIGHTMET UNITED

Secretary: Roy Haslam, Tel: 01204 535933 or 07796 134093
Ground: Moss Park, Bury Road, Breightmet, Manchester Tel: 01204 533930
Colours: Black & white stripes/black/red

DUKINFIELD TOWN

Formed: 1948
Secretary: Paul Bishop, 21 Church Walk, Stalybridge, Cheshire Tel: 0161 303 0398
Ground: Blocksages Playing Fields, Birch Lane, Dukinfield. Tel: 0161 343 4529
Directions: From Ashton centre follow Kings St, turn left into Chapel St. thenright turn into Foundry St/Birch Lane. Ground 880 yds on right, behind public baths.
Colours: All yellow

EAST MANCHESTER

Formed: 1960 (called ICL until 1985)
Secretary: D Wilkinson, 76 Sandy Lane, Dukinfield, Cheshire SK16 5NL Tel: 0161 330 4450
Ground: Droylsden FC, The Butchers Arms, Droylsden Tel: 0161 370 1426, 0161 301 1352
Directions: From Manchester take A662 (Ashton New Road) to junct with Market St. in Droylsden. Left into Market St. at lights, over the mini r'about. Ground entrance on the left.
Colours: All royal blue

ELTON VALE

Formed: 1957 (Formerly Elton Fold >2002)
Secretary: Guy Mallinson, 14 Lonsdale St, Bury BL8 2QD Tel: 0161 797 7090
Ground: Elton Vale Road, Bury. 0161 762 0666
Directions: A58 from Bury to Boltonto junction with Ainsworth Road (B6196). Approx. 3/4 mile right into Elton Vale Road. Ground is 150 yards on left after Foulds Ave.
Colours: Blue & black/black/black

HIGHFIELD UNITED

Secretary: Jackie Lomax, Tel: 0161 764 9986
Ground: Seedfield Sports Club, Parkinson Street, Bury
Colours: Jade and black

IRLAM MITCHELL SHACKLETON

Formed: 1970 (called Mitchell Shackleton until 2001)
Secretary: Ian Street, 11 Senior Road, Peel Green, Eccles, M30 7PZ Tel: 0161 789 7061
Ground: Salteye Park, Peel Green, Eccles Tel: 0161 788 8373
Directions: Leave M63 at Peel Green r'bout (jct 2), take A57 Liverpool Roadtowards Irlam, ground entrance half mile on left behind Kara Cafew opposite Barton airport. Or, follow A57 from Manchester via Salford & Eccles, then follow Irlam signs.
Colours: Blue & white

LEIGH ATHLETIC

Formed: 1959
Secretary: Rick Wilson. Tel: 01942 518328
Ground: Madley Park, Charles St., Leigh Tel: 01942 673500
Directions: Exit A580 at junction with A574 onto Warrington Road and follow into Leigh town centre. Turn right into King Street and turn right into Church Street ('Boars Head' Pub). Take 6th left into Charles Street and ground straight ahead.
Colours: Yellow/ Blue/ Blue

MONTON AMATEURS

Formed: 1916
Secretary: Tony Lee, 28 Wheatley Rd, Swinton, Manchester M27 3RW Tel: 0161 793 8033
Ground: Granary Lane, Worsley, Manchester
Directions: From Eccles Centre turn right into Worsley Rd at Patricroft Bridge.Ground approx 1 mile on left, entrance just before Bridgewater Hotel
Colours: All royal blue

NEW MILLS

Formed: 1987 (re formed)
Secretary: Barry Land, 165 Lowleighton Road, New Mills, High Peak SK22 4LR Tel: 01663 746174
Ground: Church Lane, New Mills, Derbys. Tel: 01663 747435
Directions: From A6 (Buxton Road), turn into Albion Road (A6015) at New Mills Newtown Train Station. Follow to junction of Church Road/Church Lane and ground on left.
Colours: Amber/black/black

PRESTWICH HEYS

Formed: 1938
Secretary: Norman Deardon Tel: 0161 959 1305
Ground: Sandgate Rd, Whitefield Tel: 0161 773 8888
Directions: Follow Old Bury Rd (A665) from Manchester to Prestwich, right into Heywood Rd, 3rd left into Mount Rd/Sandgate Rd - ground on right.
Colours: Red & white/red/red

ROYTON TOWN

Secretary: Phil Dean (0161 287 8436)
Ground: Crompton Cricket Club, Glebe Road, Shaw, Oldham.Tel: 01706 847421
Directions: J20, M62 onto A627(M) signed Oldham. At 1st exit follow A663 (broadway) onto A66 (Shaw Road). At r'about take 2nd exit (Crompton Way), and then 1st left onto Rochdale Road. Glebe Road is 4th turning on right and ground is at end of the road.
Colours: Yellow and Black

SPRINGHEAD

Formed: 1926
Secretary: Alex Simmons Tel: 0161 620 0959 or 07764 836918
Ground: St John St, Lees, Oldham Tel: 0161 627 0260
Directions: From Oldham (Mumps r'bout) follow A669 towards Lees for approx onemile, left into St John St, ground 500yds on right.
Colours: Black & red/black/black

STOCKPORT GEORGIANS

Formed: 1987
Secretary: Ged Newcombe, 7 Chiltern Close, Hazel Grove, Stockport SK7 5BQ Tel: 0161483 0004
Ground: Cromley Rd, Woodsmoor, Stockport, Tel: 0161 483 6581
Directions: Follow A6 from Stockport centre, turn right at Cemetery intoBranhall Lane. After 1 mile turn left at r/about into Woodsmoor Lane. Take 1st right Flowery Fields then right into Cromley Road
Colours: Red and black

WILMSLOW ALBION

Formed: 1919

Secretary: Norma Winn, 236 Derbyshire Lane, Stretford, Manchester (0161 2869520)

Ground: Oakwood Farm, Styal Road, Wilmslow

Tel: 01625 535823

Directions: From J5, M56 follow signs for Wilmslow. Turn right at the end of Ringway Road into Styal Road (B5166). Take 3rd right onto Altrincham Road and ground on right.

Colours: Yellow and blue

WYTHENSHAWE AMATEURS

Formed: 1959

Secretary: John Sobierajsh, 5 Wensley Drive, Withington, Manchester Tel: 0161 445 3415

Ground: Longley Lane, Northenden, Wythenshawe, Manchester. Tel: 0161 998 7268

Directions: Princess Parkway from Manchester to Post House hotel, via PalatineRd & Moor End Rd to Longley Lane - ground entrance opposite Overwood Rd.

Colours: Blue & white stripes/blue/blue

DIVISION ONE CLUBS

AFC BLACKLEY
Previous Names: Belden>2003; B.I.C.C.
Secretary: Rob Fuller, Tel: 0161 681 6948 or 07971 177475
Ground: Belden Works, Blackley New Road, Blackley.
Tel: 0161 740 9151
Colours: Maroon and blue

ASHTON ATHLETIC
Secretary: Steve Halliwell, 20 Kings Road, Golborne, Warrington Tel: 01942 517728 (H) 07774 180165 (M)
Ground: Brocstedes Park, Farm Road, Ashton-in-Makerfield
Tel: 01942 716360.
Colours: Orange and navy blue

AVRO
Secretary: Karen Birch, 27 Brooks Drive, Failsworth, Manchester M35 0L5 Tel: 0161 682 6731
Ground: Lancaster Club, Broadway, Failsworth
Colours: Red & black/red/red

HEYWOOD ST. JAMES
Ground:
Previous Lge: Lancs & Cheshire Amateur Lge.

HINDSFORD
Secretary: Eddie Evans, 17 Belmont Avenue, Atherton M46 9RR RTel Nos: 01942 895869 (H) 07767 492411 (M)
Ground: Squires Lane, Tyldesley
Colours: Red /blue/red & blue

HOLLINWOOD
Secretary: Ken Evans, 20 Meadow Rise, High Crompton, Shaw, Oldham OL2 7QG Tel: 01706 840987 or 07740 442818.
Ground: Lime Lane, Hollinwood, Oldham (0161 681 3385).
Colours: Yellow & Navy/ Navy / Navy

MANCHESTER TITANS
Previous name: Warth Fold
Secretary: Felix Daniel. Tel: 0161 232 0392 or 077877 880407
Ground: The Elms, George St., Whitefield, Bury. Tel: 0161 767 9233
Colours: Yellow and blue

MILTON
Secretary: Andrew Cole, 21 Whittle Drive, Shaw, Oldham OL2 8TJ Tel: 01706 291973 (H) 07754 482393 (M)
Ground: Athletic Stadium, Springfield Park, Rochdale.
Colours: Green& Black,Black/Black

OLD ALTRINCHAMIANS
Secretary: Phil Lewis, 10 Woodfield Grove, Sale, M33 6JW Tel: 0161 973 7082 or 07796 475550 (M))
Ground: Crossford Bridge Playing Fields, Meadows Rd, Sale.
Tel: 0161 767 9233
Colours: Black & white stripes/black/black

OLD STANDIANS
Ground: t.b.a.
Previous Lge: Lancs & Cheshire Amateur Lge.

ROCHDALE SACRED HEART **Formed:** 1955
(called Robinson's >1985; RSH>87 & Sacred Heart>2001)
Secretary: Joe Devlin, 61 Buersil Ave., Rochdale, Lancs. OL16 4TR Tel: 01706 712602
Ground: Fox Park, Belfield Mill Lane, Rochdale
Directions: From Rochdale town centre follow the A640 to Milnrow, at Kingsway junction turn left into Albert Royds Street and turn right again into Bellfield Mill Lane.
Colours: All red

STAND ATHLETIC Founded: 1964
Secretary: Dave Jackson, 26 Brookdene Rd, Unsworth, Bury Bl9 8ND
Tel: 0161 796 0353
Ground: Ewood Bridge, Manchester Rd, Haslingden, Lancs. BB4 6JY Tel: 01706 217814
Previous Lges: Bury Amateur, S. E. Lancs., Lancs & Cheshire, Manchester, N.W.C. 01-03
Colours: Blue & yellow/blue/blue

SWINTON TOWN **Formed:** 1977
Secretary: Frank Miller, 11 Edmund Street, Salford, Manchester Tel: 0161 737 2411 or 07761 486146
Ground: Agecroft Sports Ground, Agecroft Rd., Salford.
Directions: From Manchester, follow signs for A580(East Lancs Road) and exit at IRlas o' th' Height. At r'about take 4th exit, following signs for A666 (Kearsley/Bury). At 1st set of lights, right onto Agecroft Road (at Henry Boddington P.H.). Travel approx. 1/3 mile, & ground on left.
Colours: Red and white

TINTWISTLE VILLA
Secretary: Bill Higginbottom, 61 West Drive, Tintwistle, Glossop Tel: 01457 852467
Ground: West Drive, Tintwistle, nr Glossop, Derbys.
Colours: Black & white stripes/black/black

UNSWORTH
Secretary: Suzanne Angle Tel: 0161 766 4073 or 07775 522351
Ground: Hillock Playing Fields, Mersey Close, Whitefield, Bury.
Colours: Blue and Yellow

WHALLEY RANGE
Secretary: Paul Pestell. Tel: 0161 881 5297 or 07712 840125
Ground: Kings Rd, Whalley Range, Manchester. Tel: 0161 613 5467
Colours: Red & black stripes/black/black

WHITWORTH VALLEY
Secretary: Alan Riley, 31 John Street, Whitworth, Rochdale OL12 8BT Tel: 01706 852619 (H) 07930 543924 (M)
Ground: Rawstron Street, Whitworth Tel: 01706 853045.
Colours: Black & white/black/red

WYTHENSHAWE TOWN
Secretary: Norman Hardman. Tel: 0161 437 8236.
Ground: Ericstan Park, Timpson Rd, Wythenshawe, Manchester. Tel: 0161 998 5076. **Colours:** All royal Blue

Goole striker Jason Harris holds off the double challenge of Thackley's Mark Senior and Craig Sugden in the Dennyfield mud, during teh sides' 1-1 league draw.

Photo: Darren C Thomas.

Jason Harris and Craig Sugden challenge for the ball again.
Photo: Darren C Thomas.

Eccleshill United's Mark Burnham fends off the challenge of Ade Carter.
Photo: Darren C Thomas

Mickleover Sports F.C. Back Row (L-R): Dave Middleditch, Karl Reynolds, Wayne Sutton, Ross Mays, Kenny Lawson, Mark Wilson, Mark Wood, Matt Warren, Bev Hudson.
Front Row: Paul Cliff, Paul Stevens, Rob McGovern, Carl Cunningham, Karl Yeoman, Karl Payne, Corin Holness.
Photo: Bill Wheatcroft.

Eastwood Town F.C. Back Row (L-R): Antony Bedward, Deon Meikle, Scott Huckerby, Paul Gould (Capt), Matt Millns, Jamie Morgan, Danny Bryant, Steve Smith.
Front Row: Clayton Garfitt, Craig Housley, Jamie McGowan, James Hutchinson, Craig Wilson, Jason Bedward.
Photo: Peter Fenton.

NORTHERN COUNTIES EAST FOOTBALL LEAGUE

FEEDER TO: NORTHERN PREMIER LEAGUE

President: H Frank Catt **Chairman:** Tom Dixon

Secretary/Treasurer:

Barry Wood, 6 Restmore Avenue, Guiseley, Leeds LS20 9DG

Tel & Fax: 01943 874 558

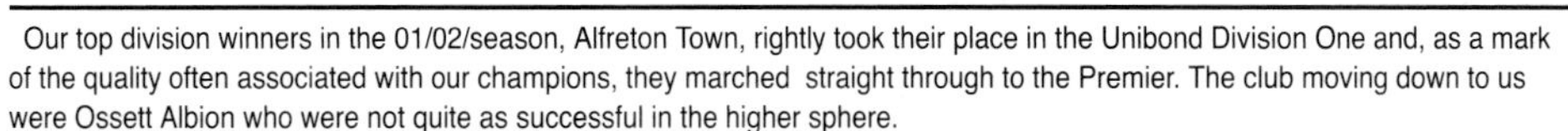

Our top division winners in the 01/02/season, Alfreton Town, rightly took their place in the Unibond Division One and, as a mark of the quality often associated with our champions, they marched straight through to the Premier. The club moving down to us were Ossett Albion who were not quite as successful in the higher sphere.

The re-emergence of the 'new' Bridlington Town in the last 4 years has been a remarkable success story after the sad demise of the original outfit. Respectable positions in division one in their first two seasons resulted in a runners-up position at the end of the 01/02 campaign and so promotion to the premier division where they have shot forward to take the championship 20 points ahead of their nearest rivals, Brigg Town, to ensure promotion to the Unibond league from where Eastwood Town will re-join our ranks.

It was by no means certain that 'Brid' would win the division though as Goole, along with Ossett Albion and Brigg Town, were vying for important championship points. Goole led the division well into early March when Town's games in hand became crucial and their consistency proved decisive. Goole slipped a little towards the end of the campaign and Brigg Town pipped them by a single point in the final run-in. Ossett Albion, the demoted Unibond club, finished in fifth place behind Buxton, another club which has encouraged its growing support by some first class performances towards the end of the season.

Borrowash Victoria had occupied bottom place in the division since early November and it seemed almost certain that they would be relegated but a very last day win against Thackley put them above Garforth Town, and saw them survive on account of only one club being promoted from division one.

Derbyshire clubs have figured prominently this year at the bottom of the premier division and at the top of division one, where Mickleover Sports achieved their championship win with a seven point cushion over Shirebrook Town who, in their first league campaign, can be well-satisfied with runners-up spot, only missing out on promotion due to their ground not being up to premier league standard. The other new club, Long Eaton United, were in the honours race for most of the season too but won only one of their last five matches - against Mickleover!

The bottom two clubs applying for re-election, a procedure that could well be a thing of the past after the Central Midlands League confirmed additional clubs would be nominated to the division, are Tadcaster Albion and Staveley MW. Nominations from the CML who have achieved minimum grading standards are the first three clubs in their supreme division - Carlton Town, Sutton Town and South Normanton Athletic. A rule amendment detailing the demotion/promotion procedure is now to be incorporated within our rules.

Our old reserve division now has to operate with a name change to division two whilst last season's champions. Emley Reserves, also decided to add 'Wakefield' to their title. The name-change didn't make any difference to their success in the division and they won it again from main rivals Liversedge Reserves.

The Reserves of Selby and Rossington have dropped out for next season and, at one point, the viability of the division was in jeopardy. However, the remaining clubs wanted it to continue and, with Goole Reserves coming in, it will operate with 12 teams. A review of the position for the future will take place towards the end of the season.

Some clubs' matches in the league cup were concertinaed into a short period at the end of the season due to a number of factors but finally emerging as winners were Ossett Albion who defeated Sheffield 3-0 in the climax to their season at Brigg Town's ground. The sponsors of the competition, Uhlsport, were on hand to present the winners and runners-up cheques.

The initiative in the President's Cup was taken by the eventual winners, Harrogate Railway, in the first leg away to Bridlington Town, when they won 3-2 with some late goals. In the second leg at Starbeck, they confirmed their superiority by adding a 4-0 win to achieve a 7-2 aggregate scoreline and our president, Frank Catt, was on hand to present his trophy.

The Wilkinson Sword Trophy was also a two-legged affair involving Pontefract Colls and Mickleover Sports. As in the President's Cup, a 2-0 away win for Sports tipped the scales in their favour and, although it was 1-1 in the second leg in Derby, the aggregate 3-1 score gave the 'Sword' to Mickleover.

The reserve team cup final was played at Ossett Albion where Liversedge Reserves won the trophy with a 3-1 win against Thackley Reserves.

There is absolutely no doubt this time that our clubs have taken the spotlight nationally to reinforce, what we already know, that our standard of football is as good as, if not better, than other areas of the country.

It was only a few days ago that Brigg Town crowned a wonderful FA Vase campaign by lifting the trophy for a second time to emulate their victory in 1996. This time a 2-0 win against Jewson Eastern Counties side AFC Sudbury at West Ham was ample reward for some hard work on the day and in earlier round along the way - none more so than when they defeated Bridlington Town in the quarter final. It was a great victory for manager, Ralph Clayton, the players and all the back-room staff and brought many congratulations from those present in the 6634 crowd plus, of course, an extra £5000 prize fund money.

FINAL LEAGUE TABLE 2002-03

PREMIER DIVISION		P	W	D	L	F	A	Pts
1	Bridlington Town	38	29	5	4	92	33	92
2	Brigg Town	38	22	6	10	75	42	72
3	Goole	38	20	11	7	68	36	71
4	Buxton	38	21	7	10	84	56	70
5	Ossett Albion	38	21	7	10	70	52	70
6	Thackley	38	17	11	10	53	39	62
7	Sheffield	38	17	8	13	74	55	59
8	Eccleshill United	38	16	7	15	61	57	55
9	Liversedge	38	16	6	16	59	65	54
10	Harrogate Railway Athletic	38	15	7	16	87	71	52
11	Clapwell	38	14	7	17	52	59	49
12	Glasshoughton Welfare	38	13	9	16	65	74	48
13	Pickering Town	38	14	5	19	49	51	47
14	Brodsworth MW	38	13	7	18	64	84	46
15	Arnold Town	38	12	8	18	58	53	44
16	Selby Town	38	11	7	20	44	73	40
17	Hallam	38	10	9	19	50	75	39
18	Armthorpe Welfare	38	10	6	22	53	85	36
19	Borrowash Victoria	38	9	5	24	41	97	32
20	Garforth Town	38	9	4	25	47	89	31

RESULTS GRID 02-03	1	2	3	4	5	6	7	8	9	10	11	12	13	14	15	16	17	18	19	20
1 Armthorpe Welfare		2-2	0-2	0-3	2-1	3-5	2-4	2-0	1-2	4-1	1-5	1-4	1-1	4-3	0-0	2-2	1-4	2-1	0-0	2-3
2 Arnold Town	3-1		1-2	1-3	2-3	3-1	0-1	2-2	4-0	3-0	3-0	0-3	1-0	3-0	6-0	1-2	2-1	1-1	0-0	1-2
3 Borrowash Victoria	2-4	2-1		1-4	0-2	2-1	0-2	0-1	2-0	3-2	1-1	0-5	1-1	3-6	2-2	0-3	2-0	4-2	2-3	2-1
4 Bridlington Town	2-1	3-0	7-0		4-0	4-0	2-1	4-0	5-1	2-0	1-1	1-0	5-1	2-1	1-0	4-0	2-1	3-1	1-0	3-1
5 Brigg Town	2-0	1-0	4-0	0-0		5-0	1-3	0-2	2-0	3-1	2-3	1-1	5-0	2-2	4-1	1-0	2-1	0-1	4-2	0-0
6 Brodsworth M.W.	2-1	1-0	6-2	4-2	1-4		0-4	1-4	5-4	1-1	3-3	0-4	0-2	2-6	1-4	6-0	3-0	0-1	2-1	0-1
7 Buxton	3-0	0-3	3-1	4-3	2-4	5-1		2-0	3-0	3-2	2-3	0-2	2-1	2-1	2-2	5-0	2-1	1-1	1-1	0-0
8 Eccleshill United	0-2	2-1	3-0	0-2	0-0	3-0	2-0		3-1	2-2	4-1	1-2	2-1	0-2	0-1	1-2	1-1	1-1	4-2	0-1
9 Garforth Town	1-2	2-5	0-0	1-1	1-1	1-0	0-6	1-3		1-2	2-4	0-2	1-4	1-4	1-0	0-2	2-3	2-0	1-2	2-0
10 Glapwell	0-2	1-0	1-1	0-1	1-4	2-0	2-3	0-2	4-1		1-2	1-3	1-1	3-2	4-1	0-1	2-1	1-0	0-1	0-2
11 Glasshoughton W.	0-1	2-0	4-1	2-4	1-6	0-0	7-2	2-4	2-1	0-1		1-1	1-1	2-2	2-1	0-2	2-0	2-3	1-4	2-2
12 Goole	3-1	1-1	1-0	2-2	2-1	0-1	0-0	4-3	3-0	1-1	0-1		1-2	2-1	2-1	0-4	0-0	0-0	2-0	2-2
13 Hallam	1-0	1-1	6-0	2-0	1-3	1-2	1-1	4-2	0-3	1-0	3-6	1-2		0-6	0-3	0-2	1-1	0-4	4-0	0-5
14 Harrogate Railway A.	7-1	2-0	3-1	1-1	0-2	1-3	0-2	4-3	2-1	2-2	2-0	3-3	2-0		3-4	1-4	1-3	3-0	2-3	2-2
15 Liversedge	1-0	3-2	2-0	1-2	1-2	3-3	2-2	0-2	4-2	0-2	3-1	1-0	3-2	1-3		0-2	2-0	4-0	1-0	0-3
16 Ossett Albion	2-2	2-2	4-0	0-1	1-2	1-1	3-2	1-1	5-3	1-1	2-0	1-4	4-1	2-0	1-3		1-3	2-0	0-2	1-1
17 Pickering Town	4-1	0-1	2-1	0-2	1-0	1-4	3-1	3-0	0-1	0-1	3-0	0-2	0-2	1-0	2-1	0-3		4-1	0-1	1-1
18 Selby Town	3-1	2-2	3-1	0-3	2-0	2-2	0-3	1-2	2-3	0-3	2-0	2-1	1-1	1-5	0-3	1-2	1-0		3-1	0-1
19 Sheffield	5-3	2-0	5-0	5-1	3-0	2-2	3-1	1-1	1-1	2-3	1-1	0-2	1-1	4-1	6-0	1-2	0-3	7-1		2-0
20 Thackley	1-0	2-0	1-0	0-1	0-1	1-0	2-4	3-0	0-3	2-3	2-0	1-1	2-1	1-1	0-0	0-3	1-1	2-0	4-0	

FINAL LEAGUE TABLE 2002-03

	DIVISION ONE	P	W	D	L	F	A	Pts
1	Mickleover Sports	32	24	3	5	62	26	75
2	Shirebrook Town	32	21	5	6	79	38	68
3	Long Eaton United	32	17	7	8	66	52	58
4	Pontefract Collieries	32	16	7	9	68	56	55
5	Hatfield Main	32	17	4	11	49	42	55
6	Gedling Town	32	14	9	9	70	49	51
7	Lincoln Moorlands	32	14	6	12	56	42	48
8	Parkgate	32	12	10	10	66	52	46
9	Hall Road Rangers	32	12	8	12	55	67	44
10	Winteton Rangers	32	10	8	14	48	54	38
11	Yorkshire Amateur	32	10	8	14	39	45	38
12	Louth United	32	10	7	15	49	62	37
13	Rossington Main	32	9	10	13	45	59	37
14	Worsbrough Bridge MW	32	10	5	17	41	56	35
15	Maltby Main	32	10	3	19	51	80	33
16	Tadcaster Albion	32	6	4	22	30	59	22
17	Staveley Miners Welfare	32	5	6	21	34	69	21

RESULTS GRID 02-03		1	2	3	4	5	6	7	8	9	10	11	12	13	14	15	16	17
1	Gedling Town		4-1	2-0	1-1	0-1	2-1	0-2	2-2	2-2	2-3	1-1	4-5	4-0	2-1	3-1	4-0	5-1
2	Hall Road Rangers	2-4		0-5	4-2	1-1	3-3	2-2	1-3	2-2	2-4	3-1	1-4	4-3	1-0	0-0	0-1	0-0
3	Hatfield Main	2-1	1-2		1-3	0-1	3-1	3-0	0-2	1-0	1-2	0-1	2-2	3-2	2-0	0-0	3-0	1-1
4	Lincoln Moorlands	1-0	3-1	1-2		2-3	0-2	3-1	1-2	2-1	2-2	2-1	0-1	2-0	2-0	1-2	3-0	2-0
5	Long Eaton United	1-3	1-2	5-1	1-1		0-0	4-3	1-1	3-2	2-3	4-1	0-2	3-1	5-1	2-2	2-1	3-2
6	Louth United	3-4	2-1	2-0	1-4	0-2		3-4	1-4	0-0	3-5	2-1	1-1	0-2	3-1	1-2	1-3	2-1
7	Maltby Main	0-4	2-3	1-2	3-1	1-1	0-3		0-1	2-6	1-4	3-4	1-6	0-2	1-6	3-2	1-0	1-1
8	Mickleover Sports	0-1	4-1	2-0	3-1	1-3	1-0	2-1		2-1	0-1	3-0	1-3	4-0	1-2	1-0	1-1	1-0
9	Parkgate	1-1	0-3	3-4	0-3	5-1	2-0	2-1	2-4		4-1	1-1	0-1	3-0	4-0	3-2	0-0	1-1
10	Pontefract Collieries	3-3	4-2	0-1	0-0	5-4	3-0	3-0	0-3	3-3		4-2	1-3	3-0	2-0	3-0	3-0	0-0
11	Rossington Main	1-0	2-2	0-1	3-2	2-0	2-2	1-2	1-2	2-2	1-1		2-1	1-6	1-1	2-1	2-1	3-1
12	Shirebrook Town	6-1	6-2	5-0	1-5	2-1	1-2	3-0	0-2	1-1	7-2	1-0		2-1	1-0	1-0	4-1	3-0
13	Staveley Miners Welfare	1-4	1-1	0-2	1-1	2-3	2-1	1-4	0-1	1-6	1-1	1-1	1-5		1-2	0-2	1-1	0-1
14	Tadcaster Albion	0-2	0-2	1-2	1-0	0-1	1-1	1-3	1-4	2-4	2-0	1-1	1-1	0-1		1-2	0-1	0-1
15	Winterton Rangers	3-3	1-3	1-3	1-1	2-2	0-1	3-2	1-2	3-4	3-0	3-1	0-0	1-0	2-3		2-2	1-3
16	Worsbrough Bridge MW	1-0	1-2	0-2	1-0	1-2	2-3	2-4	0-1	3-0	3-2	3-1	3-0	1-1	4-1	3-4		0-3
17	Yorkshire Amateur	1-1	0-1	1-1	2-4	2-3	5-3	1-2	0-1	0-1	1-0	2-2	2-0	2-1	1-0	0-1	3-1	

WILKINSON SWORD CUP 2002-03

QUARTER-FINALS

Mickleover Sports v Gedling Town	3-2	Pontefract Collieries v Worsbrough Bridge MW	2-1
Shirebrook Town v Tadcaster Albion	2-1	Yorkshire Amateur v Hatfield Main	1-2

SEMI-FINALS

Mickleover Sports v Hatfield Main	2-1	Pontefract Collieries v Shirebrook Town	5-2

FINAL

Pontefract Collieries v Mickleover Sports	0-2	First leg 8th April
Mickleover Sports v Pontefract Collieries	1-1	Second leg 21st April

LEAGUE CUP 2002-03

FIRST ROUND

Pontefract Collieries v Rossington Main	1-2	Shirebrook Town v Maltby Main	1-0
Winterton v Mickleover Sports	3-4 (aet)	Yorks Amateur v Worsbrough Bridge	3-1

SECOND ROUND

Arnold Town v Harrogate Railway Athletic	3-6	Borrowash Victoria v Staveley Miners Welfare	1-0
Brigg Town v Goole	0-2	Buxton v Gedling Town	2-0
Eccleshill United v Hallam	0-1	Glapwell v Rossington Main	1-0
Glasshoughton v Bridlington Town	1-4	Lincoln Moorlands v Louth United	1-2
Liversedge v Hatfield Main	2-3	Mickleover Sports v Brodsworth Miners Welfare	2-1
Ossett Albion v Hall Road Rangers	3-1	Pickering Town v Tadcaster Albion	4-0
Selby Town v Armthorpe Welfare	2-2 (aet)	Replay - Armthorpe Welfare v Selby	3-2
Sheffield v Garforth Town	3-0	Shirebrook Town v Parkgate	4-3
Thackley v Yorkshire Amateur	1-0		

THIRD ROUND

Borrowash Victoria v Bridlington Town	0-4	Glapwell v Sheffield	1-2
Goole v Buxton	0-2	Hallam v Harrogate Railway Athletic	1-2
Hatfield Main v Louth United	1-2	Mickleover Sports v Thackley	3-2 (aet)
Pickering Town v Ossett Albion	0-1	Shirebrook Town v Armthorpe Welfare	5-2

QUARTER-FINALS

Buxton v Shirebrook Town	1-2	Harrogate Railway Athletic v Sheffield	0-0 (aet)
Replay - Sheffield v Harrogate Railway Ath.	3-1	Louth United v Bridlington Town	1-4
Mickleover Sports v Ossett Albion	2-3		

SEMI-FINALS

Ossett Albion v Bridlington Town	3-1	Shirebrook Town v Sheffield	0-1

FINAL

Ossett Albion v Sheffield	3-0	6th May at Brigg Town.

Note: Long Eaton United did not take part in the League Cup being elected to the League after the draw had been made.

PRESIDENT'S CUP 2002-03

FIRST ROUND

Bridlington Town v Armthorpe Welfare	5-0	Gedling Town v Brigg Town	4-3
Hallam v Winterton Rangers	2-0	Harrogate Railway Athletic v Pickering Town	3-2
Lincoln Moorlands v Sheffield	0-3	Maltby Main v Thackley	2-4
Mickleover Sports v Worsbrough Bridge MW	5-1	Rossington Main v Selby Town	2-4

QUARTER-FINALS

Bridlington Town v Thackley	4-0	Harrogate Railway Athletic v Selby Town	1-0
Mickleover Sports v Gedling Town	1-2	Sheffield v Hallam	5-1

SEMI-FINALS

Harrogate Railway Athletic v Sheffield	3-1	Bridlington Town v Gedling Town	2-0

FINAL

Bridlington Town v Harrogate Railway Athletic	2-3	First leg 27th March
Harrogate Railway Athletic v Bridlington Town	4-0	Second leg 31st March

ARMTHORPE WELFARE

Secretary: Maureen Cottam, The Orchards, Whiphill Lane, Armthorpe, Doncaster DN3 3JP. Tel: 01302 832514 (H)
Ground: Welfare Ground, Church St, Armthorpe, Doncaster DN3 3AG.Tel:(M) 07771 853899-(match days only)
Directions: M18 junc 4, A630, left at r'bout then proceed to next r'bout and turn right. Ground 400yds on left behind Plough Inn. Doncaster (BR) 2 1/2 miles. Buses A2, A3 & 181 pass ground
Capacity: 2,500 Seats: 200 Cover: 400 Floodlights: Yes Club Shop: No

Clubhouse: No. Refreshments on ground. Wheatsheaf Hotel used after matches

HONOURS Northern Co's East Lg R-up 87-88, Lg Cup R-up 91-92, Div 1 R-up 83-84, East Central Div 1 84-85; Doncaster & Dist. Lg 82-83, Div 1 81-82, Div 2 79-80, Div 3 78-79; Lg Cup 79-80 80-81 81-82 82-83; Challenge Cup 82-83; West Riding Chall. Cup 81-82 82-83; Goole & Thorne Dist. Cup 82-83
PREVIOUS **League:** Doncaster Senior
RECORD **Attendance** : 2,000 v Doncaster R., Charity match 85-86
Appearances: Gary Leighton **Scorer:** Martin Johnson
Win: 7-0 v Stocksbridge PS NCE 84-85 & Brodsworth MW NCE 00-01
Defeat: 0-7 v Belper Town NCE 86-87
BEST SEASON **FA Vase:** 3rd Round 84-85 **FA Cup:** 3rd Qual. Rd. 86-87

FACT FILE
Founded: 1926
(Disbanded 1974, re-formed 1976)
Nickname: Wellie
Club Sponsors: Houston Transport
Colours: Green & white hoops/green/ green.
Change colours: Navy/white/navy
Midweek matches: Tuesday
Programme: 24 pages
Editor: John Morgan 01302 834475 (H)
Local paper: Doncaster Evening Star

CLUB PERSONNEL
Chairman: Stephen Taylor (01302 323522)
Vice Chairman: James Houston
Comm. Manager: Peter Camm
Press Officer: Sharon Morgan
Manager: Carl Leighton
Asst Manager: John McKeown
Coach: Steve Taylor
Physio: Joey Johnson

ARNOLD TOWN

Secretary: Tony Beale, 6 Elms Gardens, Ruddington, Nottm NG11 6DZ (0115 921 1451)
Ground: King George V Recreation Ground, Gedling Rd, Arnold, Notts (0115 9263660)
Directions: From M1 jct 26, take A610 to B6004 (Stockhill Lane) 3 miles to A60. Right at A60, immediate left (St Albans Rd), thru lights by Wilkinsons left onto Hallams Lane. Ground on right opposite market. From A1(M)/A614/A60 to lights (Harvester on right), left thru lights to, St. Albans Rd then as above. Nottingham Midland (BR) 4 miles. Buses 55,57.58, 59 pass ground. From A6514 left onto A60 for 1/4 m then rt onto Nottingham Rd to town centre by Wilkinsons.
Capacity: 3,400 **Seats**: 150 **Cover:** 950 **Floodlights:** Yes **Club Shop:** Sells progs, scarves, badge, mugs, baseball caps, ski hats, sweaters etc.(Martin Williams 0115 9598759)
Clubhouse: Licensed bar open matchdays & training nights. Also tea-bar on matchdays.

HONOURS (Arnold & Arnold Town): Central Mids Lg 92-93 (R-up 88-89, Lg Cup 87-88 (R-up 90-91), F/lit Cup 89-90); NCE Lg 85-86, R-up 83-84, 94-95; Div 1 94-95; Presidents Cup 94-95; Central All 62-63; Notts Snr Cup x9, r-up x 5; Midland Co's Lg R-up 70-71 75-76, Lg Cup 74-75 (R-up 68-69 70-71 80-81). **PREVIOUS Leagues:** Central Mids 89-93. Arnold FC: Bulwell & Dist, Notts Spartan, Notts Comb (pre 55), Central All. 55-63/ Midland 63-82/ NCE 82-86/ Central Mids 86-89. Kingswell: Notts Yth/ Notts Amat./Notts Spartan/ E. Mids Reg.(pre'76)/Midland 76-82/ NCE 82-86/ Central Mids 86-89. **Names:** Arnold FC (founded 1928 as Arnold St Marys) merged with Arnold Kingswell(founded 1962) 1989 **BEST SEASONS: FA Cup:**1st Rd replay 77-78
FA Vase.: 5th Rd 01-02 **FA Trophy:** 2nd Rd Replay 71-2

FACT FILE
Founded: 1989 Nickname: Eagles
Sponsors: Mapperley Sports/Neartone Printers
Colours: Yellow (blue trim)/blue/yellow
Change Colours:All red
Midweek matches: Tuesday
Programme:44 pages £1
Editor: Mel Draycott (0115 926 1574)
2002-03 Captain: Chris Hudson
Top Scorers : Sean Burrell 10
P.o.Y :. David Wilkins

CLUB PERSONNEL
President: Alan Croome Chairman: David Law
Vice-Chairman: Roy Francis
General Manager: Ray O'Brien
Comm. Manager: Len Robinson
Team Manager: Iain McCulloch
Asst Man: Bill Brindley Physio: Trevor Wells
Press Officer: Brian Howes (0115 9856986)
Website: www.arnoldfc.com
Email: mail@arnoldfc.com

BORROWASH VICTORIA

Secretary.: Ian Collins, 30 Margreave Road, Chaddesden, Derby DE21 6JD Tel: 01332 739437
Ground: Robinson Construction Bowl, Borrowash Road, Spondon, Derby Tel: 01332 669688.
Directions: M1 jct 25, A52 towards Derby, 3rd left off by-pass into Borrowash Rd, ground 400 yds on left. 2 miles from Spondon (BR). Nottingham to Derby buses pass nearby.
Capacity: 5,000 Seats: Yes Covered: 500 Floodlights: Yes
Clubhouse: Normal pub hours. Hot & cold food. **Club Shop:** No

PREVIOUS **Leagues:** Derby Sun. School & Welf. 52-57; Derby Comb.; Midland 79-82; N.C.E.; Cen Mid Lg. **Ground:** Dean Drive 1911-84

RECORDS **Attendance:** 2,000 v Nottim Forest,(floodlight opening 22/10/85)
Win: 11-1 **Defeat**: 3-8 **Goalscorer:** Paul Acklam **Appearances:** Neil Kellogg

BEST SEASON **FA Cup** 3rd Qual. Rd 91-92. **FA Vase:** 4th Rd 90-91,00-01

HONOURS N.C.E. Lg Div 1 00-01,Div 1 Sth 83-84 (R-up 84-85, Div 2 Sth R-up 82-83), Derby Comb. 77-78 (R-up(10) 65-66 68-74 75-77 78-79, Lg Cup 68-69 75-76 (R-up 63-64 66-67), Midland Co's Lg Div 80-81 (Div 1 Cup 80-81), Derbys Snr Cup R-up 90-91, Derbys Div. Cup 73-74 (R-up 70-71 72-73), Cen. Midl Lg B E Webbe Cup R-up 88-89 (Res. Cup 94-95)

FACT FILE
Founded: 1911
(Reformed 1963)
Nickname: Vics
Club Sponsors: Robinson Construction
Colours: Red & white stripes/black/black
Change Colours: Navy blue/sky/sky
Mid matches: Tues Prog: 16 pages, 50p
Editor: Max Anderson (01332 669688)

CLUB PERSONNEL
Chairman: Ian Anderson
Press Officer: Secretary
Manager/Coach: Bob Sykes
Asst Man: John Kinane

2002-03
Leading Goalscorer: Lee Bestwick
Captain: Matt Hutchings

BRIGG TOWN

Secretary: Robert B Taylor, `Highfield House', Barton Rd, Wrawby, Brigg, Lincs DN20 8SH
Tel: 01652 652284 (H) 01724 402749 (W) **Email Address:** bob taylor60@aol.com

Ground: The Hawthorns, Hawthorn Avenue, Brigg (01652 652767) Office: 01652 651605

Directions: From M180 Junc 4 Scunthorpe East, A18 through Brigg leaving on Wrawby Rd, left into recreation ground and follow road into BTFC.
Capacity: 4,000 Seats: 250 Cover: 2 Stands Floodlights: Yes

Clubhouse: Licensed club open matchdays

HONOURS F.A. Challenge Vase 95-96; Northern Co's East Lg Presidents Cup R-up 91-92 92-93, R-up 95-96; Lincs Lg 49-50 53-54 73-74 75-76 (Div 1 68-69 69-70 70-71 71-72, Lg Cup 49-50 65-66 68-69 69-70 72-73); Mids Co's Lg 77-78 (Lg Cup 77-78); Lincs `A' Snr Cup 75-76 76-77 94-95 99-00; Lincs `B' Snr Cup (5), NCE (Premier) 00-01

PREVIOUS **Leagues:** Lindsey; Lincs 48-76; Midland Counties 76-82
Grounds: Manor House Convent, Station Rd (pre 1939); Brocklesby Ox 1939-59

BEST SEASON **FA Vase:** Winners 95-96, 02-03 **FA Cup:** 4th Rd Q

RECORD Attendance: 2,000 v Boston U. 1953 (at Brocklesby Ox)

FACT FILE
Formed: 1864 Nickname: Zebras
Colours: Black & white stripes/black/red
Change colours: Yellow/Blue
Midweek Matchday: Wednesday
Programme: 24 pages
Editor: Match Secretary
Club Website: zebras@briggtown.co.uk

CLUB PERSONNEL
President: Mike.Harness
Chairman: Mike Harness 01724 869893 (H)
Match Sec: John Martin. Tel: 01652 654526 (H)
Manager: Ralph Clayton
Coach:Dave McLean

BRODSWORTH WELFARE

Secretary: Nigel Hyde, 5 Stonegate, Thorne, Doncaster DN8 5NP
Tel Nos: 01405 818330 (H) 01405 818330 (FAX) 07952 812811(M)
Ground: Welfare Ground, Woodlands, Nr. Doncaster (01302 728380).

Directions: From A1 take A638 to Doncaster, take left after Woodlands Pub into Welfare Road, ground 50yds on left.
Regular bus service from North Bridge Bus Station, Doncaster.
Capacity: 3,000 Seats: 228 Cover: 500 Floodlights: Yes

Clubhouse: Yes, Matchday drinks and snacks **Club Shop:** Yes

HONOURS Yorks Lg 24-25, Donc. & Dist. Lg 84-85 (Lg Cup 85-86, Div 2 78-79, Div 2Cup 78-79), Sheffield Jnr Cup 83-84, Mexborough Montagu Cup 91-92 92-93.R-up N.C.E. Div 1 98-99

PREVIOUS **Leagues:** Doncaster Snr; Sheffield; Yorkshire.
Name: Brodsworth Main, Brodsworth Miners Welfare

BEST SEASON **FA Cup:** 4th Qual. Rd 26-27 **FA Vase:** 3rd Rd 97-98

RECORD **Win:** 9-0 v Blidworth MW, NCE 97-98
Fee received: £2,550 (+ Payments for apps) for Danny Schofield from Huddersfield Town, Jan 99

FACT FILE
Founded: 1912
Nickname: Broddy
Colours: Navy & light blue/white/white
Change colours: Yellow & black
Midweek home matchday: Wednesday
Programme: 50 pages
Editor: Secretary

CLUB PERSONNEL
Chairman: Gordon Jennings Tel: 01302 781121
Press Officer Mark Bell (0797 779 4893)
Tel: 01302 725794H) 07720 832147 (M)
Manager: AlanRradford
Physio: Eric Beaumont

BUXTON

Secretary: Sarah Barton,20 Danesway,Chapel en-le-Frith,High Peak SK23 0RF
Tel: No & Fax : 01298 813268 (please telephone before faxing).email:mike@buxtonfc.co.uk
Ground : The Silverlands, Buxton, Derbyshire (01298 24733)

Directions: 200 yards of Buxton Market Place, opp. County Police HQ. Buxton (BR) 1/2 mile.
Capacity: 4,000 **Cover:** 2,500 **Seats:** 490 **Floodlights:** Yes
Club Shop: Yes, Mike Barton,01298 813268
Clubhouse: (01298 23197). Open nightly + Sunday lunchtimes. licensed, no hot food

HONOURS N.P.L Lg Cup 90-91, Presidents Cup 81-82; Cheshire County 72-73(R-up 46-47 62-63, Lg Cup 56-57 57-58 68-69); Manchester Lg 31-32 (R-up 04-05 28-29 29-30 30-31, Lg Cup 25-26 26-27); Derbys. Sen. Cup 38-39 44-45 45-46 56-57 59-60 71-72 80-81 85-86 86-87.

PREVIOUS **Leagues:** The Combination 1891-99; North Derbyshire; E Cheshire; Manchester 07-32; Cheshire County 32-73; NLP 73-98.]

BEST SEASON **FA Trophy:** Qtr Finals 70-71 71-72. **FA Vase:** 98-99
FA Cup: 3rd Rd 51-52. 2nd Rd 58-59, 1st Rd 62-63League clubs defeated: Aldershot 51-52

RECORDS **Attendance:** 6,000 v Barrow, FA Cup 1st rd 51-52
Goalscorer: Dave Herbert 104 in 263 games **Fee Paid:** £5,000 for Gary Walker (Hyde Utd)
Appearances: David Bainbridge 635Fee **Received:** £23,500 for Ally Pickering (Rotherham 89)

FACT FILE
Formed: 1877
Nickname: The Bucks
Sponsors: Paintmaster
Colours: Royal blue & white /royal/royal
Change colours:Yellow & Black
Midweek matchday: Tuesday
Programme: 36 pages £1.00
Editor: Tony Tomlinson (01484 718907)
Website: www.buxtonfc.co.uk
Local Press: Buxton Adverftiser and Matlock Mercury. Local Radio: Radio Derby and Radio High Peak

CLUB PERSONNEL
Chairman: Tony Tomlinson
Manager: Ronnie Wright
Director of Football: Kenny Johnson
Asst Manager/Coach: David Bainbridge
Res Man: JohnCohenPhysio: Dave Percival
2002-2003 Top Score & P.o.Y.:
Caine CheethamCapt: Tim Willis.

Goole A.F.C. 2003-04
Back Row: Scott Pinder, Steve Price, Rob Hanby, Neil Harrison, Andy Saville, John Hood, Mick Trotter, Graham Remmison, Stuart Baldwin.
Front Row: Andy Cox, Richard Hepworth, Duncan Richards, Jermaine Manners, Darren Rushton, A.N.Other, Steve Ward, Wayne Noteman, Mark Roldan.

EASTWOOD TOWN

Secretary / Press Officer: Paddy Farrell, 7 Primrose Rise, Newthorpe, Notts. NG16 2BB
Tel/Fax: 01773 786186 email: patriciafarrell777@hotmail.com

GROUND: Coronation Park, Eastwood, Notts. Tel: 01773 715823

Directions: From North - M1 jct 27, follow Heanor signs via Brinsley to lights in Eastwood. Turn left then first right after Fire Station - ground entrance on Chewton Street. From South - M1 jct 26, A610 to Ripley, leave at 1st exit(B6010), follow to Eastwood, left at lights, first left at `Man in Space' -ground entrance on Chewton Street. Nearest station - Langley Mill. Buses every10 mins (R11, R12 or R13) from Victoria Centre, Nottingham - approx 40 mins

Capacity: 5,500 Cover: 1,150 Seats: 650

Clubhouse: Social club open normal licensing hours (Sat 11am-11pm, midweek matches 6.30-11pm). Hot & cold food available. Steward; Jane Rowley

Club Shop: Sells programmes, mugs, scarves, badges etc. Contact R K Storer - 0115 9199596

PREVIOUS Leagues: Notts Alliance 53-61; Central Alliance 61-67; East Mids 67-71; Midland Counties 71-82; N.C.E. 82-88; N.P.L. 88-03

RECORDS: Attendance: 2,723 v Enfield, FA Amateur Cup, Feb 1965.

Appearances: Arthur Rowley, over 800 1st team games, but not a single booking, 1955-76

HONOURS: Northern Counties (East) Lg R-up 82-83 84-85; Midland Counties Lg 75-76 R-up 74-75 77-78, Lg Cup 77-78 79-80; Central Alliance 63-64 R-up 64-65; Notts Alliance 56-57 R-up x 6, Lg Cup 55-56; E. Mids Lg R-up 68-69; Notts Senior Cup x 9 R-up x 5; Evans Halshaw F'lit Cup 94-95 R-up 89-90 97-98; Mid Reg. All (Prem) 99-00 R-up 97-8, 98-9. MRA Chall. Cup 01-02

FACT FILE

Formed: 1953
Nickname: The Badgers
Sponsors: T.B.A.
Colours: White with black trim/black/black
Change Colours: All Red or Blue
Midweek matchday: Tuesday
Programme: Pages: 50 Price: £1.00
Editor: Paddy Farrell 01773786186
Website: www.eastwoodtownfc.com

2002-2003

Captain: Paul Gould
Top Scorer: Jamie Morgan
Player of the Year:Danny Bryant

CLUB PERSONNEL

President: George Belshaw
Chairman: Gary Hardy
Vice Chairman: Roy Cheatle
Manager: Bryan Chambers
Ass.Manager: Paul Cox
Physio: David Nicholls

ECCLESHILL UNITED

Secretary: Mrs. LyndaAndrews,46 Stott Terrace,Eccleshill, Bradford BD2 2DX (01274 640346)

Ground: Plumpton Park, Kingsway, Wrose, Bradford BD2 1PN (01274 615739)

Directions: M62 jct 26 onto M606, right on Bradford Ring Road A6177, left on to A650 for Bradford at 2nd r'bout. A650 Bradford Inner Ring Road onto Canal Rd,branch right at Staples (Dixons Car showrooms on right), fork left after 30mph sign to junction with Wrose Rd, across junction - continuation of Kings Rd, 1st left onto Kingsway - ground 200 yds on right. 2 miles from Bradford (BR). Buses 624 or 627 for Wrose

Capacity: 2,225 Seats: 225 Cover: 415 Floodlights: Yes

Clubhouse: Open normal licensing hours. Bar, lounge, games room, hot &cold snacks

Club Shop: Sells range of souvenirs.

HONOURS N.C.E.Div 1 96-97, Div 2 R-up 86-87, Res Div 86-87 89-90, R-up 87-88 94-95; Bradford Amtr Lg Cup 61-62; Bradford & Dist. Snr Cup 84-85; Bradford & Dist. FA Snr Cup 85-86; W. Riding County Amat. Lg 76-77; West Riding Cup R-up 99-00

PREVIOUS Leagues: Bradford Amat; W Riding Co Amat **Name:** Eccleshill FC
Ground: Myers Lane

BEST SEASON FA Vase: 99-00, 5th Rd

RECORDS Attendance: 715 v Bradford C 96-97 **Win:** 10-1 v Blackpool Mechs (H), F.A.C /!Q

Defeat: 0-6 v Rossington Main (A), N.C.E. Lge Cup 2nd Rd 92-93, & v Gt. Harwood T. (A), FA Cup Prel. Rd 91-92

FACT FILE

Founded: 1948
Nickname: Eagles
Colours: Blue & white stripes/blue/blue
Change colours: All yellow
Midweek matches: Wednesday
Reserves' Lge: NCE Res. Div
Programme: 24-28 pages, 50p
Editor: Lynda Andrews
Tel: 01274 640346
Local Press: Bradford Telegraph & Argus, Bradford Star Free Press

CLUB PERSONNEL

Chairman: Keith Firth Tel: 01274 583440 (H)
Press Officer: Bill Rawlings (01274 635753)
Manager: Tony Brown
Physio: Gordon Raynor

Player to Progress:Terry Dolan (Hudd'sfied U)

GLAPWELL

Secretary: Ellen Caton, High Ridge, 111 The Hill, Glapwell, Chesterfield. S44 5LU.
Tel: 01246 854648 (H & Fax) 07976 838423 (M)
Email: ellen@decaton.fsnet.co.uk

Ground: Hall Ground, Hall Corner, Glapwell, Chesterfield, Derbyshire
Tel: 01623 812213

Directions: M1 Junc. 29 A617 towards Mansfield, after Young Vanish Inn take filter lane left onto Bolsover Road, ground facing, use rear entrance next to garden centre
Floodlights: Yes

HONOURS Central Midlands Lg 93-94, Floodlit Cup 93-94, Evans Halshaw Floodlit Cup 96-97 Derbyshire Senior Cup 97-98 R-Up 00-01 (lost onpenalties) NCE Lg. Cup Finalists 99-00.

BEST SEASON FA Vase: 2nd Rd 96-97

FACT FILE

Founded: 1985
Colours: Black & white stripes/blackj/black
Change colours: All yellow
Midweek matches: Tuesday
Programme: 48 pages £1.00
Editor: Paul Harrison
01623 842588 (H) 07966 500521 (M)
Web site: www.glapwellfc.co.uk

CLUB PERSONNEL

Chairman: Roger Caton
Match Secretary: Malcolm Hol;mes
Tel No: 01246 558892
Manager:Andy Kirk
Assistant Manager: Junior Glave
Commercial Manager: Andrew Saunders

GLASSHOUGHTON WELFARE

Secretary: Eric Jones, `Marrica', Westfields Ave, Cutsyke, Castleford WF10 5JJ.
Tel: 01977 556257 (H) 01977 514157(B)

Ground: Glasshoughton Welfare, Leeds Rd, Glasshoughton, Castleford (01977518981)

Directions: From M62 use either Junct. 31 or 32 towards Castleford. From Junction 32 the road comes into Glasshoughton. From Junct. 31 turn right at 2nd roundabout at Whitwood Tech. College. The ground is on the left in Leeds Road. Car park on ground. Castleford (BR) 1 mile.
Capacity: 2,000 Seats: None Covered: 250 Floodlights: Yes

Clubhouse: Bar & refreshment facilities **Club Shop:** No

HONOURS West Riding County Cup 93-94

PREVIOUS **League:** West Yorkshire **Name**: Anson Sports 1964-76
Ground: Saville Park 1964-76

RECORD **Attendance:** 300 v Bradford C, 90
Win: 8-1 v Garforth Town, WR Cup 00-01
Defeat: 0-8 v Hucknall Town, NCE 97-98

BEST SEASON **FA Cup:** 2nd Qual Rd. 98-99 **FA Vase:** 2nd Round 00-01

FACT FILE

Founded: 1964
Club colours: All Blue
Change colours: All yellow
Midweek Matchday: Tuesday
Reserves' Lge: N.C.E. Res. Div.
Programme: 20 pages, 20p
Prog. Editor: Nigel Lee (0113 247 6186)-W

CLUB PERSONNEL

President: R Rooker
Chairman: Gordon Day
Tel: 01977 514178 (H)
Match Sec: Barry Bennett
Tel: 01977 682593 (H)
Manager: Wayne Day
Asst Manager/Coach: M Ripley

GOOLE AFC

Secretary: AnnSmith, 8 Boothferry Road Avenue, Howden, Goole. E Yorks. DN14 7TB
Tel No: 01430 432048

Match Secretary: Graeme Wilson, 12 Thorntree Close, Goole, E. Yorks DN14 6LN
Tel: 01405 763316 (H)

Ground: Victoria Pleasure Grounds, Marcus St, Goole DN14 6AR
Tel: 01405 762794 Website: www.gooleafc.freeserve.co.uk

Directions: M62 to Junc 36, then follow signs for town centre.
Turn right at 2nd lights into Boothferry Rd, then after 300 yards turn right again into Carter St, and the ground is at the end of road.

Capacity: 3000 Seats: 200 Cover: 800 Floodlights: Yes
Club Shop: Yes **Clubhouse:** Matchdays only

HONOURS NCE Div. 1 99-00, Div. 1 Trophy 99-00; Cen. Mids. Lge. 97-98

PREVIOUS **League**: Central Midlands 97-99

RECORDS **Attendance**: 964 v Leeds Utd. 99
Appearances: Phil Dobson 187 (1999-2001)
Goalscorer: Kevin Severn (97-01)

BEST SEASON **FA Vase:** 4th Round 98-99 **FA Cup:** 2nd Qual. Rd. 00-01

FACT FILE

Founded: 1997
Colours: Red/ white/ black.
Change Colours: Gold/black/gold & black
Midweek Matchday: Tuesday
Programme Editor: Andrew Lawson

CLUB PERSONNEL

Chairman: Des O'Hearne
Tel: 01405 704292 (H)

Manager:Steve Richards

2002-2003

Captain: Steve Price
Top Scorer: Darren Fell
Player of the Year: Kevin Graham

HALLAM

Secretary: Mrs Susan Muzyczka, 24 Meadow Bank Avenue, Sheffield, S7 1PB.
Tel: 0114 255 3173(H) Club Email: hallamfc@supanet.co.uk Website:www.sportsworldwide.co.uk

Ground: Sandygate, **(The oldest club ground in the world 1860)** Sandygate Road, Crosspool, Sheffield S10.Tel: 0114 230 9484. Two new stands and full access & facilities for wheelchair users. New changing rooms and Social Club. Plus Refreshmants Canteen.

Directions: A57 Sheffield to Glossop Rd, left at Crosspool shopping area signed`Lodge Moor' on to Sandygate Rd. Ground half mile on left opposite Plough Inn. 51 bus from Crucible Theatre

Capacity: 1,000 Seats: 250 Cover: 400 Floodlights: Yes **Club Shop:** Yes
Clubhouse: Social Club. Hot & cold snacks on ground for matches

HONOURS: Northern Counties (East) Lg Div 1 R-up 90-91 94-95, Yorkshire Lg Div 2 60-61 (R-up 56-57), Sheffield & Hallamshire Snr Cup (4) Finalists 01-02

BEST SEASON **FA Vase:** 5th Rd 80-81 **FA Cup:** 3rd Qual. Rd 1957

PREVIOUS **League:** Yorkshire 52-82

CLUB RECORDS **Attendance:** 2,000 v Hendon, FA Amtr Cup 3rd Rd 59 &13,855 v Dulwich at Hillsborough, FA Amtr Cup 55) **Goalscorer:** A Stainrod 46 **Appearances:** P Ellis 500+
Win: 7-0 v Hatfield Main (H) 92-93, & v Kiveton Pk H) 69-70 **Defeat:** 0-7 v Hatfield Main (A) 88-9

Players progressing: Sean Connelly (Stockport C), Howard Wilkinson (Sheff. Wed) -The F.A.'s Technical Director, L Moore (Derby C.)

FACT FILE

Formed: 1860 Nickname: Countrymen
Sponsors: Hallamshire Holdings Ltd.
Colours: Blue & white hoops/blue/blue
Change colours: Red/black/black
Midweek Matches: Wednesday
Programme: Yes£1.00
Editor: Mark Radford (Press Off.)
Local Press: Star, Green'Un, Sheffield Telegraph, Yorkshire Post

CLUB PERSONNEL

Chairman: Tony Scanlan -
Tel Nos: 01246 415471(H) 07720072492(M)
Vice Chairman:R.Merry
President: A Cooper
Press Off: Mark Radford Tel: 0114 249 7287
Manager: Guy Glover Physio:J.Beachell

2002-2003

Top Goalscorer: Craig Woprsfold
Player of the Year: Danny Spooner

HARROGATE RAILWAY ATHLETIC

Secretary: Stuart Lloyd, 61 Jesmond Road, Harrogate, N.Yorks.
Tel Nos: 01765 601711 (W) 01423 889924 (H) 0788 4012797 (M)
Club e-mail: hgterailafc@ntlworld.com

Ground: Station View, Starbeck, Harrogate.Tel: 01423 885539 & 01423 883104 (Fax)

Directions: A59 Harrogate to Knaresborough road. After approx 1.5 miles turn left just before railway level crossing. Ground is 150 yds up the lane
Adjacent to Starbeck (BR).
Served by any Harrogate to Knaresborough bus.

Capacity: 3,500 Seats: 800 Cover: 600 Floodlights: Yes Clubshop Yes

Clubhouse: Games, TV room, lounge. Open normal pub hours. Hot food available.

HONOURS N.C.E. Div 1 98-99, Div. 2 North 83-84, Lg Cup 86-87 Pres Cup 02-03

PREVIOUS **Leagues:** West Yorkshire; Harrogate District; Yorkshire 55-73 80-82.
Names: Starbeck LNER

RECORD **Attendance:** 3,500 v Bristol City F.A.Cup 02-03

BEST SEASON **FA Cup:** 2nd Rd Rd. 02-03 v Bristol C 3,500 **FA Vase:** 4th Round 88-89
FA Amateur Cup: 2nd Round 52-53

2002-2003 **Captn: & P.o.Y.:** Nigel Danby **Top Scorer:**Steve Davey 32 (10 in F.A.Cup)

FACT FILE

Founded: 1935 Nickname: The Rail
Sponsors: Sports Network
Colours: Red /green/red
Change: White/black/white
Midweek matchday: Wednesday
Programme Editor: Gordon Ward
Tel: 01423 880423 (H) 01423 880423 (Fax)
Local Press: Yorkshire Post, Harrogate Herald & Advertiser, York Press

CLUB PERSONNEL

President: J Robinson
Chairman: Dennis Bentley
Comm. Man: Alan Smith
Press Officer/Prog. Editor: Gordon Ward
Tel: 01423 880423 (H)
Manager:Dave Harmson
Assistant.Man.: John Francis
Physio: Steve Abbott

LIVERSEDGE

Secretary: Michael Balmforth, 7 Reform St., Gomersal, Cleckheaton BD19 4JX (01274 862123)
Ground: Clayborn Ground, Quaker Lane, Hightown Rd, Cleckheaton, W. Yorks (01274 862108)
Directions: M62 jct 26, A638 into Cleckheaton, right at lights on corner of Memorial Park, through next lights & under railway bridge, 1st left (Hightown Rd) and Quaker Lane is approx 1/4 mile on left and leads to ground. From M1jct 40, A638 thru Dewsbury and Heckmondwike to Cleckheaton, left at Memorial Park lights then as above. Buses 218 & 220 (Leeds-Huddersfield) pass top of Quaker Lane
Capacity: 2,000 Seats: 250 Cover: 750 Floodlights: Yes
Clubhouse: Matchdays, Tues, Thursday. TV. Snacks **Club Shop:**Scarves & Badges only

HONOURS W. Riding Co. Chal. Cup 48-49 51-52 69-70; W. Riding County Cup 89-90;
North Counties East Lg Div 1 R-up 89-90 (Div 2 R-up 88-89);
West Riding Co.Amtr Lg(6) 23-24 25-27 64-66 68-69 (Lg Cup 57-58 64-65).

PREVIOUS **Leagues:** Spen Valley; West Riding County Amateur 22-72; Yorkshire 72-82.
Ground: Primrose Lane, Hightown. **Name:** None

BEST SEASON **FA Cup:** 2nd Qual. Rd. 93-94 97-98 99-00
FA Vase: 2nd Round 74-75 91-92 93-94 98-99

RECORD **Attendance:** 986 v Thackley

Players progressing: Garry Briggs (Oxford), Martin Hirst (Bristol City) Leigh Bromby (Sheffield Wed)

FACT FILE

Founded: 1910 Nickname: Sedge
Colours: All blue Change: Red & Yellow
Midweek Matches: Tuesday
Reserves League: NCEL Div. 2
Programme: 28 pages, 50p
Editor: Secretary
Local Press: Yorkshire Evening Post, Telegraph & Argus, Spenbrough Guardian

CLUB PERSONNEL

Chairman: Robert Gawthorpe
Press Officer: Secretary
Manager: Eugene Lacy
Coach:Kym Farrand

2002-2003

Captaiin: Rob Dunderdale
Lerading Goalscorer: James Nestor 9
Player of the Year: Adam Goldthorpe

MICKLEOVER SPORTS

Secretary: Tony Shaw, 80 Onslow Road, Mickleover, Derbys. DE3 5JB
Tel: 01332 512826 (H & Fax)

Ground: Mickleover Sports Ground, Station Rd, Mickleover, Derby (01332 521167).
Club Website: www.mickleoversports.fsnet.co.uk

Directions: Derby ring road A38 to A52, turn off at Markeaton Park Island.Take turn to Ashbourne A52, then 2nd left into Radbourne Lane. Take 3rd left into Station Road, ground on corner.

Capacity: 1,500 **Seats:** 280 **Cover:** 200

Clubhouse: Open Thursdays and Fridays (7-11 p.m) Saturdays and Sundays (11am-11pm)
Snacks available only on Matchdays

Club Shop: No

HONOURS Champions N.C.E.L. Division 1 2002-2003, Wilkinson Sword Trophy Winners and Derbyshire Senior Cup Finalists 2002-03

Last Season **FA Cup:** 1st Qual Rd. 0-1 v Shepshed Dynamo (A)
FA Vase: 3rd Round replay, 2-3 v Oadby Town (H) after 2-2 (A)

FACT FILE

Founded: 1948
Colours: Red & White shirts/black/red
Change Colours: All blue
Midweek Matchday: Tuesday
Programme Editor: Stephen Pritchard
Tel: 01332 516271

CLUB PERSONNEL

Chairman Keith Jenkinson
Tel: 01332 516 271 (H)
Match Sec.: Cath Grant
Tel: 01332 511359

Manager: Martin Rowe

OSSETT ALBION

Secretary: David Chambers, 109 South Parade, Ossett, Wakefield, WF5 0BE. Tel:01924 276004 (H)
GROUND: Dimple Wells, Ossett (01924 273618-club, 01924 280450-grd)
Directions: M1 jct 40. Take Wakefield road, right at Post House Hotel down Queens Drive. At end right then second left down Southdale Rd. At end right,then first left down Dimple Wells (cars only). Coaches take second left following the road for 200yds bearing left twice. Four miles from both Wakefield and Dewsbury BR stations. Buses 116 and 117
Capacity: 3,000 Seats: 200 Cover: 500 Floodlights: Yes
Clubhouse: 3 bars + function room, open 7 days per week - catering available
Club Shop: Selling various souvenirs & programmes. Contact chairman
PREVIOUS **Leagues:** Heavy Woollen Area 44-49; West Riding Co. Amtr 49-50; West Yorks 50-57; Yorks 57-82. **Ground:** Fearn House
RECORDS **Attendance:** 1,200 v Leeds Utd, floodlight opening 1986
Win: 12-0 v British Ropes(H), Yorks. Lge Div. 2 6/5/59
Defeat: 2-11 v Swillington (A), W. Yorks. Lge Div. 1 25/4/56
Goalscorer: John Balmer **Appearances:** Peter Eaton, 800+ (22 yrs)
HONOURS: Yorks Lg 74-75 R-up 59-60 61-62, Lg Cup 75-76, 76-77, Div 2 78-79, 80-81 R-up 58-59; N.C.E. Prem. Div. R-up 00-01 Div 1 86-87 Lg Cup 83-84; West Yorks Lg 53-54 55-56 Div 2 52-53, Lg Cup 52-53; W. Riding County Cup 64-65 65-66 67-68; Wheatley Cup 56-57 58-59
Players progressing: Gary Brook (Newport, Scarborough, Blackpool) 1987, Ian Ironside (Barnsley, Middlesbrough, Scarborough) 1980.

FACT FILE
Founded: 1944 Nickname: Albion
Sponsors: Arco
Colours: Old gold & black/black/black
Change colours: All white
Midweek matches: Wednesday
Reserves' Lge: NCEL Res Div
Prog: 44 pages Price: £1
Editor: N Wigglesworth (01924 275630)
Website: www.pyke42.freeserve.co.uk

CLUB PERSONNEL
President: Miss Helen Worth
Chairman: Neville A Wigglesworth
Vice-Chairman: S B Garside
Commercial Man.: D Riley 01924 240247
Press Officer: Neville Wigglesworth 01924 275630
Manager: Eric Gilchrist
Physio: Nicky Davies Coach: Tony Passmore

PICKERING TOWN

Secretary: Anthony Dunning,13 Mill Lane, Pickering, North Yorkshire YO18 8DJ
Tel No: 01751 473697
Ground: Recreation Club, Mill Lane (off Malton Rd), Pickering, North Yorkshire
Tel: 01751 473317
Directions: A169 from Malton. On entering Pickering take 1st left past Police Station and B.P. garage into Mill Lane, ground 200 yards on right
Capacity: 2,000 Seats: 200 Cover: 500 Floodlights: Yes
Clubhouse: Open 1.30pm for Saturday games, 6pm for midweek games.
Food available from Football Club Kitchen at half-time and after games.
Club Shop: No
PREVIOUS **Leagues:** Beckett; York & District; Scarborough & District; Yorkshire 72-82.
RECORD **Attendance:** 1,412 v Notts County, friendly, August 1991
HONOURS Northern Co's East Lg R-up 92-93 Div 2 87-88, Div 1 R-up 91-92, 00-01, Yorks Lg Div 3 73-74, Div 2 R-up 74-75 North Riding Snr Cup R-up 93-94 94-95, N. Riding Co. Cup 90-91, Wilkinson Sword Trophy 2000-01.
BEST SEASON **FA Cup:** 2nd Qual. Rd. 99-00,01-02 **FA Vase:** 4th Round 01-02,02-03
Players progressing: Chris Short (Stoke City), Craig Short (Everton) both via Scarborough

FACT FILE
Founded: 1888
Nickname: Pikes
Club Sponsors: Flamingoland
Colours: Royal bluewhite/royal blue
Change colours: All Green
Midweek matches: Tuesday
Reserves' League: N.C.E. Res. Div.
Programme: 48 pages, £1.00
Editor: Gerry Gregory (01751 473818)

CLUB PERSONNEL
Chairman: Anthony Dunning (01751 473697)
President: J.P.Jennison
Match Secretary: Geoff raw (01751 474528)
Manager: Steve Brown
Assist. Manager: Richard Rose
Physio: Clive Reynolds
Coach: Steve Brown
2002-2003
Captain & P.o.Y.: Alex Willgrass
Top DScorer: Luke Ibbetson

SELBY TOWN

Secretary: Thomas Arkley,176 Abbots Rd,Selby, N.Yorks.O8 8AZ Tel: 01757 700356 (H) 07974691437(M) Email Address: toonarkley@hotmail.com
Ground: Flaxley Rd Ground, Richard St, Scott Rd, Selby, N YorksYO8 0BS.Tel: 01757 210900
Directions: From Leeds, left at main traffic lights in Selby down Scott Rd.then 1st left into Richard St. From Doncaster go straight across main traffic lights into Scott Road then 1st left. From York right at main traffic lights into Scott Rd, and 1st left. 1 mile from Selby (BR)
Capacity: 5,000 Seats: 220 Cover: 350 Floodlights: Yes
Clubhouse: Bar at ground open first and second team matchdays **Club Shop:** Yes
HONOURS Yorkshire Lg 32-33 34-35 35-36 52-53 53-54 (R-up 24-25 25-26 27-28 28-29 30-31 31-32 50-51 55-56, Div 3 R-up 74-75, Lg Cup 37-38 53-54 54-55 62-63); N.C.E. Div 1 95-96, Div 2 R-up 89-90, Presidents Cup 00-01; W. Riding Snr Cup 37-38; W. Riding Co Cup 27-28 48-49; W. Riding Chall. Cup 34-35 35-36
PREVIOUS **League:** Yorkshire (1920-82) **Ground**: Bowling Green, James St. 1920-51
BEST SEASON **FA Cup:** Second Round Proper 54-55 **FA Vase:** 4th Round 95-96
RECORD **Attendance:** 7,000 v Bradford Park Avenue (FA Cup 1st Rnd 1953-54)
Goalscorer: Graham Shepherd 158 (63-82)
Win: 14-1 v Altoffs, W. Rid. Cup 35
Defeat: 0-14 v Bradford PA Res. Yorkshire Lge 28

FACT FILE
Founded: 1918 Nickname: The Robins
Sponsors: Aaron Riccal Garage
Colours: All red
Change colours: Amber/black/amber
Midweek Matches: Tuesday
Reserves' League: N.C.E. Res. Div.
Programme: 30 pages, 50p
Editor: Sean Gleeson (01757 703098)
Local Newspaper: Selby Times

CLUB PERSONNEL
Chairman: Michael Dunn (01757 228605)
President: J.Belbin
Match Sec:As Secretary.
Manager: B Lyon
Asst Manr/Coach: G.Cygan
2002-2003
Captain: Dominic Moyles
Top Scorer: Andrew Cygan 12
Player of the Year: Andrew Hart

SHEFFIELD

Secretary: Stephen Hall, 12 Haddon Way, Aston, Sheffield S26 2EH
Tel: 0114 287 3578 (H), 01246 258918 (B)
Ground: Coach & Horses Ground, Sheffield Road, Dronfield. Sheffield
Directions: M1, J 29, A617 into Chesterfield. At traffic island turn right onto dual carriageway A61 (Sheffield). Follow over two islands and at third island follow sign 'Dronfield/Gosforth Valley'. At entrance to Dronfield, The Coach & Horses ground is at bottom of hill on the right.
Capacity: 2,000 Seats: 250 Floodlights: Yes
Clubhouse: Licensed Bar **Club Shop:** Yes

PREVIOUS **League:** Yorks 49-82 **Grounds:** Abbeydale Park, Dore (1956-1989); Sheffield Amateur Sports Club, Hillsborough Park 1989-91; Sheffield International (Don Valley) Stadium 1991-94; Sheffield Sports Stadium Don Valley 94-97.
HONOURS FA Amateur Cup 02-03; FA Challenge Vase Runners-up 76-77; Northern Co's East Lg Cup 94-95 ,Div 1 88-89 90-91; Yorkshire Lg Div 2 76-77, Lg Cup 77-78
BEST SEASON **FA Cup:** 4th Qual. Rd 00-01 **FA Vase:** R-up 76-77
FA Amateur Cup: Winners 1903-04
RECORD **Attendance:** 2,000 v Barton Rovers, FA Vase SF 76-77
Player progressing: Richard Peacock, Hull 94-95,

FACT FILE

Founded: 24th October1857
Nickname: The Club
Sponsors: Production Company
Colours: Red & black /black/red
Change: All blue
Midweek matchday: Tuesday
Programme: 16 pages, 50p
Editor:Craig Williamson(0114 258 1108)

CLUB PERSONNEL
Chairman: Richard Tims
Tel: 0114 2728888 (B)
President: Alan Methley
Manager: David McCarthy
Asst Manager: Lee Walshaw
Physio: Steve Naylor

2002-2003
Captain: Robert Moorland
Top Scorer: Robert Bray
Ps.o.Y.:Duncan Bray & Andy Slowe

THACKLEY

Secretary: Stewart Willingham, 3 Kirklands Close, Baildon, Shipley, Yorks BD17 6HN
Tel: 01274 598589
Ground: Dennyfield, Ainsbury Avenue, Thackley, Bradford (01274 615571).
Directions: On main Leeds/Keighley A657 road, turn off at Thackley corner which is 2 miles from Shipley traffic lights and 1 mile from Greengates lights.Ainsbury Avenue bears to the right 200yds down the hill. Ground is 200yds along Ainsbury Avenue on the right. 3 miles from Bradford Interchange (BR), 1.5 miles from Shipley (BR). Buses to Thackley corner (400 yds)
Capacity: 3,000 Seats: 300 Cover: 600 Floodlights: Yes
Clubhouse: Tue-Sun evenings,matches and w/e lunchtimes. Hot & cold snacks on matchdays
Club Shop: Progs, Metal badges- £2.50 + s.a.e.Contact Geoff Scott (01274 611520)
HONOURS N.C.E. Lg R-up 94-95, Lg Cup R-up 94-95; Yorks Lg Div 2 73-74; West Yorks Lg 66-67; W. Riding Co. Amtr Lg (x3) 57-60; W. Riding Co. Cup 73-74 74-75; W. Riding Co. Chal. Cup 63-64 66-67, R-up 94-95; Bradford & Dist. Snr Cup 12.
PREVIOUS **Leagues:** Bradford Amateur, W. Riding County Amateur, W. Yorks, Yorks 67-82.
Name: Thackley Wesleyians 1930-39
BEST SEASON **FA Vase:** 5th Rd 80-81 (01-2 v Whickham) **FA Cup:** 2nd Qual. Rd.(x3)
RECORD **Attendance:** 1,500 v Leeds Utd 1983
Players progressing: Tony Brown (Leeds), Ian Ormondroyd (Bradford City).

FACT FILE

Founded: 1930
Sponsors: Diamond International Shipping
Colours: Red /white/red
Change colours: All white
Midweek matches: Tuesday
Programme: 20 pages, 50p Editor: Secretary
Local Press: Bradford Telegraph & Argus, Bradford Star, Aire Valley Target.

CLUB PERSONNEL
Chairman: Derek Stokes
42 Ryedale Way,Allerton, Bradford
Match Secretary : June Willingham
Treasurer: Steven Paley
Manager/Coach: Andrew Taylor
Asst Manager: Warren Fletcher
Physio: John Laidler

The official view of
Arnold Town F.C.
2002/2003

Northern Counties East
Premier Division
ARNOLD TOWN
V
ARMTHORPE WELFARE

Saturday, 19th April, 2003
3.00 pm

£1.00

Sponsored by
MAPPERLEY SPORTS

EASTWOOD TOWN FOOTBALL CLUB

UNIBOND LEAGUE - DIVISION 1

EASTWOOD TOWN
V
SPENNYMOOR UNITED
Saturday 12th April, 2002. Kick off 3pm
OFFICIAL PROGRAMME
PRICE £1

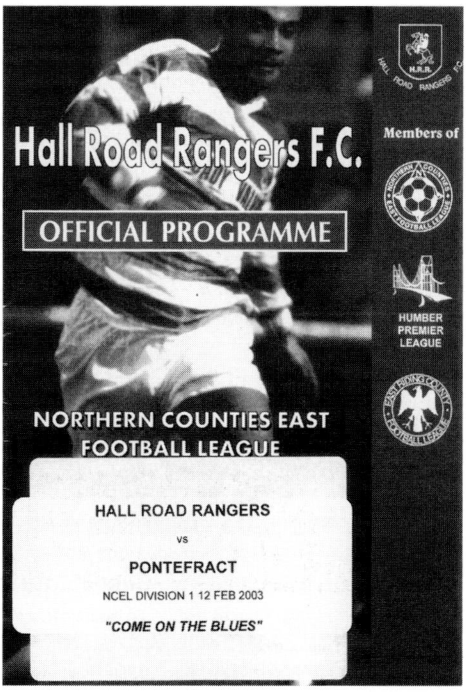

CARLTON TOWN

Secretary: Paul Shelton, 28 Freda Close, Gedling, Nottingham NG4 4GP.
Tel: 0115 987 7527 (H) 07808 576778 (M)
email: paul.shelton1@btopenworld.com

Ground: Stoke Lane Gedling, Nottingham. Tel: 0115 987 3583

Directions: A612 Nottingham to Southwell Road. Stoke Lane is situated off A612 between Gedling & Burton Joyce (signed Stoke Bardolph).
Ground 200 yards on left over level crossing. **Nearest BR Station:** Carlton.

Capacity: 1000 **Seats:** None **Cover:** 200 **Floodlights:** Yes

Clubhouse: Yes Tel: 0115 940 2531 **Club Shop:** No

PREVIOUS **Name:** Sneiton F.C.
Leagues: Central Midlands >2003

HONOURS: Notts Alliance - Div 1 92-93, Div 2 84-85; Notts Intermediate Cup 91-92;
Central Midlands Supreme Division Champions: 2002-2003

Founded: 1904
Colours: Yellow/Blue/Blue
Change colours: Red & Black
Midweek Matchday: Tuesday
Programme: £1.00 Editor: Martin Bell

Chairman & Chief Executive: Mick Garton
President: John Stokeld

Coach: Tom Brookbanks
Asst. Managers: Dave Nairn & Brian Franks
Physio: Martin Jepson

2002-03
Captain: Steve Garrett
Top Scorer: Phil Bignall 47
Player of the Year: David Jephson

GARFORTH TOWN

Secretary: Antony Clough, 44 Lowther Grove, Garforth, Leeds LS25 1EN (0113 286 6023)
Fax: 0113 286 2728 e mail: garforthtown@hotmail.com

Ground: Wheatley Park Stadium, Cedar Ridge, Brierlands Lane, Garforth, Leeds LS25 2AA
Tel: 0113 286 4083 Website: www.garforth.town.com

Directions: M1 junction 47. Take turning signed 'Garforth' (A642). Approx 200 yards turn left into housing estate opposite White Ho. (Cedar Ridge). Stadium at end of lane.

Capacity: 3,000 Seats: 278 Cover: 200 Floodlights: Yes

Clubhouse: Full Licensing Hours. Closed Mondays **Club Shop:** Yes

HONOURS NCE Div 1 97-98, R-up 96-97, Div 2 R-up 85-86, Lge Cup 99-00; Yorks Lg Div 3 R-up 79-80; Barkston Ash Snr Cup x6; Wilkinson Sword Tphy 96-97; W. Riding Co. FA Cup 97-98 99-00

PREVIOUS **Leagues:** Leeds Sunday Comb 64-72; West Yorks 72-78; Yorks 78-82.

BEST SEASON **FA Vase:** Q-F 85-86 **FA Cup:** 2nd Qual. Rd. 91-92, 97-98

RECORDS **Attendance:** 1,014 Brendan Ormsby Testimonial v Comb. Leeds/A. Villa XI

2002-03 Leading Goalscorer & P.o.Y: Gavin Birmingham Captain: Richard Hand

FACT FILE
Founded: 1964 Nickname: The Miners
Sponsors: TWS/FDS
Colours: Yellow/Blue/Yellow
Change colours: Red/black/red
Midweek matches: Tuesday
Reserves' League: NCE Div.2
Programme: 32 pages, £1.00
Editor: Chris Mather 0113 286 3453 (H)

CLUB PERSONNEL
President: Norman Hebbron
Chairman: Stephen Hayle
Manager/Coach: Dave Holmes
Asst Manager: Trevor Best
Physio: Paul Cavell Coach: Steve Swallo

GEDLING TOWN

Secretary: Albert Graves, 32 Shelford Road, Gedling NottinghamNG4 4HW
Tel Nos: 0115 987 8185 (H) 07889 954285 (M)

Ground: Riverside Ground, (rear of Ferryboat Inn), Stoke Lane, Stoke Bardolph, Nott'm NG14 5HX

Directions: A612 Nottingham-Lowdham-Southwell road. Just before Burton Joyce turn right into Stoke Lane to Ferryboat P.H. Approx 1.5 miles. Ground at rear of pub.

Capacity: 2,000 Seats: None Cover: 500 Floodlights: Yes

Clubhouse: Matchdays only. Refreshments. Licensed bar. **Club Shop:** No

Honours: Central Mids Lg Prem 97-98 R-up 91-92, Div 1 90-91, (Res Prem 96-97 97-98); Wakefield Floodlit Trophy 92-93 R-up 95-96; Ken Marsland Cup (Res) 93-94; Notts Amtr Lg 89-90 (Snr Cup R-up 89-90).Res Lg & Cp Winners 98-99, NCECup 01-02, Notts Cup 01-02

Best season FA Vase: 3rd Rd 96-97

RECORDS **Attendance:** 250 v Arnold Town.
Win: 11-0 v Radford 91-92 **Defeat:** 2-5 v Staveley MW 93-94.
Goalscorer: Rob Orton 98 in 124 **Appearances:** Gary Ball 300+

FACT FILE
Founded: 1986
Colours: Blue & yellow/blue&yellow/blue
Midweek Matchday: Tuesday
Prog 32 pages 50p
Editor:Mark Batchford (0115 940 3361)

Chairman: Roland Ash (0115 9403361)

Managers: Gary Haywood
Assistant Manager: darren Davies
Physio: Dick Henton

HALL ROAD RANGERS

Secretary: Alan Chaplin,33 Lee Street,Holderness Road,Hull HU8 8NH Tel No: 01482 703775

Ground: Dene Park, Dene Close, Beverley Rd, Dunswell, Nr Hull (01482 850101).

Directions: M62 to A63, turn left before Humber Bridge onto A164 to Beverley,after approx 5 miles turn right onto A1079. In 2 miles turn left at large roundabout to ground 20 yards on right.

Capacity: 1,200 Seats: 250 Cover: 750 Floodlights: Yes

Clubhouse: Open all week for drinks and bar snacks, snooker, pool and darts. **Shop:** Yes

HONOURS N.C.E. Lg Div 2 90-91, Yorks Lg Div 3 72-73 79-80, E. Riding Snr Cup 72-73 93-94.

PREVIOUS **Leagues:** East Riding Co.; Yorks 68-82 **Ground:** Hull Co-Op (to 1968)

BEST SEASON **FA Cup:** Never entered **FA Vase:** 3rd Round 99-00

RECORDS **Attendance:** 1,200 v Manchester City Aug 93

Goalscorer: G James **Apps:** G James **Players progressing:** Gerry Ingram (Blackpool),. Mark Greaves (Hull City) **2002-03: Capt & Top Scorer**:Jamie Barnwell **P.o.Y.**: Steve Underwood

FACT FILE
Founded: 1959 Nickname: Rangers
Sponsor: Admiral Signs of Hull Ltd.
Colours: Blue & white hoops/ blue/ blue.
Change : Red & Black Stripes,black/black
Midweek Matches: Wednesday
Reserves' League: East Riding Co.League
Prog: 36 pages, 50p Editor/Press Off: Sec
Local Press: Hull Daily Mail

CLUB PERSONNEL
Chairman:Robert Smailes (01482 821354 (H))
Director of Football: Nigel Dalee)
Press Officer: Craig Ellyard (01482 812530)
Man:Jamie Barnwell Coach: Ray Daniel

LINCOLN MOORLANDS

Secretary: Graham Peck, 128 Granson Way, Washingborough,Lincoln LN4 1HF
Tel Nos: 01522 792170 (H) 07815 458196 (M))
Ground: Moorland Sports Ground, Newark Rd, Lincoln LN5 9LY
Tel: 01522 520184 Office & Fax: 01522 874111
Directions: From north A1 to Markham Moor. Take A57 until Lincoln by-pass and then turn right onto A46. At 3rd r'about left into Doddington Rd. Continue until Newark Rd. - ground on left after 800 yards.
From Newark enter Lincoln on A1434, go past Forum Shopping Centre for approx. 3/4 mile. Ground on left signposted 'Moorlands Club'.
Capacity: Seats: 100 Cover: 200 Floodlights: Yes
Clubhouse: Yes **Club Shop:** No
HONOURS: Central Midlands Supreme 99-00, R-up 00-01, Lincolnshire Senior A 00-01

FACT FILE
Founded: 1989
Nickname: The Moors
Colours: Sky Bue + Navy trim/Navy/ Sky Blue
Change colours: Orange/black/orange
Midweek Matchday: Wednesday
Programme: 2 pages price 75p
Editor:Paul Stafford 07796 887319(M)

CLUB PERSONNEL
Chairman: Graham Longhurst(07976 357684)
Match Secretary: 07748 764398 (M)
Manager: Garry Goddard

LONG EATON UNITED

Secretary: Jim Fairley, 13 Redland Drive,Chilwell, Nottingham NG9 5JZ9726343.
Tel No: 0115 9199447 (H)
Ground: Grange Park, Station Road, Long Eaton, Nottingham (0115 973 5700).
Directions: M1 Junc 25, take A52 towards Nottingham, to island by `Bardills Garden Centre', left onto B6003 to t/lights. Right A453, 2nd left Station Rd. Entrance on left opposite the Speedway Stadium
Capacity: 5,000 Seats: None Cover: 500 Floodlights: Yes
Clubhouse: Open matchdays, snacks available
Club Shop: None
Record **Attendance:** 2,000 1973 FA Cup
Honours: Derbys Snr Cup 64-65 75-76, Midland Co's Lg R-up 76-77, Central Alliance Div South 58-59, Northern Co's (East) Div 1 South 84-85.

FACT FILE
Founded: 1956
Nickname: Blues
Sponsor: Beeston Suite Co
Colours: All Blue
Change colours: Red/black/black
Midweek Matchday: Tuesday
Programme: 20 pages 50p
Editor: Geoff Whitehead (01332 872849)

CLUB PERSONNEL
Chairman: J C Fairley
Manager:Adam Bamford
Physio: John Burns

LOUTH UNITED

Secretary: Albany Jordan,180 High Holme Road,Louth, Lincs. LN110JX Tel No: 01507 607356
Ground: Park Avenue, Louth, Lincs Tel: 01507 607351 FAX: 01507 607351
Directions: A16 To Louth Market Place, exit via Eastgate/Eastfield Rd, to Fire Station turn right into Park Avenue. Ground at bottom of avenue of prefabricated bungalows.
Capacity: 2,500 Seats: None Cover: 400 Floodlights: Yes **Club Shop:** No
Clubhouse: Weekdays 6.30-11.45, Sat 12-11.45. Full bar facilities. Snacks available.
HONOURS Lincs Lg Prem 72-73 85-86 86-87 (Div 1 57-58 66-67 67-68; Lg Challenge Cup 73-74 86-87; Lg Charity Cup 55-56 56-57 67-68; Central Mids Lg Cup R-up 92-93; Wakefield F'lit Cup R-up 91-92; Lincs Snr `A' Cup 77-78. R-Up 00-01 Lincs Sen Cup R-up: 98-99
PREVIOUS **Leagues:** Lincs 47-75 82-88; Central Midlands 88-93.
Names: Louth Nats & Louth Town - merged **Grounds:** None
BEST SEASON **FA Cup:** 3Rd Q 0-2 v Emley **F.A Vase:** 4th Rd v Halesowen Town 85-86
RECORDS: **Goalscorers:** Peter Rawclife 39 **Appearances:** Steve Newby 510 **Att::** 2,500

FACT FILE
Founded: 1947 Nickname: The Lions
Sponsors: 'Brother'
Colours: Blue with red trim/blue/blue
Change:All Yellow
Midweek matches: Tuesday
Reserves League: Lincolnshire
Prog:50p Ed.: Scott Santus 01507 606252)

CLUB PERSONNEL
Chair: Jim Waumsley V-Chair: George Horton
Ch Exec:Jim Walmsley Pres: Dave Fairburn
Commercial Manager: Simon Hewson
Man: Steve Newby Coach: Nigel Fanthorpe.
Physio: Kenny Vincent

MALTBY MAIN

Secretary: Dave Morris, 2 Buckingham Way, Maltby. S66 7EA Tel No: 01709 814400
Email: david@morris1984.fsnet.co.uk
Ground: Muglet Lane, Maltby , Rotherham. Tel: 017941 057883
Directions: Exit M18 at junct 1 with A631. Two miles into Maltby, right at traffic lights at Queens Hotel corner on to B6427 Muglet Lane. Ground 3/4mile on left. Bus 101 from Rotherham stops at ground. Bus 287 from Sheffield to Queens Hotel, then follow as above
Capacity: 2,000 Seats: 150 Cover: 300 Floodlights: Yes
Clubhouse: No, Miners Welfare Club opposite **Club Shop**: No
HONOURS Sheff. & Hallamshire Snr Cup 77-78, N.C.E. Lge Presidents Cup 92-93, Mexborough Montague Cup 76-77 80-81 90-91,Yorks Lg R-up 77-78, Sheff. Wharncliffe Cup 80-81.
CLUB RECORDS **Attendance:** 1,500 v Sheffield Wed., June 91-92 (friendly)
PREVIOUS **Leagues:** Sheffield County Senior; Yorkshire 73-82.
Name: Maltby Main 1916-65 (disbanded); Maltby Miners Welfare 1970-96
BEST SEASON **FA Cup:** 2nd Qual. Rd. 23-24 **FA Vase:** 3rd Round 87-88 93-94

FACT FILE
Founded: 1916 Nickname: Miners
Sponsors: Millgate Computer Systems
Colours: Red/white/red Change: All yellow
Midweek matchday: Wednesday
Programme: 36 pages, 70p
Editor: Nick Dunhill Tel: 017941 057 883

CLUB PERSONNEL
Chair: Gary Kitching V-Ch:Graham McCormick
Pres H Henson Sec: Dave Morris
Man:Shaun Goodwin Asst. Man: Bryn Webster
2002-03 Leading Goalscorer:Scott Somerville
Captain & P.o.Y.: Russ Ward

PARKGATE

Secretary: Bruce Bickerdike, 2 Cardew Close, Rawmarsh, Rotherham S62 6LB
Tel: 01709 522305 Fax: 01709 528583.
Ground: Roundwood Sports Complex, Green Lane, Rawmarsh, Rotherham S62 6LA
Tel: 01709 826600 Website: www.parkgatefc.co.uk Email: bruce@parkgatefc.co.uk
Directions: From Rotherham A633 to Rawmarsh. From Doncaster A630 to Conisbrough, then A6023 through Swinton to Rawmarsh. Grd at Green Lane - right from Rotherham, left from Conisbrough at the Crown Inn. Grd 800yds right
Capacity: 1,000 Seats: 300 Cover: 300 Floodlights: Yes **Club Shop:** No.
Clubhouse: Licensed bar, 2 lounges. Meals available lunchtime Wed-Sat.
HONOURS S&HSC Finalists 0-3 v Emley 97-98, Wilkinson Sword Trophy R-up 98-99
PREVIOUS Leagues: Sheffield County Senior Lge; Yorkshire 74 **Names:** BSC Parkgate (82-86); RES Parkgate (pre-1994). **RECORD Attendance:** v Worksop 1982
BEST SEASON FA Cup: 2nd Qual. Rd 97-98 **FA Vase:** 1st Round, 6 times
2002-2003: **Captain** : Neil pickering **Top Scorers:** Peter Smith & b Brian Cusworth

FACT FILE
Founded: 1969
Nickname: The Gate or The Steelmen
Kit Sponsors: JBB Investigations
Colours: All red Change: Blue & yellow
Midweek matches: Tuesday
Programme: 20 pages, £1.00
Editor: Stuart Bisby (01709 545219)

CLUB PERSONNEL
President: Paul Cristinacce
Chairman: Neil Freeman
Press Officer: Secretary
Manager: Stewart Evans
Asst Man: Vincent Brady
Coach: John Eagle
Physio: David Proctor

PONTEFRACT COLLIERIES

Secretary: Frank Maclachlan, 188 Watling Road, Ferry Fryston, Castleford WF102QY
,Tel: 01977 512085 (H), 01977 601327 (B), 07710 586447 (M) Email: ponterod@tiscali.co.uk
Ground: Skinner Lane, Pontefract, West Yorkshire (01977 600818)
Directions: M62 jct 32 towards Pontefract. Left at lights after roundabout for park entrance and retail park. Traffic thro town should follow racecouse signs thro lights to roundabout and back to lights. Monkhill (BR) 1/2 mile. Baghill (BR) 1 mile. Tanshelf (BR) 1/2 mile .All Leeds and Castleford buses pass ground. **Capacity:** 1,200 **Seats:** 300 **Cover:** 400 **Floodlights:** Yes
Clubhouse: Fully licensed. Hot & cold snacks. Openmatch days **Club Shop:** Occasionally
HONOURS N.C.E. Lg Div 1 83-84 95-96 (Div 2 R-up 82-83); Lg Cup, R-up: 96-97 Floodlit Comp 87-88 88-89; Yorks Lg Div 3 81-82; W. Riding Co. Cup R-up 87-88 90-91;Embleton Cup (4) Castleford FA Cup (5) Wilkinson Sword 95-96 R-Up: 99-00.02-03
PREVIOUS Leagues: West Yorkshire 58-79; Yorkshire 79-82 **RECORD Attendance:** 1,000 v Hull City, floodlight opening 1985. **Players progressing:** David Penney (Derby Co., 85), Andy Hayward (Rotherham U) and Dean Trott (Northampton Town)

FACT FILE
Founded: 1958 Nickname: Colls
Sponsors: Easy Hire
Colours: Blue & black halves/black/black
Change :All green Midweek Matches: Tuesday
Programme: 36 pages £1.00
Editor:Rod Naylor(01977 602266
Local Press: Pontefract & Castleford Express
Website: www.nce-league.freeserve.co.uk

CLUB PERSONNEL
Chairman: T.B.A.
Man::Pete Daniels Asst Man: Dave Robinson
Physio: MickSlater

2002-2003
Captain: & P.o.Y.: Richard Britten
Top Scorers: Ian Twitchen 33 Jon Leigh 29

ROSSINGTON MAIN

Secretary: Gerald Parsons, School Bungalow, Hayfield Lane, Auckley, Doncaster DN8 3NB, Tel: 01302 770249(H) 07941 811217 (M)
Ground: Welfare Ground, Oxford Street, Rossington, Doncaster Tel: 01302 865524
Directions: Enter Rossington and go over the railway crossings. Pass the Welfare Club on right, Oxford Street is next right - ground is at bottom.8miles from Doncaster (BR)
Capacity: 2,000 Seats: 200 Cover: 500 Floodlights: Yes
Clubhouse: Evenings & matchdays, Sandwiches, rolls, satellite TV, pool. **Club Shop:** No
HONOURS Cen. Mids. Prem Div. 84-85, Lg. Cup 83-84 84-85;
Doncaster Sen Lge 44-45, Lg. Cup 44-45; DDSALShield 90-91 R-up 89-90.
PREVIOUS Leagues: Doncaster Sen, Yorkshire Lge, Sheffield County Sen, Cent Mids.
RECORDS Attendance: 864 v Leeds United 8/91.
Goalscorer: Mark Illman **Appearances:** Darren Phipps
BEST SEASON FA Cup: 2nd Qual. Rd. 25-26 **FA Vase:** 2nd Round 88-89

FACT FILE
Founded: 1920 Nickname: The Colliery
Sponsor: RJB Mining
Colours: All blue
Change colours: Blue & black
Midweek matches: Tuesday
Reserves' League: Beefeater County Sen
Programme: 50p
Editor:Peter Murden

CLUB PERSONNEL
Chairman: Gerald Murden (01302 867542)
Joint Managers: D Ridley & L Ostle
Physio: J White

SHIREBROOK TOWN

Secretary: S.Wall,26 Carter Lane,Shirebrook, Mansfield, Notts. Ng20 8NA (01623 747638)
Ground: BRSA Sports Ground, Langwith Rd, Shirebrook, Mansfield(01623 742535).
Directions: M1 jct 29, A617 to Mansfield, 2.5 miles, onto B6407 to Shirebrook, then through town to Langwith Rd.
Capacity: 2,000 **Seats:** 165 **Cover:** 400 **Floodlights:** Yes

Clubhouse with refreshments at the ground.
Club Shop: No
Honours:
Central Midlands Supreme Champions 00-01 01-2 R-Up 99-00 Lg Cup winners 00-01 Res Prem Div 94-95 95-96. Floodlit Cup winners 97-98 N.Co E Div 1 R-up 2002-03
Records:
Most Appearances : .Tansley 289
2002-2003: Captain: A.Starkey Leading Goalscorere: Rob Orton

FACT FILE
Founded 1985
Sponsors: Warsop Tyre Service
Colours: All Red & black
Change : All Blue
Midweek Matchday: Wednesday

Programme 12 pages 50p
Editor: G.Howarth

CLUB PERSONNELL
Chairman: Stephen S. Brown
Tel: 01623 748375
Manager:Gary Quincey

SOUTH NORMANTON ATHLETIC

Secretary: Andrew Meredith, 40 Hilcote Street, South Normanton, Derbys. Tel: 01773 776477 (H)

Ground: South Normanton Athletic FC, Lees Lane, South Normanton, Derby Tel: 01773 581491

Directions: M1 Junc 28, B6019 towards South Normanton. Turn right after 1mile (in South Normanton) at BP garage into Market Street, after 1/4 mile turn left, immediately after The Clock pub into Lees Lane, ground at bottom on right.

Capacity: 3000 **Seats:** 150 **Cover:** 300 **Floodlights**:Yes

Clubhouse Open on matchdays. Food available.
Club Shop: No

PREVIOUS **Leagues:** Central Midlands League

Re-Formed: 1980
Colours: Yellow/navy/yellow
Change colours: Black & white/black/white
Midweek Matchday: Tuesday
Programme: Yes - The Shiner
Editor: Lance Henderson (07763 7339176)

Chairman: Peter Kane

Manager: Rob Aitkin
Asssistant Manager: Marcus Brameld

STAVELEY MINERS WELFARE

Secretary: Keith Burnand, 2 Woodland Grove, Clowne, Chesterfield S43 4AT Tel: 01246 811063
Ground: Inkersall Road, Staveley, Chesterfield, Derbyshire Tel: 01246 471441
Directions: M1 jct 30, follow A619 Chesterfield - Staveley is 3 miles from jct30. Turn left at GK Garage in Staveley town centre into Inkersall Rd - ground 200yds on right at side of Speedwell Rooms. Frequent buses (47, 70, 72, 75, 77) from Chesterfield stop in Staveley town centre - 3 mins walk to ground
Capacity: 5,000 Cover: 400 Seats: 220 Floodlights: Yes
Clubhouse: The Staveley Miners Welfare, 500 yds from ground, open before and after games
Club Shop: Yes, contactRod Walker 01246 473655
HONOURS County Sen Lg Div 2 92-93, Div 3 91-92, Chesterfield & D. Amat Lg R-up89-90 90-91, Byron (Lge) Cup 89-90, R-up 90-91.NCE Div 1 R-up 97-98
PREVIOUS **Leagues:** Chesterfield & D. Amat 89-91; County Sen 91-93.
BEST SEASON **FA Cup:** **FA Vase:** 98-99, 3rd Rd at least
RECORDS **Attendance:** 280 v Stocksbridge, Sheffield Senior Cup 22/1/94
Goalscorer: Mick Godber **Appearances:** Shane Turner

FACT FILE
Founded: 1989 Nickname: The Welfare
Colours: All Blue
Change colours: Yellow/Green/Green
Midweek matches: Wednesday
Programme: 32pages, £1.00
Editor: Steve Duncan (01246 471441)

CLUB PERSONNEL
Chairman: Dennis Burnand
Tel: 01246 475644 (H)
2002-2003
Captain: Rob Cowlishaw
Top Scorer: Glenn Nattriss 9
Player of the Year: Carl Vickers

SUTTON TOWN

Secretary: Keith Mayes, 22 Allington Drive, Mansfield, Notts. NG19 6NA Tel: 01623 407064 (H) 07831 881469 (M)

Ground: Hosiery Mills Ground, Huthwaite Road, Sutton-in-Ashfield, Notts. NG17 3LA Tel: 01623 552376

Directions: M1 Jct. 28 - A38 towards Mansfield. Take the A38 at Kings Mill Island, 1st left (Sutton sign), then 1st rt into Hosiery Mills ground.

Capacity: 1,500 Covered Seating: Covered Standing: Floodlights:

Clubhouse: 01623 405660

PREVIOUS **Name:** North Notts
Leagues: Central Midlands League >03
HONOURS R-up CM Lge Supreme Div. 02-03

FACT FILE
Re-Formed: (as Sutton Town) 2002
Colours: Claret & sky/white/white.
Change: All royal blue - with yellow trim
Midweek Matchday: Tuesday
Programme: Price: Pages:
Editor:

Chairman: ????

Manager: Les McJannett
Tel: 01623 655834 (H) 07951 061236 (M)

TADCASTER ALBION

Secretary: Howard Clarke,17 Springhill Court,Tadcaster,N.Yorks.LS24 8DN (0193735017)
Ground: The Park, Ings Lane, Tadcaster, LS24 9AY. Tel: 01937 834119
Directions: From West Riding and South Yorks, turn right off A659 at John Smith's Brewery Clock.
From East Riding turn left off A659 after passing over river bridge and pelican crossing (New Street).
Capacity: 1,500 **Seats**: Planned this season **Cover:** 400 **Floodlights**: Yes
Clubhouse: Yes **Club Shop:** No
HONOURS None
RECORD **Attendance:**1,200 v Winterton F.A.Vase 4th Rd 1996-7
Win: 13-0 v Blidworth MW, NCE 97-98 **Defeat**: 2-10 v Thackley
PREVIOUS **Leagues:** York, Harrogate, Yorkshire (73-82)
BEST SEASON **FA Cup:** 2nd Qual. Rd. 98-99 **FA Vase:** 5th Round 77-78

FACT FILE
Founded: 1892
Colours: Yellow + Navy & Red trim /navy & red/navy
Change colours: Green & Yellow halves
Midweek Matchday: Tuesday
Programme: 20 pages
Prog Ed: Mrs Elaine Targett (01977 780964)
CLUB PERSONNEL
Chairman: Wayne Day Tel No: 01924 896446
President: Lord Edward Stourton
Match Sec: 01937 835017 (H/B)
Manager: Wayne Day
2002-03
Leading Goalscorer: Steve Batley
Captain & P.o.Y.: Lee Maguire

WINTERTON RANGERS

Secretary: G Spencer, 2 Dale Park Ave.,Winterton,Scun'pe,N Lincs.DN15 9UY (01724 732039)

Ground: West Street, Winterton, Scunthorpe, South Humberside (01724 732628).
Directions: From Scunthorpe take A1077 Barton-on-Humber for 5 miles. On entering Winterton take 3rd right (Eastgate), 3rd left (Northlands Rd)and 1st right (West St.). Ground 200yds on left
Capacity: 3,000 Seats: 200 Covered: 200 Floodlights: Yes **Club Shop:** No.
Clubhouse: Open matchdays & evenings Mon-Sat, hot & cold food available on matchdays

HONOURS Lincs Jnr Cup 47-48 61-62; Lincs Snr `B' Cup 69-70; Yorks Lg 71-72 76-77 78-79 (Lg Cup 80-81); N.C.E. Div 2 89-90; S'thorpe Lg & Cup many times.
PREVIOUS **Leagues:** Scunthorpe & Dist. 45-65; Lincs 65-70; Yorkshire 70-82.
BEST SEASON **FA Vase:** QF 76-77 **FA Cup:** 4th Qual Rd replay 76-77, 2-3 after 3-3
RECORD **Attendance:** 1,200 v Sheffield Utd, official floodlight opening, Oct. 78
Fee received: £5,000 for Henry Smith (Leeds United, 1979)

Players progressing Henry Smith (Leeds), Keith Walwyn (Chesterfield), Rick Greenhough(Chester)

FACT FILE
Founded: 1930 Nickname: Rangers
Colours: Blue & white/Black/Blue
Change colours: All red
Midweek matches: Wednesday
Programme: 28-36 pages, 50p
Editor: Mark Fowler (01724 734570)
Local Press: Scunthorpe Evening Telegraph

CLUB PERSONNEL
Chairman:David Crowder V- Chair: Ken Edgehill
Press Officer: as Secretary
Manager: J. Wilkinson
2002-2003
Captain: Billy Green
Top Scorer & P.o.Y.: Chris McDonald

WORSBROUGH M.W. & ATHLETIC

Secretary: Garry Wiggan, 9 Pantry Well, Worsbrough Bridge, Barnsley, S. Yorks S70 4SW
Tel: 01226 247023 (H) 01226 247023 (Fax) 07817 068752 (M)
Ground: Park Road, Worsbrough Bridge, Barnsley Tel: 01226 284452
Directions: On the A61 Barnsley-Sheffield road two miles south of Barnsley, 2miles from M1 jnt 36 opposite Blackburns Bridge. Two and a half miles from Barnsley (BR). Yorkshire Traction run buses every 10 mins thru Worsbrough Bridge.
Capacity: 2,000 Seats: 175 Cover: 175 Floodlights: Yes
Clubhouse: Yes **Club Shop:** No
HONOURS Northern Co's East Div 1 R-up 90-91 (Div 3 R-up 85-86); Sheffield SnrCup R-up 72-73; County Snr Lg 65-66 69-70 (R-up 62-63, Lg Cup 65-66); Barnsley Lg 52-53 58-59 59-60, Lg Cup 56-57 58-59 (R-up 53-54), Beckett Cup 57-58.
PREVIOUS **Leagues:** Barnsley 52-61; Sheffield County Snr 62-71; Yorkshire 71-82.
RECORD **Attendance:** 1,603 v Blyth Spartans, FA Amateur Cup 1971
BEST SEASON **FA Cup:** 1st Qual. Rd 78-79 79-80 80-81 **FA Vase:** 3rd Round 90-91

FACT FILE
Founded: 1923
Reformed: 1947
Colours: All red
Change colours: Yellow/blue
Midweek Matchday: Wednesday
Programme: 60 pages, 50p
Editor: Secretary

Chairman: John Cooper

Record Holders
Appearances: Billy Pickering
Goals: Frank Briscoe

YORKSHIRE AMATEUR

Secretary: David Packham, 30 Roxholme Avenue, Leeds LS7 4JF (0113 262 0758)
Ground: The Bracken Edge, Roxholme Road, Leeds LS8 4DZ Tel: 0113 262 4093
Directions: From South M1 to Leeds, then A58 Wetherby Road to Fforde Green Hotel, left at lights and proceed to Sycamore Ave. (on right). From East A1 to Boot & Shoe Inn then to Shaftesbury Hotel, turn right into Harehills Lane, then to Sycamore Avenue. Two and a half miles from Leeds (BR). Buses 2, 3 & 20 from Briggate to Harehills Ave.
Capacity : 1,550 Seats: 200 Cover: 160 Floodlights: Yes **Club Shop:** Yes
Clubhouse: Bar, tea bar, games, lounge. Every night 8.30-11, Sat matchdays 12-11, Sun 12-3.

HONOURS FA Amtr Cup SF 31-32; West Riding Co. Cup(3); Yorks Lg 31-32, Div 2 58-59 (R-up 52-53 71-72), Div 3 77-78, Lg Cup 32-33; Leeds & Dist. Snr Cup. **PREVIOUS League:** Yorks 20-24 30-82. **Ground:** Elland Road 1919-20 **RECORD Attendance:** 4,000 v Wimbledon, FA Amateur Cup QF 1932. **Players progressing:** Gary Strodder & Stuart Naylor (W.B.A.), Peter Swan (Leeds U) Brian Deane (Doncaster R) **BEST SEASONS: FA Cup:** 1st Rd 31-32 45-46 **FA Vase:** 3rd Round 93-94 **FA Amateur Cup:** Semi-Finals 31-32

FACT FILE
Founded: 1918 Nickname: Ammers
Sponsors: Screeching Parrot
Colours: White/navy/red
Change colours: All red
Midweek Matches: Tuesday
Programme: 12 pages, 50p
Editor: Secretary
Local Press: Yorkshire Post, Yorkshire Evening Post and North Leeds Advertiser

CLUB PERSONNEL
Chairman: Andrew Wilkinson (0113 260 9521)
President: Rayner Barker
Manager: Denis Metcalfe
Coach:Jim McKay Physio: Terry Davies

HEANOR TOWN
FOOTBALL CLUB LTD

MAIN SPONSOR
BURCHELL EDWARDS

OFFICIAL
PROGRAMME

KIT SPONSOR
ATI SRS
SERMATECH
Codnor Gate

KITClub CENTRAL MIDLANDS LEAGUE
COMPUTER PRODUCTS
SUPREME DIVISION
Monday 21st April 2003
HEANOR TOWN
versus
BLACKWELL MINERS WELFARE

SEASON 2002/2003

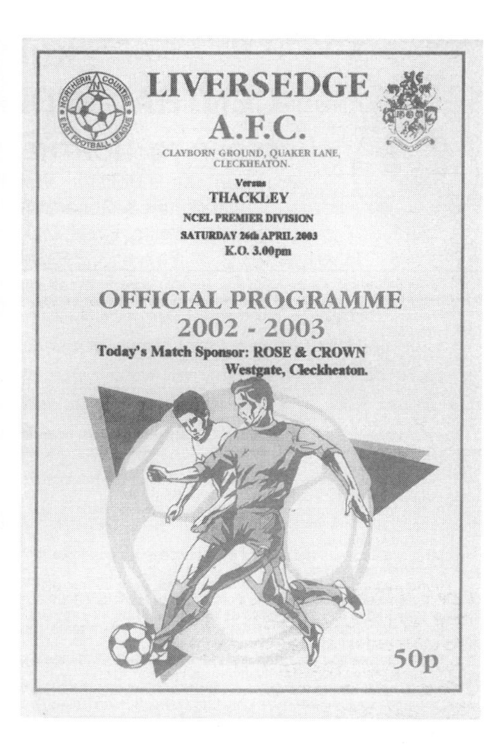

NORTHERN COUNTIES
EAST FOOTBALL LEAGUE
LIVERSEDGE
A.F.C.
CLAYBORN GROUND, QUAKER LANE,
CLECKHEATON.
Versus
THACKLEY
NCEL PREMIER DIVISION
SATURDAY 26th APRIL 2003
K.O. 3.00pm
OFFICIAL PROGRAMME
2002 - 2003
Today's Match Sponsor: ROSE & CROWN
Westgate, Cleckheaton.
50p

KitClub
CENTRAL MIDLANDS LEAGUE

FEEDER TO: NORTHERN COUNTIES LEAGUE

President: Mr R Holmes **Vice President:** Mr D Capenerhurst
Chairman & General Secretary: Frank Harwood
103 Vestry Road, Oakwood, Derby DE21 2BN
Tel: 01332 832372 Fax: 01332 835004 e-mail: frankharwood@onetel.co.uk

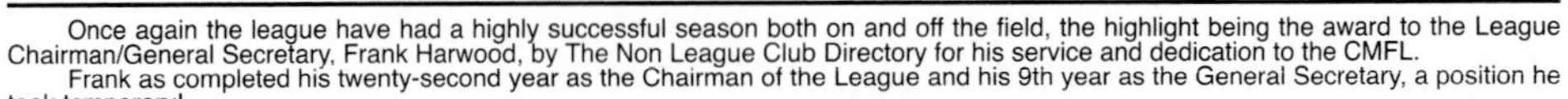

Once again the league have had a highly successful season both on and off the field, the highlight being the award to the League Chairman/General Secretary, Frank Harwood, by The Non League Club Directory for his service and dedication to the CMFL.

Frank as completed his twenty-second year as the Chairman of the League and his 9th year as the General Secretary, a position he took temporary!

Claimed by the followers of football through out the country, the CMFL is recognised as being the outstanding league both off and on the field at Level Four of the National game.

On the field there have been many notable performances in outside competitions with the most outstanding performance going to Teversal who reached the final of the Nottinghamshire Football Association Senior Cup Competition before losing 2-0 to Unibond side Hucknall Town, Hucknall are a former CMFL side and are one of many clubs who have reached the higher spheres of Non-League football since being promoted from the CMFL.

Teversal's achievements in the Notts Cup may well have been the reason for a drop in their league form which saw them lose what seemed like certain being certain champions slump to such an extent that they finally finished in 5th place. In April they lost four of the five games they played.

Two CMFL Reserves sides met in the Final of the Nottinghamshire F A Intermediate Cup and it was Pelican Reserves who took the trophy after a 1-0 victory over Carlton Town Reserves.

In the league Carlton Town (Nottinghamshire) made a late run to win the Computer Products Supreme Division and thus gain promotion to the Northern Counties East League. In their last 16 games Carlton won 13 drew 2 and lost only one, a shock home defeat 2-1 to mid table Dunkirk.

Their away record was the key to their success, through out the season they lost only two games, they where successful in winning thirteen games by the odd goal.

Sutton Town by winning 2-1 at Dinnington Town in their last league game finished runners up, again they came from behind to take this honour, April was the turning point for this Nottinghamshire club when they played six league games and won them all. The only 'hiccup' they had in this month was defeat in the Phoenix Trophies Floodlit Cup Final when they lost 8-7 on penalties to Dunkirk.

South Normanton Athletic finished in 3rd place but some consolation for this club was the news that they along with Carlton Town and Sutton Town would be promoted to the NCEL.

South Normanton also had a good April in their six league games they lost only once crashing to embarrassing 4-0 home defeat against inconsistent fellow Derbyshire club Heanor Town.

At the other end of the division Bottesford Town had a dreadful season and finished adrift by eleven points conceding 151 goals in their 38 league games, they won only four times, 3 at home and one away, 5-2 win at Nettleham in October. They had started the season so well winning 2-0 at home against Teversal.

Due to the promotion of Sutton Town and South Normanton Athletic it means that only Bottesford will be relegated and both Graham St Prims and Blackwell Miners Welfare retain their Supreme Division status despite finishing in relegation places.

Prims have improved their ground so much that it would have been a tragedy if they had gone down but it is hoped their reprieve can be beneficial next season.

They throughout the season had a dread of playing away from the "Asterdale" only winning one game on their travels, a 2-1 win at Nettleham last August.

Blackwell Miners Welfare started their return to the Supreme Division well and their demise as been surprising again the away form was the problem only winning three times on their travels one being a 2-1 win at the champion club Carlton Town. They scored ten times twice both against the bottom club Bottesford Town winning at home 10-2 and away 10-4.

Pelican in their first season in the league became the champions of the R & R Scaffolding Premier Division, impressive throughout the season they won 22 matches out of the 32 games played and their away form was the key to their success only losing two on their travels, the 'scrap' for runners up went to the last games of the season and Yorkshire club Kiveton Park surprised everybody by surging up the table to 'pip' Radford by goal difference. Needing to win their last game at GAD Khalsa Sports by six clear goals they duly obliged winning 8-2!

They became the most consistent team in the league winning their last thirteen league games during which they took four out of the champion club Pelican, drawing at Pelican and then winning the return at Kiveton.

At the turn of the year they where in 9th place fifteen points behind leaders Pelican and in the end they reduced that tally to three points at the conclusion of the season.

A dismal season however for Yorkshire Main who have to apply for re-election for the second year running, this club is ably run of the field and they deserve better fortune on the field.

Playing at home must have been a "death wish" because they only won once in front of their long-suffering supporters and they had to wait until March when they caused something of a sensation defeating Thoresby Colliery Welfare 5-1!

In all they only gained three victories all told winning away at GAD Khalsa and Harworth CI who earlier in the season had won 7-2 at Main's Edlington Lane Ground.

Selston who had been relegated from the Supreme Division continued their 'slide' and finished third from bottom and also must seek re-election.

They opened the season with a win at Kiveton Park 1-0 but there onwards the decline set in and they only won one more game on their travels.

Their best performance was perhaps their League Challenge Cup 3rd game at the eventual cup winners Supreme Division Dinnington Town, they lost 2-1 but the home team stated they had been fortunate.

Gad Khalsa Sports finished in second from bottom place and have withdrawn from the league, they have found CMFL football difficult during their two years of membership but they have been a credit on the field and their problems off the field may have contributed greatly to their final league placing, in their last twelve league games they did not have a victory losing eight times.

The Lee's Reserves Divisions where both keenly fought, in the Premier Division Shirebrook Town Reserves always seemed to have to much for the rest of the teams and they finally won the title with 13 points to spare, Worksop Town Reserves fought of the challengers Carlton Town Reserves and graham St Prims Reserves to secure runners up.

Rolls Royce Leisure Reserves, Ollerton Town Reserves and Selston Reserves finished in the bottom three positions.

The Reserves Division One title went to the last game of the season, Ripley Town Reserves need to win by five clear goals to take the title but they only won 4-1 in their last game at home to Sutton Town Reserves so the title went to Pelican Reserves who made it a double for the Nottinghamshire club.

Carlton Town 'A' where a creditable third.

The Humber Inspection Services Challenge Cup was won by Yorkshire club Dinnington Town 2-0 in a match played at Alfreton Town Ground on a lovely sunny Sunday, the first time the league have played a match on a Sunday, amongst the spectators was The Football Association National League Manager, Mike Appleby.

Dunkirk had consolation by winning the Phoenix Trophies Floodlit Cup in a game described as a credit not just to the CMFL but Non League Football Dunkirk defeated Sutton Town 8-7 on penalties after the game had ended 3-3 after extra time. This match was played at the excellent Lido Ground, home of Clipstone Welfare.

The Phoenix Trophies Reserves Cup went to the 'underdogs' Holbrook who defeated 'hot' favourites Shirebrook Town Reserves 1-0 at Lees Lane, South Normanton and the league where delighted that the sponsors of the competition proprietor, Stuart Howarth, journeyed down from Bradford to make the presentations.

Frank Harwood. Chairman/General Secretary.

COMPUTER PRODUCTS SUPREME DIVISION

	P	W	D	L	F	A	Pts
Carlton Town	38	22	9	7	80	46	75
Sutton Town	38	23	5	10	75	47	74
South Normanton Ath.	38	22	5	11	103	67	71
Retford United	38	19	11	8	69	40	68
Teversal	38	20	6	12	90	53	66
Dinnington Town	38	19	9	10	78	50	66
Holbrook FC	38	17	12	9	67	49	63
Sandiacre Town	38	17	10	11	67	60	61
Ripley Town	38	17	9	12	81	57	60
Rolls Royce Leisure	38	19	3	16	72	64	60
Heanor Town	38	17	6	15	78	50	57
Dunkirk	38	17	6	15	75	64	57
Barton Town Old Boys	38	18	1	19	62	77	55
Nettleham	38	11	9	18	52	72	42
Greenwood Meadows	38	11	8	19	48	71	41
Clipstone Welfare	38	11	7	20	50	73	40
Askern Welfare	38	10	9	19	53	70	39
Graham St Prims	38	9	4	25	55	93	31
Blackwell Miners Welf.	38	8	4	26	65	106	28
Bottesford Town	38	4	5	29	40	151	17

R & R SCAFFOLDING PREMIER DIVISION

	P	W	D	L	F	A	Pts
Pelican	32	22	6	4	89	28	72
Kiveton Park	32	21	6	5	95	46	69
Radford FC	32	21	6	5	76	28	69
Gedling Miners Welf (-3)	32	19	8	5	78	36	62
Thorne Colliery (-1)	32	17	7	8	90	51	57
Ollerton Town	32	16	7	9	60	34	55
Bentley Colliery	32	15	9	8	78	62	54
Thoresby Colliery Welf	32	13	7	12	50	55	46
Harworth C.I.	32	14	2	16	63	71	44
Forest Town	32	11	10	11	50	58	43
Blidworth Welfare	32	12	5	15	52	52	41
Sheffield City	32	8	8	16	44	67	32
Kimberley Town	32	6	8	18	35	64	26
Welbeck Welfare	32	6	8	18	60	92	26
Selston	32	6	7	19	43	87	25
Gad Khalsa Sports	32	4	9	19	47	89	21
Yorkshire Main	32	3	3	26	29	119	12

Computer Products Supreme Division	1	2	3	4	5	6	7	8	9	10	11	12	13	14	15	16	17	18	19	20
1 Askern Welfare		1-0	0-0	6-2	2-3	2-3	3-1	0-2	2-0	0-2	1-1	1-1	0-2	0-0	0-3	1-2	1-2	0-2	1-4	2-1
2 Barton Town Old Boys	3-2		2-0	3-1	1-2	1-2	0-2	2-0	2-1	2-0	2-1	1-0	1-1	2-3	3-1	2-1	3-2	2-5	2-3	1-2
3 Blackwell Miners Welfare	1-5	0-4		*-2	3-5	1-3	3-5	1-5	2-2	3-3	0-3	3-4	0-2	2-1	1-0	3-5	0-1	1-2	1-6	0-3
4 Bottesford Town	1-4	3-1	4-*		2-2	1-1	0-5	4-4	2-1	0-1	0-3	0-1	0-3	1-4	0-4	0-3	1-2	1-3	1-4	2-0
5 Carlton Town	2-2	5-1	1-2	4-0		2-0	1-0	1-2	5-0	0-0	1-2	1-2	2-3	1-1	3-2	2-1	2-0	1-0	1-0	2-2
6 Clipstone Welfare	4-0	4-2	1-3	2-2	1-1		0-3	1-1	4-1	1-2	0-4	1-2	2-1	0-2	2-2	2-3	2-4	1-1	1-0	2-0
7 Dinnington Town	2-0	5-0	2-0	4-0	0-1	2-0		3-2	2-0	3-0	2-0	1-1	1-0	0-2	0-0	5-0	1-1	2-6	1-2	3-2
8 Dunkirk	1-0	3-1	1-2	6-0	1-3	2-1	3-4		1-1	0-1	3-1	2-1	3-1	0-0	1-1	4-0	1-1	3-6	2-3	2-0
9 Graham St Prims	1-2	2-1	1-0	5-1	1-4	4-1	1-1	0-2		5-4	1-3	1-2	3-1	0-4	2-2	5-3	1-0	1-3	2-3	1-3
10 Greenwood Meadows	0-0	1-2	2-2	1-1	0-0	3-1	1-1	4-0	4-2		5-3	0-2	0-2	1-2	1-2	1-2	0-2	1-2	0-1	3-2
11 Heanor Town	1-3	0-2	4-1	6-0	0-1	0-1	3-1	3-0	4-2	5-1		3-0	0-0	0-1	1-1	3-1	2-4	0-2	2-3	2-4
12 Holbrook FC	4-1	3-1	3-1	6-1	1-3	2-0	2-2	0-1	3-1	4-1	0-0		2-1	0-1	1-3	2-2	2-2	4-0	0-2	1-0
13 Nettleham	0-5	2-3	3-1	2-5	2-2	1-0	2-2	0-1	1-2	1-3	0-4	1-1		1-0	3-1	2-3	2-0	0-2	1-3	1-5
14 Retford United	1-1	3-0	2-3	6-0	4-3	1-0	1-1	5-1	4-0	0-0	1-0	0-0	2-2		0-3	2-0	2-2	2-1	2-1	2-3
15 Ripley Town	3-0	2-3	3-2	7-0	0-3	4-1	4-1	1-5	3-0	2-0	2-2	2-2	2-3	2-0		2-4	2-2	5-3	2-0	2-1
16 Rolls Royce Leisure	4-1	4-1	2-0	3-0	0-1	5-0	0-3	2-1	2-0	0-1	0-1	1-1	4-0	2-1	0-2		3-1	3-4	1-3	0-2
17 Sandiacre Town	2-2	1-2	2-1	3-1	2-3	2-1	2-2	3-1	4-2	1-0	2-0	4-2	1-1	2-2	1-0	1-2		1-0	2-1	1-3
18 South Normanton Athletic	2-0	7-1	6-0	9-0	4-3	2-2	1-2	3-2	2-1	3-1	0-4	2-2	4-2	2-3	2-2	3-3	4-1		1-2	1-2
19 Sutton Town	2-2	1-0	3-1	2-0	0-1	0-1	3-2	3-2	3-1	7-0	0-5	1-1	1-1	1-0	1-0	1-0	3-3	1-2		0-0
20 Teversal	5-0	1-2	3-1	*-1	2-2	4-1	3-1	1-4	3-1	5-0	2-2	1-2	1-1	2-2	3-2	0-1	2-0	5-1	2-1	

R & R Premier Division	1	2	3	4	5	6	7	8	9	10	11	12	13	14	15	16	17
1 Bentley Colliery		1-2	0-0	3-1	2-2	5-0	0-0	3-3	0-0	1-3	1-6	7-3	3-1	2-1	3-0	5-2	2-1
2 Blidworth Welfare	0-1		1-1	5-2	0-3	4-2	0-0	0-2	3-2	0-2	1-1	3-3	1-3	1-0	0-1	2-0	1-0
3 Forest Town	0-4	0-6		3-2	1-2	2-3	1-1	4-2	2-0	0-2	1-1	2-2	0-1	3-1	2-2	3-2	1-1
4 Gad Khalsa Sports	1-1	2-4	1-5		1-7	1-3	2-2	2-8	0-2	1-3	1-2	4-3	5-0	0-6	1-1	3-3	0-2
5 Gedling Miners Wlefare	5-2	3-1	1-2	1-0		4-1	4-2	1-4	1-1	1-0	1-1	4-1	2-1	1-2	2-2	1-0	3-1
6 Harworth C.I.	4-2	2-0	1-3	4-2	0-1		3-1	2-3	2-1	0-3	3-1	2-1	2-2	4-1	0-3	3-1	2-4
7 Kimberley Town	1-1	1-0	1-1	3-1	0-	1-2		1-6	0-2	0-6	0-2	3-1	3-2	0-1	2-3	2-0	2-2
8 Kiveton Park	3-3	2-1	6-1	5-1	0-0	3-2	2-0		2-1	3-2	2-1	0-2	1-1	3-0	4-1	2-3	5-0
9 Ollerton Town	2-1	1-0	1-2	0-0	0-0	4-1	3-0	2-4		0-2	3-0	2-1	4-0	3-1	0-2	5-0	7-1
10 Pelican	1-3	2-1	6-0	4-2	0-0	4-1	1-0	3-3	1-0		2-1	5-1	4-1	0-1	2-1	8-0	6-1
11 Radford FC	4-1	4-1	2-0	1-1	4-1	2-0	3-2	2-0	1-2	2-2		3-0	1-0	2-0	1-0	7-1	3-0
12 Selston	1-5	2-1	0-0	2-2	3-2	2-3	1-0	2-7	0-2	1-5	0-6		1-4	0-2	3-6	2-2	1-0
13 Sheffield City	2-3	2-3	0-0	1-1	0-7	2-1	1-1	1-3	0-0	1-3	0-2	0-0		3-1	1-0	0-3	5-1
14 Thoresby Colliery Welfare	0-0	1-4	1-0	1-2	1-1	3-1	1-0	3-2	1-1	1-1	1-1	2-1	2-2		2-2	3-1	4-0
15 Thorne Colliery	5-2	4-0	1-2	4-1	1-2	1-0	5-1	2-2	3-3	1-1	0-3	3-1	5-3	6-0		6-2	*-0
16 Welback Welfare	5-7	2-2	4-2	0-0	2-3	2-2	6-2	0-2	3-4	0-0	0-3	0-0	3-2	3-5	3-5		0-0
17 Yorkshire Main	3-4	0-4	0-6	0-4	0-*	2-7	0-3	0-1	0-2	0-5	1-3	0-3	1-2	5-1	2-4	1-7	

HUMBER INSPECTION SERVICES LEAGUE CHALLENGE CUP 2002-03

FIRST ROUND

Bentley Colliery	v	Rolls Royce Leisure	2-4
Gedling Miners Welf.	v	Pelican	2-1
Retford United	v	Yorkshire Main	6-0
Thorne Colliery	v	Radford	3-2
Bottesford Town	v	Thoresby Colliery W.	0-2
Nettleham	v	Teversal	2-3
Sutton Town	v	Carlton Town	0-2

SECOND ROUND

Barton Town Old Boys	v	Greenwood Meadows	4-0
Dinnington Town	v	GAD Khalsa Sports	4-0
Gedling Miners Welfare	v	Ollerton Town	0-1
Heanor Town	v	Ripley Town	1-0
Kimberley Town	v	Rolls Royce L (expelled)	
Selston	v	Blidworth Welfare	2-1
Teversal	v	Graham Street Prims	2-3
Kiveton Park	Bye		
Blackwell Miners W.	v	ThoresbyCW	4-4,4-4*(3-2p)
Forest Town	v	Askem Welfare	3-3, 2-3
Harworth Colliery Int.	v	Welbeck Welfare	0-2
Holbrook	v	Retford United	6-1
Sandiacre Town	v	South Normanton A.	1-0
Sheffield City	v	Clipstone Welfare	0-2
Thorne Colliery	v	Carlton Town	0-1
Dunkirk	Bye		

THIRD ROUND

Carlton Town	v	Clipstone Welfare	4-1
Dunkirk	v	Sandiacre Town	4-1
Heanor Town	v	Barton Town Old Boys	2-0
Kimberley Town	v	Blackwell Miners Welf.	1-4
Dinnington Town	v	Selston	2-1
Graham Street P.	v	Ollerton Town	2-0
Holbrook	v	Welbeck Welfare	6-0
Kiveton Park	v	Askern Welf.	2-2, 2-1

QUARTER FINALS

Blackwell Miners Welf.	v	Graham Street Prims	3-3
Heanor Town	v	Dunkirk	1-6
Carlton Town	v	Kiveton Park	4-1
Holbrook	v	Dinnington Town	1-6

SEMI FINALS

Dinnington Town	v	Carlton Town	2-1	at Clipstone Welfare FC
Dunkirk	v	Blackwell Miners Welf.	4-3	at Heanor Town FC

FINAL

Dinnington Town	v	Dunkirk	2-0	at Alfreton FC

PHOENIX TROPHIES FLOODLIT CUP 2001-02

FIRST ROUND			1st Leg	2nd Leg	Aggregate
Blackwell Miners Welf	v	Sutton Town	0-1	1-3	1-4
Blidworth Welfare	v	Harworth Colliery Institute	1-2	1-2	2-4
Carlton Town	v	Clipstone Welfare	1-2	4-4	5-6
Graham Street Prims	v	South Normanton Athletic	0-2	0-3	0-5
Heanor Town	v	Sandiacre Town	3-3	3-2	6-5
Kimberley Town	v	Dunkirk	0-2	0-5	0-7
Nettleham	v	Bottesford Town	0-1	2-0	2-1
Rolls Royce Leisure	Bye				

Retford United removed from competition for not having floodlights by 1st October 2002.

QUARTER FINALS

Dunkirk	v	Clipstone Welfare	4-0	4-2	8-2
Harworth Colliery Inst.	v	Nettleham	0-1	4-1	4-2
Rolls Royce Leisure	v	South Normanton Athletic			
Sutton Town	v	Heanor Town	2-1	2-2	4-3

SEMI FINALS

Dunkirk	v	Rolls Royce Leisure	3-0	3-3	6-3
Sutton Town	v	Harworth Colliery Institute	7-1	3-0	10-1

FINAL

Dunkirk	v	Sutton Town	3-3*	8-7 pens

at Ciptsone Welfare FC

ASKERN WELFARE

Chairman: John Metcalfe **President:** R.Redhead
Secretary: Jon Stewart, 43 Sutton Road, Askern,Doncaster,S.Yorks. DN6 0AG
& Match Sec Tel Nos: 01302 702502 (H) 01302 703035 (W)
Ground: Askern Welfare Sports Ground, Doncaster Road, Askern,Doncaster
Tel: 01302 700957. Clubhouse open normal hours and all day Saturdays
Directions: A1/A639 Pontefract. Follow sign for Askern/Campsall.At T-junction turn right. Left at Anne Arms, right at Supersave, ground on right.
Capacity: 3,000 **Cover** 200**Floodlights** Yes **Club shop:**Yes(01226 771900)

Formed: 1924 Nickname: The Welly
Colours: Black & white stripes/black/black
Change colours: All Red with white trim
Midweek Matchday: Wednesday
Reserves Lg: Doncaster & Dist. Sen. Prem.
Programme: 30 Pages £1.
Editor & Com Man: Martin Terrell 01302 701964
Manager: Paul Curtis
Asst Man/Coach: Martin Terrell
Physio: Kevin Lewis

BARTON TOWN OLD BOYS

Secretary: Peter Mitchell, 56 Brigg Rd., Barton-on-Humber, North Lincs. DN18 5DR
Tel: 01682 632382 (H) 07900 105204 (M)
Ground: Marsh Lane Football Ground, Marsh Lane, Barton-on-Humber, North Lincs.
Tel: 07900 105204 (Secretary's Mobile)
Directions: Approaching from south on A15, Barton is the last exit before Humber Bridge. Follow A1077 into town. Right at mini r'about, at bottom of hill onto 'Holydyke'. 2nd left onto George St., then into King St. Marsh Lane is opp. junction of King St. & High St.

Colours: Light blue/dark blue/dark blue
Change colours: Red & black stripes/black/black

BLACKWELL MINERS WELFARE

Secretary: Steve Harris, 6 Pennine Close, Newton, Alfreton, Derbys DE55 5UD.
Tel: 01773 779172(H) 01246 501561(W) 01773 779173 (F)
Email: steve-harris@bdrmg.co.uk
Club Website: www.blackwellmwfc.org.uk - Club Email: manor@globalnet.co.uk
Ground: Welfare Ground, Primrose Hill, Blackwell, Derbyshire DE55 5JE. Tel: 01773 811295.
Directions: M1 Junc 28, A38 towards Mansfield, left onto B6406, left again at Hilcote Arms, ground 1 mile on left just past Miners Welfare. Matchday Tel: 07890 198776

Founded:
Colours: Red & white stripes/red/red
Change cols: White/black/black

Midweek Matchday: Wednesday

Manager: Paul Jones 01623 405608 (H)
Physio:

CLIPSTONE WELFARE

Secretary: Barry Clarke, 40 Church Road, Clipstone, Mansfield, NG21 9DG (01623640829).
Ground & Directions: Clipstone Lido Ground Clipstone Road West, Mansfield,Notts (01632 655674). B6030 from Mansfield, between Forest Town & Clipstone, on left entering Clipstone.
Capacity: 3000 **Seats:** 90 **Cover:** 200 **Floodlights:** Yes **Club Shop:** No
Honours: Notts Snr Cup 85-86 94-95, Notts Alliance 72-73 73-74 74-75 92-93 94-95 (Lg Cup 72-73 73-74 74-75 94-95 (R-up 92-93)), Notts I'mediate Cup 55-56. Central Midlands Premier Championship 94-95 96-97

Founded 1927
Colours: Red/black/black
Change Colours: All B lue
Midweek Matchday: Tuesday or Wednesday
Programme: Yes

Chairman: Carl Hardwick
Manager: Steve Bingley

DINNINGTON TOWN

Secretary: Wallace Chambers, 26 Mackenzie Way,Kiveton Park, Sheffield S26 6QMM
Tel No: 07932 677881
Ground: Resource Centre, 131 Laughton Road, Dinnington.
Tel: 01905 518555
Directions: M1 J31 onto A57 towards Worksop. At 1st lights turn left to Dinnington. Follow road into town centre and the ground is on the left.

Founded:
Colours: Yellow/black/black
Change: Green & Black/white/white

Midweek Matchday:

Manager: Steve Toyne
Tel: 01142 347584 (H) 07960 616129 (B)

DUNKIRK

Secretary: Steve Throssell, 24 Kingfisher Wharf, Castle Marina, Nottingham NG71GA (0115 9473903 or 07903 322446
Ground & Directions: The Ron Steel Sports Ground, Trentside Farm, Clifton Bridge, Nottingham (0115 9850803). Ring Road - Clifton Bridge (North End),Ind Estate, Lenton Lane.
Honours: FA Vase 5th Rd 93-94; Cen Mid Sup Div R-up 96-97, Prem Div R-up 95-96,KO Cup 97-98; Notts Alliance Div 1 84-85, Div 2 82-83, Lg Cup R-up 84-85;02-03 Notts I'mediate Cup 83-4 Floodlit CupWoinners: 2002-2003**Capacity:**1,500 **Seats:** No **Cover**: 200 **Floodlights**: Yes **Shop:** No **Clubhouse:** Yes
Record Attendance: 821 v Tiverton Town, F.A.Vase 5th Rd 93-94
2002-2003: Captain: Mark Smith **Top Scorer**: Darryl Thomas **P.o.Y.**: Chris Murdock

Founded: 1946
Colours: Red/black/black
Change Colours: All Blue
Midweek Matchday: Tuesday
Programme : Yes
Chairman:Jack Riley
Manager: Andy Freeman
Assistant Manager: Ian Henry
Players Progressing: Roger Willis and Matthew McKemzie (Grimsby T), Wes Morgan (Nottm F)

GEDLING M.W.

Secretary: Norman Hay, 182 Gedling Rd., Arnold, Nottingham NG5 6NY
Tel: 0115 926 5598 (H)
Ground: Plains Sports & Social, Plains Road, Mapperly, Nottingham
Tel: 0115 926 6300
Location: The ground is situated on the B684 in Mapperley

Colours: Yellow/blue/yellow
Change: Blue/white/blue

Manager: Mark Allison
Tel: 0115 931 2650 (H)

GRAHAM STREET PRIMS

Secretary: Mrs E Wright, 6 Athol Close, Sinfin Moor, Derby DE24 9LZ
Tel. Nos.: 01332 606837 (H) 01332 340131 x6855 (B)
Match Secretary: D.J.Tice, North Bank Cottage,Church Lane,Swarkestone, Derbys. DE73 1JB
Tel. No.: 01332 704054
Ground: Asterdale Sports Centre, Borrowash Road, Spondon, nr Derby. Tel: 01332 668656
Directions: M1 Junc 25, take A52 to Derby. 3rd left Borrowash Road - golf driving range on left, approx 400m further turn left into Asterdale Sports Centre. Ground at rear.
Capacity: 1,000 Seats: No Cover: Yes Floodlights: Yes Club shop: No Clubhouse: Yes

Formed: 1904
Colours: Red & white stripes/black/black
Change Colours: Yelow/red/red
Midweek Matchday: Tuesday
Programme: Yes
Chairman:
Manager: Gerry McElhinney

GREENWOOD MEADOWS

Secretary: Peter Hynes,64 Wallis Street,Basford,Nottingham NG6 0EP
0115 9705132
Ground: Greenwood Meadows, Lenton Lane, Clifton, Nottingham.
Tel: 0115 986 5913
Directions: M1 Junc 24 take A453Nottingham-Clifton Bridge to Lenton Ind Estate. Left into Old Lenton Lane.Ground second on right on lane.

Founded:
Colours: Green & white/black/green
Change:Red & black.black/black

Midweek Matchday:

Managers: Brian Cawthorn & Chris Nicholson

HEANOR TOWN

Secretary: Keith Costello, 45 Stainsby Avenue, Heanor, Derbys. DE75 7EL(01773 719446).
Ground & Directions: The Town Ground, Mayfield Avenue, Heanor (01773713742/715815).
M1 (J26), take A610 onto A608, ground 200yds from Market Square
Capacity: 4,000 and new stand being built `**Cover:** 2,000 **Floodlights:** Yes
Honours: Central Midlands League Cup 94-95 (Runners-up 86-87 92-93, B E Webbe Removals Cup 88-89), West Midlands Reg. League Runners-up 72-73; Midland Co's League Runners-up 65-66 67-68; Derbys Senior Cup(9) 1892-94 1946-47 65-69 70-7178-79; FA Cup 1st Rd 58-59 63-64.Central Midlands Supreme Champions:94-5,96-7 Central All.Lg(2) R-up4
2002-2003 Top Scorer: Chris Henson 27: Captain & P.o.Y.: Matt Johnson 27

Nickname: The Lions
Colours: Black& white Halves/black/black
Change Colours: All Red
Midweek Matchday: Wednesday
Programme: 32pages £1.00 Ed: Stan Wilton
01332 880199 (H) & 01332 881049 (Fax)
Club House: On ground.Hot food (match days)
Chair: John McCulloch Manr:Richard preston
F.A.Vase 2001-02 4th Round

HOLBROOK

Secretary: Alan Pace,5 Belvedere Close,Swanwick,Derbys. DE56 1BY Tel No: 01773 528224
Ground: The Welfare Ground, Shaw Lane, Holbrook, Derbyshire Tel: 07932 930298
Directions: From A38 take B6179 for Kilburn, turn left at lights for Belper. 1mile on left at Bulls Head for Holbrook. 2 miles on turn right at Venturegarage into Shaws Lane.
Capacity: 1,000 **Seats:** None **Cover:** 250 **Floodlights:** No
Clubhouse: Holbrook Miners Welfare, Shaw Lane.(01332 880259) **Shop:** No
Honours: Central Midlands Premier Division 99-00

Founded: 1996
Nickname: The Brookies
Colours:Blue & black halves/black/black
Change:All Yellow
Midweek Matchday:Wednesday
Programme: Yes / 24pages 50price

Chairman: T.B.A.
Manager: Mark Webster

KIVETON PARK

Secretary: Kevin Hull, 3 Chapel way, Kiveton Park, Sheffield S26 6QT
Tel: 01909 772152
Ground: Hard Lane, Kiveton Park, Sheffield. Tel: 0797 4247074.
Directions: M1 J31. Take A57 Worksop road, first right to Todwick, at T junct. turn right. Follow road to Kiveton crossroads. Go over & ground is on right after approx 100m.

Colours: Green & Blue/Blue/Green
Change Colours:: All Red

Manager: Stuart Holmes

NETTLEHAM

Secretary: Andrew Bandelow,104 Wragby Road,Bardney,Lincoln.LN3 5XW
Tel: 01526 399520 (H) 01522 530363 (W)
Ground: Mulsanne Park, Field Close, Nettleham Tel: 01522 750007.
Directions: A46 - 3 miles north of Lincoln, right at Brown Cow Pub, past Church 2nd turning on right, ground at end
Floodlights: Yes

Honours: Central Mids Lg Premier Div. Cup R-up 87-88, Village Tphy, Nursing Cup, Kelly Read Cup, Blankney Hunt Cup, Lincoln & Dist. Amtr Cup R-up, Joe Miller Tphy(2).

Founded: 1905
Sponsors: Double 'M' Catering (Home)
J W Bandelow Plastering (Away)
Colours: All Royal Blue
Change: Yellow/Green/Yellow
Midweek Matchday: Tuesday
Programme: Price £1
Editor: A Bandelow
Chairman: Clive Mason
Manager: Jim Masterton
2002-03
Leading Goalscorer: Lee Beesley
Captain: Ian Wheatley
Player of the Year: Lee Beesley/Danny Lynn

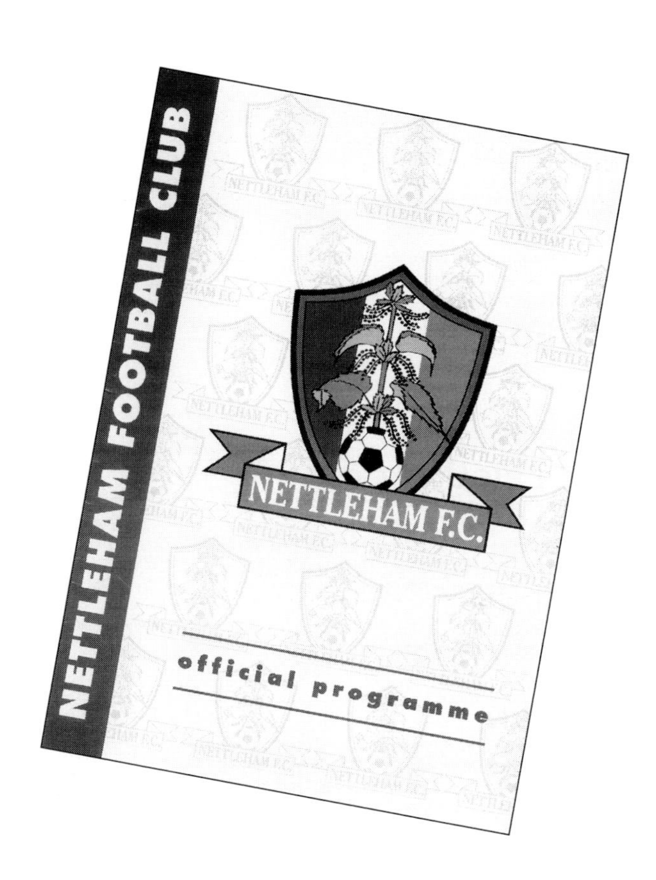

PELICAN

Secretary: Neil Swift, 21 Lancaster Way, Strelley, Nottingham NG8 6PH
Tel: 0115 929 4728 (H) 0776 77778765 (B)
Ground: Brian Wakefield Sports Ground, Lenton Lane, Nottingham
Tel: 0115 986 8255
Directions: M1 J26 take A610 to ring road. Follow signs A52 Grantham.
Go under Clifton Bridge, Ground last on Lenton Lane.
Honours: Notts Alliance Lg Cup 90-91(R-up 91-92 93-94).

Colours: All Blue
Change: Red/black/black

Manager: Glen Russell

RADFORD

Colours: Claret & sky blue/claret/claret
Change: Red & Blue stripes/red/red
Midweek Matchday: Tuesday

Manager: Matt Keetley

Secretary: Miss Joanne Smith, 63 Hilcot Drive, Aspley, Nottingham NG8 5HS
Tel: 0794 9091477
Ground: Radford FC, Berridge Rd. West, off Radford Road, Radford, Nottm
Tel: 0115 943250
Directions: M1 Junc 26,take A610 to Nottingham, at dual carriageway turn left. Move to right lane and go immediately right into Wilkinson St. At top turn right & right again at 2nd crossing.

RETFORD UNITED

Secretary: John Hodgkinson, Richmond Ho., York St., East Markham, Notts. NG22 0QW
Tel: 01777 705570 (H) 07850 975978 (B)
Ground: Cannon Park, Leverton Rd., Retford, Notts.
Tel: 0794 9454694 or 01777 710300
Directions: From A1 take A620 past Ranby Prison and into Retford. At large r'about take 3rd exit. Pass Morrisons superstore to lights. Right at lights, then left at next set. Follow Leverton Rd. out of town. Cannon Park on RHS after two bridges.
Capacity: 2,000 Covered Seating:&Standing:300 Floodlights: Yes June 03

Founded: 1987
Colours: Black & white stripes/black/black
Change colours: Yellow/blue/white
Midweek Matchday:
Programme: Price: Pages:28-40
Editor: Matt Hickin, Bubble Design

President: Dean Vivian
Chairman: Dave Hickin
Manager:Paul Hyde Tel: 01777 228158 (H)

RIPLEY TOWN

Secretary: Michael E Boam, 5 Valley Drive, Newthorpe, Notts. NG16 2DT.
Tel: 01773 715277 (H) 0374 876794 (B)
Ground: Hanson Brick Works, Peasehill Road, Ripley, Derbys.
Tel: 01773 742200
Directions: M1, J 28, A38 south to A610 signed Nottingham. Continue approx. 1 mile. Turn right into Steam Mill Lane, continue to Peasehill Road to brickworks.

Colours: Blue & White/ Blue/ Blue
Change: White/black/white

Midweek Matchday:

Manager: Paul MacFarland
Tel: 01773 609030 (H)

ROLLS ROYCE LEISURE F.C.

Secretary: Gary Warbrick, 20 Balmoral Road, Hucknall, Nootts. NG15 8ES
Tel. No: 0115 9640384 (H) 07732426283 (M)
Ground: Rolls Royce Sports & Social Club, Watnall Road, Hucknall Notts. Tel. 0115 963 0134
Directions: M1 Junc 27. Follow sign A611 to Hucknall. Turn right onto by-pass. 2nd r/about turn right on to Watnall Road. Take 2nd left after fire station on R.R. Sports Ground.
Capacity: 1,000 **Cover:** Yes **Floodlights**: No
Clubhouse: Social Club always open with food

Colours: All Blue
Change colours: Yellow/yellow/white
Midweek Matchday: Wednesday
Programme: Yes Price: Pages:
Editor:
Chairman: Darryl Claypole
Manager: Phil Towle
Reserves: Peter Needham & Paul Hopkins

SANDIACRE TOWN

Secretary: Mel Williams, 38 Pasture Rd.,Stapleford, Nottingham NG9 8GL Tel: 0115 9174079
Ground: St Giles Park, Stanton Road, Sandiacre, Nottingham NG105EP Tel:0115 9392880.
Directions: M1 jct 25, follow signs to Sandiacre passing Post House on right, straight over cross-roads into Rushy Lane and towards Stanton Rd, 1st right after 1000yds into Stanton Rd, ground at bottom after another1000yds. **Web:** homepage.ntlworld.com/sandiacretownfc
Capacity: 2,000 Seats: None Cover: 250 Floodlights: Yes Club Shop: No
Clubhouse: Members Club 8-11pm. Sunday lunch, Saturday1.30-11pm. Snacks available
Honours: Central Mids Prem. Div 92-93, Lg Cup 92-93 R-up 95-96, Mids Regional All. R-up 91-92

Founded: 1978 Nickname: Saints
Cols: Red/navy/red
Change: Yellow/sky/yellow
Midweek Matchday: Tuesday
Programme: 44 pages 50p
Editor/Press Officer: Mel Williams
Tel: 0115 917 4079
Chairman: ?????
Manager: Tony Roe and Mark Harvey

TEVERSAL

Secretary: Kevin Newton, 8 Vere Ave., Sutton in Ashfield, Notts NG17 2ES
Tel: 01623 461145
Ground: Teversal Grange Country Inn, Carnarvon Street, Teversal, Sutton-in-Ashfield, Notts.
Tel: 01623 442021
Directions: M1, J28, A38 towards Mansfield. At r'about take A6075 Mansfield Woodhouse. Next lights left B6014, Stanton Hill. At r'about take A6014 Tibshelf. 2nd on right Carnarvon St., ground at the top.

Colours: Red & white/ black/red
Change: Blue / white/white

Chairman:
Managers: John Courtie
Physio:

APPLEBY FRODINGHAM ATHLETIC

Ground: Brumby Hall Sports Ground, Ashby Road, Scunthorpe, North Lincs Tel: 01724 843024

Previous League: Lincolnshire Lge.. > 2003

BENTLEY COLLIERY

Secretary: James P Tooth, 38 East St., Darfield, Barnsley, South Yorks. S73 9AE Tel: 01226 754012 (H/Fax)
Ground: Bentley Miners' Welfare, The Avenue, Bentley, Doncaster, S. Yorks. Tel: 01302 874420 **Directions:** North from Doncaster on A19: Selby Road. In Bentley turn right at mini r'about on Arksey Lane. Left at shops onto The Avenue and the ground is 60 yards on left.
Colours: All Yellow **Change colours:** White & Claret/claret/claret **Manager:** Roy Butterworth

BLIDWORTH WELFARE

Secretary: Graham Redfern, 1 Dennbigh Close,Rainworth,Notts NG21 0HY Tel No: 01623 403019
Ground: Welfare Ground, Mansfield Rd, Blidworth, Mansfield (01623 793361). **Directions:** On B6020, Rainworth side of Blidworth. From M1 jct 27 take A608 to Kirby at lights follow A611 to Kirby then take B6020through Ravenshead to Blidworth -thru village and up hill ground on right. From A1 follow A614 /A617 to Rainworth, left at lights then 1st right on to B6020 to Blidworth - ground on left at top of hill.
Colours: Orange/black/orange **Change colours:** Blue/whiteblue. **Manager:** Rudi Funk

BOTTESFORD TOWN

Secretary: Tony Reeve, 61 Skelton Road, Scunthorpe, North Lincs. DN17 1RB Tel 01724 352939 (H)
Ground: Birch Park, Ontario Road, Bottesford, Scunthorpe, N. Lincs. Tel: 01724 871833
Directions: Exit M180 via M181 - Scunthorpe. At r'about right into Scotter Road. Over next r'about then 2nd left into South Park Rd., on to Sunningdale Rd. Right into Goodwood Rd, ground at end.
Colours: Orange/Black/Black **Change**: Blue & Yellow/blue/yellow **Manager**: Vic Jubber

FOREST TOWN

Secretary: Jan Nieloojadio, 14 Bransdale Avenue, Forest Town, Mansfield, Notts. NG19 0LZ Tel No: 01623 648588
Ground: Forest Town Welfare Sports Ground, Clipstone Rd West, Forest Town, Mansfield, Notts. Tel: 01623 624678
Directions: From Mansfield follow signs for Clipstone/Forest Town. The ground is situated at the Mansfield end of Forest Town on the right.
Colours: All blue **Change Colours:** All red **Manager:**Mat Vardy

HARWORTH COLLIERY INSTITUTE

Secretary: Tom Brogan, 30 Lindsey Road, Harworth, Doncaster, Sth Yorks DN11 8QH Tel: 01302 750132.
Ground: Recreation Ground, Scrooby Rd, Bircotes, Doncaster Tel: 01302 750614.
Directions: Off A1(M) at Blyth, head towards Bawtry for approx 2 miles, 3rd left, ground in village at top of hill on left. Or, from Doncaster to Bawtry then head for A1(M) and turn left after caravan site - ground at top of hill.
Colours: Amber & black/black/amber & black **Change Cols:** Claret and Blue **Midweek Matchday:** Wednesday **Manager:** Alan Needham

KIMBERLEY TOWN

Colours:White/navy/red Chairman/Manager: Graeme Critchley
General Manager/Match Secretary: Mrs Patricia Critchley, 21 Rowborn Drive,Oughtbridge, Sheffield S35 0JR Tel: 0114 2517742
Ground: Stag Ground, Nottingham Road, Kimberley Tel: 0115 938 2788. e-ail:info@kimberleytownfc.co.uk Website:www.kimberleytownfc.co.uk
Directions: Thro' Nuthall from M1 J 26 to Kimberley, ground entrance 150 yds after Stag Inn. **Capacity**: 2,500 Seats: None Cover:250
Floodlights: Yes **Clubhouse:** Evenings (Except Sun) & matchdays. Hot & cold snacks available
Honours: Notts Amateur Lg Div 1 54-55, Central Alliance Div 2 R-up 57-58. **2002-2003** Captain & Player of the Year: Andrew Peters

KIVETON PARK

Secretary: Kevin Hull,3 Chapel way, Kiveton Park, Sheffield S26 6QTTel No: 01909 772152
Ground: Hard Lane, Kiveton Park, Sheffield. Tel: 0797 4247074. **Directions:** M1 Junct. 31. Take A57 Worksop road, first right to Todwick, at T junct. turn right. Follow road to Kiveton crossroads. Go over and ground is on right after approx 100m.
Colours: Green & Blue/Blue/Green. **Change Colours:**: All Red **Manager:** Stuart Holmes

MATLOCK UNITED

Ground: Cavendish Road Playing Fields, Cavendish Park, Matlock, Derbyshire

Previous League: Midlands Regional Alliance > 2003

OLLERTON TOWN

Gen. Secretary: Les Brown,14 Holly Rise,New Ollerton, Notts NG22 9UZ Tel No: 01623 836023
Secretary: Les Brown, 14 Holly Rise, New Ollerton, Notts. NG22 9UZ Tel: 01623 836023 (H)
Ground: Walesby Lane, New Ollerton, Notts
Directions: From Ollerton r'about om A614 take A6075 to Ollerton. At r'about first left & after 30m left into Walesby Lane
Colours: All red **Change colours:** Blue/white/blue **Manager:** Alan Owen

PUNJAB UNITED

Ground: The Wharf, Shardlow, Derby
Previous League: East Midlands Senior Lge. > 2003

RADCLIFFE OLYMPIC

Secretary: C Johnson, 2 The Firs, Holme Pierpoint, Nottingham NG12 2LT Tel: 0115 933 3791
Ground: Wharf Lane, Radcliffe-on-Trent, Nottingham
Colours: All black with beige & red trim

RAINWORTH MINERS WELFARE

SELSTON

Secretary: George Elliott, 3 Derwent Drive,Selston, Notts. NG16 6QU9 Tel: 01773 781540 (H) 07786 574452 (M)
Ground: The Parish Hall Ground, Mansfield Road, Selston, Notts Tel: 01773 812540 **Directions:** J27 M1. Take A608 (Heanor). 1st right onto B600 (Alfreton/Selston). Into Selston & take 2nd right onto B6018 (Kirby-in-Ashfield). Ground 600 yds on left.
Colours: Black & white/white/white **Change**: Navy & sky halves/navy/black **Manager:** John Dawn

SHEEPBRIDGE

Ground: Sheepbridge Miners Welfare, Chesterfield, Derbyshire
Previous League: Matlock & Dist. > 2003

SHEFFIELD CITY

Secretary: John Wilson, Whitewalls Farm, Swinston Hill Rd, Dinnington, Sheffield S25 2RY. Tel: 01909 563466 (H) 01909 569973 (B)
Ground: Meadowhall Stadium, 101 Ferrers Road, Tinsley, Sheffield S9 1RZ. **Directions**: J34, M1 South exit Tinsley Viaduct. Take A6178 to Templeborough/Rotherham. 2nd road on rt. past "Fox & Duck" P.H., is Ferrers Rd. Ground at bottom.
Colours: Red/black/black **Change**: Blue/white/white **Manager**: Mick Dakin

SOUTHWELL CITY

Secretary: Pat Johnson, 63 The Ropewalk, Southwell, Notts. NG25 0AL Tel: 01636 8126594
Ground: War Memorial Recreation Ground, Bishops Drive, Southwell, Notts. Tel: 01636 814386
Previous League: Notts Alliance. > 2003 **Colours**: Black & white stripes/black/black

THORESBY COLLIERY WELFARE

Secretary: Barry Reece, 125 Henton Rd., Edwinstone, Mansfield, Notts. NG21 9LD Tel: 01623 822415 (H) 01623 491422 (B)
Ground: Thoresby Colliery Sports Ground, 4th Avenue, Edwinstone, Notts. Tel: 01623 822283 (Ground & Clubhouse)
Directions: A614 Ollerton r'about take A6075 Mansfield/Edwinstone. Turn left opposite 'Manvers Arms' onto 5th Avenue. Opposite Nursing Home turn right onto 4th Ave. Ground entrance ahead.
Colours: Blye & white/ blue/blue **Change Colours:** Gold/black/black **Manager:** Mick Heron

THORNE COLLIERY

Secretary: Glyn Jones, 21 Haynes Close, Thorne,Doncaster, S Yorks DN8 5HR Tel No: 01405 741062
Ground & Directions: Miners Welfare, Grange Road, Moorends, Thorne, Doncaster.(01374 996474), M18 Junc 6, in THorne, turnat lights to Moorends, go almostthrough village, Grange Road on right.
Manager: Graham Jones **Colours:** All Navy **Change:** Green & Navy/green/green **Midweek Matchday:** Tuesday

WELBECK MINERS WELFARE

Secretary: Gillian Gibbonbs,21 Cumberland Avenue,Warsop, Mansfield, Notts. NG20 0JJ Tel No: 01623 844616
Ground: Elksley Road, Meden Vale, Mansfield. (01623 842611) **Directions:** 1 1/2 miles off A60 between Worksop and Mansfield. Signed Meden vale. (do NOT follow signs for Welbeck Colliery.) Turn off at Warsop Church.
HONOURS: Notts Alliance Div 2 93-94 (Intermediate Cup 93-94), Chesterfield & Dist. Lg 92-93
Colours: All black/white **Change colours:** Grey/grey/red **Manager:** Neil Gibbons

YORKSHIRE MAIN

Secretary: Dennis Tymon, 22 Pamela Drive, Warmsworth, Doncaster DN4 9RP Tel: 01302 852455
Ground: Yorkshire Main Welfare, Edlington Lane, Edlington, Doncaster Tel: 01709 864075
Directions: A1M junc 36. Proceed on A630 towards Rotherham. At 1st lights turn on to B6376. Ground on left after Fire Station.
Colours: Yellow/green/yellow **Change Colours:** Red/black/red **Manager:** Derek Wynne

NOTTS FOOTBALL ALLIANCE

Founded 1894

Chairman: Alan Wright

10 Faraday Road, Mansfield NG18 4ES Tel: 01623 624379

Treasurer: Godfrey Stafford

7 The Rushes, Gotham, Nottingham NG11 0HY Tel: 01509 820737

FINAL LEAGUE TABLES 2002-03

SENIOR DIVISION		P	W	D	L	F	A	Pts
1	Radcliffe Olympic	30	23	4	3	87	28	73
2	Boots Athletic	30	19	5	6	73	41	62
3	Southwell City	30	18	3	9	87	51	57
4	Cotgrave Colliery W.	30	14	5	11	77	68	47
5	Rainworth Miners W.	30	13	6	11	61	50	45
6	Linby Colliery Welf.	30	14	2	14	69	62	44
7	Newark Flowserve	30	12	7	11	47	52	43
8	Clifton	30	12	6	12	56	57	42
9	Wollaton	30	12	5	13	70	56	41
10	Keyworth United	30	9	11	10	66	67	38
11	Kimberley Miners W.	30	9	7	14	55	79	34
12	Attenborough	30	10	4	16	34	61	34
13	Kingswell	30	9	4	17	44	81	31
14	Awsworth Villa	30	7	8	15	49	66	29
15	Ruddington United	30	8	5	17	55	81	29
16	Notts Police	30	7	6	17	46	76	27

DIVISION ONE		P	W	D	L	F	A	Pts
1	AC Bulwell	28	22	2	4	83	33	68
2	Bestwood Miners W.	28	18	4	6	66	28	58
3	ASC Dayncourt	28	17	4	7	74	40	55
4	Bilborough	28	16	4	8	67	53	52
5	Magdala Amateurs	28	15	3	10	48	48	48
6	Newark Flowserve Res.	28	14	4	10	58	48	46
7	Calverton Miners W.	28	11	7	10	46	47	40
8	Boots Athletic Res.	28	10	5	13	52	54	35
9	Southbank	28	8	9	11	45	41	33
10	Southwell City Res.	28	8	8	12	58	64	32
11	Bilsthorpe	28	7	8	13	42	63	29
12	Chaffoteaux	28	7	7	14	41	63	28
13	Wollaton Res.	28	7	6	15	35	54	27
14	Basford United	28	5	5	18	39	75	20
15	Matrixgrade	28	5	4	19	30	73	19

Note – Stapleford Borough withdrew during the course of the season.

DIVISION TWO		P	W	D	L	F	A	Pts
1	Santos	30	23	3	4	94	31	72
2	Bestwood Miners Welfare Res.	30	21	3	6	80	34	66
3	Keyworth United Res.	30	19	4	7	82	42	61
4	BTSC	30	18	6	6	79	46	60
5	Radcliffe Olympic Res.	30	17	6	7	77	47	57
6	Chaffoteaux Res.	30	16	5	9	64	38	53
7	East Leake Athletic	30	14	6	10	70	63	48
8	Bottesford St Mary's	30	14	5	11	84	68	47
9	Burton Joyce	30	13	6	11	86	71	45
10	Kimberley Miners Welfare Res.	30	12	2	16	56	60	38
11	Kirton Brickworks	30	11	3	16	48	59	36
12	Durham Ox	30	9	0	21	53	73	27
13	Ruddington United Res.	30	8	3	19	44	75	27
14	Sandhurst	30	7	3	20	33	78	24
15	Newark Town	30	6	3	21	54	92	21
16	Pinxton North End	30	3	0	27	27	154	9

SENIOR DIVISION RESULTS CHART 2002-03

		1	2	3	4	5	6	7	8	9	10	11	12	13	14	15	16
1	Attenborough		0-4	1-1	0-0	0-1	1-2	0-0	2-1	3-1	1-0	1-2	0-3	0-2	1-0	2-9	2-5
2	Awsworth Villa	2-3		0-4	2-2	3-3	1-1	2-2	7-1	0-4	2-2	1-3	2-2	3-2	1-3	0-0	1-0
3	Boots Athletic	5-0	3-0		5-1	5-2	2-0	4-1	0-3	2-1	1-1	1-2	0-1	3-1	6-3	0-5	1-0
4	Clifton	3-0	2-1	3-1		2-1	4-2	3-1	5-0	2-0	3-2	3-2	2-2	1-0	1-2	1-4	1-1
5	Cotgrove Colliery Welfare	2-0	1-3	2-2	3-2		1-2	3-3	3-0	1-2	4-3	0-0	0-4	0-4	5-3	5-1	3-2
6	Keyworth United	1-0	1-4	1-2	2-2	2-7		1-1	3-4	6-3	1-2	6-3	1-4	2-2	1-1	2-2	2-1
7	Kimberley Miners Welfare	0-3	1-3	2-2	4-3	1-5	2-7		1-3	6-2	4-0	2-2	1-5	0-1	3-2	1-7	2-1
8	Kingswell	0-4	2-1	1-2	3-1	5-3	1-1	1-3		1-2	1-4	4-3	0-3	1-6	1-1	1-4	1-1
9	Linby Colliery Welfare	5-1	5-0	2-4	4-3	3-1	0-4	4-1	0-2		1-2	4-0	0-0	3-2	2-3	2-3	0-2
10	Newark Flowserve	2-2	1-0	0-3	2-0	0-6	1-1	0-1	3-0	1-3		3-1	1-1	0-3	3-2	2-0	2-1
11	Notts Police	0-1	2-0	1-4	2-2	0-1	2-2	2-2	1-1	3-5	3-4		1-4	2-3	1-0	1-2	0-4
12	Radcliffe Olympic	4-0	2-0	4-1	4-0	6-2	4-2	1-0	4-1	2-4	1-0	3-0		5-1	5-2	2-3	2-3
13	Rainworth Miners Welfare	1-2	4-3	1-3	0-2	1-1	2-2	1-2	3-0	1-1	3-3	2-0	0-1		0-1	3-1	1-0
14	Ruddington United	3-2	1-1	1-4	3-2	2-5	2-2	3-6	1-2	0-5	0-1	2-4	1-2	3-5		4-3	1-4
15	Southwell City	1-0	4-1	0-1	2-0	4-2	1-2	3-2	4-2	3-0	1-0	8-0	0-2	3-4	1-1		5-2
16	Wollaton	1-2	5-1	1-1	2-0	3-4	5-4	5-0	5-1	3-1	2-2	1-3	0-4	2-2	2-4	6-3	

SENIOR CUP

FIRST ROUND

AC Bulwell	v	Boots Athletic	0-6	Attenborough	v	Awsworth Villa	0-1
Bilborough	v	Matrixgrade	6-2	Calverton MW	v	Bilsthorpe	3-1
Chaffoteaux	v	Radcliffe Olympic	1-5	Cotgrave CW	v	Ruddington United	1-2
Keyworth Utd	v	Stapleford Borough	6-2	Kingswell	v	Bestwood MW	3-1 (aet)
Magdala Amateurs	v	Wollaton	0-3	Newark Flowserve	v	Basford United	6-1
Southbank	v	Kimberley MW	3-1	Southwell City	v	ASC Dayncourt	3-4

SECOND ROUND

Awsworth Villa	v	Keyworth United	1-2	Bilborough	v	ASC Dayncourt	1-3
Boots Athletic	v	Wollaton	0-2	Calverton MW	v	Rainworth MW	0-3
Clifton	v	Kingswell	0-0 (aet)	Replay - Kingswell	v	Clifton	2-0
Notts Police	v	Ruddington United	1-3	Radcliffe Olym.	v	Newark Flowserve	5-1
Southbank	v	Linby Colliery W.	1-2				

QUARTER-FINALS

Keyworth United	v	Kingswell	3-0	Radcliffe Olympic	v	ASC Dayncourt	5-2
Rainworth MW	v	Linby CW	2-1	Wollaton	v	Ruddington United	1-2

SEMI-FINALS

Keyworth United	v	Ruddington United	6-0	at Cotgrave
Radcliffe Olympic	v	Rainworth Miners Welfare	5-2 (aet)	at Southwell

FINAL

Keyworth	v	Radcliffe Olympic	1-1 (aet)	29th April at Southwell
REPLAY				
Radcliffe Olympic	v	Keyworth Utd	4-0	8th May at Southwell

INTERMEDIATE CUP

QUARTER-FINALS

Bestwood MW Res.	v	Durham Ox	7-1	Clifton Res.	v	Newark Flow. Res.	2-2 (aet)
Replay - Newark F. Res.	v	Clifton Res.	3-1	Santos	v	Wollaton Res.	4-0
Southwell Res.	v	Keyworth Utd Res.	2-4				

SEMI-FINALS

Bestwood MW Res.	v	Keyworth Utd Res.	3-3 (aet)	at Bilborough
Bestwood MW Res.	v	Keyworth Utd Res.	1-4	at Southwell
Santos	v	Newark Flowserve Res.	0-1	at Rainworth

FINAL

Newark F. Res.	v	Keyworth Res.	1-2	6th May at Southwell City

SENIOR DIVISION

ATTENBOROUGH

Secretary: Terry Allen, 5 Coningsby Road, Woodthorpe, Nottingham NG54LG Tel: 0115 920 0698
Ground & Directions: The Village Green, The Strand, Attenborough, Beeston, Nottingham. Midway between Beeston & Long Eaton on A6005 - adjacent to Nature Reserve (via Attenborough Lane).
Colours: All Royal Blue
Change colours: White/black/black.

AWSWORTH VILLA

Secretary: Paul Wilkinson
15 Barlow Drive North, Awsworth, Nottingham NG16 2RQ.
Tel: 0115 930 4905 (H) 0115 932 8721 (B)
Ground: Shilo Park, off Attewell Road, Awsworth, Nottm.
Colours: Red & white/red/red.

BESTWOOD MINERS WELFARE

Secretary: Alan Fisher,5 Skipton Close, Ilkeston, Derbyshire DE7 9HX (0115 932 7717)
Ground: Bestwood Workshops, Park Rd, Bestwood
Colours: Red/navy blue/navy blue.

BILBOROUGH

Secretary: Duncan Costin, 12 Calstock Road, Woodthorpe, Nottingham NG5 4FH Tel: 0115 919 9371 (H)
Ground: Birchover Park, Brindley Road, Bilborough, Notts.

BOOTS ATHLETIC

Secretary: Ian Whitehead, 21 Rosthwaite Close, West Bridgford, Nottingham NG26RA Tel: 0115 981 2830 (H) 0115 968 7535 (B)
Ground: Lady Bay, West Bridgford, Nottingham Tel: 0115 981 2392
Colours: Blue & white stripes, bue,blue.
Honours: Notts Alliance Div 1 91-92 (Lg Cup 91-92), Notts Snr Cup R-up 93-94, Notts Inter R-up 91-92.

CLIFTON

Secretary: Mrs Pat Brodie, 21 Cerne Close, Clifton, Nottingham. Tel: 0115 9215113
Ground: Green Lane, Clifton Est., Nottm Tel: 0115 984 4903
Colours: All white(Blue trim

COTGRAVE COLLIERY WELFARE

Secretary: Kevin Whitehead, 51 Crosshill, Cotgrave, Nottinham. NG12 3NB Tel: 0115 989 4043
Ground: Woodview, Cotgrave, Nottingham
Colours: Red/blue/blue

KEYWORTH UNITED

Secretary: Stuart Douglas, 29 Ashley Crescent, Keyworth, Nottm. NG12 5GF Tel: 0115 937 5358
Ground: Platt Lane, Keyworth Tel: 0115 937 5998
Colours: Green/black/green

KIMBERLEY MINERS WELFARE

Secretary: Stephen Hobster, 35 Truman Street, Kimberley, Nottingham NG16 2HA
Tel Nos: 0115 938 4067 (H) 07866 77376 (M)
Ground: Digby Street, Kimberley, Nottingham Tel: 0115 938 2124
Colours: Black & red/black/black & red

KINGSWELL

Secretary: Phil Smith
1 Mowbray Rise, Arnold, Nottm NG5 5DW
Tel: 0115 956 9585 (H) 07977 633051 (M)
Ground: Williams Lee Memorial Ground
Park Road, Calverton, Nottingham Tel: 0115 965 3097
Colours: Red & White (home) All blue (away)

LINBY COLLIERY WELFARE

Secretary: J.Riley, 70 Bolingey Way, Hucknall, Notts.NG15 6TQ
Tel: 0115 953 3025
Ground: Church Lane, Linby, Nottingham (07971 023622)
Colours: Red, black& white/red & black shorts

MAGDALA AMATEURS

Secretary: Alan Gilmour, 9 Adbolton Grove, West Bridgford, Nottingham NG2 5AR Tel: 0115 982 1071
Ground: Civil Service Sports Ground, Wilford Lane, W Bridgford.
Colours: Amber/Black/Tangerine

NEWARK FLOWERSERVE

Secretary: Kevin Presland, Appleby Lodge, Barnby Road, Newark, Nottingham NG24 2NE Tel: 01636 704606, 07771 507065
Ground: Lowfield Works, off hawton Lane, Balderton, Newark, Nottingham. Tel: 01636 702672
Colours: Orange/blue/orange

NOTTINGHAMSHIRE POLICE

Secretary: John Beeston, 17 Alandene Ave, Watnall, Nottingham NG16 1HH Tel: 0115 938 2110
Ground: Calverton Recreation Centre, Hollingwood Lane, Calverton, Nottingham Tel: 0115 965 4390
Honours: Notts Snr R-up 91-92, Notts All. Div 1 & Lge Snr Cup R-up 85-86, PAAN Nat. K-O Comp 63-64.
Club Colours: All Red

RUDDINGTON UNITED

Secretary: John Fisk, 3 Savages Rd., Ruddington, Nottm NG11 6EW
Tel: 0115 9842552
Ground & Directions: The Elms Park Ground, Loughborough Road, Ruddington (0115 984 4976) On A60 Nottm to Loughborough, 5 miles out of Nottingham.
Colours: Yellow & blue/blue/blue
Honours: Notts Comb. Lg 79-80, Lg Cup 70-71 76-77 80-81

WOLLATON

Secretary: Paul King, 18 Lancaster Way, Strelley, Nottingham NG8 6PH
Ground: Wollaton Sports Association, Wollaton Village, Nottm. Tel: 0115 9133 134
Colours: All Sky Blue
Honours: Notts All. Div 1 R-up 92-93, Div 2 91-92, I'mediate Cup R-up 91-92.

DIVISION ONE CLUBS

A.C. BULWELL
Secretary: Neil Fitch, 4 Hoefield Crescent, Bulwell, Nottingham NG6 8AY Tel: 0115 849 8652 (H) 07903 153105 (M)
Ground: River Leen School, Squires Avenue, Bulwell. Tel: 0115 927 8425

ARNOLD SOUTHBANK
Secretary: Gerry Bishop, 4 Foxearth Ave., Clifton, Nottm. NG11 8JQ Tel: 0115 984 2363
Ground: Carlton Hill, Nottingham
Colours: Red & White Stripes/White/Red

BASFORD UNITED
Secretary: Maria Smith, 17 Snenfield Gardens, Rise Park, Nottingham NG5 5BH (0115 955 8045)
Ground: Greenwich Ave., Bagnall Rd, Basford, Nottm (0115 942 3918).
Directions: M1, J26 follow signs A610 Nottingham then B6004 Arnold into Mill St.
Colours: Yellow/black/yellow

BOTTESFORD ST. MARYS
Secretary: Miss Micci Angeloni, 129 Stamford St., Grantham, Lincs. NG31 7BF Tel: 01476 593581
Ground: Village hall Playing Fields, Belvoir Rd., Bottesford
Colours: Dark red & black stripes/black/black

BURTON JOYCE
Ground: Station Road, Burton Joyce, Notts.

CALVERTON M.W.
Secretary: John Daniel, 13 Renals Ways, Calverton, Nottingham NG14 6PH 0115 965 4447 (H) 0771 5306032 (M)
Ground: Calverton Recreation Centre, Hollingwood Lane, Calverton, Nottingham Tel: 0115 965 4390
Colours: Sky Blue & navy/navy

DALE HOTEL
Ground: Standhill Road, Carlton, Nottingham
Previous name: BTSC

EAST LEAKE ATHLETIC
Secretary: Andrew Fletcher, 62 Suthers Road, Kegworth, Derby DE74 2DF Tel: 01509 674752
Ground: Costock Road, East Leake, Loughborough.

NUTTALL CHAFFOTEAUX
Secretary: Mark Nicholls, 31 Telford Drive, Newthorpe, Nottm. NG16 3NN 01773 534169 (H) 0115 942 2400(B)
Ground: Basil Russell Playing Fields, Maple Drive, Nuthall, Nottingham 0115 938 4765
Colours: Red & black/red&black/black

RETFORD TOWN
Ground: Badworth Road, Retford, Notts. Tel: 01777 703163
Previous League: Lincolnshire Lge.

SANTOS
Ground: William Lee Memorial Ground, Park Road, Calverton, Notts. Tel: 0115 965 3097

WOLLATON RESERVES

WOODHOUSE
Secretary: Tony Dove, 1 Greenwood Close, Sutton-in-Ashfield, Nottm. Tel: 01623 554466
Ground: Debdale Lane, mansfield Woodhouse, Nottm. Tel: 01623 631747
Colours: Red & blue stripes/blue/blue & red

plus

BESTWOOD M.W. RESERVES

BOOTS ATHLETIC RESERVES

KEYWORTH UNITED RESERVES

NEWARK FLOWSERVE RESERVES

DIVISION TWO

BILSTHORPE WELFARE
Secretary: Mick Gresswell, 40 Scarborough Road, Bilsthorpe, Nottingham. (01623 8700320
Ground: Bilsthorpe CW, Eakring Road, Bilsthorpe, Notts
Colours: All royal blue

KIRKTON BRICKWORKS
Secretary: Stuart Douglas, 29 Ashley Crescent, Keyworth, Nottingham NG12 5GF Tel: 0115 937 5358
Ground: Kirkton Brickworks, Nr. New Ollerton, Nottingham Tel: 01623 860481

MATRIXGRADE
Secretary: Stephen Farmery
Tel: 0115 910 6694 (H) 07979 238209 (M)
Ground: Carrington Sports Ground, Mansfield Rd., Nottm.
Colours: Yellow & black/black/black

NEWARK TOWN
Secretary: David Wildes, Forest Cottage, Brough, Newark, Nottingham NG23 7QZ Tel: 01636 676038
Ground: Devon Park

NOTTINGHAMSHIRE
Ground: Bluecote School, Aspley Lane, Nottingham, Notts.
Previous League: Midland Amateur Lge.

SANDHURST
Secretary: Robert Crawford, 4 The Brambles, Walesby, Newark, Nottingham NG22 9PH Tel: 01623 862985
Ground: Walesby Sports & Social Club, Retford Road, Walesby.

plus
ARNOLD SOUTHBANK RESERVES
ATTENBOROUGH RESERVES
AWSWORTH VILLA RESERVES
BILBOROUGH RESERVES
CALVERTON MW RESERVES
CLIFTON RESERVES
COTGRAVE CW RESERVES
DURHAM OX
KIMBERLEY M.W. RESERVES
LINBY CW RESERVES
MAGDALA AMATEURS RESERVES
NOTTS. POLICE RESERVES
NUTTALL CHAFFOTEAUX RESERVES
RUDDINGTON UTD RESERVES

Radcliffe Olympic celebrate after picking up the Notts Alliance Championship trophy.

Photo: Gordon Whittingham.

Ruddington United F.C. Photo: Gordon Whittington

Burton Joyce F.C. Back Row (L-R): Gary Holland (Asst. Manager), John Stevenson, IanLockwood, Rick Newton, Lawrie Jenkins, Paul Wilstead, Steve Eley, Danny Cane, Adrian Spencer, Pat Eley (Manager). Front Row: Michael Matthews, Paul MacMillan, Darren Petch, Ben Snowden, Nev Gill, Phil Riley, Adam Smith. Photo: Gordon Whittingham.

Durham OX F.C. Photo: Gordon Whittingham.

NORTHERN LEAGUE

Founded 1889

President: George Courtney MBE **Chairman:** Mike Amos
Hon. Secretary & Treasurer: A Golightly, 85 Park Road North, Chester-le-Street, Co Durham DH3 3SA
Tel: 0191 388 2056 Fax: 0191 3891 1385 E-mail: tonygol@northernlge.fsnet.co.uk

FINAL LEAGUE TABLES 2002-03

DIVISION ONE		P	W	D	L	F	A	Pts
1	Brandon United	40	26	10	4	77	28	88
2	Bedlington Terries	40	24	9	7	96	42	81
3	Billington Town (-3)	40	23	5	12	100	56	71
4	Billingham Synthonia	40	21	8	11	73	47	71
5	Durham City	40	21	5	14	77	54	68
6	Shildon	40	19	7	14	83	74	64
7	Guisborough Town	40	19	6	15	58	43	63
8	Dunston Federation	40	17	11	12	52	43	62
9	Jarrow Roofing BCA	40	17	7	16	64	67	58
10	Whitley Bay (-3)	40	17	8	15	68	62	56
11	Morpeth Town	40	15	11	14	67	67	56
12	Washington	40	16	8	16	52	60	56
13	West Auckland Town (-3)	40	16	9	15	87	74	54
14	Chester Le Street	40	14	11	15	60	63	53
15	Tow Law Town	40	14	8	18	58	63	50
16	Marske United	40	13	10	17	64	74	49
17	Esh Winning (-3)	40	15	7	18	54	84	49
18	Peterlee Newtown	40	8	9	23	44	89	33
19	Prudhoe Town	40	7	10	23	52	89	31
20	Consett	40	7	8	25	44	83	29
21	Newcastle Blue Star	40	3	9	28	37	105	18

DIVISION TWO		P	W	D	L	F	A	Pts
1	Penrith	38	26	10	2	102	28	88
2	Horden CW	38	26	7	5	83	38	85
3	Thornaby	38	25	8	5	84	32	83
4	Seaham Red Star	38	26	4	8	91	45	82
5	Ashington	38	22	13	3	101	37	79
6	Washington Nissan	38	21	5	12	102	57	68
7	Easington Colliery	38	19	5	14	83	72	62
8	South Shields	38	16	11	11	86	70	59
9	Northallerton Town	38	17	5	16	72	58	56
10	Whickham	38	14	9	15	68	2	51
11	Kennek Ryhope CA	38	12	9	17	63	67	45
12	Hebburn Town	38	13	5	20	55	66	44
13	Evenwood Town	38	12	6	20	58	95	42
14	Murton	38	10	8	20	55	95	38
15	Alnwick Town (-3)	38	10	8	20	50	69	35
16	Crook Town (-6)	38	11	8	19	64	92	35
17	Shotton Comrades	38	8	5	25	46	103	29
18	Norton & Stockton Anc.	38	5	9	24	38	81	24
19	Willington	38	6	5	27	50	132	23
20	Eppleton CW (-15)	38	8	6	24	45	87	15

DIVISION ONE	1	2	3	4	5	6	7	8	9	10	11	12	13	14	15	16	17	18	19	20	21
1 Bedlington Ter.		0-2	4-5	0-1	2-2	1-1	4-1	3-2	3-0	6-0	0-1	5-1	6-0	3-0	3-1	1-1	2-2	3-1	2-1	2-2	2-1
2 Billingham Syn.	0-2		0-0	2-3	4-2	3-2	0-2	0-1	4-0	3-0	3-1	3-1	3-3	2-0	3-1	2-1	4-1	2-0	2-0	2-2	4-1
3 Billingham T.	2-3	0-3		0-1	1-4	5-1	1-2	2-0	0-0	2-0	5-1	6-1	1-0	1-1	2-1	2-0	5-1	6-2	1-2	1-2	4-2
4 Brandan United	1-1	0-1	1-2		1-1	2-0	0-1	1-0	4-0	1-0	2-1	3-2	1-1	3-0	5-0	3-0	1-1	2-0	3-0	5-0	3-0
5 Chester-le-Street	0-2	4-1	1-1	0-2		2-1	1-0	1-2	1-1	1-0	1-2	1-1	1-2	6-3	0-1	2-1	0-0	3-1	0-5	1-1	0-3
6 Consett	1-1	0-2	3-3	2-2	0-1		1-4	2-0	5-1	0-3	0-2	1-2	0-2	1-2	2-1	3-1	0-3	1-1	0-1	3-1	1-0
7 Dunston Fed.	3-2	2-2	1-0	0-0	0-1	1-1		2-1	1-0	0-1	4-2	0-1	2-1	4-2	0-1	3-1	0-1	2-1	0-0	1-2	1-2
8 Durham City	1-2	1-1	0-3	1-0	5-3	4-2	0-3		2-0	1-0	1-1	1-1	3-2	5-0	1-1	3-2	3-1	0-2	3-0	3-2	0-1
9 Esh Winning	0-1	3-0	0-7	0-3	4-2	1-0	1-1	2-4		0-0	2-6	2-1	0-4	2-1	4-1	2-0	2-0	0-1	2-1	4-1	2-1
10 Guisborough T.	0-1	1-1	1-2	2-4	2-1	3-1	1-2	2-4	6-0		3-0	4-0	2-0	2-1	3-0	3-1	4-1	1-0	1-1	2-0	1-0
11 Jarrow Roofing	1-6	3-2	1-0	1-1	1-2	2-0	0-0	0-0	1-2	1-0		1-0	3-0	4-1	3-2	1-1	0-1	2-2	4-1	2-4	1-4
12 Marske United	0-4	2-0	1-2	3-4	1-1	2-0	0-0	2-0	1-3	3-0	3-1		2-4	3-1	5-1	1-1	2-3	3-0	3-1	0-1	0-0
13 Morpeth Town	1-1	1-0	2-2	1-2	3-1	6-0	1-0	3-1	2-2	0-3	3-2	2-2		1-1	4-1	1-3	1-3	2-2	1-1	1-0	3-0
14 Newcastle B.S.	1-2	0-1	0-8	0-0	0-3	2-1	0-0	0-5	2-2	1-1	0-2	2-3	1-1		0-2	1-3	2-4	2-5	1-0	1-4	1-2
15 Peterlee Newtown	0-4	1-1	1-4	1-2	2-2	1-0	2-0	0-3	2-2	0-1	1-2	1-5	0-0	3-1		1-1	0-2	1-2	0-0	0-3	3-1
16 Prudhoe Town	0-3	2-0	0-3	2-3	0-0	3-1	2-3	2-1	2-2	2-1	2-3	1-1	1-3	1-1	6-4		1-3	2-2	0-0	1-5	0-4
17 Shildon	0-3	0-4	2-4	0-0	1-3	2-0	0-1	1-5	2-1	0-2	3-1	1-1	4-1	4-0	6-0	2-1		3-1	7-3	5-2	3-3
18 Tow Law Town	2-1	1-0	0-3	1-1	1-3	2-2	1-1	0-2	4-0	2-0	1-0	2-1	0-2	4-0	0-1	4-1	2-3		0-1	1-2	0-1
19 Washington	1-3	0-2	0-2	1-2	2-2	1-3	3-1	2-1	1-0	0-0	1-0	5-0	3-1	3-2	2-1	1-0	2-1	0-0		2-5	1-0
20 West Auckland	1-1	2-3	5-0	0-2	2-0	2-2	2-2	1-2	1-2	0-2	2-2	4-1	5-1	2-2	1-1	7-2	3-2	2-4	2-3		4-1
21 Whitley Bay	2-1	1-1	3-2	0-2	1-0	5-0	1-1	1-5	5-0	0-0	1-2	2-2	2-0	2-1	3-3	3-1	4-4	1-3	2-0	2-0	

DIVISION TWO	1	2	3	4	5	6	7	8	9	10	11	12	13	14	15	16	17	18	19	20
1 Alnwick Town		0-5	5-2	3-1	3-3	2-2	0-1	3-4	0-2	0-1	3-2	0-1	0-0	0-2	1-1	2-3	1-0	3-2	1-1	2-4
2 Ashington	0-0		4-0	1-3	6-0	3-1	3-1	2-3	1-1	0-0	1-0	2-1	1-1	1-1	4-0	3-1	2-2	5-1	1-1	3-2
3 Crook Town	3-2	1-1		1-3	0-0	3-1	1-0	1-6	3-0	2-4	0-2	1-1	1-4	2-1	4-3	2-3	2-2	0-2	0-4	4-0
4 Easington Coll.	3-1	1-2	4-3		1-3	1-2	1-1	1-3	3-1	2-1	3-7	4-1	1-1	2-1	4-1	3-1	1-6	4-0	0-0	2-2
5 Eppleton Coll.W.	2-0	0-2	1-2	1-5		1-0	0-2	0-2	0-2	3-1	3-1	1-2	3-6	0-1	0-1	1-1	0-3	0-4	1-3	2-1
6 Evenwood Town	1-0	1-4	2-2	3-3	4-2		3-1	2-2	2-2	2-1	0-3	2-2	0-3	1-4	1-4	1-3	1-4	0-4	2-1	3-0
7 Hebburn Town	2-1	2-3	0-2	1-2	0-3	1-2		0-1	4-3	1-1	1-2	3-1	1-2	1-1	3-2	2-2	3-2	2-0	2-2	2-1
8 Horden Coll.W.	1-1	1-1	2-1	2-0	3-2	4-0	2-0		1-1	2-0	3-0	2-1	0-0	0-2	3-0	3-1	1-0	2-2	2-1	5-2
9 Kennek Ryhope	1-4	0-3	5-1	1-4	2-2	3-4	2-0	1-1		3-0	2-1	1-1	0-1	3-4	0-0	1-0	1-1	1-4	2-0	5-0
10 Murton	1-2	1-1	3-2	3-0	5-1	3-0	0-2	0-3	3-1		0-0	3-2	1-7	1-8	2-0	0-0	1-2	3-2	4-5	2-2
11 Northallerton T.	3-0	1-2	5-2	1-3	3-1	5-2	3-1	2-3	3-4	1-0		0-0	2-3	0-1	1-2	2-1	0-4	1-2	1-1	4-1
12 Norton & Stock.	0-1	0-4	1-4	1-2	1-1	0-1	4-3	0-2	0-5	4-2	1-2		2-2	1-4	1-2	2-2	0-4	0-3	1-1	1-3
13 Penrith	0-0	2-2	3-0	2-0	3-1	6-1	3-0	1-0	1-0	9-0	0-0	2-0		1-0	4-1	2-2	0-0	2-0	2-1	8-0
14 Seaham R. S.	5-0	1-1	2-1	2-0	3-1	2-1	2-1	2-1	1-0	3-2	1-3	0-0	3-1		4-0	3-2	1-2	1-2	2-1	4-1
15 Shotton Com.	1-2	0-7	4-4	1-6	3-2	1-5	0-3	0-1	2-1	2-2	1-4	1-0	1-4	1-3		1-3	0-2	3-3	1-2	2-4
16 South Shields	3-1	0-4	3-3	3-0	2-2	4-0	3-2	4-2	1-1	7-1	2-3	2-0	2-6	3-1	3-1		1-2	3-1	3-3	5-2
17 Thornaby	2-1	2-1	5-1	1-3	1-0	5-3	4-1	0-1	1-0	3-0	0-0	4-0	1-0	3-0	1-0	2-0		2-2	4-1	4-1
18 Washington N.	2-0	1-3	3-1	6-2	4-0	3-0	1-0	1-3	5-0	5-1	3-2	2-0	0-2	0-2	5-0	3-3	0-0		5-2	13-0
19 Whickham	1-0	3-3	1-2	0-4	4-0	2-0	1-2	2-1	4-2	5-1	1-0	2-1	0-3	3-7	3-0	0-2	2-2	0-3		0-3
20 Willington	1-5	1-9	0-0	2-1	0-2	1-2	0-3	1-5	1-3	1-1	0-2	1-4	1-5	2-6	1-3	2-2	0-1	4-3	2-4	

LEADING GOALSCORERS 2002-03

Player	Club	Goals
Adam Johnston	Washington Nissan	36
Paul Chow	Jarrow Roofing BCA	35
John Milner	Bedlington Terriers	35
Alan Hogg	Ashington	28
Roy Allen	Bedlington Terriers	26
Carl Chillingsworth	Billingham Town	25
Andrew Wright	Penrith	24
James Swordy	Alnwick Town	23
Jamie Clarke	Thornaby	23
Lee Ellison	Shildon	21
David Taylor	Easington Colliery	21
Paul Taylor	Seaham Red Star	21
David Onions	Northallerton 1994	20
Barry Irving	Penrith	20

Billingham Synthonia F.C. Back Row (L-R): Chris Rooney (coach), Michael Cater, Tommy Marron, John Mohan, david O'Gorman, Paul wilson, James Bridge, Dean McGee, Tommy Cuchley (physio), Lenny Gunn (coach).
Front Row: Stuart Coleby (manager), Chris Fawcett, Nathan Haslam, Liam Smith, Andy Harbron, David Wells, Andrew Ripley.

Chester-Le-Street F.C. Back Row (L-R): Gary Shields, Mark Errington, Danny O'Brien, John Heggarty, Ian Aitken, Gary Andison, Jamie Elrington, Phil Sowerby, Andy Blower.
Front Row: Steve Cuggy, David Turner, Colin Wake, Martin Bowes, David Lowther.

ALBANY LEAGUE CUP 2002-03

FIRST ROUND

Billingham Synthonia	v	West Auckland Town	3-0	Billingham Town	v	Easington Coll.	6-1
Eppleton CW	v	Evenwood Town	1-5	Murton	v	Northallerton Town	2-1
Newcastle BS	v	Guisborough Town	2-1	Prudhoe Town	v	Chester-le-Street	4-1
Washington	v	Kennek Ryhope CA	3-2	Washington Nissan	v	Consett	1-5
Willington	v	Horden CW	0-4				

SECOND ROUND

Billingham Synthonia	v	Norton & Stockton An	5-1	Billingham Town	v	Whitley Bay	1-2
Brandon United	v	Crook Town	5-1	Dunston Federation	v	Esh Winning	3-2
Durham City	v	Marske United	1-2 (aet)	Evenwood Town	v	Ashington	1-2 (aet)
Hebburn Town	v	Horden CW	1-2	Morpeth Town	v	Shotton Comrades	6-1
Murton	v	Newcastle B. S.	2-3 (aet)	Penrith	v	Jarrow Roofing BCA	3-1
Peterlee Newtown	v	Prudhoe Town	2-1	Seaham Red Star	v	Alnwick Town	2-1
Shildon	v	Thornaby	3-0	Tow Law Town	v	South Shields	2-0
Washington	v	Consett	0-1	Whickham	v	Bedlington Terriers	1-2

THIRD ROUND

Billingham Synthonia	v	Consett	2-0	Brandon United	v	Horden Colliery W.	4-0
Dunston Fed. B.	v	Bedlington Terriers	0-2	Marske United	v	Newcastle BS	1-0
Morpeth Town	v	Ashington	3-1	Peterlee Newtown	v	Seaham RS	1-3
Shildon	v	Whitley Bay	2-1	Tow Law Town	v	Penrith	1-0

QUARTER-FINALS

Billingham Synthonia	v	Bedlington Terriers	2-1	Marske United	v	Tow Law Town	1-2
Seaham Red Star	v	Brandon United	1-5	Shildon	v	Morpeth Town	1-0

SEMI-FINALS

Shildon	v	Tow Law Town	0-0 (aet) 3-1p	Brandon	v	Billingham Synthonia	1-2

FINAL

Shildon	v	Billingham Synthonia	3-2 (aet)	5th May at Darlington

CRAVEN CUP 2002-03

FIRST ROUND

Easington Colliery	v	Kennek Ryhope CA	0-3	Evenwood Town	v	Murton	4-0
South Shields	v	Northallerton Town	3-2 (aet)	Thornaby	v	Eppleton CW	1-1 (aet) 5-3p

SECOND ROUND

Alnwick Town	v	Norton & Stockton A.	3-2	Ashington	v	Whickham	5-0
Evenwood Town	v	Kennek Ryhope CA	3-1	Hebburn Town	v	Penrith	1-3
Horden Colliery W.	v	South Shields	1-4	Seaham Red Star	v	Shotton Comrades	5-1
Thornaby	v	Washington Nissan	6-1	Willington	v	Crook Town	4-1

QUARTER-FINALS

Alnwick	v	Seaham Red Star	1-2	Ashington	v	Penrith	1-0
Evenwood Town	v	Willington	1-0	South Shields	v	Thornaby	4-3 (aet)

SEMI-FINALS

Ashington	v	Seaham Red Star	3-1	Evenwood Town	v	South Shields	2-0

FINAL

Evenwood Town	v	Ashington	0-2	6th May at Horden CW

BEDLINGTON TERRIERS

Secretary: Shaun Campbell,106 Wright St., Blyth. Northumberland NE24 1HG
Tel: 01670 353823 (H) 07703 529869 (M)
Ground: Welfare Park, Park Rd., Bedlington, Northumberland. Tel: 01670 825485
Directions: Into Bedlington, turn left at `Northumberland Arms' on Front St., then 2nd Right, ground on right 100 yds . Club Website: www.btfc.fsnet.co.uk
Capacity: 3,000 Seats: 300 Cover:500 Floodlights: Yes
Clubhouse: Open every evening, 7-11pm Sat. & Sun lunch. Pool, darts etc Club Shop: Yes
Record Att: 2,400 v Colchester Utd **Record Seasons Scorer:** John Milner 63 , 98-99
HONOURS Northern League Div One 97-98 98-9 99-00 00-01 01-02 R-up: 85-86 9596 Div 2 94-95 (R-up 84-85), Northern Alliance 66-67 (R-up 67-68 69-70 71-72) Lg Cup 57-58 66-67 69-70 81-82, Lge Chall Cup 96-97 00-01,Northumberland Sen Cup 96-97. 97-98 01-02Cleator Cup 97-88, 98-99, 99-00

PREVIOUS **Leagues:** Northern Alliance **Names:** Bedlington Mechanics 49-53; Colliery Welfare 53-56; Mechanics 56- 61; Bedlington United 61-65; Bedlington Colliery 65-68; Bedlington Town 68-74.

BEST SEASON **FA Cup:** 2nd Rd v Scunthorpe(a) 0-1 **FA Vase:** Final 98-9 VTiverton T 0-1

RECORDS **Attendance:** 1,013 v Blyth Spartans, Northern Lg 85-86
Win: 11-0 v West Auckland, (H) Lge 96-97 **Scorer:** John Milner63

FACT FILE
Formed: 1949
Colours: Red & white/red&white/white
Change colours: Blue & whitw/blue&white/blue
Midweek Matches: Wednesday
Programme: 50 pages, £1.00

CLUB PERSONNEL

Chairman: David Perry
(0468 195350)
Vice Chairman: John Feary
Press Officer:Jeff King
Tel Nos: 01670 735824 or 07730285558
Managers: Keith Perry & Tony Lowrey
Coach: Melvyn Harmison
Physio: Dave Robertson

BILLINGHAM SYNTHONIA

Secretary: Graham Craggs, 10 Embleton Grove, Wynard,Stockton on TeesTS22 5SY
Tel No: 01740 645367
Ground: The Stadium, Central Avenue, Billingham, Cleveland (Press Box 01642 532348)
Directions: Turn off A19 onto A1027 signposted Billingham, Norton (this applies from either north or south), continue straight on along Central Avenue, ground on left opposite office block. 1 mile from Billingham (BR)
Capacity: 1,970 Seats: 370 Cover: 370 Floodlights: Yes
Clubhouse: Onthe ground. Normal club hours **Club Shop:**Yes(Lapel Badges)
HONOURS Northern Lg 56-57 88-89 89-90 95-96, R-up 49-50 50-51 51-52, Lg Cup 51-52 87-88 89-90, Div 2 86-87, Teeside Lg 36-37 (Lg Cup 34-35 38-39), Durham Chall. Cup 88-89 90-91, North Riding Snr Cup 66-67 71-72, North Riding Amat. Cup 38-39 56-57 62-63 63-64.

PREVIOUS **League:** Teeside (1923-War) **Name:** Billingham Synthonia Recreation

BEST SEASON **FA Amateur Cup** 4th Rd 48-49 **FA Vase:** 3rd Rd 01-02
FA Trophy: Q-F replay 93-94, 1-2 v Woking after 1-1 (A)
FA Cup:1st Rd 48-49 51-52 56-57 57-58 87-88 89-90

RECORDS **Attendance:** 4,200 v Bishop Auck. 6/9/58
Scorer: Tony Hetherington **Appearances:** Andy Harbron

FACT FILE

Founded: 1923
Nickname: Synners
Sponsors: Darlington Building Society
Colours: Green & White quarters/white/white
Change colours: Blue & White
Midweek Matches: Tuesdays
Programme: 20 pages (+ads),50p
Editor: David Lealman (01642 559540)

CLUB PERSONNEL

Chairman: Stuart Coleby
President: Frank Cook
Press Officer: Secretary
Manager: Stuart Coleby
Physio: Tommy Cushley
Coach: Lenny Gunn

2002-03
Leading Goalscorer:Tony Wood 23
Captain & P.o.Y.::Tommy Marron

BILLINGHAM TOWN

Secretary: Glenn Youngman,13 Blackthorne Grove, fairfield, Stockton, Cleveland TS19 7DG
Tel/Fax: 01642 655516 and Tel: 01642 862058

Ground: Bedford Terrace, Billingham, Cleveland. Tel: 01642 560043

Directions: Leave A19 on A1027 (signed Billingham). Turn left at 3rd r/bout,over bridge 1st left, 1st left again to grd
Capacity: 3,000 Seats: 176 Cover: 600 Floodlights: Yes
Clubhouse: Open matchdays. Hot & cold food **Club Shop:** No

HONOURS Durham Cup 76-77 77-78, R-up: 01-02Teesside Lg 77-78 81-82, Nth Riding Snr Cup R-up 76-77 81-82, Stockton & Dist. Lg(3)
PREVIOUS **Leagues :** Stockton & Dist. 68-74; Teesside 74-82.
Name: Billingham Social Club (pre-1982) **Ground:** Mill Lane (pre-1974)
BEST SEASON **FA Cup:** 1st Rd Proper 55-56
FA Vase: 5th Rd Proper
RECORDS **Attendance:** 1,500 v Manchester City, FA Youth Cup 1985
Scorer: Paul Rowntree 396 (1990-2001)
Appearances: Paul Rowntree 505 (including 2000-01)
Players progressing: Gary Pallister (Middlesbrough), Gerry Forrest (Southampton), Dave Robinson (Halifax), Tony Barratt (Hartlepool), Mark Hine (Grimsby), Tony Hall(Middlesbrough), Graham Hall (Arsenal).

FACT FILE
Founded: 1967 Nickname: The Social
Colours: All Blue
Change colours: Yellow/green/green
Midweek Matches: Tuesday
Programme: 28 pages, 50p
Editor:Peter Martin

CLUB PERSONNEL
Chairman: Tommy Donnelly
Hon. President: F Cook M.P.
President: G A Maxwell
Press Officer: Tom Donnelly
(01642 555332(H) 01642 370101(W)
Fax : 01642 651033
Manager: Alan Robinson
Asst Manager: Michael Watson
Coaches: Lee Tucker

2002-03
Leading Goalscorer: Carl Shillingworth
Captain: David Gallagher
Player of the Year: Rob Hutchinson

BRANDON UNITED

Secretary: Brian Richardson, Flat 2, 30 Commercial St, Brandon, Durham DH7 8PL
Tel: 0191 378 1373

Ground: Welfare Ground, rear of Commercial St., Brandon, Durham Tel: 0191 378 2957

Directions: A690 - 3 miles west of Durham City. Buses 49 & 49A from Durham

Capacity: 3,000 Seats: 200 Cover: 300 Floodlights: Yes **Club Shop:** No
Clubhouse: Open every day, lunch & evening. Pool Entertainment at weekends

HONOURS Northern Lg Div 1 Champions 2002-03 Div 2 84-85 99-00 Northern All.(2) 77-79, Lg Cup 77-78 79-80 Sunderland Shipowners Cup 81-82, Durham Co. Sunday Cup 73-74 75-76 76-77,Durham & Dist Sunday Lg(4) 73-77 (Div 2 69-70, Div 3 68-69), Staffieri Cup 75-76 FA Sunday Cup 75-76,

PREVIOUS **Leagues:** Durham & Dist. Sunday 68-77; Northern All. 77-80; Northern Amtr 80-81; Wearside 81-83.

BEST SEASON **FA Cup:** 1st Rd replay 88-89 (lost to Doncaster). Also 1st Rd 79-80
FA Vase: QF 82-83 83-84 **FA Trophy:** 3rd Qual. Rd 87-88 89-90

RECORD **Gate:** 2,500, FA Sunday Cup SF **Record Goalscorer:** Tommy Holden
Most Appearances: Derek Charlton 1977-86

Players progressing: Bryan Liddle (Hartlepool 1984) Dean Gibb (Hartlepool 1986), Paul Dalton (Manchester Utd 1988), Neil Richardson (Rotherham).

FACT FILE
Founded: 1968
Nickname: United
Sponsors: Bramble Down Landscapes
Colours: All red Change colours: All blue
Midweek Matches: Wednesday
Programme: 40 pages, 30p
Editor: Keith Nellis (0191 378 0704)

CLUB PERSONNEL
Chairman: Neil Scott
Vice Chairman: John Dickinson
President: Brian Hewitt
Press Officer: Secretary

Manager: Ken Lindoe
Physio: Keith Glendenning
2002-2003
Captain: Richard Pitt
Player of the Year: Ben Cole
Top Goalscorer: Mark Patterson

CHESTER-LE-STREET TOWN

Secretary: Melvyn Atkinson, 1 St Marys Close, Chester-le-Street, Co Durham DH2 3EG
Tel: 0191 288 3664
Ground: Moor Park, Chester Moor, Chester-le Street, County Durham (0191 388 3363)
Directions: Ground lies approx 2 miles south of town on A167 (C.-le-S. to Durham). Regular buses from C.-le-S. and Durham pass ground. Railway station 2 miles distant in town centre
Capacity: 3,500 Seats: 150 Cover: 1,500 Floodlights: Yes
Open Matchdays- midweek 6.30p.m.- 11.00 p.m. Saturday 12.00p.m.-7.00.Open Monday 7..30-11.00pm **Club Shop:** No, but old programmes available from editor
GROUNDS Ravensworth Welfare, Low Fell 72-73; Riverside Pk 73-78; Sacriston Welfare 78-79.
HONOURS Northern Lg Div 2 83-84 97-98; Wearside Lg 80-81 (R-up 82-83); Monkwearmouth Cup 80-81 81-82; Washington Lg; Durham Minor Cup; Washington AM Cup.

PREVIOUS **Leagues:** Newcastle City Amtr 72-75; Washington 75; Wearside 77-83
Names: Garden Farm 72-78

BEST SEASON **FA Cup: 4th Qual. Rd. 86-87, 2-3 v Caernarfon Town (H)**
FA Vase : 5th Rd v Fleetwood Town 84-85 (1-1,2-2,0-3)

RECORD **Gate:** 893 v Fleetwood FA Vase 18/2/85,
(3000 Sunderland v Newcastle,Bradford appeal match 85)
Appearances: Colin Wake 361
Win: 9-0 v Washington N.L. 28/2/98 **Defeat:** 0-7 v Consett 6/11/96

FACT FILE
Founded: 1972 Nickname: Cestrians
Colours: Blue & white hoops/white/white
Change colours: All yellow
Midweek Matches: Tuesday
Programme: 40 pages, 50p
Editor: K.Greener
email:keith@ greener82fsnet.co.uk
Club Website: chester-le-street-townfc.co.uk

CLUB PERSONNEL
Chairman: John Tomlinson
Vice Chairman: Jack Thornback
President: John Holden
Press Off.: Jack Thornback (0191 3883554)
Manager: Stuart Sherwood
Asst Manager: tony Heslop Stuart Sherwood
Physio: Mark Parkinson
2002-2003
Captain:ColinWake
Player of the Year: David Turner
Top gaolscorer: Steve Cuggy 14

DUNSTON FEDERATION BREWERY

Secretary: Bill Montague, 12 Dundee Close, Chapel House, Newcastle-upon-Tyne NE51JJ
Tel: 0191 2672250
Ground: Federation Park, Wellington Road, Dunston, Gateshead Tel: 0191 493 2935
Directions: Dunston/Whickham exit off A1(M), grd 400 yds north. along Dunston Rd on L. 1 mile from Dunston or Metrocentre stations. Buses from Gateshead & Metrocentre stop outside ground
Capacity: 2,000 Seats:120 Cover: 400 Floodlights: Yes
Clubhouse: Matchdays only. Hot & cold snacks, darts. **Club Shop:** No
HONOURS Northern Lge Div 1 R-up 00-01, Div 2 92-93, Challenge Cup 97-8, 98-9, 99-00; Northern Amtr Lg 77-78 R-up 2, Lg Cup 77-78 78-79 R-up 75-76, Lg Shield 78-79 79-80, Wearside Lg 88-89, 89-90. R-up 90-91, Lg Cup 90-91, N. Comb. 86-87 R-up 3, Lg Cup 83-84, 86-87 R-up 3, Sunderland Shipowners Cup 87-88, Durham Co Tphy 81-82 R-up 2, Minor Cup 79-80 R-up 78-79, Gateshead Chy Cup 77-78 80-81, Heddon Homes Cup 80-81. Cleator Cup 00-01
PREVIOUS **Ground:** Dunston public park 75-86
Names: Whickham Sports; Dunston Mechanics Sports
BEST SEASON **FA Vase:** Quarter-Finals 92-93, 0-2 v Gresley Rov. (A)
FA Cup: 3rd Qual. Rd 92-93, 0-3 v Northallerton T.
RECORDS **Attendance:** 1,550 - Sunderland Shipowners Cup Final 1/4/88
Win: 13-0 v Crook T. (H), Northern Lge Div. 1, 00-01 **Scorer:** Paul King
Defeat: 1-6 v Billingham Synthonia (A), Northern Lge Div. 1, 94-95 **Appearances:** Paul Dixon

FACT FILE
Founded: 1975 Nickname: The Fed
Sponsors: Federation Brewery
Colours: All blue with white trim
Change colours :Yellow/black
Midweek matchday: Tuesday
Reserve s' League : None
Programme: 28 pages 50p
Editor: Ian McPherson (0191 420 5583)

CLUB PERSONNEL
Chairman: Malcolm James
Vice-Chairman: Fred Fowles
President: John Smart
Press Officer: Ian McPherson (0191 420 5583)
Commercial Secretary: Malcolm James
Manager: Bobby Scaife
Asst Manager: Perry Briggs
Physio: Matt Annan
2002-2003
Captain & P.o.Y.: Billy Irwin
Top Goalscorer: Benn Thompson

DURHAM CITY

Secretary: Kevin Hewitt, 21 Cerrytree Drive, Langley Park,Co Durham DH7 9FX
& Press Officer Tel: 0191 3733878 (H & FAX) 0191 383 4200 (W)
Ground: Archibalds Stadium, Durham Tel No: 0191 3869616
Directions At J62 on A1M take A690 towards Durham City. Follow signposts for Belmont Industrail Estate.
Capacity: **Seats:** 300 **Cover:** 700 **Floodlights: Yes**
HONOURS Northern Lg 94-95 (R-up 70-71, Div 2 R-up 30-31 91-92), Durham Benevolent Bowl 55-56, Durham Challenge Cup R-up (2).Northern Div 2 Champions 98-99, Div 2 Champions 98-99 Durham Challenge Cup R-up (3)
PREVIOUS **Leagues:** Victory 18-19; N Eastern 19-21 28-38; Football Lge 21-28; Wearside 38-39 50-51.
Grounds: Holliday Park 21-38; Ferens Park 49-94. NB club disbanded in 1938
BEST SEASON **FA Cup:** 2nd Rd 25-26 57-58 (Also 1st Rd 27-28 55-56)
FA Vase: SF 01-02, QF 87-88 **FA Amateur Cup:** 2nd Rd rep. 57-58
FA Trophy: 1st Rd 83-84, 94-95
RECORD **Appearances:** Joe Raine, 552

Players progressing: Harry Houlahan (Newcastle 51), Derek Clark (Lincoln 51), Leo Dale & David Adamson (Doncaster 54/70), Stan Johnstone (Gateshead 54), Dennis Coughlan (Barnsley 57), John Wile (Sunderland 66), Brian Taylor(Coventry 68), Paul Malcolm (Rochdale 84), Gary Pearson (Darlington 02)

FACT FILE
Reformed: 1949 Nickname: City
Sponsors: Archibalds and Arnotts
Colours: Blue & gold halves/blue & gold stripe/ blue with gold top socks
Change colours: Red & black stripes
Midweek Matches: Tuesday
Progr: 50 pages Editor: Gordon Wright
Local Press: Northern Echo, Sunderland Echo, Evening Chronicle

CLUB PERSONNEL
President&Chairman: Stewart Dawson
Vice Chairman: David Asbery
Commercial Manager: Richrd Rodden
Press Officer: Secretary
Manager: Billy Cruddas
Asst Manager/Coach: Richard Ord
Physio: Gordon Ellis

2002-2003
Captain & P.o.Y.::Steve Walklate
Top Scorer: Michael Dunwell 36

ESH WINNING

Secretary: Roli Bell,12 Park Rd.Central, Chester-le-Street, Co Durham 0191 388 1458 (H)

Ground: West Terrace, Waterhouses, Durham Tel: 0191 373 3872 (Fax: 0191 387 1983)

Directions: Durham to Ushaw Moor, to Esh Winning; ground 1 mile further at Waterhouses
Capacity: 3,500 Seats: 160 Cover: 500 Floodlights: Yes
Clubhouse: Open daily. Snacks served **Club Shop:** No

HONOURS Durham & Dist. Sunday Lg 78-79 79-80, Durham Co. Sun. Cup R-up 78-79, Staffieri Cup 74-75, Guards Cup 72-73, N. Durham Yth Lg 94-95, Auckland Yth Lge 94-95.

PREVIOUS **Leagues:** Durham & Dist Sunday; Northern Alliance 81-82.
Grounds: None **Names:** Esh Winning Pineapple (pre-1982)

BEST SEASON **FA Cup:** 2nd Qual Rd 90-91 **FA Vase:** 2nd Round 83-84

RECORDS **Gate:** 900 v Liverpool Fantail, FA Sunday Cup 1982
Goalscorer: Mark Drake **Appearances:** Paul Hewitson 40
Win: 11-0 v Norton (H) **Defeat:** 0-10 v Shotton Comrades
Fee Paid: £1,000 for Steven Burns **Received:** £500 for Paul Ward (Brandon U)

FACT FILE
Formed: 1967
Nickname: `Esh'
Sponsors:Lumsden & Carroll
Colours: Yellow/green/green/ green
Change colours: Green & Navy
Midweek Matches: Wednesday
Programme: 20 pages, 50p
Editor: Nigel Quinn

CLUB PERSONNEL
Chairman: Charles Ryan
Vice Chairman: David Parkinson
President: Jack Lumsden
Press Officer: Secretary
Manager:Barrie Fleming
Physio:Trevor Best

2002-03
Captain & P.o.Y.: Marc Irwin
Leading Scorer: Gary Messer

GUISBOROUGH TOWN

Secretary: Keith Smeltzer, 212 Woodhouse Road, Guisborough, Cleveland TS14 6LP
Tel: 01642 226181 (W) 01287 201561 (H) 07811 850388 (M)
Ground: King George V Ground, Howlbeck Rd, Guisborough, Cleveland (01287 636925)
Directions: From west: bear left at 2nd set of lights, left into Howlbeck Rd after quarter mile, ground at end. Buses from Middlesbrough
Capacity: 3,500 Seats: 150 Cover: 400 Floodlights: Yes Club Shop: Yes
Clubhouse: Open evenings & weekends. Hot & cold snacks & drinks from kitchen on matchdays

HONOURS FA Vase R-up 79-80; Northern Lg Cup 87-88 (Div 2 R-up 86-87), Northern Alliance 79-80 (R-up 78-79, Lg Cup 78-79); N. Riding Sen. Cup 89-90 90-91 91-92 92-93 94-95.
PREVIOUS **Leagues:** Middlesbrough & District; South Bank; Northern Alliance 77-80; Midland Counties 80-82; Northern Counties (East) 82-85.
BEST SEASON **FA Cup:** 1st Round Proper 88-89, 0-1 v Bury **F.A.Vase:** Finalists 79-80
FA Trophy: 1st Rd Proper 90-91 91-92 92-93
CLUB RECORDS **Gate:** 3,112 v Hungerford, FA Vase SF, 1980
(at Middlesbrough FC - 5,990 v Bury, FA Cup 1st Rd 1988)
Goalscorer: Mark Davis 341 **Appearances:** Mark Davis 587
Win: 6-0 v Ferryhill & v Easington **Defeat:** 0-4 v Billingham Synthonia

FACT FILE
Founded: 1973 Nickname: Priorymen
Sponsors: Hensons Windows & Conservatories
Colours: Red & white stripes/Black/Red
Change colours:Yellow
Midweek matchday:Wednesday
Reserves ' League: Teesside Strongarm
Programme: 32pages, 50p
Editor: Stuart Burns
Local Press: Northern Echo, Middlesbrough Evening Gazette

CLUB PERSONNEL
Chairman: Richard Corden
Vce Chairman: Keith Watson
Press Officer: Stuart Burns
Manager: Steve Corden
Asst Manager: Tiger Wyke
Physio: Gary Hinchley

2002-03
Leading Goalscorer,Captain & P.oY.
Darren Mowdray

Billingham Synthonia F.C.
Founded 1923
The Synners
DARLINGTON
The ALBANY Northern League

The Cestrian
Match Programme of
Chester-le-Street Town F.C.
ALBANY
CLAIMS MANAGEMENT
24hr HELPLINE
Proud to sponsor the
NORTHERN LEAGUE
www.chester-le-street-townfc.co.uk
50p

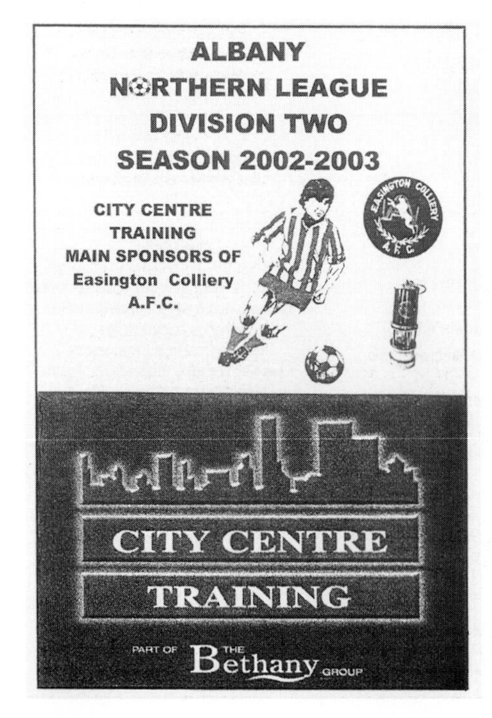
ALBANY
NORTHERN LEAGUE
DIVISION TWO
SEASON 2002-2003
CITY CENTRE
TRAINING
MAIN SPONSORS OF
Easington Colliery
A.F.C.
EASINGTON COLLIERY A.F.C.
CITY CENTRE
TRAINING
PART OF THE Bethany GROUP

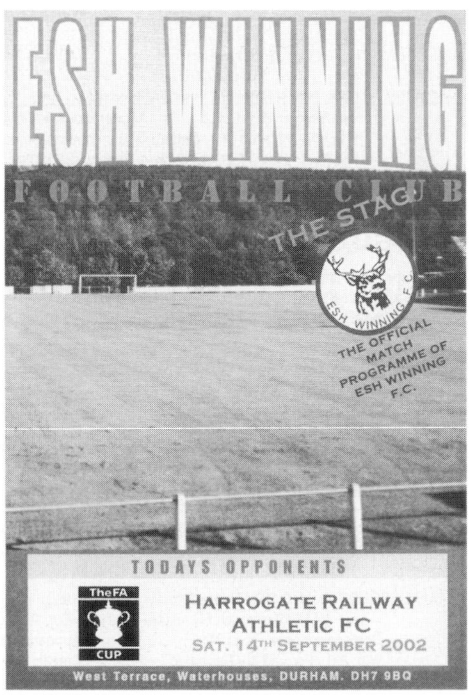
ESH WINNING
FOOTBALL CLUB
THE STAG
ESH WINNING F.C.
THE OFFICIAL MATCH PROGRAMME OF ESH WINNING F.C.
TODAYS OPPONENTS
The FA CUP
HARROGATE RAILWAY
ATHLETIC FC
SAT. 14TH SEPTEMBER 2002
West Terrace, Waterhouses, DURHAM. DH7 9BQ

HORDEN COLLIERY WELFARE

Ground: Welfare Park , Park Rd, Horden, Peterlee, Co. Durham
Tel: 0191 587 3549 (Club)

Directions: A19 to Peterlee, signposted from there

Capacity: 3,000 Seats: 220 Cover: 370 Floodlights: Yes

Clubhouse: Open during normal licensing hours. Hot & cold snacks, darts, pool

HONOURS Northern Lge. Div. 2 R-up 02-03;
North Eastern Lg 37-38 63-64 ('Non-Reserve' Medal 50-51)
Durham Challenge Cup 35-36 63-64 80-81 81-82, Durham Benevolent Cup 33-34,
Wearside Lge 11-12 12-13 13-14 33-34 64-65 67-68 69-70 70-71 71-72 72-73,
Lg Cup 33-34 49-50, Monkwearmouth Charity Cup 12-13 23-24 32-33 69-70 72-73,
Sunderland Shipowners Cup 65-66 72-73, .

PREVIOUS **Leagues:** Wearside 07-35 63-75; N. Eastern 35-58 62-64;
Midland (Co's) 58-60; Northern Co's 60-62. **Names:** Horden Athletic

BEST SEASON **FA Cup:** 2nd Rd 38-39, 2-3 v Newport Co. (H)
Also 1st Rd 25-26 52-53 53-54 54-55 81-82

RECORD **Attendance:** 8,000 - FA Cup 1937

Players progressing: Paul Dobson (Hartlepool Utd), Stan Anderson (Sunderland), Colin Bell (Bury), Tommy Garrett (Blackpool), Bob Taylor (Leeds Utd)

FACT FILE

Reformed : 1980
Nickname: Colliers
Colours: Red/black/red
Change colours:Sky/navy/navy
Reserves League: Wearside Div 2
Midweek Matches: Tuesday
Programme: 10 pages, 50p

CLUB PERSONNEL

Chairman: Norman Stephens
Secretary: Rob Jones
17 Aspatria Avenue, Blackhall,
Hartlepool. TS27 4EG
Tel: 0191 587 0949 (H) 07932 951842 (M)
Press Officer: Secretary

JARROW ROOFING BOLDON C.A.

Secretary/Manager: Richard McLoughlin, 8 Kitchener Terrace, Jarrow NE32 5PU
Tel: 0191 489 9825

Ground: Boldon CA Sports Ground, New Road, Boldon Colliery (0191 519 1391)

Directions: A19 to junction with A184 (Sunderland/Newcastle). Follow signs to Boldon Asda stores, then to North Road Social Club. Ground behind. East Boldon(BR) 800 yds.

Capacity: 3,500 Seats: 150 Cover: 800 Floodlights: Yes Club Shop: Yes

Clubhouse: Open eves.& w/e lunchtimes. Hotdogs, burgers etc from tea bar on matchdays

HONOURS Wearside Lg Div 2 R-up 91-92 95-96; Sunderland Shipowners Cup R-up 93-94, 94-95; Tyneside Amtr Lg R-up 90-91, Chal. Shield 90-91 (R-up 89-90); Bill Dixon Cup 90-91; Mid-Tyne Lg 87-88; Fred Giles Cup R-up 87-88; Gateshead Charity Cup SF 90-91; Monkwearmouth Cup 94-95; Craven Cup 96-97, Northern League Div One Cup R-Up 98-98

PREVIOUS **Leagues:** Mid-Tyne; Tyneside Amtr 88-91; Vaux Wearside

RECORD **Attendance:** 500 v South Shields
Appearances: Mick Haley **Goalscorer:** Paul Chow

FACT FILE

Founded: 1987Nickname: Roofing
Sponsors: Jarrow Roofing Co
Colours: Yellow with Blue trim shirts,
Royal Blue & Yellow sjhorts and socks
Change colours: Red & Black
Midweek matchday: Tuesday
Programme: 20 pages, free with entry
Editor: Brian Marshall (0191 4217011)

CLUB PERSONNEL

Chairman: Richard McLoughlin
Press Officer/Treasurer: Rose McLoughlin
Manager/ Secretary: Richard McLoughlin
Coaches: Colin Myers, Tony Metcalfe
Physio: John Cullen

2002-03

Leading Goalscorer: Paul Chow
Captain: Scott Garrett
Player of the Year:Paul Chow

MARSKE UNITED

Secretary: Ian Rowe, 19 High Row, Loftus, Saltburn By The Sea, Cleveland. TS134SA
& Press Officer Tel: 01287 643440 (H) 01642 230546 (B) 01642 241273 (Fax)

Ground: Mount Pleasant, Mount Pleasant Ave., Marske, Redcar, Cleveland. Tel: 01642 471091

Directions: From A19 take A174 exit marked Yarm, Teesport, Redcar, Whitby and head east towards Saltburn until Quarry Lane r/about. Take 1st left (A1085) into Marske, 1st right (Meadow Rd) then 1st left (Southfield Rd),then 1st left again Mount Pleasant Ave directly into car park.
By train: Darlington to Saltburn, Marske station 300 yds from ground.

Capacity: 2,500 Seats: 169 Cover: 300 Floodlights: Yes

Clubhouse: Open every night and weekend lunchtimes. Food served after all games
Contact : Janet Pippen (01642 474985)

HONOURS N Riding Sen Cup 94-95; N Riding County Cup 80-81 85-86; Teesside Lg 80-81 84-85; Wearside Lg 95-96, R-up 93-94 94-95 96-97, Cup 92-93 94-95 95-96; M/mouth Charity Cup 93-94 95-96; Sunderland Ship. Cup 95-96 96-97.N.Lg Cup R-up: 00-01

PREVIOUS **Leagues:** Cleveland & South Bank 56-76, Teesside 76-85, Wearside 85-97.

BEST SEASON **FA Cup:** 2nd Qual Rd., 00-01 **FA Vase:** Qtr Final replay, 00-01

RECORDS **Attendance:** 1,359 v Bedlington Terriers (F.A.Vase) **Win:** 16-0 v North Shields
Defeat: 3-9 **Goalscorer:** Chris Morgan 169 **Appearances:** John Hodgson 476

Players progressing: Peter Beagrie (Middlesbrough), Tony Butler (Blackpool),
Roy Hunter (Northampton), Dave Logan (Mansfield T.)

FACT FILE

Founded: 1956 Nickname: The Seasiders
Colours: Yellow/royalblue/white
Change: Royal/sky/yellow
Midweek matchday: Tuesday
Programme: 60 pages £1.00
Editor: Moss Holtby (01642 475612)
Local Press: Sunday Sun, Middlesbrough
Evening Gazette, Northern Echo

CLUB PERSONNEL

Chairman: John Hodgson
Vice Chairman: John Corner
President: Raymond Jarvis
Commercial Manager: Steve Davies
Manager: Charlie Bell
Assistant Manager: Stephen Dowling
Physios: Eric Barrett & Owen Hughes
Coaches: Charlie Bell & Stephen Dowling
Kit Manager: Colin Gilbert

Shildon F.C. Back Row (L-R): Phil Owers (coach), Lee Ellison, Stephen Tobin, James Middleton, Adam Clementson, Mark Rutter, Nigel Bolton, Charlie Walton, Ray Gowan (Manager).
Front Row: Gareth Clarkson (mascot), Joseph Jennings (mascot), David Bayles, Danny Key, Lee Collings, Keith Emmerson, Jennifer Jennings (mascot).

Morpeth Town F.C.

Photo: Roger Turner.

MORPETH TOWN

Secretary: Les Scott,1 Bennetts Walk, Morpeth, Northumberland NE61 1TP
Tel: 01670 517390 (H) 0780 3483509 (M) e-mail: les@craikpark.fsnt.co.uk

Ground: Craik Park, Morpeth Common, Morpeth, Northumberland
Tel: 01670 513785

Directions: Morpeth is signed off the A1 onto A197.
Take the B6524, right at Mitford sign, then right after about a mile into the ground, next to Morpeth Common

Capacity: 1000 Seated: 150 Cover: 150 Floodlights Yes

Clubhouse: Yes

Club Shop: No

PREVIOUS **Leagues:** Northern Alliance pre 1994
Ground: Storey Park, Morpeth. pre 1992

BEST SEASON **FA Cup:** 4th Q Rd v Burton Albion 1998-99

HONOURS Northern Alliance 83-84, 93-94 (R-up 37-38, 65-66, 73-74, 81-82, 84-85); Challenge Cup Winners 38-39, 85-86, 93-94 (R-up 36-37, 62-63, 73-74).

FACT FILE

Colours:
Amber & black stripes/black/black
Change colours: Blue,white,blue
Midweek Matchday: Tuesday
Programme: Yes

Chairman: Ken Beattie
Tel.: 01670 515271 (H)
01670 520565 (B)
Press Officer: Les Scott (Secretary)

PENRITH

Secretary: John Balmer, 48 Macadam Way, Penrith, Cumbria
Tel: 01768 866736

Ground: Southend Road Ground, Penrith, Cumbria
Tel: 01768 895990

Directions: M6 Jct 40, onto dual carriageway to Appleby & Scotch Corner, first left at next r'bout, approx 1/2 mile into Penrith on A6 into town, take 1st left for ground. 3/4 mile from Penrith (BR)

Capacity: 4,000 Seats: 200 Cover: 1,000 Floodlights: Yes
Clubhouse: Yes **Club Shop:** No

PREVIOUS **Leagues:** Carlisle & Dist., Northern 48-82, NWC. 82-87 90-97, NPL 87-90.

RECORDS **Attendance:** 2,100 v Chester 1981
Goalscorer: C Short **Appearances:** Lee Armstrong
Win: 13-2 v Parton Utd **Defeat:** 0-13 v Bishop Auckland
Fee paid: £750 for A Carruthers (Netherfield)
Fee received: £1,000 for B Brown (Queen of the South)

BEST SEASON **FA Cup:** 2nd Rd 81-82 League Clubs beaten: Chester 81-82

HONOURS Northern Lg R-up 61-62, Div 2 Champions 02-03; NW Co's Lg R-up 83-84; NW Co's F/Light Trophy 95-96 96-97; Cumberland Snr Cup [13], Craven Cup 00-01

Players progressing: K Sawyers, G Fell, G Mossop (all Carlisle)

FACT FILE
Founded: 1894
Nickname: Blues
Sponsors: Primasonics
Colours: Blue/white/blue
Change colours: All yellow
Midweek Matches: Tuesday
Reserve team: Yes
Programme: 24 pages, 70p
Press Officer: Secretary
Local Press: Cumberland & Westmorland Herald, Cumberland News

CLUB PERSONNEL
Chairman: Don Cameron
Vice Chairman:Walter Brogden
Manager: David Heslop

2002-2003
Captain: Mark Jones
Top Scorer: Andrew Wright
P.o.Y.: Wayne Robertson

PETERLEE NEWTOWN

Secretary: Arnie Church, 38 Hatfield Place, Peterlee, Co. Durham SR8 5SS (0191 586 4804)
Ground: Eden Lane, Peterlee, County Durham (0191 586 3004)

Directions: From town centre Fire Station, turn left into Edenhill Rd, thenright into Robson Ave. Left at the next junction and ground is on the right

Capacity: 6,000 Seats: 50 Cover: 200 Floodlights: Yes

Clubhouse: Open normal licensing hours. Sandwiches etc available **Club Shop:** No

HONOURS Northern Lg Div 2 82-83, North Eastern F'lit League, 4th Qual Rd FA Cup

PREVIOUS **Leagues:** Northern Alliance 76-79; Wearside 79-82

RECORD **Attendance:** 2,350 v Northern, Hillsborough Fund match 1989
Scorer : Keith Fairless **Appearances** : Keith Bendelow

BEST SEASON **FA Cup:** 4th Qual. Rd replay 85-86 **FA Vase:**

Players progressing: Keith Fairless (Scarborough) 1986, Brian Honour(Hartlepool) 1988)

FACT FILE
Formed: 1976
Nickame: Newtowners
Sponsors: Artix Ltd
Colours: Yellow/black/yellow
*Midweek Matches: Wednesday
Programme: 10 pages, 30p
Editor: Secretary
Local Press: Hartlepool Mail, Sunderland Echo, Northern Echo

CLUB PERSONNEL
Chairman: Carl Paylor
Vice-Chairman: Colin Austin (07817 707565)
President: David Brown
Press Officer: Ray Matthews (07720 548424)
Manager: Tommy Smith
Asst Manager: Eddie Freeman
Physio: Ron Lamdrel

SHILDON

Secretary /Press Officer: Mike Armitage, 22 Hambleton Court, Byerley Park, Newton Aycliffe, Co.Durham DL5 7HR Tel: 01325 316322

Ground: Dean Street, Shildon, County DurhamTel: 01388 773877 **Directions:** In the town centre 1 mile from BR station and 300yds from Darlington-Bishop Auckland bus stop

Capacity: 4,000 Seats: 480 Cover: 1000 Floodlights: Yes **Club Shop:** No

Clubhouse: .Matchdays only.

HONOURS Northern Lg 33-34 34-35 35-36 36-37 39-40 (R-up 32-33 38-39, Div 2 Champions 2001-02 Lg Cup 33-34 34-35 37-38 38-39 39-40 52-53 2002-03), Durham Challenge Cup 07-08 25-26 71-72, Durham Amateur Cup 01-02 02-03, Durham Benevelopment Bowl 24-25.

PREVIOUS Leagues: Auckland & District 1892-96; Wearside 96-97; North Eastern 07-32.

BEST SEASON FA Cup: 2nd Rd 36-37 1st Rd 27-28 29-30 34-35 36-37 55-56 59-60 61-62 **FA Trophy:** 3rd Qual. Rd 74-75 **FA Amateur Cup:** 4thRd 58-59 **FA Vase:** 1st Rd 86-87

RECORDS **Attendance:** 13,000 - Leeholme v Perkinsville, schoolboys game, 1920s. (Shildon game); 11,000 Shildon v Ferryhill Ath., Durham Sen. Cup 1922
Appearances: Bryan Dale **Goalscorer:** Jack Downing, 61 (1936-37)

Players progressing: Ken Whitfield (Wolves 47), James Smith(Chelsea 51), Mike Peacock, Philip Shute, Nigel Bolton (Darlington 60, 84, 95), Kevin Stonehouse (Blackburn 79), Alan White (Middlesbrough 93).

FACT FILE
Founded: 1890
Nickname: Railwaymen
Sponsors:Ashfield
Colours: Purple/black/black
Change: Yellow/blue/blue
Midweek Matches: Wednesday
Programme: 48 pages, 50p
Editor: Secretary

CLUB PERSONNEL
Chairman: Gordon Hampton
Vice Chairman: G. Elliott
President: John Atkinson
Manager: Ray Gowan
Assistant Manager: David Bayles
Physio: Neil Jennings

2002-2003
Captain: & P.o.Y.: Danny Key
Leading Goalscorer: Lee Ellison 24

THORNABY

Ground: Teesdale Park, Acklam Road, Thornaby, Stockton-on-Tees TS17 8TZ Tel: 01642 606803

Directions: A19 to Thornaby turn off, ground half mile on right. One mile fromThornaby BR station. Any Stockton-Middlesbrough bus - stop at Acklam Rd,Thornaby

Capacity: 5,000 Seats: 150 Cover: 350 Floodlights: Yes

Clubhouse: 150+ seater social club with concert room, pool/games room and bar. Open every night and Sunday lunchtimes and all day Saturday. Sandwiches avail. in bar, canteen in ground sells pies, burgers, soup, drinks etc

Club Shop: No

PREVIOUS Leagues: Stockton & District 80-81; Wearside 81-85.
Names: Stockton Cricket Club 65-80; Stockton 80-99: Thornaby-on-Tees 99-00

Grounds: Grangefield Youth & Community Centre, Stockton 80-82; Tilery Sports Centre 82-83.

RECORD **Attendance:** 3,000 v Middlebrough, pre-season friendly August 1986
Appearances: Michael Watson
Win: 11-0 v Horden C.W.(H) Buchanan Cup 94-95

BEST SEASON **FA Vase:** 3rd Rd 89-90 **FA Trophy:** 3rd Rd 92-93
FA Cup: 4th Qual. Rd replay 92-93,1-2 v Blyth (H) after 1-1

HONOURS Northern Lg Div 2 87-88 91-92, Nth Riding Co. Cup 85-86, Inaugralwinners of Craven Cup (Northern Div 2 clubs) 94-95..

FACT FILE
Formed: 1980
Colours:Yellow and blue/Navy & white/yellow
Change colours: All sky
Midweek Matches: Wednesday
Reserves' Lge: Wearside & Teesside Lgs
Programme: 24 pages, 50p
Editor: Peter Morris (01642 585625)
Local Press: Northern Echo, Evening Gazette

CLUB PERSONNEL
Chairman: Lol Lyons
Press Officer: Paul Beards ()1642 897861)
Secretary: Peter Morris
20 Wheatear Lane, Ingleby Barwick, Stockton-on-Tees, Cleveland TS17 0TB
Tel: 01642 760779

Manager: Michael Watson
Asst Mgr: Peter May
Coach: Paul Sharkey

TOW LAW TOWN

Secretary: Bernard Fairbairn, 3 Coppice Walk, Mowden Park, Darlington, Co. Durham DL3 9DP Tel: 01325 350743

Ground: Ironworks Road, Tow Law, Bishop Auckland Tel: 01388 731443

Directions: Just of High Street in Tow Law town centre

Capacity: 6,000 Seats: 200 Cover: 300 Floodlights: Yes

Clubhouse: Every evening 8.30 -10.30 **Club Shop:** Yes

HONOURS FA Vase R-up 97-98; Rothmans National Cup 1977, Northern League Champions 23-24 24-25 94-95, R-up 28-29 88-89, Lg Cup 73-74; Rothmans Overseas Cup 76-77, Durham Chal. Cup 1895-96, Durham Amtr Cup 1892-93.

PREVIOUS **Leagues:** None

BEST SEASON **FA Cup:** 2nd Rd rep. 67-68, 2-6 v Shrewsbury T. (A) after 1-1. Also 1st Rd 68-69 84-85 89-90. League Clubs defeated:Mansfield Town 67-68
FA Amateur Cup: 3rd Rd rep. 70-71 **FA Trophy:** 2nd Rd rep. 82-83
FA Vase: Runners-up 1997-98

RECORD **Gate:** 5,500 v Mansfield Town, FA Cup 1967

Players progressing: Reuben Cook & Ralph Guthrie (Arsenal 1951 & 53), Gordon Hughes, Terry Melling & Chris Waddle (Newcastle 1956 & 65 & 80), EricJohnstone & Kevin Dixon (Carlisle 1963 & 83), Keith Adamson (Barnsley 1966),Tom Henderson (Bradford PA 1969), Vincent Chapman (Huddersfield 1988)

FACT FILE
Founded: 1890
Nickname: Lawyers
Colours:
Black & white stripes/black/black & white
Change colours: Red & white
Midweek Matches: Tuesday
Programme: Yes
Editor:Chairman
Local Press : Northern Echo

CLUB PERSONNEL
Chairman: John Flynn
Press Officer: John Flynn (01388 730525)
Manager: Graeme Forster
Assistant Manager: Andy Sinclair

WASHINGTON F.C.

Secretary: George Abbott,14 Grosvenor St, Southwick, Sunderland, Tyne & Wear SR5 2DG
Tel Nos: 0191 5491384 (H) 0191 4177779 (W)

Ground: Albany Park, Spout Lane, Concord, District 11, Washington
Tel: 0191 417 7779

Directions: Ground situated opposite bus station.

Capacity: 3,000 Seats: 25 Cover: Yes Floodlights: Yes Club Shop: No

Clubhouse: Open normal licensing hours, with live entertainment, pool etc

PREVIOUS **Leagues:** Washington Amateur; Northern Alliance 67-68; Wearside 68-88
Ground: Usworth Welfare Park

RECORD **Gate:** 3,800 v Bradford Park Avenue, FA Cup 1970

2002-2003 Captain: James Curtis Top Goalscorer: Ben Chambers 20
Player of the Year: Kevin Leighton

FACT FILE
Founded: 1949
Nickname: Mechanics
Colours: All red
Change colours: Yellow'Blue
Midweek Matches: Wednesday
Programme: 8 pages, 50p
Editor: Rob Goodwin

CLUB PERSONNEL
Chairman: Derek Armstrong
Tel: 0191 416 3956 (H)
Press Officer:John Oliver
Tel: 0191 416 3527
Manager:John Oliver
Physio:Jim McGrath

WEST AUCKLAND TOWN

Secretary: Allen Bayles, 11 Edith Terrace, West Auckland, Co.Durham.DL14 9JT
Tel: 01388 833783 (H) & FAX, 01388 605221 (B) 01388 661366

Ground: Darlington Road, West Auckland, Co.Durham Tel: 01388 834403

Directions: Leaving West Auckland take A68-ground on right before leavingvillage. Bus route via Bishop Auckland fron Newcastle or Darlington
Capacity: 3,000 Seats: 250 Cover: 250 Floodlights: Yes **Club Shop:** No
Clubhouse: On Gound. (The Thomas Lipton Trophy is on display at the local Working Mans Club five minutes away). Tel No: 01388 661366

HONOURS FA Amateur Cup Finalists 60-61; Northern League Champions 59-60, 60-61 Div 2 90-91,Lg Cup 59-60,62-639r-UP;48-49,61-62,63-64)
Durham Challenge Cup 63-64 Durham Benevolent Bowl 62-63; Sir Thomas Lipton Tphy`First World Cup'(as featured in `The Captains Tale') 1909, 1911.

PREVIOUS **League:** Auckland & District
Names: St Helens Utd (1919 only), West Auckland Town.

BEST SEASON **FA Cup:** 1st Rd 58-59, 61-62,98-99 **FA Trophy:** 3rd Rd. 77-78
FA Vase: 4th Rd. 2001-02 **FA Amateur Cup:** Runners-up 60-61; Q-F 59-60

RECORD **Gate:** 6,000 v Dulwich Hamlet, FA Amateur Cup 58-59
Victory: 11-0 in Durham County Cup

FACT FILE
Founded: 1892
Nickname: West
Sponsors:Rushlift Mechanical Handling and F.Hudson Transport
Colours: White with black & amber band s and amber collar & cuffs/white/white
Change Colours: All Yellow
Midweek Matches: Tuesday

CLUB PERSONNEL
Chairman: Jim Polfreyman
Press Officer:Stuart Alderson (01388 834211)
Manager: Allan Oliver
Ass.Manager & Coach: Paul Cross

WHITLEY BAY

Secretary: Derek Breakwell 27 Kings Rd, Whitley Bay, Tyne & Wear, NE26 3BD 0191 252 7940
GROUND Hillheads Park, Rink Way off Hillheads Road, Whitley Bay, Tyne& Wear NE25 8HR 0191 291 3637 Club. Fax & matchday office 0191 291 3636 Website: www.whitleybayfc.co.uk
Directions: 1 mile walk from bus station - leave St Pauls Church southward, turn right at r-about, ground 3rd left at rear of ice rink.Whitley Bay (25mins from Newcastle) or Monkseaton metro stations, both 1 mile. Email: derek.breakwell@blueyonder.co.uk
Capacity: 4,500 Cover: 650 Seats: 450
Clubhouse: Open 6-11pm Mon-Fri, 12pm 11pm Sat, 7pm 10.30 pm Sun.Bar,Darts,Pool.functions
Club Shop: Sells progs, scarves, hats, metal badges etc. Contact Tom Moody (0191 291 1618)
PREVIOUS **Leagues:** Tyneside 09-10, Northern All. 50-55, North Eastern Lge 55-58, Northern Lge 58-88; N.P.L. 88-00 **Name:** Whitley Bay Athletic 1950-58
CLUB RECORDS **Attendance:** 7,301 v Hendon, FA Amateur Cup 1965
Win: 12-0 v Shildon 1961 **Defeat:** 1-8 v Bishop Auckland 1979 **Goalscorer:** Billy Wright 307
Appearances: Bill Chater 640 **Fee Paid:**£3,00 for Craig Melrose from Bedlingtobn Terriers
Fee Received: £10,000 for Kevin Todd from Berwick Rangers
BEST SEASON **FA Amateur Cup:** Semi Final 65-66 68-69 **FA Trophy:** 3rd Rd 86-87
FA Cup: 3rd Rd 89-90 (0-1 v Rochdale [A]). **F.A.Vase:** Winners 2001-02
HONOURS: Northern Premier Lg Div 1 90-91 (Div 1 Cup 88-89 90-91), Northern Lg 64-65 65-66 (R-up 59-60 66-67 68-69 69-70), Lg Cup 64-65 70-71 (R-up 67-68); Northern Alliance 52-53 53-54 (Lg Cup 52-53 53-54); Northumberland Sen. Cup x10, R-up x8

FACT FILE
Formed: 1897
Nickname: The Bay
Colours: Blue & white stripes/white/white
Change colours: Yellow or white
Midweek home matchday: Tuesday
Programme Pages: 24 Price: £1.00
Website: www.whitleybayfc.co.uk

CLUB PERSONNEL
Chairman: Peter Siddle
President: Sid Cope
Press Officer: Peter Fox (0773 982 7237 (M)
Manager:T.B.A.
Asst Manager/Coach: T.B.A.
Physio:T.B.A.

2002-2003
Captain: Steve Locker
Top Scorer: Lee Ludlow 23
Player of the Year: Kevin Walton

ALNWICK TOWN

Secretary: Darren Middleton, 1 Fire Station Houses, Alnwick, NE66 2PB(1665 603781)
Ground: St James' Park, Alnwick, Northumberland Tel: 01665 603162
Directions: 35 miles north of Newcastle on A1, take the slip road to Alnwick,then first left. At roundabout turn left, ground is then on your left.
Capacity: 2,500 Seats: 100 Cover: 200 Floodlights: Yes
HONOURS Northern Lg Div 2 R-up 88-89, Northern Alliance 37-38 62-63 63-64 65-66 67-68 68-69 69-70 70-71 71-72 (R-up 59-60 61-62 66-67 72-73, Lg Cup 61-62 65-6667-68 68-69 70-71, Subsidiary Cup 80-81), Durham Central Lg Cup 64-65, Northumberland Benevolent Bowl 86-87, Northumberland SNR Cup R-up 61-62,Northumberland Amtr Cup 71-72.
PREVIOUS **League:** Northern Alliance 35-39 46-64 64-82
Names: Alnwick United Services; Alnwick United.
BEST SEASON **FA Cup:** 3rd Qual. Rd 51-52 (3-4 at Blyth), 57-58 (4-6 at Easington Coll.).
FA Trophy: 3rd Qual. Rd 90-91.
RECORD **Attendance:** 600 v Bedlington Terriers, Northern Alliance 1971.

FACT FILE
Founded: 1879
Colours: Black & white stripes/black/black
Change colours: Green and yellow
Midweek Matches: Tuesday

Local Press: Northumberland Gazette

CLUB PERSONNEL
Chairman: Alan Wilcox
Manager: Malcolm Beusle
Press Officer: Secretary
Players progressing: George Turnbull (Grimsby 1950) and Brian Pringle (1973)

ASHINGTON

Secretary: Brian Robinson, 80 Milburn Road, Ashington, N/thumberland NE63 0PG
Tel: 01670 852832 (H) 01670 521212 (B) Fax: 01670 852832
Ground: Portland Park, Ashington NE63 9XG (01670 811991 Social Club)
Directions: 200 yds north at traffic lights in centre of town
Capacity: 2,000 Seats: 350 Cover: 2,200 Floodlights: Yes
Clubhouse: Open 6-11 eves & from11am Tues (market day), closed Wed & Sun. Snacks etc.
Club Shop No but jumpers, baseball caps etc. behind bar
PREVIOUS **Leagues:** Northern All. 1892-93 1902-14 69-70; Football League; North Eastern 14-21 29-58 62-64; Midland 58-60; Northern Counties 60-62; Wearside 64-65; N.P.L. 68-69.,
RECORD **Attendance:** 13,199 v Rochdale, FA Cup 2nd Rd 9/12/50
BEST SEASON **FA Cup:** 3rd Rd 26-27 **FA Amateur Cup** SF 73-74
HONOURS Northumberland Snr Cup x9, N'berland Chall. Bowl x6, Midland Lg 58-59, North Eastern Lg Cup 33-34(jt) 39-40; Northern Alliance x 4, R-up x 6 Lg Cup 47-48, Craven Cup 98-99

FACT FILE
Formed: 1883 Nickname: The Colliers
Club colours: Black & white stripes/black/black
Change colours: Green/white/green
Midweek Matches: Tuesday
Programme: Yes, 50p
Editor: A Marchett (01670 854585)

CLUB PERSONNEL
Chairman: Jim Lang
Joint Presidents:
Sir Bobby Charlton & Jackie Charlton OBE
Press Officer: Brian Bennett (01670 856606)
Manager: Tony Harrison
Asst.Manager: Paul Anderson
Physio: Mick Harrison

CONSETT

Secretary: Ian Hamilton, 29 Grange St. Delves Lane, Consett, Co. Durham DH87AG
Tel: 01207 509366 (H) 07947 130726 (M) email: thesecretarycafc@aol.com
Ground: Belle Vue Park, Ashdale Road, Consett, County Durham (01207 503788)
Directions: Quarter of mile north of town centre - along Medomsley Rd, left down Ashdale Rd, ground 100m yards on left. Follow signs for Sports Centre and Baths
Capacity: 4,000 Seats: 400 Cover: 1,000 Floodlights: Yes
Clubhouse: Matchdays, and evenings on request. Darts & pool **Club Shop:** No
PREVIOUS **Leagues:** Northern Alliance 19-26 35-37; North Eastern 26-35 37-58 62-64; Midland 58-60; Northern Counties 60-62; Wearside 64-70
BEST SEASON **FA Cup:** 1st Rd 58-59, 0-5 v Doncaster Rov. (A) **FA Trophy:** 2nd Rd 78-79
HONOURS North Eastern Lg 39-40 Div 2 26-27, Lg Cup 50-51(jt) 53-54, Durham Challenge x5 R-up x2, Northern Lg R-up 76-77 Div 2 88-89, Lg Cup 78-79 80-81, Northern Counties Lg 61-62, Sunderland Shipowners Cup 67-68, Monkwearmouth Charity Cup 67-68, Wearside Lg R-up 68-69 69-70.

FACT FILE
Founded: 1899 Nickname: Steelmen
Colours: Red with black & white trim/black/red
Change colours: Sky blue/dark blue/sky blue
Midweek Matches: Wednesday
Programme: 16 pages, 30p
Programme Editor: Andrew Pearson

CLUB PERSONNEL
Chairman: Derek .Nicholls
Vice Chairman: Stuart Moffat
President: John Hirst
Press Officer: Andrew Pearson, 01207 506194
Manager: Colin Carr
Physios: Brian Nicholson & Jim Vipond

CROOK TOWN

Secretary/Press Officer: Kieron Bennett, Flat 4, Robertson Court, Salisbury Ave,,Chester le Street, Co.Durham. DH3 3FB Tel Noi: 0191 3825078
Ground: Millfield Ground, West Road, Crook, County Durham (01388 762959)
Directions: 400 yds west of town centre on Wolsingham Road (A689). Nearest BR station is Bishop Auckland (5 miles). Buses 1A & 1B from Bishop Auckland or X46& X47 from Durham
Capacity: 3,500 Seats: 400 Cover: 300 Floodlights: Yes
Clubhouse: Lic Bar open matchdays. Hot & Cold Food available from Shop **Club Shop:** Yes
PREVIOUS **Leagues:** Auckland & Dist. 1894-96; Northern 1896-28 29-30; Durham Central 28-29; North Eastern 30-36; Wartime Durham & Northumberland 40-41;Durham Cen. 41-45.
BEST SEASON **FA Trophy:** 3rd Rd 76-77 **FA Cup:** 3rd Rd, v Leicester 31-32. 2nd Rd (4), 1st Rd.(10) **FA Vase:** 4th Rd 99-00 **FA Amateur Cup:** Winners 5 times, plus S-F x 3
HONOURS FA Amateur Cup Winners 00-01 53-54 58-59 61-62 63-64; Northern Lg 5, (R-up 4) Lg Cup 3, (R-up 4); Durham Chall. Cup 26-27 31-32 54-55 59-60; Durham Benevolent Bowl 6; Ernest Armstrong Mem Trophy 97.

FACT FILE
Formed: 1889 Nickname: Black & Ambers
Sponsors: NEMS
Colours: Amber/black/black
Change colours: All White
Midweek Matches: Wednesday
Programme: Yes Editor: Secretary

CLUB PERSONNEL
Chairman: Stephen Buddle
Vice-Chairman:William Neil
Chief Executive: Tom Chopra
President: Sir Tom Cowie O.B.E.
General Manager: David Buchanan
Manager: Ronan Liddane
Asst. Manager: Dennis Pinkney
Physio: Dave Southern

EASINGTON COLLIERY

Secretary: Alan Purvis, 12 Wark Crescent, Jarrow, Tyne & Wear, NE32 4SH (0191 489 6930)

Ground: Easington Colliery Welfare Ground, CW Park, Easington, Co Durham. (0191 527 3047)
Directions: A19 Easington turn-off, B1284 thru Easington to 'Derby' PH (next to zebra crossing), ground on the right**Clubhouse:** Normal licensing hours. Pies, soup and sandwiches.

Capacity: 2,450 Seats: 175 Cover: 475 Floodlights: Yes **Club Shop:** No
HONOURS Northern Lg Div 2 R-up 85-86; Wearside Lge 29-30 31-32 32-33 47-48 48-49, R-up 28-29 46-47 73-74, Lg Cup 32-33 45-46 61-62; Monkwearmouth Cup 30-31 47-48 75-76; Sunderland Shipowners Cup 74-75 79-80.
PREVIOUS **Leagues:** Wearside 13-37 39-64 73-88
BEST SEASON **FA Cup:** 1st Round Proper 55-56
FA Trophy: 2nd Qual. Rd replay 88-89 **FA Vase:** 4th Rd replay 82-83
RECORD **Attendance:** 4,500 v Tranmere Rovers, FA Cup 1st Round 1955
Scorer: Andrew McKenna **Appearances:** David Howard **Ex Players**:: Ron Greener (Newcastle 1951), Frank Wayman (Darlington1957), John Langridge (Hartlepool 1982).

FACT FILE
Founded: 1913 Nickname: The Colliery
Colours: Green & white stripes/green/green
Change colours: Yellow/green/green
Midweek Matches: Tuesday
Programme: Yes Editor: Charlie Dodds

CLUB PERSONNEL
Chairman: Allan Barkas
Press Officer: Alan Purvis
Manager:Graeme Hedley
Asst Manager: Andy McCreash
2002-2003
Captain: Graeme Carter
Top Scorer: David Taylor
Player of the Year: Paul Milner

EVENWOOD TOWN

Secretary: The Football Secretary, Evenwood Town F.C.c/o Evenwood Sports & Social Club, Stones End, Evenwood, Co.Durham
Ground: Welfare Ground, Stones End, Evenwood, County Durham Tel: 01388 832281

Directions: In village centre by Sports & Social club in StonesEnd
Capacity: 3,500 Seats: 150 Cover: 350 Floodlights: Yes
Clubhouse: Open lunch & evening every da except Monday

HONOURS Northern Lg 48-49 69-70 70-71 (Lg Cup 35-36), Durham Challenge Cup 69-70.
PREVIOUS **Leagues:** Barnard Castle & Dist. 1894-95; Auckland & Dist. 1894-96 1903-04 08-23 28-31; Wear Valley 1896-99 1904-06 24-25; Gaunless Valley 06-07; South Durham 27-28. Names: None
BEST SEASON **FA Cup:** 1st Rd 1936 FA Vase:
RECORD **Gate:** 9,000 v Bishop Auckland, FA Amtr Cup 1931
2002-2003: **Captain:** S.Moore **Player of the Year:** C.Warburton **Top Scorer:** K.Dinhey

FACT FILE
Founded: 1890
Nickname: The Wood
Sponsors: C A Roofing
Club colours: All blue
Change:Yellow
Midweek Matches: Tuesday
Programme: 50p Editor: Rev .Frank Campbell
CLUB PERSONNEL
Chairman: Craig Latcham
President: N Colegrove
Press Officer: Secretary
Manager: Ken Houlahan
Assistant Manager:Andy Turner

HEBBURN TOWN

Secretary: Tom Derrick, 63 Staneway, Felling, Gateshead, NE10 8LS.Tel: 0191 442 1563
Tel Nos: 0191 4421563 (H & Fax) 0191 2251444 (W)
Ground: Hebburn Sports & Social Ground, Victoria Road West, Hebburn Tel: 0191 483 5101
Directions: On the main road through the town about 1 mile from railway station. Hebburn lies on the Metroline - excellent bus service from Heworth Metro **Clubhouse:** 7-11 mon,11am-1pm Sat and 12-2.0 p.m. Sun.Pool ,darts etc.**Ground Capacity:** 2,000 **Seats**:153 **Cover**:420 **Lights**:Yes
PREVIOUSLeagues: Jarrow & Dist. Jnr 12-14; S Shields Comb. 19-22; Tyneside Comb. 22-27; Tyneside 27-39; Northern Comb. 41-44 45-59; North Eastern 44-45 59-60; Wearside 60-89.
Names: Reyrolles; Hebburn Reyrolles (pre-1988), Hebburn 88-00 **Club Shop:** No
HONOURS Shields Gazette Cup 91-92, Wearside Lg 66-67 (Monkwearmouth Charity Cup 68-69), Durham Challenge Cup 42-43 91-92, Tyneside Lg 38-39, Northern Comb. 43-44, Gateshead Charity Cup 35-36 37-38, Palmer Hospital Cup 27-28, Hebburn Aged Miners Cup 35-36, Heddon Homes Cup 42-43, Hebburn Infirmary Cup 35-36 36-37 37-38 38-39, Craven Cup 99-00.
BEST SEASON FA Vase: 2nd Rd 91-92 **FA Cup:** 2nd Qual. Rd rep. 89-90, 0-3 v South Bank (A)
RECORD Attendance: 503 v Darwen, FA Cup Prel. Rd replay 7/9/91 **Win:** 10-1 **Defeat** 3-10

FACT FILE
Founded: 1912
Nickname: Hornets
Colours: Yellow& navy stripes /navy blue yellow & navy blue.
Change colours:Blue and White stripes/black
Midweek Matches: Wednesday
Programme: 24 pages, 30p
Editor: Steve Newton
CLUB PERSONNEL
Chairman: Bill Laffey
Vice-Chairman: Brian Errington
Press Officer: Alan Armstrong 0191 483 2046
Manager: Tony Robinson
Coach: Norman Dryden

KENNEK RYHOPE C.A.

Secretary: Owen Haley, 34 Charter Drive,east Herrington, Sunderland SR3 3PG
Tel No: 0191 5200827 (H) 07957 621364 (M)
Ground: Meadow Park, Stockton Road, Ryhope, Sunderland (0191 523 6555)
Directions: Ground on Waterworks Road near Ryhope & Cherry Knowle Hospitals. From Sunderland follow signs for A19 South
Capacity: 2,000 Seats: 150 Cover: 200 Floodlights: Yes

HONOURS Northern League Div 2 R-Up: 1981. Northern Al'ce Lg Cup:1981.Wearside Lg (4) Lg Cup 63-64 77-7), Durham Chal.Cup 77-78, Monkwearmouth Charity Cup (3) Sunderland Shipowners Cup 61-62 (S.C.Vaux) 86-87
PREVIOUS **Names:** Ryhope C.W. (est.1898, prev.Ryhope Villa) merged with Sporting Club Vaux (est.1968 as Monkwearmouth, later Bishopwearmouth, South Hetton) in 1988; Sunderland Vaux Ryhope C.W. 88-93. Amalgamated with Kennek Roker fromWearside Lg 99
Leagues: S. C. Vaux: Tyne & Wear; N.Eastern Amat.
BEST SEASON **FA Cup** 4th Q Rd 88-89 **FA Vase** 2nd Rd 1985 **F.A.Trophy:** 3rd Rd 86

FACT FILE
Founded: 1988
Colours: Red & white stripes/black/red Change colours: All Blue
Midweek Matchday:Tuesday
Programme: Price: 50p Pages:24
Editor: Owen Haley

CLUB PERSONNEL
Chairman: W.Mathieson
Tel: 0191 534 5496 (H)
Press Officer: Secretary
Manager: Les Dodd
Physio: Iasn Palfreyman

MURTON

Secretary: Chris Fahey, 16 D'Arcy Square, Murton, Seaham, Co. Durham SR7 9LZ
Tel No: 0191 5171355(H) 07814 523289 (M) e-mail: murtonafc@yahooo.co.uk
Ground: Recreation Park, Church Lane, Murton, Co. Durham (07814 523289)
Directions: Exit A19 onto B1285 heading west into Murton - Church Lane on left opposite catholic church
Capacity: 3,500 Seats: 100 Cover: 320 Floodlights: Yes Club Shop: No
Clubhouse: `The International' 300 yards from ground on B1285. Normal pub hours. Restaurant upstairs. Matchday snacks at ground
HONOURS Northern Lg Div 2 89-90, Wearside Lg 28-29 36-37 59-60 (Lg Cup 58-5970-71), Sunderland Shipowners Cup 59-60 69-70 70-71, Monkwearmouth Charity Cup 21-22 28-29 34-35 35-36 63-64 70-71 87-88, Durham Chall. Cup 92-93, Durham Jnr Cup 50-51.
PREVIOUS **Leagues:** Wearside 13-46 51-88; North East Counties 46-51.
RECORD **Gate:** 3,500 v Spennymoor Utd, Durham Challenge Cup 1951
Appearances: Robert Welch 500 (1962-78)

FACT FILE
Founded: 1904 Nickname: Gnashers
Club Sponsors: John Hellyns
Colours: All white with red trim
Change colours: Red/black/red
Midweek matchday: Wednesday
Programme: 12 pages, 30p
Programme Editor: Stuart Upperton
CLUB PERSONNEL
Chairman: Tom Torrence
Vice Chairman: J Hudson
President: John Hellens
Press Officer: Secretary
Commercial Mgr: T Carr
Manager: Jeff Cranson
Asst Mgr: Brian Burlinson
Coach: Richie Madden Physio: Vince Symmonds

NEWCASTLE BENFIELD SAINTS

Secretary: Tony Baird, 3 Rathmore Gardens, North Shields, Tyne & Wear NE30 2SX
Ground: Benfield Park, Benfield Road, Newcastle-upon-Tyne.
Tel: 0191 265 9357
Directions: From Newcastle towards coast take 2nd exit after Corner House pub lights, right into Benfield Rd, ground on left opp. Walkergate Hosp. & adjacent to school.

FACT FILE
Colours: All Navy Blue
Change colours:All White

Chairman: Jimmy Rowe

Manager: Allan Bell
Coach: Steve Burn

NEWCASTLE BLUE STAR

GROUND: Wheatsheaf Sports Ground, Woolsington, Newcastle-on-Tyne. NE13 8DF
Tel: 0191 286 0425 **Email Address:** nbsfc@blueyonder**Club Website**: www.nbsfc,co,uk
Directions: From central station follow airport signs for 7 miles - ground next to Wheatsheaf Hotel on left, approx. 800yds before airport. Callerton Parkway metro station is 400yds from ground
Capacity: 2,000 Seats: 300 Cover: 500 Floodlights: Yes **Clubhouse:** Open every day

HONOURS FA Vase 77-78; Northern Lg R-up 87-88, Lg Cup 85-86, R-up(1), Div 2 85-86; Wearside Lg 73-74 75-76 82-83 83-84 84-85, R-up 74-75 77-78 79-80, Lg Cup76-77 79-80 80-81 82-83 83-84; Sunderland Shipowners Cup 82-83 84-85; Monkwearmouth Charity Cup 74-75 79-80 82-83 88-89; Northern Comb. 62-63 68-69, Lg Cup 66-67 71-72; Northumberland Snr Cup 76-77 82-83 85-86 87-88, R-up 74-75 78-79 80-81, Minor Cup 64-65; J R Cleator Cup 86-87.
PREVIOUS **Leagues:** Newcastle Business Houses 32-38; North East Amateur; Tyneside Amateur; Northern Comb.; Wearside 75-85
BEST SEASON FA Trophy: Qtr-finals 88-89, 1-4 v Telford Utd (H)
FA Vase: Winners 77-78, SF 81-82 **FA Cup:** 1st Rd 84-85, 0-2 v York C. (A)

FACT FILE
Founded: 1930 Nickname: `Star'
Colours: All Blue
Change colours: Red/Black/red
Midweek matchday: Tuesday
Programme: 44 pages, 60p Editor: M.Gault
CLUB PERSONNEL
Secretary: Jim Anderson
38 Western Ave., West Denton,
Newcastle NE5 5BU Tel: 0191 243 1025
Chairman: Derek Sayers
Manager/Coach: Warren Teasdale
Asst. Man.: Dean Gibb Physio: Jim Gelatly
2002-2003 Captain: Andy Cunningham
Top Scorer: Kris Heron
P.o.Y.: Michael Cunningham

NORTHALLERTON TOWN

Secretary: Ken Lomer, 28 Aysgarth Grove, Romanby, Northallerton, N. Yorks DL7 8HY
Tel: 01609 779686(H) 01609 773970 (W) **Website:** www.northallertontown.co.uk
Ground: Ainderby Rd, Romanby, Northallerton, N. Yorks. Tel: 01609 772418
Directions: Leave A1 at Leeming Bar (A684) to Northallerton, approaching town take B1333 to Romanby - ground 250yds on left. 3/4 a mile from Northallerton BR station - bus from town
Capacity: 3,000 Seats: 150 Cover: 500 Lights: Yes **Shop:** Yes, Nigel Taylor 07990 948574
Clubhouse: Mon-Fri 7.30-11pm, Sat noon-7.30pm, Sun 12-2 & 7.30-10.30pm
HONOURS Northern Lg Cup 93-94, Div 2 96-97 R-up 89-90, Harrogate & Dist. Lg.; N.Riding Snr Cup R-up 83-84; Harrogate Invit; Alverton Trophy.
PREVIOUS **Leagues:** Allertonshire; Vale of Mowbray; Ripon & Dist.; Teesside; North Yorks; Darlington & Dist.; Harrogate & Dist. **BEST SEASONS FA Cup:** 4th Qual. Rd 92-93**FA Trophy:** 3rd Rnd 92-93 **RECORD Gate:** 671 v Farnborough, FAT 3rd Rd 20/2/93
RECORD Scorer: John Woods **Appearances:** Lee Wasden **Win**: 11-0 v Ferryhill (A) **Defeat:** 1-9 v Ryhope CA (A) **Players progressing**: Andy Toman (Hartlepool)

FACT FILE
Founded: 1994 Nickname: Town
Colours: Black & White stripes,black
Change Colours: All Yellow
Midweek matchday:Wednesday
Reserves ' League: Harrogate & District
Prog.: 16 pages, 50p Ed: Ian Bolland
Local Press : N Echo, Darlington & Stockton Times, N Yorks News **CLUB PERSONNEL**
Chair: Ralph Alderson V- Chair: Les Hood
Press Officer: Ian Bolland (01609 776900)
Manager: Paul Burton Physio: T.B.A.
PREVIOUS Names: Northallerton Alliance; Northallerton Town (pre-1994).
Ground: Bluestone Ground (pre-1975)

the

town crier

Evenwood Town

Versus

South Shields

Albany Northern League Division 2

Saturday 5 April 2003

OFFICIAL PROGRAMME 50p

KENNEK RYHOPE C.A.F.C.

MEADOW PARK

ESTABLISHED 1961

Members of the Albany Northern League Division II

Main Sponsor

50p

OFFICIAL PROGRAMME

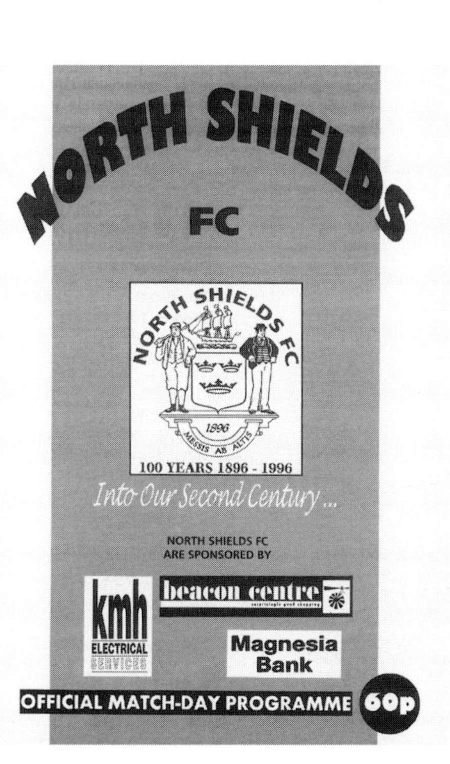

NORTH SHIELDS
FC
NORTH SHIELDS FC
1896
MESSIS AB ALTIS
100 YEARS 1896 - 1996
Into Our Second Century...
NORTH SHIELDS FC
ARE SPONSORED BY
kmh
ELECTRICAL SERVICES
beacon centre
Magnesia Bank
OFFICIAL MATCH-DAY PROGRAMME
60p

BAY WATCH
THE OFFICIAL MATCHDAY PROGRAMME OF WHITLEY BAY F.C
Whitley Bay V Guisborough Town
ALBANY NORTHERN LEAGUE
Div 1 - 2002 / 2003
WINNERS : F.A. CARLSBERG VASE
2001 / 2002
PRICE: £1.00

NORTON & STOCKTON ANCIENTS

Secretary: Anne Turnbull, 19 Tibbersley Avenue, Billingham TS23 1JP
Tel No: 01642 555712

Ground: Norton (Teesside) Sports Complex,Station Road, Norton, Stockton-on-Tees, Cleveland (01642 530203) Clubhouse (01642 5540310

Directions: Norton village 2 miles from Stockton centre, turn into Station Road on outskirts of village

Capacity: 2,000 Seats: 200 Cover: Yes Floodlights: Yes

Clubhouse: Full bar facilities, 150 yds from ground

HONOURS Northern Lg Cup 81-82

PREVIOUS **Leagues:** Teesside (pre-1982) **Name:** Norton & Stockton Cricket Club Trust

BEST SEASON **FA Cup:** 1st Qual Rd(4) 88-89 90-93 **FA Vase:**

RECORD **Attendance:** 1,430 v Middlesbrough, Friendly 88

FACT FILE

Formed: 1959 Nickname: Ancients
Colours: Amber&black side panel/black&amber side stripe/black socks
Change: White/blue/white
Midweek Matches: Tuesday
Programme: 12 pages with entry
Club Website: nortonfootball .co.uk

CLUB PERSONNEL

Chairman: Peter Aldridge
President: Barry Lee
Press Officer: Ken Steele (01642 898787)

PRUDHOE TOWN

Secretary: Chris Lowther, 10 Westhills,Tantobie, Stanley, Co.Durham DH9 9RZ
Tel: 01207 230108

Ground: Kimberley Park, Broomhouse Road, Prudhoe, Northumberland NE42 5EH
Tel/Fax: 01661 835900

Directions: To Prudhoe along A695, turn right at `Falcon' Inn, 200 yds down Eastwood Rd., left into Broomhouse Rd., ground on right

Capacity: 5,000 Seats: 150 Cover: Yes Floodlights: Yes

Clubhouse: Open every evening plus Sat/Sun lunchtimes

HONOURS Hexham & Dist. Lg 68-69 (Lg Cup 68-69), Newcastle & Dist. Lg 69-70 70-71, Lg Cup 69-70, Charity Shield 69-70 70-71), Northern Comb. 79-80, Northerm AmtrLg 71-72, Clayton Charity Cup 68-69, Northumberland Minor Cup 78-79, Northumberland Benevolent Bowl 79-80, Heddon Homes Charity Cup 81-82

PREVIOUS **Leagues:** Hexham & Dist 59-69; Newcastle & Dist 69-71; N. Comb.; N.Amtr; Northern All. 84-88 **RECORD** **Attendance:** 2,500 v Blyth, N'mberland Snr Cup 1981

FACT FILE

Founded: 1959
Nickname: Citizens
Sponsors: Swinton Insurance
Colours: Orange/blue/orange
Change: White & blue chevrons/navy/sky
Midweek Matches: Tuesday
Programme: 8 pages, 50p
Editor: Rev. Frank Campbell

CLUB PERSONNEL

Chairman: Alex Waters
Press Officer:ErnieGoodfellow (01661 836941)
Manager: Steve Smith
Asst Manager: Shaun McKenna
Physio: Ernie Goodfellow

SEAHAM RED STAR

Secretary: John Smith, 33 Frederick St.,Seaham, Co.Durham.SR7 7HX Tel: 0191 5810423 H& W

Ground: Seaham Town Park, Stockton Road, Seaham, Co. Durham (0191 581 1347)

Directions: From Tyne Tunnel: A19 Teeside approx 8 miles; B1404 Seaham slip road, left at top of slip road. Right at traffic lights & first left past school into ground

Capacity: 4,000 Seats: 60 Cover: 200 Floodlights: Yes **Club Shop:** No

Clubhouse: Mon-Sat 11am-11pm, Sun 12-2, 7-10.30pm Bars & restaurant, snooke & pool

HONOURS Northern Lg Cup 92-93, Phillips F'lit Tphy 78-79, Durham Chal. Cup 79-80, Wearside Lg 81-82 (Lg Cup 81-82, Div 2 R-up 87-88, Monkwearmouth Charity Cup R-up 79-80).

PREVIOUS **Name:** Seaham Colliery Welfare Red Star 78-87
Leagues: Sunday f'tball; Houghton & Dist. 73-74; Northern Alliance74-79; Wearside 79-83.

BEST SEASON **FA Cup:** **FA Vase:** 5th Rd 78-79 **FA Trophy** 2nd Rd 89-90

RECORDS Gate: 1,500 v Guisborough, Wearside Lg & v Sunderland, floodlight opener 1979
Scorer: Tom Henderson **Appearances:** Michael Whitfield

FACT FILE

Formed: 1973 Nickname: The Star
Colours: Red & white stripes/blacjk/black
Change colours: All blue
Midweek matchday: Wednesday
Reserves ' League: Banks Youth League
Programme: 20 pages
Editor: David Copeland (0191 581 8514)

CLUB PERSONNEL

Chairman: JohnSmith
President: Michael English
Press Officer: Secretary (079030 33014)
Manager: Chris Copeland
Asst Man.: Paul Walker
Physio: Allan Jackson

SHOTTON COMRADES

Secretary: Billy Banks, 7 Weldon Close,The Parklands,Shotton Collierey, County Durham DH6 2YJ (0191 526 7134)

Ground: Shotton Re., Station Road, Shotton Colliery, Co. Durham(0191 526 2859)

Directions: A19 to Peterlee to Shotton, right at the War Memorial t-junction, follow round 800yds, ground on right

Capacity: 1,700 Seats: 80 Cover: 400 Floodlights:Yes **Clubhouse:** No **Club Shop:** No

HONOURS Houghton & District Lg 78-79, Lg Cup x 2, Northern Alliance Lg Cup SF, Hetton Charity Cup 78-79, Peterlee Sunday Lg 75-76, Div 2 74-75; Northern Lg.Div 2 Cup R-Up. 94-95. Durham Challenge Cup QF 78-79

PREVIOUS **Leagues:** Peterlee Sunday 74-76; Houghton & Dist. 76-80; Northern Alliance 80-83

BEST SEASON **FA Cup:** 2nd Qual. Rd 85-86, 0-2 v Wingate(H) **FA Vase** 1st Rd 86-87 90-91

RECORDS **Attendance:** 1,726 v Dennis Waterman XI**Goalscorer:** Keith Willets 50
Win: 8-0 v Bedlington Ter. (H), '92 **Defeat:** 1-7 v Brandon Utd (A), FA Cup Prel. Rd 91-92
Appearances: J Cudlip **Transfer Fee received**: £500 for G Gudlip (Shildon)

FACT FILE

Formed: 1973 Nickname: Coms
Colours: Red & white stripes/black/black
Change colours: All orange
Midweek matches: Tuesday

CLUB PERSONNEL

Chairman: Colin Jobes
Vice Chairman: T Robinson
President: G Taylor
Press Officer: Secretary
Manager: Mark Watson
Physio: Bryan Maitland

2002-2003

Captain: Lee BeestonTop Scorers: Ian Bicjklerstaff & Graham Irvine

SOUTH SHIELDS F.C.

Secretary: David Fall, 50 Basil Way, South Shields NE34 8UD Tel& FAX: 0191 519 6612
Ground: Mariners Club, Filtrona Pk, Shaftesbury Ave, Jarrow, T. & W.r NE349PH(.01914279839)
Directions: From A1(M) take A194(M) to South Shields, A194 town centre road for 5 miles,ignore A1300 (Sunderland & coast) & turn left at next lights beside Co-op store into Simonside Ind. Est. (Shaftesbury Ave.), ground at bottomon right.
Capacity: 2,500 Seats: 150 Cover: 400 Floodlights: Yes
Clubhouse: Two function suites, club kitchen **Club Shop:** Yes
HONOURS Northern Lge Div 2 R-up 95-96, Northern Alliance 74-75 75-76, Wearside Lg 76-77 92-93 94-95, Monkwearmouth Charity Cup 86-87 (R-up 94-95), Shipowners Cup 92-93 (R-up 83-84)), Durham Chal. Cup 76-77 R-up 94-95. **BEST SEASON** **FA Vase** QF 75-76
PREVIOUS **Leagues:** Northern Alliance 74-76 **Ground:** Jack Clarke Park 74-92
RECORD **Attendance:** 1,500 v Spennymoor, Durham Challenge Cup Final 94-95
2002-03 Leading **Goalscorer:** Michael Haley **Captain**: Mar Jarvis P.o.Y.Ian McQueeney
L ocal Press: Shields Gazette, Newcastle Journal, Chronicle

FACT FILE
Founded: 1974 Nickname: Mariners
Colours: Claret & blue/white/white
Change: All white
Midweek matchday: Tuesday
Reserve team: None
Programme: 50p Editor: Steve Leonard

CLUB PERSONNEL
Chairman: John Rundle
Vice Chairman:T.B.A.
Press Officer: Secretary
Manager: Tony Gibson
Asst Manager:Alan Weir
Physio: Jim Wilkinson

WASHINGTON NISSAN

Secretary: Harry English, 22 Rushcliffe, Fulwell , Sunderland SR6 9RG
Tel: 0191 548 7194 (H) 0191 415 2340 (W) 07889 469961 (M)

Ground: Nissan Sports Complex, Washington Road, Sunderland SR5 3NS
Tel: 0191 415 2354 or 0191 415 2773
Directions: North along A1 (M) use A690 (signed Sunderland) connect withA19, north on A19, after passing the A1231 turn off, plant on the left. Past plant & follow signs 'Nissan Offices'.
Clubhouse: Open Mon-Fri 5-11pm, Sat 11am-11pm, Sun noon-3 & 7-10.30pm

PREVIOUS **League:** Wearside to 2001
HONOURS: Wearside Lg Div 1 93-94 (Lg Cup R-up 91-92, Div 2 Cup 92-93 93-94), Nissan European Trophy 3.

FACT FILE
Founded: 1988
Colours:Blue & Black stripes/Blue/Blue
Change colours: Red & white/white/white.
Mlidwek Matchday:
Programme: Price: Pages:
Editor:

CLUB PERSONNEL
Chairman: Alan Hill
Treasurer: J.Taylor
Press Officer: Secretary
Manager: Stan Fenwick
Assistant Manager: Keith Robertson.
Coach: Darren Ward

WHICKHAM

Secretary: Harry Hodgson, 2, Dockendale Hall, Dockendale Lane, Whickham, Newcastle upon Tyne,NE16 4EN Tel: 0191 488 2493
Ground: Glebe Ground, Rectory Lane, Whickham (0191 420 0186) **Directions:** A692 (Consett) from A69. Left at r'bout signed Consett/Whickham. Uphill and right at mini-r'bout. Continue along & turn left into Rectory Lane (by Lloyds Bank) for 500 yds, clubhouse on right
Capacity: 4,000 Seats: 100 Cover: Yes Floodlights: Yes
Clubhouse: Mon-Fri. 12-3 & 7-11, Sat.11-11, Sun. 12-2, 7.30-11 Souvenir Shop: No
HONOURS FA Vase 80-81, Wearside Lg 77-78 87-88 (R-up 80-81 84-85, Lg Cup 86-87, Monkwearmouth Charity Cup 76-77, Sunderland Shipowners Cup 77-78 80-81), Northern Comb. 69-70 72-73 73-74 (Lg Cup 60-61 73-74)
PREVIOUS **Leagues:** Derwent Valley -55; Northern Comb. 55-57 59-74; Tyneside Amtr 57-59; Wearside 74-88 **Ground:** Rectory Rec. Field
BEST SEASON **FA Cup:** 1st Qual. Rd. 89-90 **FA Vase:** Winners 80-81
RECORD **Gate**: 3,165 v Windsor & Eton, F.A. Vase SF 81

FACT FILE
Founded: 1944
Colours: Black & White stripes/ Black/Black
Change colours: All white
Midweek Matches: Wednesday Prog20p
Local Press : Newcastle Journal, Sunday Sun, Evening Chronicle
CLUB PERSONNEL
Chairman: Brian Smith Manager: Toiny Ainley
Press Officer: Tony Ainley
2002-03 Captain & P.o.Y.: Danny Hall
Top Goalscorer: Thomas Scott
Players progressing: Nigel Walker (Newcastle 1977), David Norton (Hartlepoo'l 1981), Mike Carroll (Chesterfield 1981)

WILLINGTON

Secretary: Bob Nichols, 46 Cavendish Ct, Brandon,Durham DH7 8UW Tel/ FAX 0191378 1981
Ground: Hall Lane, Hall Lane Estate, Willington, County Durham (01388 746221
Website: www.willingtonafc.free-online.co.uk
Directions: Willington is on A690 7 miles west of Durham City & 2 miles east of Crook. Northern Bus Co. operates a service through Willington from Crook or Durham City
Capacity: 2,680 Seats: 350 Cover: 400 Floodlights: Yes Club shop: Occasionally
Clubhouse: Open eves 7-11pm &Sat. matchdays 1-11pm. Bar facilities.Tea shop on matchdays
HONOURS FA Amateur Cup 49-50, R-up 38-39; Northern League 13-14 25-26 29-30, R-up 12-13 57-58 75-76, Lge Cup 24-25 25-26 27-28 30-31 31-32 48-49 56-57 74-75; Durham Benevolent Cup 48-49 50-51 57-58.
BEST SEASON FA Cup: 1st Rd rep. 73-74, 1-6 v Blackburn R (A) after 0-0.Also 1st Rd 45-46 & 50-51
FA Trophy 3rd Rd 75-76 **FA Amat. Cup:** Winners 49-50
PREVIOUS **Leagues:** Auckland & Dist. 1906-11 **Names:** Willington Temperance 1906-11
RECORD Attendance: 10,000 v Bromley, FA Amateur Cup 2nd Rd 24/1/53**Goalscorer:** Brett Cummings(92-03) 137.**Appearances:** Brett Cummings(92-03) 377

FACT FILE
Founded: 1906 Nickname: Blue & Whites
Sponsor:T.B.A.
Colours: Blue & white stripes/blue/blue
Change colours: Yellow/green/green
Midweek Matches: Tuesday
Youth League: Auckland & Dist League
Programme: 50p Editor: Keith Newton
CLUB PERSONNEL
Chairman: John Phelan
Vice-Chair:Alan Hardy
President: Hilary Armstrong M.P.
Press Officer: Sec Manager :Alan Shoulder
2002-03 Capt: Brett Cummings P.o.Y.: Marc Adamson Top Scorer: Chris Taylor

NISSAN WEARSIDE LEAGUE

FEEDER TO:
ARNOTT INSURANCE NORTHERN LEAGUE

President: W Robson **Chairman:** P J Maguire

Secretary: T Clark, 55 Vicarage Close, New Silksworth, Sunderland SR3 1JF
Tel: 0191 5211 242 Email: tclark2@virgin.net

FINAL LEAGUE TABLE 2002-03

		P	W	D	L	F	A	Pts
1	Birtley Town	34	26	4	4	120	39	82
2	Wolviston	34	25	4	5	96	43	79
3	Stokesley SC	34	25	2	7	110	49	77
4	New Marske Spts Club	34	19	4	11	85	53	61
5	Boldon Comm. Assoc.	34	18	6	10	80	55	60
6	Windscale	34	17	7	10	63	37	58
7	Darlington Railway Ath.	34	15	10	9	75	40	55
8	North Shields	34	15	6	13	74	47	51
9	Whitehaven Amateurs	34	13	4	17	49	67	43
10	Annfield Plain	34	12	6	16	53	83	42
11	Ryhope CW	34	11	5	18	60	75	38
12	Harton & Westoe (-9)	34	13	7	14	71	76	37
13	Cleadon SC	34	11	4	19	37	90	37
14	Stanley United	34	10	6	18	74	94	36
15	Jarrow	34	10	4	20	56	92	34
16	Redcar Town	34	8	7	19	54	96	31
17	Barnard Castle Glaxo	34	8	4	22	71	98	28
18	Ferryhill Athletic	34	4	2	28	44	138	14

RESULTS GRID 2002-03

		1	2	3	4	5	6	7	8	9	10	11	12	13	14	15	16	17	18
1	Annfield Plain		1-4	3-0	2-2	0-5	3-0	3-0	1-1	0-0	1-2	4-1	2-1	2-1	6-3	1-3	1-0	2-1	0-5
2	Barnard Castle Glaxo	4-1		1-6	1-3	0-5	5-2	2-2	2-5	0-2	1-1	3-4	0-1	3-3	2-1	3-4	2-2	1-5	0-3
3	Birtley Town	4-0	3-2		4-3	6-2	15-0	2-0	2-1	4-2	3-1	2-1	12-1	6-1	1-1	2-1	3-0	0-2	0-1
4	Boldon Community Assoc.	0-1	2-1	1-4		2-1	9-3	3-0	1-1	1-3	3-0	3-0	6-0	1-1	3-0	1-2	0-4	4-1	2-2
5	Darlington Railway Ath.	3-2	1-0	1-1	2-2		7-1	3-3	0-1	2-1	2-0	3-0	3-0	5-1	1-2	1-2	0-0	0-0	5-0
6	Ferryhill Athletic	2-2	0-7	3-4	1-3	0-3		5-2	1-4	0-1	1-6	1-3	5-1	0-1	2-2	1-3	6-0	0-2	1-5
7	Jarrow	3-0	4-1	0-5	1-2	1-3	3-2		3-2	2-7	5-0	0-4	2-2	4-1	4-2	2-2	3-0	0-3	0-1
8	New Marske Sports Club	6-0	5-2	1-3	0-3	2-1	7-2	7-0		0-2	4-0	1-0	5-1	3-0	5-1	2-5	2-1	2-1	1-4
9	North Shields	9-0	1-5	0-2	3-3	0-0	3-0	4-1	2-0		1-2	2-0	5-0	0-0	1-3	4-1	1-2	0-2	0-2
10	Redcar Town	2-2	2-1	0-7	1-4	2-1	5-0	7-3	1-1	1-1		0-2	1-2	0-3	3-3	0-3	0-5	0-6	0-3
11	Ryhope Colliery Welfare	6-2	4-2	2-2	1-4	1-1	1-3	3-0	0-0	0-2	9-1		1-0	3-2	1-3	1-5	3-1	0-1	2-5
12	South Shields Cleadon SC	1-1	2-0	1-3	0-2	1-1	3-0	1-2	3-2	0-5	2-1	1-1		2-4	2-1	1-3	1-2	0-1	1-4
13	South Sheilds Harton & W.	2-4	7-4	3-1	1-3	0-2	7-1	1-0	4-3	2-4	3-2	1-1	0-1		1-5	4-1	1-1	2-1	3-3
14	Stanley United	1-4	5-3	1-3	3-1	3-3	6-0	1-2	1-2	4-3	4-4	6-3	4-0	0-2		2-6	1-2	2-2	0-2
15	Stokesley SC	5-1	2-1	1-3	5-0	4-3	4-0	3-2	4-2	3-2	3-2	4-0	9-0	4-1	8-1		3-0	1-1	1-2
16	Whitehaven Amateurs	3-1	1-4	0-4	2-0	0-4	5-1	2-1	0-1	1-0	1-3	2-1	1-2	1-4	3-1	2-1		0-3	1-2
17	Windscale	1-0	1-3	2-2	1-2	1-1	3-0	5-0	1-2	1-1	3-1	3-1	0-1	1-0	2-0	0-4	2-2		2-3
18	Wolviston	2-0	7-1	0-1	3-1	1-0	3-0	3-1	1-4	3-2	3-3	5-0	1-2	4-4	7-1	1-0	5-2	0-2	

LEAGUE CUP 2002-03

FIRST ROUND

Barnard Castle Glaxo	v	Windscale	3-5	Ferryhill Athletic	v	North Shields	1-3

SECOND ROUND

Birtley Town	v	Annfield Plain	4-1	Darlington Railway Ath	v	Stanley United	4-2
Jarrow	v	New Marske Spts Club	1-1 aet (3-4p)				
Redcar Town	v	North Shields	0-1	Sth Shields Harton & Westoe	v	Whitehaven Amateurs	3-0
Stokesley SC	v	Ryhope Colliery Welfare	2-1	Windscale	v	Boldon Community Ass.	1-0
Wolviston	v	Sth Shields Cleadon SC	2-4 aet				

QUARTER-FINALS

New Marske Spts C.	v	Darlington Railway Ath.	0-4	North Shields	v	Stokesley SC	4-3
Sth Shields Harton & Westoe	v	Birtley Town	1-2	Windscale	v	Sth Shields Cleadon SC	2-1

SEMI-FINALS

Birtley Town	v	Windscale	4-1	North Shields	v	Darlington R'way Ath	2-3 aet

FINAL

Birtley Town	v	Darlington Railway Ath.	1-3 aet	16th May at Birtley Town

SUNDERLAND SHIPOWNERS CUP 2002-03

FIRST ROUND

New Marske S.C.	v	North Shields	3-0	Redcar Town	v	Windscale	5-0

SECOND ROUND

Barnard Castle Glaxo	v	Jarrow	3-2	Darlington Railway Ath.	v	Boldon Community Ass.	3-1
Redcar Town	v	Birtley Town	1-5	Ryhope Colliery W.	v	Stokesley SC	1-7
Sth Shields Cleadon SC	v	Whitehaven Amateurs	2-0	Sth Shields H & W	v	Annfield Plain	2-0
Stanley United	v	Ferryhill Athletic	8-0	Wolviston	v	New Marske S.Club	1-0

QUARTER-FINALS

Darlington Railway A	v	Birtley Town	1-0	Sth Shields Cleadon SC	v	Barnard Castle Glaxo	1-0
Stokesley SC	v	Sth Shields H & Westoe	3-1	Wolviston	v	Stanley United	3-2

SEMI-FINALS

Sth Shields Cleadon SC	v	Darlington Railway Athletic	2-2 aet (4-5p)
Wolviston	v	Stokesley SC	3-1

FINAL

Wolviston	v	Darlington Railway Athletic	1-0	5th May at Wolviston

MONKWEARMOUTH CHARITY CUP 2002-03

FIRST ROUND

Stanley United	v	Annfield Plain	3-1	Windscale	v	Whitehaven Amateurs	4-1

SECOND ROUND

Boldon Com. Ass.	v	Darlington Railway Ath	0-2	Ferryhill Athletic	v	Wolviston	3-2
Jarrow	v	North Shields	1-3	New Marske Sports C.	v	Birtley Town	0-1
Sth Shields Cleadon SC	v	Ryhope Colliery Welfare	4-2	Stanley United	(walkover)	Redcar Town	
Stokesley SC	v	South Shields H. & W.	2-5	Windscale	v	Barnard Castle Glaxo	1-2

QUARTER-FINALS

Ferryhill Athletic	v	Sth Shields Cleadon SC	1-0	North Shields	v	Birtley Town	2-0
Sth Shields H. & W.	v	Barnard Castle Glaxo	4-0	Stanley United	v	Darlington Railway Ath	0-5

SEMI-FINALS

Darlington Railway Ath.	v	South Shields H. & W.	3-1 aet	North Shields	v	Ferryhill Athletic	6-0

FINAL

Darlington Railway Ath.	v	0 North Shields	0-3	21st April at Darlingon Railway Athletic

ANNFIELD PLAIN

Secretary: M Lawson, 24 Northgate, Anfield Plain, Stanley, Co. Durham DH9 7UY
Ground: Derwent Park, West Road, Annfield Plain
Directions: On A693 road to Consett, 200yds west of junction with A6067. Ground behind new housing estate. 6 miles fromDurham (BR). Buses from Sunderland, Newcastle & Durham.
Capacity: 6,000 Seats: 20 Cover: 200 Floodlights: No
HONOURS Wearside Lg 84-85 (Monkwearmouth Charity Cup 92-93),
FA Cup: 1st Rd 26-27 28-29 64-65.

Founded: 1890.
Colours: Claret/white/blue
Change colours: All blue.
Programme: 16 pages, 20p

Chairman: Frank Ross
Treasurer :Marshall Lawson
Manager: D Longstaff
Press Officer: Frank Ross

BARNARD CASTLE GLAXO

Ground: Glaxo Sports & Social Club, Harmire Road, Barnard Castle, Co. Durham
Tel: 01833 638926

BIRTLEY TOWN

Secretary: Kevin McConnell, 8 Laybourn Place, Birtley DH3 1PL Tel No: 0191 4100 495
Commercial Manager: Ray Stafford.
Ground: Birtley Sports Complex. **Directions:** (From Durham) Off A1(M) signpsted for Chester-le-Street, take 2nd turn off r-bout signed Birtley, take last turnoff next r-bout (still signed Birtley), after one and a half miles take 1stleft after AEI Cables - ground at rear of sports complex.
Capacity: Unknown Seats: None Cover: None Floodlights: No.
Clubhouse: Matchdays only
HONOURS: Wearside Lg 45-46 (Lg Cup 35-36), Northern Alliance 23-24 (R-up 13-14).

Founded: 1890 Reformed: 1986
Colours: Green&white hoops/white/green
Change colours: Yellow/blue/red.
Midweek matches: Wednesday
Sponsors: C & C Coachworks
Chairman: John Heslington
Vice-Chairman: J Grainger.
Manager: Barry Fleming
Asst Manager: David Smith
Coach: Malcolm Thompson

BOLDON COMMUNITY ASSOCIATION

Secretary: Tom Robson, 16 Hardie Drive, West Boldon ,Tyne & Wear NE36 0JH.
Ground: Boldon Community Association, New Road, Boldon Colliery.
Directions: A19 to junc A184 Sunderland/Newcastle. Follow signs to Boldon Asdastores, then to North Road Social Club (SHACK). Ground behind. 800 yds fromEast Boldon (BR). Buses 533, 531, 319, 528.
Capacity: 3,500 Seats: 100 Cover: 400 Floodlights: No
Clubhouse: Matchdays only. Bar snacks
HONOURS: Wearside Lg 3, (Lg Cup 3), M/mouth Char Cup 2, Shipowners Cup 6.

Founded: 1892. Nickname: Villa
Colours: Black & Blue Stripes/ Black/Blue
Change: Scarlet & black
Chairman:Kevin Oliver
Vice Chairman: G Smith
President: A Brewster.
Manager: Bill Newham
Asst Manager: P Quinn
Coach: Tommy Frazer.
Press Off. / Comm. Man.: Secretary

DARLINGTON RAILWAY ATHLETIC

Secretary: Martyn Jackson, 6 Westlands Rd., Darlington,Co.Durham DL3 9JJ
Tel Nos: 01325 240495 (H) 0870 370095 (M)
Ground: Railway Social Club, Brinkburn Road,Darlington, Co Durham
Capacity: 1,000 **Seats:** None **Cover**: 50 **Floodlights** : Planned
Directions: Take A68 off A1 towards Darlington. Turn left opposite pub on right into Brinkburn Road and ground is 400 yards on left.
Clubhouse: Yes. It serves all sports at complex.
Honours: Auckland & Dist Lg & Cup, Darlington & The SacristonCharity Cups, 00-01

Reformed 1996

Colours: Dark blue & light blue stripes, blue shorts and socks.
Change Colours: Red & black quarters, black shorts and socks.

Manager: Dave Woodcock
Programme : Yes Editor: Robert Harman

FERRYHILL ATHLETIC

Secretary: Norman Bellwood, 49 Rush Park, Bishop Auckland DL14 6NS
Tel: 01388 451065 (H)
Football Secretary: Rob Ridley, 31 Ravensworth Road, Ferryhill Tel: 0780 3803335
Ground: Dean Bank Recreation Ground
Directions: The ground is situated on the old Dean & Chapter Colliery Welfare site west of the old Athletic ground at Darlington Road. From the top of Darlington Road with the Black Bull on your right, pass over the bridge crossing the A167 cutting. Dean Bank school is immediately on your left, turn left at the one way traffic restriction. Follow the signs to Dean Bank Rec.

Colours: Black & amber/amber/black & amber
Change: Red & white/red/red & white

Chairman: Secretary
Press Officer: Jimmy O'Sullivan
Tel: 01740 635524

GATESHEAD RESERVES

Secretary: Ray Kipling Tel: 07789 846333
Ground: International Stadium, Neilson Road, Gateshead, NE10 0EF.
Tel: 0191 478 3883 Fax : 0191 427 5211.
Directions: From the South follow A1(M) to Granada services (Birtley),take right hand fork marked A194(M) (Tyne Tunnel, South Shields) follow A194 to first roundabout, turn left onto A184 - then 3 miles to stadium. Turn right at traffic lights into Neilson Road. BY RAIL to Newcastle Central Station,transfer to the Metro System and then to Gateshead Stadium.
Capacity: 11,795 Seats: 11,795 Cover: 3,300

Formed: 2003
Colours: White with black trim/ black/ white
Change colours: Claret & Blue

Chairman: Mike Gulson
Press Officer: Dean Ranyard

JARROW

Secretary: Susan Scott,46 Breamish Street, Jarrow. NE32 5SH (0191 4248610)

Ground: Perth Green Community Centre.
Directions: From A19 or A1(M) followdrections to South Shields, right onto John Reid Road. First slip road ontoBrockley Whinns Estate, follow road past Red Hackle pub, third left left ontoInverness Road, then right into Perth Green Community Centre.

HONOURS: Sth Tyne Lg & Lg Cup, Washington Lg R-up 89-90 (Lg Cup 90-91, Aged Peoples Tphy R-up 90-91), Gateshead Charity Cup 90-91, Durham Tphy R-up 90-91.

Founded: 1980.
Colours: Blue & white/blue/blue
Change: Green/black/green

Chairman: B.Tyreman
Treasurer: Jimmy Kane

NEW MARSKE

Secretary: Peter Livingstone, 5 Guisborough Rd, Thornaby on Tees TS17 8BE
Tel: 01642 646428 (H) 01642 606803 (B)

Ground: Gurney Street, New Marske, Redcar
Directions: A19 south onto A174 Redcar- Teesport. Follow A174 towards Saltburn turn right at roundabout with footbridge over road. Ground 500 yds on left.

Colours: Yellow & black/navy/navy or white
Change colours: Blue & black/navy/navy

Charmain: Errol Richter
Tel: 01947 600296
Press Officer: Tony Saunders

NORTH SHIELDS

Secretary: Dave Thompson, 38 Barnstable Road, North Shields. Tel: 0191 259 0249
Ground: Ralph Gardner Park, West Percy Rd., N.Shields, Tyne & Wear, NE29 OES
Directions: South: Through Tyne Tunnel, follow signs to North Shields. Travel along Howden Rd (A187) past N.Shields sports centre on left. Continue to next r'about and take 2nd left onto Coach Lane (signposted Tynemouth) then take 4th left into West Percy Rd. Ground on left, entrance next left. West: From Newcastle take A1058 Coast Rd. At Billy Mill r-about turn right, signed N.Shields, continue over min r-about towards Town Centre. At next r'about (Collingwood Arms) turn right, then second left, ground on left.
Clubhouse: None
HONOURS: FA Amateur Cup 68-69, Northern Lge 68-69, N.C.E. Prem. Div. 91-92, R-up 89-90, 90-91, Lge. Cup 90-91, Presidents Cup 91-92. Wearside Lge 98-99, 01-02 R-up 00-0. Sunderland Suipwneas Cup 98-99. Monkwearmouth Charity Cup 00-01. Northumberland Senior Bowl 98-99, 00-01.

Founded: 1896
Nickname: Robins
Sponsors: Beacon Centre/E.D.S.
Colours: All red
Change colours: Blue & black/black/black

Chairman: Alan Matthews.
Treasurer:Mike Taylor
Manager: T.B.A .Coach: Wilf Keilty.

2002-03
Leading Goalscorer: Micahel Chilton
Captain: Anthony Robson
Player of the Year: Anthony Robson

RYHOPE C.W.

Secretary: George McKitterick, 8 Kilburn Close, Ryhope Village, Sunderland. SR2 0QU
Tel: 0191 523 8436)
Ground: Ryhope Recreation Park, Ryhope Street, Ryhope, Sunderland Tel: 0191 521 2843
Directions: Take A19 (3 miles south of Sunderland centre) to Ryhope village, atVillage Green turn into Evelyn Terrace/Ryhope Street and carry on up bank pastPresto's for 600 yds - ground appears on left. 3 miles from Sunderland Central(BR), bus every 10 mins from Sunderland centre.
Capacity: 1,000 Seats: No Cover: No Floodlights: Yes
HONOURS: Wearside Lg 4, (Lg Cup 2), Durham Chall Cup 77-78, M/mouth Charity Cup3, S/land Shipowners Cup 2

Founded: 1988.

Colours: Yellow/black/black & red
Change colours: Red/white/red & white

Chairman:: G. Routledge
Press Officer: Peter Grainge

SOUTH SHIELDS CLEADON F.C.

Secretary: Douglas Keys,3 Paragon Way,Holder Hause Estate, South Shields. NE34 8TA
Tel No: 0191 536 7434
Ground: Jack Clarke Park, South Shields.
Directions: Enter South Shields on A194 to r'bout taking you on to A1300 JohnReid Rd. 2nd left at 3rd r'bout into King George Rd then Sunderland Rd, rightat lights into Grosvenor Rd, left into Horsly Hill Rd. Ground on right
Clubhouse: Cleadon Social Club, Fulwell Ave, S Shields. Normal pub hours except Saturday.
HONOURS: Wearside Lg Div 2 90-91, Shields & Dist. Lg, Washington Lg 77-78 84-85

Nickname: The Club
Sponsors: Cleadon & Dist. Soc. Club
Colours: Yellow/black/black
Change: All red
Midweek matches: Wednesday
Chairman: Gordon Ferries
Vice-Chairman/Press Off . /Manager:
David Wood (0191 455 4607).
Asst Man: Steve Duguid
Commercial Manager: Joan Wood

SOUTH SHIELDS HARTON & WESTOE

Colours: All Blue
Change colours: All red

Chairman: Ronald Wightman
Treasurer: Gordon Smith

Secretary: Alan Bell, 31 Meldon avenue, South Shields, Tyne & Wear NE34 0EL
Tel Nos: 0191 4218233 (H) 0191 4301446 (W)

Groun: Harton Colliery Welfare.

Directions: A1M at Whitemare Pool take A194 to South Shields for 2 1/2 miles. At third roundabout turn right onto A1300. At 2nd roundabout turn left onto Boldon Lane. Ground 50 yards on right

STOKESLEY SPORTS CLUB

Colours: Red & black/black/black
Change: White/red/red

Chairman: Eric Taylor 01642 273934
Press Officer: secretary

Secretary: Peter Grainge, 77 Darnton Drive, Easterside, Middlesbrough TS4 3RF
Tel: 01642 273934

Ground: Stokesley Sports Ground, Broughton Road, Stokesley

Directions: A19 to Middlesbrough, then A174 turn to Whitby/Teesport. At 3rd turning up slip road A172 to Stokesley. Go over the 1st r'about, at next r'about turn to Stokesley, 5 miles. At next r'about keep left to next r'about. Ground 100 yards on left.

NISSAN UK (formerly Washington Nissan reserves)

Colours:Blue & Black stripes/Blue/Blue
Change colours: Red & white/white/white.

Chairman: Alan Hill
Treasurer: J.Taylor
Press Officer: Secretary

Secretary: Harry English, 22 Rushcliffe, Fulwell , Sunderland SR6 9RG
Tel: 0191 548 7194 (H) 0191 415 2340 (W) 07889 469961 (M)

Ground: Nissan Sports Complex, Washington Road, Sunderland SR5 3NS
Tel: 0191 415 2354 or 0191 415 2773

Directions: North along A1 (M) use A690 (signed Sunderland) connect withA19, north on A19, after passing the A1231 turn off, plant on the left. Past plant & follow signs 'Nissan Offices'

PREVIOUS **League:** Wearside Combination

WHITEHAVEN AMATEURS

Colours: Yellow/blue/yellow
Change colours: White/navy/white

Chairman: Bill Robson.
Press Officer: Secretary
Manager: Ian Green
Assistant Manager: Ian Atkins

Secretary: Richard Stamp, Johnson House, Hillcrest Avenue, Whitehaven, CA28 6SU
Tel: 01946 61877

Ground: Whitehaven County Ground, Coach Road, Whitehaven

Directions: Barrow on A595, ignore branch to town centre at B.P. garage turn right at t/lights on A5094. 1/2 mile turn left at Esso garage into Coach Rd. Narrow lane ent immed after level crossing to grd behind Rugby Lge Stadium.

HONOURS: Cumberland Cup 90-91, County League 87-88 88-89, Wearside Lg Div 2 Cup R-up 93-94.

WINDSCALE

Founded: 1950
Colours:White & Navy Blue/ Navy/White
Change: Blue & white/royal/royal

Chairman: R Napier
Press Officer: Secretary
Treasurer: A Barwise

Secretary: Craig Heggie, 12 Bookwell, Egremont, Cumbria CA2 2LS
Tel: 01946 823587 (H) 01946 788337 (W)

Ground: Falcon Field, Egremont.

Directions: A66 to Bridgefoot. A595 Barrow,bottom of hill approaching Egremont take 3rd turn off island (signed)Smithfield/Gillfoot, ground in housing estate

HONOURS: Furness Senior Cup 1985-86

WOLVISTON

Founded: 1910 Nickname: Wolves
Sponsors: R.C.I. Industrial Cleaners
Colours: Royal blue/blue/white
Change: Red & white/red/white
Chairman: Eddie Poole
President: Bob Smith
Vice Chairman: Derek Stockton
Press Officer: Andy Anderson
Manager: John Johnson
Asst Manager: Kevin Smith
Coach: Alan Lucas

Secretary: Keith Simpson, 14 Lodore Grove, Acklam, Middlesbrough TS5 8PB 01642 823734

Ground: Metcalfe Way, Wynyard Road, Wolviston, Billingham, Cleveland TS22 5NE.

Directions: On Wynyard Road between Thorpe Thewles & Wolviston. A19 onto A689 into Wolviston village, take Wynyard Road towards Thorpe Thewles, grd left before Sir John Halls Estate.

Capacity: 2,000 Seats: None Cover: 200 Floodlights: No Club Shop: No.

Clubhouse: Licensed bar. Hot & cold meals. Open 11am-11pm on matchdays.

HONOURS: Wearside Lg Div 2 89-90, Lg Cup R-up 92-93, Teesside Lg R-up 84-85, Lg Cup 86-87, Durham FA Trophy R-up 89-90, Stockton & Dist. Lg 3, LgCup 3, Lg Charity Cup 79-80.

Record Gate: 500 v Middlesbrough 27/7/93

HUMAN
KINETICS

HUMAN
KINETICS

WADE ASSOCIATES NORTHERN FOOTBALL ALLIANCE

President: Les Todd **Chairman:** George Dobbins
Secretary: John McLackland, 92 Appletree Gardens
Walkerville, Newcastle upon Tyne NE6 4SX Tel: 0191 2621636
Press Officer: Bill Gardner Tel/Fax: 0191 4883422 Email: bill.gardner@eidosnet.co.uk

FINAL LEAGUE TABLES 2002-03

PREMIER DIVISION		P	W	D	L	F	A	Pts
1	Newcastle Benfield Saints	30	23	3	4	81	35	72
2	Carlisle City	30	20	6	4	64	29	66
3	West Allotment Celtic	30	19	8	3	71	25	65
4	Shankhouse	30	17	7	6	61	41	58
5	Northbank Carlisle	30	16	3	11	64	40	51
6	Ponteland United	30	12	6	12	65	52	42
7	Winlaton Hallgarth	30	10	9	11	45	50	39
8	Harraby Catholic Club (-6)	30	11	10	9	38	47	37
9	Ryton	30	10	6	14	56	67	36
10	Walker Central (-3)	30	9	8	13	38	45	32
11	Amble United	30	8	8	14	30	54	32
12	Bedlington Terriers 'A'	30	8	7	15	41	51	31
13	Newcastle University (-3)	30	9	6	15	50	52	30
14	Spittal Rovers (-3)	30	8	3	19	47	72	24
15	Percy Main Amateurs	30	4	10	16	29	61	22
16	Seaton Delaval Amateurs	30	3	6	21	23	82	15

DIVISION ONE		P	W	D	L	F	A	Pts
1	Chopwell Top Club	26	19	2	5	71	41	59
2	Northumbria University	26	17	3	6	86	25	54
3	Walker Fosse	26	15	6	5	75	45	51
4	Procter & G. Heddon	26	14	6	6	55	39	48
5	Heaton Stannington	26	12	5	9	75	48	41
6	Cramlington Town	26	13	2	11	55	47	41
7	Haydon Bridge United	26	11	5	10	69	52	38
8	Cullercoats (-3)	26	12	3	11	42	57	36
9	Wark	26	9	3	14	66	92	30
10	Newbiggin Cent. Welf.	26	6	9	11	49	79	27
11	Wallington	26	7	5	14	30	59	26
12	Cowgate Sports Club (-6)	26	8	5	13	51	60	23
13	Rutherford Newcastle	26	4	4	18	42	85	16
14	Hebburn Reyrolle (-3)	26	4	4	18	25	62	13

DIVISION TWO		P	W	D	L	F	A	Pts
1	Blyth Town	22	18	2	2	69	26	56
2	Newc. EE Rail Club	22	15	2	5	60	31	47
3	Wallsend Town	22	13	4	5	54	38	43
4	Newcastle BT	22	11	3	8	64	46	36
5	Forest Hall	22	10	6	6	50	52	36
6	Ashington Colliers	22	10	5	7	48	28	35
7	Stobhill Rangers	22	7	5	10	33	39	26
8	Highfields United (-3)	22	8	5	9	38	58	26
9	Birtley (-3)	22	6	4	12	48	53	19
10	Walker Stack FOS	22	3	3	16	38	76	12
11	Otterburn (-13)	22	6	4	12	38	57	9
12	Walker Wincomblee	22	1	5	16	42	78	8

PREMIER DIVISION RESULTS CHART 2002-03

		1	2	3	4	5	6	7	8	9	10	11	12	13	14	15	16
1	Amble United		1-0	1-1	1-0	2-5	0-3	0-3	1-1	1-0	4-2	1-1	1-3	3-0	0-1	0-0	2-1
2	Bedlington Terriers 'A'	3-0		0-2	0-0	1-3	0-1	1-1	1-1	4-3	2-4	4-1	3-1	1-2	1-0	1-3	5-1
3	Carlisle United	2-0	1-0		1-1	2-2	0-0	2-0	3-0	2-1	5-1	4-0	3-1	3-0	0-2	3-3	5-1
4	Harraby Catholic Club	2-1	2-1	1-3		0-3	3-2	0-2	1-1	2-1	0-0	1-1	1-0	3-1	2-0	1-5	1-0
5	Newcastle Benfield Saints	0-2	3-0	3-0	4-0		1-0	3-0	1-0	4-2	2-1	6-1	2-0	3-0	1-1	0-5	2-1
6	Newcastle University	0-0	2-3	1-4	3-0	2-3		0-3	2-0	1-4	3-0	7-0	2-3	1-2	2-1	0-3	5-0
7	Northbank Carlisle	3-1	6-1	0-1	1-2	3-0	3-0		5-0	3-2	2-3	2-1	0-2	7-1	2-2	1-3	5-2
8	Percy Main Amateurs	1-1	0-2	3-2	1-1	0-2	1-0	1-2		2-5	1-2	2-2	1-3	1-0	0-2	1-1	1-1
9	Ponteland United	4-0	1-1	2-3	2-0	1-6	1-1	0-2	2-2		3-0	7-0	2-2	4-2	3-0	0-2	0-0
10	Ryton	2-3	2-0	0-1	0-3	3-3	2-1	3-0	1-0	3-4		8-2	2-2	5-2	3-4	1-1	0-0
11	Seaton Delaval Amateurs	1-0	0-0	0-1	3-3	0-7	1-1	0-2	0-2	0-2	2-4		1-2	1-0	1-2	0-2	0-1
12	Shankhouse	2-0	1-1	3-2	2-2	2-4	3-1	2-0	4-3	3-2	7-2	1-0		1-1	2-0	0-0	1-0
13	Spittal Rovers	6-0	3-2	0-1	2-4	0-2	4-4	1-1	4-2	1-3	3-0	2-0	3-4		3-1	0-2	2-4
14	Walker Central	2-2	2-1	2-4	1-1	0-2	0-1	1-2	0-0	1-1	4-0	1-2	0-3	3-0		0-2	1-1
15	West Allotment Celtic	4-1	1-1	1-1	4-0	5-1	4-1	3-2	3-1	1-2	1-0	5-1	0-0	4-1	2-3		0-2
16	Winlaton Hallgarth	1-1	3-1	0-2	1-1	1-3	3-3	2-1	7-0	3-1	2-2	2-1	2-1	2-1	1-1	0-1	

STAN SEYMOUR LEAGUE CUP

FIRST ROUND

Amble United	v	Carlisle City	0-3
Cullercoats	v	Newbiggin Central W.	4-0
Heaton Stannington	v	Seaton Delaval Am.	1-2
Percy Main Amateurs	v	Shankhouse	2-4
Spittal Rovers	v	West Allotment Celtic	1-2
Cramlington Town	v	Harraby Catholic Club	5-2
Haydon Bridge Utd	v	Rutherford Newcastle	2-1
Hebburn Reyrolle	v	Winlaton Hallgarth	3-4
Ponteland United	v	Northumbria Uni.	3-2
Walker Fosse	v	Newcastle Benfield S	0-7

SECOND ROUND

Ashington Colliers	v	N'castle East End R.C.	4-1
Carlisle City	v	Blyth Town	3-3 (aet) 5-4pens
Cramlington Town	v	Otterburn	2-1
Newcastle Benfield S.	v	Chopwell Top Club	3-1
Newcastle University	v	Wallsend Town	4-3
Procter & Gamble He.	v	Highfields United	3-0
Walker Central	v	Cullercoats	4-1
Wark	v	Walker Wincomblee	5-2
Bedlington Ter. 'A'	v	Northbank Carlisle	0-2
Cowgate Sports Club	v	Walker Stack FOS	3-1
Haydon Bridge Utd	v	Forest Hall	15-1
Newcastle British Tel.	v	West Allotment Celtic	1-7
Ponteland United	v	Shankhouse	0-5
Seaton Delaval Am.	v	Birtley	2-4
Wallington	v	Stobhill Rangers	3-1 (aet)
Winlaton Hallgarth	v	Ryton	1-2

THIRD ROUND

Ashington Colliers	v	Shankhouse	1-0
Cowgate Sports Club	v	Newcastle Benfield S	2-3
Haydon Bridge United	v	Ryton	1-2
Walker Central	v	Newcastle University	0-1
Carlisle City	v	Wark	4-0
Cramlington Town	v	Wallington	3-2
Procter & Gamble H	v	Northbank Carlisle	0-5
West Allotment Celtic	v	Birtley	8-0

QUARTER-FINALS

Ashington Colliers	v	West Allotment Celtic	0-1
Newcastle University	v	Cramlington Town	0-0 (aet) 3-0pens
Northbank Carlisle	v	Carlisle City	3-3 (aet) 2-4pens
Newcastle Benfield S	v	Ryton	6-3

SEMI-FINALS

Newcastle Benfield S	v	Newcastle University	3-0
West Allotment Celtic	v	Carlisle City	5-1

FINAL

West Allotment Celtic v Newcastle Benfield Saints 3-2 (aet) 5th May at Heaton Stannington

CHALLENGE CUP

FINAL

Carlisle City v West Allotment Celtic 3-4 (aet)
30th April at Penrith

COMBINATION CUP

FINAL

Cramlington Town v Northumbria Uni 0-0 (aet) 3-4p
28th April at Percy Main Amateurs

PREMIER DIVISION

CARLISLE CITY

Secretary: Jackie Williamson,14 Etterby Street, Stanwix, Carlisle Tel No: 01228 523798
Ground: The Sheepmount Sports Complex, Carlisle (01228 265599).
Directions: B6264 Brampton-Carlisle road & follow Workington signs, dual-c'way down hill (Carlisle Castle on right), where road intersects double back on yourself and take turning left just before castle, follow down hill keeping left until ground.

Colours: Sky & Navy hoops/navy
Change colours: White/navy

Chairman: Jackie Ewbank
Manage/Coach: Willie Armstrong.

CHOPWELL TOP CLUB

Ground Chopwell Park, Chopwell, Newcastle-upon-Tyne, Tyne & Wear

EPPLETON COLLIERY WELFARE

Secretary: John Tweddle, 40 Station Road, Hetton le Hole, Tyne & Wear DH50AT
Te: 0191 526 9633
Ground: Eppleton Welfare Park, Park View, Hetton-le-Hole, Tyne & Wear (01915261048)
Directions: Situated behind Front Street Post Office & directly behind Hetton swimming baths, Hetton-le-Hole on A182. Buses 194, 535, 231, X5, X94 in Front Street. 8 miles from Durham BR station; buses 154 and 254 from Durham
Capacity: 2,500 Seats: 250 Cover: 500 Floodlights: Yes
HONOURS Northern Lg Div 2 R-up 92-93, Wearside Lg 90-91 91-92 (Lg Cup 74-75 78-79 87-88, Sunderland Shipowners Cup 47-48 85-86 90-91 (R-up 91-92), Monkwearmouth Charity Cup 89-90 90-91 91-92), Durham Challenge Cup 89-90.
PREVIOUS **Leagues:** Wearside 51-65 74-92; Houghton & Dist. 65-74; Northern Lge 92-2003

Founded: 1929
Nickname: Welfare
Colours: Black & sky/black/black
Change colours : Yellow/green/green
Midweek matchday: Wednesday
Programme: 16 pages, 50p Editor:

Chairman: Ralph Lawson
President: J. Storey
Press Officer: Secretary
Manager: Vin Pearson
Asst Manager: John Cullen

HARRABY CATHOLIC CLUB 1999

Secretary: Mike Little, 34 Springfield Road, Harraby, Carlisle CA1 3QR (01228 512887)
Ground: Harrowby Community Centre, Edghill Road,Harraby
Directions: A69 over M^ to Rosehill roundabout.Second ledft on Eastern Way. First left after 3/4 mile into Arnside Road. End of road left into Edghill Road

Colours:All white
Change colours: Old gold and black

Chairman/Press Officer: Richard Wilson
Manager/Coach: Bobby Rutherford & Kevin Robson

NEWCASTLE UNIVERSITY

Secretary: Simon Kent, 8/10 Myrtle Grove,JesmondNewcastle -u-TyneNE2 3HT(0191 2093609)
Ground: Cochrane Park, Etherstone Avenue, Newcastle -u-Tyne
Directions: From Newcastle via Jesmond to coast road.Take first slip road after Jesmond Dene and immediately after lights at the Corner House.Then take first slip road and left again onto A188 and right at first roundabout at the garage into Etherstone Avenue. Ground is 200 metres on left

Colours: All blue
Change colours: White/navy

Chairman: Simon Kent
Manager: T.B.A.

NORTHBANK CARLISLE

Secretary: David Bell,4 Carlislwe Road, Dalston ,Cumbria CA5 7NG (01228 711095)
Ground: Sheepmount Sports Complex, Carlisle
Directions: B6264 from Bampton to Carlisle, follow Workington sign, past Carlisle Castle on right. Where dual carriageway intersects take next right and travel back towards Castle. Turn left before castle & keeping left follow the road to Complex

Colours: Red & white/red
Change colours: Yellow & navy/navy

Chairman: Kenny Brown
Manager: Bob Lancaster

NORTHUMBRIA UNIVERSITY

Ground Bullocksteads Sports Ground, Kenton Bank Foot, Newcastle-upon-Tyne

PERCY MAIN AMATEURS

Secretary: Len Renham, 7 Stanley Crescent, Whitley Bay, Tyne & wear NE26 2 EB
Tel No: (0191 2902768)
Ground: Purvis Park , St John's Green,Percy Main, North Shields.
Directions: A19 Tyne tunnel follow signs for Royal Quays and take seconsd left after school Ground is first turning on the right adjacent to Percy Main cricket club.t after Percy Main schol

Colours: Claret & blue/claret
Change colours: All Blue

Chairman: G.Marsh
ManagerBob Rodgerson
Coach: John Humbertson

PONTELAND UNITED

Secretary: L McMahon, 1 Wardle Drive, Annitsford, Cramlingham NE23 7DB (0191250 0463).
Ground: Ponterland leisure Centre Ponteland (01661 825441)
Directions: Left at lights entering Ponteland from N'castle, ground 100m on left adjacent to Leisure Centre.
Colours: Black & White stripes/Black **Change Colours:** All yellow

Chairman:Alan Birkinshaw
Manager : Barry Wardrobe
Coach:Steve Baxter

RYTON

Secretary: Les Robson, 31 Park View Gardens, Runhead, Ryton, Tyne & wear NE40 3JD
Tel: 0191 413 7628
Ground: Kingsley Park, Crawcrook, (Tel No: 0191 413 4448)
Directions: West from Newcastle, over Scotswood Bridge and take A695to Blaydon roundabout. A617 and go through Ryton until traffic lights at Crawcrook. Turn righ when signposted to Wylam and Clara Vale ground is 400 yds on right.

Colours: Blue & black/black
Change colours: Orange/black

Chairman: Michael Williams
Manage Stevan Kendall
Coach: K.Dixon

SEATON DELAVAL AMATEURS

Secretary: Bill Fellows, 11 Ridley Street, Klondyke, Cramlington NE23 6RH (01670 731833)
Ground: Wheatridge Park, Seaton Delaval.
Directions: A189 from Newcastle, at Annitsford r'bout A190 to Seaton Delaval,left at r'bout entering village, ground 450yds on right next to Deal Garage and behind Market Garden. 3 miles from Cramlington BR station. Bus 363 from Newcastle passes ground.

Colours: Sky/black
Change colours: Yellow/blue

Chairman: Tom Ashburn
Manager/Coach: Steve Armstrong

SHANKHOUSE

Secretary: Syd Ramsey, 6 Brinkburn Ave, Cramlington, Northumberland NE23 6TB
Tel: 01670 715943
Ground: Action Park, Dudley.
Directions: Tyne Tunnel A19 to Moor Farm roundabout at Anitsford. A1 exit to Morpeth and leave at first slip road.Left at junction (to Dudley) turn right to Seaton Burn at roundabout.Then immediate right after Weetslade club and ground is signposted.

Colours: Yellow/blue
Change colours: White/blue

Chairman: George Davison
Manager: Garry Kirkup

SPITTAL ROVERS

Secretary: G Burn, 7 Sea Road, Spittal, Berwick-on-Tweed TD15 1RN (01289306049).

Ground: Newfields, Berwick-on-Tweed.
Directions: From south take Berwick by-pass to 3rd r'bout. Safeway Store on right - pitch reached by taking 2nd left on r'bout.

Chairman: Noel Evans
Vice Chairman: Paul Renton
Manager/Coach: Carl Hudson

Colours: Black & white stripes/black
Change colours: Green/Black

WALKER CENTRAL

Secretary: BobMulroy, 31 Dalton Cres., Byker Wall, Newcastle-upon-Tyne NE62DA
Tel: 0191 265 7803

Ground: Monkchester Recreation Ground, Walker, Newcastle.
Directions: From City: Shields Rd to Union Rd, to Welbeck Rd, right into Monkchester Rd, left into pitch (between houses) opposite Norbury Grove.

Club colours: White and black
Change colours: All Blue
Chairman: R T McClellan
Manager/Coach: Ray Mulroy/Billy Johnson

WEST ALLOTMENT CELTIC

Secretary: Mark Hedley,12 Co-operative Terrace,West Allotment, Tyne and Wear NE27 0DU
Tel No: 0191 2702178
Ground: Blue Flames Sports Ground, Benton
Directions: From Newcastle take A189 to the roundabout at junction with A191. Folllow road east for one and a half miles.Immediatley after Station Road (B1317) junction and traffic lights, turn right into ground.

Colours: Green& white hoops, green,green
Change colours: All Blue

Chairman: Joe Mather
Manager: Terry Mitchell

WINLATON HALLGARTH

Secretary: Robert Young, Alwinton, 21B California, Winlaton Tyne & Wear NE21 6NG
Tel No: 0191 4144363)
Ground: Shibdon Park, Shibdon Road, Blaydon-on-Tyne, Tyne & Wear.
Directions: From north, over A1 Scotswood Bridge to 1st slip road, take Swalwell and Consett road to r'bout, right, Blaydon Baths car park and ground 400yds on right. From South past Metro Centre to Swalwell, then on to Blaydon and the Blaydob Baths car park.

Colours: Green & Black
Change colours: Blue & white/blue
Chairman: R obertYoung
Manager/CoachStephen Brown

SOUTH CLEVELAND GARAGES TEESSIDE FOOTBALL LEAGUE

FEEDER TO: NORTHERN LEAGUE

President: J Corner **Chairman:** L Crossman

Secretary: R D Marsay, 12 Aislaby Court, Wilton Lane, Guisborough, Cleveland TS14 6TG

Tel: 01287 637087 Fax: 01287 281051 Email: dmarsay@ntlworld.com

HONOURS LIST 2002-03

League Champions	Grangetown BC	**JV Madden Trophy Winners**	Grangetown BC
Runners up	Nunthorpe Athletic	Finalists	Thornaby FC
Macmillan Bowl Winners	Grangetown BC	**Player of the Year**	Ian Thompson
Finalists	Bedale FC		(Wolviston Reserves)
RT Raine Trophy Winners	Fishburn Park	**Match Official of the Year**	Ted Popple
Finalists	Carlin How		(Stockton)

FINAL LEAGUE TABLES 2002-03

DIVISION ONE		P	W	D	L	F	A	Pts
1	Grangetown Boys Club	28	20	4	4	97	39	64
2	Nunthorpe Athletic	28	20	3	5	84	25	63
3	Thornaby	28	19	3	6	67	38	60
4	Bedale Athletic	28	18	3	7	87	46	57
5	Acklam SW (-3)	28	15	2	11	69	47	44
6	Fishburn Park	28	13	5	10	52	36	44
7	Thornaby YC	28	11	8	9	53	44	41
8	Richmond Town	28	12	3	13	38	44	39
9	BEADS FC	28	10	5	13	53	44	41
10	Carlin How	28	9	7	12	62	63	34
11	Wolviston Reserves	28	7	6	15	41	76	27
12	Mackinlay Park	28	8	2	18	36	80	26
13	Whitby Town Reserves	28	5	8	15	43	82	23
14	New Marske SC	28	4	6	18	32	71	18
15	Stokesley SC	28	4	5	19	25	87	17

DIVISION TWO		P	W	D	L	F	A	Pts
1	SMG Redstripes	20	13	6	1	44	18	45
2	Teesside Arriva	20	13	3	4	67	25	42
3	Darlington CB	20	10	4	6	48	35	34
4	Dormans FC (-3)	20	12	0	8	50	44	33
5	Teesside Athletic	20	8	1	11	48	48	25
6	Billingham Wanderers	20	7	3	10	41	44	24
7	Whinney Banks	20	6	5	9	46	52	23
8	Teesside Link	20	7	1	12	48	48	22
9	Darlington SRM	20	5	5	10	26	46	20
10	Guisborough Town Reserves (-3)	20	7	2	11	20	46	20
11	Darlington RA Reserves	20	5	4	11	30	62	19

PREVIOUS HONOURS

LEAGUE CHAMPIONS

2001-02	Grangetown BC
2000-01	Acklam Steelworks
1999-00	Grangetown Boys Club
1998-99	Grangetown Boys Club
1997-98	Acklam Steelworks
1996-97	Acklam Steelworks
1995-96	Acklam Steelworks

R T RAINE TROPHY WINNERS

2001-02	Bedale Athletic
2000-01	Bedale Athletic
1999-00	Nunthorpe Athletic
1998-99	Cargo Fleet
1997-98	Dormans Athletic
1996-97	BSC Redcar
1995-96	BSC Redcar

PLAYER OF THE YEAR

2001-02	Lee Atkinson, Acklam SW
2000-01	Adam Bramley, Bedale Athletic
1999-00	Nicholas Agiadis, Acklam Steelworks
1998-99	John Newton, Whitby Town Reserves

MACMILLAN BOWL WINNERS

2001-02	Thornaby SC
2000-01	Grangetown Boys Club
1999-00	Grangetown Boys Club
1998-99	Nunthorpe Athletic
1997-98	Acklam Steelworks
1996-97	Acklam Steelworks
1995-96	Acklam Steelworks

J V MADDEN TROPHY

2001-02	Grangetown BC
2000-01	Acklam Steelworks
1999-00	Nunthorpe Athletic
1998-99	Acklam Steelworks
1997-98	Acklam Steelworks
1996-97	Acklam Steelworks
1995-96	Tees Components

MATCH OFFICIAL OF THE YEAR

2001-02	Bill Mounter, Billingham
2000-01	Gary Coxon, Middlesbrough
1999-00	Mark Tilling, Guisborough
1998-99	Chris Lane, Hutton Rugby

CLUBS IN MEMBERSHIP 2003-04

FIRST DIVISION CLUBS

B.E.A.D.S.
Dave Kane, 27 Edgeworth Court, Hemlington, Middlesbrough TS8 9EP Tel: 01642 280586

BEDALE ATHLETIC
Mike Allen, 1 Sycamore View, Nosterfield, Bedale, North Yorks DL8 2QR Tel: 01677 470739

CARLIN HOW WMC
Simon Whitwell, 10 Harebell Close, North Skelton, Saltburn TS12 2FE Tel: 01287 652135

FISHBURN PARK
Richard & Karen Hutton, 24 Abbots Road, Whitby, North Yorks YO22 4EB Tel: 01947 602537

GRANGETOWN BOYS CLUB
Kevin Larkin, 19 Braemar Grove, Teesville, Middlesbrough TS6 0AN Tel: 01642 452095

HARTLEPOOL FC
Barry Murray, 110 Spalding Road, Hartlepool TS25 2JP Tel: 01429 299428

MACKINLAY PARK
Martin Coates, 221 High Street, Marske, Redcar TS11 7LR Tel: 01642 475707

NEW MARSKE SPORTS CLUB
Jimmy Allen, 5 Rosewood Court, Marton, Middlesbrough TS7 8QR Tel: 01642 279786

NUNTHORPE ATHLETIC
Kevin Levitt, 131 Burlam Road, Middlesbrough TS5 5AX Tel: 01642 824332

RICHMOND TOWN
Wendy Prosser, 19 Glebe Court, Melsonby, Richmond, North Yorks DL10 5NU Tel: 01325 718924

SMG REDSTRIPE
Mark McCabe, 2 Atwick Close, Billingham TS23 3YD Tel: 01642 566345

STOKESLEY SC
Peter Grainge, 77 Darnton Drive, Easterside, Middlesbrough TS4 3RK Tel: 01642 273934

THORNABY FC
Dave Watson, 13 Mainside, Redmarshall, Stockton TS21 1HY Tel: 01740 631028

THORNABY YOUTH CLUB
Geoff Kirk, 9 Tipton Close, Thornaby, Stockton TS17 9QF Tel: 01642 676516

WOLVISTON RESERVES
Keith Simpson, 14 Lodore Grove, Acklam, Middlesbrough TS5 8PB Tel: 01642 823734

SECOND DIVISION CLUBS

Billingham Wanderers
Darlington Albion
Darlington Cleveleand Bridge
Darlington Railway Athletic Res.
Darlington SRM SC
Dormans
Guisborough Town Reserves
North Ormesby
Richmond Mavericks
Teesside Athletic
Teesside Link
Whinney Banks

SHEFFIELD COUNTY SENIOR LEAGUE

President: M Matthews Esq. **Chairman:** A Goodison Esq.

Secretary & Treasurer: Brian Gould **Press Officer:** Bill Ownsworth

	PREMIER DIVISION	**P**	**W**	**D**	**L**	**F**	**A**	**Pts**
1	Wombwell Main	24	17	5	2	57	17	56
2	Penistone Church	24	15	4	5	43	22	49
3	Mexboro. Main Street	24	15	2	7	70	39	47
4	Athersley Recreation	24	15	1	8	47	25	46
5	Hallam Reserves	24	13	4	7	69	32	43
6	S. Kirkby Colliery	24	13	4	7	55	41	43
7	Parkgate Reserves	24	11	3	10	56	55	36
8	Groves Social	24	9	5	10	46	46	32
9	Wickersley OB	24	9	5	10	46	56	32
10	Grapes Roy Hancock	24	9	0	15	43	47	27
11	Thorpe Hesley	24	7	4	13	29	45	25
12	Swinton Athletic	24	3	1	20	26	71	10
13	Phoenix	24	0	2	22	16	107	2

	DIVISION ONE	**P**	**W**	**D**	**L**	**F**	**A**	**Pts**
1	Elm Tree	26	18	3	5	64	33	57
2	HSBC	26	15	7	4	70	35	52
3	Sheffield Lane Top	26	15	4	7	66	42	49
4	Oughtibdge WMSC	26	14	3	9	51	40	45
5	Hollinsend Amateur	26	13	5	8	57	40	44
6	Parramore Sports	26	11	4	11	55	48	37
7	Rising Sun	26	11	4	11	60	61	37
8	Stocksbridge Reserves	26	11	2	13	50	37	35
9	The Wetherby	26	10	5	11	45	42	35
10	Frecheville CA	26	9	6	11	42	50	33
11	Georgia Pacific	26	10	3	13	46	60	33
12	Ecclesfield Red Rose	26	7	8	11	36	47	29
13	Avesta Polarit	26	6	6	14	45	74	24
14	Caribbean Sports	26	1	2	23	20	98	5

	DIVISION TWO	**P**	**W**	**D**	**L**	**F**	**A**	**Pts**
1	Edlington WMC	26	22	3	1	66	23	69
2	High Green Villa	26	17	3	6	63	32	54
3	Renishaw Juniors	26	17	1	8	83	39	52
4	Treeton	26	13	7	6	65	39	46
5	Wath Athletic	26	12	8	6	60	38	44
6	Sheff'ld Centralians	26	13	5	8	50	44	44
7	Grimethorpe MW	26	11	8	7	56	48	41
8	Gate 13	26	10	7	9	49	54	37
9	Penistone Church Reserves	26	8	5	13	40	60	29
10	Dinnington T Reserves	26	9	1	16	56	61	28
11	Davy	26	7	6	13	50	58	27
12	Manvers Park	26	6	6	14	49	56	24
13	Psalter Vigo	26	6	1	19	38	66	19
14	Harworth Colts	26	0	1	25	19	126	1

WEST YORKSHIRE ASSOCIATION FOOTBALL LEAGUE

Founded 1928

President: J Hill **Chairman:** B Chaplin

Secretary: Kevin Parkinson, 9 Lake Lock Drive, Stanley, Wakefield WF3 4HN Tel: 01924 825491

FINAL LEAGUE TABLES 2002-03

PREMIER DIVISION		P	W	D	L	F	A	Pts
1	Carlton Athletic	28	20	5	3	91	37	65
2	Horsforth St Margaret's	28	17	7	4	60	34	58
3	Nostell Miners Welfare	28	16	5	7	91	57	53
4	Beeston	28	15	4	9	73	62	49
5	Pontefract Sports & Social	28	14	6	8	58	46	48
6	Pudsey	28	13	7	8	53	44	46
7	Whitkirk Wanderers	28	13	5	10	53	47	44
8	Aberford Albion (-3)	28	13	5	10	52	47	41
9	Wetherby Athletic (+3)	28	9	6	13	51	54	36
10	Bardsey	28	9	5	14	55	71	32
11	Baildon Trinity Athletic	28	8	4	16	40	55	28
12	Knaresborough Town	28	7	7	14	36	60	28
13	Wakefield	28	6	5	17	39	61	23
14	Tadcaster Magnet Sports	28	4	9	15	33	60	21
15	Ripon City Magnets	28	3	6	19	36	86	15

DIVISION ONE		P	W	D	L	F	A	Pts
1	Boroughbridge	30	25	4	1	117	30	79
2	Ossett Common Rovers	30	23	4	3	93	20	73
3	Churwell Lions	30	19	3	8	102	53	60
4	Howden Clough	30	17	8	5	84	51	59
5	Barwick	30	18	2	10	80	55	56
6	Sandy Lane	30	16	3	11	58	49	51
7	Pool	30	15	4	11	73	56	49
8	Upper Armley Old Boys	30	14	7	9	72	55	49
9	Rothwell Athletic	30	12	6	12	82	73	42
10	Featherstone Colliery	30	11	3	16	56	68	36
11	Sherburn White Rose	30	11	1	18	65	79	34
12	Mount St Mary's	30	7	6	17	40	73	27
13	Rothwell Town	30	7	4	19	47	74	25
14	Robin Hood Athletic	30	7	1	22	44	107	22
15	Armley Athletic	30	5	1	24	43	133	16
16	Kirk Deighton Rangers	30	4	1	25	41	121	13

DIVISION TWO		P	W	D	L	F	A	Pts
1	Kellingley Welfare	26	22	3	1	96	25	69
2	Ryhill & Havercroft Sports	26	19	2	5	91	36	59
3	Hartshead Senior	26	14	4	8	59	51	46
4	Camerons	26	14	2	10	77	55	44
5	Boston Spartans	26	12	7	7	55	51	43
6	Hunslet	26	12	4	10	66	52	40
7	Woodhouse Hill WMC	26	11	7	8	60	51	40
8	Kippax Athletic	26	13	0	13	58	52	39
9	Great Preston	26	10	2	14	54	74	32
10	Kippax Welfare	26	8	7	11	56	62	31
11	Stanley United	26	7	7	12	47	66	28
12	Pontefract Town	26	7	3	16	44	78	24
13	Swillington Saints	26	5	1	20	37	100	16
14	Dewsbury Moor Athletic	26	2	3	21	45	92	9

PREMIER DIVISION RESULTS CHART 2002-03

		1	2	3	4	5	6	7	8	9	10	11	12	13	14	15
1	Aberford Albion		0-2	3-2	1-1	1-3	0-1	3-1	2-2	0-1	1-0	4-0	5-0	1-3	3-1	2-1
2	Baildon Trinity Athletic	2-0		1-0	0-1	1-2	1-2	1-2	0-6	0-3	3-3	5-0	1-0	2-1	1-3	4-0
3	Bardsey	4-2	3-3		5-2	0-5	1-7	4-1	6-7	1-2	1-2	2-2	1-4	2-2	2-0	2-1
4	Beeston	1-2	2-0	1-2		0-5	6-1	5-1	3-2	5-2	4-1	5-5	4-3	1-0	4-4	5-2
5	Carlton Athletic	4-4	5-2	6-2	4-3		2-2	2-0	3-5	2-1	0-1	4-1	5-1	3-4	3-1	3-3
6	Horsforth St Margaret's	3-0	3-1	1-2	0-1	1-1		6-0	2-0	3-1	4-3	5-2	1-0	1-0	2-0	2-1
7	Knaresborough Town	1-3	4-3	0-3	2-1	0-1	1-1		2-3	4-0	0-1	4-1	0-0	3-2	1-1	0-0
8	Nostell Miners Welfare	2-3	4-1	5-2	3-1	2-4	2-2	4-4		2-3	5-2	7-5	3-0	6-0	3-3	1-3
9	Pontefract Sports & Social	3-1	2-0	2-1	6-1	0-4	1-1	4-0	0-1		1-3	6-0	3-0	4-4	2-1	2-2
10	Pudsey	4-1	1-0	6-2	1-2	1-5	0-1	2-2	0-0	2-2		4-0	1-0	1-0	1-0	1-2
11	Ripon City Magnets	1-3	1-2	2-0	2-2	0-9	1-1	0-1	0-1	0-0	1-3		2-1	3-0	2-3	0-6
12	Tadcaster Magnet Sports	3-4	0-0	1-1	1-3	0-1	1-1	2-2	3-6	1-1	1-1	0-0		4-3	3-1	2-0
13	Wakefield	0-0	2-2	0-2	1-4	0-3	1-3	3-0	0-3	0-1	2-2	2-1	6-1		2-0	0-3
14	Wetherby Athletic	1-1	2-1	2-2	2-3	1-1	5-1	3-0	0-4	2-3	1-3	4-3	3-0	2-0		1-2
15	Whitkirk Wanderers	0-2	3-1	1-0	4-2	0-1	0-2	1-0	3-2	5-2	3-3	2-1	1-1	3-1	1-4	

PREMIER DIVISION CUP

FIRST ROUND

Aberford Albion v Wakefield 2-1

Baildon Trinity Ath v Knaresborough T. 3-0

Bardsey v Nostell Miners Welfare 4-3

(Bardsey expelled - use of an ineligible player)

Pontefract Sports & S. v Tadcaster Magnets 1-2

Pudsey v Carlton Athletic 3-4

Ripon City Magnets v Horsforth St Margaret's 1-2

Wetherby Athletic v Beeston 0-5

QUARTER-FINALS

Baildon Trinity Athletic v Nostell Miners Welfare 1-3

Beeston v Tadcaster Magnet Sp 5-2

Carlton Athletic v Whitkirk Wanderers 0-2

Horsforth St Margaret's v Aberford Albion 1-0

SEMI-FINALS

Horsforth St Margaret's v Beeston 3-0

Whitkirk Wanderers v Nostell Miners W. 1-2

FINAL

Horsforth St Margaret's v Nostell Miners Welfare 1-0

10th May at Whitkirk Wanderers

DIVISION ONE CUP FINAL

SEMI-FINALS

Boroughbridge v Ossett Common Rovers 2-1

Sandy Lane v Barwick 0-1

FINAL

Boroughbridge v Barwick 3-0

3rd May at Knaresborough Town

DIVISION TWO CUP FINAL

SEMI-FINALS

Camerons v Hartshead Senior (walkover)

Ryhill & Havercroft S. v Woodhouse Hill WMC 1-0

FINAL

Ryhill & Havercroft S. v Hartshead Senior 2-0

26th April at Nostell Miners Welfare

MUMTAZ WEST RIDING COUNTY AMATEUR FOOTBALL LEAGUE

President: J Jones Esq.

General Secretary: Stuart Marsden, 28 Church View, Crigglestone, Wakefield WF4 3PF
Tel: 01924 249 302

FINAL LEAGUE TABLES 2002-03

PREMIER DIVISION		P	W	D	L	F	A	Pts
1	Silsden	24	17	7	0	63	19	58
2	Brighouse Town	24	16	6	2	54	16	54
3	Ovenden West Riding	24	13	5	6	55	44	44
4	Wibsey	24	11	3	10	45	36	36
5	Hemsworth Miners W.	24	11	3	10	35	33	36
6	Golcar United	24	9	4	11	48	51	31
7	Campion	24	8	6	10	37	45	30
8	Bay Athletic	24	8	5	11	51	64	29
9	Tyersal	24	7	6	11	38	56	27
10	Storthes Hall	24	6	6	12	35	47	24
11	Littletown	24	6	4	14	39	53	22
12	Otley Town	24	5	7	12	35	64	22
13	Lower Hopton	24	5	6	13	45	52	21

DIVISION ONE		P	W	D	L	F	A	Pts
1	Hall Green United	30	23	2	5	94	35	71
2	Steeton	30	22	3	5	103	38	69
3	Altofts	30	21	2	7	88	39	65
4	Ardsley Celtic	30	16	5	9	76	53	53
5	Keighley Shamrocks	30	15	5	10	67	43	50
6	Wakefield City	30	13	5	12	62	55	44
7	Dudley Hill Rangers	30	12	5	13	52	62	41
8	Eastmoor	30	12	4	14	55	59	40
9	Salt Old Boys	30	11	6	13	56	52	39
10	Stump Cross	30	12	3	15	65	71	39
11	Marsden	30	11	6	13	59	81	39
12	Heckmondwike Town	30	10	6	14	62	74	36
13	Hunsworth	30	10	6	14	67	87	36
14	Halifax Irish Club	30	10	5	15	58	83	35
15	Rawdon Old Boys	30	5	6	19	45	94	21
16	Dudley Hill Athletic	30	1	3	26	41	124	6

DIVISION TWO		P	W	D	L	F	A	Pts
1	Salts	22	16	4	2	70	30	52
2	Westwood	22	16	3	3	78	29	51
3	Roberttown	22	14	2	6	68	41	44
4	Westbrook Wanderers	22	12	2	8	71	40	38
5	Bowling	22	10	5	7	58	44	35
6	Farnley	22	10	3	9	55	46	33
7	Barclays	22	9	1	12	55	46	28
8	Ventus/Yeadon Celtic	22	8	4	10	56	67	28
9	Morley Town	22	6	4	12	43	67	22
10	Green Lane	22	5	5	12	45	74	20
11	Dynamoes	22	5	3	14	33	69	18
12	Crag Road United	22	2	2	18	36	115	8

PREMIER DIVISION RESULTS CHART 2002-03

	1	2	3	4	5	6	7	8	9	10	11	12	13	14
1 Bay Athletic		2-2	3-4	2-7	3-1	n/a	4-2	3-3	5-1	1-3	1-1	1-0	1-2	3-1
2 Brighouse Town	4-2		4-0	1-0	0-1	n/a	2-0	2-1	3-1	1-1	0-1	5-1	1-1	3-2
3 Campion	3-1	0-0		2-2	0-3	4-0	2-1	0-0	1-1	0-1	1-6	1-0	3-0	1-2
4 Golcar United	1-5	0-3	1-0		3-0	n/a	2-2	3-4	5-1	1-4	2-3	3-2	2-0	0-2
5 Hemsworth Miners Welfare	1-3	1-3	3-2	1-1		n/a	1-0	2-0	0-0	4-1	0-0	1-0	4-0	0-3
6 Keighley Phoenix	n/a	0-9	n/a	1-2	2-4		1-7	n/a	2-8	1-3	n/a	n/a	n/a	n/a
7 Littletown	2-2	0-1	1-3	2-3	2-0	8-0		0-4	5-0	1-4	1-2	2-2	5-3	1-5
8 Lower Hopton	7-1	0-2	1-1	2-3	1-3	8-1	1-3		4-2	1-2	1-2	1-2	1-1	3-1
9 Otley Town	1-2	0-3	3-5	3-1	2-1	n/a	2-1	3-3		2-3	0-3	3-2	4-4	2-2
10 Ovenden West Riding	6-1	0-2	0-0	1-1	1-4	n/a	2-1	5-2	4-1		2-4	0-3	2-2	3-2
11 Silsden	2-2	1-1	6-1	3-1	2-0	6-1	6-2	2-0	0-0	4-1		1-1	5-1	3-0
12 Storthes Hall	5-1	1-5	2-1	1-2	3-1	7-2	1-2	0-0	2-2	3-3	1-5		1-1	1-0
13 Tyersal	2-1	0-6	1-4	4-3	1-0	n/a	0-2	7-4	0-1	3-4	0-0	2-0		0-1
14 Wibsey	3-1	0-0	3-2	3-1	2-3	n/a	1-1	2-1	5-0	0-2	0-1	4-1	1-3	

Keighley Phoenix withdrew during the season. Their results are shown above but are expunged from the league table.

PREMIER DIVISION CUP 2001-02

FIRST ROUND

Bay Athletic v Otley Town 1-0
Golcar United v Campion 2-3
Tyersal v Storthes Hall 2-2 (aet) 2-3p
Brighouse Town v Silsden 0-3
Keighley Phoenix v Ovenden West Riding 1-2
Wibsey v Hemsworth M. W. 2-0

QUARTER-FINALS

Campion v Silsden 1-4
Lower Hopton v Ovenden West Riding 4-1
Littletown v Storthes Hall 4-5 (aet)
Wibsey v Bay Athletic 6-4

SEMI-FINALS

Silsden v Lower Hopton 3-0 at Altofts
Storthes Hall v Wibsey 1-2 (aet) at Otley Town

FINAL

Silsden v Wibsey 2-0 16th May at Brighouse Town

In winning the Premier Division Championship, the Premier Division Cup, the West Riding County F.A. Challenge Cup and the Keighley and District F.A. Cup, **Silsden FC**, equalled a record set in 1939/40 by Bradford Rovers. Silsden also set a club record of remaining undefeated in all games throughout the 2002/03 season, a total of 36.

LEAGUE CONSTITUTION FOR 2003-04

PREMIER DIVISION

Bay Athletic
Brighouse Town
Campion
Golcar United
Hall Green United
Hemsworth Miners Welfare
Littletown
Otley Town
Ovenden West Riding
Silsden
Steeton
Storthes Hall
Tyersal
Wibsey

DIVISION ONE

Altofts
Ardsley Celtic
Dudley Hill Rangers
Eastmoor
Heckmondwike Town
Hunsworth
Keighley Shamrocks
Lower Hopton
Marsden
Salt Old Boys
Salts
Stump Cross
Wakefield City
Westwood

DIVISION TWO

Barclays
Bowling
Crag Road United
Dudley Hill Athletic
Dynamoes
Farnley
Green Lane
Halifax Irish Club
Morley Town
Rawdon Old Boys
Roberttown
South Bradford (formerly TFD Centre)
Ventus & Yeadon Celtic
Westbrook YMCA

LINCOLNSHIRE FOOTBALL LEAGUE

Hon. Secretary: Colin Barraclough
14 Lichfield Road, Bracebridge Heath, Lincoln LN4 2SS
Tel: 01522 560912

FINAL LEAGUE TABLE 2002-03

		P	W	D	L	F	A	Pts
1	Grimsby Amateurs	24	17	3	4	76	30	54
2	Sleaford Town	24	17	2	5	68	24	53
3	Wyberton	24	12	7	5	54	30	43
4	Limestone Rangers (+1)	24	11	6	7	56	35	40
5	Lincoln Moorlands Reserves	24	10	5	9	41	44	35
6	Alstom Sports	24	10	4	10	43	46	34
7	Hykeham Town	24	9	6	9	52	54	33
8	Skegness Town	24	9	5	10	39	43	32
9	Appleby Frodingham Athletic	24	8	4	12	36	42	28
10	Lincoln U. Reserves (-1)	24	6	9	9	39	41	26
11	Horncastle Town	24	6	7	11	27	41	25
12	Louth United Reserves	24	4	7	13	30	71	19
13	Retford Town	24	3	3	18	24	84	12

		1	2	3	4	5	6	7	8	9	10	11	12	13
1	Alstom Sports		3-3	1-1	2-1	0-2	1-4	1-1	2-1	4-1	6-1	4-0	1-4	0-4
2	Appleby Frodington Athletic	0-1		1-3	2-0	0-1	2-3	0-0	2-2	HW	1-3	2-1	0-1	3-3
3	Grimsby Amateurs	2-1	5-1		3-0	6-0	3-3	4-1	4-3	6-0	6-0	3-2	1-0	1-1
4	Horncastle Town	0-1	0-3	2-4		4-3	0-0	1-0	4-1	0-0	2-1	0-1	1-0	0-1
5	Hykeham Town	2-2	3-0	1-3	2-2		1-2	1-0	2-2	4-3	4-2	3-3	2-1	5-1
6	Limestone Rangers	2-0	0-1	2-3	6-0	4-0		0-4	2-2	4-0	4-0	2-3	1-3	1-1
7	Lincoln Moorlands Reserves	2-3	1-0	3-1	1-1	1-0	2-1		0-1	5-2	5-0	3-3	2-1	0-0
8	Lincoln United Reserves	4-0	4-1	0-6	0-1	5-2	2-2	0-3		0-0	7-1	2-0	0-2	1-1
9	Louth United Reserves	1-0	0-4	3-2	4-4	1-7	3-3	4-0	0-0		0-1	2-2	0-5	0-8
10	Retford Town	1-2	0-4	0-6	1-1	4-4	1-4	3-4	0-0	2-4		0-1	1-2	0-5
11	Skegness Town	3-4	0-2	3-1	2-1	2-1	0-3	7-2	2-0	0-0	0-1		1-2	1-1
12	Sleford Town	3-2	4-2	0-2	1-1	4-0	2-1	9-1	1-1	8-2	7-0	3-0		3-1
13	Wyberton	3-2	4-2	2-0	2-1	2-2	1-2	1-0	3-1	2-0	5-1	1-2	1-2	

HW - Given as a Home Win.

LEAGUE CUP 2002-03

FIRST ROUND

Alstom	v	Grimsby Amateurs	1-2
Lincoln United Res.	v	Horncastle Town	6-4 (aet)
Wyberton	v	Retford Town	5-2
Limestone	v	Skegness	1-0
Louth United Res.	v	Lincoln M'lands Res.	1-0

QUARTER-FINALS

Appleby Frod. Athletic	v	Lincoln United Res.	1-2
Limestone Rangers	v	Sleaford Town	2-3
Grimsby Amateurs	v	Wyberton	4-0
Louth United Res.	v	Hykeham Town	0-2

SEMI-FINALS

Lincoln United Res.	v	Hykeham Town	0-2
Sleaford Town	v	Grimsby Am.	2-1 (aet)

FINAL

Hykeham Town v Sleaford Town 3-2 — 14th May at Lincoln Moorlands

SUPPLEMENTARY CUP 2002-03

SEMI-FINALS

Louth United Res.	v	Lincoln United Res.	0-1
Sleaford Town	v	Limestone Rangers	4-3

FINAL

Sleaford Town v Lincoln United Res. 6-1 — 21st May at Wyberton

NORTH EASTERN FINAL LEAGUE TABLES 2002-03

EAST RIDING AMATEUR LEAGUE

PREMIER DIVISION	P	W	D	L	F	A	Pts
Pinefleet Wolfreton	18	17	0	1	54	16	51
Discount Carpets	18	14	2	2	57	27	44
Kinloss	18	8	5	5	42	25	29
AFC Charleston	18	8	3	7	57	41	27
Springhead OB	18	8	3	7	51	42	27
Hider Foods	18	6	4	8	35	50	22
Malet Lambert YC	18	6	1	11	24	40	19
East Hull Amateurs	18	4	4	10	30	52	16
FC Robbies	18	3	3	12	38	75	12
Auto Matrix	18	2	3	13	16	36	9

YORKSHIRE OLD BOYS LEAGUE

SENIOR A DIVISION	P	W	D	L	F	A	Pts
Centralians	20	14	4	2	51	18	46
Roundhegians	20	14	2	4	50	15	44
Modernians	20	12	2	6	42	32	38
Leeds Medics	20	11	3	6	44	28	36
Almondburians	20	10	5	5	41	33	35
Leeds University	20	7	5	8	30	32	26
Yorkshire Bank	20	6	5	9	33	34	23
Abbey Grange	20	6	2	12	43	42	20
Adel	20	5	5	10	25	34	20
Ealandians	20	4	7	9	31	59	19
Wheelwright	20	0	2	18	18	81	2

HUDDERSFIELD & DISTRICT LEAGUE

DIVISION ONE	P	W	D	L	F	A	Pts
Brackenhall United	22	14	5	3	56	24	47
Diggle	22	12	4	6	46	29	40
Wooldale Wanderers	22	9	8	5	51	43	35
Kirkheaton Rovers	22	8	8	6	37	30	32
Shepley	22	9	4	9	35	28	31
Slaithwaite United	22	7	9	6	53	38	30
Honley	22	8	5	9	43	45	29
Heywood Sports	22	6	8	8	34	40	26
Skelmanthorpe	22	7	5	10	30	44	26
Britannia Sports	22	6	7	9	45	48	25
Grange Moor	22	5	4	13	37	74	19
Sovereign Sports	22	4	5	13	21	45	17

YORK & DISTRICT FOOTBALL LEAGUE

PREMIER DIVISION	P	W	D	L	F	A	Pts
Pocklington Res.	26	23	2	1	80	18	71
Dringhouses	26	21	2	3	89	22	65
Malton Bacon Fact.	26	16	3	7	91	37	51
Osbaldwick	26	13	5	8	76	47	44
Dunnington	26	12	5	9	56	49	41
Huntington Rovers	26	12	3	11	53	58	39
Old Malton	26	11	3	12	63	51	36
Kartiers	26	9	5	12	36	44	32
Wigginton G'hopp.	26	9	4	13	41	58	31
Rufforth United	26	8	5	13	45	72	29
Nestle Rowntree	26	7	5	14	50	62	26
Bishopthorpe	26	7	3	16	45	68	24
Crayke	26	6	5	15	36	60	23
Riccall United	26	2	2	22	24	139	8

SPEN VALLEY & DISTRICT LEAGUE

PREMIER DIVISION	P	W	D	L	F	A	PTS
Overthorpe SV	17	12	3	2	69	21	39
Lord Nelson	18	11	4	3	69	42	37
Salfia Rangers	18	10	7	1	48	26	37
Mount SV	18	9	4	5	57	35	31
Commonside	18	8	2	8	52	43	26
Airedale Celtic	17	6	3	8	38	56	21
Howden Clough	18	6	0	12	37	53	18
Norfolk	18	4	4	10	44	57	16
FC Bosnia	18	4	4	10	50	71	16
Hare & Hounds	18	3	1	14	35	95	10

SOUTHERN LEAGUE

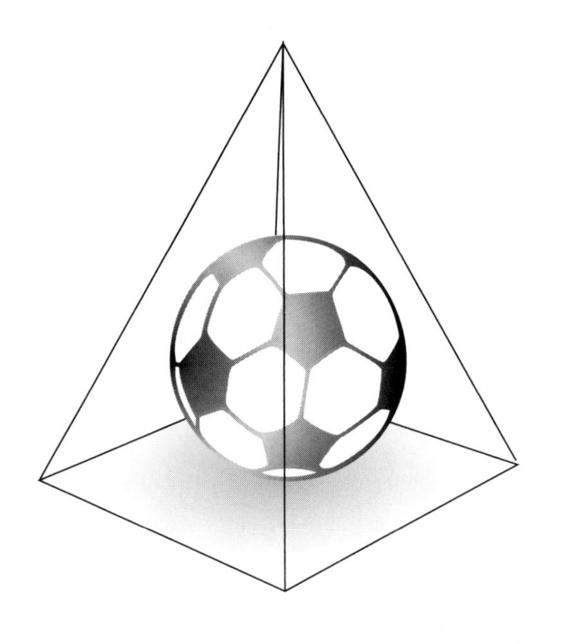

PYRAMID SECTION

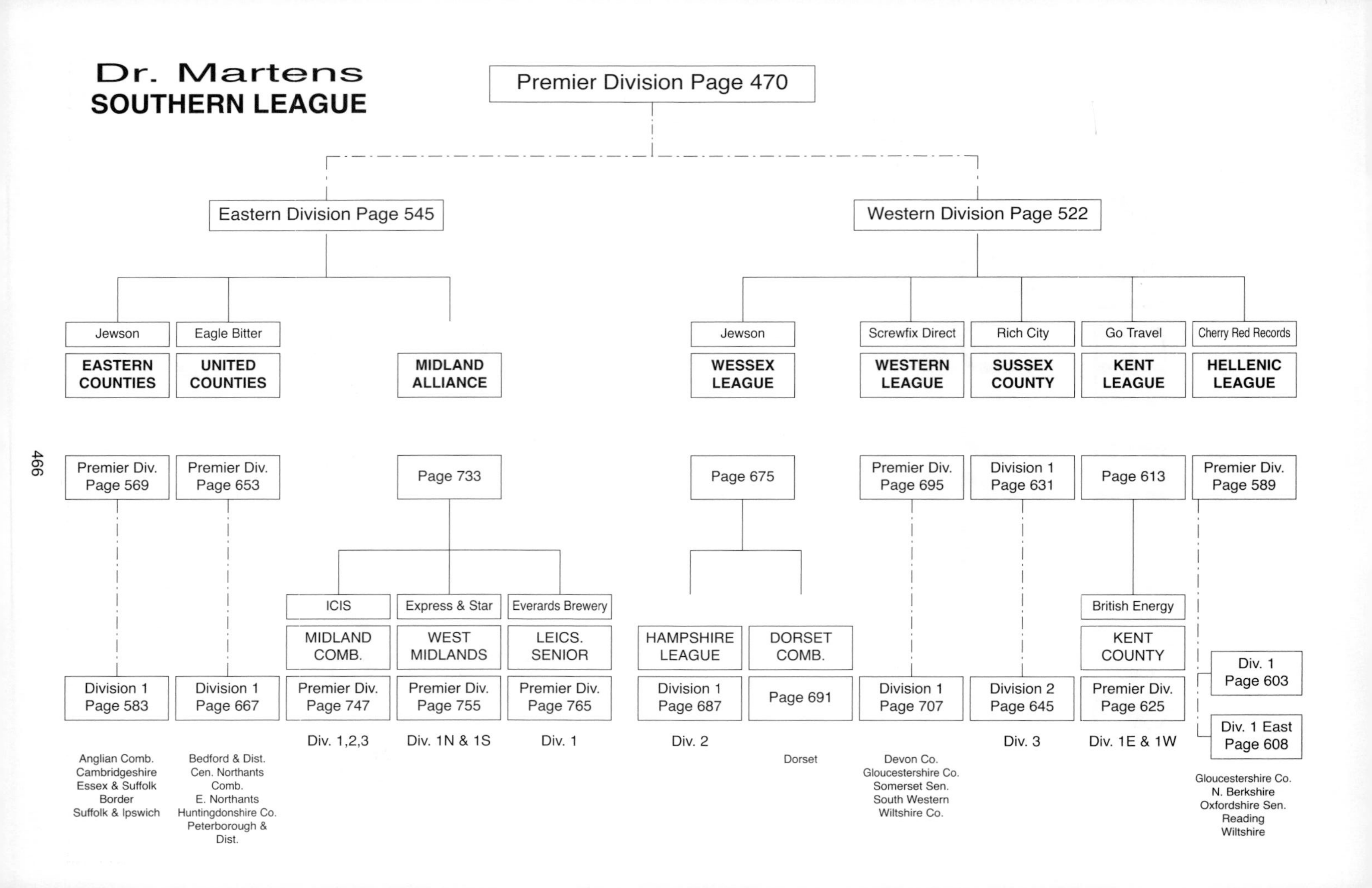
Dr. Martens
SOUTHERN LEAGUE
Premier Division Page 470
Eastern Division Page 545
Western Division Page 522
Jewson
EASTERN COUNTIES
Premier Div. Page 569
Division 1 Page 583
Anglian Comb.
Cambridgeshire
Essex & Suffolk Border
Suffolk & Ipswich
Eagle Bitter
UNITED COUNTIES
Premier Div. Page 653
Division 1 Page 667
Bedford & Dist.
Cen. Northants Comb.
E. Northants
Huntingdonshire Co.
Peterborough & Dist.
MIDLAND ALLIANCE
Page 733
ICIS
MIDLAND COMB.
Premier Div. Page 747
Div. 1,2,3
Express & Star
WEST MIDLANDS
Premier Div. Page 755
Div. 1N & 1S
Everards Brewery
LEICS. SENIOR
Premier Div. Page 765
Div. 1
Jewson
WESSEX LEAGUE
Page 675
HAMPSHIRE LEAGUE
Division 1 Page 687
Div. 2
DORSET COMB.
Page 691
Dorset
Screwfix Direct
WESTERN LEAGUE
Premier Div. Page 695
Division 1 Page 707
Devon Co.
Gloucestershire Co.
Somerset Sen.
South Western
Wiltshire Co.
Rich City
SUSSEX COUNTY
Division 1 Page 631
Division 2 Page 645
Div. 3
Go Travel
KENT LEAGUE
Page 613
British Energy
KENT COUNTY
Premier Div. Page 625
Div. 1E & 1W
Cherry Red Records
HELLENIC LEAGUE
Premier Div. Page 589
Div. 1 Page 603
Div. 1 East Page 608
Gloucestershire Co.
N. Berkshire
Oxfordshire Sen.
Reading
Wiltshire

Dr MARTENS LEAGUE

Chairman: D S R Gillard

Secretary: D J Strudwick

PO Box 90, Worcester WR3 8RX Tel: 01905 757509

Tamworth won the Dr. Martens League championship with three weeks and four matches to spare. The Lamb's winning margin of 13 points, whilst being helped by just about all the main challengers shooting themselves in the foot, was an amazing accomplishment after last season's final day disappointment and the loss of manager Gary Mills in the summer.

An unbeaten run of 17 matches saw Dorchester Town clinch the Eastern Division, but not until the final day of the season, and even then only on goal difference.

Merthyr Tydfil took just one season to return to the PRemier Division. Having clinched promotion with three weeks of the campaign remaining nearest rivals Weston-Super-Mare inexplicably lost their last home fixture of the season against relegated Racing Club Warwick, to present the Western Division championship to the Glamorganshire club.

And two years after being losing finalists Crawley Town lifted the league's Challenge Cup after a close encounter with Halesowen Town.

PREMIER DIVISION

Grantham Town and Worcester City occupied the top of the table until the beginning of November. Only Crawley Town interrupted their dominance, and only then for one week. Tamworth emerged as league leaders after the results on 9th November. Worcester then regained top spot for two weeks but from 7th December, apart from the first two weeks of the New YEar, it was the Lambs all the way to the finishing line.

At times, Tamworth's stranglehold on the Division was as much as 14 points, and even on the rare occasion the Lambs did slip up, or when they were engaged on their fine FA Trophy run, none of the challengers could take advantage. As Worcester City slipped off the pace and back into sixth place; Crawley Town dropped to seventh and Grantham Town fell so far back that a victory was needed on the last day of the season to avoid relegation. Stafford Rangers, Dover Athletic, Tiverton Town and Chippenham Town emerged as Tamworth's nearest rivals. So badly did the challengers shoot themselves in the foot, the Lamb's built a lead sufficient to clinch the championship three weeks before the end of the season. The challenge petered away so much, Tamworth won the league with 88 points. Only Kettering Town had won the competition with fewer points during the previous five years. Tamworth's effort, however, is all the more commendable given the disappointment on the final day of last season when the championship slipped from their grasp, mainly due to a penalty saved by Folkstone's Dave Wietecha, and the loss of manager Gary Mills in the summer.

A change of management, towards the end of last season, also paid dividends for Stafford Rangers. Former Aston Villa, Wolves and Birmingham City midfielder, Phil Robinson, led 'Borough' into runners-up spot.

It is frequently suggested the 'strength in depth' in the Dr. Martens League is unrivalled at our level of the game. (At least, it is never us that suggests when a club opts for another competition, they have chosen an 'easier route'). So after establishing themselves quite comfortably in the premier division last season, Folkstone Invicta and Ilkeston Town would not necessarily have been favourites for relegation. It was surprising, therefore, to learn they were the first two clubs to 'qualify' for the drop.

On the other hand, as if to emphasise the quality of the premier division, and demonstrate the tangible difference between the regional first divisions and the top flight, two clubs who were promoted this year (Hastings United and Halesowen Town) also fell through the trapdoor. It is significant to note too, both clubs qualified for promotion at the end of the last season as champions!

EASTERN LEAGUE

The leadership of the Eastern Division changed almost weekly. In the early stages of the campaign Eastbourne Borough, Stamford, Rothwell Town, Histon, Ashford Town, Bashley, Dorchester Town, Banbury United and Salisbury City all spent time as 'Kings of the Castle' during the first half of the season.

Dorchester's results suddenly took a downturn in mid-season. A sequence of two victories in nine matches saw the Magpies slip to eighth place during January and February. Just as quickly, however, a recovery was launched by Mark Morris's men. A run of fifteen wins in the final seventeen games of their season swept Dorchester to the top of the table and saw them clinch the championship on the final day of the season, on goal difference over Eastbourne Borough.

After being comfortably placed all season, Eastbourne Borough forced their way onto the leader board in March. Five weeks in first place subsequently followed before Dorchester inched ahead with a better goal-difference in the penultimate week of the campaign. Eventually, the East Sussex club was piped at the post by the narrowest of margins.

WESTERN LEAGUE

The last time Merthyr Tydfil won a first division I seem to remember the Martyrs being in the relegation zone at Christmas. after failing to win any of their first four matches last August, they seemed intent on giving themselves a similar uphill task. Manager Andy Beattie, had other ideas and by Yuletide 2002, his side were in second place chasing long-time leaders Bromsgrove Rovers.

BY February the side from South Wales was in a clear lead. Merthyr, however, could not shake off Weston-Super-Mare despite losing only four matches in 38 outings. With 26 victories under their belt, the Seagulls were still in the race for the championship with three games to go when incredibly they lost at home to Racing

Club Warwick, whose relegation had already been confirmed. The title was gifted to Merthyr Tydfil.

As for Bromsgrove, a spell of eight defeats and only four wins in fourteen games, ended their hopes and allowed Merthyr Tydfil and Western-Super-Mare to secure promotion by mid-April.

LEAGUE CHALLENGE CUP

Crawley Town won the Worcester Vase, two years after their last appearance in the final when they lost to Worcester City.

By taking the lead on the hour in the first leg of the final tie, at Halesowen Town, the Reds looked to have lain to rest 'the ghosts of seasons past'. However, two goals by the Yeltz in the final four minutes haunted Crawley for the two weeks before the second leg.

In the return match at Broadfield Stadium, the hosts scored after twelve minutes to level the tie. A further goal shortly after half time put Crawley ahead and despite a spirited battle and a grandstand finish, it was Halesowen's lack of decisive thrust in front of goal that prevented the visitors from making inroads into the deficit. Crawley Town won 3-2 on aggregate.

Before moving on to the next topic, it would be remiss not to mention the progress of King's Lynn to the semi-final of this year's competition. As a first division club, losing to the eventual winners 1-0 was no disgrace, partic
ularly as the Linnets reached last year's final.

PREMIER DIVISION FINAL LEAGUE TABLE 2002-03

			HOME			AWAY			TOTAL						
		P	W	D	L	W	D	L	W	D	L	F	A	GD	Pts
1	Tamworth	42	12	6	3	14	4	3	26	10	6	73	32	41	88
2	Stafford Rangers	42	11	7	3	10	5	6	21	12	9	76	40	36	75
3	Dover Athletic	42	11	4	6	8	10	3	19	14	9	42	35	7	71
4	Tiverton Town	42	11	4	6	8	8	5	19	12	11	60	43	17	69
5	Chippenham Town	42	9	9	3	8	8	5	17	17	8	59	37	22	68
6	Worcester City	42	12	6	3	6	7	8	18	13	11	60	39	21	67
7	Crawley Town	42	9	8	4	8	5	8	17	13	12	64	51	13	64
8	Havant & Waterlooville	42	10	6	5	5	9	7	15	15	12	67	64	3	60
9	Chelmsford City	42	8	5	8	7	7	7	15	12	15	65	63	2	57
10	Newport County	42	8	7	6	7	4	10	15	11	16	53	52	1	56
11	Hednesford Town	42	10	7	4	4	6	11	14	13	15	59	60	-1	55
12	Moor Green	42	8	7	6	5	7	9	13	14	15	49	58	-9	53
13	Hinckley United	42	9	6	6	3	10	8	12	16	14	61	64	-3	52
14	Bath City	42	8	7	6	5	6	10	13	13	16	50	61	-11	52
15	Welling United	42	8	7	6	5	5	11	13	12	17	55	58	-3	51
16	Grantham Town	42	10	5	6	4	4	13	14	9	19	59	65	-6	51
17	Weymouth	42	7	10	4	5	5	11	12	15	15	44	62	-18	51
18	Cambridge City	42	6	5	10	7	5	9	13	10	19	54	56	-2	49
19	Halesowen Town	42	7	8	6	5	5	11	12	13	17	52	64	-11	49
20	Hastings Town	42	7	6	8	3	7	11	10	13	19	44	57	-13	43
21	Ilkeston Town	42	8	3	10	2	7	12	10	10	22	54	92	-38	40
22	Folkstone Invicta	42	5	4	12	2	3	16	7	7	28	57	105	-48	28

	PREMIER DIVISION 02-03	1	2	3	4	5	6	7	8	9	10	11	12	13	14	15	16	17	18	19	20	21	22
1	Bath City		1-1	0-1	1-1	0-1	1-0	2-0	3-2	3-0	1-0	1-1	4-1	2-2	1-1	1-1	4-3	0-1	0-2	0-1	0-2	1-1	1-0
2	Cambridge City	0-1		2-3	0-1	3-0	1-1	2-1	1-1	0-1	1-2	4-5	2-2	1-1	2-2	1-2	1-3	1-0	0-1	3-0	2-1	0-1	1-0
3	Chelmsford City	2-0	1-2		2-3	1-2	0-1	3-2	1-2	1-0	1-0	1-2	2-2	1-1	2-1	4-0	1-1	0-2	0-4	3-0	1-1	3-1	1-1
4	Chippenham Town	1-2	2-0	3-1		1-0	0-0	1-0	0-0	1-2	0-0	3-1	1-3	3-1	3-0	1-1	0-0	1-1	3-0	1-1	4-0	1-1	0-0
5	Crawley Town	1-2	4-2	0-0	1-1		0-3	2-2	2-0	4-0	1-1	2-1	2-2	0-2	2-1	2-2	2-0	2-4	1-0	1-1	1-0	5-0	0-0
6	Dover Athletic	2-0	2-1	1-0	0-1	2-1		2-1	2-1	0-3	1-0	0-0	1-0	2-0	1-1	1-2	0-0	0-2	0-3	0-0	2-1	0-2	2-1
7	Folkestone Invicta	2-4	0-3	3-2	1-2	1-3	1-2		0-2	2-2	1-0	3-3	4-1	4-0	0-3	0-1	2-3	1-2	2-3	1-1	2-2	4-1	1-2
8	Grantham Town	0-0	1-0	2-3	1-1	0-3	3-1	4-1		3-3	2-1	1-1	3-0	2-1	2-2	4-0	1-2	1-2	2-1	0-2	3-1	2-0	2-3
9	Halesowen Town	1-1	1-1	0-2	3-2	0-2	0-0	5-0	1-0		2-1	1-0	0-1	2-1	2-1	0-1	1-2	1-1	0-0	0-0	0-0	0-1	0-0
10	Hastings United	1-1	1-2	1-1	2-1	0-0	1-1	1-2	2-1	3-2		1-1	2-0	1-0	3-0	3-1	1-3	0-2	2-3	0-3	1-4	1-1	1-4
11	Havant & Waterlooville	3-1	0-2	1-0	1-0	2-4	1-1	6-2	3-3	3-1	0-0		2-1	2-2	1-3	3-3	1-0	1-1	0-3	2-1	1-0	0-1	2-1
12	Hednesford Town	2-2	3-2	2-2	1-3	0-0	2-2	3-1	1-0	3-2	1-0	3-0		0-0	6-2	0-0	1-0	2-2	0-1	2-3	4-1	0-1	2-0
13	Hinckley United	3-1	3-2	2-1	1-2	3-1	1-1	3-3	0-0	1-1	3-2	2-1	0-1		5-2	1-2	0-2	2-0	1-1	1-1	1-3	2-1	0-1
14	Ilkeston Town	1-1	0-2	2-2	2-6	2-1	0-1	2-1	1-2	1-3	3-1	1-5	3-1	1-1		2-0	1-0	2-5	0-1	1-3	1-6	3-1	3-2
15	Moor Green	1-0	1-1	1-1	1-0	0-2	0-2	3-0	3-0	4-0	0-0	0-1	0-1	2-2	5-0		1-2	1-1	0-2	2-1	1-0	2-2	1-1
16	Newport County	1-1	1-1	2-5	3-1	3-3	0-1	1-2	3-2	1-1	1-1	0-0	1-0	3-2	3-0	1-1		1-0	0-1	0-1	0-2	3-0	2-1
17	Stafford Rangers	5-0	0-1	1-1	0-0	2-1	3-1	6-0	4-0	4-2	1-1	1-3	1-1	2-2	2-0	4-0	1-0		1-2	2-1	1-1	0-0	2-1
18	Tamworth	6-1	3-1	3-1	0-1	1-1	1-2	2-0	3-1	3-1	2-0	3-3	1-0	2-0	1-1	2-2	0-0	2-1		1-1	2-0	3-0	1-2
19	Tiverton Town	2-1	0-2	3-3	1-1	0-1	0-0	4-0	0-2	4-2	0-1	3-1	2-1	0-2	3-1	1-0	3-1	2-1	0-1		3-1	3-0	0-0
20	Welling United	1-3	1-0	0-2	1-1	2-2	0-0	2-1	2-0	3-1	0-3	1-1	2-2	1-2	2-0	1-0	1-0	1-2	1-1	1-1		4-2	0-1
21	Weymouth	2-0	0-0	1-3	1-1	2-0	0-0	3-3	3-1	1-4	1-1	1-1	0-0	2-2	1-1	3-1	2-0	1-0	0-1	0-2	2-1		0-0
22	Worcester City	2-1	2-0	5-0	0-0	2-1	0-1	6-0	2-0	1-1	2-1	2-1	3-1	2-2	0-0	4-0	2-1	0-3	0-0	0-2	1-1	3-1	

DR MARTENS CHALLENGE CUP 2002-03

PRELIMINARY ROUND

Crawley Town	v	Sittingbourne	2-0	Mangotsfield Utd	v	Gloucester City	3-0

FIRST ROUND

Bashley	v	Havant & Waterlooville	3-2	Bath City	v	Tiverton Tn 2-2(aet)	1-3p
Bedworth United	v	Atherstone United	1-0	Burnham	v	Erith & Belvedere	4-2
Chatham Town	v	Chelmsford City	0-3	Cirencester Town	v	Cinderford Town	3-1
Crawley Town	v	Hastings United	1-0	Dartford	v	St Leonards	2-0
Dover Athletic	v	Folkestone Invicta	2-1	Fisher Athletic	v	Ashford Town	1-3
Fleet Town	v	Eastbourne Borough	0-1	Grantham Town	v	Histon	3-1
Gresley Rovers	v	Hinckley United	1-2	Ilkeston Town	v	Banbury United	2-1 (aet)
Mangotsfield United	v	Weston-super-Mare	2-0	Merthyr Tydfil	v	Chippenham Town	0-1
Moor Green	v	Stafford Rangers	2-1	Newport County	v	Clevedon Town	2-0 (aet)
Newport IOW	v	Weymouth	3-1	Redditch United	v	Evesham United	4-5 (aet)
Rocester	v	Hednesford Town	1-2	Rugby United	v	*Cambridge City	0-3
Salisbury City	v	Dorchester Town	3-2	Shepshed Dynamo	v	Corby Town	3-2
Solihull Borough	v	Racing Club Warwick	6-2	Spalding United	v	King's Lynn	1-3
Stamford	v	Rothwell Town	3-2 (aet)	Stourport Swifts	v	Bromsgrove Rovers	1-4
Tamworth	v	Sutton Coldfield Town	1-3	Taunton Town	v	Swindon Supermarine	3-1
Tonbridge Angels	v	Welling United	1-2 (aet)	Worcester City	v	Halesowen Town	0-1

*Cambridge City expelled, tie awarded to Rugby United.

SECOND ROUND

Ashford Town	v	Crawley Town	1-2	Bedworth United	v	Hednesford	3-1
Chippenham Town	v	Bashley	2-1	Dartford	v	Dover Athletic	1-6
Eastbourne Borough	v	Burnham	2-3 (aet)	Halesowen Town	v	Evesham United	4-3
Hinckley United	v	Moor Green	2-1	King's Lynn	v	Stamford	2-1
Newport IOW	v	Salisbury City	3-2	Rugby United	v	Grantham Town	1-2
Shepshed Dynamo	v	Ilkeston Town 3-3 (aet)	4-2p	Solihull Borough	v	Bromsgrove	3-0
Sutton Coldfield	v	Newport County	2-1	Taunton Town	v	Mangotsfield Utd	1-7
Tiverton Town	v	Cirencester Town	4-2	Welling United	v	Chelmsford City	2-3

THIRD ROUND

Burnham	v	Crawley Town	1-4	Dover Athletic	v	Chelmsford City	0-1
Halesowen Town	v	Sutton Coldfield	4-1	King's Lynn	v	Hinckley United	3-0
Mangotsfield United	v	Chippenham	0-1	Newport IOW	v	Tiverton Town	1-7
Shepshed Dynamo	v	Grantham	2-5	Solihull Borough	v	Bedworth United	2-3

QUARTER-FINALS

Bedworth United	v	Halesowen Town	0-2	Crawley Town	v	*Chelmsford City	1-2
King's Lynn	v	Grantham Town	2-0	Tiverton Town	v	Chippenham Town	2-3

*Chelmsford played an ineligible player, tie awarded to Crawley Town.

SEMI-FINALS

Crawley Town	v	King's Lynn	1-0	Halesowen Town	v	Chippenham	2-1

FINAL 1st LEG 15th April

Halesowen Town v Crawley Town 2-1

FINAL 2nd LEG 29th April

Crawley Town v Halesowen Town 2-0 Crawley Town won 3-2 on aggregate.

PREMIER DIVISION LEADING GOALSCORERS 2002-03

22	Jame Taylor	Havant & Waterlooville	16	Martin Paul	Chippenham Town
17	Gary Bull	Grantham Town	16	Dale Watkins	Chelmsford City
17	Stephen Piearce	Hednesford Town	15	Christopher Freestone	Ilkeston Town
17	David Sadler	Hinckley United	15	Lee Phillips	Weymouth
16	Phil Everett	Tiverton Town	15	Allan Tait	Folkestone Invicta
16	Nathan Lamey	Moor Green	15	Nicholas McDonnell	Crawley Town
16	Darren Middleton	Worcester City	14	James Mudge	Tiverton Town

SOUTHERN LEAGUE - PREMIER DIVISION - LAST TEN YEARS

	93-94	94-95	95-96	96-97	97-98	98-99	99-00	00-01	01-02	02-03
Ashford Town	-	-	-	19	21r	-	-	-	-	-
Atherstone United	4	15	17	11	9	16	22r	-	-	-
Baldock Town	-	-	18	20r	-	-	-	-	-	-
Bashley	21r	-	-	-	-	-	-	-	-	-
Bath City	-	-	-	-	6	4	4	15	17	14
Boston United	-	-	-	xfer from NPL		2	1p	-	-	-
Bromsgrove Rovers	-	-	-	-	19	22r	-	-	-	-
Burton Albion	11	3	16	6	3	13	2	2	-	-
Cambridge City	17	9	19	18	13	20	14	16	14	18
Chelmsford City	6	15	12	22r	-	-	-	-	18	9
Cheltenham Town	2	2	3	2p	-	-	-	-	-	-
Chippenham Town	-	-	-	-	-	-	-	-	-	5
Clevedon Town	-	-	-	-	-	-	8	19r	-	-
Corby Town	9	22r	-	-	-	-	-	-	-	-
Crawley Town	5	11	9	17	10	11	12	11	4	7
Dorchester Town	18	6	13	15	4	18	18	21r	-	-
Dover Athletic	-	-	-	-	-	-	-	-	-	3
Farnborough Town	1p	-	-	-	-	-	-	-	-	-
Fisher Athletic	-	-	-	-	-	-	-	20r	-	
Folkestone Invicta	-	-	-	-	-	-	-	17	13	22r
Forest Green Rovers	-	-	-	-	-	1p	-	-	-	-
Gloucester City	10	4	4	3	11	6	20r	-	-	-
Gravesend & Northfleet	-	14	11	14	to Isthmian Lge		-	-	-	-
Grantham Town	-	-	-	-	-	17	19r	-	-	16
Gresley Rovers	14	8	5	1	17	21r	-	-	-	-
Halesowen Town	3	13	2	4	5	8	11	22r	-	19r
Hastings United	12	12	8	16	14	5r	-	-	-	20r
Havant & Waterlooville					**	-	13	6	3	8
Hednesford Town	13	1p	-	-	-	-	-	-	16	11
Hinckley United	-	-	-	-	-	-	-	-	12	13
Ilkeston Town	-	-	20r	-	-	3	9	14	10	21r
Kettering Town	-	-	-	-	-	-	-	-	1p	-
King's Lynn	-	-	-	5	8	10	5	3	20r	-
Leek Town	-	7	-	-	-	-	-	-	-	-
Margate	-	-	-	-	-	-	3	1p	-	-
Merthyr Tydfil	-	-	7	9	2	15	17	18	21r	-
Moor Green	19r	-	-	-	-	-	-	9	7	12
Newport AFC (County from 99-00)	-	-	14	21r	-	-	7	10	5	10
Newport I.o.W.	-	-	-	-	-	-	-	-	19r	-
Nuneaton Borough	22r	-	-	7	12	1p	-	-	-	-
Rothwell Town	-	-	-	-	16	19	21r	-	-	-
Rushden & Diamonds	-	5	1p	-	-	-	-	-	-	-
St Leonards	-	-	-	-	22r	-	-	-	-	-
Salisbury City	-	-	15	12	18	12	16	13	22r	-
Sittingbourne	8	20r	-	8	20r	-	-	-	-	-
Solihull Borough	6	19r	-	-	-	-	-	-	-	-
Stafford Rangers	-	-	21r	-	-	-	-	7	9	2
Sudbury Town	-	18	10	11	to Eastern Lge.		-	-	-	-
Trowbridge Town	7	21r	-	-	-	-	-	-	-	-
Tamworth	-	-	-	-	15	9	6	12	2	1p
Tiverton Town	-	-	-	-	-	-	-	-	6	4
V.S. Rugby	-	17	22r	-	-	-	-	-	-	-
Waterlooville	20r	-	-	-	-	**				
Welling	-	-	-	-	-	-	-	4	15	15
Weymouth	-	-	-	-	-	14	10	5	11	17
Worcester City	15	10	6	10	7	7	15	8	8	6

BATH CITY

CLUB OFFICIALS

Chairman: Stephen Hall
Directors: G.Todd,P.Weaver,M.Hughes. P.Williams and A Pierce

Secretary: Quentin Edwards c/o the club, 01225 423087 (B) & 07785 795532 (M)

Commercial Director: G.Todd
Safety Officer: J Watt
Press Officer:Q.Edwards

FOOTBALL MANAGEMENT TEAM

Manager: Alan Pridham
Assistant Manager: Gary Smart
Physios:Dave Lukins

FACT FILE

Founded: 1889
Nicknames: The City or The Romans
Midweek home matchday: Tuesday
Colours: Black & white stripes/black/b & w
Change: All red
Youth League: South West Counties
Ladies Team: Yes
Unofficial Club Website:www.bathcityfc,com
2002-2003
Captain: Paul Milsom
Top Scorer:Jason Eaton
Player of the Year:Andy Williams

Pages: 48 Price £1.50

Editor: Chris Stillman
Tel: 01761 433528

GROUND Twerton Park, Twerton, Bath Avon BA2 1DB. Tel: 01225 423087/313247
Fax: 01225481391 Email Address: ofice@bathcityfc.freeserve.co,
Directions: Twerton Park is situated on the A4/A36 Lower Bristol Road - on theBristol side of Bath City Centre (Approx 2.5 miles). The area is serviced byJ18 on the M4. From the centre of Bath the bus route is No.5 - Twerton HighStreet
Capacity: 8,840 Seated: 1,017 Covered Terracing: 4,800
Clubhouse: Several bars open all week and full service with menu on match-days catering for up to 250 people Club Shop: Contact MrM.Brush

PREVIOUS
Grounds: The Belvoir Ground, Lambridge 1889-1932
Leagues: Southern League, Vauxhall Conference

CLUB RECORDS
Attendance: 18,020 v Brighton & Hove Albion, FA Cup.
Defeat: 9-0 Yeovil Town 46-47 **Victory:** 8-0 v Boston United 98-99
Career goalscorer: Paul Randall. **Career appearances:** David Mogg (530)
Transfer fee paid: £15,000 for Micky Tanner from Bristol City
Transfer fee received: £80,000 for Jason Dodd from Southampton

BEST SEASON
FA Cup: Third Round 63-64, 0-3 v Bolton W. (A) after 1-1: 93-94 **FA Trophy:** 4th Round, 89-90

HONOURS
Southern League Champions 59-60, 77-78; R-up 29-33, 61-62, 89-90; Southern League Cup 78-79; Somerset Premier Cup 51-52, 52-53, 57-58, 59-60, 65-66, 69-70, 77-78, 80-81, 81-82, 83-84, 84-85, 85-86, 88-89, 89-90, 93-94, 94-95;Anglo-Italian Cup R-up 76-77, 77-78

Players progressing: Alan Skirton (Arsenal),Tony Book (Plymouth A.), Kenny Allen (Bournemouth), Peter Rogers (Exeter C.), R Bourne (Torquay), Martyn Rogers (Exeter City)Dave Wiffil (Manchester C.), , Brian Wade (Swindon Town), Jeff Meacham (Bristol R.), Martin Hirst (BristolC.), Paul Bodin (Swindon), Graham Withey (Coventry), Jason Dodd (Southampton), Paul Adcock (Torquay)

L-R - Back row: Gary Thorne, Giuseppe Sorbara (now Team Bath), Gary Kemp, Paul Milsom, Gary Horgan (now Chippenham Town), Mark Hervin, Mike Trought, Jason Drysdale, Dean Birkby (Now Weston s-Mare), Jim Rollo and Adrian Foster. **Middle:** John Archer (Youth Team Coach), Gary Smart (Asst Man.), Andy Minturn, Danny Cleverley, Jason Eaton,Jamie Gosling, Frankie Bennett, Andy Williams, Chris Honor, Iain Harvey and Dave Lukins (Physio). **Front:** Roy Pitman (Chief Scout), Mike Hughes (Director), Paul Williams (Director), Alan Pridham (Manager), Frank Entwistle (President), Steve Hall (Chairman), Geoff Todd (Vice Chairman), Andrew Pierce (Director), Phil Weaver (Director), Dave Edler (Commercial Executive),and Quentin Edwards (Secretary).

Date	Comp.	Opponents	Att.	Score	Goalscorers
17/08	D.M. P	Ilkeston Town	575	1 - 1	Eaton 58
20/08	D.M. P	HAVANT & WATERLOOVILLE	768	1 - 1	Gosling 28
24/08	D.M. P	FOLKESTONE INVICTA	639	2 - 0	Gosling 49[p], Cleverley 75
26/08	D.M. P	Chippenham Town	1906	2 - 1	Gosling 30[p], Birkby 90
31/08	D.M. P	CRAWLEY TOWN	818	0 - 1	
04/09	D.M. P	Tiverton Town	903	1 - 2	Horgan 71
07/09	D.M. P	CAMBRIDGE CITY	734	1 - 1	Drysdale 20[p]
10/09	D.M. P	HALESOWEN TOWN	588	3 - 0	Cleverley 40, Williams 69, Horgan 76
14/09	D.M. P	Hinckley United	314	1 - 3	Bennett 32
17/09	D.M. P	Moor Green	243	0 - 1	
21/09	D.M. P	CHELMSFORD CITY	663	0 - 1	
28/09	FAC Q2	MERTHYR TYDFIL	744	5 - 0	Rollo 1 20, Thorne 40, Foster 65 75
05/10	D.M. P	Tamworth	831	1 - 6	Thorne 85
08/10	D.M. P	WORCESTER CITY	635	1 - 0	Eaton 63
12/10	FAC Q3	Weston-super-Mare	1029	5 - 0	Kemp 26, Rollo 36, Eaton 67 68 78[p]
19/10	D.M. P	Welling United	635	3 - 1	Seabury 60[og], Eaton 75[p], Thorne 78
27/10	FAC Q4	YEOVIL TOWN	3470	1 - 1	Cleverley 36
29/10	FAC Q4 rep	Yeovil Town	4393	1 - 3	Foster 79
02/11	FAT 1	Halesowen Town	403	3 - 4	Eaton 37 78, Thorne 59
05/11	Lge Cup 1	TIVERTON TOWN	318	2 - 2	Gosling 42[p], M Keen 74 Lost 1 3 after pens.
09/11	D.M. P	Hednesford Town	624	2 - 2	Eaton 11, Williams 72
12/11	D.M. P	TIVERTON TOWN	513	0 - 1	
16/11	D.M. P	HINCKLEY UNITED	595	2 - 2	Cleverley 24, Eaton 42[p]
26/11	Som. PC 2	Odd Down	214	3 - 4	Rollo 68, Minturn 86, Eaton 88
07/12	D.M. P	WELLING UNITED	589	0 - 2	
14/12	D.M. P	Dover Athletic	781	0 - 2	
21/12	D.M. P	NEWPORT COUNTY	898	4 - 3	Milsom 55, Eaton 65, Gosling 86[p], Bennett 88
26/12	D.M. P	CHIPPENHAM TOWN	1972	1 - 1	Eaton 13
28/12	D.M. P	Crawley Town	886	2 - 1	Eaton 30, Cleverley 52
04/01	D.M. P	MOOR GREEN	678	1 - 1	Eaton 51
18/01	D.M. P	Folkestone Invicta	316	4 - 2	Bennett 44 54, Williams 73, Shaw 79
25/01	D.M. P	Newport County	856	1 - 1	Bennett 24
01/02	D.M. P	HEDNESFORD TOWN	702	4 - 1	Rollo 19, Gosling 23[p], Williams 28, Eaton 67
08/02	D.M. P	Cambridge City	317	1 - 0	Jefferies 87
22/02	D.M. P	Hastings United	452	1 - 1	Trought 83
01/03	D.M. P	Chelmsford City	535	0 - 2	
04/03	D.M. P	HASTINGS UNITED	536	1 - 0	Shore 77
08/03	D.M. P	Grantham Town	368	0 - 0	
11/03	D.M. P	STAFFORD RANGERS	558	0 - 1	
15/03	D.M. P	DOVER ATHLETIC	651	1 - 0	Toomey 60
22/03	D.M. P	Halesowen Town	507	1 - 1	Milsom 62
25/03	D.M. P	Weymouth	551	0 - 2	
29/03	D.M. P	ILKESTON TOWN	628	1 - 1	Cleverley 77
12/04	D.M. P	GRANTHAM TOWN	610	3 - 2	Tweddle 40 42[p], Williams 55
19/04	D.M. P	Worcester City	753	1 - 2	Harvey 31
21/04	D.M. P	WEYMOUTH	788	1 - 1	Coupe 28
26/04	D.M. P	Stafford Rangers	982	0 - 5	
01/05	D.M. P	Havant & Waterlooville	357	1 - 3	Jefferies 90
03/05	D.M. P	TAMWORTH	1116	0 - 2	

PLAYING SQUAD

Goalkeepers: Mark Bryant (Weston-super-Mare)

Defenders: Nathan Coupe (Forest Green R.), Chris Honor (Basingstoke T.), Gary Kemp (Newport County), Andy Mintum (Cirencester T.), Michael Trought (Bristol R.), Andy Williams (Swindon T.).

Midfield: Joe Collins (Paulton R.), Iain Harvey (Clevedon T.), Marco Micciche (Clevedon T.), Jim Rollo (Merthyr Tydfil), Drew Shore (Bristol R.), Gary Smart (Clevedon T.), Ben Trace (Clevedon T.).

Forwards: Frankie Bennett (Weston-super-Mare), Jamie Crandon (Paulton R.), Jason Eaton (Basingstoke T.), Adrian Foster (Forest Green R.), Dave Toomey (Barry T.)

CAMBRIDGE CITY

CLUB OFFICIALS

Chairman: Denis Rolph

President: Sir Neil Westbrook, CBE MA FRICS

Secretary: Stuart Hamilton
1 Parsonage Close, Highfield
Caldicote,Cambridge
Tel No: 01954 212602

Press Officer: Secretary
email: stuart@cambridgecityfc.com

FOOTBALL MANAGEMENT TEAM

Manager: Gary Roberts
Asst. Manager: T.B.A.
Physio: DamionT.B.A.

FACT FILE

Formed: 1908
Nickname: Lilywhites
Sponsors: Lancer UK
Colours:White /black/ white. Change All Sky
Midweek matchday: Tuesday
Reserves' League: Eastern Counties
Website: www.cambridgecityfc.com

2002-2003

Captain : Rob Nightingale
Players of the Year: Danny Bllomfield & Martin Davies
Leading Goalscorer: Danny Bloomfield

Welcome to Milton Road home of
Cambridge City Football Club
Formed in 1908 - 94th season
2002/3 Season
CAMBRIDGE CITY
1985-6
Dr Martens League - Premier Division
City v Halesowen Town
Saturday 14 September - Kick off 3pm
Vol 6
Issue 05
£1.50
Main Club Sponsors
LANCER

Pages: 44 Price: £1.50
Editor: Secretary
Local Press: Cambridge Evening News
Local Radio: BBC Radio Cambridge

GROUND City Ground, Milton Road, Cambridge CB4 1UY Tel: 01223 357973

Directions: Fifty yards on left from start of A1309, Cambridge to Ely Rd. (Behind Westbrook Centre). Thirty minutes walk from Cambridge BR

Capacity: 2000 Cover: 1,400 Seats:533 Floodlights: Yes

Clubhouse: 11am-11pm Mon-Sat, 12-3 & 7pm-10.30 Sun. Bingo, Dances, Pool, Darts

Club Shop: Sells badges, scarves, pennants, replica shirts and leisurewear. Contact Neil Harvey (01223 235991)

PREVIOUS **Leagues:** Bury & Dist. 08-13 19-20, East Anglian 08-10, Southern Olympian 11-14, Southern Amateur 1913-35, Spartan 35-50, Athenian 50-58 **Name:** Cambridge Town 1908-51

CLUB RECORDS **Attendance:** 12,058 v Leytonstone, FA Amateur Cup 1st Rd, 1949-50
Scorer: Gary Grogan **Appearances:** Mal Keenan
Fee Paid: £8,000 for Paul Coe (Rushden & Diamonds) **Fee Received:**£100,000 from Millwall for Neil Harris 1998

BEST SEASON **FA Amateur Cup:** Semi Final 27-28 **FA Trophy:** 2nd Rd. 86-87 87-88
FA Cup: 1st Rd; v Ashford 66, v Swindon 46, v Walthamstow Ave. 48, v Hereford 93, v Wigan Ath. 99, v Exeter City 01

HONOURS Southern Lg 62-63 (R-up 70-71, Southern Div 85-86, Div 1 R-up 69-70, Champ Cup62-63; E Anglian Cup (9); Eastern Prof Floodlit Lg 65-66 72-73, Cambs Prof Cup(6); Cambs Invitation Cup (8); Spartan Lg 47-48 48-49 (R-up 49-50); EasternDiv Champs 45-46); Southern Amat Lg 20-21 27-28 28-29 30-31 31-32; Bury & Dist.Lg (4); E Anglian Lg (6); AFA Snr Cup 30-31 46-47 47-48(shared) 48-49 49-50;AFA Invitation Cup 50-51; Hunts Prem Cup 62-63 64-65; Suffolk Sen Cup 09-10; Addenbrookes Hosp Cup 87-88; The Munns Youth Cup 82-83 83-84 84-85; ChilternYouth Lge Cup R-up 75-76; South Mids Lg Youth Trophy 82-83; Robinson Cup 87-8889-90; Jim Digney 89-90; Essex & Herts Youth Lg 89-90 Southern Lg Cup R-up 98-9

Players progressing: K Wright (West Ham 46), A Gallego(Norwich 47), A Stokes (Watford 61), D Weddle (Middlesbrough 61), D Hicksen(Bury 62), B Harvey (Blackpool 62), R Whitehead (Darlington 62), G Cummins(Hull 62), R Pearce (Peterborough 63), A Banks (Exeter 63), T Carroll (Ipswich66), Dominic Genovese (Peterborough 88), Roy Jones (Swindon), Winston Dubose(Oldham), K Wilkin (Northampton Tn 91), S Flack (Cardiff City 95), D Hedcock(Sheffield Wed 96), Neil Harris (Millwall 1998), Tesfaye Bramble, Shane Wardley (Southend United)

Back row left to right: Martin Fox, Kevin Wilkin, Matt Nurse, Andy Taylor and Tim Wooding
Front row: John O'Flynn, Matt Hann, Steve Wenlock, Adam Wilde, Chris Tovey and Jon Challinor.

Date	Comp.	Opponents	Att.	Score	Goalscorers
10/08	Cambs PC F	Histon	n/k	1 - 3	
17/08	D.M. P	NEWPORT COUNTY	426	1 - 3	Gutzmore 3
20/08	D.M. P	Grantham Town	611	0 - 1	
24/08	D.M. P	Hednesford Town	516	2 - 3	Gutzmore 23, Wooding 58
26/08	D.M. P	CHELMSFORD CITY	407	2 - 3	Wilde 79, Hayes 81[p]
31/08	D.M. P	Stafford Rangers	677	1 - 0	Clements 17
03/09	D.M. P	DOVER ATHLETIC	370	1 - 1	Wilkin 79
07/09	D.M. P	Bath City	734	1 - 1	Wilkin 10
10/09	D.M. P	FOLKESTONE INVICTA	416	2 - 1	Clements 33, Collins 36
14/09	D.M. P	HALESOWEN TOWN	343	0 - 1	
17/09	D.M. P	Ilkeston Town	523	2 - 0	Wilkin 11 46
21/09	D.M. P	Weymouth	561	0 - 0	
28/09	FAC Q2	King's Lynn	1041	0 - 1	
05/10	D.M. P	TIVERTON TOWN	316	3 - 0	Collins 7, Clements 10, Nightingale 28
08/10	D.M. P	HASTINGS UNITED	419	1 - 2	Collins 7
19/10	D.M. P	Worcester City	974	0 - 2	
26/10	D.M. P	HEDNESFORD TOWN	584	2 - 2	Bloomfield 24 84
29/10	Lge Cup 1	Rugby United	128	3 - 0	Simpson 45, Herin 54, Hayes 72
02/11	FAT 1	Worthing	256	4 - 1	Wardley 6, Nightingale 43, Wooding 80, Hayes 90
09/11	D.M. P	Tamworth	785	1 - 3	Collins 69
16/11	D.M. P	CHIPPENHAM TOWN	555	0 - 1	
30/11	FAT 2	CRAWLEY TOWN	327	0 - 1	
07/12	D.M. P	WEYMOUTH	437	0 - 1	
14/12	D.M. P	ILKESTON TOWN	383	2 - 2	Bloomfield 48 55
21/12	D.M. P	Moor Green	230	1 - 1	Sturgess 4
28/12	D.M. P	STAFFORD RANGERS	522	1 - 0	Vowden 68
04/01	D.M. P	Tiverton Town	737	2 - 0	Simpson 71 87
11/01	D.M. P	Folkestone Invicta	412	3 - 0	Nightingale 34[p] 84, Vowden 51
18/01	D.M. P	GRANTHAM TOWN	536	1 - 1	Vowden 70
25/01	D.M. P	Hastings United	468	2 - 1	Clements 39, Bloomfield 80
08/02	D.M. P	BATH CITY	317	0 - 1	
22/02	D.M. P	Crawley Town	734	2 - 4	Bloomfield 23, Hayes 73[p]
25/02	Cambs IC QF	FORDHAM	116	5 - 0	Hayes 8 47, Nightingale 12, Vowden 65, Wilson 68
01/03	D.M. P	HINCKLEY UNITED	444	1 - 1	Bloomfield 88
04/03	Cambs IC SF	Sawston United	126	2 - 0	Hayes 80 89
08/03	D.M. P	Halesowen Town	506	1 - 1	Niven 39
10/03	D.M. P	Chelmsford City	480	2 - 1	Simpson 14 90
15/03	D.M. P	Newport County	548	1 - 1	Wilkin 74
18/03	D.M. P	MOOR GREEN	285	1 - 2	Simpson 78
22/03	D.M. P	CRAWLEY TOWN	402	3 - 0	Bloomfield 32, Simpson 38, Wilkin 44
25/03	D.M. P	Havant & Waterlooville	359	2 - 0	Fennimore 11[og], Bloomfield 78
29/03	D.M. P	Chippenham Town	445	0 - 2	
01/04	D.M. P	WELLING UNITED	278	2 - 1	Bloomfield 2, Wilkin 46
05/04	D.M. P	WORCESTER CITY	453	1 - 0	Bloomfield 51
12/04	D.M. P	Dover Athletic	752	1 - 2	Simpson 85
14/04	Cambs IC F	HISTON	n/k	2 - 2	Bloomfield 57 78 Won 8 7 after pens (at Cambridge Utd)
19/04	D.M. P	TAMWORTH	825	0 - 1	
21/04	D.M. P	Welling United	540	0 - 1	
26/04	D.M. P	HAVANT & WATERLOOVILLE	648	4 - 5	Nightingale 30 90[p], Simpson 63 89
03/05	D.M. P	Hinckley United	411	2 - 3	Hayes 54, Vowden 90

PLAYING SQUAD

Goalkeepers: Martin Davies (Llanelli), Nicky Rust (Braintree T.)

Defenders: Tom Liberatore (Club Academy), Rob Miller (Bedford T.), Craig Pope (Barnet), Matt Rice (Club Academy), Shane Wardley (Enfield), Jack Wignall (Dagenham & Redbridge),Tim Wooding (Boston Utd).

Midfield: Lewis Baillie (Heybridge Swifts),Danny Bloomfield (A.F.C.Bournemouth), Laurie Church (St Ives T.), Rob Nightingale (Youth Team), Rob Sturgess (Peterborough Utd).

Forwards: Mathy Clements (Kings Lynn), Leon Gutzmore (Braintree T.), Ryan Jenner (Norwich C.), Stuart Niven (Marlow T.), Robbie Simpson (Norwich C.), Steve Thacker (Club Academy).

CHELMSFORD CITY

CLUB OFFICIALS

Chairman: **Trevor Wright**

Secretary: **David Clarke**
186 The Avenue, Lowestoft, Suffolk.
NR33 7LW
Tel 01502 580079 or
0781 8267555

FOOTBALL MANAGEMENT TEAM

Manager: Steve Moseley
Coach: Keith Day
Physio: Paul Smith

FACT FILE
Formed: 1878(Turned Pro 1938)
Nickname: City or 'The Clarets'
Sponsors:T.B.A.
Colours: All Claret with white trim
Change colours: All white with claret trim
Midweek matches : Monday
Club Website: www.chelmsfordcityfc.com

2002-2003
Captain: Mike Rutherford
Top Scorer: Dale Watkins
Player of the Year: Danny Slatter

Pages: 52 Price: £1.50
Editor: Trevor Smith (01473 824782)

Local Press: Essex Chronicle,
Chelmsford Weekly News,
East Anglian Daily Times, Evening Gazette
Local Radio: Essex Radio/Breeze AM,
BBC Essex, Chelner FM

GROUND Ground Share with Billericay Town
New Lodge, Blunts Wall Road, Billericay CM12 9SA Tel: 01277 652188

Directions: From Shenfield (A129) right at 1st lights then 2nd right. FromBasildon (A129) over 1st lights in town, then left at next lights and 2nd right. Half mile from Billericay (GER) station (London Liverpool St. - Southend line). Ground 5 mins walk from buses 222, 251, 357, 255, 551

Capacity: 3,500 Seats: 424 Cover: 600 Floodlights: Yes

Clubhouse: Open eves 8-11pm (except Mon),1pm-11pm Sat & w/e lunch noon-2.30pm.
Club Shop: Sells progs, badges, scarves, mugs etc. Contact Sharon Chantryvia club

PREVIOUS **Leagues:** None **Grounds:** New Writtle Street 38-97, Maldon Town 97-98
Name: None (Brentwood Town were incorporated in 1970)

CLUB RECORDS **Attendance:** 16,807 v Colchester, Southern League 10/9/49
Goalscorer: Tony Butcher, 287 (1957-71) **Appearances:** Derek Tiffin, 550 (1950-63)
Win: 10-1 v Bashley (H) Dr Martens Leagu 26/4/2000
Defeat: 2-10 v Barking (A), FA Trophy, 11/11/78
Fee - Paid: £10,000 for Tony Rogers (Dover Athletic, 1992) **Received:** £50,000 for David Morrison (Peterborough 94)

BEST SEASON **FA Cup:** 4th Rd, 1938-39 (v Birmingham City). 1st Rd 26 times
FA Trophy: Semi-final 69-70 v Telford Utd

HONOURS Southern Lg 45-46 67-68 71-72 (R-up 48-49 60-61 63-64 65-66); Southern Div 88-89, R-up 97-98, Lg Cup 45-46 59-60 (R-up 60-61); Merit Cup 71-72; Southern Lg War-Time (East) 39-40); Essex Prof Cup 5; Essex Snr Cup 85-86 88-89 92-93; Non-League Champs Chall Cup 71-72; E Anglian Cup 48-49; Eastern Co's Lg(3) 46-49(Lg Cup 59-60); Eastern F'lit Comp 6, (Cup 72-73 74-75); Metropolitan Lg 67-68, Lg Prof Cup 67-68, Autumn Shield 70-71; Essex Snr Lg Cup 84-85; Harry Fisher Mem. Tphy 88-89

Players progressing: G Merton (Watford 48), G Adams (Orient 49), W O'Neill(Burnley 49), B Farley/S McClellan/L Dicker/P Collins (Spurs 49/49/51/68), O Hold (Everton 50), R Marden (Arsenal 50), C McCormack (Barnsley 50), D Sexton(Luton 51), W Bellet & R Mason & A Nicholas (Orient 61 & 63 & 65), R Gladwin(Norwich 66), B King (Millwall 67), J O'Mara (Bradford City 74), N Spink (Aston77), M Dziadulewicz (Wimbledon 79), M Cawston (Southend 84), P Coleman (Exeter84), J Keeley & A Owers (Brighton 86 & 87), I Brown (Bristol C 93), D Morrison (Peterborough 94)

L-R - Back row: Brian Statham, Dale Watkins, Lewis Reed, Simon CLarke, Mike Rutherford, Paul Nicholls, Ian Cousins, Austin Berkley, Gary Cross, George Lay, Barry Lakin.**Front**: Keith Sharman, Steve Sanders, Lee Kelsey, Jack Midson, Ian Wiles, Danny Slatter, Tony Samuels.

Date	Comp.	Opponents	Att.	Score	Goalscorers
17/08	D.M. P	Chippenham Town	702	1 - 3	Keevil 32
19/08	D.M. P	HINCKLEY UNITED	443	1 - 1	Owusu 84
24/08	D.M. P	WORCESTER CITY	421	1 - 1	Sanders 45
26/08	D.M. P	Cambridge City	407	3 - 2	Samuels 25, Wiles 44, Gray 60[p]
31/08	D.M. P	HALESOWEN TOWN	481	1 - 0	Rutherford 54
03/09	D.M. P	Havant & Waterlooville	530	0 - 1	
07/09	D.M. P	Tamworth	649	1 - 3	Gray 50[p]
09/09	D.M. P	CRAWLEY TOWN	486	1 - 2	Samuels 89
14/09	D.M. P	NEWPORT COUNTY	496	1 - 1	Gray 27
17/09	D.M. P	Hastings United	397	1 - 1	Keevill 25
21/09	D.M. P	Bath City	663	1 - 0	Cross 52
28/09	FAC Q2	Carshalton Athletic	577	1 - 1	Gray 32[p]
02/10	FAC Q2 rep	CARSHALTON ATHLETIC	537	1 - 0	Samuels 98
05/10	D.M. P	WEYMOUTH	535	3 - 1	Gray 2 88, Samuels 90
07/10	D.M. P	Dover Athletic	1038	0 - 1	
12/10	FAC Q3	St Albans City	839	0 - 1	
19/10	D.M. P	MOOR GREEN	501	4 - 0	Gray 11, Berkeley 18 21, Cross 35
26/10	D.M. P	Welling United	669	2 - 0	Gray 45, Watkins 55
29/10	Lge Cup 1	Chatham Town	136	3 - 0	Slatter 25, Watkins 56, Boyle 61[og]
02/11	FAT 1	Hastings United	599	0 - 1	
09/11	D.M. P	STAFFORD RANGERS	560	0 - 2	
19/11	Essex SC 3	Halstead Town	189	5 - 0	
23/11	D.M. P	Tiverton Town	772	3 - 3	Samuels 45, Cross 71, Lakin 79
26/11	Lge Cup 2	Welling United	206	3 - 2	Gray 28, Watkins 31, Cross 70
03/12	Essex SC 4	Canvey Island	273	4 - 1	Cross 23, Slatter 46 87, Samuels 83
07/12	D.M. P	CHIPPENHAM TOWN	429	2 - 3	Kersey 34, Slatter 75
14/12	D.M. P	TAMWORTH	627	0 - 4	
16/12	Lge Cup 3	Dover Athletic	401	1 - 0	Slatter 13
21/12	D.M. P	Worcester City	911	0 - 5	
28/12	D.M. P	Moor Green	334	1 - 1	Berkley 7
04/01	D.M. P	ILKESTON TOWN	455	2 - 1	Cross 60, Kersey 90
18/01	D.M. P	TIVERTON TOWN	516	3 - 0	Cross 3, Watkins 78 89
25/01	D.M. P	Grantham Town	381	3 - 2	Reid 8, Watkins 19, Gowshall 81[og]
04/02	Essex SC QF	Heybridge Swifts	174	2 - 0	Watkins 77, Cross 89
08/02	D.M. P	Folkestone Invicta	420	2 - 3	Watkins 43[p] 89
11/02	Lge Cup QF	Crawley Town	359	2 - 1	Dean 25 50
15/02	D.M. P	GRANTHAM TOWN	481	1 - 2	Watkins 32
17/02	Essex SC SF	SOUTHEND UNITED	424	2 - 0	Slatter 3, Watkins 7
22/02	D.M. P	Halesowen Town	462	2 - 0	Dean 32, Watkins 43
01/03	D.M. P	BATH CITY	535	2 - 0	Watkins 55, Berkeley 62
03/03	D.M. P	Hednesford Town	378	2 - 2	Dean 9, Rutherford 89
08/03	D.M. P	HAVANT & WATERLOOVILLE	450	1 - 2	Watkins 20
10/03	D.M. P	CAMBRIDGE CITY	480	1 - 2	Samuels 83
15/03	D.M. P	Weymouth	679	3 - 1	Samuels 19, Slatter 72, Cross 84
22/03	D.M. P	WELLING UNITED	579	1 - 1	Berkeley 59
24/03	Essex SC F	AVELEY (at Southend United)	857	5 - 0	Slatter 16, Watkins 28, Cross 40, Lakin 74, Samuels 84
29/03	D.M. P	Hinckley United	333	1 - 2	Samuels 62
05/04	D.M. P	DOVER ATHLETIC	470	0 - 1	
08/04	D.M. P	Ilkeston Town	275	2 - 2	Watkins 24 34[p]
12/04	D.M. P	Stafford Rangers	739	1 - 1	Watkins 54[p]
14/04	D.M. P	HASTINGS UNITED	504	1 - 0	Watkins 14
19/04	D.M. P	Crawley Town	880	0 - 0	
22/04	D.M. P	FOLKESTONE INVICTA	434	3 - 2	Dean 9, Nicholls 61[p], Sharman 88
26/04	D.M. P	HEDNESFORD TOWN	618	2 - 2	Moss 54[og], Samuels 78
03/05	D.M. P	Newport County	890	5 - 2	Nicholls 24[p] 45[p], Sharman 28, Samuels 67, Cross 68

PLAYING SQUAD

Goalkeepers: Paul Nicholls (Havant & Waterlooville).

Defenders: Simon Clarke (Hendon), Garry Cross (Slough T.), Russell Edwards (Welling Utd), Steve Sanders (British Universities), Keith Sharman (Crawley T.), Ian Wiles (Heybridge Swifts).

Midfield: Rio Alderton (Sheffield Utd), Dean Gibbs (Stoke C.), Dean Gray (Welling Utd), Matt Jones (Canvey Island), Barry Larkin (Erith & Belvedere), Steve Norman (Dover Ath.), Gareth Street (Witham T.).

Forwards: Danny Curran (Aveley), Ben Fuller (Witham T.), Tony Sammuels (Boreham Wood), **Dale Watkins** (Kettering T.)

CHIPPENHAM TOWN

CLUB OFFICIALS

President: Doug Webb
Chairman: Malcolm Lyus
Vice-Chairman: Wayne Devine
Treasurer: Richard Terrell
Press Officer: Chris Blake
Comm Man: Sue Evans (01249 705912)
Secretary: Chris Blake, 28 Sadlers Mead, Chippenham, Wilts SN15 3PB
Tel: 01249 658212

FOOTBALL MANAGEMENT TEAM

Manager: Tommy Saunders
Physio: Paul Watts

FACT FILE

Formed: 1873
Nickname: The Bluebirds
Club Sponsors: D.L.Windows, Costcutters, Shoestrings, Crane Merchandising Systems,
Club colours: All Navy blue
Change colours:All white or All yellow
Midweek matches: Wednesday
Local Press: Chippenham News, Wilts Gazette, Wiltshire Chronicle

2002-2003

Captain: Colin Towler
Leading Goalscorer: Martin Paul 19
Player of the Year: Wayne Thorne

PROGRAMME
Pages: 32 Price: £1.50
Editors: Will Hulbert & Chris Blake

GROUND Hardenhuish Park, Bristol Road, Chippenham SW 14 6LR Tel: 01249 650400
Website: www.chippenhamtownfc.co.uk email: chrisblake@chiptownfc.freeserve .co.uk

Directions: M4 jct 17, A350 into Chippenham, follow signs for Trowbridge/Bath until r'about, left onto A420 into town, ground 800yds on left 15 mins walk from railway station on main A420 Bristol Road

Capacity: 4,000 Seats: 300 Cover: 1,000 Floodlights: Yes
Clubhouse: Yes, open matchdays. Food available **Club Shop:** Yes

PREVIOUS **Leagues:** Hellenic, Wiltshire Senior, Wiltshire Premier, Western League
Grounds: Westmead, Lowden, Little George Lane, Malmesbury Rd

RECORD **Gate:** 4,800 v Chippenham Utd, Western League 1951
Goalscorer: Dave Ferris **Appearances:** Ian Monnery

BEST SEASON **FA Cup:** 1st Round 51-52 **FA Vase:** Finalists 99-00

HONOURS F.A. Vase R-up 99-00, Western Lg 51-52 R-up 00-01, Div 1 80-81, Div 2 52-53 (Res) 80-81. Wilts Senior Cup; Wilts Senior League; Les Phillips Cup (Western Lg Cup) 99-00 00-01, Wilts Premier Shield 2001-02. Dr Martens Division 1 Western Division: Runners-Up 2001-02

L-R - Back Row: Ellis Wilmot, Simon Gilbert, Scott Walker, Gary Horgan, Wayne Thorne, Steve Brown. **Middle**: Clive Garraway (Kit Man.), Lee Collier, Martin Paul, Dean Birkby, Mark Hervin, Matt Rawlings, Charlie Griffin, Mark Harrington, Paul Watts (Physio), Paul Summers (GK Coach). **Front:** Susan Evans (Commercial man.), Colin Towler, Adie Mings (player/Asst. Man.), Tom Saunders (Manager), Chris Blake (Secretary), Gareth Davies, Tom Gould, Sean Hughes (Scout).

Date	Comp.	Opponents	Att.	Score	Goalscorers
17/08	D.M. P	CHELMSFORD CITY	702	3 - 1	Brown 6 72, Paul 22
20/08	D.M. P	Welling United	500	1 - 1	Rawlins 12
24/08	D.M. P	Stafford Rangers	669	0 - 0	
26/08	D.M. P	BATH CITY	1906	1 - 2	Griffin 88
31/08	D.M. P	Tamworth	805	1 - 0	Griffin 42
04/09	D.M. P	WEYMOUTH	817	1 - 1	Paul 68
07/09	D.M. P	Grantham Town	466	1 - 1	Griffin 20
11/09	D.M. P	HAVANT & WATERLOOVILLE	661	3 - 1	Griffin 37, Paul 57[p] 80
14/09	D.M. P	ILKESTON TOWN	645	3 - 0	Paul 29, Gould 61, Mings 81
16/09	D.M. P	Newport County	741	1 - 3	Brown 45
21/09	D.M. P	Folkestone Invicta	339	2 - 1	Davies 32, Gould 60
28/09	FAC Q2	WEYMOUTH	917	1 - 4	Paul 29
05/10	D.M. P	MOOR GREEN	577	1 - 1	Towler 56
08/10	D.M. P	Weymouth	653	1 - 1	Griffin 71
19/10	D.M. P	HINCKLEY UNITED	541	3 - 1	Rawlins 8, Paul 20 41
29/10	Lge Cup 1	Merthyr Tydfil	238	1 - 0	Rawlins 37
02/11	FAT 1	DORCHESTER TOWN	534	4 - 1	Mings 28, Horgan 45, Griffin 78, Paul 83
09/11	D.M. P	HASTINGS UNITED	592	0 - 0	
16/11	D.M. P	Cambridge City	555	1 - 0	Brown 66
20/11	Wilts PS SF(1)	SALISBURY CITY	368	3 - 3	Griffin 30 41 90
23/11	D.M. P	FOLKESTONE INVICTA	531	1 - 0	Rawlins 90
27/11	Lge Cup 2	BASHLEY	301	2 - 1	Brown 28 70
30/11	FAT 2	AYLESBURY UNITED	580	0 - 1	
03/12	D.M. P	Crawley Town	956	1 - 1	Paul 23
07/12	D.M. P	Chelmsford City	429	3 - 2	Paul 16 51, Griffin 67
14/12	D.M. P	WORCESTER CITY	1014	0 - 0	
17/12	Lge Cup 3	Mangotsfield United	205	1 - 0	Griffin 18
21/12	D.M. P	Ilkeston Town	395	6 - 2	Mings 8 53, Robinson 32[og], Paul 50 70, Futcher 75
26/12	D.M. P	Bath City	1972	1 - 1	Paul 10
28/12	D.M. P	TAMWORTH	1209	3 - 0	Tweddle 11 87, Griffin 15
18/01	D.M. P	NEWPORT COUNTY	1067	0 - 0	
25/01	D.M. P	Dover Athletic	1009	1 - 0	Paul 75[p]
29/01	Lge Cup QF	Tiverton Town	435	3 - 2	Griffin 18 85, Brown 46
01/02	D.M. P	CRAWLEY TOWN	796	1 - 0	Gould 85
08/02	D.M. P	GRANTHAM TOWN	669	0 - 0	
12/02	D.M. P	TIVERTON TOWN	608	1 - 1	Gould 65
15/02	D.M. P	Havant & Waterlooville	461	0 - 1	
22/02	D.M. P	Hinckley United	286	2 - 1	Mills 80 89
24/02	D.M. P	Hednesford Town	486	3 - 1	Rawlins 40, Mings 72, Paul 73
01/03	D.M. P	Worcester City	1346	0 - 0	
04/03	Lge Cup SF	Halesowen Town	348	1 - 2	Griffin 28
08/03	D.M. P	STAFFORD RANGERS	761	1 - 1	Walker 15
15/03	D.M. P	HALESOWEN TOWN	605	1 - 2	Walker 57
22/03	D.M. P	Moor Green	335	0 - 1	
25/03	Wilts PS SF(2)	Salisbury City	381	0 - 2	
29/03	D.M. P	CAMBRIDGE CITY	445	2 - 0	Mings 32, Griffin 35
05/04	D.M. P	HEDNESFORD TOWN	491	1 - 3	Kear 69
12/04	D.M. P	Hastings United	433	1 - 2	Griffin 82
21/04	D.M. P	Tiverton Town	832	1 - 1	Harrington 14
26/04	D.M. P	DOVER ATHLETIC	556	0 - 0	
28/04	D.M. P	WELLING UNITED	273	4 - 0	Walker 4, Paul 61, Davies 78, Thorne 90
03/05	D.M. P	Halesowen Town	730	2 - 3	Mings 26, Paul 70

PLAYING SQUAD

Goalkeepers: Liam Bull (Swindon Supermarine), Mark Hervin (Cirencester T.), Paul Thompson (Devizes T.).

Defenders: Shane Andrews (Clevedon T.), Gareth Davies (Swindon T.), **Murray Fishlock** (Woking), Tom Gould (Team Bath), Andy Pitman (Afan Lido), Mark Robinson (Swindon T.), ColinTowler (Bath C.)

Midfield: Mark Badman (Bath C.), Andy Catley (Weston-super-Mare), Simon Charity (Paulton R.), Will Halliwell (Southampton), Mark Harrington (Bath C.), Gary Horgan (Bath C.), Wayne Thorne (Clevedon T.), Scott Walker (Newport County), Ellis Wilmot (Mangotsfield Utd), Jason Wood (Brislington).

Forwards: Steve Brown (Calne T.), Charlie Griffin (Woking), Adie Mings (Basingstoke T.), Martin Paul (Newport County), Matt Rawlings (Gloucester C.).

CRAWLEY TOWN

CLUB OFFICIALS

Chairperson: **Ms Jo Gomm**
Vice Chairman: **Dave Brown**
President: **Les Turnbull**
Secretary: **Dave Haining**
20 Irving Walk, Tilgate, Crawley RH10 5BQ
Tel: 01293 535683
Chief Executive: **John Duly**
Managing Director: **Steve Duly**

FOOTBALL MANAGEMENT TEAM

Manager: Francis Vines
Assistant Man: Victopr Bettinelli
Physio: R Massimo

FACT FILE

Formed: 1896
Nickname: Red Devils
Sponsors: Providian Bank
Colours: All red Change:White/black/white
Midweek matchday: Tuesday
Reserves' League: Suburban
Website: www.crawley-town-fc.co.uk

2002-2003

Captain: Pater Fear
Top Scorer: Nic McDonnell
Player of the Year: Marc Pullan

Pages: 32 Price: £1.50
Editors: Jim Green & Steve Duly
Tel: 01293 410000
Local Press: Crawley Observer, Crawley News, The Argus Local Radio: Radio Mercury, BBC Southern Counties

GROUND Broadfield Stadium, Brighton Road, Crawley RH11 9RX Tel: 01293 410000

Directions: M23 exit 11, 2nd exit off roundabout, A23, towards Crawley. Turn left at next r/about into ground

Capacity: 4,996 Cover: 4,200 Seats: 1,080 Floodlights: Yes

Clubhouse: Mon-Fri: Evenings 7-11 Sat: 12-11 Sun 12-8
Club Shop: Programmes, metal badges, hats, scarves, mugs, replica kits and other items

PREVIOUS **Leagues:** Sussex County 1951-56; Metropolitan 56-63 **Grounds:** Malthouse Farm 1896-1914 38-40; Victoria Hall + Rectory Fields 18-38;Yetmans Field 45-49, Town Mead 49-53 54-97, Ifield Rec Grd 53-54

CLUB RECORDS **Attendance:** 4,516 v Dagenham & Redbridge FA Cup 2nd Rd 7.12.2002
Goalscorer: Phil Basey 108 (68-72) **Appearances:** John Maggs 652 (63-73 75-79)
Win: 10-0 v Chichester United, Sussex Co. Lge Div. 2 17-12-55 and v Crowborough A,Sussex Floodlit Cup 25-09-01
Defeat: 0-10 v Arundel (A), Sussex County Lge 09-02-52
Fee Paid: £5,000 for David Thompson (Wokingham, May 92)
Fee Received: £75,000 for Jay Lovett from Brentford ,2000.

BEST SEASON **FA Trophy:** 3rd Rd 98-99
FA Cup: 3rd Rd Proper 91-92, 0-5 v Brighton & HA (A) League Clubs defeated: Northampton Town 91-92

HONOURS Sussex Snr Cup (3) 89-91-03 (R-up 58-59 95-96); Sussex I'mediate Cup 26-27,01-02Sussex Prof. Cup 69-70; Southern Lg S Div.R-Up 83-84; Merit Cup 70-71;Sussex Floodlit Cup (3) 90-93; Sussex Lg Div 2 R-up 55-56; Gilbert Rice F'lit Cup 79-80 83-84; Southern Co's Comb. Floodlit Cup 85-86; Met Lg Chal. Cup 58-59; Mid-Sussex Snr 02-03; Montgomery Cup 25-26 Sussex Floodlit Cup 98-99 Southern Lg Cup R-up:20 00-01, Southern League Cup Winners 2002-03

Players progressing: Ray Keeley, Graham Brown (Mansfield 68), Andy Ansah (Brentford 87), Craig Whitington (Scarborough 93),Ben Abbey (Oxford United 99), John Mackie (Reading 99), Jay Lovett (Brentford 2000)

Crawley line up prior to the Sussex Senior Cup Final. **Photo**: Roger Turner

Date	Comp.	Opponents	Att.	Score	Goalscorers
17/08	D.M. P	HEDNESFORD TOWN	863	2 - 2	Stevens 56, Le Bihan 89
19/08	D.M. P	Dover Athletic	1038	1 - 2	McDonnell 65
24/08	D.M. P	Tamworth	758	1 - 1	Holmes 53
26/08	D.M. P	WELLING UNITED	872	1 - 0	Bagnall 25
31/08	D.M. P	Bath City	818	1 - 0	Stevens 46
03/09	D.M. P	Folkestone Invicta	407	3 - 1	Stevens 42, Bagnall 46, Holmes 51
07/09	D.M. P	NEWPORT COUNTY	1041	2 - 0	McDonnell 66, Hockton 69
09/09	D.M. P	Chelmsford City	486	2 - 1	Hooper 35, Stevens 79
14/09	D.M. P	WORCESTER CITY	1738	0 - 0	
17/09	D.M. P	DOVER ATHLETIC	956	0 - 3	
21/09	D.M. P	Halesowen Town	547	2 - 0	McDonnell 75 81
28/09	FAC Q2	GREAT YARMOUTH TOWN	723	3 - 0	Stevens 43[p], Hockton 82, McDonnell 90
01/10	Lge Cup P	SITTINGBOURNE	260	2 - 0	Hockton 31, Patterson 48
05/10	D.M. P	GRANTHAM TOWN	1556	2 - 0	Stevens 32, Holmes 74
08/10	D.M. P	FOLKESTONE INVICTA	970	2 - 2	Stevens 20, McDonnell 35
12/10	FAC Q3	Lymington & New Milton	480	2 - 0	Fear 69, Hockton 89
19/10	D.M. P	Stafford Rangers	874	1 - 2	Stevens 8
26/10	FAC Q4	Flackwell Heath	567	4 - 1	Hooper 3, Cooksey 18, Harkin 36, Holmes 90
02/11	D.M. P	Moor Green	303	2 - 0	Stevens 37, Hockton 89
05/11	Lge Cup 1	HASTINGS UNITED	443	1 - 0	Hemsley 45
09/11	D.M. P	HINCKLEY UNITED	1217	0 - 2	
16/11	FAC 1	Tiverton Town	1840	1 - 1	McDonnell 36
19/11	Sussex SC 2	Bognor Regis Town	n/k	3 - 1	
26/11	FAC 1 rep	TIVERTON TOWN	3907	3 - 2	McDonnell 66 80, Bagnall 87
30/11	FAT 2	Cambridge City	327	1 - 0	McDonnell 20
03/12	D.M. P	CHIPPENHAM TOWN	956	1 - 1	Hemsley 45
07/12	FAC 2	DAGENHAM & REDBRIDGE	4516	1 - 2	McDonnell 3
09/12	D.M. P	Worcester City	877	1 - 2	Stevens 26
14/12	D.M. P	STAFFORD RANGERS	848	2 - 4	Bagnall 17, Hockton 28
17/12	Lge Cup 2	Ashford Town	149	2 - 1	Stevens 45 55[p]
26/12	D.M. P	Welling United	800	2 - 2	McDonnell 7, Le Bihan 63
28/12	D.M. P	BATH CITY	886	1 - 2	Hockton 87
14/01	FAT 3	Hayes	296	1 - 2	McDonnell 14
18/01	D.M. P	Havant & Waterlooville	599	4 - 2	McDonnell 7, Fear 9, Cooksey 11, Holmes 62,
25/01	D.M. P	ILKESTON TOWN	874	2 - 1	Bagnall 13, McDonnell 19
28/01	Sussex SC 3	Horsham	742	3 - 1	Bagnall 18, McDonnell 81, Hockton 86
01/02	D.M. P	Chippenham Town	796	0 - 1	
04/02	Lge Cup 3	Burnham	95	4 - 1	McDonnell 15 35 50, Hockton 74
08/02	D.M. P	Weymouth	654	0 - 2	
11/02	Lge Cup QF	CHELMSFORD CITY	359	1 - 2	Payne 69
15/02	D.M. P	HALESOWEN TOWN	679	4 - 0	Fear 14, Harkin 61, McDonnell 72, Holmes 90
17/02	Sussex SC QF	BRIGHTON & HOVE ALBION	534	1 - 0	Payne 17[p]
22/02	D.M. P	CAMBRIDGE CITY	734	4 - 2	Brake 32 40, Harkin 66, McDonnell 82
25/02	D.M. P	HASTINGS UNITED	783	1 - 1	Harkin 2
04/03	Lge Cup SF	KING'S LYNN	565	1 - 0	Bagnall 21
12/03	D.M. P	Tiverton Town	537	1 - 0	Bagnall 19
15/03	D.M. P	MOOR GREEN	813	2 - 2	Hockton 8, Brake 12
19/03	Sussex SC SF	Rye & Iden United (at Lewes FC)	350	3 - 0	Hockton 112, Cookson 114, Holmes 119
22/03	D.M. P	Cambridge City	402	0 - 3	
25/03	D.M. P	Grantham Town	375	3 - 0	Sadough 24, Fear 79, Brake 89
29/03	D.M. P	HAVANT & WATERLOOVILLE	824	2 - 1	Cooper 53, Holmes 83
01/04	D.M. P	Hinckley United	291	1 - 3	Le Bihan 15
07/04	D.M. P	Hednesford Town	490	0 - 0	
12/04	D.M. P	Newport County	583	3 - 3	Hockton 34, McDonnell 58, Harkin 68
15/04	Lge Cup F(1)	Halesowen Town	401	1 - 2	Bagnall 60
19/04	D.M. P	CHELMSFORD CITY	880	0 - 0	
21/04	D.M. P	Hastings United	491	0 - 0	
23/04	D.M. P	TIVERTON TOWN	365	1 - 1	Cooksey 29
26/04	D.M. P	Ilkeston Town	254	1 - 2	Cooksey 19
29/04	Lge Cup F(2)	HALESOWEN TOWN	1049	2 - 0	Brake 12, McDonnell 54
01/05	D.M. P	TAMWORTH	411	1 - 0	Kirkwood 20
03/05	D.M. P	WEYMOUTH	643	5 - 0	Hockton 44 60 66, Harkin 45, Sadough 75
05/05	Sussex SC F	Eastbourne Borough		0 - 0	Won 6 5 after pens. (at Eastbourne Bor.)1705

PLAYING SQUAD

Goalkeepers: Andy Little (Banstead Ath.).

Defenders: Justin Gregory (Stevenage Borough), Stewart Holmes (Saltdean Utd), Ellis Hooper (Horsham YMCA), Ben Judge (Croydon), Ian Payne (Vancouver, Canada), Marc Pullen (Wick), John Ugbah (Welling Utd).

Midfield: Paul Armstrong (Airdrie), Ernie Cooksey (Chesham Utd), Peter Fear (Kettering T.), David Harlow (Sutton Utd), Neil le Bihan (Dover Ath.), Barry Moore (Woking).

Forwards: Warren Bagnall (Lewes), Nigel Brake (Redhill), Maurice Harkin (Nuneaton Borough), Andrew Julius (Barnet), Charlie McDonald (Stevenage Borough), Joff Vansittart (Farnborough T.)

DORCHESTER TOWN

CLUB OFFICIALS
Chairman: **E. C. G. Belt**
President: **A. E. Miller**
Vice Chairman: **K. Miller**
Comm Mgr: **Brian Benjafield**
Secretary: **David Martin**
21 Diggory Crescent, Dorchester
01305 262345
General Manager: **Keith Kellaway**

FOOTBALL MANAGEMENT TEAM

Manager: Mark Morris
Physio: Geoff Dine

FACT FILE
Formed: 1880
Nickname: The Magpies
Sponsors: A.J.Dennis & Son
Colours: Black & white stripes/black/black
Change colours: All red
Midweek games: Tuesdays (7.45)
Newsline (Magpies Hotline): 0839 664412
Reserves' League: Dorset Comb

2002-2003
Captain: Andy Harris
Top Scorer: Justin Keeler
Player of the Year: Matty Holmes

Pages: 32 Price: £1.50
Editor: Melvin Cross (01305 848365)

Local Press: Dorset Evening Echo, Western Gazette, Western Daily Press
Local Radio: Radio Solent, Wessex FM

GROUND Avenue Stadium, Weymouth Avenue, Dorchester DT1 2RY Tel: 01305 262451

Directions: Situated at the junction of the town bypass (A35) and the Weymouth road (A354)
Nearest station: Dorchester South
Capacity: 5,009 Cover: 2,846 Seats: 697 Floodlights: Yes

Clubhouse: Dorchester Lounge Club - access via main entrance to stadium.
Cold food and snacks
Club Shop: Sells replica shirts, badges, mugs, etc

PREVIOUS **Leagues:** Dorset; Western 1947-72
Grounds: Council Recreation Ground, Weymouth Avenue 1880-1929; The Avenue Ground, Weymouth Avenue 29-90

CLUB RECORDS **Attendance:** 4,000 v Chelsea, official ground opening 1990. Competitive: 4, 159 v Weymouth, Southern Lge Prem Div , 99
Goalscorer: Dennis Cheney 61 (in one season) **Appearances:** Derek (Dinkie) Curtis 458 50-66
Win: 7-0 v Canterbury (A), Southern Lge Southern Div 86-87
Defeat: 0-13 v Welton Rovers Western Lge 66
Fee Paid: £12,000 for Chris Townsend (Gloucester City, 1990)
Fee Received: £35,000 for Trevor Senior (Portsmouth, 1981)

BEST SEASON **FA Trophy:** 3rd Rd replay 71-72, 96-97
FA Cup: 2nd Rd Replay 81-82, 1-2 v A.F.C. Bournemouth after 1-1. 2nd Rd 54-55 57-58; 1st Rd8 times

HONOURS Southern Lg 85-85, R-up 79-80 Div 1 Sth R-up 77-78, Lg Cup 86-87 R-up 91-92; Western Lg 54-55 R-up 60-61, Div 2 R-up 49-50, Lge Cup 54-54; Dorset Snr Cup 50-51 60-61 67-68 68-69 71-72 93-94 94-95; Dorset Lg 37-38

Players progressing: Len Drake (Bristol Rov. 57), David Noake (Luton 59), Mike Turner (Swindon 61), Trevor Senior (Portsmouth 81), David West (Liverpool 83), Mike Squire (Torquay 84), Jeremy Judd (Torquay 84),Tony White (Bournem'th 85), Graham Roberts (Spurs, Chelsea, Rangers, England) who progressed via Weymouth. Darren Garner (Rotherham U, 95), Craig Taylor (Swindon),Syfyan Ghazghazi (Club African De Tunis 98)

Dorchester celebrate - L-R - Back: Matty Holmes, Derek Taylor, Geoff Dine, Jamie Brown, Mike Walker, Justin Keeler, (arm raised), Martin Shepherd, Oliver Cherrett and Mark Morris.**Middle:** Matt Groves and Stuart Cooper. **Front:** Mark Ormorod,Marcus Aldbury, Mark Rawlinson, Carl Poore, Simon Radcliffe, Andy Harris, Mark Jermyn, Mike White and Matt Hann. **Photo:** Dorset Evening Echo

Date	Comp.	Opponents	Att.	Score	Goalscorers
27/07	SL Shield	Kettering Town	525	2 - 0	Shepherd 56, Keeler 88[p]
17/08	D.M. E	Spalding United	121	2 - 2	Keeler 27, Shepherd 45
20/08	D.M. E	NEWPORT IOW	427	1 - 1	Keeler 32[p]
24/08	D.M. E	BANBURY UNITED	459	3 - 1	Keeler 16[p], Andrews 76, Shepherd 77
26/08	D.M. E	Bashley	304	0 - 0	
31/08	FAC P	Porthleven	284	5 - 0	Keeler 7, Shepherd 9 88, Oldbury 44, Harris 49
07/09	D.M. E	Rothwell Town	133	2 - 2	Shepherd 56, Holmes 88
10/09	D.M. E	SALISBURY CITY	469	5 - 1	Keeler 6 14, Hann 36, Shepherd 79, Groves 83
14/09	FAC Q1	Clevedon Town	195	0 - 2	
21/09	D.M. E	Tonbridge Angels	318	2 - 2	Groves 26 70
24/09	D.M. E	Eastbourne Borough	519	3 - 1	Jermyn 2, Shepherd 6[p], Groves 73
28/09	D.M. E	ASHFORD TOWN	455	3 - 1	Brown 49, Shepherd 63[p], Harris 66
05/10	FAT P	YEADING	316	4 - 1	Jermyn 35 88, Groves 48 61
12/10	D.M. E	SITTINGBOURNE	472	3 - 0	Jermyn 1, Holmes 43, Radcliffe 54
19/10	D.M. E	Corby Town	60	5 - 2	Holmes 32, Oldbury 60, White 77, Cherrett 86 89
22/10	D.M. E	Salisbury City	553	0 - 0	
26/10	D.M. E	ST LEONARDS	447	8 - 1	Holmes 3, Shepherd 14 34 38[p] 54, Keeler 31, Cooper 63, Jermyn 84
29/10	Lge Cup 1	Salisbury City	441	2 - 3	Groves 21, Keeler 47
02/11	FAT 1	Chippenham Town	534	1 - 4	Hann 90
09/11	D.M. E	DARTFORD	469	3 - 0	Keeler 51, Hann 53 55
16/11	D.M. E	CHATHAM TOWN	459	4 - 0	Holmes 51, Sheppard 60, Hann 66 73
04/12	Dorset SC 3	Poole Town	123	2 - 0	Holmes 41, Keeler 82
07/12	D.M. E	Sittingbourne	160	3 - 0	Cooper 54, Groves 67 90
14/12	D.M. E	STAMFORD	444	2 - 1	Keeler 23, Shepherd 63
21/12	D.M. E	Burnham	129	2 - 1	Keeler 15, Shepherd 60
26/12	D.M. E	BASHLEY	854	0 - 2	
28/12	D.M. E	Banbury United	743	1 - 2	Groves 80
04/01	D.M. E	ROTHWELL TOWN	433	0 - 2	
14/01	Dorset SC QF	HAMWORTHY UNITED	118	7 - 0	Groves 16 43 57 71, Keeler 47 58, Cherrett 81
18/01	D.M. E	King's Lynn	747	2 - 2	Groves 22, Shepherd 53
25/01	D.M. E	Erith & Belvedere	137	1 - 0	Groves 29
01/02	D.M. E	BURNHAM	421	3 - 4	Hann 16, Keeler 61, Holmes 89
08/02	D.M. E	Stamford	242	1 - 2	Keeler 58
15/02	D.M. E	TONBRIDGE ANGELS	359	5 - 1	Jermyn 3, Keeler 31 34[p], Hann 41, Groves 81
18/02	D.M. E	Fleet Town	101	0 - 0	
22/02	D.M. E	FISHER ATHLETIC	370	2 - 0	Keeler 49, Groves 82
01/03	D.M. E	Ashford Town	260	5 - 1	Shepherd 18 81, Groves 23, Hann 42 66
04/03	Dorset SC SF	Portland United	401	2 - 0	Holmes 69, Shepherd 74
08/03	D.M. E	SPALDING UNITED	416	9 - 0	Hann 11 41 62, Keeler 17 89, Shepherd 24 32 76, Cooper 90
11/03	D.M. E	Histon	217	2 - 0	Keeler 74, Groves 83
15/03	D.M. E	ERITH & BELVEDERE	423	6 - 2	Rawlinson 13, Hann 32 41 67, Groves 43, Shepherd 86
22/03	D.M. E	CORBY TOWN	453	3 - 1	Jermyn 9, Shepherd 41, Marshall 55[og]
25/03	D.M. E	Newport IOW	152	1 - 0	Keeler 33
29/03	D.M. E	Dartford	266	1 - 1	Cooper 60
01/04	D.M. E	EASTBOURNE BOROUGH	776	2 - 1	Hann 11, Holmes 83
05/04	D.M. E	Chatham Town	178	4 - 0	Groves 4 86, Keeler 48[p], Shepherd 74
12/04	D.M. E	HISTON	536	2 - 1	Keeler 27 44
15/04	Dorset SC F	WEYMOUTH	708	2 - 0	Groves 51, Shepherd 75[p]
19/04	D.M. E	St Leonards	115	2 - 0	Groves 61, Walker 77
21/04	D.M. E	FLEET TOWN	602	5 - 1	Keeler 15 59, Groves 19, Shepherd 29, Jermyn 48
26/04	D.M. E	Fisher Athletic	141	5 - 1	Groves 1 45, Holder 56[og], Shepherd 65, Walker 72
03/05	D.M. E	KING'S LYNN	1259	1 - 0	Keeler 37

PLAYING SQUAD

Goalkeepers: Mark Ormorod (Woking)

Defenders: Alex Browne (Weymouth), Mark Jermyn (Torquay Utd), Mark Morris (Hastings Utd), Marcus Oldbury (Lymington & New Mills), Simonn Radcliffe (Bridport), Michael White (Wimborne T.).

Midfield: John Bailey (Brockenhurst), Jamie Brown (B.A.T.Sports), Matthew Holmes (Charlton Ath.), Matt Lonnen (Bournemouth Poppies), Ron Murray (Hampton & Richmond B.)

Forwards: Phil Andrews (Bashley),Stuart Cooper (Bashley), Chris Evans (Bridport), Matthew Groves (Portsmouth), Matthew Hann (Cambridge C.), Andy Harris (Weymouth), Justin Keeler (AFC Bournemouth), Steve Legg (Wareham Rangers), Martin Shepherd (Salisbury C.)

DOVER ATHLETIC

CLUB OFFICIALS

Chairman:Mike Kemp
Directors:Steve Cattermole & John Farringdon
Secretary: Judy Yetman
General Manager 01304 822373
Commercial Manager & Press Officer:
Dave Scoggins Tel: 01304 240041

FOOTBALL MANAGEMENT TEAM

Manager: Clive Walker
Assistant Manager: Paul Hyde
Reserve Team Manager: Richard Langley
Physiotherapist: T.B.A.
Club Doctor: Dr. J.P.Allingham

FACT FILE

Founded: 1983
Nickname: The 'Whites'
Club Sponsors: Hoverspeed
Club colours:White/Blackwhite
Change colours:Yellow/blue/yellow
Yellow shirts yellow shorts, yellow socks
Reserve team's league: Kent League Div. 1
Midweek home matchday: Tuesday
email: dover.athletic@virgin.net

2002-2003

Captain: Andy Arnott
P.o.Y.: Jamie Day
Top Scorer: Tommy Tyne 12

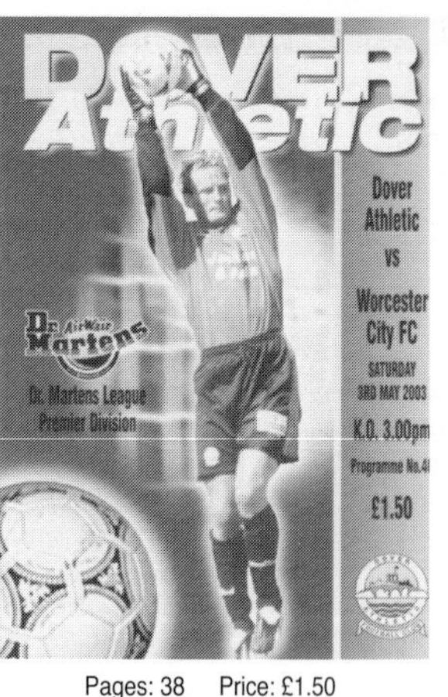

Pages: 38 Price: £1.50
Editor: Chris Collins
Tel: 01304 822373
email: dover.athletic@virgin.net

Local Press: Dover Express; Dover Mercury
Local Radio: Radio Kent; Invicta FM
KFM Radio

GROUND Hoverspeed Stadium,Crabble Athletic Ground, Lewisham Road, River, Dover, Kent. CT17 0JB Telephone No : 01304 822373 Fax: 01304 821383
Directions: Follow the A2 from Canterbury until you pass the Forte Posthouse on your left and approach a r-about with McDonalds & petrol station on your left. Turn right signed 'Town Centre' & follow down the hill.
Capacity: 6,500 Covered Terracing: 4,900 Seats: 1,000
Clubhouse: Social Club open 7 days a week. Meals available. **Contact:** Gavin Hughes 01304 822306/01304 822373
Club Shop: At the ground. Open matchdays for general souvenirs. Contact 01304 822373

PREVIOUS **Leagues:** Kent League, Southern League, Conference
Grounds: None **Names:** Dover FC

CLUB RECORDS **Attendance:** 4,186 v Oxford United (FAC1st Rd) Nov .02
Win: 7-0 v Weymouth 03.04.1990 **Defeat:** 1-7 v Poole Town
Career Goalscorer: Lennie Lee 160 **Career Appearances:** Jason Bartlett 359
Transfer Fees Paid: £50,000 for David Leworthy (Farnborough Town) Aug. 93
Received: £50,000 for Ricky Reina (Brentford) '97

BEST SEASON **FA Cup:** Fourth Qualifying Round x 8
(as Dover FC) 2nd Round 75-76 1-4 v Southend Utd. (A) League club defeated Colchester Utd.
FA Trophy: Semi-Final 97-98 **FA Amateur Cup:** Did not compete
League: 6th Conference 99-00

HONOURS Southern League - Premier Division 89-90, 92-93; Southern Division 87-88; Championship Match 1990, 1983; Premier Inter League Cup 90-91; Challenge Cup 91-92. Kent Senior Cup 90-91, R-up 93-94, 96-97

Players progressing: Ricky Reina (Brentford) 1997

L-R - Back Row: Nicky Dent, Simon Glover, Dave Wietecha, Paul Hyde (Player/ Asst. Man), P Egan (now left), Andy Arnott (Capt.), Dean Readings. **Middle**: Robin Hastie (Kit Manager), Kenny Dyer, Nicky Humphrey, Craig Wilkins, Danny Welsh, Matt Carruthers, Danny Chapman, Tommy Tyne, Frank Clark (Physio). **Front**: Ingus Martin, Darren Davies, Tony Browne, Michael Smissen, Mike Kemp (Chaiman), Clive Walker, Jamie Day, Lee Spiller, Mark Patterson, Israel Amadi

Date	Comp.	Opponents	Att.	Score	Goalscorers
17/08	D.M. P	Moor Green	338	2 - 0	Tyne 53, Carruthers 76
19/08	D.M. P	CRAWLEY TOWN	1038	2 - 1	Sykes 35, Day 54
24/08	D.M. P	WEYMOUTH	851	0 - 2	
26/08	D.M. P	Folkestone Invicta	1446	2 - 1	Dent 4 5
31/08	D.M. P	HINCKLEY UNITED	810	2 - 0	Carruthers 66, Dent 87[p]
03/09	D.M. P	Cambridge City	370	1 - 1	Spiller 55
07/09	D.M. P	Halesowen Town	463	0 - 0	
09/09	D.M. P	HASTINGS UNITED	1004	1 - 0	Dent 60[p]
14/09	D.M. P	STAFFORD RANGERS	901	0 - 2	
17/09	D.M. P	Crawley Town	956	3 - 0	Humphrey 51, Arnott 56 81
21/09	D.M. P	Grantham Town	581	1 - 3	Chapman 13
28/09	FAC Q2	BASINGSTOKE TOWN	825	2 - 0	Glover 50, Dent 78
05/10	D.M. P	Hednesford Town	542	2 - 2	Chapman 60, Carruthers 73
07/10	D.M. P	CHELMSFORD CITY	1038	1 - 0	Dent 83
12/10	FAC Q3	WELLING UNITED	1302	2 - 2	Dent 44, Glover 55
15/10	FAC Q3 rep	Welling United	735	3 - 1	Day 45, Dent 55, Spiller 76[p]
19/10	D.M. P	Newport County	643	1 - 0	Tyne 72
26/10	FAC Q4	WOKING	1636	1 - 1	Dent 33
29/10	FAC Q4 rep	Woking	1806	2 - 1	Day 44[p], Carruthers 85
02/11	D.M. P	TAMWORTH	1127	0 - 3	
04/11	Kent SC 1	SITTINGBOURNE	332	2 - 3	Sykes 18 40
09/11	D.M. P	Ilkeston Town	491	1 - 0	Tyne 39
11/11	Lge Cup 1	FOLKESTONE INVICTA	408	2 - 1	Carruthers 52, Glover 88
16/11	FAC 1	OXFORD UNITED	4186	0 - 1	
23/11	D.M. P	NEWPORT COUNTY	1006	0 - 0	
26/11	Lge Cup 2	Dartford	179	6 - 1	Carruthers 22 49, James 30, Tyne 47, Day 57, Glover 71
30/11	FAT 2	FORD UNITED	804	2 - 0	Spiller 4, Glover 86
07/12	D.M. P	Stafford Rangers	664	1 - 3	Carruthers 83
14/12	D.M. P	BATH CITY	781	2 - 0	Day 30, Tyne 90
16/12	Lge Cup 3	CHELMSFORD CITY	401	0 - 1	
21/12	D.M. P	Welling United	771	0 - 0	
26/12	D.M. P	FOLKESTONE INVICTA	1609	2 - 1	Spiller 37, Tyne 80
28/12	D.M. P	Hinckley United	321	1 - 1	Day 52
14/01	FAT 3	GRAVESEND & NORTHFLEET	814	1 - 0	Spiller 78
18/01	D.M. P	Worcester City	1258	1 - 0	Browne 54
25/01	D.M. P	CHIPPENHAM TOWN	1009	0 - 1	
11/02	FAT 4	Scarborough	965	1 - 1	Dent 70
15/02	D.M. P	WELLING UNITED	859	2 - 1	Carruthers 24 60
17/02	FAT 4 rep	SCARBOROUGH	801	2 - 1	Carruthers 88, Day 99[p]
22/02	FAT 5	FOREST GREEN ROVERS	932	0 - 3	
24/02	D.M. P	MOOR GREEN	703	1 - 2	Sykes 68
01/03	D.M. P	Hastings United	630	1 - 1	Sykes 26
08/03	D.M. P	ILKESTON TOWN	756	1 - 1	Day 69
10/03	D.M. P	HALESOWEN TOWN	604	0 - 3	
15/03	D.M. P	Bath City	651	0 - 1	
19/03	D.M. P	Tiverton Town	465	0 - 0	
22/03	D.M. P	Tamworth	1529	2 - 1	Tyne 6, Brown 43
24/03	D.M. P	TIVERTON TOWN	715	0 - 0	
29/03	D.M. P	GRANTHAM TOWN	803	2 - 1	Tyne 8 79
05/04	D.M. P	Chelmsford City	470	1 - 0	Arnott 89
08/04	D.M. P	Havant & Waterlooville	282	1 - 1	Tyne 36
12/04	D.M. P	CAMBRIDGE CITY	752	2 - 1	Tyne 43, Day 45[p]
14/04	D.M. P	HEDNESFORD TOWN	662	1 - 0	Spiller 6
19/04	D.M. P	Weymouth	668	0 - 0	
21/04	D.M. P	HAVANT & WATERLOOVILLE	744	0 - 0	
26/04	D.M. P	Chippenham Town	556	0 - 0	
03/05	D.M. P	WORCESTER CITY	1013	2 - 1	Day 18 72

PLAYING SQUAD

Goalkeepers: Paul Egan (Folkestone Invicta).

Defenders: Andy Arnott (Stevenage B.), Tony Browne (Folkestone I.), Craig Cloke (Youth), Darren Davies (Greenock Morton), Nicky Humphrey (Tonbridge A.), Jason Moore (Ramsgate), Mark Pattterson (Gillingham), Craig Wilkins (Gravesend & Northfleet).

Midfield: David Bathgate (Youth Team), Matt Carruthers (Newport I.o.W.),Danny G. Chapman (Folkestone Invicta), Jamie Day (AFC Bournemouth), John Elliot (Airdrie), Steve Haffner (Sittingbourne), Tom Hickman (Youth Team), Kristian James (Port Talbot), Lee Spiller (Chesham Utd).

Forwards: Nicky Dent (Folkestone Invicta), Simon Glover (Welling Utd), Roy Godden (St Leonards), John Ovard (Youth Team), Tommy Tyne (Millwall)

EASTBOURNE BOROUGH

76 Pages Price: £150
Programme Editor: Mike Spooner
Tel./Fax: 01323 471071(H)
Website: www.eastbourne borough fc.co.uk
Local Press: Eastbourne Gazette & Herald

CLUB OFFICIALS

Chairman: Len Smith

President: J Stonestreet

Secretary: Mrs Myra Stephens,
9 Gwent Road,St James Rd.,Eastbourne,
BN22 7BX
Tel/Fax: 01323 642834 07754174406(M)
email: myra@stephens529.fsnet.co.uk

FOOTBALL MANAGEMENT TEAM

Manager: Garry Wilson

Coach: Nick Greenwood

Physio: Ray Tuppen

FACT FILE

Founded: 1966 Nickname: Sports
Sponsors: 1st Class Window Systems Ltd.
Colours: Red & Black
Change: White/red/white
Midweek Matchday: Tuesday
Reserve League:Sussex Co.Prem Res.

2002-2003

Captain: Daron Pearce
Top Scorer: Scott Ramsay
Players o.Year.: John Price & Stuart Tuck

GROUND Langney Sports Club, Priory Lane, Eastbourne, E, Sussex Tel: 01323 766265 or 01323 743561 Email Address: head@stoucrosse-sussex.sch.uk

Capacity: 3,000 Seats:500 Cover: 2,500 Floodlights: Yes

Directions: A22 to Polegate, A27 @ junction of A27/A22 new by-pass follow signs to cre matorium and then first right to Priory Lane
One mile from Pevensey & Westham(BR). Buses from Eastbourne

Clubhouse: Open every evening & lunchtime with adjoining sports hall, boardroom and matchday tea bar **Club Shop:** Yes

HONOURS Sussex County League Champions 99-00 R-up: 2002-03, Sussex Co. Lg R-up 91-92, Div 2 87-88, Lg Cup 89-90, Div 3 86-87, Div 3 Cup 86-87, 5-aside 1990; Sussex I'mediate Cup 85-86, Eastbourne Chall. Cup 85-86 86-87 99-00 00-01
Sussex Senior Cup 2001-02, Dr Martens Eastern Div R-up 02-03

PREVIOUS **League:** Eastbourne & Hastings, Unijet Sussex Oo League.**Name:** Langney Sports
Grounds: Princes Park, Wartling Rd, Eastbourne/ Adjacent pitch

RECORDS **Attendance:** 1703 Sussex Senior Cup Final v Crawley Town 2003
Goalscorer: Nigel Hole 146 **Appearances:** Darren Baker 500
Win: 10-1 v Haywards Heath Town, Sussex County Lg Div. 1 11/4/92
Defeat: 0-8, v Sheppey United (A), FA Vase Prel. Rd 9/10/93
v Peacehaven & Telscombe (A), Sussex County Lg Div. 1 9/11/93

Date	Comp.	Opponents	Att.	Score	Goalscorers
17/08	D.M. E	Banbury United	263	3 - 0	Allen 42 55, Westcott 76
20/08	D.M. E	DARTFORD	416	4 - 0	Crabb 38, Pearce 59[p], Allen 72, Adams 79
24/08	D.M. E	HISTON	426	4 - 1	Price 30, Westcott 66, Ramsay 68, Pearce 72
26/08	D.M. E	St Leonards	459	1 - 1	Goodwin 90
31/08	FAC P	Croydon Athleitc	185	0 - 0	
03/09	FAC P rep	CROYDON ATHLETIC	412	4 - 1	Smart 12, Allen 35, Pearce 81[p], Crabb 90
07/09	D.M. E	Stamford	225	0 - 1	
10/09	D.M. E	TONBRIDGE ANGELS	526	3 - 2	Pearce 11[p], Adams 66 79
14/09	FAC Q1	AFC NEWBURY	397	6 - 2	Adams 18 45, Ramsey 40, Westcott 44, Price 87, Austin 90
21/09	D.M. E	Ashford Town	320	0 - 1	
24/09	D.M. E	DORCHESTER TOWN	519	1 - 3	Ramsey 79
28/09	FAC Q2	AFC Wallingford	238	1 - 0	Goodwin 85
05/10	D.M. E	Chatham Town	235	3 - 0	Smart 63, Price 67, Tuck 90
12/10	FAC Q3	Bishop's Stortford	452	0 - 1	
19/10	D.M. E	FLEET TOWN	472	2 - 1	Pearce 12, Ramsey 83
22/10	D.M. E	Tonbridge Angels	394	1 - 0	Price 60
26/10	D.M. E	Burnham	122	0 - 0	
29/10	Lge Cup 1	Fleet Town	72	1 - 0	Ducille 18
02/11	FAT 1	HERTFORD TOWN	335	4 - 1	Ducille 29, Ramsey 39 53, Smart 84
04/11	D.M. E	Fisher Athletic	134	4 - 2	Pearce 32, Bower 41[og], Ramsay 42 89
09/11	D.M. E	SITTINGBOURNE	517	3 - 0	Ramsay 22 75, Price 89
16/11	D.M. E	BANBURY UNITED	551	1 - 2	Ramsay 62
19/11	Sussex SC 2	SHOREHAM	n/k	5 - 0	
23/11	D.M. E	Corby Town	80	2 - 2	Pearce 24, Adams 75
30/11	FAT 2	Hastings United	906	2 - 0	Ducille 9, Ramsay 77[p]
03/12	Lge Cup 2	BURNHAM	194	2 - 3	Longhurst 53, Read 83
07/12	D.M. E	ROTHWELL TOWN	402	3 - 1	Pearce 60[p] 79, Ramsay 67
10/12	D.M. E	SALISBURY CITY	357	0 - 0	
14/12	D.M. E	Spalding United	93	1 - 0	Smart 60
21/12	D.M. E	ASHFORD TOWN	524	2 - 0	Goodwin 18, Tuck 40
04/01	D.M. E	NEWPORT IOW	456	7 - 0	Ramsay 3 65 68 79, Pearce 30[p], Goodwin 40 41
11/01	FAT 3	FARNBOROUGH TOWN	1576	0 - 1	
14/01	Sussex SC 3	Wick	119	3 - 1	Ducille 7 17, Ramsey 41
18/01	D.M. E	BASHLEY	561	2 - 2	Ramsey 30, Price 90
25/01	D.M. E	Newport IOW	294	1 - 0	Tuck 41
08/02	D.M. E	Salisbury City	561	2 - 1	Baker 23, Ramsay 41
12/02	Sussex SC QF	EASTBOURNE TOWN	746	3 - 1	Westcott 29, Ramsay 46, Goodwin 78
15/02	D.M. E	CHATHAM TOWN	415	3 - 0	Ramsay 55 84, Baker 75
18/02	D.M. E	ST LEONARDS	345	4 - 0	Ramsay 17 30 59, Peacock 28[p]
22/02	D.M. E	Sittingbourne	236	2 - 0	Pearce 12, Ducille 25
01/03	D.M. E	KING'S LYNN	541	4 - 1	Ramsay 40 55, Smart 83, Austin 90
04/03	D.M. E	Dartford	247	1 - 0	Price 44
11/03	D.M. E	Erith & Belvedere	140	1 - 0	Harris 62
15/03	D.M. E	STAMFORD	669	2 - 1	Ramsay 45, Price 70
18/03	D.M. E	Histon	227	2 - 0	Ramsay 5 43
22/03	D.M. E	Rothwell Town	215	0 - 2	
26/03	Sussex SC SF	Pagham (at Burgess Hill Town)	342	1 - 0	Pearce 78
29/03	D.M. E	BURNHAM	689	3 - 1	Crabb 14, Pearce 21[p], Austin 71
01/04	D.M. E	Dorchester Town	776	1 - 2	Ramsay 62
05/04	D.M. E	Fleet Town	202	2 - 1	Smart 40, Pearce 64
08/04	D.M. E	CORBY TOWN	488	2 - 2	Harris 10, Goodwin 83
12/04	D.M. E	SPALDING UNITED	615	4 - 0	Ramsay 7, Price 55, Huggins 66[og], Adams 84
19/04	D.M. E	Bashley	272	6 - 1	Ducille 31, Smart 35, Ramsay 48 62, Adams 79, Goodwin 89
21/04	D.M. E	ERITH & BELVEDERE	783	3 - 0	Pearce 30, Crabb 42, Smart 45
26/04	D.M. E	King's Lynn	661	0 - 2	
03/05	D.M. E	FISHER ATHLETIC	937	2 - 0	Crabb 14, Ramsay 79
05/05	Sussex SC F	CRAWLEY TOWN	1705	0 - 0	Lost 5 6 after pens. (at Eastbourne Borough)

PLAYING SQUAD

Goalkeepers: Lee Hook (Sittingbourne), Dean Lightwood (Saltdean Utd), Paul Stark (U.S.A.)

Defenders: Ben Austin (Eastbourne T.), Darren Baker (Littlehampton T.), Nathen Godden (Sidley Utd), Grant Harrison (Eastbourne Utd), Ron Longhurst (Wealden), Stuart Playford (Hastings Utd), John Price (Newoport I.o.W.), John Scarborough (Herne Bay), Stuart Tuck (Worthing), Ben White (Gillingham).

Midfield: Luke Denton (Eastbourne T.), Andrew Ducille (St.Leonards), Justin Harris (Lewes), Darren Pearce (East Preston), Danny Simmonds (Eastbourne Utd), Matthew Smart (Horsham), Paul Stevens (Burgess Hill T.), Ian Verow (Eastbourne T.), Steve Yates (Hastings Utd).

Forwards: Dave Adams (Hailsham T.), Peter Baker (St.Leonards), Matt Crabb (Eastbourne Utd), Steve Dallaway (Eastbourne T.), Mark Goodwin (Eastbourne T.), Scott Ramsay (Dover Ath.), John Westcott (Sutton Utd)

GRANTHAM TOWN

Programme: 38 pages £1.50

Local Press: Grantham Journal, Nottingham Evening Post, Melton & GranthamTrader, Grantham Citizen, Lincolnshire Echo
Local Radio: Radio Lincolnshire, Lincs FM

CLUB OFFICIALS

Chairman: Barry Palmer
President:George Freeston
Secretary: Pat Nixon
72 Huntingtower Road, Grantham,
Lincs NG31 7AU
Tel: 01476 419391 FAX: 01476 419392

FOOTBALL MANAGEMENT TEAM

Manager:Roger Ashby
Asst MgrKevin Wilkin
Physio: Nigel Marshall

FACT FILE

Formed: 1874
Nickname: Gingerbreads
Sponsors: Crystal Motors
Colours: Black & White stripes/black/black
Change: Orange
Midweek matchday: Tuesday
Reserve League: Central Conference
Club Website: www..granthamtownfc.co.uk
www.cheiroa.domon.co.uk/gtfc

2002-2003
Captain: Adrian Speed
Captain & P.o.Y.: Gary Bull

GROUND South Kesteven Sports Stadium, Trent Road, Grantham, Lincs Tel: 01476 402224
Directions: Midway between A1 and A52 on edge of Earlesfield Industrial Estate; from A1 take A607 to Earlsfield Ind. Est and continue into Trent Rd
Capacity: 7,500 Cover: 1,950 Seats: 750 Floodlights: Yes

Clubhouse: (01476 402225) Open evenings and weekends. Bar, darts, pool etc.Frequent live entertainment. Available for functions **Club Shop:** Programmes and a wide range of souvenirs. Contact club number.

PREVIOUS **Leagues:** Mid Amat All, Central All. 11-25 59-61, Midland Co's 25-59 61-72,Southern Lge 72-79, Northern Prem. 79-85
Names: Grantham FC, pre-80. Grounds: London Rd up to 90

CLUB RECORDS **Attendance:** 3,695 v Southport. F.A.Trophy Quarter Final 97-98
Win: 13-0 vRufford Colliery (H), FA Cup Preliminary Rd 15/9/34
Defeat: 0-16 v Notts County Rovers (A), Midland Amateur All. 22/10/1892
Transfer Fee - Paid:undisclosed for Mario Ziccari **Received:** £20,000 for Gary Crosby (Notts Forest 87)
Career Goalscorer: Jack McCartney 416
Career Appearances: Chris Gardiner 664

BEST SEASON **FA Cup:** 3rd Rd 1883-84 86-87 1973-74. Comp Proper on 23 occasions
FA Trophy: Quarter Final 1971-72, 97-98

HONOURS Southern Lg R-up 73-74 (Div 1 Nth) 72-73 78-79, Merit Cup 72-73), Southern Lg Mid Div Champions 97-98. Eastern Division R-up. 2001-02 Midland Co's Lg(3) 63-64 70-72 (R-up 37-38 64-65 69-70, Lg Cup 68-69 70-71), Midland Amtr Lg10-11 (Lg Cup R-up 10-11), Central All. 24-25 (Southern Div R-up 59-60), Lincs Snr Cup 1884-851936-37 (R-up(5) 34-36 39-40 45-47), Lincs Co. `A' Cup(3) 53-54 60-62 (R-up 49-50 52-53 57-58), Lincs Co. Snr Cup 71-72 82-83 (R-up 80-81)

Players progressing: E Morris (Halifax 50), P Thompson/R Cooke (Peterborough 64/80), J Rayner (Notts County 64), D Dall (Scunthorpe 79), N Jarvis/H Wood (Scunthorpe 80), D White (Bristol Rvrs 86), T Curran (Grimsby 87), G Crosby (Nottm Forest 87), A Kennedy (Wrexham 87), R Wilson (Lincoln 87)

Back row left to right: Ian Wilkins, Seamus Lawless, Mario Ziccardi, Rick Wright, Danny George and Dave Gilbert.
Middle row: Peter Day (Finance Director), Paul Teare (Youth Developement Director), Matt Carvell, Migg Hogg (Coach), John Wilkinson (Manager), Tony Simmons (Asst. man.), Nigel Marshall (Physio), Mark Foster, Chris Hall, George Freeston and Pat Nixon (Secretary).
Front row: Tim Harrison (Director), Dave Taylor, Darren Dye, Brendon McDaid, Stuart Wilson, Adrian Speed, Gary Bull, Rick Ranshaw, Lee Marshall, Ken Healey (Commercial Director) and Barry Palmer (Chairman) **Photo:** Dean Fardell

Date	Comp.	Opponents	Att.	Score	Goalscorers
01/08	Lincs SC 01-02 F	SCUNTHORPE UNITED	n/k	0 - 3	
13/08	Lincs SC 1	Lincoln City	n/k	3 - 1	McDaid, Marshall, Ranshaw
17/08	D.M. P	Folkestone Invicta	378	2 - 0	Ranshaw 64, Hallows 66
20/08	D.M. P	CAMBRIDGE CITY	611	1 - 0	McDaid 3
24/08	D.M. P	HALESOWEN TOWN	518	3 - 3	Dye 23, Neil 29, Bull 44
26/08	D.M. P	Ilkeston Town	703	2 - 1	Bull 22, Marshall 41
31/08	D.M. P	WEYMOUTH	538	2 - 0	Ranshaw 53, Neil 64
02/09	D.M. P	Hednesford Town	644	0 - 1	
07/09	D.M. P	CHIPPENHAM TOWN	466	1 - 1	Bull 77[p]
10/09	D.M. P	Stafford Rangers	617	0 - 4	
14/09	D.M. P	Tiverton Town	823	2 - 0	Clark 18, McDaid 84
17/09	D.M. P	TAMWORTH	534	2 - 1	McDaid 43, Bull 88
21/09	D.M. P	DOVER ATHLETIC	581	3 - 1	Neil 44 90, Clarke 56
28/09	FAC Q2	Solihull Borough	349	2 - 0	Clarke 50 84
05/10	D.M. P	Crawley Town	1556	0 - 2	
08/10	D.M. P	Moor Green	295	0 - 3	
12/10	FAC Q3	WORKSOP TOWN	915	1 - 0	Neil 58
19/10	D.M. P	HAVANT & WATERLOOVILLE	488	1 - 1	Clarke 61
26/10	FAC Q4	Morecambe	1055	1 - 3	Clarke 73
29/10	Lge Cup 1	HISTON	151	3 - 1	Clarke 59, Wilson 71 83
02/11	FAT 1	HINCKLEY UNITED	413	3 - 2	Clarke 11 31, Minett 55
09/11	D.M. P	NEWPORT COUNTY	458	1 - 2	Bull 58
16/11	D.M. P	Welling United	583	0 - 2	
26/11	Lge Cup 2	Rugby United	225	2 - 1	Wilson 30, Marshall 75
30/11	FAT 2	GAINSBOROUGH TRINITY	547	0 - 1	
07/12	D.M. P	Newport County	571	2 - 3	Bull 62[p] 79
14/12	D.M. P	FOLKESTONE INVICTA	317	4 - 1	Wilson 3, Bull 5, McDaid 23 79
17/12	Lge Cup 3	Shepshed Dynamo	120	5 - 2	George 27, Wilson 48 57, Ranshaw 58, Bull 77
21/12	D.M. P	Tamworth	868	1 - 3	Bull 38
26/12	D.M. P	ILKESTON TOWN	563	2 - 2	Lawrence 17[og], Bull 48
28/12	D.M. P	Weymouth	723	1 - 3	Dye 56
07/01	D.M. P	Hastings United	252	1 - 2	Bull 90
18/01	D.M. P	Cambridge City	536	1 - 1	Wilson 36
25/01	D.M. P	CHELMSFORD CITY	381	2 - 3	Bull 17, Wilson 29
01/02	D.M. P	STAFFORD RANGERS	424	1 - 2	Speed 6
08/02	D.M. P	Chippenham Town	669	0 - 0	
12/02	Lge Cup QF	King's Lynn	396	0 - 2	
15/02	D.M. P	Chelmsford City	481	2 - 1	Bull 36, Hallows 86
22/02	D.M. P	WORCESTER CITY	372	2 - 3	Wilson 9 18
01/03	D.M. P	Havant & Waterlooville	389	3 - 3	Bull 15, Speed 30, Hemstock 85
04/03	Lincs SC SF	Stamford	229	1 - 0	Wilson 24
08/03	D.M. P	BATH CITY	368	0 - 0	
15/03	D.M. P	HASTINGS UNITED	330	2 - 1	Wilson 24, Hawley 69[p]
18/03	D.M. P	Hinckley United	332	0 - 0	
22/03	D.M. P	HEDNESFORD TOWN	362	3 - 0	McDaid 10 12, Bull 89
25/03	D.M. P	CRAWLEY TOWN	375	0 - 3	
29/03	D.M. P	Dover Athletic	803	1 - 2	George 38
05/04	D.M. P	TIVERTON TOWN	356	0 - 2	
12/04	D.M. P	Bath City	610	2 - 3	Bull 59, Hall 82
15/04	D.M. P	WELLING UNITED	385	3 - 1	Ranshaw 18 70, George 48
19/04	D.M. P	Halesowen Town	501	0 - 1	
21/04	D.M. P	HINCKLEY UNITED	470	2 - 1	Ranshaw 80, Speed 90
26/04	D.M. P	Worcester City	1003	0 - 2	
29/04	Lincs SC F	Gainsborough Trinity	390	0 - 4	
03/05	D.M. P	MOOR GREEN	640	4 - 0	McDaid 42, Peer 48[og], Ranshaw 79, Marshall 89

PLAYING SQUAD

Goalkeepers: Marianno Ziccardi (Lincoln Utd).

Defenders: Graham Bowater (Spalding Utd), Darren Dye (Lincoln Utd), Rob Gould (St.Albans C.), Joby Gowshall (KIngstonian), Jim Neil (Gainsborough Trinity), Matthew Pitts (Nettleham), Adrian Speed (Holbeach Utd), Steve Wenlock (Cambridge C.), Rick Wright (Lincoln Utd).

Midfield: Wayne Hallcro (Kingstonian), Jamie Kearns (Roithwell T.), Guy Last (Peterborough Utd), Lee Marshall (Scunthorpe Utd), Jason Minett (Kingstonian).

Forwards: Jamie Clarke (Kings Lynn), Nigel Hemstock (Frickley Ath.), Mark Paul (Kingstonian), Kevin Slinn (Stamford), Kevin Wilkin (Cambridge C.), Stuart Wilson (Shepshed Dynamo).

HAVANT & WATERLOOVILLE

CLUB OFFICIALS

Chairman: Derek Pope
President: Arthur Saitch, Maurie Hibberd
Vice Chairman: Peter Demott
Directors: Trevor Brock, Ray Jones, John Carter, Peter Faulkner, Sandy Peters, Dave Crook
Secretary: Trevor Brock, 2 Betula Close, Waterlooville, Hampshire. PO7 8EJ
Tel:02392 267276

FOOTBALL MANAGEMENT TEAM

Joint Managers: Mick Jenkins & Liam Daish
Physio: Phil Ashwell

FACT FILE

Formed: 1998
Nickname: Hawks
Sponsors: Thomas Sanderson
Colours: All White
Change colours: Gold & Blue
Midweek matchday: Tuesday
Reserves' League:Capital

2002-2003

Captains : Tim Hambley & Gareth Hall
Top Scorer: James Taylor
Player of the Year:Bobby Howe

Pages: 32 Price: £1.60
Editor: Adrian Gardiner

Local Press: News (Portsmouth)
Radio:Radio Solent,Power FM,The Quay

GROUND Westleigh Park, Martin Road, West Leigh, Havant PO9 5TH Tel: 02392 787822

Directions: Take B2149 to Havant off the A27 (B2149 Petersfield Rd if coming out of Havant). 2nd turning off dual carriageway into Bartons Road then 1st right into Martins Road.
1 mile from Havant station

Capacity: 4,500 Cover: 2,500 Seats: 560 Floodlights: Yes

Clubhouse: Open every day, lunchtime and evening. 2 bars, function suites. Hot & cold food available Club Shop: Sells various souvenirs & progs

PREVIOUS (Havant) **Leagues:** Portsmouth 58-71; Hants 71-86; Wessex 86-91. **Names:** Leigh Park; Havant & Leigh Park; Havant Town **Grounds:** Front Lawn 1958-83 (Waterlooville) **Leagues:** Waterlooville & District, Portsmouth 38-53, Hants1953-71. **Grounds:** Convent Ground 10-30, Rowlands Avenue Recreation Ground 30-63, Jubliee Park 63-98

CLUB RECORDS **Attendance:** 3,500 v Wisbech Town, FA Vase QF 85-86
(Havant) **Win:** 10-0 x3; v Sholing Sports (H), FA Vase 4th Rd 85-86, v Portsmouth R.N. (H), Wessex League 90-91; & v Poole Town, Southern Lge SouthernDiv. 94-95. **Defeat:** 1-7 v Camberley Town (H), FA Vase 3rd Rd 88-89
Career Goalscorer: Tony Plumbley 348 **Career Appearances:** Tony Plumbley 510

BEST SEASON (Havant) **FA Cup:** 1st Rd Proper (H) 1-2 2000-01 **FA Vase:** Qtr Final 85-86 **F.A.Trophy:** As H& WS-Final 2002-03 V Tamworth
(Waterlooville) **FA Trophy:** 3rd Rd 98-99 (lost 0-1 at Worcester City) **FA Amateur Cup:** 1st Rd 59-60
FA Cup: 1st Rd 2nd replay 83-84, 0-2 v Northampton T. (A) after two 1-1 draws

HONOURS (Havant): FA Sunday Cup 68-69, Wessex Lg 90-91 R-up 88-89, Hampshire Lg Div 372-73 Div 4 71-72, Hampshire Sen. Cup 93-94,94-95 R-up 91-92 Hants.I'mediate Cup, Hants Junior Cup, Russell Cotes Cup 91-92, Portsmouth Sen. Cup 83-84 84-85 91-92, Gosport War Mem. Cup 74-75 91-92 92-93 94-95, Southern Cos F'lit Cup R-up 91-92, 00-01, Hants F'lit Cup 85-86, Portsmouth Lg.
(Waterlooville): Southern Lg Div 1 Sth 71-72 Lg Cup 86-87, R-up 82-83, Hants Lg R-up 69-70 Div 2 59-60 64-65, Div 3 East R-up 53-54, Hants Sen. Cup 69-7072-73 84-85 R-up 75-76 90-91, 00-01, Russell Cotes Cup 88-89, Portsmouth Lg 49-50 50-51 51-52 Div 2 46-47, Div 3 38-39, Portsmouth Sen. Cup 68-69, Portsmouth Victory Cup 59-60 69-70,00-01
(H&W): Southern Lg.Southern 98-99, Capitol Lg R-up: 00-01 Hampshire Senior Cup R-up 00-01, 01-02

L - R - Back row: Gareth Hall, Shaun Gale and Chris Ferrett. **Middle:** Dave Leworthy (Youth Man.), Mick Catlin (Reserves Man.), Jamie O'Rourke (now Newport IOW), Neil Davis, James Taylor, Steve Sladen (now Alton T.), Aaron Kerr, Alec Masson, Steve Black (now Fleet T.), Luke Middleton (now Gosport Bor.), Steve May (Reserves Asst.Man) and Bobby de St Croix (Youth Team Manager). **Front:** Louis Savage, Bobby Howe, Paul Wood, Dean Blake, Warren Haughton, LIam Daish and Miick Jennings (Co-Managers), Tim Hambley (now Welling Utd), Gary Connolly (now Bashley), Neil Champion, Phil Barnett and James Ford.

Date	Comp.	Opponents	Att.	Score	Goalscorers
17/08	D.M. P	TAMWORTH	582	0 - 3	
20/08	D.M. P	Bath City	768	1 - 1	Haughton 45
24/08	D.M. P	Tiverton Town	603	1 - 3	Daish 26
26/08	D.M. P	HASTINGS UNITED	487	0 - 0	
31/08	D.M. P	Moor Green	241	1 - 0	Woods 5
03/09	D.M. P	CHELMSFORD CITY	530	1 - 0	Blake 85
07/09	D.M. P	STAFFORD RANGERS	490	1 - 1	Wood 70
11/09	D.M. P	Chippenham Town	661	1 - 3	Pope 23
14/09	D.M. P	Hednesford Town	555	0 - 3	
17/09	D.M. P	WEYMOUTH	346	0 - 1	
21/09	D.M. P	HINCKLEY UNITED	395	2 - 2	Afandiyev 18[og], Taylor 44
28/09	FAC Q2	HARROW BOROUGH	210	2 - 1	Taylor 70 83
01/10	Hants RC 1	PIRELLI GENERAL	n/k	3 - 1	
05/10	D.M. P	Worcester City	1003	1 - 2	Taylor 73[p]
08/10	D.M. P	WELLING UNITED	399	1 - 0	Howe 30
12/10	FAC Q3	EVESHAM UNITED	329	4 - 0	Wood 7, Taylor 12, Haughton 85, Hambley 88[p]
19/10	D.M. P	Grantham Town	488	1 - 1	Taylor 29
26/10	FAC Q4	BILLERICAY TOWN	631	3 - 1	Taylor 7, Haughton 18, Blake 29
29/10	Hants SC 2	WHITCHURCH UNITED	167	6 - 0	Barnett 9, Davis 41, Leworthy 51, Masson 58, Middleton 85, Ford 86
02/11	D.M. P	Newport County	571	0 - 0	
05/11	Lge Cup 1	Bashley	105	2 - 3	Barnett 22, Leworthy 47
09/11	D.M. P	HALESOWEN TOWN	436	3 - 1	Taylor 18 37, Hall 33
16/11	FAC 1	Dagenham & Redbridge	1546	2 - 3	Haughton 21 26
30/11	FAT 2	BILLERICAY TOWN	277	1 - 1	Hambley 49
03/12	FAT 2 rep	Billericay Town	327	2 - 1	Taylor 44 105
07/12	D.M. P	Ilkeston Town	469	5 - 1	Hambley 9, Taylor 45 83, Haughton 54 68
10/12	Hants SC 3	Lymington Town	150	4 - 1	Davis 17, D Leworthy 50 68, C Leworthy 59
14/12	D.M. P	MOOR GREEN	409	3 - 3	Hanson 50, Taylor 72, Middleton 74
17/12	Hants RC 2	Wimborne Town	69	1 - 5	
21/12	D.M. P	Folkestone Invicta	320	3 - 3	Taylor 13 28 56
28/12	D.M. P	HEDNESFORD TOWN	510	2 - 1	Haughton 43, Taylor 53
04/01	D.M. P	Welling United	501	1 - 1	Blake 60
11/01	FAT 3	Sutton United	645	3 - 1	Howe 25, Haughton 55, Hambley 59
14/01	D.M. P	Stafford Rangers	672	3 - 1	Howe 20, Blake 35, Taylor 45[p]
18/01	D.M. P	CRAWLEY TOWN	599	2 - 4	Haughton 34, D Leworthy 84
25/01	D.M. P	Weymouth	655	1 - 1	Masson 45
28/01	Hants SC QF	Christchurch	191	4 - 0	Taylor 15, Haughton 23, Davis 25, Blake 44
01/02	FAT 4	Colwyn Bay	351	2 - 0	Hambley 2 44
08/02	D.M. P	Halesowen Town	429	0 - 1	
15/02	D.M. P	CHIPPENHAM TOWN	461	1 - 0	Poate 76
22/02	FAT 5	HAYES	456	3 - 0	Davis 32, Blake 56, Taylor 80
01/03	D.M. P	GRANTHAM TOWN	389	3 - 3	Haughton 7, Taylor 24, Howe 89
04/03	Hants SC SF(1)	Bashley	165	0 - 2	
08/03	D.M. P	Chelmsford City	450	2 - 1	Wood 6, Gale 90
11/03	D.M. P	NEWPORT COUNTY	349	1 - 0	Poate 50
15/03	FAT QF	Forest Green Rovers	1016	2 - 1	Wood 62, Hambley 76
18/03	Hants SC SF(2)	BASHLEY	301	1 - 2	Howe 60
22/03	D.M. P	WORCESTER CITY	502	2 - 1	Howe 20, Taylor 73
25/03	D.M. P	CAMBRIDGE CITY	359	0 - 2	
29/03	D.M. P	Crawley Town	824	1 - 2	Masson 24
01/04	D.M. P	Hastings United	318	1 - 1	Blake 37
05/04	FAT SF(1)	Tamworth	2165	0 - 1	
08/04	D.M. P	DOVER ATHLETIC	282	1 - 1	Turner 76
12/04	FAT SF(2)	TAMWORTH	1331	1 - 1	Taylor 42
15/04	D.M. P	Hinckley United	317	1 - 2	Masson 29
19/04	D.M. P	TIVERTON TOWN	401	2 - 1	Leworthy 78 79
21/04	D.M. P	Dover Athletic	744	0 - 0	
23/04	D.M. P	Tamworth	408	3 - 3	Taylor 10, Champion 80, Blake 90
26/04	D.M. P	Cambridge City	648	5 - 4	Haughton 7 62, Taylor 14 43, Poate 45
29/04	D.M. P	FOLKESTONE INVICTA	274	6 - 2	Taylor 1 57 72 83, Poate 11, Ford 27
01/05	D.M. P	BATH CITY	357	3 - 1	Haughton 11, Fennymore 45, Blake 85
03/05	D.M. P	ILKESTON TOWN	484	1 - 3	Haughton 31

PLAYING SQUAD

Goalkeepers: Gareth Howells (Aldershot T.)

Defenders: Liam Daish (Coventry C.),Chris Ferrett (Dorchester C.), Shaun Gale (Exeter C.), Gareth Hall (Swindon T.), Christian Hanson (Middlesbrough), Alec Masson (Wick), Karl Miller (Youth Team), Ben Price (Portsmouth).

Midfield: Brett Poate (Southampton), Dean Blake (Bognor Regis), Neil Campion (Aldershot), Neil Davis (Southampton), James Ford (AFC Bournemouth), Bobby Howe (Swindon T.).

Forwards: Phil Barnett (Portsmouth), Lee Disney (Youth Team), Warren Haughton (Woking), Steve Harding (Liss Ath.), Craig Leworthy (Youth Team), **David Leworthy** (Kingstonian), Norman Sylla (Banbury Utd), **James Taylor** (Bashley), David Town (Boston Utd), Paul Wood (Happy Valley, Hong Kong)

HEDNESFORD TOWN

CLUB OFFICIALS

Directors: Steve Price & Carole Price

President: T.B.A.

Chairman: Steve Price

Managing Director: Terry Brumpton

Press Officer: Neil Holde

FOOTBALL MANAGEMEN TE AM

Manager: Barry Powell
Assistant Manager: Chris Brindley

FACT FILE
Founded: 1880
Nickname: The Pitmen
Club Sponsors: Extra Personnel
Club colours: White/black/red&black
Change colours: Sky Blues
Midweek home matchday: Tuesday
Reserves' league: Central Conference,
Web site: www.hednesfordtownfc.co.uk
Hotline Number: 09066 555880

Season 2000-01
Leading Scorer: Steve Piearce 26
P.o.Y.: Chris Brindley
Captain: Les Robinson

Pages: 32 Price: £1.50
Editor: Terry Brumpton
Local Press: Express & Star; Sporting Star; Chase Post; Cannock Mercury; Birmingham Evening Mail &Birmingham Post; Sports Argus; The Chronicle
Local Radio: Radio WM; BRMB; WABC; Beacon; Signal; BBC Radio Stoke,Capital Gold

GROUND Keys Park,Keys Park Road, Hednesford, Cannock, Staffordshire S12 2DZ Tel:015 43 422870, **Fax**: 01543 428180, **Hotline:** 0930 555880 **e-mail**:fc@darby7782freeserve.co.uk
SIMPLE DIRECTIONS: M6 J11 to Cannock, through traffic lights to island , 3rd exit, next island, 2nd exit onto Lichfield Rd. Next island 1st exit, next island straight on, next island 3rd exit, continue to mini-island. Keys Park is straight on (signposted from 2nd island.)
CAPACITY: 6,039 **SEATED:** 1,010 **COVERED TERRACING:** 4,324
CLUB SHOP: Open throughout the week
SOCIAL FACILITIES: Strikers Bar - Open matchdays and every evening 7-11 except Sunday. Chase Suite holds functions and conferences

PREVIOUS **Leagues:** Walsall & District; Birmingham Combination 08-15, 45-53; West Midlands 19-39, 53-72, 74-84; Midland Counties 72-74; Southern League 84-95; Conference 95-01.
Grounds: The Tins (behind Anglesey Hotel) until 1904, Cross Keys until 1995. **Names:** None

HONOURS Welsh Cup R-up 91-92; Southern League - Prem. Div. 94-95; Midland Div. R-up 91-92, Lge. Cup R-up 86-87; West Midlands. Lge 77-78, R-up 83-84; Lge. Cup 83-84; Birmingham Comb. 09-10 50-51, R-up 12-13 52-53; Staffs Senior Cup 69-70, 73-74; R-up 92-93; Birmingham Sen. Cup 35-36; R-up 93-94.

CLUB RECORDS **Attendance:** (at Cross Keys) 10,000 v Walsall F.A.Cup 1919-20 (at Keys Park): 3,169 v York City F.A.Cup 13.01.97
Win: 12-1 v Birmingham City, B'ham Wartime Lge Cup 40-41, 12-1 v Redditch United, B'ham Comb. 52-53
Defeat: 0-15 v Burton, B'ham Comb. 52-53
Career goalscorer: Tosh Griffiths, Joe O'Connor (post-war) **Career appearances:** Kevin Foster
Transfer fee paid: £12,000, for Steve Burr (Macclesfield Town 1991)
Transfer fee received: £50,000, for Dave Hanson (Leyton Orient)

BEST SEASON **FA Cup:** Fourth Round 1996-97 2-3 v Middlesbrough (A)
League clubs defeated: Blackpool 96-97, York City 96-97, Hull City 97-98, Barnet 98-99
FA Trophy: 1997-98, 3rd Round 1-2 v Grantham Town (A) **League:** 3rd, Conference 95-96

Players Progressing (Post War): Brian Horton (Port Vale 70), Vernon Allatt (Halifax T. 79); Chris Brindley (Wolverhampton W. 86), Scott Cooksey (Shrewsbury T. 98), Dave Hanson (Leyton Orient), Paul Ware (Macclesfield T.), Keith Russell (Blackpool 97)

Match Facts 2002-03

Date	Comp.	Opponents	Att.	Score	Goalscorers
17/08	D.M. P	Crawley Town	863	2 - 2	Francis 11, Rae 66
19/08	D.M. P	HALESOWEN TOWN	802	3 - 2	Lucas 42[p], Jones 68, Brindley 87
24/08	D.M. P	CAMBRIDGE CITY	516	3 - 2	Brindley 70, Francis 72 88
26/08	D.M. P	Moor Green	486	1 - 0	Brindley 72
31/08	D.M. P	Hastings United	506	0 - 2	
02/09	D.M. P	GRANTHAM TOWN	644	1 - 0	Wray 18
07/09	D.M. P	Weymouth	654	0 - 0	
09/09	D.M. P	HINCKLEY UNITED	540	0 - 0	
14/09	D.M. P	HAVANT & WATERLOOVILLE	555	3 - 0	Pierce 63 77, Ware 69
17/09	D.M. P	Stafford Rangers	1675	1 - 1	Lucas 63[p]
21/09	D.M. P	Tiverton Town	742	1 - 2	Pierce 57
28/09	FAC Q2	HUCKNALL TOWN	506	0 - 0	
01/10	FAC Q2 rep	Hucknall Town	355	3 - 3	Simkin 63[p], Jones 70, Rae 94 Lost 5 6 after pens.
05/10	D.M. P	DOVER ATHLETIC	542	2 - 2	Ware 15, Ryder 90
08/10	D.M. P	Tamworth	1078	0 - 1	
19/10	D.M. P	ILKESTON TOWN	545	6 - 2	Brindley 37, Pierce 49 51 53, Lancashire 50, Wray 89
26/10	D.M. P	Cambridge City	584	2 - 2	Simkin 51[p], Brindley 58
29/10	Lge Cup 1	Rocester	134	2 - 1	Francis 13, Airdrie 18
02/11	FAT 1	Clevedon Town	172	4 - 2	Francis 44, S Pierce 52 55, Airdrie 78
09/11	D.M. P	BATH CITY	624	2 - 2	Pierce 25, Thorne 74[og]
11/11	Staffs SC 2	CHASETOWN	192	7 - 0	Pierce 3 7 38, Airdrie 32, Maguire 62, Lancashire 81, Charie 88
16/11	D.M. P	Newport County	628	0 - 1	
18/11	Birm SC 2	RUGBY UNITED	n/k	7 - 2	
23/11	D.M. P	STAFFORD RANGERS	1241	2 - 2	Pierce 7 77
26/11	Lge Cup 2	Bedworth United	116	1 - 3	Francis 62
30/11	FAT 2	Ilkeston Town	436	1 - 3	McGuire 68
14/12	D.M. P	Halesowen Town	512	1 - 0	Pierce 87
21/12	D.M. P	HASTINGS UNITED	471	1 - 0	Rae 72
26/12	D.M. P	MOOR GREEN	647	0 - 0	
28/12	D.M. P	Havant & Waterlooville	510	1 - 2	Lancashire 85
01/01	D.M. P	Worcester City	1251	1 - 3	Francis 71
13/01	Birm SC 3	OLDBURY UNITED	130	0 - 3	
18/01	D.M. P	Ilkeston Town	523	1 - 3	Pierce 53
25/01	D.M. P	WELLING UNITED	542	4 - 1	Pierce 28 73, Francis 65, Lake 84
01/02	D.M. P	Bath City	702	1 - 4	Airdrie 5
03/02	Staffs SC QF	Burton Albion	203	2 - 1	Ware 16, Jones 81
12/02	Birm SC QF	WOLVERHAMPTON WANDERERS	859	1 - 3	Airdrie 49
15/02	D.M. P	TIVERTON TOWN	452	2 - 3	Brindley 78 89
22/02	D.M. P	Welling United	518	2 - 2	Simkin 20, Francis 37
24/02	D.M. P	CHIPPENHAM TOWN	486	1 - 3	Pierce 86
03/03	D.M. P	CHELMSFORD CITY	378	2 - 2	Simkin 25[p] 49
08/03	D.M. P	NEWPORT COUNTY	454	1 - 0	Berks 55
15/03	D.M. P	Folkestone Invicta	325	1 - 4	Jones 53
19/03	Staffs SC SF	STOKE CITY	248	2 - 6	Pierce 64, Simkin 90
22/03	D.M. P	Grantham Town	362	0 - 3	
29/03	D.M. P	TAMWORTH	1182	0 - 1	
05/04	D.M. P	Chippenham Town	491	3 - 1	Corbett 17, Moss 43, Pierce 83
07/04	D.M. P	CRAWLEY TOWN	490	0 - 0	
12/04	D.M. P	WEYMOUTH	480	0 - 1	
14/04	D.M. P	Dover Athletic	662	0 - 1	
19/04	D.M. P	Hinckley United	372	1 - 0	Dakin 69[og]
21/04	D.M. P	WORCESTER CITY	497	2 - 0	Moss 85, Pierce 88
26/04	D.M. P	Chelmsford City	618	2 - 2	Berks 17, Pierce 25
03/05	D.M. P	FOLKESTONE INVICTA	525	3 - 1	Brindley 45, Jones 82, Moss 84

PLAYING SQUAD

Goalkeepers: Michael Bingham (Mansfield T.), Adam Jenkins(Youth Team), Ryan Young (Hucknall T.).

Defenders: Chris Brindley (Kidderminster H.), Alex Gibson (Stafford Rangers), Tom Griffiths (Youth Team), Les Robinson (Mansfield T.), Stuart Ryder (Stafford Rangers), Darren Simpkin (Blakenall), **Wayne Simpson** (Nuneaton Bor.), Bryan Small (Kettering T.), Allen Tankard (Mansfield T.), Ashley Williams (Youth Team).

Midfield: David Berks (Stafford R.), Karl Brown (Stafford Rangers), Danien Charie (York C.), Ashley Dodd (Moor Green), Steve Evans (Tamworth), Les Hines (Halesowen T.), Mark Jones (Raith R.), Stuart Lake (Walsall), Spencer Lloyd (Youth, Robbie Meacham (Youth), Steve Palmer (Telford Utd), Derek Rae (Elgin C.), Paul Ward (Rochdale), Shaun Wray (Stafford R.).

Forwards: Stewart Airdrie (Guiseley), Steve Anthrobus (Total Network Solutrions), Kevin Francis (Hull C.), Graham Lancaster (Rochdale), Micky Moore (Stourport Swifts), Steve Pierce (Hereford Utd), Michael Swann (Tamworth), Simon Tucker (Sutton Coldfield T.)

HINCKLEY UNITED

CLUB OFFICIALS

Chairman: **Kevin Downes**
Vice Chairman: **Rob Mayne**
Secretary: **Ray Baggott**
37 Laneside Drive, Hinckley, Leics.
LE10 1TG (01455 447278)
Press Officer: **Andy Gibbs** (01455 617828)

FOOTBALL MANAGEMENT TEAM

Manager: Dean Thomas
Coach:Charlie Palmer
Physio: Julie Hayton

FACT FILE

Formed: 1997
Sponsors: Vacon Drives
Colours: Red & blue stripes/blue/red
Change colours: Amber & black stripes/black/amber
Midweek matchday: Tuesday
Reserves' League: Mid Comb Res Div
Unofficial Website: www.hinckleyunitedfc.co.uk

2002-2003
Captain: Andy Penny
Leading Goalscorer: David Sadler
Player of the Year: T.B.A.

HINCKLEY UNITED FOOTBALL CLUB
Sponsored by Transco
THIS IS MIDDLEFIELD LANE - HOME OF "THE KNITTERS"
Dr Martens FOOTBALL LEAGUE
SATURDAY 3RD MAY 2003
HINCKLEY UNITED
CAMBRIDGE CITY
DR MARTENS LEAGUE PREMIER DIVISION
2002-2003 SEASON
OFFICIAL MATCH PROGRAMME £1.50

Pages: 60 Price: £1 Editor:Andy Gibbs
Local Radio: BBC Radio Leicester, Fosseway Radio
Local Press: Heartland Evening News, Hinckley Times, Leicester Mercury, Coventry Evening Telegraph

GROUND Middlefield Lane, Hinckley, Leics. LE10 0RB 01455 613553/615012
Directions: From M69 junction 1 take A5 north to Dodwells Island, then A47(sign Leicester). At 3rd r/about turn right (Stoke Road) then first left(Tudor Road), until crossroads. Turn left (Middlefield Lane), ground at end oflane on left
Capacity: 5,000 Cover: 1,300 Seats: 320 Floodlights: Yes
Clubhouse: Social club with lounge, games room and concert hall
Club Shop: Sells programmes, books, vidoes, badges, mugs , replica shirts,scarves, hats,etc.

PREVIOUS **Names:** Hinckley Athletic (1889) & Hinckley Town (prev. Westfield Rovers 58-66) merged in 1997
Grounds: Westfield Playing Field 58-60; Coventry Rd Rec Grd 60-68; Leicester Rd68-97
Leagues: Town: S Leicester & Nuneaton Amat, Leics Snr 72-86, Central Mids 86-88, West Mids 88-90
Athletic: Leics. & Northants; Leics. Sen.; Birmingham Comb. 14-39 47-54; West Midlands (Regional) 54-59 64-94; Southern 63-64

CLUB RECORDS **Attendance: Town:** 2,000 v Real Sociedad 86. **Athletic:** 5,410 v Nuneaton Boro 49
United: 2,661 v Cheltenham Town (F.A.Cup 2nd Rd. (H) 2001-02
Win: 9-1 vRocester (Away) 28.8.2000 **Defeat:** 0-6 v Redditch United (a) 7.11.1988
Career Goalscorer: David Sadler 72 **Career Appearances:** Morton Titterton 213

BEST SEASON **FA Trophy:** United: 4th Rd 2-3 v Yeovil Town 98-99
FA Cup: 2nd Round Proper v Cheltenham Town (Home) 0-2. 2001-02

HONOURS Dr. Martens (Southern) Western Division Champions 2000-2001, Westerby Challenge Cup Winners 2000-2001,2001-02
Players progressing: Athletic: John Allen (Port Vale), Keith Scott (Swindon via Wycombe W.), Gary Pick (Hereford), Mike Love (Wigan)

L - R - Back row: Lol Chamberlain (Goalkeepers coach), Charlie Palmer (Asst.Man), Buster Kendall (Kitman), Jamie March, Leon Mitchell, Justin Jenkins, Andy Penny, Farhad Afandiyev, Guy Hadland, Simon Dakin, Niki Preston, Paul Hunter, Jamie Williams, Phil Preston (Asst.Res.& Youth Manager), Julie Hayton (Physio) and Steve Cook (Res & Youth Manager). **Front row**: Tim Wilkes, Richard Mitchell, Dave Crowley, Gavin O'Toole, Leon Blake, Stuart Storer, Dean Thomas (Manager), Neil Cartwright, Leon Doughty, Martin Fox, Zeke Rowe and Ashley Hamilton.

Date	Comp.	Opponents	Att.	Score	Goalscorers
17/08	D.M. P	TIVERTON TOWN	393	1 - 1	Fox 33
19/08	D.M. P	Chelmsford City	443	1 - 1	R Mitchell 59
24/08	D.M. P	Hastings United	431	0 - 1	
26/08	D.M. P	TAMWORTH	791	1 - 1	Sadler 23
31/08	D.M. P	Dover Athletic	810	0 - 2	
03/09	D.M. P	Ilkeston Town	543	1 - 1	Jenkins 89
07/09	D.M. P	WELLING UNITED	287	1 - 3	Mitchell 89
09/09	D.M. P	Hednesford Town	540	0 - 0	
14/09	D.M. P	BATH CITY	314	3 - 1	Sadler 68, Penny 70, Fox 90[p]
17/09	D.M. P	WORCESTER CITY	354	0 - 1	
21/09	D.M. P	Havant & Waterlooville	395	2 - 2	Price 55[og], Preston 87
28/09	FAC Q2	KIDSGROVE ATHLETIC	283	3 - 0	Sadler 16 88, Jenkins 29
05/10	D.M. P	NEWPORT COUNTY	344	0 - 2	
08/10	D.M. P	STAFFORD RANGERS	346	2 - 0	Sadler 43 90
12/10	FAC Q3	TAMWORTH	1139	1 - 3	Mitchell 45
19/10	D.M. P	Chippenham Town	541	1 - 3	Sadler 58
26/10	D.M. P	WEYMOUTH	272	2 - 1	Sadler 51, Dyer 61
29/10	Lge Cup 1	Gresley Rovers	225	2 - 1	Rowe 34, James 38[og]
02/11	FAT 1	Grantham Town	413	2 - 3	March 52, Dakin 80
09/11	D.M. P	Crawley Town	1217	2 - 0	Penney 12, C Smith 90
12/11	Lge Cup 2	MOOR GREEN	147	2 - 1	Smith 16, Doughty 22
16/11	D.M. P	Bath City	595	2 - 2	Voice 32 76
23/11	D.M. P	MOOR GREEN	290	1 - 2	Sadler 17
30/11	D.M. P	FOLKESTONE INVICTA	241	3 - 3	March 57, Dyer 70, Smith 90
07/12	D.M. P	Worcester City	828	2 - 2	Voice 9, Preston 27
14/12	D.M. P	Weymouth	604	2 - 2	Dyer 63, Voice 71
17/12	Lge Cup 3	King's Lynn	331	0 - 3	
21/12	D.M. P	HALESOWEN TOWN	346	1 - 1	Voice 50
26/12	D.M. P	Tamworth	1208	0 - 2	
28/12	D.M. P	DOVER ATHLETIC	321	1 - 1	Smith 24
04/01	D.M. P	Newport County	658	2 - 3	Smith 59, Dakin 69
18/01	D.M. P	HASTINGS UNITED	294	3 - 2	Smith 54, Doughty 56, Voice 61
21/01	Leics CC QF	Barwell	225	7 - 1	Penny 8, Dyer 9 90, Voice 14 25, Smith 48 54
25/01	D.M. P	Stafford Rangers	862	2 - 2	Sadler 87, Fox 90
01/02	D.M. P	ILKESTON TOWN	391	5 - 2	Fox 45 52[p] 77[p], Sadler 66, Dyer 70
08/02	D.M. P	Moor Green	334	2 - 2	Lenton 85, Sadler 86
22/02	D.M. P	CHIPPENHAM TOWN	286	1 - 2	Wilkes 10
27/02	Leics CC SF	LEICESTER CITY	168	0 - 7	
01/03	D.M. P	Cambridge City	444	1 - 1	Penny 57
11/03	Rolleston QF	THURNBY RANGERS	95	3 - 1	Sadler 43, Wilkes 57, Fox 80
15/03	D.M. P	Welling United	530	2 - 1	Doughty 57, Fox 90
18/03	D.M. P	GRANTHAM TOWN	332	0 - 0	
22/03	D.M. P	Folkestone Invicta	338	0 - 4	
29/03	D.M. P	CHELMSFORD CITY	333	2 - 1	Sadler 14 85
01/04	D.M. P	CRAWLEY TOWN	291	3 - 1	Voice 28 48, Doughty 77
05/04	D.M. P	Halesowen Town	535	1 - 2	Sadler 70
08/04	Rolleston SF	FRIAR LANE OLD BOYS	63	8 - 0	Piercewright 12 37 70, Jenkins 47 68 84, Sadler 58, Jackson 75
15/04	D.M. P	HAVANT & WATERLOOVILLE	317	2 - 1	Sadler 20 77
19/04	D.M. P	HEDNESFORD TOWN	372	0 - 1	
21/04	D.M. P	Grantham Town	470	1 - 2	Jackson 22
26/04	D.M. P	Tiverton Town	660	2 - 0	Sadler 16 53
03/05	D.M. P	CAMBRIDGE CITY	411	3 - 2	Jenkins 1 10, Cartwright 37
05/05	Rolleston F	ANSTEY NOMADS	253	6 - 0	Jenkins 15 71 84, Lenton 55[p], Wilson 64[og], Thomas 87 (at LCFA, Holmes Park)

PLAYING SQUAD

Goalkeepers: Farhad Afandiyev (Azerbaijan), Thomas Whittle (Oldham Ath.).

Defenders: Bevan Browne (Cambridge C.), Neil Cartwright (Youth Team), Simon Dakin (Kings Lynn), Scott Eustace (Stevenage Bor.), Martin Fox (Cambridge C.), Tommy Goodwin (Shepshed Dynamo),Guy Hadland (Aston Villa), Andy Penny (Solihull Bor.), Brad Piercewright (Kettering T.), Craig Smith (Belper T.), Gavin Stone (Halesowen T.).

Midfield: Dave Crowley (Nuneaton B), Leon Doughty (Atherstone Utd), Wayne Dyer (Sutton Coldfield T.), Leon Jackson (Worcester C), Jamie Lenton (V.S.Rugby), Shaun Murray (Kettering T.), Gavin O'Toole (Aberystwyth), Stuart Storer (Chesham Utd).

Forwards: Zeke Rowe (Kings Lynn), David Sdaler (Kingstonian), Chris Smith (Solihull Borough)

MERTHYR TYDFIL

CLUB OFFICIALS

Chairman: Wyn Holloway
Vice Chairman: Paul Sugrue
Football Sec: Anthony Hughes,4 BrynmorlaisSt.,Penydarren, Merthyr Tydfil CF47 9YE
Tel: 01685 359921 (H&F)
07958006911 (M)
Press Off. Mike Donovan

FOOTBALL MANAGEMENT TEAM

Manager: Andy Beattie
Assistant Manager: John Relish

FACT FILE

Formed: 19445
Nickname: The Martyrs
Sponsors: Rainbow Print
Colours: Black & white stripes/black/black
Change colours:Red with yellow trim
Midweek home matchday: Tuesday
Reserves' League: None
Club Website: www.themartyrs.com
Local Press: Merthyr Express
Local Radio: Valleys Radio

GROUND Penndarren Park, Merthyr Tydfil, Mid Glamorgan
Tel: 01685 384102 Email: pughy@tinyonline.co.uk
Directions: (South) A470 Express Way to Merthyr Centre to Pontmorlais (traffic lights) turn left then first right, first right at Catholic Church and right again into Park Terrace . (North) Heads of theValley road to Town Centre, to Pontmorlais(traffic lights) turn right, then as above
Capacity: 10,000 Seats: 1,500 Cover: 5,000 Floodlights: Yes
Clubhouse: Open Mon. to Sun. 6.30 - 11.00pm. 2 club cafes open on matchdays for hot food
Club Shop: Sells replica kits, club souvenirs & programmes.
Contact Mel Jenkins01443 692336

PROGRAMME

Pages: 36 Price: £1.50
Editor:Mike Donovan 07788 185149 (M)

PREVIOUS **Leagues:** Southern League 46 -89 (Southern League 46-59, 1st Division 59-61, 64-71, !st Div. North 72-79, Premier Div. 61- 64, 71-72, 88-89, Midland Div. 79-88), G M Conference 89-95.
Names: None **Grounds:** None

CLUB RECORDS **Attendance:** 21,000 v Reading FA Cup 2nd Rnd 1949/50
Win: 11-0 v Rushden 1987 **Defeat:** 9-2 v Altrincham 1993
Transfer fee paid: £10,000 to Cardiff City for Robbie James 1992
Transfer fee received: £12,000 for Ray Pratt from Exeter City 1981

BEST SEASON **Welsh FA Cup:** Winners 48-49 50-51 86-87
FA Trophy: 3rd Rd v Northwich Vic 95-96
FA Cup: 2nd Round on six occasions. League clubs defeated: Bristol Rovers

HONOURS Welsh FA Cup 48-49, 50-51, 86-87; Southern League 47-48, 49-50, 50-51, 51-52, 53-54; Southern League (Midland) 87-88; Southern League (Premier) 88-89;Southern League Cup 47-48, 50-51

Players Progressing : Syd Howarth (Aston Villa), Cyril Beech, Gilbert Beech,Bill Hullet, Ken Tucker (Cardiff City), Nick Deacy (Hereford United), Gordon Davies (Fulham), Ray Pratt (Exeter City), Peter Jones, Paul Giles (Newport County)

L-R - Back: John Chicken (Director), Jane Price (Asst. Physio), Owen Money (Director), John Relish (Asst. Man.), Gethin Jones, Jason Price, Cortez Belle, Craig Evans, Brendan Cropley, Ian Edwards, Kevin Aherne-Evans, Gareth Elliott, Dean Clarke, Andy Beattie (Manager), Mel Jenkins (Director), Alan Pyke (Physio), Anthony Hughes (Secretary). **Front**: Richard French, Danny Carter, Simon Heal, Ryan Dorrian, Adrian Needs, Chris Bale, Paul Keddie, Grant Thomas, Kristian Whitcombe, Mike Regan, Gary Thorne, Shaun Hughes (mascot)

Date	Comp.	Opponents	Att.	Score	Goalscorers
17/08	D.M. W	Bedworth United	251	1 - 2	Pritchard 12
20/08	D.M. W	WESTON-SUPER-MARE	465	1 - 2	Prichard 85
24/08	D.M. W	REDDITCH UNITED	422	2 - 2	Pritchard 61[p], Belle 66
26/08	D.M. W	Gloucester City	422	2 - 2	Bell 9, Pritchard 45
31/08	FAC P	CHRISTCHURCH	353	5 - 0	Price 29, Dorrian 34, Regan 44 74, Belle 85
07/09	D.M. W	RACING CLUB WARWICK	485	3 - 0	Keddle 8, Rollins 49[og], Carter 58
11/09	D.M. W	Swindon Supermarine	189	2 - 0	Evans 32, Price 60
14/09	FAC Q1	CHARD TOWN	461	2 - 0	Price 33 85
21/09	D.M. W	ROCESTER	456	4 - 1	Mainwaring 6 8 45, Price 35
24/09	D.M. W	CLEVEDON TOWN	439	1 - 0	Price 5
28/09	FAC Q2	Bath City	744	0 - 5	
05/10	FAT P	EVESHAM UNITED	391	2 - 0	Dorrian 53, Mainwaring 65
12/10	D.M. W	Cinderford Town	272	1 - 1	Belle 78
19/10	D.M. W	SHEPSHED DYNAMO	495	3 - 0	Evans 36, Keddle 50, Belle 59
22/10	D.M. W	Weston-super-Mare	273	2 - 0	Belle 40, Pritchard 90
26/10	D.M. W	Bromsgrove Rovers	557	2 - 1	Mainwaring 35 41
29/10	Lge Cup 1	CHIPPENHAM TOWN	238	0 - 1	
02/11	FAT 1	Taunton Town	346	2 - 1	Pritchard 58, Russell 68[og]
05/11	D.M. W	Mangotsfield United	325	3 - 2	Mainwaring 52, Edwards 73, Belle 75
09/11	D.M. W	EVESHAM UNITED	521	2 - 0	Mainwaring 12, Belle 68
12/11	D.M. W	Stourport Swifts	102	3 - 2	Pritchard 68[p], Price 72, Evans 85
16/11	D.M. W	SOLIHULL BOROUGH	557	2 - 3	Belle 5, Evans 57
23/11	D.M. W	Atherstone United	203	1 - 0	Belle 16 F
30/11	FAT 2	Gloucester City	417	0 - 0	
03/12	FAT 2 rep	GLOUCESTER CITY	340	0 - 1	
07/12	D.M. W	Clevedon Town	209	1 - 0	Pritchard 56
14/12	D.M. W	Racing Club Warwick	115	2 - 1	Pritchard 13, Belle 87
21/12	D.M. W	GRESLEY ROVERS	502	1 - 1	Pritchard 48
26/12	D.M. W	GLOUCESTER CITY	570	3 - 2	Edwards 8, Evans 11, Pritchard 62
28/12	D.M. W	Redditch United	306	1 - 0	Pritchard 33
01/01	D.M. W	Cirencester Town	240	0 - 2	
04/01	D.M. W	RUGBY UNITED	524	3 - 0	Belle 31 34, Bale 54
18/01	D.M. W	Taunton Town	441	4 - 1	C Evans 39, K Evans 70, Belle 73, Dorrian 90
25/01	D.M. W	SWINDON SUPERMARINE	586	4 - 0	Pritchard 11 37[p], Belle 16, Dorrian 32
28/01	D.M. W	TAUNTON TOWN	533	1 - 0	Price 48
01/02	D.M. W	Rugby United	328	1 - 2	Bale 85
08/02	D.M. W	BROMSGROVE ROVERS	1105	2 - 0	Pritchard 10, Carter 20
15/02	D.M. W	MANGOTSFIELD UNITED	659	0 - 0	
22/02	D.M. W	Shepshed Dynamo	179	2 - 0	Pritchard 23, Carter 87
25/02	D.M. W	STOURPORT SWIFTS	479	1 - 3	Belle 85
08/03	D.M. W	Sutton Coldfield Town	203	2 - 0	Evans 76, Belle 87
15/03	D.M. W	BEDWORTH UNITED	571	1 - 0	Dorrian 90
22/03	D.M. W	Rocester	182	2 - 0	Belle 12 90
28/03	D.M. W	CINDERFORD TOWN	506	0 - 0	
05/04	D.M. W	Gresley Rovers	404	1 - 0	Mainwaring 68
12/04	D.M. W	ATHERSTONE UNITED	575	5 - 0	Pritchard 1 28, Mainwaring 35 44, Price 55
19/04	D.M. W	Evesham United	325	2 - 0	Pritchard 12 87
21/04	D.M. W	CIRENCESTER TOWN	679	2 - 0	Belle 66[p], Mainwaring 75
26/04	D.M. W	Solihull Borough	282	0 - 0	
03/05	D.M. W	SUTTON COLDFIELD TOWN	780	2 - 2	Mainwaring 74 86

PLAYING SQUAD

Goalkeepers: Brendan Cropley (Hinckley Utd), Neil Thomas (Ton Pentre).

Defenders: Gareth Elliott (Youth Team), Kevin Evans (Cardiff C.), Paul Keddle (Rhayader), Adrian Needs (Ebbw Vale), Jason Price (Havorfordwest County), Gary Thorne (Bath C.).

Midfield: Chris Bale (Cinderford T.), Danny Carter (Barry T.), Dean Clarke (Newport County), Ryan Dorrian (Clevedon T.), Ian Edwards (Maestag Park), Craig Evans (Havorfordwest Co.), Mike Regan (Cinderford T.), Grant Thomas (Swansea C.), Kristian Witcombe (Caerleon).

Forwards: Gavin Beddard (Port Talbot T.), Andy Mainwaring (Clevedon T.), Justin Pritchard (Weston-super-Mare)

MOOR GREEN

CLUB OFFICIALS

Chairman: Ian Childs
Vice-Chairman: John Bassford

Secretary: Nigel Collins
7 The Morelands, West Heath,
Birmingham B31 3HA
Tel: 0121476 4944 (H) 0121 777 8961 (W)
07801248211133 (M)
Email: nigelcollins@lineone.net
Press Officer: Peter Clynes 0121 745 3262
Commercial Man.: Commercial Dept.0121 777 8961

FOOTBALL MANAGEMENT TEAM

Manager: Bob Faulkner
Coach: Mark Harrison
Physio: Steve Shipway

FACT FILE

Formed: 1901
Nickname: The Moors
Sponsors:Alexander Forbes Insurance
Colours: Navy Blue with sky blue band
Change colours: Yellow & Green
Midweek matchday: Tuesday
Reserve League: No reserve team
Website:www.moorgreenfc.co.uk

2002-2003

Captain: Chris Gillard
Top Scorer: Nathan Lamey
Ps.o.Y: Adam Rachel & Dean Peer

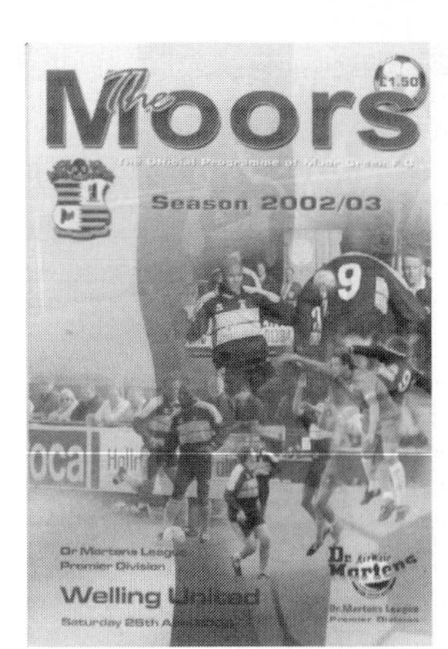

Programme: Pages: 40 Price: £1.50
Editor:Martin North(0121 603 7357)
Local Press: Solihull News, Solihull Times,
Birmingham Post & Mail, Express &Star
Local Radio: Radio WM, BRMB

GROUND `The Moorlands', Sherwood Rd., Hall Green. B28 OEX
Tel: 0121 777 8961 or 0121 624 2727

Directions: Off Highfield Rd, which is off A34 (B'ham to Stratford)
Hall Green & Yardley (BR) half mile

Capacity: 3,250 Cover: 1,200 Seats: 250 Floodlights: Yes

Clubhouse: Two bars, dance floor. Open nightly & weekend lunch

Club Shop: Selling scarves, mugs, stickers, programmes etc

PREVIOUS **Leagues:** (friendlies only 1901-21) Birmingham & Dist. A.F.A. 1908-36; Central Amateur 36-39; Birmingham Comb 45-54; West Mids 54-65; Midland Comb 65-83
Grounds: Moor Green Lane 1901-02; numerous 02-22; Windermere Road 1910-30

CLUB RECORDS **Attendance:** 5,000 v Romford, FA Amtr Cup 51
Career Goalscorer: Phil Davies 221 **Career Appearances:** Michael Hawkins 800
Transfer fee paid: £1,000 for Adrian O'Dowd (Alvechurch)
Transfer fee received: £90,000 for Ian Taylor (Port Vale)

BEST SEASON **FA Cup:** 1st Rd Proper 79-80 (lost 2-3 Stafford Rgs),02-03 v Barrow 0-2
FA Trophy: 1st Rd Prop 90-91, 0-3 v Burton Albion; 96-97, 3-5 v AshtonUnited

HONOURS Southern Lg Mid Div R-up 87-88, Mids Comb 80-81 (R-up(4) 74-76 79-80 82-83, Div 185-86, Presidents Cup(2) 66-68 78-79), Mids Comb Chall Cup 80-81 (R-up 69-7082-83), Lord Mayor of B'ham Charity Cup 90-91, Mids F'lit Cup(2) 90-92, Tony Allden Tphy 81-82, B'ham Snr Cup 57-58, Worcs Snr Cup 2000-01 R-up 86-87, 01-02 B'ham Jnr Cup66-67, Worcs Jnr Cup 85-86, Solihull Charity Cup 85-86, Smedley Crook Mem.Cup 87-88, Cent Amat Lg 36-37 37-38 38-39, Verviers (Belg) Tphy 32-33 36-37,AFA Chall Cup 38-39, AFA Snr Cup 26-27 35-36, Mids F'lit Yth Lg Cup R-up 87-88,B'ham County Yth Lg Cup R-up 83-84. Birmingham Senior Cup: 2000-01

Players progressing: H Smith/R Jefferies (Aston Villa 47/50), F Pidcock(Walsall 53), P Woodward/B Mack (W B Abion 54), S Cooper (Birmingham City 83), K Barnes (Manchester City), P Brogan (Mansfield Town), I Taylor (Pt Vale 92), S Talbot (Pt Vale 94), D Busst (Coventry 92)

Back row, left to right: Guy Sanders, Dean Peer, Nathan Lamey, Jamie Petty, Rob Elmes, Adam Rachel, Joe Martin, and Josh Walker.
Front: Richard Robinson, Danny Scheppel (now Bromsgrove Rovers), Peter Foulds, Chris Gillard, Jai Stanley, Craig Woodley, Declan Chinedu

Date	Comp.	Opponents	Att.	Score	Goalscorers
17/08	D.M. P	DOVER ATHLETIC	338	0 - 2	
20/08	D.M. P	Tamworth	1012	2 - 2	Myers 31 64
24/08	D.M. P	Welling United	510	0 - 1	
26/08	D.M. P	HEDNESFORD TOWN	486	0 - 1	
31/08	D.M. P	HAVANT & WATERLOOVILLE	241	0 - 1	
02/09	D.M. P	Worcester City	1202	0 - 4	
07/09	D.M. P	TIVERTON TOWN	268	2 - 1	Blake 46 79
10/09	D.M. P	Ilkeston Town	494	0 - 2	
14/09	D.M. P	HASTINGS UNITED	256	0 - 0	
17/09	D.M. P	BATH CITY	243	1 - 0	Lamey 89
21/09	D.M. P	Newport County	789	1 - 1	Lamey 62
28/09	FAC Q2	Bedworth United	270	4 - 1	Lamey 25 61, Robinson 60, Walker 88
05/10	D.M. P	Chippenham Town	577	1 - 1	Blake 85
08/10	D.M. P	GRANTHAM TOWN	295	3 - 0	Stanley 31, Lamey 69 72
12/10	FAC Q3	HALESOWEN TOWN	649	3 - 1	Lamey 42[p] 86[p], Scheppel 57
19/10	D.M. P	Chelmsford City	501	0 - 4	
26/10	FAC Q4	LEIGH RMI	525	2 - 1	Gayle 45 50
29/10	Lge Cup 1	STAFFORD RANGERS	184	2 - 1	Faulds 31, Martin 61
02/11	D.M. P	CRAWLEY TOWN	303	0 - 2	
09/11	D.M. P	Folkestone Invicta	302	1 - 0	Evans 70
12/11	Lge Cup 2	Hinckley United	147	1 - 2	Lamey 18
16/11	FAC 1	Barrow	2650	0 - 2	
19/11	Birm SC 2	Bromsgrove Rovers	n/k	3 - 0	
23/11	D.M. P	Hinckley United	290	2 - 1	Lamey 85 90[p]
30/11	FAT 2	BLYTH SPARTANS	323	2 - 3	Blake 33, Sanders 66
07/12	D.M. P	HALESOWEN TOWN	421	4 - 0	Elmes 25 71, Martin 89, Scheppel 90
10/12	Birm SC 3	SUTTON COLDFIELD TOWN	73	2 - 1	Scheppel 31, Martin 70[p]
14/12	D.M. P	Havant & Waterlooville	409	3 - 3	Lamey 16 63, Martin 38
21/12	D.M. P	CAMBRIDGE CITY	230	1 - 1	Martin 73
26/12	D.M. P	Hednesford Town	647	0 - 0	
28/12	D.M. P	CHELMSFORD CITY	334	1 - 1	Lamey 55
04/01	D.M. P	Bath City	678	1 - 1	Martin 88
11/01	D.M. P	STAFFORD RANGERS	443	1 - 1	Elmes 67
13/01	Worcs SC QF	Solihull Borough	249	3 - 2	Martin 36 58, Scheppel 74
18/01	D.M. P	Halesowen Town	598	1 - 0	Martin 56
25/01	D.M. P	WORCESTER CITY	675	1 - 1	Peer 61
08/02	D.M. P	HINCKLEY UNITED	334	2 - 2	Peer 6, Martin 7
15/02	D.M. P	Weymouth	604	1 - 3	Elmes 54
22/02	D.M. P	ILKESTON TOWN	326	5 - 0	Myers 7 18, Martin 55 64, Elmes 87
24/02	D.M. P	Dover Athletic	703	2 - 1	Saunders 55, Stanley 69
01/03	D.M. P	TAMWORTH	1007	0 - 2	
08/03	D.M. P	WEYMOUTH	249	2 - 2	Lamey 21[p] 68
11/03	Birm SC QF	TAMWORTH	213	1 - 3	Martin 87
15/03	D.M. P	Crawley Town	813	2 - 2	Lamey 62[p] 64
18/03	D.M. P	Cambridge City	285	2 - 1	Stanley 15, Lucas 35[p]
22/03	D.M. P	CHIPPENHAM TOWN	335	1 - 0	Martin 25
25/03	Worcs SC SF	Evesham United	122	0 - 1	
29/03	D.M. P	FOLKESTONE INVICTA	297	3 - 0	Lamey 6, Martin 70, Elmes 80
01/04	Birm SC SF	WOLVERHAMPTON WANDERERS	237	2 - 1	Lamey 17 78
05/04	D.M. P	Hastings United	407	1 - 3	Elmes 55
12/04	D.M. P	Tiverton Town	638	0 - 1	
19/04	D.M. P	NEWPORT COUNTY	254	1 - 2	Martin 78
21/04	D.M. P	Stafford Rangers	757	0 - 4	
26/04	D.M. P	WELLING UNITED	236	1 - 0	Elmes 82
28/04	Birm SC F	Birmingham City	701	0 - 2	(at Solihull Borough)
03/05	D.M. P	Grantham Town	640	0 - 4	

PLAYING SQUAD

Goalkeepers: Andy de Pont (Stourbridge), Adam Rachel (BLackpool).

Defenders: Dave Barnett (Halesowen T.), Lee Collins (Halesowqen T.), Chris Gillard (Port Vale),Garry Hughes (Kettering T.), Richard Robinson (GMP Sports), Guy Sanders (Bedworth Utd).

Midfield: Peter Faulds (Kidderminster H.), Simon Gosssage (Romulus), Dean Peer (Shrewsbury T.), Ben Petty (Burton Alb.), Jamie Petty (Solihull Borough), Danny Scheppel (Worvester C.), Jai Stanley (Bedworth Utd), Andy Turner (Northwich Victoria), Josh Walker (Shrewsbury T.), Craig Woodley (Nuneaton Borough).

Forwards: Rob Elmes (Halesowen T.), John Gayle (Torquay Utd), Nathan Lamey (Hitchin T.), Jae Martin (Woking).

NEWPORT COUNTY A.F.C.

Pages: 40 Price: £1.50
Editor: Wallace Brown (01633 265500)
Local Press:
South Wales Argus, South Wales Echo
Local Radio: Red Dragon, Real Radio

CLUB OFFICIALS

Chairman: Wallace Brown
Secretary: Mike Everett
43 Downing Street, Newport. NP19 0JL
Tel: 01633 669572

Club Website: www.newport-county.co.uk

Club's Email : hq.newportcounty@virgin.net

FACT FILE

Formed: 1989
Nickname: The Exiles
Sponsors: Acorn Recruitment
Colours: Amber shirts and black shorts
Change colours: Blue & Black Stripes/Blue
Midweek matchday: Wednesday
Reserve League: Severnside League
Youth League: South West Counties Youth

FOOTBALL MANAGEMENT TEAM

Manager: Peter Nicholas
Physio: John Fitzgerald
Kit Manager: Tony Gilbert

2002-2003

Captain: Matt Rose
Top Scorer & P.o.Y.: Garry Shephard

GROUND Newport Stadium, Spytty Park, Langland Way, Newport, South Wales
Fax 01633 666107 Tel: 01633 662262

Directions: From Severn Bridge on M4 take 1st exit signed Newport (jct 24), 1st left at r'bout follow signs for industrial area, left at r'bout after 2 1/2miles, over 2 r'bouts, next left for ground. Ample free parking available at ground

Capacity:4,300 Cover: 3,236 Seats: 1,236 Floodlights: Yes

Clubhouse: Small bar at ground with hot and cold snacks also available.

Club Shop: Open matchdays, sells a wide selection of souvenirs & programmes

PREVIOUS **Names:** Newport AFC were formed after the demise of Newport County in1988-89, name change 1999. **Leagues:** Hellenic 89-90
Grounds: London Road, Moreton-in-Marsh 89-90; Somerton Park, Newport 90-92; Gloucester City FC 92-94 (exile period due to dispute with FAW re League of Wales)

CLUB RECORDS **Attendance:** 3,721 v Blackpool. F.A.Cup , First Round Replay 2001-02
Win: 9-0 v Pontlottyn Blast Furnace (A), Welsh Cup First Round 1/9/90
Defeat: 1-6 v Stafford Rangers (A) BHL 6/1/96, 1-6 v Wrexham F.A. of Wales Premier Cup Final 08/05/03
Career Goalscorer: Chris Lilygreen 93 **Career Appearances:** Mark Price 275 (222 Lg + 53 cup)
Transfer fee paid:£5,000 for Shaun Chapple from Forest Green Rovers £1,000 from RedditchU for Paul Burton
Transfer fee received: £5,000 from Merthyr Tydfil for Craig Lima

BEST SEASON **FA Cup:** First Round 2001-02 **FA Trophy:** 3rd Rd 99-00, 00-01, 02-03 **FA Vase:** N/A

HONOURS Hellenic Lge Prem Div 89-90 (Lge Cup 89-90); Glos Sen Cup Winners 93-94;Southern Lg. Mid Div Champions 94-95, R-up 98-99 Merit Cup Jnt Win 94-95, 98-99 Gwent FA Sen.Cup Winners 96-97,97-98,98-99,99-00,00-01,01-02 Herefordshire Sen Cup. 98-99, F.A.W. Premier Cup R-Up 2002-2003. S.W.Co Youth League 2002-03 R-Up: 2000-01, 01-02

L-R - Back Row: Russell Jones (Staff), Lloyd Stone, Mark Dickeson, Jeff Eckhardt, Pat Mountain, Gareth Wesson, Andrew Thomas, Nathan Davies, Raith Plant, Nicky Palmer, John Fitzgerald (Physio). **Front**: Bobby Morris (Staff), Gethin Jones, Steve Williams, Terry Evans, Neil Davis, Peter Nicholas (Manager), Matt Rose, Garry Shephard, Gareth Phillips, Gary Lloyd, Tony Gilbert (Kit Man). **Kneeling:** Chris Rogers, Allan Stevenson.

Date	Comp.	Opponents	Att.	Score	Goalscorers
17/08	D.M. P	Cambridge City	426	3 - 1	Davis 4 18, Shephard 60
19/08	D.M. P	WEYMOUTH	906	3 - 0	Rose 14, Shephard 72, Dickeson 81
24/08	D.M. P	ILKESTON TOWN	887	3 - 0	James 39, N Davies 66, French 83
26/08	D.M. P	Worcester City	1549	1 - 2	Shail 33[og]
31/08	D.M. P	FOLKESTONE INVICTA	884	1 - 2	Walker 6
03/09	D.M. P	Stafford Rangers	631	0 - 1	
07/09	D.M. P	Crawley Town	1041	0 - 2	
09/09	D.M. P	TIVERTON TOWN	674	0 - 1	
14/09	D.M. P	Chelmsford City	496	1 - 1	Shepherd 76
16/09	D.M. P	CHIPPENHAM TOWN	741	3 - 1	Davis 21, Thomas 46 71
21/09	D.M. P	MOOR GREEN	789	1 - 1	Davis 39
24/09	FAW Prem B	Connah's Quay Nomads	182	1 - 1	Clark 49
28/09	FAC Q2	Gloucester City	774	1 - 1	Davis 21
30/09	FAC Q2 rep	GLOUCESTER CITY	619	4 - 0	Davis 33 68, Steadman 40[og], Walker 65
05/10	D.M. P	Hinckley United	344	2 - 0	Shepherd 55, D'Auria 86
07/10	Gwent SC 1	NEWPORT YMCA	126	0 - 1	
08/10	D.M. P	Tiverton Town	697	1 - 3	Eckhardt 16
12/10	FAC Q3	TEAM BATH	736	0 - 3	
19/10	D.M. P	DOVER ATHLETIC	643	0 - 1	
21/10	FAW Prem B	TOTAL NETWORK SOLUTIONS	305	1 - 0	French 13
28/10	Lge Cup 1	CLEVEDON TOWN	280	2 - 0	Rose 94, Davis 117
02/11	D.M. P	HAVANT & WATERLOOVILLE	571	0 - 0	
04/11	FAW Prem B	CONNAH'S QUAY NOMADS	258	1 - 1	Walker 18
09/11	D.M. P	Grantham Town	458	2 - 1	Fowler 23, Shepherd 90
12/11	FAW Prem B	Total Network Solutions	168	0 - 3	
16/11	D.M. P	HEDNESFORD TOWN	628	1 - 0	Shepherd 80
18/11	FAW Prem B	BANGOR CITY	n/k	1 - 1	Walker
23/11	D.M. P	Dover Athletic	1006	0 - 0	
26/11	Lge Cup 2	Sutton Coldfield Town	92	1 - 2	Davis 22
30/11	FAT 2	EPSOM & EWELL	489	2 - 1	Cowe 20, Shepherd 87
07/12	D.M. P	GRANTHAM TOWN	571	3 - 2	Eckhardt 38, Shephard 40, Thomas 71
10/12	FAW Prem B	Bangor City	301	1 - 1	Shephard 60
14/12	D.M. P	WELLING UNITED	602	0 - 2	Farley 49[p], Seabury 80
21/12	D.M. P	Bath City	898	3 - 4	Rose 20, Fowler 42, Eckhardt 83
26/12	D.M. P	WORCESTER CITY	927	2 - 1	Plant 43, Shepherd 82
28/12	D.M. P	Folkestone Invicta	456	3 - 2	Ashington 71, Eckhardt 82, Walker 85
04/01	D.M. P	HINCKLEY UNITED	658	3 - 2	Fowler 10, Luntala 16, Shephard 86
13/01	FAT 3	Worcester City	1128	2 - 3	Walker 76, Plant 79
18/01	D.M. P	Chippenham Town	1067	0 - 0	
25/01	D.M. P	BATH CITY	856	1 - 1	Plant 40
28/01	FAW Prem QF	SWANSEA CITY	843	3 - 1	Eckhardt 4, Ashington 27, Shephard 80
08/02	D.M. P	HASTINGS UNITED	667	1 - 1	Davies 6
15/02	D.M. P	TAMWORTH	804	0 - 1	
01/03	D.M. P	Weymouth	823	0 - 2	
08/03	D.M. P	Hednesford Town	454	0 - 1	
11/03	D.M. P	Havant & Waterlooville	349	0 - 1	
15/03	D.M. P	CAMBRIDGE CITY	548	1 - 1	Davis 38
18/03	D.M. P	Halesowen Town	555	2 - 1	Shepherd 46, Dimond 79
22/03	D.M. P	Hastings United	430	3 - 1	Rose 35, Shepherd 78[p], Plant 88
24/03	FAW Prem SF	CARDIFF CITY	1160	0 - 0	Won 4 2 after pens.
30/03	D.M. P	Welling United	559	0 - 1	
01/04	D.M. P	Ilkeston Town	312	0 - 1	
05/04	D.M. P	STAFFORD RANGERS	548	1 - 0	Rose 64
12/04	D.M. P	CRAWLEY TOWN	583	3 - 3	Dimond 21, Fox 73, Davis 79
19/04	D.M. P	Moor Green	254	2 - 1	Davies 55 60
21/04	D.M. P	HALESOWEN TOWN	604	1 - 1	Clark 19
26/04	D.M. P	Tamworth	1396	0 - 0	
03/05	D.M. P	CHELMSFORD CITY	890	2 - 5	Dickeson 6, Stevenson 65
08/05	FAW Prem F	Wrexham	n/k	1 - 6	(at Wrexham)

PLAYING SQUAD

Goalkeepers: Pat Mountain (Gloucester C.), Gareth Wesson (Newport YMCA).

Defenders: Josh Dupres (Cardiff C.), Jeff Eckhardt (Cardiff C.), Terry Evans (Swansea C.), Jason Perry (Hull C.), Lloyd Stone (Youth Team), Andrew Davies (Youth Team).

Midfield: Ryan Ashington (Torquay Utd), Chris Collins (Swindon T.), Matthew Currie (Youth Team), Nathan Davies (Youth Team), Kristian Dimond (Cardiff C.), Michael Fowler (Woking), Richard French (Cardiff C.), Gethin Jones (Youth Team), Matthew Rose (Gloucester C.), Allan Stevenson (Chester C.).

Forwards: Neil Davis (Hednesford T.), Mark Dickeson (Llanelli), Raith Plant (Cwmbran T.), Garry Shepherd (Merthyr Tydfil).

NUNEATON BOROUGH

CLUB OFFICIALS

Chairman: Roger Stanford
Secretary: Paul Lewis
7 Garfitt Road, Kirby Muxloe, Leics.
Tel: 0116 239 4981 (H) 07711 410642 (M)
General Manager: Alan Prince c/o the club
Commercial Manager: Graham Wilson
Press Officers: Phil Clayton c/o the club

FOOTBALL MANAGEMENT TEAM

Manager: Alan Lewer
1st Team Coach: Lee Howey
Physio: Helen Cooper
Reserves Managers: Ian Charlton/Graham Wilson
Youth Team Manager: Mick Dewis
Scout: Andy Fern

FACT FILE

Formed: 1937
Nickname: The Boro
Club colours:
Blue & white stripes,blue shorts
Change colours: White & blue,white
Reserves' league: Central Conference
Midweek matchday: Tuesday 7.45pm
Club Sponsors:
Website: www.nuneatonborough.co.uk

2002-03
Captain: Chris McKenzie
P.o.Y.: Michael Love
Leading Scorer: Mark Quayle

GROUND Manor Park, Beaumont Road, Nuneaton, Warks. CV11 5HD
Tel.: 02476 385738 Fax: 02476 342690 Clubcall: 09066 555 848
Simple Directions: A444 to Nuneaton from M6 junction 3, 2nd exit at 1st roundabout, 2nd exit at 2nd r'about, left at 3rd r'bout, 2nd right into Greenmoor Rd, turn right at the end, grd on left. Ground 1 mile from Nuneaton Trent Valley (BR)
Capacity: 6,500 **Seated:** 520 **Terracing - Covered:** 3,000 **Uncovered:** 3,500
Clubhouse: Open every evening, weekend lunchtimes & matchdays.
Club Shop: Sells souvenirs, programmes & club kits. Contact Commercial department

Pages: 56 **Price:** £2.00
Editor:Graham Wilson
Tel: 01400250332 (H), 07788 800505 (M)

Local Press:
Nuneaton Telegraph & Weekly Tribune
Local Radio: Mercia Sound, BBC CWR

PREVIOUS **Leagues:** Central Amateur 37-38; B'ham Comb 38-52; West Mids (B'ham) 52-58;Southern 58-79 81-82 88-99. GM Conference (Alliance Premier & Gola) 79-81 82-88 99-03 **Names:** None **Ground:** None

CLUB RECORDS **Attendance:** 22,114 v Rotherham, FA Cup 3rd Rd 1967
Defeat: 1-8 (55-56 & 68-69) **Win:** 11-1 (45-46 & 55-56)
Goalscorer: Paul Culpin 201 (Career), 55 (Season - 92/93)
Career Appearances: Alan Jones 545 (62-74)
Transfer Fee Paid: £35,000 to Forest Green R. 2000 for Marc McGregor
Transfer Fee Received: £80,000 from Kidderminster H. 2000 for Andy Ducros

BEST SEASON **FA Cup:** Third Round replay 66-67Rotherham U(H)1-1(A 0-1). 1st Rd 19 times
League Clubs defeated: Watford (53-4),Swansea C(66-67), Oxford U(77-78),Swansea C. (93-4) Stoke City (2001-02)
FA Trophy: Quarter final- 76-77(rep), 79-80, 86-87 **League:** Runners-up Conference 83-84, 84-85

HONOURS Alliance Prem Lge R-up (2) 83-85; Southern Lg Premier Div. 98-99, R-up 66-67 74-75, League Cup Win 95-96, Midland Div 81-82 92-93, Champ 95-96, Lg Cup R-up 62-63, Merit Cup 92-93 (jt); Birmingham Lg 55-56 (Nth Div 54-55); Birmingham Comb. R-up 3; Birmingham Snr Cup 7(inc 2001-02), R-up 3

Players P rogressing: A Morton (Fulham 70), R Edwards (Port Vale 72), K Stephens (Luton 78), T Peake (Lincoln C. 79), P Sugrue (Man City 80), M Shotton & T Smithers (Oxford U. 80), D Thomas (Wimbledon 81), P Richardson (Derby C. 84), P Culpin (Coventry 85), R Hill/T Morley/E McGoldrick/A Harris, (North'ton 85/86), D Bullock (Hudd'field 93), M Christie (Derby Co. 98), A Ducros (Kidd'minster H) 2000 S.Weaver (Lincoln C)

Season	League	Div.	Pos.	P	Home W	D	L	F	A	Away W	D	L	F	A	Pts	Manager
02-03	Conference	-	20	42	9	4	8	27	32	4	3	14	24	46	46	Steve Burr
01-02	Conference	-	10	42	9	3	9	33	27	7	6	8	24	30	57	Steve Burr
00-01	Conference	-	13	42	9	5	7	35	26	4	10	7	25	34	54	B Phillips/Steve Burr
99-00	Conference	-	15	42	7	6	8	28	25	5	9	7	21	28	51	Brendal Phillips
98-99	Southern	Premier	1	42	16	3	2	52	15	11	6	4	39	18	90	Brendan Phillips
97-98	Southern	Premier	12	42	12	3	6	39	22	5	3	13	29	39	57	Brendan Phillips
96-97	Southern	Premier	7	42	15	2	4	44	20	4	7	10	17	32	65	Brendan Phillips

Season	League	Div.	Pos.	P	W	D	L	F	A	Pts	Manager
95-96	Southern	Midland	1	42	30	5	7	82	35	95	Brendan Phillips
94-95	Southern	Midland	7	42	19	11	12	76	55	68	Elwyn Roberts
93-94	Southern	Premier	22	42	11	8	23	42	66	41	John Barton

Date	Comp.	Opponents	Att.	Score	Goalscorers
17/08	Conf.	Southport	1311	0 - 1	
20/08	Conf.	WOKING	1241	1 - 1	Thackeray 36
24/08	Conf.	STEVENAGE BOROUGH	1206	3 - 0	Quayle 32 55 81
26/08	Conf.	Yeovil Town	2504	2 - 3	Jones 32, Quayle 90at Dorchester Town
31/08	Conf.	HEREFORD UNITED	1354	0 - 3	
03/09	Conf.	Dagenham & Redbridge	1541	2 - 1	Jones 45, Harris 90
07/09	Conf.	Gravesend & Northfleet	1044	1 - 4	Woodley 17
14/09	Conf.	MARGATE	918	3 - 2	Quayle 77, Woodley 78, Jones 82
17/09	Conf.	Leigh RMI	401	1 - 1	Quayle 86
21/09	Conf.	FOREST GREEN ROVERS	1136	3 - 2	Jones 4, Woodley 50, Turner 58
24/09	Conf.	NORTHWICH VICTORIA	1012	1 - 4	Squires 39
28/09	Conf.	Halifax Town	1402	1 - 3	Quayle 14
05/10	Conf.	DONCASTER ROVERS	1759	0 - 3	
08/10	Conf.	Chester City	2564	2 - 1	Angus 1, Quayle 78
12/10	Conf.	Barnet	1421	1 - 2	Quayle 82
19/10	Conf.	TELFORD UNITED	1007	1 - 0	Quayle 50
26/10	FAC Q4	BARROW	1678	1 - 1	Love 73
29/10	FAC Q4 rep	Barrow	1919	3 - 4	Maxfield 18[og], McGregor 23, Quayle 45
02/11	Conf.	Farnborough Town	644	2 - 0	McGregor 21, Quayle 75
09/11	Conf.	SCARBOROUGH	1237	1 - 1	McGregor 6
12/11	Birm SC 2	Rushall Olympic	70	5 - 1	Quayle 11 68 87, Thackeray 30, McGregor 36
23/11	Conf.	Doncaster Rovers	2913	1 - 1	Quayle 56
30/11	Conf.	Kettering Town	1386	0 - 3	
07/12	Conf.	BARNET	868	3 - 2	B Williams 14, Walling 63, McGregor 82
14/12	Conf.	GRAVESEND & NORTHFLEET	969	0 - 1	
21/12	Conf.	Margate	504	1 - 1	Ducros 10
26/12	Conf.	BURTON ALBION	2337	1 - 2	Quayle 71
28/12	Conf.	Woking	1786	1 - 2	Quayle 20
01/01	Conf.	Burton Albion	2523	0 - 1	
11/01	FAT 3	Tamworth	2045	0 - 3	
14/01	Birm SC 3	BEDWORTH UNITED	456	6 - 0	McGregor 20[p] 29, Alford 41, Williams 47, Turner 67, Peake 74
18/01	Conf.	Stevenage Borough	1651	1 - 3	Alford 22
21/01	Conf.	MORECAMBE	718	1 - 1	Lavery 90
25/01	Conf.	YEOVIL TOWN	1717	1 - 1	Ricketts 50
08/02	Conf.	Hereford United	2071	1 - 2	Alford 74[p]
11/02	Birm SC QF	WALSALL	n/k	0 - 5	
15/02	Conf.	DAGENHAM & REDBRIDGE	1105	1 - 3	Paschalis 38
01/03	Conf.	LEIGH RMI	1187	0 - 2	
04/03	Conf.	SOUTHPORT	774	3 - 2	Murphy 13, Williams 34 83
08/03	Conf.	Northwich Victoria	582	1 - 3	Brown 69
15/03	Conf.	HALIFAX TOWN	1231	2 - 0	Brodie 18, Brown 48
22/03	Conf.	KETTERING TOWN	1549	1 - 0	Brodie 52
25/03	Conf.	Forest Green Rovers	679	1 - 6	Brodie 11
29/03	Conf.	Morecambe	1604	2 - 3	Murphy 25[p], Mansell 45
12/04	Conf.	Telford United	987	2 - 1	Murphy 38, Mansell 40
19/04	Conf.	CHESTER CITY	1371	1 - 0	Guyett 11[og]
21/04	Conf.	Scarborough	1451	1 - 4	Brodie 58
26/04	Conf.	FARNBOROUGH TOWN	1710	0 - 2	

PLAYING SQUAD

Goalkeepers: Darren Acton (Tamworth), Chris Taylor (Evesham Utd).

Defenders: Terry Angus (Slough T.), Mark Clifford (Boston Utd), Adam Cooper (Youth Team), Mickey Love (Stevenage Borough), **Neil Moore** (Mansfield T.), Dean Scott (Kidderminster H.), James Squires (Doncaster R.), Ross Weatherstone (Boston Utd), Bobby White (Northampton T.).

Midfield: Gary Birch (Walsall), Mickey Brown (Chester C.), Matt Collins (W.B.A), Daire Doyle (Kidderminster H.), Gary Fitzgpatrick (Telford Utd), Brian McGorry (Tamworth), John Turner (Coalville T.).

Forwards: Andy Corbett (Siolihull Borough), Gez Murphy (Kettering T.), Brian Quailey (Halifax T.), Stuart Whittaker (Leigh RMI).

STAFFORD RANGERS

STAFFORD RANGERS
£1.50
MAIN SPONSOR - FULWOOD ROOFING SUPPLIES

CLUB OFFICIALS

Chairman: Jon.Downing
Vice-Chairman: C.Went
Secretary: Michael Hughes,1 Rambleford Way,Parkside,Staffoord St16 1TW
Tel: 01785 661492 (H) 07850 996386 (M)

FOOTBALL MANAGEMENT TEAM

Manager: Phil Robinson
Coach: T.B.A.
Physio: T.B.A.

FACT FILE

Formed: 1876
Nickname: The Boro
Colours: Black & White stripes/black/black
Change: All Red
Midweek matchday: Tuesday
Reserves' League: T.B.A.
Local Press: Staffordshire Newsletter, Express & Star, Evening Sentinel
Local Radio:
Radio Stoke, Beacon Radio, Signal Radio

PROGRAMME

Pages: 40 Price: £1.50
Editor: Secretary

GROUND Marston Road Stafford ST16 3BX Tel: 01785 602430 Fax : 01785 602431
Club Website: www.staffordrangers.co.uk

Directions: From M6 junction 14, A34 (Stone) to roundabout, straight over into Beaconside, take third right into Common Road, ground one mile ahead. From Town Centre, follow signs for B5066 (Sandon) turn left by new housing estate. Two miles from railway station

Capacity 3,000 Cover 1,500 Seats: 426 Floodlights: Yes

Clubhouse: Yes - Open every evening
Club Shop: Two shops, one old programmes and one souvenirs

PREVIOUS
Leagues: Shropshire 1891-93, Birm 1893-96, 21-40, N Staffs 1896-1900, Cheshire 00-01, Birm Comb 00-12, 46-52, Cheshire Co. 52-69, N.P.L. 69-79, 83-85, Alliance Prem 79-83, GMVC 85-95
Grounds: Lammascotes, Stone Rd, Newtown, Doxey (until 1896)

CLUB RECORDS
Attendance: 8,536 v Rotherham Utd FA Cup 3rd Rd 75
Win: 11-0 v Dudley Town FA Cup 6.9.58 **Defeat:** 0-12 v Burton Town Birmingham Lge 13.12.30
Career Goalscorer: M Cullerton 176 **Career Appearances:** Jim Sargent
Transfer fee paid: £13,000 for S Butterworth from VS Rugby 90
Transfer fee received: £100,000 for Stan Collymore from Crystal Palace 1990

BEST SEASON
FA Trophy: Winners 1971-72 & 78-79. R-up 75-76
FA Cup: 4th Rd 74-75, 1-2 v Peterborough Utd. (H) League clubs defeated: Halifax, Stockport, Rotherham

HONOURS
Birm Comb Champ 12-13; Birm Lge Champ 25-26; N.P.L. Champ 71-72, 84-85, Champ Shield 84-85; FA Trophy 71-72, 78-79, R-up 75-76; Bob Lord Trophy 85-86; Wednesday Charity Cup 20-21; Mid F/light Cup 70-71; Jim Thompson Shield 86-87; Staffs Sen Cup 54-55 56-57 62-63 71-72 77-78 86-87 91-92 Dr.Martens Western Division 99-00

Players progressing: M Aleksic (Plymouth), J Arnold (Blackburn), R Williams/MCullerton/T Bailey (Port Vale), K Barnes (Man City), A Lee (Tranmere), ECameron (Exeter), W Blunt (Wolves), G Bullock (Barnsley), K Mottershead(Doncaster), McIlvenny (WBA), S Collymore (C Palace), P Devlin (Notts Co.),R Price (Birmingham C.)

Date	Comp.	Opponents	Att.	Score	Goalscorers
17/08	D.M. P	Weymouth	702	0 - 1	
20/08	D.M. P	ILKESTON TOWN	808	2 - 0	Balley 4, Davidson 55
24/08	D.M. P	CHIPPENHAM TOWN	669	0 - 0	
26/08	D.M. P	Halesowen Town	736	1 - 1	Berks 85
31/08	D.M. P	CAMBRIDGE CITY	677	0 - 1	
03/09	D.M. P	NEWPORT COUNTY	631	1 - 0	Heath 40
07/09	D.M. P	Havant & Waterlooville	490	1 - 1	Lovatt 38
10/09	D.M. P	GRANTHAM TOWN	617	4 - 0	Robinson 17 24, Davidson 25, Edwards 55
14/09	D.M. P	Dover Athletic	901	2 - 0	Davidson 54, Gibson 77
17/09	D.M. P	HEDNESFORD TOWN	1675	1 - 1	Davidson 61
20/09	D.M. P	Worcester City	2711	3 - 0	Edwards(2), Davidson
28/09	FAC Q2	Shepshed Dynamo	315	2 - 0	Edwards 57[p] 82
05/10	D.M. P	WELLING UNITED	819	1 - 1	Gibson 60
08/10	D.M. P	Hinckley United	346	0 - 2	
12/10	FAC Q3	ROTHWELL TOWN	849	3 - 0	Gibson 22, Lovatt 25, Davidson 90
19/10	D.M. P	CRAWLEY TOWN	874	2 - 1	Bailey 21[p], Robinson 90
26/10	FAC Q4	Ilkeston Town	903	5 - 0	Atkinson 33[og], Lovatt 48, Heath 77, Davidson 86, Bailey 90
29/10	Lge Cup 1	Moor Green	184	1 - 2	Bailey 26
02/11	D.M. P	TIVERTON TOWN	847	2 - 1	Davidson 10, Heath 34
09/11	D.M. P	Chelmsford City	560	2 - 0	Davidson 48, Bailey 60[p]
16/11	FAC 1	Shrewsbury Town	5114	0 - 4	
19/11	Staffs SC 2	PELSALL VILLA	155	7 - 0	McAughtrie 11 46, Berks 45, Barrow 52, Heath 54, Gibson 68 71
23/11	D.M. P	Hednesford Town	1241	2 - 2	Heath 38, McAughtri 90
30/11	FAT 2	ALFRETON TOWN	782	0 - 2	
07/12	D.M. P	DOVER ATHLETIC	664	3 - 1	Gibson 29, Edwards 72 75
10/12	D.M. P	Tamworth	844	1 - 2	Bailey 49
14/12	D.M. P	Crawley Town	848	4 - 2	Beale 21, Heath 33, Jones 43, Bailey 45
21/12	D.M. P	WEYMOUTH	811	0 - 0	
26/12	D.M. P	HALESOWEN TOWN	1187	4 - 2	Lovatt 16, Davidson 66[p] 73, Simpson 78
28/12	D.M. P	Cambridge City	522	0 - 1	
04/01	D.M. P	FOLKESTONE INVICTA	737	6 - 0	Heath 38 58, Gibson 48, Davidson 55, Szewczyk 80 84
11/01	D.M. P	Moor Green	443	1 - 1	Carey-Bertram 1
14/01	D.M. P	HAVANT & WATERLOOVILLE	672	1 - 3	Hambley 44[og]
18/01	D.M. P	Welling United	569	2 - 1	Edwards 5[og], Bailey 34
25/01	D.M. P	HINCKLEY UNITED	862	2 - 2	Bailey 58, Gibson 72
28/01	Staffs SC QF	NEWCASTLE TOWN	327	4 - 0	Bailey 3, McAughtrie 16, Carter 75, Davidson 79
01/02	D.M. P	Grantham Town	424	2 - 1	Carter 7, Bailey 48
08/02	D.M. P	WORCESTER CITY	1301	2 - 1	Bailey 4, Barrow 68
01/03	D.M. P	Folkestone Invicta	301	2 - 1	Lovatt 43, Bailey 64
08/03	D.M. P	Chippenham Town	761	1 - 1	Barrow 11
11/03	D.M. P	Bath City	558	1 - 0	Downs 62
22/03	D.M. P	Tiverton Town	661	1 - 2	Bailey 18
25/03	Staffs SC SF	Port Vale	n/k	2 - 1	Davidson 75, Szewczyk 77
29/03	D.M. P	HASTINGS UNITED	964	1 - 1	Bailey 16
05/04	D.M. P	Newport County	548	0 - 1	
12/04	D.M. P	CHELMSFORD CITY	739	1 - 1	Davidson 34
15/04	D.M. P	TAMWORTH	1884	1 - 2	Murphy 70
19/04	D.M. P	Ilkeston Town	495	5 - 2	Murphy 4 44, Brown 25, Davidson 45, Barrow 46
21/04	D.M. P	MOOR GREEN	757	4 - 0	Gibson 44 46, Faulds 50[og], Daniel 77
26/04	D.M. P	BATH CITY	982	5 - 0	Daniel 5, Lovatt 45, Gibson 80, Murphy 89, Fife 90
30/04	Staffs SC F	STOKE CITY	881	5 - 1	Robinson 10, Davidson 18 69 71, Heath 70 (at Port Vale)
03/05	D.M. P	Hastings United	410	2 - 0	Fife 43, Szewczyk 44

PLAYING SQUAD

Goalkeepers: Ryan Price (Telford Utd), Karl Ward (Youth Team).

Defenders: Lee Barrow (Hednesford T.), Richard Beale (Reddditch Utd), Darren Boughey (Stoke C.), Andrew Brookes (Youth Team), Wayne Daniel (Boldmere St.Michaels), Craig McAughtrie (Carlisle Utd).

Midfield: Robert Heath (Stoke C.), Craig Lovatt (Leek T.), Mark Lowry (Hereford Utd), Alex Mortimer (Shrewsbury T.) Ian Reed (Worcester C.), Phil Robinson (Hereford Utd).

Forwards: Dennis Bailey (Halesowen T.), Alfie Carter (Evesham Utd), Danny Davidson (Hereford Utd), Robin Gibson (Wrexham), Harry Singh (Chaset.), Paul Szewczyk (Stourbridge)

TIVERTON TOWN

CLUB OFFICIALS

President: Dr Gavin Haig F.R.C.S.
Chairman: Dave Wright
Vice-Chairman: Pete Buxton
Football Secretary: Ramsay Findlay
35 Park Road, Tiverton, Devon EX16 6AY
Tel: 01884 256341
Treasurer: Kim Smith
General Secretary: Tony Floyde

FOOTBALL MANAGEMENT TEAM

Manager: Martyn Rogers
Assistant Manager: Martin Grimshaw
Physio: Dai Morgan
Assistant Physio: Mike Perry

FACT FILE

Formed: 1920 Nickname: Tivvy
Colours: All Yellow
Change colours: All white
Midweek matches: Tuesday
Reserves' League: None

2002-2003

Captain: Jason Rees
Top Goalscorer: Jamie Mudge
Player of the Year: Phil Everett

GROUND: Ladysmead, Bolham Road, Tiverton, Devon EX16 8SG Tel: 01884 252397
Website: www.tiverton-town-fc.co.uk

Directions: Leave M5 at Jct 27. Take second Tiverton turn off A361, at end of dual carriage-way . Turn left and then cross over new roundabout after 500 yards. Carry on again straight over mini roundabout and ground is on right after 200 yards.
Capacity: 3,500 Seats: 520 Cover: 2,300
Clubhouse: Lunctimes, evenings. All day Sat during season. 3 bars. Food(burgers, chips etc)
Club Shop: Yes

Pages: 56 Price: £1.50 (with colour)
Editor/ Press Officer: John Reidy
Tel: 01884 2534509 & 07979 858512

PREVIOUS **League:** Devon & Exeter; Western League **Ground:** The Elms, Blundell Road 1920-39

RECORD **Attendance:** 3,000 v Leyton Orient, FA Cup First Round Proper 1994-95
Career Goalscorer: Phil Everett
Record Win: (DML) 7-1 v Cirencester 2001 **Record Defeat:** (DML) 2-6 v Stafford Rangers (A) 2001-02

BEST SEASON **FA Vase:** Winners 97-98 98-99, R-up 92-93 **FA Cup:** 1st Round 90-91 91-92 94-95 97-98

HONOURS FA Vase 97-98 98-99; Western Lg 93-94 94-95 96-97 97-98 (R-up 92-93 95-96 98-99); Les Phillips Cup 92-93 94-95 95-96 96-97 97-98; Amateur Trophy 77-78 78-79, Div 1 R-up 88-89; Devon St Lukes Cup 90-91 91-92 92-93 94-95 96-97 (R-up 89-90); Devon & Exeter Lg 51-52 66-67 70-71 84-85; Devon Snr Cup 55-56 65-66; East Devon Snr Cup 35-36 37-38 52-53 55-56 60-61 62-63 66-67; North Devon Charity Cup 72-73 86-87. Devon St Luke's Bowl 99-00; Dr. Martens Western Div. R-up 2000-01

Players progressing: Jason Smith (Coventry City 93 & Swansea City 98), Mark Saunders (1995) & Kevin Nancekivell (2000) Plymouth Argyle

L-R - Back: Luke Vinnicombe, Ben Harris, Danny Haines, James Mudge, Steve Ovens, Shaun Goff. **Middle**: Dai Morgan (Physio), Matthew Aubrey, Steve Peters, Stuart Fraser, David Steele, Rob Cousins, Kevin Nancekivell, Mike Perry (Asst. Physio). **Front**: Richard Pears, Steve Winters, Martyn Rogers (Manager), Jason Rees, Martyn Grimshaw (Asst. Man.), Chris Holloway, Paul Chenoweth

Date	Comp.	Opponents	Att.	Score	Goalscorers
17/08	D.M. P	Hinckley United	393	1 - 1	Mudge 90
21/08	D.M. P	WORCESTER CITY	714	0 - 0	
24/08	D.M. P	HAVANT & WATERLOOVILLE	603	3 - 1	Everett 70, Haines 71, Mudge 72
26/08	D.M. P	Weymouth	808	2 - 0	Browne 35[og], Mudge 52
31/08	D.M. P	ILKESTON TOWN	704	3 - 1	Rogers 22, Everett 49, Haines 51
04/09	D.M. P	BATH CITY	903	2 - 1	Rogers 30, Everett 40
07/09	D.M. P	Moor Green	268	1 - 2	Everett 77
09/09	D.M. P	Newport County	674	1 - 0	Everett 19
14/09	D.M. P	GRANTHAM TOWN	823	0 - 2	
17/09	D.M. P	Halesowen Town	430	0 - 0	
21/09	D.M. P	HEDNESFORD TOWN	742	2 - 1	Lynch 27, Nancekivell 81[p]
28/09	FAC Q2	TAUNTON TOWN	1380	1 - 1	Chenoweth 28
02/10	FAC Q2 rep	Taunton Town	1365	2 - 0	Ovens 33 80
05/10	D.M. P	Cambridge City	316	0 - 3	
08/10	D.M. P	NEWPORT COUNTY	697	3 - 1	Nancekivell 32 51[p], Ovens 45
12/10	FAC Q3	WEYMOUTH	1191	4 - 2	Peters 33 54, Browne 42[og], Nancekivell 70
19/10	D.M. P	HASTINGS UNITED	761	0 - 1	
22/10	Devon SLCB 1	Exmouth Town	n/k	3 - 3	Lynch, Mudge(2) Won 2 1 after pens.
26/10	FAC Q4	Barnet	1390	2 - 0	Mudge 39 57
02/11	D.M. P	Stafford Rangers	847	1 - 2	Chenoweth 84
05/11	Lge Cup 1	Bath City	318	2 - 2	Honor 68[og], Nancekivell 78 Won 3 1 after pens.
09/11	D.M. P	WELLING UNITED	701	3 - 1	Pears 63, Nancekivell 82 90
11/11	Devon SLCB QF	PLYMOUTH ARGYLE	214	3 - 2	Ovens 17, Trotman 19 28
12/11	D.M. P	Bath City	513	1 - 0	Mudge 77
16/11	FAC 1	CRAWLEY TOWN	1840	1 - 1	Ovens 18
23/11	D.M. P	CHELMSFORD CITY	772	3 - 3	Everett 61 68, Nancekivell 72
26/11	FAC 1 rep	Crawley Town	3907	2 - 3	Pears 8 64
30/11	FAT 2	Grays Athletic	334	1 - 3	Mudge 90
07/12	D.M. P	Folkestone Invicta	334	1 - 1	Pears 30
11/12	Lge Cup 2	CIRENCESTER TOWN	330	4 - 2	Mudge 46 75, Nancekivell 54 58
14/12	D.M. P	Hastings United	417	3 - 0	Everett 13, Nancekivell 52, Mudge 80
17/12	Lge Cup 3	Newport IOW	161	7 - 1	Nancekivell 9, Mudge 52 71 75, Rogers 64 78, Pears 80
28/12	D.M. P	Ilkeston Town	440	3 - 1	Rogers 45, Everett 74, Steele 90
04/01	D.M. P	CAMBRIDGE CITY	737	0 - 2	
14/01	D.M. P	Tamworth	799	1 - 1	Everett 86
18/01	D.M. P	Chelmsford City	516	0 - 3	
25/01	D.M. P	FOLKESTONE INVICTA	650	4 - 0	Curran 15, Rudge 49, Pears 54, Steele 77
29/01	Lge Cup QF	CHIPPENHAM TOWN	435	2 - 3	Curran 31, Everett 88
08/02	D.M. P	TAMWORTH	981	0 - 1	
12/02	D.M. P	Chippenham Town	608	1 - 1	Pears 11
15/02	D.M. P	Hednesford Town	452	3 - 2	Everett 16, Mudge 75 80
12/03	D.M. P	CRAWLEY TOWN	537	0 - 1	
15/03	D.M. P	Worcester City	1000	2 - 0	Everett 13, Mudge 78
19/03	D.M. P	DOVER ATHLETIC	465	0 - 0	
22/03	D.M. P	STAFFORD RANGERS	661	2 - 1	Chenoweth 44, Ovens 65
24/03	D.M. P	Dover Athletic	715	0 - 0	
29/03	D.M. P	HALESOWEN TOWN	731	4 - 2	Everett 20 36, Rogers 89, Mudge 90
01/04	D.M. P	WEYMOUTH	566	3 - 0	Cousins 11, Rogers 25, Everett 39
05/04	D.M. P	Grantham Town	356	2 - 0	Chenoweth 35 90
09/04	Devon SLCB SF	BIDEFORD	531	2 - 0	Chenoweth 37, Ovens 90
12/04	D.M. P	MOOR GREEN	638	1 - 0	Ovens 54
19/04	D.M. P	Havant & Waterlooville	401	1 - 2	Rudge 8
21/04	D.M. P	CHIPPENHAM TOWN	832	1 - 1	Ovens 87
23/04	D.M. P	Crawley Town	365	1 - 1	Nancekivell 68
26/04	D.M. P	HINCKLEY UNITED	660	0 - 2	
03/05	D.M. P	Welling United	578	1 - 1	Nancekivell 66
30/07	Devon SLCB F	Torquay United	n/k	1 - 0	

PLAYING SQUAD

Goalkeepers: Stuart Fraser (Exeter C.).

Defenders: Rob Cousins (Forest Green R.), Danny Haines (Merthyr Tydfil), Russell Gee (Exeter C.), Shaun Goff (Exeter C.), Marcus Gross (Exeter Ciity), Steve Peters (Clevedon T.), Nathan Rudge (Chipenham T.), Luke Vinnicombe (Clevedon T.).

Midfield: Paul Chenoweth (Gloucester C.), Ben Harris (Exeter C.), Chris Holloway (Exeter C.), Kevin Nancekivell (Plymouth Argyle), David Steele (Willand R.), Steve Winter (Basingstoke T.).

Forwards: James Mudge (Exeter C.), Steve Ovens (Witney T.), Richard Pears (Clyst R.)

WELLING UNITED

CLUB OFFICIALS

President: E Brackstone
Chairman: Paul Websdale
Vice Chairman: Steven Pain
General Manager: Graham Hobbins
Club Secretary: Barrie Hobbins
c/o the club
Tel: 0208 301 1196 Fax:0208 301 5676
Press Officer: Paul Carter
c/o the club

FOOTBALL MANAGEMENT TEAM

Manager: Paul Parker
Player-Coach: Brian Statham
Physio: Peter Green

FACT FILE

Founded: 1963
Nickname: The Wings
Club Sponsors:
E. Coomes, Bookmakers
Colours: Red/red/white
Change colours: Yellow/blue/white
Midweek home matchday: Tuesday
Welling Wingsline: 09068 80 06 54
Local Press: Kentish Times;
Bexleyheath & Welling Mercury
Local Radio: Radio Kent;
Radio Invicta; R.T.M.

2002-03

Captain: Tim Hambley
Leading Goalscorer: Paul Booth 15
Player of the Year: Billy Burgess

PROGRAMME
Pages: 40 Price: £1.80
Editor: Gary McHolland-Pilcher

GROUND Park View Road Ground, Welling, Kent DA16 1SY
Tel: 0208 301 1196 Fax: 0208 301 5676

DIRECTIONS: M25, then A2 towards London. Take Welling turn-off, ground 1 mile.
By rail to Welling station (BR) - ground 3/4 mile.

CAPACITY: 4,000 **SEATED:** 1,070 **CLUBHOUSE:** Open on match days

CLUB SHOP: Sells programmes (League & non-League), scarves, mugs, caps, hats, badges, replica kits etc. Manager Peter Mason.

PREVIOUS **Leagues:** Eltham & Dist. Lge 1963-71, London Spartan Lge 1971-77, Athenian Lge 1977-79, Southern Lge 1979-86, 2001 Conference 86-2000 **Grounds:** Butterfly Lane, Eltham - 1963-78

RECORDS **Attendance:** 4,100 v Gillingham, FA Cup
Win: 7-1 v Dorking 1985-86 **Defeat:** 0-7 v Welwyn garden City 1972-73
Career Goalscorer: John Bartley - 533 **Career Appearances:** Nigel Ransom - 1,066 & Ray Burgess - 1,044
Transfer fee paid: £30,000 for Gary Abbott from Enfield
Transfer fee received: £95,000 from Birmingham City for Steve Finnan.1995

BEST SEASON **FA Cup:** Third Round 1988-89 0-1 v Blackburn Rovers League clubs defeated: Gillingham
FA Trophy: Quarter Final 1988-89 0-1 v Macclesfield

HONOURS London Spartan League 1978; Southern League Premier Division 1985/86; Kent Senior Cup 1985/86 98-99; London Senior Cup 1989/90; London Challenge Cup 1991/92, Runners-up 1993/94.

PLAYERS PROGRESSING: Paul Barron(Plymouth A), Andy Townsend (Southampton), Ian Thompson (AFC Bournemouth), John Bartley (Millwall), Dave Smith (Gillingham), Murray Jones (C. Palace), Kevin Shoemake (Peterborough), Tony Agana (Watford,), Duncan Horton (Barnet), Mark Hone (Southend), Steve Finnan & Steve Barnes (Birmingham City),Dean Standen (Luton Town)

L-R - Back Row: B Statham, J Farley, L Watts, T Hambley, J Ventor, G Knight, I Cousins, P Collins, T O'Shea, P Green.
Front Row: D Powell, B Burgess, A Rivere, D Standen, P Parker, D Slatter, A Berkley, P Booth, A Henry.

Date	Comp.	Opponents	Att.	Score	Goalscorers
17/08	D.M. P	Halesowen Town	566	0 - 0	
20/08	D.M. P	CHIPPENHAM TOWN	500	1 - 1	Virgo 41
24/08	D.M. P	MOOR GREEN	510	1 - 0	Edwards 20
26/08	D.M. P	Crawley Town	872	0 - 1	
31/08	D.M. P	WORCESTER CITY	558	0 - 1	
03/09	D.M. P	HASTINGS UNITED	540	0 - 3	
07/09	D.M. P	Hinckley United	287	3 - 1	Nade 15, Sodje 45, Aboaye 70
10/09	D.M. P	WEYMOUTH	457	4 - 2	Powell 44, Nade 45, Lorraine 82, Sodje 88
14/09	D.M. P	Tamworth	740	0 - 2	
17/09	D.M. P	Folkestone Invicta	338	2 - 2	Sodje 6, Hogg 45
21/09	D.M. P	ILKESTON TOWN	520	2 - 0	Sodje 79, Virgo 90
28/09	FAC Q2	Maidenhead United	285	2 - 1	Nade 84, Sodje 89
05/10	D.M. P	Stafford Rangers	819	1 - 1	Jones 9
08/10	D.M. P	Havant & Waterlooville	399	0 - 1	
12/10	FAC Q3	Dover Athletic	1302	2 - 2	Nade 17, Riviere 60
15/10	FAC Q3 rep	DOVER ATHLETIC	735	1 - 3	Powell 4
19/10	D.M. P	BATH CITY	635	1 - 3	Farley 90
26/10	D.M. P	CHELMSFORD CITY	669	0 - 2	
29/10	Lge Cup 1	Tonbridge Angels	283	2 - 1	Virgo 47, Standen 106
02/11	FAT 1	Windsor & Eton	174	2 - 2	Seabury 60, Standen 84
05/11	FAT 1 rep	WINDSOR & ETON	247	3 - 5	Nade 42 52, Hogg 47
09/11	D.M. P	Tiverton Town	701	1 - 3	Powell 51
16/11	D.M. P	GRANTHAM TOWN	583	2 - 0	Booth 48, Powell 87
19/11	Kent SC 1	THAMESMEAD TOWN	n/k	1 - 1	Won 3 1 after pens.
23/11	D.M. P	TAMWORTH	651	1 - 1	Virgo 55[p]
26/11	Lge Cup 2	CHELMSFORD CITY	206	2 - 3	Riviere 35, Booth 80
07/12	D.M. P	Bath City	589	2 - 0	Honor 69[p], Booth 83
14/12	D.M. P	Newport County	602	2 - 0	Farley 49[p], Seabury 80
17/12	London SC 3	Hanwell Town	42	1 - 2	Virgo 73[p]
21/12	D.M. P	DOVER ATHLETIC	771	0 - 0	
26/12	D.M. P	CRAWLEY TOWN	800	2 - 2	Little 2[og], Booth 41
28/12	D.M. P	Worcester City	1176	1 - 1	Heeley 7[og]
04/01	D.M. P	HAVANT & WATERLOOVILLE	501	1 - 1	Booth 62
18/01	D.M. P	STAFFORD RANGERS	569	1 - 2	Hogg 66
25/01	D.M. P	Hednesford Town	542	1 - 4	Booth 36
04/02	Kent SC QF	Folkestone Invicta	156	6 - 1	Booth 2 62 66, Powell 22, Sodje 58, Riviere 68
08/02	D.M. P	Ilkeston Town	432	6 - 1	Riviere 3 60 82, Farley 21, Abbott 45, Booth 84
15/02	D.M. P	Dover Athletic	859	1 - 2	Booth 19
22/02	D.M. P	HEDNESFORD TOWN	518	2 - 2	Farley 70[p], Jones 90
25/02	D.M. P	FOLKESTONE INVICTA	443	2 - 1	Riviere 36, Burgess 52
08/03	D.M. P	Hastings United	511	4 - 1	Jones 55 69, Booth 88, Riviere 90
15/03	D.M. P	HINCKLEY UNITED	530	1 - 2	Edwards 70
22/03	D.M. P	Chelmsford City	579	1 - 1	Booth 29
30/03	D.M. P	NEWPORT COUNTY	559	1 - 0	Booth 51
01/04	D.M. P	Cambridge City	278	1 - 2	Abbott 32
05/04	D.M. P	Weymouth	604	1 - 2	Booth 5
08/04	Kent SC SF	BROMLEY	337	2 - 0	Farley 22[p] 90[p]
12/04	D.M. P	HALESOWEN TOWN	548	3 - 1	Aboagye 56, Abbott 73, Booth 77
15/04	D.M. P	Grantham Town	385	1 - 3	George 72[og]
21/04	D.M. P	CAMBRIDGE CITY	540	1 - 0	Virgo 10
26/04	D.M. P	Moor Green	236	0 - 1	
28/04	D.M. P	Chippenham Town	273	0 - 4	
30/04	Kent SC F	MARGATE	704	1 - 2	Abbott 31

PLAYING SQUAD

Goalkeepers: Glenn Knight (Boreham Wood), James Simpson (Millwall)

Defenders: Ian Cousins (Chelmsford C.), John Farley (Fisher Ath.), Tim O'Shea (Farnborough T.), Kevin Seabury (Dover Ath.), Danny Slater (Chelmsford C.), Brian Stathem (Chelmsford C.), Danny Twin (Youth Team).

Midfield: Ray Aboagye (Whitstable T.), Steve Barnes (Chesham Utd), Billy Burgess (Youth Team), **Tim Hambley** (Havant & W'ville), Danny Hogarth (Youth Team), Paul Lorraine (Youth Team), Adam Morrish (Dartford), Anthony Riviere (Faversham T.), Mike Rutherford (Chelmsford C.), Steve Sodje (Whitstable T.), Dean Standen (Luton T.).

Forwards: Austion Berkley (Chelmsford C.), Paul Booth (Gravesend & Northfleet), Phil Collins (Margate), Paul Jones (Hastings Utd), Dave Powell (Crawley T.)

WESTON-super-MARE

CLUB OFFICIALS

President: **D A Usher**

Chairman: **Paul T Bliss**

Secretary/Press Officer: **Stuart Marshall**
c/o Weston Super Mare FC
Tel: 01934 621618

FOOTBALL MANAGEMENT TEAM

Manager: Frank Gregan
AssistantManager: David Mehew
Physio: Bob Baird

FACT FILE

Formed: 1899
Nickname: Seagulls
Sponsors:
Colours: White/blue/blue
Change colours: All yellow
Midweek matches: Tuesday
Reserves' League: Somerset Senior

2002-2003
Captain: Ryan Cross
Leading Goalscorer: Jody Bevan
Players o. Y: Stuart Slater & Alan Bird

Pages: 32 Price: £1
Editors: Stuart Marshall & Phil Sheridan
Tel. 01934 621618

Local Press:
Bristol Evening Post, Western Daily Press
Local Radio: Somerset Sound, Radio Bristol

GROUND Woodspring Park, Winterstoke Road, Weston-super-Mare BS23 3YG
Tel: 01934 635665

Directions: M5 Jct 21. A370 along dual carriageway to 4th roundabout. First left and immediately right at small roundabout. FromSouth: M5 Jct 22, follow Weston signs for approx 7 miles, right at first r'bout(by Hospital), left at next r'bout, ground 1 mile on left. Twenty minutes walk fromWeston-super-Mare (BR)

Capacity: 3,000 Seats: 278 Cover: 1,300

Clubhouse: Mon-Fri 7-11pm, Sat 12-11pm, Sun 12-3 & 7-11pm.
2 skittle alleys, 2bars. Bar meals and hot meals everyday

Club Shop: Sells a wide range of souvenirs & programmes.Contact Alan White at the club.

PREVIOUS
League: Western 1900-92 (Not continuous) **Name:** Borough of Weston-super-Mare
Grounds: The Great Ground, Locking Road 48-55, Langford Road 55-83

CLUB RECORDS
Attendance: 2,623 v Woking, FA Cup First Round Proper replay 23/11/93
At Langford Road: 2,500 v Bridgwater Town, FA Cup First Round Proper replay 1961-62
Win: 11-0 v Paulton Rovers **Defeat:** 1-12 v Yeovil Town Reserves
Career Goalscorer: Matthew Lazenby, 180 **Career Appearances:** Harry Thomas, 740
Transfer fee received: £20,000 Stuart Jones fromSheffield Wednesday 98 **Transfer fee paid:** None

BEST SEASON
FA Cup: 1st Rd Proper replay 61-62, 0-1 v Bridgwater Town after 0-0; 94-95, 0-1 v Woking (A) after 2-2
FA Trophy: 4th Round 98-99 **FA Vase:** Have not entered

HONOURS
Somerset Snr Cup 23-24 26-27; Western Lg Champions 91-92 (R-up 76-77), Lg Cup 76-77 (R-up 89-90), Merit Cup 76-77 77-78; Somerset Snr Lg (Reserves) Div 1 87-88 (R-up 90-91), Div 2 R-up 85-86, Div 3 84-85 Div 3 2000-01, Div 201-02.

Players progressing: Shaun Rouse (Carlisle United 94), Ian Maine, John Palmer(Bristol City),Wayne Brown(Chester City 97), Stuart Jones (Sheffield Wed 98), Ryan Souter (Bury 99)

L-R - Back: Alan Bird, Billy Clark, Ian Howell, Dean Wilson, Ian Ganfield, Frank Gregan, Stuart Jones, Ryan Cross, Danny O'Hagan, Steve Benton.
Front: Jonathon Mills, Ricky Hodge, Guiseppe Sorbara, Michael Jackson, Danny Guibara, Kevin Parker, Tony David.

Date	Comp.	Opponents	Att.	Score	Goalscorers
17/08	D.M. W	SOLIHULL BOROUGH	270	1 - 2	Thomas 49
20/08	D.M. W	Merthyr Tydfil	465	2 - 1	Slater 62, Bevan 73
24/08	D.M. W	Stourport Swifts	80	3 - 0	Bevan 18, Davis 88[og], Wilson 89
26/08	D.M. W	TAUNTON TOWN	370	5 - 1	Harris 10[og], Mehew 13, Thomas 50, Slater 66 84
31/08	FAC P	CALNE TOWN	160	4 - 0	Bevan 11 69, Lee 45, Mehew 51
07/09	D.M. W	Atherstone United	265	2 - 0	Bevan 14, McGregor 59
10/09	D.M. W	GLOUCESTER CITY	242	3 - 2	McGregor 55, Bevan 66, Parker 70
14/09	FAC Q1	WIMBORNE TOWN	243	3 - 1	Cross 30, Mehew 34, Birkby 69
21/09	D.M. W	Sutton Coldfield Town	161	3 - 0	Lee 4[p], Sullivan 65, Bevan 86
24/09	D.M. W	Cinderford Town	146	2 - 0	McGregor 17, Lee 63[p]
28/09	FAC Q2	CLEVEDON TOWN	552	2 - 0	Bevan 73, Mehew 90
05/10	D.M. W	Rugby United	271	0 - 1	
08/10	Som. PC 1	Brislington	n/k	1 - 1	Won 5 3 after pens.
12/10	FAC Q3	BATH CITY	1029	0 - 5	
19/10	D.M. W	Cirencester Town	135	4 - 0	O'Hagan 17 77, Bevan 19, Slater 20
22/10	D.M. W	MERTHYR TYDFIL	273	0 - 2	
26/10	D.M. W	GRESLEY ROVERS	302	1 - 0	Sullivan 68
29/10	Lge Cup 1	Mangotsfield United	145	0 - 2	
05/11	FAT 1	CIRENCESTER TOWN	135	2 - 2	O'Hagan 43, Bevan 76
07/11	FAT 1 rep	Cirencester Town	120	2 - 3	Bevan 1, O'Hagan 90
09/11	D.M. W	Solihull Borough	212	3 - 0	O'Hagan 35 73, Wilson 90
12/11	D.M. W	CINDERFORD TOWN	155	3 - 3	Slater 72, Bevan 82, Kilgour 90
16/11	D.M. W	BEDWORTH UNITED	208	3 - 3	Cross 3[p], Slater 37, Bevan 87
19/11	Som. PC 2	BITTON	n/k	4 - 1	O'Hagan 7 77, Bevan 69 86
23/11	D.M. W	Evesham United	137	5 - 3	Bevan 7, Lee 30, Edwards 61 90, Mehew 87
30/11	D.M. W	REDDITCH UNITED	196	1 - 0	Lee 84[p]
07/12	D.M. W	RUGBY UNITED	200	1 - 0	Edwards 19
14/12	D.M. W	Redditch United	140	0 - 3	
21/12	D.M. W	EVESHAM UNITED	217	1 - 3	Mehew 30
26/12	D.M. W	Taunton Town	460	2 - 2	O'Hagan 6, Parker 74
28/12	D.M. W	STOURPORT SWIFTS	226	1 - 0	O'Hagan 21
04/01	D.M. W	Mangotsfield United	425	0 - 3	
18/01	D.M. W	Bedworth United	121	2 - 0	O'Hagan 46, Edwards 90
25/01	D.M. W	SUTTON COLDFIELD TOWN	207	3 - 1	Bevan 57, O'Hagan 60, Mehew 83
01/02	D.M. W	Bromsgrove Rovers	511	0 - 0	
08/02	D.M. W	Shepshed Dynamo	126	1 - 0	Parker 32
15/02	D.M. W	SWINDON SUPERMARINE	248	2 - 1	Mehew 44, Slater 90
22/02	D.M. W	ROCESTER	231	3 - 2	Jackson 2, Lee 58, Bevan 83
01/03	D.M. W	Gloucester City	583	2 - 0	Bevan 47, Bird 73
04/03	D.M. W	CLEVEDON TOWN	325	1 - 1	Mehew 34
11/03	D.M. W	ATHERSTONE UNITED	197	4 - 1	O'Hagan 44 64 79, Mehew 56
15/03	D.M. W	Swindon Supermarine	121	2 - 0	Bevan 84, Miller 88
18/03	Som. PC QF	BRISTOL CITY	420	1 - 4	Kilgour 38
22/03	D.M. W	SHEPSHED DYNAMO	214	1 - 1	Parker 28
29/03	D.M. W	Racing Club Warwick	88	2 - 0	Bevan 13, O'Hagan 26
05/04	D.M. W	CIRENCESTER TOWN	253	3 - 1	Slater 18, O'Hagan 66, Haldene 71
12/04	D.M. W	Rocester	118	2 - 0	Mills 27, O'Hagan 32
19/04	D.M. W	MANGOTSFIELD UNITED	431	1 - 1	Lee 77
21/04	D.M. W	Clevedon Town	438	1 - 0	Bevan 87
26/04	D.M. W	BROMSGROVE ROVERS	345	0 - 1	
29/04	D.M. W	RACING CLUB WARWICK	211	0 - 1	
03/05	D.M. W	Gresley Rovers	348	1 - 2	Haldane 57

PLAYING SQUAD

Goalkeepers: Ian Ganfield (Weston St Johns), Stuart Jones (Barry T.).

Defenders: Steve Benton (Newport County), Alan Bird (Trowbridge T.), Billy Clark (Newport County), RyanCross (Weymouth), Ian Howell (Bath C.).

Midfield: Michael Jackson (Bath C.), Mark McKeever (Bristol R.), Jonathon Mills (Chippenham T.), Kevin Parker (Weymouth), Justin Skinner (Brechin C.), Stuart Slater (Aberystwyth T.).

Forwards: Jonathon French (Barry T.), Ricky Hodge (Western College Acadany), Ryan King (Salisbury C.), David Mehew (Brislington), Danny O'Hagan (Dorchester T.), Giuseppe Sorbara (Clevedon T.)

WEYMOUTH

CLUB OFFICIALS

Chairman: Ian Ridley
President: Bob Lucas
Secretary: Robert Mowlem,
43 Celtic Crescent, Dorchester DT1 2TG
Tel:01305 267619 (H) 07742139209 (M)

FOOTBALL MANAGEMENT TEAM
Manager: Steve Claridge
Physio: Malcolm Coe

FACT FILE
Formed: 1890
Nickname: The Terras
Sponsors: Park Engineering
Colours: Claret & sky/claret & sky
Change colours: White/claretr/white
Midweek matchday: Tuesday
Reserves' League: Wessex Comb
Lcal Press: Dorset Evening Echo
Local Radio: Wessex FM

PROGRAMME
Pages: 36 Price: £1.50
Editor:James Murphy
01305 815656 Tel & Fax

GROUND Wessex Stadium, Radipole Lane, Weymouth, Dorset DT4 9XJ Tel: 01305 785558

Directions: Arriving from Dorchester on A354, turn right following signs to Granby Industrial Estate at Safeway r'bout - ground on right as you enter estate
Capacity: 6,600 Cover: all sides Seats : 800

Clubhouse: Matchdays & functions. Hot & cold food available
Club Shop: Matchdays only. Progs & souvenirs.During week contact Amanda 01305 815752

PREVIOUS **Leagues:** Dorset Lge, Western 1907-23 28-49, Southern 23-28 49-79, Alliance Premier 79-89
Ground: Recreation Ground (until 1987)

CLUB RECORDS **Attendance:** 4,995 v Manchester Utd, ground opening, 21/10/87
Career Goalscorer: W Farmer, Haynes. 275 **Career Appearances:** Tony Hobson 1,076
Transfer fee - Paid: £15,000 for Shaun Teale (Northwich) **Received:** £100,000 for Peter Guthrie (Spurs, 1988)

BEST SEASON **FA Cup:** Fourth Round 61-62, 0-2 v Preston N.E. (A). 1st rd on 29 occasions
League clubs defeated: Merthyr Town 24-25, Aldershot 49-50, Shrewsbury T. 56-57, Newport County 61-62, Cardiff C. 82-83
FA Amateur Cup: First Round 1900 **FA Trophy:** Fifth Round 2000-2001

HONOURS Alliance Prem Lg R-up 79-80, Lge Cup 81-82; Prem Inter Lg Cup R-up 87-88 QF 90-91; Southern Lge 64-65 65-66 R-up 54-55 77-78, Lg Cup 72-73 R-up x5, Southern Div R-up 91-92; Wstn Lg 22-23, Div 2 33-34 36-37, (R-up 35-36 47-48); Dorset Sen. Cup (27);Mark Frowde Cup (13)

Players progressing: A Smith (Accrington 61), G Bond/T Spratt/A Donnelly/M Cave(Torquay 61/65/67/68), P Leggett (Swindon 62), R Fogg (Aldershot 63), B Hutchinson (Lincoln 65), A Wool (Reading 71), A Beer (Exeter 74), B Iles(Chelsea 78), G Roberts (Spurs 80), T Gulliver/R Hill/N Townsend/P Morrell/JSmeulders (Bournemouth 66/67/79/83/84), T Agana (Watford), A Townsend/D Hughes(Southampton), S Claridge (C Palace), B McGorry/S Teale (Bournemouth), T Pounder/R Evans (Bristol Rvrs), R Pethick (Portsmouth 93)

L-R Back Row: Roger Hoare (Physio), Lee Philpott, Lee Russell, Mark Robinson, Lee Phillips, Simon Browne, Jason Matthews,Jamie Impey, Mark Kenway, Scott Dennis, Carl Mutch,Jon Lamb, Scott Partridge. **Front Row:** Pete Dennis (Kit Man.), Martin Barlow, Kevin Gill, Leon Green, Steve Claridge (player/manager), John Waldock, Martyn Sullivan, Ian Hutchinson, Steve Tully, Gary Borthwick (Asst. Trainer)

Date	Comp.	Opponents	Att.	Score	Goalscorers
17/08	D.M. P	STAFFORD RANGERS	702	1 - 0	Rawlinson 76[p]
19/08	D.M. P	Newport County	906	0 - 3	
24/08	D.M. P	Dover Athletic	851	2 - 0	Phillips 51, Giles 55
26/08	D.M. P	TIVERTON TOWN	808	0 - 2	
31/08	D.M. P	Grantham Town	538	0 - 2	
04/09	D.M. P	Chippenham Town	817	1 - 1	Giles 85
07/09	D.M. P	HEDNESFORD TOWN	654	0 - 0	
10/09	D.M. P	Welling United	457	2 - 4	Robinson 6, Giles 89
14/09	D.M. P	FOLKESTONE INVICTA	531	3 - 3	Phillips 11 43, Rawlinson 32
17/09	D.M. P	Havant & Waterlooville	346	1 - 0	Hutchinson 43
21/09	D.M. P	CAMBRIDGE CITY	561	0 - 0	
28/09	FAC Q2	Chippenham Town	917	4 - 1	Phillips 7 90, Jones 47, Dean 53
05/10	D.M. P	Chelmsford City	535	1 - 3	Charles 44
08/10	D.M. P	CHIPPENHAM TOWN	653	1 - 1	Charles 41
12/10	FAC Q3	Tiverton Town	1191	2 - 4	Ashford 3, Whiteman 69
19/10	D.M. P	HALESOWEN TOWN	602	1 - 4	Charles 73
26/10	D.M. P	Hinckley United	272	1 - 2	Phillips 14
02/11	FAT 1	Aveley	74	4 - 1	Rawlinson 48[p], Phillips 80, Whiteman 89, Charles 90
05/11	Lge Cup 1	Newport IOW	140	1 - 3	Spencer 1
09/11	D.M. P	WORCESTER CITY	583	0 - 0	
30/11	FAT 2	Heybridge Swifts	314	1 - 2	Hutchinson 50[p]
07/12	D.M. P	Cambridge City	437	1 - 0	Phillips 34
10/12	Dorset SC 3	WAREHAM RANGERS	116	4 - 0	Dean 16, Hale 29, Whiteman 30, Hutchinson 33
14/12	D.M. P	HINCKLEY UNITED	604	2 - 2	Robinson 26 45
21/12	D.M. P	Stafford Rangers	811	0 - 0	
28/12	D.M. P	GRANTHAM TOWN	723	3 - 1	Hutchinson 33, Hale 76, Phillips 82
07/01	Dorset SC QF	CRANBORNE	173	3 - 0	Redwood 34, Waldock 35, Lamb 46
18/01	D.M. P	TAMWORTH	753	0 - 1	
21/01	D.M. P	Hastings United	330	1 - 1	A Browne 87
25/01	D.M. P	HAVANT & WATERLOOVILLE	655	1 - 1	Sullivan 23
08/02	D.M. P	CRAWLEY TOWN	654	2 - 0	Sullivan 40, Phillips 57
15/02	D.M. P	MOOR GREEN	604	3 - 1	Phillips 50 88, Bailey 63
18/02	D.M. P	Tamworth	895	0 - 3	
22/02	D.M. P	Folkestone Invicta	305	1 - 4	Laws 55
25/02	D.M. P	Halesowen Town	294	1 - 0	Phillips 40
01/03	D.M. P	NEWPORT COUNTY	823	2 - 0	Sullivan 6, Robinson 86
05/03	Dorset SC SF	BRIDPORT	267	2 - 1	Robinson 35, Whiteman 70
08/03	D.M. P	Moor Green	249	2 - 2	Phillips 10, Sullivan 52
11/03	D.M. P	ILKESTON TOWN	502	1 - 1	Phillips 90
15/03	D.M. P	CHELMSFORD CITY	679	1 - 3	Laws 55
22/03	D.M. P	Ilkeston Town	363	1 - 3	Phillips 65
25/03	D.M. P	BATH CITY	551	2 - 0	Hutchinson 72, Tulley 77
29/03	D.M. P	Worcester City	826	1 - 3	Tulley 34
01/04	D.M. P	Tiverton Town	566	0 - 3	
05/04	D.M. P	WELLING UNITED	604	2 - 1	Tully 7[p], Jackson 54
12/04	D.M. P	Hednesford Town	480	1 - 0	Phillips 40
15/04	Dorset SC F	Dorchester Town	708	0 - 2	
19/04	D.M. P	DOVER ATHLETIC	668	0 - 0	
21/04	D.M. P	Bath City	788	1 - 1	Phillips 72
26/04	D.M. P	HASTINGS UNITED	690	1 - 1	Tully 23
03/05	D.M. P	Crawley Town	643	0 - 5	

PLAYING SQUAD

Goalkeepers: Jason Matthews (Clevedon T.)

Defenders: Lee Bradford (Newport I.o.W.,), Simon Browne (Salisbury C.), Michael Cooper (Salisbury C.), Matthew Hale (Mangotsfield Utd), Mark Kenway (Portland Utd), Toby Redwood (Taunton T.), Steve Tully (Torquay Utd), John Waldock (Clevedon T.).

Midfield: Paul Buckle (Aldershot T.), Ian Hutchinson (Halifax T.), Mark Rawlinson (Exeter C.), Martyn Sullivan (Weston-super-Mare).

Forwards: Steve Claridge (Millwall), Mark Fitch (Portland Utd), Michael Jackson (AFC Totton), Lee Phillips (Plymouth Argyle), Mark Robinson (Gravesend & Northfleet), Darren Rowbotham (Exeter C.), Martin Underhay (Wimborne), Marc Whiteman (Bury)

WORCESTER CITY

CLUB OFFICIALS

Chairman: Dr Michael Sorensen
Vice Chairman: Laurie Brown

Secretary: Steve Bond
4 Ferry Close, Worcester, Worcs WR2 5PQ
Tel: 01905 423120/23003

FOOTBALL MANAGEMENT TEAM

Manager: John Barton
Assistant Manager: Mick Tuohy
Physio: Archie Richards

FACT FILE

Formed: 1902 Nickname: The City
Sponsors: E.E.Engineering
Newsline: 0930 555 810
Colours:White/blue/white
Change colours: Blue/white/blue
Midweek matchday: Monday
Reserve Lge: Midland Comb Reserves
Local Press: Berrows Journal, Worcester Evening News
Local Radio: Radio Wyvern, BBC Hereford & Worcester

2002-003
Captain: Carl Heeley
P.o.Y: Danny McDonnell
Top Scorer: Darren Middleton

PROGRAMME

Pages: 32 Price: £1.50
Editor: Julian Pugh (01905 723234)

GROUND St George's Lane, Barbourne, Worcester WR1 1QT Tel: 01905 23003 Fax: 26668

Directions: M5 jct 6 (Worcester North), follow signs to Worcester, right at first lights, St Georges Lane is 3rd left. 1 mile from Foregate Street (BR)station

Capacity: 4,004 Cover: 2,000 Seats: 1,125 Floodlights: Yes

Clubhouse: Open every evening and Saturday and Sunday daytime. Cold snacks available
Club Shop: One outside - souvenirs, and one inside - programmes Contact club for details.

PREVIOUS **Leagues:** West Mids (Birmingham) 1902-38, Southern 38-79, Alliance Premier 79-85
Names: Berwick Rangers **Grounds:** Severn Terrace, Thorneloe, Flagge Meadow

CLUB RECORDS **Attendance:** 17,042 v Sheff Utd (lost 0-2), FA Cup 4th Rd 24/1/59
Win: 18-1 v Bilston, Birmingham League 21/11/31 **Defeat:** 0-10 v Wellington, Birmingham League 29/8/20
Career Goalscorer: John Inglis 189 (1970-77) **Career Appearances:** Bobby McEwan 596 (1959-75)
Transfer fee paid: £8,500 for Jim Williams (Telford United, 1981)
Transfer fee received: £27,000 for John Barton (Everton, 1979)

BEST SEASON **FA Cup:** 4th Rd 58-59. 1st Rd (12)
FA Trophy: QF 69-70 73-74 80-81 81-82 **Welsh Cup:** Semi-Final 78-79

HONOURS Southern Lg 78-79, Div 1 67-68, Div 1 Nth 76-77, Lg Cup R-up 45-46 59-60, Chal.Cup 39-40, Champs Cup 78-79; West Mids (B'ham) Lg(4) 13-14 24-25 28-30 (R-up (3) 31-34); Worcs Snr Cup (26) 07-14 28-30 32-33 45-46(jt) 48-49 55-59 60-61 62-63 64-65 69-70 77-78 79-80 81-82 83-84 87-88 96-97; B'ham Snr Cup 75-76; Staffs Snr Cup 76-77; Inter Lg Champs Cup 78-79

Players progressing: A Awford (Portsmouth 91), P King/K Ball (Cardiff C.60/65), JWilliams/M Gayle (Walsall 79/91), J Fairbrother (Peterborough 65), DTennant (Lincoln 66), R Davies (Derby 71), N Merrick (Bournemouth 74), J Barton(Everton 79), A Preece (Wrexham 90), D Lyttle (Swansea 92) M.Griffiths (Torquay United 99)

Back: John Morris (Scout), Jon Holloway, Stewart Hadley, Carl Heeley, Marc Burrow, Mark Shail, Leon Jackson, Adam Webster, Rat Woods (Youth Dev. Off.). **Middle:** Martin Obrey (Asst. Physio), Archie Richards (Physio), Michael Blackwoood, Duncan Willetts, Danny McDonnell, Paul Wyatt, Darren Middleton, Paul Carty, Graham Selby (Chief Scout), Mick Tuohy (1st Team Coach). **Front:** Pat Lyons, Mark Owen, John Snape, John Barton (Manager), David Foy, Duncan Jones, Allan Davies. Photo by Paul France

Date	Comp.	Opponents	Att.	Score	Goalscorers
17/08	D.M. P	HASTINGS UNITED	872	2 - 1	Middleton 33, Holloway 89
21/08	D.M. P	Tiverton Town	714	0 - 0	
24/08	D.M. P	Chelmsford City	421	1 - 1	Middleton 75[p]
26/08	D.M. P	NEWPORT COUNTY	1549	2 - 1	Heeley 44, Holloway 86
31/08	D.M. P	Welling United	558	1 - 0	Middleton 43
02/09	D.M. P	MOOR GREEN	1202	4 - 0	Snape 24 90, Middleton 62 82
07/09	D.M. P	Folkestone Invicta	344	2 - 1	Webster 49, Middleton 88
09/09	D.M. P	TAMWORTH	1530	0 - 0	
14/09	D.M. P	Crawley Town	1738	0 - 0	
17/09	D.M. P	Hinckley United	354	1 - 0	Webster 28
20/09	D.M. P	STAFFORD RANGERS	2711	0 - 3	
28/09	FAC Q2	STAMFORD	810	3 - 3	Lyons 14, Middleton 31, Jackson 44
01/10	FAC Q2 rep	Stamford	365	2 - 1	Heeley 11, Owen 63
05/10	D.M. P	HAVANT & WATERLOOVILLE	1003	2 - 1	Webster 79, Middleton 87
08/10	D.M. P	Bath City	635	0 - 1	
12/10	FAC Q3	Hucknall Town	652	0 - 1	
19/10	D.M. P	CAMBRIDGE CITY	974	2 - 0	Middleton 10, Owen 81
26/10	D.M. P	Halesowen Town	803	0 - 0	
28/10	Lge Cup 1	HALESOWEN TOWN	651	0 - 1	
02/11	D.M. P	ILKESTON TOWN	1008	0 - 0	
09/11	D.M. P	Weymouth	583	0 - 0	
23/11	D.M. P	Hastings United	560	4 - 1	Wilde 7, Holmes 11, Webster 29, Owen 88
30/11	FAT 2	ALDERSHOT TOWN	1562	1 - 0	Wilde 38
07/12	D.M. P	HINCKLEY UNITED	828	2 - 2	Webster 4, Holloway 26
09/12	D.M. P	CRAWLEY TOWN	877	2 - 1	Wilde 16, Heeley 51
14/12	D.M. P	Chippenham Town	1014	0 - 0	
17/12	Worcs RIC 1	Malvern Town	82	2 - 4	Willetts 69 76
21/12	D.M. P	CHELMSFORD CITY	911	5 - 0	Wilde 7, Davies 13, Webster 31, Middleton 37, Samuels 52[og]
26/12	D.M. P	Newport County	927	1 - 2	Middleton 7[p]
28/12	D.M. P	WELLING UNITED	1176	1 - 1	Holmes 82
01/01	D.M. P	HEDNESFORD TOWN	1251	3 - 1	Holloway 4, Middleton 75 88
04/01	D.M. P	Tamworth	1610	2 - 1	Blount 48, Webster 67
13/01	FAT 3	NEWPORT COUNTY	1128	3 - 2	Webster 26 73, Middleton 55[p]
18/01	D.M. P	DOVER ATHLETIC	1258	0 - 1	
25/01	D.M. P	Moor Green	675	1 - 1	Holmes 36
28/01	Worcs SC QF	Halesowen Town	178	1 - 2	Hadley 44
01/02	FAT 4	MARGATE	1304	0 - 2	
08/02	D.M. P	Stafford Rangers	1301	1 - 2	Webster 58
15/02	D.M. P	FOLKESTONE INVICTA	751	6 - 0	Webster 3 32 55, Hadley 44, Davies 48, Blount 68
22/02	D.M. P	Grantham Town	372	3 - 2	Wenlock 22[og], Webster 25, Counsell 26
01/03	D.M. P	CHIPPENHAM TOWN	1346	0 - 0	
15/03	D.M. P	TIVERTON TOWN	1000	0 - 2	
22/03	D.M. P	Havant & Waterlooville	502	1 - 2	Shail 35
24/03	D.M. P	HALESOWEN TOWN	817	1 - 1	Webster 6
29/03	D.M. P	WEYMOUTH	826	3 - 1	Middleton 18[p] 52[p] 87
05/04	D.M. P	Cambridge City	453	0 - 1	
12/04	D.M. P	Ilkeston Town	435	2 - 3	Webster 12, Middleton 60
19/04	D.M. P	BATH CITY	753	2 - 1	Hadley 15, Wilde 67
21/04	D.M. P	Hednesford Town	497	0 - 2	
26/04	D.M. P	GRANTHAM TOWN	1003	2 - 0	Wilde 5, Hadley 47
03/05	D.M. P	Dover Athletic	1013	1 - 2	Heeley 22

PLAYING SQUAD

Goalkeepers: Danny McDonnell (Halesowen T.), Dan Jones (Kidderminster H.).

Defenders: Allan Davies (Burton Alb.), Carl Heeley (Sutton Coldfield T.), **Mark Shail** (KIdderminster H.).

Midfield: Paul Carty (Hednesford T.), Mitch Counsell (Bishops Cleeve), David Foy (Tamworth), Jon Holloway (Bath C.), Pat Lyons (Burton Alb.), John Snape (Hereford Utd), **Adam Wilde** (Cambridge C.).

Forwards: Srewart Hadley (Kidderminster H.), David Holmes (Ilkeston T.), Darren Middleton (Forest Green R.), Marek Owen (Willenhall T.), Adam Webster (Bedworth Utd).

FOLKESTONE INVICTA

Match Facts 2002-03

Date	Comp.	Opponents	Att.	Score	Goalscorers
10/08	Sid Burvill Trophy	TONBRIDGE ANGELS	n/k	3 - 1	Restarick(2), Tait
17/08	D.M. P	GRANTHAM TOWN	378	0 - 2	
20/08	D.M. P	Hastings United	525	2 - 1	Hafner 44, Lindsey 61
24/08	D.M. P	Bath City	639	0 - 2	
26/08	D.M. P	DOVER ATHLETIC	1446	1 - 2	Tait 70[p]
31/08	D.M. P	Newport County	884	2 - 1	Dryden 32, Restarick 53
03/09	D.M. P	CRAWLEY TOWN	407	1 - 3	Millar 9
07/09	D.M. P	WORCESTER CITY	344	1 - 2	Tait 14
10/09	D.M. P	Cambridge City	416	1 - 2	Tate 33
14/09	D.M. P	Weymouth	531	3 - 3	Tate 12 59, Everett 56
17/09	D.M. P	WELLING UNITED	338	2 - 2	Millar 21 47
21/09	D.M. P	CHIPPENHAM TOWN	339	1 - 2	Millar 13
28/09	FA Cup Q2	Canvey Island	429	1 - 2	Ayling 78
05/10	D.M. P	Ilkeston Town	475	1 - 2	Dryden 68
08/10	D.M. P	Crawley Town	970	2 - 2	Dryden 39 64
19/10	D.M. P	TAMWORTH	413	2 - 3	Hafner 46, McGorry 55[og]
02/11	FA Trophy 1	Carshalton Athletic	347	1 - 2	Tait 63
09/11	D.M. P	MOOR GREEN	302	0 - 1	
11/11	Lge Cup 1	Dover Athletic	408	1 - 2	Millar 37
16/11	D.M. P	Halesowen Town	476	0 - 5	
19/11	Kent SC 1	DARTFORD	146	1 - 0	Azzopardi 107
23/11	D.M. P	Chippenham Town	531	0 - 1	
30/11	D.M. P	Hinckley United	241	3 - 3	Tait 54, Everitt 63, Ayling 78
07/12	D.M. P	TIVERTON TOWN	334	1 - 1	Dryden 90
14/12	D.M. P	Grantham Town	317	1 - 4	Towse 67
21/12	D.M. P	HAVANT & WATERLOOVILLE	320	3 - 3	Ayling 24, Tait 36 38
26/12	D.M. P	Dover Athletic	1609	1 - 2	Chandler 65
28/12	D.M. P	NEWPORT COUNTY	456	2 - 3	Millar 63, Dryden 74
04/01	D.M. P	Stafford Rangers	737	0 - 6	
11/01	D.M. P	CAMBRIDGE CITY	412	0 - 3	
18/01	D.M. P	BATH CITY	316	2 - 4	Tait 19, Millar 50
25/01	D.M. P	Tiverton Town	650	0 - 4	
04/02	Kent SC QF	WELLING UNITED	156	1 - 6	Ayling 26
08/02	D.M. P	CHELMSFORD CITY	420	3 - 2	Millar 16, Morris 70[p], Chandler 90
15/02	D.M. P	Worcester City	751	0 - 6	
22/02	D.M. P	WEYMOUTH	305	4 - 1	Chandler 17, Tait 46 89, Dryden 57
25/02	D.M. P	Welling United	443	1 - 2	Guest 44
01/03	D.M. P	STAFFORD RANGERS	301	1 - 2	Chandler 15[p]
08/03	D.M. P	Tamworth	1395	0 - 2	
15/03	D.M. P	HEDNESFORD TOWN	325	4 - 1	Chambers 51[p], Tait 63 67 79
22/03	D.M. P	HINCKLEY UNITED	338	4 - 0	Tait 5, Millar 36 43 57
29/03	D.M. P	Moor Green	297	0 - 3	
05/04	D.M. P	ILKESTON TOWN	339	0 - 3	
19/04	D.M. P	HASTINGS UNITED	401	1 - 0	Chandler 90[p]
22/04	D.M. P	Chelmsford City	434	2 - 3	Millar 4, Ayling 56
26/04	D.M. P	HALESOWEN TOWN	351	2 - 2	Chandler 26[p], Millar 37
29/04	D.M. P	Havant & Waterlooville	274	2 - 6	Turner 60[og], Chandler 64
03/05	D.M. P	Hednesford Town	525	1 - 3	Morris 81

HASTINGS TOWN

Match Facts 2002-03

Date	Comp.	Opponents	Att.	Score	Goalscorers
17/08	D.M. P	Worcester City	872	1 - 2	Simmonds 71
20/08	D.M. P	FOLKESTONE INVICTA	525	1 - 2	Simmonds 83[p]
24/08	D.M. P	HINCKLEY UNITED	431	1 - 0	Simmonds 24[p]
26/08	D.M. P	Havant & Waterlooville	487	0 - 0	
31/08	D.M. P	HEDNESFORD TOWN	506	2 - 0	Myall 27, Remi 61
03/09	D.M. P	Welling United	540	3 - 0	Zahna-Oni 25, Remy 44 59
07/09	D.M. P	ILKESTON TOWN	433	3 - 0	Myall 35, Hegley 44, Zahna-Oni 81
09/09	D.M. P	Dover Athletic	1004	0 - 1	
14/09	D.M. P	Moor Green	256	0 - 0	
17/09	D.M. P	CHELMSFORD CITY	397	1 - 1	Flanagan 33
21/09	D.M. P	TAMWORTH	521	2 - 3	Zahna-Oni 3, McArthur 51
28/09	FA Cup Q2	SELSEY	400	4 - 1	Flanagan 62 65, Playford 72, Webb 90
05/10	D.M. P	HALESOWEN TOWN	543	3 - 2	Zahna-Oni 31, Ruddy 34, Simmonds 88
08/10	D.M. P	Cambridge City	419	2 - 1	Simmonds 50, Myall 90
12/10	FA Cup Q3	HENDON	795	2 - 1	Simmonds 55, Webb 86
19/10	D.M. P	Tiverton Town	761	1 - 0	Simmonds 58[p]
26/10	FA Cup Q4	KETTERING TOWN	1538	0 - 0	
29/10	FA Cup Q4 rep	Kettering Town	1144	5 - 0	Playford 22, Remy 35, Zahana-Oni 71 81, Yates 78
02/11	FA Trophy 1	CHELMSFORD CITY	599	1 - 0	Zahana-Oni 69
05/11	Lge Cup 1	Crawley Town	443	0 - 1	
09/11	D.M. P	Chippenham Town	592	0 - 0	
16/11	FA Cup 1	Stevenage Borough	1821	0 - 1	
19/11	Sussex SC 2	Brighton & Hove Albion	n/k	0 - 1	@ Worthing
23/11	D.M. P	WORCESTER CITY	560	1 - 4	Zahana-Oni 51
30/11	FA Trophy 2	EASTBOURNE BOROUGH	906	0 - 2	
07/12	D.M. P	Tamworth	744	0 - 2	
14/12	D.M. P	TIVERTON TOWN	417	0 - 3	
21/12	D.M. P	Hednesford Town	471	0 - 1	
28/12	D.M. P	Halesowen Town	517	1 - 2	Ruddy 44
07/01	D.M. P	GRANTHAM TOWN	252	2 - 1	Yates 16, Hegley 66
18/01	D.M. P	Hinckley United	294	2 - 3	Zahana-Oni 9, Ruddy 19
21/01	D.M. P	WEYMOUTH	330	1 - 1	Hegley 40
25/01	D.M. P	CAMBRIDGE CITY	468	1 - 2	Remy 49
08/02	D.M. P	Newport County	667	1 - 1	Bevis 75
15/02	D.M. P	Ilkeston Town	402	1 - 3	Honey 43
18/02	Hast SC SF	RYE & IDEN UNITED	n/k	3 - 1	
22/02	D.M. P	BATH CITY	452	1 - 1	Simmonds 51
25/02	D.M. P	Crawley Town	783	1 - 1	Zahana-Oni 32
01/03	D.M. P	DOVER ATHLETIC	630	1 - 1	Honey 16
04/03	D.M. P	Bath City	536	0 - 1	
08/03	D.M. P	WELLING UNITED	511	1 - 4	Simmonds 64[p]
15/03	D.M. P	Grantham Town	330	1 - 2	Bevis 78
22/03	D.M. P	NEWPORT COUNTY	430	1 - 3	McArthur 61
29/03	D.M. P	Stafford Rangers	964	1 - 1	Bevis 87
01/04	D.M. P	HAVANT & WATERLOOVILLE	318	1 - 1	Simmonds 39[p]
05/04	D.M. P	MOOR GREEN	407	3 - 1	Zahana-Oni 63, Simmonds 74, Suleymanoglu 83
12/04	D.M. P	CHIPPENHAM TOWN	433	2 - 1	Burt 42, Simmonds 55
14/04	D.M. P	Chelmsford City	504	0 - 1	
19/04	D.M. P	Folkestone Invicta	401	0 - 1	
21/04	D.M. P	CRAWLEY TOWN	491	0 - 0	
26/04	D.M. P	Weymouth	690	1 - 1	Hegley 89
30/04	Hast SC F	WESTFIELD	210	1 - 0	
03/05	D.M. P	STAFFORD RANGERS	410	0 - 2	

HALESOWEN TOWN

Match Facts 2002-03

Date	Comp.	Opponents	Att.	Score	Goalscorers
17/08	D.M. P	WELLING UNITED	566	0 - 0	
19/08	D.M. P	Hednesford Town	802	2 - 3	Elmes 58, Hines 75
24/08	D.M. P	Grantham Town	518	3 - 3	Burnham 6[p], Hines 41, Quiggin 46
26/08	D.M. P	STAFFORD RANGERS	736	1 - 1	Quiggin 44
31/08	D.M. P	Chelmsford City	481	0 - 1	
03/09	D.M. P	TAMWORTH	656	0 - 0	
07/09	D.M. P	DOVER ATHLETIC	463	0 - 0	
10/09	D.M. P	Bath City	588	0 - 3	
14/09	D.M. P	Cambridge City	343	1 - 0	Elmes 9
17/09	D.M. P	TIVERTON TOWN	430	0 - 0	
21/09	D.M. P	CRAWLEY TOWN	547	0 - 2	
28/09	FA Cup Q2	Sutton Coldfield Town	269	2 - 0	Leadbeater 32, Ashby 85
05/10	D.M. P	Hastings United	543	2 - 3	Ashby 57, Elmes 87
08/10	D.M. P	ILKESTON TOWN	477	2 - 1	Elmes 88, Taylor 90
12/10	FA Cup Q3	Moor Green	649	1 - 3	Ashby 9
15/10	Worcs SC 1	Stourport Swifts	98	3 - 0	Ashby 31, Phillips 65, Master 75
19/10	D.M. P	Weymouth	602	4 - 1	Colwell 13, Master 26 88, Leadbeater 89
26/10	D.M. P	WORCESTER CITY	803	0 - 0	
28/10	Lge Cup 1	Worcester City	651	1 - 0	Ashby 30
02/11	FA Trophy 1	BATH CITY	403	4 - 3	Ashby 14 55, Colwell 47, Quiggin 83
09/11	D.M. P	Havant & Waterlooville	436	1 - 3	May 50
12/11	Birm SC 2	STUDLEY	212	3 - 0	May 21, Reece 35, Leadbeater 87
16/11	D.M. P	FOLKESTONE INVICTA	476	5 - 0	Hines 6 89, Ashby 21 87, Colwell 90
26/11	Lge Cup 2	EVESHAM UNITED	257	4 - 3	Master 9 11, Trainer 40 86
30/11	FA Trophy 2	Spennymoor United	268	1 - 1	Stone 57
03/12	FA Trophy 2 rep	SPENNYMOOR UNITED	391	4 - 1	Leadbeater 23, Hines 42[p], Ashby 64 90
07/12	D.M. P	Moor Green	421	0 - 4	
14/12	D.M. P	HEDNESFORD TOWN	512	0 - 1	
17/12	Lge Cup 3	SUTTON COLDFIELD TOWN	181	4 - 1	Reece 17, L Collins 18, Brennan 37, Master 43
21/12	D.M. P	Hinckley United	346	1 - 1	Skidmore 17
26/12	D.M. P	Stafford Rangers	1187	2 - 4	Ashby 44, Hines 69[p]
28/12	D.M. P	HASTINGS UNITED	517	2 - 1	Ashby 8, Leadbeater 64
11/01	FA Trophy 3	Alfreton Town	681	1 - 2	R Collins 70
18/01	D.M. P	MOOR GREEN	598	0 - 1	
20/01	Birm SC 3	BIRMINGHAM CITY	402	1 - 3	Trainer 66
25/01	D.M. P	Tamworth	1150	1 - 3	Ashby 29
28/01	Worcs SC QF	WORCESTER CITY	178	2 - 1	McHugh 13, Master 50
08/02	D.M. P	HAVANT & WATERLOOVILLE	429	1 - 0	May 13
11/02	Lge Cup QF	Bedworth United	138	2 - 0	Williams 1, Master 90
15/02	D.M. P	Crawley Town	679	0 - 4	
22/02	D.M. P	CHELMSFORD CITY	462	0 - 2	
25/02	D.M. P	WEYMOUTH	294	0 - 1	
01/03	D.M. P	Ilkeston Town	452	3 - 1	Danks 33, McHugh 60[p], Ashby 65
04/03	Lge Cup SF	CHIPPENHAM TOWN	348	2 - 1	McHugh 32[p] 55[p]
08/03	D.M. P	CAMBRIDGE CITY	506	1 - 1	Danks 67
10/03	D.M. P	Dover Athletic	604	3 - 0	Danks 14, McHugh 74 83[p]
15/03	D.M. P	Chippenham Town	605	2 - 1	Williams 44, Stone 45
18/03	D.M. P	NEWPORT COUNTY	555	1 - 2	Ashby 44
22/03	D.M. P	BATH CITY	507	1 - 1	Stone 74
24/03	D.M. P	Worcester City	817	1 - 1	Blackwood 87
29/03	D.M. P	Tiverton Town	731	2 - 4	Blackwood 16, Collins 70
01/04	Worcs SC SF	Bromsgrove Rovers	295	3 - 1	Leadbeater 10, Spencer 18, Stone 87
05/04	D.M. P	HINCKLEY UNITED	535	2 - 1	Ashby 5, Gibson 13
08/04	Worcs SC F(1)	EVESHAM UNITED	268	2 - 0	Leadbeater 71, Danks 75
12/04	D.M. P	Welling United	548	1 - 3	Ashby 9
15/04	Lge Cup F(1)	CRAWLEY TOWN	401	2 - 1	Leadbeater 87, Judge 88[og]
19/04	D.M. P	GRANTHAM TOWN	501	1 - 0	Hines 71
21/04	D.M. P	Newport County	604	1 - 1	Ashby 88
23/04	Worcs SC F(2)	Evesham United	179	1 - 0	Danks 48
26/04	D.M. P	Folkestone Invicta	351	2 - 2	Hines 32, Ashby 53
29/04	Lge Cup F(2)	Crawley Town	1049	0 - 2	
03/05	D.M. P	CHIPPENHAM TOWN	730	3 - 2	Stone 39, Leadbeater 80, Hines 86[p]

ILKESTON TOWN

Match Facts 2002-03

Date	Comp.	Opponents	Att.	Score	Goalscorers
17/08	D.M. P	BATH CITY	575	1 - 1	Walters 28
20/08	D.M. P	Stafford Rangers	808	0 - 2	
24/08	D.M. P	Newport County	887	0 - 3	
26/08	D.M. P	GRANTHAM TOWN	703	1 - 2	Kelly 48
31/08	D.M. P	Tiverton Town	704	1 - 3	Holmes 10
03/09	D.M. P	HINCKLEY UNITED	543	1 - 1	Kiely 76
07/09	D.M. P	Hastings United	433	0 - 3	
10/09	D.M. P	MOOR GREEN	494	2 - 0	Dundas 63, Burton 88
14/09	D.M. P	Chippenham Town	645	0 - 3	
17/09	D.M. P	CAMBRIDGE CITY	523	0 - 2	
21/09	D.M. P	Welling United	520	0 - 2	
28/09	FA Cup Q2	ATHERSTONE UNITED	435	7 - 0	Kelly 7[p] 20 37[p] 78, Nwadike 47, Mitchell 69, Kiely 77
05/10	D.M. P	FOLKESTONE INVICTA	475	2 - 1	Kiely 30, Ford 88
08/10	D.M. P	Halesowen Town	477	1 - 2	Kelly 40
12/10	FA Cup Q3	KING'S LYNN	694	6 - 1	Woolley 26, Kiely 28 88, Kelly 63[p], Mitchell 84, Whitehead 90
19/10	D.M. P	Hednesford Town	545	2 - 6	Kiely 75, Kelly 86
26/10	FA Cup Q4	STAFFORD RANGERS	903	0 - 5	
30/10	Lge Cup 1	BANBURY UNITED	136	2 - 1	Robinson 19, Kelly 113[p]
02/11	D.M. P	Worcester City	1008	0 - 0	
09/11	D.M. P	DOVER ATHLETIC	491	0 - 1	
19/11	Derbys SC 3	Long Eaton United	n/k	3 - 2	
26/11	Lge Cup 2	Shepshed Dynamo	98	3 - 3	Ford 86, Kelly 88 107[p] Lost 2 4 after pens.
30/11	FA Trophy 2	HEDNESFORD TOWN	436	3 - 1	Kelly 61, Freestone 78 89
07/12	D.M. P	HAVANT & WATERLOOVILLE	469	1 - 5	Freestone 63
14/12	D.M. P	Cambridge City	383	2 - 2	Heggs 60, Freestone 88
21/12	D.M. P	CHIPPENHAM TOWN	395	2 - 6	Heggs 10, Robinson 90
26/12	D.M. P	Grantham Town	563	2 - 2	Freestone 34, Heggs 77
28/12	D.M. P	TIVERTON TOWN	440	1 - 3	Ford 33
04/01	D.M. P	Chelmsford City	455	1 - 2	Heggs 86
14/01	FA Trophy 3	BURSCOUGH	248	0 - 3	
18/01	D.M. P	HEDNESFORD TOWN	523	3 - 1	Heggs 27 79, C Freestone 63
21/01	Derbys SC QF	MICKLEOVER SPORTS	142	0 - 2	
25/01	D.M. P	Crawley Town	874	1 - 2	Impey 60
01/02	D.M. P	Hinckley United	391	2 - 5	Freestone 11, Hemmings 27
08/02	D.M. P	WELLING UNITED	432	1 - 6	Freestone 62
15/02	D.M. P	HASTINGS UNITED	402	3 - 1	Woolley 16, Kelly 60, Freestone 78
22/02	D.M. P	Moor Green	326	0 - 5	
25/02	D.M. P	TAMWORTH	691	0 - 1	
01/03	D.M. P	HALESOWEN TOWN	452	1 - 3	O'Connor 75
08/03	D.M. P	Dover Athletic	756	1 - 1	Kelly 17
11/03	D.M. P	Weymouth	502	1 - 1	O'Connor 43
22/03	D.M. P	WEYMOUTH	363	3 - 1	Robinson 3, Freestone 55, Kelly 71
29/03	D.M. P	Bath City	628	1 - 1	Kelly 1
01/04	D.M. P	NEWPORT COUNTY	312	1 - 0	O'Connor 75
05/04	D.M. P	Folkestone Invicta	339	3 - 0	Woolley 29, Kelly 72, Freestone 86
08/04	D.M. P	CHELMSFORD CITY	275	2 - 2	Woolley 45, O'Connor 88
12/04	D.M. P	WORCESTER CITY	435	3 - 2	Freestone 10 53, O'Connor 51
19/04	D.M. P	STAFFORD RANGERS	495	2 - 5	Freestone 43, Westwood 80
21/04	D.M. P	Tamworth	1583	1 - 1	Freestone 83
26/04	D.M. P	CRAWLEY TOWN	254	2 - 1	Kelly 54 77
03/05	D.M. P	Havant & Waterlooville	484	3 - 1	Freestone 22, Kelly 61[p] 80

DR. MARTENS CHAMPIONSHIP TROPHY
KETTERING TOWN 0 V 2 DORCHESTER TOWN
Photos by Peter Barnes

ABOVE: Dorchester Town skipper Michael White receiving the Championship Trophy from Doug Gillard.

ABOVE
Gez Murphy showing good control with support from Gareth Hopkins.

RIGHT
The Dorchester goalscorers - Justin Keeler & Martin Shepherd.

First half pressure from the poppies in an packed Dorchester goal area, but what on earth is the goal-keeper doing? - he looks like he's on traffic control.

WESTERN DIVISION

		P	W	D	L	W	D	L	F	A	GD	Pts
1	Merthyr Tydfil	42	13	5	3	15	3	3	78	32	46	92
2	Weston-Super-Mare	42	11	5	5	15	2	4	77	42	35	85
3	Bromsgorve Rovers	42	14	3	4	9	4	8	73	41	32	76
4	Solihull Borough	42	12	6	3	9	7	5	77	48	29	76
5	Gloucester City	42	13	4	4	9	5	7	87	58	29	75
6	Mangotsfield United	42	13	5	3	8	5	8	106	53	53	73
7	Redditch United	42	15	1	5	7	5	9	76	42	34	72
8	Rugby United	42	15	3	3	5	6	10	58	43	15	69
9	Gresley Rovers	42	11	5	5	8	5	8	63	54	9	67
10	Taunton Town	42	9	5	7	11	2	8	76	78	-2	67
11	Sutton Coldfield Town	42	10	5	6	8	5	8	63	53	10	64
12	Evesham United	42	12	2	7	7	4	10	76	72	4	63
13	Clevedon Town	42	7	5	9	7	8	6	54	60	-6	55
14	Cirencester Town	42	9	3	9	6	4	11	62	82	-20	52
15	Cinderford Town	42	8	7	6	5	5	11	50	67	-17	51
16	Shepshed Dynamo	42	8	2	11	4	4	13	48	76	-28	42
17	Stourport Swifts	42	4	7	10	6	4	11	48	66	-18	41
18	Bedworth United	42	8	1	12	3	6	12	46	74	-28	40
19	Swindon Supermarine	42	5	3	13	6	2	13	52	85	-33	38
20	Atherstone United	42	5	7	9	4	3	14	45	78	-33	37
21	Rocester	42	5	5	11	4	5	12	34	74	-40	37
22	Racing Club Warwick	42	2	7	12	1	2	18	33	104	-71	18

		1	2	3	4	5	6	7	8	9	10	11	12	13	14	15	16	17	18	19	20	21	22
1	Atherstone Utd		1-1	1-2	2-2	0-0	0-3	1-2	1-1	1-2	0-4	0-1	3-1	0-0	2-1	2-0	0-0	3-4	1-1	4-1	3-2	1-4	0-2
2	Bedworth United	2-1		2-1	2-1	0-1	0-2	2-1	2-2	1-2	0-1	2-1	2-1	1-0	1-2	1-3	1-4	0-1	3-2	0-2	0-1	0-1	0-2
3	Bromsgrove Rov.	3-0	1-0		5-2	5-1	5-1	0-1	2-4	4-1	2-1	1-2	1-0	0-0	4-1	3-2	1-0	1-1	3-0	2-0	1-3	3-0	0-0
4	Cinderford Town	2-2	1-1	1-0		2-1	1-1	1-3	4-0	2-2	2-1	1-1	0-0	1-0	0-0	1-2	2-3	1-2	1-0	0-1	1-0	4-0	0-2
5	Cirencester Tn	3-1	3-1	2-0	1-1		0-1	1-2	0-3	1-3	2-5	2-0	1-0	2-0	1-0	2-0	2-4	0-1	0-4	3-1	3-3	5-5	0-4
6	Clevedon Town	1-2	1-2	1-1	2-3	2-4		3-1	1-1	0-0	0-2	0-1	2-1	1-0	1-2	1-0	2-1	1-1	1-1	1-2	2-1	4-0	0-1
7	Evesham United	3-0	4-3	1-0	3-1	4-1	2-4		0-1	1-0	1-0	0-2	4-0	1-2	3-0	0-0	5-1	2-1	1-3	0-0	3-2	1-2	3-5
8	Gloucester City	1-2	4-1	1-0	4-0	5-4	1-1	6-1		1-0	4-3	2-2	3-1	2-5	0-0	0-0	3-1	4-2	1-2	3-1	2-1	4-2	0-2
9	Gresley Rovers	4-1	1-0	2-0	3-0	3-1	2-3	3-0	1-1		2-1	0-1	2-0	0-0	2-0	1-1	3-3	1-1	1-2	0-1	2-1	2-3	2-1
10	Mangotsfield Utd	4-1	1-1	2-2	3-0	3-0	4-0	5-0	1-4	7-0		2-3	3-0	1-1	1-1	4-2	1-0	3-3	4-0	3-1	5-1	0-1	3-0
11	Merthyr Tydfil	5-0	1-0	2-0	0-0	2-0	1-0	2-0	3-2	1-1	0-0		3-0	2-2	4-1	3-0	3-0	2-3	1-3	2-2	4-0	1-0	1-2
12	R.C. Warwick	0-4	2-3	1-1	0-2	1-2	2-2	0-6	1-6	1-5	2-2	1-2		0-3	1-1	1-4	2-0	1-1	1-0	0-0	2-2	1-7	0-2
13	Redditch Utd	2-0	2-1	2-1	3-0	4-0	0-1	2-1	1-0	1-2	3-3	0-1	4-1		0-1	3-1	4-0	2-0	5-0	4-1	2-1	1-2	3-0
14	Rocester	1-0	1-2	0-1	2-1	1-1	0-0	2-2	2-2	0-1	0-6	0-2	2-1	1-0		0-0	2-0	0-2	1-2	1-2	0-1	0-2	0-2
15	Rugby United	0-0	3-1	0-2	5-1	0-3	2-2	3-0	1-0	1-0	2-1	2-1	4-0	1-2	4-2		2-0	2-0	3-0	1-1	1-0	1-0	1-0
16	Shepshed Dyn.	1-2	4-1	0-5	4-0	1-2	2-1	0-1	1-0	0-0	2-1	0-2	4-3	0-4	2-0	1-0		1-3	1-1	0-2	0-2	0-2	0-1
17	Solihull Boro'	1-0	1-1	2-2	0-1	2-0	2-0	2-2	2-1	4-0	4-2	0-0	4-0	2-1	5-0	0-1	1-1		2-0	0-0	2-0	7-2	0-3
18	Stourport Swifts	1-1	1-0	1-2	1-2	1-1	0-0	1-1	0-1	1-1	0-0	2-3	2-1	2-3	5-0	0-1	3-0	1-1		1-2	1-2	0-3	0-3
19	Sutton C'fld Tn	2-0	1-1	0-1	0-0	3-1	6-0	3-2	0-1	0-2	2-3	0-2	1-1	3-2	1-1	1-0	2-1	2-1	2-0		9-0	1-1	0-3
20	Swindon S'marine	2-1	1-0	0-1	2-0	0-3	1-3	3-3	1-2	2-4	2-4	0-2	2-0	1-2	1-2	1-1	2-0	2-3	2-2	0-2		1-2	0-2
21	Taunton Town	2-0	5-1	0-3	0-2	1-1	1-1	3-2	0-2	3-0	1-5	1-4	2-1	3-1	3-1	1-1	1-4	1-1	3-1	2-1	1-2		2-2
22	Weston-s-mare	4-1	3-3	0-1	3-3	3-1	1-1	1-3	3-2	1-0	1-1	0-2	0-1	1-0	3-2	1-0	1-1	1-2	1-0	3-1	2-1	5-1	

ATHERSTONE UNITED

CLUB OFFICIALS
Chairman: Ku Akeredolu
President: Keith Allen
Secretary:Steve Clark,
19 Arden Forest Estate, Ridge Lane,
Nuneaton,Warwicks.CV18 ORE
07739 113050 (M)

FOOTBALL MANAGEMENT TEAM
Manager: Kenny Willis
Asst Manager: Mick Bayley
Physio: Maurice Ayre

PROGRAMME
Pages: 28 Price: £1
Editor: Secretary

FACT FILE
Formed: 1979 Nickname: The Adders
Colours: Red & white stripes/red/red
Change colours: Yellow & blue/blue/yellow
Midweek home matchday: Monday 7.30pm
Reserve's Lge: Midland Comb. Reserve Div.
Club Website: www.atherstoneunited.co.uk
Local Press: Tamworth Herald,
Evening News, Atherstone Herald,
Coventry Telegraph.
Local Radio: Mercia Sound, CWR

GROUND Sheepy Road, Atherstone, Warwickshire. CV9 1HG Tel: 01827 717829
Directions: Half mile north of town centre on B4116 Twycross/Ashby road.
Capacity: 3,500 Cover: 1,000 Seats: 373 Floodlights: Yes
Clubhouse: Open during normal licensing hours, all usual facilities.
Club Shop: Programmes, magazines, souvenirs etc. Contact: Sreve Clark 01827 712812

PREVIOUS **Leagues:** West Midlands 1979-87

CLUB RECORDS **Attendance:** 2,873 v V.S. Rugby, F.A. Cup 1st Round Proper 1987-88
Win: 12-2 vTipton Town (H), West Midlands (Regional) League Premier Division 86-87
Defeat: 1-7 v Rushden & Diamonds, Beazer League Premier Division 94-95
Goalscorer: Alan Bourton **Appearances:** Lee Spencer
Fee Paid: £4,500 toGloucester City for Gary Bradder, 1989
Fee Received: £40,000 for Andy Rammellfrom Manchester United, September 1989

HONOURS Southern Lge Midland Div 88-89; West Midlands Lge 81-82 86-87 (Lge Cup 81-82,Premier Div Cup 86-87, Div 2 Cup (Res.) 86-87); Walsall Senior Cup 83-84; Midland Combination Reserve Division 87-88; Birmingham Senior Cup R-up 89-90

BEST SEASON **FA Cup:** 2nd Rd Proper 1990-91, 0-1 v Crewe Alexandra (A)
FA Trophy: 1st Round 88-89 91-92.

Players progressing: Andy Rammell (Manchester United)

BEDWORTH UNITED

CLUB OFFICIALS
Chairman: Bill Haywood
Vice Chairman: Wayne Harris
Secretary: Graham J Bloxham
43 Mount Pleasant Road, Bedworth,
Warwicks CV12 8EX
Mobile: 07748 640613
Press Officer: David Leone

FOOTBALL MANAGEMENT TEAM
Managers: Billy Hollywood
Player Coach: Matty Wileman
Club Doctor: Philip Earl
Physio: John Roberts

PROGRAMME
Pages: 60 Price: £1.20
Editor: Ron Kemp 02476 318014

2002-03
Leading Goalscorer: Lee Ross
Player of the Year: Jamie Hood
Captain: Leigh Everitt

FACT FILE
Formed: 1896 Nickname: Greenbacks
Sponsors: Worthington
Colours: Green & white/Green/Green.
Change colours: Yellow & green
Midweek matchday: Tuesday
Res: Mid Comb .Youth Lg:MidFloodlit
Club website:www.bedworthunited.fwsi.com
Local Press: Heartland Evening News,
Weekly Tribune, Bedworth Echo,
Coventry Evening Telegraph
Local Radio: Mercia Sound, BBC CWR

GROUND The Oval, Miners Welfare Park, Coventry Road, Bedworth CV12 8NN Tel: 02476 314302 Email: ronald@dkemp.3freeservice.co.uk
Directions: M6 jct 3, into Bedworth on B4113 Coventry to Bedworth road, ground200yds past past Bedworth Leisure Centre on this road. Coaches should park at this Leisure Centre. Buses from Coventry and Nuneaton pass ground
Capacity: 7,000 Cover: 300 Seats: 300 Floodlights: Yes
Clubhouse: Social club open every day 7.30-11pm & w/e noon-3pm. Hot and cold bar food
Club Shop: Selling a wide range of souvenirs & programmes. Contact : Ron Kemp 01203 318014

PREVIOUS **Leagues:** Birmingham Comb. 47-54; West Mids (at first Birmingham) Lg 54-72
Name: Bedworth Town 47-68 **Ground:** British Queen Ground 11-39

CLUB RECORDS **Attendance:** 5,127 v Nuneaton Borough, Southern Lg Midland Division 23/2/82
Win: 11-0 **Defeat:** 1-10
Career Goalscorer: Peter Spacey (1949-69) **Career Appearances:** Peter Spacey
Transfer fee paid: £1,750 for Colin Taylor (Hinckley Town, 1991-92)
Transfer fee received: £30,000 for Richard Landon (Plymouth Argyle, January 1994)

BEST SEASON **FA Trophy:** Second Round 80-81 **FA Cup:** 4th Qualifying Rd 1983/89/90

HONOURS Birmingham Comb.(2) 48-50, Birmingham Snr Cup(3) 78-79 80-82, Midland Floodlit Cup 81-82 92-93

Players progressing: Phil Huffer (Derby County 1953), Geoff Coleman(Northampton Town 1955), Ian Hathaway (Mansfield Town 1989), Richard Landon(Plymouth Argyle 1994),Robert Oddy (Coventry City 2002), Dan Pitham (Burnley 2002), Inderpaul Khela , Ashley Pringle and Phil Garner (all Kidderminster Harriers), Tom Bates (Coventry C. 2003)

BROMSGROVE ROVERS

CLUB OFFICIALS

Chairman: Tom Herbert

President: Charles W Poole

Secretary: Brian Hewings c/o Club

Commercial Managers: Helen Herbert

FOOTBALL MANAGEMENT TEAM

Manager:George Rooney

Physios: LStuart Ellwell

FACT FILE

Formed: 1885

Sponsors: T.B.A. Banks ?

Nickname: Rovers or Greens

Colours: Green & White stripes/green/black

Change colours: Red/black/black

Midweek matchday: Tuesday

Reserves' league: Central Conference.

Newsline: 0891 88 44 96

2002-2003

Captain:Steve Pope

Top Goalscorer: Richard Burgess

P.o.Ys.: Stev e Pope & Steve Frost

BROMSGROVE ROVERS FOOTBALL CLUB

Dr. Martens Western Division

ROVERS

versus

CLEVEDON TOWN

OLD ROVER

Main Sponsor

BANKS'S

Match Sponsor Bromsgrove Rovers Supporters Society Ltd

PROGRAMME £1.00

Pages: 40   Price: £1.20

Editor: Phil Baker

Tel No: 01527 870861

GROUND: Victoria Ground, Birmingham Road, Bromsgrove, Worcs, B61 0DR
Tel: 01527 876949

Directions: Ground is situated on the north side of Bromsgrove on the Birmingham Road, off the A38 Bromsgrove by pass. The M5 and M42 join theA38 to the north of the town making it easy to get to the ground without havingto go into town. The 144 Midland Red bus runs from New Street StationBirmingham and passes the ground.

Capacity: 4,893   Seated: 394   Covered Terracing: 1,344

Clubhouse: Victoria Club (01527 878260) - Serves hot & cold food. Big screenTV, pool table & darts. Open matchdays and week-day evenings.

Club Shop: Selling replica clothing & souvenirs. Contact Tracy Kite (01527 876949)

PREVIOUS **Leagues:** Birmingham Lge 1898-08 53-65, Birmingham Comb. 1908-53, West Midlands 65-72, Southern Lge - Northern Div. 73-79, Midland Div. 79-86, Premier Div. 86-92, GMVC 92-97, Southern 97-01, Midland Alliance 01-02
Grounds: Old Station Road 1885-87, Recreation Ground 87-88, Churchfields 88-97,Well Lane 1897-1910.

CLUB RECORDS **Attendance:** 7,389 v Worcester City - 1957
Career - Goalscorer: Chris Hanks 238, 83-94   **Appearances:** Shaun O'Meara 763, 75-94
Win: 11-0 - v Hinckley Ath. 1970, v Halesowen Town `A' 1939    **Defeat:** 0-12 v Aston Villa `A' 1939
Fee paid: £3,000 for Recky Carter (Solihull B.) 93-94   **Fee received:** Undisclosed for Scott Cooksey (Peterborough) Dec. 93

HONOURS Vauxhall Conference R-up 92-93, Lge Cup 94-95 95-96; Southern Lge Prem 91-92, R-up 86-87, Cup 92-93, R-up 86-87, Midland Div 85-86, Merit Cup 85-86, Cup 85-86, R-up 73-74 87-88; Bill Dellow Cup 85-86; Worcester Sen Cup (8), R-up (10); Birmingham Sen Cup 46-47, R-up 47-48 88-89; W Mid Lge R-up 67-70, Cup 67-68 70-71; Birminham Lge 59-60, R-up 04-05 56-57 60-61; Birmingham Comb 46-47, R-up 49-50 50-51; Hereford Charity Chall Cup 46-47, R-up 47-48.

Players progressing: M McKenna (Northampton 46),R Hartle (Bolton 52), A McLean (Bury 53), A Smith (A.Villa 54), M Deakin (CPalace 54), B Puster (Leicester 58), Tom Smith (Sheff Utd 1978), MalcolmGoodman (Halifax 1979), Steve Smith (Walsall 1980), Gary Hackett (Shrewsbury 1983), Bill McGarry, Martyn O'Connor (C Palace 1992), Scott Cooksey (Peterborough 1993), Steve Taylor (Crystal Palace 1995).

L-R - Back row: Pete O'Connell (Director), Steve Frost, Steve Pope, Brian Hewings (Football Secretary), Mark Clifton, James Dyson, Mark Crisp, Chris Taylor (now left the club), Matt Southwick, Neil Cartwright, Ross Collins (on loan from Halesowen Town), Steve Taylor (now Stourbridge FC), Phil Baker (Club/Company Secretary), Scott Laydon, Lee O'Neill (Physiotherapist)
Front row: Gary Hackett (Co-Manager), Stewart Brighton (Team Captain), Kevin Banner, Ashley Read, Paul Danks, Tom Herbert (Chairman), Mark Benbow, Les Palmer, Grant Beckett, Richard Burgess, Jon Ford (Co-Manager)
Missing: Matt Lowe, Paul Lloyd, Leon Broadhurst, Steve Thomas, Tony Partridge (Director), Wes Mole (Director), Steve Ingram (Coach).

CINDERFORD TOWN

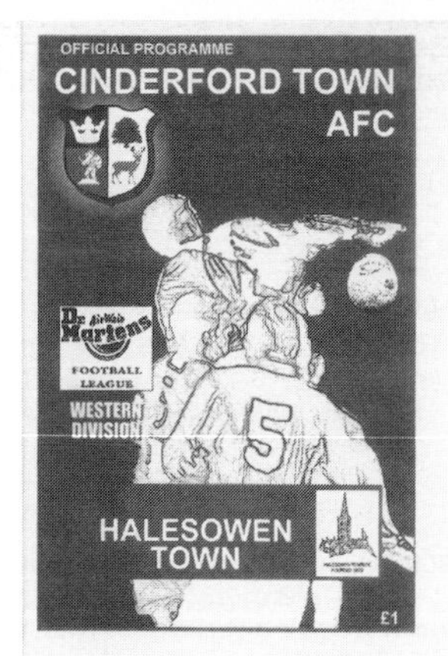

CLUB OFFICIALS

Chairman: Ashley Saunders
President: S Watkins
Vice Chairman: Ray Reed

Secretary: Chris Warren
9c Tusculum Way, Mitcheldean,
Glos GL17 0HZ
01594543065 (H) 01594 542421 x 2360 (B)

Press Officer: Andy Little

FOOTBALL MANAGEMENT TEAM

Manager: Tommy Callinan
Physio: Keith Marfell

FACT FILE

Formed: 1922 Nickname: Town
Sponsors: T.B.A.
Colours: Black & white stripes/black/black
Change colours: All Red
Midweek matchday: Tuesday
Reserves' League: No reserve team

PROGRAMME
Pages: 50 Price: £1.00
Editor: Dave Roberts
Tel: 01594 824365

GROUND The Causeway, Hilldene, Cinderford, Glos. Tel: 01594 827147 or 822039

Directions: From Gloucester take A40 to Ross-on-Wye, then A48 - Chepstow. In 8miles turn right at Elton garage onto A4151 signed Cinderford, thru Littledean, up steep hill, right at crossroads, second left into Latimer Rd. Ground 5 minswalk from town centre
Capacity: 2,500 Cover: 1,000 Seats: 250 Floodlights: Yes
Clubhouse: Open every day. 2 bars, kitchen, 2 skittle alleys, darts, dancehall,committee room
Club Shop: Souvenirs, club badges (£"3.00), ties, mugs , scarves and pennants

PREVIOUS **Leagues:** Glos Northern Snr 22-39 60-62, Western 46-59, Warwickshire Comb 63-64,West Midlands 65-69, Gloucestershire County 70-73 85-89, Midland Comb. 74-84,Hellenic 90-95
Names: None **Grounds:** Mousel Lane, Royal Oak

CLUB RECORDS **Attendance:** 4,850 v Minehead, Western League, 1955-56
Win: 13-0 v Cam Mills 38-39 **Defeat:** 0-10 v Sutton Coldfield 78-79
Career Appearances: Russell Bowles 528 **Career Goalscorer:** Unknown

BEST SEASON **FA Cup:** 2nd Rd v Gravesend 95-96 **FA Trophy:** 2nd Qual Rd
FA Vase: 2nd Rd 91-92 **FA Amateur Cup:** 3rd Qual Rd 52

HONOURS Hellenic Lg Premier Champions 94-95, Premier Lg.Cup 94-95, Floodlit Cup 93-94,Div 1 90-91; Glos Northern Snr Lg Div 1 38-39 60-61, R-up (6); Nth Glos Lg Div1 38-39 60-61; Glos Snr Amtr Cup (Nth) (6), R-up (3); Western Lg Div 2 56-57; Warwickshire Comb. 63-64; W Mids Lg Prem Div Cup 68-69; Glos Jnr Cup (Nth) 80-81; Midland Comb. 81-82; Glos Co. Lg R-up 69-70 71-72 73-74; Glos FA Trophy R-up 92-93; Hungerford Cup 94-95, Glos.Sen Cup Finalists 00-01

L-R - Back: Keith Marfell (Physio), Damien Edwards, Simon Truman, Clayton Hook, Andy Fisher, Jason Hoskins, Leigh Hall, Jamie Thompson.
Fron: Tony Hopkins, Scott Griffin, Jason Donovan, Daryl Addis, Jamie Hammond and Richard Pugh. **Photo**: Peter Barnes

CIRENCESTER TOWN

CLUB OFFICIALS

Chairman: Steven Abbley,
17 Dianmer Close, Hook, Swindon. SN4 8ER.
Tel: 01743853293 (H) 01793 884900 (B)

Secretary: Jim Saunders,
16 Arnold Way Cirencester, Glos. GL7 1TA
Tel: 01285 659002 (H)

Commercial Manager: Stephen Abbley

Press Officer: Jim Saunders

FOOTBALL MANAGEMENT TEAM

Manager: Brian Hughes

Physio: T.B.A.

FACT FILE

Founded: 1889
Nickname: Centurians
Sponsors: P.H.H./Cheltenham Windows
Colours: Red & black/ black/ red
Change colours: Blue & white
Midweek Matchday: Tuesday
Reserves' League: Cirencester & District
Local Press:
Standard, Western Daily Press
Local Radio:
BBC Radio Gloucester, Severn Sound

PROGRAMME

Pages: Varies Price: £1
Editor: Martyn Herbert

GROUND Corinium Stadium,Kingshill Lane, Cirencester Tel: 01285654543

Directions: Leave by-pass at Burford Road roundabout to the left. Then right at lights,laft at junction first left and ground is 250 yards on right.
Capacity: 4,500 Seats: 550 Cover: 550 Floodlights: Yes

Clubhouse: Open Tuesday - Friday evenings & Saturday. Snacks are available onmatchdays. Club Shop: None

PREVIOUS **Leagues:** Hellenic League Names: None. Grounds: Smithfield Stadium

CLUB RECORDS **Attendance:** 2,600 v Fareham 1969
Win: Unknown **Defeat:** Unknown
Career Goalscorer: Unknown **Career Appearances:** Unknown
Transfer fee paid: None **Transfer fee received:** None

BEST SEASON **FA Trophy:** 1st Qual. Round 1996-97 (1st season in comp.)
FA Vase: Never past the 1st Round **FA Cup:** 4th Qualifying Round, 2001-02

HONOURS Gloucestershire Senior Amateur Cup 89-90; Hellenic League Div One Challenge Cup 90-91; Hellenic League Prem Div 95-96, League Cup 95-96; Gloucestershire County Cup 95-96

Players progressing: None

CLEVEDON TOWN

CLUB OFFICIALS

Chairman: John Croft
Directors: R.J.Ayers, B.W.Bradshaw, S.T.Haas, T Walsh and G,Thomas
Secretary: Mike Williams
34 Robinia Walk, Whitchurch,
Bristol BS14 0SHTel: 01275 833835
Commercial Manager: Gary Bradshaw
(M) 07768 270718

FOOTBALL MANAGEMENT TEAM

Manager: Steve Fey
Coach: David Mogg Physio: Steve Tregale
Youth Team Manager:Barry Dudbridge

FACT FILE

Formed: 1880
Nickname: The Seasiders
Sponsors: Bradshaw Group
Colours: Blue & white stripes/blue/blue
Change colours: All yellow or all green
Midweek Matches: Tuesday
Youth Team: Som Youth Floodlit, SWCo
Web-site: www.clevedontownafc.co.uk

2002-03
Captain:S.Lester
Top Goalscorer: S.Lester 12
Ps.o.Y .J.Zabeck, J.Lester ,R.Scott

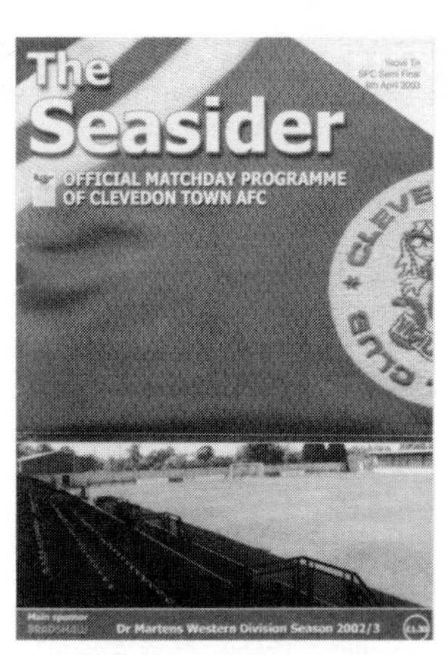

The Seasider
OFFICIAL MATCHDAY PROGRAMME OF CLEVEDON TOWN AFC
Dr Martens Western Division Season 2002/3

Pages: 34 Price:£1.30
Editor: Russell Isaac (01275 343000)

Local Radio: Radio Bristol, Star 107.7 FM
Local Press: Clevedon Mercury
Evening Post, Western Daily Press

GROUND Ha nd Stadium, Davis Lane, Clevedon email: info@handstadium.co.uk
Fax: 01275 871601 Tel: 01275 871600(ground) 01275 341913 (office)

Directions: M5 Jct 20 - follow signs for Hand Stadium; first left into Central Way (at island just after motorway), 1st left at mini-r'bout into Kenn Rd, 2nd left Davis Lane; ground half mile on right. Or from Bristol(B3130) left into Court Lane (opposite Clevedon Court), turn right after 1mile, ground on left. Nearest BR station: Nailsea & Backwell. Buses from Bristol
Capacity: 3,650 Seats: 300 Cover: 1,600 Floodlights: Yes
Clubhouse: Open every day and evening. Separate function suite & lounge bar.Hot food available. Matchday refreshment bar within ground sells confectionary, teas & hot food
Club Shop: Sells all types of souvenirs, programmes and replica kit. Exchanges welcome. Contact Stev Small **Supporters Club Chairman:** Russell Coneybeare

PREVIOUS
Leagues: Weston & District, Somerset Senior, Bristol Charity, Bristol & District, Bristol Suburban, Western 74-93
Grounds: Dial Hill ('till early 1890's); Teignmouth Road ('till 1991)
Names: Clevedon FC, Ashtonians (clubs merged in 1974)

CLUB RECORDS
Attendance: 1,600 v Bristol City, Friendly. 27/7/98 Ground Record: Bristol Rovers v Ipswich Town 24/7/02
(At Teignmouth Road: 2,300 v Billingham Synthonia, FA Amateur Cup, 52-53)
Win: 18-0 v Dawlish Town (H), Western League Premier Division 24/4/93
Defeat: 13-3 v Yate YMCA (A), Bristol Comb 67-68

BEST SEASON
FA Cup: 3rd Qual. Rd 2nd replay 92-93 v Newport AFC, 2-4 after two 1-1
FA Amateur Cup: 3rd Round Proper, 52-53 **FA Vase:** 6th Round 87-88, v Sudbury Town (A) **FA Trophy:** 2nd Round 98-99

HONOURS Southern League, Midland Division 98-99, Western League 92-93 (R-up 91-92), League Cup (R-up 92-93), Bristol Charity League 37-38,40-41, Somerset Senior Cup 01-02 04-05 28-29 , 00-01,01-02 Somerset Snr League 36-37, Div 1(Res.) 92-93, Bristol & suburbanLeague 25-26,27-28,28-29, Weston & District League: 39-40,43-44,44-45, Somerset Premier Cup;86-87,98-99, 00-01,01-02 Somerset Junior Cup 1897-98,Somerset Medal Competition: 87-88, Clevedon Charity Cup 26-27,30-31.

Players Progressing: Jason Eaton (Bristol City) and Jonathon Gould (Halifax Town)

L-R - Back Row: Steve tregale (Physio), Arthur Atherton, Mike Wyatt, Phil Walsh, Danny Greaves, Steve Weaver, Simon Bryant, James Zabek, Lee Zabek, David Hillier, Tony Hopkins. **Front Row:** Geraint Bater, Lewis haldene, Shane Hobbs, Andy Smith, Rob Scott, Lee Vickerman, Simon Dew, Mark Fey, Fidel Richards, Oliver Price.

EVESHAM UNITED

CLUB OFFICIALS

Chairman: **Jim Cockerton**

Vice Chairman: **Steve Lane**

President: **M E H Davis**

Treasurer: **Dave Wright**

Secretary/Press Officer: **Mike J Peplow**
68 Woodstock Rd, St Johns,
Worcester WR2 5NF
Tel: 01905 425993

FOOTBALL MANAGEMENT TEAM

Manager: Phil Mullen

Asst Manager: Gary Narnett

Physio:Phil Greenway

FACT FILE

Formed: 1945
Nickname: The Robins
Sponsors; Dane Valley/Banks's
Colours: Red & white/black/black
Change Colours: All blue
Midweek matches: Tuesday
Reserves' League: No reserve team
Local Press: Evesham Journal,
Worcester Evening News, Gloucester Echo
Local Radio: Classic Gold
BBC Hereford & Worcester, FM102 The Bear

2002-2003
Captain: Nathan Jukes

PROGRAMME
Pages: 58 Price: £1
Editor: Mike Peplow (01905 425993)

GROUND Common Road, Evesham, Worcestershire WR11 4PU Tel: 01386 442303
Directions: From Evesham High Street turn into Oat St, and join one-way system,turn right between Willmotts factory called Conduit Hill into Common Rd, ground 200yds down on right just before railway bridge. 5 minutes walk from Evesham BR station
Capacity: 2,000 Seats: 350 Cover: 600 Floodlights: Yes
Clubhouse: Open matchdays and training nights. Cold food available in club, and hot food from tea hut on matchdays
Club Shop: Contact John Hawkins c/o the club

PREVIOUS **Leagues:** Worcester, Birmingham Combination, Midland Combination 51-55 65-92, West Midlands Regional 55-62
Name: Evesham Town **Ground:** The Crown Meadow (pre-1968)

CLUB RECORDS **Attendance:** 2,338 v West Bromwich A., friendly 18/7/92
Win: 11-3 v West Heath United **Defeat:1-8 v Ilkeston Town**
Career Goalscorer: Sid Brain **Career Appearances:** Rob Candy
Transfer fee paid: £1,500; to Hayes for Colin Day, 1992
Transfer fee received: £5,000 for Simon Brain (to Cheltenham Town)

BEST SEASON **FA Vase:** Quarter Finals 1991-92 **FA Amateur Cup:** Runners-up 1923-24
FA Trophy: 3rd Qual Rd 96-97 **FA Cup:** 2nd Qual Rd 96-97

HONOURS FA Amateur Cup R-up 23-24, Worcestershire Snr Urn(2) 76-78 (R-up 90-91), Midland Comb.(6) 52-53 54-55 65-66 67-69 91-92 Chal. Cup 53-54 87-88 91-92 R-up (5) 54-55 71-72 83-84 88-90, Worcestershire Comb. 52-53 54-55; B'gham Combination R-up 30-31, Evesham Hosp. Cup 89-90, Tony Allden Mem. Cup 1973 19881992

Players progressing: Billy Tucker, Gary Stevens (Cardiff 77), Kevin Rose(Lincoln 78), Andy Preece (Northampton 86), Simon Brain (Hereford, via Cheltenham Town), Billy Turley (Northampton Tn)

Photo courtesy of The Evesham Journal.

GLOUCESTER CITY

Dr Martens

FOOTBALL LEAGUE

CLUB OFFICIALS

Chairman: Colin Gardner

President: R F Etheridge

Secretary: Jason Mills
25 Hewlett Road, Cheltenham,
Gloucestershire GL52 6AD
Tel/Fax: 01242 700496 Mob: 07768 750590
Club Email: mills.jason@virgin.net

Press Off: Ashley Loveridgel
Tel: 07760 417119

FOOTBALL MANAGEMENT TEAM

Manager: Chris Burns

Assistant Manager: Mike Cook

Coaches: Chris Gardner & Karl Bayliss

Physio: Adrian Tandy

FACT FILE

Formed: 1889
Nickname: The Tigers
Sponsors: Keyway
Colours: Yellow & black/black/black
Change colours: All White
Midweek games: Tuesday
Local Press: Gloucester Citizen,
Western Daily Press
Local Radio: Severn Sound,
BBC Radio Gloucestershire

2002-2003

Captain: Neil Griffiths
Player of the Year:Adie Harris
Top Scorer: Jimmy Cox

PROGRAMME

Pages: 44 Price: £1.00
Editor: Mike Dunstan Tel: 01242 250087

GROUND Meadow Park, Sudmeadow Road, Hempsted, Gloucester GL2 6HS Tel: 01452 421400

Directions: From North: A40 then then A4301 towards City Centre & Historic Docks, right into Severn Road over swingbridge, right into Llanthony Road/Hempsted Lane, 2nd right into Sudmeadow Road, ground 50yds on left

Capacity: 3,500 Cover:2,500 Seats: 560 Floodlights: Yes

Clubhouse: Meadow Park Sports & Social Club in ground. Normal licensing hours. **Club Shop:** Yes

PREVIOUS
Leagues: Bristol & Dist. (now Western) 1893-96, Gloucester & Dist. 97-1907, NorthGlos. 07-10, Glos. North Senior 20-34, Birmingham Comb. 1935-39
Grounds: Longlevens 1935-65, Horton Road 65-86 **Name:** Gloucester Y.M.C.A

CLUB RECORDS
Attendance: 4,000 v Dagenham & Redbridge, FA Trophy S-F 2nd Leg, 12.4.97
Win: 10-0 v Sudbury Town (H), FA Cup 3rd Rd Q., 17.10.98
Defeat: 1-12 v Gillingham 9.11.46
Goalscorer: Reg Weaver, 250 **Appearances:** Stan Myers & Frank Tredgett in 1950s
Fee Paid: £25,000 for S Fergusson (Worcester City), and D Holmes (Gresley R.)
Fee Received: £25,000 Ian Hedges (AFC Bournemouth, 1990)

BEST SEASON **FA Cup:** 2nd Rd 89-90 **FA Trophy:** Semi-Final 1996-97

HONOURS Southern Lg R-up 90-91, Lg Cup 55-56 R-up 81-82, Midland Div 88-89), Glos NthSen Lg 33-34, Glos Sen. Cup 37-38 49-58 65-66 68-69 70-71 74-75 78-79 79-80 81-82 82-83 83-84 90-91 92-93; Sen Amat Cup (Nth) 31-32)

Players progressing: Numerous including - William Teague (61) & Rod Thomas (64) to Swindon, John Layton (Hereford 74), Ian Main (Exeter 78), Mike Bruton (Newport 79), Mel Gwinnett (Bradford C. 84), Steve Talboys (Wimbledon 91)

Photo: Tony Hickey, 07767 400414

GRESLEY ROVERS

CLUB OFFICIALS

Chairman: Mark Evans
President: Gordon Duggins
Vice Chairman: George Sutton
Secretary / Press Officer: Neil Betteridge,
34 Thorpe Downs Road, Church Gresley,
Swadlincote, Derbys DE11 9FB
Tel: 01283 226229
Commercial Director: Mark Evans

FACT FILE

Formed: 1882
Nickname: The Moatmen
Sponsors: Ashley Adams
Colours: Red/white/red
Change colours: White/black/white
Midweek matchday: Tuesday
Reserves' League: Midland Comb (Res. Div.)
Club Website: www.gresleyrovers.com

FOOTBALL MANAGEMENT TEAM

Manager: Gary Norton
Asst Manager: Alan Titterton
Physio: Jody Brooks

2002-2003

Captain: Stuart Evans
Top Scorer: Chris Gray
Player of the Year: Andy Cheetham

GRESLEY ROVERS v RUGBY UNITED
Tuesday 19th August 2003 (Kick off 7.30pm)
DR. MARTENS LEAGUE WESTERN DIVISION

Pages: 32 Price: £1.00
Editor:Chairman

Local Press: Derby Evening Telegraph, Burton Mail, Burton Trader, SwadlincoteTimes
Local Radio: BBC Radio Derby

Ground Moat Ground, Moat Street, Church Gresley, Swadlincote, Derbys., DE11 9RE. Tel: 01283 216315

Directions: To A444 via either the A5, A38, A5121 or M42 , Junction 11. On reaching A444 head for Castle Gresley. Take exit at large island to Church Gresley, at next island 2nd exit (Church St), then 2nd left (School St) then 1st left into Moat St. 5 miles Burton-on-Trent (BR). Buses from Swadlincote and Burton

Capacity: 2,000 Cover: 1,200 Seats: 400 Floodlights: Yes

Clubhouse: Inside ground, open Mon & Thurs evenings & matchdays

Club Shop: Sells merchandise, programmes, metal badges etc.

PREVIOUS
Leagues: Burton Lge 1892-95 97-01 09-10 43-45, Derbyshire Sen 1895-97 02-03,Leics Sen 1890-91 98-99 08-09 10-12 15-16 35-42 45-49, Notts 01-02, Midland 03-06, Central All 11-15 19-25 49-53 59-67, Birmingham Comb 25-33 53-54, Birmingham (now West Mids) 54-59 75-92, Central Comb 33-35, East Mids 67-75
Grounds: Mushroom Lane, Albert Village 1882-95, Church Str., Church, Gresley. 1895-1909

CLUB RECORDS
Attendance: 3,950 v Burton Albion, Birmingham (now West Mids) Lg Division One 57-58
Win: 23-0 v Holy Cross Priory, Leics Jun Cup 1889-90 **Defeat:** 1-15 v Burton Crusaders 1886-87
Career Goalscorer: Gordon Duggins 306 **Career Appearances:** Dennis King 579
Transfer fee received: £30,000 for Justin O'Reilly (Port Vale 1996)
Transfer fee paid: £2,500 for David Robinson (Ilkeston Town 97)

BEST SEASON
FA Vase: Runners-up 90-91, (SF 92-93) **FA Trophy:** Qtr Finals 95-96
FA Cup: 1st Rd Proper: 30-31 (1-3 at York City), 94-95 (1-7 at Crewe Alex.) League clubs defeated: None

HONOURS
Southern Lge Champ 96-97; FA Vase R-up 90-91; West Mids Lg 90-91 91-92 (R-up 85-86 88-89); Lg Cup 88-89 R-Up. 86-87 91-92; Southern Lg Mid Div R-up 92-93; Derbys Snr Cup (7), (R-Up (3); Leics Snr Cup 1898-99 46-47 (R-Up 1899-90 45-46); Leics Sen Lg 00-01 46-47 47-48 R-Up (7); Coalville Charity Cup 46-47; Derby Senior Cup (S) (2) R-Up 00-01 01-02 Bass Vase (6); Cent All 64-65 66-67 R-Up(3) (Lg Cup 52-53); East Mids Reg Lg (2) R-Up (2); Dr.Martens (S Lge) Cup Fin 93-94

Players progressing: Phil Gee (Derby County 85), Mark Blount (Sheffield Utd 94), Colin Loss (Bristol City 94), Justin O'Reilly (Port Vale 96)

HALESOWEN TOWN

CLUB OFFICIALS

Chairman:NigelPitt

President: Laurence Wood

Vice Chairman: Paul Floud

Secretary: Stewart Tildesley
83 Bloomfield Street, Halesowen B63 3RF
Tel: 0121 5508443(H) 07710 434708(M)

Commercial Manager: Nigel Pitt

Press Officer: Colin Brookes

FOOTBALL MANAGEMENT TEAM

Manager: Brendan Phillips

Physio: Jeff Jones

2002-2003

Captain: Lee Collins
P.oY.: Richard Colwell
Top Scorer: Jason Ashby 20

FACT FILE

Formed: 1873
Nickname: Yeltz
Sponsors: T.B.A.
Newsline: 09066 555818
Colours: Blue with white trim
Change colours: White & Black
Midweek home matchday:Tuesday
Reserve's League: None
Local Press: Sports Argus, Express & Star, Birmingham Mail, Halesowen News, Stourbridge & Halesowen Chronicle
Local Radio: BBC West Midlands, B.R.M.B., Beacon

PROGRAMME

Pages: 44 Price: £1.50p Editor: R Pepper

GROUND The Grove, Old Hawne Lane, Halesowen, West Midlands B63 3TB Fax: 01902 714221 Tel: 0121 550 2179

Directions: M5 jct 3, A456 (signed Kidderminster) to 1st island turn right (signed A459 Dudley), left at next island (signed A458 Stourbridge), at next island take 3rd left into Grammar School Lane, then Old Hawne Lane - ground 400 yds on left

Capacity: 5,000 Cover: 1,518 Seats: 518 Floodlights: Yes

Clubhouse: (0121 602 2210) 12-2.30 & 7-11 (10.30 Sun) pm daily.Cold snacks served.

Club Shop: Sells replica strips, T-shirts, waterproof tops, coats, scarves, progs, badges etc

PREVIOUS **Leagues:** West Mids 1892-1905 06-11 46-86, Birmingham Comb. 11-39

CLUB RECORDS **Attendance:** 5,000 v Hendon F.A. Cup 1st Rd Proper 1954, (18,234 v Southall,1986 FA Vase Final at Wembley)
Goalscorer: Paul Joinson 369 **Appearances:** Paul Joinson 608
Win: 13-1 v Coventry Amateurs, Birmingham Senior Cup, 1956
Defeat: 0-8 v Bilston, West Midlands League, 7/4/62
Fee Paid: £7,250 for Stuart Evans (Gresley 1996)
Fee Received: £40,000 for Jim Rodwell (Rushden & Diamonds 96)

BEST SEASON **FA Vase:** Winners 84-85, 85-86 R-up 82-83 **FA Trophy:** 3rd Round Proper 94-95
FA Cup: 1st Rd 9 times: 54-55 then each season from 84-85 to 91-92

HONOURS Southern Lg Premier Div R-up 96, Southern Lg Midland Div 89-90, Western Division 01-02 W Mids Lg(5) 46-47 82-85 85-86 (R-up 64-65, Lg Cup 82-83 84-85 R-up 02-03),B'ham Snr Cup 83-84,97-98 (R-up 51-52 67-68), Staffs Snr Cup 88-89 (R-up 83-84), FA Vase (2) 84-86 (R-up 82-3) Worcs Snr Cup 02-03 Winners 51-52 61-62 (R-up 87-88), Midland Comb. Res Div 89-90

Players progressing Arthur Proudler (A. Villa), Cyril Spiers (A. Villa), Billy Morris (Wolves), Dean Spink (A. Villa), Stuart Cash (Nottm Forest), Andrew Pearce, Tim Clarke & Sean Flynn (Coventry), Dean Stokes (Port Vale), Frank Bennett (Southampton), Julian Alsop (Bristol R.)

L-R - Back Row: Lewis Baker, Bryan Small, Shaun Wray, Matthew Hollis, Mark Gale, Darren Grocutt, Joshua Skidmore, Andrew Spencer, Mark Hallam, Richard Kavanagh, Kelvin Phillips. **Front**: Gavin Blackwell (Physio), Leon Mitchell, Asa Charlton, jason ashby, Richard Colwell, Jamie March, Stuart Skidmore, Ben Steane, Neil Smith

ILKESTON TOWN

FOOTBALL LEAGUE

CLUB OFFICIALS

Chairman: Paul Millership

President: Robert Lindsay

Secretary: Robert Easton, 15 Regina Crescent, Ravenshead, Notts.NG15 9AE
Tel: 01623 793927(H) 07831 303031(M)

Commercial Management:
J Sports Promotions Ltd

FOOTBALL MANAGEMENT TEAM

Manager: Charlie Bishop

Asst Manager: Andy Mason

FACT FILE

Re Formed: 1945
Nickname: The Robins
Sponsors: Ron Brooks Ilkeston Toyota
Colours: Red/whitek/red
Change colours:White/Black/White
Midweek matchday:Tuesday
Reserves' League: Midland Reg. Alliance

PROGRAMME

Pages: 32 Price: £1
Editors: Mic Capill, J Shiels, D Payne

GROUND New Manor Ground, Awsworth Rd, Ilkeston Tel: 0115 932 4094

Directions: M42 to M1 junc 23A, continue on M1 to junc 26, exit left onto A610 towards Ripley, take 1st exit signed Awsworth and Ilkeston (A6096), follow bypass signed Ilkeston A6096. Turn right after 1/2 mile signed Cotmanhay. Ground 200 yards on left

Capacity: 3,500 Seats: 270 Cover: 1,100 Floodlights: Yes

Clubhouse: Open Wed-Fri 7-11pm, Sat-Sun noon-3 & 7-11pm, and Mon or Tue if there is a match. Snacks behind bar. Large tea bar open matchdays 2-5pm (6.30-9pm for night games)

Club Shop: Sells wide range of souvenirs & programmes. Contact Manager (0115 9305 622) or club secretary

PREVIOUS

Leagues: Midland 1894-1902 25-58 61-71; Notts & Derby Senior 1945-47; CentralAlliance 47-61; Midland Counties 1961-71 73-82; Southern League 1971-73; Northern Co.East 1982-86; Central Midlands 86-90; West Midlands (Regional) 90-94.
Ground: Manor Ground, Manor Rd (1945-92)

CLUB RECORDS

Attendance: 2,504 v Boston United FA Cup 1st Rd 15/11/97
Win: 14-2 v Codnor M.W 46-47: 13-0 v Swanwick OB 46-47
Defeat: 1-11 v Grantham T. 47-48: 0-10 v VS Rugby 85-86
Career Goalscorer: Jackie Ward 141. **Career Appearances:** Terry Swincoe 377
Season Goalscorer: Barry Jepson 62, 1952-53
Transfer fee paid: £7,500 Justin O'Reilly (Southport 1998) **Fee received:** £25,000 for Francis Green (Peterborough Utd)

BEST SEASON

FA Cup: 2nd Round - 1997-98 1-1, 1-2 v Scunthorpe Utd, 1999-00 0-3 (A) after 1-1 (H) v Rushden & Diamonds
FA Vase: 4th Round 88-89 1-2 v Tamworth
FA Trophy: 3rd Round 82-83 1-5 v Enfield, 94-95 2-2, 1-2 v Kidderminster H

HONOURS

Southern Lge, Midland Div 94-95, R-up 97-98; West Mids (Regional) Lg 93-94, Lg Cup 93-94, Div 1 91-92, Lg Cup 91-92; Central Mids Lg Cup 87-88; Midland Lg 67-68 R-up 1898-99; Midland Co Lg 67-68; Central Alliance 51-52 52-53 53-54 54-55 R-up 47-48 55-56

MANGOTSFIELD UNITED

CLUB OFFICIALS

President: Richard Davis

Chairman: Roger Pullin

Vice Chairman: Len Street

Secretary & Press Off: Roger Gray
105 Chiltern Close, Warmley, Bristol
BS15 5UW Tel: 0117 961 6523
(Mobile) 07768 467851

FOOTBALL MANAGEMENT TEAM

Manager: Andy Black

Assistant Manager: Shaun Penny

Physio:Tammy Mullin

FACT FILE

Founded: 1950
Nickname: The Field
Sponsors: Flo Cas
Colours: Sky & maroon/maroon/sky
Change colours:White/maroon/maroon
Midweek matchday: Tuesday 7.45
Reserve League: Somerset County

2002-2003

Captain: Scott Hendy
Top Scorer: David Seal
Player of the Year: Mark Summers

PROGRAMME

Pages: 32 Price: £1.00
Editor: Bob Smale (0117 9401926)

GROUND Cossham Street, Mangotsfield, Bristol BS17 3EW Tel: 0117 956 0119

Directions: M4 jct 19, M32 jct 1; A4174 marked Downend, through lights, over double mini-r'bout to Mangotsfield, left by village church onto B4465 signposted Pucklechurch, ground quarter mile on right. From central Bristol take A432 thru Fishponds, Staple Hill, to Mangotsfield and turn right by village church onto B4465. From Bath/Keynsham follow A4175, right at island at Willsbridge onto A431, then rejoin A4175 at next island (Cherry Garden Hill) to Bridge Yate, straight over double mini-r'bout and take 1st left, right into Carsons Rd after 1 mile and follow to Mangotsfield village & turn right by church onto B4465

Capacity: 2,500 Seats: 300 Cover: 800 Floodlights: Yes

Clubhouse: Open 11-11. Snacks - hot food on matchdays. Lounge bar for functions etc **Club Shop:** Yes

PREVIOUS **Leagues:** Bristol & District 50-67; Avon Premier Combination 67-72; Western League 72-00

RECORD **Attendance:** 2,386 v Bath City, FA Cup 77-78

Goalscorer: John Hill **Appearances:** John Hill 600+

Win: 14-0 v Dawlish (a) 1993 Western League **Defeat:** 3-13 v Bristol City United (Bristol & District Div 1)

& 17-0 v Hanham Sports (Bristol & District League `Div 6)

HONOURS Western Lg 90-91r-up 99-00, Lg Cup 73-74 r-up 86-87, Div 1 r-up 82-83; Somerset Prem. Cup 87-88, r-up 88-89 95-96; Glos Snr Cup 68-69 75-76 02-03; Glos FA Trophy 84-85 86-87 90-91 94-95 96-97; Hungerford Invitation Cup 74-75; Rothmans Nat. Cup r-up 77-78; Hanham Invit. Charity Cup 84-85 85-86; Youth honours: Glos Yth Shield 81-82 84-85 (R-up 82-83); Somerset Floodlit Yth Lg 81-82 82-83 83-84 84-85 87-88 98-99; Somerset Yth Shield 76-77
Reserve honours Somerset Snr Lg (Res.) Div 1 98-99 Div 2 97-98 75-76, Div 3 74-75; Somerset Comb. Cup 74-75

BEST SEASON **FA Vase:** Semi Final 95-96 **FA Cup:** 4th Qualifying Rd Replay v Lewes 0-0 (H) 0-2 (A) 2001-02

Players progress ing: G Megson, S White, G Penrice, P Purnell, N Tanner, M Hooper

L-R - Back Row: Alan Ball (Coach), Andy Black (Manager), Gary Warren, David Seal, Darren Edwards, Nick Yeo, Tony Mellesa, Scott Henedry, Simon Clark, Jason Drysdale, Adam Simms, Gareth Loyden, Tammy Mullah. **Middle**: James Turner, Justin Bishop, Leon Cousins, Steve Campbell, Dean Pendry, Adam Missiat, Mark Summers, Neil Ward. **Front**: Ryan Orr, Matt Huxley, Jack Pitcher, Dean Griffiths.

REDDITCH UNITED

CLUB OFFICIALS

Chairman: Pat Cremin

President: Major Jim Gillespie MBE

Secretary: Colin Lowe,
5 Hartford Road, Hardwood Park,
Bromsgrove, Worcs. Tel: 01527 876913

Commercial Manager: Pat Cremin

Press Off: Rod Brown

FOOTBALL MANAGEMENT TEAM

Manager: Rod Brown
Assistant Manager: Gary Whild
Coach: Kim Casey
Physio: Peter James

FACT FILE

Formed: 1891
Nickname: The Reds
Colours: Red with Blue collar & cuffs
Change colours: Blue with red collar & cuffs
Midweek matchday: Tuesday
Reserves' League: Midland Comb. Res Div
Local Press: Redditch Advertiser, Birmingham Evening Mail, Redditch Standard
Local Radio: BBC Hereford & Worcester
The Bear Radio FM102

2002-2003

Captain: Mark Taytlor

PROGRAMME

Pages: 50 Price: £1.00
Editor: Steve Townsend

GROUND Valley Stadium, Bromsgrove Road, Redditch B97 4RN Tel: 01527 67450

Directions: Access 7 on town centre ring-road takes you into Bromsgrove Road (via Unicorn Hill) - ground entrance 400yds past traffic lights on right.Arriving from Bromsgrove take first exit off dual carriageway. Ground 400 ydsfrom Redditch BR station and town centre

Capacity: 5,000 Cover: 2,000 Seats: 400 Floodlights: Yes

Clubhouse: Large clubroom and lounge boardroom. Open matchdays and for private hire. Food available on matchdays; steaks hot dogs, burgers, chips, bovril etc **Club Shop:** Not at Present

PREVIOUS — **Leagues:** B'ham Comb. 05-21 29-39 46-53, West Midlands 21-29 53-72, Southern 72-79, 81- Alliance Premier (Conf) 79-80
Name: Redditch Town **Ground:** HDA Spts Ground, Millsborough Rd

CLUB RECORDS — **Attendance:** 5,500 v Bromsgrove, league match 54-55
Transfer fee paid: £3,000 for Paul Joinson from Halesowen Town
Transfer fee received: £42,000 for David Farrell (Aston Villa, 1991)

BEST SEASON — **FA Cup:** 1st Rd replay 71-72, 0-4 v Peterborough U (A) after 1-1 draw. Also 1st Rd 71-72
FA Trophy: 4th Round 1998-99 0-2 v Boston Umited

HONOURS — Southern Lg Div 1 Nth 75-76 (Midland Div R-up 85-86) S.Lg Cup R-up 97-98 West Mids (B'ham) Lg Southern Sect. 54-55, Birmingham Comb. 13-14 32-33 52-53 (R-up 06-07 14-15 51-52), Staffs Snr Cup 90-91, Birmingham Snr Cup 24-25 31-32 38-39 76-77, Worcs Snr Cup 894-95 1930-31 74-75 76-77 (R-up 1888-89 1929-30 52-53 73-74), Worcs Jnr Cup 90-91

Players progressing: Hugh Evans (Birmingham 1947), Trevor Lewes (Coventry1957), David Gilbert (Chesterfield 1960), Mike Tuohy (Southend Utd 1979), NeilSmith (Liverpool), David Farrell (Aston Villa 1992), Neil Davis (Aston Villa 1991)

RUGBY UNITED

CLUB OFFICIALS

Chairman: Brian Melvin
Secretary: Doug Wilkins,
298 Rocky Lane, Great Barr,
Birmingham B42 1NQ
Tel: 0121 681 1544 (H 0121 686 4068 (F)
Press Officer: Alan Turner
Tel: 01788 567181
Commercial Manager:Lisa Melvin

FOOTBALL MANAGEMENT TEAM

Manager:Tony Dobson
Asst Manager: Steve Shea
Physio: Bob Gardner

FACT FILE

Formed: 1956 Nickname: The Valley
Sponsors: Rugby Telegraph & Melbros Ltd
Colours: Navy & sky/navy/navy
Change colours: All Red
Midweek matchday: Tuesday
Club Newsline: 0930 555971
Reserves' League: Midland Combination
Website: www.rugbyutd.co.uk

2002-2003

Captain: Craig Herbert
Top Scorer: Robbie Beard
Player of the Year: Adam Hart

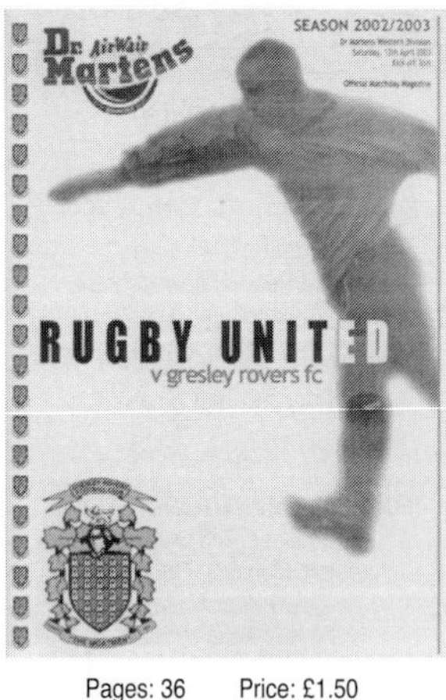

Pages: 36 Price: £1.50
Editor: N.Melvin 01788 567717

Local Press: Rugby Advertiser, Coventry Evening Telegraph, Rugby Observer
Local Radio: Mercia Sound, CWR

GROUND: Butlin Road, Rugby, Warks. CV21 3ST Tel: 01788 844806
Directions: The ground is situated off Clifton (B5414) on the north side of Rugby. 1 mile walk from the station Club Call Line: 09066 555971
Capacity: 6,000 Cover: 1,000 Seats: 750 Floodlights: Yes
Clubhouse: Open every night and weekend lunchtimes. Entertainment Saturday nights. Excellent facilities include Long Alley Skittles, darts and pool
Club Shop: Yes

PREVIOUS **Name:** Valley Sports, Valley Sports Rugby
Leagues: Rugby & District 1956-63, Coventry & Partnership, North Warks 63-69, United Counties 69-75, West Midlands 75-83

CLUB RECORDS **Attendance:** 3,961 v Northampton FA Cup 1984 **Defeat:** 1-11 v Ilkeston Town (A) 18.4.98
Win: 10-0 v Ilkeston Tn FA Trophy Preliminary Rd 4/9/85 *All-time record FA Trophy win
Career Goalscorer: Danny Conway, 124 **Career Appearances:** Danny Conway, 374
Transfer fee paid: £3,500 R Smith, I Crawley, G Bradder **Transfer fee received:** £15,000 T Angus (Northampton)

BEST SEASON **FA Cup:** 2nd round 87-88, plus 1st Rd 84-85 85-86 86-87 94-95 League clubs defeated: None
FA Trophy: **FA Vase:** Winners 82-83

HONOURS Southern Lg Midland Div 86-87 (R-up 94-95, Lg Cup 89-90), FA Vase 82-83,Mid Floodlit Cup 84-85 89-90 98 -00(R-up 86-87), Birmingham Snr Cup 88-89 91-92, Utd Co's Lg Div 3 Cup 69-70.

Players progressing: S Storer (Birmingham 1985), S Bicknell (Leicester), S Norris (Scarborough), T Angus (Northampton Town), Ashley Walker (Peterborough), Ian King (Stoke City)

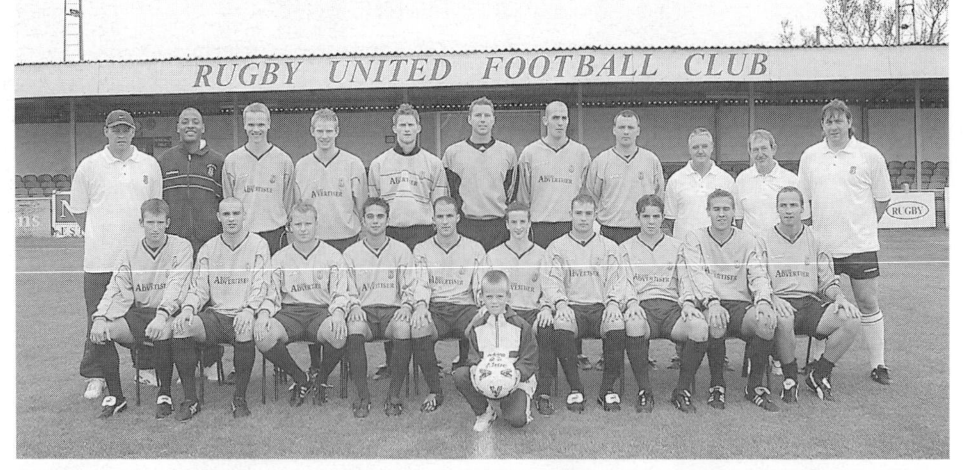

L-R - Back Row: Tony Dobson (manager), Jermaine Gordon, Lee Tatton, Andy Commander, Dean Thomas, Jason Pearcey, Ben Milner, Craig Herbert, Steve Townsend (assistant), Bob Gardner (physio), Steve Shea (asst. manager). Front: Nathan Thompson, Jamie Williams, Paul O'Brien, Karl Brennan, Dave Pearson, Neil Melvin, Danny Hall, Ryan Nash, Rory Squire, Gary Redgate. (Mascot: Jack Dobson).

SHEPSHED DYNAMO

CLUB OFFICIALS

Chairman: Michael Voce

President: Gilbert Kinch

Secretary: Peter Bull

17 Welland Rd, Barrow-on-Soar,
Leicestershire LE12 8NA
Tel: 01509 413338

Press Officer: John Brindley
Tel: 07971 339105

FOOTBALL MANAGEMENT TEAM

Manager: Dave Williams

Coach: Frank Benjamin

Physio: Alan Cook

FACT FILE

Re-formed: 1994
Nickname: Dynamo
Sponsors: Coalville Paints
Colours: Black & white stripes/black/black
Change colours: All Yellow
Midweek matchday: Tuesday
Reserves' League: Midland Comb.
Local Press: Loughborough Echo,
Leicester Mercury, Coalville Times
Local Radio: Radio Leicester, Oak FM

PROGRAMME

Pages: 40 Price: £1.20
Editors: Andy Macmilllan (01509 822587)
& Andy Reed
email: andy.macmillan@ntlworld.com

GROUND The Dovecote, Butthole Lane, Shepshed, Leicestershire Tel: 01509 650992
Directions: M1 J 23, A512 towards Ashby, right at first lights, right at garage in Forest Street, right into Butthole Lane opposite Black Swan. Five miles from Loughborough (BR)
Capacity: 5,000 Cover: 1,500 Seats: 400 Floodlights: Yes
Clubhouse: Takes 120 in main room, 50 in others **Club Shop:** Yes (Steve Straw & Alan Gibson)

PREVIOUS
Leagues: Leicestershire Senior 07-16 19-27 46-50 51-81, Midland Counties 81-82, Northern Counties (East) 82-83, Southern 83-88, Northern Premier 88-93, Midland Combination 93-94, Midland Alliance 94-96
Names: Shepshed Albion 1890-1975 91-94, Shepshed Charterhouse 75-91
Grounds: Ashby Road (pre-1897), Little Haw Farm

CLUB RECORDS
Attendance: 2,500 v Leicester C. (friendly) 96-97
Win: 10-0 v Bloxwixh T. (H), Mid. Comb. 93-94 **Defeat:** 0-7 v Hyde Utd. (A) NPL 90-91
Career Goalscorer: Jeff Lissaman 104 (81-86) **Career Appearances:** Austin Straker 300
Transfer fee paid: £2,000 for Doug Newton (Charterhouse)
Transfer fee received: £10,000 for John Deakin from Birmingham City (Charterhouse)

BEST SEASON
FA Vase: Semi-Finalists 78-79 **FA Trophy:** 3rd Rd Replay v Emley 98-99
FA Cup: 1st Rd 82-83, 1-5 v Preston North End (A), 96-97 v Carlisle United (a) 0-6

HONOURS
Southern Lge Midland Div. R-up 83-84, N.C.E. Lge 82-83, Lge Cup 82-83; Midland Counties Lge 81-82, Lge Cup 81- 82; Leicestershire Senior Lge 10-11 20-21 78-79 79-80 80-81, R-up 21-22, Div 2 53-54 65-66 77-78, Div 2 Cup 77-78; Leicestershire Senior Cup (7); Loughborough Charity Cup 92-93 01-02; Midland Alliance Winners 95-96

Players progressing: Neil Grewcock (Burnley 84), Gordon Tucker (Huddersfield 87), Devon White (Bristol R. 87), John Deakin (Birmingham City)

L-R - Back Row: Andy Davis, Darren Grassby, Carl Lawrence, Andy Harland, Adam Stevens, Duncan O'Brien, Scott Mackay, Richard Keeling, Lee Quincey. **Front Row:** Martin Emery, Matt Dorian, Damien Esky, Jason Weafer, Paul Robilliard, Rob Johnson, Simon Forsdick.

SOLIHULL BOROUGH

CLUB OFFICIALS

Chief Executive: T.B.A.

President: Joe McGorian

General Manager: Trevor Stevens

Secretary: Joe Murphy, 25 Coombe Drive, Nuneaton, Warwicks. CV10 9DD
Tel: 079711 89952 (M) Fax: c/o club

Press Officer: Richard Crawshaw
Tel: 01564 702746 or 07712 791202(M)

FOOTBALL MANAGEMENT TEAM

Manager: Paul Holleran

Assistant Manager:Guy Russell

Physio: Rob Williams

FACT FILE

Formed: 1953 Nickname: Boro
Sponsors: Carling Black Label
Colours: Red/white/red
Change colours: White/black/white
Midweek matchday: Monday
Local Press: Solihull Times, Solihull News, Sunday Mercury, Sports Argus
Local Radio: Radio WM, BRMB
Website: www.sbfc 2000.co.uk

2002-2003

Captain: Matt Smith
Player of the Year: Andy Corbett
Top Scorer: Andy Corbett 25

PROGRAMME

Pages: 44 Price: £1.50
Editor: Dave Woodbridge (07769 675382)

Ground: Damson Park, Damson Parkway, Solihull, W. Mids B91 2PP Tel: 0121 705 6770 Fax: 0121 711 4045
Directions: Leave M42 at Jnct 6. A45 for 2 miles towards B'ham.Past Honda Garage and opp Forte Posthouse Hotel, left at filter to traffic lights into Damson Parkway.(Signpost Landrover/Damsonwwod) Go round roundabout, down other side of dual crriageway for 100 jds .Ground on left. From Coventry use A45 to Posthouse. Solihull,A41 into Hampton Lane and Yew Tree LaneLane.
Capacity: 3,050 Cover: 1,000 Seats: 280 Floodlights: Yes
Clubhouse: Country Club facilities and all type of functions can be booked.(0121 705 6770)

PREVIOUS **Leagues:** Mercian; Midland Combination 69-91
Name: Lincoln FC **Grounds:** Widney Stadium, Solihull 65-88,Moor Green 88-98,Redditch 98-00

CLUB RECORDS **Attendance (at new ground):** 2,000 v Birmingham City Friendly 2002-03
Win: 9-0 v Glossop North End (H) F.A.Cup 1st Q Rd 2002-03
Defeat: 1-6 v Tiverton Town (A) Southern League (Western) 99-00
Career Goalscorer: Joe Dowling 138 **Career Appearances:** Darrel Houghton 360
Transfer fee paid: £15,000 for Recky Carter, from Kettering Town
Transfer fee received: £30,000 from Coventry City for Andy Williams

BEST SEASON **FA Cup:** 1st Rd 97-98; 1-1,3-3 (2-4pen) v Darlington and 92-93, 2-2,2-3 v V.S.Rugby
FA Vase: 5th Rd 74-75 **FA Trophy:** 4th Rd Prop 97-98 and 2001-02

HONOURS Southern Lg Midland Div 91-92; Midland Comb. R-up 84-8590-91, Chall Cup R-up 73-74 90-91, Presidents Cup R-up 69-70; Lord Mayor of Birmingham Charity Cup 91-92 92-93 94-95 96-97; Worcs Sen. Cup R-up 92-93 96-97 97-98; 99-00Birmingham Sen. Cup 94-95

Players Progressing: Kevin Ashley (Birmingham C.), Andy Williams (Coventry C.), Geoff Scott . Danny Conway ,Nicky Cross and Alan Smith (LeicesterC.), Dean Spink (Aston Villa), John Frain (Northampton T.), Jamie Campbell (Walsall) and John Gayle (Birmingham City)

2002-2003 Squad: Back row left to right: Jamie Campbell, Andy Corbett, Andy Lovelock, Matt Smith, Gary Hateley, Mike Payne, Gary Knight, Morton Titterton and Lee Saunders.**Middle row:** MarkShepherd, Martin Hier, Graham Jones (Physio), Dave Busst (Manager), Joe Murphy (Secretary/Director), Paul Holleran (Asst. Manager), Michael Hayde and Simon Hollis.
Front row: Ceaig Dutton, Brett Healy, Chris Smith, Dave Haywood. Ian Cooper, Stuart Hamilton and Leon Thomas.

STOURPORT SWIFTS

CLUB OFFICIALS

Chairman: Chris Reynolds

President: Roy Crowe

General Manager: John McDonald

Secretary & Matchday Contact
John McDonald
65 Princess Way, Stourport
Worcs. DY13 0EL
Tel: 01299 82088

FOOTBALL MANAGEMENT TEAM

Manager: Dave Titterton

Asst Manager/Coach: Kevin Sweeney

Physio: MalcolmCowell

FACT FILE

Founded: 1882 Nickname: Swifts
Sponsors: Reynolds of Rushock
Colours: All Yelow
Change colours: White/black/black
Midweek matchday: Tuesday
Website: www.fly.to/swifts

2002-2003

Captain: Simon Marsh
Top Scorer: Richard Ball
Players of the Year: John Shirley, Dave Davies and Sean Wright

PROGRAMME

68 pages £1.50
Editor: Malcolm Cowell c/o Club
Tel: 01299 250800 (B)

PROGRAMME SPONSOR
SHUTTLE
Times News
SWIFTS V MANGOTSFIELD UTD
Dr Martens Western Division • Saturday 26th April 2003 • kick-off 3.00pm

GROUND Walshes Meadow, Harold Davis Drive, Stourport-on-Severn.
Tel: 01299 825188

Directions: Follow one-way system through Stourport sign posted Sports Centre.Go over River Severn Bridge, turn left into Harold Davies Drive. Ground is at rear of Sports Centre. Nearest rail station is Kidderminster.

Capacity: 2,000 Seats: 250 Cover: 150 Floodlights: Yes

Clubhouse: Open matchdays. Hot snacks available. Licensed bar. **Club Shop:** No

PREVIOUS
Leagues: Kidderminster/ Worcester/ West Midland Regional, Midland Football Alliance 1998-2001
Grounds: Bewdley Rd; Moor Hall Park; Feathers Farm; Olive Grove; Hawthorns.

RECORDS
Attendancee: 4,000 v Birmingham, charity match.
Goalscorer: Gary Crowther **Appearances:** Ian Johnson
Win: 10-0 **Defeat:** 1-7

BEST SEASON **FA Cup:** 3rd Q Rd 2001-02 **F.A.Vase:** 6th Rd 20001 **FA Trophy:** 2nd Rd.

HONOURS West Mids Prem Div R-Up 94-95 96-97 97-98, Lg Div 1 R-up 87-88, Prem Div Cup 92-93, Div 2 Cup R-up 82-83; Worcs Snr Urn 92-93 93-94 94-95 97-98 Worcs Infirmary Cup 94-95 95-96 97-98; MFA 2000-01

L-R - Back: Andrew Wright, Jan Mulders, Dave Davies, Lee Evans, John Newall (Captain), Steve Ulfig, Craig Harris, Kerry Giddings, James Wood.
Front: Jon Hill, Craig Webb, Ronnie Sayer, John Shirley, John Cotterill, Mark Jones, Alex Kilgour, Steven Hawkes.

SUTTON COLDFIELD TOWN

CLUB OFFICIALS

Chairman: Tom Keogh

Secretary: The Rev Ken Hawkins
70 Holifast Rd.,Wylde Greem
West Midlands B721AE
Tel: 01213501630(H) 07812 771365(M)

FOOTBALL MANAGEMENT TEAM

Manager: Chris Keogh

Asst Man: Brian Kenning

Physio: Ed Judge

FACT FILE

Formed: 1897
Nickname: Royals
Colours: All Blue
Change colours: All Yelow
Midweek matchday: Tuesday
Feeder Team: Sutton Town(Mid Comb)
Local Press:
Sutton Coldfield News, Sutton Observer
Local Radio: BRMB, Radio WM

PROGRAMME

Pages: 28 Price: £1.20
Editor:Terry Coley 0121 240 4521 (H)

GROUND Central Ground, Coles Lane, Sutton Coldfield B72 1NL
Fax/Tel: 0121 354 2997 or 0121 355 5475 email: alan.fleming1@btinternet.com

Directions: A5127 into Sutton, right at Odeon cinema (Holland Rd), then first right into Coles Lane - ground 150 yds on left. 10 mins walk from SuttonColdfield (BR), bus 104 from Birmingham

Capacity: 4,500 Cover: 500 Seats: 200 Floodlights: Yes

Clubhouse: Brick built lounge & concert room, fully carpeted and extensively decorated Open daily, food available

Club Shop: Selling metal badges, scarves, hats, pens, rosettes, progs. Contact: Bill Portman

PREVIOUS
Leagues: Central Birmingham, Walsall Sen., Staffs Co., BirminghamComb. 50-54, West Mids (Regional) 54-65 79-82, Midlands Comb. 65-79
Name: Sutton Coldfield FC 1879-1921
Grounds: Meadow Plat 1879-89/ Coles Lane (site of current ambulance station) 90-1919

CLUB RECORDS
Attendance: 2,029 v Doncaster Rovers, F.A. Cup 80-81 (Receipts £2,727)
Career Goalscorer: Eddie Hewitt 288
Career Appearances: Andy Ling 550
Fee paid: £1,500 twice in 1991, for Lance Morrison (Gloucester) , Micky Clarke(Burton A.) and Steve Farmer (Atherstone U)
Fee received: £25,000 for Barry Cowdrill (WBA 1979)

BEST SEASON
FA Cup: 1st Rd 80-81, 0-1 v Doncaster R (H), 92-93, 1-2 v BoltonWanderers (A)
FA Trophy: 1st Round replay 1989-90
FA Amateur Cup: 2nd Round 1970-71

HONOURS Southern Lg Midland Div R-up 82-83, West Mids Lg 79-80 (Lg Cup 80-81 81-82), Midland Comb.(2) 77-79 (R-up(2) 69-71, Lg Cup 69-70), Walsall Senior Lg 46-47, Walsall Sen. Cup(3) 77-80 (R-up 80-81), Staffs Sen. Cup R-up 89-90, Lord Mayor of Birmingham Charity Cup 95-96, R-up 93-94, Worcs Sen. Cup SF 88-89, Walsall Challenge Cup R-up 46-47 47-48, Sutton Charity Cup 46-47 65-66 71-72 86-87 89-90 90-91, Express & Star Cup 44-45 Dr Martens Cup 98-99

Players progressing: Arthur Corbett (Walsall 49), Paul Cooper (Manchester C.), Noel Blake (Leeds), Steve Cooper (Barnsley), Peter Latchford (WBA), Mark Smith (Wolves), John Barton (Everton), Barry Cowdrill (WBA 79),Colin Dryhurst (Halifax 79), Dale Belford (Notts Co. 87), Ellis Laight (Torquay 92)

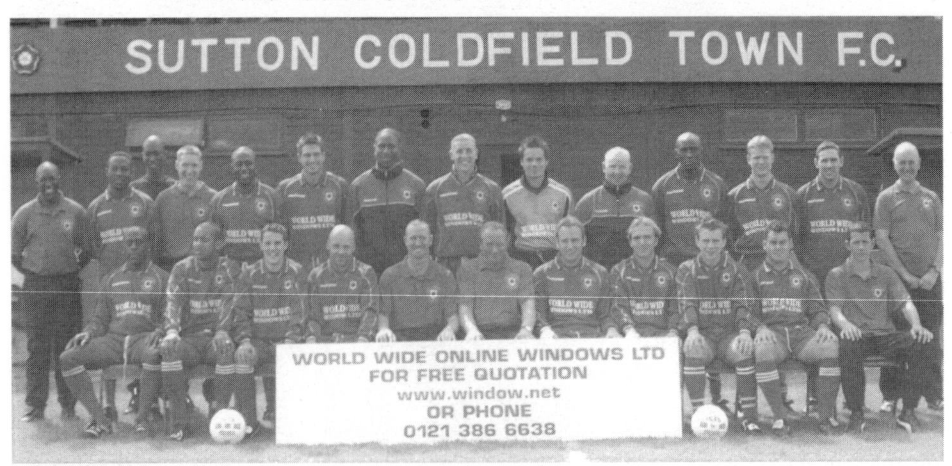

Back Row,left to right: R. Richardson (Coach),K. Murragh, C.Ferguson, D. Massingham, M.Gray, S.Farmer, E. Ejiofor, D.Baker, J. Bray, B. Burns, W. Dyer, K. Jones, D.Shaw and E.Judge (physio) **Front Row:** K.Thompson, L.B ailey, D. Burrows, A. Ling, C. Keogh (Manager), B. Kenning (Assistant Manager),S. Tucker, M. Smioz, M. Gardiner, S. Randall and A. Hughes

SWINDON SUPERMARINE

FOOTBALL LEAGUE

CLUB OFFICIALS

Chairman: Steve Moore

President: Cliff Puffett

Secretary: Judi Moore,
Chardon Rise, Bell Lane,
Liddington,Swindon, SN4 0HH
Tel: 01793 828778

Press Officer: Leigh Moore
01793 790685

FOOTBALL MANAGEMENT TEAM

Manager: Ray Baverstock

Physio: Wayne Roberts

FACT FILE

Founded: 1992
Nickname: 'Marine'
Sponsors: Fuelforce
Colours: Blue & white hoops/blue/blue
Change colours: Red & White/Red/Red
Midweek Matchday: Wednesday

PROGRAMME

Pages: 40 Price: £1.00
Editor: Keith Yeomans
Tel: 07721 885728 01793 487461

GROUND Hunts Copse, South Marston, Swindon
Tel: 01793 828778. E-mail: supermarinefc@aol.com.

Directions: On A361 Swindon/Highworth road, adjoining South Marston Ind. Estate. Six miles from Swindon (BR) - buses in direction of Highworth, Fairford & Lechdale. If lost ask for Honda.

Capacity: 3,000 Seats: 300 Cover: 300 Floodlights: Yes

Club Shop: Opening this season - contact Andy Garrett **Clubhouse:** Yes

PREVIOUS **Leagues:** Wiltshire Lge., Hellenic League to 2001
Names: Vickers Armstrong 46-81,Supermarine 82-91 (merged 1992), Penhill Youth Centre 70-84, Swindon Athletic 84-89 (merged)
Ground: Supermarine: Vickers Airfield (until mid-1960s); Swindon Ath.: Merton 70-84; `Southbrook', Pinehurst Road 84-92

RECORD **Attendance:** 1,550 v Aston Villa

HONOURS: Hellenic Lge - Premier Div. 97-98, 00-01, R-up 95-96 98-99; Div. One 85-86 86-87; Reserve Section 96-97; Lge Cup 96-97,99-00; Floodlit Cup 97-98.,99-00, 00-01. Wiltshire Senior Cup 82-83, 86-87, 89-90. Wilts Premier Shield 96-97.Wilts Youth Cup 01-02, Hellenic Challenge Cup 96-97, 99/00.

TAUNTON TOWN

Taunton Town
Football Club
Somerset FA
Home of the Peacocks
2002-03

CLUB OFFICIALS

Chairman: T F Harris

Secretary: Joan Ellis
c/o the club
Tel: 01823 333833 (H)

Press Officer: Les Gill

FOOTBALL MANAGEMENT TEAM
Manager: Russell Musker
Asst. Man: Tom Kelly
Physio: Kevin Matthews

FACT FILE
Formed: 1947
Nickname: Peacocks
Club Sponsors: T.G.Roofing
Colours: All Sky blue
Change colours: All gold
Midweek matches: Wednesday
Reserves ' League: None
Local Radio: Orchard FM, Radio Bristol
Local Press: Somerset County Gazette

PROGRAMME
Pages: 32 Price: £1
Editor: T.B.A.Newsline: 0930 555 849

Ground: Wordsworth Drive, Taunton, Somerset TA1 2HG Tel: 01823 278191
Directions: Leave M5 Jct 25, follow signs to town centre, at 2nd set of lights turn left into Wordsworth Drive; ground on left. 25 mins walk from Taunton (BR); turn left out of station and follow road right through town centre bearing left into East Reach. Follow road down and turn right into Wordsworth Drive shortly after Victoria pub
Capacity: 4,000 Seats:400 Cover: 1,000 Floodlights: Yes
Clubhouse: Social club to accommodate 300, full bar facilities. Separate bar & hall for private functions
Club Shop: Yes

PREVIOUS
Leagues: Western 54-77; Southern 77-83, Western 83-2002
Grounds: Several prior to 1953

CLUB RECORDS
Attendance: 3,284 v Tiverton Town, **FA Vase:** Winners 00-01
Appearances: Tony Payne **Scorer** (in a season) : Reg Oram 67
Win: 12-0 v Dawlish Town (A), FA Cup Prel. Rd, 28/8/93
Defeat: 0-8 v Cheltenham Town (A), FA Cup 2nd Qual. Rd, 28/9/91

BEST SEASON
FA Cup: 1st Rd Proper 81-82, 1-2 v Swindon T. (A)
FA Trophy: 1st Rd Proper 80-81, 1-5 v Hendon at Q.P.R
FA Vase: Winners 00-01, R-up 93-94, S-F 97-98 98-99

HONOURS
FA Vase Winners 00-01 R-up 93-94, Western Lge Champions 68-69 89-90,95-6,98-9,99-00, 00-01 (R-up 93-94 97-98, Les Phillips R-up 93-94 97-98, Alan Young Cup 73-74 75-76 (jt with Falmouth), Charity Chall. Cup 49-50, 50-51), Somerset Snr Lg 52-53, Som Prem.Cup R-up 82-83 89-90 92-93 98-99

Players progressing: Charlie Rutter (Cardiff), Stuart Brace (Southend), Steve Winter (Torquay) Kevin Maloy (Exeter C.)

L-R - Back Row: Michael Booth, Grantley Dicks, Gary Head, Danny Lewis, Dean Jones, Antony Lynch, Paul Edwards, Alex Watson, Gary Fisher, Craig Russell, Sean McCarthy, Mark Reynolds, Ben Smith. **Front**: Danny Harris, Derek Fields, Paul West (Coach), Chris Myers, Russell Musker (Manager), Tom Kelly (Asst. Man.), Graham Webster (Physio), Pete Shepherd, Simon Winstone.

TEAM BATH

FOOTBALL LEAGUE

CLUB OFFICIALS

Chairman: Ivor Powell
c/o Univ. of Bath, Sports Development,
Claverton Down, Bath BA2 7AY
Tel: 01225 826656

Secretary: Phil Searle
12 Chepstow Close, Chippenham SN14 0XP
Tel: 01249 460857 (H)
01225 383518 (W)
email:phil@matchtight.co.uk

FOOTBALL MANAGEMENT TEAM

Manager: Ged Roddy Tel: 01225 826339
Coach: Paul Tisdale
Physio:

FACT FILE

Formed: 2000
Colours: Yellow & Blue/blue/gold
Change colours: All blue
Midweek Matchday: Monday

PROGRAMME
Editor: Lorna Dagger
01225 386656(W)
01225 386755 (FAX)

GROUND University of Bath, Sports Training Village, Claverton Down, Bath.
Tel: 01225 826339

Directions: Follow signs to Claverton Down and Park & Ride (University).
Take the Norwood Ave. entrance to the campus and as you drive towards the university you will approach two "hanger" like buildings on the right.
This is the Sports Training Village. Follow signs to free car park.

PREVIOUS **Leagues:** Western 2000-03

CLUB RECORDS **Attendance:** 5469 v Mansfield Town, FA Cup 1st Round

BEST SEASON **FA Vase:** 01-02 - 3rd Round, 0-1 v Arlesey Town (H)
FA Cup: 02-03 -1st Round proper, 2-4 v Mansfield Town (H)

HONOURS Western Lge Div. 1 00-01, Premier Division 02-03

Players P rogressing: Barry Lavety 03 (St Mirren, Bertrand Covic 03 (Cheltenham Town)

L-R - Back Row: Paul Tisdale (Player-Coach), James Edgerley, Douglas Keen, Nick Hudson, Chris Holland, Brad Williams, Chris Lewis, Kes Metitri, Tom Stocco, Ali Otto, Greg Sharp. **Middle**: Ged Roddy (Manager), Luke Prince, David Blake, Matt Locke, Kevin Watson, Daver Horseman, Dean Smith, Matt Townley, Ivor Powell. **Front**: Stuart Gibbs, Matt Lewis, Stefan Wojciechowski, Mike Gillingham, Peter Ball, Craig Fullam, Matt Reeves.

YATE TOWN

YATE TOWN
Football Club
Cherry Red Records
Hellenic Football League
Premier Division
2002-03
Main Club Sponsor
THE ERH GROUP
E.R. Hemmings (Building) Ltd.
ERH Communications Ltd.
A B Johnson

CLUB OFFICIALS

Chairman: Peter Jackson

President: Roger Hawkins

Secretary: Terry Tansley
1 Tyning Close, Yate, Bristol. BS37 5PN
Tel: 01454 324305

Press Officer: Secretary

FOOTBALL MANAGEMENT TEAM

Manager : Richard Thompson

Physio: Steve Carter

FACT FILE

Formed: 1946
Nickname: The Bluebells
Colours: White/navy/navy
Change colours: All Red
Midweek matchday: Tuesday
Reserve Team's League: Bristol Suburban
Website: www.yatetownfc.com

2002-2003

Captain: Ben Trotman
Top Scorer: Paul Metheringham 39
Player of the Year: Ross Casey

PROGRAMME

Pages: 40 Price: £1
Editor: Terry Tansley c/o Club

GROUND Lodge Road, Yate, Bristol BS37 7LE Tel: 01454 228103

Directions: M4 jct 18, A46 towards Stroud, then A432 to Yate. Turn right into Green Goose Way. at 1st R'bout into link road and Yate shopping centre. Turn right at third main traffic lights into North Road. 1st left into lodge Road. Five miles from Bristol Parkway BR main line station, half mile from Yate BR station. Buses 329, X68 and 328

Capacity: 2,000 Cover: 400 Seats: 236 Floodlights: Yes

Clubhouse: Open every night & weekend lunchtimes. Skittles, darts, pool, live entertainment

Club Shop: Selling programmes & usual souvenirs. Contact: Secretary

PREVIOUS **Leagues:** Gloucestershire County 68-83; Hellenic 83-89, 00-03; Southern Lge 89-00
Name: Yate YMCA 1946-70 **Grounds:** Yate Aerodrome 50-54, Newmans Field 54-60, Sunnyside Lane 60-84

CLUB RECORDS **Attendance:** 2,000 for Bristol Rovers v Bristol Rovers Past, Vaughan Jones testimonial 90
Win: 13-3 v Clevedon, Bristol Premier Comb 67-68
CareerGoalscorer: Kevin Thaws **Career Appearances:** Gary Hewlett
Transfer fee - Paid: None **Received:** £15,000 for Mike Davis (Bristol Rovers 93)

BEST SEASON **FA Vase:** Fifth Round 1991-92

HONOURS Hellenic Lg (x2) 87-89 Premier R-up 02-03 Lg Cup Winners 02-03 Div 1 R-up 84-85, Lg Skol Cup R-up 87-88), Glos Chall. Trophy 88-89, 00-01 (R-up x2), Glos Snr Amtr Cup Sth 77-78 91-92 (res) 92-93 (res), Glos Snr Chal. Cup (Nth) R-up 89-90 92-93 94-95, Stroud Charity Cup R-up 74-75 81-82 84-85 (Sect. A Winners(6) 76-78 79-80 82-83 87-89), Berkeley Hosp. Prem.Cup(3) 73-75 80-81, S.W. Co's Sutton Vase 85-86 Dr.Martens Fairplay award 98-99, 99-00

Players Progressing:
Richard Thompson (Newport Co.), Phil Purnell (Bristol R.), Darren Tilley (York C.), Steve Winter (Walsall), Mike Davis (Bristol R. 93)

L-R - Back Row: Richard Thompson (Manager), Leon Simpson, Tony Court, Neil Long, Darren Hobbs, Steve Carter (physio), Lee Barlass. **Middle**: Leigh Williams, Ian Howse, Kevin Coles, Gary Powell, Andy Neal, Ali Hines. **Front**: Tony Bennett, Dave Elsey, Paul Dempsey, Dave Bright, Ross Casey, Paul Hetherington. Missing: Ben Trotman.

EASTERN DIVISION

		P	W	D	L	W	D	L	F	A	GD	Pts
1	Dorchester Town	42	17	1	3	11	8	2	114	40	74	93
2	Eastbourne Borough	42	16	3	2	13	3	5	92	33	59	93
3	Stamford	42	17	2	2	10	4	7	80	39	41	87
4	Salisbury City (-3)	42	16	4	1	11	4	6	81	42	39	86
5	Bashley	42	13	6	2	10	6	5	90	44	46	81
6	King's Lynn	42	14	4	3	10	3	8	98	62	36	79
7	Rothwell Town	42	13	4	4	9	6	6	77	52	25	76
8	Banbury United	42	12	5	4	9	6	6	75	50	25	74
9	Tonbridge Angels	42	12	5	4	8	6	7	71	55	16	71
10	Histon	42	12	5	4	8	2	11	99	62	37	67
11	Ashford Town	42	12	4	5	6	5	10	63	57	6	63
12	Sittingbourne	42	8	6	7	7	2	12	57	69	-12	53
13	Burnham	42	9	4	8	6	3	12	62	79	-17	52
14	Fisher Athletic (London)	42	5	2	14	10	3	8	57	80	-23	50
15	Chatham Town	42	9	2	10	5	3	13	54	84	-30	47
16	Newport IOW	42	7	3	11	5	3	13	53	87	-34	42
17	Dartford	42	7	4	10	4	4	13	48	78	-30	41
18	Erith & Belvedere	42	8	2	11	3	4	14	65	96	-31	39
19	Corby Town	42	5	6	10	4	5	12	49	84	-35	38
20	Fleet Town	42	3	6	12	5	2	14	34	80	-46	32
21	Spalding United	42	3	4	14	1	2	18	40	108	-68	18
22	St Leonards	42	2	3	16	2	1	18	38	116	-78	16

		1	2	3	4	5	6	7	8	9	10	11	12	13	14	15	16	17	18	19	20	21	22
1	Ashford Town		1-2	1-0	2-1	2-0	1-0	3-0	1-5	1-0	3-1	1-4	3-1	1-1	0-0	3-2	1-0	0-1	0-1	1-0	8-1	1-1	1-1
2	Banbury United	3-0		2-2	1-0	4-0	3-1	1-0	2-1	0-3	3-0	1-2	4-1	1-2	2-2	2-0	2-2	0-1	4-1	4-2	2-1	1-1	2-2
3	Bashley	4-1	0-0		4-2	4-0	2-0	4-0	0-0	1-6	0-0	4-1	4-0	5-1	1-2	5-1	1-1	3-1	4-0	1-1	6-0	2-1	1-1
4	Burnham	3-4	1-0	1-2		1-0	4-3	3-0	1-2	0-0	2-2	3-4	2-1	1-4	0-3	2-0	1-1	1-1	3-2	1-0	1-2	0-1	4-3
5	Chatham Tn	1-1	3-4	1-0	2-0		3-2	0-1	0-4	0-3	1-2	0-1	3-1	1-1	1-3	2-1	2-1	0-2	2-0	3-1	2-1	1-2	1-2
6	Corby Town	2-5	2-1	2-2	0-1	2-2		1-1	2-5	2-2	1-4	0-2	1-1	1-0	1-1	2-0	1-3	0-4	1-3	2-0	2-0	0-1	1-4
7	Dartford	1-1	1-2	1-3	3-3	3-6	4-0		1-1	0-1	0-0	1-3	1-2	0-2	3-0	4-0	2-0	1-4	1-0	2-1	4-2	2-3	0-1
8	Dorchester Town	3-1	3-1	0-2	3-4	4-0	3-1	3-0		2-1	6-2	2-0	5-1	2-1	1-0	1-1	0-2	5-1	3-0	9-0	8-1	2-1	5-1
9	Eastbourne Boro	2-0	1-2	2-2	3-1	3-0	2-2	4-0	1-3		3-0	2-0	2-1	4-1	4-1	7-0	3-1	0-0	3-0	4-0	4-0	2-1	3-2
10	Erith & Belvedere	1-2	4-4	1-4	4-0	3-1	1-0	4-1	0-1	0-1		1-2	2-1	3-4	2-4	5-3	0-2	3-2	1-4	7-0	2-3	1-2	2-2
11	Fisher Athletic	0-2	0-1	1-2	2-0	3-0	0-1	1-1	1-5	2-4	1-1		0-1	3-2	0-5	1-3	0-3	0-1	2-5	2-1	3-1	0-3	0-1
12	Fleet Town	0-0	0-1	0-1	0-1	0-2	0-0	0-0	0-0	1-2	2-1	1-3		3-2	1-5	0-2	0-2	0-2	1-2	0-4	1-0	0-0	1-1
13	Histon	3-2	0-3	6-0	2-0	3-1	1-1	5-0	0-2	0-2	6-0	2-0	4-0		4-2	1-1	2-2	1-1	3-0	5-1	8-1	2-3	1-1
14	King's Lynn	1-0	2-1	2-1	5-1	7-2	4-1	2-0	2-2	2-0	3-0	1-1	5-0	2-8		1-3	3-4	3-1	1-1	4-0	1-1	1-0	3-0
15	Newport IOW	1-1	0-3	0-4	0-1	3-1	2-2	0-3	0-1	0-1	3-0	2-3	1-0	2-1	3-0		0-2	0-4	1-1	3-2	2-0	1-6	2-3
16	Rothwell Town	1-0	0-0	0-0	2-1	2-2	3-0	0-1	2-2	2-0	5-1	3-2	3-1	3-2	2-5	2-4		0-1	2-0	2-1	2-1	4-2	2-1
17	Salisbury Town	3-1	0-0	2-2	5-2	2-0	3-1	3-0	0-0	1-2	2-1	3-1	2-1	3-2	2-1	3-2	0-0		3-0	1-0	3-2	2-1	2-0
18	Sittingbourne	2-1	0-0	1-0	2-2	0-1	2-2	1-2	0-3	0-2	4-1	1-1	3-0	0-1	1-2	0-0	0-0	3-2		5-2	2-1	1-4	2-1
19	Spalding United	0-2	4-1	0-2	1-5	0-2	1-2	1-1	2-2	0-1	1-0	2-2	0-1	1-2	1-2	0-3	2-4	1-4	1-2		1-0	0-0	1-3
20	St Leonards	2-3	0-3	1-2	0-0	0-4	1-3	3-1	0-2	1-1	0-1	2-3	3-5	0-2	0-4	3-1	0-2	0-2	1-3	1-1		0-1	1-2
21	Stamford	1-0	2-0	1-3	2-0	5-1	2-0	3-1	2-1	1-0	3-1	3-0	0-0	2-1	2-0	3-0	2-1	0-0	2-1	4-2	6-0		0-2
22	Tonbridge Angels	1-1	2-2	0-0	1-2	0-0	0-1	1-0	2-2	0-1	4-0	2-0	1-4	1-0	4-1	1-0	3-2	2-1	2-1	6-1	2-1	2-0	

ASHFORD TOWN

CLUB OFFICIALS

Chairman: Tim Thorogood
President: Ashley M Batt
Secretary/Press Officer: Alan Lancaster
128 Kingsnorth Rd, Ashford, Kent
TN23 2HY Tel: 01233 621325
Commercial Director: Peter Young
Tel: 01233 611838(Ground)

FOOTBALL MANAGEMENT TEAM
Manager: Tim Thorogood
Asst Manager: Gary Anderson
Coach: Tim Thorogood
Physios: George Sargeant& Stuart Unthank

FACT FILE
Formed: 1930
Nickname: Nuts & Bolts
Colours: Green/navy/green
Change colours: White&green/green/white
Midweek home matchday: Tuesday
Reserves' League: Go Travel Kent Lge
2002-2003
Captain: Ian Gibbs
Top Scorer: Adrrian Stone 23
Players of the Year: Ian Gibbs & John Whitehouse

Pages: 32 Price: £1.50
Editor: Dereek West

Local Press: Kentish Express& Adscene
Local Radio: Radio Kent, Invicta Radio

GROUND The Homelands, Ashford Road, Kingsnorth, Ashford, Kent TN26 1NJ Tel: 01233 611838
Directions: M20 jct 10, follow A2070 signs towards Brenzett & Lydd airport, dual carriageway to junction of old A2070, ground 1 mile on left thro' village of Kingsnorth. 4 miles south of Ashford
Capacity: 3,200 Cover: 1,250 Seats: 500 Floodlights: Yes
Clubhouse: Open matchdays and for special functions. Licensed bar, function room. Limited food - sandwiches & simple snacks.
Club Shop: Sells old progs, pennants, scarves, badges etc. Contact: Sue Brown at Ground

PREVIOUS **Names:** Ashford United, Ashford Railway, Ashford F.C.
Leagues: Kent 30-59. Ground: Essella Park, Essella Rd 30-87

CLUB RECORDS **Attendance:** 6,525 (at Essella Park, previous ground), v Crystal Palace, FA Cup 1st Rd 1959.
3,363 (at current ground), v Fulham FA Cup 1st Round 1994.
Goalscorer: Dave Arter 197. **Appearances:** Peter McRobert 765
Win: 10-1 v Bury Town, February 1964. **Defeat:** 0-8 v Crawley Town, November1964
Fee Paid: £7,000 for J Ross & D Arter (Sittingbourne, March 94)
Fee Received: £25k for Jeff Ross & Dave Arter (Hythe Tn, 90). Individually: £20k for Lee McRobert (Sittingbourne, 93)

BEST SEASON **FA Trophy:** Semi Final 72-73, 96-97 2nd Rd
FA Cup: 2nd Rd 61-62, 0-3 v QPR (H), 66-67, 0-5 v Swindon (A). 1st Rd 7 times. League clubs defeated: None.

HONOURS FA Trophy SF 72-73; Southern Lg Southern Div R-up 86-87 95-96; Kent Lg 48-49(R-up 31-32), Lg Cup 38-39; Kent Senior Cup 58-59 62-63 92-93 95-96

Players progressing: Ollie Norris (Rochdale 61), HowardMoore (Coventry 66), Tony Godden (WBA 75), Lee McRobert (Millwall 94)

Back row, left to right: Gary Anderson (Asst.Man), Stuart White, Paul O.Brien, Simon Elliott, Dave Hassett, John Whitehouse, Martin Anderson, Ian Gibbs, Dean Hill and Stuart Unthank (Physio).**Front row:** George Sergeant (Asst.physio, standing), Sam Saunders, Barry Gardner, Adrian Stone, Lee McRobert, Kevin Skinner, Ian Ross, Aaron O'Leary and Tim Thorogood (Manager, standing). **Photo:** D. F. West.

BANBURY UNITED

CLUB OFFICIALS

Chairman: Paul Saunders
Vice Chairman: Brian Kay
President: David Jesson
Commercial Mgr: Dave Bennett
Press Officer: Dave Bennett
Secretary: B Worsley, c/o Sol Systems, Unit 4 Mallorie Hse, Beaumont Rd,Banbury, OX16 1RH
Tel: 01295 265638 (H), 07941 267567
Email: bworsley@solsystems.freeserve.co.uk

FOOTBALL MANAGEMENT TEAM

Manager: Kevin Brock
Assistant Manager: Brian Robinson
Physio: Wally Hastie

FACT FILE

Founded: 1933 Reformed: 1965
Nickname: Puritans
Sponsors: Alex Lawrie Factors.
Colours: Red & gold/red/red
Change colours: White /white/white
Midweek matches: Tuesday
Reserves' Lge: Hellenic Res Div 1
Club Website: www.banburyunited.co.uk
Unofficial sites:
www..banbury-united.cityslide.com
www.expage.com.bufc

2002-2003

Captain: Jonathon Corbett
Top Scorer: Norman Sylla
Player of the Year: George Redknapp

The Puritan
www.banburyunited.co.uk
Banbury United Football Club
Official Matchday Programme
2002/2003 Season
BANBURY UNITED
V
KING'S LYNN
Dr. Martens Southern League Eastern Division
Saturday 19 April 2003
Kick off 3.00 p.m.
Alex Lawrie Factors

Pages: 40 Price: £1.00
Editor: Kevin Hicklin

GROUND Spencer Stadium, off Station Rd, Banbury, Oxon . OX16 5TA.
Tel: 01295 263354
Directions: M40 jct 11, follow signs for Banbury then BR station, turn right down narrow lane before entering station forecourt; eastern end of town
Capacity: 6,500 Seats: 250 Cover: 500 Floodlights: Yes
Clubhouse: Open match days & week-ends. Mid-week on hire.
Hot food available during after matches **Club Shop:** Yes

HONOURS Oxon Snr Cup 78-79 87-88 (R-up7); Birmingham Comb. R-up 47-48; Oxon Prof. Cup 52-53(jt) 70-71(jt) 72-73 77-78 79-80(jt); Hellenic premier Winners 99-00 Hellenic Lg.Cup R-Up 91-92; Birmingham Snr Cup R-Up 48-49 59-60 (S.F.46-47); Oxon Snr Lg. 34-35 39-4047-48 (res); Oxon Hosp. Cup 46-47 (R-up 45-46); Oxon Benev. Cup R-up 77-78 80-8182-83; Daventry Charity Cup 88-90 02-03; Smiths Mem. Cup 68-70 (R-up 66-68); Hitchin Centenary Cup 68-69 (R-up 67-68); Leamington Charity Cup 51-52; Bucks Charity Cup 00-01 Warks Comb. R-up 57-58 60-61, Presidents Cup R-up 60-61; Midland Floodlit Cup 67-68; Wallspan Comb. 85-86

PREVIOUS **Leagues:** Banbury Jnr 33-34; Oxon Snr 34-35; Birmingham Comb. 35-54; W.Mids 54-66; Southern 66-90
Name: Banbury Spencer

BEST SEASON **FA Cup:** 1st Rd replay 73-74 (Also 1st Rd 47-48 61-62 72-73) **FA Trophy:** 3rd Rd 70-71 73-74

RECORDS **Attendance:** 7,160 v Oxford City, FA Cup 3rd Qual.Rd, 30/10/48
Goalscorer: Dick Pike (1935-48), Tony Jacques (65-76) - both 222
Appearances: Ian Bowyer (557) Fee Paid : £2,000 for Phil Emsden (Oxford Utd, Jan 1980)
Fee Received: £20,000 Kevin Wilson (Derby, December 1979)
Win: 12-0 v RNAS Culham, Oxon Snr Cup 45-46
Defeat: 2-11 v West Bromwich Albion `A', Birmingham Comb. 38-39

Players progressing:
Ollie Kearns (Reading), Kevin Wilson & Richard Pratley(Derby), Mick Kearns & Terry Muckleberg (Oxford), Martin Singleton (Coventry)

Back row, left to right: Mark Essex, Liam O'Neill, Brian Robinson (Asst.Manager), Luke Grady, Ady Fuller, Wayne Blossom, Norman Sylla, Simon Tricker, Jason Allen, Jody McKay, Kevin Brock (Manager) and Wally Hastie (Physio).
Front Row: Matty Travers, Sam Ibrahim, Ollie Stanbridge, Ryan Breslin, Lewis Travers, Jon Corbett, Kieran Sullivan and George Redknapp.

BASHLEY

FOOTBALL LEAGUE

CLUB OFFICIALS

Chairman: Ray Pinney
President: Trevor Adams
Vice Chairman: Derick Binns
Secretary: Pete Plowman,
c/o Bashley F.C.
Mobile:07944 629383

FOOTBALL MANAGEMENT TEAM

Manager:Barry Blanckley
Assistant Manager: Fraser Quirk
Reserves Manager: Chris Collinge

FACT FILE

Formed: 1947
Nickname: The Bash
Sponsors: Spaceage
Colours: Yellow & black
Change colours: Blue & white
Midweek matchday: Tuesday
Reserves' League: Wessex Comb
Local Press: Bournemouth Echo, Southern Pink, New Milton Advertiser
Local Radio: 2CR, Solent, Ocean Sound

GROUND Recreation Ground, BashleyRd., New Milton,Hampshire BH25 5RY.
Tel: 01425 620280 FAX: 01425 638376
Directions: A35 Lyndhurst towards Christchurch, turn left down B3058 towards New Milton, ground on left in Bashley village. Half hour walk from New Milton (BR) station .New Cargo Bus service C32 (NewMilton-Lymington)
Capacity: 4,250 Cover: 1,200 Seats: 300 Floodlights: Yes
Clubhouse: Usual licensing hours. Snacks available **Club Shop:** Open matchdays

Pages: 36 Price: £1
Editor: Richard Millbury
Tel: 01590 645201 (W)

PREVIOUS **Leagues:** Bournemouth 50-83; Hants 83-86; Wessex 86-89

CLUB RECORDS **Attendance:** 3,500 v Emley, F.A. Vase S.F. 1st Leg 87-88
Win: 21-1 v Co-operative (A), Bournemouth Lge, 64 **Defeat:** 2-20 v Air Speed(A), Bournemouth Lge, 57
Career Goalscorer: Colin Cummings **Career Appearances:** John Bone
Transfer fee paid: £7,500 for J Stagg from Andover**Transfer fee received:** £7,500 for Darren Powell from Weymouth 95

BEST SEASON **FA Cup:** 2nd Rd Proper 1994-95, 0-1 v Swansea City
FA Vase: Semi Final 87-88, Qtr Final 88-89 FA Trophy: 2nd Round 91-92

HONOURS Southern Lg Southern Division 89-90 (Lg Cup SF 89-90), Wessex Lg 86-87 87-88 88-89, Hants Lg Div 3 84-85, Hants Lg Combination 88-89, Russell Cotes Cup 88-89 90-91 92-93

Players Progressing : Wayne Brown (Bristol C 1994), David Billington Peterborough 1996), Ryan Young (Plymouth 1997), Dean Higgins (Torquay 1998), Danny Smith (Bournemouith 1998), Craig Davies (Cardiff City 1998), Tony Wallis (Cardiff C 1999), Wade Elliott (AFC Bouremouth 2000)

Back Row, Left To Right: Glen Botterill (Reserve Physio), John Clare (1st Team Physio), Lee Harvey, Paul Wilson, Derek Brown, Gary Williams (Reserve Manager), James Heeps, Andy Lomas (Assistant Manager), Steve Jackman, Eddie Lawley, Paul Turner, Kevin Slinn, Steve Gee (Reserve Team Assistant), Kenny Mist (Chief Scout) **Front Row:** Grant Haley, Carl Adams, Josh Sozzo, Paul Covington, Roger Ashby (Manager), Ian Edge, Rob Miller, Mark Paul, Steve Berry.

BURGESS HILL TOWN

CLUB PERSONNEL

Chairman: Gary Croydon

Patron: Jack Lake

Secretary: Roger Puttick
48 Maple Drive,Burgess Hill RH15 8AW
Tel: 01444 243080
Email : bhtfcsocial@ aol.com

FOOTBALL MANAGEMENT

Manager: Danny Bloor

Asst. Man. / Coach:

Physio:

FACT FILE

Founded: 1882

Nickname: Hillians

Sponsors: Time 24

Colours: Yellow/black/yellow

Change colours: All red

Midweek matchday: Tuesday

2002-03

Leading Goalscorer:Steve Harper

Captain: Adie Doloney

Player of the Year: Ben Andrews

DR MARTENS
SOUTHERN LEAGUE
EASTERN DIVISION

SEASON 2003 - 2004

CLUB SPONSOR
Time 24

MATCHDAY
PROGRAMME

PROGRAMME
Pages: 60 Price: £1

GROUND Leylands Park, Burgess Hill, West Sussex RH15 8AW
Tel: 01444 242429 Website: www.bhtfc.org.uk

Capacity: 2,000 Seats: 307 Cover: Yes Floodlights: Yes

Directions: Turn east from A273 London Road into Leylands Road, take 4th left signposted Leyland Park. Nearest station Wivelsfield

Clubhouse: Bar & social facilities. Tea bar

Club Shop: Yes Club badges available

PREVIOUS **Leagues:** Mid Sussex League, Sussex County >03

CLUB RECORD **Attendance:** 1,598 v Tiptree United F.A.Vase 6th Round

BEST SEASON **FA Cup:** 4th Qual. Rd. 99-00, 1-4 v Hereford United
F.A.Vase: Quarter -Final v Tiptree United 2001-02

HONOURS Sussex County Lg 75-76, 96-97, 97-98, 98-99; 01-02, 02-03; Lg Cup 73-74 79-80 97-98 98-99 (R-up 90-91), Div 2 74-75 (Cup 73-73), F/lit Cup 96-97, Res 76-77 77-78 91-92, Res. Sect. East 77-78 82-83 84-85, Res. Cup 82-83 98-99, 02-03; Yth Sect. West 91-92 East 95-96 96-97 97-98 98-99 North 96-97 97-98, 02-03; Sussex Fives 80; Mid-Sussex Lg 1900-01 03-04 39-40 46-47 56-57 Div 2 03-04 (res), Div 3 20-21 36-37, Div 4 (res) 56-57; Mid Sussex Snr Cup 94-95 96-97; 01-02 Montgomery Cup 39-40 56-57; Mowatt Cup 45-46; Sussex RUR Charity Cup 91-92; Sussex I'mediate Cup 76-77; Sussex Yth Lge 96-97 97-98, Cup 91-92 97-98

The Championship winning squad celebrate at the annual Awards' Dinner & Dance

BURNHAM

32 pages Editor: Cliff Sparkes

Local Press:
Slough Observer, South Bucks Express,
Maidenhead Advertiser, Buckingham Advertiser

Local Radio:
Star FM, BBC Thames Valley, Swan F.M.

CLUB OFFICIALS

Chairman: Malcolm Higton
Vice Chairman: Mark Green
Secretary: David Thomas, 631A Bath Rd, Cippenham, Slough, Berks SL1 6AE
Tel Nos: 01628 416488 (H)
07729 621204 (M)
Press Officer: Alan King
(01494523920 (H) 078999 41414(M)

FOOTBALL MANAGEMENT TEAM

Manager: Jim Greenwood
Assistant Manager:Jackie Stuart
Coach:Steve Mellor
Physio: Sally Carey

FACT FILE

Founded: 1878
Sponsors: T.B.A.
Colours: Blue & white/blue/white
Change colours: Yellow/yellow/black
Midweek matchday: Tuesday 7.30
Reserve Team's Lge: Suburban

2002-2003

Captain: Paul Brett
Top Goalscorer: Michael Bartley 22
Players of the Year: Michael Bartley and Stev Lockhart

Ground: The Gore, Wymers Wood Road, Burnham, Slough SL1 8JG
Tel: 01628 602467/602697

Directions: North west of village centre, 2 miles from Burnham BR station, 2miles from M4 junction 7, 5 miles from M40 junction 2, 100yds north of Gorecrossroads - fork right into Wymers Wood Rd and ground is immediately on right

Capacity: 2,500 Cover: 250 Seats: 250 Floodlights: Yes

Clubhouse: Open every evening and w/e lunch.
Darts and pool, two bars, usual matchday food **Club Shop:** Yes

PREVIOUS **Leagues:** Sth Bucks & East Berks; Maidenhead Intermediate; Windsor, Slough & Dist; Gt Western Comb. 48-64; Wycombe Comb. 64-70; Reading Comb. 70-71; Hellenic 71-77; Athenian 77-84; London Spartan 84-85; Southern 85-95; Hellenic 95-99
Name: Burnham & Hillingdon 1985-87 **Ground:** Baldwin Meadow (until 20's)

RECORD **Attendance:** 2,380 v Halesowen Town, FA Vase 2/4/83
Scorer: Fraser Hughes 65, 69-70 **Win:** 18-0 v High Duty Alloys, 70-71
Defeat: 1-10 v Ernest Turners Sports, 63-64

BEST SEASON **FA Cup:** 3rd Qualifying Rd **FA Vase:** Semi-Final 82-83, Q-F 77-78.
FA Trophy: 4th Round Replay 99-00

HONOURS Athenian Lg R-up(2) 78-80, Hellenic Lg 75-76 98-99 Div 1 R-up 72-73, Lg Cup 75-76 98-99, Div 1 Cup 71-72, London Spartan Lg 84-85 Lg Cup 84-85, Reading Comb. Lg Cup 70-71 All Champions Cup 70-71, Wycombe Comb. R-up (4) 65-67 68-70

Players progressing: D Hancock (Reading), R Rafferty (Grimsby Town), D Payne (Barnet)

Left to right

Back row:
Arron Lennon, Michael Bartley, Terry Mitchell, Danny Honey, Paul Brett and James Bracken.

Front Row:
Steve Lockhart, Laurence Brown, Terry Davies, Steven Noakes and Stewart Lloyd.

Photo: Alan Coomes

CHATHAM TOWN

CLUB OFFICIALS

Chairman: Frank Skinner

Secretary: Brian Burcombe
4 Hallwood Close, Parkwood, Rainham,
Kent ME8 9NT
Tel: 01634 363419

FOOTBALL MANAGEMENT TEAM

Manager: Peter Coupland
Asst Manager: Phil Miles

FACT FILE

Founded: 1882
Nickname: Chats
Sponsors: Topps Scaffolding
Colours: Red & black/black/black
Change Colours: All Blue
Midweek matchday: Tuesday

56 pages Price: £1.00
Editor: Tony Smith
07776 165446 (M)

GROUND Maidstone Road Sports Ground, Maidstone Road, Chatham, Kent
Tel: 01634 812194

Directions: M2, A229 Chatham turn-off, follow signs to Chatham, ground one and a half miles on right opposite garage. 1 mile from Chatham (BR).

Capacity: 5,000 Seats: 500 Cover: 1,000 Floodlights: Yes

Clubhouse: Matchdays and functions

PREVIOUS
Names: Chatham FC; Medway FC (1970s)
Leagues: Southern (several spells); Aetolian 59-64; Metropolitan 64-68;Kent (Sev. spells),
Ground: Great Lines, Chatham 1882-90

RECORD
Gate: 5,000 v Gillingham, 1980

BEST SEASON
FA Cup: QF 1888-89 (incl 2-0 v Nottm Forest 2-0)
FA Trophy: 3rd Rd 70-71

HONOURS
Kent Lg (9) 1894-95 03-05 24-25 26-27 71-72 73-74 76-77 79-80 00-01 R-up 02-03 23-24 25-26 70-71 74-75 80-81,
Lg Cup 71-72 76-77 (R-up(3), Thames & Medway Comb.(5) 1896-97 04-06 19-20 23-24,
Kent Snr Cup 1888-89 1904-05 10-11 18-19, Kent Snr Shield 19-20

Back row, left to right: Peter Coupland, Garry Tilley, Kevin Fewell, Chris Cooke, Cliff Hearn, Lee Riley, Mark Freeman, Simon Austin, Andy Larkin and Phil Miles. **Front:** Joe Dowley, Steve Best, Dave Monteith, Lee Bremner, Shawn Mitchell, Matt Hoggins and Jon Neal.
Photo: Alan Coomes

CORBY TOWN

CLUB OFFICIALS

Chairman: James Kane C.B.E.

President: Vacant

Secretary: Gerry Lucas, 8 Richmond Avenue, Kettering, Northants NN15 5JG

Tel: 01536 513507 (H) 07932 633343 (M)

FOOTBALL MANAGEMENT TEAM

Manager: Lee Glover
Assistant Manager:Rob Dunion
Physio: Rob Earley

FACT FILE

Formed: 1948
Nickname: The Steelmen
Sponsor:Corus
Colours: White/black/black
Change colours:All Yellow
Midweek matchday: Wednesday
Reserves' League: United Counties Res Div

2002-2003

Captain: Garry Kennedy
Player of the Year: Richard Lavin
Top Scorer: Kevin Byrne.

Pages: 32 Price: £1
Editor: David.Tilley

Local Press: Northampton Evening Telegraph
Local Radio: BBC Radio Northampton, Hereward, Connect F.M.

GROUND Rockingham Triangle Stadium, Rockingham Road, Corby NN17 2AE
Tel: 01536 406640 email : corbytownfc@ talk21.com

Directions: On northern outskirts of town at junction of A6003 and A6116,opposite entrance to Rockingham Castle grounds. Nearest Station: Kettering (rail bus to Corby)

Capacity: 3,000 Cover: 1,150 Seats: 960 Floodlights: Yes

Clubhouse: Trackside Bar open matchdays and during the week for hot food etc.

Club Shop: Sells badges, progs etc.(Before & half time) C .Woolmer Tel: 01536 260900

PREVIOUS **Leagues:** United Counties 35-52, Midland 52-58

CLUB RECORDS **Attendance:** 2,240 v Watford, pre-season friendly 86-87
At Old Ground; 10,239 v Peterborough Utd, FA Cup 3rd Qual. Rd 52-53
Win: 14-0 v Gainsborough Trinity, 56-57 **Defeat:** 0-10 v Paget Rangers, 95-96
Career Goalscorer: David Hofbauer 141 (84-95) **Career Appearances:** Derek Walker600 (78-92)
Transfer fee - Paid: £2,700 for Elwyn Roberts (Barnet, 81) **Received:** £20,000 for Matt Murphy (Oxford U. 93)

BEST SEASON **FA Cup:** 3rd Rd 65-66 (lost to Plymouth). 1st Rd on five occasions; 54-55 63-6667-68
League clubs defeated: Luton Town 65-66 **FA Trophy:** 3rd Rd, 1986-87

HONOURS UCL 50-51 51-52 (R-up 37-38), Midland Lg R-up 52-53, Southern Lg Midland Div R-up 90-91 (Merit Cup 63-64 90-91), Northants Snr Cup 6; Maunsell Cup 83-84, Daventry Charity Cup 94-95, Midland Floodlit Cup 74-75, Evans Halshaw F'lit Cup 91-92, Anglia Floodlit Trophy 68-69 72-73, Chelmsford Invitation Cup 63-64 64-65 65-66 (jt), Kettering & Dist Samaritan Cup 60-61(joint) 68-69, Wellingborough Charity Cup 50-51, Desborough Nursing Cup 48-49 50-51 (joint), Bob Cumning Cup 6

Players progressing: A McCabe (Chesterfield 55), L Chalmers (Leicester C. 56), K Brown (Nottm Forest 56), P Kearns (Aldershot 62), N Dean (Southampton 63), H Curran (Millwall 64), D McNeil/A McGowan/G Reilly (Northampton69/75/76), P Chard (Peterborough 79), T Morley (West Ham), J Flower (SheffieldUtd), M Murphy (Oxford Utd 93), C McKenzie (Hereford 94)

Back row, left to right: Gary Kennedy, Rob Dunion, Dean Hutchinson, Wayne Spencer, Lee Glover, Andy Brown, Paul Mackay, Jaime Hawthorn, James Le Masurier and Greg Randall. **Front Row:** George Stevenson, Scott Marshall, Danny Maye, Danny Marlow, Brian Hardie, Richard Lavin and Lee Vallanie with mascot Rebecca Spencer. **Photo**: David Tilley.

DARTFORD

CLUB OFFICIALS

Chairman: **David Skinner**

Vice Chairman: **Norman Grimes**

Secretary: **Peter Martin**

10 Pembroke Place,Sutton-at-Hone,

Dartford, Kent DA4 9GN

(01322 864038)

Com.Man.: **Bill Archer**

FOOTBALL MANAGEMENT TEAM

Manager: Tommy Sampson

Ass Man:Martin Farnie Physio:Dave Phillips

Coach: Paul Sawyer

FACT FILE

Formed: 1888

Nickname: The Darts

Colours: White & black/black/black

Change colours: All Red

Midweek home matchday: Tuesday

Res League:Go Travel Kent Div 1

Website: www.darfordfootballclub.co.uk

2002-2003

Captain: Alan Tutton

Player of the Year;Terry Ratchford

Top Scorer: Martin Buglione

Pages: 40 Price: £1

Editor: John Hall Tel No: 01322 381991

Press: Dartford Times, Dartford Messenger

Local Radio: Radio Kent.

GROUND c/o Gravesend & Northfleet FootballClub

Directions: From Dartford Town Centre: Take A226 to Gravesend/Swanscombe for 4 miles until Swansccombe. At bottom of Galley Hill through lights and ground is immediately on left.
From A2 coastbound: Take Bluewater/Greenhithe exit (B255) and at second roundabout, with McDonalds onright) turn right towards Swanscombe junction with A226 . Then as above.
British Rail: Northfleet Station two minutes from ground
Dartford F.C. Email Address: peter@martinpe.freeserve.co.uk

PREVIOUS **Leagues:** Kent League 1894-96 1897-98 1899-1902 1909-14 21-26 93-96; Southern League 1896-98, 1899-1900, 26-81, 82-84, 86-92; GMVC 81-82, 84-86
Grounds: The Brent/ Westgate House, Potters Meadow, Engleys Meadow, Summers Meadow, Watling St, then groundshares with Cray Wanderers, Erith & Belverdere & Purfleet

CLUB RECORDS **Attendance:** 11,004 v Leyton Orient FA Cup 48
Career Appearances: Steve Robinson 657
Win: 11-1 v Faversham Tn Kent Snr Cup 65 **Defeat:** 0-10 v Guildford City SouthernLge 46
Transfer fee paid: £6,000 for John Bartley (Chelmsford 88) **Received:** £25,000 forAndy Hessenthaler (Redbridge Forest)

BEST SEASON **FA Trophy:** Runners-up 74 **FA Vase:** 2nd Qual Rd 95/96
FA Cup: 3rd Rd Prop 35-36 & 36-37 League clubs defeated: Cardiff (1935), Exeter(1961), Aldershot (1968)

HONOURS Southern Lg 1930-31, 31-32, 73-74, 83-84, R-up 87-88, 88-89, Eastern Div 30-31,31-32, Southern Div 80-81, Southern Lg Div 2 1896-97, Lg Cup 76-77, 87-88, 88-89, Championship Shield 83-84, 87-88, 88-89; Kent Lg 1995-96, Lg Cup 24-25,Kent Snr Cup 29-30, 34-35, 38-39, 69-70, Snr Trophy 95-96, Inter Lg Chall 1974;FA Trophy R-up 1974

Players progressing: Idris Hopkins (Brentford 32), Fred Dall(West Ham 36), Riley Cullum/Fred Alexander/Ted Croker (Charlton 47/48/48) Frank Coombs (Bristol C 49), James Kelly (Gillingham 51), Tom Ritchie (Grimsby 58), Dave Underwood (Watford 60), Derek Hales (Luton 72), Andy Hessenthaler (Watfordvia Redbridge F),Jimmy Bullard (West Ham United)

Left to right

Back row: Terry Ratchford, Paul McCarthey, Danny Lye, Steve Marriner, Jimmy Simpson, Paul Lorraine and Alan Tutton.

Front row Martin Buglione, Richard Usherwood, Darren Smith and Ted Ansell.

Photo: Alan Coomes.

EASTLEIGH

CLUB OFFICIALS

Chairman: Roger Sherwood

President: Clive Wilson

Secretary: John Dunn
21 Vale Drive, Midanbury,
Southampton SO18 4SW
Tel: 023 8032 2884 (H) 07730 734044 (M)

FOOTBALL MANAGEMENT TEAM

Manager:Paul Doswell

Coach: David Hughes

Physio: Bert Wyatt

FACT FILE

Founded: 1946
Nickname: None
Sponsors: Southern Exhaust Services
Colours: White & Navy/Navy /White & Navy
Change colours: All red
Midweek matches: Wednesday

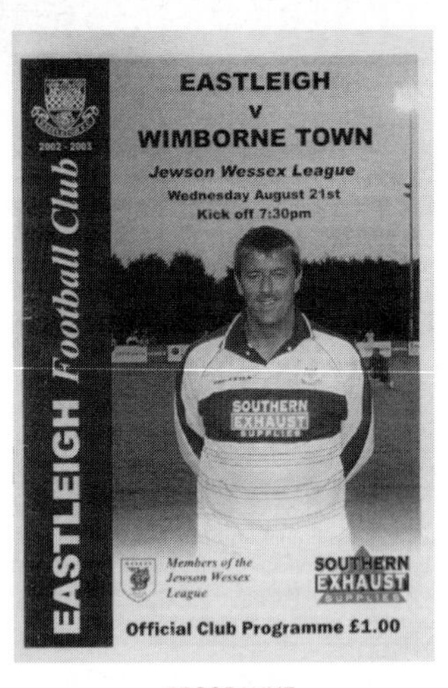

PROGRAMME
32 pages with admission
Editor: Mark Pearce & Tommy Whale

GROUND `Ten Acres', Stoneham Lane, North Stoneham, Eastleigh SO50 9HT
Tel: 02380 613361

Directions: M27, J 5, to r'bout - exit marked Stoneham Lane. Carry on to r'bout & come back down Stoneham Lane, turning right opp. Concord Club. Ground 400 yds on left. Bus 48 (S'hampton-Winchester) to Stoneham Church stop Southampton Parkway (BR) 3/4 mile.

Capacity: 2,300 Seats: 175 Cover: 210 Floodlights: Yes

Club Shop: No

Clubhouse: 11-11 Mon-Sat plus Sundays. Extensive function facilities. All catering undertaken

PREVIOUS
Leagues: Southampton Jnr & Snr 46-59, Hampshire 50-86, Wessex 86-2003
Names: Swaythling Ath. 46-73; Swaythling 73-80
Grounds: Southampton Common 46-47; Walnut Avenue, Swaythling 47-75

CLUB RECORDS
Gate: 2,500 v Southampton, floodlight opener 30/9/75
Scorer : Johnny Williams, 177 **Appearances** : Ian Knight, 611
Win: 12-1 v Hythe & Dibden (H) 11/12/48 **Defeat:** 0-11 v Austin Spts (A) 1/1/47

BEST SEASON **FA Vase:** 4th Round 82-83, 90-91, 94-95

HONOURS Wessex Lg Cup R-up 91-92, Hants Lg Div 2 69-70 R-up 54-55 60-61 62-63 64-65 (Res), Div 3 (W) 50-51 53-54 70-71(Res), Comb.(Res) (3) R-up 96- Hants Comb Cup (Res) 96-7, 97-8 Midweek F'lit Cup 78-79, Southampton Snr Lg (W) 49-50 R-up 51-52(Res), Div 1 56- 57 57-58 (Res), Russell Cotes R-up 76-77 80-81 89-90, Hants I'mediate Cup 50-51 56-57(Res) 74-75 (Res) R-up 73-74 (Res), Soton SnrCup (Res) 74-75 78-79 87-88 96-97 R-up (7) 55-56 57-59 60-61 66-67 71-72 80-81 87-88), Soton Jnr Lg Div 2 47-48 (Res), Reg Mathieson Tphy (Res) 74-75 78-79 87-88

ERITH & BELVEDERE'S NEW STAND

ERITH & BELVEDERE

CLUB OFFICIALS

Chairman: **John McFadden**
President: **L O'Connell**
Vice Chairman: **Peter Bird**
Secretary: **Kellie Discipline**
108 Chastilion Road, Dartford, Kent DA1 3LG Tel: -01322 275766
Press Off./Commecial Man.: Martin Tarrant
Tel: 01322 275766

FOOTBALL MANAGEMENT TEAM

Manager: Mike Acland 01322 225594
Asst Man ager: Dave Hough
Physio: Rob Couldwell

FACT FILE

Formed: 1922
Nickname: Deres
Colours:Blue & white/blue/blue
Change colours: All red
Midweek home matchday:Tuesday
Reserves' League:Kent League Div1

2002-2003

Captain: Darren Gowler & Richard Vercesi
Top Goalscorer: Darren Adams
Players Of the Year: Barry Gitson,Clark Hunt & Richard Vercesi

Pages: 30 Price: £1.50p
Editor: Mike Tarrant Tel: 01322 275766

Local Press:
Kentish Times, Kentish Independent
Local Radio: Radio Kent, Radio Mellenium

GROUND: Park View Rd Ground, Welling, Kent DA16 1SY Tel: 0181 301 1196
Email: kelliedt@tinyworld.co.uk
Directions: As for Welling United F.C.:M25,then A2 towards London.Take Welling turn-off, ground one mile. By rail to Welling stationBR (BR) ground 3/4 mile.
Capacity: 1,500 Cover: 1,000 Seats: 500 Floodlights: Yes
Club Shop: Sells programmes, badges and pens
Clubhouse: Licensed social club open matchdays and weekends. Cold snacks available. Separate canteen provides hot food on matchdays

PREVIOUS **Leagues:** Kent 22-29 31-39 78-82, London 29-31, Corinthian 45-63, Athenian 63-78
Names: Belvedere & District FC (Formed 1918, restructured 1922)

CLUB RECORDS **Attendance:** 5,573 v Crook Colliery Welfare Amt Cup 3rd Rd 1949
Win: 14-2 v Royal Marines, Kent Lge 18/11/33. (16-2 v RAF Friendly 4/9/41) **Defeat:** 0-15 v Ashford, Kent Lge 28/4/37
Career Appearances: Dennis Crawford 504, 56-71 **Career Goalscorer:** Colin Johnson284, 61-71

BEST SEASON **FA Amateur Cup:** Runners-up 1923-24, 37-38 **FA Trophy:** Third Qualifying Round second replay 89-90
FA Vase: Third Round 76-77 **FA Cup:** 4th Qual Rd 1924-25 (Equiv to 1st Rd Prop). League clubs defeated: None

HONOURS FA Amat Cup R-up 23-24 37-38; Athenian Lge Div 1 R-up 70-71 Lge Cup 73-74, Memorial Shield 67-68; Corinthian Lge R-up 62-63, (Lge Cup 47-48 48-49 49-50); Kent Lge 81-82, (Lge Cup R-up 81-82); London Sen Cup 44-45 (R-up 38-39); Kent Amat Cup 6, (R-up 4); Kent F/lit Lge R-up 67-68; Kent Interm Cup R-up 90-91; Kent Jun Cup 67-68; Kent County Yth Lge 90-91; Kent Yth Cup 87-88. Bromley Hosp Cup 38-39; Essex & Herts Border Comb Cup 73-74.

Players progressing: John Coshall (West Ham 28), Fred Ford 36/ Cyril Hammond 46/ KeithPeacock 62 (Charlton), Tommy Ord (Chelsea 72), Sean Devine (Barnet 95)

Back row, left to right: Steve Portway Tim Bealey, Clark Hunt, Richard Vercesi, Karl Emerick and James Vercesi.

Front Row: Darren Adams, Paul Roberts, Barry Gibson, Ryan Briggs and Scott Saunders.

Photo: Alan Coomes

FISHER ATHLETIC (LONDON)

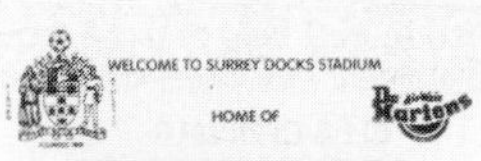

FISHER ATHLETIC F.C.

ERITH & BELVEDERE

CLUB OFFICIALS

Chairman : Richrad Jones

Secretary: John Leyden,33 Carew Close,Chafford100,Nr Grays,Essex Tel No: 01375 481224

General Manager: Elaine O'Keefe

FOOTBALL MANAGEMENT TEAM

Manager: Bob Davies

Player-Coach: Tony Dolby

Physio: Joe Miller

FACT FILE

Formed: 1908
Nickname: The Fish
Colours: Black & white stripes/black/black
Change colours: Yellow&Blue/white/white
Midweek matchday: Tuesday
Reserves' League: Suburban Premier
Local Press: Southwark News, South London Press
Local Radio: Capital & Capital Gold
PROGRAMME
Pages: 40 Price: £1.50
Editor: Teresa Watson(07776 138982(M)

GROUND The Surrey Docks Stadium, Salter Road, London SE16 5LH
Tel: 0207 231 5144 Fax:0207 2520060

Directions: 8 minutes walk from Rotherhithe (tube).2 miles from London Bridge (main line). Buses 381,225

Capacity: 5,300 Cover: 4,283 Seats: 400 Floodlights: Yes

Clubhouse: None **Club Shop:** None

PREVIOUS **Leagues:** Parthenon, West Kent, Kent Amateur, London Spartan 76-82, Southern 82-87, GMV Conference 87-91
Names: Fisher Athletic 08-93, Fisher`93 93-96 **Ground:** London Road, Mitcham

CLUB RECORDS **Attendance:** 4,283 v Barnet, GMV Conference 4/5/91
Win: 7-0 v Lewes Sept 95, FA Cup **Defeat:** 1-8 v Clevedon (away) 10.03.01
Career Goalscorer: Paul Shinners 205 **Career Appearances:** Dennis Sharp 720
Transfer fee paid: £2,500 for Ben Taylor (Sittingbourne)
Transfer fee received: £45,000 for Paul Gorman (Charlton 1991)

BEST SEASON **FA Cup:** 1st Rd 84-85 (0-1 at home to Bristol City), 88-89 (0-4 at BristolRovers)
FA Trophy: Third Round replay 87-88 **FA Vase:** Second Round replay 82-83 **FA Amateur Cup:**

HONOURS Southern Lg 86-87 (R-up 83-84, Southern Div 82-83, Lg Cp 84-85, Championship Cup 87-88, Merit Cup), London Spartan Lg 80-81 81-82 (R-up 78-79, Senior Div77-78, Div 2 R-up 76-77), Parthenon Lg 61-62 (Lg Cup 63-64 65-66), Kent AmateurLg 73-74 74-75 (R-up 72-73),Kent Intermediate 97-98.98-99 London Senior Cup 84-85 87-88 88-89, LondonIntermediate Cup 59-60 (R-up 75-76), Kent Senior Cp 83-84, Kent Senior Trophy 81-82 82-83, Surrey Inter Cup 61-62,Southern Lg. Eastern Div 99-00

Players progressing:John Bumstead (Chelsea), Trevor Aylott (Bournemouth), Paul Shinners (Orient 84), Dave Regis (Notts Co. - via Barnet), Paul Gorman(Charlton 91), Sean Devine (Barnet via Okonia Nicossia), George Barry (LeytonOrient), Dean Martin (West Ham Utd), Jason Lee (Charlton), Ken Charlery (Barnet), Steve Watts (Leyton Orient)

Adam Day getting the better of Erith's Jason Dory.

Photo: Bill Wheatcroft

FLEET TOWN

Dr Martens

FOOTBALL LEAGUE

CLUB OFFICIALS

Chairman: Martn Griffiths

President: Tony Frost

Vice Chairman: Jon Goodyear

Secretary: John Goodyear
25 Velmead Road,Fleet,Hants GU52 7LJ
Email: goodyear.john@btinternet.com

FOOTBALL MANAGEMENT TEAM

Manager:Mark Dennis

Asst Man: Dave Skilton

Coach: Jesse Bone & Mervyn Grifiths

Physio: David Keir

FACT FILE

Founded: 1890

Re-Formed: 1947

Nickname: The Blues

Sponsors: Southern Coating Contractors Ltd.

Colours: Navy & sky stripes/sky/navy & sky

Change: Red & Black/black/red&black

Midweek Matches: Tuesday

Reserves' League: Suburban(Wednesdays)

Website: www.fleettownfc.co.uk

PROGRAMME

20 Pages Price: £1.00

Editor: Stuart Reeves

07881 737934 (M)

GROUND: Calthorpe Park, Crookham Road, Fleet, Hants Tel: 01252 623804

Directions: Leave the M3 at Junction 4A. Follow signs to Fleet via A3013. At 5th roundabout (a T-junction), turn left over railway bridge. Carry on past `Oatsheaf' pub on the right - ground is 1/4 mile further on right.

Capacity: 2,000 Seats: 200 Cover: 250 Floodlights: Yes

Clubhouse: Yes. Hot & cold food served

Club Shop: Yes

PREVIOUS
Leagues: Hampsire 61-77, Athenian, Combined Co's, Chiltonian, Wessex 89-95, Southern 95-00, Wessex 00-02
Names: None **Grounds:** None

CLUB RECORDS
Win: 15-0 Pertersfield 26.12.94 **Defeat:** 0-6 v Margate 1999
Attendance: 1,050 v Coventry City 1995 (Pre-Season Frirerndly)
Transfer fee paid: £3,000 to Aldershot Dec 99 for Mark Russell 1991
Career Goalscorer: Mark Frampton 428 **Appearances:** Mark Frampton250

BEST SEASON
F.A.Cup: 2nd Q 97-98 F.A.Trophy: 2nd Rd 97-98 F.A.Vase: 3rd Rd 94-95

HONOURS
Wessex Lg 94-95 Runners-Up 01-02, Lg Cup R-up 92-93, 01-02; Hants Lg Div 2 R-up 61-62 (Div 1 R-up 60-61), Aldershot Snr Cup 92-93, 99-00; Simpsonair Challenge Shield 1993, Hants Yth Lg Div 3 92-93.

Fleet Town before their Aldershot Senior Cup Final v Ashford (Middlesex). **Photo**: Eric Marsh

FOLKESTONE INVICTA

CLUB OFFICIALS

Chairman: **Bob Dix**

President: **Bill Hewson**

Secretary: **Frank Clarke**
c/o Football club

FOOTBALL MANAGEMENT TEAM

Manager: Neil Cugley
Asst Manager: Dave Williams
Physio: Frank Clarke

FACT FILE

Founded: 1936
Sponsors: Eurotunnel (Le Shuttle) & Silver Spring
Colours: Amber & black stripes/black/amber
Change Colours:white/blue/white
Midweek matchday: Tuesday
Reserves League: Winstonlead Kent Div 1
Club Website: www.folkestoneinvicta.co.uk

2002-2003
Captaiun: Scott Lindsey
Top Goalscorer; Allen Tait

Pages: 60 Price: £1.50
Editor: Richard Morrell (01303 276517)

Local Press: Folkstone Herald
Local Radio: K.M.F.M., Invicta Radio

GROUND The New Pavilion, Cheriton Road, Folkestine, Kent CT20 5JU
Tel: 01303 257461 FAX:01303 255541

Directions: On the A20 behind Safeway foodstore, midway between Folkestone Central & West BR stations

Capacity: 6,500 Seats: 900 Cover: 3,500 Floodlights: Yes

Clubhouse: Yes, Stripes Club & Invicta Club
Club Shop: Yes (01303 257266)

PREVIOUS **Ground:** South Rd, Hythe (pre-1991). Kent County Lg matches were played on council pitches
Leagues: Kent County (pre-1991-98)

CLUB RECORDS **Attendance:** 2,332 v West Ham Utd Friendly Nov 96
Ground Record: 7,881 Folkestone Town v Margate, Kent Snr.Cup 1958
Win: 9-0 v Crockenhill WHL Div 1 **Defeat:** 0-7 v Crockenhill WHL Div 1

BEST SEASON **FA Vase:** Last sixteen 97-98
FA Cup: 2nd Qual Rd 95-96 Leagues Clubs Defeated: None

HONOURS (since joining Winstonlead Kent League) Kent Lge R-up 97-98, Kent Senior Trophy R-Up 93-94, 94-95,98-99,99-00
Dr.Martens League ,Eastern Division Runners-up: 99-00 Promotion to Dr.Martens Premier Division 1999-2000

Back row, from left: Steve Hogg, Michael Everitt, Allan Tait, Steve Hafner, Steve Restarick.
Middle row: Neil Pilcher (boardroom hospitality), Dave Williams (assistant manager), Mark Towse, Tony Henry, Dave Wietecha, Paul Egan, Jimmy Dryden, Lee Dyson, Brian Merryman (director), Bob Dix (chairman). **Front row:** Dayne Southern (kit manager), Andy Morris, Paul Chambers, Scott Daniels, Neil Cugley (manager), Dan Larkin, Martin Chandler, Scott Lindsey, Frank Clarke (associate director, physic, secretary and groundsman). **Photo** courtesy of the Folkestone Herald

HASTINGS UNITED

CLUB OFFICIALS
Chairman:David Ormorod
President: Mick Maplesden
Vice Chairman: T.B.A.
Secretary : R A Cosens
22 Baldslow Road, Hastings TN34 2EZ
01424 427867 (H) 01424 444635 (B)
0771 2634288 (M)

FOOTBALL MANAGEMENT TEAM
ALL T.B.A. at time of going to press

2002-03
Captain: Tony Burt
P.o.Y.:David King
Top scorer:Danny Simmonds 17

FACT FILE
Formed: 1894
Nickname: The Arrows
Colours: Claret & Blue
Change colours:Blue/Yellow
Midweek matchday: Tuesday
Reserves' League: Go Travel Kent Div 1
Newsline: 09066 555 879
Local Press: Hastings Observer, Evening Argus
Local Radio: BBC Southern Counties
Southern Sound, Arrow FM

PROGRAMME
Pages: 76 Price: £1
Editor: David Bealey Tel: (01797 253310)

GROUND The Pilot Field, Elphinstone Road, Hastings TN34 2AX Tel: 01424 444635

Directions: From A21 turn left at 3rd mini-r'bout into St Helens Rd, left after 1 mile into St Helens Park Rd, this leads into Downs Rd, at end of Downs Rd (T-junction) turn left, ground 200yds on right. From town centre take Queens Road (A2101). Right at roundabout into Elphinstone Road - ground 1 mile on right. 1 1/2 miles from Hastings BR station - infrequent bus service fromtown centre to ground

Capacity: 4,050 Cover: 1,750 Seats: 800 Floodlights: Yes

Clubhouse: Open matchdays and every evening

Club Shop: Sells replica kits, scarves, programmes, pens, key-rings, badges etc

PREVIOUS **Leagues:** South Eastern 04-05, Southern 05-10, Sussex County 21-27 52-85,Southern Amateur 27-46, Corinthian 46-48
Name: Hastings & St Leonards Amateurs **Ground:** Bulverhythe Rec Gd (pre 76)

CLUB RECORDS **Attendance:** 4,888 v Notts Forest, friendly 23/6/96. Competitive: 1,774 v DoverAthletic, Southern Lge Prem. Div. 12/4/93
Goalscorer: (Season) Terry White (33) 99-00
Transfer Fee Paid: £8,000 for Nicky Dent from Ashford **Received:** £50,000 for Paul Smith from Notts Forest

BEST SEASON **FA Cup:** 1st Round Proper 2002-2003 v Stevenage Bor. (A) 0-1 **FA Trophy:** 3rd Rd 1998-99
FA Amateur Cup: 3rd Rd. 38-39 **FA Vase:** 5th Rd. rep. 90-91

HONOURS Southern Lg Cup 94-95, Southern Div 91-92, Div 2 R-up 08-09, Div 2(B) 09-10; Sussex Co Lg R-up 21-22 25-26, Lg Cup 80-81, Div 2 79-80 (R-up 59-60), Div 2Cup 79-80; Sussex Sen Cup 35-36 37-38 95-96 97-98; AFA Snr Cup 37-38; Gilbert Rice F/lit Cup 89-90

Players progressing: Peter Heritage (Gillingham), Paul Smith (Nottm Forest)

EASTERN DIVISION ACTION Photo by Alan Coomes

Eastbourne Borough's John Price (5) put this header just wide against Sittingbourne

HISTON

CLUB OFFICIALS

Chairman: Gareth Baldwin
President: G P Muncey
Secretary: Mrs Lisa Baldwin,
5 Caxton Lane, Foxton,
Cambridge CB2 6SR (Tel: 01223 872246)
Press Officer: Steve Wells(01353 862367)
Email:stevenwells1@ composerve.com

FOOTBALL MANAGEMENT TEAM

Manager: Steve Fallon
Coach: Chris Tovey
Physio: Lee Petrucci

FACT FILE

Founded: 1904
Nickname: 'The Stutes'
Sponsors:Webster Building & Civil Engineers
Colours: Red and blackstripes/black/black
Change colours: Sky & Navy/navy/sky ?
Midweek Matches: Tuesday
Reserves League: Jewson Premier
Website: http://.histonfootballclub.tripod.com

2002-03

Leading Goalscorer: James Rowe
Captain: Neil Andrews
Player of the Year: Louie Farrington

GROUND Bridge Rd, Impington, Cambridge
Tel: 01223 232301 Fax: 01223 237373
email: gareth@corporate innovations.co.uk
Directions: Leave A14 northern Cambridge bypass on B1049 (signposted Histon and Cottenham). Ground half a mile on right.
5 miles from Cambridge (BR). Bus No.104
Capacity: 3,250 Seats: 250 Cover: 250 Floodlights: Yes
Clubhouse: Bar/lounge open matchdays only.Snacks available

PROGRAMME

42 pages £1.50
Editor: Sreve Wells 07734205555 (M)

Local Press : Cambridge Evening News
Local Radio: Q103, Star FM
BBC Radio Cambridgeshire

HONOURS Eastern Co's Lg - Prem. Div. 99-00, Div 1 R-up 96-97, Cup 90-91;
Cambridge Invitation Cup 77-78 79-80 96-97,00-01 R-up 50-51 52-53 53-54 2001-02 02-03;
Spartan Lg Div 1 (East) 50-51; Cambs Chall Cup; Cambs Lg Section;
Kershaw Prem Lge 00-01R-up 97-98, Sen Lge A 96-97, Cup 96-97;00-01
Auto Trader Lge & Cup (U18) 96-97 Kershaw Champions Co Cup (U18) 98-99, Colts League (U17) Champions 98-99

PREVIOUS **Leagues:** Cambridgeshire 04-48; Spartan 48-60; Delphian 60-63; Athenian 63-65; Eastern Counties 66-00
Name: Histon Institute 04-51

BEST SEASON **FA Cup:** 4th Qual. Rd. 89-90 **FA Vase:** 4th Rd 96-97, 97-98 **F.A .Trophy:** 4th Round 2000-2001

RECORD **Attendance:** 6,400 v King's Lynn, FA Cup 1956

L-R - Back Row: Lee Petrucci (Physio), Chris Tovey, Steve Holden, Neil Kennedy, Paul Barber, Colin Vowden, Roscoe Hipperson, Ian Cambridge, Graham Rush, Steve Fallon (Manager). **Front Row:** James Rowe, Wayne Goddard, Neil Coburn, Louie Farrington, Neil Andrews, Jamie Barber, Matt Haniver, Adrian Cambridge.

KING'S LYNN

CLUB OFFICIALS
Chairman: Colin Nichols
President: Jim Chandler
Secretary: Nigel Link
58 Hall Lane, West Winch,
Kings Lynn PE33 0PP
Tel:01553 841089 (H) 07885 144039 (M)
Director of Football: Kevin Boon

FOOTBALL MANAGEMENT TEAM
Manager:Peter Morris
Physio: Dave Edgeley

PROGRAMME
Pages: 24 Price: £1.20
Editor: Secretary

FACT FILE
Formed: 1879 Nickname: The Linnets
Sponsors: Lynn News
Colours: Royal Blue with gold trim/Blue/Blue & Gold hoops
Change : White with blue & gold trim
Midweek home matchday: Tuesday
Reserves League: Jewson Eastern Div 1

GROUND The Walks Stadium, Tennyson Road, King's Lynn PE30 5PB Tel: 01553 760060 **Directions:** At mini r-about arriving from A10/A47 take Vancouver Avenue. Ground on left after a half mile. Quarter mile from King's Lynn (BR), half mile from bus station
Capacity: 8,200 Cover: 5,000 Seats: 1,200 Floodlights: Yes
Clubhouse: Normal licensing hours, with extension on matchdays **Club Shop:** Sells metal badges and other merchandise

PREVIOUS **Leagues:** Norfolk & Suffolk; Eastern Co.s 35-39 48-54; UCL 46-48; Midland Co.s54-58; NPL 80-83
Name: Lynn Town **Ground**: None

CLUB RECORDS **Attendance:** 12,937 v Exeter, FA Cup 1st Rd 50-51
Win: 17-0 v Beccles 29/30 **Defeat:** 0-11 v Aston Villa FA Cup 1905/6
Career Appearances: Mick Wright 1,152 (British Record) **Career Goalscorer:** Malcolm Lindsay 321
Transfer Fee Paid: Shaun Keeble Wisbech 98-99 **Transfer Fee Received:** Mark Paul , Southampton.98-99

BEST SEASON **FA Cup:** 3rd Rd 61-62 (0-4 at Everton). Competition Proper on 14 occasions; 05-06 37-38 49-50 51-52 58-63 64-65 68-69 71-72 73-74 84-85. Rd 2 97-98 League clubs defeated: Aldershot 59-60, Coventry 61-62, Halifax 68-69
FA Trophy: 2nd Rd 78-79 **FA Vase:** 5th Rd 94-95 (0-2 at Diss Town **FA Amateur Cup:** R-up 1900-01

HONOURS FA Amateur Cup R-up 1900-01, Southern Lg R-up 84-85 (Div 1 R-up 63-64), NPLPresidents Cup 82-83, Eastern Co's Lg 53-54 (R-up 49-50 52-53 (Lg Cup 53-54),Norfolk & Suffolk Lg(8)(R-up(6)), E Anglian Lg R-up(2), Norfolk Snr Cup(19)(R-up(20), Norfolk Invitation Cup 94-95, Norfolk Premier Cup 68-69(jt) 73-74, EastAnglian Cup(4)(R-up(3), Eastern Prof Floodlit Lg 68-69, Southern Lg Midland R-up 95-96 ,U.C.L. Reserve Division, League & Cup 'double', 99-00. Southern League Cup. R-up: 2001-02

Players progressing: N Rowe (Derby 1949), B Taylor & P Ward (Bradford P. A. 54& 55), T Reynolds (Darlington 54), G Reed (Sunderland 55), P McCall (Bristol C55), J Neal (Swindon 57), T Dryburgh (Oldham 57), J Hunter (Barrow 59), JStevens (Swindon), G Catleugh (Watford), George Walters (Chesterfield 64), PMcNamee (Notts County 1966), W Biggins (Burnley), Jackie Gallagher(Peterborough 80), Andy Higgins (Rochdale 83), Neil Horwood (Grimsby 86),Darren Rolph (Barnsley 87), Mark Howard (Stockport 88), Andy Hunt, Malcolm Lindsay

NEWPORT I.W.

CLUB OFFICIALS
Chairman: Bill Manuel **Pres:** W Bunday
Director of Football: Tony Mount
Secretary: Chris Cheverton
40 Whitehead Crescent, Wootton Bridge,
I.o.W. PO33 4JF Tel: 01983 883879
Office Manager: Pauline Crisp

FOOTBALL MANAGEMENT TEAM
Manager: Steve Tate
Assistant Manager: Taffy Richardson
Physio: Chris Cheverton

FACT FILE
Formed: 1888 Nickname: The Port
Colours: all Yellow with blue trim
Change colours: Sky blue with navy trim
Midweek matchday: Tuesday
Reserves' League: Isle of Wight League
Clubcall: 09066 555 890
Local Press: Portsmouth Evening News, I.o.W. County Press, Southampton Evening Echo
Local Radio:
Solent, Isle of Wight Radio, Ocean Sound

2002-2003
Captain.: Joe McCormack
Leading Goalscorer: Gareth Keeping
Players of the Year:
Joe McCormack & Simon Pilcher

PROGRAMME
Pages: 28 Price: £1
Editor: Alan Phillips (07811 509706 (M)

GROUND: St. George's Park, St George's Way, Newport, Isle of Wight, PO30 2QH. Tel: 01983 525027
Directions: Roads from all ferry ports lead to Coppins Bridge R-abt at eastern end of town. Take Sandown/Ventnor exit, go to small r-about, St George's way is 1st exit, ground on left 5 mins walk from Newport Bus station along Church Litten (past old ground) turn left then right at r-about.
Capacity: 5,000 Cover: 1,000 Seats: 300 Floodlights: Yes
Club Shop: Sells souvenirs & progs. Contact Roger Sanders 01983 825925
Clubhouse: Open every evening & weekend lunch times. 2 bars, full range of hot and cold bar snacks. Snack Bar inside ground

PREVIOUS **Leagues:** Isle of Wight 1896-1928; Hants 28-86; Wessex 86-90
Ground: Church Litten (previously Well's Field) 1888-1988

CLUB RECORDS **Attendance:** 2,270 v Portsmouth (Friendly) : 7th July 2001 and 2,217 FA Cup 1st Rd Nov 1994 v Aylesbury U.,
Win: 14-1, v Thornycroft Athletic (H),Hampshire Lge Div. One, 22.12.45
Defeat: 1-11 v Emsworth(A) Hampshsire Div. Lge 1926-27 **Career Appearances:** Jeff Austin 540 (69-87)
Career Goalscorer: Roy Gilfillan 220 1951-57 **Record Goalscorer:** Frank Harrison 62 1929-30
Fee paid: £5,000 for Colin Matthews (Bognor Regis Town 00) **Fee received**: £2,250 for Mick Jenkins (Havant) 92-3

BEST SEASON **FA Trophy:** 4th Rd 99-00 **FA Vase:** Fifth Round 91-92, 92-93
FA Cup: 2nd Rd 35-36 45-46. 1st Rd another 8 times - 52-53, 53-54, 54-55, 56-57, 57-58, 58-59, 94-95, 95-96
League clubs defeated: Clapton Orient 45-46

HONOURS Dr. Martens Lge Eastern Div. 00-01, Wessex Lg R-up 89-90, Comb. 91-92, 99-00 (res 2.) League Cup 01-02 (res); Hants Lg (11), R-up (7), Div 2 R-up 70-71, Hants Snr Cup (8); Russell Cotes Cup (3); Pickford Cup (4); Isle of Wight Snr (Gold) Cup (34); Hants F'lit Cup 76-77 77-78; Isle of Wight Lg (4) 07-09 23-24; Hants I'mediate Cup 31-32 96-97; Hants Comb. Cup 38-39

Players progressing: Gary Rowatt (Cambridge United)

EASTERN DIVISION ACTION Photos by Alan Coomes

ABOVE: Burnham's Paul Brett clears the danger with this powerful header against Tonbridge's Ryan Royston.

BELOW: Sittingbourne goalkeeper Lee Hook rising well above Eastbourne Borough's Andy Ducille at this corner.

ROTHWELL TOWN

CLUB OFFICIALS

Chairman: **Keith Johnson**
President: **Ken Cheney**
Secretary: **Roger Barratt**
18 Norton St., Rothwell, Northants NN14 2DE
Tel: 01536 507744
Press Officer : **Mark Southon**
Tel: 07870 551428

FOOTBALL MANAGEMENT TEAM
Manager: Nick Platnauer
Physio: Bob Bramah

FACT FILE
Founded: 1895
Nickname: The Bones
Sponsors:Springfir Country Homes
Colours: Blue with white trim/blue/blue
Change : Red, black & white trim, black/red
Midweek matchday: Tuesday
Newsline: 0930 555 829
Reserves' League: Utd Counties Res Div

2002-2003
Captain: Paul Ede
Top Scorer:SteveOloaker
Players o. Y.:Paul Ede & Andy Colclough

Rothwell Town
Football Club
Matchday Programme £1.00

Pages: 48 Price: £1.00 Editor & Media Relations Officer: Mark Southon
Tel: 07860 551428

Local Press: Northants Evening Telegraph, Chronicle & Echo, Herald & Post
Local Radio: BBC Radio Northants, KCBC

GROUND Cecil Street, Rothwell, Northants NN14 2EZ Tel: 01536 710694
Directions: A14/A6 to Rothwell. At town centre r'about turn into BridgeStreet (right if northbound, left if southbound), take 3rd left into TreshamStreet, ground is at top on left.
3 miles from Kettering (BR); Rothwell is served by Kettering to Market Harborough buses
Capacity: 3,500 Seats: 264 Cover: 1,264 Floodlights: Yes
Clubhouse: Rowellian Social Club, open every evening and weekend lunchtimes.Crisps and rolls available on mätchdays (hot food and drinks available in ground). `Top of the Town Ballroom', lounge seats 200
Club Shop: Sells various souvenirs incl. metal badges.

PREVIOUS **Leagues:** Northants 1896-1911 21-33, Kettering Amateur 11-21 33-48, Leics.Senior 48-50, United Counties 50-56 61-94, Central Alliance 56-61 **Grounds:** Harrington Rd, Castle Hill **Name:** Rothwell Town Swifts

CLUB RECORDS **Attendance:** 2,508 v Irthlingborough Diamonds, United Counties League 1971
Win: 17-0 v Stamford, FA Cup Preliminary Round replay 1927
Defeat: 1-10 v Coalville Town, Leicestershire Sen Lge 1949
Transfer fee paid: Undisclosed for Andy Wright (Aylesbury 1992)
Transfer fee received: Undisclosed for Matty Watts (Charlton 1990)

BEST SEASON **FA Cup:** Fourth Qualifying Round 99-00
FA Trophy: Second Round Proper 94-95 **FA Vase:** Fifth Round 92-93 (1-2 v Bridlington Town)

HONOURS Northants Lg1899-1900 (R-up 1895-96 96-97 97-98), Northants Snr Cup 1899-1900 23-24 59-60 88-89 95-96 01-02 (R-up 24-25 71-72 87-88), United Counties Lg 92-93 94-95 (R-up 69-70 70-71 87-88 89-90 90-91), KO Cup 55-56 70-71 71-72 91-92 92-93 (R-up 77-78 79-80 82-83), Div 2 52-53 53-54, Div 2Cup 52-53 53-54, Benevolent Cup 92-93 94-95 (R-up 89-90 90-91) Southern League Mid Div R-up 96-97

Players progressing: Lee Glover (Nottingham Forest) 1987, Matty Watts (CharltonAth.) 1990, Mathew Lawrence (Wycombe Wanderers) and Chris McKenzie (Leyton Orient)

Back row, left to right: Ossie Mintus Paul Rice Craig McIlwain Adam Sturgess Nick Preston and John Hughes.

Front Row: Richard Weale Ryan Nash Jason Turner Carl Lake and Micky Garside.

Photo: Alan Coomes

SALISBURY CITY

Alternative Chairmen: M Griffiths, D.Harrold,N Beal and S McGlashan
Secretary: Douglas Ferraro, Flat 2, 13 Mea dow Rd, Salisbury, Wilts SP2 7BN
Tel No: 07803 247874(H) 07803247874
Email douglasfJ@aol.com
Press Off: Alec Hayter Tel: 02380 867195
Youth Development Off: Symon Pickett
Football in Community Off.: Andy Cook
Commercial Manager: Trevor Cross

FOOTBALL MANAGEMENT TEAM
Manager: Nick Hoilmes
Asst. Manager: Tommy Killick
Youth Coach: Terry Hatt
Physio: Conrad Parrott

ACT FILE
Formed: 1947
Nickname: The Whites
Sponsors: In-Excess
Colours: White/black/white
Change colours:Red/navy/navy
Midweek matchday: Tuesday
Reserve Team's League: Wessex Comb
Club Line: 'City Line' 0906 555 864
Website:www.salisbury-city-fc.com

2002-2003
Captain: Scott Bartlett
Top Scorer: Adam Wallace
Player of the Year: Wayne Turk

GROUND The Raymond McEnhill Stadium, Partridge Way, Old Sarum, Salisbury SP4 6PU
Tel:01722 326454, Fax 01722 323100 Club Website: www.salisbury-city-fc.com
Directions: The Stadium is situated off A345 (Salisbury - Amesbury) road on the northern edge of the city 2 miles from the City centre. Continue on this road, turn right onto A338 signed Old Sarum Business Park, Partridge Way & ground on left (well signposted)
Capacity: 4,038 Cover:2,300 Seats: 462 Floodlights: Yes
Clubhouse: On ground, . Hot & cold snacks. Hospitality Boxes available for hire.
Club Shop: Sells replica shirts, memorabilia, programmes, scarves, metal badges, souvenirs. Open all week. Contact Lynn Tucker, Commercial Office (01722 326454)

Pages: 48 Price: £1.50
Editors: Dave Todd & Alec Hunter

Local Press: Salisbury Journal, Evening Echo & Sports Echo, Western DailyPress
Local Radio: Wiltshire Sound, Spire F.M

PREVIOUS **Leagues:** Western 47-68 **Name:** Salisbury FC, 47-92 **Ground:** Hudson Field 47-48, Victoria Park 48-97

CLUB RECORDS **Attendanceat Victoria Park:** 8,902 v Weymouth, Western League 48 New Ground: 2,570 v Hull City F.A. Cup 1998.
Win: 11-1 v R.A.F Colerne (H) Western League Div 2 1948 **Defeat:** 0-7 v Minehead, Southern League 1975
Career Goalscorer: Royston Watts 180 (59-65) **Career Appearances:** Barry Fitch 713 (63-75)
Transfer fee paid: £5,750 for Peter Loveridge (Dorchester Town, 90)
Transfer fee received: £20,,000 for Adrian Randall (Forest Green Rovers)

BEST SEASON **FA Trophy:** 2nd Rd 96-97 (lost to Dorchester Town)
FA Amateur Cup: 2nd Rd 49-50 (lost to Dulwich Hamlet)) **FA Cup:** 2nd Rd 59-60 (lost to Newport County)

HONOURS Southern Lg Southern Div Champ 94-95, R-up 85-86 92-93; Western Lg 57-58 60-61,R-up 58-59 59-60 61-62 67-68; Div 47-48 Lg Cup 55-56 Hants Senior Cup 61-62 63-64; Wilts PremierShield(11) Western Co Floodlit Cup: 1982-83

Players progressing: Eric Fountain (Southampton 48), Cyril Smith (Arsenal 48), Tony Alexander (Fulham 65), John Evans (Stockport County 67), Graham Moxon (Exeter 75), Eric Welch (Chesterfield 76), Ian Thompson (Bournemouth 83), Trevor Wood (Port Vale 88), Denny Mundee (Bournemouth 88), Matthew Carmichael (Lincoln 90), Frank Monk (Southampton 47),George Marks 49), Joe Stocks (Millwall 64), Jason Matthews (Exeter C), James Hayter (Bournemouth 1999) and Steve Mildenhall (Swindon Town 1997)

L-R - Back Row: Nick Holmes (Gen. Manager), Conrad Parrott (Trainer), Tommy Killick (Asst. Player Manager), John Purches, Michael Cooper, Stuart Brown, Kevin Sawyer, Matthew Davies, Josh Thomas, Reza Sotoudeh, Sam Wyeth, Roger Emms. **Front Row:** Rhys Schell, Adam Wallace, Andy Cook, Steve Stone, Scott Bartlett, Tyronne Bowers, Steve Strong, Darren Crook. Players missing: Wayne Turk, Steve Witt, Leigh Phillips, Dean Bowden, Andy McGlashan. **Photo** courtesy of Salisbury Newspapers

SITTINGBOURNE

CLUB OFFICIALS

Chairman: Andy Spice

President: Jim Clarke

Secretary: John Pitts, 4 Silverdale Grove Sittingbourne, Kent ME10 1UY (Tel No: 01795 476809 Fax 07092 112833) email: John@bourne.plus.com

Commercial Manager: John Cooper

FOOTBALL MANAGEMENT TEAM

Manager: Mark Beeney

Assistant Manager/Coach: Steve Nolan

Physio: Gary Wisdom

FACT FILE

Formed: 1881 Nickname: Brickies

Sponsors: B.W.May & Sons

Colours: Red & black stripes/black/red

Change colours: All yellow

Midweek matchday: Tuesday

Reserves' league: Go Travel Kent

2002-2003

Captain: Ben Taylor

Top Scorer: Andrew Drury 18

Players of the Year:

Lee Hook, Andrew Drury, Adam Marshall

Editor: John Pitts Pages: 44 Price: £1.20

Local Press: East Kent Gazette, Kent Today, Kent Messenger Extra, Sittingbourne & Sheppy Adscene.
Local Radio: Invicta Supergold, BBC Radio Kent, K.M.F.M.,Invicta FM,Medway, Mercury F.M.

GROUND Bourne Park, Central Park Stadium, Eurolink, Sittingbourne, Kent ME10 3SB Tel: 01795 435077/420444 Fax: 01795 420444 Email Address: club@sittingbournefc.co.uk
Directions: Through Sittingbourne on main A2, club signposted clearly and regularly from both east and west. 1 mile from Sittingbourne BR station.
Capacity: 3,000 Cover: 600 Seats:300 Floodlights:Yes
Clubhouse: The Cabin (01795 435077)
Club Shop: Sells a wide selection of souvenirs etc. Open matchdays or contact Ann Morrison (01795 664436) Official Club Website: www.sittingbournefc.co.uk

PREVIOUS
Leagues: Kent 1894-1905 09-27 30-39 46-59 68-91, South Eastern 05-09, Southern 27-30 59-67
Grounds: SittingbourneRec. Ground 1881-90, Gore Court Cricket Ground 90-92, The Bull Ground1892-1990
Names: Sittingbourne United 1881-86

CLUB RECORDS
Attendance: 5,951 v Tottenham Hotspur, friendly 26/1/93
Transfer fee paid: £20,000 to Ashford Town for Lee McRobert, 1993.
Transfer fee received: £210,000 from Millwall for Neil Emblen and Michael Harle, 1993

BEST SEASON
FA Cup: 2nd Rd 25-26 (0-7 at Swindon Town), 28-29 (1-2 at Walsall), plus 1st Rd26-27 30-31 62-63

HONOURS
Southern Lg Southern Div 92-93 95-96; Kent Lg 1897-98 1902-03 57-58 58-59 75-76 83-84 90-91 (Lg Cup 25-26 58-59 73-74 80-81, Div 2 Cup 54-55 57-58 83-84 86-8787-88); Kent Senior Cup 01-02 28-29 29-30 57-58; Kent Senior Shield 25-26 27-28 53-54; Kent Senior Trophy 89-90; Thames & Medway Cup 55-56 58-59; Thames & Medway Comb 02-03 07-08 11-12 24-25 25-26; Chatham Charity Cup 03-04 19-20;" Kent Midweek Lg(res) 91-92 (Lg Cup 90-91).

Players progressing: Jason Lillis (Walsall 93), Neil Emblen & Michael Harle 93, Steve Forbes 94, Lee McRobert 95 (Millwall) Jimmy Case (Brighton 93), Lee Harper (Arsenal 94)

Back row, left to right: Paul Campbell, Jamie Coyle, Paul Davies, Ben Taylor, Lee Hook, Kieran Marsh and James Campbell.
Front row: Andrew Drury, Bradley Spice, Cliff Cunningham and Clint Gooding. **Photo**: Alan Coomes

STAMFORD

CLUB OFFICIALS

Chairman: **Ken Joynson**
Vice-Chairman: **Richard Jacobs**
Secretary: **Jeremy Biggs**
`The Essendine', Essendine, Stamford, Lincs., PE9 4LD Tel: 01780 763048
Press Officer: **As Secretary**

FOOTBALL MANAGEMENT TEAM

Manager:Billy Jeffrey
Assistant: Nick Ashby
Coach: Andy Drummond
Physio: Pete Foskett

FACT FILE

Founded: 1896 Nickname: Daniels
Sponsors: V.Couzens(Stamford) Ltd & Newflame
Colours: Red
Change Colours: Yellow & green
Midweek matchday: Tuesday

2002-2003
Captain: Andy Peaks
Top Scorer: Malcolm Ndekwe 21
Player of the Year: Danny Steadman

STAMFORD
PROGRAMME
AFC
Southern League Football (Eastern Division)
At the Newflame Stadium
SEASON 2002 – 2003

Pages : 44 Price:£1,00
Editor: Robin Peel
Local Press: Stamford Mercury, Peterborough Evening Telegraph, Herald & Post
Local Radio: Rutland Radio, LincsFM Radio Lincolnshire & Radio Cambridgeshire

GROUND Newflame Stadium, Kettering Road,, Stamford, Lincs
Tel: 01780 763079 (Clubhouse) 01780 766027 (Pressbox)

Directions: Off A43 Kettering Rd, 1 mile east of A1. 200 yds from station
Capacity: 5,000 Seats: 250 Cover: 1,250 Floodlights: Yes
Clubhouse: Open matchdays and functions
Food available matchdays - hot and cold
Club Shop: Wide range of Lge + non-Lge progs & club souvenirs.

PREVIOUS **Leagues:** Peterborough; Northants (UCL) 08-55; Central Alliance 55-61; Midland Co's 61-72; UCL 72-98
Grounds: None **Names:** None

CLUB RECORDS **Attendance:** 4,200 v Kettering, FA Cup 3rd Qual Rd 53
Win: 13-0 v Peterborough Reserves, Northants Lge 29-30 **Defeat:** 0-17 v Rothwell,FA Cup 27-28
Appearances: Dick Kwiatkowski 462 **Goalscorer:** Bert Knighten 248

BEST SEASON **FA Cup:** 12-13 5th Qual. Round
FA Vase: Winners 79-80, R-up 75-76 83-84 **FA Trophy: 00-01** (1st season) 2nd Round

HONOURS FA Vase 79-80 R-up 75-76 83-84; Utd Co's Lg 75-76 77-78 79-80 80-81 81-82 96-97 97-98 KO Cup 51-52 75-76 79-80 81-82 85-86); Northants Lg 11-12; Lincs Snr`A' Cup 78-79 82-83 97-98, 00-01; Lincs Snr `B' Cup 51-52 53-54; William Scarber Mem. Cup 70-71 82-83 85-86 88-89 93-94 94-95; Stamford Chal. Cup 89-90; Lincs Jnr Cup 48-49 Hinchbrooke Cup 1906-07, 07-08, 97-98

Players progressing: A Birchenall (Chelsea), R Chester(Aston Villa), T Tye (Chelsea), G Fell (Brighton), C Chapman (Wolves), S Collins (Peterborough), K Alexander (Grimsby), A Tillson (Grimsby), B Stubbs (Notts Co.), D Genovese (Peterborough), J Johnson, C MacCarney (Notts Co), B McNamara (Northampton), D Norris (Bolton), M.Clifford (Boston United)

Stamford AFC 2003-04 - Back row (left to right): Ludek Michalik, Matt Green, Garath Pritchard, Jamie Gilsenan, Richard Thompson, Robbie Blowers, Nick Ashby, Rob Maddox, Tom Webster, Billy Jeffrey (manager). **Front row:** Pete Foskett (physio), Trevor Smith, Warren Donald, Andy Peaks (captain), Kevin Byrne, Kevin Ainslie, Michael Mckenzie. **Photo** courtesy of the Rutland and Stamford Mercury.

TONBRIDGE ANGELS

CLUB OFFICIALS

Chairman: Paul Dainty
Vice Chairman: Maurice Brown
Secretary: Charlie Cole
30 Faraday Ride,Tonbridge TN10 4RL
Tel No: 01732 354985
Press Officer:T.B.A.
Commercial Manager:Tamsin Jeffrey

FOOTBALL MANAGEMENT TEAM

Manager: Alan Walker
Physio: Chris Dunk

FACT FILE

Founded: 1948
Nickname: The Angels
Sponsors: Brewers
Colours: Royal Blue with white trim
Change Colours: Yelow/Black/Yellow
Midweek matchday: Tuesday
Reserves League: Suburban

2002-2003
Captain:Lloyd Hume
Player of the Year: Peter Overton
Top Scorers:Ray Powell & Hamid Barr

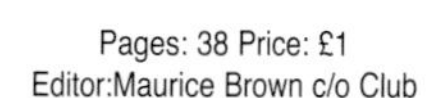

Pages: 38 Price: £1
Editor:Maurice Brown c/o Club

Local Press: Kent Messenger, Courier, Sevenoaks Leader
Local Radio: Mercury, Radio Kent, K,F.M.

GROUND Longmead Stadium, Darenth Avenue, Tonbridge, Kent TN10 3JW
Tel: 01732 352417
Directions: From Tonbridge BR station, through High Street, north up Shipbourne Rd (A227 Gravesend road) to 2nd mini-r'bout ('The Pinnacles' pub), left into Darenth Avenue, ground at bottom of Avenue, far side of car park
Capacity: 5,000 Seats: 202 Cover: 400 Floodlights: Yes
Clubhouse: Open Mon-Sat evenings and Sunday lunchtimes.
Hot food on matchdays from burger bar
Club Shop: Yes, progs, replica kits etc, contact Lorraine Parks (01732 350865)

PREVIOUS **Leagues:** Southern 48-89, Kent 89-93
Ground: The Angel 48-80 **Names:** TonbridgeAngels, Tonbridge F.C., Tonbridge A.F.C

CLUB RECORDS **Attendance:** 1,463 v Yeovil Town, FA Cup 4th Qualifying Round 26/10/91.
At theAngel Ground: 8,236 v Aldershot, FA Cup 1st Round 1951
Win: 11-1 v WorthingFA Cup 1951 **Defeat:** 2-11 v Folkstone, Kent Sen Cup 1949
Career Goalscorer: Unknown **Career Appearances:** Mark Gillham, 520 to date
Transfer fee paid: **Transfer fee received:** £7,500 for Paul Emblen (Charlton Ath 97)

BEST SEASON **FA Cup:** First Round (proper) 50-51 51-52 52-53 67-68 72-73

HONOURS Kent League 94-95 (League Cup (2)), Southern League Cup Runners-up (2) (SF(1)), Kent Senior Cup 64-65 74-75 Runners-up x2, Kent Senior Shield 51-5255-56 57-58 58-59 63-64

Players progressing: R Saunders, M McMcDonald, T Burns, I Seymour, G Moseley, T Morgan, Neil Emblen, Paul Emblen.

L-R - Back row: Lee Cooper, Peter Overton, Hamid Barr, Nick Barnes, Paul Emblen, Lloyd Hume, Paul Ainsworth, Craig Roser and Ray Powell.
Front row: Keith Moore, Kieran Wilson, Tony Reynolds, Luke Piscina, John Beales and Charlie Cole (Sec.)
Photo: Mrs Antoinette Jarrett

Dr. AirWair Martens
Supporting British Football
www.drmartens.com

JEWSON EASTERN COUNTIES LEAGUE

Feeder to: Dr Martens League
Founded 1935

Hon. Patron: Derek Needham **President:** Roger Pauley

Secretary: B Badcock, 41 The Copse, Southwood, Farnborough, Hants GU14 0QD
Tel: 01252 518 586
www.jewsonleague.co.uk

PREMIER DIVISION FINAL LEAGUE TABLE 2002-03

		P	W	D	L	F	A	Pts
1	AFC Sudbury	44	31	10	3	122	37	103
2	Wroxham	44	29	6	9	121	53	93
3	Soham Town Rangers	44	25	11	8	91	61	86
4	Lowestoft Town	44	25	7	12	108	65	82
5	Diss Town	44	26	3	15	98	62	81
6	Wisbech Town	44	23	9	12	101	73	78
7	Stowmarket Town	44	22	9	13	65	56	75
8	Great Yarmouth Town	44	19	11	14	66	57	68
9	Bury Town	44	18	11	15	75	66	65
10	Mildenhall Town (-1)	44	18	11	15	68	65	64
11	Clacton Town	44	17	10	17	62	61	61
12	Tiptree United	44	17	7	20	73	90	58
13	Histon Res.	44	15	11	18	80	84	56
14	Fakenham Town	44	13	16	15	61	61	55
15	Gorleston	44	13	10	21	79	90	49
16	Norwich United	44	13	10	21	44	63	49
17	Maldon Town	44	13	8	23	57	63	47
18	Newmarket Town	44	11	13	20	58	76	46
19	Dereham Town	44	12	9	23	55	86	45
20	Woodbridge Town	44	11	12	21	55	96	45
21	Ipswich Wanderers	44	11	8	25	59	92	41
22	Harwich & Parkeston	44	10	6	28	58	126	36
23	Ely City (-4)	44	5	10	29	38	111	21

	1	2	3	4	5	6	7	8	9	10	11	12	13	14	15	16	17	18	19	20	21	22	23
1 AFC Sudbury		1-1	3-0	4-0	0-2	6-0	2-0	4-2	2-1	2-1	1-1	4-0	1-1	2-1	5-0	2-0	2-1	4-0	4-0	2-0	4-1	2-2	1-2
2 Bury Town	0-2		1-0	2-2	4-1	1-1	1-1	3-3	1-1	2-2	0-2	3-1	1-0	1-2	0-2	2-2	1-0	1-2	0-0	4-0	2-1	2-1	4-1
3 Clacton Town	1-2	1-0		1-2	2-0	2-2	0-0	2-1	0-3	1-2	2-0	1-0	1-2	0-3	1-1	4-1	0-0	1-3	2-1	2-1	2-3	2-0	0-1
4 Dereham Tn	0-0	1-2	1-2		2-0	6-1	0-2	1-1	0-2	1-3	4-0	1-5	4-0	2-2	1-4	2-3	1-3	0-3	2-3	3-5	0-4	0-0	0-5
5 Diss Town	5-3	1-1	3-1	0-1		3-2	2-0	1-2	0-1	3-1	0-3	2-1	4-2	3-1	3-1	0-1	1-0	0-1	6-1	3-1	3-1	2-3	2-0
6 Ely City	0-3	0-3	1-4	1-2	0-1		1-5	0-0	0-4	3-2	3-1	0-2	2-6	1-0	1-5	0-2	0-0	1-2	1-3	2-1	2-3	2-0	1-2
7 Fakenham T.	1-4	0-2	0-1	0-0	1-4	2-2		4-0	2-2	0-0	2-2	2-2	2-1	0-3	2-2	2-2	2-0	4-0	1-1	1-5	2-0	1-1	1-3
8 Gorleston	0-4	4-2	1-2	1-2	4-1	3-0	0-0		1-1	6-2	3-6	7-1	0-6	0-0	3-1	4-1	2-0	1-1	1-2	1-3	1-2	6-3	1-5
9 Gt Yarmouth	1-3	1-0	0-2	2-0	1-3	4-0	0-3	0-2		4-1	3-2	1-4	1-1	1-2	2-0	1-0	2-1	1-1	3-3	0-0	1-3	3-0	2-1
10 Harwich & P.	0-10	0-1	3-1	0-1	0-8	1-0	2-2	4-2	1-1		1-5	0-2	2-4	2-0	1-3	2-0	1-0	1-4	1-2	2-4	0-3	2-3	0-6
11 Histon Res.	2-3	3-1	1-4	0-0	0-4	1-1	0-1	1-1	2-3	4-3		3-2	2-2	1-1	2-2	4-0	4-1	3-3	0-1	5-1	0-3	3-2	0-2
12 Ipswich W.	2-3	0-1	2-1	1-0	1-2	0-0	1-1	3-2	2-3	2-3	0-1		2-6	3-2	1-3	3-1	2-1	1-2	1-4	3-1	2-2	2-2	0-3
13 Lowestoft T.	0-0	2-0	1-2	8-0	3-2	5-1	2-1	4-3	0-1	4-2	3-1	1-0		1-0	5-0	3-3	3-0	2-1	1-2	2-1	4-5	2-2	3-0
14 Maldon Town	3-3	1-2	1-3	1-4	0-2	5-0	0-2	1-2	0-1	5-0	3-2	2-2	0-1		2-1	1-0	3-0	0-1	0-4	0-0	3-1	0-0	3-2
15 Mildenhall T.	1-4	2-1	1-1	2-2	0-0	2-0	2-0	1-2	2-1	4-0	2-3	2-0	2-2	1-0		1-1	2-2	1-3	2-2	1-3	0-2	2-0	0-2
16 Newmarket T.	2-2	4-1	2-1	1-1	4-3	0-0	1-2	0-0	0-1	2-2	0-1	1-1	1-3	1-0	0-1		4-0	1-1	1-2	3-1	3-2	0-4	0-1
17 Norwich Utd	0-3	1-0	1-1	1-0	1-1	3-1	0-1	1-1	2-1	2-0	0-0	2-0	0-1	1-0	1-0	4-1		0-2	0-1	0-0	1-0	1-0	0-1
18 Soham Tn R.	1-1	7-2	4-4	1-2	1-2	2-2	2-0	3-0	3-1	1-0	0-0	1-0	2-1	0-1	1-1	2-1	4-3		2-1	1-1	1-2	3-1	1-0
19 Stowmarket T.	0-1	3-2	0-0	1-0	1-4	2-0	1-0	2-0	0-0	3-1	3-0	1-0	1-2	1-0	1-0	0-0	2-2	1-3		3-0	1-1	1-0	1-2
20 Tiptree Utd	1-8	2-5	3-1	2-0	5-0	2-1	2-1	3-1	1-1	3-4	1-5	1-1	1-3	2-1	1-2	2-4	1-0	1-3	2-1		2-4	2-0	0-3
21 Wisbech Tn	0-1	3-3	1-1	2-0	1-4	2-2	4-0	3-2	2-0	4-1	5-2	2-0	3-1	3-2	1-3	3-1	3-3	4-4	4-0	1-2		2-2	1-2
22 Woodbridge T.	0-3	0-5	1-0	2-4	1-6	2-0	0-6	2-1	0-0	2-2	2-0	2-1	3-2	1-1	0-1	2-1	2-3	1-7	2-1	0-1	2-2		1-8
23 Wroxham	1-1	2-4	2-2	3-0	2-1	6-0	1-1	2-1	4-3	6-0	5-2	9-0	3-2	3-1	0-2	2-2	6-2	6-1	2-1	2-2	1-2	1-1	

DIVISION ONE FINAL LEAGUE TABLE 2001-02

		P	W	D	L	F	A	Pts
1	Halstead Town	36	24	7	5	76	37	79
2	King's Lynn Res.	36	24	4	8	108	56	76
3	Whitton United	36	21	8	7	93	44	71
4	Hadleigh United	36	20	9	7	65	40	69
5	Stanway Rovers	36	19	10	7	78	39	67
6	Long Melford	36	18	10	8	69	38	64
7	Leiston	36	18	9	9	76	51	63
8	Swaffham Town	36	18	3	15	62	62	57
9	Cambridge City Res.	36	16	7	13	66	49	55
10	Haverhill Rovers	36	16	6	14	67	55	54
11	Needham Market	36	15	8	13	71	59	53
12	Godmanchester Rovers	36	10	13	13	53	53	43
13	Cornard United	36	11	5	20	44	70	38
14	Somersham Town	36	11	5	20	59	87	38
15	March Town United	36	9	10	17	54	85	37
16	Felixstowe & Walton Utd	36	10	6	20	51	71	36
17	Thetford Town	36	9	5	22	38	74	32
18	Downham Town	36	4	6	26	33	88	18
19	Warboys Town	36	2	3	31	18	123	9

		1	2	3	4	5	6	7	8	9	10	11	12	13	14	15	16	17	18	19
1	Cambridge City Res.		5-0	4-2	0-1	1-0	2-0	4-2	2-0	2-3	3-3	0-2	6-0	5-1	6-1	2-3	3-1	2-0	1-0	1-6
2	Cornard United	2-2		1-2	2-1	1-2	0-2	1-2	1-3	1-1	4-1	0-2	1-2	2-0	2-1	1-7	0-3	3-1	0-0	2-1
3	Downham Town	0-1	0-3		0-0	1-2	0-1	1-2	2-1	2-5	1-1	0-1	2-2	1-4	1-2	1-1	1-1	0-0	2-3	0-1
4	Felixstowe & W. Utd	2-3	1-2	5-2		1-1	1-5	0-1	1-2	2-1	2-3	1-3	6-0	1-1	1-2	2-1	0-2	4-1	2-1	0-3
5	Godmanchester R.	0-0	2-0	3-1	3-0		1-1	5-0	0-4	0-1	1-2	0-2	1-1	1-1	1-2	0-0	0-3	2-4	3-0	0-0
6	Hadliegh United	1-0	2-1	3-2	2-2	3-0		1-1	5-1	0-2	0-0	0-3	4-3	2-1	3-1	0-0	2-0	2-1	6-0	1-4
7	Halstead Town	1-0	1-0	8-2	2-0	3-0	0-0		0-1	1-1	2-2	1-0	1-1	3-1	4-3	1-0	2-0	3-0	7-1	2-1
8	Haverhill Rovers	2-1	3-1	3-1	4-0	2-2	0-1	1-2		1-1	0-1	1-4	1-1	4-1	1-1	1-0	5-3	1-1	9-0	0-2
9	King's Lynn Reserves	3-1	5-1	8-0	2-1	4-4	2-0	1-0	4-1		3-2	6-4	5-1	4-1	6-2	1-3	3-1	4-1	9-1	1-2
10	Leiston	1-2	1-0	2-0	2-0	3-2	0-1	1-0	1-2	4-2		1-1	2-1	0-3	5-1	2-2	6-2	4-1	10-1	1-0
11	Long Melford	0-0	2-1	0-1	1-2	3-1	0-0	0-0	2-1	2-1	1-1		2-2	2-3	4-1	2-2	0-1	5-1	2-0	2-3
12	March Town United	2-2	1-3	3-0	4-1	1-1	1-5	2-8	0-2	0-4	0-0	0-2		0-3	3-1	2-2	1-3	1-0	2-3	2-0
13	Needham Market	1-1	1-2	5-2	3-2	1-1	0-1	2-3	1-0	5-0	0-0	1-1	2-4		3-4	1-4	4-0	1-1	5-1	2-0
14	Somersham Town	1-0	3-0	5-1	0-1	2-2	1-1	2-3	5-2	2-3	1-4	1-6	3-2	1-2		0-6	0-2	0-2	3-1	1-4
15	Stanway Rovers	3-2	4-0	2-0	6-2	3-3	2-0	0-4	0-0	1-2	3-1	1-0	1-1	3-1	1-1		3-1	3-0	6-0	1-0
16	Swaffham Town	0-0	3-2	2-1	2-2	0-2	2-1	0-1	2-1	2-1	4-2	1-3	3-0	0-2	3-1	1-0		4-1	5-1	1-4
17	Thetford Town	1-0	1-2	1-0	2-1	0-1	2-3	1-2	2-1	0-1	0-3	1-1	1-3	1-3	0-4	0-2	1-0		4-0	1-1
18	Warboys Town	0-1	0-0	0-1	0-1	0-5	1-3	0-1	1-2	1-7	0-2	0-2	0-3	0-3	0-0	0-1	0-4	2-3		0-4
19	Whitton United	4-1	2-2	2-0	2-2	2-1	3-3	2-2	3-4	4-1	5-2	2-2	4-2	2-2	1-0	4-1	6-0	5-1	4-0	

DIVISION ONE TROPHY

PRELIMINARY ROUND

1st LEG				2nd LEG			
Hadleigh United	v	Needham Market	4-0	Needham Market	v	Hadleigh United	2-1
Long Melford	v	Cornard United	5-3	Cornard United	v	Long Melford	2-2
March Town United	v	Downham Town	1-1	Downham Town	v	March Town United	2-4
Thetford Town	v	Godmanchester R.	2-1	Godmanchester Rovers	v	Thetford Town	6-1

FIRST ROUND

Cambridge City Res.	v	King's Lynn Res.	0-3	King's Lynn Res.	v	Cambridge City Res.	1-2
Felixstowe & Walton Utd	v	Whitton United	2-5	Whitton United	v	Felixstowe & W. Utd	1-0
Hadleigh United	v	Stanway Rovers	0-5	Stanway Rovers	v	Hadleigh United	0-2
Halstead Town - Walkover		Brightlingsea United					
Leiston	v	Long Melford	0-0	Long Melford	v	Leiston	6-1
March Town United	v	Warboys Town	5-1	Warboys Town	v	March Town United	1-4
Somersham Town	v	Haverhill Rovers	0-0	Haverhill Rovers	v	Somersham Town	2-3
Swaffham Town	v	Godmanchester R.	0-2	Godmanchester Rovers	v	Swaffham Town	0-1

QUARTER-FINALS

Godmanchester Rovers	v	Stanway Rovers	0-0	Stanway Rovers	v	Godmanchester R.	3-2
Halstead Town	v	King's Lynn Res.	1-2	King's Lynn Res.	v	Halstead Town	0-2
Long Melford	v	Somersham Town	1-1	Somersham Town	v	Long Melford	3-3

Long Melford through on away goals rule.

Whitton United	v	March Town United	5-0	March Town United v Whitton United - walkover			

SEMI-FINALS

Halstead Town	v	Long Melford	1-0	Long Melford	v	Halstead Town	0-2
Whitton United	v	Stanway Rovers	2-2	Stanway Rovers	v	Whitton United	2-3

FINAL

Whitton United v Halstead Town 1-2 (aet) — 5th May at Hadleigh United

LEAGUE CUP 2002-03

PRELIMINARY ROUND

AFC Sudbury	v	Needham Market	4-1
Cornard United	v	Harwich & Parkeston	2-1
Histon Reserves	v	Cambridge City Res.	4-0
Lowestoft Town	v	Godmanchester R.	5-1
Thetford Town	v	Diss Town	0-2
Wroxham	v	Gorleston	5-0
Brightlingsea United v Mildenhall Town - walkover			
Fakenham Town	v	Wisbech Town	4-2
Ipswich Wanderers	v	Soham Town R.	0-2
Swaffham Town	v	Downham Town	3-2
Whitton United	v	Tiptree United	1-0

FIRST ROUND

AFC Sudbury	v	Woodbridge Town	4-2
Diss Town	v	Mildenhall Town	3-3 (aet)
Fakenham Town	v	Norwich United	1-2
Halstead Town	v	Cornard United	2-5 (aet)
Lowestoft Town	v	Bury Town	4-1
March Town United	v	Haverhill Rovers	2-1
Soham Town Rangers	v	Dereham Town	5-3
Stowmarket*	v	Ely City	3-1
Whitton United	v	Long Melford	4-0
Clacton Town	v	Stanway Rovers	5-1
Replay - Mildenhall Tn	v	Diss Town	0-5
Felixstowe & Walton Utd	v	Wroxham	0-3
Histon Res.	v	Warboys Town	7-0
Maldon Town	v	King's Lynn Res.	6-2
Newmarket Town	v	Great Yarmouth Tn	1-0
Somersham Town	v	Leiston	8-3
Swaffham Town	v	Hadleigh United	1-3

*Expelled.

Defeated clubs from the above rounds entered into the Millennium Cup below.

SECOND ROUND

AFC Sudbury	v	Clacton Town	0-1
Lowestoft Town	v	Diss Town	3-2
Newmarket Town	v	Cornard United	5-0
Whitton United	v	Soham Town R.	2-1
Hadleigh United	v	Somersham Town	2-3
Maldon Town	v	Histon Res.	3-2
Norwich United	v	March Town United	2-0
Wroxham - walkover v Ely City			

QUARTER-FINALS

Clacton Town	v	Maldon Town	2-0
Somersham Town	v	Wroxham	0-2
Norwich United	v	Lowestoft Town	2-1
Whitton United	v	Newmarket Town	0-3

SEMI-FINALS

Norwich United	v	Clacton Town	0-1
Wroxham	v	Newmarket Town	3-1

FINAL

Clacton Town	v	Wroxham	1-2

16th March at Diss Town

MILLENNIUM CUP

PRELIMINARY ROUND

Downham Town	v	Dereham Town	3-3 (aet)
Godmanchester	v	King's Lynn Res.	2-0
Halstead Town	v	Tiptree United	0-4
Long Melford	v	Leiston	2-4 (aet)
Needham Market	v	Harwich & Park.	1-3
Replay - Dereham Town	v	Downham	4-0
Gorleston	v	Fakenham Tn	3-5 (aet)
Ipswich Wdrs	v	Woodbridge Town	0-1
Mildenhall	v	Cambridge City Res.	3-0
Warboys Town	v	Swaffham Town	0-1

FIRST ROUND

Bury Town	v	Felixstowe & Walton	3-1
Godmanchester	v	Swaffham	1-1 (aet)
Great Yarmouth Town	v	Wisbech	3-1
Harwich & Parkeston	v	Tiptree Utd	3-3 (aet)
Thetford Town	v	Haverhill Rovers	0-4
Fakenham Town	v	Dereham Town	6-2
Replay - Swaffham	v	Godmanchester	3-0
Mildenhall Town	v	Leiston	3-0
Reply - Tiptree	v	Harwich & P.	3-4 (aet)
Woodbridge Town	v	Stanway Rovers	0-2

QUARTER-FINALS

Bury Town	v	Haverhill Rovers	0-1
Harwich & Parkeston	v	Fakenham	3-2
Great Yarmouth	v	Swaffham	3-1 (aet)
Mildenhall Town	v	Stanway Rovers	2-0

SEMI-FINALS

Harwich & Parkeston	v	Haverhill	8-2
Mildenhall	v	Great Yarmouth Town	1-2

FINAL

Great Yarmouth Town	v	Harwich & Parkeston	4-2

8th May at Woodbridge Town

BURY TOWN

Secretary: Mrs Wendy Turner, 64 Winthrop Rd., Bury-St-Edmunds, Suffolk. IP333UF
Tel Nos: 01284 753688 (H) 01284 762291 (W) Club Website: www.burytownfc.co.uk
Ground: Ram Meadow, Cotton Lane, Bury St Edmunds, Suffolk IP33 1XP Tel: 01284 754721
Directions: Leave A14 at sign to Central Bury St Edmunds, follow signs to town centre at exit r'bout, at next r'bout 1st exit into Northgate St, L. at `T' junct (lights) into Mustow St, left immediately into Cotton Lane - ground 350 yds on right, through `Pay & Display' car park. 10 mins from station
Capacity: 3,500 Cover: 1,500 Seats: 300 Floodlights: Yes
Clubhouse: Members'/Public Bars open at matchdays **Club Shop:** Yes

HONOURS Eastern Counties Lg 63-64, R-up 37-38, Lg Cup 61-62 63-64; Metropolitan Lg 65-66, R-up 67-68 70-71, Lg Cup 67-68, Professional Cup 65-66; Suffolk Premier Cup (9); Suffolk Senior Cup 36-37 37-38 38-39 44-45 84-85
PREVIOUS **Leagues:** Norfolk & Suffolk; Essex & Suffolk Border; Eastern Co's 35-64 76-87; Metropolitan 64-71 **Names:** Bury St Edmunds 1895-1902; Bury Utd 02-06, Bury Town(1995) Ltd.
BEST SEASON **FA Cup:** 1st Rd replay 68-69, 0-3 v AFC Bournemouth (A) after 0-0
FA Vase: Qtr Finals 88-89 **FA Trophy:** 2nd Rd 70-71
CLUB RECORDS **Attendance:** 2,500 v Enfield, FA Cup 3rd Qual. Rd 1986 **Goalscorer:** Doug Tooley 58 **Appearances:** Doug Tooley **TransferFee Paid**: £1,500 for Mel Springett (Chelmsford 1990) **Fee Received**: £5,500 forSimon Milton (Ipswich) .**Players progressing:** D Lewis (Gillingham), L Carberry T.Pearce+S.Milton(Ipswich), T Bly (NorwichCity) + G Stevens (Brighton),

FACT FILE
Formed: 1872
Nickname: The Blues
Colours: All blue
Change colours:White/black/white
Midweek matchday: Tuesday
Programme: 40 pages 80p
Editor: Mrs Wendy Turner

CLUB PERSONNEL
Chairman: Russell Ward
Vice Chairman: Robin Calton
President: Cyril Elsey
Manager: Richard Wilkins
Asst Manager: Trevor Collins
Physio: Darren Gibbs

2002-03
Leading Goalscorer:Alex Harrison
Captain:Andrew Eady
Player of the Year:Andrew Eady

CLACTON TOWN

Secretary: Mrs Linda Pigeon c/o Club Tel: 01255 476133 email: secretary@clacton-town.com

Ground: The Rush Green Bowl, Rushgreen Road, Clacton-on-Sea, Essex CO16 7BQ
Tel/Fax: 01255 432590 email: supporters@clacton-town.com
Directions: A133 to Clacton, at r'bout right into St Johns Rd, 4th left CloesLane, 3rd right Rushgreen Rd, ground approximately half mile on right. From B1027 take main Jaywick turn off (Jaywick Lane), then 2nd left after about half a mile into Rushgreen Rd. Ground 400 yds. 2 miles from Clacton (BR), buses 3, 5or 5a to Coopers Lane/Rushgreen Rd
Capacity: 3,000 Seats: 200 Cover: Yes Floodlights: Yes Club Shop: Yes
Clubhouse: Licensed club. Open 7-11pm Mon-Fri, all day Sat & Sun.
Hot & cold food available at all times.

HONOURS Southern Lg Div 1 59-60; Eastern Co's Lg R-up 36-37 53-54 64-65 74-75 (Lg Cup 73-74), Div 1 98-99 (Lg Cup 98-99); Eastern F/lit Cup 95-96; East Anglian Cup 53-54,99-00; WorthingtonEvans Cup 56-57 67-68 74-75.
PREVIOUS **Leagues:** Eastern Co's 35-37 38-58; Southern 58-64
Grounds: Clacton Stadium, Old Road 06-87; Gainsford Av (temp)
RECORD **Attendance:** 3,505 v Romford, FA Cup 1st Qual. Rd 1952 (at Old Road)
BEST SEASON **FA Vase:** 4th Rd 74-75,99-00 ,**FA Cup:** 1st Rd,1-3 v Southend U. (H) 60-61
Players progressing: Vivian Woodward (Spurs), Mick Everitt (Arsenal), Christian McLean (Bristol R.)

FACT FILE
Founded: 1892
Nickname: Seasiders
Colours: White/white/royal blue
Change colours: yellow/yellow/royal blue
Midweek Matches: Tuesday
Programme: 40 pages, £1
Editor: Jon Gooding (01473 420731)
Local Press: Clacton Gazette
web site: www.clacton-town.com

CLUB PERSONNEL
Owner: Jeff Dewing
Chairman: Mick Brpoadbent
Commercial Manager: Michelle Stanley
Tel:01255822169
Team Manager: Richie Powling

2002-03
Leading Goalscorer:
Captain:
Player of the Year:

DEREHAM TOWN

Secretary & Fixture Sec Tim Warner, Aldiss Park, Norwich Road, Dereham, Norfolk NT20 3AL
Tel No: 01362 692419

Ground: Aldiss Park, Norwich Road, Dereham, Norfolk NR20 3AL
Tel/Fax: 01362 690460
Capacity: 3,000 Seats: 50 Cover: 500 Club Shop: (01362 690460)
Directions: **From Swaffham** (A47) turn off to Bawdeswell/Swanton Morley, pass Little Chef on left and Ground is on right. **From Dereham** town centre follow A47. Aldiss Park is onleft before A47 **From Norwich** (A47)turn offas above ,left at ist T jct then right at 2nd Jct Ground on left.

HONOURS Anglian Combination 97-98, Jewson Eastern Div 1 R-up 2000-01
Jewson League Cup R-Up: 2001-2002

PREVIOUS **Leagues:** Dereham & Dist., East Anglian, Anglian Combination >98
Names: Dereham, Dereham Hobbies
Grounds: Recreation Ground 1890-1998

RECORD **Defeat:** 0-13, v Gorleston, Norfolk Sen. Cup 9.1.1926

FACT FILE
Formed: 1890
Nickname: The Magpies
Colours: Black & white/black/white
Change colours: all Red
Midweek matchday; Tuesday
Programme - 20 pages 50p
Editor: Barnes Print
Tel: 01362 860781 Fax: 01362 860977
Website: www.derehamtownfc.com

CLUB PERSONNEL
Chairman: Tim Warner Tel: 01362 692419 (H)
Managers:Jim Landamore & Greg Owens

2002-03
Leading Goalscorer:Jason Parr
Captain:Matthew Henman
Player of the Year: Jason Parr

DISS TOWN

Secretary: Pam Lattimore, 7 Station Road, Pulham St. Mary, Diss, Norfolk, IP21 4QT.
01379 608905 Tel/Fax - 07711 470858M

Ground: Brewers Green Lane, Diss Tel: 01379 651223

Directions: Just off B1066 Diss-Thetford road, near Roydon School. 1 1/2 miles from Diss (BR)
Capacity: 2,500 Seats: 280 Cover: Yes Floodlights: Yes
Club Shop: Yes, incl. pennants
Clubhouse: Open evenings (except Sunday), Sat/Sun lunchtimes, and matchdays

HONOURS FA Vase 94-95; Eastern Co's Lg Div 1 91-92, Anglian Comb. 76-77 78-79(R-up 74-75, Div 1 67-68 73-74, Lg Cup 67-68 79-80 81-82), Norfolk & Suffolk Lg R-up 55-56 (Applegate Cup 56-57 57-58(joint)(R-up 55-56)), Norfolk Snr Cup 74-75 95-96, Norfolk Jnr Cup 1891-92, Jewson Prem Lge R-up 95-96 R-up Millennium Trophy 2001

PREVIOUS **Leagues**: Norwich & District; Norfolk & Suffolk 35-64; AnglianComb. 64-82
Ground: Roydon Road 1886-1982

BEST SEASON **FA Vase:** Winners 94-95, QF 91-92

RECORDS **Attendance:** 1,731 v Atherton LR, FA Vase SF 1st leg 19/3/94

Players progressing A Thurlow (Man City), M Cawston (Norwich), T Whymark(Ipswich), C Stafford, P Gibbs (Colchester)

FACT FILE
Founded: 1888
Nickname: Tangerines
Sponsors: Apple Garages
Colours: Tangerine/navy/tangerine
Change colours: Sky blue/navy/navy
Midweek Matches: Tuesday
Reserve's League: Anglian Combination
Programme: 16 pages, 80p
Editor: Gary Enderby (01379 608767)

CLUB PERSONNEL
Chairman: Des Tebble
President: Roger Weeks
Treasurer: Tony Collins
Manager: Robert Fleck
Physio: Adrianna Brookman

2002-03
Leading Goalscorer:
Captain:
Player of the Year:

FAKENHAM TOWN

Secretary: Mrs Tania King, 27 The Patch, Dunton, Fakenham NR21 7PF Tel No: 01328 855843
Ground: Clipbush Lane, Fakenham NR21 8SW Tel/Fax: 01328 856222

Directions: Corner of A148 & Clipbush Lane
Capacity: 3,000 Seats: 264 Cover: 500 Floodlights: Yes

Clubhouse: Bar, TV. Refreshments available Tel: 01328 855859
Club Shop: Yes

HONOURS Norfolk Snr Cup 70-71 72-73 73-74 91-92 93-94 94-95;,98-99 Eastern Co's Premier Division R-up: 98-99, Lg Div1, R-up 91-92; Anglian Comb. Cup 78-79

PREVIOUS **Leagues:** N Norfolk 1884-1910; Norwich & Dist 10-35; Norfolk & Suffolk 35-64; Anglian Comb 64-87
Grounds: Hempton Green 1884-89; Star Meadow 89-1907; Barons Hall Lawn 1907-96

BEST SEASON **FA Vase:** 98-99 3rd Rd **FA Cup:**

RECORD **Gate:** 1100 v Watford-official opening of new ground

Players progressing Nolan Keeley (Scunthorpe)

FACT FILE
Founded: 1884
Nickname: Ghosts
Sponsors:Warner Paperbacks
Colours: Amber & black/black/amber
Change colours: All White
Midweek Matchday: Tuesday
Reserves' League: Anglian Comb
Programme: 32 pages, 50p
Editor: John Cushion
Tel: 01328 862548
Local Press : Dereham & Fakenham Times

CLUB PERSONNEL
Chairman: Tim Amos
President:Tony Fisher
Press Officer: J Cushion
Commercial Manager: T.Vertigan
Managers: Wayne Coe/Stuart Woodhouse

2002-03
Captain:Steve Lewis Top Scorerr:Paul Reeve
Players of theYear: Paul Reeve & Martin mcNeil

GORLESTON

Secretary: Arthur Ottley,60 Peterhouse Avenue,Gorleston, Great Yarmouth, Norfolk NR31 7PZ
Tel Nos: 01493 603353 (H) 01263 738335 (W) 07774 205949 (M)
Ground: Emerald Park, Woodfarm Lane, Gorleston, Great Yarmouth Tel: 01493 602802

Directions: On Magdalen Estate - follow signs to Crematorium, turn left and follow road to ground. Five and a half miles from Great Yarmouth Vauxhall (BR)
Capacity: 5,000 Seats: 2000 Cover: 4,000 Floodlights: Yes
Clubhouse: Bar, colour TV, snacks. Matchday Tea, coffee,cold drinks, burgers, hotdogs, rolls **Club Shop:** No

HONOURS Eastern Co's Lg 52-53 72-73 79-80 80-81; Lge Cup 55-56; Norfolk Snr Cup x 13, R-up x 25; Anglian Comb. 68-69, Norfolk & Suffolk Lg x 7; E Anglian Cup (3);Jewson Lge Div 1 95-96

PREVIOUS **Leagues:** Gt Yarmouth & Dist; Norfolk & Suffolk; Anglian Comb

BEST SEASON **FA Cup:** 1st Rd. 51-52, 57-58 **FA Vase:**

RECORD **Attendance:** 4,473 v Orient, FA Cup 1st Rd 29/11/51

Players progressing: J Joblins (Norwich), M Bailey (Wolves), D Stringer(Norwich), R Carter (Aston Villa), D Carter (Man City), A Brown (Charlton), S Morgan (Cambridge), P Gibbs (Colchester)

FACT FILE

Founded: 1884
Nickname: Greens
Colours: Green & White/whitw/white
Change colours: All blue
Midweek Matchday: Tuesday
Programme: 56/60 pages £1.00
Editor:Simon Barnes Printing

CLUB PERSONNEL

Chairman & President: Jimmy Jones

Managers: Alan Smith

2002-03
Leading Goalscorer:
Captain:
Player of the Year:

GREAT YARMOUTH TOWN

Secretary: Brian Smith, The Bungalow, Humberstone Farm, Cobholm, Great Yarmouth, Norfolk NR31 0AZ. Tel & Fax: 01493 656099
Ground: Wellesey Recreation Ground, Wellesey Road (01493 843373)

Directions: Just off Marine Parade, 200yds north of Britannia Pier.1/2 m from Vauxhall BR(BR)
Capacity: 3,600 Seats: 500 Cover: 2,100 Floodlights: Yes Club Shop: Yes

Clubhouse: (01493 843373). Committee Room, Sky TV, darts, pool. Hot & cold food
HONOURS Eastern Co's Lg 68-69 (R-up 56-57 67-68 77-78 78-79), Lg Cup 37-38 74-75 80-81; East Anglian Cup(3); Norfolk Senior Cup x 12, R-up x 22; Norfolk Premier Cupx 2 jt; Norfolk & Suffolk Lg 13-14 26-27 27-28; Anglian Comb. Cup 65-66(res); E Anglian Lg 56-57(res)

PREVIOUS **Leagues:** Norfolk & Suffolk

BEST SEASON **FA Cup:** 2nd Rd 52-53, 1st Rd 47-48 **FA Vase:** Semi-Final 82-83
RECORD **Attendance:** 8,944 v Crystal Palace, FA Cup 1st Rd 52-53
Appearances: Mark Vincent 627 games (1984-2003)
Scorer: Gordon South 298 (1927-47) **Win:** 14-0, 2.2.10

Players progressing: R Hollis (Norwich), M Blyth & N Keeley (Scunthorpe), S Davy (West Ham), K Ready (Aston Villa), G Butcher (Blackburn)

FACT FILE

Founded: 1897
Nickname: Bloaters
Colours: Amber & black stripes/black/black
Change colours: All blue
Midweek Matches: Tuesday
Programme: 40 pages, #1.00
Editorial: Barnes Print, Dereham

CLUB PERSONNEL

Chairman: Arthur Fiske
Manager: Paul Tong

2002-03

Leading Goalscorer:Robert George
Captain:Lee Humphreys
Player of the Year: Rob George

HALSTEAD TOWN

Secretary: Stephen Webber, 12 Ravens Ave, Halstead, Essex CO9 1NZ
Tel: 01787 476959 (H) 01284 767278 (B)

Ground: Rosemary Lane, Broton Ind Est, Halstead, Essex CO9 2HR Tel: 01787 472082
Directions: A131 Chelmsford to Braintree - follow signs to Halstead.
In Halstead, 1st left after Police Station, then 1st right, and left to ground
Clubhouse: Open evenings and matchdays

PREVIOUS **Leagues:** North Essex; Halstead & District; Haverhill; Essex & Suffolk Border; Essex Senior 80-88
Grounds: Three Gates 1879-1948, Coggeshall Pieces, Ravens Meadow, King George Pl'y Field
RECORD **Attendance:** 4,000 v Walthamstow Avenue, Essex Senior Cup 1949
HONOURS Eastern Co's Lg 94-95 95-96, R-up 93-94 (Div 1 R-up 89-90), Cup 95-96; Essex Senior Trophy 94-95 96-97; Knight Floodlit Cup R-up 90-91; Essex &Suffolk Border Lg 57-59 77-78 94-95 (res), (R-up 49-50 54-55 60-61), Div 1 (res) 94-95); Essex Snr Lg Cup R-up 79-80; Essex Jnr Cup 01-02 46-47 (R-up 00-01)
Players progressing Steve Allen (Wimbledon Physio)

2002-03: **Captain**: Lloyd Pentney **Top Scorer**: Jimmy Chatteris **P.o.Y.:** Matt Chinnery

FACT FILE

Founded: 1879
Nickname 'The Town'
Colours: White /black/white
Change colours:Red/white/red
Midweek Matches: Tuesday

Programme

Page 24 Price 50p
Editor: Paul Downes Tel: 01787 477320 (H)
Local Press : Halstead Gazette

CLUB PERSONNEL

Chairman: Tony Lister
Vice-Chairman: Ralph Wilkin
President: Philip Partridge
Fixture Sec.: Steve Webber
Manager: Paul Grimsey
Physio: B Dunster

HISTON RESERVES

Secretary: Mick W Collis, 22 Haddows Close, Longstanton, Cambridge CB4 5DJ
Tel: 01954 201083 (H)

Ground Bridge Rd, Impington, Cambridge
Tel: 01223 232301 Fax: 01223 237373
Club Website: Website: www.histonfootballclub.tripod.com
EMAIL Address: gareth@corporate innovations.co.uk

Directions: Leave A14 northern Cambridge bypass on B1049 (signposted Histon and Cottenham). Ground half a mile on right.
5 miles from Cambridge (BR). Bus No.104
Capacity: 3,250 Seats: 250 Cover: 250 Floodlights: Yes

Clubhouse: Bar/lounge open Tues-Sun eves, Sun lunch and matchdays.Snacks available

HONOURS Eastern Co's Lg Div 1 R-up 01-02, Div.1 Lge Cup R-up 01-02.

FACT FILE

Founded: 1904
Colours: Red & black stripes/black/red & black
Change colours: Sky & navy/navy/sky & navy
Midweek matches: Wednesday

CLUB PERSONNEL

Chairman: Gareth Baldwin
President: G P Muncey
Manager: Nacer Relizani

2002-03

Leading Goalscorer:
Captain:
Player of the Year:

Godmanchester Rovers. Photo: Gordon Whittingham.

Felixstowe & Walton United. Back Row (L-R): Tony Barnes (Chairman), Paul Adams (Manager), Dean Sadler, Robbie Evans, Micky Felgate, Ismail Etti, Ross Charters, Andy Crump, Robbie Fuller, Jimmy Andrews, David Thurkettle, Chris Sawyer (Asst. Manager), Chris Hunton (Vice Chairman). Front Row: Lee Parry, Mark Cooper, Ryan Hunn, Nicky Barker (Capt), Ton Childs, Mark Anderson, Phil Hazelwood (Physio).

Great Yarmouth Town . Back Row: Derek Bevan (Asst. Manager), Kevin Howes, Jodie Harrison, Michael Shade, Robert Thornton, Nick Banham, Mark Vincent, Michael Tierney, Lee Brown, terry Reeves (physio).
Front Row: Neil Adcock, Kevin Winkworth, Alan Darby, Nathan Drake, robert george, Grant Pierpoint, Daniel Self, Neil Bilham.

KING'S LYNN RESERVES

Secretary: Ken Rout, Mandlyn, Fen Lane, Ashwicken, King's Lynn, Norfolk PE32 1AW
Tel: 01553 630532 (H) 01553 764494 (B) 07850 395422 (M)
email: anglian.access@btinternet.com (office hours)

GROUND The Walks Stadium, Tennyson Road, King's Lynn PE30 5PB
Tel: 01553 760060

Directions: At mini r-about arriving from A10/A47 take Vancouver Avenue. Ground on left after a half mile. Quarter mile from King's Lynn (BR), half mile from bus station

Capacity: 8,200 Cover: 5,000 Seats: 1,200 Floodlights: Yes

Clubhouse: Normal licensing hours, with extension on matchdays
Club Shop: Sells metal badges and other merchandise

FACT FILE

Colours: Blue & gold stripes/blue/blue & gold
Change colours: All purple and navy
Midweek matches: Tuesday

CLUB PERSONNEL

Manager: Darren Bloodworth

LOWESTOFT TOWN

Secretary: Terry Lynes, 31 Avondale Road Lowestoft, Suffolk NR32 2HU
Tel: 01502 564034 (H) 07930 872947(M) Email: terry@ltfcblues.freeserve.co.uk
Ground: Crown Meadow, Love Rd, Lowestoft Tel: 01502 573818
Directions: Just off A12, 10 mins from Lowestoft (BR)
Capacity: 3,000 Seats: 466 Cover: 500 Floodlights: Yes
Clubhouse: Pub hours, Snacks available **Club Shop:** Yes (incl metal badges)

HONOURS Eastern Co's Lg(8) 35-36(jnt) 37-38 62-63 64-65 67-68 69-71 77-78, Lg Cup(8) 38-39 54-55 65-67 68-69 75-76 83-84; 00-01Norf. & Suffolk Lg(8) 1897-99 1900-04 28-29 30-31; Suffolk Prem. Cup(7) 66-67 71-72 74-75 78-80; 99-00,00-01Suffolk Snr Cup(10) 02- 03 22-24 25-26 31-32 35-36 46-49 55-56; E Anglian Cup(10); Anglian Comb. (Res.) 77-78 79-80 (Lg Cup 76-77); E Anglian Lg (Res.) 57-58 63-64

PREVIOUS **League:** Norfolk & Suffolk 1897-1935
BEST SEASON **FA Cup:** 1st Rd 26-27 38-39 66-67, 67-68, 77-78
RECORDS **Attendance:** 5,000 v Watford, FA Cup 1st Rd 67
Goalscorer: M Tooley 383 **Appearances:** C Peck 629
Win: 19-0 v Thetford Town (H), Eastern Counties League

Players progressing: Eddie Spearitt (Ipswich 1965), Nigel Cassidy (Norwich1967), Richard Money (Scunthorpe 1973), Graham Franklin (Southend 1977)

FACT FILE

Founded: 1885
Nickname: Blues
Sponsors: CWA Group
Colours: Royal Blue/white/blue
Change colours: White & Navy
Midweek Matches: Tuesday
Reserves' Lge: Anglian Combination
Programme:44 pages £1.00
Editor: Shaun Cole
Website: www.lowestofttownfc.co.uk

CLUB PERSONNEL

Chairman: Shaun Cole
President: Roy Harper
Manager: Michael Chapman

2002-03

Leading Goalscorer:gary McGee 43
Captain:Ian Smith
Player of the Year: Gary McGee

MALDON TOWN

Secretary: Phil Robinson, 9 Lyndhurst Drive, Bicknacre, Essex CN3 4XL
Tel No: 01245 222633 (H) 07759 066636 (M)
Email Address: robbophil@hotmail.com

Ground: Wallace Binder Ground, Park Drive, Maldon CM9 5XX (01621 853762)
Capacity: 2,500 Seats: 250 Cover: 500 Floodlights: Yes

HONOURS Essex Snr Lg 84-85 (Sportsmanship Award 87-88,88-89,94-95, Res Shield 93-94), Res Cup:94-95, Essex & Suffolk Border Lg 55-56 (Cup 64-65),Essex Intermediate Cup 51-52, Tolleshunt D'Arcy Cup 93-94,99-00, Eastern Div 1 R-Up 96-97

PREVIOUS **Leagues:** Mid Essex, N. Essex, Essex & Suffolk Border, Essex Senior
Ground: Fambridge Road (pre-1994)

BEST SEASON **FA Cup:** 2000-01 **FA Vase:** 20003 Semi- Final v AFC Sudbury

RECORDS **Attendance:** 1,163 v AFC Sudbury April @003

FACT FILE

Founded: 1946
Nickname: 'The Town'
Colours: Blue & white hoops/blue/blue
Change colours: Red & black hoops/black/black
Midweek Matchday: Tuesday
Programme:24 pages £1.00
Editor: Alan Drewer
Club Website: http://www.maldontownfc.co.uk

CLUB PERSONNEL

Chairman:Mike Kirkham
Manager: Colin Wallington
Physio:Ian Jenkins

2002-03

Leading Goalscorer:Terry Warwick
Captain:Nicky Smith
Player of the Year: Paul Goodacre

Leiston Town Photo: Gordon Whittingham.

Halstead Town

MILDENHALL TOWN

Secretary: Val Clarke, Crundale House,Manor Road, Mildenhall,Suffolkl IP28 7EL
Tel No: 01638 718324

Ground: Recreation Way, Mildenhall, Suffolk (01638 713449)

Directions: Next to swimming pool/carpark, quarter of a mile from town centre

Capacity: 2,000 Covered Seats: 50 Covered Standing:200 Floodlights: Yes

Clubhouse: Open matchdays & functions. Light refreshments available

HONOURS Suffolk Junior Cup 1899-1900

PREVIOUS **Leagues:** Bury & District; Cambs Lg 2B, 1B & Premier

RECORD **Attendance:** 450 v Derby County

. Friendly July 2001**BEST SEASON** **FA Cup:** **FA Vase:**

2002-03

Leading Scorer: Rob Allis Captain: Mark Reeder Player of the Year: Matt Mitchell-King

FACT FILE

Founded: 1890
Nickname: The Hall
Colours: Amber/black/black
Change colours:White/sky blue/white
Midweek Matchday: Tuesday
Programme: £1.00
Editor: Frank Marshall (01638 720616)
Local Press : Bury Free Press,
Newmarket Journal,
Cambridge Evening News,East Anglian Daily Times,Green 'Un

CLUB PERSONNEL

Chairman: Martin Tuck
Vice Chairman: Frank Marshall
Fixture Sec:Eric Lloyd Tel: 01638 718324
Managers: Trevor Munns

NEWMARKET TOWN

Fixture Secretary: Elaine Jeakins, 140 New Cheveley Road,Newmarket CB88BY
Tel Nos: 01638 602525 (H) 01638 750201 (W) 07801 815682 (M)

Ground: Cricketfield Road, off New Cheveley Road, Newmarket (01638 663637)

Directions: 400 yds Newmarket (BR) - turn right into Green Rd, right at cross roads New Cheveley Rd, ground at top on left

Capacity: 1,750 Seats: 144 Cover: 150 Floodlights: Yes

Clubhouse: Matchdays only. Refreshments available

HONOURS Suffolk Snr Cup 34-35 93-94; Cambs Invitation Cup 58-59; Cambs Chall. Cup 21-22 26-27; Cambs Snr Lg, 19-20; Ipswich Snr Lg 30-31 31-32 32-33 33-34; Peterborough Lg 57-58; Suffolk Premier Cup 93-94 94-95 96-97

PREVIOUS **League:** Bury Snr; Ipswich Snr; Essex & Suffolk Border; Utd Co's 34-37; Eastern Co's 37-52

BEST SEASON **FA Cup:** 4th Qual. Rd 92-93, 0-2 v Hayes (H)
FA Vase: 4th Round 91-92

RECORD **Attendance:** 2,701 v Abbey Utd (now Cambridge Utd), FA Cup 1st Qual.Rd 1/10/49

Players progressing: Mick Lambert (Ipswich), M Wright (Northampton), G Tweed(Coventry), R Fuller (Charlton), Colin Vowden (Camb.Utd.)

FACT FILE

Founded: 1877
Nickname: Jockeys
Colours: Yellow & navy/navy/yellow
Change Colours: All Red
Midweek Matches: Tuesday
Programme:£1.00
Editor: Tony Pringle (01638 669438)

CLUB PERSONNEL

Chairman: Alan Collen
President: M J Nicholas
Manager: Chris Nunn

2002-03

Leading Goalscorer:Alex Rhodes
Captain:Darren Coe
Player of the Year: Darren Coe

NORWICH UNITED

Secretary: Keith Cutmore,42 Desmond Drive,Old Catton, Norwich NR6 7JN
Tel. No.: 01603 407148 (H) 07946033588 (M)

Ground: Plantation Road, Blofield, Norwich, Norfolk NR13 4PL
Tel: 01603 716963
Website:www.norwichunited.fsnet.co.uk

Directions: Half a mile from Blofield village - coming from Norwich on Yarmouth Rd turn left in Blofield at Kings Head pub & follow to Plantation Rd (grd on right after bridge over bypass). 1/2 hour Brundall BR (Norwich-Yarmouth line)

Capacity: 3,000 Seats: 100 Cover: 1,000 Floodlights: Yes

Clubhouse: Matchday food & drink: Tea, coffee, cold drinks, hotdogs, burgers, soup, sandwiches, rolls

Club Shop: Yes incl. metal badges & pennants

HONOURS Eastern Co's Lg Div 1 90-91 01-02, R-up 89-89, Lg Cup 91-92, Anglian Combination 88-89. Jewson League Div 1 2001-02

PREVIOUS **Ground:** Gothic Club, Heartsease Lane, Norwich (until end of 90-91)

RECORD **Attendance:** 401 v Wroxham, League match, 2/10/91
Goalscorer: M Money **Appearances:** Tim Sayer

FACT FILE

Founded: 1903
Nickname: Planters
Colours: Yellow/blue/blue
Change colours: All red.
Midweek Matches: Tuesday
Programme: 24 pages, 50p
Editor:Barnes Print
Local Press : Eastern Counties Newspapers

CLUB PERSONNEL

Chairman: John Hilditch, Pres Michael Miles
Vice-Chairman: Peter Bowyer
Managers: Paul Franklin & Donny Pye
Physio: Martyn Parker

2002-03

Leading Goalscorer:
Captain:
Player of the Year:

SOHAM TOWN RANGERS

Secretary: Peter Luck, Flat 5 17-21 Churchgate Street,Soham,Ely,Cambs. CB7 5DS
Tel No: 01353 727765 (H) 0775 951 3898

Ground: Julius Martin Lane, Soham, Ely , Cambs.CB7 5DE Tel: 01353 720732

Directions: A142 between Newmarket and Ely, at roundabout at northern end of by-pass turn left towards town centre and then right at the corner shop into Julius Martina Lane. Ground is on left

Capacity: 2,000 Seats: 250 Cover: 1,000 Floodlights: Yes Shop: Yes

Clubhouse: Function Room, Lounge Bar, Stud Bar, Public Bar.Available for private hire
Clubhouse Manager: M.Howe **Club Shop:** Yes

HONOURS Eastern Co's Lg Div 1 R-up 92-93; Peterborough & District League (3), Milleniuim Cup 2000-01, Cambs Invitation Cup 1990-91, 97-98, 98-99

PREVIOUS **Leagues:** Peterborough & Dist
Ground: Soham Rangers: Brook Street 1919-47
Names: Soham Town and Soham Rangers merged in 1947

RECORD **Attendance:** 3,000 v Pegasus, FA Amateur Cup 1963

BEST SEASONS **F.A.Cup:** 3rd Q v Kings Lynn (A) 70-71
F.A.Vase: 4th Round v Aldershot Town (A) 93-94

FACT FILE
Founded: 1947
Nickname: Town or Rangers
Main Sponsor: C.J.Murfitt
Colours: Green & white/ black/green
Change colours: Blue/black/ black
Midweek Matchday: Tuesday
Reserves ' League: Cambs Senior. A
Programme: £1.00 Editor : 01473 420731
Local Press : Ely Standard, Newmarket Journal, Cambridge Evening News

CLUB PERSONNEL
Chairman: C.J.Murffitt Pres: Vinnie Jones
Manager R Goodjohn Coach: K. Murray
Physio: M. Drury

2002-03
Leading Goalscorer:
Captain:
Player of the Year:

STOWMARKET TOWN

Secretary: Mr Mark Bolton,45 Primrose Way, Needham Market, Suffolk.
Ground: Green Meadows Stadium, Bury Road, Stowmarket
Tel: 01449 612533

Directions: About 800 yds from Stowmarket BR station - turn right at 1st lights and head out of town over r'bout into Bury Road - ground on right
Capacity: 2,000 Seats: 200 Cover: 450 Floodlights: Yes

Clubhouse: Bar open 6.30pm onwards Mon-Fri, weekends 12.0pm onwards.
Matchday food available Club Shop: Yes, incl. metal badges.

HONOURS Eastern Co's Lg R-up 91-92, Suffolk Premier Cup(4), Suffolk Snr Cup(10)
Suffolk Jnr Cup., Churchman Cup: 99-00.91-92,92-93

PREVIOUS **Leagues:** Ipswich & Dist.; Essex & Suffolk Border 25-52
Grounds: The Cricket Meadow, 1883-1984
Names: Stowupland Corinthians; Stowmarket Corinthians; Stowmarket FC

BEST SEASON **FA Cup: 2nd Q Rd 1992** **FA Vase:** 4th Rd 1983-84

RECORD **Attendance:** 1,200 v Ipswich Town, friendly July 1994
At Cricket Meadow: 3,800 v Romford, FA Amtr Cup 1st Rd 15/12/51

Players progressing: Craig Oldfield (Colchester), Les Tibbott, Ted Phillips & Brian Klug (Ipswich)

FACT FILE
Founded: 1883
Nickname: Stow
Colours: Gold & black/black/black
Change colours: All Red
Midweek Matches: Wednesday
Reserves' Lge: Essex & Suffolk Border
Programme: 20 pages,60p
Ed: Jonathon Gooding (01473 420731)
Local Press: East Anglian, Bury Free Press

CLUB PERSONNEL
Chairman: Andrew Horrex
President: John Bultitude
Fixture Sec: Christine Gillingham
23 Windermere Road,Stowmarket, Suffolk
Tel: 01449 674507(H) 07880 732416(M)
Manager: Mel Aldis Coach: Mark Barnard
Physio: John Chandler

2002-03
Leading Goalscorer:Stuart Jopling
Captain:Colin Yeomans

AFC SUDBURY

Ground: Kingsmarsh Stadium, Brundon Lane, Sudbury, Suffolk CO10 1WQ (01787 376213)

Directions: From Sudbury centre follow Halstead/Chelmsford signs for about 1mile. 1st right after railway bridge at foot of steep hill, and 1st right after sharp left hand bend

Capacity: 2,500 Seats: 200 Cover: 150 Floodlights: Yes

Clubhouse: Matchdays/ training nights Shop: Yes Contact: Darren Witt (M) 0402 159375)

HONOURS **WANDERERS -** Eastern Co's Lg Div 1 92-93, Ess. & Suff. Border Lg(2) 89-91 (R-up 88-89), Suffolk Snr Cup 90-91**TOWN:**Southern Lge -Lge Cup 93-94, R-up 97,Champonship 93-94, Southern Div (Post War)R-up 93-94; Eastern Counties Lg x 7, R-up x 6, Lg Cup x 6, Suffolk Prem.Cup x 13, R-up x 8, Suffolk Sen. Cup(2); E. Anglian Cup 85-86 91-92, R-up 83-84 95-96; Essex Suff Border Lg x 5; E.S.B.L.Cup 49-50, R-Up 46-47; East F'lit Group -94 & 95
A.F.C.: Eastern League Champiuons 2001-02 Suffolk County Premier Cup Winners 2001-02

PREVIOUS **Names:** Sudbury Town (1885) & Sudbury Wanderers (1958) merged 1999
Leagues: Wanderers- Essex & Suffolk Border. Town Suffolk & Ipswich; Essex & Suffolk Border; Eastern Co 55-90; Southern 91-97 Eastern Co. 98-99

BEST SEASON **FA Vase:** 2002-03 FA Vase Final
(as A.F.C.) **FA Cup:** 1st Round Proper, 00-01 (1-6 v Darlington)
TOWN **FA Vase:** Runners-up 88-89 **FA Trophy:** 3rd Rd.Proper 95-96
FA Cup: 2nd Rd Proper 96-97, 1-3 v Brentford. Played at Colchester Utd. F.C.

FACT FILE
Founded: 1st June,1999
Colours: Yellow/blue/yellow
Change Colours: All Red
Midweek Matchday: Tuesday
Programme: 48 + pages £1
Editor:Peter Scott (01787 379123)
Local Press : Suffolk Free Press, East Anglian Daily Times

CLUB PERSONNEL
Joint Chairmen: Nick F Smith & Phil Turner
Secretary: David Webb
6 Melford Road, Sudbury, Suffolk CO10 1LS
Tel: 01787 372352 (H) 01787 886000 x6223 (B)
Manager: Keith Martin

2002-03
Leading Goalscorer:
Captain:
Player of the Year:

Halstead Town F.C.
JEWSON
1
HTFC
JIMMY GREAVES
H T F C
H T F C
Season 2002/03

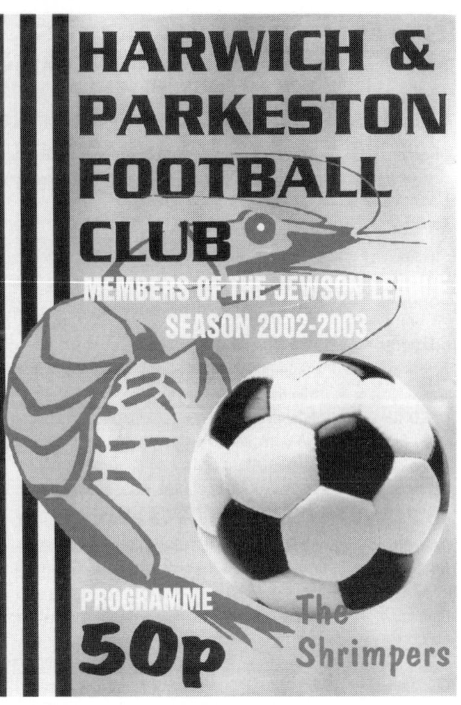
HARWICH &
PARKESTON
FOOTBALL
CLUB
MEMBERS OF THE JEWSON LEAGUE
SEASON 2002-2003
PROGRAMME
50p
The
Shrimpers

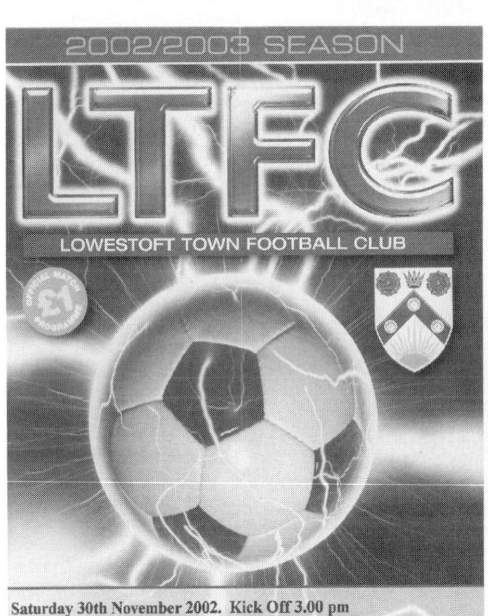
2002/2003 SEASON
LTFC
LOWESTOFT TOWN FOOTBALL CLUB
OFFICIAL MATCH
£1
PROGRAMME
Saturday 30th November 2002. Kick Off 3.00 pm
Jewson League Premier Division
Lowestoft Town V Histon Reserves
Winners Jewson League
Cup & Suffolk Premier Cup 2001
LTFC sponsored by
OWA
group limited

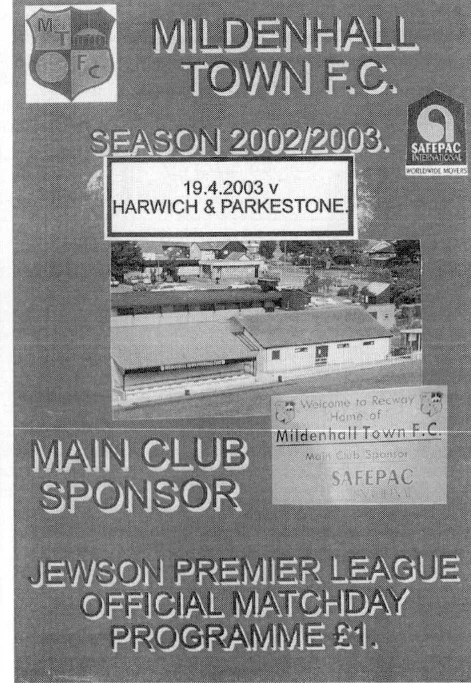
MILDENHALL
TOWN F.C.
SEASON 2002/2003.
SAFEPAC
INTERNATIONAL
WORLDWIDE MOVERS
19.4.2003 v
HARWICH & PARKESTONE.
Welcome to Recway
Home of
Mildenhall Town F.C.
Main Club Sponsor
SAFEPAC
MAIN CLUB
SPONSOR
JEWSON PREMIER LEAGUE
OFFICIAL MATCHDAY
PROGRAMME £1.

TIPTREE UNITED

Secretary: John Wisbey, 103 Peace Road, Stanway, Colchester, Essex
Tel Nos: 01206 564222 (H) 0403 585814 (M)
Email: john.wisbey@talk21.com

Ground: Chapel Road, Tiptree, Essex Tel: 01621 815213

Directions: Enter town on B1023 - Chapel Road is left at second crossroads, ground 200yds on left. 3 miles from Kelverdon (BR). Served by Eastern NationalColchester to Maldon bus

Capacity: 2,500 Seats: 150 Cover: 300 Floodlights: Yes

Clubhouse: Open daily 7-11pm (all day Fri & Sat) & 12-2.30, 7-10.30 Sun. Large bar, two snooker tables, pool, darts, netball, badminton, pigeon club, bingo. Dance hall seats 180, small hall seats 60. **Club Shop:** No

HONOURS Essex Snr Tphy 80-81, Eastern Co's Lg 81-82 (Lg Cup 81-82 84-85), Essex Snr Lg R-up 75-76 77-78, Harwich Charity Cup (4), Jewson Eastern Div 1 Champions 99-00

PREVIOUS **Leagues:** Essex & Suffolk Border; Essex Snr 78-84

RECORD **Attendance:** 1,210 v Spurs, floodlight inauguration Dec 1990

FACT FILE
Founded: 1933
Nickname:The Jam -Makers
Sponsors: Tiptree Building Supplies
Colours: Red& blackstripes/black/black
Change colours: Yellow/blue/white
Midweek Matchday: Tuesday
Reserves: Essex & Suffolk Border Lg Div 1
Programme: 32 pages, 50p Editor: Secretary
Local Press : Colchester Evening Gazette, Essex County Standard'
* Voted Eastern' Programme of the Year'
Website: www.tiptreeunited.com

CLUB PERSONNEL
Chairman: T.B.A.
President: Peter Fidge
Manager: Neil Farley

2002-03
Leading Goalscorer:
Captain:
Player of the Year:

WISBECH TOWN

Secretary: Mrs Dorothy Hill, 19 Mansell Road, Wisbech ,Cambs. PE13 2SP Tel: 01945 581767

Ground: Fenland Park, Lerowe Road, Wisbech, Cambs Tel: 01945 584176

Directions: Follow A47 bypass to the West Walton turn off roundabout where there is a Little Chef, turn left for Wisbech, Lerowe Road is first left after 30mph sign. Entering town from north along A1101 cross Freedom Bridge, atroundabout go straight over sign Walsoken/West Walton

Capacity: 3,800 Seats: 284 Cover: 1,000 Floodlights: Yes

Clubhouse: Open every evening. Matchday food & drink - Tea, coffee, cold drinks, confectionary, burgers, hotdogs, soup, sandwiches, rolls Club Shop (open matchdays): Contact Secretary

PREVIOUS **Leagues:** Peterborough 1920-35; Utd Co's 35-50; Eastern Co's 50-52 70-97; Midland 52-58; Southern 58-70, 97-02

CLUB RECORDS Attendance: 8,004 v Peterborough United, Midland League 25/8/57
Goalscorer: Bert Titmarsh 246 (31-37) **Appearances**: Jamie Brighty (731)

BEST SEASON **FA Cup:** 2nd Rd 57-58, 97-98 League clubs defeated: Colchester
FA Trophy: 3rd Qual Rd. 97-98 **FA Vase:** Semi-Finals 84-85, 85-86

HONOURS Southern Lg Div 1 61-62; Utd Co's Lg (3) 46--47-48 49-50+ 61-62 (res) (R-up 48-49, Lg Cup 35-36 (R-up 46-47); Midland Lg R-up 57-58; Eastern Co's Lg 71-72 76-77 90-91, R-up 70-71 73-74 83-84 92-93 96-97, Lg Cup x4, R-up x3; Cambs Invit Cup x8; E Anglian Cup 87-88 (R-up 40-41 48-49); Peterborough Lg x5; Peterborough Snr Cup 32-33 76-77 89-90 97-98

FACT FILE
Founded: 1920 Nickname: Fenmen
Newsline: 09066 555865
Colours: All Red
Change colours: Yellow/Green/Yellow
Midweek Matchday: Tuesday
Programme: Pages: 44 Price: £1
Editor: Gordon Smith Tel: 01945 581767

CLUB PERSONNEL
Chairman: Barry Carter
Vice Chairman: George Campion
President: J W A Chilvers
Press Off.: Chris Smith (01945 476325)
Manager: Ian Benjamin
Assistant Manager: Roy McManus
Res. Manager: Jackie Gallagher
Assistant Gary Shailes

2002-03
Leading Goalscorer:Andy Furnell
Captain:Ian Pledger
Player of the Year: Andy Furnell

WOODBRIDGE TOWN

Secretary: Eric Smy,10 Peterhouse Crescent,Woodbridge, Suffolk IP12 4HT
Tel No: 01394 384213

Ground: Notcutts Park, Seckford Hall Road, Woodbridge, Suffolk IP12 4DA Tel: 01394 385308

Directions: Turning into Woodbridge off last rounda'bout from Lowestoft, or first roundabout from Ipswich. Take first turning left and first left again. Drive to ground at end of road on left.

Capacity: 3,000 **Seats:** 50 **Cover:** 200 **Floodlights**: Yes

Clubhouse: Visitors bar, lounge bar, function hall.Matchday Tea, coffee, cold drinks, hotdogs, soup, burgers, sandwiches, rolls.

HONOURS Suffolk Sen Cup(4), Jun Cup (4); Eastern Co Lg Cup 93-94 97-98, Lge Div 1 R-up 93-94; Ipswich Sen Lge (2)

PREVIOUS **Leagues:** Suffolk & Ipswich Ground: Kingston PF

BEST SEASON **FA Cup:** 3rd Rd Q 97-98 & 00-01 **FA Vase:** 6th Round 98-99

RECORD **Attendance:** 3,000 v Arsenal, floodlight opener 2/10/90

FACT FILE
Founded: 1885
Nickname: The Woodpeckers
Sponsors: John Grose
Colours: Black & white stripes/black/black
Change colours: All blue
Midweek Matchday: Tuesday
Reserves League: Essex & Suffolk Border
Programme: 20-24 pages ,50p
Editor: D Crowley
Local Press : East Anglian Daily Times

CLUB PERSONNEL
Chairman: Keith Dixon
President:Andrew Dalby
Football Sec: David Crowley (01394 384853)
Commercial Manager: Richard Snelham
Manager: David Hubbick

2002-03
Leading Goalscorer:
Captain:
Player of the Year:

WROXHAM

Secretary : Chris Green, 24 Keys Drive, Wroxham, Norfolk NR12 8S Tel: 01603 783936 (H) 079412385 (M) Email Address: secretary@wroxhamfc.com
Ground: Trafford Park, Skinners Lane, Wroxham, Norfolk Tel: 01603 783538

Directions: Arriving from Norwich turn left at former Castle PH and keep left to ground. One and a half miles from Wroxham + Hoveton (BR). Buses 722, 724 and717
Capacity: 2,500 Seats: 50 Cover: 250 Floodlights: Yes
Clubhouse: Bar, pool, darts etc. Drinks, hot & cold food Club Shop: No

HONOURS Eastern Co's Lg 91-92 92-93 93-94 96-97 97-98, 98-99, R-Up 94-95,99-00,01-02 Lg.Cup 92-93, 99-00, 92-93R-up 90-91), Div 1 88-89; Norfolk Snr Cup 92-93 96-97 97-98;99-00,01-2 Anglian Comb(6) (LgCup(7); Res did the double in 94-95.Jewson Res K.O. Cup 00-01

PREVIOUS **Leagues:** Norwich City; East Anglian; Norwich & Dist.; Anglian Comb. 64-88
Grounds: Norwich Road; The Avenue; Keys Hill (all pre-1947)

BEST SEASON **FA Vase:** Quarter Final v Durham City 2001-02

RECORDS **Attendance:** 1,011 v Wisbech Town, E. Counties Lge Prem. Div. 16/3/93
Goalscorer: Matthew Metcalf. Appearances: Stu Larter
Win: 15-2 v Thetford Town (H), E. Counties Lge Prem. Div. 17/1/92
Defeat: 1-24 v Blofield (A), Norwich & District League, early 1960s

Players progressing: Matthew Metcalf (Brentford) 93, Paul Warne (Wigan Athletic) 97

FACT FILE
Founded: 1892
Nickname: Yachtsmen
Colours: All Blue
Change colours: All Red
Midweek Matchday: Tuesday
Reserves ' League: Anglian Comb Prem Div
Programme: 20 pages
Editor: Matt Carpenter
Local Press : North Norfolk
Eastern Football (Norwich 628311)
Web-site:www.wroxhamfc.com

CLUB PERSONNEL
Chairman: Ray Bayles President: L King
Press Officer: Secretary
Manager: Bruce Cunningham
Physio: P.Terrington
2002-03
Leading Goalscorer: Russell Stock
Captain:Darren Gill
Player of the Year: Gavin Pauling

CAMBRIDGE CITY RESERVES

Secretary: Stuart Hamilton, 55 Crowhill, Godmanchester, Huntingdon, Cambs
Tel: 01480 382675

Ground: City Ground, Milton Road, Cambridge CB4 1UY Tel: 01223 357973
Directions: 50 yards on left from start of A1309, Cambridge to Ely Rd.
30 minswalk from Cambridge BR
Capacity: 5,000 Cover: 1,400 Seats:423 Floodlights: Yes

Clubhouse: 11am-11pm Mon-Sat, 12-3 & 7pm-10.30 Sun. Bingo, Dances, Pool, Darts

Club Shop: Sells programmes, club history, badges, scarves, pennants, replica shirts etc.
Contact Neil Harvey (01223 235991)

FACT FILE
Colours: White & black halves/black/white & black hoops
Change colours: Green & Yellow halves,green,green& yellow hoops
Midweek matchday: Monday
Programme Editor: Secretary

CLUB PERSONNEL
Chairman: Dennis Rolph
Fixtures Sec.: Andy Dewey
50 Doggett Rd., Cherry Hinton, Cambridge
01223 245694 (H) 01223 555410 (Bus. Fax)
Manager:Jeremy George
Tel; 01954 782484

CORNARD UNITED

Secretary: Chris Symes, 22 Greenacres, Mile End, Colchester, Essex CO4 (01206 851627)
Ground: Blackhouse Lane Sportsfield, Great Cornard, Suffolk (01787 376719)
Directions: Left off r'bout on A134 coming from Ipswich/Colchester intoSudbury, follow signs for Country Park - ground is immediately opposite along Blackhouse Lane
Capacity: 2,000 Seats: 250 Cover: 500 Floodlights: Yes Club Shop: No
Clubhouse: Open matchdays & Sunday lunchtimes. Matchday Tea, coffee, colddrinks, & snacks
HONOURS Eastern Co's Lg Div 1 89-90 (Lg Cup R-up 92-93), Essex & Suffolk BorderLg 88-89 (Lg Cup 88-89), Suffolk Snr Cup 89-90, Suffolk Jnr Cup R-up 84-85, Harwich Senior Charity Cup 2001-02, Eastern Floodlight League Cup 2001-02
PREVIOUS Leagues: Sudbury S/day 64-65; Bury St Edmunds & Dist 65-72; Colchester71-78; Essex Suffolk Bord 78-89. Grounds: Cornard Rec 64-71; Great CornardUpper School 71-85
RECORDS: Appearances: Keith Featherstone **Goalscorer :** Andy Smiles
Attendance: 400 v Colchester Utd 1997 **Win:** 18-2 v St Peters House, Colchester Lge 14/9/72
Defeat: 4-10 v Finningham, Bury Lge 7/2/68

FACT FILE
Founded: 1964 Nickname: Ards
Sponsors: Pizza Town
Colours: Blue & white/white/blue
Change colours: Yellow
Midweek Matches: Tuesday
Reserve League: Essex & Suffolk Border
Prog:16 pages Ed:Neil Cheese(01787311368)
Local Press : Suffolk Free Press, East Anglian Daily Times

CLUB PERSONNEL
Chairman: Chris Symes Vice-Chair: Mike FordManager: Chris Symes
Assistant.Managaer: Mike Ford
Asst Man.: Jason Stalker Physio: Mike Ford

DOWNHAM TOWN

Secretary: F. Thorne, 6 Maple Rd., Downham Market, Norfolk, PE38 9PY. (01366 382563)

Ground: Memorial Field, Lynn Road, Downham Market, Norfolk (01366 388424)

Directions: One and a quarter miles from Downham Market (BR) - continue to townclock, turn left and ground is three quarters of a mile down Lynn Road
Capacity: 1,000 Seats: 60 Cover: Yes Floodlights: Yes
Clubhouse: Bar open matchdays, refreshments & snacks available

HONOURS Peterborough Lg (5) 62-63 73-74 78-79 86-88;
Norfolk Senior Cup 63-64 65-66 (R-up(3) 66-69)

PREVIOUS **Leagues:** Peterborough

RECORD **Attendance:** 325 v Wells Town Norfolk Senior Cup, 1998-99

FACT FILE
Founded: 1881
Nickname: Town
Sponsor: Lynwere Engineering
Colours: Red/white/red
Change colours: Sky/Navy/sky
Midweek Matches: Tuesday
Programme: Yes, with entry
Editor: Chairman

CLUB PERSONNEL
Chairman: John Fysh
President: Louis Barker
Manager: Steve Tyres

ELY CITY

Secretary: Derek Oakey, 11 Frederick Talbot Close, Soham, Nr. Ely Cambs, CB7 5EY
Tel: 01353 722141 (H) 01353 722179 (W) email: derk.oakey@tesco.net
Ground: Unwin Sports Ground, Downham Road (01353 662035)
Directions: A10 Ely by-pass turn off for Downham. 3 miles (approx) from Ely(BR)
Capacity: 1,500 Seats: 150 Cover: 350 Floodlights: Yes
Clubhouse: Open matchdays, refreshments available
Club Shop: Metal Badges: Yes
HONOURS Cambs Snr Cup 47-48, Eastern Co's Lg R-up 69-70 (Lg Cup 79-80)
Jewson Eastern Div 1 Winners 1996-97,R-up 1999-00,Cup Winners 99-00
PREVIOUS **Leagues:** Peterborough; Central Alliance 58-60
Grounds: Paradise Ground (1890 1986)
BEST SEASON **FA Cup:** 1st Rd 56-56 (2-6 v Torquay)
RECORD **Gate:** 260 v Soham, Eastern Co's Lg Div 1, 12/4/93
At old ground: 4,260 v Torquay, FA Cup 56-57

FACT FILE
Founded: 1885
Nickname: Robins
Colours: All red with white trim
Change colours: Jade/black/jade
Midweek Matches: Tuesday
Programme: 24 pages- 50p
Editor: Derek Oakley
Local Press: Ely Standard (01353 667831)
Club Website: elycityfc.com

CLUB PERSONNEL
Chairman: Brian Jordan
Manager: Steven Taylor

FELIXSTOWE & WALTON UNITED

Secretary: Chris& Jane Ryan,43 Brook Lane,Felixstowe,Suffolk IP11 7LG
Tel No: 01394 275873
Ground: Dellwood Avenue, Felixstowe IP11 9HT Tel: 01394 282917
Email:felixstowe@btinternet.com**Web**: http:/www.felixstowe,btinternet.co.uk
Directions: A14 to Felixstowe. Turn right at 3rd r'bout then 1st left - left. 5 mins walk from Felixstowe (BR) and town centre ground100 yds on
Capacity: 2,000 Seats: 200 Cover: 200 Floodlights: Yes
Clubhouse: Bar, snack bar, TV, **Club Shop:** Yes, including enamel badges
HONOURS Suffolk Senior Cup 66-67, 74-75 and 98-99 (as Walton United)
PREVIOUS **Leagues:** Essex & Suffolk Border; Ipswich & District
Names: Felixstowe Port & Town, Felixstowe Town, Felixstowe United
Merged with Walton United in 2000
Grounds: Tennis Club,Ferry Road.
RECORD **Attendance:** 1,500 v IpswichTown, floodlight inauguration 25/1/91

FACT FILE
Founded: 1890 Nickname: Seasiders
Colours: Red & white stripes/black/red
Change: Yelow & Blue/yellow/yellow
Midweek Matches: Tuesday
Programme: 48 pages, £1.00
Editor: Phil Griffiths Tel: 01394 277156
Local Press: East Anglia Daily Times

CLUB PERSONNEL
President: Dave Ashford
Chairman: Tony Barnes
Fixture Sec: Chris Ryan (01394 275873)
Manager: Paul Adams (01473 404559)

2002-2003
Captain: Nicky Barker
Top Scorer: Ismail Ett 21

GODMANCHESTER ROVERS

Secretary: June Coxhead, 28 Dovehouse Close, Godmanchester, Cambs PE29 2DY
Tel: 01480 383357 Fax: 01480 395137
Ground: Bearscroft Lane, Godmanchester, Cambs.
Directions: From A14 turn off for Godmanchester. Take A1198 towards Wood Green Animal Shelter, half mile from A14 on left down Bearscroft Lane
Capacity: **Cover:** 150 **Floodlights:** Yes
Clubhouse:
Club shop: No
Previous League: Cambridgeshire Lge. >2002
Honours:
Club Records: **Attendance:**

FACT FILE
Founded: 1911 Nickname: Goddy/Rovers
Sponsors: Terry Allgood, Sainsbury, Amec
Colours: Sky blue/navy/navy
Change: Green/black/black
Midweek Matches: Tuesday
Programme: 16-20 pages, £1.00
Editor: Tim Holmes, 23 Post St, Godmanchester, Cambs

CLUB PERSONNEL
President: Jack Hills
Chairman: Keith Gabb
Manager: Eric Cheesewright
Assistant Managers:
Daryl Potter, Neil Morean, Paul Allgood
Physio: Sandra Holmes
General Manager: Roger Coxhead

HADLEIGH UNITED

Secretary: Peter Hutchings, 3 Mowlands, Capel St Mary, Ipswich. IP9 2XB Tel: 01473 311093

Ground: Millfield, Tinkers Lane, Duke Street, Hadleigh, Suffolk Tel: 01473 822165

Directions: Turn off A12 approx halfway between Ipswich & Colchester. Take B1070 & follow signs to Hadleigh. Duke Street is off the High Street - turn left by Library
Capacity: 3,000 Seats: 250 Cover: 500 Floodlights: Yes
Clubhouse: Open matchdays. **Website**: hadleigh-utd.co.uk

HONOURS Ipswich & Dist./Suffolk & Ipswich Lg 53-54 56-57 73-74 76-77 78-79 (Mick McNeil) Lg Cup 76-77 80-81 81-82 86-87;
Suffolk Senior Cup 68-69 71-72 82-83. Eastern Co.Lg Champions 93-94
PREVIOUS **Leagues:** Suffolk & Ipswich (prev. Ipswich & D.)(pre-1991)
Grounds: Grays Meadow, Ipswich Road
RECORDS - Gate: 518 v Halstead Town, FA Vase Replay 17.1.95 **Win:** 8-1 v Chatteris(A) 17/1/95
Defeat: 0-7 v Harwich & Parkston (H) 12/10/96, & Wisbech (H) 26/4/97

FACT FILE
Founded: 1892
Nickname: Brettsiders
Sponsors: T.B.A.
Colours: White & navy/navy/navy
Change colours: All yellow
Midweek Matches: Tuesday
Reserves' Lge: Essex & Suff. Border
Programme: 12 pages, 50p
Editor: Peter Hutchings (01473 311093)

CLUB PERSONNEL
President: K.Grimsey
Chairman: Rolf Beggerow
Manager: Louis Newman

HARWICH & PARKESTON

Secretary: Andy Schooler, 21 The Vineway, Harwich, Essex CO12 4AX
01255 504590 (H) 01255 509700 (B) 01255 509718 (Bus. Fax)

Ground: Royal Oak, Main Road, Dovercourt, Harwich CO12 4AA Tel: 01255 503649
Directions: On main road into Dovercourt. 600 yds from Dovercourt (BR)
Capacity: 5,000 Seats: 350 Cover: 1,000 Floodlights: Yes
Clubhouse : Open every day. Dances, bingo, darts, pool, function room **Club Shop:** No

PREVIOUS **Leagues:** Eastern Co's 35-37 38-64; Essex County 37-38; Athenian 64-73 83-84; Isthmian 73-83 **Ground:** Phoenix Field, Seafront
RECORD **Attendance:** 5,649 v Romford, FA Amat Cup 4th Rd 1938
BEST SEASON **FA Vase:** Q-F 90-91 **FA Amateur Cup:** R-up 1898-99, 52-53
HONOURS: FA Amateur Cup R-up 1898-99 52-53; Eastern Counties 35-36(jt) Lg Cup 35-36 36-37 96-97; Essex County 37-38; Athenian Div 1 R-up 65-66 Div 2 64-65, Lg Cup 64-65; Essex Sen. Cup 1898-99 36-37; Essex Sen. Trophy 89-90; AFA Senior Cup 35-36 36-37; Worthington Evans Cup 80-81

FACT FILE
Founded: 1875 Nickname: Shrimpers
Colours: White & black/black/black
Change colours: All Red
Midweek Matches: Tuesday
Reserves: Essex & Suffolk Border Lge Prem. Div
Programme: 28 pages, 50p
Editor: Carl Allen Tel: 01255 552510
Website: mysite.freeserve.com/the shrimpers

CLUB PERSONNEL
Chairman:Tony Armstrong
President:Terry Rowlands
Press Officer: Carl Allan
Manager: Mitchell Springett

2002-03
Captain & Leading Goalscorer: Gareth Heath

HAVERHILL ROVERS

Secretary: Chris Rice, 23 Ovington Place, Haverhill, Suffolk. CB9 0BA
Tel: 01440 712396 (H) 07880 966423 (M)
Ground: Hamlet Croft, Haverhill, Suffolk Tel: 01440 702137
Directions: Centre of Haverhill
Capacity: 3,000 Seats: 200 Cover: 200 Floodlights: Yes
Clubhouse: Open matchdays and functions. Snacks available

HONOURS Eastern Co's Lg 78-79 Lg Cup 64-65; Essex & Suffolk Border Lg 62-63 63-64; East Anglian Cup 90-91; Suffolk Sen Cup 96-97
PREVIOUS **League:** Essex & Suffolk Border
RECORD **Attendance:** 1,537 v Warrington Town, FA Vase QF 86-87
Players progressing: R Wilkins (Colchester)

FACT FILE
Founded: 1886 Nickname: Rovers
Colours: All red
Change colours:All yellow
Midweek Matches: Tuesday
Programme: 24 pages,50p
Editor: Ray Esdale (01440 704670)
Local Press : Haverhill Echo,Cambridge Evening News
CLUB PERSONNEL
Chairman: Terry McGerty
President: N Haylock
Press Officer: Ray Esdale
Manager: Paul Goodman
Physio: Nel Franklin

IPSWICH WANDERERS

Secretary: Martin Head, 246 Sidelate Lane, Ipswich, Suffolk. IP4 3DH Tel: 01473 414390
Email address: headmartin@hotmail.com
Ground: Humberdoucey Lane, Ipswich, Suffolk Tel: 01473 728581
Directions: Take Woodbridge Road out of Ipswich,then left fork into Playford Road.
Take first left into Humberdoucy Lane Ground 300yds on right
Capacity: 2,000 Seats: 50 Cover: Yes Floodlights: Yes
Clubhouse: Bar,Tea, coffee, cold drinks, confectionary, burgers, hotdogs,sandwiches, rolls
PREVIOUS **Leagues:** Little David SundayNames: Loadwell Ipswich
RECORD **Attendance:** 335 v Woodbridge, ECL Div 1 4/4/94
BEST SEASON **FA Cup:** 2nd Qual Rd 2000-01
FA Vase: 1st Round 2002-03
HONOURS Eastern Lge Div 1 97-98

FACT FILE
Founded: 1983
Nickname: Wanderers
Sponsors: N.T.L.
Colours: All Blue
Change colours: Red & black/black/red & black
Midweek Matches: Tuesday
Programme: Yes
Editor: Alan Haste (01473 711877)
Local Press: East Anglian Daily Times, Evening Star
CLUB PERSONNEL
Chairman: A.Haste
President: P.Emmerson
Manager: Alan Dilloway

KIRKLEY

Secretary:
Ground: Kirkley Recreation Ground, Walmer Road, Lowestoft, Suffolk
Tel: 01502 513549
Directions:
Capacity:
Clubhouse:
Club Shop:
PREVIOUS **Leagues**: Anglian Combination ??-2003
RECORDS
HONOURS Anglian Combination Champions 2002-03, Lge Senior Cup R-up: 02-03

FACT FILE
Formed:
Colours:
Change colours:
Midweek Matchday:
Programme - ?? Pages ?? Price
Editor:
CLUB PERSONNEL
Chairman:

Manager:
Physio:

LEISTON

Chairman: Barry Spall, 'Loucarand', 5 Queen Elizabeth Close, Leiston, Suffolk IP16 4XB
Tel: 01728 831950 (H & B)
Secretary: Mark Pattinson, 'Fernhouse', 40 Eastward Ho, Leiston, Suffolk IP16 4XB
Tel: 01728 635016 (H) 01473 608230 (B) 01473 608607 (Bus. Fax)
email: mark.L.pattinson@bt.com
Ground: LTAA, Victory Road, Leiston, Suffolk IP16 4LD
Tel: 01728 830308
Directions:
Capacity: Covered Seating: Covered Standing: Floodlights: Yes/No
Honours:
Previous: **Leagues:** **Names:**
Club Records: **Attendance:**

FACT FILE
Formed:
Colours: Blue & whaite/blue/red
Change colours: Amber & red/red/red
Midweek matches: Wednesday
Programme: Yes
Editor: David Rees
Tel: 01728 833549

Manager: Mark Hood
Tel: 01502 501963

LONG MELFORD

Secretary: John Campany, 12 Swinton Close, Ipswich IP2 9RL
Tel: 01480 383357 (H) 01480 861544 (B)

Ground: Stoneylands, New Road, Long Melford, Suffolk. Tel: 01787 312187
Directions:
Capacity: Covered Seating: Covered Standing: Floodlights: Yes/No
Clubhouse:
Club Shop:
Previous Leagues: Essex & Suffolk Border Lge. >2002
Honours:
Club Records: Attendance:
Best Season: **FA Vase:** **FA Cup:**

FACT FILE
Formed
Colours:
Change Colours:
Midweek Matchday:
Programme: Price: Pages:
Editor:

CLUB PERSONNEL
Chairman:
President:
Manager:
Asst. Man.:
Physio:

MARCH TOWN UNITED

Secretary: R S Bennett, 47 Ellingham Ave, March, Cambs PE15 9TE (01354 653271)

Ground: GER Sports Ground, Robin Goodfellows Lane, March (01354 653073)
Directions: 5 mins from town centre, 10 mins from BR station
Capacity: 4,000 Seats: 500 Cover: 2,000 Floodlights: Yes
Clubhouse: On ground, seating 150. Light refreshments available

HONOURS Eastern Co's Lg 87-88 (Lg Cup 60-61), Utd Co's Lg 53-64, Cambs Invitation Cup 54-55, East Anglian Cup 53-54 (jt withBarking)

PREVIOUS **Leagues:** Peterborough; Isle of Ely; Utd Co's 48-54
Ground: The Avenue (prior to 1946)

BEST SEASON FA Cup 1st Rd53-54 77-78,

RECORD **Gate:** 7,500 v King's Lynn, FA Cup 1956

FACT FILE
Founded: 1885
Nickname: Hares
Club colours: Orange & black/black/black
Change colours: Yellow/blue/blue
Midweek Matches: Tuesday
Programme: 30p
Editor: R Bennett
Local Press : Cambs Times, Fenland Advertiser, Peterborough Evening Telegraph

CLUB PERSONNEL
Chairman: Gary Wesley
President: D Wilkinson

NEEDHAM MARKET

Secretary: D Bloomfield, 33 Quinton Road, Needham Market, Suffolk IP6 8DA
Tel: 01449 720693

Fixture Secrtary: P Collier, 9 The Knoll, Framlingham, Woodbridge IP13 9DH
Tel: 01728 724108

Ground: Bloomfields, Quinton Road, Needham Market, Suffolk
Tel: 01449 721000

Directions: Quinton Road is off Barretts Lane which in turn is off Needham Market High Street
Capacity: 1,000 Seats: 250 Cover: 250 Floodlights: Yes **Club Shop:** No

PREVIOUS **Leagues:** Ipswich & District; Suffolk & Ipswich >96
Grounds: Youngs Meadow; Crowley Park >96 **Names:** None

HONOURS Suffolk & Ipswich Lge 95-96

FACT FILE
Founded: 1927
Nickname: N/A
Colours: All Green
Change Coloures: All white
Midweek Matchday: Tuesday
Programme Editor: Ian Verneau
Tel No: 01473 413957

CLUB PERSONNEL
Chairman: A.Sparkes
Managers: Colin Macrow & Colin Sinclair

2002-03
Leading Goalscorer:
Captain:
Player of the Year:

SOMERSHAM TOWN

Secretary: Matthew Dunster, 29 Windsor Gardens,Somersham,Huntingdon, Cambs. PE17 3DY
Tel No: 01487 740786

Ground: West End Ground, St Ives Road, Somersham, Cambs (01487 843384)

Directions: On A604 St Ives to Somersham on right as you enter town
Capacity: 1,500 Seats: None Cover: 200 Floodlights: Yes
Clubhouse: Open Friday, Sat/Sun lunchtimes

HONOURS Hunts Snr Cup 72-73 94-95, Peterboro Snr Cup 84-85, Hinchingbrooke Cup 53-54, Cambs Lg Premier B Div 94-95 (reserves)

PREVIOUS **League:** Peterborough & District

RECORDS **Attendance:** 538 v Norwich City, floodlights inauguration 91
Goalscorer & Appearances: Terry Butcher

Local Press : Hunts Post, Cambs News, Citizen Express, St Ives Weekly

FACT FILE
Founded: 1893 Nickname: Westenders
Sponsors: Rapidtech (UK) Ltd
Colours: All old gold with black trim
Change colours: red&blue stripes/ blue/ red
Midweek Matchday: Tuesday
Reserve League: Kershaw Senior A
Programme: 76 pages, 50p
Editor: Tim Egan

CLUB PERSONNEL
Chairman: Alan Bailey
Vice-Chairman: Norman Burkett
President: Jack Marjason
Manager: Norman Hudson
Coach: Bob Barnett Physio: Alan Magnus

STANWAY ROVERS

Secretary: Alan Brierley, 19 Barley Way, Stanway, Colchester CO3 5YD (01206 521606 + Fax)
Ground: `Hawthorns', New Farm Road, Stanway, Colchester, Essex (01206 578187)
Directions: Take turn off marked Stanway off A12. Turn right(from London)or left from Ipsw ch+ go over flyover to Tollgate r'bout, 1st rt into Villa Rd, after 25 yds turn left into Chaple Rd, 200 yds on left into New Farm Rd, ground 400 yds on left.Nearest BR station is Colchester North
Capacity: 1,500 Seats: None Cover: 250 Floodlights: Yes Shop: No
Clubhouse: 6.45-11pm eves, 12-11pm Sats. Rolls, soup, tea, coffee etc available matchdays
Club Shop: Pennants & ties (Club website:lineone.net/ m alan brierley
HONOURS Esx Intermediate Cup R-up 89-90 90-91, Esx & Suffolk Border Lg R-up 91-2 (Div 1 86-87, Div 2 81-81 85-86), Esx Jnr Cup R-up 74-75
PREVIOUS **Leagues:** Colchester & E Essex; Essex & Suffolk. Border (pre-1992)
Ground: Stanway Secondary School, Winstree Road (20 years)
RECORD **Gate:** 166 v Sudbury Town FA Vase 4/10/97 **Win:** 8-1 v Swaffham Town (H), E. Counties Lge Div. 1 26/3/94 **Defeat:** 0-10 v Sudbury Townt (A), E.C.L. Cup

FACT FILE
Founded: 1955 Nickname: Rovers
Sponsors: David Martin Eastate Agents
Colours: Gold& black stripes/black/black
Change : Red & blue halves/ blue/yellow
Midweek matchday: Wednesday
Reserves' Lge: Essex & Suff. Border
Programme: 12 pages, 50p
Editor: Alan Brierleylocal Press:
Essex Co. Standard, Evening Gazette

CLUB PERSONNEL
Chairman: Peter Cracknell
President: Richard Deguille
Manager:Steve Ball
Physio: Stuart Bevis

SWAFFHAM TOWN

Secretary: D.R.Ward, 14 Mount Close,Swaffham. PE37 7BX
Tel: 01760 722516 (H) 01760 720130 (Fax) 07771 960863 (M)
Email Address: pepward@aol,com
Ground: Shoemakers Lane, Swaffham, Norfolk (01760 722700)
Capacity: 2,000 Seats: 50 Cover: 250 Floodlights: Yes
Clubhouse: Open Tuesday, Thursday, Saturday plus functions
HONOURS Norfolk Snr Cup (2), Anglian Comb. 89-90 (Div 1 88-89)
Jewson Divison 1 Champions 00-01
PREVIOUS **Leagues:** Dereham, Anglian Combination
RECORD **Attendance:** 250 v Downham Town, Eastern Co's League Cup 3/9/91

2002-03
Leading Goalscorer: Captain: Player of the Year:

FACT FILE
Founded: 1892
Nickname: Pedlars
Midweek Matchay: Tuesday
Colours: Black & white stripes/black/black
Change: Yellow/Blue/Blue
Programme: 36 pages, Free
Editor: Simon Barnes

CLUB PERSONNEL
Chairman:Les Elmer
President: Stewart Collins
Manager: Robin Sainty

THETFORD TOWN

Secretary: R.Richards, 60 Nunnery Drive, Thetford, Norfolk IP243EN Tel Nos: 01842 764282 (H) 01284 701121 (W) Email Address: omwgh@lineone.net
Ground: Mundford Road, Thetford, Norfolk Tel: 01842 766120
Directions: Off bypass (A11) at A143 junction - ground 800yds next to sports ground
Capacity: 2,000 Seats: 400 Cover: 400 Floodlights: Yes
Clubhouse: Bar, teas, refreshments, light meals & snacks **Club Shop:** No
HONOURS Eastern Co's Lg R-up 89-90, Norfolk & Suffolk Lg 54-55;
Norfolk Senior Cup 47-48 90-91
PREVIOUS **Leagues:** Norfolk & Suffolk **Grounds**: None
RECORD **Attendance:** 394 v Diss Town, Norfolk Snr Cup 91
Players progressing: Dick Scott (Norwich C.), Kevin Seggie (Leeds U.),Simon Milton (Ipswich T.)
Local Press: Thetford & Watton Times, Bury Free Press

FACT FILE
Founded: 1883
Sponsors: Thetford Garden Centre
Colours: Claret & blue//claret/claret
Change: Yellow & blue
Midweek Matches: Wednesday
Reserves League: Anglian Comb
Programme: 50p
Editor: Denise Jones (01842 761876)
Club Website: thetford townfc.fsnet.co.uk

CLUB PERSONNEL
Chairman: Peter Jones
Vice-Chairman: Mike Bailey
Press Officer: Paul Stevenson
Manager: Steve Livingstone

WARBOYS TOWN

Secretary: Martin England, 39 High Street, Warboys, Huntingdon, Cambs PE28 2TA
Tel: 01487 822503
Ground: Sports Field, Forge Way, off High Street, Warboys, Cambs Tel: 01487 823483
Directions: Access through Forge Way, half way along south side of High Street
Capacity: 2,000 Seats: 50 Cover: 200 Floodlights: Yes
Clubhouse: Bar, lounge, function hall. Open every eve. & Sun. lunch. Entertainment, drinks & snacks
HONOURS Utd Co's Lg Div 2 R-up 54-55, P'boro Lg R-up(2) 59-60 61-62, P'boro SnrCup 63-64, Hunts Snr Cup 26-27 28-29 31-32 32-33,94-95. (R-up 92-93,95-96), Hunts Scott Gatty Cup 30-31. Reserves: Hunts Benevolent Cup 57-58, Hunts Junior Cup 24-25 27-28 52-53, Hunts Lower Junior Cup 75-76 77-78. Eastern League Div 1 R-up: 95-96, Lg.Cup R-up: 97-98,
PREVIOUS **Leagues:** Peterborough & Dist 46-48 56-88; Utd Co's 50-56; Huntingdonshire 48-50
RECORD **Attendance:** 500 v Ramsey Town, Hunts Senior Cup Semi Final
Players progressing: Alec Chamberlain (Ipswich and Watford)

FACT FILE
Founded: 1885
Nickname: Witches
Colours: Red /black/red
Change colours: White/red/white
Midweek Matches: Tuesday
Programme: 12 pages,50p
Editor: Martin England
Local Press : Hunts Post (01480 411481)

CLUB PERSONNEL
Chairman: Roger Pauley
Manager: Ian Jones

WHITTON UNITED

Secretary: David Gould, 7 Karen Close, Ipswich, Suffolk IP1 4LP   Tel: 01473 253838

Ground: King George V Playing Field, Old Norwich Road, Ipswich, Suffolk. Tel: 01473 464030

Directions: Turn off A14, junction A1156 approx 3 miles west of A12/A14junction
Capacity: 600   Seats: No   Cover: 100   Floodlights: Yes
Club Shop: No
Clubhouse: Licensed Bar. Hot & Cold Food available

HONOURS Suffolk Senior Cup 58-59 62-63 92-93; Suffolk & Ipswich Lge 46-47 47-48 65-66 67-68 91-92 92-93, Jewson Fairplay Trophy 96-97, 97-98

PREVIOUS **Leagues:** Suffolk & Ipswich   Grounds: Old Norwich Rd, Ipswich

RECORD **Attendance:** 528 v Ipswich Town 29/11/95
League 244 v Ipswich Wanderers13/1/96

FACT FILE
Formed: 1926   Nickname: None
Sponsors: Speedyhire
Colours: Green & white/white/green
Change colours: All red
Midweek Matches: Wednesday
Youth's League: U18 Eastern Jun Alliance
Programme: 24pages- 50p
Editor/ Press Officer:Mark Woodward

CLUB PERSONNEL
Chairman: John Watkins
President: Russell Woodward
Fixture Sec: Alan Elliott (01473 461931)
Manager: Paul Smythe

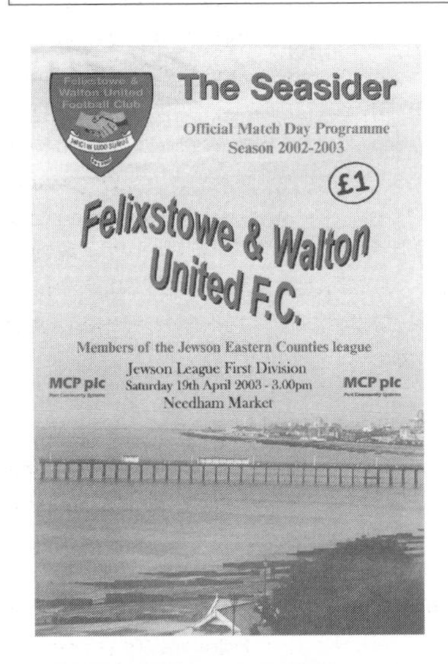

CHERRY RED RECORDS HELLENIC FOOTBALL LEAGUE

Patron: Sir Henry Cooper OBE, KSG. (2001)
Chairman: Michael Broadley

Secretary: Brian King, 83 Queens Road, Carterton, Oxon OX18 3YF
Tel: 01993 212738 **Fax:** 01993 212775 **E-mail:** hellenic_league_office@ntlworld.com

PREMIER DIVISION

North Leigh won the Premier Division Championship for the second successive season but were unable to be promoted to the Dr Martens League due to delays with their planning application.Yate Town, unbeaten in April winning five and drawing two matches won the runners-up place and promotion back to the Dr Martens League after three seasons. Carterton finished third losing only one league match all season but unfortunately they drew seventeen. Champions North Leigh showed consistency throughout the season losing only five league matches in the season. Yate Town were always going to be a threat and proved this by their final position pushing Carterton into third place on goal difference. Highworth Town finished in fourth place winning five and drawing three of their last eight matches. Didcot Town finished in fifth place and flattered to deceive at times during the season in April they managed only three wins, and failed to score in five of their nine fixtures. Fairford Town 11th at the turn of the year finished sixth with a run of good results in the second half of the season.

DIVISION ONE (WEST)

Once again a new club in the league won the title. Newcomers Slimbridge promoted from the Gloucestershire County League won the title displaying a high level of consistency throughout the season suffering only three defeats in the league and conceding only twenty-six goal sin thirty-eight matches. In securing the title Slimbridge have won five consecutive promotions. In season 1998-99 the club were in Division One of the Stroud & District League and consequent promotions through the Gloucestershire Northern Senior League Division Two and Division One was followed by promotion from the Gloucester County League as runners-up in season 2001-2002 and promotion to the Hellenic League. As they say, the rest is history and next season Slimbridge will be competing in the Hellenic Premier Division and possibly looking for a 6th successive promotion to the Dr Martens League. Chipping Norton Town pushed all the way but ran out of legs in April finishing eleven points behind the champions. Both Slimbridge and Chipping Norton Town will play in the Premier Division next season. Purton finished in third place thanks to seven straight win s in the last ten days of the season. Winterbourne United finished fourth and Ardley United fifth. Leading goal scorers were Slimbridge who scored 114 league goals with Purton FC scoring 99.

DIVISION ONE (EAST)

18 months ago Quarry Nomads almost folded but they became a force to be reckoned with in the past season as the new management team of Derek Beesley and Kevin McMahon took the club to the Division One East championship although it was not until the last week of the season that Quarry claimed the title. Penn & Tylers Green finished as runners-up on goal difference of one from last season's champions Finchampstead who took third place. Rayners Lane finished fourth and Eton Wick fifth. Quarry were top goal scorers netting 76 goals, Binfield, who finished eighth scored 73 but had a bad spell collecting only eight points in February and March and suffered five defeats in a row during this period.

FINAL LEAGUE TABLES 2002-03

PREMIER DIVISION		P	W	D	L	F	A	Pts
1	North Leigh	40	29	6	5	84	36	93
2	Yate Town	40	25	8	7	87	42	83
3	Carterton Town	40	22	17	1	61	29	83
4	Highworth Town	40	23	10	7	79	41	79
5	Didcot Town	40	22	6	12	77	39	72
6	Fairford Town	40	21	8	11	65	30	71
7	Brackley Town	40	18	12	10	84	42	66
8	Abingdon Town	40	20	6	14	70	52	66
9	Bishops Cleeve	40	19	7	14	68	50	64
10	Henley Town	40	17	10	13	69	48	61
11	Southall Town	40	18	7	15	75	65	61
12	Hook Norton	40	15	13	12	67	55	58
13	Shortwood United	40	15	10	15	64	60	55
14	Tuffley Rovers	40	12	9	19	56	76	45
15	Wootton Bassett Tn	40	10	10	20	36	70	40
16	Gloucester Utd (-3)	40	9	8	23	48	89	32
17	Almondsbury Town	40	8	7	25	43	77	31
18	Pegasus Juniors	40	8	7	25	45	108	31
19	Pewsey Vale	40	7	8	25	45	93	29
20	Bicester Town	40	5	8	27	40	99	23
21	Wantage Town	40	5	7	28	36	98	22

DIVISION ONE WEST		P	W	D	L	F	A	Pts
1	Slimbridge	38	29	6	3	114	26	93
2	Chipping Norton Town	38	24	10	4	76	33	82
3	Purton	38	25	1	12	99	49	76
4	Winterbourne United	38	22	6	10	80	41	72
5	Ardley United	38	21	6	11	93	47	69
6	Old Woodstock Town	38	19	6	13	65	54	63
7	Kidlington	38	15	9	14	67	76	54
8	Headington Amateurs	38	13	13	12	71	70	52
9	Cheltenham Saracens	38	13	12	13	61	54	51
10	Easington Sports	38	15	6	17	54	67	51
11	Adderbury Park	38	14	8	16	70	85	50
12	Shrivenham	38	13	10	15	55	65	49
13	New College Academy	38	14	4	20	57	67	46
14	Malmesbury Victoria	38	12	8	18	54	63	44
15	Witney United	38	9	13	16	54	74	40
16	Middle Barton	38	10	9	19	49	83	39
17	Cirencester United	38	9	10	19	49	77	37
18	Harrow Hill	38	10	5	23	45	78	35
19	Clanfield	38	9	7	22	43	82	34
20	Ross Town	38	7	5	26	45	110	26

DIVISION ONE EAST		P	W	D	L	F	A	Pts
1	Quarry Nomads	32	21	4	7	76	41	67
2	Penn & Tylers Green (-3)	32	19	6	7	63	33	60
3	Finchampstead	32	17	9	6	61	32	60
4	Rayners Lane	32	18	5	9	66	40	59
5	Chalfont Wasps	32	18	4	10	67	44	58
6	Eton Wick	32	16	9	7	72	49	57
7	Milton United	32	14	9	9	53	39	51
8	Binfield	32	14	6	12	73	46	48
9	Letcombe	32	11	6	15	45	53	39
10	Englefield Green Rovers	32	12	3	17	47	62	39
11	RS Basingstoke	32	10	7	15	55	64	37
12	Bisley Sports	32	10	7	15	43	64	37
13	Hounslow Borough	32	9	8	15	61	73	35
14	Prestwood	32	8	10	14	43	63	34
15	Holyport	32	10	2	20	37	78	32
16	Martin Baker Sports	32	4	11	17	41	74	23
17	Drayton Wanderers	32	5	6	21	38	86	21

Aston Clinton withdrew during the course of the season.

	1	2	3	4	5	6	7	8	9	10	11	12	13	14	15	16	17	18	19	20	21
1 Abingdon United		1-1	7-0	1-0	2-1	1-3	1-4	1-0	3-1	1-3	2-5	2-2	2-3	1-1	4-0	0-3	3-1	1-0	3-0	0-0	0-2
2 Almondsbury Tn	0-2		1-0	1-2	0-1	0-2	1-4	1-2	1-3	3-7	0-4	1-5	0-1	4-0	2-2	0-2	4-1	1-2	0-3	1-2	0-1
3 Bicester Town	0-0	3-1		1-0	2-2	1-3	0-4	0-1	3-3	2-5	0-1	1-2	0-6	1-3	2-3	1-1	2-5	3-5	4-0	1-3	0-3
4 Bishops Cleeve	3-0	1-2	2-0		2-1	1-1	1-0	2-4	2-2	0-0	3-0	2-0	2-3	1-2	1-3	1-0	1-0	2-1	2-1	8-0	0-1
5 Brackley Town	2-0	0-0	4-0	1-1		2-2	1-0	1-3	4-0	0-1	1-2	2-2	0-2	7-0	3-0	3-1	2-2	6-1	0-3	1-0	3-3
6 Carterton Town	2-1	1-0	1-1	1-1	2-2		0-0	2-1	1-0	1-0	2-2	0-0	2-1	5-1	2-0	0-3	0-0	2-1	3-0	2-2	1-1
7 Didcot Town	1-2	5-1	6-0	1-0	1-0	2-2		0-3	2-0	1-0	0-2	5-2	0-2	2-0	3-1	1-3	1-0	1-1	7-0	2-1	0-0
8 Fairford Town	2-0	1-0	5-0	2-4	0-0	0-1	0-1		2-0	1-2	1-1	3-0	0-0	2-0	1-0	1-0	0-2	0-1	7-1	2-0	0-1
9 Gloucester United	0-2	0-0	2-0	1-5	0-5	0-0	0-3	0-4		3-0	1-3	0-0	1-4	3-2	4-3	1-3	0-2	2-4	1-1	1-3	0-2
10 Henley Town	1-2	4-0	1-0	4-0	2-1	0-1	3-1	0-0	2-2		3-0	3-1	1-2	5-0	4-1	0-0	0-2	2-1	0-0	3-2	0-1
11 Highworth Town	0-2	3-0	1-0	0-1	1-4	0-0	3-0	2-1	2-2	1-1		1-1	1-2	3-2	3-0	1-1	3-2	8-1	1-1	1-0	1-2
12 Hook Norton	0-2	2-1	1-1	3-0	3-4	0-2	1-0	0-0	3-0	2-2	1-2		0-0	5-0	2-0	1-0	2-3	2-1	5-1	0-0	1-3
13 North Leigh	1-1	1-1	3-2	1-0	0-4	0-2	2-0	3-2	2-0	1-1	2-5	2-0		2-0	3-0	2-0	3-1	2-1	1-0	4-0	0-0
14 Pegasus Juniors	0-3	1-2	1-2	1-4	0-5	1-1	0-2	1-2	1-4	2-0	0-6	0-3	0-2		4-1	5-3	2-1	1-1	1-1	2-0	2-8
15 Pewsey Vale	1-5	0-3	2-3	0-2	1-1	0-0	2-2	0-4	0-2	3-1	0-1	1-3	1-3	2-2		0-3	0-0	2-2	4-1	1-0	1-2
16 Shortwood United	3-2	1-3	3-0	3-1	0-0	1-1	0-3	1-1	1-2	2-2	0-0	2-2	1-4	2-2	5-3		1-3	3-0	4-2	1-0	1-5
17 Southall Town	1-2	1-0	2-1	3-3	1-2	0-1	2-2	0-1	4-3	3-2	0-1	1-1	2-3	6-1	1-0	4-2		2-1	4-3	5-1	3-2
18 Tuffley Rovers	3-2	1-1	1-1	0-0	0-4	0-2	1-0	1-4	1-3	1-0	0-0	1-3	1-2	1-0	2-3	0-2	3-2		3-0	1-1	2-2
19 Wantage Town	0-1	1-3	1-1	2-3	0-4	0-1	1-6	0-0	2-0	0-1	1-3	1-1	1-6	3-0	2-3	0-1	1-3	0-4		0-1	1-2
20 Wootton Bassett T.	0-4	1-1	2-0	2-1	2-0	1-3	0-2	0-1	2-1	1-1	0-2	2-4	1-0	2-2	1-1	2-1	0-0	1-3	0-1		0-0
21 Yate Town	2-1	3-2	2-1	1-3	0-0	2-3	0-2	1-1	5-0	3-2	1-3	3-1	0-3	0-2	4-0	1-0	5-0	3-2	4-0	6-0	

THE CHERRY RED RECORDS CHALLENGE CUP 2002-03

PRELIMINARY ROUND

Ardley United	2-1	Slimbridge FC
Bicester Town	3-2	Southall town
Binfield	2-1	RS Basingstoke
Bishops Cleeve	6-0	New Coll. Academy
Bisley Sports	1-0	Letcombe FC
Carterton Town	2-3	Martin Baker Sports
Cheltenham Saracens	0-1	Winterbourne United
Clanfield	0-4	Shrivenham
Didcot Town	1-3	Finchampstead
Easington Sports	1-2	Cirencester United
Englefield Green Rovers	1-0	Rayners Lane
Eton Wick	3-1	Drayton Wanderers
Fairford Town	2-0	Malmesbury Victoria
Headington Amateurs	5-3	Holyport
Henley Town	2-1	Hounslow Borough
Hook Norton	2-0	Milton United
Old Woodstock Town	2-1	Adderbury Park
Pegasus Juniors	2-1	Harrow Hill
Penn & Tylers Green	2-0	Aston Clinton
Pewsey Vale	3-0	Wootton Bassett Town
Prestwood	1-4	Chalfont Wasps
Purton	3-0	Chipping Norton
Quarry Nomads	1-2	Brackley Town
Ross Town	1-4	Alondsbury Town
Shortwood United	3-1	Kidlington
Tuffley Rovers	3-0	Middle Barton
Wantage Town	1-2	Highworth Town

FIRST ROUND

Abingdon United	3-0	Headington Amateurs
Ardley United	4-1	Pegasus Juniors
Bicester Town	0-1	North Leigh
Binfield	1-3	Finchampstead
Shrivenham	3-2	Almondsbury Town
Cirencester United	1-2	Pewsey Vale
Englefield Green Rovers	2-3	Brackley Town
Eton Wick	2-4	Highworth Town

First round continued....

Fairford Town	2-1	Winterbourne United
Gloucester United	0-4	Shortwood United
Henley Town	5-0	Bisley Sports
Old Woodstock Town	2-3	Bishops Cleeve
Penn & Tylers Green	0-1	Hook Norton
Chalfont Wasps	1-0	Martin Baker Sports
Purton	1-3	Tuffley Rovers
Witney United	1-5	Yate Town

SECOND ROUND

Abingdon United	1-0	Finchampstead
Bishops Cleeve	1-0	Chalfont Wasps
Shortwood United	3-2	Fairford Town
Highworth Town	4-3	Brackley Town
Hook Norton	0-4	North Leigh
Pewsey Vale	4-0	Ardley United
Shrivenham	2-5	Yate Town
Tuffley Rovers	2-1	Henley Town

QUARTER-FINALS

Abingdon United	1-0	Highworth Town
North Leigh	1-4	Shortwood United
Pewsey Vale	1-2	Yate Town
Tuffley Rovers	0-1	Bishops Cleeve

SEMI-FINALS

1st LEG

Abingdon United	0-2	Yate Town
Shortwood United	1-0	Bishops Cleeve

2nd LEG

Yate Town	2-0	Abingdon United
Bishops Cleeve	0-0	Shortwood Town

FINAL

Shortwood Town	1-3	Yate Town

SUPPLEMENTARY CUP 2002-03

SECOND ROUND

Cheltenham Saracens	0-1	Wootton Bassett Town
Chipping Norton	1-0	RS Basingstoke
Didcot Town	3-0	Binfield
Headington Amateurs	3-0	Middle Barton
Purton	5-3	New Coll. Academy
Slimbridge	2-1	Bisley Sports
Southall Town	7-2	Hounslow Borough
Winterbourne United	3-1	Wantage Town

QUARTER-FINALS

Didcot Town	5-0	Wootton Bassett Town
Headington Amateurs	1-4	Purton
Slimbridge	0-1	Southall Town
Winterbourne United	5-1	Chipping Norton

SEMI-FINALS

1st LEG

Didcot Town	6-1	Winterbourne United
Purton	1-3	Southall Town

2nd LEG

Winterbourne United	0-0	Didcot Town
Southall Town	2-2	Purton

FINAL

Southall Town	1-2	Didcot Town

NORMAN MATTHEWS FLOODLIT CUP 2002-03

FIRST ROUND

Abingdon United	5-1	Pewsey Vale
Finchampstead	3-0	Harrow Hill
Fairford Town	1-2	Tuffley Rovers
Bishops Cleeve	0-1	Brackley Town
Didcot Town	2-1	Henley Town
Bicester Town	0-1	Pegasus Juniors
Wootton Bassett Town	1-0	North Leigh
Carterton Town	1-2	Gloucester United

QUARTER-FINALS

Abingdon United	2-0	Gloucester United
Tuffley Rovers	4-0	Pegasus Juniors
Didcot Town	0-1	Brackley Town
Wootton Bassett Town	6-0	Finchampstead

SEMI-FINALS

1st LEG

Abingdon United	3-3	Tuffley Rovers
Brackley Town	5-1	Wootton Bassett Town

2nd LEG

Tuffley Rovers	4-0	Abingdon United
Wootton Bassett Town	1-0	Brackley Town

FINAL

1st LEG

Brackley Town	0-1	Tuffley Rovers

2nd LEG

Tuffley Rovers	3-2	Brackley Town

Brackley Town - Norman Matthews Floodlit Cup runners-up.
Back Row: T Fowler (Manager), M Mounsdon, P Eldridge, S Ayris, R Darvill, V Byfield, J Bedford, J McCalmon, P Salt (Asst. Manager).
Front Row: P Hammond, N Jenkins, A Bunney, N King, A Prescott, J Blencowe, L Dawson.

ABINGDON UNITED

Secretary: John Blackmore,91 Gainsborough Green, Abingdon, Oxon OX14 5JL(01235 202124)
Ground: Northcourt Road, Abingdon OX14 1PL Tel: 01235 203203
Capacity: 2,000 Seats: 52 Cover: 120 Floodlights: Yes

Directions: From north (Oxford) leave A34 at Abingdon north sign and Northcourt Rd is 1st major turning after r'bout. From South, East or West leave Abingdonon A4183 and turn left into Northcourt Rd after 1 mile. 2 miles from Redley (BR)
Clubhouse: Two bars, food available. Open normal pub hours every day

HONOURS N Berks Lg 53-54 (Lg Cup R-up 53-54), Charity Shield 52-53;
Hellenic Lge - Prem Div R-up 96-97, Div 1 R-up 76-77 81-82, Res. Div 97-98, F/Lit Cup 96-97, Lg Cup R-up 89-90, Div 1 Cup 65-66 81-82 R-up 66-67, Reserve Cup 98-99 R-up 93-94;
Berks & Bucks Senior Cup R-up 83-84, Senior Trophy 97-98 R-up 93-94 96-97

PREVIOUS **League**: North Berks
Grounds: None

RECORD **Gate:** 1,500 v Oxford Utd 1994
Appearances: D Webb

FACT FILE
Founded: 1946
Nickname: The U's
Colours: All yellow
Change colours: All Blue
Midweek matchday: Tuesday
Reserves' Lge: Suburban
Programme: 50p
Editor: W Fletcher, ACJI (01235 203203)
Website: abingdonunitedfc.co.uk

CLUB PERSONNEL
Chairman: Derek Turner
General manager: John Blackmore
Manager: Ray Hayward
Coach: Mark O'Hara
Physio: JamesFoote & Chris Janes
Press Officer: Bill Fletcher (01235 203203)

2002-03
Leading Goalscorer:
Captain:
Player of the Year:

ALMONDSBURY TOWN

Secretary: Roger Perry, 61 Brookbridge House, Standfast Road, Henbury, Bristol BS10 7HW
Tel No: 0117 959 0309

Ground: Oakland Park, Gloucester Rd., Almondsbury, Bristol BS12 4AGTel: 01454 612220

Directions: Adjacent to M5 junction 16 - follow A38 Thornbury - ground first left. 4 miles from Bristol Parkway (BR). County bus services to Thornbury,Stroud and Gloucester
Capacity: 2,000 Seats: None Cover: No Floodlights: Yes
Clubhouse: 7 days, all sports, refreshments, function room, entertainment,skittles

HONOURS Glos Co. Lg(4) 76-78 79-81 (R-up 75-7681-82), GFA Chal. Tphy 78-79 (R-up 80-81), Avon Prem. Comb. 74-75, Glos SnrAmtr Cup 87-88, Hellenic Lg 83-84 (R-up 82-83, Lg Cup(2) 83-85)

PREVIOUS **Leagues:** Bristol Weslyan; Bristol Suburban; Bristol Premier Comb.; GlosCo
Ground: Almondsbury Rec. (until 1986)

BEST SEASON **FA Vase:**R-up 78-79, SF 77-78

RECORD **Gate:** 2,100,Hellenic Cup Final replay 89-90 (Newport AFC v Abingdon U)

FACT FILE
Founded: 1897
Nickname: Almonds
Colours: Royal blue/navy/navy
Change colours: Tangerine/black/black
Midweek Matchday: Tuesday
Programme: 20 pages 25p
Editor: Roger Perry
Tel: 0117 959 0309

CLUB PERSONNEL
Chairman: Brian Tufton
President: Peter Howarth
Manager: Shaun Honor
Coach: Micky Jefferies & Shaun Heyes
Physio: Peter Allen & Brian North

2002-03
Leading Goalscorer:
Captain:
Player of the Year:

BICESTER TOWN

Secretary: Duncan Currie Tel No: 01869 327308 (H)

Ground: Sports Ground, Oxford Rd, BicesterTel: 01869 241036 (office& fax)
Capacity: 2,000 Seats: 250 Cover: 550 Floodlights: Yes

Directions: From Oxford; past Tescos on outskirts of Bicester - ground on right
From Aylesbury; turn left at first island on outskirts of Bicester ontobypass, right at next island, pass Tescos & ground on right
Clubhouse: One bar

HONOURS Hellenic Lg 60-1 77-78 (Lg Cup 90-91 (R-up 92-93), Div 1 76-77)

PREVIOUS **League**: Oxon Senior
Name: Slade Banbury Road (pre-1923)

RECORD **Attendance:** 955 v Portsmouth, floodlight inauguration 1/2/94

FACT FILE
Founded: 1876
Nickname: Foxhunters
Colours: Red & black/black/red or white
Change: Green & yellow/green/green
Club's Email:philip@bassett38,freeserve,co.uk
Midweek Matchday: Tuesday
Reserves' league: Hellenic Lge Res. Div.
Programme: With entry
Editor:Phil Allen (01869 252125)

CLUB PERSONNEL
Chairman: David Simpson
Vice Chairman: Ray Honour
President: Michael Kinane
Fixture Secretary: Phil Allen
Press Officer: David Simpson
Manager: Barry Grant
Coach: Kevin Leach
Physio: Ray Huntley

BISHOPS CLEEVE

Secretary: Phil Tustain, 36 Hardy Road, Bishops Cleeve, Cheltenham GL52 4BN
Tel: 01242 697281 (H) 01242 673333 x 2287 (B)

Ground: Kayte Lane, Bishops Cleeve, Cheltenham
Capacity: Covered Seating: 50 Floodlights: Yes

Directions: North of Cheltenham on the A534, pass Racecourse then turn right at traffic lights and then left into Kayte Lane, ground half a mile on the left.

Clubhouse: Full facilities, bar, dance area

HONOURS Hellenic Lg Cup R-up 90-91, Helleneic Div 1West R-up: 2001-02

PREVIOUS **Leagues:** Cheltenham, Nth Glos
Grounds: The Skiller (pre-1913), Village Field (pre-1950)

RECORD **Attendance**: 1,000 v Newport AFC

FACT FILE

Founded: 1892
Nickname: Skinners
Colours: Green&black/black/black
Change colours: Yellow/blue/green
Midweek Matchday: Wednesday

CLUB PERSONNEL

President: John Davies
Chairman: David Walker
Manager: Paul Collicutt
Press Officer:Will Pember
Tel: 01242 673800
Programme Editor: John Banfield

Coach:John Banfield
Physio: Will Pember

BRACKLEY TOWN

Secretary/Press Officer: Pat Ashby, 2 Barrington Court, Ward Road, Brackley, NN13 7LE
Tel: 01327 262955(H) 01280 840900(O) 07930 143504(M)
Ground: St James Park, Churchill Way, Brackley, Northants NN13 7EJ. Tel: 01280 704077
Office: 01280 703652: Club Website: www.the-saints.co.uk Club Email: btfc1890@aol.com

Directions: Churchill Way, east off A43, south end of town
Capacity: 3,500 Cover: 150 Seats: 300 Floodlights: Yes

Clubhouse: Fully licensed. Lounge & main hall. Food available. Open all week.
Club Shop: Yes, selling club merchandise,programmes and badges etc.
PREVIOUS **Leagues:** Banbury & District; North Bucks; Hellenic 77-83; United Counties 83-94; Hellenic 94-97,Southern 97-99 **Names:** None
Ground: Banbury Road, Manor Road, Buckingham Road (up to 1974)
CLUB RECORDS **Attendance:** 720 v Kettering, Northants Senior Cup 1989
Fee Received: £2,000 for Phil Mason from Oxford City 98
BEST SEASON **FA Trophy:** 1st Qual Rd 97-98
FA Cup: 2nd Qual Rd 97-98 League clubs defeated: **HONOURS**
United Counties R-up 88-89 (Div 1 83-84); Northants Snr Cup R-up 88-89;
Buckingham Charity Cup (3); Hellenic Lg Prem 96-97, Div 1 Cup 82-83. **Players progressing**:
Jon Blencowe (Leicester) **Transfer Fee Paid:** None

FACT FILE
Formed: 1890 Nickname: Saints
Colours:Red /white/white
Change colours: All Orange
Midweek matchday: Tuesday or Wednesday
Programme: Price: £1
Editor: Brian Martin(01280 706619)
Local Press: Brackley Advertiser,
Banbury Guardian, Herald & Post
Milton Keynes Citizen - Local Radio: Fox FM
CLUB PERSONNEL
Managlng Director: Mike Bosher
Chairman:Ray Styles
Com. Man: Ray Styles: 0772 040587
President: Clive Lomax
Press Officer: Brian Martin
Manager: Tim Fowler Asst.Man: Pete Salt
2002-03
Leading Goalscorer:Andy Baird
Captain:Vinny Byfield
Player of the Year:Julian McCalmon

CARTERTON TOWN

Secretary: CathrynTaylor, 23 Mirfield Road,Witney, Oxon. OX28 5BD (01993 840628)

Ground: Kilkenny Lane, Carterton, Oxfordshire (01993 842410)

Directions: Enter Swinbrook Rd which off the Burford-Carterton road, proceed into Kilkenny Lane (one track road), ground car park 200yds on left before sharp corner.
Hourly buses to Carterton from Oxford
Capacity: 1,500 Seats: 75 Cover: 100 Floodlights: Yes
Clubhouse: Lounge & fully licensed bar open every day 7.00-11pm, Sat & Sun: noon-11pm
Sat 4-6pm. Snacks & meals available

HONOURS Oxon Junior Shield 85-86; Oxon Snr Cup R-up 90-91 96-97 98-99 Witney & Dist.Lg 65-66 (Div 1 84-85 76-77); Hellenic Lg Div 1 89-90 93-94 (Reserve Div 1989-90 (R-up 93-94)); Oxon Intermediate Cup R-up 93-94(res.)Hellen Supplementary Cup 99-00, Hellenic League Challenge Cup 2000-01, Reserves Diovision 1. 2001-02
PREVIOUS Leagues: Witney & District

RECORD **Gate:** 600 v Oxford Utd, Oxon Snr Cup 93-94
Goalscorer: Phil Rodney

FACT FILE
Founded: 1922
Reformed: 1946/1983
Colours: Black & white/black/black
Change colours: Yellow&blue/blue/blue
Midweek matches: Tuesday
Programme: 20 pages 50p
Editor: Phil Lewis
Website: www.cartertontownfc.co.uk

CLUB PERSONNEL
President: T.B.A.
Chairman: Robert Taylor
Match Secretary: Glynn Yates

Manager: Terry merriman
Physio: Andy Slater
Coach:Terry Merriman

2002-03
Leading Goalscorer: Kevin Lewis
Captain:Nick Heritage
Player of the Year: James Mortimer Jones

CHIPPING NORTON TOWN

Secretary: Bob Tanner, 36 Fox Close, Chipping Norton, Oxon. OX7 5BZ
Tel: 07881 712624
Match Secretary Terry Maycock, 31 Newlands, Witney, Oxon. OX28 3JL
Tel: 01993 778260
Ground: Walterbush Road, Chipping Norton, OX7 5DP
Tel: 01608 645311 or 01608 642562
Capacity: ????? Covered Seating: ????? Covered Standing: ???? Floodlights: Yes
Directions: From South – A361 to Chipping Norton, past school on right, take 1st left turning into Walterbush Road.
From North – drive through town and take A361 towards Burford by Kings Arms, past fire station on left, then take 1st right into Walterbush Road.

RECORD **Attendance:** 1000 v Wolverhampton Wanderers 1981
HONOURS Hellenic Lge. Div.1 West R-up 02-03

FACT FILE
Re-formed 2001
Nickname: The Magpies
Colours:
Black & white stripes/black/black & white
Change colours: Yellow/blue/yellow
Midweek fixtures: Tuesday

CLUB PERSONNEL
Chairman: Nigel Harrison
email: happyhaulier@btinternet.com
Tel: 01993 703319
Program Editor: Terry Maycock
Tel: 01993 778260

Manager: Alan Dore
Coach: TBA Physio: TBA

DIDCOT TOWN

Secretary: Phil Hussey c/o Loop Meadow Stadium
Ground: Loop Meadow Stadium, Bowmont Water, Didcot, OX11 7GA.
Website: http://users.tinyoline.co.uk/stevetclare/DTFC1/
Capacity: 5,000 Seats: 250 Cover: 500 Floodlights: Yes

Directions: From Town Centre: Take station road (old ground) and turn right under bridge just before station into Cow Lane. Left by Ladygrove Pub into Tamar Way. Then first left at roundabout. From A34: leave at Milton interchange and take Didcot road for approximately one mile. At roundabout take perimeter road Cross three more roundabouts and turn right at third into Avon Way
Clubhouse: Every evening and 12 noon to close at weekends and national holidys.

HONOURS Hellenic Lg 53-54,Lg Cup 1965-66 66-67 92-9397-98 Div 1 76-77,Div1 Cup 76-7, Supplementary Cup 2002-03 Berks & Bucks SeniorTrophy 2000-01, 2002-03

PREVIOUS **Leagues:** Hellenic 53-54; Metropolitan League 57-63
RECORD **Attendance:** 825 v Oxford United, 2001

FACT FILE
Founded: 1907
Nickname: Railwaymen
Colours: All red & white
Change colours: Blue & yellow stripes
Midweek Matchday: Tuesday
Programme: 50p
Editor: Steve Clare & Andy Selby
CLUB PERSONNEL
Chairman: John Bailey
Press Officer: Simon Kelly
e-mail: didcopt1907@aol.com
Manager:Peter Foley
Ass.Managar: Stuart Peace
Player-Coach: Andy Cooper
Physio: Mark Roberts
2002-2003
Player of the Year: Andy Cooper
Top Scorer: Ian Concanon

FAIRFORD TOWN

Secretary: William Beach, 33 Park Close, Fairford, GL7 4LF Tel: 01285 712136 (H)
Email address: ftfc00@hotmail.com
Ground: Cinder Lane, London Road, Fairford, Cirencester Tel: 01285 712071

Directions: Entering Fairford on A417 from Lechlade turn left down Cinder Lane150yds after 40mph sign. From Cirencester on same road, follow thru village andturn right down Cinder Lane 400yds afterRailway Inn.
Buses from Swindon,Lechlade and Cirencester
Capacity: 2,000 Seats: 100 Cover: 150 Floodlights: Yes
Clubhouse: Open each evening, weekend lunches & before and after all games
Club Shop: Yes
HONOURS Glos Challenge Trophy 79-80, 98-99 02-03 (R-up 82-83); Hellenic Lg R-up 78-79
79- 80 90-91 94-95, (Premier Div Cup 78-79, Div 1 71-72, Div 1 Cup 71-72);
Glos Jnr Cup 62-63; Swindon & Dist Lg 64-65 68-69 ,Hellenic floodlit Trophy: 2001-02
PREVIOUS **Leagues:** Cirencester & District (pre-1946)/ Swindon & District 46-70
Grounds: None
RECORD **Attendance:** 1,525 v Coventry City, friendly July 2000
Goalscorer: Pat Toomey **Win:** 9-0 v Moreton T **Defeat**: 0-9 v Sharpness

FACT FILE
Founded: 1891 Nickname: Town
Colours: Red/white/red
Change colours:All Blue
Midweek matchday: Wednesday
Reserves' League: Hellenic Reserve section
Prog: 20 pages Editor/Press Officer: President
Club Website: http://welcometo/ftfc

CLUB PERSONNEL
President: Michael Tanner
Manager: Mark Webb
Physio: Ian Watkins

2002-03
Leading Goalscorer:Lee Stoddart
Captain:Lee Clark
Player of the Year: Lee Kilfoyle

GLOUCESTER UNITED

Secretary: Dave Phillips, 14 Woodcock Close, Abbeydale, Gloucester GL4 4WT
Tel: 01452 414766 (H/Fax) 07754 088063 (M - matchdays only)

Ground City Stadium, Meadow Park, Sudmeadow Road, Hempsted, Gloucester GL2 5HS
Tel: 01452 421400

Capacity: 3,500 Cover:2,500 Seats: 560 Floodlights: Yes

Directions From junction 11 of M5 take A40 towards City Centre, follow signs for Historic Docks. On approach to docks turn right over narrow bridge into Severn Road (signposted Hempsted). Turn right into Hempsted Lane and then second right into Sudreadow Road. Ground is 50 yards on the left.

Clubhouse: Meadow Park Sports & Social Club in ground. Normal licensing hours.

Record **Attendance:** 120 v Shortwood Utd, 25.10.00

Honours: Hellenic D1 West 99-00; Floodlite Cup R-up 99-00

FACT FILE

Formed:
Colours : All blue
Change colours: Red/red/white
Midweek fixtures: Wednesday
Programme: Price: Pages:
Editor:

CLUB PERSONNEL

Chairman: Richard Bull
Vice Chairman: Pat Casey
Press Officer: Dave Phillips
Man: Douglas Foxwell 01452 538116
Coach: John Hamilton
Physio: Ricky Clutterbuck

HENLEY TOWN

Secretary: Tony Kingston, 50 Birdhill Avenue Reading Berks. RG2 7JU
Tel: 01189 670196(H) 07712139502 (M); 01189 844496 (B);
Fax: 01189 842201;E-mail: ad.kingston@ntlworld.com

Ground: The Triangle, Mill Lane ,Henley-on-Thames
Tel: 01491 411083

Directions: From Henley Town Centre take the A4155 Reading Road.
Mill Lane is approx. 1 mile on the left past the Newtown Ind. Est. and immed. before the Garage and roundabout for Tesco.
The ground is on the left, over the railway bridge.
Henley-on-Thames Railway Station ten minutes walk.
Buses 328 Reading or 329 Wycombe

Capacity: 2,500 **Seats:** 60 + disabled **Cover:** 160 **Floodlights:** Yes

Clubhouse: Open lunchtimes & evenings weekdays plus all day Sat,Sun

Record Gate: 2000+ v Reading, 1922 at old Reading Road ground

Recent Honours: Hellenic Lge Div1 East 00-01 Oxon Senior Cup (5)

Best Season: **FA Vase:** **FA Cup:**

2002-2003: **Capt:** Graham Jack **P.o.Y.:** Danny Isaiew **Top Scorer:** Phil Arden 22

FACT FILE

Founded 1871
Nickname: The Lillywhites or TheTown
Colours: White /black/black
Change cols.: Yellow & Green /green/green
Midweek fixtures: Tuesday 7.30
Prog Ed: Raf Lobato (0118 9019326)
Web site: www.henleytown.co.uk

CLUB PERSONNEL

Chairman: Andrew Bryan
Press Officer: As Secretary
Director of Coaching:Keith Stiles
Manager:Albie Stevenson
Assistant Manager: George Friel
Physio: Richard Ellis
Youth Development: Jack Hollidge

HIGHWORTH TOWN

Secretary: Fraser Haines, 222 Windrush, Highworth, Swindon SN6 7EB (01793861109)

Ground: Elm Recreation Ground, Highworth. (01793 766263)

Directions: Enter on A361 from Swindon, past Simpsons Garage, straight overisland, next sharp left into Green by Vet's Surgery - ground & car park 60ydson left next to Sports Hall

Capacity: 2,000 Seats: 50 Cover: 250 Floodlights: Yes Club Shop: No

Clubhouse: Sat 12-2.30 & 4.30-11pm. Mon to Fri 7-11pm. Rolls & Hot food

HONOURS Wilts Snr Cup 63-64 72-73 95-96 97-98(R-up 88-89), Hellenic Div 1 Cup 88-89,Arthur Shipway Cup 88-89 93-94, Swindon & District Lg 63-64 64-65 65-66 68-69 Hellenic Supplementary Cup Winners: 98-99, Hellenic Reserve Division Two Winners 98-99, Hellenic Premier Division R-Up 9-00

PREVIOUS **Leagues:** Wilts; Swindon & Dist

RECORD **Attendance:** 2,000 v QPR opening Floodlights
Scorer: Kevin Higgs **Appearances:** Rod Haines
Win: 12-0 v Beeches, Arthur Shipway Cup 1992
Defeat: 2-8 v Milton United, Hellenic Lge Div. 1, 1987

FACT FILE

Founded: 1893
Nickname: Worthians
Sponsors: Logic Builders
Colours: Red & black/black/red
Change colours: Blue/white/blue
Midweek matchday: Tuesday
Reserves Lge: Hellenic Reserve Div
Programme: 16 pages, 60p
Editor: Mike Markham (01793 763462)

CLUB PERSONNEL

President: Alan Vockins
Chairman: Geoff Melcott
Match Secretary: Dave Evans (01793 763548)
Press Officer:Chairman
Manager: John Fisher
Coach: Dave Webb Physio:Alan Jenning

2002-03

Leading Goalscorer: Justin Miller
Captain:John Reeves
Player of the Year: John Reeves

Carterton Town - 3rd in the Premier Division 2002-03

Back Row (L-R): Terry Merriman, Jamie Cole, Paul Sherwood, Karl Dodds, Nick Heritage (Capt), Adrian Holder, Jamie Butt, Paul Berry.
Front Row (L-R): Mark Threlfall, Craig Muncall, Kevin Lewis, David Hamill, Michael Duerden, James Mortimer-Jones, Alan Rogers.

HOOK NORTON

Secretary: Geoff James, Speedwqell, Brick Hill, Hook Norton, Oxon
Tel No: 01608 737476

Ground: The Bourne, Hook Norton OX15 5PB 01608 737132

Capacity: 2000 Covered Seating: 500 Covered Standing: 1000Floodlights: Yes

Directions: From Oxford – A44 to junction with A361 turn right, take 1st left to a 'T' junction, turn right & enter village, after 30 MPH turn left then 1st right into 'The Bourne', take 1st left into ground.

Clubhouse: On ground

Previous League: Oxfordshire Senior League

Record Gate: 244 v Banbury United 12th Dec 1998

Honours: Oxford Senior League Champions 1999-2000
Hellenic Lge Div.1 West Champions 01-02

Best Season FA Vase: 2nd Q rd. FA Cup:

FACT FILE
Founded: 1901
Nickname: Hooky
Colours: All maroon with silver grey trim
Change colours: Yellow with blue trim
Midweek fixtures: Wednesday
Program Editor: Mark Willis 01608 664101
email: repro@kmslitho.co.uk

CLUB PERSONNEL
Chairman: Michael Barlow
Deputy Chairman: Michael Barlow
Press Officer: Geoff james 01608 737476
Manager John evans
Coach:Matty Haycock
Physio: Steve Slaughter & Louisa White

2002-2003
Captain: Karlton Stratford
Top Scorer: Ben Spiro P.o.Y.: Andy Parrott

HUNGERFORD TOWN

Ground: Town Ground, Bulpit Lane, Hungerford RG17 0AY
Tel: 01488 682939 (club) 01488 684597 (boardroom) 01488 684597 (Fax)

Directions: M4 jct 14 to A4, right and left at Bear Hotel, through town centre on A338, left into Priory Rd, second left into Bulpit Lane, over crossroads, ground on left. 3/4 mile from Hungerford BR station

Capacity: 3,000 Seats: 300 Cover:320 Floodlights: Yes **Club Shop**: Yes

Clubhouse: Open eves & lunchtimes including Sunday. 2 bars, dancehall, boardroom/ committee room, darts, pool, fruit machines. Hot & coldsnacks. Steward: Dianne Tanner (01488 682939)

HONOURS: Berks & Bucks Snr Cup 81-82 (R-up 75-76 76-77); Hellenic Lg Div 1 70-71, PremDiv Cup 77-78, Div 1 Cup 70-71, Benevolent Cup 60-61; Hungerford Cup 96-97, Isthmian Lge Representatives in Anglo-Italian Tournament 81.

PREVIOUS **Leagues:** Newbury & D.; Swindon & D.; Hellenic 58-78

CLUB RECORDS **Attendance:** 1,684 v Sudbury Town, FA Vase SF 1st leg 88-89
Scorer: Ian Farr (268) **Appearances:** Dean Bailey (approx 400)
Transfer Fee Paid: £4,000 for Joe Scott (Yeovil T.)
Received: £3,800 for Joe Scott (Barnstaple T.)

BEST SEASON **FA Cup:** 1st Rd 79-80, 1-3 v Slough T. (A)
FA Vase: Semi-Final 77-78 79-80 88-89

Players progressing to Football League: Steve Hetzke (Reading, Blackpool,Sunderland), Bruce Walker (Swindon, Blackpool), Des McMahon (Reading), BrianMundee (Bournemouth, North'ton)

FACT FILE
Founded: 1886 Nickname: Crusaders
Club Sponsors: Kerridge Insurance
Colours: White/navy blue/blue
Change colours: All yellow
Midweek Matchday: Tuesday
Reserves' League: Suburban (North)
Programme: 24 pages, 50p
Editor:Martyn Leach (01488 683682)

CLUB PERSONNEL
Chairman: Alan Holland
Vice Chairman: Ron Tarry
President: Sir Seton Wills
General Secretary: Eric Richardson
Match Secretary: Norman Matthews
Press Officer: Ron Tarry (01488 682539)
Manager: Gary Ackling
Asst.Man: Tim North Physio: Richard Fox

2002-03
Leading Goalscorer:Darren Howell
Captain:Darren Howell
Player of the Year: Martin Fox

NORTH LEIGH

Secretary: Peter J Dix, 8 Windmill Close, North Leigh, Nr Witney, Oxon OX8 6RP
Tel: 01993 881199

Match Secretary: Keith Huxley, The Orchard, Cote, Bampton, Oxon. OX18 2EG
Tel: 01993 851497 (H) 0118 913 3223 (B)
email: keith_huxley@fwuk.fwc.com

Ground: Eynsham Hall Park Sports Ground, North Leigh, nr Witney, Oxon OX8 6PW
Tel: 0993 881427

Directions: Ground is situated off A4095 Witney to Woodstock road 3 miles east of Witney. Entrance to ground is 300yds east of Main Park Entrance

Capacity: 2,000 Seats: 100 Cover: 200 Floodlights: Yes

Clubhouse: Bar open matches. Snacks available **Club Shop:** No

PREVIOUS **Leagues:** Witney & District 08-89

CLUB RECORDS **Attendance:** 300 v Oxford United, Friendly August 1998
Scorer: P Coles **Appearances:** P King

HONOURS Hellenic Lg Div 1 R-up 92-93 (Reserves Cup 93-94), Oxon Jnr Shield 56-57 83-84, Oxon Charity Cup 84-85 88-89, Witney & Dist. Lg(13) 50-57 84-90 LgCup (10) 47-48 51-52 53-55 56-57 81-82 85-89), Oxon Yth Cup 93-94 94-95,OxonYth u17 Lg & Cup 93-94. Oxford Sen. Cup R-Up 94-95. Marriott Cup 95-96; Oxon U-16 Youth Cup 98-99, Allied Counties Under 18 Youth (West Div)Winners

FACT FILE
Founded: 1908
Nickname: None
Sponsors: Various
Colours: Yellow & red/red/yellow
Change colours: All claret & blue
Midweek matches: Tuesday
Programme: 20 pages, £1 with entry
Editor: Janice Carter

CLUB PERSONNEL
President: Mrs Christine Smith
Chairman: Peter King
Press Officer: Barry Norton
Tel: 01993 881777

Manager: Mark Gee
Asst Manager: David Ebsworth
Physio: Andrew Davidson

PEGASUS JUNIORS

Secretary: K.Alden, 3 Walton Close, Hereford. Tel No: 01432 358623
Ground: Leisure Centre, Holmer Road,Hereford
Directions: A49 Ross Road over Greyfriars Bridge, Victoria Street to end of Edgar Street, then turn left to next mini roundabout and then right.Leisure Centre 500 yds on left.
Capacity: 1,000 Seats 50 Cover : Yes Floodlights: Yes
Clubhouse: 48 St Owens Street

HONOURS Herefordshire Snr Amtr Cup 71-72; Worcs Senior Urn 85-86; Herefordshire Co. Chal. Cup (6) 81-83 84-85 87-88 89-90, 98-99, R-up 93-94; Hellenic Lg Div 1 84-85 98-99, R-up 93-94, Div 1 Cup R-up 93-94)

PREVIOUS **Leagues:** Leisure Centre

RECORD **Attendance:** 1,400 v Newport AFC 89-90

BEST SEASON **FA Cup:** **FA Vase:**

FACT FILE
Founded: 1955
Colours: All red
Change colours: All blue
Midweek Matchday: Tuesday/Wednesday
Programme: 50p
Editor: Kevin Bishop (01432 353805)

CLUB PERSONNEL
President: Mark Ellis
Chairman: T.B.A.
Press Officer: Chris Wells
Manager: P.Mann
Assistant. Manager:T.B.A.
Physio: A.Trumper

2002-03
Leading Goalscorer:
Captain:
Player of the Year:

PEWSEY VALE

Secretary: Liz Montague, 39 Swan Meadow, Pewsey, Wilts, SN9 5HP
E-mail: montymadhouse@btinternet.com

Ground: Recreation Ground, Ball Rd, Pewsey Tel: 01672 562990

Directions: On entering Pewsey from A345, at the Market Place proceed to end of High Street and turn right into Ball Rd, entrance to ground on right opposite pub. BR to Pewsey station
Capacity Unlimited Cover: Yes Floodlights: No
Clubhouse:

PREVIOUS **League:** Wiltshire County (pre-1993), Western League 93-01
Name: Pewsey Y.M. (until late 1940s)

HONOURS Wiltshire County League 92-93

BEST SEASON **FA Vase:** **FA Cup:**

FACT FILE
Formed: ?????
Colours: Black & White]/Black/Black
Change colours:
Navy & lime green/navy/lime green & navy
Midweek matchday: Tuesday
Programme: Price: Pages:
Editor:

CLUB PERSONNEL

Chairman: Rob Thompson

Manager: Don Rogers

SHORTWOOD UNITED

Secretary: Mark Webb, 1 The Bungalow, Shortwood, Nailsworth, Stroud, Glos GL60SD
Tel: 01453 833204 (H) 0781 2842724 (M)
Ground: "Meadow Bank", Shortwood, Nailsworth, Gloucestershire (01453 833936)
Directions: In Nailsworth turn into Spring Hill then first left. Continue pastshop and and keep left past "Britannia" (signposted Shortwood) - continue toend for ground. 4 miles from Stroud (BR)
Capacity: 5,000 Seats: 50 Cover: 150 Floodlights: Yes Club Shop: No
Clubhouse: Mon-Sat 7-11pm, Sun 12-2 & 7-10.30pm.. Hot food kitchen on matchdays

HONOURS Glos.Co.Lg 81-82 (R-up 80-81), Glos Tphy 83-84 91-92,94-95,(R-up 79-80), Hellenic Lg 84-85 91-92 (R-up 85-86 89-90 94-95, Div 1 R-up 83-84, Div 1Cup83-84), Prem Lge Cup R-up 95-96, Hungerford Merit Cup, Glos Snr AmCup 85-86,99-00 R-up 79-80), Stroud Charity Cup 91-92 92-93 94-95 00-01(R-up 95-96), Stroud Lg 27-28 (Div 2 26-27 64-65(res), Div 3 25-26 49-50(res) 62-63(res)), Glos Northern Snr Lg R-up (3)res)(Div 2 62-63 80-81(res) 90-91(res)), Arthur Shipway Cup 78-79 79-80, Supp'tary Cup R-up 98-99, Glos N. Sen 2 R-up 98-99

PREVIOUS **Leagues:** Stroud; Glos Northern Snr; Glos Co
Ground: Table Land, Wallow Green

RECORD **Attendance:** 1,000 v Forest Green Rovers, FA Vase 5th Rd 81-82
Goalscorer: Peter Grant **Appearances:** Peter Grant
Win: 11-0 **Defeat:** 0-9 **Fee Received:** Paul Tester (Cheltenham, 80-81)

FACT FILE
Founded: 1900
Nickname: The Wood
Sponsors: Ecotricity
Colours: Red & white,red,white
Change: Blue/Blue/Yellow
Midweek matchday: Tues or Wed
Reserves' League: Glos Northern Snr 1
Programme: 18 pages, 50p
Editor:Kenton Posthlethwaite

CLUB PERSONNEL
Chairman: Peter Webb
Vice C'men: W Stratford, W Lewis
President: R T Tanner
Press Officer: Keith Norbury
Tel: 01453 83 5094 (H) 07816205152 (M)
Manager: T.B.A. Coach: Ryan Gannaway

2002-2003
Captain:Mike Green
Top Scorer:Craig Cole 20
Player of the Year:Steve Walker

SLIMBRIDGE TOWN

Secretary: David Phillips, 14 Woodcock Close Abbeydale Gloucester GL4 4WT
Tel: 01452 414766 (T & F) 07754 088063 (Match Days Only)

Ground: Wisloe Road, Cambridge, Glos. GL2 7AF Tel: 01453 890361

Directions: From the A38 take the A 4135 to Dursley ground is 100 yards on left.
Clubhouse:

HONOURS: Hellenic Lge Div.1 West 02-03, Glos. County Lge 01-02

PREVIOUS **League:** Gloucestershire County Lge.

RECORD **Attendance:** 110 v Pucklechurch 18th August 2001 (Glos County Lge)

FACT FILE
Founded:
Colours: Blue/blue/white
Change: Red/black/red
Program Editor: Martin Tudor
Tel: 01453 549447
Midweek matchdays: Tuesday

CLUB PERSONNEL
Chairman: John Mack
Tel: 01453 543104

Manager: Doug Grey
Tel: 01453 544306
Coach: Alan Ward
Physio: Harry Brooks

SOUTHALL TOWN

Secretary: George Twyman, 119 Dormers Wells Lane Southall Middlesex UB1 3JA
Tel & Fax: 0208 574 5047(H & B) Email: craig@craig brown.co.uk

Match Sec.: Eddie Mee, 78 Manor Lane, feltham, Middlesex TW13 4TQ
Tel: 07940 287 985 (Bus)

Ground: Yeading FC. The Warren Beconsfield Road Hayes Middx
Tel 0208 848 7362

Capacity: 3,500 Cover: 1,000 Seats: 250 Floodlights: Yes

Directions: Leave M4 at junction 3, The Parkway onto Hayes by-pass. Continue to the second filter road and turn right onto A4020 Uxbridge Road, then take first turning on right into Springfield Road. Continue to end of road, turn left into Beconsfield Road, ground on right hand side at end of the road.the left hand side opposite the Church.

PREVIOUS **Leagues:** Isthmian League to 20 00.

RECORD **Attendance:** 46 v Bishops Cleeve 2001-2002

2002-03 Leading Goalscorer: Michael Meaker 29 Captain: leon Lewis
Players of the Year: Dale Godfrey & Michael Meaker

FACT FILE

Nickname: The Town
Colours: Red & white stripes/black/black
Change colours: Yellow & blue/blue/blue
Midweek Matchday: Wednesday
Programme: £1
Editor: Craig Brown:0208861 6215
email: craig@craigbrown.co.uk

CLUB PERSONNEL
Chairman: Manjit S Lit

Press Officer: Manjit S Lit
Tel: 0208 893 5373 Fax: 0208 571 9410

Manager: Dennis Bainborough
Coach: Del Deanus
Physio: TBA

TUFFLEY ROVERS

Secretary: Graham Moody, 50 Giles Cox, Quedgeley, Gloucester GL2 4YL
Tel: 01452 724083 (H & Fax) 01452 522009 (B)

Ground: Glevum Park, Lower Tuffley Lane, Gloucester Tel: 01452 423402

Directions: Follow Gloucester city ring-rd to traffic lights signed M5 South & Bristol. Turn right signed Hempsted & city centre, after 200yds turn right (McDonalds on corner) into Lower Tuffley Lane, ground 400yds on left
Capacity: Seats: 50 Cover: Yes Floodlights: Yes

Clubhouse: 800 yds from ground. Open before & after matches, and normal pub hours at other times. Snacks available. Club Shop: No

HONOURS Hellenic Lg Div 1 92-93 (Div 1 Cup 92-93, F'lit Cup 98-99), Glos Co. Lge 90-91, Glos SnrAmtr Cup 87-88, Stroud Lg 72-73,94-95, Glos Northern Sen. Lg. Div 1 87-88 98-99 (res) Div2 79-80.

PREVIOUS **Leagues:** Stroud; Glos Northern Senior; Glos County (pre-1991)
Grounds: Stroud Rd, Gloucester; Randwick Park, Tuffley

RECORD **Attendance:** 150 v Cinderford Town 94-95

FACT FILE

Founded: 1929
Nickname: Rovers
Club Sponsors: Albell Construction
Colours: Claret & blue/claret/claret
Change colours: White/blue/blue
Midweek Matchday: Tuesday
Reserve League: Glos.Northern Senior Lge
Programme: approx 10 pages with entry
Editor: Graham Moody

CLUB PERSONNEL

President: T.B.A.
Chairman: Tony Newport

Manager: Chris Gardner
Coach: Rob Whittington
Physio: Sean Tracey

WOOTTON BASSETT TOWN

Secretary: Rod Carter, 14 Blackthorn Close, Wootton Bassett, Swindon SN4 7JE
Tel: 01793 851386 (H); 01793 494367 (B); 01793 494355 (F);
07946 034999 (M) Email: rod.carter@woolworths.co.uk

Ground: Gerard Buxton Sports Ground, Rylands Way, Wootton Bassett, Swindon 01793 853880

Directions: M4 jnct 16 to Wootton Bassett (A3102), left at 2nd r'bout (Prince of Wales pub on right), 2nd left into Longleaze (just after Mobil garage) and Rylands Way is 3rd right by shops, ground 100yds on right. From Calne/Devizes direction proceed thru town centre and turn right into Longleaze after Shell petrol station on right - Rylands Ave. is 3rd left. Coming from Malmesbury take last exit off r'bout by Prince of Wales pub and Longleaze is 2nd left

Capacity: 4,000 Seats: None Cover: 350 Floodlights: Yes Club Shop: No
Clubhouse: Open every matchday. Matchday refreshments - teas, coffees, soups & light snacks

PREVIOUS **Leagues:** Wilts (pre-1988) **Grounds:** None
RECORD **Gate:** 2,103 v Swindon T., friendly 7/91 **Win:** 11-2 **Defeat:** 0-9
Scorer: Brian (Toby) Ewing **Appearances:** Steve Thomas
HONOURS Hellenic Lg Div 1 Cup 89-90 93-94, Wilts Lg 87-88 (Div 2 84-85,Subsidiary Cup 78-79), Wilts Snr Cup R-up 02-03 03-04 87-88, Ghia Snr 83-84,Ghia Jnr Cup R-up 88-89, FA Amateur Cup QF 26-27

FACT FILE
Founded: 1882
Colours: Blue & yellow/blue/yellow
Change colours: Red/black/black
Midweek matchday: Tuesday
Reserve's League: Wiltshire
Programme: 12 pages, free
Editor: Roger Williamson Tel: 01793 850751

CLUB PERSONNEL
Chairman: Paul Harrison
President: Keith Lodge
Press Officer: Rod Carter (see Sec)

Manager: Peter Yeardley
Coach: Mike Byrne
Physio: TBA

ADDERBURY PARK

Secretary Clive Boddy 5 Coppice Close Banbury Oxon OX16 9SW
Tel: 01295 255641 (H) 01295 225004 (B) 01295 225005 (F)

Ground: Adderbury Park Playing Fields, Round Close Road, Oxford.
Tel: 07788 867532

Directions: Take the A4260 from Oxford, enter village and turn left at village green into High Street, then into New Road, turn sharp left into Round Close Road. Ground entrance is 100 yards on left.

Clubhouse:
Previous League: Oxfordshire Senior Lge.>2002
Honours:
Record Attendance:

FACT FILE
Formed: ????
Colours: Green & white hoops/white/green
Change: Red/black/black
Midweek matchday: Tuesday
Program Editor: James Easterbrooke
01295 810847 email: jimbo111@tinyworld.co.uk

CLUB PERSONNEL
Chairman: Pete Spicer
01295 265635 email: peejay@supanet.com
Press Officer: Joel Bloxham 01295 253355 email: Topstriker69@aol.com

Manager: Jim Hay
Coach/Physio: Dennis Horrocks

ARDLEY UNITED

Secretary: Alan Mitchell, 24 Orchard Road,Ardley,Bicester,Oxon OX27 7PW
Tel: 01869 346854(H) 01865 846799(W) 01865 846333(FAX)

Ground: The Playing Fields, Ardley Road,Ardley (01869 346429)

Directions: M40 junc 10 take B430 towards Middleton Stoney on the right after1/2 mile. From Oxford take A430 through Weston-on-the-Green & Middleton Stoney on the left hand side.
Capacity: Cover: Seats: Floodlights

Clubhouse:
HONOURS Oxon Snr Lg R-up 92-93 (Pres. Cup R-up 90-91 91-92) Hellenic League Div One 96-97,97-98 Division One Cup 94-5,95-6,96-7,97-98

PREVIOUS **Leagues:** Oxon Snr (pre-1993)

RECORD **Attendance:** 91 v North Leigh (1999)

FACT FILE
Founded:
Colours: Sky/navy/sky
Change colours: Yellow/black/yellow
Midweek matchday: Tuesday
Programme Yes Ed: Barbara Gow

CLUB PERSONNEL
President: Ben Gow
Chairman: Norman Stacey
Secretary: Alan Mitchell
Tel: 01869 346854 (H)
Manager: Paul Spittle
Coach: Tony Blossom
Physio: Clive Wright

CHELTENHAM SARACENS

Secretary: Robert Attwood, 179 Arle Road, Cheltenham GL51 8LJ
Tel: 01242 515855 (H) 01242 241819 (B) 01242 222994 (Fax)
Ground: Petersfield Park, Tewkesbury Road, Cheltenham GL51 9DX(01242 584134)
Directions: Take A40 west out of Gloucester, follow A40 for 8 miles then takeA4136 to Longhope, pass by on the outskirts of Michealdean, up steep hill (Plump Hill), then second turn on the right signed Harrow Hill. At phone box on the left turn right into Larksfield Road, ground on right at top of hill. Reserves' Ground: Petersfield Park, Tewkesbury Road, Cheltenham (01242 584134) Directions: 1 mile from Cheltenham centre on A4019 Tewksbury Road (next to B &Q) - 1st left over railway bridge, 1st left and follow service road
Clubhouse: 2 mins away at 16-20 Swindon Rd, Cheltenham
HONOURS Glos Snr Cup 91-92 Glos Primary Cup 71-72, Winners Hellenic Div 1 99-00
PREVIOUS **League:** Cheltenham 1964-86
RECORD **Attendance:** 120 v Bishops Cleeve, 1.1.95
Players progressing: S Cotterill (Wimbledon) 88, K Knight (Reading) 89

FACT FILE
Founded: 1964 Nickname: Saras
Colours: Blue&yellow/blue/yellow
Change colours: Black, white stripe/black/black
Midweek Matchday: Wednesday
Reserves League: Hellenic Reserve section
Programme : 20 pages, 50p
Editor: Kevin Dix 01242 690405
Email: kevindix@blueyonder.co.uk

CLUB PERSONNEL
Chairman : Paul Passey (01452 856275)
Press Officer: Bob Attwood(01242 515855)
Manager: Ian Ford
Coach:Gerald Oldham Physio: Chris Hawkins

CIRENCESTER UNITED

Secretary/Press Officer: Gordon Varley, 95 Vaisey Rd, Cirencester, Glos GL7 2JW
Tel: 01285 657836 (H) 0973 631650 (M) 01367 718259 (B)
Ground: Four Acres P.F., Chesterton Lane, Cirencester Tel: 01285 885460
Directions: Follow by-pass towards Bristol, under footbridge, first left , ground 200yds on left hand side
Seats: None Cover: No Floodlights: No Club Shop: No
Clubhouse: Training nights & matchdays. Rolls & sundries available
HONOURS Glos Snr Amtr Cup R-up 86-87 89-90; Cirencester Lg 72-73 74-75 (Div 2(3)71-73 74-75, Lg Cup 74-75, Res. Cup 74-75); Cheltenham Lg 76-77 83-84 (Div 275-76, Lg Cup 83-84 (R-up 86-87), Snr Charity Cup 86-87); Stroud Charity Cup86-87 (Section A 82-83 83-84); Arthur Shipway Cup 86-87 (R-up 87-88 92-93);Fairford Hospital Cup R-up(4) 83-85 90-91 92-93; Hellenic Res Div 95-96, Cup96-97
PREVIOUS **Leagues:** Cirencester & Dist.(4 yrs); Cheltenham (8 yrs)
RECORDS **Scorer:** M Day **Appearances:** J.Stratford 310

FACT FILE
Founded: 1970 Nickname: Herd
Colours: Red & black/black/red
Change colours: All Blue
Midweek Matchday: Wednesday
Programme: 40 pages, 50p
Editor: N Warriner (01285 656187)

CLUB PERSONNEL
President:R.Trinder
Chairman: Paul King
Press Officer: As Secretary
Manager: Ivor Probert
Coach: P.Messenger
Physio: Brian Muir

CLANFIELD

Secretary: John Osborne, 70 Lancut Road, Witney, Oxon OX28 5AQ Tel: 01993 771631

Ground: Radcot Road, Clanfield, Oxon Tel: 01367 810314

Directions: Situated on the A4095, 8 miles west of Witney & 4 miles east of Faringdon, at the southern end of Clanfield. Buses from Witney - contact Thames Transit for details

Capacity: 2,000 Seats: No Cover: 300 Floodlights: No
Clubhouse: Every evening & Sat/Sun lunch Club Shop: No

HONOURS Oxon Jnr Shield 32-33, Oxon I'mediate Cup 67-68, Witney & Dist. Lg 66-67 (Div 1 65-66, Div 2 64-65), Hellenic Lg Div 1 69-70 (Premier Div Cup 72-73, Div1 Cup 69-70 85-86), Jim Newman Mem. Tphy 83-84 87-88, Faringdon Thursday Memorial Cup 69-70 71-72 96-97

PREVIOUS **Leagues:** Nth Berks; Witney & Dist
RECORD **Attendance:**102 v Witney Acadeny 2000 Top Goalscorer: D.Hamill(9)

FACT FILE
Founded: 1890 Nickname: Robins
Sponsors: Green King
Colours: All red
Change colours: Yellow & Black/black/black
Reserves' League: Hellenic Lge Res. section
Prog: 8 pages, with admission Ed: Secretary

CLUB PERSONNEL
President: B Wallis Chairman: J Osborne
Manager: Jason Court
Press Officer & Physio: Trevor Cuss

2002-03
Leading Goalscorer:
Captain:
Player of the Year:

EASINGTON SPORTS

Secretary: Matthew Wiggins, 26 Victoria Place, Banbury, OX16 3NN. Tel: 01295 256714
Ground: Addison Road, Banbury, Oxon, OX16 9DH (01295 257006)
Club Email: matt@wiggins1.freeserve.co.uk

Directions: From Oxford A423. After passing under flyover on the outskirts of Banbury take first turning left into Grange Road then third right into AddisonRd. Ground at top on left. One and a half miles from Banbury (BR)
Capacity: 1,000 Seats:0 Cover: 30Floodlights: No Programme: Yes

Clubhouse: Changing rooms, showers, bar facilities and food

HONOURS Oxon Snr Cup R-up, Oxon Intermediate League & Cup, Oxon Snr Lg

PREVIOUS **Leagues:** Banbury Jnr; Oxon Snr; Warkwick Combination
Ground: Bodicote

RECORD **Attendance:** 250 v Witney Town 68

FACT FILE
Founded: 1946
Colours: Red & white/black/red & white
Change colours: Blue/ white
Midweek Matchday: Wednesday
Reserves' League: Hellenic Res. section

CLUB PERSONNEL
Chairman: T.B.A.
President: Bob Cogbill
Manager/Coach: Andy Maguire
Physio: Bernie Jarvis
Press Officer: T.B.A.

HARROW HILL

Secretary/Match Sec: Robert Partridge, 20 Littledean Hill Road, Cinderford, Glos., GL14 2BE
Tel: 01594 825360 (H) 01594 825225 (B)
Club Email: geoff@tuffley33.freeserve.co.uk

Ground: Larksfield Road, Harrow Hill Tel: 01594 543873

Directions: Take A40 west out of Gloucester, follow A40 for 8 miles then takeA4136 to Longhope, pass by on the outskirts of Michealdean, up steep hill(Plump Hill), then second turn on the right signed Harrow Hill. At phone box onthe left turn right into Larksfield Road, ground on right at top of hill

RECORD **Attendance:** 350 v Cinderford Town 92
Previous Leagues:
HONOURS:
BEST SEASON **FA Vase:** **FA Cup:**

FACT FILE
Founded: 1932
Nickname: Harry Hill
Colours: Claret & blue/sky/sky
Change Colours: Purple & green/black/black
Midweek Matchday: Wednesday

CLUB PERSONNEL
Chairman: Reg Taylor
Press Officer: Geoff Tuffley
10A Bilson, Cinderford, Glos., GL14 2LJ
Tel 01594 825655(H) 077524 75514 (M)

Manager: Neil Walding
Coach: Steve Boseley
Physio: Martin Burford

HEADINGTON AMATEURS

Secretary: Stephen Giles, 67 Lucerne Ave.,Bure Park,Bicester, Oxon.OX26 3EG
Tel No: 01869 246141 Email Address: steve.giles3@ btinternet.com
Ground: Barton Rec., Barton Village Road, Barton, Oxon Tel: 01865 760489
Directions: From Green Rd r'bout, Headington, (on A40) take Barton/Islip exit(1st exit coming from Witney, last coming from London), turn left into NorthWay, follow road for half mile - ground at bottom of hill on left Seats: None Cover: None Floodlights: No Club Shop: No
Clubhouse: Tues & Thurs 6-11, Sat matchdays 4.45-11. Rolls, chips,burgers, hot dogs, etc
HONOURS Oxon Snr League(4) 72-74 75-77 (R-up 71-72 74-75 77-78 81-82 84-85, Div1 68-69, Presidents Cup(2) 72-74 (R-up 71-72 77-78 84-85)), Oxon Charity Cup75-76 (Intermediate Cup 88-89), Hellenic League Div 1 R-up 87-88 (Res. Sect.92-93, Res. Cup 91-92)
PREVIOUS Leagues: Oxford City Junr 49-66; Oxford Sen 67-88 **Grounds:**Romanway,Cowley
RECORDS Attendance: 250 v Newport AFC 91 **Scorer:** Tony Penge **Appearances:**Kent Drackett **Win:** 6-0 v Carterton (H) 91 **Defeat:** 0-9 Highworth Town (a) 2002 RPM Records Cup
Player Progressing: James Light (Oxford United) 1970s

FACT FILE
Founded : 1949 Nickname: A's
Sponsors: Shaun Bradford Decorating & Construction
Colours: All red
Change: Blue/blue/white
Midweek matchday: Tuesday
Programme: 8 pages, £1 with entry
Editor: Stan Hawkswood (01865 876485)

CLUB PERSONNEL
Pres: Shaun.Bradford Chairman: Donald Light
Press Officer: Donald Light
Manager: Phil Major
Coach/Physio: Graham McAnulf

KIDLINGTON

Secretary: David Platt, 57 Cherry Close,Kidlington, Oxon OX5 1HHJ (01865 370266 (H) 01865 244161(W) EMail Address: david@jplatt99,freeserve.co.uk

Ground: Yarnton Rd, Kidlington, Oxford Tel: 01865 375628 f loodlights: No

Clubhouse: Two bars open after matches

Directions: From Kidlington r'bout (junction of A4260 & A34) A423 north toKidlington; after 3rdlights take 2nd left (Yarnton Road), ground is 200yds onthe left ,just passes the turning to Morton Avenue.

HONOURS Oxon Snr Lg 53-54 (R-up 47-48), Hellenic Lg Cup 74-75 (R-up 68-69 73-7474-75, Div 1 R-up 63-64 78-79), Oxon Intermediate Cup 52-53 84-85 (R-up 68-69 73-74 74-75), FA Vase 5th last sixteen 76-77

PREVIOUS **League**: Oxon Snr 47-54

RECORD **Attendance:** 2500 v Showbiz XI 1973

2002-03 **Captain**: **Top Scorer:**

P.o.Y.:

FACT FILE

Founded: 1909
Colours: Green & black/black/green
Change colours: Red & white stripes/redk/red
Midweek Matchday:Tuesday/ Wednesday
Programme: 32pages £1.50
Editor: M A Canning

CLUB PERSONNEL

President: Gordon Norridge
Chairman: Geoff Talboys
Manager: Anton Vircavs
Coach: Martin Baker Physio: Michelle Hopcroft
General Manager: Karl Grossman

LETCOMBE

Secretary: Des Williams, 8 Larkdown, Wantage, Oxon. OX12 8HE
Tel: 01235 764130 (H)

Ground: Bassett Road, Letcombe Regis, Wantage, Oxon

Directions: B4507 Swindon road from Wantage, left for Letcombe Regis, follow road thru Letcombe Regis; ground on right on far side of village

Unofficial Club Website: www.letcombefc.co.uk

Seats: No Cover: No Floodlights: No Club Shop: No

Clubhouse: Open matchdays and functions only

HONOURS Chiltonian Lg Div 1 90-91, North Berks Lg 89-90 (Lg Cup 87-88, WarMemorial Cup 89-90, A G Kingham Cup 89-90, Faringdon Mem Cup 97-8 98-99 99-00

PREVIOUS **Leagues:** North Berks 60-90; Chiltonian 90-93

RECORDS **Attendance:** 90 v Courage (Reading) 03.90

Scorer: R Taylor **Appearances:** P Davies

FACT FILE

Founded: 1960
Nickname: Brooksiders
Sponsors: T.B.A.
Colours: Purple/Navy/Purple
Change colours: Blue& Green/Green/Green
Midweek Matchday: Wednesday
Reserves' Lge: Hellenic Res. sect
Programme: £1.50p with entry
Editor: Russell Stock (01235 762387)

CLUB PERSONNEL

Pres Jim VennartChairman: Dennis Stock
Vice-Chairman: Russell Stock
Manager: Matty Goddard
Coach & Physio: Des Williams

MALMESBURY VICTORIA

Secretary: Sue Neale, 30 Gastons Road, Malmesbury, Wilts. SN16 0BE
Tel: 01666 823560 E-Mail: sue@paulneale.freeuk.com

Ground: Flying Monk Ground, Gloucester Road, Malmesbury
Tel: 01666 822141

Website: www.malmesbury-victoria.com

Directions: From A429 turning signposted Tetbury (by Nurdens Garden Centre), go past school and take next left B4014 signposted Sherston. Go down hill to mini roundabout, straight over roundabout. Go past Somerfield's super store, narrow right turning into ground behind super store.

Previous Leagues: Wiltshire Premier League

Honours: Wiltshire League Champions 99-00 Wiltshire Senior Cup 01-02

FACT FILE

Founded:
Nickname: The Vic's
Colours: Black & white stripes/black/black
Change colours:
Maroon, blue sleeves/blue/maroon
Midweek fixtures: Tuesday or Wednesday

CLUB PERSONNEL

Chairman: Brian Slade 01666 825705
Press Officer: Brian Slade 01666 823211
Programme Ed: Paul Neale 01666 823560
Manager: John Norris 01666 840450
Coach: Graham Learmonth

MIDDLE BARTON

Secretary: Julie Reed, 5 Hillside Road, Middle Barton, Oxon OX7 7EY
Tel: 01869 347388

Match Secretary: Jeane Beale, 3 Dorne Closer, Middle Barton, Oxon OX7 7HD
Tel: 01869 340753

Ground: Worton Road, Middle Barton, Oxon. Tel: 01869 347597

Directions: Middle Barton village is situated on the B4030, 5 miles east of Enstone. 200 metres passed the Fox PH turn left at cross roads, ground 200 metres on right.

Clubhouse: Open every evening

Previous League: Oxfordshire Senior League

Honours: Oxfordshire Sen. Lge R-up 98-99

FACT FILE

Founded: 1952
Midweek Matchday: Wednesday
Colours: Blue & white/blue/white
Change colours: Yellow/black/black
Programme: Yes, first season

CLUB PERSONNEL

President: Derrick Jarvis
Chairman: John Hanks
Press Officer: Phil Smith (01869 347471)
Manager/Coach: Tim Fowler
Physio: Lucy Waring

NEW COLLEGE ACADEMY

GROUND Swindon Supermarine FC, Hunts Copse, South Marston, Swindon
Tel: 01793 729176

Directions: On A361 Swindon/Highworth road, adjoining South Marston Ind. Estate. Six miles from Swindon (BR) - buses in direction of Highworth, Fairford & Lechdale. If lost ask for Honda.

Capacity: 3,000 Seats: 300 Cover: 300 Floodlights: Yes

FACT FILE

CLUB PERSONNEL

OLD WOODSTOCK TOWN

Secretary: Ian F. Lenegan
c/o Workplace Systems plc.,Precedent Drive, Rooksley, Milton Keynes MK13 8PP
Tel:08362 42300(H), 01908 251301or 251311 (W) 01908 201287 (Fax)

Ground: New Road, Woodstock

Directions: A44 from Oxford into centre of Woodstock, turn right opposite The Crown into Hensington Road. After half a mile the road bends to the right, take the first turning right into New Road, ground half-way along on the left.

HONOURS Oxfordshire Sen. Lge 98-99

PREVIOUS **Leagues:** Oxfordshire Senior League

FACT FILE
Founded:
Midweek Matchday: Tuesday
Colours: Blue & red/blue/ red
Change colours: White/green/blue
Programme : Yes Ed: Mike Harris

CLUB PERSONNEL
President: Ian F Lenagan
Chairman: Ted Saxton
Press Officer: Mick Harris (01865 376018)
Manager: Andrew Townsend
Coach:Trevor Stokes
Physio: Graham Bowerman

PURTON

Secretary: Alan Eastwood, 12 Hylder Close,Woodhall Park,Swindon,Wilts. SN2 2SL
Tel: 01793 729844 **Email Address:** eastwood@hylder.fsnet.co.uk

Ground: The Red House, Purton, Tel: 01793 770262 (Saturday afternoons only)

Directions: Purton is on B4041 Wootton Bassett to Cricklade Road. Ground nearvillage hall

Capacity: Unlimited Seats: None Cover: None Floodlights: No

Clubhouse: Open after matches and before matches on Saturdays

HONOURS Wiltshire Lg Div One 48-49 85-86, Div 2 83-84, Div 3 86-87; Wilts Senior Cup (6) 38-39 48-49 50-51 54-55 87-88, 88-89,94-95 Wilts Yth Cup 77-78 85-86 88-89, Fairford Hosp. Cup (3) 87-89 93-94 Hellenic Lg. Div One 95-96, Hellenic Supplement Cup 2001-02

RECORD **Attendance:** 508 v Dorcan 5.5.85

PREVIOUS **Leagues:**

FACT FILE
Founded: 1923
Nickname: The Reds
Sponsors: The Care Company
Colours: All red
Change colours: All purple
Midweek Matchday: Wednesday
Programme: 36 pages
Editor: Alan Eastwood (01793 729844)

CLUB PERSONNEL
President: Graham Price
Chairman: Tony Brown
Press Officer: Alan Eastwood
Manager: Alan Clark

QUARRY NOMADS

Secretary: Keith Dolton, 58 Pitts Road Headington Oxford OX3 8AZ 01865 450256 (H)

Match Sec.: Linda Dolton, 58 Pitts Road Headington Oxford OX3 8AZ 01865 450256 (H)

Ground: Margaret Road, Headington, Oxford Tel: 07860 408769

Directions: Exit M40 J 8, then A40 towards Oxford to Green Road r'about (McDonalds on left), straight over towards Headington.Take third left into Wharton Road, then at T junction turn left into Margaret Road. Ground on left.

Clubhouse:

Club Shop:

RECORD **Attendance:** 267 v Witney Town, 1994

PREVIOUS **League**: Chiltonian

HONOURS

FACT FILE
Formed:
Web Site: www.qnfc.co.uk
Colours: Black & white/black/black
Change colours: All yellow or all red
Midweek fixtures: Tuesday
Prog. Editor: Andrew Molden 01865 433686
E-mail: ac.mold@hotmart.com

CLUB PERSONNEL
Chairman: Richard Lawrence 01865 873258
Press Officer: Paul Dolton 01865 768970
Manager: Darren Henderson
Physio: Paul Dolton

ROSS TOWN

Secretary: Alan Bridges, Re-adel, Willowbrook,Greytree,Ross-On-Wye HR9 7JS.
Tel: 01989 564432 (H) 01594 542421 x 1276 (W)

Ground: Cinderford Town FC, Causeway Ground, Hilldene, Cinderford (01594822039)

Directions: From Gloucester take A40 to Ross-on-Wye, then A48 - Chepstow. In 10miles turn right at Elton garage onto A4151to Cinderford, thru Littledean, up steep hill, right at crossroads, and left into Latimer Rd.(F.C signposted).
Ground 5 mins walkfrom town centre

Capacity: 3,500 Cover: 1,000 Seats: 250 Floodlights: Yes

HONOURS Hereford Lge 94-95, Charity Shield 95-96; Hereford FA Charity Bowl 94-95; Worcester & Dist Lge 95-96, Baylis Cup 95-96; Hereford FA County Chall Cup 97-99 R-up 95-96; 98-99 Pershore Hospital Charity Cup R-up 95-96, Hellenic Lg Cup R-up: 99-00

PREVIOUS **Leagues:** Hereford Lg, Worcester & District League.

RECORD **Attendance:** 147 v Harrow Hill 26/3/97

FACT FILE
Founded:1993
Nickname: Riversiders
Colours: Red /black/black
Change colours:Green/Green/White
Midweek Matchday: Tuesday/Wednesday

CLUB PERSONNEL
Patron: Dave Sexton
Chairman: Geoff Jones
Director of Football and
Press Officer: Chris Parsons (01989 566712)
Manager: Martin Thomas
Coach: Chris Parsons
Physio: Sylvia Durham

SHRIVENHAM

Secretary: Matthew Hampson, 12 Grange Drive, Swindon, Wilts SN3 4LD
Tel: 01793 330983(H) 01793 423033 (B 07748 804593 M
E-mail: brad@currybeast.com

Match Secretary: Robb Forty, 40 Stallpitts, Shrivenham, Swindon, Wilts
Tel: 01793 783309(H) 01793 643744(B)

Ground: The Recreation Ground, Shrivenham SN6 8BJ Tel: 01793 784453

Directions: 'Off Highworth Road, Shrivenham' Village is signposted off A420, six miles east of Swindon, four miles west of Faringdon

Previous League: North Berks League

Record Gate 800 v Aston Villa X1 21st May 2000

Honours North Berks League Champions 00-01

FACT FILE
Founded:
Colours: Blue & white hoops/blue/white.
Change colours: All Red & black
Midweek fixtures: Tuesdays
Programme: Yes
Editor: Dan Prescott (Press Officer)

CLUB PERSONNEL
Chairman: Ian Richardson 01793 782033
Press Officer: Dan Prescott 07989 603948
Manager: Dave Clauson
Coach: Dave Clauson
Physio: P Mansfield

WINTERBOURNE UNITED

Secretary: John Lloyd, 9 Stanford Close, Frampton Cotterell, Bristol. BS36 2DG
Tel: 01454 775841(H) 0117 9552048(B) E-mail john-lloyd@1-nil.co.uk

Ground Parkside Avenue, Winterbourne, Bristol BS36 1LX 01454 850059

Directions Leave Junction 1 of M32 turn left then left again at traffic lights, sign posted Yate. Keep on road for two miles into Winterbourne After Ridings High School turn right into Parkside Avenue, ground on right.

Clubhouse:

Previous League: Gloucester County League

Honours: Gloucester County League Champions 00-01

Record Attendance:

FACT FILE
Formed:
Nickname: The Bourne
Colours: White/red/red
Change colours: Red/white/white or red
Midweek fixtures: Tuesday or Thursday

CLUB PERSONNEL
Chairman: Robyn Maggs
Tel: 01454 887338
Press Officer: as Chairman
Program Editor: John Lloyd 01454 775841
Manager Stewart Jones
Coach: Richard Dunn
Physio: Ken Purnell

WITNEY UNITED

Secretary: Adrian Bircher 13 Colwell Drive Witney Oxon OX28 5NJ
Tel: 01993 200913 (H) 01865 393356 (B) 07779 326074 (M)

Ground: Marriotts Stadium, Downs Road, Witney OX8 5LY
Tel: 01993 702549

Directions: From West: A40 eastbound towards Oxford. At Minster Lovell r'about, take the first exit towards Minster Lovell. After two miles turn right into Downs Road (signposted for Witney Lakes Golf Club), ground half a mile on right.
From Witney town centre: head west down Welch Way, at r'about take 3rd exit into Curbridge Road. At r'about, take 3rd exit into Deer Park Road, at traffic lights turn left into Range Road, at end turn left ground is 400 yards on right.

Capacity: 3,500 Cover: 2,000 Seats: 280 Floodlights: Yes

FACT FILE
Formed 2002
Colours: Gold/black/black
Change: Green/white/green
Midweek matchday: Tuesday
Program Editor: Kieren Bushell
Tel: 07768 071102

CLUB PERSONNEL
Chairman: Philip Webb
Tel: 01993 844666
email: PAWebb01@aol.com
Manager:T.B.A.
Coach/Physio: John Nolan

BADSHOT LEA

Ground: Recreation Ground, Badshot Lea, Farnham, Surrey Tel: 01252 316076
PREVIOUS Leagues: Surrey Intermediate League (West)
RECORDS:
HONOURS:

FACT FILE
Formed
Colours:
Change Colours:
Midweek matchday:
Programme:

CLUB PERSONNEL
Chairman:
Manager:
Physio:

BINFIELD

Secretary: Vernon Bradshaw, 21 Audley Way Ascot Berks SL5 8EE
Tel: 01344 886144 (H); 01344 356651 (B)

Ground: Stubbs Lane Binfield 01344 860822
Directions From A329 Bracknell to Wokingham Road, turn by the Travel Lodge into St. Marks Road, through the village into Terrace Road South & North, then at T junction by All Saints' Church turn right & then left into Stubbs Hill.

Record Gate: 268 v Englefield 2001-02
Previous League: Chiltonian

FACT FILE
Colours: All reded.
Change colours:All Blue
Midweek fixtures: Tuesday
Nickname: Moles
CLUB PERSONNEL
Chairman: Bob Alloway
Press Officer: Glen Duggleby
Programme Editor: Rob Jones
Manager:T.B.A.
Coach: T.B.A.

BISLEY SPORTS

Secretary Michael Clement, 3 Lower Guilford Road, Knaphill, Woking, Surrey, GU21 2EE
Tel: 01483 475003 (H) 01483 736286 (B) E-mail: mclem0@aol.com
Ground: Burghfield Sports Grnd, Church Lane, Bisley GU24 9EB
Tel: 07796 094941

Directions: Exit M3 at Junction 3. Head southbound on A322 towards West End & Bisley. Go over two roundabouts then turn left opposite the Hen & Chicken P. House into Church Lane, ground is about 400 yards on left hand side.

FACT FILE
Colours:Shirts – Blue & black/black/black
Change colours: All red
Midweek fixtures: Tuesday
CLUB PERSONNEL
Chairman: Peter Lucas
email: sales@carfiles.co.uk Tel: 01276 671314
Press Officer: See Secretary
Program Editor: Bruce Henderson
Tel: 01483 472432
Manager: Andy Clement Tel: 01276 24374
Coaches: John Cook & Bruce Henderson

CHALFONT WASPS

Secretary: Bruce Keen, 25 Albion Crescent, Chalfont St Giles, Bucks. HP8 4ET
Tel: 01494 875129 (H) email: bruce.keen@tesco.net

Match Sec/Press Off. & Prog. Editor.: Bob Isherwood 01494 871445 (H)

Ground: Crossleys, Bowstridge Lane, Chalfont. HP8 4QN Tel: 01494 875050

Directions On entering Chalfont St. Giles Village from A413 (Aylesbury - Uxbridge Road), turn left into Bolostridge Lane immediately after the shops. After a quarter of a mile turn right into Crossleys by a small green. Ground is directly ahead through the gates
Record Attendance: 50 v Harrow Hill Rovers 00-01
Previous League: Chiltonian

FACT FILE
Colours: Yellow & black striped/black/black.
Change colours: All Green
Midweek fixtures: Tuesday
Nickname: The Stingers

CLUB PERSONNEL
Chairman: Steven Waddington
Manager: John Franks
Coach: Denis Higgs

CHINNOR

Ground: Station Road, Chinnor, Oxfordshire
PREVIOUS **Leagues**: Oxford Senior league
RECORDS:
HONOURS:

FACT FILE
Formed
Colours:
Change Colours:
Midweek matchday:
Programme:

CLUB PERSONNEL
Chairman:
Manager:
Physio:

DRAYTON WANDERERS

Web Site: http://website.lineone.net/~drayton_wanderers

Secretary: Tom Ash, 28 Stonecroft Ave., Iver, Bucks. SL0 9QF Tel: 01753 654413

Ground: Cowley Hall, Cowley Road Uxbridge 01895 258269

Directions: 1 1/2 miles south of Uxbridge town centre, follow signs to Heathrow Airport, entrance to ground opposite the Grand Union Public House.

Honours:

Record Attendance: 105 v Uxbridge 1995

Previous League: Chiltonian League

FACT FILE

Colours: Black & white stripes/black/black
Change cols: Red & yellow stripes/red/red
Midweek fixtures: Wednesday
Nickname: Wanderers
Program Editor:Mick Turtle 01895 446575

CLUB PERSONNEL

Chairman: Kevin Kelly Tel: 01895 824465
email: kevin.l.kelly@bt.com
Manager: Mick Turtle
Coach: Mick Stafford & Alan Carter

ENGLEFIELD GREEN ROVERS

Secretary Jon West, 74 Lindsay Road, New Haw, Surrey KT15 3BE
Email Address: www.goode @ terry.com

Ground: Coopershill Lane Englefield Green 01784 43566

Directions: Leave M25 at junction 13, A30 by passing Egham, at top of Egham Hill turn right at traffic lights. After passing Village Green on the left take 2nd turning right at the north east of green. Ground on the right after half a mile.

Record Gate: 100 v Eton Wick, 1999

FACT FILE

Colours: All green & white
Change cols.: Red & white halves/white/white
Midweek fixtures: Tuesday
Nickname: The Rovers

CLUB PERSONNEL

Chairman: Terence David Goode
Manager:Gerry Kelly
Coach: Walter Reynolds
Physio, Press Off & Prog Ed: Peter Casey

ETON WICK

Secretary : Barrie Shurville, 21 The Wheat Butts, Eton Wick, Berks., SL4 6JH.
& Press Officer& Programme Editor 01753 862969 (H) 07860262614 (B)

Ground: 01753 852749

Directions: From M4 junction 7 follow A4 to Maidenhead. At first roundabout (Sainsbury's) take B3026 towards Eton Wick. Ground is on the right after theparade of shops. From Eton take B3026 and ground is on the left after the Catholic church.

Honours:

Record Gate 500 v Andover, 1993 FA Vase

Previous Leagues: Chiltonian League

FACT FILE

Nickname: The Wick
Cols:Amber/black/black Change:All white
Midweek fixtures: Tuesday

CLUB PERSONNEL

Chairman: Micky Foulkes 01753 733629
Man/Coach:Rob Curtis 01753 851877
Physio: Bobby White

FINCHAMPSTEAD

Secretary: David Hobbs, 57 Welford Road, Woodley, Berkshire RG5 4QS
Tel : 01189 696195 Web Site: www.finchampsteadfc.co.uk

Match Sec.: Michael Husk, 16 Sadlers Lane, Winnersh, Berks RG41 5AJ
01189 785949 (H)

Press Officer: Stephen King 01189 732890 E-mail: Stephen@kingsb.fsnet.co.uk

Ground: Finchhampstead Memorial Park, The Village, Finchampstead RG114JR
Tel: 01189732890

Directions: A321 from Wokingham, then fork right onto B3016. At the Greyhound pub turn right onto the B3348. The ground is 200 yards on the right.

Record Gate 425 v Sandhurst, 1958/ 9 **Previous League:** Chiltonian

FACT FILE

Formed:
Nickname: Finch
Colours: Sky blue & white/black/black
Change colours: All red
Midweek fixtures: Wednesday

CLUB PERSONNEL

Chairman: Kieron Brown (01344 452007)
E-mail: aquaspec@globalnet.co.uk
Manager: Steven McClurg
Coach : Willie Graham

HOLYPORT

Secretary: Eddie Pearce 1 Australia Ave Maidenhead Berks SL6 7DJ
Tel: 01628 673554 (H) 01628 680680 (B) 01628682700 (F)
E-mail: EddieP@Maidenads.co.uk

Ground: Braywick Sports Centre, Braywick Road, Maidenhead, Berks.
Tel: 01628 627066 Floodlights: No

Directions: From M4 exit at junction 8/9 take Maidenhead Central road, at roundabout take 1st left, follow dual carriageway for 300 yards and turn right into complex, signed Maidenhead Rugby club. In sports park follow road to the end, main pitch is on the left with changing rooms in front of you.

Previous League: East Berks. Lge >2002

FACT FILE

Colours: Claret/green/yellow
Change: Blue/red/red
Midweek matchday: Wednesday

CLUB PERSONNEL

Program Editor: Mark Burton
Tel: 01494 436331
Chairman: Norman House
Tel: 01628 626882
Manager: Mark Burton

HOUNSLOW BOROUGH F.C.

Secretary: Stefano Poulos, 7 Fairways Isleworth Middlesex TW7 4NS
0208 560 9763 (H); 0208 5800591 (B); 0208 560 1295 (F)
07765305003 (M) E-mail hounslowborough.f.c@lineone,net
Program Editor: Lee-John Tansey 07889 342865 E-mail: l.tansey@talk21.com
Ground: White Lodge Syon Lane Isleworth 0208 560 8829
Capacity: ????? Covered Seating: ????? Covered Standing: ???? Floodlights: Yes/No
Directions: From M25 onto M4 at junction 3 then follow signs to Central London. At Gillett Corner turn left into Syon Lane. Ground 100 metres on the left.
From A40 turn at Target Roundabout and follow A312 Hayes by pass to A4 then follow signs to Central London until Gillett Corner, turn left and ground on the left.
Record Gate 200 v Rayners Lane, 3rd Jan. 2000 **Previous Leagues:** Chiltonian League

FACT FILE
Colours: Blue & white quarters/blue/blue
Change cols.: Red & black quarters/red/red
Midweek fixtures: Tuesday
Web site: www.sportworldwide.com

CLUB PERSONNEL
Chairman: James Stefanopoulos
0208 667 1269
Manager:Jamie Rooke (07760213481)
Coach:Antony Yersley Physio: Rehana Iqbal

LETCOMBE

Ground: Bassett Road, Letcombe Regis, Berkshire Tel: 01235 832999
PREVIOUS Leagues:
RECORDS:
HONOURS:

FACT FILE
Formed
Colours:
Change Colours:
Midweek matchday:
Programme:

CLUB PERSONNEL
Chairman:
Manager:
Physio:

MARTIN BAKER SPORTS

Secretary: Michael Hayselden, 53 Leven Way Hayes Middlesex UB3 2SS
Press Off. & Prog. Editor 0208 5732887 (H); 0208 8406992 (B)

Ground: Martins Field Tilehouse Lane Denham 01895 833077
Club Email: mick.hayselden@bt.com

Directions: A412 from the A40 London / Oxford Road. (Do not confuse the A40 with the M40 which runs parallel). The entrance to the ground is approximately 150 yards on the right between the houses.
Previous League: Chiltonian League

FACT FILE
Colours: White & blue/blue/blue
Change colours: Green or gold/green or black/green or black
Midweek fixtures: Tuesday
Nickname: Baker Boys

CLUB PERSONNEL
Chairman: John Curd
Manager: Ray Flegg 0956 980880
Coach & Physio: Ron Wise

MILTON UNITED

Secretary: Sue Walker, 122 High St, Sutton Courtney, Abingdon, OX14 4AX Tel: 01235 847158 (H)
Ground: The Sportsfield,Milton Hill, Potash Lane,Milton Heights,Oxon Tel:01235 832999
Directions: Exit A34 at Milton, 10 miles south of Oxford & 12 miles north of J 13, M4. A4130 towards Wantage, after 100m 1st left, then 1st right into Milton Hill. Entrance 200m on left.
Capacity: Covered Seats: 50 Floodlights: Yes Club Shop: No
Clubhouse: On ground, open matchdays
HONOURS Hellenic Lg 90-91 (Div 1 89-90 R-Up.94-95)), Nth Berks Lg(4) 85-86 87-89(R-up 84-85 86-87, Lg Cup(3) 84-86 88-89, Div 2 80-81, Charity Shield(4) 84-86 87-89 (R-up 82-83), Nth Berks War Mem. Cup(3) 83-85 87-88, Berks & Bucks Intermediate Cup 90-91
RECORD **Attendance:** 500 v Almondsbury Picksons, Hellenic Lg 90-91
Goalscorer: Nigel Mott

FACT FILE
Founded: 1926
Colours: Sky & claret/claret/sky & claret
Change colours: Orange/white/white
Midweek matchday: Tuesday
Programme Editor / Press Officer:
David Taylor (01235 816376)

CLUB PERSONNEL
Chairman: Ken Tull President: John Cannon
Match Secretary: Sid Tindall (01491 835630)
Manager: Paul Biddle
Coach: Nigel Mott Physio: John Belcher

PENN & TYLERS GREEN

Secretary: Malcolm James, Woodlands, Forty Green Rd, Forty Green, Beaconsfield HP9 1XS
Tel: 01494 677311 (H) 0207 777 0602 (B) email: malcolm.d.james@chase.com
Ground: Elm Road, Penn, Bucks HP10 8LF Tel: 01494 815346

Directions: Entrance to ground is off the main Hazlemere to Beaconsfield road. From Beaconsfield follow the road through Penn towards Hazlemere, pass the pond on green & ground entrance is on the right before going downhill.
Record Attendance: 125 v Chalfont Wasps 00-01
Previous League: Chiltonian

FACT FILE
Colours: Blue & white striped/blue/white
Change colours: All yellow
Midweek fixtures: Tuesday
Program Editor: Neil Bellamy 01494 812492

CLUB PERSONNEL
Chairman & Match Secretary:
Robert Dalling 01494 671424
Press Officer: Neil Bellamy
Manager: Richard Mikurenda

PRESTWOOD

Secretary: Paul Mullen, 16 Maybush Gardens, Prestwood, Bucks HP 16 9EA
Tel No: 01494 864048 EMail: paul.mullen @the-fa,org

Ground: Prestwood Sports Centre 01494 865946

Directions: From the Chequers Public House in the Centre of Prestwood, take the road signposted to Great Hampden. The ground is approximately half a mile on the left.

Previous Leagues: Chiltonian League

Record Attendance:

Honours:

FACT FILE

Formed: ????

Colours: Claret / claret

Change colours: orange/ blck/orange

Midweek fixtures: Tuesday

CLUB PERSONNEL

Chairman:

Manager:Steven Simmons 01494 725217

Reserves Manager: A Henney 01494 712544

RAYNERS LANE

Secretary: Tony Pratt, 4 Stirling Close Cowley Uxbridge Middx. UB8 2BA
01895 233853 (H)

Ground: 151 Rayners Lane, Rayners Lane, South Harrow 0208 8669659

Directions: From A40 Polish War Memorial (First junction after Northolt Aerodrome) turn left into A4180 (West End Road), approx. 500m turn right into Station Approach, at lights turn right into Victoria Road Sainsbury's on the right). At next roundabout continue straight on to lights at junction with Alexandra Avenue (Farmers House pub on left). Continue straight on over lights and take 2nd turning on left into Rayners Lane. Ground is approx. half a mile on left.

Record Gate 550 v Wealdstone, 1983 Season 2000/2001: Member of the Hellenic Lg

FACT FILE

Nickname: The Lane

Colours: Yellow/green/yellow

Change colours: White/blue/white

Midweek fixtures: Tuesday

CLUB PERSONNEL

Chairman: Richard Mitchell 020 8422 6340

Press Off/Prog.Ed: Tom Lynn 0208 868 4671

Manager/Coach: Richard Hedge 020 8480843

Physio: Ron Fairhead

WANTAGE TOWN

Secretary: Alan Parker, Little Orchard, Manor Rd, Wantage, OX12 8DW Tel: 01235 763842(H & F)

Ground: Alfredian Park, Manor Road, Wantage, Oxon Tel: 01235 764781

Directions: Take Hungerford Road from Wantage (A338) The ground is signposted on right opposite recreation ground **Capacity**: 1,500 Seats: 50 Cover: 300 Floodlights: Yes

Clubhouse: Mon-Fri 7.30-11pm, Sat noon-2.30, 4-7pm **Club Shop:** No

Programme: 28 pages, 50p Editor: Tony Woodward (01367 241328)

PREVIOUS Leagues: Swindon & Dist. 1901-12 30-35 47-56; N Berks 12-22 38-40 46-47; Reading & D. 22-30 35-38

RECORD Attendance: 500 v Newport AFC 89

HONOURS Hellenic R-up 81-82, Div 1 80-81 R-up 69-70 87-88 91-92 95-96, Div1 Cup R-up 91-92; Oxon Snr Cup 82-83; Berks & Bucks Intermediate Cup 54-55; Swindon & Dist. x4

FACT FILE

Founded: 1892

Nickname: Alfredians

Colours: Green &white/white/white

Change Colours: Blue& white/black/black

Midweek Matchday:Tuesday

CLUB PERSONNEL

Chairman: Tony Woodward

President: John Hutchings

Match Sec.: Colin Blunsden 01235 768605 (H)

1st Team Manager: Stuart Peace

Coach: Terry Delaney Physio: Ian Howard

CARTERTON TOWN
CT
FC
FOOTBALL CLUB
WATSON
WATSON PETROLEUM
Brackley Town
Football Club
Brackley Town v Carterton Town
Cherry Red Records Hellenic League
Division
DIDCOT TOWN
Football Club
OFFICIAL MATCHDAY PROGRAMME
Saturday 17th August 2002
DIDCOT TOWN F.C.
versus
TUFFLEY ROVERS
Hellenic Prem League
Kick-off 3.00pm
CHERRY
ASDA
Hellenic Football League
Premier Division
2002/2003
SOUTHALL TOWN
F.C.
Hellenic League
Premier Division
Southall Town vs Shortwood United
Saturday 29th March 2003
Kick Off: 3 pm
Season 2002 / 2003
INVESCO
PERPETUAL
HENLEY TOWN
FOOTBALL CLUB
Members of the:
Oxfordshire Football Association
Hellenic Football League
Allied Counties Youth Football League
Reading & District Sunday Football League
Official Programme

GO TRAVEL
KENT LEAGUE

FEEDER TO: DR MARTENS LEAGUE

President: D D Baker **Chairman:** P C Wager **Vice Chairman:** D Richmond
Hon. Secretary & Treasurer: A R Vinter, Bakery House, The Street, Chilham, Nr Canterbury, Kent CT4 8BX Tel: 01227 730457 Fax: 01227 738880

PREMIER DIVISION FINAL LEAGUE TABLE 2002-03

		P	W	D	L	F	A	Pts
1	Cray Wanderers*	29	19	5	5	68	23	62
2	Maidstone United	30	18	9	3	76	31	63
3	Thamesmead Town	30	19	6	5	76	39	63
4	Deal Town*	28	15	9	4	62	40	54
5	Ramsgate	30	16	7	7	57	35	55
6	Whitstable Town*	30	15	8	6	56	45	53
7	VCD Athletic	30	13	9	8	51	36	48
8	Hythe Town	30	13	6	11	46	54	45
9	Slade Green*	29	10	5	14	57	54	35
10	Herne Bay	30	9	7	14	53	54	34
11	Beckenham Town*	29	9	6	14	41	53	33
12	Tunbridge Wells*	29	7	8	14	53	66	29
13	Lordswood	30	5	9	16	37	66	24
14	Greenwich Borough	30	5	5	20	36	72	20
15	Erith Town*	30	4	6	19	36	71	18
16	Faversham Town	22	2	1	19	18	88	7

**Finishing position determined by points per game average following resignation of Faversham.*

		1	2	3	4	5	6	7	8	9	10	11	12	13	14	15	16
1	Beckenham Town		0-2	2-2	3-0	2-1	3-1	1-3	6-0	4-0	0-4	1-1	2-0	1-4	3-0	1-4	2-1
2	Cray Wanderers	3-0		1-1	5-0	8-0	0-1	5-3	2-2	2-0	2-1	4-2	2-0	1-2	5-1	3-0	7-0
3	Deal Town	1-1	2-1		5-2	N.r	2-1	2-1	2-0	7-1	2-2	4-3	3-0	1-3	7-2	1-1	2-1
4	Erith Town	1-1	0-0	0-1		N.r	2-1	2-3	1-1	1-2	2-4	1-1	0-3	2-5	1-5	1-4	2-2
5	Faversham Town	N.r	N.r	N.r	1-5		1-0	0-6	2-3	0-2	1-5	0-1	N.r	0-4	2-6	0-1	N.r
6	Greenwich Borough	1-0	0-2	1-1	2-1	3-1		4-2	3-4	0-0	0-5	2-3	0-4	0-3	3-3	0-1	2-4
7	Herne Bay	1-2	0-1	1-3	0-1	6-1	3-1		3-3	1-1	1-4	0-0	3-1	2-1	3-1	1-3	1-1
8	Hythe Town	2-0	0-1	1-3	1-0	3-0	3-1	2-1		3-1	0-3	0-2	3-2	2-3	3-1	1-1	0-2
9	Lordswood	1-1	1-3	6-3	3-4	0-1	2-2	1-0	2-1		1-2	0-1	0-4	1-3	1-1	1-1	2-3
10	Maidstone United	5-2	2-1	1-2	2-0	8-1	1-0	1-1	1-1	1-1		2-1	4-2	2-0	0-0	0-0	4-0
11	Ramsgate	2-0	1-1	0-0	3-1	8-1	4-3	4-1	3-0	2-1	0-0		1-0	2-2	3-1	0-2	0-2
12	Slade Green	3-2	0-2	1-2	2-0	4-2	3-1	1-1	1-1	2-2	2-2	0-4		2-3	5-1	2-2	1-2
13	Thamesmead Town	5-0	0-1	2-2	4-3	8-0	1-0	2-0	1-2	2-1	2-2	4-3	3-2		0-2	1-1	1-1
14	Tunbridge Wells	3-0	0-1	3-0	5-2	N.r	1-1	2-2	1-2	2-2	1-4	1-0	1-3	2-4		1-2	3-3
15	VCD Athletic	1-1	3-1	1-1	1-0	1-1	6-1	2-1	1-2	7-0	1-2	0-2	0-4	0-2	3-2		1-2
16	Whitstable Town	1-0	1-1	1-0	1-1	4-2	4-1	1-2	4-0	2-1	4-2	1-2	5-3	1-1	1-1	1-0	

N.r - No result, matches not played.

MANAGER OF THE MONTH AWARDS 2002-03

Aug Jim Ward (Maidstone United)
Sept Simon Bryant (Deal Town)
Oct Jason Bragg (Whitstable Tn)
Nov Simon Bryant (Deal Town)
Dec Barry Zillwood (Lordswood)
Jan Jim Ward (Maidstone United)
Feb Ian Jekins (Cray Wanderers)
Mar Ian Jekins (Cray Wanderers)
Apr Ian Jekins (Cray Wanderers)

GOLDEN BOOT AWARD 2002-03

28 Steve Jones (Deal Town)
22 Mo Takaloo (Ramsgate)
21 Richard Sinden (Maidstone United)
21 Dean Bowey (Slade Green)

DIVISION ONE FINAL LEAGUE TABLES 2002-03

DIVISION ONE NORTH		P	W	D	L	F	A	Pts
1	Cray Wanderers Reserves	22	18	2	2	68	18	56
2	Thamesmead Town Reserves	21	16	1	5	65	34	49
3	Danson Furness	22	12	4	6	52	39	40
4	Corinthian	22	11	3	8	44	40	36
5	Erith Town Reserves	21	10	4	8	33	39	34
6	Dartford Reserves (-3)	22	10	4	8	30	26	31
7	Chatham Town Reserves	22	8	6	8	47	38	30
8	Beckenham Reserves	22	7	3	12	40	59	24
9	Tunbridge Wells Reserves	22	7	3	12	34	56	24
10	Lordswood Reserves	22	4	6	12	27	44	18
11	VCD Athletic Reserves	22	5	2	15	44	58	17
12	Erith & Belvedere Reserves (+3)	22	3	4	15	29	62	16

Thamesmead v Erith Town was not played. Match declared as a draw.

DIVISION ONE SOUTH		P	W	D	L	F	A	Pts
1	Deal Town Reserves	22	13	7	2	55	25	46
2	Dover Athletic Reserves	22	12	6	4	69	35	42
3	Herne Bay Reserves	22	11	8	3	47	26	41
4	Ashford Town Reserves	22	12	3	7	43	26	39
5	Ramsgate Reserves	22	11	2	9	41	42	35
6	Hastings United Reserves	22	9	5	8	40	27	32
7	Sittingbourne Reserves (-3)	22	9	2	11	45	69	26
8	Folkestone Invicta Reserves	22	7	4	11	49	52	25
9	Maidstone United Reserves	22	6	7	9	38	43	25
10	Whitstable Reserves (+3)	22	5	5	12	35	46	23
11	Margate Reserves	22	5	7	10	29	46	22
12	Hythe Town Reserves	22	3	2	17	25	79	11

DIVISION ONE CHAMPIONSHIP PLAY-OFF

Deal Town Reserves 3-2 Cray Wanderers Reserves (aet)

GOLDEN BOOT AWARD 2002-03

33 Lewis Wood (Cray Wanderers Res.)
31 John Main (Danson Furness)
25 Stephen Wright (Beckenham Tn Res.)
24 Paul Vines (Cray Wanderers Res.)

DIVISION ONE FLOODLIGHT TROPHY TABLE 2002-03

		P	W	D	L	F	A	Pts
1	Chatham Town Reserves (-1)	16	10	4	2	37	18	33
2	Hastings United Reserves	16	8	4	4	32	21	28
3	Deal Town Reserves	16	8	3	5	38	30	27
4	Maidstone United Reserves (-3)	16	8	3	5	33	24	24
5	Ramsgate Reserves	16	7	2	7	22	27	23
6	Ashford Town Reserves (+2)	16	5	5	6	34	27	22
7	Herne Bay Reserves	16	5	6	5	27	26	21
8	Hythe Town Reserves	16	5	3	8	19	32	18
9	Lordswood Reserves (+3)	16	1	0	15	17	54	6

PREMIER DIVISION CUP 2002-03

FIRST ROUND

Tunbridge Wells	v	Hythe Town	3-0
Faversham Town	v	Maidstone United	2-5
Deal Town	v	Greenwich Borough	3-1
VCD Athletic	v	Ramsgate	3-2
Beckenham Town	v	Herne Bay	1-2
Cray Wanderers	v	Thamesmead Town	2-1
Lordswood	v	Slade Green	0-3
Erith Town	v	Whitstable Town	1-0

SECOND ROUND

Tunbridge Wells	v	Herne Bay	3-2
Deal Town	v	Slade Green	3-2
Maidstone United	v	Cray Wanderers	0-2
VCD Athletic	v	Erith Town	2-0

SEMI-FINALS (Two Legs)

Tunbridge Wells	v	Cray Wanderers	0-2, 1-3
Deal Town	v	VCD Athletic	0-1, 0-3

FINAL

Cray Wanderers	v	VCD Athletic	2-0

DIVISION ONE CUP 2002-03

FIRST ROUND (Two Legs)

Whitstable Town	v	Herne Bay	0-2, 0-4
Tunbridge Wells	v	Ramsgate (w/o for Tunbridge)	
Cray Wanderers	v	Folkstone Invicta	4-1, 6-2
Dartford	v	Margate	2-1, 3-1
Thamesmead Town	v	Danson Furness	3-4, 4-4
VCD Athletic	v	Deal Town	0-2, 1-2
Corinthian	v	Chatham Town	2-1, 1-2
Erith & Belvedere	v	Dover Athletic	1-8, 1-1

SECOND ROUND (Two Legs)

Herne Bay	v	Sittingbourne	1-3, 1-2
Erith Town	v	Tunbridge W	2-2, 2-2, 4-2p
Corinthian	v	Hastings Town	1-2, 1-1
Dover Athletic	v	Ashford Town	1-0, 4-1
Maidstone United	v	Danson Furness	3-0, 2-3
Deal Town	v	Cray Wanderers	2-2, 3-7
Hythe Town	v	Dartford	1-3, 0-3
Lordswood	v	Beckenham Tn	0-0, 1-3

THIRD ROUND

Sittingbourne	v	Maidstone United	2-2, 4-3p
Hastings Town	v	Dartford	1-3
Erith Town	v	Cray Wanderers	1-3
Dover Athletic	v	Beckenham Town	2-1

SEMI-FINALS (Two Legs)

Sittingbourne	v	Cray Wanderers	0-4, 1-5
Dartford	v	Dover Athletic	0-4, 0-1

FINAL

Cray Wanderers	v	Dover Athletic	3-2

GOALS OF THE MONTH

	Premier Division	First Division
September	Maidstone United	Chatham Town Reserves
October	Herne Bay	Deal Town Reserves
November	Cray Wanderers Ramsgate	Cray Wanderers Reserves Hastings United Reserves
December	Cray Wanderers Maidstone United	Tunbridge Wells Reserves
January	Lordswood	Cray Wanderers
February	Maidstone United Ramsgate Thamesmead Town	Cray Wanderers Reserves Danson Furness Maidstone United Reserves
March	Thamesmead Town	Thamesmead Town Reserves
April	Beckenham Town	Corinthian

FAIR PLAY AWARD (sponsored by Ladbrokes)

Premier Division	Division One
VCD Athletic	Dartford

BECKENHAM TOWN

Secretary: Peter Palmer,36 Inglewood,Pixton Way, Selsdon, Surrey CR0 9LP
Tel: 020 86513363 Mobile 07774 728758
Website: www.beckenhamtownfc.co.uk
Ground: Eden Park Avenue, Beckenham, Kent Tel: 07774 728758
Directions: M25, A21 to Bromley then follow signs to Beckenham.
Ground 1 mile west of town off A214.
2 mins walk from Eden Park (BR) station - trains from London Bridge. Bus 264
Capacity: 4,000 Seats: 120 Cover: 120 Floodlights: Yes
Clubhouse: All day opening at weekends.
Hot & cold food, teas, etc. Bar & dance area.
Club Shop: Yes

HONOURS London Spartan Lg Cup R-up 77-78 78-79, Kent Snr Tphy R-up 81-82 93-94, Kent Lg Cup R-up 84-85 92-93 (Div 2 Cup R-up 90-91)

PREVIOUS **Leagues:** S. E. London Amtr 71-73; Metropolitan 73-75; London Spartan 75-82
Ground: Stanhope Grove, Beckenham (60 yrs)

RECORD **Gate:** 720 v Berkhamstead F.A.Cup 94-95
Scorer: Ricky Bennett **Appearances:** Lee Fabian 985

FACT FILE
Reformed: 1971
Nickname: Reds
Colours:All Red
Change Colours:Yellow/blue/blue
Midweek matchday: Tuesday
Programme: 16 pages, 31.00
Editor:Secretary

CLUB PERSONNEL
Chairman: John Weatherhead
Vice Chairman: B Hollaway
Manager: Kevin Sugrue
Asst Manager: Jason Taylor
2002-03
Leading Goalscorer: Jason Claws
Captain:Matthew Belton
Player of the Year:David Weatherhead

CRAY WANDERERS

Secretary: Dave Brown,16 Westhurst road, Chislehurst, Kent BR7 6HT (020 8467 2128)
Ground: Bromley F.C. Hayes Lane, Bromley, Kent BR2 9EF (0181 460 5291 or 0181 313 3992)
Websites: http://hometown.aq.com\cray or wanderersfc/club.html
Directions: One mile from Bromley South (BR). Buses 316, 146 and 119 passground. Junction 4 off M25, then A21 towards London
Capacity: 5,000 Cover: 2,500 Seats: 1,300 Floodlights: Yes
Clubhouse: Open pub hours (freehouse). Hot & cold food available **Club Shop:** Yes

HONOURS London Lg(2) 56-58 (Lg Cup 54-55), Aetolian Lg 62-63 (Lg Cup 63-64), GtrLondon Lg 65-66 (Lg Cup(2) 64-66), Metropolitan Lg Cup 70-71 (Amtr Cup(2) 66-68), London Spartan Lg(2) 76-78, Kent Lg 01-02 80-81 02-03 (R-up 79-80 90-91, Lg Cup 83-84 02-03, Kent Snr Tphy 92-93, Kent Amtr Cup(4) 30-31 62-65

PREVIOUS **Leagues:** Kent 1894-1903 6-7 9-14 34-38; W Kent 03-06 07-09; London 20-34 51-59; Kent Amtr 38-39 46-51; S London All 43-46; Aetolian 59-64; GtrLondon 64-66; Metropolitan 66-71; London Metropolitan 71-75; London Spartan 75-78
Grounds: Star Lane; Tothills; Twysden; Fordcroft; Grassmeade, St Mary Cray

CLUB RECORDS **Gate:** 1,523 v Stamford, F.A. Vase QF 79-80
Goalscorer: Ken Collishaw, 272 **Appearances:** John Dorey c500, 61-72
Win: 15-0 v Sevenoaks, 1894-95 **Defeat:** 1-11 v Bromley, 20-21

FACT FILE
Founded: 1860
Nickname: Wands
Sponsors: Hillman Grant
Colours: Amber & black
Change Colours: White/black/black
Midweek matchday: Wednesday
Programme: 32 pages, 50p
Editor/Press Officer: Greg Mann
Tel: 0181 318 9604(H) 0171 500 4496B)

CLUB PERSONNEL
Chairman: Gary Hillman
President: Bill Faulkner
Team Manager: Ian jenkins
Asst.Manager: John Allwright
Reserve Team Manager: Sam Wright

2002-03
Leading Goalscorer:
Captain:
Player of the Year:

DEAL TOWN

Secretary: Colin Adams,156 Mill Hill, Deal, Kent CT149JA (01304 372784)

Ground: Charles Sports Ground, St Leonards Road, Deal, Kent Tel: 01304 375623
Directions: A258 through Walmer, left into Cornwall Road, continue intoHamilton Road, veer left into Mill Rd, follow round to right into Manor Road, right into St Leonards Road, ground 100 yards on right. 1 mile from both Walmerand Deal BR stations. Local buses stop near ground
Capacity: 2500 Seats: 180 Cover: 180 Floodlights: Yes
Clubhouse: Matchdays & functions. Bar. Tea bar with hot & cold food Club Shop: Yes

HONOURS F.A.Vase Winners 99-00, Kent Lg 53-54,99-00 (R-up 88-89,98-99) Lg Cup 57-58, 81-82 , 98-99 (R-up 94-95), Kent Snr Tphy 94-95 , 99-00 R-up 82-83 90-91, Gtr London Lg Cup 67-68, Aetolian Lg R-up 59-60

PREVIOUS **Leagues:** Kent 09-59; Aetolian 59-63; Southern 63-66; Gtr London 66-71

RECORDS **Gate:**(Competitive) 2,495 v Newcastle Town F.A.Vase, S-Final 2nd Leg. 26.3.00
Scorer: Joe Brayne 175
Appearances: Alan Barrow 544 (recent times)

Player progressing: Danny Wallace (Southampton)
2002-03
Leading Goalscorer:Steve Jones 36 Captain: Ian Hayes

FACT FILE
Founded:1908
Nickname: Town
Sponsors: Adamson Motors
Colours: Black & white hoops/white/white
Change: Yellow & Blue halves/blue/blue
Midweek matchday: Tuesday
Reserves' Lge: Go Travel Kent Div 1
Programme: 36/40 pages, £1.00
Editor: Colin Adams (01304 372784)

CLUB PERSONNEL
Chairman: David Saunders
Vice-Chairman: Bob Chivington
Fixture Sec: Colin Adams (01304 372784)
Manager:Derek Hares
Asst. Man.Andy Bigginton
Physio:Brenton Duke

Beckenham Town FC

Deal Town FC

Back Row (L-R)
Daryl Bartholomew
Andy Bowyer
Matt Goodban
Jason Hughes
Carl Rook
Marc Sutton-Foster

Front Row (L-R)
Darren Hover
Martin James
Ian Hayes
Steve Jones
Jamie Marriott
Steve Smith

Photo: Alan Coomes.

Erith Town FC. Photo: Alan Coomes

ERITH TOWN

Secretary: Jim Davie, 6 Dashwood Close, Broomfield Road, Bexleyheath, Kent. DA6 7NU
Tel: 020 8306 7068

Ground: Erith Sports Stadium, Avenue Road, Erith, Kent DA8 3AJ (01322 350 271)
Directions: Off the A206 at Erith, into Victoria Road, then left at T junction into Avenue Road. First right along driveway which leads to leisure car park, stadium on left.600 yards from Erith BR.
Capacity: 1,450 Seats: 1,006 Cover: 60Floodlights: Yes (156 lux)
Clubhouse: Use Leisure Facilities Shop: No

PREVIOUS **Leagues:** London Metropolitan Sunday 1959-91, London-Spartan 1991-96
Names: Woolwich Town 1959-89 and 1990-97 Woolwich Heathway 1989-90

CLUB RECORDS Appearances: Alan Hanlon 192 (8)
Victory: 7-2 v Canterbury City, Kent Sen. Trophy 20.12.00 **Defeat:** 0-8 v Deal
Goalscorer: Ben Hackett 42 **Goals in Season:** Dean Bowey 18 00-01
Attendance: 325 v Charlton 11.08.01Athletic x1 (Friendly)

HONOURS: Met Sunday Lge: Senior Section 1966, 1971, 1975.
London Spartan Lge: Intermediate Cup R-up 1994 & 1995. Div 1 R-up: 1995.
London F.A. Intermediate Cup R-up 1995. London F.A. Senior Cup R-up 2000

FACT FILE
Founded: 1959
Nickname: The Dockers
Colours: Red& blackstripes/black/black
Change Colours: White/red/red
Midweek matchday: Monday
Reserve League: Kent League(Go Travel) Div 1
Programme: 40-52 pages £1.00 (Ian Birrell)

CLUB PERSONNEL
Chairman: Albert Putnam
Vice Chairman: Phil Legg
President: Cyril Rebak
General Manager: Ian Birrell
Press Secretary: Matthew Panting

Manager: Fabio Rossis
Coach: Lloyd Bradley

2002-03
Leading Goalscorer: Ben Hackett 10
Captain: Alan Hanlon
Player of the Year: Prul Votier

GREENWICH BOROUGH

Secretary: Sheila Crowhurst (Letters c/o club)
Tel Nos: 0207 3543509 07970 986537M
Ground: Harrow Meadow, Eltham Green Rd, Eltham, London SE9 Tel: 0208 8595788

Directions: South Circular (A205) to McDonalds, grd opposite.
1 mile from both Eltham and Kidbrooke BR stations
Capacity: 2,500 Seats: 5o Cover: 50Floodlights: Yes
Clubhouse: Yes

HONOURS London Spartan Lg 79-80 (Lg Cup 82-83), Kent Lg 86-87 87-88 (Lg Cup 84-85 86-87), Kent Snr Tphy 84-85, FA Vase 5th Rd 89-90

PREVIOUS **Leagues:** South London Alliance; Kent Amateur; London Spartan 77-84
Ground: Erith & Belvedere F.C. 1992-93
Name: London Borough of Greenwich

RECORD **Gate:** 2,000 v Charlton, floodlight opening, 1978
Defeat : 0-8 v Faversham Town, August 1989

FACT FILE
Founded: 1928
Nickname: Boro
Colours: All Red
Change Colours: All white
Midweek matchday: Tuesday
Programme: 16 pages, 50p
Editor: Keith Harmer
Tel: 07930 618911 (M)

CLUB PERSONNEL
Chairman: T. Hassan

Manager: L. Hussein
Asst Manager: K. Crowhurst

2002-03
Leading Goalscorer:
Captain:
Player of the Year:

HERNE BAY

Secretary: Simon Harris 72 Station Road, Herne Bay, Kent CT6 5QH
Email: roland@hernebay,co.uk

Ground: Winch's Field, Stanley Gardens, Herne Bay, Kent Tel: 01227 374156

Directions: Leave new Thanet Way at Herne Bay/Canterbury exit. Follow signs toHerne Bay via Canterbury Road. After railway bridge (1/2 mile), take first left into SpencerRoad, then first left into Stanley Gardens, Ground on left **Clubhouse:** Open matchdays **Club Shop:** Yes
Capacity: 4,000 Seats: 200 Cover: 1,500 Floodlights: Yes

HONOURS Kent Lg 91-92 94-95 96-97 97-98, (R-up 92-93 00-01), Div 2 62-63 63-64, R-up92-93(res) 94-95(res), Lg Cup 96-97, R-up 78-79 97-98, Div 2 Cup 53-54; Kent Snr Tphy 78-79, 96-97; Kent Amtr Cup 57-58 (R-up 58-59 63-64 68-69 72-73); Aetolian LgDiv 2 62-63 63-64 (Lg Cup R-up 62-63), Div 2 Cup 62-63 63-64; Athenian Lg Div 2 70-71 (Lg Cup 66-67); Kent Amtr Lg Cup 53-54 54-55; Thames & Medway Comb. CupR-up 61-62; FA Cup 4th Qual. Rd 70-71 86-87.

PREVIOUS **Leagues:** East Kent, Faversham & Dist, Canterbury & Dist, Kent Amateur, Kent 53-59, Aetolian 59-64, Athenian 64-74 **Ground:** Memorial Park 1886-1953

RECORDS **Attendance:** 2,303 v Margate, FA Cup 4th Qual. Rd 70-71
Win: 19-3 v Hythe 1900
Defeat: 0-11 v RAF Manston, Kent Amateur Lge 1935
Fee received: £3,000 for Mark Munday (Gravesend) 1994

FACT FILE
Founded: 1886Nickname: The Bay
Colours: Blue & white halves
Change Colours: Red & black halves
Midweek matchday: Tuesday
Reserves' League: Kent Lge Div One
Programme: 36 pages, 70p
Editor/Press Off.: Doug Smith (01227742182)
Website: www.hernebayfc.co.uk

CLUB PERSONNEL
Chairman: J Bathurst
Vice Chairman: W Dordoy
President: T.B.A.
Manager: Nick Denly
Asst. Manager: Gerry Allen
Physio: H.Roberts

2002-03
Leading Goalscorer:
Captain:
Player of the Year:

Maidstone United's Richard Sinden completes the 4-2 win over Erith Town with this penalty. Photo: Francis Short.

Maidstone's Jamie Kempster gets in a diving header against Herne Bay.

Herne Bay FC
Back Row (L-R)
Dave Bathgate
Scott Appleton
Martin Collins
Jon Warden
Stephen Lloyd
Nigel Floyd
Front Row (L-R)
Julian Beal
Andy Thompson
Lee Jones
Robbie Summers
Gavin Theze
Photos: Alan Coomes

HYTHE TOWN (2001)

Secretary: Martin R Giles, 21 Wych Elm Way, Hythe, Kent. CT21 6QE
Tel: 01303 265962 (H) 01303 267619 (B)
Email Address: infohythetownfc.co.uk

Ground: Reachfields Stadium, Fort Rd, Hythe, Kent. Tel: 01303 264932 or 238256

Directions: On A259 west out of Hythe, turn left after light railway lights (Fort Road), entrance at end
Capacity: 3,000 Seats: 400 Cover: 2,400 Floodlights: Yes

Clubhouse: Bar open weekends/matchdays & training nights
Club Shop: No

HONOURS None as Hythe United or Hythe Town (2001)

PREVIOUS **Leagues**: Kent County and Southern
Names: Hythe Town and Hythe Town 1988 Ltd
BEST SEASON **FA Vase:** Semi-Final 89-90 **FA Cup:** ???
RECORD **Attendance**: 2,147 v Yeading 1990 F.A.Vase Semi-Final

FACT FILE
Founded: 1992
Sponsors:Saga Group,Portex and Sotirio's Restaurant
Colours: All Red
Change Colours:Blue & White
Midweek Matchday: Tuesday
Programme: 60p
Website: www.huthetownfc.co.uk
Editor: Martin Whybrow

CLUB PERSONNEL
Chairman: Paul Markland
President: Rt Hon Michael Howard QC
Press Officer: Richard Giles
Manager: Paul Fisk
Physio: Dave Garlinge

2002-03
Leading Goalscorer:Mark Roberston
Captain:Gary MillerP.o.Y.: Nick Day

LORDSWOOD

Secretary: Steve Lewis, Sunnybrook, Gorsewood Road, Hartley, Longfield, Kent DA3 7DF
Tel: 01474 708233 (H) 01233 822300 (B) 07775 541573 (M)
Email: s.lewis@claas.com

Ground: Lordswood Sports & Social Club Tel: 01634 669138
North Dane Way, Walderslade, Chatham, Kent ME5 9XX
Website: www.lordswoodfc.co.uk

Capacity: 600 Seats: 125 Cover: No Floodlights: Yes

Clubhouse: Yes
Club Shop: No

HONOURS None

PREVIOUS **Leagues:** Kent County Lge 68-

RECORD **Attendance:** 650
Biggest Win: **Biggest Defeat:**

BEST SEASON **FA Vase: FA Cup:**

FACT FILE
Founded: 1968
Nickname: Lords
Colours: Orange/black/black
Change Colours: Maroon
Midweek Matchday: Tuesday/Thursday
Reserve or Youth League: Both
Programme: Yes Editor: T.B.A.

CLUB PERSONNEL
Chairman: J. O'Halloran
Vice Chairman: T.B.A.
Press Officer: T.B.A.
Manager: B.Zillwood
Asst. Man. / Coach:

2002-03
Leading Goalscorer:
Captain:
Player of the Year:

MAIDSTONE UNITED

Secretary: Adrian Hubbard
Ground: Ground share with Sittingbourne FC - Bourne Park Eurolink Industrial Park, Church Road, Sittingbourne ME10 3SB Tel: 01795 435077
Website: www.maidstoneunited.co.uk Hotline 09068 800691
Directions: Through Sittingbourne on main A2, club signposted clearly and regularly from both east and west. 1 mile from Sittingbourne BR station.
Capacity: 8,000 Cover: 3,300 Seats: 2,000 Floodlights: 420 lux
HONOURS Kent Lg 01-02 R-up 02-03 Kent Lg Cup 02 Kent LG Shield 02
Kent Sen Trophy 03 Kentb Junior Cup 95Kent Co Lg Div 1 99,Div2 95 Div4 94 West kent Challenge Shield 94,99 R-up 95 Tunbridge Wells Charity Cup 94 Weald of Kent Cup 00,01
\PREVIOUS **Names:** Maidstone Invicta **Grounds:** London Rd 92-01 Central Park 01-02 **Leagues:** Kent County League 93-01
BEST SEASON **FA Vase:** 2nd Rd 01-02 0-3 v Mildenhall
FA Cup: 2nd Q Rd 02-03 v Boreham Wood
RECORDS **Attendance:** 1,589 v Gillingham (friendly) 12.03.02 937 v Boreham Wood F.A.Cup 29.09.02 **Victory**: 12-1 v Aylesford K Co Lg Div 1 26.03.94 **Defeat:** 2-8 v Scott Sports Kent Co Lg Div 1 24.0296

FACT FILE
Founded: 1966 Nickname: The Stones
Reformed 1992
Sponsors: joebec.com
Colours: Amber/black/gold
Change Colours: All white
Midweek matchday: Tuesday
Programme: Yes Editor Ian Tucker
Editor: Steve Hemsley Tel: 01892 514006

CLUB PERSONNEL
Chairman: Paul Bowden-Brown
Vice Chairman:Richard Bowden-Brown
Life President:George Gray
Manager:Jim WardCoach:Mal Watkins
Physio:Simon Kavanagh
2002-2003 Capt: Paul Foley
P.o.Y.: Neil Davey
Top Scorer: Richard Sinden 26

Lordswood FC
Back Row (L-R): Shaun Friend, Ben chell, Paul Piggott, Sam Colyer, Dean Woodland, Jason Lillis.
Front Row (L-R): Glen Barlow, Grant Gallagher, Steve Weeks, Gary Burrows, Steve Clements, Ian Docker.
Photo: Alan Coomes.

Maidstone United - Kent League Runners-up
Front Row (L-R): Jim Ward (Manager), Ian Court, Steve Coatham, Adam Morrish, Kevin Hudson, Nick Davis, Paul Foley, Danny Ward (Assistant Manager.
Back Row (L-R): Aaron Lacey, Paul Ribbens, Jamie Kempster, Steve Hogg, Neil Davy.
Photo: Alan Coomes.

RAMSGATE

Secretary: Martin Able, 1 Parkside Villas,Tivoli Rd., Margate, Kent CT9 5PZ (01843 290272)
Ground: Southwood Stadium, Prices Avenue, Ramsgate, Kent Tel: 01843 591662

Directions: From London on A229, A253 into Ramsgate - left into Netherhill atr'bout, right into Ashburnham Rd, right into Southwood Rd. 15 mins walk from Ramsgate BR station; walk thru Warre Recreation Ground, along St Lawrence HighStr., left at `St Lawrence Tavern', follow Southwood Rd and turn right into PricesAvenue

Capacity: 5,000 Seats: 400 Cover: 600 Floodlights: Yes

Clubhouse: Open matchdays & private functions. Two bars, two pool tables,darts. Hot & cold food on matchdays Club Shop: Yes (First team home matches)

HONOURS Kent Lg 49-50 55-56 56-57 98-99(Lg Cup 48-49 92-93 93-94 94-95 00-01) Kent I'mediate Cup 54-55, Kent Snr Cup 63-64, Thames & Medway Cup 60-61, KentSnr Shield 60-61, Kent Floodlit Tphy 69-70, Kent Snr Tphy(3) 87-89 98-99 Kent Lg Charity Shield 97-98

PREVIOUS **Leagues:** Southern 59-75
Name: Ramsgate Athletic

RECORDS **Gate:** 5,200 v Margate, 56-57
Scorer: Mick Williamson
Win:11-0(H) & 12-1 (A) v Canterbury City, Kent League 2000-01

FACT FILE
Founded: 19469 (1898 as Ramsgate Town)
Nickname: Rams
Sponsors: Thanet Waste
Colours: Red & white stripes/red/red
Change Colours: Green/green/yellow
Midweek matchday: Tuesday
Reserves' League: Kent Lge Div. One
Programme: 28 pages
Editor: Steve Redford (01843 596138)

CLUB PERSONNEL
Chairman: Richard Lawson
Vice Chairman: Paul Jefcoate
President: Tom Pendry
Commercial Manager: Martin Power
Tel: 01843 597703
Manager: Peter Hook Asst Man: Lee Bosham
Physio: Gallvic Walker
2002-03 Capt: Paul Downey
Po.yY:Danny Twyman
Top Scorer: Mo Takaloobighashi

SEVENOAKS TOWN

Secretary: Edwin Diplock, 23 Holly Bush Lane, Sevenoaks, Kent TN13 3TH
Tel: 01732 454280

Ground: Greatness Park, Seal Road, Sevenoaks Tel: 01732 741987
Directions:

Capacity: Seats: Cover: Floodlights: Yes/No
Clubhouse: **Club Shop:**

PREVIOUS **Leagues:** Kent County Lge >2003

CLUB RECORDS

HONOURS:

FACT FILE
Founded: 1883
Colours:
Azure & black stripes/black/black
Change colours:
Navy & scarlet quarters/navy/navy

CLUB PERSONNEL

2002-03

Thamesmead FC.
Back Row (L-R): Paul Sringett, Dean Kearley, Wayne Barrett, Chris Tuley, Peter Deadman, Dean Burns.
Front Row (L-R): Aran Heyrettin, Mark Simmons, Marc Merridan, Steve Northwood, Barry Stewart.
Photo: Alan Coomes.

SLADE GREEN

Secretary: Bruce Smith, 15 Gumping Rd, Orpington, Kent BR5 1RX Tel: 01689 858782

Ground: The Small Glen, Moat Lane, Slade Green, Erith, Kent Tel: 01322 351077

Directions: Off A206 between Erith & Dartford.
400 yards from Slade Green BR station. Buses 89 & B13

Capacity: 3,000 Seats: 150 Cover: 400 Floodlights: Yes

Clubhouse: Yes; Hall, Directors Lounge & Canteen Club Shop: No

HONOURS Kent Snr Tphy 91-92 (R-up 80-81); Kent Lg Cup 82-83; Kent Amtr Lg 52-53 53-54 60-61 (Lg Cup 60-61); Kent Intermediate Cup 61-62; Kent Benevolent Cup46-47; West Kent 60-61 65-66; Dartford Lg R-up 48-49 (Lg Cup 47-48 (R-up 46-47)); Erith Hospitals Cup 46-47 48-49; Gtr London Lg R-up 68-69; Plumstead Challenge Cup 48-49

PREVIOUS Leagues: Dartford 46-52; Kent Amateur 52-62; Greater London 62-70
Name: Slade Green Athletic 46-86

RECORDS **Attendance:** 3,000 v Millwall, friendly 25/7/92
Goalscorer: Colin Dwyer **Appearances:** Colin Dwyer
Win: 14-0 v Island Social, Kent Amtr Lge 1953 **Defeat:** 1-9 v Whitstable Greater London 64-65

Players progressing : Roy Dwight (Nottm Forest), Alan Clark (Charlton) , Fred Lucas (Charlton)Tommy Tute (Millwall Jan. 1999)

FACT FILE

Founded: 1946 Nickname: The Green
Sponsor: T.B.A.
Colours: All white
Change Colours: Yellow /black/yellow
Midweek matchday: Tuesday
Reserve League:
Programme: 44 pages, incl. with admission
Editor: Robert Smith (01322 287982)

CLUB PERSONNEL

Chairman: Brian Smith
President: William Dudley
Press Officer: Robert Smith (01322 287982)
Manager: Srteve Waite
Coach: Micky Orme
Physio: Alan Martin

2002-03

Leading Goalscorer:
Captain:
Player of the Year:

SPORTING BENGAL UNITED

Ground: Mile End Stadium, Rhodeswell Road, Burdett Road, Poplar, London
Tel: 020 8980 1885

PREVIOUS **Leagues**: London Intermediate Lge >2003

FACT FILE

CLUB PERSONNEL

2002-03

Leading Goalscorer:
Captain:
Player of the Year:

THAMESMEAD TOWN

Secretary: Albert Panting,97 Sydney Road, Bexleyheath,Kent DA6 8HQ (0208303 1350 (H)

Ground: Bayliss Avenue, Thamesmead, London SE28 8NJ Tel: 0181 311 4211

Directions: By road: From Dartford tunnel A2 to London, exit Danson Interchange and follow signs for Thamesmead and Abbey Wood. From Blackheath tunnel exit on south side and follow signs to Woolwich, to Plumstead and then to Thamesmead

From Abbey Wood (BR) north east along Harrow Manor Way, into Crossway at 3rd r'bout, Bayliss Av. is 3rd right (Bexley bus 272 stops in Crossway near Bayliss Av.

Capacity: 400 Seats: 125 Cover: 125 Floodlights: Yes Club Shop: No

Clubhouse: Mon-Fri 6-11pm, Sat 12-11pm, Sun 12-3 & 7-10.30pm. Double bar,lounge, dance-floor, children's games room, video machines, hot & cold food.New members Bar

HONOURS Spartan Lg Div 3 79-80 (Lg Cup 84-85 86-87; I'mediate champs 85-86);Kent I'mediate Cup 83-84 94-95; 4 promotions & 9 trophies (inc London & Kent FA Cups) in progress thru Spartan I'mediate Divs, 1980-87; Kent Lge Div 2 94-95, Div 2 Cup 94-95

PREVIOUS **Leagues:** London Spartan 80-91
Ground: Meridian Sports Ground, Charlton

RECORDS **Attendance:** 400 v Wimbledon, ground opening 1988
Appearances: Delroy D'Oyley **Win** : 9-0 v Kent Police, Kent League 19/4/94

FACT FILE

Founded: 1970
Nickname: The Mead
Sponsors: Courage Brewery
Colours: Green& White/Green/Green
Change Colours: All blue
Midweek matchday: Tuesday
Reserves League: Winstonlead Kent D2
Programmes: Yes. 50p
Editor: Secretary

CLUB PERSONNEL

Chairman: Brian Morris
Vice Chairman: John Kelly
President: Albert Panting
Press Officer: Matthew Panting
Manager: Paul Blade
Physio: Allen Martin

2002-03

Leading Goalscorer:
Captain:
Player of the Year:

TUNBRIDGE WELLS

Secretary: Mrs J.Rogers, 21 Bluebell Walks, Hunters Chase,Paddock Wood, Kent. Wadhurst, East Sussex TN5 6PU Email Address: ronrogers@skynew.net
Ground: Culverden Stadium, Culverden Down, Tunbridge Wells, Kent TN4 Tel: 01892 520517

Directions: Leaving town on main Tonbridge rd (A26), turn left into Culverden Down ground half mile. 1 mile from Tunbridge Wells Central(BR). Served by any Tunbridge Wells-Tonbridge bus - to St Johns
Capacity: 3,750 Seats: 250 Cover: 1,000 Floodlights: Yes
Clubhouse: Open matchdays and as required Club Shop: No

HONOURS Kent Lg 84-85 (R-up 68-69, Lg Cup 74-75 77-78 85-86 87-88) Kent SnrTphy R-up 85-86 91-92

PREVIOUS **Names:** None. predecessors: T . Wells FC 1886-1910 47-50 T. Wells Rgrs 03-09 63-67; T. Wells Utd 51-62
Grounds: Down Lane 1906; Combley Park 06-10; Swiss Cottage 06-14;Down Farm 19-39; St Johns 47-50; Eridge Road 50-67

RECORDS **Attendance:** 967 v Maidstone United, FA Cup 1969
Goalscorer: John Wingate 151 **Appearances:** Tony Atkins 410
Win: 10-0 v Deal (H), May'86
Defeat: 1-11 v Deal Town (H), 20/2/93

FACT FILE
Founded: 1886
Reformed: 1967
Nickname: Wells
Colours: Red/Red/White
Change Colours: Blue/Blue/White
Midweek Matchday: Tuesday
Prog: 20 pages, 50p Editor: Secretary
Web: www.@team2.com/tunbridge wellsfc

CLUB PERSONNEL
Chairman: R.Rogers
Vice Chairman:
President:
Manager: Steve Clark
Asst. Man. / Coach:

2002-03
Leading Goalscorer:
Captain:
Player of the Year:

VICKERS CRAYFORD, DARTFORD ATHLETIC

Secretary: Brian Norris,Peelers Lodge ,21 St Edith's Road, Kemsing,Sevenoaks, Kent TN15 6PT. Tel No: 01689 854302
Ground: Thamesmead Town FC, Bayliss Avenue, Thamesmead, London, SE28 8NJ
Tel: 0208 311 4211 (Temporary Groundshare)
Home Ground (Pending floodlights) Oakwood, Old Road, Crayford, Kent, DA1 4DN.
Home clubhouse: Lounge Bar every day and evening. Plus snack bar on matchdays.
Directions: From Abbey Wood (BR) north east along Harrow Manor Way, into Crossway at 3rd r'bout, Bayliss Av. is 3rd right (Bexley bus 272 stops in Crossway near Bayliss Av. By road: From Dartford tunnel A2 to London, exit Danson Interchange and follow signs for Thamesmead and Abbey Wood. From Blackheath tunnel exit on south side and follow signs to Woolwich, to Plumstead and then to Thamesmead.
Capacity: 400 **Seats:** 125 **Cover:** 125 **Floodlights**: Yes

PREVIOUS **League:** Kent County. **Grounds:** Flamingo Park, Sidcup (pre 1994); VCD Sports & Social Club,Old Road, Crayford

RECORD **Victory:** 10-1 v Canterbury City 14.5.01 **Defeat:** 0-5 v Deal Town 20.4.02

HONOURS Kent County Cup 61-62, 63-64, 94-95, R-Up: 84-85, 89-90. Kent County Lg Div One 96-97 Kent County Premier 96-97. West Kent Cup 87-88.Kent Lge Cup: Winners 99-00 ,Runners up 98-99, 02-03. Kent Intermediate Shield (2) R-up(1), Erith Hosp Cup x4, R-Up x4; Kent Sen, Tphy. R-up 00-01

FACT FILE
Founded: 1916
Nickname: The Vickers
Sponsors: MB Fire Protection
Colours: Green & white/green/green
Change Colours: Blue & white/blue/blue
Midweek matchday: Wednesday
Programme: 40 pages 50p

CLUB PERSONNEL
Chairman: Michael Bonello
Vice Chairman:
President:
Manager:Martin Ford
Asst. Man.: Peter Burke
Coach: Roy Passey
Physio: Peter Burke

2002-03
Leading Goalscorer:
Captain:
Player of the Year:

WHITSTABLE TOWN

Secretary: George Corney, 46 Elizabeth Way, Herne Bay, Kent CT6 6ET (01227 363496)
Ground: Belmont Road, Belmont, Whitstable, Kent Tel: 01227 266012

Directions: From Thanet Way (A299), left at Tescos r'bout and down MillstroodRd - ground at bottom of road, 400yds from Whitstable (BR) station. Car park atGrimshall Rd entrance
Capacity: 2,000 Cover: 1,000 Seats: 500 Floodlights: Yes Club Shop: Yes
Clubhouse: Social & recreation purposes, open all matchdays. Bar. Hot food &drinks at tea-bar

HONOURS Kent Lg Div 2 27-28 33-34 49-50 (Lg Cup 79-80 (R-up 89-90 91-92)), KentAmtr Lg East 60-61, Kent Amtr Cup 28-29, Kent Snr Tphy R-up 78-79 89-90 92-93,Gtr London Lg Cup R-up 65-66, Kent Amtr Cup 28-29, Kent Midweek Lg Cup 92-93

PREVIOUS **Leagues:** E. Kent 1897-1909; Kent 09-59; Aetolian 59-60; Kent Amtr 60-62 63-64; S E Anglian 62-63; Gtr London 64-67; Kent Premier 67-68 (also in New Brompton, Thanet & Faversham & Dist. Lges over the years)
Names: Whitstable Utd (pre-1886); Whitstable Swifts 93-95; WhitstableTown 95-1905; Whitstable FC 08-66
GroundsSaddleston's Field 1885-94; Westmeads (Cromwell Rd) 94-95; Joy Lane 95-1908; Church Rd 08-09

RECORDS **Gate:** 2,500 v Gravesend & N, FA Cup 3rd Q. Rd,19/10/87 **Goalscorer**: Barry Godfrey **Appearances:** Frank Cox 429 (1950-60) **Win:** 18-0 v Greenstreet (H), Faversham & Dist. Lge 20-21 **Defeat**: 0-10 v Sittingbourne (A), FA Cup 1st Qual. Rd 62-63

FACT FILE
Founded: 1885
Nickname: Oystermen, Reds, Natives
Sponsors: D & J Tyres
Colours: Red & White/ Black/Red
Change colours: Yellow/blue/yellow
Midweek matchday: Tuesday
Programme: 48 pages, 80p
Editor/Press Off:Tony Rouse
Tel: 01227 274138

CLUB PERSONNEL
Chairman: Joe Brownett VChair: Trevor Rapley
President: George Gifford
Fix Sec:Bruce Smith (01227 274138)
Manager: Matt Toms
Asst Manager: Glen Atkin
Physio: Tony Pattenden

2002-03
Leading Goalscorer:John Utterson
Captain: Ada Burrorough
Player of the Year:Andy Skinner

BRITISH ENERGY KENT COUNTY FOOTBALL LEAGUE

Founded: 1922

President: W C Manklow **Chairman:** C T C Windiate

General Secretary: B H Bundock

Press Secretary: G Jenkins

Kings View, Shottenden Lane, Molash, Canterbury, Kent CT4 8EZ

Tel: 01233 740143 Email: geoff@kcfl2000.freeserve.co.uk

Inclement weather, particularly around Christmas and New Year, meant that the British Energy Kent County League, for the second time in three seasons, had to extend their playing season, albeit on this occasion by only five days, in order to allow the completion of outstanding league games.

Following the League's representative sides representation of England in the third U.E.F.A. Regions Cup in Estonia, a full list of Premier Division matches was not played until the third week in September - four weeks later than usual. Bearsted, who had won the league for the last two seasons, never really threatened a hat-trick of successes, and left the door open for last season's runners-up, Sevenoaks Town, to win the title by just two points from Stansfeld O&B Club. Sevenoaks Town's successful application to join the Go travel Kent League means they will play their football next season one step up the ladder of the National League System, and our Leagues' good wishes go with them.

In Division One East Tenterden Tigers, runners-up last season, won the Division by a two point margin over University of Kent, whose academic year interruptions were not always to their advantage. The Division One West Championship was close with Cray Valley (PM) and AFC Blackheath needing to win their respective matches on the final day. As the season's proceedings came to a conclusion it was Cray Valley who took the title and AFC Blackheath, who had led the Division since late March, finished as runners-up.

A 'two-horse' race in Division Two East with Tyler Hill and Woodstock Park, both in their debut seasons, occupying the top two positions for virtually the whole campaign. Tyler Hill, the only unbeaten side in the entire league, eventually reigned supreme by three points over their Sittingbourne rivals. In Division Two West another of the League debutants, Bromleians Sports, made use of their matches in hand, and won the title in their penultimate game from second placed Halls who had led the table for most of the latter part of the season.

A fourth new side to be amongst the honours was Lanes End, who made up for their County Cup disappointment by winning Division Three West from Samuel Montagu Youth Club, the side that finished third that previous season.

In Reserve Division One Sevenoaks Town, eight points clear at Christmas, retained their title by ten points from second placed Greenways. Having scored 85 goals (three more than last season) in 22 league matches played, Sevenoaks were the League's highest scorers, and for the second successive season finished with the most superior goal difference throughout the League. Like their first team Sevenoaks Town will play their football in the Go Travel Kent League next season. Reserve Division Two saw new team Aylesford Paper Mills top the table in January, maintain that position and win the Division by mid-April by a 12 point advantage over Halls at the end of the season.

In the County Cup Competitions five teams competed in the 'Lea Ray' Kent Senor Trophy but none could match Milton Athletic's achievements of last season in reaching the semi-finals. Bearsted, Stansfeld O&B Club and Milton all suffered first round defeats at the hands of Kent League opposition, with Crockenhill and Sevenoaks Town eliminated in the second round. Division One West champions Cray Valley (PM) lifted the much coveted London Intermediate Cup following a penalty shoot-out win over Kent League side Thamesmead Town Reserves, and another Intermediate side to win County honours was Sheerness East who defeated Kent League side Danson Furness Athletic in the final if the Kent Intermediate Challenge Shield, recovering from a two goal deficit to eventually win by the odd goal in five.

The League's domestic Cup competitions saw Stansfeld O&B Club retain the Inter-Regional Challenge Cup following a penalty shoot-out defeat of Sheerness East in the final at Dr Martens League side Ashford Town. Another final requiring a penalty shoot-out to decide the winner was the Eastern Section Senior Les Leckie Cup at Chatham Town's ground with Lydd Town eventually proving more accurate from 12 yards than holders Milton Athletic. Hythe Town F.C. hosted the Eastern Section Junior Cup final, which saw Sheerness East Reserves overcome the second string of Kennington. A close final of the West Kent challenge Shield, played at Sevenoaks Town F.C., was won by Oakwood who defeated their Division One rivals Pembury by the only goal of the game. Lordswood F.C. was the venue for the final of the Western Section Reserve Division's Cup, where Sevenoaks Town Reserves retained the cup when they defeated Oakwood Reserves.

Geoff Jenkins - Press Secretary.

FINAL LEAGUE TABLES 2002-03

PREMIER DIVISION		P	W	D	L	F	A	Pts
1	Sevenoaks Town	26	17	6	3	65	22	57
2	Stansfeld O&BC	26	17	4	5	71	29	55
3	Old Roan	26	15	7	4	63	32	52
4	Lydd Town	26	14	4	8	49	52	46
5	Bearsted	26	11	10	5	45	28	43
6	Sheerness East	26	11	7	8	48	42	40
7	Greenways	26	10	7	9	50	47	37
8	Kennington	26	8	7	11	38	47	31
9	Milton Athletic	26	9	3	14	47	46	30
10	New Romney	26	7	6	13	36	61	27
11	Beauwater	26	7	4	15	29	56	25
12	Wickham Park (R)	26	6	4	16	27	54	22
13	Crockenhill	26	5	6	15	40	54	21
14	Snodland	26	5	5	16	33	71	20

PREMIER DIVISION	1	2	3	4	5	6	7	8	9	10	11	12	13	14
1 Bearsted		4-1	4-2	0-3	3-0	4-2	1-0	0-0	2-2	0-2	0-0	6-0	1-2	2-0
2 Beauwater	0-2		3-5	1-1	1-1	1-0	0-2	3-0	0-2	0-2	2-3	3-1	0-4	2-1
3 Crockenhill	0-1	0-2		2-2	2-3	1-1	1-3	5-0	1-2	1-3	1-1	2-2	2-3	3-0
4 Greenways	1-1	2-0	1-3		4-2	3-3	2-1	2-2	2-5	1-1	1-1	3-0	4-3	2-1
5 Kennington	1-1	0-0	1-1	3-1		0-1	2-1	3-1	2-2	1-0	1-4	1-2	0-3	4-1
6 Lydd Town	3-2	3-2	1-0	3-2	2-1		6-5	2-1	1-1	1-3	3-3	3-0	2-1	0-6
7 Milton Athletic	1-2	0-1	3-2	1-0	2-2	3-1		0-0	1-2	0-2	0-1	5-0	1-3	4-0
8 New Romney	2-2	2-1	1-0	3-1	3-2	0-2	0-6		3-1	1-3	0-4	3-5	2-2	1-3
9 Old Roan	2-1	0-0	4-1	1-2	4-0	4-1	3-3	6-2		1-1	5-0	2-0	1-1	4-1
10 Sevenoaks Town	1-1	8-1	5-1	1-0	1-1	4-0	4-1	0-0	2-3		4-1	6-2	0-1	1-1
11 Sheerness East	1-1	0-1	1-2	5-3	4-2	2-1	3-1	3-1	2-1	1-3		0-0	2-2	2-0
12 Snodland	2-2	3-2	4-2	1-3	1-4	3-4	1-2	1-4	0-1	1-5	2-1		1-1	0-0
13 Stansfeld Oxford & Bermondsey Club	0-2	7-0	3-0	2-0	2-0	0-1	3-0	3-1	3-1	1-2	4-3	5-1		6-1
14 Wickham Park	0-0	3-2	0-0	1-4	0-1	0-2	4-1	1-3	0-3	0-1	1-0	1-0	1-6	

DIVISION ONE WEST

	P	W	D	L	F	A	Pts
1 Cray Valley PM	26	16	5	5	74	33	53
2 AFC Blackheath	26	15	4	7	57	35	49
3 Moonshot Athletic	26	12	5	9	51	45	41
4 Holmesdale	26	10	8	8	45	36	38
5 Fleetdown United	26	12	2	12	42	50	38
6 Thames Poly (-1)	26	11	5	10	50	52	37
7 Oakwood	26	10	6	10	37	31	36
8 Bly Spartans	26	12	0	14	46	45	36
9 Aylesford P. Mills	26	11	3	12	46	48	36
10 Belvedere	26	10	6	10	41	46	36
11 Pembury	26	10	2	14	34	55	32
12 Eynsford	26	8	6	12	29	42	30
13 Rusthall	26	7	6	13	42	46	27
14 Phoenix Sports	26	8	2	16	37	67	26

DIVISION ONE EAST

	P	W	D	L	F	A	Pts
1 Tenterden Tigers	24	14	5	5	67	36	47
2 University of Kent	24	14	3	7	59	44	45
3 Bromley Green	24	11	5	8	43	43	38
4 Bliby	24	11	4	9	65	46	37
5 Betteshanger Welfare	24	9	10	5	56	41	37
6 Norton Sports	24	11	3	10	57	43	36
7 St Margarets	24	8	6	10	40	44	30
8 Snowdown Colliery Welfare	24	8	4	12	45	50	28
9 Smarden	24	1	2	21	20	105	5

INTER-REGIONAL CHALLENGE CUP 2002-03

FIRST ROUND EAST

Lydd Town	v	Smarden	1-0
Betteshanger Welfare	v	Tenterden Tigers	3-1
Norton Sports	v	Kennington	1-2 (aet)
Bromley Green	v	Bliby	0-5
Snowdown Colliery Welf.	v	Sheerness East	0-6
New Romney	v	St Margarets	5-3

FIRST ROUND WEST

Sevenoaks Town	v	Thames Poly	10-2
Stansfeld O&B Club	v	Fleetdown United	2-0
Bearsted	v	Belvedere	2-0
Oakwood	v	Wickham Park	4-2
Crockenhill	v	Eynsford	2-2 (aet) 4-3p
Phoenix Sports	v	Snodland	1-2
AFC Blackheath	v	Bly Spartans	1-2

SECOND ROUND EAST

Bliby	v	Kennington	2-0
University of Kent	v	Sheerness East	1-2
Milton Athletic	v	Lydd Town	5-2
Betteshanger Welfare	v	St Margarets	5-3

(Winners through to County wide Quarter-finals)

SECOND ROUND WEST

Cray Valley (PM)	v	Pembury	3-0
Beauwater	v	Stansfeld O&B Club	0-2
Holmesdale	v	Crockenhill	0-2
Aylesford Paper Mills	v	Bearsted	1-0
Snodland	v	Bly Spartans	2-3 (aet)
Moonshot Athletic	v	Greenways	2-1
Sevenoaks Town	v	Old Roan	2-2 (aet) 6-5p

THIRD ROUND WEST

Bly Spartans	v	Crockenhill	1-2
Stansfeld O&B Club	v	Moonshot Athletic	5-3 (aet)
Aylesford Paper Mills	v	Cray Valley (PM)	2-0
Old Roan	v	Oakwood	1-4

QUARTER-FINALS

Milton Athletic	v	Oakwood	0-2
Bliby	v	Crockenhill	3-2
Stansfeld O&B Club	v	Betteshanger Welfare	7-1
Sheerness East	v	Aylesford Paper Mills	3-0

SEMI-FINALS

Sheerness East	v	Bliby	6-1
Stansfeld O&B Club	v	Oakwood	2-1

FINAL

Stansfeld O&B Club	v	Sheerness East	2-2 (aet) 3-1p

LES LECKIE CUP 2002-03

QUARTER-FINALS

Lydd Town	v	Betteshanger	3-2
Tenterden Tigers	v	St Margarets	3-3 (aet) 4-5p
Norton Sports	v	Milton Athletic	0-2
Univercity of Kent	v	Kennington	2-3

SEMI-FINALS

Milton Athletic	v	Kennington	3-2 (aet)
St Margarets	v	Lydd Town	1-2

FINAL

Milton Athletic	v	Lydd Town	2-2 (aet) 4-5p

WEST KENT CHALLENGE SHIELD 2002-03

QUARTER-FINALS

Bromlians Sports	v	Fleetdown United	2-3 (aet)
Oakwood	v	Lane End	2-1
Holmesdale	v	Cray Valley (PM)	2-1 (aet)
Pembury	v	Thames Poly	1-0

SEMI-FINALS

Fleetdown United	v	Oakwood	2-4
Pembury	v	Holmesdale	2-1

FINAL

Pembury	v	Oakwood	0-1

BEARSTED
Founded: 1895
Secretary: Mrs Liz Owen, 21 Copsewood Way, Bearsted, Maidstone, Kent ME15 8PL(01622 737709)
Ground: Honey Lane, Otham, Maidstone. (0411 128034)
Colours: White/blue/blue
Change Colours: Yellow/blue/blue

BEAUWATER
Founded: 1927
Secretary: Robert Taylor, 24 Sun Lane, Gravesend, Kent DA12 5HG (01474 332208)
Ground: Beauwater Leisure Club, Nelson Road, Northfleet (01474 359222)
Colours: Blue/blue/white
Change Colours: Red/Navy/Red

CRAY VALLEY PaperMills
Founded: 1981
Secretary: Steve Chapman, 97 Yorkland Ave., Welling DA16 2LG
Tel: 020 8304 5387 (H) 01293 802208 (B)
Ground: Badgers Sports Ground, Middle Park Ave., London SE9
Tel: 020 8850 4273
Colours: Green/black/black
Change colours: Blue & white/white/green

CROCKENHILL
Founded: 1946
Secretary: Mike Floate, Newlands Cottages, 71 Stones Cross Road, Crockenhill,Swanley, Kent BR8 8LX Tel No: 01322 668275
Ground: The Wested Meadow, Wested, Eynsford Road, Crockenhill, Kent. (01322 662097)
Colours: Red & white stripes/ black/ red
Change Colours: All navy

GREENWAYS
Founded: 1965
Secretary: William Miller, 14 Cygnet Gardens, Northfleet, Kent DA11 7DN (01474 560913)
Ground: Beauwater Leisure Centre, Nelson Road, Northfleet, (01474 359222)
Colours: Green & white/green/green
Change Colours: Red & black/black/black

KENNINGTON
Founded: 1888
Secretary: Kevin Hayden, 36 Alec Pemble Close, Kennington, Ashford, Kent. TN24 9PF Tel No: 01233 627826
Ground: Kennington Cricket Club Club, Ulley Road, Kennington, Ashford, Kent
Colours: Sky blue/yellow/sky blue
Change Colours: Red/navy/navy

LYDD TOWN
Founded: 1885
Secretary: Bruce Marchant, 14 Quested Road, Folkestone, Kent.CT19 4BY Tel No: 01303 275403
Ground: The Lindsey Field, Dengemarsh Road, Lydd, Romney Marsh (01797 321904)
Colours: Red & green/green/green
ChangeColours:All Blue

MILTON ATHLETIC
Founded: 1926
Secretary: Paul Duffin, 18 Hales Road, Tunstall, Sittingbourne, Kent ME10 1SR (01795 422882)
Ground: UK Paper Sports Ground, Gore Court Road, Sittingbourne, Kent (01795 564213)
Colours: Royal blue/royal blue/white
Change Colours: Yellow & navy/navy/yellow

NEW ROMNEY
Founded: 1895
Secretary: Alan Chandler, 124 Jefferstone Lane, St Marys Bay, romney Marsh (01303 873872)
Ground: The Maud Pavilion, Station Road, New Romney, Kent (01797 364858)
Colours: All Navy blue & yellow
Change Colours: Orange/royal blue/orange

OLD ROAN
Founded: 1905
Secretary: Brian Riley, 33 Buckler Gardens, Mottingham, London SE9 3BD (020 8857 0401)
Groud: John Roan Playing Fields, Kidbrooke Park Road, KIdbrooke, London SE3 (020 8856 1915 or 020 8856 1012)
Colours: Blue & black stripes/ black/ black & blue.
Change Colours: Red & white/red/red

SHEERNESS EAST
Founded: 1932
Secretary: Jonathan Longhurst, 34 Sunnyside Avenue, Minster Sheerness, Kent ME12 2EN (01795 870093)
Ground: Sheerness East Working Mens Club, Queenborough Rd., Halfway, Sheerness (01795 662049)
Colours: Yellow/royal blue/royal blue
Change colours: Royal blue/black/royal blue

SNODLAND
Founded: 1940
Secretary: Terry Reeves, 136 Townsend Road, Snodland, Kent ME6 5RN (01634 240076)
Ground: Potyn's Field, Paddlesworth Road, Snodland, Kent. (01634 243961)
Colours: Yellow/ /red/black
Change colours:Red/red/black

STANSFELD OXFORD & BERMONDSEY CLUB
Founded: 1897
Secretary: Edward Ellis, 40 Tilbrook Road, Kidbrooke, London SE3 9QE (0208 319 0903)
Ground: F.K.G.Sports,Eltham Rd .,Lee Green SE12 (020 8852 6622)
Colours: Yellow/blue/blue
Change Colours: All white

TENTERDEN TOWN
Founded: 1889
Secretary: Stephen Saxby, 46 Hopes Grove,High Halden,Ashford, Kent TN26 3ND Tel No: 01233 850741
Ground: Recreation Ground, Recretaion Ground Rd., Tenterden (07786 932151)
Colours: Blue & white hoops/red/red
Change Colours: Blue & white/ blue/blue

KENT COUNTY LEAGUE DIVISION ONE WEST

APM Mears
Founded: 1919. Re-formed 2003
Secretary: Phillip Allen, 397 Lower Woodlands Road, Gillingham Kent ME7 2TR. Tel: 07949 048 695
Ground: Cobdown Sports & Social Club, Station Rd, Ditton, Maidstone. Tel: 01622 717771
Colours: Black & white stripes/black/black
Change Colours: Sky blue/navy/sky blue

BELVEDERE
Founded: 1923
Secretary: Paul Bell, 10 Abbotswood Road, Dulwich, London SE22 8DL Tel: 020 8693 6521 (H)
Ground: Belvedere Sports & Social Club, Woolwich Road, Belvedere. Tel: 01322 436724
Colours: Yellow/blue/blue
Change: Green/blue/blue

BLY SPARTANS
Founded: 1982
Secretary: Tony Wheeler, 14 Lynnette Ave., Rochester, Kent ME2 3NH Tel: 01634 713404 (H)
Ground: Bly Spartans Sports Ground, Rede Court Road, Strood. Tel: 01634 710577
Colours: Maroon & sky blue/maroon/maroon
Change: Grey/black/black

BROMLEIANS SPORTS
Founded 1922
Secretary: Stephen Millward, 24 Palace Road, Bromley Kent BR1 3JT. Tel: 020 8466 1911
Ground: Lower Gravel Road, Bromley, Kent Tel: 020 8462 5068
Colours: Light blue/dark blue/light blue
Change Colours: Red/red/red

EYNESFORD
Founded: 1895
Secretary: Robert Graham, 48 Goddington Lane, Orpington, Kent BR6 9DS Tel: 01689 821425
Ground: STC Ivor grove, New Eltham, SE9
Tel: 020 8850 2057
Colours: Black & white/black/black
Change Colours: Yellow & black/black/black

FLEETDOWN UNITED
Founded: 1971
Secretary: Brian Wakeman, 670 Princes Road, Dartford, Kent DA2 6JG (01322 228680)
Ground: Lower Heath Lane, Dartford, Kent (01322 273848)
Colours: Tangerine/blue/blue
Change colours: Blue &White/ blue/blue

HALLS
Founded: 1919
Secretary: Steven Poile, 33 Carlton Avenue, Horns Cross, Greenhithe, Kent DA9 9DR. Tel: 01322 383 587
Ground: Princes Golf & Leisure Club, Darenth Road, Dartford, Kent Tel: 01322 276565
Colours: Yellow & royal blue stripes/royal blue/yellow
Change Colours: All navy

HOLMESDALE
Founded 1956
Secretary: Mark Hayes, 12 Danson Way, Rainham, Kent. ME8 7EW (01634 327954)
Ground: Holmesdale Sports & Social Club, Oakley Road, Bromley Common (020 8462 4440)
Colours: Yellow & Green/ Green/ Green
Change Colours: Red/ Black/Black

LEWISHAM BOROUGH (COMMUNITY)
Founded: 2003
Secretary: Joseph Collymore, 37 Vaughan Williams Close, Deptford SE8 4AW (0208 691 2543)
Ground: Ladywell Arena, Doggett Road, Catford SE6 4QX
Tel: 020 8314 1986
Colours: All Blue & gold stripes
Change Colours: All gold & blue stripes

OAKWOOD
Founded: 1924
Peter Mannering, 24 Ellenswood Close, Otham, Maidstone, Kent ME15 8SQ Tel: 01622 862482
Ground: Otham Sports Club, Honey Lane, Otham, Maidstone, Kent. Tel: 07745 383328
Colours: Red & white stripes/black/red
Change colours: Green & red/green/red

PEMBURY
Founded1908
Secretary: Michael Waterman, 26 The Coppice, Pembury, Tunbridge Wells Kent TN2 4EY
Tel: 01892 824137
Ground: Woodside Recreation Ground, Henwoods Mount, Pembury
Tel: 07970 026628
Colours: Black & White stripes/ black/black
Change Colours: All red

WICKHAM PARK
Founded: 1934
Secretary: Robbie Devlin,117 Hazlebank Road,London SE6 1LT
Tel No: 07939 556737
Ground: 228-230 Pickhurst Rise, West Wickham.
Tel: 020 8777 2550
Colours: Navy & tangerine/navy & tangerine/navy
Change Colours: Black & white stripes/black/black

KENT COUNTY LEAGUE DIVISION ONE EAST

BETTESHANGER WELFARE
Founded: 1939
Secretary: Ms Kim Ashton, 12 Douglas Road, Deal Kent CT14 9HT
Tel: 01304 364550
Ground: Betteshanger Welfare Ground, Cavell Square, Mill Hill, Deal.
Tel: 01304 372080
Colours: Red & white/blue/red
Change colours: All blue

BLIBY
Founded: 1994
Secretary: Mrs Jacqui Barker, Frithfield, Aldington Frith, Ashford, Kent TN25 7HH Tel: 01233 720469 (H) 01233 720973 (B)
Ground: Sandyacres, Sandyhurst Lane (from January 2004), Ashford.
Tel: 01233 627373
Temporary Ground: The Ridge, Spearpoint, Kennington.
Colours: Navy & amber/navy/navy
Change: Amber & navy/navy /navy

BROMLEY GREEN
Founded: 1930
Secretary: Stanley Donald,12 Oast Meadow ,Willesborough, Ashford,Kent TN24 0AS Tel No: 01233 627916
Ground: The Swan Centre, Newtown Road, South Willesborough, Ashford, Kent Tel: 01233 645982
Colours: All Green & blue.
Change Colours: White/green/green

NORTON SPORTS
Founded: 1927
Secretary: Colin Page, 22 Haysel, Sittingbourne, Kent ME10 4QE
Tel: 01795 426675
Ground: Norton Park, Provender Lane,Norton,Kent Tel: 01795 520088
Colours: Sky Blue & white stripes/ navy / navy
Change Colours: Red & black/navy/navy

SNOWDOWN COLLIERY WELFARE
Founded: 1927
Secretary: Mr Patrick Sutcliffe, 14 Park View, Sturry, canterbury Kent CT2 0NP. Tel: 01227 712673 (H). 01304 840309 (B)
Ground: Spinney Lane, Aylesham, Canterbury CT3 3AF (01304 840278)
Colours: Black & white stripes/black/black
Change Colours: Green & white/white/white
Previous League: Kent

St MARGARETS
Founded: 1970 Re-formed:1993
Secretary: Dennis Mitchell, 178 St Davids Avenue, Dover Kent CT17 9HJ. Tel: 077734 77781 (M). 07855 013412 (B)
Ground: The Alexandra Field, Off Kingsdown Road, St Margarets at Cliffe, Nr Dover. Tel: 07973 139966
Colours: Red &blue/ navy/ red
Change Colours: White/blue/red

TYLER HILL
Founded: 1950
Secretary: Bill Clark, 23 Hanscombe House, Forty Acres Road, Canterbury Kent CT2 7TL. Tel: 01227 768358 (H). 07930 100034 (B)
Ground: Hersden Recreation Ground, Hersden, Nr. Canterbury.
Tel: 07930 100034
Colours: Black & white stripes/black/white
Change Colours: All red & white

UNIVERSITY OF KENT
Founded: 1967
Secretary: Aaron Campbell, Sports Federation, Kent Union, Mandela Building, ,University of Kent, Canterbury, Kent CT2 7NW
Tel: 01227 823 074
Ground: Oast House, Parkwood Road, Off Giles Lane, Canterbury, Kent. Tel: 01227 827430
Colours: Black & white stripes/black/black
Change Colours: Red & blackstripes/red/red

WOODSTOCK PARK
Founded: 1970
Secretary: Maurice Dunk, 29 Shurland Avenue, Sittingbourne Kent ME10 4QT. Tel: 01795 478927 (H)
Ground: Woodstock Park, Broadoak Road, Sittingbourne, Kent
Tel: 07774 654 912
Colours: All royal blue
Change colours: Maroon/maroon/sky blue

DIVISION TWO WEST

BOROUGH UNITED Glentworth Club, Lowfield Street, Dartford, Kent Tel: 01322 401802
BRIDON ROPES Meridian Sports Club, Charlton Park Road, Charlton, London SE7 8QF Tel: 020 8856 1923
ELTHAM PALACE Beaverwood Lodge, Beaverwood Road, Chislehurst, Kent Tel: 020 8300 1385
FARNBOROUGH OLD BOYS GUILD Farnborough (Kent) Sports Club, High St, Farnborough, Kent Tel: 01689 862949
LANES END Waller Park, Wood Lane, Darenth, Dartford, Kent Tel: 01322 221006
LARKFIELD & NEW HYTHE WDRS Larkfield Sports Ground, New Hythe Lane, Larkfield, Aylesford Tel: 07786 221262
ORPINGTON Westcombe Park & Orpington SC, Goddington Lane, Orpington, Kent Tel: 01689 834902
OTFORD UNITED Otford Recreation Ground, High Street, Otford, Sevenoaks, Kent Tel: 01959 524405
PHOENIX SPORTS Phoenix Sports Club, Mayplace Road East, Bexleyheath, Kent Tel: 01322 526159
RUSTHALL Jockey Farm, Nellington Lane, Rusthall, Tunbridge Wells. Tel: 07940 277138
SAMUEL MONTAGU YOUTH CLUB Broadwalk, Kidbrooke, London SE9 Tel: 020 8856 1126
SUTTON ATHLETIC The Roaches, Parsonage Lane, Sutton-at-Hone, nr Dartford, Kent Tel: 01322 280507
WESTERHAM Westerham Sports Association, King George V Playing fields, Costells Meadow, Westerham, Kent Tel: 01959 561106

DIVISION TWO EAST

BETTESHANGER WELFARE **RESERVES**
BORDEN VILLAGE Borden & Playstool Parish Council Ground, Borden, Sittingbourne, Kent . Tel: 07903 016794
KENNINGTON Kennington Cricket Club, Ulley Road, Ulley Road, Kennington, Ashford TN25 4PE. Tel: 07887 995219
LYDD TOWN **RESERVES**
NEW ROMNEY **RESERVES**
SHEERNESS EAST **RESERVES**
SHEPPEY UNITED Medways Ports Authority Ground, Holm Place, Sheerness, Kent. Tel: 01795 668054
TENTERDEN TIGERS **RESERVES**
UNIVERSITY OF KENT **RESERVES**

MATTHEW CLARK SUSSEX COUNTY LEAGUE

FEEDER TO: DR MARTENS LEAGUE

FOUNDED 1920

President: P H Strange **Chairman:** Peter Bentley

Secretary: P Beard, 2 Van Gogh Place, Bersted, Bognor Regis PO22 9BG

Tel: 01243 822063 (H) 07966 457908 (M) Fax: 01243 822063 www.scfl.org.uk

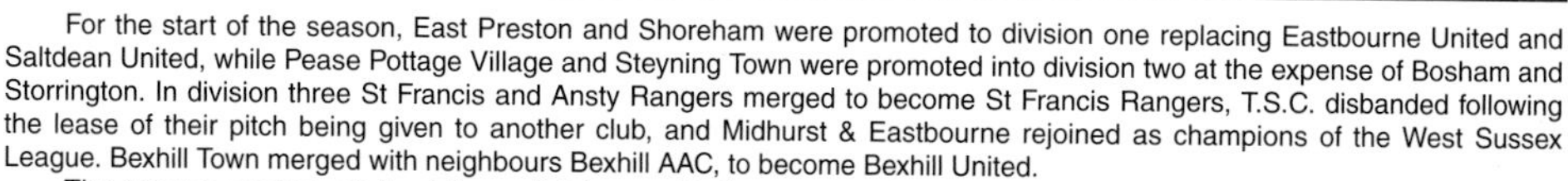

For the start of the season, East Preston and Shoreham were promoted to division one replacing Eastbourne United and Saltdean United, while Pease Pottage Village and Steyning Town were promoted into division two at the expense of Bosham and Storrington. In division three St Francis and Ansty Rangers merged to become St Francis Rangers, T.S.C. disbanded following the lease of their pitch being given to another club, and Midhurst & Eastbourne rejoined as champions of the West Sussex League. Bexhill Town merged with neighbours Bexhill AAC, to become Bexhill United.

The reserve section retained three divisions, with the premier division going to 17 clubs, Horsham YMCA escaping relegation, with East and West both having 16. Saltdean and Oving were relegated, while Worthing disbanded their reserve team again, this time to allow Withdean to ground share. Eastbourne Town and Lewes were promoted from East and Selsey and Shoreham from West. Bexhill took out their reserve team to concentrate on cementing the new club but Pease Pottage Village entered the East for the first time. This was, however, short-lived as they were forced to withdraw very early on. In the West St Francis re-entered in the name of the new merged club but this division was also reduced to 15 when Bosham encountered problems. Before the end of the season, Peacehaven were forced to withdraw from the premier division with only a few games remaining, due to a lack of off the field help. The youth section again had three regionalised divisions.

First team fixtures were completed by 3rd May, with just one reserve match outstanding to the Bank Holiday Monday (5th May). Burgess HIll were again champions and their strenuous efforts during the season to upgrade their ground has resulted in a successful application to join the DR Martens Southern Division - having finished first or second for the past seven years they certainly deserve it. Whitehawk, with a tremendous late run, finished as runners-up with Horsham YMCA third. Littlehampton, Wick and Peacehaven & Telscombe, all former division one champions, filled the relegation spots and they will be replaced by Rye & Iden United, having upgraded their ground which prevented them being promoted last season, Eastbourne Town and East Grinstead Town. Finishing in the relegation places were Pease Pottage Village and Oving. Division three champions were Midhurst & Eastbourne after just one season, with Haywards Heath Town coming in second. In the relegation zone were Uckfield Town and Bosham. Eastbourne United and Shinewater Association, both in division two, have made known their intentions to merge forming Eastbourne United Association, and will remain in the division. After much deliberation, and as a result of Oving disbanding, it was decided that Pease Pottage Village would not be relegated, whilst Bosham and Uckfield were also spared their fate in division three. Wardhurst United will be joining from the East Sussex League and Bexhill United Reserves will be entering Reserve East.

Eastbourne Borough retained the reserve premier title, with Burgess Hill runners-up. They also won the County FA Intermediate Cup at Lancing, by defeating Loxwood from the West Sussex League. Reserve East was won by East grinstead Town, with Rye & Iden United runners-up and reserve west by Whitehawk with Mile Oak coming in second. Relegated from the premier division were Lancing, Littlehampton Town, Peacehaven & Telscombe, Selsey and Shoreham.

In the youth section the North division was won by Burgess Hill with Crowborough second. The east division saw Lewes take the title with runners-up spot going to Hailsham, whilst in the West, Wick were champions followed by Chichester City. In the play-offs to determine the overall champions Lewes went to Wick and won 3-0 in one semi-final, whilst Burgess Hill lost at home to the top runner-up, Chichester, 2-3 after extra time. In the final, played at Hassocks, Chichester defeated Lewes 2-0 to become champions.

In the FA Cup Extra Preliminary Round, Ringmer, Three Bridges and Whitehawk recorded victories over Chessington United, Greenwich Borough and Walton Casuals respectively, whilst Chichester and East Preston were unable to convert away draws to home wins in their respective replays. In the Preliminary Round Ringmer won 3-0 at Erith Town, Peacehaven knock-out Redhill 3-1 whilst Pagham, Selsey and Three Bridges were all victorious at home. First Qualifying Round only brought victories for Selsey, 2-1 after drawing 2-2 at Tonbridge Wells, and Three Bridges who beat Chipstead 3-1. Both teams were drawn away in the next round but neither progressed further.

In the FA Vase First Qualifying Round, Eastbourne Town, Redhill and Whitehawk all won away, whilst Ringmer progressed from home. Horsham YMCA lost out in a replay having drawn at home. The Second Qualifying Round saw East Grinstead win 4-3 at home to Herne Bay, Broadbridge Heath convincingly defeat Whitchurch United 7-0, Hailsham winning 1-0 away to Lancing and Whitehawk through after a home win. Broadbridge were not the only club to score seven, as Redhill were on the wrong end of the same result against Sidlesham. In the First Round of the competition Arundel won at AFC Wallingford, then top of their league, Sidlesham travelled to Maidstone and came away with a 4-2 win, whilst Selsey and Whitehawk both recorded 3-0 victories over Lymington Town and Broadbridge Heath respectively.The Second Round saw wins for Arundel, 1-0 at home to Erith Town, Selsey, 3-2 at Soham Town rangers, Whitehawk, 2-0 at home to Abingdon Town, and Burgess Hill, exempt until this round due to their past successes, won 2-1 at home to Stanway Town. The Third Round saw only Burgess Hill and Arundel progress through to the next round. Burgess with a 4-1 away win against Holbeach United, leaders of the United Counties League, whilst a 5-2 win after extra time away to Whitehawk saw Arundel through. Burgess Hill again proved their pedigree in the FA Vase by winning 3-0 at Northallerton to progress to the Fifth Round, however, their run in the competition came to end after losing 2-1 at home to Winchester City.

Teams of the season were Burgess Hill, winning the championship again and for their run in the FA Vase, Rye & Iden United in division two for winning the title again, despite the disappointment of not being able to be promoted last season, whilst in division three Midhurst take the honours for doing the 'double' in their first season back in the league.

FINAL LEAGUE TABLES 2002-03

DIVISION ONE	P	W	D	L	F	A	Pts	GD
Burgess Hill Town	38	29	4	5	97	27	91	70
Whitehawk	38	22	4	12	79	41	70	38
Horsham YMCA	38	21	6	11	101	51	69	50
Chichester City Utd	38	20	9	9	79	51	69	28
Sidlesham	38	20	6	12	65	62	66	3
Southwick	38	18	6	14	67	50	60	17
Ringmer	38	17	9	12	55	56	60	-1
Hassocks	38	16	8	14	67	65	56	2
Pagham	38	16	7	15	69	52	55	17
East Preston	38	16	6	16	63	66	54	-3
Selsey	38	14	11	13	59	44	53	15
Redhill	38	16	5	17	53	62	53	-9
Sidley United	38	15	6	17	55	51	51	4
Three Bridges	38	14	7	17	88	83	49	5
Hailsham Town	38	13	8	17	54	60	47	-6
Shoreham	38	13	6	19	54	69	45	-15
Arundel	38	11	11	16	50	65	44	-15
Peacehaven & Tel.	38	9	5	24	43	95	32	-52
Wick	38	7	5	26	51	123	26	-72
Littlehampton Town	38	4	9	25	34	110	21	-76

DIVISION TWO	P	W	D	L	F	A	Pts	GD
Rye & Iden United	34	27	4	3	77	35	85	42
Eastbourne Town	34	25	7	2	97	28	82	69
East Grinstead Tn	34	17	12	5	67	39	63	28
Oakwood	34	17	5	12	70	55	56	15
Saltdean United	34	15	6	13	70	55	51	15
Westfield	34	13	10	11	54	53	49	1
Wealden	34	14	6	14	64	60	48	4
Eastbourne United	34	14	6	14	63	60	48	3
Lancing	34	12	11	11	47	49	47	-2
Steyning Town	34	13	7	14	47	43	46	4
Shinewater Ass.	34	13	7	14	46	59	46	-13
Seaford	34	11	7	16	51	51	40	0
Broadbridge Heath	34	11	5	18	54	74	38	-20
Worthing United	34	11	5	18	41	64	38	-23
Crawley Down	34	9	10	15	43	51	37	-8
Mile Oak	34	9	6	19	47	74	33	-27
Pease Pottage Vill.	34	9	4	21	38	79	31	-41
Oving	34	5	4	25	37	84	19	-47

Division One	1	2	3	4	5	6	7	8	9	10	11	12	13	14	15	16	17	18	19	20
1 Arundel		1-3	4-3	2-2	1-1	1-1	1-4	0-0	2-4	3-0	1-0	0-3	0-0	3-1	2-0	2-3	0-4	0-0	1-0	3-0
2 Burgess Hill Town	5-1		4-0	2-0	4-1	1-1	1-1	3-2	2-1	7-0	4-0	3-0	1-0	0-1	4-0	2-1	2-0	3-0	1-0	6-1
3 Chichester City United	3-1	1-0		1-3	5-2	1-1	1-4	5-1	3-1	2-0	0-0	1-2	2-0	1-0	4-1	2-1	3-1	2-4	1-1	0-1
4 East Preston	0-4	0-6	1-2		4-0	2-3	2-0	3-1	1-0	2-1	0-0	0-3	1-0	1-2	0-3	1-2	2-2	3-2	2-1	5-1
5 Hailsham Town	1-1	0-2	2-4	3-3		1-1	0-1	1-0	2-3	3-0	4-0	0-1	1-3	0-1	0-1	2-2	2-0	3-0	0-1	2-1
6 Hassocks	3-0	1-2	1-1	2-3	2-0		2-2	3-0	2-1	6-2	1-2	0-3	1-4	2-1	2-1	1-0	2-4	3-1	0-2	5-0
7 Horsham YMCA	4-0	0-0	3-3	0-2	1-4	2-1		22-1	5-2	2-0	2-0	1-4	0-0	6-0	4-1	0-1	0-1	5-3	1-1	3-0
8 Littlehampton Town	0-0	0-3	1-5	2-1	1-2	3-0	0-2		0-2	3-1	2-2	1-0	0-3	0-3	1-2	1-2	1-2	0-5	0-4	2-2
9 Pagham	2-1	0-1	1-1	0-1	0-0	4-0	4-0	5-2		1-1	0-2	1-1	1-1	2-0	1-0	0-1	0-1	4-2	1-2	7-2
10 Peacehaven & Telscombe	2-1	0-3	0-5	2-1	1-4	2-1	0-1	1-1	1-3		1-4	4-1	2-2	0-1	1-2	1-3	2-0	0-7	0-2	7-3
11 Redhill	2-1	4-1	0-1	2-0	1-2	3-5	1-3	1-0	2-0	4-1		4-2	0-2	1-2	0-2	1-0	0-3	3-2	1-2	2-0
12 Ringmer	1-0	1-2	1-1	3-1	1-0	1-3	2-1	2-1	3-0	1-0	0-0		1-4	3-0	3-3	0-5	0-0	4-2	0-5	2-1
13 Selsey	0-1	1-1	0-2	1-2	2-2	4-2	1-0	2-2	2-1	1-1	1-0	1-1		5-0	2-3	1-2	0-0	3-1	0-2	5-1
14 Shoreham	1-3	1-0	0-0	4-1	5-0	2-2	1-3	1-1	0-1	4-0	2-3	0-0	1-3		4-0	1-1	3-2	2-4	0-1	3-3
15 Sidlesham	1-1	0-4	1-0	0-2	1-3	5-3	3-2	2-2	2-2	5-1	2-0	1-1	1-0	1-0		1-0	2-1	4-1	2-1	1-2
16 Sidley United	2-0	0-2	2-5	1-1	1-1	0-1	1-2	6-0	0-5	1-2	0-1	0-0	1-0	2-1	4-0		3-1	2-2	0-1	3-1
17 Southwick	2-2	1-2	2-0	0-4	1-2	3-0	1-4	3-0	4-2	1-0	0-1	5-1	1-1	3-0	0-3	2-0		1-1	3-1	5-0
18 Three Bridges	4-4	1-4	2-2	2-1	0-2	1-1	3-2	5-0	0-1	1-1	2-1	3-1	1-3	3-2	1-4	5-2	1-3		4-1	6-2
19 Whitehawk	0-1	3-2	1-2	3-2	3-1	0-1	1-4	3-1	1-1	2-3	7-1	2-1	3-0	7-0	1-1	1-0	0-2	2-1		6-0
20 Wick	3-1	2-4	1-4	3-3	1-0	0-1	2-4	1-1	1-5	1-2	4-4	0-1	2-1	1-4	2-3	1-0	3-2	2-5	0-5	

Division Two	1	2	3	4	5	6	7	8	9	10	11	12	13	14	15	16	17	18
1 Broadbridge Heath		1-1	0-1	0-5	3-4	2-1	1-5	1-1	4-1	1-2	1-2	2-5	2-2	2-1	2-1	5-4	4-3	4-0
2 Crawley Down	0-2		1-1	1-4	1-1	1-2	1-1	2-1	2-1	6-1	0-0	3-1	3-0	5-1	0-4	0-2	0-1	1-0
3 East Grinstead Town	3-0	2-2		0-0	0-3	0-0	4-3	1-1	2-0	3-0	1-1	6-0	2-1	5-0	3-1	3-0	0-0	0-1
4 Eastbourne Town	4-2	2-0	1-1		5-1	2-0	4-1	3-1	3-1	2-0	1-1	3-0	2-0	2-1	4-0	0-0	4-1	3-1
5 Eastbourne United	3-0	2-1	2-3	0-3		0-2	5-1	1-2	3-2	2-0	0-3	0-4	2-1	4-3	0-1	3-3	2-2	1-1
6 Lancing	2-1	1-1	2-4	2-1	0-0		1-0	4-4	3-1	2-0	0-1	1-1	0-2	1-1	1-1	3-1	2-2	0-1
7 Mile Oak	4-0	0-0	0-5	0-7	2-1	2-5		0-3	1-1	4-1	0-1	1-2	2-4	4-1	3-2	0-0	0-1	4-3
8 Oakwood	2-0	2-0	3-0	1-3	2-6	3-2	2-0		3-1	3-0	0-2	4-1	3-1	2-1	2-4	3-4	1-3	4-0
9 Oving	3-1	1-2	2-2	0-2	1-3	1-3	3-0	3-1		2-4	0-1	0-6	2-0	3-1	1-4	0-5	0-1	2-5
10 Pease Pottage Village	1-2	3-0	2-1	1-7	1-4	5-1	0-0	2-1	5-1		1-1	0-3	0-4	1-2	0-0	1-3	0-2	1-3
11 Rye & Iden United	2-0	2-1	1-2	3-6	3-2	2-0	1-0	3-2	1-0	4-0		2-5	3-2	3-1	3-0	7-2	3-0	3-0
12 Saltdean United	2-5	1-1	1-1	1-1	1-3	3-0	4-1	1-2	5-0	0-1	2-3		0-1	6-2	0-2	2-1	0-0	0-2
13 Seaford	1-1	2-1	2-2	1-5	2-0	0-2	1-1	1-3	1-0	3-0	1-2	1-2		0-1	0-0	0-1	3-3	5-1
14 Shinewater Association	2-1	3-1	2-2	1-2	0-0	0-0	1-0	1-0	3-0	1-1	0-3	2-5	1-1		1-0	3-1	0-2	1-0
15 Steyning Town	1-2	1-0	5-0	0-2	2-1	1-1	2-0	3-3	0-0	1-2	0-1	0-2	0-4	1-1		2-1	1-0	3-0
16 Wealden	1-0	3-1	1-2	2-0	1-3	4-1	3-4	1-1	3-2	4-0	2-4	2-0	3-2	1-2	1-0		1-1	0-1
17 Westfield	2-2	1-1	0-3	3-3	1-0	1-2	3-1	0-3	3-1	4-1	0-1	0-2	1-0	0-2	1-4	3-3		6-1
18 Worthing United	2-0	1-3	1-2	1-1	3-1	0-0	1-2	0-1	1-1	2-1	3-4	2-2	0-2	0-3	1-0	1-0	2-3	

LEADING SCORERS 2002-03

(League goals only)

DIVISION ONE		DIVISION TWO		DIVISION THREE	
36 Pat Massaro	**Three Bridges**	**34 Yemi Odubade**	**Eastbourne Tn.**	**29 Jack Singer**	**Crowborough A.**
23 Nick Flint	HorshamYMCA	25 Scott McDonald	Eastbourne Utd	23 Clinton Moore	Haywards Heath
		Gary Brockwell	Eastbourne Tn.	James Lattimer	Crowborough A.
21 Matt Huckett	East Preston	22 Scott Price	Rye & Iden Utd	20 Kumbar Francis	Haywards Heath
20 Phil Gault	Three Bridges	19 Adam Burton	Saltdean United	16 Robert Pearce	Midhurst & E.
Pat Harding	Hassocks			Paul Cheal	Newhaven
Roger Moore	Chichester City				

TEAMS OF THE MONTH

MONTH	DIVISION ONE	DIVISION TWO	DIVISION THREE
August	Pagham	Shinewater Assoc.	Franklands Village
September	Whitehawk	Steyning Town	St. Franics Rangers
October	Arundel	Rye & Iden United	Storrington
November	Shoreham	Eastbourne Town	Midhurst & Ease
December	Sidlesham	Eastbourne Town	Upper Beeding
January	Burgess Hill Town	Rye & Iden United	Storrington
February	Southwick	East grinstead	Hurstpierpoint
March	Redhill	Rye & Iden United	Crowborough Athletic
April/May	Whitehawk	Rye & Iden United	Midhurst & Ease

HONOURS LISTS

LEAGUE DIVISION ONE

1981-82	Peacehaven & Tels
1982-83	Peacehaven & Tels
1983-84	Whitehawk
1984-85	Steyning Town
1985-86	Steyning Town
1986-87	Arundel
1987-88	Pagham
1988-89	Pagham
1989-90	Wick
1990-91	Littlehampton Town
1991-92	Peacehaven & Tels
1992-93	Peacehaven & Tels
1993-94	Wick
1994-95	Peacehaven & Tels
1995-96	Peacehaven & Tels
1996-97	Burgess Hill Town
1997-98	Burgess Hill Town
1998-99	Burgess Hill Town
1999-00	Langney Sports
2000-01	Sidley United
2001-02	Burgess Hill Town
2002-03	**Burgess Hill Town**

LEAGUE DIVISION TWO

1981-82	Wick
1982-83	Horsham YMCA
1983-84	Portfield
1984-85	Shoreham
1985-86	Wick
1986-87	Pagham
1987-88	Langney Sports
1988-89	Seaford
1989-90	Bexhill Town
1990-91	Newhaven
1991-92	Portfield
1992-93	Crowborough Athletic
1993-94	Shoreham
1994-95	Mile Oak
1995-96	Saltdean United
1996-97	Littlehampton Town
1997-98	East Preston
1998-99	Sidley United
1999-00	Sidlesham
2000-01	Southwick
2001-02	Rye & Iden United
2002-03	**Rye & Iden United**

LEAGUE DIVISION THREE

1984-85	Oakwood
1985-86	Seaford Town
1986-87	Langney Sports
1987-88	Midway
1988-89	Saltdean
1989-90	Worthing United
1990-91	Ifield
1991-92	Hassocks
1992-93	Withdean
1993-94	Bosham
1994-95	Midhurst & Easebourne
1995-96	Ifield
1996-97	Sidlesham
1997-98	Lingfield
1998-99	Oving SC
1999-00	Bosham
2000-01	Rye United
2001-02	Pease Pottage Village
2002-03	**Midhurst & Easebourne**

LEAGUE CHALLENGE CUP

1981-82	Horsham YMCA
1982-83	Whitehawk
1983-84	Steyning Town
1984-85	Littlehampton Town
1985-86	Steyning Town
1986-87	Arundel
1987-88	Wick
1988-89	Pagham
1989-90	Langney Sports
1990-91	Littlehampton Town
1991-92	Peacehaven & Tels
1992-93	Peacehaven & Tels
1993-94	Whitehawk
1994-95	Hailsham Town
1995-96	Shoreham
1996-97	Wick
1997-98	Burgess Hill Town
1998-99	Burgess Hill Town
1999-00	Saltdean United
2000-01	Sidley United
2001-02	Horsham YMCA
2002-03	**Selsey**

DIVISION TWO LEAGUE CUP

1981-82	Lancing
1982-83	Shoreham
1983-84	Haywards Heath
1984-85	Chichester City
1985-86	Pagham
1986-87	Selsey
1987-88	Chichester City
1988-89	Midhurst
1989-90	Oakwood
1990-91	Chichester City
1991-92	Redhill
1992-93	Lancing
1993-94	Shoreham
1994-95	Horsham YMCA
1995-96	Selsey
1996-97	Sidley United
1997-98	Three Bridges
1998-99	Sidley United
1999-00	Sidlesham
2000-01	Peacehaven & Tels
2001-02	Rye & Iden United
2002-03	**Rye & Iden United**

MERIT TABLE WINNERS

1981-82	Wick
1982-83	Peacehaven & Tels
1983-84	Portfield
1984-85	Steyning Town
1985-86	Wick
1986-87	Pagham
1987-88	Three Bridges
1988-89	Wick
1989-90	Wick
1990-91	Littlehampton Town
1991-92	Peacehaven & Tels
1992-93	Pagham
1993-94	Wick
1994-95	Wick
1995-96	Wick
1996-97	Wick
1997-98	Burgess Hill Town
1998-99	Horsham YMCA
1999-00	Arundel
2000-01	Redhill
2001-02	
2001-02	**Midhurst & Easebourne**

Horsham YMCA before their final league match against Arundel on April 26th 2003.
Back Row (L-R): J. Dumbrill, W. Potter, S. Langridge, M. Francis, G. Taylor, R. Andrews, J. Suter (Manager).
Front Row (L-R): N. Flint, N. Sleat, M. Duffield (Capt), D. Carden, D. Oakes, M. Hennessey. Photo: Clive Turner.

Eastbourne United. Photo: Roger Turner.

Hailsham Town. Photo: Roger Turner.

ARUNDEL

Secretary: Doug Feest, 142 Aldsworth Road, Worthing. BN12 4UU Tel: 01903 249276

Ground: Mill Road, Arundel, West Sussex. Tel: 01903 882548

Directions: A27 from Worthing to Arundel over railway bridge to roundabout. Second exit into Queen Street to town centre, turn right over bridge. Car park leading to ground 100yards right

Capacity: 2,200 Seats: 100 Cover: 200 Floodlights: 206 lux

Clubhouse: 2 bars, kitchen, toilets, telephone, pool, darts, Sky TV. Normal pub hours. No food

HONOURS Sussex Co. Lg 57-58 58-59 86-87 (Lg Cup 86-87, Div 2 Cup 76-77, Res. Sect. 78-79, Res. Sect. Cup 78-79, Merit Table 80-81,Sussex Fives 1984 1987), Sussex RUR Charity Cup 68-69 72-73 78-79 79-80, Sussex Jnr Cup 07-08, West Sussex Lg (Res.) 70-71 (Malcolm Simmonds Cup 70-71)

PREVIOUS **League** : West Sussex 1896-1975 **Grounds:** Castle Park; Station Rd Ground

RECORD **Gate:** 2,200 v Chichester, League 67-68
Scorer: Paul J Bennett **Appearances:** 537, Paul Bennett (goalkeeper)
Win : 13-0 v Horsham YMCA (H), Sussex Co. Lge Div 1 21/12/85

Players progressing: John Templeman (Brighton & Hove Albion 1966)

FACT FILE

Founded: 1889
Nickname: Mulletts
Colours: Red & white halves/white/red
Change colours: Green/black/green
Midweek matchday: Tuesday
Reserves' Lge: Sussex Co. Res Div (West)
Programme: 8 pages, free Editor: P Wells
Local Press: Arun Herald

CLUB PERSONNEL

Chairman: Bob Marchant
Vice Chairman: S Brennan
Manager: Mike Rowland

CHICHESTER CITY UNITED

Secretary: Peter Down, 14 Edith Cottages,Mill Road, West Ashling, Chichester PO18 8DG
Tel: 01243 574597 (H) email: peter.down1@btinternet.com

Ground: Church Road, Portfield, Chichester, West Sussex PO19 4HN Tel: 01243 779875
Capacity: 2,000 Seats: 20 Cover: 200 Floodlights: Yes

Directions: A27 from Arundel to Chichester, take road to signposted city centre then 1st left (Church Rd) after supermarket r'bout. 1 mile from Chichester(BR)

Clubhouse: 2 bars, pool, snooker, seating for 100, dance floor, darts. Teabar selling h & c food.

PREVIOUS **Names**: Chichester FC (pre-1948), Chichester City 48-00. Amalgamated with Portfield in 2000

HONOURS as Portfield: Sussex Co. Lg Div 2 72-73 83-84 91-92 (Div 2 Cup 70-71 72-73, Res Sect Prem Lge 94-95, Cup 91-92), W Sussex Lg 46-47 48-49 (Malcolm Simmonds Cup 46-47), Sussex Jnr Cup 45-46, Benevolent Cup 46-47

HONOURS as Chichester City: Sussex Co. Lg(5) 59-61 67-68 72-73 79-80 Invit. Cup 47-48 54-55 56-57 63-64, Div 2 Cup 84-85 87-88 90-91, Sussex Snr Cup 25-26, Sussex RUR Charity Cup 60-61(jt with Brighton & HA) 63-64, Sussex I'mediate Cup 67-68

FACT FILE

Formed 2000
Chichester (1873)Portfield (1896)
Sponsors: Covers
Nickname: Lilywhites
Colours: All white with green piping
Change colours: Green & blue/blue/blue
Midweek matchday: Tuesday
Programme Editor: T Wallis
Local Press: Chichester Observer

CLUB PERSONNEL

Chairman: Simon Kenny
Match Secretary:Phil Littlejohns
Tel: 01243 528007
Press Officer: T Wallis (01705 464438)
Manager: Adrian Girdler
Chief Coach: Gary Brockway
Physio: Hannah Alen
2002-03: Capt: Tony Stephens
Top Scorer: Roger Moore
P.o.Y.: Ben O'Connor

EAST GRINSTEAD TOWN

Secretary Martin Hill, The Flat, 2A Saxbys Lane, Lingfield, Surrey RH7 6DN

Ground: East Court, East Grinstead Tel: 01342 325885

Directions: A264 Tunbridge Wells road (Moat Road) until mini-r'bout at bottom of Blackwell Hollow, turn immediately right by club sign then 1st left, ground 200yds down lane past rifle club on right.

Capacity: 3,000 Seats: None Cover: 400 Floodlights: Yes Club Shop: No

Clubhouse: Open 1.30-10.30 matchdays, 6-11 midweek matches. Available for hire. Darts, pool, satellite TV. Hot food available Saturday match days, hot snacks rolls etc available at midweek matches.

PREVIOUS **Leagues:** Mid-Sussex 1900-15 35-37; Sussex Co. 20-32; Southern Amateur 32-35.
Grounds: West Street Cricket Ground (pre-1963); King George's Field 63-68.

RECORD **Attendance:** 2,006 v Lancing, FA Amateur Cup 8/11/48
Appearances: Guy Hill in 19 seasons - 1977-94

HONOURS Sussex RUR Charity Cup (R-up 74-75); Sussex Co. Lg Invitation Cup 51-52; Sussex Jnr Cup (jt) 07-08; Sussex Youth Cup 86-87; Southern Amtr Lg.Snr Div 3 31-32; Mid-Sussex Lg x 6, Lg Cup x 7; Brighton Lg x 3, Lg Cup x 3,Mid Sussex Junior Cup 2001-02

Players progressing: None

FACT FILE

Founded: 1890
Nickname: Wasps
Sponsors: Rydon Group.
Colours: Gold/black/black
Change colours: All Blue
Midweek Matchday: Tuesday.
Reserves Lge: Sussex Co. Reserve Div East
Website: www.egffc.co.uk
Programme
36 pages, 50p Editor: Bruce Talbot
Press Off.: Bruce Talbot 01293 543809
Local Press: East Grinstead Observer/East Grinstead Courier, Sports Argus

CLUB PERSONNEL

Chairman:Bruce Talbot
President: Colin Dixon

Manager: Bobby Smith
Physio: Pam Presland

EAST PRESTON

Secretary: Keith Freeman, 41 Ambersham Cres., East Preston, West Sussex BN161AJ Tel: 01903 771158

Ground: Roundstone Recreation Ground, East Preston, West Sussex Tel: 01903 776026
Capacity:1,000 Seats: 50 Cover: 100 Floodlights: Yes

Directions: Less than a mile from Angmering (BR) station. A259 from Worthing to Roundstone Hotel (6 miles), turn south over railway crossing, left past Centurion garage, right into Roundstone Drive

Clubhouse: Licensed bar open Mon-Fri evenings, Sat noon-11pm, Sun noon-11pm. Kitchen serves light refreshments on matchdays

HONOURS Sussex Co. Lg Div 2 Champions 97-98Div 3 83-84, (R-up 90-91), Div 3 Cup 87-88 (R-up 89-90); West Sussex Lg 77-78 80-81 81-82 82-83 (Malcolm Simmonds Cup 80-81 82-83), Div2 Sth 81-82, Div 3 Sth 79-80, Div 5 Sth 82-83; Chichester Cup 87-88; BorehamTphy 77-78 90-91 (R-up 93-94); Vernon Wentworth Cup 80-81 89-90; 99-00 Worthing Lg 67-68 (Div 2 68-69 (res); Benevolent. Trophy 66-67 68-69; Worthing Charity Cup 68-69

PREVIOUS **Leagues:** Worthing; W Sussex

FACT FILE
Reformed: 1966
Nickname: None
Sponsors: Argyl insurance
Colours: White with black trim,black/white
Change: Black & yellow stripes/white/black
Reserves Lge: Sussex Co. Res. Div (Prem)
Programme: Yes
Editor: Doug Hall
Local Press: Littlehampton Gazette

CLUB PERSONNEL
President: Greg Stanley
Chairman:Doug Hall
Manager: Vic Short
Asst Managers: Kevin Valentine & Simon Butler

2002-2003
Captain: Jim Smith
Player of the Year: Simon Clayton
Top Scorere: Matthew Huckett

EASTBOURNE TOWN

Secretary: Viv Greenwood, 102 Latimer Rd., Eastbourne BN22 7DR (01323 411117)

Ground: The Saffrons, Compton Place Road, Eastbourne, East Sussex (01323723734)
Capacity: 3,000 Seats: 200 Cover: Yes Floodlights: Yes

Directions: Turn south west off the A22 into Grove Road (opposite BR station), and the ground is 1/4 mile on the right

Clubhouse: Fully licensed bar. Board room. Tea bar with Hot Food.

HONOURS Sussex County Lg. 76-77; Sussex Sen Cup x12 1889-91, 93-95, 98-1901, 02-03, 21-22, 31-35, 52-53; Sussex RUR Charity Cup 32-33, 47-48, 49-50; SouthernAmat. Lge. x2; AFA Sen. Cup 21-22, 24-25, R-up 22-23, 23-24; AFA Invitation Cup69-70, R-up 56-57, 68-69, 70-71

PREVIOUS **Leagues:** Southern Amtr 07-46; Corinthian 60-63; Athenian 63-76

RECORD **Attendance:** 7,378 v Hastings Utd. 1953

FACT FILE
Founded: 1882 Nickname: `Bourne'
Sponsor: Owen Contractord
Colours: yellow/blue/yellow
Changes: Sky blueblack/black
Prog Ed: Dave Pelling Tel: 01323 460695

CLUB PERSONNEL
Chairman: Roger Addems
Manager: Dave Winterton

2002-03
Captain:MarkReeve Top Scorer:YemiOdubade
Player of the Year: Gary Brockwell

HAILSHAM TOWN

Secretary: /Press Officer Derek York, 59 Anglesey Avenue, Horsebridge, Hailsham BN27 3BQ Tel: 01323 848024 (H)

Ground: The Beaconsfield, Western Road, Hailsham, East Sussex Tel: 01323 840446

Directions: A22 to Arlington Road, turn east, then left into South Road - left into Diplocks Way until Daltons. Four miles from Polegate (BR - Brighton-Eastbourne line); regular bus service from Eastbourne

Capacity: 2,000 Seats: None Cover: 300 Floodlights: Yes

Clubhouse: Hot and cold snacks. Open every evening, matchdays and Sundays, teabar

HONOURS Sussex County Lg Div 2 R-up 80-81, Southern Co'sComb. 74-75, Sussex RUR Charity Cup, Sussex I'mediate Cup, Hastings Snr Cup,Sussex Jnr Cup, E Sussex Lg Cup, Hailsham Charity Cup, John O'Hara Cup 95-96

PREVIOUS **League:** E Sussex, Southern Comb

BEST SEASON **FA Vase:** 5th Rd 88-89

RECORD **Gate:**1,350 v Hungerford, FA Vase Feb '89
Goalscorer: H Stevens 51, 95-96 **Appearances:** P Comber 713

FACT FILE
Founded: 1885
Nickname:The Stringers
Colours: Yellow &Green/Green/gGreen
Change colours: All blue
Midweek matchday: Tuesday
Programme: Yes
Editor: Secretary
Admission: ˜3.00

CLUB PERSONNEL
President: J.Whippy
Chairman: S.Richardson
Manager: Brian Dennis

2002-03
Leading Goalscorer: S.French 14
Captain & Player of the Year:M.Richardson

HASSOCKS

Secretary: Dave Knight, 21 Farnham Avenue, Hassocks, BN6 8NR
Tel No: 01273 842023

Ground: The Beacon, Brighton Rd, Hassocks Tel: 01273 846040
Capacity: 1,500 Seats: None Cover: 100 Floodlights: Yes

Directions: Off A273 Pyecombe Road to Burgess Hill, 300yds south of Stonepound cross roads (B2116) to Hurstpierpoint or Hassocks

Clubhouse: Clubroom, bar, kitchen Club Shop: No

HONOURS Sussex County Lg Div 3 91-92, Div 2 R-up 94-95, Res. Sect. East R-up 92-93; Southern Counties Comb. 76-77, Lg Cup R-up 79-80; Brighton Hove & Dist. Lg 71-72; Sussex Intermediate Cup 74-75 (R-up 80-81)

PREVIOUS **Leagues:** Mid Sussex; Brighton Hove & Dist.; Southern Co's Comb
Ground: Adastra Park, Hassocks (pre-1992)

RECORD **Attendance:** 610 v Burgess Hill Town, Sussex County Lge 96-97

FACT FILE
Founded: 1902
Nickname: The Robins
Sponsors: Icon
Colours: Red/white/red
Change colours: Blue/white/blue
Midweek Matchday: Tuesday/Wednesday
Programme: 24 pages, 50p
Editor: Dave Knight
Admission: £1.50
Local Press: Mid Sussex Times, Evening Argus

CLUB PERSONNEL
President: Maurice Boxall
Chairman: JimGoodrum (01273 842023)
Manager: Dave John

HORSHAM YMCA

Secretary: Bob Brading, 16 Hazelhurst Crescent, Horsham,.RM12 1XB
Tel No: 01403 250270 (H)
Ground: Gorings Mead, Horsham Tel: 01403 252689
Capacity: 1000 Seats: 150 Cover: 200 Floodlights: Yes

Directions: Approaching Horsham fron the East on A281 Brighton Road, the ground is on left & signposted opposite Gorings Mead

HONOURS Sussex Co Lge Div 2 65-66 82-83 R-up 94-95 (Lg Cup 81-82, Invitation Cup66-67 67-68, Div 2 Invit. Cup 59-60 61-62 94-95) Sussex RUR Cup Winners 2000-01

PREVIOUS **Leagues:** Horsham & Dist/Brighton & Hove/Mid Sussex
Grounds: Lyons Field, Kings Road

RECORD **Attendance:** 950 v Chelmsford City , FA Cup 2000
Victory: 22-1 v Litt;lehampton 15th Octpober 2002 (Nick Flint 10)

BEST SEASON: **FA Cup:** 4th Qual. Rd. 99-00 2-3 v Chelmsford City

FACT FILE
Founded: 1898
Nickname: YM's
Sponsors: Principal Corporation
Colours: White/black/white
Change colours: All Red
Midweek Matchday: Tuesday
Local Press: West Sussex County Times

CLUB PERSONNEL
Chairman:Mick Browning
Manager: John Suter
Match Secretary:Bob Brading
Manager: John Suter
Physio: Robin Bishop

2002-03
Leading Goalscorer:Nick Flint 28
Captain: Matt Duffield
Player of the Year: Wayne POtter
Ever present (51 games) Jason Dumbrill

PAGHAM

Secretary: David Bolland, 23 Tennyson Road, Bognor `Regis PO21 2SB
Tel No: 01243 829973
Ground: Nyetimber Lane, Pagham, West Sussex Tel: 01243 266112
Capacity: 2,000 Seats: 200 Cover: 200 Floodlights: Yes

Directions: Turn off A27 Chichester by-pass (signposted A259 Pagham). Ground invillage of Nyetimber. Three miles from Bognor (BR). Buses 260 & 240

Clubhouse: Bar open matchdays and some evenings. Hot food, pool, darts,satellite TV. Tea bar
Club Shop: No

HONOURS Sussex Co. Lg R-up 80-81 87-88 88-89 92-93 (Div 2 78-79 86-87, Lg Cup88-89, Div 2 Cup 71-72 85-86, Res. Sect. West 80-81, Res Section Cup 77-78 80-81 87-88 88-89 90-91 96-97; Sussex F'lit Cup R-up 88-89; Sussex RUR Charity Cup88-89 (R-up 93-94); West Sussex Lg 65-66 68-69 69-70; Malcolm Simmonds Cup 67-68; Sussex I'mediate Cup 66-67

PREVIOUS **Leagues:** Chichester 1903-50; West Sussex 50-69 **Grounds:** None

RECORDS **Gate:** 1,200 v Bognor, 1971 **Scorer:** Mark Vickers/ R Deluca
Win: 10-1 v Seaford Town (A), Sussex County League Division Two, 1970
Defeat: 0-7 v Newport IOW (H), FA Amateur Cup, mid-1970s

FACT FILE
Founded: 1903
Nickname: Lions
Sponsors: City Sales Centre
Colours: White/black/red
Change colours: Yellow/green/green
Midweek Matchday: Tuesday
Reserve's League: Sussex Co. Res Premier
Programme: 12 pages, 50p
Editor: Rob Peach
Local Press: Bognor Observer

CLUB PERSONNEL
Chairman: Graham Peach
Vice-Chairman: Steve Newdick
President: A Peirce
Press Officer: John Rose(01243 545694)
Comm. Manager: Chairman
Manager: Paul Gilbert
Asst Manager: Kevin Hotson

Ringmer FC. Photo: Roger Turner.

Arundel attack the Hassocks goal during their 1-1 draw at Mill Road. Photo: D. Nicholson.

Rye & Iden United, Division Two Champions, line up before their Sussex County Division Two Cup final success. Photo: Roger Turner.

REDHILL

Secretary: Neil Hoad, 2b Earlswood Rd, Redhill, Surrey RH1 6HE Tel: 01737 213847
Ground: Kiln Brow, Three Arch Road, Redhill, Surrey Tel: 01737 762129
Emails: michael-stewart 7@ ntlworld.com & neil@ nhoad.fsnet.co.uk
Directions: On left hand side of A23, two and a half miles south of Redhill
Capacity: 2,000 Seats: 150 Cover: 150 Floodlights: Yes
Club Shop: Sells usual range of souvenires. Contact Spencer Mitchell - 01737 780634
Clubhouse: Social club, bar, canteen, board room, club shop, tanoy, toilets
HONOURS Athenian 24-25 83-84 (Lg Cup 69-70 70-71), East &West Surrey Lg1902-3, Southern Sub Sen West Lg. 1902-03, Surrey Snr Cup 28-29 65-66, Gilbert Rice F'lit Cup 80-81, Sussex Co. Lg Div 2 Cup 91-92, Southern Co's Comb. Cup 90-91,98-99

PREVIOUS **Leagues:** E & W Surrey; Spartan 09-10; Southern Sub; London 21-23; Athenian 23-84; Spartan 84-88
Grounds: Memorial Sports Ground, London Road 1894-1986

BEST SEASON **FA Amtr Cup:** Semi-Final 25 **FA Cup:** 1st Round 57-58

RECORDS **Attendance:** 8,000 v Hastings United F.A.Cup 1956
Goalscorer: Steve Turner 119 **Appearances:** Brian Medlicott 766
Win : 12-1 v Southall (H) Athenian Lg. 1928-29
Defeat : 1-13 v Bromley (A) Athenian League 1945-46

FACT FILE
Founded: 1894 Nickname: Reds/Lobsters
Sponsors: Morrisons
Colours: All red Change: White/black
Midweek matchday: Tuesday
Reserve League: Sussex Co.Lg
A4 size Programme: 72 pages 50p
Winners of all Programme Awards 2002-3
Editor: Michael Stewart
New Editors: Dave & Dan Best
Website: http://redhillfc.tripod.com/kilnbrow
Local Press:Surrey Mirror/Redhill&Reigate Life

CLUB PERSONNEL
Chair: Nick Creasey V.Chair: Alan Thurlbeck
President: Malcolm Chatfield
Press Officer: Michael Stewart
Man: Ian Dawes Assistant: : John Framks
Physio: Brian Watts
2002-03
Captain& Player of the Year:
SteveGillett

RINGMER

Secretary: Gary Bullen, 13 Browns Parth, Uckfield, East sussex TN22 1LN
Tel Nos: 07769 936272 (M) 01825 769748 (H)

Ground: Caburn Ground, Anchor Field, Ringmer Tel: 01273 812738
Capacity: 1,000 Seats: 100 Cover: Yes Floodlights: Yes

Directions: From Lewes road turn into Springett Avenue opposite Ringmer village green. Anchor Field first left. Three miles from Lewes (BR)

Clubhouse: 2 bars, function room, boardroom, tea bar
Club Shop: Club ties & metal badges

HONOURS Sussex Co. Lg 70-71, R-up: 01-02Div 2 68-69, Invit Cup 66-67; Res. Sect. East 79-80 80-81 (R-up 89-90), Yth Section 87-88, Yth SectionEast 87-88; Sussex Snr Cup 72-73 (R-up 80-81); Sussex Jnr Cup 25-26; Sussex Express Sen Charity Cup 94-95

PREVIOUS **League:** Brighton **Grounds:** None **Names:** None

BEST SEASON **FA Cup** 1st Rd Proper 70-71

RECORD **Gate:** 1,200 in FA Cup

FACT FILE
Founded: 1906
Nickname: The Blues
Colours: Sky & navy/navy/navy
Change colours: All yellow
Midweek Matchday: Tuesday
Programme: Yes
Editor: Martin BUrke (01797 230572)
Admission: £3.00
Local Press: Sussex Express

CLUB PERSONNEL
President: Sir G Christie
Chairman: Richard Soan
Manager: Glen Geard
Press Officer: Martin Burke(01797 230572)
Match Sec:John McWhirter (01323 847743)
2002-03
Leading Goalscorer:
Captain:
Player of the Year:

RYE-IDEN UNITED

Secretary: Ged Say,18 Parkwwod Iden, nr Rye,East Sussex TN31 7XE
Tel: 01797 280495 (H) 07776 101993 (M)
email: ged@sayiden.fsnet.co.uk

Ground: Sydney Allnut Pavilion, Rye Football & Cricket Salts, Fish Market Rd., Rye, East Sussex Tel: 01797 223855

Directions: Outskirts of Rye on the A268, joins A259 opposite Skinners Rover garage. Fishmarket Road.

Previous **Leagues:** Sussex Co., Kent Co. >00

Honours: Sussex Co. Lge Div. 3 Champions 01-02
Sussex Co. Lge Div. 2 Champions 02-03
Sussex Co. Lge Div. 2 Cup Winners 02-03

SELSEY

Secretary: Denny Lee, 29 Malthouyse Cottages, West01243 605027

Ground: High Street Ground, Selsey, Chichester, West Sussex Tel: 01243 603420
Capacity: 2,250 Seats: 50 Cover: Yes Floodlights: Yes

Directions: Through Selsey High Street to fire station. Take turning into car park alongside the station. Entrance is in the far corner. Regular buses from Chichester
Clubhouse: Bar, hospitality room, lounge, toilets, kitchen

HONOURS Sussex Co. Lg R-up 89-90 (Div 2 63-64 75-76 (R-up 86-87), Div 2 Cup 86-87 (R-up 84-85), Div 2 Invitation Cup 63-64, Sussex 5-aside 88-89), Sussex SnrCup R-up 63-64, Sussex I'mediate Cup 58-59, Sussex Jnr Cup(Reserves) 76-77,West Sussex Lg 54-55 55-56 57-58 58-59 60-61 (Malcolm Simmonds Cup 55-56 56-57 57-58 58-59)

PREVIOUS **Leagues:** Chichester & Dist.; West Sussex

RECORD **Gate:** 750-800 v Chichester or Portfield, 50's

FACT FILE
Founded: 1903
Nickname: Blues
Sponsors: Ariel Cars
Colours: Blue/white/blue
Change colours:All red
Midweek Matchday: Tuesday
Programme Editor: Secretary
Match Secretary: Mandie Glew

CLUB PERSONNEL
President: Roy Glew
Chairman: Mike Hurst
Press Officer: Secretary
Manager:Danny Hinshelwood

SHOREHAM

Secretary: Glenn Hilton, 2 Loneycourt, Wilmot Road,Shoreham by Sea, BN43 6JQ
Tel No: 01273 705902(H) 01273 430775 (W)

Ground: Middle Road, Shoreham-by-Sea, West Sussex Tel: 01273 454261
Capacity: 1,500 Seats: 20 Cover: 1 stand Floodlights: Yes

Directions: Half mile from Shoreham-by-Sea (BR) - east across level crossing, up Dolphin Road, ground 150yds on right. Or, A27 to Shoreham. At Southlands Hospital turn left down Hammy Lane, left at end, ground opposite
Clubhouse: Seats 70. Bar, pool, darts, tea bar **Club Shop:** No

HONOURS Sussex Co. Lg 51-53 77-78 (R-up 34-35, Div 2 61-62 76-77 84-85 93-94,Div 2 Cup 74-75 82-83, Invitation Cup 57-58), Sussex Snr Cup 01-02 05-06,Sussex F'lit Cup R-up 89-90, Sussex RUR Charity Cup 02-03 05-06, VernonWentworth Cup 86-87
PREVIOUS **League:** West Sussex **Ground:** Buckingham Park (pre-1970)
RECORD **Gate:** 1,342 v Wimbledon (f/lt opening 86)

FACT FILE
Founded: 1892
Nickname: Musselmen
Sponsors: Len German Wholesalers
Colours:All royal blue
Change colours: All red
Midweek Matchday: Wednesday
Programme: Yes
Editor: Michael Wenham
Local Press: Shoreham Herald

CLUB PERSONNEL
President: Alf Bloom
Chairman: John Bell
Press Officer: Michael Wenham
Tel: 01273 596009
Manager: Roger Vrace

SIDLESHAM

Secretary: Michael Homer, 20 McNair Close, Selsey, Chichester, W. Sussex PO20 9JB
Contact details - TelNo: 01243 603977(h) 07803 617176 (M)01243 603977(Fax)
e-mail: mbheh.0428@virgin.net

Ground: Sidlesham Recreation Ground,Selsey Road Sidlesham.Chichester.E.Sussex PO20 7RD Tel No: 01243 603977
Capacity:1,500 **Covered Seating:** No **Covered Standing:** Yes **Floodlights:** Yes
Clubhouse: Open evenings 8-11 p.m. **Club Shop**: No

Directions: From the Chichester bypass take the B2145, signposted Hunston/Selsey Head towards Selsey. Upon entering Sidlesham the ground is on the right between houses.
Best Season: F.A.Vase: Second Round 2002-2003

HONOURS West Sussex League 1963-64 W.Sussex Lg Cup 1963-64,19787-79,1990-91 Sussex Intermediate Cup 1q9909-91. Sussex Co. Lg Cup Div 3 1991-92,1996-97.Div 3 Champipons1996-97, Division 2 Champions 1999-2000 Div 2 CP 99-00 Div1 Cup r-uyp: 2000-01

FACT FILE
Founded: 1936
Colours: Yellow & Green/green/yellow
Change colours: Red /white/red
Midweek Matchday: Tuesdays
Prog: Yes 24 Pages 50P Ed: Sec.

CLUB PERSONNEL
Chairman: Alan Parker
Tel: 01243 513891 (H)
07887 507351 (M)
Vice Chairman: Roy Parker
Manager: Richard Towers
(01243 586887)
Assistant .Manager: Shaun Standing

2002-03
Leading Goalscorer:Richie Davies
Captain:David Towers
Player of the Year:Mark Wozniak

SIDLEY UNITED

Secretary: Mike Gardner, 24 Magpie Close, St Leonards on Sea, E Sussex TN38 8DY

Ground: Gullivers Sports Ground, Glovers Lane, Sidley, Bexhill-on-Sea
Tel: 01424 217078
Capacity: 1,500 Seats: None Cover: 150 Floodlights: Yes

Directions: From Brighton on A259 to Bexhill bypass traffic lights, left intoLondon Road, continue into Sidley, right into Glovers Lane and 1st left into North Road.
One mile from Bexhill (BR)

Clubhouse: Large bar area & function room. Tea bar
Club Shop: No, but metal badges are available.

HONOURS Sussex Co. Lg Div 1 00-01 Jphn O'Hara League Cup: 00-01 01-02Div 2 58-59 64-65 98-99, Div. 2 Cup 98-99, Div 2 Invit. Cup 57-58; Sussex Intermediate Cup 47-48, Sussex Jnr Cup 24-25

PREVIOUS **Leagues:** East Sussex; Hastings & District
Grounds: None

RECORD **Attendance:** 1,300 in 1959

FACT FILE

Founded: 1906
Nickname: Blues
Sponsors: M.T.Drains
Colours: Navy & sky/navy/navy & sky
Change colours: Yellow & Black
Midweek Matchday: Tues/ Weds
Programme: Yes
Local Press: Bexhill Observer, Bexhill News

CLUB PERSONNEL
President: Tom Hyland
Chairman: Dickie Day
Joint Managers: Glen Sully & Peter Heritage

2002-03
Leading Goalscorer:
Captain:
Player of the Year:

SOUTHWICK

Secretary: Gary Milliis, 21 Grover Avenue, Lancing, West Sussex. BN15 9RG
Tel: 01903 761396 (H) 07801 477979 (M)
Ground: Old Barn Way, off Manor Hall Way, Southwick, Brighton BN43 4NT
Tel: 01273 701010
Directions: Five minutes walk from either Fishergate or Southwick BR stations.
By car A27 from Brighton take 1st left after `Southwick' sign to Leisure Centre. Ground adjacent.
Capacity: 3,500 Seats: 220 Cover: 1,220 Floodlights: Yes Shop: Badges only
Clubhouse: Weekdays 12-3 & 6-11, all day Sat., normal hrs Sunday.
Members bar & boardroom with bar. Matchday snacks from tea bar.
HONOURS Isthmian Lg Div 2 Sth 85-86; Sus. Co. Lg 25-26 27-28 29-30 47-48 68-69 74-75, R-up x 9, Lg Cup 77-78 ,Div 1 Invit. Cup 65-66, Div 2 R-up 65-66; Combined Co's Lg R-up 84-85, Sus.Snr Cup x 10, Sus. RUR Charity Cup (10) 1896-97 08-09 10-11 24-26 27-30 37-38 76-77, W. Sus. Lg1896-97 97-98 1908-09 10-11, Sus. Jnr Cup 1891-92.
PREVIOUS Leagues: West Sussex 1896-1920; Sussex County 20-52 54-84; Metropolitan 52-54; Combined Co's 84-85; Isthmian 85-92.Sussex RUR Charity Cup 02-03
Previous Grounds: Croft Avenue; The Green; Oldfield Crescent.
BEST SEASON FA Cup: 1st Round 74-75, 0-5 v Bournemouth **FA Amtr Cup:** 3rd Rd. 28-29
FA Vase: 3rd Rd. 79-80 85-86 **RECORD Attendance:** 3,200 v Showbiz side 1971
Players progressing: Charles & William Buttenshaw (Luton 1948)

FACT FILE
Founded: 1882
Nickname: Wickers
Sponsors: City Woodfloors
Colours: Red & black stripes/black/red
Change Blue& blackstripes/black/blue
Midweek matchday: Tuesday
Reserve League: Sussex Co. Res Div
Programme: Yes
Editor/ Press Off.:
Paul Symes 01273 594142
Local Press : Evening Argus, Shoreham Herald
CLUB PERSONNEL
Chairman: Barry Noonan
President: Dr D W Gordon.
Manager: Jason Rutherford
Asst Manager: Mick Fogden
2002 -2003
Captain: Jamie Ash
Top Scorers: Tony Holden & Simon Funnell 15
P.o.Y.: Danny Smith

Horsham YMCA's Nick Flint (left) is unsettled by an East Preston defender, during Horsham's 0-2 league defeat.

Photo: Clive Turner.

ST. LEONARDS

GROUND The Firs, Elphinstone Rd, Hastings, E. Sussex
Tel: 01424 434755 (Matchday) 01424 716362 (Office) Club Website: www.freezone.co.uk/stlfc
Directions: From north approach Hastings on A21. Immediately after junct with A28 on the northern borough boundary, turn right into Junction Rd. At T junct with B2093 turn right onto The Ridge. After 2 miles turn right, opposite cemetary, into Elphinstone Rd, grd 600 yds downhill on left. Nearest station; Ore (Connex South East), 1 mile uphill (no bus or taxi). Hastings (Connex South East) 1.5 miles. Bus service from town centre to ground
Capacity: 3,768 (Day), 3,015 (Even) Seats: 251 Cover: 1,000 Floodlights: Yes
Clubhouse: Open normal pub hours. Hot food available on matchdays, plus matchday tea bar.
Club Shop: Open matchdays
PREVIOUS **Leagues:** Eastbourne & Hastings 71-82, Southern Counties Comb 82-88, Sussex County 88-96, Southern Lge 96-2003
CLUB RECORDS **Attendance:** 1,798 v Tiverton Town, FA Vase 4th Rd. 15/01/95
Appearances: Keith Miles 292 1995-2001 **Goalscorer:** Keith Miles 134 1995-2001
BEST SEASON: **FA Cup:** 3rd Qual Rd 96-97 97-98 **FA Vase:** 5th Rd 94-95
FA Trophy: 3rd Rd 96-97
HONOURS: Sussex Sen Cup 96-97; Sussex RUR Charity Cup R-up 94-95; Hastings Snr Cup 89-90 95-96 96-97, R-up 92-93 97-98; Southern Lge Southern Div R-up 96-97, Merit Cup 96-97; Sussex County Div 1 R-up 94-95 95-96, Div 2 R-up 92-93, Cup R-up 89-90 90-91, Div Three R-up 88-89, Cup R-up 88-89 Kent Midweek Lg.Cup Winners 98-99

FACT FILE
Formed: 1971
Nickname: Saints Sponsors:
Shirt Sponsor: Hastings Direct (Insurance)
Colours: Blue/white/blue
Change colours: White/black/white
Midweek Matchday: Monday
Reserves' League: Sussex County
Programme: Pages: 60 Price: £1 Editor:T.B.A.

CLUB OFFICIALS
Chairman: John Cornelius
Patron: Leon Shepherdson
President: Mrs K Shepperdson
Vice-Chairman: Danny Bossum
Secretary: Tony Leppard c/o The Club
Business Manager: Dale Seymour
Tel: 01424 434755 or 0797 6626716
Press Officer: Roy Russell 01424 846008

Manager: Glyn White
Physio: Rob Greig

THREE BRIDGES

Secretary: Martin Clarke, 18 Mannings Close, Pound Hill, Crawley RH10 3TX
Tel: 01293 883726 (H), 07885 662940 (Mob)
Ground: Jubilee Field, Jubilee Walk,Three Bridges, Crawley, West Sussex
Tel: 01293 442000
Capacity: 3,500 Seats: 120 Cover: 600 Floodlights: Yes
Directions: From Three Bridges station, turn L. to Crawley. At 2nd T'light turn R. into Three Bridges road. Take 1st left (opp. Plough Inn) into Jubilee Walk.
Clubhouse: Open every day 12 noon - 11pm (10.30pm Sunday) Carpeted lounge. Bar serving food, Players bar, Pool, Darts, Satelite big screen TV, Dance floor. Separate Tea Bar serving hot food on match days. Disabled toilet facilities.
Club Shop: No
HONOURS Sussex I'mediate Cup 84-85 Sussex Co. Lg R-up 85-86 87-88 88-89 Div 2 54-55, R-up 68-69, 73-74, 79-80, 98-99, Invitation Cup 70-71, Div 2 Invitation Cup 62-63, 73-74, Sussex RUR Charity Cup 82-83 R-up 85-86, 87-88, 88-89. Co. Lge Div. 2 5-a-side 97-98, R-up 98-99

PREVIOUS **League s:**Mid Sussex; E. Grinstead, Redhill&District 36-52 **Grounds:** None
Names: Three Bridges 01-18, Three Bridges Worth 19-53, Three Bridges United 54-64.

RECORD **Attendance:** 2,000 v Horsham, 1948

FACT FILE
Founded: 1901
Nickname: Bridges
Sponsors:Canadian Spaco Ltd
Colours: Amber & black/black/black
Change colours: Blue & white/blue/white
Midweek Matchday: Tuesday
Programme: Yes
Editor: Andy West (01293 883163)
Local Press: Crawley Observer, Crawley News

CLUB PERSONNEL
Chairman: Alan Bell
Press Officer: Alf Blackler
Manager: Sam Donnelly
Asst. Manager: Derek Pyle
2002-2003
Leading Goalscorer: Pat Massaro 43
Captain: Jamie Edwards
Player of the Year: Pat Massaro

WHITEHAWK

Secretary: John Rosenblatt, 25 Arundel Street, Brighton BN2 5TH Tel: 01273 680322

Ground: The Enclosed Ground, East Brighton Park Tel: 01273 609736
Capacity: 3,000 Seats: None Cover: 500 Floodlights: Yes

Directions: Follow Brighton seafront road towards Newhaven, turn inland (Arundel Road) oppo site Marina, 3rd right into Roedean Road, 1st left intoWilson Ave. 3 miles from Brighton (BR); take Newhaven, Eastbourne or Saltdean bus to Marina
Clubhouse: Licensed bar, pool, darts. Board room. Tea bar Club Shop: No

Honours: Sussex Co. Lg 61-62 63-64 83-84 (Div 2 67-68 80-81, Lg Cup 82-83 93-94, Invitation Cup 60-61 69-70, Div 2 Cup 80-81), Sussex Snr Cup 50-51 61-62,Sussex RUR Charity Cup 54-55 58-59 90-91, Sussex I'mediate Cup 49-50, Sussex Jnr Cup 48-49 51-52, Brighton Charity Cup 51-52 59-60 61-62 82-83 87-88 88-89 89-90 90-91 97-98 98-99 99-00 Worthing Charity Cup 82-83

PREVIOUS **League:** Brighton Hove & Dist**Grounds:** None
Name: Whitehawk & Manor Farm Old Boys (until 1958)

BEST SEASON **FA Vase:** 5th Round 93-94

RECORDS **Gate:** 2,100 v Bognor Regis Town, FA Cup 4th Qualifying Rd replay 88-89
Scorer: Billy Ford **Appearances:** Ken Powell 1,103

FACT FILE
Founded: 1945
Nickname: Hawks
Sponsors: Precision Metal Products
Colours: All red
Change colours: All blue
Midweek Matchday: Tuesday
Programme: £3.50 with admission
Editor: Fred Moore (01273 689433)
Local Press: Evening Argus

CLUB PERSONNEL
President: Ron Wiltshire
Chairman: Wally Sweetman
Match Sec: Fred Moore
Manager:Ian Chapman
Asst Manager: Glen Burvill

Above: Jim Smith, East Preston's number three, clears the danger during a Sidley United attack.
Photo: Roger Turner.

Right: Chris Hewitt shows his commitment to Hassocks when he throws his body in front of Jason Wimbleton's shot, during their league match against Arundel.
Photo: D. Nicholson.

Below: In the same match, Arundel's Steve Blake finds himself in plenty of space to tee up a shot at goal.....
....unfortunately for Blake his shot went wide.
Photo: D. Nicholson.

BROADBRIDGE HEATH

Secretary: Richard Solman, 13 Monks Court, Monks Walk, Reigate, Surrey RH2 0SR
Tel: 01737 212335

Ground: Broadbridge Heath Sports Centre, Wickhurst Lane, Horsham Tel: 01403 211311
Capacity: 1,300 Seats: 300 Cover: 300 Floodlights: Yes

Directions: Alongside A24, Horsham north/south bypass. From the A24 Horsham Bypass, at thelarge roundabout/underpass take the Broadbridge Heath Bypass towards Guildford and then at the first roundabout turn left into Wickhurst Lane.

Clubhouse: Bar. Kitchen serving meals,

HONOURS Sussex Yth Lg N. Div. 99-00, Southern Yth Lg S. Div. 00-01

PREVIOUS **Leagues:** Horsham, West Sussex, Southern Co's Comb

RECORD **Attendance:** 240

FACT FILE
Founded: 1919 Nickname: Bears
1st Team Sponsors: Maltaward Ltd.
Colours :Royal blue Change: Red/black or white
Midweek matches: Tuesday
Programme Editor: Andy Crisp (01403 252273)
Admission: £2.50

CLUB PERSONNEL
Chairman: Keith Soane
President: G W Manketelow
Manager: Allan Winton

2002-03
Leading Goalscorer:Ramin Jaruand 14
Captain:Paul Stevens
Player of the Year: Ramin Jaruand

CRAWLEY DOWN

Secretary: Bob Rashbrook, 3 Collier Row, Southgate, Crawley, West Sussex RH10 6ES
Tel 01293 411457 (H)

Ground: The Haven Sportsfield, Hophurst Lane, Crawley Down.
Tel: 01342 717140 Website: www.partners-solutions.co.uk/crawley down.info
Capacity: 1000 Seats: None Cover: 50 Floodlights: No

Directions: From B2028, follow signpost for village to War Memorial, turn left into Hophurst Lane, ground 100 yards on left. From A22, Felbridge, left into Crawley Down Road, ground 2 miles uphill on right.

HONOURS Sussex County Lge Div 3 R-Up 95-96
Sussex Intermediate Chall. Cup R-up 95-96

PREVIOUS **League:** Mid Sussex Football League

FACT FILE
Formed: ?????
Colours: All red
Change: White/black/black
Midweek Matchday: ?????
Programme:Yes

CLUB PERSONNEL
Chairman: Brian Suckling
Vice-Chairman: Michael Martin
President: Tony Clements
Match Secretary: Andy hale

Managers : Shaun Donnelly & Alan Watson
Physio: Mike Green

EASTBOURNE UNITED ASSOCIATION

Secretary: c/o Peter Snashall, 3 Gilbert Road, Eastbourne BN 22 8JA Tel: 01323 644038(H)
Ground: The Oval, Channel View Rd, Eastbourne, East Sussex (011323-726989)
Capacity: 3,000 Seats: 160 Cover: 160 Floodlights: Yes
Directions: From A22 follow signs to eastbourne East/Seafront. Turn left onto seafront. Turn left into Channel View Rd at Princess Park & ground 1st right. 2 miles from Eastbourne (BR)
Clubhouse: Bar, lounge, dancefloor, stage, tea bar, board room **Club Shop:** Yes
PREVIOUS **Ground:** Lynchmere **Leagues:** Sussex Co. 21-28 35-56; Metropolitan 56-64; Athenian 64-77; Isthmian 77-92
Names: Eastbourne Old Comrades, Eastbourne Utd (merged with Shinewater Assoc 2003)
RECORD **Attendance:** 11,000 at Lynchmere
HONOURS Sussex Co. Lg 54-55, Div 2 R-Up 99-00 Sussex Snr Cup(5) 60-61 62-64 66-67 68-69(R-up 89-90), Sussex RUR Charity Cup 55-56,Metropolitan Lg Cup 60-61,Athenian Lg Div 2 66-67 (Div 1 R-up 68-69), Sussex I'mediate Cup 65-66 68-69
Players progressing: B Salvage, T Funnell, M French, L.Barnard

FACT FILE
Founded: 1894 Nickname: The 'Us'
Colours: White/black/white
Change colours: All Sky Blue.
Midweek Matchday: Wednesday
Reserve Lge: Sussex County Res. Premier

Programme
36 pages Editor:Kevin Townsend

CLUB PERSONNEL
Chairman: Peter Snashall
Vice-Chairman: Kevin Townsend
President: Doug Sissons
Manager: Micky French
Asst Manager: Dave Shearing
Physio: Jo Henderson

HAYWARDS HEATH TOWN

Secretary: Steve Weller, 52 Kents Road,Haywards Heath, Sussex RH16 4HQ
Tel: 01444 457230

Ground: Hanbury Park Stadium, Haywards Heath Tel: 01444 412837

Directions: A272 to Haywards Heath town centre. At Sussex roundabout, north on B2708 (Hazelgrove Road) take first right into New England Road, then the 4th right (Allen Road) leads to ground.

FACT FILE
Colours: Blue & white stripes/blue/blue

CLUB PERSONNEL

LANCING

Secretary: Brian Hill,17 Annweir Ave., Lancing, W. Sussex BN15 9NF
Tel: 01903 756165 (H&F) email: brian@whill20.fsnet.co.uk
Ground: Culver Road, Lancing, West Sussex Tel: 01903 764398
Web-site: www.lancingfc.co.uk
Directions: From A27 turn south at Lancing Manor r'about into Grinstead Lane, 3rd turning on right North Farm Rd. Turn left then immed. right into Culver Rd. From railway station take 3rd turning on left heading north. Capacity: 2,400 Seats: 350 Cover: 350 Floodlights: Yes
Clubhouse: Open matchdays & training nights. Separate tea bar. **Club Shop:** Yes
HONOURS Sussex Co. Lg R-up 49-50 64-65 (Div 2 57-58 69-70 (R-up 82-83), Div 2 Cup 81-82 92-93, Invitation Cup), Sussex RUR Charity Cup 65-66, Brighton Lg 46-47 47-48, Sussex Intermediate Cup 46-47, Brighton Charity Cup 83-84 84-85 86-87.
PREVIOUS League: Brighton Hove & District **Name:** Lancing Athletic
RECORDS Attendance: 2,591 v Tooting, FA Amateur Cup 22/11/47 At Culver Road: 2,340v Worthing 25/10/52 **Career Appearances:** Dave Menzies 462 **Goals:** Paul Steele 113

FACT FILE
Founded: 1941 Nickname: Lancers
Sponsors: Bacon & Co. Estate Agents
Colours: Yellow/blue/yellow
Change colours: All red
Midweek Matches: Wed Programme: Yes
Reserves League: Sussex Co Res.West
Editor/Press Off.: Len Ralph (01903 763913)
2002-03 Captain: Glen Souter
Top Scorers Jamie Cole 14
P.o.Y.: Simon Davey
CLUB PERSONNEL
Chairman: John Brown President: R G Steele
Match Sec: Don Stevens (01273 592653 (H)
Commercial Man.: SteveTaylor(01903 851919)
Manager: Alf Ford Physio: Peter Towell

LITTLEHAMPTON TOWN

Secretary: John Savage, 66 Nelson Road, Worthing. BN12 6EN. (01903 502850)

Ground: The Sportsfield, St Flora's Road, Littlehampton (01903 713944)
Capacity: 4,000 Seats: 260 Cover: 260 Floodlights: Yes
Directions: 10 minutes walk from Littlehampton station (BR) - turn left alongTerminus Rd, continue through High Street and Church Rd to junction with St Flora's Rd (left)
Club Shop: No, but metal badges available
Clubhouse: Sportsman (Private Club). Separate board room & tea bar
HONOURS Sussex Co. Lg 58-59 (jt with Shoreham) 75-77, 84-85, 90-91, 96-97
Sussex Senior Cup 1949, 1970
RECORD Gate: 4,000 v Northampton, FA Cup 1st Rd Proper 90-91
BEST SEASON FA Vase Semi-Final 90-91 v Gresley Rovers 1-3 (A), 1-2 (H)
FA Cup: 1st Round 90-91 v Northampton Town(H) 0-4
2002-03 Leading Scorer: Jan Miller Captain: Cameron Johnson Player o.Y: Chris Hazel

FACT FILE
Founded: 1894
Nickname: Marigolds
Colours: Gold/black/black
Change: All white
Midweek Matches: Tuesday
Programme: 50p Pages: 52
Editor: Paul Hooker
Local Press: Littlehampton Gazette

CLUB PERSONNEL
President: Ian Cunningham
Chairman:Andy Taylor

Manager: Carl Stabler

MIDHURST & EASEBOURNE

Secretary: Ted Dummer, 14 Nine Acres, June Lane, Midhurst, W. Sussex GU29 9EP
Tel: 01730 813887 (H) email: acs@harrisonrenwick.com

Ground: Rotherfield, Dodsley Lane, Easebourne, Midhurst, W. Sussex
Tel: 01730 816557
Directions: Ground one mile out of Midhurst on London Road (A286) opposite Texaco Garage. Ample car parking. Buses pass ground every hour

FACT FILE
Colours: Royal blue/black/royal
Change colours: All red
CLUB PERSONNEL

MILE OAK

Secretary: Colin Brown, 19 The Crescent, Southwick, West Sussex BN42 4LB
Tel: 01273 591346
Ground: Mile Oak Recreation Ground, Graham Avenue, Mile Oak.Tel: 01273423854

Directions: From A27 take Mile Oak Road or Locks Hill & Valley Road to Chalky Road, ground 500yds on right along Graham Avenue which runs up valley fromcentre of Chalky Road
Capacity: Seats: None Cover: Yes Floodlights: Yes
Clubhouse: Mile Oak Pavillion; Hall and tea bar **Club Shop:** No
HONOURS Sussex Co.Lg.Div 2 Champions, Div 3 R-up 91-92 (Div 2 Cup R-up 92-93), Southern Counties Combination 86-87, Brighton Hove & District Lg 80-81, VernonWentworth Cup 85-86, Sussex Intermediate Cup R-up 88-89
PREVIOUS Leagues: Southern Counties Combination; Brighton Hove & District
Ground: Victoria Rec., Portslade
RECORD Attendance: 186

FACT FILE
Founded: 1960
Nickname: The Oak
Colours: Tangerine/black/tangerine
Change colours: All blue
Midweek Matchday: Tuesday
Programme: Yes
Editor: C Tew (01273 416036)
Admission: £1.50
Local Press: Brighton Evening Argus, Shoreham Herald
CLUB PERSONNEL
Chairman: L.Hamilton
President: D Bean
Manager: M.Cox

OAKWOOD

Secretary: S.A.Wildy, 45 Holmcroft, Southgate, Crawley, West Sussex (01293 409410)
Ground: Tinsley Lane, Three Bridges, Crawley, West Sussex Tel: 01293 515742

Directions: From A23 to Gatwick, take 1st set of lights into Manor Royal, pass next lights, over r'bout to warehouse marked Canon, turn right signposted Oakwood. Last clubhouse down lane. Two miles north of Three Bridges (BR)

Capacity: 3,000 Seats: 20 Cover: Yes Floodlights: Yes
Club Shop: Yes, incl. metal badges
Clubhouse: Large bar area, pool tables, multidart boards. Board room & tea bar

HONOURS Sussex Snr Cup R-up 92-93, Sussex Co. Lg Div 2 R-up 89-90 (Div 2 Cup 89-90, Div 3 84-85), Southern Comb. Cup 83-84
PREVIOUS **Leagues:** Crawley & Dist., Southern Co's Comb
Ground: Park pitches
RECORD **Attendance:** 367 **Appearances:** Peter Brackpool

FACT FILE
Founded: 1966 Nickname: Oaks
Sponsors: Linden Plc
Colours: Red & black/black/black
Change colours: Blue& black/white/blue
Midweek Matchday: Tuesday
Reserves' Lge: Sussex Co. Reserve section
Programme: 24 pages
Editor: Scott Packer Local Press: Crawley Observer, Crawley News

CLUB PERSONNEL
Chairman: Stuart Lovegrove
Press Officer & Match Sec: Scott Packer
Manager:Andy Maddox
Physios: Ms.S Widy & Frank Pushman

PEACEHAVEN & TELSCOMBE

Secretary: Mrs Margaret Edwards, 2,Tuscan Court, The Esplanade, Telscombe Cliffs, East Sussex BN10 7HF Tel: 01273 583022 (H) 07803 845329 (M)
Ground: Piddinghoe Avenue, Peacehaven, E. Sussex (01273 582471)
Directions: From Brighton on A259, over r'bout & Piddinghoe Ave. is next left after 2nd set of lights - ground at end. From Newhaven, Piddinghoe Ave. is 1st right after 1st set of lights. 3 miles from Newhaven(BR). Peacehaven is served by Brighton to Newhaven & Eastbourne buses
Capacity: 3,000 Seats: None Cover: 250 Floodlights: Yes
Clubhouse: Bar open evenings and weekends, pool darts, hot and cold food available. Tea bar
RECORD Attendance: 1,420 v Littlehampton, Lge 91 **PREVIOUS Leagues:** Lewes; Brighton
BEST SEASON FA Cup: 4th Qual. Rd 90-91 **FA Vase:** 6th Rd (Q-F) 95-96, 5th Rd 92-93
HONOURS Sussex Co. Lg 78-79 81-82 82-83 91-92 92-93 94-95 95-96 R-up x 3, Lg Cup 91-92 92-93, Div 2 R-up 75-76, Div 2 Cup 75-76, Norman Wingate Tphy 82-83 91-92 92-93, Hayden Tphy 82-83 92-93, Div 2 Invitation Cup 69-70, Sussex Snr Cup R-up 81-82 92-93, Sussex RUR Charity Cup 77-78 81-82 92-93 R-up x 5, Brighton Charity Cup (x3) 91-94, Vernon Wentworth 91-92 92-93

FACT FILE
Founded: 1923
Nickname: The Tye
Sponsors: Anchor Garage
Colours: All white and black
Change colours: Royal Blue
Midweek Matches: Tuesday
Programme: Yes
Editor: Secretary

CLUB PERSONNEL
Chairman: Jim Edwards
Match Sec: Fred Parris
Press Officer: Secretary
Manager: Peter Edwards

PEASE POTTAGE VILLAGE

Secretary: Mrs Sue Brooks, 115 Lark Rise, Langley Green, Crawley, W. Sussex RH11 7QG
Tel: 01293 410657 (H) 01293 848100 (B) 07754 163029 (M)
email: suebrooks57@aol.com

Ground: Finches Field, Pease Pottage, Crawley, W. Sussex
Tel: 01293 538651

Directions: Off M23/A23 towards Brighton, turn off at Pease Pottage (turn off just past Crawley). Past service station to roundabout, take 3rd exit over bridge sharp left, follow signs to Finches Field. Approx. 300 yards past "Grapes" P.H., on the right.

FACT FILE
Colours:
Royal blue & white/royal/raoyal & white
Change: Yellow/blue/yellow

CLUB PERSONNEL
Chairman: Tony Read
29 Westpark Road, Handcross, W. Sussex RH17 6DN
Tel: 01444 400059 (H) 01444 881565 (B)
Manager: Mick Butler

SALTDEAN UNITED

Secretary: Iain Fielding, 40 Rowan Way, Rottingdean, Brighton BN2 7FP
Tel: 01273 304995

Ground: Hill Park, Combe Vale, Saltdean, Brighton Tel: 01273 309898
Capacity: 2,000 Seats: 50 Cover: Yes Floodlights: Yes
Club Shop: No Club Website: www.the-tigers.co.uk
Directions: A259 coast road east from Brighton to Saltdean Lido, left into Arundel Drive West, and Saltdean Vale to bridle path at beginning of Combe Vale. Club 200yds along track
Clubhouse: Licensed bar, lounge, darts, video games, board room, tea bar.Pool table

HONOURS Sussex Co. Lg Div 3 88-89, Div 2 95-96: John O'Hara Lg Cup Winners 2000
PREVIOUS **League:** Sussex County **Ground:** None
RECORD **Attendance:** 676
2002-2003 **Captain**: Ashley Walker **Top Scorer**: Leigh Bavis **P.o.Y.:** Daniel Jordan

FACT FILE
Founded: 1966 Nickname: Tigers
Sponsors: Camkal
Colours: Red & blackstripes/black/black
Change : Blue & whitestripes/blue/white
Programme: Yes Editor:Alex Panton
Local Press: Brighton Evening Argus & Sussex Express

CLUB PERSONNEL
Chairman: Robin Hall
Vice Chairman:Mike Walker
President: Jim Bower
Press Officer:Alex Panton
Manager: Mark Cox
Physio: Gary West

East Grinstead Town before their FA Vase Preliminary Round tie against Herne Bay.

Photo: Roger Turner.

East Grinstead goalkeeper, Scott Kenward, comes off his line to close down a shot from Herne Bay's Arundel, during their FA Vase Preliminary tie. Photo: Roger Turner.

Westfield line up before their Sussex County Division Two Cup final.

Photo: Roger Turner.

SEAFORD TOWN

Secretary: Chas Pulford,14 Rosemount Cloise, Bishopstone BN25 2TPO
Tel: 01323 898286 (H) 01323 893040 (B) 07815 051128 (M)
email: charles.pulford@btopenworld.com

Match Sec.: Neil Vine, Flat 4, Miramar House West, 2 Grand Parade, Eastbourne BN21 3EH
Tel: 07811 618361 (M)

Ground: The Crouch, Seaford. Tel: 01323 892221

Directions: A259 to Seaford. At mini r'about by station, turn LEFT (coming from Newhaven) or RIGHT (from Eastbourne). At end of Church St., across junction, then left at end. After 500 m turn left up Ashurst Rd. Bramber Rd. is at the top.

FACT FILE

Colours: Red & blue/blue/red
Change: Yellow & green/green/yellow

CLUB PERSONNEL

Chairman: Kevin Moore
Tel: 01323 897369 (H) 07760 173178 (M)

Manager: Duncan Kneller
Tel: 01323 892876 (H) 07760 175746 (M)

STEYNING TOWN

Secretary: Mrs. Gina Barnes, 36 Shooting Field, Steyning W. Sussex BN44 3RQ
Tel: 01903 815387 (H)

Ground: The Shooting Field, Steyning, W. Sussex
Tel: 01903 812228)

Directions: Entering Steyning from the west. Take 1st left in the High St (Tanyard Lane) Follow into Shooting Field estate, ground is 4th turn on the left.
Entering Steyning from the east. From the High St., turn right into Church St.. Turn left by Church into Shooting Field estate.
NB Coaches MUST park in Church Street Car Park.

HONOURS

PREVIOUS **Leagues:**

CLUB RECORDS **Attendance:**

Biggest Win: **Biggest Defeat:**

FACT FILE

Colours: All Red and white
Change: All sky blue & yellow

CLUB PERSONNEL

Chairman: Russell Matthews
Tel: 01903 813372 (H)
Vice Chairman:
Manager: John Bolingbroke
Asst. Man. / Coach:

WEALDEN

Secretary: Larry Hillman,26 Framelle Mount,Framfield,Uckfield TN22 5PT
Tel: 01825 890764 (H) 07710 838843 (M)
Email: larry@addagrip.co.uk

Ground: Wealden Football Club, Old Eastbourne Road, Uckfield, East Sussex.
Tel: 01825 890905

Directions: Next to the Rajdutt Restaurant on the Old Eastbourne Road, south of Uckfield town centre.

HONOURS Sussex County Lge Div. 3 R-up 99-00

FACT FILE

Colours: Blue & white.
Change colours: Red & Black

CLUB PERSONNEL

Chairman: Tom Parker
Vice Chairman:
Manager: Gary Allen
Asst. Man. / Coach
Physio:

WESTFIELD

Secretary: J. J. Archer, Gorse Cottage, Moor Lane, Westfield TN35 4QU
Tel: 01424 754516 (H) 01424 751030 (W)

Ground: Parish Field. Westfield Tel: 01424 751011

Directions: Take A21 towards Hastings, left onto A28, Westfield Lane - signposted to Ashford. Approx. 2 miles to village, pitch on left on main road just past garage.

FACT FILE

Colours: White & Green/green/green
Change Colours: Yellow & Green/ green/green

CLUB PERSONNEL

Chairman: G.A.Drinkwater
28 Churchfield, Westfield, Hastings TN35 4QN
Tel: 01424 754032 (H) 01424 751030 (B)
Vice Chairman:
Manager: Shaun Hardy
Asst. Man. / Coach
Physio:

WICK

Secretary: Peter Turner,64 Hawthorn Road,Bognor Regis,West Sussex. PO21 2DD
Tel: 01243 822860 (H)

Ground: Crabtree Park, Coomes Way, Wick, Littlehampton, W. Sussex Tel: 01903 713535

Capacity: 2,000 Seats: 50 Cover: 200 Floodlights: Yes

Directions: A27 to Crossbush, left at lights signed Littlehampton, after 1 mile over level crossing, left into Coombes Way next to Locomotive PH - ground at end. 1.5 miles from Littlehampton (BR)

Clubhouse: First floor. Capacity 120. Tea bar Club Shop: No

HONOURS Sussex Snr Cup 92-93; Sussex Co. Lg 89-90 93-94, Lg Cup 87-88 96-97 R-up 93-94 94-95), Div 2 81-82 85-86, Div 2 Cup R-up 81-82; Norman Wingate Tphy88-89 90-91, Res. Sect West 87-88 90-91 94-95; Sussex 5-aside R-up 85-86;Sussex RURCharity Cup 89-90 97-98; 98-99 Gilbert Rice F'lit Cup R-up 80-81 81-82; Sussex Jnr Cup 59-60; Brighton Charity Cup 85-86; Sussex F'lit Cup R-Up 94-95

PREVIOUS **League:** West Sussex **Grounds:** Southfields Rec

RECORD **Attendance:** 900

FACT FILE

Founded: 1892 Nickname: Wickers
Sponsors: Swandean
Colours: Red & black/black/black
Change colours: All blue
Midweek Matchdays: Tuesday
Reserve League: Sussex Co. Reserve Div
Programme: Yes Editor:Secretary
Local Press: Littlehampton Gazette

CLUB PERSONNEL

Chairman: Barry Wadsworth
Vice-Chairman: T.B. A.
President: Jack Croft
Manager: T.B.A.
Asst Manager:T.B.A.

WORTHING UNITED

Secretary: Malcolm Gamlen, 1 Westbourne Ave., Worthing, West Sussex BN14 8DE
Tel: 01903 263655

Ground: The Robert Albon Memorial Grd, Lyons Way, Worthing Tel: 01903 234466
Capacity:1,000 Seats: 100 Cover: 500 Floodlights: No

Directions: From west past Hill Barn r'about to 2nd set of lights, turn left into Lyons Way. From east 1st set of lights at end of Sompting bypass right into Lyons Way

Clubhouse: Bar (capacity 80), refreshment facilities (tea bar) Metal badges: Yes

HONOURS As Wigmore Athletic prior to 1988. Sussex Co. Lg Challenge Cup 74-75 (Invitation Cup 59-60, Div 2 52-53, Div 2 Invitation Cup 59-60, Div 3 89-90, Reserve Section West 92-93, Sussex Jnr Cup 49-50

PREVIOUS **Names:** Wigmore Athletic (founded 1948) merged with Southdown in 1988
Grounds: Harrison Road, Worthing

RECORD **Attendance:**180 v Northwood, FA Vase 3rd Rd 91-92

FACT FILE

Founded: 1988
Nickname: None
Sponsors: Tinsley Robor
Colours: Sky & white/navy/navy
Change : Green & white/white/green & white
Programme: Yes
Editor: D.Treacy (01903 690122)
Local Newspapers: Worthing Herald

CLUB PERSONNEL

President: Bob Albon
Chairman: Dennis Stoner
Press Officer: Secretary
Manager: Derrren Woods

Midhurst & Easebourne celebrate their victory over Crowborough in the Sussex County League Division Three Cup final played at Horsham YMCA. Photo: Arthur Evans.

BEXHILL UNITED
Secretary: Mrs Leigh Quinn, 37 Colebrook Road, Bexhill-on-Sea. TN39 3PX Tel: 01424 214197
Ground: The Polegrove, Brockley Rd, Bexhill-on-Sea, E. Sussex Tel: 01424220732 **Directions**: At Little Common r'bout take 3rd exit to Cooden Sea Rd, left into Cooden Drive for one and a half miles, Brockley Rd on the right. 3/4 mile from Bexhill Central (BR)
Colours: Green & white/white/white

BOSHAM
Chairman:Terry Longland Manager: Richard Mckenna
Secretary: Dick Doncaster, 61 Manor Way,Southbourne,Nr Emsworth PO10 8LY Tel: 0143 375184
Ground: Bosham Recreation Ground, Walton Lane, Bosham, W. Sussex Tel: 01243 574011
Directions: From Chichester take the A259 towards Portsmouth. On reaching Bosham turn left at the Swan P.H. roundabout. 1/2 mile to T junction, turn left & car park 50 yds on left.
Honours: Sussex County Lge Div. 3 99-00
Colours: Red/white/red Change Colours: White/black/white

CROWBOROUGH
Founded: 1894
Secretary: Phil Sharman, High Ridge, Green Lane, Crowborough TN6 2DF Tel: 01892 668176 (H)
Ground: Alderbrook Recreation Ground, Fermor Road, Crowborough Tel: 01892 661893
Directions: Turn east off A26 at Crowborough. Cross traffic lights, through High Street, right into Croft Rd, continue into Whitehill Rd and Fermor Rd, Alderbrook is 2nd right after mini-r'bout.
Clubhous Bar facilities & tea bar on matchdays Club Shop: No
Colours: Navy Blue/white/navy blue
Change colours: Yellow/green/yellow

FOREST
Secretary: Peter Farley, 9 Owlbeech Way, Horsham, W.Sussex RH13 6AW. Tel: 01403 25256
Ground: Roffey Sports & Social Club, Spooners Rd., Roffey. Tel: 01403 210221
Directions: Spooners Rd. is off the main Crawley road, 100 yds from the `Star'PH, towards Crawley
Colours: White/Navy Blue/ White

FRANKLANDS VILLAGE
Secretary: Mrs Linsey Worsfold, 151a Franklands Village, Haywards Heath. RH163RF. Tel: 01444 416475)
Ground: Hardy Memorial Playing Field, Franklands Village. Tel: 01444 440138)
Directions: A272 (Haywards H. to Uckfield). Left at Princess Royal Hosp.r'about. 2nd left & ground at rear of social club
Colours: All Royal blue

HURSTPIERPOINT
Secretary: Rodney Wilson,12 St Mary's Road, Burgess Hill, RH15 8NU Tel: 01444 870356
Ground: Fairfield Rec. Ground, Cuckfield Road. (Tel: 01273 834783)
Directions: At Hurstpierpoint crossroads, go north into Cuckfield Road (B2117) for 1km. Ground entrance between houses nos.158 & 160
Colours: Blue & white quarters/blue/blue

IFIELD EDWARDS
Secretary: Robert Anderson, 1 Old Orchards, Church Rd, Worth, Crawley. RH107QA. Tel: 01293 886215)
Ground: Edwards Sports& Social Club, Ifield Green, Rusper Road, Crawley. Tel: 01293 536569)
Directions: From A23 Crawley by-pass going north, left at r'about signedCharlwood. Third left into Ifield Green, first right past Royal Oak (PH) into Rusper Rd
Colours: White/black/red

LINGFIELD
Secretary: Pamela Thomsett, 61 Drivers Mead. Lingfield,Surrey RH7 6EX Tel: 01342 832418 (H)
Ground: Sports Pavilion, Godstone Road, Lingfield, Surrey. Tel: 01342 834269
Directions: A22, 4 miles north of East Grinstead, to Mormon Temple roundabout, take exit Lingfield (B2028) Newchapel Road for 1 1/2 miles. Left at T junction into Godstone Road (B2029) and ground is 1/2 mile on left.
Colours: Red & yellow stripes/black/yellow Change:Blue & white stripes/white/ sky blue

NEWHAVEN
Secretary: Peter Foote, 32 Valley Dene, Newhaven BN9 9NF Tel: 01273 513232
Ground: Fort Road Recreation Ground Tel: 01273 513940
Directions: A259, follow one-way system around town, left at Police Station into South Road, which becomes Fort Road.
Colours: Red & amber/red & amber/red

OVING
Secretary: Nigel Strudwick, 28 Lamorna Gardens, Chichester, West Sussex PO20 3RL Tel: 01243 545665
Ground: Highfield Lane, Oving, Nr Chichester, W Sussex. Tel: 01243 778900 **Directions:** Into Oving past the Gribble Inn, follow road round to housing estate - Highfield Lane (left). Ground signposted 50 yards on right.
Colours: Black & white stripes/white/white Change colours:Red & white/black/red

ST. FRANCIS RANGERS
Previous Names: Ansty Rangers & St. Francis
Secretary: Pat Bucknell, 79 Priory Way, Haywards Heath, W.Sussex RH16 3NS Tel: 01444 457726 (H)
Ground: The Princess RoyalHospital, Lewes Rd., Haywards Heath. Tel: Gd. 01444 474021 Social club: 01444 441881
Directions: Enter through main Hospital entrance on Lewes road, (A272 Haywards Heath). Follow signs to Sports Complex
Colours: Black & white/black/black

STORRINGTON
Secretary: Keith Dalmon, 4 End Cottages, Turnpike Road, Amberley. BN18 9LX Tel: 01798 831887 (H)
Ground: Recreation Ground, Storrington. Tel: 01903 745860
Directions: Turn west on A283 (off A24). Ground is opposite the pond to the west of the village.
Colours: All Blue Chanbge Colours : Yellow/black/yellow

UCKFIELD TOWN
Secretary: Jennie Hickman, 10 Wilson Grove, Uckfield, E.Sussex TN22 2BU (01825 762602)
Ground: Victoria Pleasure Grounds, Uckfield. Tel: 01825 769400)
Directions: Take Eastbourne road (old A22) south of Uckfield town centre. Entrance to ground is 1/2 mile on the right (just after the Police station)
Colours: Red/black/black

UPPER BEEDING
Secretary: Mrs Anita Addison, Sheppens, Newham Lane, Steyning, W. Sussex BN44 3LR Tel: 01903 814077 (H) 01903 813109 (B)
Ground: Memorial Playing Field, High St., Upper Beeding BN44 3WN Tel: 01903 815930
Directions: From east/west A27 J A283 north to Upper Beeding. Ground opposite village hall in High St. From north/south A24 J A283 southbound. Turn left to Steyning/Upper Beeding.
Colours: Yellow & blue/blue/yellow & blue. Change: All royal blue.

WADHURST UNITED
(from East Sussex Lge)
Ground: Sparrow Green Rec., South View Road, Wadhurst, East Sussex Tel: 01892 783527

OFFICIAL PROGRAMME
HORSHAM YMCA FC
FOUNDED 1898
2002-2003 SEASON
SPONSORED BY
PRINCIPAL
23

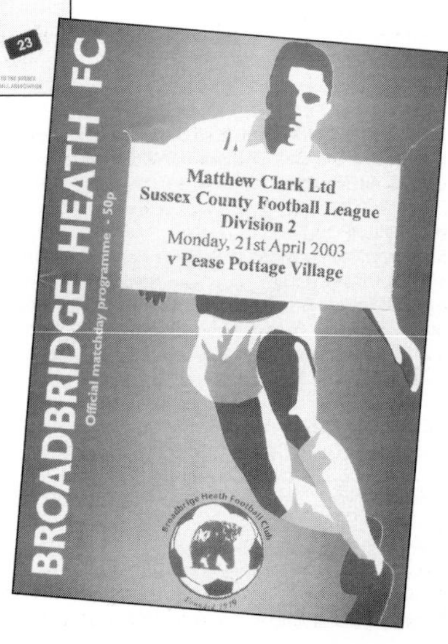

THE EAGLE BITTER UNITED COUNTIES LEAGUE

FEEDER TO: DR MARTENS LEAGUE

Chairman: Geoff Paul

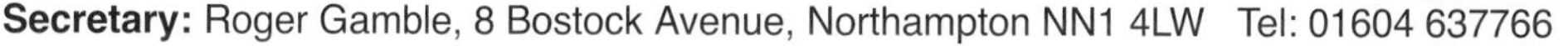

Secretary: Roger Gamble, 8 Bostock Avenue, Northampton NN1 4LW Tel: 01604 637766

Press Officer: Jeremy Biggs Tel: 01780 763048

An enthralling championship race saw Holbeach claim their second premier division championship thanks to some outstanding form in the second half of the season. On Boxing Day they were third in the table but had 27 points to make up on leaders Newport Pagnell whose advantage over second placed Deeping stood at 24 points. The Swans had a squad of vast experience at their disposal and looked certain to become the first newly promoted club to win the premier title.

Newport had supplemented their free scoring promotion winning squad with quality additions such as former Northampton Town pair Mark Parsons and Darren Harmon and classy midfielder Simon Dunlop, and with no distractions from the FA Cup and Vase they were soon setting the pace. They went to the top in mid-September and after beating Buckingham on Boxing Day to record their 14th successive win, they were almost out of sight.

Holbeach had their own share of well known names on the non-league circuit and the experience of players like Steve Appleby, Lee Hudson, Micky Nuttell and the Keeble cousins, NIck and Shaun, proved crucial as they responded to a disappointing FA Vase exit with a run of victories. After losing at Northampton Spencer on the Saturday before Christmas they were unbeaten in their remaining 24 league matches.

On 1st March 13 points separated the sides, Holbeach had two games in hand and the title chasing pair had to meet twice. A week later their Willen Road clash saw Holbeach dig deep to snatch a 2-2 draw, and defeats for Newport in their next two games added to the Holbeach belief that they could win the title. By the time the clubs met again Newport's lead was nine points and Holbeach had three matches in hand. Nick Keeble's spot kick gave the Tigers the points and the initiative for the first time.

The crown was decided on 3rd May. Going into their final match Newport led on goal difference but the Tigers had two to play. A win for both would take Holbeach into a last match decider but their 2-1 win at Stotfold with a Shaun Keeble brace proved enough as Newport were gunned down by Yaxley starlet MIchael Frew whose hat-trick ended the Swan's challenge.

Elsewhere Wootton finished third, their highest position for 22 years, free scoring Buckingham's best season in years was rewarded with fourth place and Deeping finished fifth in only their second top flight campaign.

Ford Sports lacked the previous season's consistency and never looked like retaining their title, they even lost bragging rights, finishing one place below neighbours Daventry Town. St Neots had a wretched season with their expected promotion push never getting off the ground while Raunds made a promising start only to slip back after the mid season departure of manager Adam Sandy and several key players.

Bourne made a dreadful start and were bottom until just before Christmas but the return of former title winning manager Mark Mitchell to the Wakes helm saw them rebuild and ease clear of danger in the new year. Long Buckby's promising start soon petered out and they were left to scrap it out with Kempston at the bottom. A win over Buckingham on the final day proved crucial for Buckby as they inched past their rivals to safety, thanks to a little help from Irchester.

In Division One the previous season's runners-up Sileby Rangers dominated from the off. They won their first nine matches and were unbeaten until February when they lost at Thrapston in their eighteenth outing. They did stutter later on but a burst of high scoring to end the campaign saw them to the championship.

With Sileby's Fernie Fields ground lacking floodlights, it appeared that third place might be sufficient for promotion. The minor placings were keenly contested by ambitious Harrowby, revitalised pair Potton and Eynesbury and surprise contenders Irchester.

It was the Arrows who displayed the greater consistency when it mattered and their reward was second place and a first ever promotion to the top flight. Eynesbury, with the division's outstanding strike partnership of Paul Carey and Vince Petty, and Potton, with a host of former Ryman League players recruited by the new manager Dick Newman, nonetheless came up short in the race for a podium finish as Irchester claimed third, their best finish since joining the division in 1974. The Romans' Alfred Street home was another which failed to meet premier requirements though, giving Long Buckby a reprieve from the drop from the premier.

Cup football was full of surprises as always. IN the knockout cup Blackstone claimed the trophy for the first time, beating favourites BUckingham 4-0 in the final at Kingsthorpe Mill, with the discovery of the season Graham Epps scoring twice. Harrowby, Rothwell Corinthians and Eynesbury all toppled higher grade opposition in the competition while perhaps the biggest surprise of all was the appearance of former England midfielder Steve Hodge in the Blackstone line up for their quarter final against Eynesbury. He provided a story book ending too, scoring the only goal from the penalty spot!

Wootton and Yaxley were our best FA Cup performers, reaching the Second Qualifying Round while Blue Cross also performed with distinction in the FA Vase. They reached the Fourth Round for the first time, losing in extra time to holders Whitley Bay. Buckingham also reached the last 32 with Ford Sports, Holbeach and Yaxley bowing out a stage earlier.

Both championship winners landed county cup successes. Holbeach beat FA Vase winners Brigg 3-1 to win the Lincolnshire Senior Cup A, while Sileby Rangers retained the Northamptonshire Junior Cup beating Rothwell Corinthians in the final for the second successive season. In the Huntingdonshire Senior Cup final St Neots' shootout defeat by Hotpoint summed up their campaign, there were also reverses for Stotfold in the Huntingdonshire PRemier Cup final and Harrowby, for the third season running, in the Lincolnshire Senior Cup B.

The league welcomes three new clubs for season 2003-04. Spalding United return to the premier division after their four year stint in the DR Martens League ended with relegation, while Eye United and Huntingdon Town join division one from the Peterborough and Cambridgeshire LEagues respectively. Both are ambitious and progressive and should prove excellent additions to the league.

It is also pleasing to report that Charles Wells Limited have extended their sponsorship agreement with the competition for a further three years. The league will continue to operate under the Eagle Bitter brand title.

Jeremy Biggs - Press Officer

Holbeach United - United Counties Premier Division Champions 2003

Back Row (L-R): Steven Barnes, Michael Lovell, Kevin Cross, Nick Keeble, Dean Elston, Leigh Taylor, Lee Hudson. Front Row: Jason Callaby, Shaun Keeble, Nigel Vince, Steve Appleby, Philip Barnes, Tom Fielding, James Fletcher, Andrew Stanhope. Photo: Arthur Evans.

FINAL LEAGUE TABLES 2002-03

PREMIER DIVISION		P	W	D	L	F	A	Pts
1	Holbeach United	40	28	8	4	80	25	92
2	Newport Pagnell Town	40	27	5	8	118	43	86
3	Wootton Blue Cross	40	22	10	8	72	32	76
4	Buckingham Town	40	21	8	11	90	50	71
5	Deeping Rangers	40	20	9	11	68	58	69
6	Stewarts & Lloyds	40	21	5	14	72	56	68
7	Yaxley	40	20	7	13	72	52	67
8	Boston Town	40	20	5	15	62	55	65
9	Cogenhoe United	40	18	7	15	75	59	61
10	Daventry Town	40	15	11	14	55	66	56
11	Ford Sports Daventry	40	13	14	13	62	67	53
12	Northampton Spencer	40	15	7	18	52	60	52
13	St Neots Town	40	16	4	20	59	69	52
14	Woodford United	40	15	7	18	50	60	52
15	Raunds Town	40	15	6	19	52	58	51
16	Blackstone	40	13	9	18	72	74	48
17	Stotfold	40	11	13	16	67	69	46
18	Desborough Town	40	10	13	17	48	75	43
19	Bourne Town	40	8	8	24	50	94	32
20	Long Buckby	40	3	10	27	21	107	19
21	Kempston Rovers	40	4	4	32	34	102	16

DIVISION ONE		P	W	D	L	F	A	Pts
1	Northampton Sileby Rangers	30	23	3	4	96	26	72
2	Harrowby United	30	21	4	5	81	29	67
3	Irchester United	30	20	4	6	63	36	64
4	Eynesbury Rovers	30	19	3	8	77	36	60
5	Thrapston Town	30	17	7	6	61	37	58
6	Potton United	30	16	6	8	63	40	54
7	Olney Town	30	14	7	9	65	43	49
8	Rothwell Corinthians	30	12	6	12	49	44	42
9	St Ives Town	30	11	9	10	47	50	42
10	Cottingham	30	11	6	13	49	46	39
11	Northampton ON Chenecks	30	9	7	14	54	74	34
12	Wellingborough Whitworths	30	8	2	20	39	72	26
13	Bugbrooke St Michaels	30	6	4	20	40	81	22
14	Higham Town	30	5	5	20	35	76	20
15	Blisworth	30	4	6	20	30	94	18
16	Burton Park Wanderers	30	2	5	23	27	92	11

Reserve Div One	P	W	D	L	F	A	Pts
Bugbrooke Res.	36	22	8	6	83	39	74
Rothwell Town Res.	36	22	5	9	70	39	71
Raunds Town Res.	36	21	7	8	97	49	70
Holbeach Utd Res.	36	21	4	11	85	57	67
Sileby Rangers Res.	36	20	6	10	69	44	66
Stotfold Res.	36	19	6	11	67	50	63
Newp't Pagnell Res.	36	18	5	13	74	48	59
Yaxley Res.	36	17	6	13	84	55	57
S&L Corby Res.	36	17	4	15	71	63	55
N'pton Spencer Res.	36	15	4	17	56	70	49
Blackstones Res.	36	12	11	13	64	61	47
St Neots Town Res.	36	12	10	14	47	57	46
Desborough Res.	36	10	12	14	76	72	42
Deeping Rgrs Res.	36	11	9	16	59	73	42
Whitworths Res.	36	11	8	17	50	89	41
Cogenhoe Utd Res.	36	10	9	17	47	80	39
Thrapston T. Res.	36	10	7	19	48	82	37
ON Chenecks Res.	36	6	7	23	53	80	25
Corby Town Res.	36	2	4	30	37	129	10

Reserve Div Two	P	W	D	L	F	A	Pts
Olney Town Res.	30	22	2	6	81	32	68
Potton United Res.	30	21	3	6	76	40	66
Bourne Town Res.	30	19	4	7	75	37	61
Cottingham Res.	30	17	5	8	100	50	56
Eynesbury Rv. Res.	30	17	5	8	78	47	56
Buckingham T. Res.	30	15	9	6	66	41	54
Daventry Town Res.	30	14	7	9	75	52	49
Blisworth Res.	30	14	4	12	60	57	46
Woodford Utd Res.	30	11	7	12	57	58	40
Rothwell Cor. Res.	30	11	5	14	52	60	38
Ford Spts Dav. Res.	30	10	6	14	53	67	36
Higham Town Res.	30	8	5	17	56	90	29
Burton Pk Wdrs Res.	30	7	6	17	44	70	27
Irchester United Res.	30	7	4	19	59	84	25
St Ives Town Res.	30	6	3	21	48	98	21
Long Buckby Res.	30	3	1	26	52	149	10

PREMIER DIVISION	1	2	3	4	5	6	7	8	9	10	11	12	13	14	15	16	17	18	19	20	21
1 Blackstones		3-3	1-3	0-2	1-1	2-3	2-2	4-0	2-2	0-2	2-0	4-1	2-3	3-1	6-1	1-2	1-1	1-0	0-0	2-3	0-3
2 Boston Town	1-1		3-2	3-1	1-0	8-0	2-1	1-1	0-2	1-4	3-2	0-0	2-0	1-2	2-0	2-0	3-0	3-0	0-1	0-0	3-2
3 Bourne Town	0-1	0-2		2-6	3-0	0-4	2-2	1-0	3-3	1-3	1-2	4-0	1-4	1-4	0-3	1-3	1-2	1-1	1-2	0-4	0-3
4 Buckingham Tn	2-0	4-0	2-0		2-1	4-1	6-1	0-0	3-0	0-0	3-0	2-2	1-1	1-6	1-2	6-0	1-4	0-5	4-0	3-0	7-2
5 Cogenhoe United	3-0	1-0	3-3	0-5		1-1	1-2	7-3	4-0	0-2	2-2	2-0	3-2	2-3	0-2	6-1	3-1	0-0	2-1	2-1	2-0
6 Daventry Town	3-0	0-1	1-2	3-0	3-2		0-1	0-0	4-1	2-1	3-2	0-0	0-3	2-0	0-1	3-1	2-0	1-1	0-3	0-2	0-2
7 Deeping Rangers	3-2	3-0	2-0	3-0	2-1	1-0		2-2	2-2	0-0	0-3	3-2	1-1	2-0	2-1	4-2	4-0	3-3	1-1	1-2	0-0
8 Desborough Town	1-3	0-2	2-1	2-2	2-0	1-1	2-0		3-3	0-2	2-2	2-1	0-3	1-2	3-2	0-5	1-2	1-1	2-1	1-3	0-1
9 Ford Sports Dav.	3-3	4-1	1-0	0-2	0-3	1-1	0-4	1-1		0-1	2-0	1-1	1-1	2-0	1-1	1-2	1-1	1-1	1-0	2-1	0-1
10 Holbeach United	3-1	5-0	2-2	2-1	3-1	5-1	2-1	0-0	0-0		2-1	6-0	1-0	1-0	1-0	2-0	1-0	0-0	1-0	2-0	2-0
11 Kempston Rovers	2-5	0-1	1-2	0-6	0-3	2-3	0-3	0-2	0-4	0-5		5-0	1-7	0-2	3-0	2-3	0-1	2-5	0-3	0-0	0-2
12 Long Buckby	0-2	0-1	0-3	2-1	1-4	2-2	0-4	0-3	0-1	1-2	1-1		2-1	0-2	1-0	0-5	0-5	2-8	0-2	0-5	0-4
13 Newport Pagnell Tn	4-0	2-1	8-1	2-1	3-1	6-1	6-1	2-0	2-1	2-2	5-0	4-0		3-2	4-0	7-1	1-2	4-1	4-0	1-1	1-3
14 Northampton Spen.	1-4	3-2	0-4	1-1	0-2	1-1	2-0	4-1	1-4	2-1	2-0	1-1	0-1		1-1	0-1	2-0	2-5	1-3	0-0	1-0
15 Raunds Town	3-1	0-1	3-0	2-2	0-2	1-1	1-2	1-2	3-4	2-2	1-0	5-0	0-3	1-0		2-1	0-0	0-2	2-1	2-0	2-1
16 St Neots Town	2-0	2-1	6-0	1-0	1-1	1-1	0-1	2-0	2-2	0-1	1-0	4-0	1-4	0-1	0-1		1-3	2-1	0-1	0-4	1-3
17 Stewarts & Lloyds C.	2-1	1-0	6-1	0-1	0-3	1-2	3-0	2-4	2-5	2-0	3-1	0-0	2-1	2-0	3-2	2-1		2-3	3-0	0-2	4-1
18 Stotfold	1-4	0-3	2-2	0-1	2-3	2-3	3-1	1-1	3-1	1-2	3-0	3-0	3-5	2-0	0-3	0-2	0-4		1-1	0-2	0-0
19 Woodford United	2-3	0-2	1-0	0-3	2-0	3-0	4-1	0-0	2-1	0-3	6-0	0-0	0-4	1-1	3-1	2-1	0-3	2-2		0-3	1-4
20 Wootton Blue Cross	2-1	2-0	1-1	1-2	1-1	1-1	0-1	2-1	5-0	2-1	2-0	4-0	2-0	1-1	1-0	0-0	2-2	4-1	3-1		1-2
21 Yaxley	3-3	6-2	0-0	1-1	3-2	0-1	0-1	8-1	1-3	1-5	1-0	1-1	1-3	2-0	1-0	3-1	4-1	0-0	2-0	0-2	

DIVISION ONE	1	2	3	4	5	6	7	8	9	10	11	12	13	14	15	16
1 Blisworth		3-1	2-2	0-3	1-8	2-2	0-1	0-3	1-3	1-6	1-3	1-1	0-5	2-3	2-4	2-0
2 Bugbrooke St Michaels	1-2		4-2	2-3	2-5	1-5	4-0	0-3	3-3	1-0	2-3	1-1	1-4	0-4	1-2	2-2
3 Burton Park	2-2	2-0		1-1	1-3	1-6	3-0	2-3	2-4	1-3	0-2	0-2	1-1	0-1	0-4	2-4
4 Cottingham	2-0	5-0	2-0		3-1	1-4	1-1	1-1	1-2	0-1	2-4	0-0	0-1	2-1	0-0	0-1
5 Eynesbury Rovers	7-0	1-0	4-1	4-1		0-1	2-1	0-3	3-1	3-1	0-1	3-1	1-2	1-0	1-1	4-0
6 Harrowby United	8-0	3-1	8-0	3-1	1-0		2-1	2-1	3-0	0-2	4-0	2-1	2-2	1-1	2-0	5-0
7 Higham Town	0-2	2-4	2-2	0-7	0-5	1-3		0-2	2-4	0-0	0-3	1-0	0-3	2-2	1-2	5-1
8 Irchester United	2-1	0-0	4-0	3-1	1-3	1-0	3-2		4-2	2-2	2-1	3-0	2-0	3-2	1-0	3-0
9 Northampton ON Chenecks	0-0	3-2	3-0	0-2	1-3	0-1	4-3	3-4		0-2	2-2	1-6	0-2	4-4	3-3	4-2
10 Olney Town	5-1	1-3	7-0	2-3	3-3	3-1	1-0	0-3	1-1		3-0	2-1	0-3	1-1	1-1	0-2
11 Potton United	5-1	2-1	4-0	0-0	3-2	2-3	1-1	1-1	3-0	5-0		2-1	1-3	2-2	0-1	4-1
12 Rothwell Corinthians	2-0	2-0	2-0	2-0	1-3	0-4	3-2	3-1	5-1	1-4	2-2		1-2	2-2	2-0	2-2
13 Sileby Rangers	8-0	11-1	4-0	4-1	1-1	2-0	9-2	4-1	1-2	2-1	2-1	3-1		9-0	2-0	3-0
14 St Ives Town	1-1	2-1	4-1	2-1	0-3	0-2	1-0	1-0	1-1	0-2	1-2	1-2	4-0		0-2	1-0
15 Thrapston	3-1	5-0	2-1	3-1	1-2	3-3	1-3	4-0	5-1	3-3	2-1	1-0	2-1	2-2		3-2
16 Whitworths	3-1	0-1	4-0	3-4	3-1	2-0	1-2	1-3	3-1	1-8	0-3	0-2	0-2	1-3	0-1	

MONTHLY AWARDS

Month	Manager of the Month Premier Division	Manager of the Month Division One	Goalscorer of the Month
August	Morrell Maison (Buckingham)	No award	Meshach Cole (Buckingham)
September	Danni Janes (Newport Pagnell)	John Dower/Bob Reed (Irchester)	Darren Lynch (Newport P.)
October	Jon Taylor (Wootton)	Nick Verity (Sileby)	Darren Lynch (Newport P.)
November	Mark Shackleton (Daventry)	Warren Everdell (St Ives)	Dominic Johnson (Cottingham) Paul Munday (Olney)
December	Bob Tansley (Northampton Spencer)	Dick Newman (Potton)	Vince Petty (Eynesbury)
January	Dick Creasey (Holbeach United)	Graham Leech (Cottingham)	Duncan McNish (Cottingham)
February	Mel Landin (Blackstone)	Russell Ward (Olney)	Justin Griffith (Stotfold)
March	Phil Lines (Woodford)	Gary Petts (Thrapston)	Richard Turner (Sileby)
April	Jimmy Watson (Yaxley)	John Dower/Bob reed (Irchester)	Graham Epps (Blackstone)
May	Dick Creasey (Holbeach United)	Nick Verity (Sileby)	Richard Turner (Sileby)

Manager of the Year: Dick Creasy (Holbeach United)

UNITED COUNTIES LEAGUE KNOCKOUT CUP 2002-03

PRELIMINARY ROUND

Boston Town	v	Cogenhoe United	4-1
Harrowby United	v	Woodford Utd	3-0
Northampton Spencer	v	Wootton Blue Cross	0-1
Buckingham Town	v	Olney	3-1
Kempston	v	Stew. & Lloyds	2-1 (aet)
Raunds Town	v	Sileby Rangers	3-2

FIRST ROUND

Blisworth	v	St Neots Town	0-1
Bourne Town	v	Deeping Rangers	1-0
Bugbrooke	v	Harrowby United	1-3
Eynesbury	v	Burton Park Wanderers	5-0
Long Buckby	v	Rothwell Corinthians	0-1
ON Chenecks	v	Blackstones	1-6
Stotfold	v	Kempston Rovers	0-4
Wootton BC	v	Ford Sports	2-3
Boston Town	v	Whitworths	6-1
Buckingham Town	v	Holbeach	3-2
Desborough	v	Daventry Town	1-4
Irchester	v	Raunds Town	3-5 (aet)
Newport Pagnell (walkover)	v	Wellingborough Town	
St Ives Town	v	Cottingham	1-3
Thrapston Town	v	Potton United	1-0
Yaxley	v	Higham Town	4-1

SECOND ROUND

Blackstones	v	Daventry Town	2-0
Buckingham Town	v	Harrowby United	3-1
Eynesbury Rovers	v	Kempston Rovers	4-2
St Neots Town	v	Yaxley	2-2 (aet) 3-2p
Boston Town	v	Rothwell Corinthians	4-0
Cottingham	v	Newport Pagnell	2-4
Raunds Town	v	Bourne Town	2-0
Thrapston Town	v	Ford Sports Daventry	4-6

QUARTER-FINALS

Blackstones	v	Eynesbury Rovers	1-0
Newport Pagnell Town	v	Ford Sports Daventry	2-3
Boston	v	Buckingham Town	1-2
St Neots Town	v	Raunds Town	1-0

SEMI-FINALS

Buckingham Town	v	St Neots	5-1
Ford Spts Daventry	v	Blackstones	1-2

FINAL

Buckingham Town	v	Blackstones	0-4

30th April at Northampton Spencer

UNITED COUNTIES LEAGUE LEADING SCORERS/APPEARANCES 2002-03 PREMIER DIVISION

Club	Most Appearances		Leading Scorers	
Blackstone	Richard Challinor	45	Graham Epps	28
Boston Town	Lee Rippin	44	Jamie Graham	15
Bourne Town	Darren Munton	40	Darren Munton	20
Buckingham Town	Sean Griffith	44	Meshach Cole	30
Cogenhoe United	Mark Hofford	39	Ben Foster	17
Daventry Town	Matt Finlay	40	Gareth Jones	15
Deeping Rangers	Simon Mead	40	Simon Mead	21
Desborough Town	Michael Coles	38	Sam Johnson	10
Ford Sports	Ian Pearce	41	Ian Pearce	26
Holbeach United	Kevin Cross	41	Shaun Keeble	29
Kempston Rovers	Tom Franics	41	Chris Payne	7
Long Buckby	Rick Kimbell	40	Nigel Fretwell	4
Newport Pagnell Town	Sinmon Dunlop	42	Darren Harmon	31
	Paul Edgeworth	42		
Northampton Spencer	Jamie Moss	40	Kaafi Bile	14
Raunds Town	Rob Golding	41	Rob Golding	13
St Neots Town	Paul Bloss	42	Steve Kuhne	21
	Steve Kuhne	42		
Stewarts & Lloyds	Kevin Fox	40	Matt Curtis	13
Stotfold	Paul Garrett	39	Justin Griffith	17
Woodford United	Adam Knight	39	Nick Gordon	11
Wootton Blue Cross	Jack Rashid	41	Darek Jozwaik	19
Yaxley	John-Paul Duncliffe	41	Simon Acton	13
			Michael Frew	13

BLACKSTONE

Secretary: Ian MacGillivray, 20 New Rd, Ryhall, Stamford, Lincs PE9 4HL
Tel: 01780 762263 (H),

Ground: Lincoln Road, Stamford Tel: 01780 757335
Now owned by Blackstones Sports a nd Social Club.

Directions: A6121 Stamford to Bourne road, 2nd left past MB works

Capacity: 1,000 Seats: 100 Cover: Yes Floodlights: Yes

Clubhouse: Open evenings, lunchtimes & matchdays

HONOURS UCL Div 1 R-up 87-88 (Benevolent Cup R-up), Lincs Snr Cup `A' 92-93
Eagle Bitter K.O. Cup 2002-03

PREVIOUS **Leagues:** Peterborough Works; Peterborough; Stamford & District
Names: Rutland Ironworks; Blackstone (until 1975)

RECORD **Gate:** 700 v Glinton
Win: 11-0 v Brackley, 22/1/94 (A Dunn 6 goals)
Scorer (in one game): A Dunn; 6 v Brackley Town, 22/1/94

BEST SEASONFA Vase: 2nd Round 97-98, 01-02 **FA Cup:** First Qualifying Round 91-92

Players progressing : Craig Goldsmith (Peterborough), Alan Neilson (Newcastle)

FACT FILE
Founded: 1920
Nickname: Stones
Sponsors: Ideal Shopfitters
Colours: Green& white shirts black shorts
Change Colours: Royal blue and white stripes
Midweek matchday: Wednesday
Programme: 32 pages with entry
Editor: Kevin Boor (01780 754584)
Local Press: Stamford Mercury, Herald & Post,
Peterborough Evening Telegraph

CLUB PERSONNEL
President: Bill Sewell
Chairman: Darren Laughton
Manager: Mel Landin Asst.Man.:Jim Shilling
Press Officer: IMac Gillivray
Captain: Nathan Mitchell

2002-2003
Captains: Nathan Mitchell & Garetrh Williams
P.o.Y.: Gareth Williams
Top Scorer: Graham Epps

BOSTON TOWN

Secretary: A Crick, Daisy Cottage, Shore Rd, Freiston, Boston, Lincs., PE22 0LN
Tel: 01205 760162. (H &Fax) 01205 313090 (W) 07718906053 (M)

Ground: Tattershall Road, Boston, Lincs Tel: 01205 365470

Directions: A52 Grantham-Sleaford, 2nd left into Brotherton Rd., Argyle St. to bridge, immediately over left into Tattersall road, ground 3/4 mile on left.

Capacity: 6,000 Seats: 450 Cover: 950 Floodlights: Yes Club Shop: Yes

Clubhouse: Open evenings, except Sunday, matchdays & functions. Bar & Lounge. Darts & pool

HONOURS Midland Co's Lg 74-75 78-79 80-81 (Lg Cup 76-77); Lincs Snr `A' Cup (5)73-74 79-82 89-90 (Snr `B' Cup 65-66); Central Mids Lg 88-89; Central All 65-66; Lincs Lg 64-65; Und. Co. Lg. Prem Div 94-95, 00-01

PREVIOUS **Leagues:** Lincs 63-65; Central Alliance 65-66; Eastern Co's 66-68; Midland 68-82; Northern Co's East 82-87; Central Midlands 87-91 **Ground:** Mayflower Ground

BEST SEASONFA Cup: 1st Rd Proper 76-77, 1-3 v Barnsley (A)
FA Trophy: 2nd Round 79-80, 3-6 v Mossley (A) after 0-0
FA Vase: Semi-Finals 94-95, 0-2 (agg) v Taunton Town)

RECORD **Attendance:** 2,700 v Boston Utd, FA Cup 3rd Qual. Rd 1970
Goalscorer (in a season): Carl Smaller 48, 1994-95

Players progressing: Julian Joachim (Leicester City and Aston Villa) , Neil Mann (Hull City)

FACT FILE
Founded: 1963 Nickname: Poachers
Sponsors: Barclays Brokers, Graham Gill
Carpets & Boston Snooker Centre
Colours: Sky Blue/ Royal Blue/Sky
Change: Yellow/white/yellow
Midweek Matchday: Tuesday
Reserves League: None 94-95
Programme: 40 pages, 50p(Ed-Sec)
Press Off:J.Rose 01205351501

CLUB PERSONNEL
Chairman: Mick Vines
Vice Chairman: J Rose
Treasurer: J Rose
Manager: Bob Don-Duncan
Ass.Manager: Vince Adams
Physio: Steve Greetham

2002-03
Leading Goalscorer:Jamie Graham 17
Captain & Player of the Year: Lee Rippin

BOURNE TOWN

Secretary: Jim Ashton, Tulip Cottage, Fen Road,Dunsby, Bourne, Lincs. PE10 0UE
Tel No:0177888 440022

Ground: Abbey Lawn, Abbey Road, Bourne, Lincs Tel: 01778 422292

Directions: In market place take A151 Spalding Road, ground 500 yds on right.Public transport from Peterborough, Stamford and Grantham
Capacity: 3,000 Seats: 300 Cover: 750 Floodlights: Yes
Club Shop: Contact Sec.

Clubhouse: Small, open matchdays and specific events. Food, confectionary available

HONOURS Utd Co's Lg 68-69 69-70 71-72 90-91 (KO Cup 69-70, Benevolent Cup 90-91, Res Div 2 94-95), Lincs Snr `A' Cup 71-72 (R-up 92-93), Central Alliance Division 1 South 59-60, Lincs Intermediate Cup 85-86

PREVIOUS **Leagues:** Peterborough; UCL 47-56; Central All. 58-61; MidlandCos 61-63
Ground: Adjacent to cricket field after WW2 until 1947

RECORD **Attendance:** 3,000 v Chelmsford, FA Trophy 1970
Goalscorer: David Scotney

BEST SEASON **FA Vase:** 4th Round 89-90 **FA Cup:**????

Players Progressing Peter Grummit (Nottm Forest), Shaun Cunnington (Wrexham), David Palmer (Wrexham)2002-2003

2002-2003 Captain: Darren Munton & Player of the Year:

FACT FILE
Founded: 1883 Nickname: Wakes
Sponsors:Sporting Lincs
Colours: Maroon & sky/sky/maroon
Change Colours: White & sky/white & sky/sky
Midweek matchday: Tuesday
Reserves' Lge: HSUCL Res Div 2
Programme: 30 pages, 75p
Editor: JimAshton (01778 440065)
Local Press: Stamford Mercury, Lincs Free Press, Peterborough EveningTelegraph, Bourne Local

CLUB PERSONNEL
Chairman: Terry Bates
Vice-Chairman: Don Mitchell
President: Bob feetham
Press Officer: Terry Bates
Manager: Mark Mitchell
Assistant Manager: Paul Bentley
Physio: John Handley

BUCKINGHAM TOWN

Secretary: Brian Maycock, 31 Westfield, Buckingham, Bucks Tel: 01280 815529

Ground: Ford Meadow, Ford Street, Buckingham Tel: 01280 816257
Capacity: 4,000 Cover: 420 Seats: 420 Floodlights: Yes

Directions: From town centre take Aylesbury (A413) road and turn right at Phillips Garage after 400yds. Public transport: train to Milton Keynes, then bus to Buckingham

Clubhouse: Open evenings 6.30-11 (12-11 Sat & Sun) Rolls etc available on matchdays. Bingo, dominoes, darts & pool. Concert room with stage for hire,capacity 150 **Club Shop:** Yes

HONOURS Southern Lg Southern Div 90-91, Utd Co's Lg 83-84 85-86 (Div 1 R-up 75-76, Div 2 R-up 74-75, Lg Cup 83-84, R-up: 2002-03Div 2 Cup R-up 74-75), Nth Bucks Lg 24-25 28-29 33-34 35-37 38-39 48-50(2) Aylesbury & Dist. Lg 02-03, Berks & Bucks Snr Cup 83-84, Berks & Bucks Jnr Cup 02-03 48-49 (R-up 38-39 72-73), Berks & Bucks Minor Cup 32-33, Buckingham Snr Charity Cup x12, r-up x 5

PREVIOUS **Leagues:** Aylesbury & Dist; Nth Bucks; Hellenic 53-57; Sth Mids 57-74; Utd Co's 74-86; Southern Lge 86-97

BEST SEASON **FA Cup:** 1st Round 1984-85 **FA Vase:** Quarter Finals 1990-91 & 92-93

RECORD **Attendance:** 2,451 v Orient, FA Cup 1st Rd 84-85
Fee paid: £7,000 for Steve Jenkins (Wealdstone, 1992)
Fee received: £1,000 for Terry Shrieves (Kettering)

FACT FILE

Formed: 1883
Nickname: The Robins
Sponsors: Wipac
Colours: All red
Change colours: All blue
Midweek Matchday:
Reserves' League: No reserve team
Programme: Yes Editor: Carl Waine
Newsline: 0891 884 431
Local Press: Buckingham Advertiser, MK Citizen, Herald & Post
Local Radio: Chiltern Radio, Fox FM (102.6 fm), 3 Counties Radio

CLUB PERSONNEL

Chairman: Brian Maycock
Manager: Morrell Maison
Assistant Manager: Pete Riches

COGENHOE UNITED

Secretary: Allan Standring, 33 Bedford Road, Denton, Northampton NN7 1DR (01604 890105)
Ground: Compton Park, Brafield Rd, Cogenhoe, Northants (01604 890521)
Directions: Turn off A428 at Brafield-on-the-Green, first turn right toCogenhoe or A45 to Billing Aquadrome. Carry on, take second Cogenhoe turn on left

Capacity: 5,000 Seats: 100 Cover: 200 Floodlights: Yes Club Shop: No
Clubhouse: Tues-Fri 7-11, Sat 12-3 & 4-11, Sun 12-3 & 7-10.30 Snacks. Hot food on matchdays

HONOURS UCL Div 1 R-up 86-87 (Res. Div 2 88-89), K.O. Cup 96-97; Daventry Charity Cup 91-92 95-96, (R-up 79-80); Central Northants Comb 80-81 82-83 83-84 (R-up 81-82, Prem Div Cup 82-83 (R-up 78-79), Div 1 up R-up 77-78, Charity Shield 82-83 83-84)

PREVIOUS **League:** Central Northants Combination 1967-84
Ground: Cogenhoe Village PF 1967-84

RECORD **Gate:** 1,000 v Eastenders XI, Charity match 8/7/90
Scorer & Appearances: Tony Smith
Win: 22-0 v Ravensthorpe, Cen. Northants Comb. Prem. Div. KO Cup, 79-80
Defeat: 0-6 v Yardley United, Central Northants Comb. Div. 1, 76-77

Players progressing : Darren Bazeley (Watford 89), Darren Harmon (Notts Co. 89),Matt Murphy (Oxford Utd 93), Gary Leonard (Northampton 1978)

FACT FILE

Founded: 1967
Nickname: Cooks
Sponsors: Supertrucking
Colours: All royal blue
Change: Red & black stripes/black/red
Midweek matchday: Tuesday
Reserves' Lge: UCL Res. Div 1
Programme: 32 pages with Admission
Editor:Sue Wright
Local Press: Chronicle & Echo, Northants Evening Telegraph

CLUB PERSONNEL

Chairman:Gary Deer
Vice Chairman: Bob Earl
President: Steve Brockwell
Comm. Man.: Robert Jones
Manager: Adam Sandy
Assistant Manager: Dino Cirelli
Physio: Ian Blair

DAVENTRY TOWN

Secretary: Tim Kibblewhite,78 The Medway, Daventry, Northants.
Tel: 01327 703974 (H)

Ground: Elderstubbs Farm, Browns Road, Daventry, Northants
Tel: 01327 706286
Capacity: 2,000 Seats: 250 Cover: 250 Floodlights: Yes

Directions Adjacent to A45 by-pass at top of Staverton Road Sports Complex
Clubhouse: Large bar/kitchen

HONOURS UCL Div 1(3), Lg Cup R-up 92-93, Highest Aggregate Cup.
Northants Junior Cup 36-37 60-61 91-92 Daventry Charity Cup: 1999

PREVIOUS **Leagues:** Northampton Town (pre-1987)/ Central Northants Combination 87-89

BEST SEASON **FA Cup:** Prel. Rd 94-95
FA Vase: Preliminary Rd 91-92 94-95
RECORD **Attendance:** 850 v Utrecht (Holland) 1989
Local Press : Daventry Weekly Express, Herald & Post, Northants Chronicle/Echo
Players Progressing: Martin Aldridge (Northampton)
2002-2003 **Captain**: Daniel Burke **Top Scorer:**Gareth Jonnes **P.O.Y.**: Mathew Finlay

FACT FILE

Founded: 1886
Sponsor: G.D.R.Caterers
Colours:Grey & Navy/Navy
Change colours:Claret & blue/claret/claret
Midweek Matchday: Tuesday
Reserves League: U.C.L. Reserves Div 2
Programme: 36 Pages Editor: Tony Perry

CLUB PERSONNEL

Chairman: Gary Roche
Vice Chairman: Tony Perry
Treasurert: Jo. Beau mont
President: Paul Webster
Manager: Mark Shackleton
Assistant Manager.: Lee Ault
Physio: Tony Jackson

Life Presidents

A.G.Cox,Frank Hobbs,Anne Hobbs,Malc Hobbs and Dave Liddington.

The Blackstone squad and officials celebrate their 4-0 United Counties League Cup win over Buckingham Town.

Bourne Town F.C. Back Row (L-R): Len Pick (Club patron), Paul Bentley (Asst. Manager), John Morton, Ross Nicholls, Richard Thompson, John Feetham, Mark Lovelace, P.Cook, Daniel Fisher, M.Mitchell (Manager). Front Row: Paul Pearson, Nick Lovelace, Andy Smurthwaite, Darren Munton, Steve Garfoot, Brett Bellamy, Paul Wright. Photo: Gavin J Tutcher.

Buckingham Town F.C. Back Row (L-R): Leon Cashman, Jonathan Barnett, Sean Griffiths, Paul Stanley, Stuart Blaik, Ruben Max-Grant, Adam Turner, Junior George, Morell Maison (Manager). Front Row: Paul Trott, Pete Sogbodjur, Meshach Cole, Lewis Julius, Moses Olaleye, Abdul Abdi, Marcus McGillycuddy. Photo: Arthur Evans.

DEEPING RANGERS

Secretary: Haydon Whitham, 3 Everingham, Orton Brimbles, Peterborough PE2 5XP
Tel:01733 238539 (H) 07736 548500 M)

Ground: Deeping Sports Club, Outgang Road, Market Deeping, Lincs.
Tel: 01778 344701 Website: www.deepingrangers.co.uk
Capacity: 1,000 Seats: 180 Cover: 250 Floodlights: Ys

Directions: From Deeping town centre take the A15 towards Bourne. Turn right at Towngate Tavern following signs to Industrial Estate & club is 1/4 mile on left.
Clubhouse: Bar and lounge. Changing rooms
HONOURS Peterborough & Dist. Lge Div 3 67, Div. 2 69, Div. 1 70, Prem. Div. R-up 95-96 98-99; Lincs Junior Cup 83-84 87-88 88-89, Lincs. Sen. B Cup 00-01, R-up UCL Div 1 R-up 00-01, Fair Play Award 99-00, 00-01
Peterborough FA Senior Cup 91-92 96-97 Minor Cup 67,
PREVIOUS **League:** Peterborough & District
BEST SEASON **FA Vase:** 1st Rd. F.A.Cup **F.A.Cup:** Prelim Rd 02-03 (first season)
Players Progressing:Richard Sendall (Blackpool), Eddie Herbert (Peterborough), Ben Wright (Bristoil, City), Malcolm Christie (Derby County via Nuneaton Borough) and Lewis Kileane (Sheffield Utd.)

FACT FILE

Founded: 1966
Nickname: Rangers
Colours: Claret & blue
Change colours: White/claret/sky blue
Midweek Matchday:Wednesday
Programme: Yes

CLUB PERSONNEL
President: Albert Lawrence
Chairman: Jon Sandall
Match Sec.:Robin Crowson
01778 348287(H) 07977 971796 (M)
Email: rwc@deeprang.fsnet.co.uk
Manager: Paul Kirk

2002-2003
Top Scorer: Simon Mead
Player the Year: Tuncay Korkmaz

DESBOROUGH TOWN

Secretary: John Lee, 85 Breakleys Road, Desborough, Northants NN14 2PT
Tel: 01536 760002 Email Address: johnlee@froggerycottage.fsnet.co.uk

Ground: Waterworks Field, Braybrooke Rd, Desborough Tel: 01536 761350
Capacity: 8,000 Seats: 250 Cover: 500 Floodlights: Yes

Directions: Half a mile west of A6 following signs for Braybrooke
Clubhouse: Lounge & main hall, 2 bars, games room. Every eve. & w/e lunchtimes
Club Shop: No

HONOURS Utd Co's (Prev. Northants) Lg 00-01 01-02 06-07 20-21 23-24 24-25 27-28 48-49 66-67 (R-up 02-03 10-11 19-20 22-23 79-80, 98-99), Div 2 10-11, 28-9(Res),R-up 09-10 (Res) 26-27(Res) 51-52(Res), KO Cup 77-78 96-97 00-01; Northants Snr Cup10-11, 13-14 28-29 51-52; Desborough Charity Cup 97-98,98-99,99-00, 01-02
PREVIOUS **Leagues:** None
RECORD **Attendance:** 8,000 v Kettering Town
Win: 10-1: v Huntingdon Utd (A) 1957 & v Stewarts & Lloyds (A) 1965, both UCL.
Defeat: 11-0 v Rushden Town (A) 1934
Fee received: £8,000 for Wakeley Gage, from Northampton Town
BEST SEASON **FA Vase:** 5th Round 78-79 **FA Cup:** ?????
Players progressing: Wakeley Gage (Northampton), Jon Purdie & Campbell Chapman (Wolves), Andy Tillson (Grimsby), Matt Murphy (Oxford United)

FACT FILE
Founded: 1896
Nickname: Ar Tarn
Colours: Blue
Change Colours: All red
Previous Leagues: None
Midweek matchday: Tuesday
Programme: 32 pages 30p
Editor:John Lee
Local Press: Evening Telegraph,Northants Post,Chronicle & Echo,& Harborough Mail
Website: www.artarn.co.uk
CLUB PERSONNEL
Chairman:Alan Panter
President: T.B.A. Press Off: John Lee
Manager: Kevin McGuire
Asst Manager: Somon Reilly
Physio: Dave Marlow
2002-2003
Capt: Andy Greensmith P.o.Y.: Michael Coles
Leading Gaolscorer: Sam Johnson

FORD SPORTS

Secretary: Bob Lowe, 4 Banbury Lane, Byfield, Daventry Northants. nn11 6UX
Tel No:s: 01327 705282 (H) 01327 305358 (W)

Ground: Royal Oak Way South, Daventry, Northants Tel: 01327 704914
Capacity: 1,000 Seats: Yes Cover: Yes Floodlights: Yes

Directions: Enter Daventry on A45 or A361 and follow signs for Royal Oak Way

Clubhouse: Yes -
HONOURS UCL Premier Division 2001-02 ,Div 1 92-93, 95-96, Knockout Cup 97-98, Benevolent Cup R-up 92-93; Daventry Charity Cup 201-02
Highest Agg. Goalscoring Trophy 92-93; Northants Sen Cup R-up 96-97

PREVIOUS **League:** Central Northants Comb

BEST SEASON **FA Vase:** 2nd Round 00-01, 01-02

Player progressing: Martin Aldridge (Northampton)

FACT FILE
Founded: 1968
Nickname: Motormen
Sponsors: Ford Sports & Social Club
Colours: Blue & white/blue/blue
Change : Red & white/red/red
Reserves' Lge: UCL Res Div 2
Programme: 12 pages
Editor: John Hinton

CLUB PERSONNEL
Chairman: John Bailham
Manager: Shane Geary
Assistant Manager: Mick Bulliman
Physio: Dave Bull

HARROWBY UNITED

Secretary: Michael Atter, 6 Barrowby Road, Debdale, Lincs. NG32 1BD
Tel: 01476 567426 (H) 07718 263386 (M)

Ground: Harrowby Playing Fields, Harrowby Lane, Grantham Tel: 01476 590822
Capacity: 1,500 Seats: 100 Cover: 150 Floodlights: Yes
Directions: From A1 take B6403, go past A52 roundabout, past Ancaster turn and take road to Harrowby. Continue into Grantham, ground on right opposite Cherry Tree PH.
Clubhouse: Large bar open normal licensing hours

PREVIOUS **Leagues:** Grantham; Lincs; East Mids Regional Alliance (pre-1990)

BEST SEASON **FA Vase:** Preliminary Round 91-92

HONOURS Utd Co's Lg Div 1 91-92 R-Up 02-03 Benev. Cup R-up 91-92, Mids Regional All. 89-90, Lg Cup 89-90, Lincs Snr `B' Cup x2 90-92

Players progressing: Richard Liburd (Middlesbrough), Kevin Pilkington (Mansfield Town)

FACT FILE
Founded: 1949
Nickname: Arrows
Sponsor: Crystal Grantham
Colours: Red & black hoops/black/red & black
Change : Blue & black/black/blue
Programme
16 pages Editor: Paul Wilson

CLUB PERSONNEL
Chairman: Paul Wilson
Vice Chairman: Robert Wilson
Match Secretary: Mick Atter

Manager: Graham Drury
Asst Mgr: Steve Joseph
Coach: Tony Cook
Physio: Nigel Burton
Groundsman: Malcolm Brothwell

HOLBEACH UNITED

Secretary: Dennis Sp[arrow, 112 Langwith Gardens, Holbeach, Lincs. Tel No: 01406 424366 (H)
Ground: Carters Park, Park Road, Holbeach Tel: 01406 424761
Capacity:4,000 Seats: 200 Cover: 450 Floodlights: Yes
Directions: Second left at traffic lights in town centre, 220 yds down road on left.
From King's Lynn; sharp right at traffic lights
Clubhouse: Large bar, lounge & kitchen, open every night **Club Shop:** No

HONOURS Utd Co's Lg Champions 89-90, 02-03 (KO Cup 64-65 89-90), Benevolent Cup, Evans Halshaw Cup 97-98; Lincs Snr Cup `A' 83-84 84-85 86-87 02-03 (Senior Cup `B' 57-58)

PREVIOUS **Leagues:** Peterborough; Utd Co's 46-55; Eastern Co's 55-62; Midland Co's62-63

BEST SEASON **FA Cup:** 1st Rd Proper 82-83, 0-4 v Wrexham (at Peterborough)
FA Trophy: 2nd Qual. Round 69-70 71-72
FA Vase: 5th Round 88-89, 2-4 v Wisbech Town

RECORD **Gate:** 4,094 v Wisbech 1954

Players progressing: Peter Rawcliffe (Lincoln)

FACT FILE
Founded: 1929 Nickname: Tigers
Sponsors: Ashwood Homes
Colours: Old gold & black stripes/black/black
Change Colours: All blue
Midweek matchday: Tuesday
Reserves' Lge: Peterborough
Prog: 44 pages, 50p Editor: Chris Cook
Tel No: 01205 350144
Local Press : Lincs Free Press, Spalding Guardian, Peterborough Evening Telegraph

CLUB PERSONNEL
Chairman: Chris Cooper
President: Francis Bissadike
Manager:Shaun Keeble
Assistant Manager: Shaun Keeble

LONG BUCKBY

Secretary: John Partridge, 11 Rockhill Road, Long Buckby, Northants. NN6 7PT
Tel Nos: 01327 842246 (H) and 01327 8422246 (W)
Ground: Station Rd, Long Buckby Tel: 01327 842682
Capacity: 1,000 Seats: 200 Cover: 200 Floodlights: Yes
Directions: Daventry - Long Buckby rd. 400 yds from station (Northampton -Rugby line)
Clubhouse: Bar & concert room. Open matchdays

HONOURS UCL KO Cup 84-85, UCL Div 2 70-71 71-72, Div 2 KO Cup 71-72, Div 3 69-70; Northants Snr Cup R-up; Daventry Charity Cup 96-97

PREVIOUS **Leagues:** Rugby & D.; Central Northants Comb. (pre-1968)
Name: Long Buckby Nomads 1936

BEST SEASON **FA Vase:** 2nd Rd 85-86
FA Cup: 1st Qualifying Rd 92-93

RECORD **Gate:** 750 v Kettering, Northants Snr Cup Final 1984

Players progressing: Gary Mills (Nottm Forest), Vince Overson (Burnley), Des Waldock (Northampton),Steve Norris (Scarborough)

FACT FILE
Nickname: Bucks
Sponsors: Northampton Elec Dist
Colours: All blue
Change colours: All red
Midweek matchday: Tuesday
Reserves' Lge: HSUCL Res Div 1
Programme: 8 pages
Editor: Rod Pryor (01604 845071)
Local Press : Chronicle & Echo, Daventry Weekly News

CLUB PERSONNEL
President: Alister Bruce
Chairman: Ted Thresher
Manager: Steve Renshaw
Assistant Manager: Shaun Tiernan
Physio: Robert Stafferton

NEWPORT PAGNELL TOWN

Secretary: Jim Diggins, 32 Clinton Road, Far Cotton, Northampton (07958 710118)

Ground: Willen Road, Newport Pagnell Tel: 01908 611993

Capacity: 2,000 Seats: 100 Cover: 100 Floodlights: Yes

Directions: Adjacent to A422 Newport Pagnell by-pass

Clubhouse: Open every evening Club Shop: No

HONOURS UCLPrem Div R-Up: 2002-03 Div 1 82-83,01-02 (R-up 91-92, Div 1 Cup 77-78), Daventry Charity Cup R-up 93-9; .League Goalscoroing trophy 2001-02, Berks & Bucks Intermediate Cup 2001-02

PREVIOUS **Leagues:** North Bucks 63-71; South Midlands 71-73

BEST **FA Vase:** 2nd Round 84-85

FACT FILE

Founded: 1963 Nickname: Swans

Sponsors: Brian Currie

Colours: White & green/green/green

Change colours:Sky blue/navy blue/navyblue

Midweek Matchday: Tuesday

Reserves League: United Counties

Programme: 56 pages

Editor: Secretary

CLUB PERSONNEL

Chairman: Dennis Stoyles

Vice Chairman: Ernie Print

President: Ken Inch

Manager:Danni Janes

Assistant Manager: Nick Hamper

NORTHAMPTON SPENCER

Secretary: Nick Hillery, Cowntess Road, Northampton 01604 756580 (H) 07754 665724(M)

Ground: Kingsthorpe Mill, Studland Rd., Northampton NN3 1NF Tel: 01604 718898

Capacity: 2000 Seats: 100 Cover: 350 Floodlights: Yes

Directions: Turn off Kingsthorpe Road at traffic lights into Thornton Rd., 1st right into Studland Rd. and ground is at the end.

Clubhouse: Open during normal licensing hours. Lounge and bar. **Club Shop:** No

HONOURS: UCL 91-92, r-up 92-93, 97-98, Div. 1 84-85, KO Cup 88-89 93-94, r-up 87-88 96-97 97-98, Benevolent Cup 91-92; Northants Sen. Cup r-up 90-91 93-94.

PREVIOUS **League:** Northampton Town Lge 36-68
Name: Spencer School Old Boys
Grounds: Dallington Park 36-70, Duston High School 70-72

BEST SEASON **FA Cup:** 1st Qual. Rd 93-94, 96-97
FA Vase: 4th Round 87-88, 1-2 v Gresley Rovers

RECORDS **Attendance:** 800 v Nottm. Forest, dressing room opener 1993
Most Appearances: P.Jelley 6221984-2002

Players progressing: Paul Stratford (Northampton), Wakeley Gage (Northampton)

FACT FILE

Founded: 1936

Nickname: Millers

Sponsors: Future Print

Colours: Yellow/green/yellow

Change colours: All red

Midweek matchday: Tuesday

Reserves' League: UCL Res Div 1

Programme: 20 pages 50p

Editor: Andy Goldsmith (01604 412382)

Website: www.geocities.com/kirby42000

CLUB PERSONNEL

President: J Sampson

Joint Chairmen:

Graham Wrighting & Jim Connelly

Press Off.: Andy Goldsmith (01604 412382)

Manager: Bob Tansley Coach: Keith Bowen

Assistant. Manager.: Dave Love

2002-2003

Captain: Jamie Moss TopScorer: Kaafi Bile 15

PLayer of the Year: Gavin Nullatumby

RAUNDS TOWN

Secretary Mick Walden,5 Fernie Way,Wellingborough,Northants NN8 3LB (01933 279561)

Ground: Kiln Park, London Road, Raunds, Northants NN9 6EQ
Tel: 01933 623351, Matchdays 01933 460941

Directions: Take Raunds turning at roundabout on A45 and ground is first left
Nearest station; Wellingborough. Bus services local
Capacity: 3,000 Seats: 250 Cover: 600 Floodlights: Yes

Clubhouse: On ground, open every day

Club Shop: Open matchdays, selling shirts, books programmes, contact Malc York, c/o club

PREVIOUS **Leagues:** Rushden & Dist., Cen. Northants Comb., U.C.L., Southern Lge 96-00
Grounds: Greenhouse Field (until 1948), The Berristers (1948-91)

BEST SEASON **FA Cup:** 4th Qual Rd, 98-99 (0-2 v Enfield),
FA Vase: Semi-final v Arlesey Tn 94-5
FA Trophy: 3rd Rd v Weston-super-Mare 98-99 (2-2, 0-1)

HONOURS UCL Prem Champions 95-96, UCL Div 1 82-83 (R-up 91-92), KO Cup 90-91, 01-02(R-up 83-84 93-94), Res Div 1 88-89 95-96 (R-up 86-87 87-88 89-90 90-91 91-92), Reserve KO Cup 84-85 88-89 93-94; Northants Snr Cup 90-91; Hunts Premier Cup R-up 92-93; Daventry Charity Cup R-up 83-84; Northants Jnr Cup 82-83 91-92 (res) 92-93 (res)

CLUB RECORDS **Attendance:** 1,500 v Crystal Palace, ground opening 23/7/91
Win: 9-0 v Potton 95, 11-2 v Brackley 93 **Defeat:** 0-6 v Baldock 83, vBuckingham 84-85
Career Goalscorer: Shaun Keeble 208 **Career Appearances:** Martin Lewis 355 (+29subs)

FACT FILE

Formed: 1946

Nickname: Shopmates

Colours: Red & black/black/black

Change Colours:All Yellow

Midweek matchday: Tuesday

Reserves' League: UCL Reserve Div. One

Prog: Pages: Varies Price: 50p

Editor: Malc York 01933 311586

CLUB PERSONNEL

Chairman: George Hagan

President: Mahen Perera

Manager:Adam Sinclair

Asst Manager: Dino Cirelli

2002-03

Leading Goalscorer:

Captain:

Player of the Year:

Kempston Rovers line up before their traditional Easter Monday 'derby' match against Wootton Blue Cross.
Photo: Gordon Whittingham.

St Neots Town F.C. Back Row (L-R): Craig Lambert (physio), Gareth Grant, Mick Finney, Richard Beckett, Ian Morris, Steve Kuhne, Justin Hicks, Michael McDonnell, Chris Howell (Manager).
Front Row: Trevor Smith, Matt Doyle, Warren Brown, Neil Worker, Julian Old, Paul Bloss, Phil Cavener (Asst. Manager). Photo: Gordon Whittingham.

Wootton Blue Cross F.C. Back Row (L-R): Mel Roberts (physio), Scott Houghton, Robert White, Adam Smith, Chris Price, Jack Rashid, John Hoggett (capt), Steve Atkinson, Danny Bartley, John Taylor (Manager).
Front Row: Darren Edwards, Cameron Clarke, Danny Griggs, Steve Wareham, Russell Lawes, Bobby Roberts (Asst. Manager), Ivan Finch, Derek Joswiak. Photo: Gordon Whittingham.

SPALDING UNITED

Secretary: John Franks, 2 Samworths Close, Castor, Peterborough PE5 7BQ
Tel: 01733 380609

GROUND Sir Halley Stewart Playing Field, Winfrey Avenue, Spalding Tel: 01775 713328
Directions: Town centre off A16, adjacent to bus station. 250 yds from Spalding(BR) station
Capacity: 3,500 Seats: 1,000 Cover: 2,500 Floodlights: Yes
Clubhouse: Open matchdays, and events Club Shop: Yes

PREVIOUS **Leagues:** Peterborough; U.C.L. 31-55 68-78 86-88 91-99; Eastern Co's 55-60; Central Alliance 60-61; Midland Co's 61-68; N.C.E.F.L. 82-86; Southern 88-91, 99-03
RECORD **Attendance:** 6,972 v Peterborough, FA Cup 1952
BEST SEASON **FA Cup:** 1st Round 57-58, 1-3 v Durham City (A), 64-65, 3-5 v Newport Co. (A)
FA Trophy: 3rd Rd 99-00
FA Vase: Quarter-Finals 89-90, 1-3 v Guiseley
HONOURS Utd Counties Lg 54-55 74-75 87-88 98-99 R-up 50-53(x3) 72-73 75-76 96-97; KO Cup 54-55 94-95; N.C.E.Lg 83-84; Lincs Snr Cup 52-53; Hinchingbroke Cup 98-99 Lincs Snr `A' Cup 87-88, 98-99 R-up 97-98; Snr `B' Cup 50-51; Evans Halshaw F'lit Cup 89-90
2002-2003 **Captain**: Steve Waiton **Top scorers:** Paul Goodhand & Liam Harrold
Player of the Year: Lee Sowervby
Players progressing: Carl Shutt (Sheffield Wed.)

FACT FILE
Founded: 1921
Nickname: Tulips
Sponsors: T.B.A.
Colours: Royal blue/white/royal blue
Change: Tangerine & navy/navy/T&N
Midweek matchday: Tuesday
Reserve League: Utd Counties Res Div 2.
Programme: 36 Pages Price:£1.00
Editor: Ted Conner

CLUB OFFICIALS
Chairman: Chris Toynton
President: John Chappell
Press Officer: Ray Tucker

FOOTBALL MANAGEMENT
Manager: Dick Creasey
Asst Manager: Steve Appleby
Physio: Tony Clark

ST. NEOTS TOWN

General Se: John Carroll ,95 St Neots Road, Sandy, Beds SG19 1BP Tel No: 01767 222436 (H)
Co Sec: Graham Moffitt **Fixture Sec:** Marion. Izzard (All c/o club)

Ground: Rowley Park, Cambridge Rd, St Neots, Cambs Tel: 01480 470012
Capacity: 3,000 Seats: 250 Cover: 850 Floodlights: Yes
Directions: Through the town centre, under the railway bridge, ground is first on the left
Capacity: 2,500 **Seating:** 160 **Covered Standing:** 300 **Floodlights :** Yes
Clubhouse: Yes with Conference,Banqueting and private functions all bookable

HONOURS Hunts Snr Cup(34), UCL 67-68 (KO Cup 67-68 68-69),
Metropolitan Lg 49-50(Lg Cup 79-80), South Midlands Lg 32-33,
Huntingdonshire Lg 90-91 92-92 92-93 94-95 Hunts.Prem Cup: 2001-02
PREVIOUS **Leagues:** South Midlands 27-36 46-49; United Counties 36-39 51-56 66-69 73-88; Metropolitan 49-51 60-66; Central Alliance 56-60; Eastern Counties 69-73; Huntingdonshire 90-94 **Name:** St Neots & District 1879-1957 **Ground:** Shortlands

BEST SEASON **FA Cup:** 1st Rd 66-67, 0-2 v Walsall (A)
FA Vase: 5th Rd 2001-02 **FA Trophy:** 2nd Qual. Rd 69-70 72-73

RECORD **Attendance:** 2,000 v Wisbech, 1966
Players progressing: Frank Atkins (Cambridge United), John Gregory (Aston Villa) and Matthew Oakey (Southampton)

FACT FILE
Founded: 1879 Nickname: Saints
Sponsors:Adam Kennedy, Midland Thermal, and Fleet Car Contracts
Colours:Sky & Navy Blue quarters/Navy/Navy
Change colours:Yellow/Black/Yelow
Reserves' Lge: UCL Res Div 1
Programme: Yes Editor: Mike Birch
(Tel: 01480 395505)
'Saintly Text';Revolving Information screen.
Editor:John Carroll (07752 654496
Web site: www.stneotsfc.com

CLUB PERSONNEL
Chairman: Bob Page Directors:John Carroll
Kenneth Harris and Neil Holmes
Commercial Man: Peter Hicks(01733 263656)
Team Manager: Chris Howell
Coaches: Gerald Sylvester,Barry Cavilla and Mike Brooks Physio; Craig lambertr

STEWARTS & LLOYDS

Secretary: Dave Foster, 29 Tettenhall Close, Corby, Northants NN198 9PJ
Tel: 01536 746004 (H) 01536 201234 Ext. 5292(W) 07818 264220(M)
email: carol@carol77.fsnet.co.uk
Ground: Recreation Ground, Occupation Road, Corby Tel: 01536 401497
Capacity: 1,500 Seats: 100 Cover: 200 Floodlights: Yes

Directions: The ground is situated on Occupation Rd at the rear of Stewart & Lloyds Leisure Club, next to old Corby Town F.C. ground

Clubhouse: Licensed bar **Club Shop:** No

HONOURS UCL R-up 85-86, Div 1(2) 73-75; UCL KO Cup, Prem 95-96, Div 1 Cup(2)73-75, Div 2 KO Cup(2) 75-77)

PREVIOUS **Leagues:** Kettering Amateur

BEST SEASON **FA Cup:** ??????? **FA Vase:** 3rd Round 96-97, 01-02

RECORD **Goalscorer:** Joey Martin 46 (92-93)

Players progressing : Andy McGowan (Northampton), Willie Graham (Brentford)

FACT FILE
Formed: 1935
Nickname: None
Sponsor: Weldon
Colours: yellow & blue/blue/yellow
Change Colours:Sky blue/Navy blue/blue
Midweek matchday: Tuesday
Programme: 12 pages with admission
Editor/Press Officer: Dave Foster

CLUB PERSONNEL
Chairman: Peter Webb
Vice Chairmen: Gordon Hall, Harry Nelson
Manager: Elwyn Roberts
Asst Manager:Karl Binley
Physio: Roger White

STOTFOLD

Secretary: Bill Clegg, 12 Common Rd, Stotfold, Hitchin, Herts SG5 4BX Tel: 01462 730421
Club Email: football@stotfoldfc.freeserve.co.uk Website:www.stotfoldfc.freeserve.co.uk

Ground: Roker Park, The Green, Stotfold, Hitchin, Herts Tel: 01462 730765
Capacity: 5,000 Seats: 300 Cover: 300 Floodlights: Yes

Directions: A507 from A1, right at lights, right at T-jct.
A507 from Bedford via Shefford, left at lights, right at T-jct

Clubhouse: Clubroom, bar, refreshment bar, dressing rooms, physio room

HONOURS Utd Co's Lg R-up 93-94, KO Cup Winners 98-99 R-up 91-92, Res Div 1 87-88; Sth Mids Lg 80-81 (R-up 55-56 57-58 58-59 59-60 63-64 65-66 77-78), Div 1 53-54, Chal. Tphy 81-82; Beds Snr Cup 64-65 93-94; Beds Premier Cup 81-82; 98-99 Beds I'mediate Cup 58-59; Nth Beds Charity Cup (8) Beds Colts Lg 88-89; Southern Com Cup 94-95 95-96 96-97; Hinchingbrooke Cup R-up 97-98: Win. 99-00: R-up 00-01

PREVIOUS **Leagues:** Biggleswade & District/ North Herts/ South Midlands 51-84

BEST SEASON: **FA Cup:** 00-01 **FA Vase:** 4th Round 94-95, 97-98, 00-01

RECORD **Attendance:** 1,000 v Letchworth Town, FA Amtr Cup
Scorer: Roy Boon **Appearances:** Roy Boon/Dave Chellew

FACT FILE
Founded: 1904 Reformed: 1945
Nickname: Eagles Sponsors: Astron
Colours: Amber/black/black
Change Colours: All Sky blue
Midweek matchday: Tuesday
Reserves' League: UCL Reserve Division One
Programme: 22 pages with entry
Editor: Phil Pateman (01462 834581)
Local Press: Comet, Biggleswade Chronicle

CLUB PERSONNEL
Chairman: Phil Pateman
Vice Chairman: Alan Syme
Pres: David Chellow Man: Phil Pateman
Asst Manager: Ken Baker
Press Officer: Bill Clegg
Physio: Dave Chivers

2002-03
Leading Goalscorer:Paul Garrett
Captain:Luke Gregson
Player of the Year: Gareth Cottenden

WOODFORD UNITED

Secretary: Pat Ashby, 2 Barrington Court, Ward Road, Brackley. NN13 7LE
Tel Nos: 01327 262955 (H) 07930143504 (M) 01280 840900 (B)

Ground: Byfield Road, Woodford Halse, Daventry, Northants. Tel: 01327 263734
Capacity: 3,000 Seats: 120 Cover: 120 Floodlights: Yes

Directions Off A 361 Daventry to Banbury Rd, on Woodford Road out of Byfield

Clubhouse: Yes

Website: www.wufc.net

PREVIOUS Leagues: Central Northants Comb pre 70, UCL 70-78, Northants Comb

HONOURS Northants Comb 66 67 90 92 95, KO Cup 66 90 93 95 98;
United Counties Lge Div 2 74, KO Cup 74;

FA Vase: Do not compete

FACT FILE
Founded: 1946
Nickname: United
Sponsors: Huber + Suhner Uk Ltd
Colours: Red/black/white
Change Colours:White and sky blue
Reserves' League: Utd. Co. Res. Div 2
Programme: 16 pages
Editor: Tony Perry (01327 871461)

CLUB PERSONNEL
Chairman: Andrew Worrall
Vice-Chairman: R Adams
Manager: Phil Lines
Asst. Man / Coach:
Physio:

WOOTON BLUE CROSS

Secretary: Bryan Keens, 5 Stewart Court,Wootton,Des. MK43 9PH Tel : 012134 768214
Ground: Weston Park, Bedford Road, Wootton Tel: 01234 767662
Capacity: 2,000 Seats: 50 Cover: 250 Floodlights: Yes
Directions: Four miles south of Bedford on main road through village at rear of Post Office

Clubhouse: Main hall, bar, darts, pool, bingo. Open every evening and w/e lunchtimes
Club Shop: No

HONOURS Utd Co's Lg Div 2 67-68 69-70 (KO Cup 82-83, Div 2 Cup 64-65), South Midlands Lg 47-48 (R-up 49-50), Beds Sen. Cup 70-71, Hinchinbrooke Cup(6)

PREVIOUS **Leagues:** Bedford & District; South Midlands 46-55
Grounds: Recreation Ground, Fishers Field, Rose & Crown, Cockfield

BEST SEASON **FA Vase:** 3rd Rd 74-75
FA Cup: 2nd Qual. Rd 50-51 (3-4 v Hitchin (H))

RECORD **Gate:** 838 v Luton, Beds Prem. Cup 1988

Players progressing: Tony Biggs (Arsenal)

FACT FILE
Founded: 1887
Nickname: Blue Cross
Sponsors: Vision Blinds
Colours: Blue & white/blue/blue
Change: Yellow/Red/Yellow
Reserves' League: United Counties Res. Div 1
Midweek matchday: Tuesday
Programme: 24 pages Editor: John Fl;etcher
Local Press : Bedfordshire Times, Bedford Herald, Beds Express, Beds on Sunday

CLUB PERSONNEL
President: J Clarke
Chairman: Trevor Templeman
Manager:Kenny Davidson
Assistant Manager:Danny Nicholls
Coach: Ian Evason
Physio: Trevor Templeman
Press Officer: Secretary

YAXLEY

Secretary: Alan Andrews, 3 Farringdon Close, Pterborough. PE1 4RQ
Tel Nos: 01733 342897(H) 07739 497528(M) email: alan@yaxleyfc.com

Ground: Leading Drove, off The Holme Road, Yaxley Tel: 01733 244928
Capacity: 1,000+ Seats: 150 Cover: Yes Floodlights: Yes

Directions: A1, then A15 at Norman Cross up to traffic lights. Turn right then immediately right again. Follow the road for approx. 1 mile, then turn right into Holme Rd.. The ground is approx. 200 yards on left

HONOURS UCL Div 1 96-97, Benevolent Cup 97-98; Hunts Senior Cup (5 times Inc 98-99)
Peterborough League (2); Peterborough Senior Cup (2);
West Anglia League;Scott-Gatty Cup

PREVIOUS **Leagues:** Peterborough & District, Huntingdonshire, West Anglia

BEST SEASON **FA Vase**: 2nd Round 98-99

FACT FILE

Sponsor: Reads Removals
Colours: Blue/white/blue
Change colours:Red/white/red
Programme: Yes
Editor:Jonatghon Goodinhg

CLUB PERSONNEL

President: John Dowse
Chairman:Geoff Lenton
Vice Chairman: Malcolm Whaley
Manager:Jimmy Watson
Asst Manager: Gary Cupston

Holbeach United manager Dick Creasey celebrates his club's UCL Premier Division championship win, an honour that also made him Manager of the Year.
Photo: Gavin J Tutcher.

BLISWORTH

Secretary: Kim Barnard, 5 Harrier Park, East Hunsbury, Northampton NN4 0QG
Tel Nos: 01604 660697 (H) 07768 465569 (M)
Ground: Blisworth Playing Field, Courteenhall Road, Blisworth Tel: 01604 858024
Capacity: 1,000 Seats: None Cover: None Floodlights: No
Directions: Courteenhall Road off A43
Clubhouse: Yes -
HONOURS Northants Junior Cup 88-99
PREVIOUS **League:** Central Northants Combination 1978-87
Player progressing: Dave Johnson (Northampton 83-84)
CLUB RECORDS **Attendance:**
Win: **Defeat:**
Career Appearances: **Career Goalscorer:**

FACT FILE
Founded: 1890
Sponsors: Target Furniture, JB King Plant Hire
Colours: Yellow/Green/Yellow
Change colours: All Red
Reserves' Lge: UCL Res. Div. 2
Programme: Yes Editor:Kim Barnard
Tel: as for Decretary.
CLUB PERSONNEL
Chairman: Pete Edwards
President: L Piggott
Manager: Bob Earl
Asst Man: Gary Edwards
Coach: RichardlLarge
Physio: Elaine Johnson

BUGBROOKE ST MICHAELS

Secretary: Roger Geary, 31 Kislingbury Rd, Bugbrooke, Northampton NN7 3QG
Tel: 01604 831678
Ground: Birds Close, Gayton Road, Bugbrooke Tel: 01604 830707
Capacity: 2,500 Seats: 120 Cover: Yes Floodlights: Yes **Clubhouse:** Yes - normal licensing
Directions: M1. Jct 16 Take A45 to Northampton. At 1st roundabout follow signs to Bugrooke. In villagefollow road straight through to club immediately past last house on left.
CHONOURS Northants Junior Cup 89-90, Central Northants Comb. 68-69 69-70 70-71 71-72 76-77 85-86, UCL Res Div 2 R-up 94-95 U.C.L. Div One Champions 98-99
PREVIOUS **League** : Central Northants Combination 1952-87 **Ground:** School Close
RECORD **Attendance:** 1,156 **Scorer:** Vince Thomas **Appearances:** Jimmy Nord
Players progressing: Kevin Slinn (Watford), Craig Adams (Northampton)
2002-2003 **Captain & P.o.Y.:** Paul Warnecki **Top Scorer:** Robert Frost 28

FACT FILE
Founded: 1929
Nickname: Badgers
Sponsors: Unusual Industries
Club colours: Black & white/black/black
Change colours: All Red
Reserves' Lge: UCL Res. Div. 1
Programme: Eight pages
Editor: Donna Clancy
CLUB PERSONNEL
Chairman: Tom Treacy
President: John Curtis
Manager: T.B.A.
Assistant Manager:Mark Champlovier
Press Officer: Donna Clancy

BURTON PARK WANDERERS

Secretary: Roger Patrick,16 Church Stret, Burton Latimer, Northants.NN15 5LU
Tel: 01536 724103 (H), 01536 725841 (W)
Ground: Latimer Park, Polwell Lane, Burton Latimer Tel: 01536 725841
Capacity: 1,000 Seats: 100 Cover: 150 Floodlights: No
Directions: Entering Burton Latimer, turn off A6 Station Rd and right into Powell Lane; ground on the right
HONOURS UCL Div 1 R-up, Benevolent Cup R-up
PREVIOUS **League**: Kettering Amateur
RECORD **Attendance**: 253 v Rothwell, May 1989
Players progressing : Shaun Wills (Peterborough), Laurie Dudfield (Leicester City)

FACT FILE
Founded: 1961 Nickname: The Wanderers
Sponsor: Prescott Motors
Colours: All Yellow
Change Colours: All red
Midweek matchday: Tuesday
Prog: 16 pages with entry Ed: Michael Capps
Local Press : Northants Evening Telegraph, Northants Post
CLUB PERSONNEL
Chairman: Roger Patrick
Vice Chairman: Stuart Coles
Manager: Jason Thurland
Assistant Manager: Hughie Duchan
Physio: Stuart Coles

COTTINGHAM

Secretary: Lindsay Brownlie, 30 Bancroft Rd, Cottingham, Market Harborough LE168XA
Tel: 01536 771009 (H) email: Lindsay Brownlie@Rigid.co.uk
Ground: Berryfield Rd, Cottingham Tel: 01536 770051
Capacity: 1,000 Seats: None Cover: Yes Floodlights: No
Directions: One and a half miles from Corby on A427 turn right to Cottingham.At junction of B670 turn left; Berryfield Road 200 yds on right
Clubhouse: Bar & changing rooms
HONOURS UCL Div 1 R-up 97-98; Northants Junior Cup
CLUB RECORDS **Attendance:**
PREVIOUS **Leagues:** Market Harborough; Kettering Amateur; East Midlands Alliance

FACT FILE
Sponsors: B & J Decorators
Colours: Green &Yellow/navy/yellow
Change colours: Sky blue/navy/navy blue.
Reserves' Lge: UCL Res. Div. 2
Programme: No
CLUB PERSONNEL
Chairman: Mike Beadsworth
Vice Chairman: Brian Tilley
Manager: Graham Leech

EYE UNITED

FACT FILE
CLUB PERSONNEL

Secretary:

Ground: Chestnut Avenue, Dogsthorpe, Eye, Peterborough, Cambs.
Capacity: Seats: Cover: Floodlights: Yes/No
Directions
Club House:
Club Shop:

PREVIOUS **League** Peterborough League >2003

HONOURS Peterborough League 2002-03

EYNESBURY ROVERS

Secretary: Deryck Irons, 12 Hadleigh Close, Bedford MK41 8JW. Tel: 01234 268111
Email Address: patrick.erfc@btinternet.com
Ground: Hall Road, Eynesbury, St Neots Tel: 01480 477449
Capacity: 3,000 Seats: 200 Cover: 500 Floodlights: Yes
Directions: Two miles from A1, on South side of St Neots urban area, near Ernulf School
Clubhouse: Large bar, committee room.Available for private hire **Club Shop:** No

HONOURS UCL Div 1 76-77; Hunts Snr Cup 13-14 46-47 48-51 54-55 56-57 69-70 84-85 90-93 95-96,99-00,01-02; Hunts Premier Cup 50-51 90-91 95-96; Hinchingbrooke Cup (7) 46-4748-52 57-58 66-67; Cambs Invitation Cup 61-62; E Anglian Cup R-up 90-91 91-92;Hunts Scott Gatty Cup 35-36 56-57 84-85 89-90 (R-up 93-94 res); Hunts Jnr Cup 21-22 26-27
PREVIOUS **Leagues:** Sth Mids 34-39; UCL 46-52; Eastern Co's 52-63
BEST SEASON **FA Vase:** 3rd Rd 94-95 **FA Cup:** 4th Qual. Rd 54-55, 1-3 v Camb. Utd (A)
RECORD **Gate:** 5,000 v Fulham 1953 (Stanley Matthews guested for Eynesbury)
Players progressing: Chris Turner (Peterborough), Denis Emery (Peterborough)

FACT FILE
Founded: 1897 Nickname: Rovers
Sponsors: Classic Windows
Colours: Royal & white/royal/royal
Change Colours: Yellow/black/yellow
Midweek matchday: Tuesday
Reserves' League: Utd Counties Res. Div. 2
Prog: 32 pages, 50p Ed: Graham Mills
Website: www.eynesburyrovers.org.uk
CLUB PERSONNEL
Chair: Brian Abraham V Chair:John Newland
Man:Steve Galbraith Asst.Man: Ken Churchill
2002-03: Capt: Robert Dobson
P.o.Y.: Mick McCreanor
Top Scorers:Vince Petty & Paul Carey

HIGHAM TOWN

Secretary: Chris Ruff, 23 Queensway, Higham Ferrers, Northants. NN10 8BU Tel: 01933 358862
Ground: Recreation Ground, Vine Hill Drive, Higham Ferrers Tel: 01933 353751
Capacity: 1,000 Seats: Nil Cover: 100 Floodlights: No
Directions: From Kettering 1st right on A6 after junction to St Neots. From Bedford, 3rd left after entering town on A6 from Rushden. Higham is served by London-Bedford-Corby United Counties Coachlines, and their local services Northampton-Raunds and Bedford-Kettering
Clubhouse: During season 8.30-11pm Tues, Thurs, Fri, Sat after games & 12-1.30pm Sun. Light refreshments available after Saturday games
HONOURS UCL Div 1 97-98, R-up 70-71 71-72 89-90 92-93 93-94 94-95 95-96 98-99; Northants Lg 21-22 22-23 R-up 23-24 26-27; Northants Snr Cup 21-22 R-up 30-31 32-33; Maunsell Premier Cup 22-23 33-34
PREVIOUS **Leagues:** Wellingborough 20-21; Northants (now UCL) 21-36; Rushden 46-50
RECORD **Attendance:** 5,700 v Chesterfield, FAC 4th qual. rd replay 22-23 **Scorer:** Jon Ogden 157 (Lge) **Appearances**: Brian Harbour 485 **Best Win**: 15-0 v Towcester T (H), UCL Div. 92/93

FACT FILE
Founded: 1895 Reformed: 1920 & 1946
Nickname: Lankies
Sponsors: Higham News
Colours: Sky & navy/navy/sky
Change colours:Green/black/black
Midweek matchday:: Tuesday
Reserves' Lge: UCL Reserve Div
Programme: 12 pages with admission
Editor: Secretary
CLUB PERSONNEL
Chairman: Richard Williams
Pres: Vijay Patel Vice Chairman: Brian Kirk
Manage:r: John Leeson
Asst.Man: Colin Hoyland
Physio: Keith Bates

HUNTINGDON TOWN

FACT FILE
CLUB PERSONNEL

Secretary:

Ground: Hartford Road, Huntingdon, Cambridgeshire
Capacity: Seats: Cover: Floodlights: Yes/No

Directions
Club House:
Club Shop:

PREVIOUS **League** Cambridgeshire League 'A' 2003
HONOURS

IRCHESTER UNITED

Secretary: Glynn Cotter, 3 Bank Hill View, Littlree HarrowdenWellingborough, Northants NN8 5UB
Tel Nos: : 01933 402514 (H) 07802 728736 (M)

Ground: Alfred Street, Irchester Tel: 01933 312877
Capacity: 1,000 Seats: None Cover:Yes Floodlights: No

Directions: Off Rushden Road to Wollaston Road, next to recreation ground

Clubhouse: Yes

HONOURS Northants LgDiv 2 30-31 31-32,Northants Jnr.Cup 29-30,33-34,48-49 75-6, Rushden & Dis.t Lg 28-29 29-30,32-33,33-34 36-3746-47 50-51 51-52 56-57

BEST SEASON **FA Cup:** Prel. Rd 34-35
FA Vase: Preliminary Round 77-78

PREVIOUS **Leagues:** Rushden & District 1936-69

FACT FILE
Colours: Red & Blackstripes,black,black
Change colours:Black&White stripes,black,red
Reserves' Lge: UCL Res. Div. 2
Programme: No

CLUB PERSONNEL
Chairman: Geoff Cotter
Manager: Glyn Cotter
Physio: Mick Howarth

KEMPSTON ROVERS

Secretary: Alan Scott, 26 King William Rd, Kempston, Bedford MK42 7AT
Tel: 01234 854875(H) 07813 088703 (M) Email: arscott@archchemicals.com
Ground: Hillgrounds Leisure, Hillgrounds Rd, Kempston, Bedford Tel: 01234 852346.
Capacity: 2,000 Seats: 100 Cover: 250 Floodlights: Yes
Directions: M1 jct 13, A421 to Kempston, Hillgrounds Rd is off the B531 main Kempston-Bedford road. Entrance to Hillgrounds Road is opposite Sainsburys onthe B531 - ground can be found just over twi miles from Sainsburys entrance.British Rail to Bedford Thameslink/Midland then bus No.103 from Bedford town centre stops outside ground
Club Shop: No, but old programmes available from clubhouse
Clubhouse: Open 7-11pm Tues - Sun. & w/e lunch 12-3pm. Sky TV, pool, hot pies & pasties.
PREVIOUS: League: South Midlands 27-53
BEST SEASON FA Vase: 5th Round 88-89
HONOURS U.C.L. Prem. 73-74 R-up 56-57 59-60, Div 1 57-58 85-86, Div 2 55-56 R-up 67-68, KO Cup 55-56 57-58 59-60 74-75 76-77; Beds Senior Cup 08-09 37-38 76-77 91-92 R-up 92-93

FACT FILE
Founded: 1884 Nickname: Walnut Boys
Club Sponsors: Bar Soviet
Colours: Red & white stripes/black/red
Change Colours: All yellow
Midweek matchday: Tuesday
Reserve League: Beds FA County Res. Lge
Programme: 24 pages, 40p
Editor: Tommy Tyrrell (01234 853529)

CLUB PERSONNEL
President: Mr Doug Jack
Chairman: Russell Shreeves.
Vice Chairman: Kevin Howlett
Press Officer: Secretary
Co-Managers: John Dower and Bob Reed
Coach: Steve Sava

NORTHAMPTON O.N. CHENECKS

Secretary: Trevor Cadden, 26 Greenfield Road, Spinney Hill, NNorthampton NN3 2LW
Tel Nos: 01604 407070 (H) 078887 652910 (M)

Ground: Old Northamptonians Sports Ground,Billing Road,Northampton Tel: 01604 34045
Capacity: 1,350 Seats: Yes Cover: Yes Floodlights: No

Directions: South ring road, exit A43 Kettering. Turn left at the lights, to the top of hill and the ground is 200 yds on right

Clubhouse: Yes

HONOURS UCL Div 1 77-78 79-80, Northants Jnr Cup R-up 93-94

PREVIOUS **Leagues:** N'pton Town (pre-1969)

CLUB RECORDS **Appearances:**

FACT FILE
Founded: 1946
Colours:All Navy Blue
Change colours: All red
Reserves' League: UCL Res Div 1
Midweek Matchday:
Prog.: 16 pages with entry
Editor: Eddie Slinn

CLUB PERSONNEL
Chairman: John Wilson
Vice Chairman: Eddie Slinn
President: Claude Hasdell
Manager: Peter Green
Asst Manager: Claude Hasdell
Physio: John Goodger

NORTHAMPTON SILEBY RANGERS

(formerly Northampton Vanaid)

Secretary: David Battams, 12 Geldock Road, Little Billing, Northampton NN3 9PH
Tel Nos: 01604 412654 (H) 07970 910463 (M)

Ground: Fernie Fields Sports Ground, Moulton, Northampton Tel: 01604 670366
Capacity: 700 Seats: 100 Cover: Yes Floodlights: No

Directions: R'bout at Lumbertub pub take turn to Moulton, 1st right signposted

Clubhouse: Large bar with food

HONOURS UCL Div 1 93-94,02-03 Benevolent Cup R-up 93-94; Northants Jnr Cup 93-94 96-97 97-98; 02-03 Northampton Town Lg 88-89 89-90

PREVIOUS **League:** Northampton Town (pre-1993) **Name:** Northampton Vanaid >00

RECORD **Attendance:** 78

FACT FILE
Founded: 1968Nickname: Sileby
Sponsors: Mr Removals
Colours: Red/Black/Black
Change colours:Yellow/Navy Blue/ Yellow
Reserves' League: UCL Res Div 1
Programme Editors: Terry Whenham
Tel No: 07764 158569 (M)

CLUB PERSONNEL
Chairman: Rob Clarke Vice Chairman: G,Law
President: N.Gibbs
Manager: Nick Verity Asst Man: T.Bonner
Physio: M.Arnold
Captain: Mark Pepperell

OLNEY TOWN

Secretary: Andrew Baldwin, 49 Midland Road, Olney, Bucks MK46 4BP
Tel: 01234 711071 (H) 07932 141623 (M) email: a.baldwin@cranfield.ac.uk
Club Website: www.olneytownfc.com
Ground: East Street, Olney , Bucks. Tel: 01234 712227
Capacity: 2,000 Seats: None Cover: Yes Floodlights: No
Clubhouse: Yes

Directions: Enter Olney on A509 from Wellingborough, 100yds on left enter East St, the ground is 200 yds on left

HONOURS UCL Div 1 72-73, Berks & Bucks I'mediate Cup 92-93

PREVIOUS **Leagues:** Nth Bucks, Rushden & District

CLUB RECORDS Attend

FACT FILE
Founded: 1903
Sponsors: Cyclo Sports
Colours: Green&white/green/green &white
Change colours: Black&white/white/white
Programme: 8 pages - Editor: Mickl Smith

CLUB PERSONNEL
Chairman: Malcom Thomas
President: Trevor Church
Manager: Russell Ward
Asst Manager: Pete Munting
Coach: Neil Bunker - Physio: Peter Munting

POTTON UNITED

Secretary: Derek Inskip, 16 Sheffield Close, Potton, Beds SG19 2NY Tel: 01767 260355
Ground: The Hollow, Biggleswade Road, Potton Tel: 01767 261100
Capacity: 2,000 Seats: 200 Cover: 250 Floodlights: Yes
Directions: Outskirts of Potton on Biggleswade Road (B1040). 3 1/2 miles from Sandy (BR). United Counties buses from Biggleswade **Clubhouse:** Yes
HONOURS Utd Co's Lg 86-87 88-89, KO Cup 72-73, Benevolent Cup 88-89; Beds Snr Cup(5) 47-49 63-64 75-76 77-78 (R-up 94-95 96-97); Wallspan Floodlit Cup 87-88; Hinchingbrooke Cup 51-52 84-85 89-90 90-91 91-92; Hunts Premier Cup 89-90 91-92 94-95(jt) 96-97; Beds I'mediate Cup 43-44; Southern Comb. Cup 92-93; Nth Beds Charity Cup (12); East Anglian Cup 96-97; Jess Pigott Trophy 96-97
PREVIOUS Leagues: Sth Mids 46-55; Central Alliance 56-61 **Ground:** Recreation Grnd pre-1947
BEST SEASON **FA Cup:** 3rd Qual. Round 74-75, 1-2 v Bedford Town
FA Trophy: 3rd Qual. Round 71-72 72-73 **FA Vase:** 5th Round 89-90, 1-2 v Billericay Town
RECORD **Attendance:** 470 v Hastings Town, FA Vase 1989

FACT FILE
Founded: 1943 Nickname: Royals
Colours: Blue Change : White/black/white
Midweek matchday: Tuesday
Reserves' Lge: Beds. County
Prog: 28 pages, 50p Editor: Bev Strong
Local Press: Biggleswade Chronicle,

CLUB PERSONNEL
President: Peter Hutchinson
Chairman: Nigel Westhorp
Press Officer: Secretary
Manager: Richard Newman
Assistant Manager: Roy Johnson

2002-2003
Capt: Roy Bloxham Top Scorer:Tonty Norman

ROTHWELL CORINTHIANS

Secretary: Mark Budworth, 5 Jackson way, Kettering, Northants. NN15 7DL
01536 521973 (H) 07730 416960(M) email: Mark Budworth@compuserve.com
Ground: Seargeant's Lawn, Desborough Road, Rothwell, Northants.
Tel: 01536 418688
Capacity: Unknown Seats: 50 Cover: 200 Floodlights: Yes
Directions A6 towards Desborough, on right opposite Greening Road
Club House: Yes -
Club Shop: No
HONOURS East Midlands Alliance (2)
PREVIOUS **League** East Midlands Alliance
CLUB RECORDS **Attendance:**
Career Goalscorer: **Career Appearances:**
Biggest Win: **Biggest Defeat:**

FACT FILE
Founded: 1930's
Nickname: Corinthians
Sponsor: Springfir Estates
Colours: Red& white / black/black
Change colours: Blue & white/blue/blue
Programme: Yes Editor: Nick Garley
Tel No: 01536711694

CLUB PERSONNEL
Chairman: Graham Dawson
Vice Chairmperson: May Clelland
President: Terry Smith
Manager: Colin Sinclair
Physio:John Dickson

ST. IVES TOWN

Secretary: Chris George, 16 Canberra Drive,St Ives. Terl Nos: 01480 382257 (H)
07775 854017 (M) E-mail: stivestownfc@hotmail.com
Ground: Westwood Road, St. Ives, Cambs.Tel: 01480 463207
Directions: From Huntingdon: A1123 thru Houghton, right at 2nd lighs intoRamsey Rd, after quarter mile turn right opp. Fire Station into Westwood Road
From A604: Follow Huntingdon signs past 5 r'bouts, left into Ramsey Rd at lights then follow as above.
Capacity: 5,000 Seats: 130 Cover: 300 Floodlights: Yes
Clubhouse: Bar and entertainment room. Normal licensing hours.
HONOURS Hunts Snr Cup 00-01 11-12 22-23 25-26 29-30 81-82 86-87 87-88,
Cambs League 22-23 23-24 24-25.
PREVIOUS **Leagues:** Cambs; Central Amtr; Hunts; P'boro. & D. (pre-1985).
Ground: Meadow Lane
RECORD **Gate**: 400 v Saffron Walden Town, FA Vase.

FACT FILE
Founded: 1887
Nickname: Saints
Colours: White & black/black/red
Change colours: Blue/black/black
Midweek matchday: Tuesday
Reserves' Lge: UCL Res Div 2
Programme editor:Neville Nania
Tel: 01480 494293 (H) 07850 709837 (M)

CLUB PERSONNEL
Chairman: Nevile Nania
Managers: Warren Everdale
Match Sec.:Peter Claridge,Tel Nos: 01480 466873 (H) 07889 161741 (M)

Cottingham F.C. Back Row (L-R): Phil Docherty (asst. Manager), Steve Marshall (Chairman), David Donativo, Lee Brydon, Dominic Johnson, Craig Herbert, Dave Trimble, Paul Docherty, Graham Leech (Manager).
Front Row: Sean Brennan, Graham Clark, Gary Owen, Ian Bell, Eddie McGoldrick, Duncan McNish.

Eynesbury Town F.C. Back Row (L-R): Ken Churchill (Asst. Manager), Mark Garwood, Gary Jackson, Dean Shipp, Robert Dobson, Iain Parr, Dave Goddall, Barry Albone, Tom Hobbs, Steve Galbraith (Manager).
Front Row: Dave Samal (coach), Kevin Anderson, Paul Childerley, Gareth Peck, ross West, Paul Carey, Neil Morris.

Thrapston Town United F.C. Back Row (L-R): Gary Petts (Manager), Lee Purser, Jason Lee, Glen Turner, Mike Battams, Keith Morsen, Jason Morse, Scott Witney, Barry Carter, Keith Julian. Front Row: Scott Atkinson, Tyron Wilson, Dominic Baradi, Paul Smith, Marshall Dodd, Rob Stewart, David Peet, Paul Byers.

All Photos: Gordon Whittington.

THRAPSTON TOWN

Secretary: Mark Brown, 3 Drayton Place, Irthlingborough, Northants. NN9 5TD
01933 388671 (H) 07885 640947 (M) email: mark @datsprint.co.uk

Ground: Chancery Lane, Thrapston, Northants Tel: 01832 732470
Capacity: 1,000 Seats: Yes Cover: Yes Floodlights: No

Directions: Chancery Lane off A605 in town centre

Clubhouse: Yes

HONOURS Northants Junior Cup 87-88, 98-99 Kettering Am Lg 70-71 72-73 73-74 77-78
UCL Div1 Runners -Up 99-00

PREVIOUS **League:** Kettering Amateur (pre-1978)

CLUB RECORDS Appearances:

FACT FILE
Founded: 1960
Nickname: Venturas
Sponsor: IKEA
Colours: All Blue
Change colours: All Yellow
Programme: Yes Editor: Barry Carter
Tel No: 07771 976784

CLUB PERSONNEL
President: Derek Barber
Chairman: Dave Harris
Vice Chairman: Barry Carter
Manager: Gary Petts
Asst Manager: Barry Carter
Physio: Zoe

WELLINGBOROUGH WHITWORTHS

Secretary: John Betts, 2 St Mary's Road, Bozeat, Wellingborough, Northants. NN29 7JU
Tel: 01933 664253 (H) 07789 997025 (M) email: johnsmbetts@aol.com

Ground: London Road, Wellingborough, Northants. Tel: 01933 227324
Capacity: 700 Seats: None Cover: Yes Floodlights: No

Directions: Off London Road at Dog & Duck public house

Clubhouse: Yes -

PREVIOUS **Leagues:** Rushden & Dist.; E. Mids All. (pre-1985)

HONOURS Rushden & District Lg 76-77; Northants Jun Cup 96

CLUB RECORDS **Attendance:**
Career Goalscorer: **Career Appearances:**
Biggest Win: **Biggest Defeat:**

FACT FILE
Sponsor: Whitworth Brothers
Colours: All navy blue
Change colours: Purple and Navy Blue
Reserves' Lge: UCL Res Div 2
Programme: No

CLUB PERSONNEL
Chairman: Bob Jarvis
Vice Chairman: Dave Woodley
President: Terry Faulkner
Manager: Mark Desborough
Assistant Manager: Joe Smyth
Physio: Andrew King

Blisworth F.C.

Photo: Gordon Whittington.

ISLE OF WIGHT F.A.

Chairman: K R Morris

Secretary: Andrew Justice, 12 The Mall, Binstead, Ryde, Isle of Wight PO33 3SF

Tel: 01983 565244

FINAL LEAGUE TABLES 2002-03

DIVISION ONE		P	W	D	L	F	A	Pts
1	WW Mayflower	22	16	5	1	61	22	53
2	Oakfield	22	16	2	4	84	23	50
3	Shanklin	22	13	5	4	56	23	44
4	E. Cowes Vics Reserves	22	13	2	7	56	33	41
5	Cowes Sports Reserves	22	12	5	5	48	29	41
6	Binstead & COB	22	11	3	8	59	46	36
7	Whitecroft & B. Sports	22	9	7	6	61	40	34
8	Red Star Spartans	22	7	4	11	45	56	25
9	St Helens Blue Star	22	6	4	12	32	61	22
10	Carisbrooke United	22	3	3	16	40	87	12
11	Newport Town 'A'	22	3	2	17	28	90	11
12	Brading Town Reserves	22	2	0	20	23	83	6

DIVISION TWO		P	W	D	L	F	A	Pts
1	Niton	18	13	4	1	75	25	43
2	Northwood IOW	18	12	3	3	59	23	39
3	Sandown	18	10	6	2	58	21	36
4	Plessey	18	11	3	4	47	31	36
5	GKN Westlands	18	6	5	7	30	52	23
6	Bembridge (-2)	18	6	4	8	45	48	20
7	Wakes	18	5	2	11	24	36	17
8	Kyngs Towne	18	4	4	10	26	39	16
9	Osborne Coburg	18	3	2	13	15	66	11
10	Seaview	18	2	3	13	17	55	9

JEWSON WESSEX LEAGUE

FEEDER TO: Dr MARTENS FOOTBALL LEAGUE

President: Cyril Hurlock

Chairman: Alf Peckham **Vice Chairman:** Ray Barnes

Hon. Secretary: Ian Craig, 56 Ecton Lane, Anchorage Park, Hilsea, Portsmouth, Hampshire PO3 5TA Tel: 02392 671155 Fax: 02392 651147

I would like to start this Annual Report by saying a few words about Tom Lindon the League Secretary for the past six years who sadly passed away on Tuesday 4th February 2003. He had worked tirelessly as our secretary, with others to help bring the Wessex League to what it is today, a successful thriving LEague which is highly regarded in the South of England.

The first match of the season kicked off on Friday 16th August in fine cricketing weather soon followed by F.A.Cup matches where nearly all of our teams won through to the next round. Thatcham narrowly lost away to Lewes in front of 344 fans, and Brockenhurst had a good win against Southern League Fleet Town. AFC Newbury started the season well leading the first division with four straight wins.

September brought success in the F.A.Cup and Vase for many of our clubs. In the F.A.Cup Lymington & New MIlton beating the famous Dulwich Hamlet and Hillingdon Borough, and Gosport beat Deal Town at home in front of 212 spectators. AFC Totton, Eastleigh and Bemerton joined them in the 2nd Qualifying Round. Brockenhurst narrowly lost to Lewes in front of a crowd of 240, Wimborne Town lost away to Weston Super Mare in front of 243 and BAT lost by the odd goal away to Bromley in front of 303.

In the FA Vase Eastleigh demolished Peacehaven and Gosport, whilst AFC Totton and Christchurch progressed to the next round with Portland and Downton bidding farewell. Lymington scored 11 in the next round to join up with seven other clubs from our league and ended the month with a hundred per cent record to win the Club of the Month. On the 28th September in the FA Cup 2nd Qualifying round AFC Totton drew at home with Slough, attracting 306 fans, whilst Eastleigh drew away with the strong Lewes side in front of 437 fans. AFC Newbury meanwhile still led the first division chased by free scorers Portland United. Weymouth Reserves headed the Combination Division closely followed by newcomers Winchester City Reserves.

October began with Eastleigh and AFC Totton losing their FA Cup replays in front of large crowds. Gosport lost away to Bideford in front of a massive 886 fans whilst Lymington, watched by 480 fans, lost at home to Crawley Town to bow out of the FA Cup Third Qualifying Round. The County Cup competitions also commenced with Andover, BAT, Brockenhurst, Hamble ASSC and Cowes Sports progressing to the next round of the Hampshire Cup and Lymington surprisingly eliminated. Eastleigh defeated Newport (IW) at home in front of 536 fans with Matt Le Tisser making his debut for the home side. Eastleigh took over the leadership of the first division.

November began with an incredible 15-2 victory for Alton Town against Hants League's Brading in the Hampshire Senior Cup, with Eastleigh (5-0) and Christchurch (4-0) also recording victories. The Vase brought more winners, Lymington beating much fancied Team Bath, whilst Christchurch disposed of Torrington. Cowes, Bournemouth, Eastleigh and Wimborne all slipped quietly away. November also saw the first batch of postponements due to the weather, whilst Eastleigh and Lymington finished month neck and neck in the title race.

Bournemouth narrowly lost 2-3 to a strong Aldershot side in the Senior Cup before a crowd of 657, however, Andover, Christchurch and Eastleigh all continued their fine run in this competition. Brockenhurst, Moneyfields and AFC Totton were all beaten in the Vase, whilst Christchurch overwhelmed Welton 5-0 and Lymington went through at the expense of Willand Rovers. The league cup commenced with Lymington, Andover, Bemerton, Bournemouth, Brockenhurst and Moneyfields winning through to the next round. Eastleigh were still top of the league six points ahead of the improving Gosport Borough.

As soon as the New Year arrived the weather took over and postponed matches became the norm. In amongst the frost and flooding Gosport Borough maintained their unbeaten run to put the pressure on leaders Eastleigh. In the Vase Lymington & New Milton and Christchurch finally bowed out leaving Winchester City as the only Hampshire club in the last 16. Eastleigh narrowly lost an epic Senior Cup match against Aldershot, having had the original game abandoned whilst in the lead. Over 1700 spectators watching the games. Christchurch lost to Havant but Andover mastered neighbours Basingstoke 4-2 to reach the semi finals. The month ended with Eastleigh still on top closely followed by Gosport whose unbeaten run gave them the 'Club of the Month' for January.

Eastleigh managed to edge past Wimborne to reach the league cup quarter final and then beat Lymington & New Milton to reach the semi final. Moneyfields, AFC Totton and Bemerton Heath Harlequins had already reached the semi finals. AFC Totton Reserves, Winchester City Reserves, AFC Newbury Reserves and Wimborne Town Reserves also reached the Combination Cup semi final. Neighbours Fareham Town ended Gosport's unbeaten run in front of 254 spectators, whilst Eastleigh continued on their merry way always getting one goal more than the opposition to head division one. It was nice to see Whitchurch United back to winning ways and causing stir down at the basement, whilst 'Club of the Month', Moneyfields, stormed up the table with five straight wins.

Portland United made a gallant attempt to reach the Dorest Senior Cup losing to a strong Dorchester Town side in front of 401 spectators. Eastleigh and AFC Totton reached the league cup final whilst Wimborne Town Reserves and AFC Newbury Reserves won through to the Combination Cup final.

Eastleigh won the first division by beating Gosport 2-0 and were presented with the trophy by the league's chairman Nick Spencer. They must have been still celebrating when they visited and lost 1-6 to Andover in front of a record Wessex League crowd of 702. There was a real scrap for the runners up spot with several teams in contention. It was not decided until the final weekend of the season when Gosport Borough emerged as runners up, after Wimborne were defeated by the champions letting AFC Totton slip into third place. On the same afternoon Blackfield held out for a draw at Alton, which left Whitchurch United at the bottom having narrowly lost at Christchurch.

On a windy evening at Blackfield's Gang Warily ground, AFC Newbury Reserves beat Wimborne Town Reserves 1-0 to win the Combination Cup for the first time.

Three days later AFC Newbury hosted the league cup final, which saw AFC Totton beat Eastleigh in a pulsating 2-1 victory, watched by a crowd of over 500, a fine end to another successful Wessex League season.

FIRST DIVISION FINAL LEAGUE TABLE 2002-03

		P	W	D	L	F	A	W	D	L	F	A	Pts	GD
1	Eastleigh	42	16	4	1	61	14	16	3	2	54	18	103	83
2	Gosport Borough	42	15	2	4	54	19	12	4	5	40	24	88	51
3	AFC Totton	42	14	4	3	52	22	13	2	6	44	25	87	49
4	Wimborne Town	42	14	1	6	60	25	12	6	3	53	19	85	69
5	Fareham Town	42	11	5	5	42	23	11	5	5	36	24	76	31
6	Lymington & NM	42	11	4	6	47	29	11	4	6	42	27	74	33
7	Andover	42	12	5	4	54	26	10	2	9	41	37	73	32
8	Portland United	42	12	2	7	47	26	8	6	7	34	36	68	19
9	Thatcham Town	42	9	7	5	34	25	9	6	6	34	33	67	10
10	Moneyfields	42	10	3	8	42	32	8	3	10	31	36	60	5
11	BAT Sports	42	11	4	6	29	19	7	2	12	28	46	60	-8
12	AFC Newbury	42	11	3	7	47	28	6	3	12	30	44	57	5
13	Christchurch	42	7	4	10	29	37	8	6	7	29	31	55	-10
14	Bournemouth	42	8	5	8	33	28	7	4	10	24	39	54	-10
15	Cowes Sports	42	6	9	6	35	23	7	4	9	22	32	52	2
16	Hamble ASSC	42	6	5	10	31	30	7	7	7	27	30	51	-2
17	Alton Town	42	7	3	11	42	48	7	6	8	29	32	51	-9
18	Bemerton Heath H.	42	8	2	11	34	37	5	3	13	25	46	44	-24
19	Downton	42	7	5	9	21	42	3	2	16	20	63	37	-64
20	Brockenhurst	42	3	3	15	27	53	4	2	15	23	65	26	-68
21	Blackfield & Langley	42	2	2	17	19	66	2	4	15	18	68	18	-97
22	Whitchurch United	42	1	3	17	12	47	3	0	18	15	77	15	-97

First Division	1	2	3	4	5	6	7	8	9	10	11	12	13	14	15	16	17	18	19	20	21	22
1 AFC Newbury		0-4	1-2	0-3	4-0	2-0	6-1	4-0	3-1	4-0	1-4	0-3	1-1	3-0	2-0	3-2	0-2	3-3	5-0	0-1	5-1	0-0
2 AFC Totton	4-0		1-0	1-1	2-3	5-1	1-0	2-0	4-0	5-1	2-0	2-1	2-0	2-4	1-1	1-1	5-2	4-3	4-2	0-1	3-0	1-1
3 Alton	1-0	1-4		1-2	3-2	0-2	1-1	6-1	3-0	2-2	3-0	3-2	1-3	1-4	3-4	0-3	1-2	3-1	2-2	4-6	2-4	1-3
4 Andover	0-2	3-2	2-2		3-1	2-1	4-2	0-0	0-1	0-0	1-2	8-0	6-1	2-4	5-0	1-1	3-2	3-1	1-1	4-1	3-1	3-1
5 BAT	2-1	3-2	2-3	2-1		2-0	1-1	0-0	5-0	1-0	4-1	2-1	0-1	2-0	0-0	0-1	0-3	0-2	1-0	1-1	1-0	0-1
6 Bemerton	3-2	1-2	0-2	2-1	0-0		3-2	5-1	1-3	5-2	0-1	0-1	0-7	0-1	0-2	1-3	1-2	2-2	2-0	0-2	6-0	2-1
7 Blackfield	1-3	0-3	2-1	1-2	0-2	0-1		1-3	1-4	0-5	0-0	2-2	0-1	0-5	1-6	2-1	0-6	1-4	2-4	2-4	2-3	1-6
8 Bournemouth	2-3	2-3	1-1	1-1	4-2	2-1	2-1		1-0	2-1	1-1	2-0	0-1	3-2	0-2	0-1	2-2	0-1	1-3	0-0	6-0	1-2
9 Brockenhurst	4-2	0-4	0-3	4-2	1-3	1-2	2-2	1-2		0-2	0-3	6-2	1-2	0-2	1-3	1-2	1-1	2-3	1-1	1-3	0-2	0-7
10 Christchurch	3-1	0-1	1-1	3-5	2-1	4-3	0-0	1-2	0-0		1-2	4-1	0-6	0-1	0-0	1-2	2-1	0-2	0-2	5-2	1-0	1-4
11 Cowes	0-0	2-0	1-2	1-4	2-0	2-3	7-0	1-0	1-1	0-0		8-0	1-3	0-0	1-1	2-2	1-1	0-0	1-1	1-3	3-0	0-2
12 Downton	2-3	2-1	1-0	0-3	1-1	2-2	1-0	1-1	3-0	0-5	1-0		0-3	0-0	0-3	0-2	0-3	2-1	3-7	1-1	1-0	0-6
13 Eastleigh	2-1	4-0	5-1	1-2	3-2	1-1	5-0	3-2	7-1	4-0	1-0	2-0		1-1	2-0	5-0	0-0	3-0	5-1	1-1	4-0	2-1
14 Fareham	1-1	1-1	2-2	2-4	1-0	3-0	5-0	2-1	4-1	0-1	2-1	1-1	0-1		3-0	2-1	1-3	2-1	1-1	3-0	5-0	1-3
15 Gosport	3-1	1-2	0-0	3-0	4-1	1-0	4-1	0-2	8-0	4-0	1-2	4-0	1-6	1-0		2-1	3-1	4-0	3-0	1-0	5-1	1-1
16 Hamble	0-1	3-3	0-2	1-2	6-1	2-3	5-1	0-1	3-2	1-1	2-3	2-0	0-2	0-1	0-3		0-1	1-0	0-0	1-1	2-0	2-2
17 Lymington	5-2	0-2	0-0	3-2	6-0	1-0	2-1	3-1	4-2	2-2	3-0	3-0	1-1	1-2	0-5	1-1		2-1	0-	0-1	10-0	0-4
18 Moneyfield	3-1	0-3	4-3	2-1	1-2	6-0	1-2	2-1	6-0	0-1	1-1	2-1	1-2	2-2	1-3	3-2	3-0		0-2	1-1	3-1	0-3
19 Portland	3-2	0-2	3-0	3-1	2-1	3-1	6-0	1-1	6-3	0-1	3-0	4-1	0-4	2-3	0-1	4-0	0-3	0-1		2-1	5-0	0-0
20 Thatcham	1-1	1-0	3-0	3-1	0-2	1-1	6-0	2-3	2-1	1-1	2-0	1-0	2-2	1-1	0-1	0-0	1-3	2-0	0-4		2-1	3-3
21 Whitchurch	1-2	0-3	1-4	13	0-2	2-1	0-2	1-2	1-2	0-3	0-0	2-3	0-3	0-3	2-2	0-0	0-3	1-2	0-1	0-4		0-2
22 Wimborne	3-1	1-2	2-0	2-0	1-2	4-2	6-1	3-0	2-1	0-1	3-1	5-1	1-4	3-0	2-3	1-1	3-1	1-3	4-0	5-0	8-1	

COMBINATION DIVISION FINAL LEAGUE TABLE 2002-03

		P	W	D	L	F	A	W	D	L	F	A	Pts	GD
1	Eastleigh	40	15	4	1	61	22	14	3	3	59	19	94	79
2	Weymouth	40	18	1	1	56	15	12	3	5	43	23	94	61
3	Gosport Borough	40	14	2	4	52	13	11	5	4	40	24	82	55
4	Winchester City	40	15	0	5	66	28	10	1	9	48	41	76	45
5	Bashley	40	14	2	4	66	23	9	4	7	49	32	75	60
6	Newport IW	40	12	4	4	40	30	8	5	7	31	34	69	7
7	Bemerton Heath H.	40	11	4	5	57	33	9	3	8	43	35	67	32
8	AFC Totton	40	11	6	3	54	26	8	2	10	38	37	65	29
9	Horndean	40	11	3	6	54	50	7	5	8	38	38	62	4
10	Wimborne Town	40	11	2	7	54	33	6	5	9	37	50	58	8
11	Christchurch	40	8	4	8	50	39	7	4	9	29	41	53	-1
12	Hamble ASSC	40	10	2	8	35	31	7	0	13	33	48	53	-11
13	AFC Newbury	40	8	3	9	36	33	6	4	10	26	34	49	-5
14	Brockenhurst	40	7	5	8	32	47	5	2	13	31	70	43	-54
15	Moneyfields	40	5	5	10	31	46	6	2	12	31	43	40	-27
16	BAT Sports	40	8	1	11	47	47	4	2	14	27	51	39	-24
17	Alton Town	40	5	5	10	39	43	6	1	13	32	71	39	-43
18	Lymington & NM	40	7	2	11	33	35	3	4	13	29	50	36	-23
19	Downton	40	6	4	10	26	37	4	2	14	21	58	36	-48
20	Portsmouth RN	40	8	1	11	35	52	3	1	16	22	67	35	-62
21	Andover New St.	40	7	1	12	33	55	3	3	14	31	91	34	-82

JEWSON WESSEX LEAGUE CUP

FIRST ROUND

Aggregagte Scores

BAT Sports 3
Brockenhurst 5

Cowes Sports 1
Fareham Town* 1

Moneyfields 1
Gosport Borough* 2

Portland United 6
Blackfield & Langley 4

Whitchurch United 0
Thatcham Town 3

Wimborne Town 8
Hamble ASSC 4

*Removed from the competition.

SECOND ROUND

Alton Town 2
Moneyfields 5

Brockenhurst 3
Downton 2

Christchurch 2
AFC Totton 6

Cowes Sports 4
Bournemouth 5

Lymington & NM 7
AFC Newbury 1

Portland United 1
Bemerton Heath H. 5

Thatcham Town 2
Andover 3

Wimborne Town 3
Eastleigh 5

QUARTER FINAL

AFC Totton 5
Bournemouth 0

Bemerton Heath H. 10
Brockenhurst 2

Lymington & NM 3
Eastleigh 5

Moneyfields 5
Andover 2

SEMI FINAL

Bemerton Heath H. 1
AFC Totton 1
(Totton won on away goal)

Eastleigh 4
Moneyfields 0

FINAL

AFC Totton 2
Eastleigh 1

A.F.C. NEWBURY

Secretary: Mike Hall, 27 Sanden Close. Hungerford, Berks. RG17 0LA
Tel: 01488 685070 (H) 01635 566225 (W) 07714 953784 (M)
Email Address: mike.hall o @ talk21.com

Ground: Faraday Road, Newbury, Berks. Tel: 01635 523222

Directions: A34 to Robin Hood roundabout, then A4 towards Reading. Right at lights after 100 yards into Faraday Road. Ground at end of road.

Clubhouse:
Honours:

Previous names: The club was formed in 1996 from the resources of Ecchinswell Football Club (1906), Shaw Boys and Belles Junior Football Club (established in 1972) and Wickham U17 Youth Team. The club operates from Faraday Road Stadium and this is the only link with Newbury Town F.C.

Club Records **Attendance:**
Best Season **FA Vase:**

FACT FILE
Formed: 1996
Colours: Red/white/red
Change: Green/black/green
Reserves:Wessex Combination
Midweek Matches: Tuesday
Website (under construction)
www.@fcnewbury.com
Programme - Price: Pages:
Editor:

CLUB PERSONNEL
Chairman: Steve Hartley Tel: 01488 683783(H) 0118 9304030 (W)
President:

Manager: Guy Whittingham
Asst. Man. / Coach:
Physio:

A.F.C. TOTTON

Secretary: Malcolm Tombs, 2Seymour Close,Calmore, Southampton SO40 2TW
Tel No: 023 8087 1790
GROUND: Testwood Park, Testwood Place, Totton, Southampton Tel:023 8086 8981
Directions: Five minutes walk from Totton station. Turn off at roundabout in Totton centre into Library Road.Then first left and second right into Testwood Place.

Capacity: 2,500 Seats: 200 Cover: 250 Floodlights: Yes Club Shop: No

Clubhouse: Open for matches and training sessions. Burgers, sandwiches, tea,coffee, biscuits etc available (matchdays only)

HONOURS : Hampshire League 81-82, 84-85 Russell Cotes Cup 98-99
Jewson Wessex League Cup: 2002-2003

PREVIOUS : **League:** Hants 1886-1986
Name: Totton FC until merger with Totton Athletic 1979
Grounds: Downs Park; Mayfield Park

RECORD: **Gate:** 600 v Windsor & Eton, F.A. Cup 4th Qual Rd 82-83

FACT FILE
Founded: 1886
Nickname: Stags
Colours: Blue & white stripes/blue/blue
Change colours: All Red
Midweek Matches: Tuesday
Programme: 30 pages 50p
Editor:Malcolm Thomas(02380 871790)

CLUB PERSONNEL
Chairman: John Dawson
President: D Maton
Press Officer: P Chilcott (023 80860453)
Manager: John Robson
Physio:T.B.A.

2002-2003
Captain: Martin Whiddatt
Top Scorer: Patrick James 35
Player of the Year:Daniel Barker

ALTON TOWN

Secretary: Tony Hillman, 19a Beechwood Rd, Alton, Hants GU34 1RL
Tel: 01420 87103 (H) 07796 184095 (M)

Ground: Alton/Bass Sports Ground, Anstey Rd, Alton
Tel: 01420 82465
Capacity: 2,000 Covered Seating: 200 Floodlights: Yes
Clubhouse:
Directions: A31 from Winchester to Alton, through town and ground is on junction with Anstey Road and Anstey Lane.

Previous League: Hampshire League >2002

Senior Honours: Hampshire Premier Div. Champions 2001-02 Hants.Senior Cup (4) 1958, 1969, 1972, 1978 Intermediate Cup 1949 Russell Cotes Cup Winners 1949,1957, 1965, 1970 (4) R-up 1933 Hampshire League Div 3 1948 Div 2 1949, 1955, 1987 Div1 1958,1999 Athenian League Div2 Winners 1974 Lg. Cup Winners 1978 Aldershot Challenge Cup:R-up 1986, 1988

2002-2003 **Captain:** Clive Ventham **Top Scorer:** Dave Bridger **P.o.Y.:** John Edwrads

FACT FILE
Formed: 1991
Colours:White/black/black
Change colours: Red & black/white/white.
Midweek home matchday: Tuesday
Programme - Price:£1.00 Pages: 20

CLUB PERSONNEL
Chairman: Jim McKell
Scotch Corner, Huntsmead, Alton, Hants. GU34 2SF
Tel: 01420 82725 (H) 07740 099374 (M)
Press Officer:

Manager: Dave Hawtin
Asst. Man. / Coach:Tom Powers
Physio:T.B.A.

ANDOVER

Secretary: Chris Jeremy, 23 Stubbs Court, Artists Way, Andover, Hants SP10 3QR
Tel: 01264 361973

Ground: Portway Stadium, West Portway Ind. Estate, Andover SP10 3LF Tel: 01264 391341

Directions: From the Andover By-pass A303 follow signs to Portway Ind. estate. On exiting the A303 turn right at r/about & over bridge, bear off left at next mini r/about and after 150yds turn right onto estate. Straight on until you enter Hopkinson Way, ground on left 4-500 yds

Capacity: 3,000 Cover: 250 Seats: 250 Floodlights: Yes

Clubhouse: Open matchdays & private function Club Shop: No Metal Badges: Yes

HONOURS Wessex Lg 00-01 R-up 94-95,97-98 Western Lg R-up 69-70 70-71; Hants Lg 13-14 24-25 33-34 44-45 48-49 50-51 61-62 (R-up 42-43), Northern Div 13-14, Div 2 R-up 37-38; Salisbury & Dist Lg (7) Hants Sen Cup (5); Russell Cotes Cup 23-24 31-32 37-38 44-45 52-53 58-59 60-61 61-62; Pickfords Cup 50-51; Hants Interm Cup 59-60 60-61; Hants Jun Cup 19-20 (R-up 1894-95 1910-11 12-13) N.Hants Cup 99-00 00-01

PREVIOUS **Leagues:** Salisbury & D.; Hants 1896-98, 1899-1901, 02-62; Southern 1898-99,1971-93 98-99; Western 1962-71; Wessex Lge 93-98

BEST SEASON **FA Cup:** 1st Rd 62-63, 0-1 v Gillingham
FA Trophy: 3rd Qual Rd 69-70, 70-71
FA Vase: 4th Rd 94-95, 1-3 v Falmouth Town (A)

CLUB RECORDS **Attendance:** 1,100 v Leicester, ground opening.
(3,484 v Gillingham at WalledMeadow, previous ground)

FACT FILE

Founded: 1883
Nickname: The Lions
Colours: Red & black/black/red
Change cols: All Purple.
Midweek matchday: Tuesday
Reserve Team's League: None
Programme: 50 pages #1.00

CLUB PERSONNEL

Chairman: John Cunningham-Brown
President: R Coleman
Manager: Howard Goddard
Asst Manager:
Physio: Chris Burford

2002-03

Leading Goalscorer:
Captain:
Player of the Year:

B.A.T. SPORTS

Secretary: Gill McClelland, 27 Saxon Road, Blackfield, Southampton SO45 1WY
Tel: 023 8089 2314

Ground: BAT Sports Ground, Southern Gdns, off Ringwood Road, Totton SO 40 8RW
Tel: 023 8086243

Directions: Into centre of Totton, proceed up Ringwood Road, past small roundabout, then 2nd left into Southern Gardens.
Half mile from Totton (BR)
Bus X2(Southampton-Bournemouth)

Capacity: 3,000 Seats: 150 Cover: 150 Floodlights: Yes

Clubhouse: Normal licensing hrs, all day for members' sports facilities. Hot & cold snacks

Best Season **FA Vase:** 3rd Rd 99-00
Club Records **Attendance:** 403 v AFC Bournemouth 3.05.02
Honours
Previous **Names:**

FACT FILE

Founded: 1925
Colours: All blue& yellow trim
Change: Red & black/red/red
Midweek Matches: Tuesday
Programme: 20 pages, 30p
Editor:

CLUB PERSONNEL

Chairman: Mike Geddes
Vice Chairman:
President:

Manager: Andy Leader & Ray Collins
Physio:

2002-03

Leading Goalscorer:
Captain:
Player of the Year:

BEMERTON HEATH HARLEQUINS

Secretary: Andy Hardwick, 2 Ashley Rd, Salisbury, Wilts. SP2 7BZ Tel: 01722 327232 & mobile: 07810128292

Ground: Western Way, Bemerton Heath, Salisbury, Wilts Tel: 01722 331925 :
FAX :01722 331218

Directions: Turn off A36 Salisbury-Bristol Rd at Skew Bridge (right turn if coming out of Salisbury), 1st left into Pembroke Rd for half mile, 2nd left along Western Way - ground quarter mile at end. 40 mins walk from Salisbury(BR) station.
Bus 51 or 52 from city centre stops at junction of Pembroke Rd/Western Way

Capacity : 2,100 Seats: 200 Cover: 350 Floodlights: Yes

Clubhouse: Yes - Week Days 7p.m.-11p.m.Week ends 12 noon.-11 p..m.Snacks available

HONOURS Wilts Snr Cup 92-93. Wilts Lg(3) as Bemerton Athletic

PREVIOUS **Names:** Bemerton Athletic, Moon FC & Bemerton Boys; all merged in 1989
Leagues: Bem. Ath.: Salisbury. & Wilts Comb.
Moon: Salisbury. & Andover Sunday Bem.Boys: Mid Wilts

RECORD **Attendance:** 1,118 v Aldershot Town FA Cup 1st Qual Rd Aug 94
Appearances: Keith Richardson

FACT FILE

Founded: May 1989
Nickname: Quins
Colours: Black & white diamonds/black/black & white hoops
Change colours: Yellow/white/white
Midweek Matches: Tuesday
Programme: 32 pages, 50p

CLUB PERSONNEL

Chairman: George Parker
President: Peter Say
Manager: Steve Slade
Coach:es: Andy Nash.,Jim McConnel l& Brian Leboutillier
Physio:Sandra Leboutillier

2002-2003

Leading Goalscorer:Neil Cole 25
Captain:Gary Burden
Players of the Year: Gary Burden & Colin Hopkins

Bournemouth Poppies F.C. Back Row (L-R): Steve Sharkey (Asst. Manager), Pete Littlefield (kit man), Mark Dancer, Colin Dand, Sammy Bryning, Chris Edmonds, Ross Drew, Mark Beverley, Kishan Chengadu, Keith Williams (Manager). Front Row: James Antell, Ryan Lucas, Paul Cuglietta, Lewis Till, Steve Miles, Danny Holmes, Dave Smith.

Christchurch F.C. Back Row (L-R): Stuart Underwood (Asst. Manager), Pete Murphy, Gary Horlock, Ross Edwards, Martin Saunders, Max Frampton, Neil Massie, Phil Langdown, Scott Joyce, Adie Butler, Nigel Cripps (Manager), Emma Walsh (Physio). Front Row: Duncan Wells, Lee Manning, John Wyatt, Paul Rideout, Jon Grace, James Johnson

Thatcham Town F.C. Back Row (L-R): John Haines (Secretary), Manny Preston (Physio), Pete Woodage (Match Secretary), Dave Quaintance (Lakeside Superbowl), Gareth James, Jamie Green, Paul Taplin, Russell Green, Steve Stott, Ashley Perry, Sian Howard, Jason Braidwood (Coach), Steve Melledew (Manager). Front Row: Sean Cook, Stuart Bould, Tom Melledew, Richard Sayer, Alan Mann, James Detreine, Bobby McClay.

BLACKFIELD & LANGLEY

Secretary: Doug Sangster, 3 Fir Tree Grove, Butts Ash Lane, Hythe, Hants SO45 3RA
Tel: 023 80844911 (H) 023 80313721 (B) Email: doug.sangster@tesco.net

Ground: Gang Warily Rec., Newlands Rd, Blackfield, Southampton, Hants SO45 1GA
Tel: 01703 893603

Capacity: 2,500 **Covered Seats**:180 **Covered Standing** :Nil **Floodlights**: Yes

Directions: A326 from Totton. At Holbury mini roundabout take the right fork signposted to Lepe and Fawley. After the 1st set of lights (170m) turn left into ground.
Nearest Railway station:

Clubhouse Opening hours and availability of food & snacks.

Previous **Leagues**: Southampton Senr Lg, Hampshire League, R-U Russell Cotes Cup
Names:

Honours: Hants Div97-98, Div 2 84-85, Southampton Senior Cup (4)

Club Records **Attendance:** 240

Best Season **FA Vase:** **FA Cup:**

FACT FILE
Founded: 1935
Colours: Green & white/green/green
Change colours: Red & white/red/red
Midweek home matchday: Tuesday
Programme Price:£1.00 Pages:32
Editor:Steve Nockeridge (023 8089 3065)

CLUB PERSONNEL
Chairman: Ian Hore
Tel: 023 8089 3325 (H) 023 8084 7659 (B)
Vice Chairman: Owen Lightfoot
President:Geoff Mercer

Managers:Tony Feeney & Andy Price
Asst. Man. / Coach: Bill Moore
Physio:

2002-03
Capt: Simon Eagle, P.o.Y.: Jimmy Hooper
Top Goalscorere: Steve Wheatland

BOURNEMOUTH

Secretary: Mandy Vaughan, 33 Kings Park Road, Bournemouth BH7 7AE
Tel No. & Fax: 01202 258367

Ground: Victoria Park, Namu Rd., Winton, Bournemouth, Dorset Tel: 01202 515123

Directions: Any bus to Wimborne Road, Winton. 2 miles from Bournemouth Central(BR)

Capacity: 3,000 Seats: 250 Cover: 250 Floodlights: Yes Shop: No

Clubhouse: Open daily 7-11pm. Sandwiches & hot snacks available.

HONOURS Hants Lg 13-13 21-22, B'mouth Snr Cup 66-67 89-90, Texaco F'lit Cup R-up 91-92, Hants I'mediate Cup 49-50 69-70, Hants Yth Cup 54-55 57-58 67-68

PREVIOUS **Leagues:** Hampshire **Ground:** Dene Park 1888-90
Names: Bournemouth Rovers 1875-88; Bournemouth Dene Park 1888-90

RECORD **Scorer:** B Head
Fee Received: £1,500 for Chike Onourah (Wimborne 93-94)

BEST SEASON **FA Vase:** **FA Cup:**

FACT FILE
Founded: 1875
Nickname: Poppies
Sponsors:Bradbury Roofing
Colours: All Red
Change colours: All blue.
Midweek Matches: Tuesday
Reserves' League: Jewson Wessex Comb
Programme: 58 pages, 50p
Editor: Steve Maidment
Local Press: Evening Echo

CLUB PERSONNEL
Chairman:Robert Corbin
Vice Chairman: Frank Harvey
President: Ernie Simpkins
Comm. Manager:Steve Jones
Press Officer: Steve Maidment
Manager: Keith Williams
Asst Manager: Steve Sharkey
Coach: Pete Littlefield
Physio:John Edwards

BROCKENHURST

Secretary: Paul Christopher, 31 Brookside Road, Bransgore, Christchurch, Dorset BM 23 8NA (01425 674084

Ground: Grigg Lane, Brockenhurst, Hants Tel: 01590 623544

Capacity: 2,000 **Seats:** 200 **Cover:** 300 **Floodlights:** Yes

Clubhouse: Open every evening plus Tues, Fri, Sat & Sun lunchtimes

Directions: M27 Junc 1, A337 to Lyndhurst and A337 to Brockenhurst. Turn right at Carey's Manor Hotel into Grigg Lane. Ground is 200 yds on the right
Bus : 56/56A(Lymington-Southampton)

HONOURS Hants Intermediate Cup 61-62; Bournemouth Senior Cup 60-61; Hampshire Lg 75-76, R-up 73-74 79-80, Div 2 70-71 R-up 60-61, Div 3 59-60.

PREVIOUS **League:** Hampshire Lge 24-26 47-86

RECORDS **Attendance:** 1,104 v St Albans City F.A..Amateur Cup January 1974
Win: 10-1 V Knowle Hospital Hants Inter Cup 13.02.61
Defeat: 0-11 Portsmouth Gas Co. Hants Div 2

BEST SEASON **FA Vase:** 4th Rd @000-2001 **FA Cup:** 2nd Q Rd 2001-2002
FA Amateur Cup: 2nd Round 73-4

FACT FILE
Founded: 1898 Nickname: The Badgers
Sponsor: T.B.A.
Colours: Blue & white/blue/blue
Change colours: Green/black/green
Midweek Matches: Tuesday
Reserves League: Wessex Combination
Programme: 32 pages, £1.00
Editor/Press Officer: Dave Stansbridge

CLUB PERSONNEL
Chairman:Brian Small
President: Mike Kimber
Vice Chairman: Ray Colverson
Man: Huw Lewis Asst. Man: Malcolm Cobb
Reserves Manager: Andy Colverson
Physio: Dave Lane

CHRISTCHURCH

Secretary: Alan Wilkins,59 Lingwood Avenue,Mudeford,Christchurch,Dorset. BH23 3JU
Tel No: 01202 480918 (H) 01202 488 116 (Fax) e-mail: christgol@aol.com

Ground: Hurn Bridge Sports Club, Hurn Bridge, Avon Causeway, Christchurch
Tel: 01202 473792

Directions: A338 from Ringwood, turn off signed Hurn Airport on left. Before Airport use mini roundabout & take exit signed Sopley & ground is immed. on the right. 3 miles from Christchurch (BR)

Capacity: 2,000 Seats: 215 Cover: 265 Floodlights: Yes

Clubhouse: Normal pub hours. Cooked food at lunchtimes

HONOURS Hants Jnr Cup 1892-93 1911-12 20-21; Hants Int. Cup 86-87; Pickford Cup 91; Hants Lg Div 2 37-38 47-48 85-86 (Div 3 56-57); B'mouth Snr Cup (5) 56-57 59-60 67-70; B'mouth Page-Croft Cup 94-95

PREVIOUS **League:** Hampshire **Ground:** Barrack Rd Recreation Grd (>1984)

RECORD **Appearances** : John Haynes

BEST SEASON **FA Vase:** 2nd Qual. 2002-03 **FA Cup:** 20021-2002
FA Amateur Cup:

Players progressing: Jody Craddock (Cambridge Utd 93), Dan West (Aston Villa 94)

FACT FILE

Founded: 1885
Nickname: Priory
Sponsors: Franklin Transport
Colours: All royal blue (white trim)
Change colours: All Red
Midweek Matches: Tuesday
Programme: 16 pages, 50p
Editor: Dennis Miller

CLUB PERSONNEL

Chairman: Majid Azzeddin
Vice Chairman: Ian Harley Pres: Joss Jenkins
Press Officer: Robin Osborne
Joint Managers: Nigel Cripps & Tony Brown
Physio: Kevin Jackson

2002-03

Leading Goalscorer:Duncan Wells
Captain:Steve Hillyer
Player of the Year: Steve Hillyer

COWES SPORTS

Secretary: Lee Bray, 86 Seaview Road, Cowes, Isle of Wight 7UQPO31 (01983 200626)
Website: www.cowessportsfc.co.uk

Ground: Westwood Park, Reynolds Close, off Park Rd, Cowes, Isle of Wight PO31 7NT
Tel: 01983 293793

Directions: Take Park Rd out of Cowes . Reynolds Close is a right turn half mile up hill

Capacity: 1850 Seats: 450 Cover: 450 Floodlights: Yes

Clubhouse: Yes - **Club Shop:** No

HONOURS Hants. League (7) Lg Cup 93 Isle of Wight Gold Cup (17),Wessex Lg.Cup 98-9

PREVIOUS **League:** Hampshire (pre-1994)

BEST SEASON **FA Cup:** 4th Qual. Rd replay 57-58, 1-4 v Trowbridge (A) after 2-2
FA Vase: 5th Rd 99-00

FACT FILE

Founded: 1881
Colours: Blue & white stripes,black,blue
Change colours: All Yellow
Midweek Fixtures: Tuesdays
Reserves' Lge: Wessex Combination
Programme Editor: Tony Gibbs

CLUB PERSONNEL

President: Ada Leigh
Chairman: Ian Lee
Vice Chairman: Ron Bowler
Press Officer: Simon Smith
Manager: Derek Ohren
Asst. Man. / Coach:
Physio: T.B.A.

DOWNTON

Secretary: Brian Ford, 11 Chantry Road, Wilton, Salisbury, Wilts.
Tel No: 01722 743314

Ground: Brian Whitehead Sports Ground, Wick Lane, Downton Tel: 01725 512162

Directions: Travel south from Salisbury on A338 for about 7 miles. Turn right intoWick Lane, and the ground is a qtr mile on left

Capacity: 1600 Seats: 250 Cover: Nil Floodlights: Yes

Clubhouse: Bar with kitchen facilities Club Shop: No

HONOURS Wilts Sen Cup 79-80 80-81, (R-up 55-56 91-92 94-95); Wilts Jun Cup 49-50; Bournemouth Sen Lge 60 61 62 64 65 67 68, Sen Lge Cup 61-62 63-64 66-67, Cup 62-63 79-80; Wessex Lge Cup 95-96; Wessex Comb Cup (R-up 95-96); RussellCotes Cup 95-96; Hayward Cup 64-65

PREVIOUS **League:** Bournemouth, Hants (pre-1993)

CLUB RECORDS **Attendance:**
BEST SEASON **FA Vase:** **FA Cup:**
FA Amateur Cup:

FACT FILE

Founded: 1905
Nickname: The Robins
Sponsor: Priority Mailing
Colours: Red/white/red
Change colours:Yellow/blue/yellow
Midweek Matchday: Tuesday
Programme: Yes
Editor: Paul Beaney

CLUB PERSONNEL

Chairman: James Blake
President: R Tanner
Manager: Mitch Blake
Asst.Manager: Steve Adlam
Coach: C Huxford
Physio: Pete Watts

FAREHAM TOWN

Secretary: Malcolm Harper OBE, 20 Hampton Grove, Catisfield, Fareham, Hants PO15 5NL
Tel: 01329 8413476 (H) 01329 844074 (Fax) 0410 689939 (M)

Ground: Cams Alders, Highfield Avenue, Fareham, Hants PO14 1JA Tel: 01329 231151

Directions: M27, J11, follow A27 towards Southampton. After passing Fareham station turn left at traffic lights (2nd left) into Redlands Ave.. Turn right at Redlands Inn then left into Highfields Ave.
Capacity: 5,500 Cover: 500 Seats: 450 Floodlights: Yes

Clubhouse: Open every evening except Sundays. Food available

Club Shop: Sells programmes, scarves & fanzines

HONOURS Hants Lg (8) 59-60 62-67 72-73 74-75 (R-up 55-56 60-61 67-68 71-72 76-77 78-79, Div 2 R-up 52-53, Eastern Div 24-25, Div 3 East 49-50), Hants Snr Cup 56-57 62-63 67-68 92-93, Russell Cotes Cup (6) 64-65 72-77, Gosport War Memorial Cup, SW Co's Cup (2), Pickford Cup (2),

PREVIOUS **Leagues:** Portsmouth 47-49, Hants 49-79, Southern 79-98
Name: Fareham FC **Ground:** Bath Lane

BEST SEASON **FA Trophy:** Semi Final 86-87 **FA Amateur Cup:** 2nd Rd 63-64 66-67 73-74
FA Vase: 1st Rd 98-9 **FA Cup:** 1st Rd replay 88-89, 2-3 v Torquay U. (H) after 2-2

RECORDS **Attendance:** 2,650 v Wimbledon, FA Cup 1965.
(at Southampton F.C.) 6,035 v Kidderminster H., FAT S-F 2nd leg 86-87
Fee received: £43,000 for David Leworthy (Spurs)

FACT FILE
Formed: 1947 Nickname: The Town
Sponsors: Portsmouth Evening News
Colours: Red/white/red
Change colours: Whiteblack/black
Midweek matchday: Wednesday
Reserves' League: Hampshire Comb
Programme: 36 pages £1
Editor: Ian Tewson Tel. 01329 662624

CLUB PERSONNEL
Chairman: Bob Ralls
Director of Football: John Green
President: Ken Atkins
General Manager: Tony Adams (01705 615931)
Press Officer: M Willis
Manager: Jon Gittens
Physio: James McKay

GOSPORT BOROUGH

Secretary: B V Cosgrave, 2 Cavanna Close, Rowner, Gosport PO13 0PE Tel: 01329314117

Ground: Privett Park, Privett Road, Gosport, Hants Tel: 01705 501042 (Office)

Directions: M27 Junct 11, A32 Fareham to Gosport. At Brockhurst r-about (about 3 miles) right into Military Rd passing thru H.M.S. Sultan, left into Privett Rd at next r-about, ground 300yds left signed `Privett Park Enclosure'. 2 miles from Portsmouth Harbour (BR) or Fareham (BR)

Capacity: 4,500 Cover: 500 Seats: 450 Floodlights: Yes Club Shop: No

Clubhouse: Matchdays only - from 1.30 Sat., 6.30 Wed. Refreshment hut sells hot food & drinks

HONOURS Wessex Lg Cup 92-93, Southern Lg Div 1 South R-up 84-85, Hants Lg 45-46 76-77 77-78 (Div 3 (Res.) 70-71 75-76), Portsmouth Lg R-up 44-45, Hants Senior Cup 87-88, Russell Cotes Cup R-up 94-95, Hants Intermediate Cup 70-71, Portsmouth Senior Cup 61-62 69-70 70-71 94-95, South West Counties Pratten Challenge Cup 77-78

BEST SEASON **FA Trophy:** 1st Rd 88-89 **FA Amateur Cup:** 3rd Rd 47-48 66-67
FA Vase: 6th Rd rep 77-78 **FA Cup:** 4th Qual. Rd 80-81 (lost to Windsor & Eton)

PREVIOUS **Leagues:** Portsmouth 44-45; Hants 45-78; Southern 78-92
Name: Gosport Borough Athletic

RECORD **Attendance:** 4,770 v Pegasus, FA Amtr Cup 1951
Scorer: Richie Coulbert 192 **Appearances**: Tony Mahoney 764
Win: 14-0 v Cunliffe-Owen, Hampshire Lg Div 1 45-46
Defeat: 0-9 twice v Newport, Hants Lg Div 1 47-48.
v Gloucester (A), Southern Lg Prem Div 89-90

FACT FILE
Founded: 1944 Nickname: The Boro'
Sponsors:MM Surfacine
Colours: Yellow/blue/yellow
Change colours: All red
Midweek matchday: Tuesday
Reserves ' League: Wessex Combination
Programme:40 pages, £1.00
Editor: Roy newman (02392 799198)
Press: Portsmouth Eve News, So'ton Eve Echo
Website:www.gosportboroughfc.co.uk

A club record 14 consecutive victories were achieved in 00-01 season

CLUB PERSONNEL
Chairman: JohnStimpson
President: H.Mizen
Manager: Mick Marsh Coach Hugh Doyle
Physio: Zoe Huggins

2002-03
Leading Goalscorer:Neil Scammell 43
Captain:Stuart Hensman
Player of the Year: Ian Rew

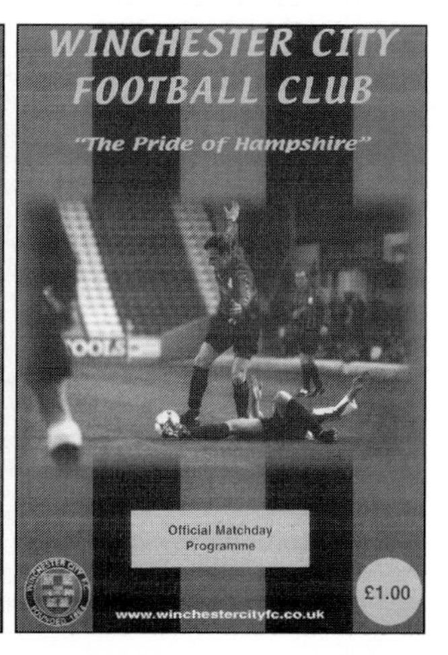

HAMBLE AEROSTRUCTURES SPORTS & SOCIAL CLUB

Secretary: Matthew Newbold, Flat 6, 70-72 Portsmouth Road, Woolsten, Southampton, Hants. SO19 9AN Tel: 023 803 24147 (H) 023 804 53371(W)

Ground: Folland Park, Kings Avenue, Hamble.,Southampton SO31 4NF Tel: 02380452173

Directions: M27 junction 8, then B3397 to Hamble. Half mile fromHamble (BR); turn right out of station, proceed for one mile then turn right before shops into Kings Avenue. Ground 1000 yards on right in works sports ground.

Capacity: 1000 Seats: 150 Cover: 150 Floodlights: Yes
Clubhouse: 300 capacity social club. Cricket & bowls

HONOURS: Hampshire Lg Div 3 80-81 (Div 4 79-80), Hampshire Intermediate Cup 79-90, Southampton Senior Cup 84-85 86-87 91-92
As Hamble AS&SC: Jewson Wessex League Cup 97-98

PREVIOUS **Name:** Folland Sports (pre-1990), Aerostructures SSC 90-97
RECORD **Defeat:** 1-10 v Andover (A), Wessex League 93-94

FACT FILE

Colours: Maroon and Sky Blue
Change colours: All navy blue
Midweek Matches: Tuesdays & Wednesdays
Reserves ' League: Wessex Comb
Under 18 & Under16: So'ton Youth Lgs
Programme - Price: Pages:
Editor:

CLUB PERSONNEL

President: Alistair Tritten
Assistant Secretary: Matthew Newbold
Treasurer: Barry Morse
Senior Manager: Larry Clay

Team Manager:
Asst. Man. / Coach:
Physio:

LYMINGTON & NEW MILTON

Secretary: John Osey, 9 Samphire Close, Lymington, Hants SO41 9LR Tel: 01590 676995
Ground: Fawcett Fields,Christchurch Rd., New Milton,Hants BH25 6QF (01425 6281910
Directions: M27 Jct 1 follow A337 to Lyndhurst one way system(A35) towards Christchurch. Left in Hinton Admiral at Cat & Fiddle.Follow Ringwood road ,then left at A337 roundabout to New Milton. Ground one mile on left past Chewton Glen Hotel.Bus service 123(Lym't -Bournemout)
Capacity: 3,000 Seats: 262 Cover: 262 Floodlights: Yes
Clubhouse: Open seven days a week 11.0 am to 11.0 pm. Hot food and functions availab le
HONOURS Wessex Lg 92-93 96-97 97-98, 98-99 , 99-00,00-01R-up 91-92 95-96, Wessex Lg Cup 88-89, R-up 94-95, 98-99 Wessex Comb. 92-93, Hants Snr Cup R-up 89-90, Texaco Cup 91-92, Bournemouth Snr Cup 92-93, R-up 96-97, Russell Cotes Cup 93-94 94-95, R-up91-92 92-93; Pickford Cup R-up 92-93. Jewson Champions Shield 98-99
BEST SEASON **FA Cup:** 4th Qual. Rd. 99-00, 1-3 v Aldershot Town (H)
FA Vase: 98-99 Quarter Final, 1-3 v Taunton Town (A)
PREVIOUS **Names:** Lymington Town (until 1988 merger with Wellworthy Ath.), AFC Lymington 88-98 (until merger with New Milton Town)
Ground: Ampress Ground (Wellworthy Ath.), until 1988 merger
RECORD **Attendance:** 2,900 v Karen Mills Memorial Day 12.3.95
Scorer: Darren Pitter 197 **Appearances:** Graham Kemp 504
Win: 11-1 v Romsey Town (H), Wessex League 9/11/92
Defeat: 0-8 v Basingstoke Town (A), Hampshire Senior Cup 10/4/90

FACT FILE

Founded as Lymington & New Milton: 1998
Nickname: Linnets
Sponsors:Parkcrest Construction
Colours: Marroon & Blue Stripes/blue/maroon
Change colours: White/black/black
Midweek Matches: Tuesday
Reserves ' League: Wessex Comb

Programme: 48 pages, £1.00
Editors: Jack Holliday & Keith Williams

CLUB PERSONNEL

Chairman: Charlie Hewlett
President: Jack Holliday & Ted Goodyer
Press Officer: Keith Williams (01202 476898)

Manager: Graham Kemp

MONEYFIELDS

Secretary: Paul Lipscombe,5 Braunston Close,Paulsgrove,Hants. PO6 4EN (07766 222718)
Ground: Moneyfields Sports Ground, Moneyfields Avenue, Copnor, Portsmouth,Hants. Tel: 023 9266 5260 (Club), 023 9265 2424 (Office) **Club Shop**: Yes
Capacity: 1,500 Seats: 150 Cover: 150 Floodlights: Yes
Clubhouse: Daily 7-11 p.m. Saturday 11-11p.m. (food from 1.0 pm)
Directions: From Southampton & the west - travel east on M27 onto A27. Take exit marked Southsea A2030. (From east take the same exit). Head south along A2030 exit and turn right into Tangier Road (4th right). Follow until`Tangiers' PH & take next right into Folkestone Road. Carry on into Martin Rd & club is in front of you.
Records: **Attendances:** Matthew Lafferty 156 (Jewson Wessex)
Goalscorer: Kevin Marsh 49 (Jewson Wessex)
Attendance: 152 v Fareham Town, Jewson Wessex League, 98-99
Best Seasons: **F.A.Cup:** 1st Qual. Rd. 01-02 **Previous Name**: Portsmouth Civil Service
F.A.Vase: 3rd Rd 01-02
Records: **Goalscorer**: Neil Damley 62 **Appearances** Matthew Lafferty 168
Attendance v Fareham T 232 01-02
Honours: Portsmouth Senior Cup: 90-91 R-up 91-92 Hampshire League Div 3 91-92, Div 2 92-93,Div 196-97,R-Up 97-98 Portsmouth Premier champions 90-91,91-92 Billy Hill Cup 90-91 Hampshireb Intermediate Cup Winners 91-92, 92-93 Russell Cotes Cup Finalists 98-99 Hants Youth Cuip (under 18) (4), Under 16 (98-99),Hants Youth League 00-01 R-up 98-99

FACT FILE
Founded: 1987 Nickname: Moneys
Sponsors: Icee Ltd & Triman
Colours: Yellow/navyblue/navy blueChange: Green & white/ green/green.
Midweek Fixtures: Wednesday
Reserves League: Wessex Combination
Programme: 26 pages £1.00
Editor: David Hayter (023 9264 3986)
CLUB PERSONNEL
Chairman: David Jupe
Tel: 023 9235 9571
Manager: Calvin Hore
Assistant Manager: Paul GregoryPhysio: Adie Hylands

2002-03
Leading Goalscorer: Lee Mould 26
Captain:Matthew Lafferty
Player of the Year: Craig Stafford

PORTLAND UNITED

Chairman: Phillip Laming, Acorn Bungalow, 1b, Straits, Portland, Dorset.
Tel: 01305 822756 (B)
Website: www.portlandunitedfc.co.uk
E.mail: portlandutdfc@aol.com

Secretary: Tony Greaves, 1 The Spinney, Lorton Lane,Weymouth, Dorset. DT3 5DJ
Ground: New Grove Corner, Grove Road, Portland, Dorset
Tel: 01305 861489
Capacity: 2000 Covered Seating: 150 Covered Standing: 50 Floodlights: Yes

Directions A354 to Portland, follow one way system to the top of island, roundabout (hotel on left, garage on right), over roundabout for 500m, turn left into Grove Road, ground on left hand side.
Clubhouse: Yes - Open one hour before kick-off. Food available
PREVIOUS Leagues: Dorset Combination
CLUB RECORDS Attendance: 651

FACT FILE
Founded: ????
Colours: All blue
Change colours: Red/black/red
Midweek matches: Tuesday
Programme: Yes - Price: 50p Pages:32
Editor:Mike Harvey
CLUB PERSONNELL
Vice Chairman: Pete Turrell
Treasurer: Alex Goracey
Manager:Nicky Preston
Asst. Man. / Coach: Andy Mason
Physio: M..Harper
2002-03 Top Scorer: James Reeves

THATCHAM TOWN

Football Secretary: Peter Woodage, 5 Elm Grove, Thatcham, Berks. RG18 3DJ
Tel: 01635 861937

Ground: Waterside Park, Crookham Rd, Thatcham, Berks Tel: 01635 862016
Capacity: 3,000 Seats: 300 Cover: 300 Floodlights: Yes
Directions: M4 junc 13, take A34 to Newbury, then left onto A4 towards Reading InThatcham turn right to the railway station. The ground is on the left beyond the station - 2 minutes walk.From South A34 to Newbury,take A339 to Basingstoke,left to Thatcham then left again down Crookham Rd. Ground on right just before station

Clubhouse: Open every evening & lunchtimes **Club Shop:** Yes
HONOURS Wessex Lg 95-96,R-up 98-99, Cup 90-91 91-92 94-95 96-97, (R-up twice)
PREVIOUS **Grounds**: Station Road 46-52; Lancaster Close 52-92
BEST SEASON **FA Cup:** 4th Qual Rd 96-97 **FA Vase:** 6th Round 1987-88
RECORD **Attendnace:** 1,400 v Aldershot, FA Vase

FACT FILE
Founded: 1895
Sponsors: Panasonic Gsm Mobile Phones
Colours: Blue & white stripes/blue/blue
Change colours:Red,black,black
Midweek Matches: Tuesday
Programme: 28 pages, 50p
Editor: Ed Houghton
CLUB PERSONNEL
Chairman: Phil Holdway
General Secretary: John Haines
Press Officer: Chairman (01635 867803)
ManagerSteve Melledew
Coach:Jason Braidwood

2002-03
Leading Goalscorer:Sean Cook
Captain:Sian Howard
Player of the Year:Ashley Perry

WHITCHURCH UNITED

Secretary: Joanna Cozzi, 39 Hartley Meadow, Whitchurch,Hants RG26
Tel: 01256 892579(H) 01344 401129 (B) 07780 663494 (M)

Ground: Longmeadow, Winchester Road, Whitchurch Tel: 01256 892493

Directions: From Whitchurch (BR) station; turn left after Railway Inn, follow road to end, turn right into main road, arriving in town turn left alongWinchester Road. Ground three quarters of a mile on left

Capacity: 2,000 Seats: 200 Cover: Yes Floodlights: Yes

Clubhouse: Hot food on matchdays. Sports hall with squash courts and indoor bowling green

HONOURS ????
PREVIOUS **Leagues:** Hampshire (pre-1992)
BEST SEASON **FA Vase:** Extra-Preliminary Rd 93-94, 1-3 v Peppard (H)
CLUB RECORDS **Attendance: ??**

FACT FILE
Founded: 1903
Colours: Red &white/black/black
Change colours: White/blue/blue.
Midweek Matches: Tuesday
Programme: 24 pages

CLUB PERSONNEL
Chairman: Tony Chivers
8 Bloswood Drive, Whichurch, Hants. RG28 7AZ
Tel: 01256 893696 (H) 07702 692200 (M)
Vice Chairman:
President:

Manager:
Asst. Man. / Coach:
Physio:

WIMBORNE TOWN

Secretary: Peter Barham,Chelmer, 17 Margards Lane,Verwood, Dorset BH31 6JP
Tel Nos: 01202 826705 (H) 07956 833346 (M)

Ground: The Cuthbury, Cowgrove Road, Wimborne, Dorset BH21 4EL Tel: 01202 884821
Capacity: 3,250 Seats: 275 Cover: 150 Floodlights: Yes

Directions: Wimborne to Blandford Road, behind Victoria Hospital

Clubhouse: Eves 7-11, Sat noon-11, Sun 12-6 Bar & Skittle alley **Club Shop:** Yes

HONOURS FA Vase 91-92; Wessex Lg 91-92 93-94 ,99-00(R-up 92-93 96-97), Lg Cup 93-94,99-00 (R-up 90-91 95-96); Dorset Lg Div 1 80-81 81-82 (R-up 38-39 72-73), Div 2 31-32 34-35 36-37(R-up 35-36), Lg Cup R-up (4) 72-74 80-82; Dorset Snr Cup 91-92 96-97, (R-up 80-82 85-86 98-99,99-00); Mark Frowde Cup 92-93 94-95;01-02 Dorset Snr Amateur Cup 36-37 63-64;Dorset Jnr Cup 31-32 36-37 (R-up 13-14 34-35); Dorset Minor Cup 12-13; Dorset Jnr Amateur Cup (3) 34-36 38-39; Bankes Charity Cup 89-90 94-95 95-96, TexacoF/Light Cup 90-91

PREVIOUS **Leagues:** Dorset Lge, Dorset Comb, Western 81-86

BEST SEASON **FA Vase:** Winners 91-92 **FA Cup:** 1st Rd Proper 82-83

RECORDS **Attendance:** 3,250 v Bamberbridge FA Vase Semi-Final 28/3/92
Goalscorer: Jason Lovell **Win** (Wessex Lg): 9-0 v E.Cowes V 98-99, Brockenhurst 99-00
Appearances: James Sturgess **Defeat** (Wessex Lg): 2-6 v Thatcham Town 91-92
Fee paid: £5,500 for J P Lovell (Bashley, 1992)
Fee received: £6,000; for J P Lovell (Bashley, 1989) & for Tommy Killick(Dorchester, 1993)

FACT FILE
Founded: 1878 Nickname: Magpies
Sponsors: Nicolas O'Hara
Colours: Black & white stripes/black/black
Change colours: Yellow/green/yellow
Midweek Matches: Tuesday
Reserve League: Dorset League
Programme: 28 pages, £1.00
Editor: Ken Fergus

CLUB PERSONNEL
Chairman: Nicholas O'Hara
President: Brian Maidment
Press Officer: Secretary
Manager:Paul Arnold
Asst, Mgr: John Macey
Coach: Darren Powell
Physio: Steve Churchill

2002-2003
Captain: Darren Powell
P.o.Y.: Stewart Kearn
Top Goalscorer: Gareth Barnes

WINCHESTER CITY

Secretary: Ray Murphy, 'Petals', 21 Villette Close, Christchurch, Dorset BH23 2NR
Tel: 01202 482067 (H) 07801 638158 (W/M)
Fax: 01202 258863 email: raymurph@supanet.com

Ground: The City Ground, Hillier Way, Abbotts Barton, Winchester. Tel: 01962 863553

Directions: M3 J9, take A33/A34 for 1 mile, then A33 for a further mile. 1st left into Kings Worthy, follow road for about 3 miles. After 30mph sign take 2nd left, 1st right, 1st left into Hillier Way. Clubhouse and pitch in front of you.

Capacity: 7,500 Covered Seating: 200 Covered Standing: No Floodlights: Yes
Clubhouse Opening match days with food available.

PREVIOUS **Leagues: 1898-99, 1903 -42, 1943-44, 1945-71, 1971-73,1973-2003 Southern**

BEST SEASON **FA Vase:** (first season) Quarter Final 2002-2003

HONOURS Hampshire League Prem Div. 2002-03, Div. 1 00-01

FACT FILE

Founded: 1884
Colours: Red & black stripes/black/black
Change colours: Yellow & blue stripes/blue/yellow
Midweek matchday: Tuesday
Programme
Price £1.00: Pages: 56

CLUB PERSONNEL

Chairman: Richard Newsome
Director of Football: David Malone
Manager: Neil Hards

2002-03
Leading Goalscorer: Andy Forbes
Captain: Danny Smith
Player of the Year: Matthew Bicknell

BAT Sports' Gary Fox (No.9) beats the St Leonards defence to send the ball goal bound, during the 1st Qualifying Round of the FA Cup. Photo: Roger Turner.

HAMPSHIRE FOOTBALL LEAGUE

Established: 1896

President: N L White
Chairman: G Cox
Secretary: I J Craig

56 Ecton Lane, Anchorage Park, Hilsea, Portsmouth PO3 5TA
Tel: 023 9267 1155 Fax: 023 9265 1147
League Development Officer: J Moody

The League welcomed three new clubs this season, DC AFC who joined from the Salisbury Football League, Lodgershall Sports FC who were runners-up in the North Hants Senior LEague and Fareham Town Reserves who joined the Combination Division. However, prior to the start of the season the league suffered two withdrawals, when 2001-02 Division Two champions Headley Athletic lost their manager and failed to secure a sponsor and King's Somborne were unable to find a manager or players up to the Hampshire League standard.

The season kicked off on August 17th in weather more akin to the cricket season. The first round of the Trophyman Cup produced it's usual giant killing results, notably Second Division Overton United beating Premier Division Locksheath 5-0, Central Sports again beating Premier opposition Hythe & Dibden and League newcomers DC AFC defeating cup specialists Hayling United after extra time and penalties.

In the FA Vase Petersfield Town and Poole Town exited the competition at the first qualifying round against Hungerford Town and Christchurch respectively. Amesbury Town lost to Devon League side NEwton Abbott after a replay in the second qualifying round but Lymington Town winners over Sussex County League opposition Oakwood, with the lowest attendance of the round, 18, and Winchester City winners over Sussex County LEague side Eastbourne Town both reached the first round proper and were rewarded with home ties.

The pick of the results in the first round of Hampshire Senior Cup saw Vosper Thornycroft beat Jewson Wessex League title favourites Lymington & New Milton 3-2. Bishops Waltham did well to lose by the only goal of the match against Brockenhurst.

Winchester City became the only league side left in the FA Vase when they beat Kent League outfit, Cray Wanderers, 5-2 and earned a home tie against Shortwood United from the Hellenic League in the next round. Our other club Lymington Town were defeated 3-0 by Selsey from the Sussex County League.

The Trophyman Cup holders East Cowes Victoria were knocked out of the competition in Round Two by Pirelli General and another Premier Division club, Petersfield Town suffered a 3-2 defeat at home to Division Two leaders Overton United. The Cup matches at this stage of the season continued with more success for our club's. The second round of the Hampshire Senior Cup saw Lymington Town pull off a tremendous 5-4 win over Jewson Wessex League high fliers, AFC Totton, whilst Winchester City convincingly defeated Jersey's St Peters 7-0. Brading Town suffered a humiliating 15-2 defeat against Alton Town and Vosper Thornycroft put up a good fight before losing 3-2 against Southern League Bashley.

Winchester City reached the last 32 of the FA Vase when they comprehensively beat Jewson Wessex League side Brockenhurst 7-0 at Gigg Lane which earned them an away tie in the Midlands against Newcastle Town and as our last representatives in the Hampshire Senior Cup were eliminated at the quarter-final stage losing 2-1 at Southern League Bashley after extra time. A 1-0 win over Newcastle Town took Winchester to the last 16 of the FA Vase, the furthest any Hampshire League side had reached, and bettered this record with a late winner over Burgess Hill Town to progress to the quarter-finals. It was at this stage that Winchester's fine run ended when they lost 1-0 to Oadby Town.

Winchester City completed a memorable season by defeating Portsmouth Royal Navy 10-1 to make sure of the Premier League title, whilst their last game of the season brought them further silverware with victory over Andover New Street in the final of the Trophyman Cup. Hayling United lifted the Division One championship trophy whilst Laverstock & Ford came out on top of Division Two. The Combination titles were taken by Paulsgrove Reserves in Division One and by Fareham Town Reserves in Division Two. Whilst Winchester City also added the Southampton Senior Cup to their season's successes.

FINAL LEAGUE TABLES 2002-03

PREMIER DIVISION		P	W	D	L	F	A	Pts
1	Winchester City	38	36	1	1	181	18	109
2	Vosper Thornycroft	38	29	5	4	116	40	92
3	East Cowes Victoria Athletic	38	23	4	11	95	47	73
4	Poole Town	38	22	6	10	79	54	72
5	Horndean	38	19	11	8	66	43	68
6	Locksheath	38	19	5	14	84	70	62
7	Liss Athletic	38	18	8	12	94	86	62
8	Andover New Street	38	16	9	13	73	65	57
9	Stockbridge	38	17	4	17	86	75	55
10	Petersfield Town	38	15	8	15	71	70	53
11	Amesbury Town	38	15	5	18	76	88	50
12	Ringwood Town	38	13	10	15	75	79	49
13	Portsmouth Royal Navy	38	14	7	17	62	84	49
14	Bishops Waltham Town	38	13	7	18	57	67	46
15	Lymington Town	38	11	11	16	75	91	44
16	Pirelli General	38	10	7	21	45	92	37
17	Brading Town	38	10	7	21	58	110	37
18	Fawley	38	6	5	27	43	130	23
19	Hythe & Dibden	38	5	7	26	46	94	22
20	Aldermaston	38	3	5	30	36	115	14

Division One	P	W	D	L	F	A	Pts
Hayling United	28	20	3	5	86	29	63
Verwood Town	28	19	1	8	51	38	58
Colden Common	28	16	5	7	70	39	53
Paulsgrove	28	17	2	9	66	37	53
Fleet Spurs	28	15	6	7	57	36	51
Farnborough Nth End	28	14	5	9	69	47	47
Fleetlands	28	13	6	9	63	62	45
Micheldever	28	11	6	11	51	44	39
Tadley Town	28	11	6	11	46	41	39
AFC Portchester	28	10	8	10	58	59	38
Alresford Town	28	11	5	12	39	50	38
Clanfield	28	5	8	15	43	75	23
Fareham Sac. Hearts	28	6	3	19	41	71	21
Co-op Sports & Hilsea	28	3	5	20	34	81	14
Yateley Green (-1)	28	3	3	22	26	91	11

Division Two	P	W	D	L	F	A	Pts
Laverstock & Ford	24	17	3	4	66	20	54
Overton United	24	16	3	5	61	26	51
Hedge End	24	15	5	4	64	33	50
Ordnance Survey	24	12	5	7	44	29	41
Netley Central Sports	24	12	3	9	49	36	39
DC AFC	24	10	5	9	38	39	35
Hamble Club	24	10	5	9	38	44	35
Otterbourne	24	10	3	11	31	37	33
Ludgershall Sports	24	7	5	12	39	44	26
Broughton	24	8	2	14	40	66	26
QK Southampton	24	7	3	14	30	51	24
M & T Awbridge	24	6	5	13	25	44	23
Romsey Town	24	1	3	20	16	72	6

PREMIER DIVISION	1	2	3	4	5	6	7	8	9	10	11	12	13	14	15	16	17	18	19	20
1 Aldermaston		0-2	1-5	1-2	0-2	0-3	3-0	1-0	2-3	2-4	0-2	4-3	0-2	1-2	0-5	0-1	2-2	1-3	1-2	1-4
2 Amesbury Town	3-0		2-0	5-2	1-2	0-2	1-2	2-3	1-0	2-3	3-2	5-7	4-1	3-1	2-3	3-0	3-1	2-5	1-3	3-2
3 Andover New Street	4-1	2-1		0-0	4-2	2-2	7-0	2-2	3-0	4-2	2-0	2-4	1-2	3-0	2-1	1-3	0-2	1-2	1-1	1-1
4 Bishops Waltham Tn	0-0	1-2	1-1		6-1	2-1	2-0	1-1	5-3	0-2	1-2	1-2	0-1	0-1	2-3	2-0	3-2	2-1	0-1	0-5
5 Brading Town	1-0	2-2	1-4	3-2		1-4	2-1	0-0	3-0	1-1	2-2	1-3	1-4	3-3	1-4	5-1	1-1	4-0	1-2	0-7
6 East Cowes Victoria	4-0	5-0	4-1	1-2	2-3		7-0	1-0	1-2	1-0	2-0	3-2	2-1	4-1	5-0	3-1	2-2	1-3	3-0	0-5
7 Fawley	5-2	0-0	1-5	2-5	3-2	1-5		1-2	3-3	0-2	0-2	1-1	0-5	2-2	4-2	0-2	0-1	0-7	1-2	0-2
8 Horndean	5-0	2-0	1-1	1-0	2-0	0-0	4-0		5-1	6-0	3-4	2-0	0-3	4-2	1-0	0-1	1-1	2-0	2-0	0-4
9 Hythe & Dibden	5-1	2-2	1-3	0-1	1-2	0-1	2-4	0-1		1-1	1-4	1-1	0-2	0-0	1-2	2-4	1-2	5-2	2-7	0-7
10 Liss Athletic	3-3	5-2	5-0	4-2	8-2	2-2	3-2	1-1	4-1		7-0	4-4	2-4	2-1	2-1	2-0	5-3	2-1	0-1	2-8
11 Locksheath	3-0	3-5	0-1	4-0	4-1	2-5	5-1	1-2	4-0	1-1		2-0	1-1	2-1	1-3	4-1	5-1	1-2	1-2	0-4
12 Lymington Town	3-0	1-1	1-2	1-0	3-3	2-5	5-0	1-3	2-2	0-1	4-4		1-0	1-2	2-2	4-1	2-2	3-1	0-3	1-3
13 Petersfield Town	3-3	2-3	2-2	2-2	2-0	0-3	2-3	2-2	1-1	3-0	1-2	1-4		1-0	4-1	2-2	1-2	2-3	1-2	0-6
14 Pirelli General	3-3	1-0	0-2	1-2	2-1	0-5	4-2	0-2	0-2	4-3	1-2	3-1	0-0		0-3	1-1	5-3	2-3	1-1	0-4
15 Poole Town	5-1	1-3	1-1	1-0	8-1	W-L	2-1	0-0	4-0	2-0	1-3	3-1	3-0	1-0		2-0	3-1	1-1	2-2	0-5
16 Portsmouth R.N.	2-1	2-2	4-1	2-2	2-1	2-1	4-0	2-2	2-1	2-1	2-2	2-2	2-4	5-0	2-4		0-2	1-2	1-2	1-10
17 Ringwood	3-0	5-2	5-1	2-3	3-1	0-3	2-2	0-1	2-1	3-3	1-4	2-2	0-4	7-0	1-2	2-1		3-0	1-1	0-2
18 Stockbridge	7-1	7-2	2-0	2-2	4-1	2-1	4-0	2-2	1-0	3-4	2-3	2-1	2-3	0-1	1-2	1-3	4-4		1-2	1-2
19 Vosper Thornycroft	6-0	3-0	2-1	3-0	4-0	3-1	12-0	7-0	2-1	7-3	3-1	7-0	4-2	6-0	1-1	4-0	2-1	4-1		2-5
20 Winchester City	3-0	5-1	5-0	3-1	10-0	5-0	7-1	2-1	2-0	6-0	3-1	10-0	6-0	7-0	2-0	6-0	6-0	4-1	3-0	

AFC ALDERMASTON
Secretary: Christine Collier,14 Brackenwood Drive,Tadley, Hampshire RG26 4YB Tel: 07884 254706 (M) 01256 363344 (W)
Chairman: George Johnstone
Ground: Aldermaston Rec. Society, Automatic Weapons Establishment, Aldermaston, Reading, Berks. Tel: 0118 982 4544
Colours: All Blue. Change Colours: Yellow/white/white

AMESBURY TOWN Founded: 1904
Secretary: Ken Lawes, 9 Bincombe Drive, Crewkerne, Somerset TA18 7BE Tel: 07967 698211 (M) Chairman: Tom Yeo Tel: 01980 622187
Ground: Recreation Ground, Amesbury, Wiltshire. Tel: 01980 623489
Capacity: 1,500 Covered Seating: 150 Floodlights: Yes
Directions: From A303 take A345 towards Salisbury to Amesbury. Turn right into Salisbury St.left at Lloyds Bank, into Church St., over bridge then 50 yds left into Recreation Road.
Colours: All blue. Change colours.: All Red
Midweek matchday: Tuesday

ANDOVER NEW STREET
Secretary: J.Dunn, Andover New Street,Sports & Social Club, Foxcotte Park, Charlton, Andover, Hants SP11 0HS Tel: 01264 337678
Chairman: T. Antrobus
Ground: Foxcotte Park, Charlton, Andover.(01264 358358)
Colours: Green & black/black/green. Change colours: White/blue/white
Midweek matchday: Tuesday or Wednesday.

BISHOPS WALTHAM TOWN
Secretary: Jim Bailey, 46 Claylands Road, Bishops Waltham, Southampton SO32 1BH Tel: 07810 600496 (M) Chairman: James Spratt
Ground: Priory Park, Elizabeth Way, Bishops Waltham, Southampton, Hant. Tel: 01489 894269
Colours: All red & black. Change Colours: All Navy Blue

BRADING TOWN
Secretary: David Munday, 67 Howgate Road, Bembridge, Isle of Wight PO35 5QU Tel: 07786 562067 Chairman: Vincent Thompson
Ground: Vicarage Lane, Brading, I. o. W. Tel: 01983 405217
Directions: Adjacent to Brading main car park near to Wax Museum and Church.
Colours: Red & white/red/red. Change colours: Blue/white/white

EAST COWES VICTORIA ATHLETIC
Secretary: Jim Thorn,12 Brigstocke Terrace, Ryde, Isle of Wight, PO33 2PD Tel: 07773 661926 (M) email: ecvics@pavwykeham.demon.co.uk
Chairman: Arthur Richards
Ground: Beatrice Avenue Ground, East Cowes, I.O.W. Tel: 01938 297165
Directions: From the ferry: 1 mile from town centre on lower main road to Newport or Ryde near Whippingham Church adjacent to Osborne Middle School
Colours: Red/black/white. Change colours: All white

FAWLEY AFC
Secretary: Steve Amos, 3 Charnwood Cres., Chandlers Ford, Southampton SO53 5QN Tel: 02380 255721 (H) 07900 928741 (M)
Chairman: J. Oliver
Ground: Waterside Sports & Social Club, Long Lane, Holbury, Southampton (01705893750)
Directions: From Totton, J2 M27, take A326 to Fawley/Holbury. Ground is 800 yds after Hardley r'about on right, immed. after Hardley School.
Colours: All blue. Change colours: All red.

HORNDEAN
Secretary: Mick Austin, 22 Abbas Green, Havant, Hampshire PO9 4EP Tel: 07881 937995 (W & M) email: michaelaustin@horndean fc.fsnet.co.uk
Chairman: J. Bryson
Ground: Five Heads Park, Five Heads Road, Horndean, Hants. PO8 9NZ (01705 591363)
Directions: From north: J3 A3M, turn off aerial flyover, past Safeways on right, over r'about. Turn right at next r'about into A3 London Road, ground on left just past Good Intent PH. From south: J2 A3M, off at Horndean sign at end of slip road, turn left - then from Safeways above.
Colours: Red/black/red. Change colours.: White & blue/blue/blue

HYTHE & DIBDEN
Secretary: Tony Moyst, 105 Hobart Drive, Hythe, Southampton SO40 6FD Tel: 02380 847335 Chairman: Robert Parsons
Ground: Ewart Rec Ground, Jones Lane, Hythe, Southampton (02380 845264 -matchdays only)
At Dibden r'about on A326, take 1st left into Southampton Rd. Continue to Waterside PH, turn left into Jones Lane. Ground 200 yards on left.
Colours: Green & white/white/green. Change colours: All blue

LISS ATHLETIC
Secretary: Neil Noble,11 Southdown View, Waterlooville, Hants. PO7 6BJ Tel: 07816 038764 Chairman: Mick Alder
Ground: Newman Collard PF, Hill Brow Rd, Liss, Hants (01730 894022)
Midweek matchday: Thursday
Colours: All Blue. Change Colours: All green

LOCKS HEATH
Secretary: Peter Smith, 20 Wildrose Crescent, Locksheath, Hampshire SO31 6TG Tel: 01489 602256 (H) 07810 585878 (M)
Chairman: Stephen Smith
Ground: Locksheath Rec, Warsash Rd, Titchfield Common, Eastleigh (01489600932)
Directions: M27 J9, follow A27 for Fareham. Past GEC factory then 4th exit at next r'about into Warmarsh Rd. Left at next r'about. Ground .75 mile on right.
Colours: Red & black/black/red & black. Change colours: All blue and yellow

LYMINGTON TOWN
Secretary: Mike Woodfield, 6 Genoa Close, Pennington, Lymington, Hants. SO41 8AU Tel: 015905676705 (H) 07759 861550 (M)
Chairman: George Shaw
Ground: Sports Ground, Southampton Road, Lymington, Hants. Tel: 01590 671305
Capacity: 3,000 Covered Seating: 200 Floodlights: Yes
Directions: Follow the A337 to Lymington. Go over the lights after the Police Station (on right) and ground is approx. 150 metres on the left.
Colours: Red/white/black. Change colours.: Blue&white/blue/white
Midweek matchday: Tuesday

PETERSFIELD TOWN
Secretary: Mark Nicholl, 49 Durford Rd, Petersfield, Hants GU31 4ER Tel: 01730 300518 (H) 07949 328240 (M) email: mnicoll@cwctv.net
Chairman : Kenneth Longland
Ground: Love Lane, Petersfield, Hants GU31 4BW Tel: 01730 233416
Directions: Off A3 circulatory system in Petersfield town centre (well signposted) or 10 min. walk from Petersfield railway station.
Colours: Red & black/black/black. Change colours: Green/white/white
Midweek Matches: Wednesday

POOLE TOWN Founded: 1880
Secretary: Bill Read, 15 Addison Close, Romsey, Hants SO51 7TL Tel: 01794 517991
Chairman: C. Robbins Tel: 01202 395004
Vive Charman: Chris Reeves 01202 674425
Manager: Paul Morrell & Dean Mooney
Ground: Oakdale School,Tatnam Ground, School Road, Poole, Dorset. Tel: 07771 604289
Directions: From M27 take A31 towards Poole/Dorchester. Follow A31 Wimborne by-pass, follow Ferryport signs, left at Merley r'about then right at next sign for Poole. Follow A3049 eventually reaching major r'about (Fleets Bridge), over into Fleets Lane then left into Palmer Rd. opposite Poole Motor Cycles. 1st right into School Lane. **Office**:153 High St. Poole Tel: 01202 674425
Capacity: 2000 Covered Seating: Planned Covered Standing: Yes Floodlights: Yes
Clubhouse: Poole Labour Club, off Wimborne Road, Poole **Website:** www.poole-town.fsnet.co.uk
HONOURS: Dorset Senior Cup(12) F.A.Cup 3rd Rd 1926-27 Anglo -Italian R-up 80-81
Western LG. 25-26, 56-57 R-U (3) Southern Lg.R-up 88-89 Southern Div 61-62 Hants (2)
PREVIOUS Western 23-26 Southern 26-30 Western 30-57 Southern57-96
Colours: Red & white halves/red/white. Change colours: Navy & white/white/red or white
Midweek matchday: Wednesday
Programme: Yes Price:£1.00 Pages:60/70
2002-03
Leading Goalscorer:Karim Banssaouda (33)
Captain:Neal Spalding and Graham Kemp
Player of the Year:Carl Woodward

PORTSMOUTH ROYAL NAVY
Secretary: John Thomas, 21 Elizabeth Court, Fareham, Hants. PO14 1DQ Tel: 07960 116806. Chairman: R. Strudwick
Ground: The Navy Stadium, HMS Temeraire, Burnaby Road, Portsmouth PO1 2EJ Tel: 0239 272 4235, Clubhouse 0239 229 1660
Directions: From Portsmouth Harbour (BR), turn right onto The Hard, pass under the rail bridge and turn left into Park Road, after approx 200yards take 1st right into Burnaby Road. Entrance to ground 100 mtrs on the right.
Colours: Navy blue/navy/sky blue. Change colours: All red
Midweek Matches: Monday

RINGWOOD TOWN
Secrtary: Mrs Shirley Crewe, 278 Windham Road, Bournemouth, Dorset BH1 4QU Tel: 012102 398975 (H & Fax) Chairman: Bob Lane
Ground: The Clubhouse, Long Lane, Ringwood, Hants.Tel: 01425 473448
Colours: Red & black/ black/red & black
Change colours: All blue

STOCKBRIDGE
Secretary: Robin Smith, Curlews Farm, Quarley, Andover, Hants. SP11 8PT Tel: 01264 773545 Chairman: Dave Gray
Ground: Recreation Ground, High Street, Stockbridge, Hants.
Directions: Off Stockbridge High Street. 1st right at the BT sub-station into the Recreation Ground
Colours: All red. Change colours: Blue & maroon stripes/blue/blue

VTFC (previously Vosper Thorneycroft)
Secretary: A.Fox, 22 Thornleigh Road, Woolston, Southampoton, Hants, SO19 9DH
Tel: 02380 493346
Chairman: William Boyle MBE
Ground: Vosper Thornycroft Spts Ground, Portsmouth Rd, Sholing, Southampton(01489 403829)
Colours: All Yellow & Blue. Change colours: Navy blue, jade & tangerine/navy/navy

DIVISION ONE CLUBS

AFC PORTCHESTER
Secretary: Christine Collier, 14 Brackenwood Drive, Tadley Hants
Tel No: 07884 254706 (M)
Ground: Portchester Community School, White Hart Lane, Portchester, Hants. Tel: 02392 364399
Colours: All Blue

ALRESFORD TOWN
Secretary: Trevor Ingram, 18 Corfe Close, Alresford, Hants. SO24 9PH
Tel: 01252 544002 (B) 07770 387462 (M)
email: trevor@ingramtribe.freeserve.co.uk
Ground: Alresbury Park, The Avenue, Alresford, Hants.
Tel: 01962 735100
Colours: Black & white stripes/black/black

CLANFIELD
Secretary:Stuart Wallis. 42 Glamorgan Road, Catherington, Waterlooville,Hampshire. PO8 OTR Tel No 07765 238231 (M)
Ground: Peel Park, Charlton Lane, Clanfield, Waterlooville, Hants.
Colours: Blue & Black/ Black/Black

COLDEN COMMON
Secretary: Angela Banford, 19 Fleming Place, Colden Common, Winchester Hants. SO21 1SL Tel NO: 07967 889670 (M)
Ground: Colden Common Recreation Ground, Main Road, Colden Common (01962712365)
Colours: Red & white stripes/black/red
Midweek home matchday: Wednesday

FARNBOROUGH NORTH END
Secretary: Steve Amos, 3 Charnwood Cres. Chandlers Ford, Southampton Hants. SO53 5QN Tel NO: 07900 928741 (M)
Ground: Farnborough Gate, Ringwood Rd., Farnborough, Hants.
Colours: Red/Black/Red

FAREHAM SACRED HEARTS
Secretary:Wallace Arnold,48 Wallington Shore Road, Fareham, Hants. PO16 8SA Tel No: 07887 528457 (M)
Ground: Bakers barracks, Thorney Island, West Sussex.
Colours: Black & White/Black/Black

FLEETLANDS
Secretary: David Bell, 72 White Hart Lane, Portchester, Hants. PO16 9BQ.(01705321781)
Ground: Lederle Lane, Gosport, Hants (01329 239723)
Colours: Red & black/black/black

FLEET SPURS
Secretary: Steve Houghton, 61 Earlsbourne, Church Crookham, Hampshire GU52 8XG Tel NO: 07966 225446
Ground: Ancells Farm, Fleet, Hants
Colours: Red & blue/blue/blue

HAYLING UNITED
Secretary: Mrs S hirley Westfield, L'Ancresse14 Harold Road, Hayling Island, Hants PO11 9LT (01705 463305)
Ground: Hayling Park, Hayling Island, Hants
Colours: Black & white stripes/black/black

HEDGE END
Ground: Norman Rodaway Sports Ground, Heathouse Lane, Hedge End, Southampton. Tel: 02380 798027

LAVERSTOCK & FORD
Ground: The Dell, Laverstock & Ford SC, 23 Church Rd., Laverstock, Salisbury. Tel: 01722 327401

MICHELDEVER
Secretary: Mrs Mary Green, 19 Southbrook Cottages, MIcheldever, Winchester Hants. SO21 3DJ Tel: 07876 728449 (M)
Ground: Lord Rank Playing Fields, Duke St., Micheldever, Winchester.
Colours: All Navy Blue and White

OVERTON UNITED
Secretary: Mrs A Wheeler, 3 Lordsfield Gardens, Overton, Hants RG25 2EW (01256771241)
Ground: Recreation Centre, Bridge Street, Overton (01256 770561)
Colours: Blue & white stripes/white/blue
Change: Green & purple/purple/purple
Midweek home matchday: Tuesday or Thursday

PAULSGROVE
Secretary: Jim Garcia, 112 Falmouth Road, Paulsgrove, Portsmouth Hants. PO6 4JT Tel NO: 07901 655485
Ground: The Grove Club, Marsden Rd (off Allaway Avenue), Paulsgrove, Portsmouth (01705 324102)
Colours: Red & black stripes/black/red

TADLEY TOWN
Secretary: Steve Blackburn, 7 Bramdean Close, Tadley, Hanrts. RG26 3RD Tel No: 07787 501028 (M)
Ground: The Green, Tadley, Hants
Cols: Blue & maroon stripes/maroon/maroon
Change: Yellow & blue/blue/blue

VERWOOD TOWN
Secretary: Mrs Judith Fry, 19a Noon Hill Rd, Verwood, Dorset BH31 7DB (01202822826)
Ground: Pottern Park, Pottern Way, Verwood, Dorset
Colours: Red with black & white/Black/Red

DIVISION TWO CLUBS

BROUGHTON
Ground: The Sportsfield, Buckholt Road, Broughton, Stockbridge, Hampshire Tel: 01794 301150

DCAFC
Ground: Victoria Park, Castle Road, Salisbury, Wiltshire Tel: 01722 415089

DURLEY
Ground: Kytes Lane, Durley, Southampton
Previous Lge: Southampton Senior Lge.

EAST LODGE
Ground: Langstone Harbour Sports Ground, Eastern Road, Portsmouth, Hampshire

HAMBLE CLUB
Ground: Shell Mex Ground, Hamble Lane, Hamble-le-Rice, Southampton, Hampshire Tel: 07881 766085

LUDGERSHALL SPORTS
Ground: Astor Crescent, Ludgershall, Hampshire Tel: 01264 398200

M & T AWBRIDGE
Ground: Michelmersh & Timsbury Sports Pavilion, Mannyngham Way, Timsbury, Romsey Tel: 01794 368955

MOTTISFONT
Ground: Bengers Lane, Mottisfont, Hampshire
Previous Lge: Southampton Senior Lge.

NETLEY CENTRAL SPORTS
Ground: Netley Rec, Station Road, Netley Abbey, Southampton, Hampshire Tel: 023 8045 2267

ORDNANCE SURVEY
Ground: Lordshill Recreation Ground, Southampton, Hampshire Tel: 023 8061 8812

OTTERBOURNE
Ground: Oakwood Park, off Oakwood Avenue, Otterbourne, Hampshire Tel: 01962 714681

QK SOUTHAMPTON
Ground: Lordshill Recreation Centre, Southampton, Hampshire Tel: 023 8073 2531

RS BASINGSTOKE
Ground: Whiteditch Playing Field, Sherborne Road, Basingstoke, Hampshire Tel: 01256 814618
Previous Lge: Hellenic

ROMSEY TOWN
Ground: The By-Pass Ground, South Front, Romsey, Hampshire Tel: 01794 512003

YATELEY GREEN
Ground: Sean Deveraux Park, Chandlers Lane Playing Fields, Chandlers Lane, Yateley, Hampshire

KEYLINE DORSET COMBINATION LEAGUE

Founded: 1957

President: Jack Cruickshank **Chairman:** Alan Burt

Secretary: Geoff Theobald, 41 South Road, Corfe Mullen
Wimborne, Dorset BH21 3HZ Tel: 01202 697994

FINAL LEAGUE TABLE 2002-03

		P	W	D	L	F	A	Pts
1	Hamworthy United	34	29	1	4	103	34	88
2	Gillingham Town	34	27	6	1	89	25	87
3	Hamworthy Recreation	34	23	3	8	92	42	72
4	Westland Sports	34	20	5	9	73	49	65
5	Dorchester Town Res.	34	17	7	10	76	39	58
6	Sherborne Town	34	15	9	10	59	42	54
7	Poole Borough	34	17	3	14	73	66	54
8	Holt United	34	12	13	9	68	56	49
9	Bridport Res.	34	14	7	13	59	47	49
10	Wareham Rangers	34	13	7	14	64	71	46
11	Bournemouth Sports	34	12	8	14	91	75	44
12	Stourpaine	34	13	3	18	62	72	42
13	Shaftesbury	34	11	8	15	48	57	41
14	Cobham Sports	34	9	4	21	39	78	31
15	Sturminster Newton Utd	34	7	8	19	40	70	29
16	Blandford United	34	7	6	21	41	71	27
17	Weymouth Sports	34	4	4	26	36	138	16
18	Swanage Town & Herston	34	3	4	27	29	110	13

		1	2	3	4	5	6	7	8	9	10	11	12	13	14	15	16	17	18
1	Blandford United		1-2	1-2	0-1	1-2	1-4	0-3	1-5	1-1	4-2	2-1	1-1	1-2	3-2	3-0	2-1	1-3	0-2
2	Bournemouth Sports	1-1		0-3	1-2	1-1	0-2	0-1	0-3	3-3	4-7	2-1	2-2	4-2	5-1	6-0	1-2	1-3	7-2
3	Bridport Reserves	3-0	2-3		2-1	3-2	0-2	2-2	0-2	1-1	3-0	1-1	1-0	4-0	0-1	2-3	1-1	1-3	3-0
4	Cobham Sports	3-2	0-5	2-2		1-2	0-2	0-2	0-4	2-3	1-3	3-3	0-3	2-6	3-0	2-2	1-3	0-1	3-1
5	Dorchester Town Reserves	2-1	0-4	1-1	5-0		0-0	3-1	1-2	1-4	5-2	4-0	3-0	0-0	4-0	4-0	4-3	0-0	6-0
6	Gillingham Town	3-2	4-3	2-0	2-0	1-0		4-2	3-1	1-1	4-1	1-1	4-3	3-0	1-0	4-0	5-0	0-0	12-0
7	Hamworthy Recreation	4-0	4-2	1-0	3-0	2-1	3-0		3-0	2-0	3-3	0-2	3-1	2-0	4-0	5-1	5-1	1-2	9-1
8	Hamworthy United	7-1	4-1	2-0	5-2	1-0	1-2	3-1		2-1	1-0	4-0	1-0	4-2	4-0	5-2	3-1	5-1	2-4
9	Holt United	1-1	2-2	4-1	2-1	2-0	2-4	1-5	2-3		2-0	1-2	0-0	3-0	2-2	3-1	4-4	1-1	6-4
10	Poole Borough	1-0	4-3	2-0	0-1	1-6	0-1	2-1	2-3	1-1		3-1	1-0	2-3	2-2	3-0	4-2	1-0	6-0
11	Shaftesbury	1-1	3-7	1-3	2-0	2-4	0-1	1-2	0-1	1-1	3-0		0-2	2-1	2-1	1-0	3-0	2-1	1-1
12	Sherborne Town	0-0	4-3	3-0	1-0	0-0	0-1	2-2	1-3	3-1	4-1	1-0		2-1	3-1	3-0	0-0	2-2	5-1
13	Stourpaine	2-1	2-2	0-1	1-2	1-0	0-2	3-1	0-3	0-1	0-3	1-7	1-2		4-2	2-1	0-4	1-3	8-0
14	Sturminster Newton United	0-1	2-2	1-1	0-1	1-1	3-3	2-1	0-1	2-2	1-2	0-1	2-0	3-4		3-1	1-0	0-4	3-0
15	Swanage Town & Herston	2-1	2-4	0-6	1-1	0-4	0-3	1-2	0-6	1-0	1-6	1-1	1-3	2-4	1-2		1-2	0-6	1-1
16	Wareham Rangers	4-1	1-0	3-6	3-1	1-2	0-0	2-3	3-3	1-6	2-0	3-0	4-2	1-1	0-0	6-1		1-3	3-2
17	Westland Sports	3-2	0-6	2-1	5-1	3-2	1-3	2-4	0-1	1-0	2-3	3-1	1-1	1-4	4-1	5-2	4-0		2-0
18	Weymouth Sports	0-3	4-4	0-3	1-2	0-6	0-5	0-5	0-8	2-4	2-5	1-1	1-5	1-6	3-1	1-0	1-2	0-1	

COMBINATION LEAGUE CUP 2002-03

FIRST ROUND

Blandford	v	Westland Sports	0-1
Cobham Sports	v	Hamworthy Rec.	1-3

SECOND ROUND

Dorchester Res.	v	Swanage	7-0
Hamworthy United	v	Bournemouth Sports	2-0
Shaftesbury	v	Sherborne	0-1
Westland	v	Stourpaine	2-2 (aet)
Weymouth Sports	v	Bridport Res.	2-3
Gillingham Town	v	Holt	0-1 (aet)
Poole Borough	v	Hamworthy Rec.	0-4
Sturminster N'ton U.	v	Wareham Rangers	2-1
Replay Stourpaine	v	Westland	1-0

QUARTER-FINALS

Bridport Res.	v	Stourpaine	1-1 (aet)
Hamworthy Recreation	v	Dorchester T Res.	3-3 (aet)
Hamworthy United	v	Sturminster N'ton Utd	3-1
Replay Stourpaine	v	Bridport Res.	1-2
Replay Dorchester	v	Hamworthy Rec	0-1
Sherborne	v	Holt United	1-2

SEMI-FINALS

Hamworthy Recreation	v	Bridport Res.	2-1
Hamworthy United	v	Holt United	2-3

FINAL

Hamworthy Recreation	v	Holt Utd	0-4

10th May at Hamworthy United

DORSET COMBINATION CLUBS 2003-04

BLANDFORD UNITED

Chairman: M.Westwood

Secretary: Mrs Catherine Johnson, 37 Damory Street, Blandford Forum, Dorset DT117EU (01258 455899)

Ground: Recreation Ground, Park Road, Blandford Forum, Dorset. (HQ Tel: 01258456374)

Cover: No Clubhouse: No Programme: Yes

Colours: All Royal Blue Change colours: Red/black/green

BOURNEMOUTH SPORTS CLUB

Chairman: I.Hansford

Secretary: Mrs June Johnson,19 Lawns Road, Wimborne BH21 2JP Tel: 01202 887195

Ground: Chapel Gate, East Parley, Christchurch, Dorset BH23 6BD Tel: 01202 581933

Cover: No Clubhouse: Yes Programme: Yes

Colours: Gold/black/gold Change colours: All blue

BRIDPORT Reserves

Chairman: David Fowler **Secretary:** Keith Morgan, 95 Orchard Cres., Bridport DT6 5HA 01308 456142(H) 01308 424269(W)

Ground: The Beehive, St Mary's Field, Bridport, Dorset 01308 423834

Colours: Red & black/black/red & black Change colours:All blue.

COBHAM SPORTS (formerly Flight Refuelling)

Chairman: A Miles

Secretary: Harry W Doyle, 27 Fairview Crescent, Broadstone, Poole BH18 9AL Tel: 01202 698393 (H) 07718 896211 (M)

Ground: Merley Park, Merley, Wimborne, Dorset (01202 885773)

Cover: No Clubhouse: Yes Programme: Yes

Colours:Sky blue/navy blue/navyblue. Change colours: All red

DORCHESTER TOWN Reserves

Chairman: C E Clarke

Secretary: David Martin, 21 Diggory Crescent, Dorchester DT1 2SP Tel: 01305 262345 (H) 07971 172795 (M)

Ground: The Avenue Stadium, Dorchester. (01305 262451)

Cover: Yes Floodlights: Yes Clubhouse: Yes Programme: Yes

Colours: Black & white stripes/black/black Change: All red.

DORCHESTER UNITED

Ground: Sandringham Sports Centre, Armada Way, Dorchester.

Previous Leagues: Dorset League

GILLINGHAM TOWN

Chairman: E Murphy **Secretary:** David J Ayles, 37 Sylvan Way, Bay Road, Gillingham SP8 4EQ (01747822065)

Ground: Hardings Lane, Gillingham (01747 823673)

Cover: Yes Programme: Yes Clubhouse: Yes

Colours: Tangerine/black/tangerine

Change colours: Yellow & green/green/green

HAMWORTHY RECREATION

Chairman: M Robson **Secretary:** Ray Willis, 52 Heckford Road, Poole BH15 2LY (01202 773 290)

Ground: Hamworthy Rec. Club, Magna Rd, Canford Magna, Wimborne, Dorset BH21 3AE(01202 881922)

Cover: No Clubhouse: Yes Programme: No

Colours: All green Change colours: Blue & White stripes/blue/blue.

HAMWORTHY UNITED

Chairman: D. Manuel **Secretary:** Peter Gallop, 51A Symes Road, Hamworthy, Poole, Dorset BH15 4PR(01202 670792)

Ground: The County Ground, Blandford Close, Hamworthy, Poole, Dorset (01202674974)

Cover: Yes Floodlights: Yes Programme: Yes Clubhouse: Yes

Colours: Maroon & Sky Blue stripes/maroon/maroon

Change colours:Yellow & black stripes/black/black

HOLT UNITED
Ground: Gaunts Common, Holt, Wimborne, Dorset. Tel: 01258 840379
Previous League: Dorset County League

POOLE BOROUGH
Ground: Turlin Moor Recretaion Ground, Blandford Moor, Hamworthy, Poole, Dorset. Club Office: 01202 674973
Previous League: Dorset County Lge.

SHAFTESBURY
Chairman: A.P.Humphries
Secretary: Phil Watts, 4 Willow Cottages, Compton Abbas, Shaftesbury SP70NF (01747 811037)
Ground: Cockrams, Coppice Street, Shaftesbury (01747 853990)
Cover: Yes Floodlights: Yes Clubhouse: Yes
Colours: Red & white striped/Red/Red
Change colours: Yellow/black/black

SHERBORNE TOWN
Chairman: F Henderson
Secretary: Mike Mock, 67 Yew TRe Close, Yeovil. BA20 2PB
Tel: 01935 426219 (H) 01935 703934 (W)
Ground: Raleigh Grove, The Terrace Playing Fields, Sherborne
Tel: 01935 816110
Cover: Yes Clubhouse: Yes Programme: Yes
Colours: Yellow/black/yellow Change: Black & white/ white/ black.

STOURPAINE
Chairman: C.Hardiman **Secretary**: Rob Turner, 35 Hod View, Stourpaine, Blandford DT11 8TN Tel : 01258 451691
Ground: Dick Draper Memorial Fields, Stourpaine, Blandford Forum
Previous league: Dorset County League
Colours: Navy blue & Yellow/navy blue/ yellow & navy blue.
Change Colours: Red & white stripes/red & white/red & white

STURMINSTER NEWTON UNITED
Chairman: A.Stockley **Secretary:** Richard Frear 44 Green Close, Sturminster Newton DT10 1BL (01258473036)
Ground: Barnetts Field, Honeymead Lane, Sturminster Newton, Dorset. (01258471406)
Cover: Yes Clubhouse: No Programme: Yes
Colours:Red & Black stripes /red/red
Change colours:Blue & Black stripes/blue/blue.

WAREHAM RANGERS
Chairman: G.Hawkes **Secretary:** Mrs Carol White, 18 Folly Lane, Wareham, Dorset BH20 4HH (01929551765)
Ground: Purbeck Sports Centre,Worgret Rd, Wareham, Dorset
Cover: No Clubhouse: No Programme: Yes
Colours: Amber & black/black/black
Change colours: Navy & light blue/ navy/ light blue

WESTLAND SPORTS
Chairman: A. Fisher
Secretary: Dean Vincent, 8 Whitemead, Abbey Manor Park, Yeovil. BA21 3RX Tel: 01935 479971 (H) 01935 705381 (W)
Ground: Westland Sports Ground, Westbourne Close, Yeovil
Tel: 01935 703810
Cover: No Clubhouse: No Programme: Yes
Colours: Red & Black/Black/Black C hange colours: All White

WEYMOUTH SPORTS
Chairman: M. Richards
Secretary: Alan Burt, 32 Preston Road, Weymouth, DT3 6PZ
Tel: 01305 833256 (H) 01305 773536 (W)
Ground: Weymouth College, Cranford Ave., Weymouth, Dorset
Tel: 01305 208859/208860
Colours: Blue & yellow stripes/yellow/blue. Change: Red/black/red
Prev. Lge: Dorset (champs 1993)

DOREST COUNTY LEAGUE

SENIOR DIVISION	P	W	D	L	F	A	Pts
Dorchester United	20	15	3	2	82	30	48
Allendale	20	16	0	4	73	23	48
Chickerell United	20	13	2	5	70	25	41
Gillingham Town Res.	20	12	1	7	47	36	37
Portland United Res.	20	12	1	7	38	28	37
Witchampton United	20	9	4	7	42	33	31
Hamworthy Utd Res.	20	7	2	11	33	39	23
Sturminster Marshall	20	4	4	12	48	70	16
Shaftesbury Res.	20	4	3	13	29	70	15
Blandford United Res.	20	3	3	14	18	68	12
Cobham Sports Res.	20	3	1	16	14	72	10

Dorchester Sports withdrew during the season.

DIVISION ONE	P	W	D	L	F	A	Pts
Cranborne	22	18	3	1	84	21	57
Weymouth United	22	15	3	4	75	43	48
Royal Oak Cougars	22	14	3	5	61	28	45
Barwick & Stoford	22	11	2	9	47	48	35
Marina Sports (-3)	22	10	4	8	42	41	31
Weymouth Post Office	22	10	1	11	61	61	31
Crossways	22	7	8	7	39	33	29
Moreton (-6)	22	7	6	9	43	40	21
Wareham Rangers Res.	22	5	5	12	38	55	20
Allendale Reserves	22	5	4	13	36	65	19
Piddletrenthide United	22	5	3	14	39	75	18
Okeford United	22	3	2	17	25	80	11

SCREWFIX DIRECT WESTERN LEAGUE

President: Rod Webber **Chairman:** Cliff Ashton

Secretary: Ken Clarke, 32 Westmead Lane, Chippenham, Wiltshire SN15 3HZ
Tel: 07790 002279 (8am - 9pm) **Fax:** 01249 652952 **Email:** westernleague@aol.com
www.firsteleven.co.uk/western

FINAL LEAGUE TABLE 2002-03

PREMIER DIVISION		P	W	D	L	F	A	Pts
1	Team Bath	34	27	3	4	109	28	84
2	Brislington	34	22	7	5	71	28	73
3	Bideford	34	21	7	6	105	35	70
4	Backwell United	34	21	4	9	70	33	67
5	Paulton Rovers	34	18	9	7	68	35	63
6	Bridgwater Town	34	17	8	9	71	43	59
7	Bath City Reserves	34	14	5	15	66	57	47
8	Melksham Town	34	12	7	15	65	68	43
9	Odd Down	34	12	6	16	49	67	42
10	Keynsham Town	34	11	7	16	55	65	40
11	Frome Town	34	11	7	16	49	62	40
12	Bishop Sutton	34	11	5	18	57	83	38
13	Dawlish Town	34	11	5	17	47	107	38
14	Bridport	34	9	8	17	40	54	35
15	Barnstaple Town	34	8	8	18	41	68	32
16	Welton Rovers	34	9	5	20	40	99	32

PREMIER DIVISION		1	2	3	4	5	6	7	8	9	10	11	12	13	14	15	16	17	18
1	Backwell United		1-0	3-1	2-1	7-0	1-0	5-1	0-0	5-0	4-0	3-2	2-1	2-2	2-2	1-3	2-0	0-1	4-0
2	Barnstaple Town	0-2		0-5	2-2	2-2	1-4	1-2	0-0	3-1	4-0	1-2	2-1	0-3	1-1	1-3	0-1	0-3	1-1
3	Bath City Reserves	2-5	0-1		1-1	1-3	2-0	3-0	4-1	4-0	2-1	1-1	0-1	1-0	2-2	6-1	2-1	1-2	0-1
4	Bideford	1-0	4-0	5-1		7-0	1-2	1-0	1-1	11-0	6-1	2-0	1-1	4-2	1-0	5-0	1-1	5-2	11-2
5	Bishop Sutton	0-1	1-2	5-1	3-2		2-2	1-0	0-3	1-3	2-0	1-1	4-0	0-3	2-5	2-3	1-2	0-5	3-0
6	Bridgwater Town	1-2	2-1	2-1	3-1	3-1		0-0	2-0	6-1	0-0	3-1	3-2	4-0	2-4	2-0	1-1	1-3	6-0
7	Bridport	1-2	5-0	0-1	2-2	0-1	2-5		0-1	1-1	2-2	3-1	1-0	2-0	4-1	0-3	0-2	0-2	0-1
8	Brislington	1-2	2-1	2-0	3-0	2-2	1-0	3-0		6-0	5-0	2-0	1-2	2-1	5-1	3-2	1-0	3-1	4-0
9	Dawlish Town	1-0	0-3	2-1	0-3	4-1	2-2	1-4	1-0		2-8	2-0	0-5	0-1	3-3	1-2	2-1	0-4	6-2
10	Devizes Town	1-0	4-1	0-2	0-1	4-2	1-3	4-2	0-1	0-2		1-3	2-2	0-2	0-2	1-5	0-1	1-1	1-0
11	Elmore	1-0	2-2	2-7	0-3	3-3	0-5	0-1	0-3	1-1	4-1		1-2	3-3	3-1	2-1	2-3	0-7	1-2
12	Frome Town	0-1	0-3	0-3	2-4	3-4	1-2	2-2	0-1	3-3	3-0	1-1		1-0	3-2	3-0	0-4	1-3	0-0
13	Keynsham Town	2-4	0-0	0-3	0-3	3-1	1-1	0-0	3-3	3-4	1-1	3-2	0-1		0-3	4-2	1-0	0-2	3-2
14	Melksham Town	2-1	3-1	3-1	1-3	4-3	3-1	2-4	0-1	5-1	2-0	1-2	1-1	1-4		1-4	1-1	0-1	1-2
15	Odd Down	1-1	3-3	2-2	0-2	1-3	1-0	1-1	1-3	2-3	2-2	0-3	0-2	3-2	0-2		0-0	1-0	1-0
16	Paulton Rovers	1-0	4-1	2-0	1-1	1-2	2-2	0-0	3-3	8-0	1-1	2-0	4-1	4-3	3-1	4-0		3-0	2-1
17	Team Bath	2-1	3-0	4-1	2-1	3-0	4-1	4-0	1-1	6-0	2-2	8-0	6-0	4-2	3-1	2-0	3-1		7-0
18	Welton Rovers	2-4	1-3	4-4	0-8	2-1	0-0	1-0	0-3	2-0	3-1	2-1	1-4	2-3	3-3	0-1	2-4	1-8	

FINAL LEAGUE TABLE 2002-03

DIVISION ONE		P	W	D	L	F	A	Pts
1	Torrington	36	27	5	4	113	47	86
2	Exmouth Town	36	26	7	3	83	29	85
3	Westbury United	36	20	8	8	92	65	68
4	Hallen	36	19	6	11	70	56	63
5	Calne Town	36	16	9	11	62	43	57
6	Clyst Rovers	36	17	5	14	67	55	56
7	Willand Rovers	36	16	6	14	63	53	54
8	Bitton	36	13	10	13	50	48	49
9	Shepton Mallet Town	36	13	10	13	53	55	49
10	Chard Town	36	12	10	14	59	60	46
11	Bristol Manor Farm	36	14	4	18	56	71	46
12	Wellington	36	12	8	16	49	57	44
13	Larkhall Athletic	36	13	4	19	48	73	43
14	Cadbury Heath	36	10	11	15	49	61	41
15	Street (-6)	36	13	7	16	59	81	40
16	Corsham Town	36	8	12	16	44	51	36
17	Weston St Johns	36	9	4	23	54	76	31
18	Ilfracombe Town	36	7	9	20	47	85	30
19	Minehead Town	36	7	5	24	34	86	26

DIVISION ONE		1	2	3	4	5	6	7	8	9	10	11	12	13	14	15	16	17	18	19
1	Bitton		2-0	1-0	1-1	5-1	2-0	0-0	1-1	4-3	1-2	0-2	3-1	1-0	1-5	1-2	0-1	0-0	4-2	0-2
2	Bristol Manor Farm	1-0		2-2	2-4	0-1	2-1	1-0	0-2	0-3	5-1	2-4	6-1	1-0	1-2	0-2	1-0	0-2	1-4	2-1
3	Cadbury Heath	1-0	1-1		3-2	1-2	0-0	4-4	0-1	2-0	1-1	2-4	2-0	1-1	0-0	2-3	3-1	0-3	3-3	1-2
4	Calne Town	2-2	2-1	1-0		3-0	1-1	1-1	0-1	1-2	1-0	3-1	4-0	0-1	2-3	1-1	1-1	0-0	5-2	0-2
5	Chard Town	1-1	4-1	1-1	3-2		1-4	3-1	0-2	1-2	3-4	0-2	4-1	2-3	2-1	3-4	1-1	1-2	3-2	0-2
6	Clyst Rovers	1-0	6-2	1-0	1-4	0-3		2-1	2-3	0-2	4-1	2-1	3-1	4-0	5-0	2-4	1-1	1-1	2-0	3-0
7	Corsham Town	0-2	0-1	4-0	0-1	1-1	1-2		2-1	0-1	1-1	0-1	1-1	0-0	3-1	1-2	3-0	2-2	2-3	0-1
8	Exmouth Town	2-0	1-3	3-1	1-2	1-1	2-0	2-0		3-2	2-1	3-0	4-0	3-3	3-0	1-1	1-0	3-2	4-0	2-0
9	Hallen	1-1	1-3	3-1	0-3	2-1	2-1	1-1	1-5		6-2	3-0	3-1	3-3	4-0	0-3	2-2	5-3	1-0	0-1
10	Ilfracombe Town	0-0	3-3	0-1	2-1	1-1	1-3	2-2	1-2	1-0		1-3	1-2	0-1	2-1	2-2	1-3	2-5	1-0	2-6
11	Larkhall Athletic	2-4	0-2	0-2	0-1	2-2	2-1	3-1	1-6	0-2	2-3		4-2	0-1	1-1	1-5	2-1	1-1	2-1	1-1
12	Minehead Town	0-1	1-0	1-2	0-1	0-3	1-0	0-2	0-3	0-2	1-1	2-0		0-0	3-1	0-2	3-1	1-6	5-2	1-1
13	Shepton Mallet Town	2-1	2-0	1-2	2-0	1-1	1-1	0-0	0-3	2-2	2-1	2-0	1-1		3-1	2-4	0-2	5-1	0-1	0-2
14	Street	1-5	2-2	3-3	2-0	0-3	2-1	1-1	2-2	0-2	5-0	2-1	3-1	3-1		2-1	3-1	2-6	0-4	3-0
15	Torrington	3-0	8-2	4-0	2-2	1-1	5-0	6-1	1-3	6-2	2-0	5-0	5-1	5-3	6-1		2-5	4-0	2-1	1-0
16	Wellington	0-0	1-3	1-0	1-1	2-0	2-5	1-3	0-2	0-1	5-1	3-1	3-1	2-0	0-2	2-0		2-2	0-0	1-3
17	Westbury United	6-1	3-1	2-1	4-3	3-2	1-4	1-0	2-2	0-2	3-3	5-0	1-0	4-3	6-3	1-2	5-1		2-4	1-0
18	Weston St Johns	0-3	1-3	1-1	0-4	1-1	0-2	1-3	0-3	2-1	4-2	0-1	5-0	2-5	5-1	1-2	0-1	1-2		1-3
19	Willand Rovers	2-2	3-1	4-5	0-2	0-2	5-1	1-2	0-0	3-3	1-0	1-3	5-1	1-2	0-0	3-5	3-1	3-4	1-0	

LES PHILLIPS CHALLENGE CUP 2002-03

PRELIMINARY ROUND

Barnstaple Town	v	Keynsham Town	2-0
Clyst Rovers	v	Larkhall Athletic	5-0
Welton Rovers	v	Frome Town	1-0
Bideford	v	Exmouth Town	0-2
Paulton Rovers	v	Weston St Johns	8-0

FIRST ROUND

Barnstaple Town	v	Hallen	1-2 (aet)
Bitton	v	Chard Town	0-1
Bristol Manor Farm	v	Welton Rovers	1-0
Dawlish Town	v	Wellington	3-0
Ilfracombe Town	v	Corsham Town	3-5 (aet)
Shepton Mallet Town	v	Bishop Sutton	2-3 (aet)
Team Bath	v	Brislington	1-2
Westbury United	v	Devizes Town	1-3
Bath City Reserves	v	Minehead Town	2-0
Bridgwater Town	v	Backwell United	3-1
Clyst Rovers	v	Cadbury Heath	2-3 (aet)
Exmouth Town	v	Calne Town	2-0
Odd Down	v	Paulton R.	1-1 (aet) 7-6p
Street	v	Elmore	2-1
Torrington	v	Melksham Town	3-2
Willand Rovers	v	Bridport	2-1

SECOND ROUND

Bath City Reserves	v	Hallen	1-1 (aet) 2-4p
Chard Town	v	Corsham Town	3-2 (aet)
Exmouth	v	Torrington	5-1
Street	v	Cadbury Heath	1-0
Bishop Sutton	v	Brislington	0-4
Dawlish Town	v	Bristol Manor Farm	3-1
Odd Down	v	Devizes Town	2-1
Willand Rovers	v	Bridgwater Town	0-2

QUARTER-FINALS

Brislington	v	Dawlish	6-3
Exmouth Town	v	Hallen	3-0
Chard Town	v	Bridgwater Town	1-2
Street	v	Odd Down	0-4

SEMI-FINALS

Bridgwater	v	Odd Down	1-0
Exmouth	v	Brislington	1-2

FINAL

Brislington	v	Bridgwater Town	0-1	3rd May at Melksham Town

PAST RECORDS
WESTERN FOOTBALL LEAGUE CHAMPIONS

1981-82	Bideford
1982-83	Bideford
1983-84	Exmouth Town
1984-85	Saltash United
1985-86	Exmouth Town
1986-87	Saltash United
1987-88	Liskeard Athletic
1988-89	Saltash United
1989-90	Taunton Town
1990-91	Weston-super-Mare
1991-92	Clevedon Town
1992-93	Tiverton Town
1993-94	Tiverton Town
1994-95	Tiverton Town
1995-96	Taunton Town
1996-97	Tiverton Town
1997-98	Tiverton Town
1998-99	Taunton Town
1999-00	Taunton Town
2000-01	Taunton Town
2001-02	Bideford

WESTERN FOOTBALL LEAGUE FIRST DIVISION CHAMPIONS

1981-82	Shepton Mallet
1982-83	Bristol Manor Farm
1983-84	Bristol City Reserves
1984-85	Portway-Bristol
1985-86	Portway-Bristol
1986-87	Swanage Town & Herston
1987-88	Welton Rovers
1988-89	Larkhall Athletic
1989-90	Ottery St Mary
1990-91	Minehead
1991-92	Westbury United
1992-93	Odd Down
1993-94	Barnstaple Town
1994-95	Brislington
1995-96	Bridgwater Town
1996-97	Melksham Town
1997-98	Bishop Sutton
1998-99	Minehead
1999-00	Devizes Town
2000-01	Team Bath
2001-02	Frome Town

LES PHILLIPS CHALLENGE CUP WINNERS

1989-90	Plymouth Argyle Reserves
1990-91	Elmore
1991-92	Plymouth Argyle Reserves
1992-93	Tiverton Town
1993-94	Tiverton Town
1994-95	Elmore
1995-96	Tiverton Town
1996-97	Tiverton Town
1997-98	Tiverton Town
1998-99	Yeovil Town Reserves
1999-00	Chippenham Town
2000-01	Chippenham Town
2001-02	Bideford

BACKWELL UNITED

Secretary: Jonathon Rpogers,114 Wellington Hill West,Westbury on Trym, Bristol BS9 4QY Tel No: 0117 985 6138

Ground: Backwell Recreation Ground, West Town Rd, Backwell, Avon Tel: 1275 462612

Directions: Near centre of Backwell on main A370 Bristol to Weston-super-Mare road. Buses from Bristol or Weston, or 20 mins walk from Nailsea & Backwell(BR) station; turn right out of station, right at traffic lights (half mile),ground quarter mile on right just past car sales

Capacity: 1,000 Seats: 60 Cover: 150 Floodlights: Yes

Clubhouse: Open 6-11pm weekdays, 12.30-11pm Sat. Snacks available Club Shop: No

HONOURS Somerset Snr Lg 77-78 79-80 80-81 81-82 82-83 (Lg Cup 82-83 (R-up 79-80) Div 1 72-73); Somerset Snr Cup 81-82; SW Co.'s Sutton Transformer Cup 81-82. Western Lge Div 1 89-90 Champions, 94-95 promoted in 3rd place

PREVIOUS **Leagues**: Clevedon & Dist; Bristol C. of E.; Bristol Surburban (pre 1970); Somerset Senior 70-83
Grounds: Two in Backwell prior to 1939. Club reformed in 1946

RECORD **Attendance**: 487 v Brislington, Gt Mills Lg. 2/5/94
Goalscorer: Steve Spalding **Appearances:** Wayne Buxton
Win: 10-1 v Dowton, F.A.Cup 1st Qualifying Round. 1998-99
Defeat: 2-6 v Tiverton Town (H), Les Phillips Cup QF 1.2.94

FACT FILE
Founded: 1911
Nickname: Stags
Club Sponsors: D.C.I.Refrigeration
Colours: Red & black,white,red &black
Change colours: Gold & Blue
Midweek Matches: Tuesday
Programme: 42 pages, 50p
Editor: Jonathon Rogers (01179 856138)

CLUB PERSONNEL
Chairman: John Southern
Vice-Chairman: MikeNaylor
President: Charlie Jones
Press Officer:Mike Naylor (01275 858576)
Manager:Jamie Patch
Asst Manager: Jeff Meacham
Physio: Dave Gould

2002-03
Leading Goalscorer: Lee Patch
Captain & P.o.Y.: Brad Haynes

BARNSTAPLE TOWN

Secretary: David Cooke, 51 Walnut Way, Whiddon Valley, Barnstaple, Devon. EX32 7RF Tel: 01271 326088

Ground: Mill Road, Barnstaple, North Devon Tel: 01271 343469

Directions: A361 towards Ilfracombe (from M5 Jct 26), in Barnstaple follow A36 1Ilfracombe signs, second left after crossing small bridge is Mill Road

Capacity: 5,000 Seats: 250 Cover: 1,000 Floodlights: Yes

Clubhouse: Full license with canteen on match days.

HONOURS Western Lg 52-53 79-80 (R-up 80-81 81-82, Div 1 49-50 94-95, Merit Cup74-75 83-84 84-85, Comb. 92-93), Devon Professional Cup 62-63 64-65 67-68 69-70 71-73 (X2) 74-75 76-81 (X5), Devon Lg, Devon St Lukes Cup 87-88, Devon Snr Cup 92-93, Devon Youth Cup 48-49 51-52

PREVIOUS **Leagues:** Nth Devon, Devon & Exeter, S. Western **Name:** Pilton Yeo Vale
Grounds: Town Wharf (> 1920); Highfield Rd, Newport (> 35), Pilton Pk, Rock Pk

RECORDS **Attendance:** 6,200 v Bournemouth, FA Cup 1st Rd, 54 **Appearances:** Ian Pope **Win:** 12-1 v Tavistock (H), FA Cup 3rd Qual. Rd 1954 **Defeat:** 1-10 v Mangotsfield Utd (A), West Lge Prem. Div. 90-91 **Fee out**: £4,000 to Hungerford T for Joe Scott **Fee in** £6,000 for Ian Doyle from Bristol City **BEST SEASON** **F.A Cup:** 1st Rd replay 51-52 **FA Vase:** 4th Rd 94-95

Players progressing: Len Pickard (Bristol R. 51), John Neale (Exeter72), Barrie Vassallo (Torquay 77), Ian Doyle (Bristol C. 78), Ryan Souter (Swindon 94), Jason Cadie (Reading 94), Simon Heal (Cardiff City -02)

FACT FILE
Founded: 1906
Nickname: Barum
Sponsors:Brend Hotels
Colours: Red/red/red
Change colours: All Blue
Midweek Matches: Tuesday
Reserve League: Devon & Exeter
Programme:£1.00
Programme Editor: David Cooke
Local Press: N. Devon Journal Herald

CLUB PERSONNEL
President: Wilf Harris
Chairman:Jeff Evans
Manager: John Hore
Physio: Dave Griffith

2002-03
Leading Goalscorer:Kevin Squire
Captain: Simon Ovey
Player of the Year:Simon Ovey

BIDEFORD

Secretary: Kevin Tyrrell, 69 Laurel Ave., Bideford, devon EX39 3AZ Tel: 01237 4707747

Ground: The Sports Ground, Kingsley Road, Bideford Tel: 01237 474975

Directions: A361 for Bideford - ground on right as you enter the town

Capacity: 6,000 Seats: 120 Cover: 1,000 Floodlights: Yes

Clubhouse: `Robins Nest' - on ground. Open lunchtimes and evenings, snacks and bar menu. Mgr: Mrs Sue Tyrell

HONOURS Western Lg 63-64 70-7171-72 81-82 82-83, Div 1 51-52, Div 3 49-50, Lg Cup 71-72 84-85; Alan Young Cup 64-65 69-70; Merit Cup 68-69; Subsidiary Cup 71-72; Devon Snr Cup 79-80; Devon St Lukes Cup 81-82 83-84 85-86 95-96 (R-up 86-87 91-92 94-95)

PREVIOUS **Leagues:** Devon & Exeter 47-49; Western 49-72; Southern 72-75
Name: Bideford Town **Ground:** Hansen Ground (1 season)

BEST SEASON **FA Cup:** 1st Rd 64-65(replay) 73-74 77-78 81-82. **FA Vase:**

RECORD **Gate:** 6,000 v Gloucester C., FA Cup 4th Qual. Rd 60
Scorer: Tommy Robinson 259 **Appearances:** Derek May 527
Win: 16-0 v Soundwell 50-51 **Defeat:** 0-12 v Paulton 96-97

Players progressing: Shaun Taylor (Swindon Town) Tony Dennis (Cambridge)

FACT FILE
Founded: 1949
Nickname: Robins
Colours: All Red
Change colours: All Blue
Midweek Matchday: Tuesday
Prog: 32 pages, 50p Editor: Ian Knight

CLUB PERSONNEL
Chairman: Paul Mitchell
President: Jimmy McElwee
Hon.Vice Predident: Kevin Keegan
Company Secretary: B.Weston
Marketing & Promotions Exec. Sean Joyce
Assistant Secrtary: Ron Ackland
Manager: Sean Joyce Ass. Man: Mike Jones
Reserves Manager: Dave Matthews
Chief Scout Dudley Barry
Physio: Tony Beal

BISHOP SUTTON

Secretary: Roy Penney, 53 Ridgway Lane, Whitchurch, Bristol BS14 9PJ Tel: 01275 541392

Ground: Lakeview Football Field, Bishop Sutton Tel: 01275 333097

Directions: On A368 at rear of Butchers Arms pub - ground signposted on left entering village from the West

Capacity: 1,500 Seats: None Cover: 200 Floodlights: yes

Clubhouse: Open matchdays. Rolls, pies and usual pub food available Club Shop: No

HONOURS Somerset Snr Lg R-up 89-90 (Div 1 83-84 (R-up 81-82), Div 2 82-83), Bristol & Avon Lg 80-81 (Div 2 79-80), Somerset Jnr Cup 80-81, Weston Yth Lg77-78, Chew Valley KO Cup 83-84, Mid-Somerset Lg(Res) R-up 82-83 (Div 3 81-82)

PREVIOUS **Leagues:** Weston & Dist. Yth; Bristol & Avon; Somerset Snr (pre 1991)
Ground: Adjacent cricket field

BEST SEASON **FA Cup:** **FA Vase: 3rd Rd 1998**

CLUB RECORDS **Attendance:** 400 v Bristol City, friendly
Win: 15-0 v Glastonbury Res

Players progressing: David Lee (Chelsea), S Williams (Southampton), J French(Bristol R.)

FACT FILE
Founded: 1977
Nickname: Bishops
Sponsors: Symes Off License
Colours: All blue
Change colours: All yellow
Midweek Matches: Wednesday
Youth team's League: Somerset Mid Week
Programme: Yes
Editor: G Williams

CLUB PERSONNEL
Chairman: George Williams
Vice Chairman: Roy Penney
President: Bob Redding
Manager: Tony Cornelious
Coach: Peter Wills
Physio: Chris Bailes

BRIDGWATER TOWN (1984)

General Secretary: Mrs Glenda Fletcher,18 Dunkery Road, Bridgwater Tel:01278 425599
Football Secretary: Ray Heard, 4 Bush Road,Spaxton, Bridgwater
Tel Nos: 01278 671373 (H) 01278 446922 (W)

Ground: Fairfax Park, College Way, Bath Road, Bridgwater Tel: 01278 446899 (matchdays and weekday mornings only -it is not a postal address).
Website: www.bridgwatertownfc.com

Directions: M5 jct 23, follow signs to Glastonbury (A39), turn right for Bridgwater (A39). Follow sign to Bridgwater College via College Way.Ground on rt after Rugby Club One mile from Bridgwater (BR) station

Capacity: 2,500 **Seats:** 150 **Cover**: 400 **Floodlights**: Yes

Clubhouse: Robins social club on the Ground with refreshmants cabin on matchdays

HONOURS Somerset Senior Cup 93-94, Somerset Senior Lge 89-90 90-91 91-92 , Lg Cup winners (3) ,Western Lge Div 1 95-96, Merit cup 96-97 Somerset Senior Cup: 93-94 95-96

PREVIOUS **League:** Somerset Snr (pre-1994)**Names:** None
BEST SEASONFA Cup: 2nd Q Rd **FA Vase:** First Round Proper

RECORDS **Attendance:** 1,112 v Taunton Town 26.2. 97

FACT FILE
Founded: 1984
(after collapse of previous BTFC)
Nickname: The Robins
Sponsor: TMB Patterns Ltd
Colours: Red,white & black/black/red
Change colours: All blue
Midweek matchday: Tuesday
Youth League.: Somerset U18 Floodlight
Prog. Editor: Mark Hollidge ,8 Conway Road, Cannington , Bridgwater TA5 2NP

CLUB PERSONNEL
Chairman: Steve French
Patron & President: Tom Pearce
Press Officer: Gordon Nelson (01823 271167)
Manager: Trevor Senior
Sports Injury Therapist: Dave Callow
L.C.S.P.(Assoc): F.A.Dip.

BRIDPORT

Secretary: Keith Morgan,95 Orchard Crescent, Bridport,Dorset DT6 5HA (01308 425113)
Email Address: ian@newsport.freeserve.co.uk and FAX: 01308 867422

Ground: The Beehive, St Mary's Field, Bridport, Dorset Tel: 01308 423834

Directions: Take West Bay road from town centre, turn right just before Palmers Brewery

Capacity: 2,000 Seats: 200 Cover: 400 Floodlights: Yes Club Shop: No

Clubhouse: Yes, open matchdays and for functions. Hot and cold snacks available

HONOURS Western Lg Cup 70-71 72-73 77-78 (R-up 76-77, Div 1 R-up 94-95, Merit Cup 69-70 71-72 73-74); Dorset Comb.(3) 85-88 (Lg Cup 86-87 87-88); Dorset Snr Cup(8) 63-64 69-71 75-76 78-81 87-88; Dorset Snr Amtr Cup(6) 48-50 54-55 56-57 70-72; W. Dorset Chal. Bowl 07-08; Perry Str. Lg 22-23; Mark Frowde Cup 76-77 88-89

PREVIOUS **Leagues:** Perry Street; Western 61-84; Dorset Combination 84-88
Grounds: Pymore (pre 1930s); Crown Field (pre 1953)

BEST SEASON **FA Cup:** **FA Vase:**5th Round 88-89

RECORD **Attendance:** 1,150 v Exeter City, 1981; 3,000 v Chelsea, at Crown, 1950
Scorer (in a season): Ellis Hoole 36
Fee received: £2,000 for Tommy Henderson
Fee paid: £1,000 for Steve Crabb

FACT FILE
Founded: 1885
Nickname: Bees
Sponsors:Nerwlands Holidays
Colours: Red & black/black/red
Change colours: Blue & black/blue/blue
Midweek Matches: Tuesday
Reserves ' League: Dorset Combination
Programme: 40pages, #1.00
Editor: Ian Hallett (01308 868795)

CLUB PERSONNEL
President: Barry Williams
Chairman: David Fowler
Manager: Peter Conning

BRISLINGTON

Secretary: David Braithwaite, 3 Ashcott, Whitchurch, Bristol BS14 0AG
Tel: 01275 542040 (H) 0796 739 5650 (M) Email: brizzsec@aol.com

Ground: Ironmould Lane, Brislington, Bristol Tel: 0117 977 4030

Directions: 4 miles out of Bristol on main A4 to Bath - turn left up lane opposite Garden Centre just before dual carriageway (500 yards past Park & Ride on right)

Capacity: 2000 Seats: 144 Cover: 1500 Floodlights: Yes

Clubhouse: Yes - on ground, open matchdays **Club Shop:** No

HONOURS Somerset Senior Cup 92-93 R-up 93-94; Western Lg R-Up: 2002-2003 les Phillips Western Lg.Cup R-Up: 2003
Somerset Senior League, Premier Cup 95-96
Somerset County League Champions 2001-02 (Reserves)

PREVIOUS **League:** Somerset Senior (pre-1991)

BEST SEASON **FA Vase**: 3rd Rd 89-90, 2-3 v Abingdon T. (A)

FACT FILE
Formed: 1956
Nickname: Bris
Sponsors: Balson 7 Co(Accountants)
Colours: Red & black/black/black & red
Change colours: White/red/red
Midweek matches: Tuesday
Reserves ' League: Somerset Senior
Programme: 50p
Editor: Laserset (0117 969 5487)

CLUB PERSONNEL
President: Paul Bishop
Chairman: M.Richardson
Vice-Chairman:B.Perrott
Manager: Nigel Webb
Asst Manager: Richard Cowley
Physio: Dave Sutor

2002-03
Leading Goalscorer:Rob Claridge
Captain:Dean Radford
Player of the Year:Rob Claridge

DAWLISH TOWN

Secretary: John Wathen, 'Yardley',Oak Hill Cross Road,Teignmouth, Devon TQ14 8TN
Tel No: 01626 776852 Fax: 01626 879854

Ground: Playing Fields, Sandy Lane, Exeter Road, Dawlish Tel: 01626 863110
Website: www.dawlishtownfc.co.uk

Directions: Approx 1 mile from centre of town, off main Exeter road (A379)
Capacity: 2,000 Seats: 200 Cover: 200 Floodlights: Yes

Clubhouse: Open nightly, all day Saturday and Sunday situated in car park opposite ground

HONOURS Western Lg Div 1 R-up 98-99, Lg Cup 80-81 83-84, Devon Premier Cup 69-70 72-73 80-81, Devon Snr Cup 57-58 67-68, Devon St Lukes Cup 82-83 (R-up 81-82), Carlsberg Cup 96

BEST SEASON **FA Cup:** **FA Vase:** Quarter Finals 86-87

PREVIOUS **League:** Devon & Exeter **Ground:** Barley Bank 1875-1900

RECORD **Gate:** 1,500 v Heavitree Utd, Devon Prem. Cup Q-Final
Defeat: 0-18 v Clevedon (A), Western Lge Prem. Div. 92-93

FACT FILE
Founded: 1889
Colours: Green/green/green
Change Colours:Blue/white/white
Midweek matchday: Wednesday
Programme: 34 pages, £1.00
Programme Editor: Roy Bolt

CLUB PERSONNEL
President & Chairman
Bob Webster
Manager: Ray Green
Coach:Pete Darke
Physio:Roger Smart

2002-03
Leading Goalscorer:
Captain:
Player of the Year:

DEVIZES TOWN

Secretary: Roy King, 20 Sand Leaze,Worton, Devizes , Wiltshire BN10 5SA
Tel Nos: 01380 720648 Email: royking100uk@hotmail.com

Ground: Nursteed Road, Devizes. Tel: 01380 722817

Directions: Off Nursteed Road (A342 signposted Andover); leaving town ground on right opposite Eastleigh Rd

Capacity: 2,500 Seats: 130 Cover: 400 Floodlights: Yes

Clubhouse:

Club Shop:

HONOURS Western League Div. 1 99-00; Wilts Snr Cup 07-08 49-50 56-57 57-58 58-59 60-61 61-62 62-63 65-66 67-68 70-71 71-72 73-74 78-79

PREVIOUS **Leagues:** Wilts Comb.; Wilts Premier
Name: Southbroom (until early 1900s) **Ground:** London Rd (pre 1946)

CLUB RECORDS **Attendance:**
Win: **Defeat:**

BEST SEASON **FA Vase:** **FA Cup:**

FACT FILE
Founded: 1883
Nckname:
Colours: Red & white stripes/black/red
Change colours: All Blue
Midweek Matchday: Tuesday
Programme: Price: Pages:
Editor:

CLUB PERSONNEL
President:
Chairman: Chris Belcher
Press Officer:

Manager: Brian Newlands
Asst. Man / Coach:
Physio:

ELMORE

Secretary: Neville Crocker, Rivercroft,4 Little Silver, Tiverton, Devon EX16 4PH
Tel: 01884 2456634 (H) 07966 642094 (M)

Ground: Horsdon Park, Tiverton, Devon EX16 4DE Tel: 01884 252341

Directions: M5 Jct 27, A373 towards Tiverton, leave at 1st sign for Tiverton &Business Park, ground 500yds on right

Capacity: 2,000 Seats: 200 Cover: Floodlights: Yes

Clubhouse: 11am-11pm Mon-Sat. Full canteen service - hot & cold meals & snacks

Club Shop: Yes

HONOURS East Devon Snr Cup 72-73 75-76, Western Lge R-up 94-95. Lge Cup 90-91,94-95, Div 1 R-up 90-91, Prem Div Merit Cup R-up 91-92, Div 1 Merit Cup 86-87 89-90 90-91, Devon St Lukes Cup R-up 90-91, Devon Snr Cup 87-88, Devon Intermediate Cup 60-61, Football Express Cup 60-61, Devon & Exeter Lg Div 2A 73-74 86-87(res)(Div 1A 76-77(res)), Devon Yth Cup 77-78.

PREVIOUS **Leagues:** Devon & Exeter 47-74; South Western 74-78 Grounds: None

RECORD **Attendance:** 1,713 v Tiverton Town Fri.April 14th 95
Appearances: P Webber **Goalscorer:**
Win: 17-0 **Defeat:** 2-7

FACT FILE

Founded: 1947
Nickname: Eagles
Club Sponsors: Ken White Signs
Colours: All Green
Change colours: Red /black/black
Midweek matches: Tuesday
Reserve League: None
Programme: 12 pages, 30p
Editor: Richard Tapp(01884 252341)

CLUB PERSONNEL

Chairman: Alan J Cockram
Vice Chairman: P.J.Garnsworthy
Manager: Peter Buckingham
Asst Manager: R Moore
Physio: M Crocker

EXMOUTH TOWN

Ground: King George V Ground, Southern Road, Exmouth Tel: 01395 263348

Directions: On right side of main Exeter to Exmouth road (A376).
Half mile from Exmouth (BR)

Capacity: 2,500 Seats: 100 Cover: 250 Floodlights: Yes

Clubhouse: Open every night and weekend lunchtimes. Snacks available

Club Shop: Yes

PREVIOUS **League:** Devon & Exeter 1933-73
Grounds: Maer Cricket Field 33-38 48-64; Raleigh Park, Withycombe 38-39

RECORD **Attendance:** 2,395 v Liverpool XI, friendly in 1987
Goalscorer: Mel Pym, 117
Appearances: Keith Sprague, Geoff Weeks 410 (Western Lg)
Victory: 11-0 v Pewsey Vale 7/10/00 (A) 10-0 v Glastonbury 27'3/99 (H)
Defeat: 0-10 v Tiverton (A), Devon St Lukes Cup QF 16/2/94

BEST SEASON **FA Vase:** Semi Final 84-85

HONOURS Western Lg x 3, R-up x 2, Lg Cup 88-89 Les Phillips Cup 00-01, Div 1 R-up 81-82 2002-03, Sportmanship Trophy x 2; Devon Premier Cup x 2 Devon St Lukes Cup x 3; Devon Senior Cup 50-51; East Devon Snr Cup x 2 Harry Wood Mem. Cup 81-82; Exmouth Chal. Cup x 7

FACT FILE
Formed: 1933
Nickname: `Town' or `Blues'
Colours: Blue & white/blue/blue
Change colours: All Red
Midweek matchday: Tuesday
Reserves' League: Devon & Exeter
Programme
36 pages, 30p
Editor: P.Hiscock

CLUB PERSONNEL
President: Brian Bradley
Chairman: Phillip Rugg
Secretary: David Richardson J.P.,
44 Whitchurch Avenue, Exeter. EX2 1NT
Tel: 01392 430985
email: davidrich43@hotmail.com

Manager: Russell Wilson

FROME TOWN

Secretary: Geoff Norris, 10 Clumber Drive, Frome, Somerset BA11 2LG (01373 464 803)

Ground: Badgers Hill, Berkeley Road, Frome Tel: 01373 464087

Directions: On the Westbury Road, 1 mile from town centre and Frome BR station
Capacity: 5,000 Seats: 250 Cover: 800 Floodlights: Yes Club Shop: No

Clubhouse: Evenings & weekends. Cold food only

PREVIOUS **League:** Somerset Senior, Wilts League and Wilts Premier

BEST SEASON **FA Trophy:** 2nd Rd v Boston Utd (a) 0-4, 1984-85
FA Cup: 1st Rd Proper v L.Orient 1954-55
FA Vase: 2nd Rd v Paulton R (a) 1-2

RECORD **Attendance:** 8,000 v Leyton Orient, F.A.Cup 1st Rd. 58
Victory: 15-0 v Glastonbury, Somerset Senior League (h) 1906-07
Defeat: 1-11 v Dorchester, Western League (a) 1958-59

HONOURS Western Lg 78-79 Div 1 2001-02 (Div 2 19-20, Div 2 R-up 54-55, Lg Cup 79-80 82-83, Merit Cup 82-83, Alan Young Cup 79-80, Subsidiary Cup 59-60), Somerset Prem Cup 66-67 68-69 82-83, Wilts Prem Lg 62-63, Wiltshire Lge 1909-10,1910-11; Western Co's F'lit Cup 83-84, Somerset Snr Cup 32-33 33-34 50-51, Somerset Snr Lg 06-07 08-09 10-11 also Div 1 (res) 90-91, Div 3 (res) 85-86, Lg Cup (res) 91-92 Lg.Cup (Res) 2001-2002

FACT FILE
Founded: 1904
Nickname: Robins
Sponsors: Woodman Furniture
Colours: All Red
Change colours: White/blue/white
Midweek matchday: Tuesday
Reserves ' League: Somerset Senior
Programme:40 pages £1.00
Editor: Ian Pearce

CLUB PERSONNEL
President: T.B.A.
Chairman: Geoff Norris
Vice Chairman: PaulEastwood
Manager: Paul Thorpe
Player-coach: Tony Pounder
Physio:Shaun Baker
2002-2003
Captain: Lee Ashton
Top scorer & P.oY.: Matt Peters

Melksham Town F.C.

KEYNSHAM TOWN

Secretary: Iain Anderson, 195 Mount Hill Road, Hanham, Bristol BS15 9SU Tel: 0117 961 6426

Ground: Crown Field, Bristol Road, Keynsham Tel: 0117 986 5876

Directions: A4 from Bristol to Bath, ground on left before entering village opposite Crown Inn. Bus service every 30 mins from Bristol passes ground. 10mins walk from Keynsham BR station
Capacity: 2,000 Seats: 120 Cover: 500 Floodlights: Yes
Clubhouse: Evenings & before & after games. Snacks Club Shop: No

HONOURS Somerset Lg Div 1 77-78; Somerset Snr Cup 51-52 57-58, 00-01; Div. 2 00-01 GFA Jnr Cup 25-26; Somerset & Avon (South) Premier Cup 79-80 (SF 93-94);

BEST SEASON **FA Cup:** 4th Qual. Rd **FA Vase:**

PREVIOUS **Leagues:** Bristol District, Bristol Comb., Bristol Premier, Somerset Senior
Grounds: The Hams 1886-1910; Gaston 1910-25; Park Road 25-30; Charlton Rd 30-39

RECORD **Attendance:** 3,000 v Chelsea, f'light opening 88-89.
Competitive:2,160 v Saltash, Amateur Cup, Oct 1952

FACT FILE
Founded: 1895
Nickname: K's
Sponsors: Hollywood Frames
Colours: All amber
Change: All blue
Midweek matchday: Wednesday
Reserves ' League: Somerset County
Programme: 32 pages, 50p
Editor: Mark Brown (0117 969 5487)

CLUB PERSONNEL
President: Lester Clements
Chairman: Martin Coles
Press Officer: Ray Parker

Manager: Nigel Lee
Physio: Guy Linley
Player of the Year:

MELKSHAM TOWN

Secretary: David Phillips, 37 Duxford Close, Bowerhill,Melksham,Wlts. SN12 6XN
Tel No: 01225 706 904)
Ground: The Conigre, Melksham (01225 702843)
Capacity: 3,000 Seats: 150 Cover: 1,500 Floodlights: Yes

Directions: Just off main square in grounds of Melksham House

Clubhouse: Inside ground, open every evening & weekend lunchtimes

HONOURS Wilts Lg 03-04 93-94 (R-up 24-25 29-30 59-60 67-68 68-69 71-72), Western Lg Div 1 79-80, 96-97, Wilts Snr Cup 03-04 69-70 77-78 (R-up 57-58 67-68 68-69), Wilts Shield 80-81 81-82 84-85 ,85-86,97-98 ,99-00(R-up 86-87).

PREVIOUS **Leagues:** Wiltshire 1894-1974 93-94; Western 74-93
Grounds: Challymead; Old Broughton Road Field

BEST SEASON **FA Cup:** 2nd Q Rd 57-58 **FA Vase:** 3rd Rd 81-82,98-99,01-02
FA Amateur Cup: 1st Rd 68-69

RECORD **Attendance:** 2,821 v Trowbridge Town, FA Cup 57-58

FACT FILE
Founded: 1876
Sponsors: Cooper Avon Tyres
Colours:yellow/black/yellow
Change :White/Navy Blue
Midweek Matchday: Moinday
Prog Editor:T.B.A.

CLUB PERSONNEL
President: T.B.A.
Chairman: Mike Perrin
Vice Chairman: Paul Smith
Manager:Nigel Tripp
Ass.Manages: Pete Tripp & Jason Lunt
Physio: Neil Young
2002-2003 Captain: Justin Messenger
To Screr: Matt Brown P.o.Y.: Andrew Sandell

ODD DOWN

Secretary: Mike Mancini, 36 Caledonian Rd., East Twerton, Bath BA2 3RD
Tel: 01225 423293 Mobile: 07788 635560

Ground: Lew Hill Memorial Ground, Combe Hay Lane, Odd Down

Directions: On main Bath/Exeter road - leaving Bath turn left into Combe Hay Lane opposite The Hustler Pub .opposite Park & Ride car park. 40 mins walk from Bath (BR)
Capacity: 1,000 Seats: 160 Cover: 250 Floodlights: Yes

Clubhouse: Yes, open noon-3 & 7-11pm. Hot & cold food available
Club Shop: No

HONOURS Western Lg Div 1 92-93, Som. Snr Cup 91-92,Som, Premier Cup: R-up 2000-01

PREVIOUS **Leagues:** Wilts Premier, Bath & District, Somerset Senior

BEST SEASON **FA Cup:** **FA Vase:** Last 64 1983-84

RECORD **Appearances:** Steve Fuller 446
Scorer: Joe Matano 104
Win: 11-1 v Minehead (H), Western Lge Prem. Div. 19/3/94

FACT FILE
Founded: 1901
Sponsors:Dunsford Landrovers
Colours: All Yellow
Change Black & White
Midweek Matches: Tuesday (7-30)
Reserves ' League: Somerset Senior
Programme: 12 pages with admission
Editor: Secretary

CLUB PERSONNEL
President:: Eric Clarke
Chairman: Ian Robertson V- Chair:T.B.A.
Manager: Chris Mountford
2002-2003
Captain: Adamo Missiato
Top Scorer: Shaun Wiles/Richards 33
P.o.Y.: Jaz Bright & James Peart

Winners of the Les Phillips Western League Cup

BRISLINGTON F.C.

Back Row (L-R): Guy Cook, Mark Pope, Jon Cronory, Rob Claridge, Richard Ollis, Don Forbes, Craig Hopkins, Ian Jones, Ben Walker, Dean Wilson, Shane Andrews, Richard Crowley (Asst. Manager).
Front Row: Steve Jenkins, Nigel Gillard, Simon Gew, Bradley Andrews, Dean Radford, Scott Morrison, Jon Miller, Deam Maggs, Chris Churchill, Tony Cook, Andrew Summers, Nigel Webb (Manager).

Western League Division One & Les Phillips League Cup Runners-up

EXMOUTH F.C.

Back Row (L-R): Jason Down, Reece Tippett, Neil Middlesditch, Mark Rock, Tim Thorne, Tom Gardiner, Jamie Densham, Danny Burwood.
Front Row: Richard Spiller, Russell Wilson, Richard Bentley, Steve Taylor, Russell Wilson, Neil Saunders, Steve May, Andrew Widger.

PAULTON ROVERS

Secretary: Tracy Curtis,12 Linden Close,Waterford Park, Westfield,Radstock Somerset BA3 3EJ
Ground: Athletic Ground, Winterfield Road, Paulton Tel: 01761 412907

Directions: Leave A39 at Farrington Gurney (approx 15 miles south of Bristol),follow A362 marked Radstock for two miles, left at junction B3355 to Paulton,ground on right. Bus services from Bristol and Bath

Capacity: 5,000 Seats: 138 Cover: 200 Floodlights: Yes

Club Shop: Old programmes available - contact Chairman
Clubhouse: 3 bars, lounge, skittle alley, dance hall. Capacity 300. Cateringfacilities

HONOURS Western Lg Div 2 R-up 1900-01; Somerset Snr Cup 00-01 02-03 03-04 07-08 08-09 09-10 34-35 67-68 68-69 71-72 72-73 74-75; Somerset Snr Lg 00-01 03-04 04-05 70-71 71-72 72-73 73-74; Somerset F/Lit Youth Lge 96-97

PREVIOUS **Leagues:** Wilts Premier; Somerset Snr
Grounds: Chapel Field; Cricket Ground; Recreation Ground 1946-48

RECORDS **Attendance:** 2,000 v Crewe, FA Cup, 1906-07
Appearances: Steve Tovey **Goalscorer:** Graham Colbourne

2002-2003 **Captain:** Mark Buxton **P.o.Y.:** Richard Perry **Top Scorer:** Graham Colbourne.

FACT FILE
Founded: 1881
Nickname: Rovers
Sponsors: Barons Property Centre/Bass Breweries
Colours: White & maroon/maroon/maroon
Change colours: Yellow/navy/navy
Midweek matches: Monday
Reserves' League: Somerset Snr
Programme: 20 pages, £1.00
Editor: D Bissex (01761 412463)
Local Press: Bath Evening Chronicle, Bristol Evening Post, Western Daily Press Somerset Guardian

CLUB PERSONNEL
President: L.Rogers
Chairman: David Bissex
Vice Chairman: D Carter
Manager: Darren Perrin
Physio: Mike Brown

TORRINGTON

Secretary: David Priscott, 6 Highfield Terrace, Bishops Tawton, Barnstaple EX32 0AN
Tel: 01271 328316 (H) 07751-149900 (M) e-mail afctorrington@msn.com

Ground: Vicarage Field, School Lane, Great Torrington Tel: 01805 622853
Directions: In town centre turn left by parish church, right at swimming pool, ground behind swimming pool. Good parking.
Red Bus from Bideford & Barnstaple (nearest BR station).Bus stop 300yds from ground
Capacity: 4,000 Seats: 100 Cover: 1,000 Floodlights: Yes Shop: No

Clubhouse: Weekdays 7-1pm, Sat 11-11 & Sun 12-3. Light snacks available on matchdays.

PREVIOUS **Leagues:** N Devon; Devon & Exeter; S Western 77-84 **Grounds**: None
BEST SEASON **FA Vase:** 5th Rd 84-85 **FA Cup**: 2nd Qual Rd. 81-82, 94-95, 96-97
RECORDS: **Scorer:** Trevor Watkins 254 **Appearances:** Mike Gilbert 527
TransferFee Rcd: £3,000 D.Walter(Yeovil)

HONOURS Western Lg R-up 90-91 Div 1 Champs 02-03; Merit Cup 91-92 93-94 95-96; South Western Lg Cup 81; Devon St Lukes Cup R-up 95-96 96-97; Devon & Exeter Lg & Cup 73-74; Festival of Britain Cup 96-97; Les Phillips Cup R-up 91-92; Torridge Cup (14),Arlington Cup 02-03

FACT FILE
Formed: 1908
Nickname: Torrie or Supergreens
Sponsors: K & J Plant Hire
Colours: Green & white Change :Yellow/blue
Midweek Matches: Tuesday
Programme
48 pages, 50p Editor: Secretary
Local Press: North Devon Journal

CLUB PERSONNEL
President: Keith Curtis
Chairman: Winston Martin
Manager: Jeff Evans
Coach: Paul Hutchings
Physio: Brian Alford
2002-03
Leading Goalscorer: Andy Stevens 44
Captain: Richard Fey
Player of the Year: Darren Polhill

WELTON ROVERS

Secretary: Geoff Baker, 6 Longfellow Road, Westfield Road, Westfield, Radstock BA3 3YZ
Email Address: weltonrovers@ yahoo.com

Ground: West Clewes, North Road, Midsomer Norton, Somerset Tel: 01761 412097

Directions: A367 Bath to Radstock ō right at lights at foot of hill onto A362,ground on right.

Capacity: 2,400 Seats: 300 Cover: 300 Floodlights: Yes Club Shop: No

Clubhouse: 7.30-11pm daily, plus Sat matchdays 1.30-2.45pm, Sun 12-2pm

HONOURS Western Lg 11-12 64-65 65-66 66-67 73-74, Div 1 59-60 87-88,Amateur Cup 56-57 57-58 58-59 59-60, Alan Young Cup 65-66 66-67 67-68(jt); Somerset Snr Cup 06-07 11-12 12-13 13-14 19-20 24-25 25-26 60-61 61-62 62-63, Som. I'mediate Cup 77-78, Som. Jnr Cup 06-07(jt) 24-25 30-31, WBC Clares City of Wells Cup 78-79

PREVIOUS **Leagues:** None **Names:** None **Grounds:** None
BEST SEASON **FA Cup:** **FA Vase:** **FA Amateur Cup:**
RECORD **Attendance:** 2,000 v Bromley, FA Amateur Cup 1963
Goalscorer: Ian Henderson, 51

FACT FILE
Formed: 1887
Nickname: Rovers
Sponsors: Young Bros (Roofing)
Colours: Green & navy/navy &green/green
Change colours: Yellow/black/yellow
Midweek matchday: Wednesday
Reserve s' League: Somerset Senior
Programme: 12 pages, 25p
Editor: M Brown
Website: www.geocities.com/weltonrovers

CLUB PERSONNEL
Chairman: Rae James
Manager: T.B.A.
Physio: John Carver

Torrington. Back Row (L-R): Dave Priscott (Secretary), Brian Alford (Physio), Andy Stevens, Jeff Parish, Kevin Pickard, Garry Pedler, Barry Yeo, Lee Langmead, Mike Hedden, Carl Armstrong, Kevin Evans (Coach), Graham Avery (Club Official).
Front Row: Martin Davey, Darren Polhill, Kevin Darch, Paul Hutchings (Manager), Karl Madge, Jon Vooght, Karl Baggaley.

Dawlish Town Back Row (L-R): Brad Cox, Aidan Saunders, Ryan Harris, Dan Harvey, Darren Armitage, Matt Coleman, Neil Cleave, Paul Wilkins.
Front Row: Dave Jarvis, Craig Fenner, Alex Warren, Carl Turner, Darren Green, Stuart Norrish, Lee Ingham.

BITTON

Secretary: Mark Tilling, 71 Howes Close, Barrs Court, Bristol BS30 8SB
Tel Nos: 0117 9604550 (H) 0781 5086198 (M)

Ground: The Recreation Ground, Bath Road, Bitton, BS30 6HX Tel: 0117 932 3222
Capacity:1000 Cover: 200 Seats: 48 Floodlights: Yes Club Shop: Yes

Directions: M4 junc 18. Take A46 towards Bath, at first roundabout take A420 for Wick/ Bridgeyate. On approach to Bridgeyate turn left at mini-roundabout onto A4175 and follow for 2.2 miles, then left for Bath on the A431. The ground is 100 yards on right. Nearest station: Keynsham, Bristol

Clubhouse: Weekdays 7.30-11, Sat.& Sun all day.

HONOURS Glos. Jun Cup r-up 90; Avon Prem. Lg r-up 94, 95; Glos Sen amat Cup 95; Glos Chall Trophy r-up 97; Glos County Lg r-up 97.

PREVIOUS **Leagues:** Avon Premier Comb.ination, Glos County

FACT FILE
Founded: 1922
Sponsors: John Dean Builders
Colours: Red & white stripes/black/black
Change colours: Yellow/green/yellow
Midweek Matcday :Tuesday 7.45
Programme: 36 pages Editor: Paul Cater

CLUB PERSONNEL
Chairman: John Langdon
V- Chairman: Paul Cater Pres: Roy Ewans
Treas: Steve Webb Manager: Keith Brown
2002-2003 Captain: Rich Lee
Top Scorer: Mike ~Branch
Player of the Year: Matt Emery

BRISTOL MANOR FARM

Secretary: John Scriven, 44 Woodleaze,Sea Mills,Bristol BS9 2HY (0117 968 4916)
Email: christopher-davis2000@hotmail.com

Ground: `The Creek', Portway, Sea Mills, Bristol BS9 2HS Tel: 0117 968 3571

Directions: M5 jct 18 (Avonmouth Bridge), follow A4 for Bristol - U-turn on dual carriageway by Bristol & West sports ground and return for half mile on A4- ground entrance is down narrow lane on left (hidden entrance). Near to Sea Mills station (BR Temple Meads-Severn Beach line)

Capacity: 2,000 Seats: 84 Cover: 350 Floodlights: Yes Club Shop: No

Clubhouse: Open every evening & lunchtime Sat & Sun. Lounge bar, skittle alley, bar meals.

HONOURS Western Lge Prem 00-01 Sportsman Awards, Western Lg Div 1 82-83, Glos Tphy 87-88, Glos Amtr Cup 89-90, Somerset Snr Lg Div 1 (Lg Cup, Div 2)

PREVIOUS **Leagues:** Bristol Suburban 64-69; Somerset Snr 69-77
Name: Manor Farm O.B. 1964-68 **Grounds:** None

RECORD **Attendance:** 500 v Portway, Western Lg 1974

FACT FILE
Formed: 1964
Nickname: The Farm
Club Sponsors: M.T.I. Ltd
Colours: Yellow
Change colours: Red& black/black/red& black
Midweek Matchday: Tuesday
Reserve s' League: Suburban League
Programme: 28 pages, 50p
Editor: Natalie & Michelle Lawrence

CLUB PERSONNEL
Chairman: Geoff Selleck
Manager: Geoff Bryant
Assistant Manager: Pete McCall

CADBURY HEATH

Secretary: Colin Trotman, 51 Deanery Road, Kingswood, Bristol BS15 9JB
Tel: 0117 983 7510 (H)

Ground: Springfield, Cadbury Heath Road, Warmley, Bristol. Tel: 0117 967 5731

Directions: Situated in East Bristol on the road between Warmley & Oldeland.
Tower Road (North & South) runs from Warmley to Oldland and passes Cadbury Heath road. Look for Spar shop and King William P.H..
Turn into Cadbury Heath Road. 20 yds on right entrance to Social Club.

PREVIOUS **League:** Gloucestershire County Lge.

HONOURS Glos. County Lge 98-99, R-up 99-00

FACT FILE
Formed:
Colours: All red
Change Cols.: yellow/black/black
Midweek Matchday: Wednesday
Programme: Price: Pages:
Editor:

CLUB PERSONNEL
Chairman: Dave Smart
1 Farm Close, Emerson Green,
Bristol BS16 7RU Tel: 0117 956 1223
Manager: Glen Smart
Asst. Man. / Coach:
Physio:

CALNE TOWN

Secretary: Laurie Drake, 22 Falcon Rd, Calne, Wilts SN11 8PL . Tel: 01249 819186

Ground: Bremhill View, Lickhill Rd., North End, Calne. 01249 816716.

Directions: Take A4 from Chippenham near Calne turn L. at 1st R'abt onto A3102 Calne B'pass at next R'abt turn R., next L, then R and R. again. Email: calnetownfc@btinternet.com

Capacity: 2,500 **Seats:** 78 **Cover**: 250 **Floodlights**: Yes **Club Shop**: No

Clubhouse: Mon-Fri 7-11pm, Sat-Sun 12-11pm. Filled rolls, hot food, tea,coffee, sweets etc

HONOURS Western Lg Div 1 R-up 92-93; Wilts Snr Cup 12-13 34-35 84-85 (R-up1894-95 94-95 1911-12 49-50); Wilts Lg 33-34, (`Ghia' Cup 8) 1-81 85-86, Div 279-81, Div 3 85-86, Div 4 81-82

PREVIOUS **League:** Wilts Co. (pre-1986) **Ground:** Anchor Road Rec. 1887-1967
Names: Calne Town (1886) & Harris Utd merged; Calne & Harris Utd (1921-67)

RECORD **Attendance:** 1,100 v Swindon, Friendly 25/7/1987
Scorer: Robbie Lardner **Appearances:** Gary Swallow, 259
Win: 11-1 v Heavitree (H) **Defeat:** 2-7 v Odd Down (A)

FACT FILE
Founded: 1887 Nickname: Lilywhites
Sponsors: Daceuninck
Colours: White/black/black
Change colours: Yellow/blue/blue
Midweek Matchday: Tuesday 7.45
Programme: 20 pages, 50p
Editor: Jacky Drake (01249 819186)

CLUB PERSONNEL
Chair: Steve Walker
President: Bill Burt
Manager: Kelvin Highmoor
2002-2003
Top Scorer & P.o.Y.: Glenn Armstrong
Captain: Martyn Wheeler

CHARD TOWN

Secretary: Brian Gidley, 64 King Atheistan Drive,Chard, Somerset TA20 2HY (0146064680)
Ground: Town Ground, Zembard Lane, Chard TA20 1JL Tel: 01460 61402
Capacity: 1,500 Seats: 60 Cover: 200 Floodlights: Yes

Directions: Follow sports centre signs off main A30 High Street along Helliers Road. Right into Upper Combe Street and left into Zembard Lane . BR 7miles Axminster or 8 miles Crewkerne
Clubhouse: Matchdays & most evenings. Snacks served

HONOURS Som. Snr Lg 49-50 53-54 59-60 67-68 69-70 (Lg Cup 61-62 71-72 76-77); Western Lg Div 1 R-up 83-84 87-88 95-96, (Merit Cup 82-83, Comb. Cup(Res) 91-92 (R-up 92-93)); Som. Snr Cup 52-53 66-67; S W Co's Cup 88-89; Western Com Lge 96-97, Cup 96-97.

BEST SEASON **FA Cup:** 2nd Qual Rd. 77-78 82-83 **FA Vase:**

PREVIOUS **Leagues:** Somerset Snr 20-24 48-75; Perry Street 25-48 **Grounds:** None

2002-03
Leading Goalscorer:Matt Corrick **Captain**:Simon Baines **Player of the Year:** James Steer

FACT FILE
Founded: 1920 Nickname: Robins
Colours: Red with white trim/red/red
Change : Blue with yellow trim/blue/yellow
Midweek matches: Wednesday
Prog: 24 pages with entry Ed: Ian Hallett

CLUB PERSONNEL
Chairman: Robert Glentworth
V-Chairman: Troy Symes
Treasurer/Gen Sec.: Mrs Rose Richards
Gen Man: Malcolm Adcock

Manager: Steve Ritchie
Asst.Man:Billy Morris
Physio: Daniel Glentworth

CLEVEDON UNITED

Secretary:
GROUND c/o Clevedon Town FC, Hand Stadium, Davis Lane, Clevedon, N. Somerset
Tel: 01275 871600 (ground) 01275 341913 (office)
Fax: 01275 871601 email: info@handstadium.co.uk
Directions: M5 Jct 20 - follow signs for Hand Stadium; first left into Central Way (at island just after motorway), 1st left at mini-r'bout into Kenn Rd, 2nd left Davis Lane; ground half mile on right. Or from Bristol(B3130) left into Court Lane (opposite Clevedon Court), turn right after 1 mile, ground on left. Nearest BR station: Nailsea & Backwell. Buses from Bristol
Capacity: 3,650 Seats: 300 Cover: 1,600 Floodlights: Yes
Clubhouse:
PREVIOUS **League:** Somerset County League >2003
RECORD **Attendance:**
HONOURS Somerset County Lge Prem. Div 98-99

FACT FILE
Founded:
Colours:
Change Colours:
Midweek Matchday:
Programme:

CLUB PERSONNEL
Chairman:
President:
Manager:
Physio:

CLYST ROVERS

Secretary: Bob Chamberlain, Orchard Cottage, Clyst St George, Exeter EX3 0NZ(01392 873498)
Ground: Waterslade Park, Clyst Honiton, Devon Tel: 01392 366424
Directions: A30 following signs for Exeter Airport. Coming from Exeter take 1st right after airport turning (ground signposted) up narrow 200yds past Duke of York Pub
Capacity: 3,000 Seats: 130 Cover: 300 Floodlights: Yes
Club Shop: Yes, Programmes, souvenirs etc
Clubhouse: Open one and a half hours before kick off and after game. Excellent food available
HONOURS Devon St Lukes Cup R-up 92-93, Western Lg Cup SF 92-93
PREVIOUS **Leagues:** Exeter & District 26-44 51-66; Exeter & District Sunday 67-82; South Western 81-92 **Grounds:** Fair Oak 1926-44
RECORD **Gate:** 768 v Tiverton, Devon St Lukes final 11/5/93
Win: 6-0 v Heavitree United, 1993
Defeat: 0-12 v Torpoint Athletic, South Western League, October 1990

FACT FILE
Founded: 1926 Reformed: 1951
Nickname: Rovers
Sponsors: Vantage Pharmacy, Paignton
Colours: All yellow
Change colours: All green
Midweek Matches: Tuesday
Programme: 32 pages, 30p
Editor:

CLUB PERSONNEL
President: Mr P W Brown
Chairman: Bob Chamberlain
Vice Chairman: Colin Dadson
Managers:Bill Potter & Martin Tooze
Physio: Bill Wreford

CORSHAM TOWN

Secretary: Richard Taylor, 7 Cresswells, Corsham, Wilts SN13 9NJ Tel: 01249 714406
Website: www.corshamtownfc.co.uk Email: info@corshamtownfc.co.uk

Ground: Southbank Ground, Lacock Road, Corsham, Wilts. SN13 9HS Tel: 01249 715609
Directions From the A4 turn into Corsham at the Hare & Hounds PH roundabout, taking the Melksham Road, B3353, past the Methuen Arms PH then straight across the next mini-r'about into Lacock Road. The ground is situated 1/2 mile on right
Capacity: 1,500 Seats: No Cover: Yes Floodlights: Yes
Clubhouse: Yes Club Shop: Yes

HONOURS Wiltshire Lge. 97-98, Wiltshire FA Sen. Cup 75-76 96-97,
Wiltshire Lge. KO Cup 95-96 96-97
PREVIOUS **League:** Wiltshire Co. Lge

FACT FILE
Founded: 1893
Sponsors: Hong Kong House Vanitec
Colours: All red
Change colours: Yellow/blue/blue
Midweek matchday: Tuesday

CLUB PERSONNEL
Chairman: Colin Hudd
Manager:Colin Bush
Assistant Manager: John Woods

2002-03
Leading Goalscorer:Dave Kilmurray
Captain:Richard Thompson
Player of the Year:Dan Beck

HALLEN

Secretary: T.B.A.
Email Address jrogers.gosw@go-region.gsi.gov.ok
Ground: Hallen Playing Fields, Moorhouse Lane, Hallen, Nr Bristol Tel: 0117 950 2265
Directions: M5 jct 17, A4018 to Henbury r'bout, right, right again at junction,next right to Station Road, left into Avonmouth Road at r'bout. One mile toHallen, ground first left, then right into lane to ground
Capacity: 2,000 Seats: 200 Cover: 200 Floodlights: Yes/No
Clubhouse: Yes - Open ????

HONOURS Glos County Lg 92-93, Glos Snr Trophy 92-93
PREVIOUS **League:** Glos County (pre-1993), Hellenic 93-00
Names: Lawrence Weston Athletic (80's), Lawrence Weston Hallen (pre-1991)
Ground: Kings Weston (early 1980's)
RECORD **Attendance:** 803 v Bristol Rovers 1997

FACT FILE
Founded: 1949
Colours: All Royal Blue
Change Colours: All Yellow
Midweek Matchday: Wednesday
Programme: No
CLUB PERSONNEL
Chairman: Barrie Phillips
Tel: 0117 950 1754
President: Ken Naish
Manager: Terry HareCoach: John Payne
Physio: Charlie Baldwin

ILFRACOMBE TOWN

Secretary: Tony Alcock, 2 Worth Road, Ilfracombe, North Devon EX34 9JA Tel: 01271 862686. Mobile: 07977 589199
Ground: Marlborough Park, Ilfracombe, Devon Tel: 01271 865939
Directions: A361 to Ilfracombe. Turn1st right in town after lights and follow Marlborough Rd to the top, ground on left.**Capacity:** 2,000 **Seats:** 60 Cover: 450Floodlights: Yes Club Shop: No
Clubhouse: Every night 7-11pm and weekend lunchtimes. Hot & cold meals on matchdays
HONOURS E Devon Prem Lg 25-26 28-29 29-30, N Devon Senior Lg, N Devon Prem Lg 66-67 70-71 81-82 82-83, Western Lg Div 2 R-up 52-53, Les Phillips Cup R-up 91
PREVIOUS Leagues: North Devon 04-14 20-22 60-84; EDevon Premier 22-31;Exeter & District t 32-39 46-49; Western 49-59 **Grounds:** Shaftesbury Field; Brimlands; Killacleave (all pre-1924)
Names: Ilfracombe FC 02-09; Ilfracombe Utd 09-14; Ilfracombe Comrades 14-20
RECORDS **Attendance:** 3,000 v Bristol City, Ground opening, 2/10/24
Goalscorer: Paul Jenkins 77 **Appearances:** Bobby Hancock 45
Players progressing: Jason Smith (Coventry City and Swansea City via Tiverton Town)

FACT FILE
Founded: 1902 Nickname: Bluebirds
Sponsors: K&J Electrical
Colours: Blue/black/blue
Change : White/navy/navy
Midweek matchday: Tuesday
Reserves ' League: North Devon
Programme: 8 pages, 40p Editor: Phil Hill

CLUB PERSONNEL
Chairman: Phil Hill
Vice-Chairman: Barry Jones
President: Mrs Jo Rose
Manager: Kevin Constantine
Physio: Ray Wooff

LARKHALL ATHLETIC

Secretary: Garry Davy, 84 London Road West, Batheaston, Bath, BA1 7DA 01225 852729
Email: garrydvy@aol.com

Ground: "Plain Ham", Charlcombe Lane, Larkhall, Bath. 01225 334952
Directions A4 from Bath, 1 mile from city centre turn left into St Saviours Rd. In Larkhall Square fork left, and right at junction, road bears into Charlcombe Lane. Ground on right as lane narrows

Capacity: 1,000 Seats: None Cover: 50Floodlights: No

HONOURS Somerset Senior Cup 75-76, Somerset Senior Lg,; Western Lg Div 1 88-89 93-94 94-95(Div 1 Merit Cup (4) 83-86 87-88 (jt with Yeovil Res)
PREVIOUS **Leagues:** Somerset Senior
CLUB RECORDS Attendance:

FACT FILE
Founded: 1914 Nickname: Larks
Colours: Royal & white/royal & white/royal
Change colours: Red & white/red & white/red
Midweek Matches: Tuesday
Programme: Yes
CLUB PERSONNEL
President: Tony Codd
Chairman: Jim McLay Tel: 01373 834050
Manager: Paul Rankin & Tommy Gilbert
Coach: John Newman
2002-03
Leading Goalscorer:
Captain:
Player of the Year:

MINEHEAD

Secretary: Alex Knight,Swallowdale,Watery Lane,Doniford,Watchet,Somerset.TA3 0TW
Tel: 01984 639212
Ground: The Recreation Ground, Irnham Road, Minehead, Somerset (01643 704989)
Directions: Entering town from east on A39 turn right into King Edward Road at Police station, first left into Alexandra Rd and follow signs to car park;ground entrance within. Regular buses to Minehead from Taunton, the nearestrailhead. (Steam train 'holiday route' Taunton to Minehead)
Capacity: 3,500 Seats: 350 Cover: 400 Floodlights: Yes
Clubhouse: Yes **Club Shop:** No
HONOURS Southern Lg R-up 76-77, Div 1 Sth 75-76, Merit Cup 75-76;
Western Lg R-up 66-67 71-72, Div 1 90-91 98-99, Alan Young Cup 67-68 (jt with Glastonbury),Somerset Premier Cup 60-61 73-74 76-77
PREVIOUS **Leagues:** Somerset Senior; Southern 72-83
RECORD **Attendance:** 3,600 v Exeter City, FA Cup 2nd Rd, 77
BEST SEASON **FA Cup:** 2nd Rd 76-77, 1-2 v Portsmouth (A); 77-78, 0-3 v Exeter City (H)

FACT FILE
Founded: 1889
Colours: All Blue
Change colours: Yellow/black/black
Midweek Matches: Tuesday
Reserves League: TBA
Programme: Yes
Editor: Brian Walder
CLUB PERSONNEL
Chairman: Colin Gardner
Tel: 01984 633932
Manager: Andy Hodgson

Odd Down F.C.

Action from Paulton Rovers' 4-1 Screwfix Premier League win over Barnstaple Town.

Photo: Mark Wood.

Screwfix Division One action between Larkhall Athletic and Westbury United, this time resulting in a 1-1 draw.

Photo: Mark Wood.

SHEPTON MALLETT

Secretary: John Bell, 43 Victoria Grove, Shepton Mallet, Somerset BA4 5NJ
Tel Nos: 01749 344687 (H) 01749 830332 (W) 07866 762372 (M)
Ground: The Playing Fields, Old Wells Rd., West Shepton, Shepton Mallett, Som. BA4 5XN
Tel: 01749 344609
Capacity: 2500 Covered Seating: 120 Floodlights: Yes
Directions: Take the Glastonbury road from Shepton Mallett town centre then turn right at the junction with Old Wells Rd (approx. 1/2 mile, near the "King William" P.H.) - the ground is 300 yards on the left.
Clubhouse:
PREVIOUS **League:** Somerset Senior
HONOURS Somerset Senior League 2000-01
CLUB RECORDS **Attendance:**

FACT FILE
Founded: 1986
Colours: Black & white/black/black
Change colours: Red & black/white/red
Midweek matchday: Tuesday
Programme: Price: Pages:
Editor:
CLUB PERSONNEL
Chairman: Brian Blinman
Manager: Gary Banfield
Asst. Man. / Coach:
Physio:
2002-03
Leading Goalscorer:
Captain:
Player of the Year:

SHREWTON UNITED

Secretary: Jayne Foot, 3 North Croft, Tilshead, Salisbury, Wiltshire SP3 4SE
Tel: 01980 621 284 (H) 01722 439516 (B) email: peterwithers@lineone.net

Ground: Recreation Ground, Mill Lane, Shrewton, Wiltshire
Directions: From A303 left at Winterbourne Stoke and left at The Royal Oak. Then turn right at mini roundabout on outskirts of village, and then turn left at the George Inn and follow Football Club signs. From Devizes A360 turn right at mini roundabout on outskirts of village, and then turn left at the George Inn and follow Football Club signs.

PREVIOUS **League:** Wiltshire League >2003

HONOURS Wiltshire Lge Prem Div. 2001-02 02-03, R-up 00-01, Lge Senior Cup 01-02 02-03

FACT FILE
Colours: Maroon & Navy/navy/navy
Change Colours: All White & jade
Midweek Matchday: Tuesday

CLUB PERSONNEL
Chairman: Brian Sainsbury
Manager: Stuart Withers

STREET

Secretary: Mark Clarke, c/o 6 Clemence Road, Street, Somerset BA16 0SR
Tel Nos: 01458 442249 (H) 07979 5144181 (W) 07979 514181 (M)
Ground: The Tannery Ground, Middlebrooks, Street, Somerset
Tel: 01458 445987 Matchdays 01458 448227
Directions: Sign posted from both ends of A39 & B3151, Station Castle Cary
Capacity: 2,000 Seating: 120 Cover: 25 Floodlights: Yes Club Shop: No
Clubhouse:
HONOURS: Western Lge R-up 52-53
RECORDS: **Attendance:** 4,300 v Yeovil Town FA Cup 17/11/47
PREVIOUS: **Leagues:**
Grounds: Victoria Field, Tunpike Ground

FACT FILE
Founded: 1880 Nickname The Cobblers
Sponsors C I C A
Colours: Green & white/white/white& green
Change colours: Red & black/black/black
Midweek home matchday: Tuesday
Programme: 44 pages 50p
Editor: M Clarke
CLUB PERSONNEL
Chairman: Andrew Walton
Manager: Gerry Pearson
Asst Mgr: Simon Culliford
Physios: Dick Pickersgill, Andrew Lee

WELLINGTON TOWN

Secretary: Dave Grabham, 12 Drakes Park, Wellington, SomersetTA21 8TB
Tel: 01823 664946 (H), 01823 355687 (B) 07817 274585 (M) email:djgrabham@msn.com
Ground: Wellington Playing Field, North Street, Wellington, Somerset Tel: 01823 664810
Directions: At town centre traffic lights turn into North St., then first left by Fire Station into the public car park that adjoins the ground
Capacity: 3,000 **Seats:** None **Cover:** 200 **Floodlights:** Yes **Clubhouse:** Yes **Club Shop:** No
HONOURS Western Lg Div 1 R-up 80-81, Merit Cup 91-92, Comb Lge 95-96;Comb Lge KO Cup 95-96 98-99; Somerset Snr Lg Div 1 R-up; Rowbarton & Seward Cup, Bill Slee Trophy
PREVIOUS **Leagues:** Taunton Saturday, Somerset Senior
RECORD **Attendance:** **Goalscorer:** Ken Jones
BEST SEASON **FA Cup:** 1st Qual Rd. 81-82, 84-85 **FA Vase:** 2nd rd Prop 98-99
Players progressing: Nick Jennings and Ian Stonebridge (Plymouth)
2002-03
Top Goalscorer: Shane Kingston: **Captain :**Mathewt Brereton **Player of the Year**:Greg Jackson

FACT FILE
Founded: 1892
Sponsors: A J Shire & Wadham Fencing
Colours: All tangerine
Change cols: Blue & claret stripes/blue/blue
Midweek Matches: Tuesday
Reserve Lge: Devon & Exeter Sen Div
Programme: Yes Editor: Chairman
CLUB PERSONNEL
Chairman: Ken Bird
Vice-Chairman:Graham Aspin
President: Alan Shire
Manager: Dave Sheehan
Res Manager: John Port
Physio: Ken Pearson

WESTBURY UNITED

Secretary: Michael Taylor, c/o W. U. F .C. Westury, Wiltshire BA13 3AF (01373 865406)
Ground: Meadow Lane, Westbury Tel: 01373 823409
Directions: In town centre, A350, follow signs for BR station, Meadow Lane on right (club signposted). Ten mins walk from railway station (on main London-South West and South Coast-Bristol lines)
Capacity: 3,500 Seats: 150 Cover: 150 Floodlights: Yes
Clubhouse: Evenings 7-11pm, Fri, Sat & Sun lunchtimes 12-3pm Club Shop: No
HONOURS Western Lg Div 1 91-92, Wilts Senior Cup 31-32 32-33 47-48 51-52, Wilts Combination, Wilts Lg 34-35 37-38 38-39 49-50 50-51 55-56, Wilts Premier Shield R-up 92-93
PREVIOUS **Leagues:** Wilts Comb.; Wilts Co. (pre-1984)
Ground: Redland Lane (pre-1935)
RECORD Gate: 4,000 - v Llanelli, FA Cup 1st Rd 37 & v Walthamstow Ave. FA Cup 37
Players progressing: John Atyeo (Bristol City)

FACT FILE
Formed: 1921
Nickname: White Horsemen
Colours: Green /white/green
Change colours: Sky & navy/navy/sky
Midweek Matches: Wednesday
Reserves' league: Wilts County Lg.
Programme: 16 pages, 50p
Editor: Mike Taylor (01373 865406)

CLUB PERSONNEL
Chairman: Phillip Alford
Vice Chairman: Bert Back
President: Ernie Barber
Managers: Derek Graham
Physio: Dave Prescott

WESTON ST. JOHNS

Secretary: Andy Jarrett, 2 College Court, Uffculme, Cullompton, Devon EX15 3EQ
Tel No: 01934 515260 (H)
Ground: Coleridge Road, Bournville Estate, Weston-s-Mare, Somerset
Tel: 01934 612862
Capacity: ????? Covered Seating: ????? Covered Standing: ???? Floodlights: Yes/No
Directions: Leave M5 at J21and take main road into Weston-s-Mare.
Turn left at the 4th r'about into Winterstoke Road, then take the 2nd right into Byron Road and then 1st left into Coleridge Road.

PREVIOUS **League:** Somerset Senior Lge.
Names: Worle & Weston St. Johns amalgamated 2000
HONOURS R-up Somerset Sen. Lge. 99-00 (Worle)
CLUB RECORDS **Attendance:**

FACT FILE
Founded:
Colours: blue & black/black/ black
Change Colours: All yellow
Midweek Matchday: Tuesday
Programme: Price: Pages:
Editor:

CLUB PERSONNEL
Chairman: Bob Flaskett
Vice Chairman:
Manager: Martin Dancey Tel: 01934 517792
Asst. Man. / Coach:
Physio:

WILLAND ROVERS

Secretary: Andy Jarrett, 2 College Court, Uffcombe, Cullompton, Devon EX15 3EQ
Tel: 01884 841210 (H) 01884 253238 (B) 07836 472708 (M)
email: henry.jarrett1@btopenworld.com
Ground: Silver Street, Willand, Devon. Tel: 01884 33885
Capacity: 2000 Covered Seating: 75 Floodlights: Yes

Directions: Leave the M5 at Junction 27 (signed Tiverton & N. Devon).
Follow signs to Willand and the ground is on the left hand side about 1/4 mile after passing Willand village sign.
PREVIOUS **League:** Devon County until 2001
HONOURS Devon County League 98-99, 00-01,
BEST SEASON **FA Vase:** 3rd Round Proper 02-03, 4-5 v Lymington & Milton (H)
CLUB RECORDS **Attendance:** 650 v Newton Abbot 1992-93

FACT FILE
Founded: 1946
Colours: All White
Change colours: Yellow/blue/yellow
Midweek matchday: Tuesday
Prog - Price::50p Editor:Dave Campion

CLUB PERSONNEL
Chairman: Mike Mitchell
General Secretary: Vicky Horsburgh
Manager: Clive Jones
Asst. Man. / Coach: Neil Greening
Physio: Keith Sutton

2002-2003
Captaiin: Brian Cann
Top Scorer: Steve Ebdy P.o.Y.: John Pengelly

SOUTH WESTERN FINAL LEAGUE TABLES 2001-02

CORNWALL COMBINATION

	P	W	D	L	F	A	Pts
St Agnes	38	28	5	5	126	39	89
Hayle	38	25	6	7	106	37	81
Illogan RBL	38	23	9	6	109	39	78
Helston Athletic	38	22	9	7	87	42	75
Newquay Res.	38	21	9	8	110	66	72
St Ives Town	38	21	4	13	83	50	67
Mullion	38	20	5	13	68	66	65
St Just	38	19	7	12	89	57	64
Goonhavern	38	19	5	14	81	74	62
Penryn Athletic Res.	38	16	8	14	67	60	56
Wendron CC United	38	17	5	16	72	72	56
Penzance Res.	38	16	6	16	80	68	54
Truro City Res.	38	14	4	20	65	84	46
Perranwell	38	11	8	19	73	70	41
RNAS Culdrose (-3)	38	12	8	18	57	68	41
Porthleven Res.	38	11	6	21	54	85	39
Mousehole	38	11	4	23	52	94	37
Falmouth Town Res.	38	11	2	25	72	116	35
Marazion Blues	38	6	1	31	41	142	19
Ludgvan	38	1	1	36	27	190	4

DEVON & EXETER LEAGUE

Premier Division	P	W	D	L	F	A	Pts
Tap & Barrel	30	22	4	4	89	28	70
Cullompton Rangers Res.	30	19	4	7	76	42	61
Seaton Town	30	18	4	8	66	29	58
Okehampton Argyle	30	18	4	8	75	40	58
Witheridge	30	15	5	10	58	46	50
Willand Rovers Res.	30	14	6	10	56	52	48
Hatherleigh Town	30	14	5	11	65	61	47
Pinhoe (-1)	30	13	6	11	65	63	44
Exeter C.S. Res. (-4)	30	13	7	10	52	47	42
St Martins	30	12	4	14	53	57	40
University of Exeter Res.	30	11	5	14	55	41	38
Budleigh Salt. Res.(-1)	30	10	3	17	47	57	32
Sidmouth Town	30	10	2	18	50	75	32
Elmore Reserves (-4)	30	8	4	18	41	85	24
Topsham Town Res.	30	6	0	24	25	100	18
Exeter St Thomas (-2)	30	4	3	23	27	77	13

PLYMOUTH & DISTRICT COMBINATION

Premier Division	P	W	D	L	F	A	Pts
Mount Gould BP	26	18	4	4	85	28	58
Plymouth CSS&L	26	16	7	3	66	35	55
Manstow	26	15	3	8	68	57	48
Wessex Rangers	26	14	4	8	67	51	46
Plympton United	26	14	3	9	50	32	45
Plymouth Univ.	26	13	4	9	61	42	43
Plymstock Utd Res.	26	12	7	7	60	43	43
Plym. Parkway Res.	26	10	6	10	62	62	36
Mainstone Sports	26	9	2	15	49	55	29
Prince Rock YC	26	7	4	15	42	81	25
Roborough	26	6	6	14	42	65	24
Tavistock Res. (-6)	26	8	4	14	52	73	22
Vospers OV Res.	26	3	7	16	41	77	16
Plym. Command (-3)	26	5	3	18	46	90	15

EAST CORNWALL PREMIER LEAGUE

	P	W	D	L	F	A	Pts
Foxhole Stars	38	33	2	3	105	30	101
Torpoint Ath. Reserves	38	26	4	8	94	32	82
Liskeard Ath. Reserves	38	23	9	6	113	50	78
Dobwalls	38	23	8	7	79	39	77
St Cleer	38	21	5	12	90	55	68
Saltash United Reserves	38	20	6	12	67	51	66
Camelford	38	19	5	14	68	50	62
St Blazey Reserves	38	19	3	16	70	74	60
Wadebridge T. Res. (-3)	38	18	6	14	61	53	57
Bude	38	16	3	19	68	68	51
Roche	38	16	3	19	52	77	51
Callington Town Res.	38	14	8	16	64	81	50
St Dennis	38	13	5	20	59	75	44
Bodmin Town Reserves	38	12	7	19	52	63	43
Nanpean Rovers	38	12	3	23	52	73	39
Probus	38	10	8	20	60	95	38
Padstow United	38	9	7	22	56	92	34
Launceston Reserves	38	7	8	23	62	122	29
Sticker	38	8	4	26	48	88	28
Millbrook Reserves	38	6	6	26	45	97	24

SOUTH DEVON LEAGUE

Premier Division	P	W	D	L	F	A	Pts
Upton Athletic	28	24	2	2	112	30	71
Teignmouth	28	22	2	4	99	34	68
Hele Rovers	28	20	4	4	76	31	64
Victoria Rangers	28	18	3	7	84	44	57
East Allington	28	14	8	6	59	40	50
Kingsteignton	28	13	5	10	71	57	44
Galmpton United (-3)	28	13	5	10	86	53	41
Totnes Town Reserves	28	11	2	15	59	56	35
Buckfastleigh	28	10	5	13	47	53	35
Dartmouth Reserves	28	10	3	15	44	66	33
Chelston	28	7	7	14	42	56	28
Kingskerswell	28	7	2	19	39	85	23
Liverton United	28	6	2	20	26	70	20
Chudleigh	28	5	2	21	34	78	17
Combined 89	28	1	6	21	29	154	9

Division One	P	W	D	L	F	A	Pts
Bovey Tracey Reserves	26	20	3	3	113	53	63
Brixham United	26	17	5	4	73	33	56
Bishopsteignton United	26	14	6	6	51	37	48
Newton Abbott Reserves	26	14	5	7	63	31	47
Newton Spurs Reserves	26	15	2	9	57	64	47
Channings Wood	26	12	8	6	100	58	44
Brixham Villa	26	11	7	8	66	43	40
Paignton Villa (-3)	26	12	4	10	50	43	37
Stoke Gabriel Reserves	26	11	4	11	51	56	37
Loddiswell Athletic	26	10	2	14	62	70	32
Chagford	26	7	4	15	50	62	25
Paignton United	26	6	7	13	50	74	25
Watts Blake Bearne	26	2	1	23	24	83	7
Buckfastleigh Reserves	26	1	2	23	27	130	2

SOUTH WESTERN FINAL LEAGUE TABLES 2002-03

BATH & DISTRICT LEAGUE

DIVISION ONE	P	W	D	L	F	A	Pts
Westgate Bath	16	16	0	0	84	11	48
Odd Down Athletic	16	10	3	3	53	31	33
Bath Arsenal	16	9	2	5	38	23	29
Oval Sports	16	8	2	6	48	39	26
Bath University	16	7	2	7	27	32	23
Saltford Res.	16	5	3	8	22	31	18
Keynsham Town 'A'	16	4	3	9	19	35	15
Claverton Academ.	16	2	4	10	24	51	10
Larkhall Ath. 'A'	16	1	1	14	15	77	4

PERRY STREET & DISTRICT LEAGUE

Premier Division	P	W	D	L	F	A	Pts
Ilminster Town Res.	20	13	3	4	52	23	42
Lyme Regis	20	11	3	6	44	25	36
Barrington	20	10	4	6	47	35	34
Merriott Rovers	20	9	5	6	45	31	32
Farway United	20	8	6	6	50	52	30
South Petherton	20	8	4	8	44	35	28
Crewkerne Res.	20	8	3	9	37	55	27
Forton Rangers	20	7	3	10	27	33	24
Shepton Beauchamp	20	6	3	11	26	47	21
Chard United	20	4	4	12	30	52	16
Combe St N. Res. -3	20	4	6	10	35	49	15

YEOVIL & DISTRICT LEAGUE

Premier Division	P	W	D	L	F	A	Pts
Ilchester	18	14	2	2	68	22	44
Wincanton Town	18	11	2	5	55	30	35
Henstridge United	18	11	2	5	59	38	35
Pen Mill	18	11	1	6	51	29	34
Milborne Port	18	10	1	7	29	21	31
Normalair RSL	18	7	2	9	23	26	23
Stoke-sub-Hamdon	18	4	6	8	32	30	18
Keinton Mandeville	18	5	1	12	33	63	16
Castle Cary Res.	18	3	6	9	40	60	15
Glastonbury Sports	18	2	1	15	15	86	7

TAUNTON & DISTRICT LEAGUE

Division One	P	W	D	L	F	A	Pts
Bishops Lydeard	20	17	1	2	62	20	52
Sydenham Rangers	20	15	0	5	78	37	45
Staplegrove	20	10	3	7	55	48	33
Alcombe Rovers	20	9	4	7	59	47	31
Galmington (-3)	20	9	4	7	61	46	28
Wellworthy Saints	20	9	1	10	49	44	28
Wyvern	20	9	1	10	43	43	28
Bridgwater Sports	20	6	3	11	37	53	21
Norton F'warren (-3)	20	7	1	12	35	55	19
Sampford Blues	20	4	2	14	26	73	14
Redgate	20	3	4	13	27	66	13

BRISTOL PREMIER COMBINATION

PREMIER DIVISION	P	W	D	L	F	A	Pts
Bitton Reserves	26	17	6	3	56	26	57
Rangeworthy	26	14	7	5	54	32	49
Hartcliffe	26	13	6	7	51	39	45
Sea Mills Park	26	14	2	10	71	46	44
Nicholas Wanderers	26	13	5	8	44	28	44
Longwell Green Sp.	26	12	6	8	45	33	42
Hillfields Old Boys	26	12	2	12	52	55	38
Highridge Utd Res.	26	10	6	10	34	45	36
Hallen Reserves	26	9	7	10	47	47	34
RMC Wick	26	10	4	12	39	50	34
Hanham Athletic	26	9	6	11	51	52	33
Bristol Union	26	7	6	13	38	48	27
St Philips Marsh AS	26	4	3	19	43	82	15
Iron Acton	26	3	4	19	25	67	13

MID-SOMERSET LEAGUE

Premier Division	P	W	D	L	F	A	Pts
Coleford Athletic	20	17	2	1	78	21	53
Meadow Rangers	20	13	3	4	62	30	42
Mells/Vobster Utd	20	10	7	3	50	38	37
Stoke Rovers	20	9	4	7	49	38	31
Chew Magna	20	8	6	6	40	42	30
Evercreech Rovers	20	9	2	9	48	43	29
Littleton Sports	20	8	2	10	41	46	26
Chilcompton	20	7	4	9	37	41	25
Belrose (-1)	20	7	3	10	48	55	23
Pensford	20	3	2	15	22	67	11
Temple Cloud (-1)	20	1	1	18	26	80	3

CARLSBERG SOUTH WESTERN FOOTBALL LEAGUE

Sponsored by The St Austell Brewery Co Ltd

President: Tristan H Scott **Chairman:** Bob Bell

Secretary: Ray Rowe, 5 Alverton Gardens, Truro, Cornwall TR1 1JA
Tel/Fax: 01872 242190 **Email:** ray@rowe57.fsbusinessco.uk

Press Officer: Mike Sampson, 23 Eliot Street, Weston Mill, Plymouth, Devon PL5 1AX
Tel/Fax: 01752 514326 **Email:** mikewrite@blueyonder.co.uk

In May 2003 all clubs within the league achieved FA Charter status for adult clubs. It is felt that this is a great achievement being the first league, as a whole, to be awarded this status in England. Les Howie of the Football Association presented the awards to club representatives at our league cup final on May Bank Holiday. Cornwall County FA Development Officer, Phil Cardew, supported this work and was instrumental in achieving this status, together with the drive of Chairman, Bob Bell and commitment of all club officers.

This season the league had five entrants involved in the FA Cup and/or FA Vase, an increase of two from the previous season. Porthleven reached the 3rd round, whilst St Blazey went out in the 5th round to Sudbury (eventual finalists) after a replay. One day we'll be there!

A repeat of St Blazey's clean sweep of the previous season looked to be on the cards until the last six weeks of the season. Truro City, who were struggling against seeking re-election, celebrated an unlikely semi-final victory against St Blazey in the Cornwall Charity Cup. Liskeard Athletic then went on to defeat St Blazey in the Cornwall Senior Cup final, after a replay, and the league cup final 2-1 on the magnificent playing surface at Penryn Athletic. By this time St Blazey had already won the league by a mile but when the championship trophy was presented, Liskeard Athletic did their best to ruin the afternoon by winning 2-1 at Blaise Park. This ended a fantastic run of 75 league games without defeat, an incredible achievement by any standards. Tavistock took runners-up spot achieving their highest ever finish.

At the bottom of the table Bodmin Town and St Austell finished in the re-election places. Bodmin were always going to finish bottom after taking just 12 points from 108 but the other position went to the last week of the season when St Austell's 2-1 defeat at Launceston meant they finished in 18th spot.

The league suffered the disappointment of losing Holsworthy after 30 years of membership, they decided to transfer to the Devon League, this means that subject to re-election issues the league will be running with 18 clubs next season.

The league is looking forward to taking part in the Level 4 National League system competition next season and we are quietly confident that our representative squad will do themselves justice.

Ray Rowe - Hon. Secretary.

		P	W	D	L	F	A	Pts
1	St Blazey	36	30	5	1	126	23	95
2	Tavistock	36	24	5	7	87	41	77
3	Porthleven	36	23	5	8	95	48	74
4	Plymouth Parkway	36	23	4	9	83	55	73
5	Liskeard Athletic	36	21	4	11	95	59	67
6	Wadebridge Town	36	17	9	10	61	46	60
7	Launceston	36	18	6	12	79	78	60
8	Holsworthy	36	17	7	12	59	48	58
9	Saltash United	36	17	3	16	79	68	54
10	Falmouth Town	36	16	5	15	60	61	53
11	Newquay	36	13	4	19	64	77	43
12	Penzance	36	12	5	19	53	55	41
13	Torpoint Athletic	36	11	8	17	48	69	41
14	Millbrook	36	12	4	20	56	80	40
15	Callington Town	36	11	6	19	64	80	39
16	Truro City	36	9	6	21	44	74	33
17	Penryn Athletic	36	7	7	22	51	84	28
18	St Austell	36	7	6	23	45	108	27
19	Bodmin Town	36	3	3	30	30	125	12

		1	2	3	4	5	6	7	8	9	10	11	12	13	14	15	16	17	18	19
1	Bodmin Town		4-3	0-4	2-2	0-1	1-5	2-3	1-0	1-1	1-4	3-6	0-3	1-5	2-3	0-4	1-2	1-2	1-2	0-4
2	Callington Town	4-0		1-1	2-1	2-3	2-5	2-1	2-4	2-0	1-4	1-1	1-4	4-6	1-1	0-9	4-2	3-0	2-2	0-2
3	Falmouth Town	2-1	2-1		1-2	1-3	0-5	3-1	2-1	3-1	1-1	1-2	1-2	2-4	3-0	0-0	2-3	2-2	5-1	0-1
4	Holsworthy	2-1	0-2	0-0		2-0	1-2	3-0	3-2	6-1	2-0	4-4	1-2	1-3	2-1	1-2	1-1	1-0	0-2	2-2
5	Launceston	3-0	3-1	6-0	1-3		0-4	5-1	1-1	5-2	0-4	0-2	1-6	2-3	2-1	0-4	3-3	3-2	4-2	2-2
6	Liskeard Athletic	6-1	2-1	1-2	1-0	7-0		1-2	2-4	1-3	0-1	2-3	1-1	4-3	3-2	0-2	1-4	5-2	5-0	2-0
7	Millbrook	2-0	2-2	2-3	1-0	4-5	2-2		1-2	0-0	2-0	2-2	3-2	2-1	3-0	0-2	0-3	0-1	2-0	1-2
8	Newquay	2-3	0-5	1-0	0-2	4-1	1-2	5-3		3-1	4-1	0-2	0-3	4-1	2-1	1-3	0-2	5-0	3-2	1-3
9	Penryn Athletic	4-0	3-1	0-3	0-2	1-1	1-2	1-2	0-2		1-5	1-2	4-4	3-1	2-3	1-5	1-2	1-2	1-1	1-3
10	Penzanze	1-1	1-2	1-2	0-1	1-2	0-2	4-0	2-2	0-0		0-2	3-4	2-1	4-0	0-2	2-1	3-0	0-2	0-2
11	Plymouth Parkway	5-0	3-2	2-1	1-2	2-2	3-1	5-3	3-1	1-2	3-1		2-1	0-3	4-1	1-3	0-3	2-1	4-1	4-1
12	Porthleven	10-1	3-1	3-0	2-1	0-3	3-0	3-0	3-3	1-3	1-0	2-1		2-1	3-0	0-0	1-2	1-1	1-0	3-2
13	Saltash United	4-0	3-2	3-2	2-2	1-4	1-2	3-1	4-1	3-0	0-2	0-1	3-2		7-2	0-3	3-1	3-3	2-1	0-2
14	St Austell	4-0	0-1	0-3	1-1	3-1	2-6	0-4	4-1	1-7	4-1	2-5	1-9	0-3		0-3	0-4	1-0	2-2	0-0
15	St Blazey	4-0	2-1	5-0	7-1	7-1	1-2	5-1	3-0	4-0	4-1	2-0	4-1	3-0	10-1		3-0	5-1	2-1	4-1
16	Tavistock	6-1	1-0	4-1	0-3	0-2	3-3	3-1	4-0	4-0	3-1	3-0	3-2	1-0	5-1	2-2		3-0	2-0	3-0
17	Torpoint Athletic	2-0	0-2	1-4	1-2	0-4	2-2	4-1	2-0	4-1	0-0	0-3	1-3	0-0	2-2	3-3	2-0		1-2	2-1
18	Truro City	4-0	2-2	0-1	0-2	0-3	3-5	1-2	2-2	1-0	2-1	1-2	0-3	3-1	2-1	1-3	0-4	0-1		1-1
19	Wadebridge Town	6-0	3-1	0-2	1-0	2-2	2-1	3-1	3-2	3-3	0-2	2-0	0-1	3-1	0-0	1-1	0-0	0-3	3-0	

CARLSBERG SOUTH WESTERN LEAGUE CHALLENGE CUP 2002-03

PRELIMINARY ROUND

Millbrook	v	Porthleven	1-3
Truro City	v	Penzance	1-3
Saltash United	v	Wadebridge Town	0-2

FIRST ROUND

Bodmin	v	Penzance	1-1 (aet)
Callington	v	Tavistock	3-0
Newquay	v	St Austell	0-1
St Blazey	v	Penryn Athletic	3-0
Replay Holsworthy	v	Torpoint Athletic	1-0
Replay Penzance	v	Bodmin Town	4-0
Liskeard Athletic	v	Plymouth Parkway	2-0
Porthleven	v	Launceston	7-1
Torpoint Athletic	v	Holsworthy	2-2 (aet)
Wadebridge Town	v	Falmouth Town	1-2

QUARTER-FINALS

Falmouth Town	v	Liskeard Athletic	1-3
Porthleven	v	Callington Town	4-1
Penzance	v	Holsworthy	3-1
St Austell	v	St Blazey	0-7

SEMI-FINALS

Liskeard Athletic	v	Penzance	2-0
St Blazey	v	Porthleven	2-0

FINAL

Liskeard Athletic	v	St Blazey	2-1 (aet)

5th May at Kernick Road

LEADING GOALSCORERS 2002-03

Glyn Hooper	St Blazey	36
Luke Hodge	Porthleven	32
Andy Sargent	Liskeard Athletic	29
Ian Rowe	Holsworthy	25
Lee Doncaster	Tavistock	23
Andy Bowker	Plymouth Parkway	22
Steve Daly	St Blazey	22
Ross Saint	Saltash United	22

SPORTING TROPHY

(avarage mark from 5)

Wadebridge Town	4.28
Falmouth Town	4.22
Launceston	4.17
Penzance	4.08
Saltash United	4.06
Liskeard Athletic	3.97

GROUND TROPHY

(avarage mark from 5)

Penryn Athletic	4.94
St Blazey	4.61
Tavistock	3.89
Penzance	3.89
Liskeard Athletic	3.83
Wadebridge Town	3.78

BODMIN TOWN

Secretary: Sheila Chapman, c/o Bodmin AFC, Bodmin, Cornwall PL31 2AF
Tel: 01208 77974 (H) 07786 923638 (M)

Ground: Priory Park, Bodmin. Tel: 01208 269033 (office) or 021208 78165 (clubhouse)
Directions: Just off town centre in Priory Park complex, at rear of town car park

Capacity: 5,000 Cover: 400 Seats: 400 Floodlights: Yes

Clubhouse: Mon-Fri 6.30-11pm (matchdays 6-11), Sat 12-11pm,
Sun 12-10.30pm Bar snacks available most times
Club Shop: No

Honours: South Western Lg 90-91 93-94 (R-up 76-77, 92-93, 94-95, Lg Cup 93-94 ,97-98 (R-up 7-78 88-89 94-95,95-96), Cornwall Snr Cup Winners 98-99 R-up 93-94, Cornwall Charity Cup 86-87 89-90,96-97.Cornish Guardian E.C.P.L.Supplimentary Cup 91-92 (R-Up. 93-94)-GordonSweet Cup 90-91,92-93,98-99, 01-02.

FACT FILE
Founded: 1889 Nickname: Black & Ambers
Sponsors: Parc Signs
Colours: Amber/black/amber
Change colours: All white
Midweek Matchday: Wednesday
Reserves' League: East Cornwall Premier
Programme: 60 pages, 40p
Programme Editor: Secretary

CLUB PERSONNEL
Chairman: Colin.Hooper
Vice-Chairman: Dave Dunckley
President: A.Gynn
Manager: Paul Hicks
Physio: Stev Trotman

CALLINGTON TOWN

Secretary: Philip Brown, Mount Pleasant Cottage, Harrowbarrow, Callington PL17 8JL
Tel: 01822 833851 (H) 01752 307102 (B)

Ground: Ginsters Marshfield Park, Callington Comm. College, Launceston Rd., Callington, Cornwall Tel: 01579 382647 **Directions** Turn into Callington Community College from the A388, Callington to Launceston road. Go to the top of the drive and bear left - the ground is 100m ahead.

Capacity: 1,500 **Seats:** No **Cover** Yes **Floodlights** : Soon **Clubhouse**: Yes

2001-02: Captain .: Matthew Hawke P.o.Y: Chris TIlbury Top scorer: Gary Williams 21

FACT FILE
Colours: Red & black/black/red & black
Change Cols.: All blue
Midweek Fixtures: Wednesday
Website: www.callington townfc.com

CLUB PERSONNEL
Chairman: Andrew Long
34 Coombe Road, Callington
Tel: 01579 383982 (H) 01752 220881 (B)

Manager: Ian Southcott
Tel: 01579 383561 (H) 07973 109609

FALMOUTH TOWN

Secretary: Colin Spargo,2 Grenville Crescent, Falmouth, Cornwall TR11 2NR
Tel: 0794 1591764 (M) & 01326314250 e-mail:
Websites; http://www.users.globalnet.co.uk/~cgdf www.falmouthtownafc.net
Ground: Bickland Park, Bickland Water Rd. Falmouth, Cornwall Tel: 01326 375156
Directions: Follow A39 to Tregoniggie Industrial Estate - will pass ground on left.
1 1/2 miles from Penmere Halt (BR) on Falmouth-Truro branch line.
Capacity: 6,000 **Seats**: 350 **Cover:** 1,200 **Floodlights**: Yes **Shop:** Yes
Clubhouse: Mon-Fri 7-11pm, Sat 11 am-11pm, Sun 12-10.30pm. Meals available
HONOURS: Cornish Senior Cup x 11 R-up x 8; Western Lg x 4, Lg Cup 74-75, Alan Young Cup x 3; South Western Lg x 14 R-up x 5, Lg Cup x 13 R-up x 5; Pratten Cup 73-74, Cornwall Charity Cup (2) R-up 00-01
BEST SEASON **FA Cup:** 1st Round 62-63 v Oxford U& 67-68 & 69-70 bothv Peterborough U
FA Trophy: 2nd Rd Round 77-78 v Hendon (A) 0-4
FA Vase: Quarter Final replay 86-87 0-1 v St Helens T 1-1 (H) after 1-1 (A)
PREVIOUS Leagues: Cornish Sen 50-51; S Western 51-74; Western 74-83
RECORDS **Gate:** 8,000 v Oxford United, FA Cup 1st Round 3/11/62
Scorer: Joe Scott 204, 72-78
Appearances: Keith Manley 580 (appr) 70-83
Players progressing to Football League: Roy Carter (Hereford 1975), Joe Scott(Bournemouth 1978), Tony Kellow (Exeter 1976), John Hodge (Exeter 1991) and Anthony Tonkin (Yeovil Town)

FACT FILE
Founded: 1949 Nickname: Town
Club Sponsors: G-J Medlin
Colours: Amber/black
Change colours: Red/white
Midweek Matchday: Tues/Wed
Reserves' League: Cornwall Comb
Programme: 44 pages, 50p
Ed/ Press Off.: Mike Williams(01326 378352)

CLUB PERSONNEL
Chairman: John Thompson
Vice Chairman: Trevor Jones
President: Sid Ridgeon
Manager: Neil Phillips
Coach:Justin Ashburn

2002-03
Leading Goalscorer:Damian Stevens 19
Captain:Robert Troon
Player of the Year: Steve Coggin

LAUNCESTON

FACT FILE
Founded: 1891
Nickname: Clarets
Colours: Alll Claret
Change colours: Yellow/blue/blue
Midweek matchday: Tues/Wed
Reserves' League:East Cornwall Prem.
Programme: Yes

CLUB PERSONNEL
Chairman: Keith Ellacott
President: Mr.S.Dawe
General Manager: Keith Ellacott
Manager: Gary Shirley
Asst. Man. / Coach:
Physio: B.Medland

2002-03
Leading Goalscorer:
Captain:
Player of the Year:

Secretary: Chris Martin, 3 Tavistock Road, Launceston, Cornwall PL15 9HA
Tel: 01566 776175 (H) Email: launcestonfc.co.uk

Ground: Pennygillam, Pennygillam Industrial Estate, Launceston PL15 7ED
Tel: 01566 773279 **Web site:** www.launcestonfc.co.uk

Directions: Follow signs to Pennygillam Ind. Est., just off main A30 - ground 400yds on left
Capacity 1000 **Seats:** 150 **Cover:** 150 **Floodlights:** Yes

Clubhouse: Open after every game. Bar meals available. Club Shop: No

HONOURS South Western Lg Winners 94-95, R-up 84-85, S.W Lg.Cup Winners: 95-96
Cornish Snr Cup 1899-1900 00-01 82-83 (R-up 92-93, Charity Cup R-up 88-89)

LISKEARD ATHLETIC

FACT FILE
Formed: 1889
Nickname: Blues
Sponsors: J P Leisure & Gilbert Outfitters
Colours: Blue & white/blue/blue or white
Change colours: Yellow & blue
Midweek matchday: Tuesday
Programme: 40 pages, 50p Editor: Ian Pook

CLUB PERSONNEL
Chairman: Ian Pook
Vice Chairman: B. Harding
President: W. N. Rawlings
Manager: Chris Burchell
Asst Manager: Roger File
Physio: Hayley Collin

2002-03
Leading Goalscorer:
Captain:
Player of the Year:

Football Secretary: Brian Oliver, Windrush, Tremeddan Lane, Liskeard, Cornwall PL14 3DS
Gen. Secretary: J. Melhuish,16 Maddever Crescent,Liskeard PL14 3PT
Ground: Lux Park, Liskeard, Cornwall Tel: 01579 42665
Directions: Take Tavistock Rd (A390) from town centre, after 1/2 mile turn left on St Cleer Rd (follow signs to Lux Park Sports Complex) & ground is 200 yards on left. Half mile from Liskeard BR station
Capacity 2,000 **Seats:** 50 **Cover:** 300 **Floodlights**: Yes **Club Shop:** No
Clubhouse Normal licensing hours. Hot & cold food available Tel: 01579 342665
HONOURS: South Western Lg 76-77 78-79 R-up 75-76 77-78, Lg Cup 76-77 78-79; Western Lg 87-88 R-up 85-86 89-90, Merit Cup 80-81; Cornwall Snr Cup 04-05 83-84 84-85 85-86 88-89 89-90 93-94 R-up.x 5; Cornwall Charity Cup 21-22 79-80, Cornwall Jnr Cup 05-06 13-14 26-27; S W Pratten Cup 78-79; E Cornwall Prem RAOB Cup 67-68, Plymouth & Dist. Lg 60-61, Div 1 59-60 R-up 54-55 73-74, Div 2 76-77 (Res), Victory Cup 60-61, Charity Cup 59-60; E Cornl Prem. Lg (Res) x3 R-up x3 Lg.Cup x4 Evely Cup (Res) 01-02
PREVIOUS **Leagues:** East Cornwall Prem., Plymouth & Dist., South Western 66-79, Western 79-95
BEST SEASON **FA Vase:**
FA Cup:
RECORDS **Goalscorer:** T Turner 59, 60-61 **Appearances:** Brian Bunney, 500+
Players progressing: Bradley Swiggs, Jon Aston

MILLBROOK

FACT FILE
Founded: 1973 Nickname: The Brook
Sponsors: Plymouth Boat Cruises Ltd
Colours: Black & white/black/red
Change colours: All Royal blue
Midweek matchday: Tuesday
Reserve's League: Plymouth & District
Programme: 20 pages, 10p
Editor: J Weekes (01752 822637)

CLUB PERSONNEL
President: Mrs E Weekes
Chairman: Martin Bettridge
Vice Chairman: K Townsend
Press Officer: W Linney
Manager: Paul Stewart
Asst Manager: S Matthews

Secretary: Lee Collins, Goosaford Cottage, St John, Torpoint, Cornwall PL11 3AR
Tel No: 01752 822892 (H)
Ground: Mill Park, Millbrook, Cornwall (01752 822113)

Directions: From Torpoint Ferry - 3 miles to Antony on A374, fork left, after 1 mile turn left again and follow B3247 to Millbrook (3 miles), take road marked `Town Centre Southdown', right at mini-r'bout after 1/4 mile, ground clearly visible. From Tamar Bridge - follow signs for Torpoint, 2 miles after Polbathic right turning marked Millbrook, 5 miles to Millbrook then proceed as above
Capacity: 2,000 **Seats:** 50 **Cover**: 200 **Floodlights**: Yes **Club Shop:** No
Clubhouse: Weekdays 7-11pm, Sat 11am-11pm, Sun noon-3 & 7.30-10.30. Hot food (chips, burgers etc) available during and after matchdays
HONOURS: South Western Lg R-up 81-82, Cornwall Snr Cup R-up 83-84 (Charity Cup 84-85, Jnr Cup 75-76), Plymouth & District Lg 80-81 (Div 1 R-up 76-77)
PREVIOUS **Leagues:** Plymouth Comb.(8yrs)/ Plymouth & Dist.(6yrs)
CLUB RECORDS **Scorer:** Unknown **Appearances:** John Horne 215

Bodmin Town. Back Row (L-R): Alan Carey (Manager), Luke Hodge, Craig Swiggs, Perran Cooke, Jon Ashton, Lee Beer, Johnny Herbert, George Torrance (Asst. Manager). Front Row: Gary Wheildon, Darren Gilbert, Jamie Morrison-HIll, Adrian Walton, Nicky Medlyn, Paul Madden.

Callington Town. Back Row (L-R): Craig West, James Crawford, Mathew Martin, Adam Fuller, Andy Brenton, Andrew Long (Chairman), Michael Ruark, Chris Tilbury, Brian Baker. Front Row: Lee Rider, Matt Head, Adam Bartlett, Matt Hawke, Ian Southcott (Manager), Geoff Battams, Chris Truscott, Peter Floyd.

Penzance. Back Row (L-R): Nick George (Asst. Manager), Darren Ball, Sol Gardner, Jamie Burr, Rob Stapleton, Liam Bennett, Andy Withers, Rob Watts, Jim Dann (President), John Mead (Manager). Front Row: Andrew Mead, Steve Burt, Dave Burt, Dennis Annear, Danny Rendle, Jamie Devine, Colin Payne.

NEWQUAY

Secretary: Bob Steggles, 12 Clemens Close, Newquay, Cornwall, TR7 2SG. Tel: 01637 872677
Ground: Mount Wise, Newquay 01637 872935
Directions: .5 mile from Newquay BR, follow 2way system for .5 mile grd sign on L.eft at Clevedon Road Website: www.newquayafc.com Email: bob@steggles.net
Capacity: 3,500 **Seats:** 250 **Cover:** 500 **Floodlights:** Yes **Club Shop**: No
Clubhouse: 7-11pm w/days, 12-11pm Sat, 12-10.30 Sun. Hot & cold snacks during matches
HONOURS: Cornish Senior Cup 34-35 52-53 54-55 56-57 91-92 (R-up (10) , S. Western Lg (7) 58-60 77-78 79-80 81-82 83-84 87-88 (R-up 3) Lg Cup 55-56 88-89 (R-up 4) Cornwall Charity Cup (13) & R-up (10) , W.Cornwall Lg 06-07,(R-up 2) ,Cornish Snr Lg Herald Cup 34-35 (R-up (7)
PREVIOUS **Leagues:** West Cornwall; Plymouth & District 21-27; Cornish Senior 31-51
BEST SEASON **FA Vase:** 3rd Round 90-91
Pl;ayers progressing: Chris Morris (Sheffield Wednesday), David Philip (Plymouth Argyle), Kevin Miller and John Hodge (Exeter City

FACT FILE
Founded: 1890 Nickname: Peppermints
Sponsors:Hunters Sports
Colours: Red & white stripes/white/white
Change colours: Blue & white/white/white
Midweek Matchday: Tuesday
Reserve League: Cornwall Combination
Programme: 24 pages, 50p Editor: J Hawkey

CLUB PERSONNEL
Chairman:Roy Swift
V.-Chairman: M.Jago
President: A.Kendall
Manager: Conrad Robins
Physio: Ross McOnie
Coach: Kelvin Hunkin

PENRYN ATHLETIC

Secretary: Mike Young, 1 Dunvegan Road, Penryn, Cornwall TR10 8HJ
Tel: 01326 374098 (H) 01326 212974 (B) 01326 374098 (F)

Ground: "Kernick", Kernick Road, Penryn, Cornwall Tel: 01736 75182 (Clubhouse)
Capacity: 800 **Seats** 20 **Cover** 40 **Floodlights** No:

Directions: From Truro take the NEW Falmouth road at Treluswell and at the Treleiver roundabout follow signs for Kernick Industrial Estate.
Turn left at the new Asda store.

PREVIOUS **League:** Cornwall Comb.
2000-20001 **Captain:** Steve Jewell **P.o.Y.:** Steve Coggin
Top Goalscorer: Paul Kneebone (central defender) 10

FACT FILE
Colours: Yelow/Blue/Yellow
Change colours: Light & dark blue stripes/ Navy Blue/Royal Blue
Midweek Matchday: Wednesday

CLUB PERSONNEL
Chairman: Peter Young
146 Little Oaks, Penryn
Tel: 01326 378035 (H)

Manager: Ronnie Barr
Tel: 01736 366742 (H) 07866 313816 (M)

PENZANCE

Secretary: John Mead, 8 Chyanclare, St Clare Street, Penzance TR18 2PG
Tel./Fax: 01736 369066 (H)

Ground: Penlee Park, Alexandra Place, Penzance Tel: 01736 361964
Capacity 3000 **Seats** 250 **Cover** 250 **Floodlights** No
Directions: Seafront road past harbour, after amusement arcade turn right at r'bout (Alexander Rd), ground second right.
Fifteen minutes walk from Penzance(BR); directions as above
HONOURS Cornish Snr Cup 1892-93 95-96 97-98 98-99 1903-04 07-08 47-48 60-61 72-73 80-81 (R-up 1896-97 99-1900 00-01 04-05 48-49 49-50 54-55 56-57 74-75), South Western Lg 55-56 56-57 74-75 (Lg Cup R-up 60-61), Cornwall Charity Cup 47-48 48-49 (R-up 21-22 63-64), Cornwall Snr Lg Div 2 57-58 (Div 2 Cup 53-54 54-55), Cornwall Comb. R-up 65-66 (Lg Cup 69-70 (R-up 81-82)), Cornwall Jnr Cup(West) 03-04 04-05 05-06 07-08 09-10
Players progressing: Gerry Gazzard (West Ham), Tony Kellow (Exeter)

FACT FILE
Founded: 1888
Nickname: Magpies
Colours: Black & white/black/black
Change colours: All sky blue
Midweek matchday: Tuesday - no lights
Reserves' league: Cornwall Comb

CLUB PERSONNEL
President: Jim Dann
Chairman: Peter George
Manager:Gary Marks
Trainer: John Mead

PLYMOUTH PARKWAY

Secretary: Stuart Cadmore, 71 Trelawny Road, Menheniot, Liskeard, Plymouth PL14 3TS
Tel: 01579 340820 (H) 01752 304096 (B) 07776 14102 (M)

Ground: Brickfields, Cumberland Road, Devonport, Plymouth
Floodlights: Yes Clubhousr : Yes

Directions: Torpoint Ferry - Ferry Road and right to Park Avenue- Chapel Street- the le then bear into Cumberland Road. Ground is on left in Madden Road

FACT FILE

Colours: Yellow/royal blue/white
Change colours: Navy/navy/white

CLUB PERSONNEL

Chairman: Mark Rowles
Tel: 01752 790436 (H) 01752 201918 (B)

Manager: Gez Baggott
Tel: 01752 302596 (H) 0966 542982 (M)

PORTHLEVEN

Team Secretary: Vidal James, 23 Parc-an -Bans, Camborne TR14 7RW Tel: 01209 710618
Ground Gala Parc, Mill Lane, Porthleven Tel: 01326 574754
Directions From Penzance on A394, B3304 into Porthleven, ground on left immediately before town. From Helston on B3304 ground on right as you exit town.
Buses from Helston & Penzance Nearest rail station: Penzance
Capacity 1,500 **Seats:** 50 **Cover:** 100 **Floodlights:** Yes **Club Shop:** No
Clubhouse Mon 7-11pm, Tue-Fri 12 pm-4.30 pm, Sat 12pm 12 am, Sun 12 pm -10.30 pm
Full food menu at week-ends Tel: 01326 574754
HONOURS South Western League R-up 72-73, 98-99, 00-01, 01-02, Lg Cup 00-01 R-up 98-99; Cornwall Combination x6, Lg Cup x6; Cornwall Charity Cup 70-71, 97-98 R-up: 01-02 Cornwall Sen. Cup R-up 68-69, 97-98, 99-00, 00-01 George Evely Cup 64-65 65-66 83-84 86-87, West Penwith Lg, Penzance Hosp. Cup, Penzance Charity Cup
PREVIOUS **Grounds:** Treza Downs; Sunset Farm
Leagues: West Penwith; Cornwall Sen; South Western 66-77; Cornwall Comb. 77-89

BEST SEASON
FA Vase: Quarter Finalists 1997-98, 0-2 v Taunton Town (A)
FA Cup: 1st Qualifying Round 2002-03
RECORD **Attendance: 2,300 v Hucknall - 5th Round FA Vase 1997-98**

FACT FILE

Founded: 1896
Nickname: Fishermen
Colours: Yellow / black/blue
Change colours: All blue
Midweek Matchday: Wednesday
Reserves' League: Cornwall Combination
Programme: 50p

CLUB PERSONNEL

President: P F Johns
Chairman: Jan Cowles
Manager: John Clarkson
Asst. Man. / Coach: Mark Damerrall
Physio: Heather Mudge

2002-03

Leading Goalscorer: Luke Hodge
Captain: Nigel Thwaites
Player of the Year: Luke Hodge

SALTASH UNITED

Secretary: Luke Ranford, 8 Rogate Walk, Thornbury, Plymouth PL6 8SZ Tel: 07817 008257
email: luke.ranford@blueyonder.co.uk
Ground: Kimberley Stadium, Callington Road, Saltash, Cornwall LP12 6DX Tel: 01752 845746

Directions: First left after crossing Tamar Bridge, through town centre, at top of town fork right at mini - roundabout, ground 400 yds ahead on left.
Capacity: 3,000 **Seats:** 200 **Cover:** 200 **Floodlights**: Yes
Clubhouse: Club attached to stand and caters for dancing and clubactivities.Sapphire Lounge caters for wedding receptions,quiz nights and private functions etc

PREVIOUS **Leagues:** Cornwall Snr; Sth Western 51-59 62-76; E Cornwall Prem 59-62; Western 76-95
HONOURS Cornwall Snr Lg 49-50 50-51, Western Lg 84-85 86-87 88-89 (R-up 83-84 87-88, Lg Cup 86-87 87-88 (R-up 88-89), Div 1 76-77, Merit Cup 79-80 87-88), Sth Western Lg 53-54 75-76 (R-up 52-53, 73-74, 74-75), Lg Cup 3, Cornwall Snr Cup 6

FACT FILE

Formed: 1945
Nickname: The Ashes
Colours: Red & white/black/black
Change: All blue
website: saltashunited.co.uk
Midweek Matchday:Tuesday/ Wednesday
Programme: 52 pages,50p
Editor: Marian Gammage

CLUB PERSONNEL

President: P Skinnard
Chairman: Darren Bennetts
Manager:Allan Evans
Asst. Manager: Eddie Shapland
Coach: Jon Sheffield
Physio: Dave Williams

St. AUSTELL

Secretary: Peter Beard, 24 Alexandra Rd, St Austell, Cornwall PL25 4QP
Tel: 01726 64138 (H) 07867 675460(M)

Ground: Poltair Park, Poltair Road, St. Austell Tel: 01726 66099

Directions: 5 mins walk north of St Austell (BR)

Capacity: 4,000 **Seats**: 200 **Cover:** 200 **Floodlights**: No

Clubhouse: Mon-Fri 7-10.30 & Sat 12-11pm Food is available

PREVIOUS **Leagues:** Rocky Park (1890s)

RECORD **Gate:** 15,000 v Penzance, Senior Cup 49

HONOURS South Western Lg 68-69 (R-up 4), Lg Cup 64-65 71-73 87-88 (R-up 4), Cornish Senior Cup(11)

FACT FILE

Founded: 1890
Sponsors: Kwik Print
Colours: White/black/black
Change colours: Yellow/red/red
Midweek Matchday: Tuesday
Reserves' League: East Cornwall Prem.

CLUB PERSONNEL

Chairman:Andrew Millington
Asst Chairman: Alan Lucas
Manager: Glyn Rowett
Asst Manager: Keith Hosbani

St. BLAZEY

Secretary: Martin Richards,2 Deeble Drive,Par Pl24 2JJ.
Email Address: admin@stblazey-football.co.uk

Ground: St Blaise Park, Station Road, St Blazey, Cornwall
Tel: 01726 814110
Website: stblazey-football.co.uk

Directions: From the A390, Liskeard-St Austell road, turn into Station Road at the taffic lights inSt Blazey village and the ground is 100 yards down on the left.
One and a half miles from Par (BR)

Capacity: 3,500 **Seats:** 200 **Cover**:600 **Floodlights**: Yes **Club Shop:** No

Clubhouse: Mon- Sat 11-11.00pm, Sun 12-11pm. Bar snacks

HONOURS S Western Lg (10), R-up (10), Lg Cup 7, (R-up 6), Cornish Snr Cup (11)
Cornish Charity Cup (5) Cornwall Snr Lg Cup (Herald Cup) 35-36 48-49

RECORDS **Gate:** 6,500 v St Austell, Cornwall Snr Cup 48-49
Goalscorer: Glynn Hooper **Appearances:** W Isbell

BEST SEASON **FA Vase:** 5th Round replay 2002-2003
FA Cup: 2000

Players progressing to the Football League: Nigel Martyn and Shaun Taylor

FACT FILE

Founded: 1896 Nickname: Saints
Sponsors: Eden Project
Colours: Green/Green /White
Change colours: Blue & white/blue/yellow
Midweek matchday: Wednesday
Reserve's League: East Cornwall Premier
Programme
24 pages, 50p Editor: Steve Paynter

CLUB PERSONNEL

Chairman: Harry Cooke
Vice Chairman: MrA Putt
Treasurer Brian Brokenshire
Manager: Trevor Mewton
Assistant Manager: Dave Jones

2002-03

Leading Goalscorer:Glynn Hooper
Captain: Glynn Hooper
Player of the Year: Steve Daly

TAVISTOCK AFC

Secretary: Philip Lowe, 14 Anderton Court, Whitchurch, Tavistock PL19 9EX
Tel: 01822 614447 (Club) 01822 613715 (W)

Ground: Langsford Park, Crowndale Rd, Tavistock (01822 614447)

Directions: A386 from Plymouth, 2nd left after Macdonalds into Crowndale Road and the ground is half mile on left opposite Tavistock College

Capacity: 2,000 **Seats:** 200 **Cover:** 200 **Floodlights:** Yes **Club Shop:** No

Clubhouse: Open all day Saturday and evenings 6.30-10.30 or 11pm. Hot & cold food

HONOURS Devon Premier Cup 01-02 R-up 94-95, Devon Snr Cup 1889-90 1968-69 77-78 81-82, South Western Lg Cup 68-69 (R-up 76-77 83-84 99-00), Bedford Cup -numerous times; Devon Charity Cup 78-79, R-up 77-78, .Plymouth & District Comb Premier Cup 01-02

RECORDS **Gate:** 5,000 v Calstock, Bedford Cup final 1952
Appearances: A Pethick 1,000+

Players progressing: Peter & Neil Langman (Plymouth A., 51 & 53); Robbie Pethick (Portsmouth); Mike Trebilcock (Plymouth A. 65); Harold Redmond & Danny Sullivan (Crystal Pal. 57 - £100)

FACT FILE

Founded: 1888
Nickname: `Tavy' or `Lambs'
Sponsors: RM Builders & Contractors
Colours: Red& blackblack/black
Change : All Blue
Midweek matchday: Wednesday
Reserves' Lge: Plymouth & Dist Comb. (Prem)
Programme: 32 pages £1.Editor:Ereic Pinch
Website: www.tavistock.afc.co.uk

CLUB PERSONNEL

Chairman: Robin Fenner
Vice Chairman:Steve Metters
Managers:Chris Abbott & Craig Smith
Asst Manager: Graeme Kirkup
Physio: Les Mewton

TORPOINT ATHLETIC

Secretary: Vic Grimwood, 43 Hemerdon Heights, Plympton PL7 3EY Tel: 01752 344263 (H)

Ground: The Mill, Mill Lane, Torpoint, Cornwall Tel: 01752 812889

Directions: Bear left from Torpoint ferry, ground down hill on left after half a mile

Capacity: 1,000 **Seats:** 100 **Cover:** 100 **Floodlights:** Soon

Clubhouse: Yes

PREVIOUS **League:** Plymouth & District League.(Premier)

BEST SEASON **FA Vase**: 4th Round 93-94, 0-3 v Diss Town (H), eventual winners

HONOURS South Western Lg 64-65 66-67 (Lg Cup R-up 65-66), Cornish Snr Cup 8

FACT FILE

Colours:Gold & black stripes/gold& black/black
Change colours: Red & white hoops/white/red
Programme: Yes

CLUB PERSONNEL

Chairman: Colin Phillips
Tel: 01752 705845 (H)

Manager: Phil Cardew
Tel: 01752 812721 (H)

TRURO CITY

Secretary: Brian Fisher, 33 Southview Road, Biscosey, Par Pl24 2HJ(01726 812238)

Ground: Treyew Road, Truro, Cornwall (01872 278853)

Capacity: 3,000 **Seats:** 20 **Cover** : 150 **Floodlights:** Yes **Clubhouse:** Yes

Directions: On A39 by-pass south of city.
10 mins walk from BR station; up hill and left at junction

HONOURS South Western Lg 60-61 69-70 92-93 95-96 97-98, (R-up 54-55 62-63 66-67 67-68 70-71 96-97), Lg Cup 59-60 66-67(jt) 92-93 (R-up 54-55 58-59 67-68 93-94 95-96 97-98); Cornish Snr Cup x13; Cornish Charity Cup x7; Cornish Snr Lg 31-32 32-33; Cornwall Combination 94-95 98-99 League Cup: 1968,78,86,88,99

FACT FILE
Formed: 1889
Colours: All red
Change colours: All Blue
Midweek Matchday: Tuesday
Programme: Yes

Reserve s' League: Cornwall Combination

CLUB PERSONNEL
Chairman: Steve Cudmore
Manager: Robbie Black

WADEBRIDGE TOWN

Secretary: Brian Williams, 4 School Walk, Wadebridge, PL27 6DY

Ground: Bodieve Park, Bodieve Road, Wadebridge (01208 812537)

Capacity 1,500 **Seats**: 20 **Cover**: 80 **Floodlights**: No **Clubhouse:** Yes

Directions: At junction of A39 and B3314 to east of Wadebridge

HONOURS South Western Lg R-up 68-69 78-79 79-80 (Lg Cup 5), (R-up 3),
CornishSenior Cup 79-80, Cornish Charity Cup 8

FACT FILE

Nickname: Bridgers
Colours:All red/white
Change colours: All blue/white
Reserve s' League: East Cornwall Premier

CLUB PERSONNEL

Chairman: Steve Cudmore
Manager:Robbie Black

Porthleven. Front Row (L-R): John Clarkson (Joint Manager), Carl Cliff-Brown, Jamie Ahern, Hugh Morgan, Sean Ingham, Neil Montadon, James Lynch, Paul Foude, Ben Williamson, Darren Vicary, Danny Gulliver, Mark Damerell (Joint Manager). Front Row: Mark Forester, Jason Heath, Andy Rolloson, Lee Williams, Simon Lewcock.

St Blazey. Front Row (L-R): Harry Cooke (Chairman), Amos Putt (Vice Chairman), Andrew Street (Asst. Manager) Dan Jeffers, Dale Band, Jay Isbell, Neil Burton, Nigel Pugh, Dan Lean, Matt Penry, Mark Vercesi, Terry Huddy (Coach), M. Eade (Physio), Martin Richards (Secretary), Ken Cocks (President). Front Row: Ellis Glassup, Chris Strike, Carlton Farnham, Justin Harrington, Glynn Hooper, trevor Mewton (Manager), Adrian Street, graham Waters, Andy Bowker, Stephen Taylor.

Tavistock. Back Row (l-r): James Cole, Steve Daymond, John Gosling, Steve Brownlow, Chris Gott, Simon Parnell. Middle Row: Lew Hewton (first aid), Chris Short, Mark Wall, Lee Beer, Andy Meeds, Darren Babb, Paul Smith, Graeme Kirkup (coach), Phil Lowe (secretary). Front Row: Lee Doncaster, Nathan Blamey, Craig Smith (jnt manager), Roger Lowe (president), Robin Fenner (chairman), Chris Abbott (jnt manager), Rob Hawkins

FIREWATCH
DEVON COUNTY LEAGUE

President: Carl Throgmorton
Chairman: Stephen Ware **Vice Chairman:** Nigel Gooding
Hon. Secretary: Philip Hiscox, 19 Ivy Close, Wonford, Exeter EX2 5LX
Tel/Fax: 01392 493995 Email: pahiscox@hotmail.com

FINAL LEAGUE TABLE 2002-03

		P	W	D	L	F	A	Pts
1	Dartmouth	38	29	5	4	96	32	92
2	Ivybridge Town	38	26	8	4	135	55	86
3	Buckland Athletic	38	23	6	9	88	47	75
4	Vospers Oak Villa	38	21	4	13	72	57	67
5	Alphington	38	19	7	12	80	54	64
6	Newton Abbot Spurs (-3)	38	19	6	13	62	49	60
7	University of Exeter	38	19	3	16	85	76	60
8	Newton Abbot	38	16	11	11	67	57	59
9	Plymstock United	38	14	13	11	72	58	55
10	Cullompton Rangers	38	15	8	15	56	65	53
11	Ottery St Mary	38	15	6	17	63	74	51
12	Heavitree United	38	14	6	18	71	84	48
13	Dartington Sports	38	13	7	18	79	70	46
14	Appledore	38	12	9	17	51	69	45
15	Elburton Villa	38	11	10	17	67	69	43
16	Budleigh Salterton (-1)	38	12	8	18	58	77	43
17	Exeter Civil Service	38	9	13	16	46	79	40
18	Stoke Gabriel	38	7	6	25	58	92	27
19	Crediton United	38	7	5	26	30	109	26
20	Topsham Town	38	7	3	28	29	92	24

DIVISION ONE		1	2	3	4	5	6	7	8	9	10	11	12	13	14	15	16	17	18	19	20
1	Alphington		2-0	1-2	2-4	3-0	0-2	4-0	2-3	1-1	3-0	3-1	3-3	3-2	3-0	6-2	1-1	2-1	5-0	0-2	0-2
2	Appledore	0-2		4-3	1-0	2-0	1-0	1-0	0-6	0-0	1-1	4-6	2-4	2-2	3-0	1-3	0-3	1-2	3-0	3-1	0-0
3	Buckland Athletic	2-1	2-1		5-1	3-0	2-1	4-0	1-2	5-0	1-1	5-0	1-5	0-0	4-1	5-2	1-1	3-1	2-0	3-2	0-3
4	Budleigh Salterton	2-0	1-0	0-3		0-0	0-3	3-3	0-3	2-0	1-1	6-2	1-4	3-3	0-2	0-2	3-1	1-3	2-0	3-1	1-0
5	Crediton United	2-5	1-2	1-1	0-4		0-0	3-1	0-5	0-7	0-2	1-3	0-5	0-6	2-0	1-2	0-2	0-9	0-1	0-5	2-1
6	Cullompton Rangers	1-3	3-0	1-2	1-0	1-0		1-2	1-1	1-1	1-1	5-0	2-4	1-3	0-3	1-0	1-2	1-0	1-0	1-4	2-0
7	Dartington Sports	2-3	2-0	0-2	4-0	1-2	4-0		0-2	2-1	6-0	1-2	6-5	0-0	1-1	8-0	3-5	2-3	6-0	1-6	2-2
8	Dartmouth	1-0	2-0	2-0	2-0	1-1	0-1	3-3		4-0	5-2	5-2	4-0	1-0	0-1	3-0	3-0	2-1	4-1	2-1	2-1
9	Elburton Villa	1-1	1-3	1-3	1-1	0-1	3-3	1-0	3-1		1-1	2-2	2-2	2-0	1-2	3-1	2-1	10-0	4-0	0-4	0-2
10	Exeter Civil Service	0-0	2-2	0-5	2-1	2-1	5-0	0-3	1-2	1-0		0-0	2-8	3-3	1-3	1-0	0-0	1-1	4-0	1-3	0-3
11	Heavitree United	0-5	3-0	2-0	3-0	4-1	2-5	1-1	0-2	2-6	3-0		2-2	3-5	2-0	2-1	0-3	3-0	4-3	1-2	7-0
12	Ivybridge Town	2-1	0-1	2-1	7-2	7-1	10-1	2-0	2-2	1-0	7-1	2-0		2-3	5-1	5-2	2-1	1-1	7-1	4-1	7-2
13	Newton Abbott	4-1	1-0	1-4	3-3	1-2	4-0	1-0	2-1	1-1	2-1	1-0	1-2		2-1	2-0	1-4	3-3	0-0	4-1	1-0
14	Newton Abbot Spurs	2-2	1-1	3-0	3-1	4-0	2-1	2-0	0-2	2-1	0-2	2-2	1-1	0-1		2-1	0-0	3-1	3-0	3-1	4-0
15	Ottery St Mary	2-3	2-2	1-0	2-2	1-1	2-2	4-0	1-1	2-0	4-0	4-3	0-3	1-1	2-1		2-1	6-3	2-0	2-0	1-3
16	Plymstock United	2-2	1-1	2-2	5-2	6-1	2-2	2-2	1-2	6-0	4-2	0-0	2-2	2-0	0-3	1-0		3-0	1-0	2-2	1-3
17	Stoke Gabriel	1-2	4-1	0-2	2-3	1-2	0-3	1-4	0-2	4-3	2-2	1-2	2-4	1-1	1-2	1-2	2-2		1-3	1-2	2-4
18	Topsham Town	0-1	2-4	1-3	0-0	5-2	0-3	0-3	2-6	0-2	0-1	2-0	0-0	2-1	1-3	0-2	1-0	0-1		1-0	1-5
19	University of Exeter	1-2	4-2	2-2	0-5	4-1	1-1	0-4	2-5	7-5	2-1	1-0	0-3	4-1	2-1	3-2	6-1	2-1	5-2		1-4
20	Vospers Oak Villa	3-2	2-2	1-4	3-0	2-1	1-2	3-2	0-2	0-1	1-1	3-2	2-3	3-0	2-0	3-0	4-1	2-0	1-0	1-0	

THROGMORTON CUP 2002-03

FIRST ROUND

Budleigh Salterton	v	Plymstock	2-0
Ottery St Mary	v	Exeter CS	1-1 (aet) 2-3p
Dartmouth	v	Vospers OV	3-1 (aet)
Stoke Gabriel	v	Heavitree Utd	1-2

SECOND ROUND

Alphington	v	Heavitree United	4-1
Crediton United	v	Buckland	0-9
Dartmouth	v	Dartington	7-2 (aet)
Ivybridge	v	Newton Abbot Spurs	3-2
Bud. Salterton	v	Appledore	4-5 (aet)
Cullompton Rangers	v	Exeter CS	0-1
Elburton Villa	v	Newton Abbot	2-1
University of Exeter	v	Topsham	1-2 (aet)

QUARTER-FINALS

Appledore	v	Buckland Athletic	3-0
Ivybridge Town	v	Dartmouth	1-0
Exeter Civil Service	v	Alphington	0-2
Topsham Town	v	Elburton Villa	0-4

SEMI-FINALS

Appledore	v	Elburton Villa	3-2
Ivybridge Town	v	Alphington	1-0

FINAL

Appledore v Ivybridge Town 0-5 — 5th May at Cullompton Rangers

CHARITY SHIELD 2002-03

Dartmouth v Topsham Town 4-0 — 11th August at Dartmouth

LEADING GOALSCORERS 2002-03

James Lynch	(Ivybridge Town)	35
Danny Hall	(Alphington)	31
Mark Collins	(Dartmouth)	30
Mark Dunford	(University of Exeter)	27
Mark Harding	(Buckland Athletic)	26
John Rimmer	(Dartington)	23
Lee Johnson	(Elburton Villa)	22
Sean Friend	(Dartmouth)	21
Roger Bonaparte	(Vospers OV)	20
Tony Hendy	(Ivybridge Town)	20

PROGRAMME AWARD 2002-03

Buckland Athletic

HOSPITALITY SHIELD 2002-03

Appledore

SPORTSMANSHIP CUP 2002-03

University of Exeter

MEDI PRINT PRESS TROPHY 2002-03

Appledore

DEVON LEAGUE CONSTITUTION 2003-04

Alphington	The Chronicles, Alphington, Exeter, Devon 01392 279556
Appledore	Marshford, Appledore, Devon 01237 477099
Buckland Athletic	Homers Lane, Kingsteignton, Devon 01626 362602
Budleigh Salterton	Greenway Lane, Budleigh Salterton, Devon 01395 443850
Crediton United	Lords Meadow, Commercial Road, Crediton, Devon 01363 774671
Cullompton Rangers	Speeds Meadow, Cullompton, Devon 01884 33090
Dartington Sports	Foxhole Sports Ground, Dartington, Devon 01803 868032
Dartmouth	Longcross, Dartmouth, Devon 01803 832902
Elburton Villa	Haye Road, Elburton, Devon 01752 480025
Exeter Civil Service	Foxhayes, Exwick, Exeter, Devon 01392 273976
Heavitree United	Wingfield Park, Wonford Hill, Exeter, Devon 01392 273020
Holsworthy	Upcott Field, North Road, Holsworthy, Devon 01409 254295
Ivybridge Town	Erme Valley, Ivybridge, Devon 01752 896686
Newton Abbot	Forde Park, Coach Road, Newton Abbot, Devon 01626 335011
Newton Abbot Spurs	Recreation Ground, Newton Abbot, Devon 01626 365343
Ottery St Mary	Washbrook Meadows, Butts Road, Ottery St Mary, Devon 01404 813539
Plymstock United	Dean Cross, Plymstock, Devon 01752 406776
Stoke Gabriel	G J Churchward Memorial Ground, Broadley Lane, Stoke Gabriel, Totnes, Devon 01803 782223
Topsham Town	Coronation Field, Topsham, Devon 01392 873678
University of Exeter	University Sports Ground, Topsham, Devon 01392 264452

SOMERSET COUNTY FOOTBALL LEAGUE

President: L J C Heal **Chairman:** Miss S A Wright

Hon Secretary: C R J Rose, Sutley House, Pilton, Shepton Mallet BA4 4BL
Telephone: 01749 890767

FINAL LEAGUE TABLE 2002-03

PREMIER DIVISION

		P	W	D	L	F	A	Pts
1	Nailsea United	34	20	6	8	73	39	66
2	Portishead	34	19	7	8	58	29	64
3	Westland United	34	19	6	9	64	33	63
4	Clevedon United	34	19	6	9	74	45	63
5	Mangotsfield United Reserves	34	19	3	12	70	48	60
6	Fry Club	34	16	10	8	51	36	58
7	Bridgwater Town Reserves	34	15	6	13	65	59	51
8	Brislington Reserves	34	15	5	14	54	47	50
9	Keynsham Town Reserves	34	14	8	12	55	56	50
10	Radstock Town	34	11	12	11	63	64	45
11	Castle Cary	34	13	5	16	54	66	44
12	Burnham United	34	12	7	15	63	66	43
13	Backwell United Res. (-1)	34	13	4	17	70	81	42
14	Stockwood Green	34	10	10	14	57	63	40
15	Wells City	34	9	10	15	53	56	37
16	Welton Rovers Reserves	34	10	7	17	57	75	37
17	Peasedown Athletic	34	5	9	20	36	81	24
18	Nailsea Town	34	4	5	25	29	102	17

		1	2	3	4	5	6	7	8	9	10	11	12	13	14	15	16	17	18
1	Backwell United Reserves		2-6	1-2	3-2	5-2	1-1	0-1	5-0	1-2	5-0	0-4	2-4	1-0	3-3	1-1	7-4	1-2	1-0
2	Bridgwater Town Reserves	2-3		0-0	2-3	0-1	3-3	2-1	0-2	3-0	5-1	1-4	3-0	1-0	1-4	2-3	5-3	3-2	1-1
3	Brislington Reserves	5-1	0-3		2-2	5-0	2-1	1-3	0-0	6-1	0-1	1-2	2-0	2-3	2-1	4-3	1-0	5-2	0-1
4	Burnham United	4-1	1-2	1-0		4-2	0-2	1-2	2-1	3-1	5-0	0-2	2-2	1-0	4-0	1-1	0-3	2-1	3-6
5	Castle Cary	0-0	3-2	1-0	2-3		1-5	3-1	3-1	3-2	1-3	1-1	1-1	0-2	2-2	1-2	2-0	2-1	1-3
6	Clevedon United	7-1	2-1	2-1	2-2	2-0		0-1	2-1	3-1	7-1	1-3	3-2	0-3	2-1	3-1	3-2	5-0	2-1
7	Fry Club	2-1	0-0	0-0	4-1	4-1	0-2		1-3	2-1	3-0	2-0	1-1	1-3	1-1	2-0	1-0	1-1	1-0
8	Keynsham Town Reserves	3-1	1-1	1-2	3-2	1-0	1-0	4-3		0-1	4-1	2-2	2-1	0-3	3-2	4-1	1-1	3-1	0-3
9	Mangotsfield United Res.	5-1	3-0	2-1	2-1	3-0	3-1	0-1	0-4		4-1	3-3	3-0	0-0	1-2	6-1	1-1	3-1	3-1
10	Nailsea Town	1-4	1-3	1-2	1-2	0-4	1-2	0-3	1-1	0-5		0-2	0-0	2-5	2-3	0-3	1-3	3-1	1-1
11	Nailsea United	4-0	3-0	2-0	1-0	1-2	3-2	0-0	4-0	0-3	3-0		5-1	1-4	3-1	1-2	1-0	1-1	1-2
12	Peasdown Athletic	4-0	1-1	0-4	1-1	0-4	2-3	0-3	2-0	0-2	2-3	1-0		0-2	0-2	0-9	3-3	4-3	0-3
13	Portishead	2-1	2-0	3-0	2-2	3-1	1-0	0-0	1-1	0-2	0-0	1-2	3-0		1-1	2-1	0-2	0-0	1-2
14	Radstock Town	0-4	2-3	1-1	4-2	2-0	1-1	2-1	3-3	0-3	4-0	1-4	1-1	1-2		3-1	2-2	2-3	1-0
15	Stockwood Green	3-2	0-2	0-1	2-2	1-4	2-0	1-1	2-2	2-3	4-1	1-1	2-1	0-3	2-2		0-1	1-1	1-1
16	Wells City	0-3	2-4	0-1	3-1	1-1	1-1	2-2	1-2	2-0	6-0	3-4	4-1	0-2	2-2	0-0		1-0	0-1
17	Welton Rovers Reserves	3-5	2-3	5-1	2-1	2-4	1-4	3-0	2-1	1-0	2-2	0-4	4-1	3-2	3-3	3-4	0-0		0-3
18	Westland United	2-3	3-0	3-0	4-2	3-1	0-0	2-2	2-0	3-1	3-0	3-1	0-0	1-2	1-3	2-0	3-0	0-1	

FINAL LEAGUE TABLE 2002-03

DIVISION ONE

		P	W	D	L	F	A	Pts
1	Cleeve West Town	34	26	3	5	69	21	81
2	Team Bath Reserves	34	25	4	5	100	35	79
3	Paulton Rovers Reserves	34	22	5	7	94	45	71
4	Hengrove Athletic	34	20	10	4	55	24	70
5	Weston-super-Mare Res.	34	14	7	13	61	65	49
6	Watchet Town	34	13	9	12	53	53	48
7	Bishop Sutton Reserves	34	13	8	13	55	51	47
8	Winscombe	34	11	11	12	53	54	44
9	Cheddar	34	13	4	17	68	76	43
10	Blackbrook	34	12	5	17	55	85	41
11	Shirehampton	34	10	9	15	50	70	39
12	Oldland Abbotonians (-9)	34	14	5	15	51	56	38
13	Crewkerne	34	11	5	18	54	67	38
14	Timsbury Athletic	34	10	7	17	45	54	37
15	Robinsons	34	9	7	18	44	62	34
16	Congresbury	34	9	7	18	43	75	34
17	Glastonbury	34	8	9	17	41	58	33
18	Sporting Club Somerton	34	4	9	21	45	85	21

PAST WINNERS

	PREMIER DIVISION	DIVISION ONE	DIVISION TWO	DIVISION THREE
2001-02	Brislington Reserves	Westland United	Weston super Mare Res.	Backwell United A
2000-01	Shepton Mallet Town	Castle Cary	Keynsham Town	Weston super Mare
1999-00	Shirehampton	Welton Rovers	Nailsea Town	University of Bath
1998-99	Clevedon United	Mangotsfield Utd	Paulton Rovers	Dundry Athletic 82
1997-98	Portishead	Timsbury Athletic	Mangotsfield Utd	Wrington Redhill
1996-97	Street	Radstock Town	Worle	Clevedon Utd Res
1995-96	Portishead	Nailsea United	Ilminster Town	Worle
1994-95	Portishead	Stockwood Green	Robinsons	Shepton Mallet Res
1993-94	Portishead	Longwell Green	Odd Down	Street
1992-93	Long Sutton	Clevedon Town	Saltford	Keynsham Cricketers
1991-92	Bridgwater T (1984)	Portishead	Bishop Sutton	Blackbrook
1990-91	Bridgwater T (1984)	Frome Town	St George E in G	Bishop Sutton Res
1989-90	Bridgwater T (1984)	Clevedon Town	Keynsham Town	Clutton
1988-89	Brislington	Stockwood Green	Ilminster Town	Fry's Club
1987-88	Robinson's DRG	Weston super Mare	Stockwood Green	Mendip Hospital
1986-87	Robinson's DRG	Bridgwater T (1984)	Shepton Mallet	Stockwood Green

LEAGUE CONSTITUTION 2003-04

Premier Division

Backwell United Res
Bridgwater Town Res
Brislington Reserves
Burnham United
Castle Cary
Cleeve West Town
Fry Club
Keynsham Town Res
Mangotsfield Utd Res
Nailsea United
Paulton Rovers Res
Portishead
Radstock Town
Stockwood Green
Team Bath Reserves
Wells City
Welton Rovers Res
Westland United

Division One

Bishop Sutton Res
Blackbrook
Cheddar
Congresbury
Crewkerne
Hengrove Athletic
Ilminster Town
Nailsea Town
Odd Down Reserves
Oldland Abbotonians
Peasedown Athletic
Robinsons
Shirehampton
Timsbury Athletic
Tunley Athletic
Watchet Town
Weston super Mare Res
Winscombe

GLOUCESTERSHIRE COUNTY LEAGUE

Chairman: A C Barrett

Hon. Secretary: D J Herbert, 8 Fernhurst Road, St George, Bristol BS5 7TQ
Tel: 0117 951 7696

FINAL LEAGUE TABLE 2002-03

		P	W	D	L	F	A	Pts
1	Patchway Town	34	23	7	4	69	18	76
2	Henbury Old Boys	34	21	6	7	73	36	69
3	Wotton Rovers	34	18	11	5	70	39	65
4	Almondsbury	34	19	5	10	76	49	62
5	Tytherington Rocks	34	18	3	13	72	57	57
6	Highridge United	34	17	5	12	54	49	56
7	Thornbury Town	34	16	7	11	65	48	55
8	DRG Stapleton	34	13	7	14	62	52	46
9	AXA	34	13	6	15	59	64	45
10	Roman Glass St George	34	12	7	15	53	60	43
11	Taverners	34	12	6	16	40	46	42
12	Old Georgians	34	12	5	17	55	70	41
13	Hardwicke	34	12	5	17	57	84	41
14	Ellwood	34	9	9	16	36	48	36
15	Pucklechurch Sports	34	10	4	20	55	88	34
16	Totterdown Port of Bristol	34	8	9	17	39	53	33
17	Viney St Swithins	34	7	10	17	35	62	31
18	Whitminster	34	6	8	20	44	91	26

		1	2	3	4	5	6	7	8	9	10	11	12	13	14	15	16	17	18
1	AXA		2-6	2-1	0-1	3-1	2-2	2-1	0-2	1-2	0-2	3-0	1-1	2-4	2-1	1-5	2-2	4-2	0-4
2	Alomdsbury	0-0		4-1	1-1	0-0	0-1	1-4	4-0	0-1	3-2	2-0	1-3	2-4	2-1	3-2	0-0	3-0	1-2
3	DRG Stapleton	3-4	1-2		2-1	4-1	0-2	1-2	3-0	0-2	2-3	1-1	0-0	2-2	2-1	2-4	1-0	8-1	1-0
4	Ellwood	0-1	0-3	2-0		2-1	0-1	4-1	0-1	0-1	3-1	0-0	0-0	2-3	0-3	1-3	1-1	1-0	1-1
5	Hardwicke	0-7	1-6	1-3	2-4		3-2	4-1	0-2	0-3	6-2	2-1	4-1	1-3	3-0	3-0	0-2	4-2	0-2
6	Henbury Old Boys	1-2	0-3	2-0	2-0	0-1		6-1	2-0	0-0	6-1	5-2	1-0	2-2	2-0	1-0	4-1	3-3	1-1
7	Highridge United	1-0	3-1	3-2	2-0	1-2	0-1		0-2	0-0	2-0	3-0	0-3	1-0	2-1	2-3	3-1	2-0	5-0
8	Old Georgians	1-2	2-3	1-4	1-0	4-2	2-4	1-3		1-5	1-4	0-0	2-1	1-0	1-3	2-3	1-1	2-3	4-4
9	Patchway Town	1-2	2-0	2-1	1-2	2-0	0-2	2-0	0-0		4-0	3-1	4-0	2-0	3-1	3-1	2-0	4-0	1-1
10	Pucklechurch Sports	3-2	4-0	1-2	2-2	2-3	1-5	1-1	3-5	0-7		2-4	2-0	0-2	2-2	0-2	1-2	4-2	1-0
11	Roman Glass St George	4-2	1-6	0-0	2-1	6-0	2-1	2-2	2-4	0-2	2-2		1-3	0-3	2-1	2-0	2-1	1-4	2-0
12	Taverners	2-2	2-4	1-2	0-2	1-2	0-1	0-2	1-0	3-2	2-0	0-2		2-1	1-0	1-3	4-0	1-0	2-2
13	Thornbury Town	1-0	3-4	0-4	3-0	4-2	0-1	1-1	1-1	0-2	4-2	2-0	1-0		0-0	0-3	5-0	3-0	5-1
14	Totterdown Port of Bristol	0-3	1-4	1-1	1-1	1-1	2-1	2-1	1-0	1-3	4-0	0-2	0-1	1-1		4-0	2-1	2-2	0-1
15	Tytherington Rocks	3-1	0-1	0-3	4-1	4-4	3-2	1-2	3-2	1-1	1-2	3-2	1-0	2-2	4-1		3-0	3-0	1-3
16	Viney St Swithins	1-1	1-1	3-2	1-1	1-1	2-4	0-0	0-1	0-2	0-3	1-1	1-3	2-0	3-0	2-1		2-4	1-3
17	Whitminster	3-2	2-4	1-1	1-0	1-1	1-4	1-2	2-7	0-0	3-2	0-6	1-1	3-4	0-0	1-4	0-2		0-3
18	Wotton Rovers	3-1	2-1	2-2	2-2	7-1	1-1	4-0	6-1	0-0	4-0	1-0	1-0	2-1	1-1	2-1	3-0	1-1	

SKURRAYS WILTSHIRE FOOTBALL LEAGUE

Secretary: Peter Ackrill, 3 Dallas Avenue, Swindon SN3 3NP
Tel: 01793 520334

FINAL LEAGUE TABLE 2002-03

PREMIER DIVISION		P	W	D	L	F	A	Pts
1	Shrewton United	34	27	5	2	147	34	86
2	Stratton Crosslink	34	23	7	4	76	27	76
3	Wroughton	34	23	3	8	94	48	72
4	Bradford Town	34	20	5	9	76	52	65
5	Trowbridge Town	34	19	6	9	53	23	63
6	Biddestone	34	16	8	10	63	51	56
7	Melksham Town Reserves	34	17	2	15	68	59	53
8	Warminster Town	34	15	4	15	63	56	49
9	Aldbourne	34	15	3	16	50	62	48
10	Cricklade Town	34	13	8	13	59	59	47
11	Corsham Town Reserves	34	14	4	16	56	58	46
12	Devizes Town Res. (-3)	34	14	5	15	67	68	44
13	Purton Reserves	34	11	6	17	41	69	39
14	Westbury United Reserves	34	10	7	17	43	60	37
15	Pewsey Vale Reserves	34	7	5	22	38	77	26
16	Malmesbury Vics Reserves	34	5	7	22	35	98	22
17	Marlborough Town	34	5	7	22	36	109	22
18	Chiseldon Castrol	34	4	4	26	33	88	16

		1	2	3	4	5	6	7	8	9	10	11	12	13	14	15	16	17	18
1	Aldbourne		2-1	0-1	3-0	4-1	3-2	2-2	3-5	3-0	0-3	2-0	1-2	0-5	0-1	1-0	2-1	2-0	1-4
2	Biddestone	4-3		2-2	2-0	1-1	5-0	4-2	1-0	1-1	3-1	6-0	2-1	1-3	0-5	1-3	1-1	1-0	3-0
3	Bradford Town	3-1	2-2		4-1	1-2	2-0	0-3	3-1	1-2	3-0	5-0	3-1	3-5	2-1	0-2	4-3	5-1	0-3
4	Chiseldon Castrol	0-3	1-2	0-2		2-0	2-4	0-1	1-1	0-0	1-2	2-4	1-2	0-6	1-3	1-2	2-4	1-2	0-3
5	Corsham Town Reserves	0-0	1-2	1-2	3-2		0-2	1-3	3-0	4-0	5-1	4-2	1-2	0-5	2-2	2-0	0-1	2-1	1-0
6	Cricklade Town	0-2	3-0	0-0	0-0	4-3		1-3	6-4	1-0	2-1	3-0	1-1	4-4	1-1	2-1	3-1	3-1	3-3
7	Devizes Town Reserves	0-2	1-1	1-4	7-2	0-0	2-0		3-0	2-1	0-2	1-3	5-1	4-2	1-5	1-1	2-0	3-4	3-4
8	Malmesbury Victoria Res.	1-1	1-3	0-1	2-3	0-5	1-1	3-3		1-2	0-4	1-0	1-2	2-6	0-5	0-0	0-6	1-1	2-9
9	Marlborough Town	2-3	2-2	3-5	2-1	3-1	0-6	0-3	1-3		2-5	1-1	3-1	0-10	0-9	2-3	0-3	1-1	1-5
10	Melksham Town Reserves	4-1	3-1	3-5	5-0	1-2	2-0	1-3	3-0	5-0		2-1	4-0	1-7	1-4	0-2	1-2	0-3	5-2
11	Pewsey Vale Reserves	1-2	2-1	2-2	1-2	1-2	2-3	3-2	1-2	2-1	0-1		1-1	0-3	0-3	1-0	1-1	0-4	1-3
12	Purton Reserves	2-0	0-2	1-1	0-4	0-3	2-0	5-0	0-1	2-0	0-3	2-1		1-2	0-1	0-2	3-1	2-2	0-2
13	Shrewton United	5-0	3-3	6-3	4-0	4-2	4-0	7-1	6-1	8-0	2-1	1-1	9-0		3-0	2-0	7-0	6-1	2-1
14	Stratton Crosslink	1-0	3-2	2-1	1-1	2-0	1-0	2-0	2-0	3-3	4-1	4-1	0-0	1-0		1-0	1-0	0-0	1-1
15	Trowbridge Town	2-0	2-0	1-2	3-0	4-0	1-0	3-1	3-0	0-0	0-0	4-1	4-1	1-1	1-0		2-0	0-0	4-1
16	Warminster Town	2-1	0-1	2-1	3-0	0-1	3-1	0-2	3-0	8-1	1-1	4-2	2-2	0-4	1-3	1-0		1-3	3-1
17	Westbury United Reserves	0-2	0-1	0-1	4-1	5-3	2-2	1-0	0-0	2-0	0-1	1-2	1-3	0-3	0-3	1-0	1-4		0-3
18	Wroughton	7-0	2-1	0-2	3-1	1-0	2-1	3-2	7-1	4-2	3-0	1-0	5-1	2-2	4-1	0-2	2-1	3-1	

You Have to Love It!

is a very special Christmas book of amusing and enlightening photos illustrating all that happens at a non-league club on an average matchday.

The photos have been taken by our team of photographers who are all in love with the game at this level, and I'm sure it will bring a great deal of enjoyment to everyone involved with the world of football outside the Football League

The book is planned for publication in November and further details are available by contacting us on 01823 490080 Tony Williams

MIDLAND FOOTBALL ALLIANCE

President: Bernard Davis **Chairman:** Pat Fellows

Secretary: Peter Dagger, 32 Drysdale Close,
Wickhamford, Worcestershire WR11 7RZ
Tel: 01386 831763 Fax: 01386 833488
E-mail: PDagger@talk21.com

THIS is the ninth annual report of the Midland Football Alliance since its inception in 1994. For the third season in succession we did not have a main sponsor, which is a concern to members of the Management Committee and club officials. Discussions have been held with several company's throughout the year and will continue until hopefully this problem is solved. The current uncertainty regarding the revision of the non-league pyramid doesn't help in the search for a sponsor and it is to be hoped that the Football Association resolves the situation as soon as possible. We remain grateful to Polymac Services for sponsoring the League Cup competition and to Baker and Joiner for their continued sponsorship of the Hospitality award. Malcolm Lycett a life member of the League, through his company Polymac Services, continues to sponsor the annual awards for the team manager and the highest goal scorer and Clubcall provide awards for the team of the month.

Such is the competitive nature of the Midland Football Alliance, the championship was not decided until the last week of the season with Stourbridge being the first club to retain the trophy, with Rushall Olympic again finishing in second place. Virtually to the end of the season several clubs were in contention, with Stratford Town, Oadby Town, Quorn and Willenhall Town all at times during the season looking as if they would be real contenders for the title.

For the second successive season, Stourbridge could not be considered for promotion to the Dr. Martens League because they ground share with the local cricket club and this means that they are not able to carry out the necessary improvements to their ground. Rushall Olympic were considered for promotion, but unfortunately because only four promotion places are available to the Dr. Martens League for the eight feeder leagues, despite having the required ground grading they missed out again on the basis that one club's ground was subjectively considered to be better than another. The Midland Football Alliance has protested about this situation and it is hoped that even if the current review of the national football pyramid does not improve the system, the Dr. Martens League will consider holding play offs where two clubs are available for one promotion spot.

The League Cup was keenly contested, the semi-finalists being Causeway Utd, Grosvenor Park, Stratford Town and Studley. The final saw Stratford Town defeat Causeway Utd 1-0 after extra-time.

For many the highlight of the season was Oadby Town reaching the semi-finals of the FA Vase. This was the first time that a club from the Midland Football Alliance had reached this stage of the competition and they were only denied a place in the final by the eventual 'winners Brigg Town losing 3-1. A magnificent effort and it is hoped that they and other clubs will emulate this success in the coming season. In the Worcestershire Senior Urn, Studley won the trophy for the third year in succession and quite rightly have been invited to take part in the Worcestershire Senior Cup next season .

Prior to the start of the season the match for the Joe McGorian Trophy competed for by the previous season's League Champions and League Cup winners saw Stourbridge take the trophy after defeating Rushall Olympic..

For the first time in several years three clubs Alvechurch, Coalville Town and Westfields wiLl be promoted to the Midland Football Alliance for season 2003/2004. Following the relegation of Rocester and Racing Club Warwick from the Dr. Martens League, it means that three clubs were relegated. Two of these Shifnal Town and Wednesfield join the Midland Football Combination and West Midlands (Regional) League respectively and the third, Halesowen Harriers, have resigned and will not compete at a senior level. Shifnal Town will be missed particularly for their superb playing facilities and Halesowen Harriers also for their facilities but also for their famous hospitality. Wednesfield also deserve special mention. After losing their manager and an entire team at the start of the season and despite many heavy defeats they completed all their matches, always fielded a full team when it would have been very easy to have resigned at many times during the season.

The season saw the introduction of a new system for the appointment of Referees and Assistant Referees. The Football Association now makes all appointments from a national list of officials. This has meant that many new officials have visited our grounds and although initially subsidised by the FA, will also mean additional costs for our clubs over the next few years. Many clubs remain to be convinced of the need for this new system.

Finally, it is interesting to note that of the twenty clubs who formed the MidLand Football Alliance in 1994, only eight (nine if Rocester are included after their relegation from the Dr. Martens League) will start with us in 2003/2004. How things change in ten years.

P.G.Dagger
General Secretary/Treasurer.

FINAL LEAGUE TABLE 2002-03

	P	W	D	L	F	A	Pts
1. Stourbridge	42	31	8	3	96	27	101
2. Rushall Olympic (-3)	42	31	6	5	94	37	96
3. Stratford Town	42	29	6	7	105	38	93
4. Oadby Town	42	26	7	9	87	52	85
5. Quorn	42	25	9	8	115	55	84
6. Willenhall Town	42	23	10	9	91	47	79
7. Studley	42	24	6	12	97	58	78
8. Oldbury United	42	22	7	13	88	58	73
9. Chasetown	42	20	8	14	79	64	68
10. Grosvenor Park	42	19	10	13	81	58	67
11. Causeway United	42	18	5	19	70	73	59
12. Barwell	42	17	7	18	70	68	58
13. Biddulph Victoria	42	17	6	19	51	69	57
14. Boldmere St Michaels	42	16	5	21	59	63	53
15. Ludlow Town	42	12	8	22	63	76	44
16. Bridgnorth Town	42	11	9	22	48	79	42
17. Stafford Town	42	11	8	23	61	93	41
18. Pelsall Villa	42	10	11	21	64	97	41
19. Cradley Town	42	8	7	27	43	87	31
20. Shifnal Town	42	6	7	29	43	93	25
21. Halesowen Town	42	4	6	32	44	107	18
22. Wednesfield	42	4	0	38	19	169	12

	1	2	3	4	5	6	7	8	9	10	11	12	13	14	15	16	17	18	19	20	21	22
1 Barwell		4-1	3-0	0-0	0-0	1-4	3-1	1-1	2-1	1-0	0-1	2-2	1-2	0-1	0-4	2-0	1-3	0-1	1-1	1-0	2-0	4-3
2 Biddulph Vic.	2-2		2-0	1-0	1-3	2-1	2-1	1-1	4-2	2-1	2-2	0-0	1-2	1-3	0-2	1-4	1-0	2-1	1-2	1-0	3-1	1-0
3 Boldmere St.M	2-0	1-0		2-1	1-2	0-1	2-0	2-2	2-0	0-4	0-4	0-2	1-4	1-1	0-3	3-0	4-2	0-2	0-1	1-5	4-0	3-0
4 Bridgnorth Tn	1-2	0-1	0-6		0-2	1-3	1-0	3-1	1-2	2-1	2-2	3-1	2-0	0-0	0-2	2-0	2-0	0-2	0-2	0-2	4-0	2-2
5 Causeway Utd	4-3	1-2	1-0	4-1		2-1	2-0	0-2	1-1	0-1	0-3	2-1	1-0	5-2	1-2	2-2	1-3	0-4	0-1	1-4	3-0	3-3
6 Chasetown	4-2	2-2	2-2	0-2	3-0		0-0	2-4	2-2	5-4	3-0	2-0	0-3	0-3	0-2	2-1	1-1	0-1	1-0	2-1	8-0	1-3
7 Cradley Town	1-3	1-0	0-5	2-2	1-0	0-2		0-0	2-1	1-3	1-3	0-3	2-2	0-2	1-3	2-1	1-3	1-4	1-2	0-3	4-0	0-2
8 Grosvenor Park	2-1	1-0	0-0	6-0	5-2	3-0	1-3		3-0	1-1	1-5	4-2	6-2	0-2	0-2	2-1	1-1	1-2	1-0	2-2	3-0	0-1
9 Halesowen H.	1-3	1-2	0-2	1-2	0-3	0-2	2-2	0-3		1-1	2-5	0-5	1-1	0-3	1-3	2-1	1-2	0-3	1-3	2-3	4-0	1-2
10 Ludlow Town	3-2	0-1	1-0	1-1	1-2	0-1	3-2	1-2	0-1		1-2	1-5	2-0	1-2	0-0	2-2	5-1	0-3	0-7	2-3	8-0	2-2
11 Oadby Town	3-2	4-1	2-1	1-0	2-5	3-2	3-1	1-4	3-1	3-2		2-2	1-0	1-2	2-0	2-0	3-0	1-2	0-0	3-2	2-0	2-2
12 Oldbury United	0-4	1-0	1-1	2-0	2-1	3-0	2-0	2-4	5-3	1-0	2-1		2-3	2-0	4-6	3-0	3-0	2-4	0-3	0-0	4-0	2-3
13 Pelsall Villa	2-3	1-1	1-3	2-2	1-1	0-3	1-1	0-0	4-0	0-1	0-4	0-1		2-7	0-2	4-2	1-5	2-2	2-5	1-1	1-2	1-1
14 Quorn	3-1	3-2	4-2	5-1	4-1	1-2	0-0	3-0	4-1	3-0	1-1	1-3	2-2		1-1	8-0	9-2	1-2	2-1	4-1	6-0	0-3
15 Rushall Olympic	2-1	2-1	1-0	4-1	2-1	2-2	4-2	1-0	4-0	1-1	1-2	2-0	4-1	1-1		4-0	3-1	0-1	2-1	0-2	4-0	0-4
16 Shifnal Town	2-0	3-0	0-3	2-2	0-1	2-2	0-2	1-4	2-2	2-4	0-1	1-5	1-3	2-2	0-2		2-1	1-3	0-2	1-2	2-0	1-2
17 Stafford Town	1-3	2-3	0-1	2-2	1-3	2-4	4-2	2-0	3-1	4-1	1-3	1-1	0-2	1-5	1-2	0-0		1-3	2-1	0-2	1-2	0-4
18 Stourbridge	0-0	4-0	1-0	3-0	2-0	3-1	2-1	3-1	5-2	4-0	1-0	1-0	5-1	1-1	1-2	2-0	1-1		0-1	0-0	2-0	1-0
19 Straford Town	3-1	6-0	3-0	4-1	4-2	2-2	5-0	1-1	2-1	1-0	2-0	1-2	6-1	3-2	1-2	3-2	2-2	1-1		4-2	8-0	2-0
20 Studley	4-2	1-0	3-0	3-1	4-2	0-2	2-1	4-1	3-2	3-0	1-0	0-2	8-2	5-1	0-5	3-1	1-1	2-2	1-2		6-0	1-3
21 Wednesfield	1-4	0-3	1-3	1-3	0-4	0-3	2-3	0-7	2-0	0-2	1-3	0-6	1-6	1-7	0-3	1-0	2-3	0-10	0-4	1-7		0-4
22 Willenhall Town	1-2	3-0	3-1	2-0	3-1	4-1	2-0	3-0	2-0	2-2	1-1	2-2	3-1	2-3	2-2	0-1	3-0	1-1	1-2	2-0	5-0	

CONSTITUTION FOR 2003-2004

Alvechurch
Barwell
Biddulph Victoria
Boldmere St. Michaels
Bridgnorth Town
Causeway United
Chasetown
Coalville Town
Cradley Town
Grosvenor Park
Ludlow Town
Oadby Town
Oldbury United
Pelsall Villa
Quorn
Racing Club Warwick
Rocester
Rushall Olympic
Stafford Town
Stourbridge
Studley
Westfields
Willenhall Town

CLUBCALL TEAM OF THE MONTH AWARDS 2002-03

August/September	Willenhall Town	January	Stourbridge
October	Oadby Town	February	Oldbury United
November	Causeway	March	Studley
December	Quorn	April/May	Stourbridge

LIST OF HONOURS

	1996-97	1997-98	1998-99	1999-00	2000-01	2001-02	2003-03
LEAGUE CHAMPIONSHIP							
Winners	Blakenall	Bloxwich T	Rocester	Oadby Town	Stourport Swifts	Stourbridge	Stourbridge
Runners up	Hinckley Ath	Rocester	Kings Norton	Stratford T	Rushall Olympic	Bromsgrove R.	Rushall Olympic
LEAGUE CUP							
Winners	Willenhall T	Knypersley V	Oldbury Utd	Willenhall T	Stourbridge	Rushall Olympic	Stratford Town
Runners up	Bloxwich T	Bloxwich T	West Mids Pol.	Knypersley V	Bridgnorth T	Barwell	Causeway United
INVITATION CUP							
Winners	Oldbury Utd	Atherstone U	Atherstone U	Bridgnorth T	Willenhall T		
Runners up	Bridgnorth T	Blakenall	Bandon	Darlaston T	Stratford T		
HOSPITALITY CUP							
Winners	West Mids Pol.	Halesowen H	Halesowen H	Halesowen H	Halesowen H	Halesowen H	Boldmere St M.
KEVIN KEEGAN - PLAYER OF THE YEAR							
Player	Adrian Horne	John Powell	Ian Long	David Davis	John Powell	Marcus Johnson	Dean Craven
Club	Pelsall Villa	Shifnal Town	Oldbury Utd	Oldbury Utd	Shifnal Town	Rushall Olympic	Bridgnorth Town
TOP GOALSCORER - THE GOLDEN BOOT							
Player	C Blakemore	S Bradbury	A Lucas	S Bradbury	L Booth	Craig Pountney	James Wood
Club	Willenhall T	Chasetown	Barwell	Chasetown	Stourport S	Studley BKL	Oldbury United
BEST DISCIPLINARY AWARD							
Club	Barwell	Stapenhill	Rocester	Boldmere St M	Stafford Town	Barwell	Boldmere St. M.
BEST PROGRAMME AWARD							
Club	Pelsall Villa	Rocester	Willenhall T	Shifnal Town	West Mids Pol.	Kypersley Vic	Rushall Olympic
MANAGER OF THE YEAR							
Manager	B Green	Knox/Folland	T Greer	T Hussy	R Brown	Joe Jackson	Joe Jackson
Club	Blakenall	Bloxwich T	Rocester	Oadby T	Stourport S	Stourbridge	Stourbridge
J McGORIAN CUP							
	Shepshed D	Willenhall T	Knypersley V	Oldbury Utd	Oadby Town	Stourbridge	Stourbridge
	1996-97	1997-98	1998-99	1999-00	2000-01	2001-02	2003-03

STUDLEY FOOTBALL CLUB
Vs HALESOWEN HARRIERS
Biddulph Victoria
Football Club
2002 - 2003
Midland Football Alliance
Saturday 12th April 2003
80p
STOURBRIDGE FC
OFFICIAL MATCHDAY PROGRAMME 2002-03
MAIN CLUB SPONSOR:
STOURBRIDGE COLLEGE
PROGRAMME SPONSOR:
www.plumbingworld.co.uk
STOURBRIDGE FOOTBALL CLUB
MIDLAND FOOTBALL ALLIANCE CHAMPIONS 2001-02
£1.20
Midland Football Alliance
Saturday, 7th December 2002
Kick Off 3.00 p.m.
STOURBRIDGE
V
BOLDMERE ST. MICHAELS
Match Sponsor:
STOURBRIDGE COLLEGE
Stourbridge FC
1876
THE GLASSBOYS

BOLDMERE
ST. MICHAELS FC
Midland Football Alliance
Saturday, 19th April 2003 - KO 3.00 p.m.
BOLDMERE ST. MICHAELS
v STOURBRIDGE
Monday, 21st April 2003 - KO 7.30 p.m.
BOLDMERE ST. MICHAELS
v STAFFORD TOWN
Official Programme - Price: £1.00
MAIN SPONSORS:
SFM
SWIFT FORWARDERS
(MIDLANDS) LTD.
The MiKES
TREVOR BROWN
TESCO
The Coors Stadium
OFFICIAL MATCHDAY MAGAZINE
£1
V Rushall Olympic
staying put
Darryl Smith
INTERVIEW
Andy Blakeley
PLAYER PROFILE
LUDLOW TOWN FOOTBALL CLUB
CRADLEY TOWN
FSC
OFFICIAL
PROGRAMME

ALVECHURCH F.C.

Secretary: Stephen Denny, 11 Shawhurst Croft, Hollywood, Birmingham B47 5PB
Tel: 01564 822302

Ground: Lye Meadow, Redditch Rd, Alvechurch, Worcs Tel: 0121 445 2929

Directions: M42 jct 2, follow signs to Redditch, taking dual carriageway. At island turn right (signed Alvechurch) ground approx one mile on right. Ground is actually on Redditch Road, just south of Alvechurch village

Capacity: 3,000 **Seats**:100 **Cover:**Yes **Floodlights**:Yes

Clubhouse: Open evenings and matchdays **Club shop:** No

HONOURS Mid Comb Prem Div 2002-03, Chall Cup R-up 95-96, Smedley Crooke Cup R-up 94-95

CLUB RECORDS **Goalscorer:** Dean Meyrick **Appearances:** Dean Meyrick

PREVIOUS **Leagues:** Midland Combination 1994-2003
Name: None (predecessors, Alvechurch FC, founded 1929, folded in 1992)

FACT FILE
Founded: 1994
Nickname: The Church
Sponsors: Centreprint
Colours: Gold/black/black
Change colours: Black &White,white/black
Midweek matchday: Wednesday

CLUB PERSONNEL
Chairman: Michael Rowley
Director of Football: Lee Shaw
Patron: Roy Yardley
Manager: Mick Preece

BARWELL

Secretary: Mrs Shirley Brown, 101 Eskdale Road, Hinckley, LE10 0NW (01455 446048)
Email address: steven.brown16@ntlworld.com

Ground: Kirkby Rd, Barwell, Leics (01455 843067)
Directions: M42 jct 10 (Tamworth Services), A5 towards Nuneaton. Remain on A5for approx 11 miles, go straight on at traffic lights at the Longshoot Motelthe 400 yards at r/about take 1st exit left sign A47 Earl Shilton, in 3 milesat traffic lights go straight ahead and in 1 mile at r/about take first leftexit sign Barwell in village centre 1/2 mile go straight over mini r/about, 20yards turn right into Kirkby Rd, ground 400 yards on right.
Capacity: 2,500 Seats: 256 Cover: 750 Floodlights: Yes
Clubhouse: Evenings & lunchtimes. Snacks available. **Club Shop:** No

HONOURS: Barwell Ath.: Leics Snr Lg Tebbutt Brown Cup 91-92, Leics Sen Cup 96-97.

PREVIOUS **Names:** Barwell Athletic F.C., Hinckley F.C. - amalgamated in 1992.
Leagues: Midland Combination 92-94
(Barwell Ath.: Leics Senior. Hinckley: Central Midlands 86-88)
Ground: Barwell Ath.: Kirkby Road pre 1992, Hinckley: groundshare at Hinckley Ath. pre-'92

RECORDS **Goalscorer:** Andy Lucas
Appearances: Adrian Baker

FACT FILE
Founded: 1992.
Nickname: The Kirkby Roaders
Sponsors: Trinity Van Centre.
Colours: Yellow,black& white/black/yellow
Change colours: All blue with white trim
Midweek matchday: Tuesday
Programme: 36 pages #1.00
Editor: I Backhouse
CLUB PERSONNEL
Chairman: David Laing.
Vice Chairman: Colin Burton
President: Derek Withers
Press Officer: Merv Nash.
Manager: Alan Hussey
Asst Manager: Kevin Julian
Physio: Viv Coleman
2002-03
Leading Goalscorer:Dave Putnam
Captain:Scott Clamp
Player of the Year:Dave Hart

BIDDULPH VICTORIA

Secretary: John A Shenton, 27 Portland Drive, Biddulph, Stoke-on-Trent ST8 6RY.
Tel: 01782 251058 Email: secretary@biddulphvictoriafc.co.ukk
Ground: Tunstall Road, Biddulph, Stoke-on-Trent, (01782 522737 club).
Directions: From South, M6 J15 join A500 to 7th Exit to A50 (Tunstall & Kidsgrove). Follow new road up the hill past Focus DIY to traffic island. Turn right towards Tunstall in half a mile turn left into Furlong Rd. at church. At bottom of road bear left onto A527. Continue up hill to island. Straight ahead for approx 2 miles and ground is on the right. **From the North** M6 J18. Follow signs to Congleton and then to Biddulph on the A527. Continue through Biddulph town to the traffic lights. Straight over and ground is 250 yards on the left.
Capacity: 1,200 Seats: 224 Cover: 224 Floodlights: Yes **Club Shop:** No
Clubhouse: Open from 1pm Saturdays, 7pm weekdays. Hot snacks at tea bar
HONOURS Industrial Rewinds Lge Cup 97-98 R-up 99-00; Joe McGorian Cup 88; West Mids Lg Div 1 92-93, Staffs Snr Lg 84-85, Lg Cup 84-85 85-86; Staffs Co. Lg R-up 79-80, Staffs FA Vase 83-84 86-87; Sentinel Cup 86-87; Leek & Moorlands Lg 72-73, Div 2 71-72.
BEST SEASON **FA Cup** 4th Qual Rd 97-98 **FA Vase:** 2nd Rd Proper 97-98
PREVIOUS **Leagues:** Leek & Moorlands 69-78; Staffs Co. (North) 78-83; Staffs Sen 83-90; W Midland (Reg) 90-94. **Names:** Knypersley Victoria >2002
RECORDS Attendance: 1,100 v Port Vale, friendly 1989 **Fee paid:** £1,000 M Biddle Congleton
Goalscorer: John Burndred 128 **Appearances:** Terry Stanway 681
Defeat: 0-9 v Meir KA, Staffs Sen. **Win:** 10-0 v Clancey Dudley, West Mids Reg. Div. 1 90-91

FACT FILE
Founded: 1969 Nickname: The Vics.
Sponsors: tba
Colours Sky blue & maroon
Change Colours: Yellow & royal blue
Midweek matchday: Tues/Thurs
Reserve League: None
Programme: 40 pages 80p.
Editor/ Press Officer: Secretary
Website: www.BiddulphVictoria FC.co.uk
CLUB PERSONNEL
Chairman: A. Farr
V/Chairman: J. Shallcross
Commercial Dept: V. Shallcross
Manager; Terry Greer
Coach: Matt Beeby
Physio: W. Harrison
2002-2003
Captain: Darren Baker
Top Scorer: James Harrow 20
P.o.Ys.: Steve Calgar & Kevin Taylor

BOLDMERE St. MICHAEL

Secretary: Dave Holvey, 38 Aldridge Road, Streetly, Sutton Coldfield, B743TT
Tel: 0121 353 6321 (H & FAX) 07787 106698 (M)

Ground: Trevor Brown Memorial Ground,Church Road, Boldmere, Sutton Coldfield
Tel: 0121 373 4435 or 0121 384 7531

Directions: A38 & A5127 from City towards S. Coldfield, left at Yenton lights onto A452 (Chester Rd), Church Rd is 6th turning on the right.
Nearest station: 400yds from Chester Road (BR).

Capacity: 2,500 **Seats:** 230 **Covered:** 400 **Floodlights:** Yes

Clubhouse: Bar & lounge, every evening and four lunchtimes.

HONOURS: Birmingham AFA 36-37; Birmingham AFA Snr Cup; Birmingham Jnr Cup, FA Amtr Cup SF 47-48; AFA Snr Cup 47-48; Central Amtr Lg 48-49; Midland Comb 85-86 88-89 89-90, Challenge Cup 77-78 89-90; Tony Allden Mem.Cup 78-79 88-89 91-92; Challenge Trophy 86-87; Sutton Charity Cup 96-97. Midland Comb. Reserve Div 2001-02

PREVIOUS: **Leagues:** West Mids 49-63; Midland Combination 63-94.

Players Progressing: John Barton (Everton, Derby County),Kevin Collins (Shrewsbury), Jack Lane (Birmingham City, Notts Co.), John Lewis(Walsall), Don Moss (Cardiff, C Palace), Harry Parkes (Aston Villa), Wally Soden (Coventry). Mike Griffiths (Torquay Un ited) , Robin Elmes, Jimmy Quiggin (Hereford United) and Paul Devlin (Birmingham City)

FACT FILE

Founded: 1883 Nickname: Mikes.
Sponsor: Swift Forwarding
Colours: White/black/black
Change Colours: Yellow/yellow/yellow
Midweek matches: Tuesday
Programme: 32 pages, £1.00
Editor: D.Holvey (0121 3536321)

CLUB PERSONNEL

Chairman: Keith Fielding
Match Secretary: as secretary
Manager: Alan Parsons

2002-03

Leading Goalscorer: David Brush
Captain:Steve Behan
Player of the Year: Matt Knight

BRIDGNORTH TOWN

Secretary: Lee Edgington, Hall Farm Cottage,Deuxhill, Bridgnorth WV16 6AF(01746 762747)
Ground: Crown Meadow, Innage Lane, Bridgnorth, Salop WV16 6PZ (01746 762747)
Directions: Follow signs for Shrewsbury (A458) over river bridge on by-pass,turn right for town centre at island, right at T junction, 1st left into Victoria Road, right at cross-road, follow road into Innage Lane, ground on left.
Capacity: 1,600 Shop: Yes Seats: 250 Cover: 700 Floodlights: Yes
Clubhouse: Evenings & weekend lunches, Dancehall, darts, pool, hot food on matchdays
Record Fee Recieved: £10,000 for Delwyn Humphries from Kidderminster Harriers
Players Progressing: Roger Davies (Derby county) and Paul Jones (Wolves via Kidd'ter H)

HONOURS: Midland Comb 79-80 82-83 (R-up 76-77 80-81); Lg Cup 78-79, Tony Allden Mem Cup R-up, Kidderminster & Dist Lge,Shropshire Snr Cup 85-86; Shropshire County Cup 70-71 75-76 76-77 78-79 79-80;Welsh Amt Cup 70-71; Shropshire County Jun Cup 98-99.

BEST SEASON: FA Cup: 3rd Qual Rd 64-65FA Vase: 5th Rd 75-76, 94-95

PREVIOUS Leagues: Kidderminster & Dist until 68; Midland Comb 68-83; Southern Lge, Midland Div. 83-96 Names: St Leonards Old Boys pre 46

RECORDS Goalscorer: Roger Davies 157 Appearances: Kevin Harris 426
Attendance: 1,600 v South Shields FA Vase 5th Rd 1976

FACT FILE

Founded: 1946
Nickname: The Town
Colours: All Blue
Change colours: All red
Midweek matchday: Tuesday
Programme: 24 pages,60p
Editor: Simon Bromley
Local Press : Shropshire Star, Bridgnorth Journal, Express & Star.. Local Radio: Beacon, BBC Radio Shropshire
Youth League: West Mids Regional Regional

CLUB PERSONNEL

Chairman: Harold Broome
Vice Chairman: Mick Tranter
President: Mike Williams
Manager:Jimmy Mullen
Asst Manager: Bernard Mackay
Physios: Chris Harkson & Jenny Stretton
2002-03 Top Goalscorer: Carl Tranter
Capt: Nicholas Guy P.o.Y: Daniel Adams

CAUSEWAY UNITED

Secretary: Frank Webb, 10 Moorfield Drive, Halesowen, West Midlands B63 3TG
Tel: 0121 550 5219 (H) 0121 550 9916 (B)

Ground: Groundshare with Halesowen Town F.C., The Grove, Old Hawne Lane, Halesowen
Tel: 0121 550 2179

Directions: M5 jct 3, A456 (signed Kidderminster) to 1st island turn right (signed A459 Dudley), left at next island (signed A458 Stourbridge), at next island take 3rd left into Grammar School Lane, then Old Hawne Lane - ground 400 yds on left

Capacity: 5,000 Cover: 1,420 Seats: 420 Floodlights: Yes

Clubhouse: (0121 602 2210) 12-2.30 & 7-11 (10.30 Sun) pm daily. Cold snacks served.

Colours: All blue
Change Colours: All white

Chairman:Steven Hulston
Vice Chairman:
President:
Other Club Personnel

Manager:
Asst. Man. / Coach
Physio:

CHASETOWN

Secretary: Chris Harris, 38 Naden House, Stafford Rd., Cannock, Staffs. WS12 4NU
tel; 01543 572927 (H) 01889 583306 (B)

Ground: The Scholars, Church Street, Chasetown, Walsall WS7 8QL Tel: 01543 682222/684609

Directions: Follow Motorways M5, M6 or M42 and follow signs for A5. A5 to White Horse Road/Wharf Lane, left into Highfields Rd (B5011), left into Church Street at top of hill, ground at end just beyond church. Buses 394 or 395 W Mids Travel, 94 Chase Bus,from Walsall, 860 Midland Red from Cannock.
Capacity: 2,000 Seats: 112 Cover: 250 Floodlights: Yes **Club Shop:** Yes
Clubhouse: Mon-Fri 7.30-11pm, Sat 11.30am-11pm, Sun 8-10.30pm. Basic snacks

HONOURS West Mids Lg R-up 90-91 92-93 (Lg Cup 89-90 90-91, Div 1 77-78 (R-up73-74 74-75 75-76 80-81 82-83), Div 1 Cup R-up 80-81 82-83, Div 2 R-up 87-88,Div 2 Cup R-up 86-87); Walsall Snr Cup 90-91 92-93; Staffs Snr Cup R-up 91-92.

PREVIOUS **Name:** Chase Terrace Old Scholars 54-72 Ground: Burntwood Rec Cte (pre'83)
Leagues: Cannock Yth 54-58; Lichfield & Dist. 58-61; Staffs Co. 61-72; West Mids 72-94.

RECORDS **Attendance:** 659 v Tamworth, FA Cup 2nd Qual Rd 1/10/88.
Appearances: A Cox 469 (+15) **Win:** 14-1 v Hanford (H), Walsall Snr Cup 17/10/92.
Goalscorer: T Dixon 172 **Defeat:** 1-8 v Telford U Res., West Mids (Reg.) Lge Div. 1

FACT FILE

Founded: 1954.
Nickname: Scholars
Colours: All blue
Change Colours: All Red.
Sponsors: Aynsley Windows
Midweek matchday: Tuesday
Reserves League: West Midlands
Programme: 26 pages, 50p
Editor/Press Officer: Mike Fletcher

CLUB PERSONNEL

Chairman: Brian Baker
Vice Chairman: B Simpson
President: A Scorey.
Manager: Mick Rowe
Asst Manager: Brian Fox
Physio: E Highfield.

COALVILLE TOWN

Secretary: Robert Brooks, 17 Ashland Drive, Coalville, Leics LE67 3NH
Tel: 01530 833269

Ground: Owen Street Sports Ground, Owen Street, Coalville
Tel: 01530 833365

Directions: From M1 J22 take A511 towards Coalville. At 3rd r'about take 3rd exit, then at 4th r'about bear left to Coalville centre. 2nd lights, left into Belvoir Rd and 2nd right into Owen St. Ground is on left at top of road

Capacity: 1000 Seats: 24 Cover:200 Floodlights: Yes

Clubhouse Open matchdays & training nights.

PREVIOUS **Names:** Ravenstoke Miners Ath 26-58; Ravenstoke FC 58-95; Coalville FC 95-98
Leagues: Coalville & Dist Amateur 1926-29, 33-35, 46-74 North Leicester 74-91; Leicestershire Senior 1991-2003
Grounds: Recreation Ground, Ravenslea, Ravenstone.

HONOURS: As Coalville Town:
Leics Sen Lg Prem. Div. 2001-02 02-03; Leics Sen Cup 99-00 R-up 01-02; Coalville Charity Cup 99-00, R-up 01-02

FACT FILE

Founded: 1926
Nickname: The Ravens
Colours: Black & white/black/red
Change Colours: All Yellow
Midweek matchday: Tuesday
Reserves League: Leics Comb Div 2

Programme

36 pages with admission
Editor: Tony Moore 01530 459055

CLUB PERSONNEL

Chairman: Steve Price
Vice-Chairman: Glyn Rennocks
President: Mick Jordan
Press Officer: Tony Moore 01530 45905

Manager: Lee Harriman.

CRADLEY TOWN

Secretary: David Attwood, 4 Birch Coppice, Quarry Bank, Brierley Hill, W Midlands DY5 1AP
Tel: 01384 637430

Ground: Beeches View, Beeches View Ave, Cradley, Halesowen, B63 2HB. (01384 569658)

Directions: M5-jct3.A456 right at 2nd island into Hagley Rd. Third left to Rosemary Rd. Straigh into Lansdowne Rd/Dunstall Rd then left at T jct into Huntingtree Rd/Lutley Mill Rd.Left at next T jct into Stourbridge Rd and left into Beecher Rd East.First left into Abbey Rd and right into Beeches View Avenue at end .Ground entrance is between houses 48 & 50,20yyds on left.

Capacity: 3,000 **Seats:** 200 **Cover:** 1,500 **Floodlights:** Yes
Clubhouse: Open matchdays only. Food available Club Shop: No

HONOURS West Mids Lg Div 1 90-91, Midland Comb. Div 2 72-73 R-up 75-76 77-78, Presidents Cup 74-75 75-76, Invitation Cup 72-73); Metropolitan Lg 70-71, Wednesbury Charity Cup 90-91, Dudley Guest Hosp. Cup 71-72 72-73 75-76 90-91

PREVIOUS **Leagues:** Metropolitan; Brierley Hill; Kidderminster; West Mids Amtr; Midland Comb. 71-82; West Midlands 82-99 **Name:** Albion Haden United **Grounds:** None

RECORDS Gate: 1,000 v Aston Villa, friendly **Goalscorer:** Jim Nugent **Apps:** R J Haywood
Win: 9-1 v Wolverhampton U (H), West Midlands Lge 1990 **Defeat:** 0-9 v Paget Rangers (A) Invitation Cup 97 **Transfer fee paid:** £1,000 for Darren Marsh (Oldswinford, 1992)
Received: £20,000 for John Williams (Swansea, 1991)
Players progressing: Alan Nicholls (Plymouth), John Williams, Jon Ford, Andy McFarlane (all Swansea), Duane Darby (Torquay)

FACT FILE

Founded: 1948
Nickname: Lukes
Sponsors:Stables Solicitors
Colours: Red/black/black
Change colours: All Yellow
Midweek matchday: Tuesday
Programme: Yes

CLUB PERSONNEL

President: Alf Hill
Chairman:Martin Knight
Vice Chairman: Paul Morris
Press Officer: Trevor Thomas (01384 569658)
Manager: Morton Bartleet
Assistant Manager:Geoff Grosvenor
Physio: Jim Williams

2002-03

Leading Goalscorer:Ian Perry
Captain:Mark Hodges
Player of the Year: Neil Dudley

Biddulph Victoria Back Row (L-R): Terry Greer (Manager), Steve Callear, Greg Briggs, Kevin Taylor, Scott Burge, Tony Kirk, Matt Beeby (Player coach). Front Row: James Marrow, Lee Mayer, Dean Wilson-Cunningham, Darren Baker (capt), Scott Beasley, Matt Davenport, Aidan Callan, Adam Beasley.

Ludlow Town Back Row (L-R): Tony Green (Kit Manager), Les Bristow (Joint Manager), Jordan Rice, Steve Moore, Martin Poole, Russell Clarke, Carl Morris, Steve Frisby (Joint Manager), Bob Jones (Trainer), Dean Yates.
Front Row: Shaun Parker (Capt), Steve Clifford, Gareth Horler, Tim Jones, Nathanael Bristow, Alan Hider, Phil Bates.

Oldbury United. Back Row (L-R): Barry Young, Phil Rowe, Jamie Wood, Steve Wilkinson, Matty Ford, Richard Ball, Phil Male, Nathan Harvey. Front Row: John wilson, Simon Hampson, Russell Dodd, Gareth Day, Greg Walters, Jason Campbell. Photo: Marshall's Sports Services

GROSVENOR PARK

Secretary: Peter Yates, 8 Crome Road, Great Barr, Birmingham B43 7NL
Tel: 0121 360 1611 (H) email: py@otal.com

Ground The Red Lion Ground, Somerfield Rd, Bloxwich,Walsall WS3 2EJ
Tel: 01922 405835

Clubhouse: At ground

Directions: From Jct 10 M6 follow signs to Walsall town centre. Left at first lights into Bloxwich Lane. At first traffic island turn right and follow signs for A34. Ground is on A34 on right after Four Crosses public house.

HONOURS: Mid Comb Div 1 99-00, B'ham County Cup R-up 99-00, Endsleigh Cup 99-00 (first non Premier club for 30 years), 00-01 R-up B'ham County Vase 00-01, MFC team of 99-00; Tony Allden Memorial Cup 2001-02.
Midland Combination Champions 2001-02

PREVIOUS **Leagues**: Midland Comb. **Names**: Sutton Town 1959-2001

FACT FILE
Founded: 1959
Colours: Tangerine/black/tangerine
Change colours: All white

Chairman: John O'Hara
Tel: 0121 360 1611
Vice Chairman:
President:
Match Secretary: Ray Fisher
Tel: 0121 360 9904

Manager:Lincoln Moses
Asst. Man. Trevor Burroughs
Physio:

LUDLOW TOWN

Secretary: Mr J Nash, 58 Hucklemarsh Road, Ludlow, Shropshire (01584 874337)
Ground: The County Ground,Bromfield Road, Ludlow, Shropshire SY8 2BN
Directions: From Kidderminster and West Midlands, take A4117 and turn right at r'about onto A49 to Shrewsbury. Then exit on B4361 after one and a half miles towards Ludlow. Ground is on right after passing under bridge after half a mile. From South , follow A49 to north end of Ludlow by-pass and turn right onto B4361. From north,Telford and Shrewsbury , at northern approach to Ludlow, exit left from A49 onto B4361.

Capacity Unlimited Seats: No Cover: 150 Floodlights: Yes
Clubhouse: Yes Official opening at beginning ofthe season 2003-2004

HONOURS: West Mids. Lg. Prem Div. 00-01, Div. 2 78-79, Lg. Cup R-up 94-95.
Div 1 Cup 90-91; Shropshire Co. Cup: 73-74, 93-94, 94-95, 96-97;
Presteigne-Otway Cup 90-91.94-95:
PREVIOUS: **Leagues**: Kidderminster League 1961-63, Shropshire Co. Lg.: 1963-1978, West Midlands Lge 1978-2001
Ground: Riddings Park, Riddings Road, Ludlow, Shropshire

BEST SEASON **F.A.Vase:** 1st Q Rd. 98-99 (1st season) **F.A.Cup:** 1st □ Rd 2002-2003

FACT FILE
Formed: 1890
Colours: Red & white/black/black
Change colours: Blue & white/white/blue
Midweek Matchdays: Tuesday
Reserve League: West Midlands
Programme: Yes

CLUB PERSONNEL
Chairman: P.Gwilliam
Vice Chaiman: Robert Leech
Co Managers: Steve Frisby - Les Bristow
Asst Manager: Paul Blakeley
Physio: Miss J Stretton

2002-03
Leading Goalscorer:
Captain:
Player of the Year:

OADBY TOWN

Football Sec. Kevin Zupp c/o Club. Tel Nos: 01455 557674 (H) 07790 728384 (M)
Match Day Sec: Ken Farrant,115 Foxhunter Drive, Oadby,Leics LE2 5FH (M) 0798 6359646
Ground: Topps Park, Wigston Rd,Oadby, Leics LE2 5QG Tel: 0116 271 5728
Club house (Available for hire) 0116 2718885 (Contact Mr M.V.Burton)
Directions: M69/M1 Jct 21. Follow A46 to Leicester take 4th turning off roundabout towards Narborough/ Enderby.Turn left on the outer ring road A563 ,towards Oadby.Turn right at lights after 2.5 miles towardsWigston.One mile to roundabout turn left first exit to Oadby follow Oadby road for another mile ground on right opposite Leicester Tigers Oval Park
Capacity: Unlimited Cover: 224 Seating: 224 Floodlights: Yes
Clubhouse: Yes - Open matchdays 11.00 am-11.00pmShop: Yes
Best Seasons: **F.A.Cup**: 2nd Q.Rd 20002-03 **F.A.Vase**: 2002-03
HONOURS Leicestershire Senior Lge: (8) Midland Football Alliance 99-00
Div. 2 51-52; Lge Cup 77-78 93-94 94-95;
Leics Senior Cup 62-63 63-64 75-76 76-77 80-81
Charity CupsRolleston 58-59 59-60 68-69 74-75 88-89 93-94 96-97 97-98;
Coalville 60-61 63-64 65-66 69-70; Harborough 83-84 88-89; Oadby 70-71;
Battle of Britain 93-94 94-95 96-97
PREVIOUS **Leagues:** Leicestershire Senior League

FACT FILE
Founded:1939
Colours: All red
Change colours: All blue
Midweek matchday: Wednesday
Programme Editor: Kevin Zupp (01858 881023)
CLUB PERSONNEL
Chairman: Brian Fletcher-Warrington
Vice Chairman: Martin Reid
Directors: K.G.Farrant., M.V.Burtion,
I Lockhead and L..C.Adam
President: Bob Mallet
Club Secretary: T.B.A.
Manager: Lee Adam
Coach: Frank Benjamin
Assistant Manager: Ian Lockhead
Physio: Martin Almen
2002-03
Leading Goalscorer: A.Warner
Captain: D.Poultney
Player of the Year: S.Towers

OLDBURY UNITED

Secretary: Lee Tomkinson, 36 Bryan Road, Walsall,WS2 9DW
Tel. Nos: 01922-447834 (H) 0121 3034468 (W) 07790 295141 (M)

Ground: The Cricketts, York Road, Rowley Regis, Warley, West Midlands (0121 5595564)

Directions: M5 jct 2, follow Blackheath & Halesowen signs, first left at lights and fourth right into York Road (turning before motorway flyover), ground 200yds on left.
One and a half miles from Sandwell & Dudley and Rowley Regis BR stations.
Bus 404 from West Bromwich, Oldbury and Blackheath.

Capacity: 3,000 Seats: 300 Cover: 1,000 Floodlights: Yes

Clubhouse: Mon-Fri 7.30-11pm, Sat-Sun 12-2.30 (12-11pm Sat matchdays).
Snacks available on matchdays. **Club Shop:** No

HONOURS West Mids Lg 92-93, Staffs Snr Cup 87-88, Midland Comb. R-up 78-79(Presidents Cup 72-73(res), Div 3 R-up 82-83(res), Chal. Vase 82-83(res)),Walsall Snr Cup 82-83, B'ham Snr Amtr Cup, Oldbury Lg Div 2 61-62, Worcs Snr Urn 86-87, Sandwell Charity Cup 86-87, Interlink Invitation Cup 96-97. Industrial Rewinds League Cup: 98-99

PREVIOUS **Leagues**: Oldbury 58-62/ Warwick & W Mids All. 62-65/ Worcs (later Midland) Comb. 65-82/ Southern 82-86.**Names:** Queens Colts 58-62/ Whiteheath Utd 62-65
Grounds: Brittania Park 61-63/ Newbury Lane (Oldbury Stadium) 63-78.

RECORDS **Attendance:** 2,200 v Walsall Wood, Walsall Snr Cup Final 1982.
Win: 10-1 v Blakenall **Defeat:** 1-9 v Moor Green.

FACT FILE

Founded: 1958
Nickname: Cricketts,The Blues.
Sponsors: Beswick Paper Group, Oldbury.
Colours: Navy with sky trim/blue/blue
Change colours: All amber
Midweek matchday: Tuesday
Programme: 28 pages, 60p
Editor: Football Secretary.

CLUB PERSONNEL

Chairman: Roy Keeling.
Vice Chairman: Ken Harris.
Press Officer: Ian Whitmore

Manager: Bob Green
Asst Mgr: Russell Dodd
Physio: Paul Millard

PELSALL VILLA

Secretary: Dave Law, 29 Blithfield Road,Brownhills West, Walsall (Tel No: 01543 361693)
Ground: The Bush, Walsall Road, Pelsall, Walsall
Tel: 01922 682018 Club, 01922 692748 Ground
Directions: M6 jct 7 marked A34 B'ham. Take A34 towards Walsall to 1st island,turn right (marked Ring Road), cross two islands. At large island at bottom of hill take last exit marked Lichfield, up hill, cross next island to lights.Continue to next set of lights and turn left (B4154 Pelsall). Over railway bridge to Old Bush pub on right (next to Pelsall Cricket & Sports Club).
Capacity: 2,000 Seats: Yes Cover: 624 Floodlights: Yes **Club Shop:** Yes
Clubhouse: Mon-Fri 7-11pm, Sat noon-11pm, Sun noon-3 & 7-10.30pm. Hot &cold meals.

HONOURS West Mids Lg - Prem. Lge 94-95 (R-up 95-96) Div Cup 95-96, Div 1 Cup 88-89 (R-up 89-90, Div 2 Cup R-up 83-84, Walsall Snr Cup R-up 89-90 92-93, Wednesbury Charity Cup 6, (R-up 7), D Stanton Shield(2) 73-75 (R-up 75-76), Sporting Star Cup 76-77 (R-up 61-62), Prem Div Tphy(res)89-90), Rugeley Charity Cup 78-79 (R-up 69-70), Bloxwich Charity Cup(2), Edge Cup 83-84, Ike Cooper Tphy R-up 89-90. Midland Triangle Cup 95-96.

BEST SEASON **FA Cup:** 3rd Qual. Rd 92-93, 2-4 V Gainsborough T. (A).
FA Vase: 5th Rd 92-93, 0-1 v Buckingham T. (A)

PREVIOUS **League:** Staffs County (South) 61-81, West Midlands 82-96 Grounds: None

RECORDS **Attendance** 2,060 v Aston Villa 29.7.98
Goalscorer: Dean Walters 244 **Appearances:** Neil Coles 679

FACT FILE

Reformed: 1961
Nickname: Villians
Sponsor: Spe-al
Colours: Red & black/blackblack
Change colours: Sky & navy/navy/sky
Midweek home matchday: Tuesday
Programme: 68 pages, 80p
Editor: Gareth Evans

CLUB PERSONNEL

Chairman: RonNew
Vice Chairman: J H Gough
President:M.Clark
Press Officer: D.Law

Manager: Steve Hinks
Asst Manager:Pall Baker
Physio:Martin Seal

QUORN

Secretary: Ms Margaret Berry, 214 Barrow Rd., Sileby, Leics.LE12 7LR
Tel: 01509 813259

Ground: Farley Way, Quorn, Leics (01509 620232)

Directions: From M1 jct 23 follow signs for A512 Loughborough. Turn right at roundabout (A6004) before town and pick up A6 (leicester).Three ,iles at large roundabout straight on to Quorn.Left at next lights ground on left.

Floodlights:Yes

HONOURS Leics Sen.Cup Winners 1940,1952,1954 Leicestershire Senior Lge 2002, Leics Sen. Lg. Premier Div Winners: 2000-01Div.1 Winners 1950-51,1987-88,1995-96Div 2: Winners 1949-50 Beacon Bitter League Cup Winners 2000-01

FACT FILE
Founded: 1924
Colours: Red/white/red
Change colours: Yellow & Blue.

CLUB PERSONNEL
- Chairman: Stuart Turner

President, Commercial Manager, Press Officer etc.

Manager: Bob Steel
Asst. Man. / Coach:
Physio:

RACING CLUB WARWICK

GROUND: Townsend Meadow, Hampton Road, Warwick CV34 6JP Tel: 01926 495786
Directions: On the B4189 Warwick to Redditch road (via Henley in Arden) next to owners' & trainers' car park of Warwick Racecourse. From M40 jct 15 (1 1/2 miles) take A429 into Warwick, left into Shakespeare Ave., straight over island, right at T-junction into Hampton Rd, ground 300yds on left. 2 miles from Warwick BR station
Capacity: 1,000 Cover: 200 Seats: 250 Floodlights: Yes
Clubhouse: 01926 495786 Open every evening & Sat &Sun lunchtimes
Club Shop: Scarves, mugs, badges, programmes - contact Secretary
PREVIOUS Leagues: Birmingham & West Mids All., Warwickshire Comb., West Midlands (Regional) 67-72, Midland Comb. 72-89, Southern 89-2003 **Names**: Saltisford Rovers 1919-68
CLUB RECORDS Attendance: 1,000 v Halesowen Town, FA Cup 1987
Transfer fee paid: £1,000 for Dave Whetton (Bedworth United) **Win:** 9-1 v Knowle
Fee received: £5,000 for Ben Foster (Stoke City) **Defeat:** 0-7 v Redditch United
Career Goalscorer: Steve Edgington 200 **Career Appearances:** Steve Cooper 600
BEST SEASON FA Vase: 4th Round 77-78 **FA Cup:** 3rd Qual Rd 92-93
HONOURS: Midland Comb. 87-88 R-up 88-89; Warwick Lg 33-34 34-35 35-36; Birmingham & West Mids Alliance 48-49; Birmingham & Dist Alliance Senior Cup 49-50; Leamington & Dist Lg 37-38 45-46 46-47 47-48; Leamington Hospital Cup 37-38; Warwick Cinderella Cup 35-36 36-37 37-38 38-39 46-47; T G John Cup 36-37; Leamington Junior Cup 38-39 46-47

FACT FILE
Formed: 1919
Nickname: Racers
Colours: Gold & black
Change colours: Red & white/red/red
Midweek matchday: Tuesday
Youth's League: Mid F/Lit Yth Lge
Programme
Pages: 20 Price: £1.00
Editor: Phil Street

CLUB OFFICIALS
Chairman: Jim Wright
Secretary: Pat Murphy
Tel: 01926 612675

FOOTBALL MANAGEMENT
Manager:Billy Hollywood

ROCESTER

GROUND Hillsfield, Mill Street, Rocester, Uttoxeter, Staffs
Tel: 01889 590463 Email: rocester@floodlight org.uk
Directions: From A50 r'bout adjoining Little Chef at Uttoxeter take B5030 to Rocester & Alton Towers, right into Rocester village after 3miles over narrow bridge, in village centre bear right at sharp left-hand bend into Mill St., ground 500yds on left just past former cotton mill.
Capacity: 4,000 Seats: 230 Cover: 500 Floodlights: Yes
Clubhouse: On matchdays (normal licensing hours). Hot drinks & snacks. **Club Shop:** Yes
PREVIOUS Leagues: Ashbourne; Leek & Moorland; Cheadle & Dist; Uttoxeter Amateur; Stafford 53-57; Staffordshire County North 57-84; Staffordshire Senior 84-87; West Midlands 87-94; Midland Alliance 94-99; Southern 99-2003.
BEST SEASON FA Cup: 3rd Qual. Round 97-98, 1-2 v Bromsgrove Rovers (A)
FA Vase: 5th Round 86-87, 1-3 v Garforth Town (H) aet.
RECORDS Attendance: 1,026 v Halesowen T., FA Vase 4th Rd Jan.'87 (at Leek T.) 3-1 a.e.t.
Appearances: Peter Swanwick.(Goalkeeper who played for 20 years -1962-82)
Fee Received: £12,000 for Mark Sale from Birmingham City 1994
HONOURS West Mids Lg R-up 89-90 Div 1 87-88, Div 1 Cup 87-88, Staffs Senior Lg (x2) 85-87, Staffordshire FA Vase 85-86 87-88; Midland Alliance 98-99

FACT FILE
Founded: 1876
Nickname: Romans
Sponsors:
Colours: Amber & black/black/black
Change colours: All blue
Reserves' Lge: North Staffs (North)
Midweek matchday: Tuesday
Programme
32 pages £1.00
Editor: Barry Brosnan Tel: 01889 567795
CLUB OFFICIALS
Chairman: Alf.Hawksworth
Secretary: Gilbert Egerton
23 Eaton Rd, Rocester, Uttoxeter, Staffs ST145LL. Tel: 01889 590101
FOOTBALL MANAGEMENT
Manager: Warren Campbell

RUSHALL OLYMPIC

Secretary: Peter Athersmith, 46 Blakenall Lane, Leamore, Walsall, W Mids WS31HG
Tel: 01922 712632 (H) 0121 553 5525 (W) 07909 792422(M)
Ground: Dales Lane, off Daw End Lane, Rushall, Nr Walsall (01922 641021).
Directions: From Rushall centre (A461) take B4154 signed Aldridge. Approx., 1mile on right, directly opposite Royal Oak P.H., in Daw End Lane. Grd on right. 2 miles Walsall (BR) station.
Capacity: 2,500 Seats: 200 Cover: 200 Floodlights: Yes **Club Shop:** No
Clubhouse: Bar/lounge, every night 8-11pm, Sat matchdays, Sun noon-2.30pm
HONOURS West Mids Lge Div 1 79-80; Walsall Amtr Lge Div 1 55-56, Div 2 52-53, Snr Cup 54-55 55-56, Jabez Cliff Cup 55-56 ; Staffs Co. Lge Div 1(4) (Div 2 56-57); Walsall Charity Cup 52-53; Walsall Chal.Cup (2).Walsall Mem. Charity Cup (x7) 55-62; W Preston Chal. Cup 56-57; Cannock & Dist. Charity Cup 56-57; Wednesbury Snr Cup (3) Sporting Star Cup (5) J W Edge 62-63 66-67; Walsall Snr Cup 64-65;99-00 Lichfield Charity64-65 66-67; Staffs Yth Cup 81-82. Mid Alliance R-up 00-01,02-03 Lg.Cup Winners 2001-02
PREVIOUS Leagues: Walsall Amateur 52-55/ Staffs County (South) 56-78/ West Midlands (Reg) 78-94. **Grounds:** Rowley Place 51-75/ Aston University 76-79.
RECORDS Attendance: 2,000 v Leeds Utd Old Boys **Goalscorer:** Graham Wiggin
Appearances: Alan Dawson (400+ apps) **Players progressing:** Lee Sinnott (Watford), Lee Palin (Aston Villa),Stuart Watkiss (Walsall), Steve Taylor (Crystal Palace via Bromsgrove £1,500 + £18,000 sell on-record club fee)

FACT FILE
Founded: 1951 Nickname: Pics.
Sponsors:Williams Bookmakers
Colours: Amber with black trim/black/amber
Change colours: White & Black/white/white
Midweek matchday: Tuesday
Youth League: Miidland.Flloodlit League.
Programme: 60 pages, £1.00
Editor/ Press Officer: Darren Stockall (01922 379153).

CLUB PERSONNEL
Chairman: John Allen
Vice Chairman: Gary Cooper
President: Brian Greenwood.
Manager: Kevin Hadley
Asst Manager: Dave Beasley
Physio: Gary McHale, Mick Andrews

2002-03
Leading Goalscorer:Lee Booth 28
Captain:Richard Brown
Players of the Year: Lee Booth & Davifd Read

STAFFORD TOWN

Secretary: Dave Rowley, 32 Lodge Rd, Brereton, Rugely, Staffs WS15 1HG
Tel: 01889 800779 (H) 07971 454217 (Mobile) Email: info@staffordtownfc.co.uk
Ground: Stafford Rangers FC, Marston Road, Stafford
Directions: From M6 junction 14, Take 3rd left to Red Hill Roundabout and follow signs for Aston Fields Ind Est along Beaconside. Aston Fields is signposted 3rd right along Common Road, having travelled over railway bridge, Stafford Rangers FC ground is on the right

Capacity: 6,000 Cover: 3,000 Seats: 426 Floodlights: Yes Club Shop: No

Club address: Chamley Club, Beconside, Stafford Tel: 01785 665739 (Mr N Payne)
Website: www.staffordtownfc.co.uk
HONOURS WMRL Div 1 93-94, Staffs Snr Lg R-up 91-92, Midland Comb. Div 2 78-79, Staffs Vase 84-85 92-93 (R-up 87-88,99-00, Bourne Sports Trophy 84-85, Walsall Sen Cup SF 91-92 W.Mids Champions 99-00 Lg.Cup R-up 99-00 Laegue Discipline Award 00-01
PREVIOUS **Leagues:** Staffs Co. (North) 74-77 82-84; Midland Comb. 77-82; Staffs Sen. 84-93, W.M.R.L. 93-2000
Grounds: Silkmore Lane 74-77 Burton Manor Spts 77-88; Riverway 88-91 Park Stadium 91-94
RECORD **Win:** 14-0 v Leek CSOB (H), Staffs Senior League 8/10/88
Goalscorer: Mick Stark - 54 goals in the 1999-2000 season

FACT FILE
Founded: 1974
Nickname: Reds or Town
Colours: All red
Change colours:All Blue
Midweek matches: Mon/Wed
Programme: 36 pages, £1.00
Editor: Chris Curtis & Graham Whitehall (01785 605561)

CLUB PERSONNEL
Chairman: Gordon Evans
President: Graham Hollinshead
Press Officer: Chris Curtis/Alan Bowers
Manager:
2002-03
Leading Goalscorer:
Captain:
Player of the Year:

STOURBRIDGE

Secretary: Hugh Clark,10 Burnt Oak Drive, Stourbridge, W. Mids DY8 1HL Tel: 01384 392975
Ground: War Memorial Ath. Grd, High St., Amblecote, Stourbridge DY8 4HN (01384 394040)
Directions: Take A491, signposted Wolverhampton, from Stourbridge ring-road -ground 300yds on left immediately beyond traffic lights and opposite `RoyalOak' pub. Buses 311, 246 from Dudley, and 256 from Wolverhampton, pass ground. 1 mile from Stourbridge Town (BR)
Capacity: 2,000 Cover: 1,250 Seats: 250 Floodlights: Yes
Clubhouse: Open most evenings from 8pm and Sunday lunchtimes
Club Shop: Programmes & souvenirs. Contact Nigel Gregg

PREVIOUS Name: Stourbridge Standard **Leagues:** West Midlands (prev. Birmingham) 1892-1939 54-71, Birmingham Comb. 45-53, Southern 71-00
Ground: None

HONOURS Welsh Cup R-up 73-74; Southern Lg Midland Div 90-91 (Lg Cup 92-93), Div 1 North73-74, Merit Cup 73-74; West Mids (prev. B'ham) Lg 23-24 (R-up 4); B'ham Comb. R-up 51-52; B'ham Snr Cup 49-50 45-46 75-76 (R-up 3); Worcs Snr Cup 9, (R-up 12); Herefordshire Snr Cup 54-55; Camkin Cup R-up 69-70; Camkin Presidents Cup 70-71; Albion Shield 43-44; Keys Cup 37-38 62-63, Worcs Comb. R-up 27-28; Worcs Jnr Cup R-up 27-28; Tillotson Cup R-up 39-40, MFC Davis League Cup 00-01. Joe McGorian Cup 01-02,02-03 Midland Alliance:01-02,02-03
BEST SEASON **FA Cup:** 4th Qual Rd: 67-68, 84-85 85-86 98-99 **FA Trophy:** Qtr Final 70-71
CLUB RECORDS **Career Goalscorer:** Ron Page 269 **Career Appearances:** Ron Page 427

FACT FILE
Formed: 1876 Nickname: The Glassboys
Sponsors: Stourbridge College
Colours: Red & white stripes
Change colours: Yellow & blue
Midweek matchday: Tuesday
Programme: Pages: 32 Price: £1.20
Editors: Hugh Clark & Nigel Gregg

CLUB PERSONNEL
Chairman: Stephen Hyde
Press Officer: Nigel Gregg
Managers:Jon Ford & Gary Hackett
Physio: T.B.A.
2002-03
Leading Goalscorer:Brian Gray
Captain:Jim Conway
Player of the Year: Andy Higgs

STRATFORD TOWN

Secretary: Robin Lamb,14 Regal Close, Scimitar Park, Two Gates, Tamworth B77 1GT
Ground: Masons Road, off Alcester Road, Stratford-upon-Avon, Warks (01789 297479).
Directions: Follow the signs for Alcester/Worcester A422 from the town centre.
Masons Road is the 1st right afterthe railway bridge.
400 yards from Stratford-on-Avon (BR)station.
Local buses for West Green Drive.
Capacity: 1,100 Seating/Cover: 200 Floodlights: Yes

Clubhouse: Open every night **Club Shop:** Yes.

HONOURS Midland Comb 56-57 86-87; Chal. Cup 86-87 88-89 (R-up 55-56); Chal. Vase 81-82; Jack Mould Tphy 81-82; Tony Allden Mem. Cup 86-87; B'ham Snr Cup62-63.

PREVIOUS **Leagues:** W Mids 57-70/ Mid Com. 70-73 75-94/ Hellenic 70-75.
RECORDS **Attendance:** 1,078 v Aston Villa, Birmingham Snr Cup, Oct 1996

Players progressing: Martin Hicks (Charlton '77), Roy Proverbs (Coventry, '56)

FACT FILE
Founded: 1944
Nickname: The Town
Sponsors: Sitel
Colours: Blue & White
Change Colours:Tangerine & Black
Midweek Matchday: Tuesday
Reserves' League: Midland Comb. Res. Div..
Programme: 24 pages, £1.00
Editor:Alan Hawkins

CLUB PERSONNEL
Chairman:Craig Hughes
Vice-Chairman: Phil Day
Manager: Lennie Darby
Physio:M.Bayliss

2002-03
Leading Goalscorer: Paul Spacey
Captain: Nigel Niblett
Player of the Year: Wayne Starkey

STUDLEY

Secretary: Mark Sealey c/o club.

Ground: Beehive, Abbeyfields Drive, Studley, Warwicks B80 7BE
Tel: 01527 853817

Directions: M42 Jct.3 onto A435 to Redditch.Over island at Dog Pub on left continue towards Studley. Ground on left signposted to Abbeyfields.

Capacity 1,500 **Seats:** 200 **Cover:** Yes **Floodlights**:Yes

Clubhouse Yes, on ground - Mon-Fri 7-11 fri-Sat 11am -11pm Sun 12-5(if dining) 7-10.30

HONOURS Midland Comb.: Prem Div R-up 2000-01,Div 1 91-92, Chall Cup R-up 91-92, MFC Challenge Vase 87-88 R-up 88-89 WFA Senior Urn 2000-01,01-02,02-03
Presidents Cup R-up 91-92, Div2 Cup 87-88;
Smedley Crooke Char. Cup 90-91 91-92; Jack Mould Trophy R-up 1987-88
Birmingham Vase R-up 96-97, Tony allden memorial Cup: 2001-02

PREVIOUS **League:** Redditch & South Warwickshire Sunday Combination 71-87
Name: BKL Works

CLUB RECORDS **Appearances:** Lee Adams 523
Goalscorer: Brian Powell
Attendance: 685 v Tamworth 1998-99

FACT FILE
Founded: 1971
Nickname: Bees
Sponsors: Persimmon Hom
Colours: All Skyblue & navy blue.
Change colours: All Yellow
Programme: 50p Editor: Gordon Wilkie

CLUB PERSONNEL
Chairman: David Robinson
Vice-Chairman: Gordon Wilkie
Press Officer: Dave Chiswell
Manager: Mark Chambers
Asst Manager: Nicky Cross
Coach: Steve Cooper
Physio: Duncan Turk

2002-03
Leading Goalscorer:Craig Pountney
Captain:Steven Hands
Player of the Year:T.B.A.

WESTFIELDS

Secretary & Chief Executive: Andrew Morris
17 Fayre Oaks Green, Kings Acre, Hereford HR4 0QT Tel: 01432 264711
Ground: Moor House, Widemarsh Common, Hereford Tel: 0860410548
Directions: New directions to come
Capacity: 2,000 Seats: 200 Cover: 250 Floodlights: Yes Club Shop: Yes
Clubhouse: On ground
PREVIOUS Leagues: Herefordshire Sunday 66-74; Herefordshire 72-74; Worcester & Dist. 74-77
RECORD
Attendance: 518 v Rushden & Diamonds FA Cup 96
Goalscorer: Paul Burton **Appearances:** Phil Powell/ Mark Tabb
HONOURS West Mids Champions 02-03 Lg Div 1 86-87, Div 2 R-up 83-84 (Div 2 Cup 79-80 83-84), H.County Snr Cup 85-86 88-89 91-92 95-96 01-202-03 (Yth Cup 92-93 95-96), Kington Chall. Cup x5; Kington Invit. Cup x4; Presteigne Ottway Cup x4, Worcs Jnr Cup 79-80,Wye Guild Cup x2, Hereford Sunday Lg Prem 75-76 76-77 (Div 1 71-72, Div 2 76-77, Div 3 75-76, Prem Div Cup x3, Div 1 Cup x2, Div 3 Cup 72-73), Smart Brown Cup 67-68, Fair Play Cup 67-68. D.Hartland Mem Trophy 95-96,99-00 00-01 R Biggart Trophy 95-6,99-00
Players progressing: Alex Sykes (Mansfield Town 92), GaryBowyer (Nottingham Forest 89), John Layton (Hereford Utd 74)

FACT FILE
Founded: 1966
Nickname: The Fields
Sponsors: Left Bank Village
Colours: Maroon & sky/sky/sky
Change colours: Sky/white/ maroon
Midweek matchday: Tuesday
Programme: Yes Editor: Andy Morris

CLUB PERSONNEL
Chairman: Alan Dunsford
V .Chair:John Morgan
President: Graham Preece
Joint Managers: Sean Edwards & Clive Harris
Coach: Darren Lynch
Physio: Mark Newman
2002-03
Capt. & P.o.Y.: Matt Phillips
Top Scorer: Paul Burton

WILLENHALL TOWN

Secretary: Simon Haynes, 6 Ingledew Close, Briarsleigh, Walsall, West Mids (01902 411758)
Ground: Noose Lane, Willenhall, West Midlands (01902 605132-club, 636586-office).
Directions: M6 Jnc 10 follow 'new' Black Country route and then 'Keyway'. On leaving 'Keyway' follow signs to Wolverhampton(A454). At 'Neachells' P H house right into Neachells Lane, and first right again into Watery Lane. At island turn left onto Noose Lane, ground is 200yds on left.
Capacity: 5,000 Seats: 324 Cover: 500 Floodlights: Yes Shop: Yes
Clubhouse: Open Mon-Fri 12-2 & 7-12pm,Sat & Sun All Day Hot food available.
HONOURS FA Vase R-up 80-81; West Mids Lg 78-79, Div 1 75-76, Prem. Div Cup 79-80, Div 2 Cup 78-79(res); Southern Midland 83-84; Birmingham Snr Cup R-up 82-83; J W Hunt Cup 73-74., Mid Alliance Cup R-up 99-00, Rameses Invitation Cup 2000-01.
BEST SEASON **FA Vase:** Finalists 80-81 **FA Cup:** 1st Rd Proper v Crewe Alexander 1981
PREVIOUS **Leagues:** Wolverhampton Amateur/ Staffs County/ West Mids 75-82 91-94/ Southern 82-91.
RECORDS **Attendance**: 3,454 v Crewe Alexandra, FA Cup 1st Rd 1981.
Goalscorer: Gary Matthews **Appearances**: Gary Matthews.
Players progressing: Sean O'Driscoll (Fulham), Joe Jackson (Wolves), Stuart Watkiss (Wolves), Tony Moore (Sheff U), Andy Reece (Bristol R.), Wayne O'Sullivan (Swindon), Adie Smith (Kidderminster H) & Peter Smith (Brighton & H)
2002-03
Leading Scorer: Captain: Player of the Year:

FACT FILE
Founded: 1953 Nickname: Reds
Sponsors: Aspray Transport Ltd.
Colours: All Red
Change colours: Yellow & Blue/Blue/Blue
Midweek matchday: Tuesday.
Reserves League: Midland Comb.
Programme: 44-46 pages, £1.00
Editor: Russ Brown (01902 681011)

CLUB PERSONNEL
President: Jack Williams
Chairman: JackWilliams
Vice-Chairman: Ed Edmunds
Football Sec: Neil Arrowsmith (01902 450613)
Commercial Dept:
Russ Brown & Robert Fletcher

Manager: Rob Smith
Asst Man:Larry Chambers
Physio: Steve Ball

Pesall. Back Row (L-R): Steve Hicks, Paul Baker, Mike Harrison, Stuart Bradford, John Bitten, Martin Dobson, Ian Whitehouse, Ian Purvey, James Pemberton.
Front Row: Micky Nichllos, Richie Allen, Stuart King, Paul James, Peter Howell, Ashley Perry, Cameron Morgan, Alany Conway.

Photo: Marshall's Sports Service (Birmingham)

Stourbridge. Back Row (L-R): Ross Pearce, Adam Bastable, Steve Hillman, Andrew Higgs, Mark Jones, Lewis Baker, Detton Franics, Nick Powell.
Front Row: Stuart Leeding, Danny Williams, Matt Webb, Tim Jackson, Zahoor Suliman, Jordon Lee, Dave Benton.

Photo: Marshall's Sports Service (Birmingham)

ICIS MIDLAND COMBINATION

FEEDER TO THE MIDLAND FOOTBALL ALLIANCE

Chairman & Treasurer: David Prust
Secretary: Nigel Wood
30 Glaisdale Road, Hall green, Birmingham B28 8PX Tel: 0121 680 0605

FINAL LEAGUE TABLE 2002-03

PREMIER DIVISION		P	W	D	L	F	A	Pts
1	Alvechurch	42	30	7	5	126	48	97
2	Coventry Marconi	42	29	5	8	94	37	92
3	Leamington	42	27	9	6	92	48	90
4	Bolehall Swifts	42	27	5	10	82	53	86
5	Romulus	42	24	5	13	107	58	77
6	Rugby Town	42	22	10	10	90	52	76
7	Coventry Sphinx	42	23	6	13	95	72	75
8	Fernhill County Sports	42	21	8	13	74	59	71
9	Highgate United (-3)	42	23	3	16	95	67	69
10	Meir KA	42	21	6	15	94	75	69
11	Castle Vale Kings Heath	42	19	6	17	86	66	63
12	Nuneaton Griff	42	17	3	22	66	80	54
13	Continental Star	42	14	9	19	86	88	51
14	Coleshill Town	42	13	9	20	54	68	48
15	Pershore Town	42	13	7	22	74	86	46
16	Massey-Ferguson	42	13	7	22	85	112	46
17	Feckenham	42	12	6	24	66	85	42
18	West Midlands Police	42	11	9	22	56	87	42
19	Handrahan Timbers	42	11	8	23	57	73	41
20	Alveston	42	9	7	26	66	114	34
21	Southam United	42	7	2	33	43	162	23
22	Cheslyn Hay	42	4	7	31	47	145	19

	1	2	3	4	5	6	7	8	9	10	11	12	13	14	15	16	17	18	19	20	21	22
1 Alvechurch		4-2	6-1	1-0	10-1	3-2	3-2	2-0	3-3	1-1	1-2	2-1	4-2	1-2	6-0	0-1	1-0	3-1	2-2	4-0	8-3	3-2
2 Alveston	1-5		0-2	0-2	3-1	2-0	0-5	0-3	3-2	1-1	1-4	2-3	3-2	0-0	3-3	1-2	5-1	2-4	0-3	0-1	4-0	1-1
3 Bolehall Swifts	2-3	3-2		2-0	3-0	2-1	4-4	0-2	6-2	2-0	0-2	2-0	2-0	1-0	2-0	1-0	3-1	2-1	2-3	3-1	5-1	3-0
4 Castle Vale KH	1-3	6-5	4-1		2-2	0-2	1-0	0-2	3-2	3-0	0-2	2-1	4-1	1-4	1-1	0-1	1-3	4-1	0-1	4-1	3-1	4-1
5 Cheslyn Hay	0-4	2-2	0-1	0-7		2-1	2-2	0-3	0-6	1-6	0-4	1-2	1-2	0-3	2-3	2-2	4-1	0-2	1-2	3-2	3-3	0-3
6 Coleshill Town	0-3	2-1	2-3	0-0	1-0		1-1	1-5	0-3	3-1	3-2	1-1	0-0	0-2	4-2	0-1	1-0	1-1	0-2	0-4	1-2	1-1
7 Continental Star	0-3	5-2	0-2	0-3	2-3	2-1		0-2	2-0	1-1	0-1	5-1	2-4	2-4	2-3	4-3	1-4	3-0	3-2	1-3	8-1	1-2
8 Coventry Marconi	2-4	4-1	2-0	2-1	5-2	1-0	2-0		1-1	2-1	4-1	0-0	1-0	2-0	1-3	4-2	0-1	2-0	2-1	0-1	5-0	5-0
9 Coventry Spinx	0-0	3-1	1-0	2-1	2-0	3-0	2-2	1-0		4-0	5-0	3-2	3-1	2-4	2-4	2-3	2-0	0-4	1-3	5-8	6-2	1-0
10 Feckenham	4-1	4-1	0-2	1-3	4-3	0-1	3-4	0-4	0-1		0-3	1-0	0-1	2-3	4-1	0-2	3-1	4-3	1-5	1-1	6-1	2-0
11 Fernhill County S	0-5	2-2	1-4	3-2	3-1	2-0	5-1	1-1	1-0	4-1		2-2	2-1	2-0	5-2	0-0	0-1	3-2	2-1	1-2	0-0	1-1
12 Handrahan Tim.	1-2	4-2	0-2	2-2	1-1	0-1	1-1	1-2	1-2	3-1	4-2		0-1	0-1	1-1	2-1	6-1	0-4	0-3	0-1	1-0	1-2
13 Highgate United	1-4	4-0	1-2	3-2	7-0	2-0	3-1	2-1	5-3	1-2	0-0	2-0		0-0	4-2	1-4	3-0	4-1	3-2	0-3	6-3	2-0
14 Leamington	3-1	2-2	2-2	0-3	5-1	1-0	3-5	0-0	1-1	2-1	1-0	2-1	5-1		3-2	3-1	2-0	2-0	4-3	0-0	5-0	5-1
15 Massey-Ferguson	2-2	1-3	0-2	3-4	2-0	3-3	4-2	3-4	1-4	3-2	1-1	1-2	0-6	2-6		3-4	2-1	4-0	0-1	0-3	2-0	2-1
16 Meir KA	1-3	2-3	1-1	1-1	6-1	1-2	2-0	3-1	2-4	0-1	2-4	3-0	0-4	1-1	5-1		1-4	3-2	2-1	4-0	4-3	5-0
17 Nuneaton Griff	0-2	0-1	1-1	2-3	7-1	1-1	1-2	1-4	2-3	4-1	1-0	1-0	4-3	1-2	4-3	1-3		5-2	0-2	1-1	1-0	1-0
18 Pershore Town	0-2	7-2	0-2	0-4	1-1	1-1	2-3	1-1	1-1	4-3	0-2	3-0	1-3	0-2	3-2	1-2	0-2		5-3	3-3	1-0	2-0
19 Romulus	1-1	4-1	6-1	2-2	6-0	2-3	0-0	0-3	5-2	2-1	1-0	7-0	0-1	1-2	0-3	2-2	5-0	2-4		2-0	6-0	3-1
20 Rugby Town	0-1	5-0	1-1	2-0	8-2	3-1	2-2	0-1	0-3	1-1	4-0	0-0	3-1	1-1	5-0	6-0	1-0	2-1	0-3		6-0	1-0
21 Southam United	0-8	3-1	0-1	2-0	3-2	0-8	0-3	1-6	0-1	1-0	1-4	0-9	1-0	1-2	1-7	2-11	2-3	0-4	0-3	1-3		1-4
22 West Mid Police	1-1	2-0	2-1	3-2	3-1	2-4	2-2	1-2	0-1	1-1	1-0	0-3	1-7	3-2	3-3	3-0	2-3	1-1	3-4	1-1	1-3	

FINAL LEAGUE TABLE 2002-03

DIVISION ONE		P	W	D	L	F	A	Pts
1	Knowle	36	27	3	6	104	40	84
2	Stockingford AA	36	26	4	6	100	45	82
3	Pilkington XXX	36	23	5	8	92	48	74
4	Dudley Sports	36	24	1	11	78	47	73
5	Polesworth North Warwick	36	20	3	13	66	46	63
6	Fairfield Villa	36	18	7	11	61	53	61
7	Wilmcote Sports & Social	36	16	5	15	65	63	53
8	Northfield Town	36	15	4	17	72	71	49
9	Kenilworth Town	36	14	6	16	69	82	48
10	Blackheath	36	12	10	14	69	73	46
11	Loughborough	36	11	11	14	59	57	44
12	Thimblemill REC	36	11	10	15	69	67	43
13	Burntwood Town	36	11	9	16	49	69	42
14	Cadbury Athletic	36	11	6	19	55	72	39
15	Handsaker	36	11	6	19	39	64	39
16	Old Hill Town	36	10	8	18	70	83	38
17	Bloxwich Town	36	11	3	22	59	82	36
18	Holly Lane	36	10	4	22	54	101	34
19	Brownhills Town	36	5	7	24	31	98	22

WILLIE KNIBBS CHALLENGE CUP

(Premier and Division One clubs)

FIRST ROUND

Burntwood Town	v	Coleshill Town	4-6 (aet)
Castle Vale Kings Heath	v	Cheslyn Hay	1-1 (aet) 7-8p
Fairfield Villa	v	Feckenham	4-2 (aet)
Holly Lane	v	Nuneaton Griff	3-2
Southam United	v	Massey-Ferguson	1-4
Cadbury Athletic	v	Alvechurch	2-4 (aet)
Continental Star	v	Old Hill Town	6-0
Handrahan Timbers	v	Stockingford	2-1
Polesworth NW	v	Highgate United	1-2

SECOND ROUND

Blackheath	v	Meir KA	1-3
Bolehall Swifts	v	Thimblemill REC	2-1
Cov. Marconi	v	Pilkington XXX	1-2 (aet)
Fernhill County Sports	v	Cheslyn Hay	2-0
Knowle	v	Brownhills Town	2-1
Northfield	v	Handrahan Timbers	0-2
Romulus	v	Massey-Ferguson	2-1
West Midlands Police	v	Loughborough	1-0
Bloxwich Town	v	Coleshill Town	2-3
Continental Star	v	Alvechurch	3-4 (aet)
Coventry Sphinx	v	Fairfield Villa	0-2
Kenilworth Town	v	Handsaker	3-0
Leamington	v	Alveston	2-0
Pershore Town	v	Dudley Sports	4-0
Rugby Town	v	Highgate United	1-2
Wilmcote Sports/Social	v	Holly Lane	4-2

THIRD ROUND

Fairfield Villa	v	Highgate United	1-3
Handrahan Timbers	v	Kenilworth	4-2
Leamington	v	Meir KA	5-2
Pilkington XXX	v	Coleshill Town	3-1
Fernhill County Sports	v	Alvechurch	0-4
Knowle	v	Bolehall Swifts	2-0
Pershore Town	v	West Mids Police	1-0
Romulus	v	Wilmcote Sports & Social	3-1

(ineligible player – Romulus expelled)

QUARTER-FINALS

Alvechurch	v	Handrahan Timbers	3-2 aet
Pershore Town	v	Leamington	0-3
Highgate United	v	Pilkington XXX	1-3
Wilmcote Sports & Social	v	Knowle	1-0

SEMI-FINALS

(played over two legs)

Alvechurch	v	Leamington	2-0
Leamington	v	Alvechurch	1-1
Pilkington XXX	v	Wilmcote S&S	1-0
Wilmcote S&S	v	Pilkington XXX	4-4

FINAL

Alvechurch v Pilkington XXX 1-1 (aet) 5-4p 10th May at Moor Green

ALVESTON

Secretary: Martin Beese, 16 The Smallholdings, Bubbenhall Road, Baginton, CV8 3BB
Tel: 02476 305294H 077744 23641M

Ground: Home Guard Club, Main Street, Tiddington, Stratford-upon-Avon. Tel: 01789 297718
Social Club Telephone : 01789 297718 Club Email martin.beese@fleet.gecapital.com

Directions: ground is on the Stratford - Wellesbourne Road (B 40860) Home Guard Club is last building on right through Tiddington

Colours: Maroon & sky blue/sky blue/ maroon & sky blue
Change Cols.: Black & white stripes/ white/ white

Chairman: Martin Beese (02476 305294)

BOLEHALL SWIFTS

Secretary: Philip Hill, 64 Rene Road, Bolehall,Tamworth,Staffs. B77 3NN (07812 449054- M)
Ground: Rene Road, Bolehall, Tamworth (01827 62637)
Directions: A51 signs south to Bolebridge island, left under railway archesinto Amington Rd, 4th left into Leedham Ave, fork right into Rene Rd, ground onright by school. From Tamworth BR station walk up Victoria Road for threequarters of a mile and catch No.3 or No.6 mini-bus to Bolehall. Alight atLeedham Avenue or Rene Road and follow as above
Capacity: 2,000 Seats: 500 Cover: 600 Floodlights: Yes Club Shop: No
Clubhouse: Large Social Club. OpenDays 12-3 & evenings 7-11 & lunchtimes. Snacks available
HONOURS: Midland Comb. Div 2 84-85, F/Lit Cup R-up 96-97, Chall. Vase 84-85, Presidents Cup R-up 85-86; Fazeley Char Cup 84-85 (R-up 85-86); Ernie Brown Mem. Cup R-up (6)Jack Mould Cup R-up 85-86 Tony Allden Nenorial Cup 98-99 Walsall Sen.Cup Winners 2002

Founded: 1953 Nickname: Swifts
Colours: Yellow/green/yellow Change : l Blue
Sponsors: Need -A-Skip-Hire Ltd.
Midweek matches: Tuesday
Programme: 24 pages, £1.00
Editor: W Gould (01827 64530)
President:.L. Fitzpatrick
Chairman: James Latham V-C D.Wright
Manager: Ron Tranter Ass.Man:T.Edmead
Coach: J.Capaldi Physio: D.Crump
2002-2003
Capt: Neil bennett P.o.Y.: Greg Walters
Top Scorer: Ryan Allmark 22. Career top scorer

BROCTON

Secretary:

Ground: Cannock Sports Stadium, Pye Green Road, Cannock, Staffordshire
Tel: 01543 571898

PREVIOUS **Leagues**: Midland League >2003

CASTLE VALE KINGS HEATH

Secretary: Stuart Maddocks, 37 Rowheath Road, Cotteridge, Birmingham B30 2EP
Tel: 0121 604 7543
Ground: Groundshare with Alvechurch F.C. See their section for details
Directions: As Alvechurch F.C.
HONOURS Midland Comb. Div 1 R-up 92-93, Div 2 R-up 82-83, Presidents Cup R-up 79-80 81-82 92-93; Birmingham Chall. Vase R-up 86-87; Worcester Sen Urn 96-97, Chall. Cup R-up 96-97
PREVIOUS **Names:** Horse Shoe FC; Kings Heath Amateur; Kings Heath
Ground: Shirley Town (pre-1994)
Player progressing: Geoff Scott (Stoke C.)

Founded: 1964
Nickname: The Kings
Colours: Old Gold/black/gold
Change Colours: All white

Programme: 12 pages
Editor: M Kite

Chairman: Ray Kite
Manager: Clive Seeley
Asst. Man. / Coach: ???
Physio: ???

COLESHILL TOWN

Secretary: George Phillips,49 Circus Avenue, Chelmsley Wood, Birmingham (0121 770 9513)
Ground: Pack Meadow, Packington Lane, Coleshill, Birmingham B46 3JQ (0167563259)
Directions: A446 to A4117 towards Coleshill, Packington Lane forks from A4117,south of village and ground is 150 yds on right. M6 jct 4, 1 mile away
Capacity: 3,000Seats: 50Cover: 50 Floodlights: Yes
Clubhouse: Bar open 7 nights a week. Bar manager resident
HONOURS: Mercian Lg 75-76, Walsall Snr Cup 82-83 R-up 83-84, Midland Comb. R-up 83-84, Div 2 69-70 R-up 74-75, Invitation Cup 70, Presidents Cup R-up x2 67-69
CLUB RECORDS: Attendance: 1,000
Players progressing: Gary Shaw (Aston Villa)

Founded: 1894
Nickname: Coalmen
Colours: Green & white/green/green
Change Colours: All blue
Midweek matches: Tues/Thurs
Programme: 30p,
Editor: Mavis Gordon

Chairman:
Manager: Christopher Davies

COVENTRY MARCONI F.C.

Chairman: D.Ryan **Vice-Chairman:** S.Canliani **Press Officer:** P Scanlon
Secretary: D.Wilson, 60 Craven Avenue, Binley Woods, Coventry. CV3 2JT (02476 544296)

Ground: Allard Way, Copswood, Coventry Tel: 02476 562831
Capacity 1,500 **Seats**: 92 **Cover:** Yes, Seats and standing **Floodlights:**Yes

Clubhouse: 12-11 Saturdays 6.00-11.00 weekdays

HONOURS: Midland Comb Div 1 96-97, Presidents Cup 96-97 , Endsleigh Comb.Cup 2001-02.
Only winners of Coventry Evening Telegraph Cup (3 years), R-up Endslegh Comb Cup 99-00

Formed: 1923
Sponsors: Home Heating
Colours: White with blue trim/bluewhite
Change colours: All red

Programme: 32 pages Price: 50p
Editor P.Scanlon

Manager: P.Mills
Assistant Manager:S.Shaw
Physio: S.Wilson

COVENTRY SPHINX

Match Secretary/Secretary: Joe Fletcher,37 B Bread Streeet, Fleshill, Coventry CV6 5ATY
Tel Nos: 02476 663365 (H) 07850 932832 (M)

Ground: Sphinx Drive, off Siddeley Avenue, Stoke Aldermoor, Coventry Tel: 01203 451361
Social Club Tel.: 02476 451361
Directions:
Capacity: 2,000 Covered Seating: 100 Covered Standing: 150 Floodlights: Yes
HONOURS:
2002-2003: Captain: Danny McSheffrey **Top Scorer:** Thomas Thacker **P.o.Y.:** James McNulty

FACT FILE

Formed: 1946
Colours: Sky blue & white/black/white
Change Colours: White/white/Sky Blue
Midweek Matchday: Tuesday

Chairman: Vic Jones
Manager: Martin Ahcroft
Asst. Man. / Coach: Steve Masterson
Physio: Steve Harris

DUDLEY SPORTS

Secretary: John Lewis, 6 Hern Rd., Brieley Hill, West Mids DY5 2PW
Tel: 01384 895782
Ground: Hillcrest Avenue, Brierley Hill, West Mids. Tel: 01384 826420

Colours: Green & white /white/ green

FECKENHAM

Secretary: M G Hawkes4 Mill Lane, Feckenhamk, Redditch, Worcs B96 6HY (01527 893341)
Ground: Groundshare with Redditch United F.C.
Valley Stadium, Bromsgrove Road, Redditch B97 4RN Tel: 01527 67450
Capacity: 5,000 Cover: 2,000 Seats: 400 Floodlights: Yes
Directions: M42 , Junction 4 take A38 towards Bromsgrov to Golf Course. Left at roundabout - A448 towards Redditch. Aftyer five miles take third exit off roundabout, cross over dual carriage-way, . First right into Birchfield Road, pastthe Foxlydiate Pubkic House.. First left into Red Lane leading into Bromsgrove rRoad. Vallley Stadium is approx 3/4 mile on the left

FACT FILE

Colours: Green & White Hoops/Green/Green
Change Colours: All Yellow

Acting Chairman: R.Freeman
28 Milford Close,Walkwood,Redditch B97 5PZ
Tel: 01527 67450 (H) 01527 401819 (W)

HANDSWORTH CONTINENTAL STAR

Secretary: Gary Christie, 21 Spouthouse Lane, Great Barr B43 5PX
Tel: 0121 357 1044 (H) 07752 202802 (M)
email: soccer@continentalstar.fsnet.co.uk
Ground: Red Lion Ground,Somerfield Road, Walsall WS32EJ (019222 405835)

Clubhouse: Bar open 7 nights a week and is available for hire. Bar manager resident
HONOURS: Midland Comb Div One R-up 96-97; Birmingham Vase.
Jack Mould Cup R-up Invitation Cup Winners. JW Hunt Cup winners

Founded: 1973
Colours: All white
Change Colours: All blue

Website: www..continentalstar.fsnet.co.uk

Chairman:Keith John Tel: 07956429046 (M)

HIGHGATE UNITED

Secretary: Simon Pretty, 8 Monastry Drive,Solihull,B91 1DN (0121 706 0933)
Ground: The Coppice, Tythe Barn Lane, Shirley, Solihull B90 1PH (0121 7444194)
Directions: A34 from City through Shirley, fork right B4102 (Tanworth Lane), half mile then right into Dickens Heath Rd, then first right & ground on the left. 100yds from Whitlocks End (BR)
Capacity: 5,000 Seats: 250 Covered: 750 Floodlights: Yes
Clubhouse: Members Club open Tue to Thur, Sat & Sun. Light refreshments available weekends
HONOURS Midland Comb (3) 72-75 (Div 2 66-67 68-69 71-72), Lg Cup (5) 72-74 75-77 84-85 (R-up 78-79 92-93); Presidents Cup 70-71 85-86); Tony Allden Mem. Cup 74-75; Invit. Cup 68-69 71-72 85-86; West Mids All. 63-64; Birmingham Snr Cup 73-74
CLUB RECORDS Attendance: 4,000 v Enfield, FA Amateur Cup QF 1967
Players progressing: John Gayle (Wimbledon), Keith Leonard (A Villa), Geoff Scott (Leicester C.)

Founded: 1947 Nickname: The Gate
Colours:Red/Black/Red & Black
Change Colours: All white
Midweek matches: Tuesday
Programme: 28 pages, 50p
Editor: Terry Bishop (0676 22788)

Chairman: Terry Bishop
Treasurer: G Read
Press Officer: N C Sawyer
Manager: Jim Simms
Physio: Richard Flynn

LEAMINGTON

Secretary: Brian Knibb, 61 Villiers Street, Leamington Spa, Warwicks. CV32 5YA Tel: 01926 429066
Ground: New Windmill Ground, Harbury Lane, Whitnash, Leamington Spa, Warwicks CV33 9JR Tel 07866 348712 **Capacity**:5,000 **Covered Seats:**120**Covered Standing**:600**Floodlights:** Yes
Record Attendance: 1.263 v Rugby Town 2001
Previous Names: Leamington Town until 193, Lockheed Leamington 1943, AP Leamington
Directions: From A40 follow signs for LeamingtonSpa.On outskirts of town,right at roundabout for Harbury. Cross Leamington-Bishops Tachbrook road along Harbury Lane to The Fosse Way Ground which is on left.
Clubhouse Under construction. Hospitality only. Hot Food on match days. **Shop:** yes
Honours Midlkand Comb.Div 2 Winners 2000-02 Div 1 R-Up 2001-02

Re-Formed:2000-2001
Colours: Gold/ Black/ Gold. Change: White
Midweek Matchday: Tuesday
Prog- Price:50p Pages: 24 Ed: Roger Vincent
Chairman: Mick Brady President: David Hucker
DeputyChairman: Vic Shepherd
Match Sec: Terry Ford (01926 771277 (H)
Managers: Jason Cadden
Assistant.Manager: Steve Thompson
Physio: Matt Papworth
2002-03 Top scorer: Paul Nicholls 30
Captain: Steve Thompson P.o.Y.: Andy Gregory

MASSEY-FERGUSON

Secretary: Terry Borras, Massey Ferguson FC, c/o Massey Ferguson Social Club, Broad Lane, Coventry CV5 9LA. Tel: 02476 675745 (H) 07909 685137 (M)
Ground: Massey-Ferguson Sports Ground, Banner Lane, Tile Hill, Coventry (01203 694400)
Directions: A45 to Meridan turn (B4104). Over two traffic islands, turn rightat 3rd island into Pickford Grange Lane, continue to Pickford Green Lane, &Hockley Lane, left into Broad Lane, right into Banner Lane, 3rd entrance right
Seats: 70 Cover: 200 Floodlights: Yes **Clubhouse**: Not on ground
HONOURS Midland Comb. Div 1 94-95, Div 2 93-94, Chall. Vase 93-94, Chall Cup 94-95, Presidents Cup 94-95; Coventry Evening Telegraph Cup 95-96
PREVIOUS **League:** Coventry Alliance (pre-1993)

Colours: Red & Black stripes,Black,Black
Change Colours: Yellow/ Blue / White

Programme: Yes

Chairman: Joe Swords

Manager: John Halford, Geoff Brassington
Coach: Carl Lascelles
Physio: Joe Doolan

MEIR K.A.

Secretary: Chris Robinson, 19 The Square, Meir, Stoke-on-Trent ST3 6DW Tel: 01782 332152
Ground: Kings Park, Hilderstone Road, Meir Heath, Stoke-on-Trent Tel: 01782 388465
Directions: M6 jct 14, A34 to Stone, A520 to Rough Close then Meir Heath, turnright (B5066) ground approx 1 mile on right. 3m Blythe Bridge (BR)
Capacity: 5,000 Seats: 200 Cover: 250 Floodlights: Yes Club Shop: No
Clubhouse: Open matchdays. Hot food available.
HONOURS: Staffs Snr Lg 88-89, 90-91; Staffs FA Vase 93-94; Walsall & Dist Sen Cup 89-90; Mid Comb Prem Lge R-up 96-97; Mid Comb Lge Chall Cup R-up 97-98
PREVIOUS **Leagues:** Staffs Alliance/ Staffs Snr 84-92 **Ground:** Normacot Rec.
Names: 'The Station' & 'Shoulder of Mutton.'

Founded: 1972 Nickname: Kings
Colours: Yellow/navy/navy
Change colours: All Red
Midweek matchday: Wednesday
Programme: 32 pages 50p
Editor: Kelly Reaney (01782 325624)
President: Peter Bott
Chairman: Des Reaney
Vice Chairman: Graham Lovatt
Manager: Des Reaney Coach: Bernie Bramwell
Press Officer: Mark Allen (01782 304472)
Commercial Mgr: Paul Robinson

NUNEATON GRIFF

Secretary: Pete Kemp,205 Haunchwood Road,Nuneaton, Warwicks. CV10 8DS Tel: 02476 737459 (H) 07761611338 (M)
Ground: The Pingles Stadium, Avenue Road, Nuneaton. Tel: 024 76 37 0688
Directions: Avenue Road (A4252) leads to Cedar Tree Pub traffic lights, where you turn left into the stadium car park service road - unsuitable for coaches.
Capacity: 2,000 **Seats:** 238 **Cover:** 400 **Floodlights:** Yes
Clubhouse: Yes / Usual Licensing hours Tel: 024 7673 5344 (Social Club) **Club Shop:** No No
HONOURS: Coventry Alliance 97-98, Coventry Telegraph Cup 98, 02, Cov. Charity Cup 99, BCFA Junior Cup 98-99 R-up 99-00, Midland Comb Prem Div 99-00 00-01 (NB Only club to be placed in Premier Division on application and win title in first season.) Cov Tel Challenge Cup 00-01, Endsleigh Challenge Cup 00-01, BCFC Challenge Vase R-up 00-01

Founded: 1972-73 Nickname: Griff
Colours: Blue & white/blue/red & blue
Change colours: All yellow
Midweek Matchday:Wednesday
Programme:20 pages 50p
Editor: Rod Grubb (02476 345023)
Chairman: John Gore
Manager: Dave Stringer
2002-03
Captain:Lee Bateman
Leading Goalscorer:Lee Smith 19
Player of the Year:Gareth Plant

PERSHORE TOWN 88

Secretary: Brian Evans, Terl No: 01905 456122 or 07771 956823
Ground: King George V Playing Fields, King Georges Way, Pershore, Worcs (01386556902).
Directions: M5 jct 7, A44 to Pershore (8 miles) cross 1st lights in Pershore,at 2nd lights turn left & fold road round into King Georges Way, ground immediately on left.
Capacity: 4,000 Seats: 200 Cover: 200 Floodlights: Yes (157 lux) Club Shop:No
Clubhouse: Open every evening, and all day Saturdays and Sundays
HONOURS Midland Comb Prem 93-94, Div 2 89-90; Worcs Jnr Cup 90-91, Robert Biggart Cup (5), R-up (3); Worcs Snr Urn 95-96, R-up 92-93, Jack Mould Cup 90-91, Alfred Terry Cup 90-91 Martley Hosp. Cup(`A') 90-91. Pershore Hospital Charity Cup 2001-02
RECORDS: Atttendance: 1,356 v Yeading, FA Cup 4th Qual. Rd 23/10/93 **Scorer**: Simon Judge
PREVIOUS Leagues: Midland Comb 89-90 90-94 Midland Alliance 94-95, 99-00

Founded: 1988 Nickname: The Town
Colours: Blue & White,blue,blueChange:Red
Midweek matchday: Tuesday
Prog: 20 pages, 60p Ed: Graham Merchant
Chairman: Anthony Cosnett
Vice-Chairman: Graham Merchant
Match Secretary: Barbara Hodgkiss
Tel Nos: 01905 452885 or 0787 9845539
Manager: Nigel Russell
2002-2003
Captain: Colin Fulloway
Top Scorer: Simon Judge P.o.Y.: Chris Tew

ROMULUS

Secretary: Andy Fitchett, 7 Saveker Drive, Sutton Coldfield, Birm. B76 1FT Tel: 0121 3111115H 07768 852784M

Ground: Vale Stadium, Farnborough Road, Castle Vale, Birm. B35 7BE. Tel: 0121 7476969 Fax: 0121 7476868 Email: information@romulus-fc.co.uk Website: www.romulus-fc.co.uk

Capacity: 2,000 Seats: 500 Cover: 600 Floodlights: Yes

Directions: From Birmingham City Centre take No. 67 bus alight at terminus. Ground is 3 mins walk. Train - exit at New Street station. Catch No. 67 bus from City centre. If travelling by car contact the secretary for directions.

Founded: 1979

Colours: Red & white stripes/red/red

Change colours: White/white/black

Chairman: John Matthews

Tel: 01827 899583 (H) 0121 693 4747 (B)

RUGBY TOWN

Secretary: David Badger, New House, Halfway Lane, Dunchurch Nr Rugby, Warwicks.CV22 6RP
Tel: 01788 522538 (H) 01812 392842 (M)
Ground: The Rugby Lions R.F.C. Webb Ellis Rd., Rugby CV22 7AU Tel: 01788 334466

Capacity: 3,396 Seated: 240 Standing- Covered 600 Uncovered 2,556

Directions: Second turn right, half mile south west of town centre on A4071,Bilton Road. From NW: M6 Jnc 1 A426 Rugby A4071
From NE: M1 Jnc 20 A426 Rugby A4071. From SE: M1 Jnc 17/M45/A4071 towards Rugby.
Nearest Railway Station: Rugby - recommend taxi 2 miles to ground

Colours: All Tangerine and Black

SHIFNAL TOWN

Secretary: Glyn Davies, 30 Drayton Road, Shifnal, Shropshire, TF11 8BT (01952460326 H)
Ground: Phoenix Park, Coppice Green Lane, Shifnal, Shropshire.
Directions: M54 jct 3, A41 towards Newport, 1st left for Shifnal (3 miles), in Shifnal take 1st right, and sharp right again up Coppice Green Lane, ground800yds on left past Idsall School.
Capacity: 3,000 Seats: 224 Cover: 300 Floodlights: Yes
Clubhouse: Not on ground but in Newport Rd, Shifnal. Open Mon-Fri 7.30-11pm, Sat 7.30-11pm , Sun 12-3 & 7.30-10-30 **Club Shop:** No
HONOURS West Mids Lg 80-81 81-82 Div 1 78-79, Shropshire Snr Cup 80-81 90-91 92-93.
BEST SEASON **FA Cup:** 1982-83 **FA Vase:** 1983-84
PREVIOUS **Leagues:** Wellington (Dist.) 64-69; Shropshire County 69-77 85-93; West Midlands 77-85; Midland Comb. 94-95; Midland Alliance 95-2003

Founded: 1964 Nickname: None.
Colours:All Red & white
Change cols: Blue & white/white/blue & white
Midweek matchday: Tuesday
Programme: 30 pages, 60p
Editor: J. Wilson (01952 274855).
Vice Chairman: Mr. R Owen
President: D Adams
Press Off: K Fullerton 01952 405274
Manager: Bernard Mackey
Assistant Manager: Dave Meachin
Physio: Charlott Lewis

SOUTHAM UNITED

Secretary: Alan D Freeman,3 Old Road, Southam, Warwickshire Cv47 1GF (01926 817711)
Ground: Banbury Road Ground, Southam, Leamington Spa.Warwicks CV 47 0BJ
Tel: 01926 812091

Directions: A423 - 12 miles south of coventry on the Banbury side of Southam
Capacity: 2000 Seats: 200 Cover: 250 Floodlights: Yes
Clubhouse: Yes, with food available Club Shop: No
HONOURS Midland Comb. Prem. Div. R-up 97-98: Birmingham County Sat. Vase 97-98; Coventry Chall. Cup; Coventry City Cup; Coventry & N. Warwicks. Lge Pre. Div.
RECORD **Attendance:** 1,500 v Coventry City, friendly 86-87

Founded: 1905
Colours: Yellow & Royal Blue/blue/blue
Change colours:White & Black/black/black
Midweek Matchday: Tuesday
Programme: 24 pages 50p Editor: Charles Hill

Chairman: Charles Hill
Presss Officer: Czaire Hughes
Manager: Ian Clarke
Assistant Manager: Dave Sturman
Player/Coach: Rob Morey
Physio: Bill Rutledge

WEST MIDLANDS POLICE

Secretary: John Black, 57 Grosvenor Close, Sutton Coldfield, W.Mids. B75 6RP. 0121 308 7673
Ground: Police Sports Ground, `Tally Ho', Pershore Road, Edgbaston, Birmingham B57RN
Tel: 0121626 8228 Website: www.wmpfc.org.uk
Directions: 2 miles south west of city on A441 Pershore Road. Ground is on the left 50yds past Priory Road lights (Warks County Cricket Ground).
3 miles from Birmingham New Street (BR) - buses 45 & 47 from city.
Capacity: 2,500 Seats: 224 Covered: 224 Floodlights: Yes
Clubhouse: 3 bars including snooker room, ballroom, kitchen. Hot &cold food. Open all day.
BEST SEASON **FA Vase:** Quarter Final 91-92 **FA Cup:** 2nd Q ual Rd 91-92

Founded: 1974
Colours: Red & black/ black/black
Change Colours: All Blue
Midweek matchday: Tues/Thurs.
Programme: 32 pages, £1.00
Editor: D.Coulson (01283 533791)
President: Chief Constable Paul Scott-Lee
Chairman: Ass. Chief Constable: Paul Blewitt
Manager: Jim Scott Coach: Tony Workman

DIVISION ONE CLUBS

BARNT GREEN SPARTAK

Ground: Alvechurch FC, Lye Meadow, Redditch Road, Alvechurch, Worcestershire. Tel: 0121 445 2929

BLACKHEATH

Secretary: Paul Boswell, 34 Princes Rd., Tividale, W. Mids. B69 2LR
Tel: 0121 532 4032 (H) 07720 956309 (M)
Ground: Invensys Brook Crompton Sports Ground, Oakemore Rd.,
Rowley Regis Tel: 0121 698 3253
Colours: Red & white/red/red

BLOXWICH TOWN

Ground: Abbey Pk, Glastonbury Crnt, Bloxwich, Walsall. Tel: 01922 477640

BURNTWOOD

Secretary: David Cox, 12 Galway Road, Burntwood, Staffs. WS7 8DT
Tel No: 07931 626887 (M)
Ground: Memorial Institute, Rugeley Road, Burntwood. Tel: 01543 675578
Colours: Red and Blue stripes/Blue/Red

CADBURY ATHLETIC

Secretary: Gerry Boyle,1 Greenway Gardens, Kings Norton, Birmingham B38 9RY (0121 628 6533 (H) 07974 382986 (M)
Ground: Cadbury Recreation Ground, Bournville Lane, B'ham. B14 6DL Tel No: 0121 458 2000 x 3316 or 0121 454 4264 **Colours:** All Purple.

FAIRFIELD VILLA

Secretary/Press Officer: C W Harris, 28 ShelleyClose, Catshill, Bromsgrove B61 0NH Tel: 01527 877203
Ground: Bromsgrove Rvrs F.C. See their details.
Colours: All Red & Black

HANDSAKER

Secretary: Claire Handsaker, 43 Bridle Lane, Streetly, Sutton Coldfield.
Tel: 0121 580 9308 (H) 07956 517258 (M)
Ground: Hollyfields Centre Club Ltd., Woodacre Road, Erdington Birmingham B24 0JT Tel: 0121 373 1018
Colours: Navy & white stripes/navy & red trim/navy & red trim

KENILWORTH TOWN

Secretary: Mrs Sally McKenzie, K.T.F.C.,Marlborough House, Holly Walk, Leamington Spa CV32 4JA 01926 855247 (H) 886632 (W)
Ground: K.T.F.C. Gypsy Lane (off Rouncil Lane), Kenilworth, Warwicks. Tel: 01926 50851
Colours: All blue

KNOWLE

Secretary: Roger Whittick, 149 Richmond Road, Solihull B92 7RZ
Tel No :0121 684 2753 (H) 07944 753551 (M)
Ground: Hampton Rd, Knowle, Solihull , W.Mid B93 0NX Tel: 01564 779807 **Colours:** Red/black/black

LITTLETON

Five Acres, Pebworth Road, North Littleton, Evesham, Worcestershire

LOUGHBOROUGH F.C.

Secretary: John Belton: 51 Farndale Drive, Loughborough, Leics.LE112RG Tel No: 01509 231583 (H) 01509 231583 (W)
Ground: The Drome, Derby Road Playing Fields, Derby Road, Loughborough Tel: 01509 610022 **Colours:** All white and blue.

NORTHFIELD TOWN

Secretary: Matthew Kirby, 53 Park Dale Drive, Birmingham B31 4RN
Tel: 0121 604 2202 (H) 07876 143121 (M)
Ground: Shenley Lane Comm. Assoc. & Sports Centre, 472 Shenley Lane, Birmingham B29 4HZ Tel: 0121 478 3900 **Colours:** yellow/blue/yellow

OLD HILL TOWN

Secretary: Scott Wilshaw, 10 Rowley Hill View, Cradley Heath, West Midlands. B64 7ER 01384 564466 (H) 07976 849022 (M)
Ground: Hingleys, Bluebell Rd, Cradley Heath, West Midlands. (01384 566827)
Colours: All maroon

PILKINGTON XXX

Triplex Sports Ground, Eckersall Road, Kings Norton, Birmingham, West Midlands
Tel: 0121 458 4570

POLESWORTH NORTH WARWICK

Secretary: Mrs Lynn Wright, 69 Chaytor Rd,.Polesworth, Tamworth Staffs. B78 1JS (01827 892896 or 0797 389 8523)
Ground: North Warwick Sports Ground, Hermitage Hill, Tamworth Road, Polesworth, Warks.
Colours: Green/ Black/ Black

STOCKINGFORD AA

Ground: The Pavilion, Ansley Road, Stockingford, Nuneaton, Warwicks. Tel: 02476 387743

THIMBLEMILL R.E.C.

Secretary: Gerry Houten, 86 Gower Road, Halesowen, W.Midlands, B62 9BT Tel Nos: 0121 422 3357 (H) 07966 374771 (M)
Ground: Thimblemill Recreation, Thimblemill Road, Smethwick, Warley. Tel: 0121 429 2459
Colours: Red & Blue/ Blue/ Blue.

WILMCOTE SPORTS & SOCIAL

Secretary: Jennifer Smith, 19 Nightingale Close, Spernal Lane, Great Alne, Warwicks. B49 6PE 01789 488077 (H)
Ground: The Patch, Rear of Wilmcote S.S.Club, Astton Cantlow Road, Wilmcote, Stratford on Avon (01789 297895)
Colours: Green & yellow / Green / Yellow

EXPRESS & STAR
WEST MIDLANDS (REGIONAL) LEAGUE

FEEDER TO: MIDLAND ALLIANCE

Hon Secretary: Neil Juggins
14 Badgers Lane, Blackwell, Bromsgrove

THE main honours went to Herefordshire this season, with Hereford-based Westfields clinching the premier division championship for the first time, whilst Kington Town claimed the runners-up spot before going on to lift the league cup.

The season began with a reduced programme of fixtures following the departures of Causeway United (promoted to the Midland Alliance), Darlston Town (attaining the dubious status of being the first club to be demoted for failing to comply with ground grading regulations for a second time) and Star (returning to the Shropshire League), whilst Sedgley White Lions had been promoted. In the league the lead changed hands several times, with Westfields heading the table initially on August Bank Holiday Monday, only for Kington to overtake them before they, too were overhauled by Little Drayton Rangers into September and October. Westfields briefly interrupted Drayton's progress in November before victory over fellow contenders Tipton Town early in December saw Westfields resume top spot. This was held until February when Tipton headed the table for a month but Westfields always had several games in hand and after going back to the top on March 15th they were never headed again.

Tipton's challenge faded and Kington emerged as the only likely contenders in the closing weeks of the season, despite Westfields leading by as many as 14 points on Easter Saturday, at which stage Kington had just six games to play, one of them a game in hand. The penultimate Saturday of the season went by with Kington still trailing by nine points and only three games to play but home and away victories for Kington over Westfields took the outcome of the championship to the final day when Westfields claimed the title with a 4-1 victory over Ettingshall. For Westfields it was the club's first championship success since winning promotion back in 1987, beating their best previous placing of fifth. Promotion to the Midland Alliance has since been confirmed, and their place in the WMRL will be filled by Wednesfield, returning after a six year absence. Kington's 24 match unbeaten run to the season's end only enabled the club to claim the Keys Cup, as runners-up, though they added the league cup with a 2-0 victory over Bustleholme. Tipton's final placing of third was their best after 12 seasons of premier division membership, and there was the added bonus of success in the newly instituted Birmingham FA Midweek Challenge Cup, Midland Combination club Rugby Town being overwhelmed 4-1 in the final.

The bottom end of the table was beginning to take shape by October, with dudley Town and Walsall Wood occupying familiar positions. Wood fell to the bottom on September 21st and did not record their first victory until mid december, in their 18th game. Thereafter a recovery of sorts was mounted, to the extent that the Oak Park club finally lifted itself off the bottom in mid-March to set up a three way tussle with Dudley and Gornal Athletic. However, it was Dudley Town that escaped the bottom two places with a 3-3 draw at Heath Hayes on the closing day of the league season, leaving the other two facing relegation to division one.

In division one (north) it soon became apparent that the title was going to be a three way tussle between Lucas Sports, Newport Town and Bilston Town. The latter is a familiar name but is actually a new club formed from the ashes of the previous season's Southern League club, which had disbanded in the summer. Lucas and Bilston both opened the season with nine consecutive victories, with Lucas leading the way from September 14th to November 9th. The first defeat was suffered in the 15th game and thereafter the club's challenge began to fade. Bilston, meanwhile, made use of the availability of floodlights to get ahead with their fixtures and by the end of 2002 led Lucas and Newport by 13 and 14 points respectively, through crucially the latter had five games in hand. Into January and victory for Bilston over Lucas in January, coupled with a rare Newport defeat, left Bilston with the title seemingly in their grasp. However, after remaining unbeaten in the first 21 games, two successive defeats followed for Bilston, the second of these coming in favour of Newport, and the race was on again. Bilston went on to win all ten remaining games but it proved to be insufficient, for Newport finished the season with a 20 game unbeaten league run, 18 of them victories, which included a sequence of 13 straight wins to finish the season. Having completed their programme on May Day Bank Holiday Monday Bilston could only watch as Newport won their two remaining fixtures, a 1-0 victory over Ashbourne on May 10th taking Newport to the top of the table for the first time all season to clinch the championship, and ensure promotion to the premier division.

At the opposite end of the table Walsall Wood reserves created a host of unwanted records. The previous season's dismal haul of five points from 30 games was actually exceeded, with just three points being taken from a 34 game programme. The side has now won just once in 64 games over two seasons and has gone 40 games since their last league victory, equalling the WMRL record set by Oldswinford in 1987-88.

In division one (south) Chaddesley Corbett headed the table for a while before Hinton (another Hereford based club) took over, opening up a seven point lead by the end of October. However, Chaddesley had overhauled this deficit a month later, only for HInton to resume top spot a couple of weeks later after inflicting what proved to be one of just two defeats suffered by Bewdley Town. Hinton then retained the lead with Bewdley close behind, with as many as six games in hand, until the championship was decided as early as March 29th. Hinton completed their league programme with a defeat, whilst a 2-0 victory for Bewdley over Leominster took them to the top of the table for the first time, in an unassailable position with five games still to play.

Due to the disparity in fixture programmes (26 as opposed to 34) the league cup competition became a supplementary cup competition, contested by south division clubs only, which was ultimately won by Wyre Forest Brintons.

In external competitions Tipton was not the only WMRL club to enjoy success this season. Both the Herefordshire Challenge Cup and Shropshire County Cup finals were all WMRL affairs, Westfields defeating Kington in the Herefordshire final, and Shawbury United overcoming Newport in the Shropshire competition. Meanwhile in the Worcestershire Senior Urn Lye Town reached the final, only to go down to Midland Alliance club Studley. However, there was little joy in the FA Vase for WMRL clubs, with only Ledbury Town, Lye Town and Malvern Town making much progress, all three being eliminated in the First Round Proper.

Steve Carr.

FINAL LEAGUE TABLES 2002-03

PREMIER DIVISION	P	W	D	L	F	A	Pts
Westfields	42	32	6	4	119	30	102
Kington Town	42	31	6	5	121	51	99
Tipton Town	42	27	8	7	95	40	89
Little Drayton Rangers	42	26	5	11	113	66	83
Tividale	42	22	10	10	104	53	76
Malvern Town	42	22	9	11	96	49	75
Shawbury United	42	21	9	12	86	68	72
Lye Town	42	19	7	16	69	64	64
Ledbury Town	42	18	9	15	90	75	63
Brierley & Hagley All	42	17	11	14	74	73	62
Wellington	42	16	10	16	59	69	58
Heath Hayes	42	15	12	15	72	75	57
W'ton Casuals	42	17	5	20	71	91	56
W'ton United	42	15	8	19	66	73	53
Smethwick Sikh Temple	42	11	11	20	58	83	44
Sedgley White Lions	42	11	9	22	48	74	42
Ettingshall H T	42	12	5	25	65	92	41
Bustleholme	42	11	7	24	69	93	40
Bromyard Town	42	11	2	29	61	125	35
Dudley Town	42	7	9	26	46	112	30
Walsall Wood	42	6	11	25	48	109	29
Gornal Athletic	42	7	7	28	41	106	28

DIVISION ONE NORTH	P	W	D	L	F	A	Pts
Newport Town	34	29	3	2	105	28	90
Bilston Town	34	28	4	2	125	29	88
Lucas Sports	34	25	3	6	124	51	78
Brereton Social	34	18	7	9	87	58	61
Ashbourne United	34	18	5	11	106	69	59
Morda United	34	16	5	13	65	57	53
Darlaston Town	34	14	8	12	76	75	50
Marston Wolves	34	14	6	14	65	58	48
Great Wyrley	34	13	7	14	84	69	46
Sikh Hunters	34	12	9	13	81	73	45
Heath Hayes Reserves	34	12	6	16	55	72	42
Wrockwardine Wood	34	10	7	17	45	77	37
Wednesbury Town	34	10	5	19	68	85	35
Shenstone Pathfinder	34	9	8	17	50	81	35
Roverway	34	9	7	18	52	91	34
Wyrley Rangers	34	10	3	21	42	82	33
W'ton Sports Gnst	34	9	4	21	51	101	31
Walsall Wood reserves	34	0	3	31	23	148	3

Sheffield Sports resigned during the season.

DIVISION ONE SOUTH	P	W	D	L	F	A	Pts
Bewdley Town	26	19	5	2	83	31	62
Hinton	26	17	1	8	74	42	52
Blackheath Town	26	14	8	4	65	36	50
Bridgnorth Town Res.	26	14	6	6	58	34	48
Mahal	26	13	5	8	55	46	44
Chaddesley Corbett	26	12	6	8	50	37	42
Ludlow Town Reserves	26	10	8	8	61	51	38
Wyre Forest Brintons	26	11	3	12	58	60	36
Lye Town Reserves	26	10	5	11	36	38	35
Malvern Town Reserves	26	8	6	12	52	62	30
Bustleholme Reserves	26	5	5	16	38	70	20
Ledbury Town reserves	26	5	4	17	38	76	19
Leominster Town	26	4	5	17	36	74	17
Malvern Rangers	26	4	5	17	33	80	17

Premier Division	1	2	3	4	5	6	7	8	9	10	11	12	13	14	15	16	17	18	19	20	21	22
1 Brierley & Hagley All		1-3	4-1	3-0	5-1	1-1	1-3	3-2	0-0	1-2	2-1	0-5	3-1	0-0	2-2	1-3	1-1	0-2	2-2	3-0	3-2	0-3
2 Bromyard Town	3-4		1-0	6-1	5-2	3-1	1-5	1-4	1-7	1-4	3-1	2-3	2-4	3-1	0-2	0-4	1-4	2-0	2-3	1-2	0-0	0-9
3 Bustleholme	3-5	2-1		0-2	0-2	2-0	1-2	1-2	3-1	2-4	5-2	2-2	4-0	4-0	3-3	1-2	1-2	1-2	1-1	2-1	2-3	1-4
4 Dudley Town	1-6	4-0	1-2		0-2	0-2	1-1	0-2	2-1	0-2	1-2	2-1	2-2	0-9	1-1	0-1	1-0	1-4	2-3	2-2	1-2	0-3
5 Ettingshall Holy Trinity	0-1	2-3	0-3	3-3		5-0	1-3	3-6	4-1	3-4	0-0	0-1	3-2	3-1	1-2	1-2	0-2	1-2	1-1	2-1	4-0	0-2
6 Gornal Athletic	0-2	2-0	2-2	1-0	5-1		0-2	1-6	2-4	0-5	0-4	1-0	1-3	1-2	0-1	0-4	1-1	2-1	0-4	1-3	1-1	1-5
7 Heath Hayes	1-1	4-3	3-2	3-3	0-4	2-2		0-1	3-4	1-2	0-2	0-1	0-0	4-	2-2	1-4	1-3	2-2	0-3	9-1	1-1	2-4
8 Kington Town	3-1	5-0	4-1	6-2	5-1	4-1	0-0		0-1	2-2	2-0	4-2	1-0	1-2	3-1	1-1	2-1	4-1	3-1	4-2	8-0	2-1
9 Ledbury Town	2-0	2-2	6-1	4-2	5-1	5-2	0-1	1-2		3-1	4-1	3-2	1-1	3-3	1-1	0-4	1-1	3-3	1-1	3-3	3-0	0-1
10 Little Drayton Rangers	3-0	3-0	3-0	8-0	5-1	3-1	2-1	2-1	4-2		1-2	0-2	3-0	2-3	3-1	1-1	2-2	5-1	1-3	4-0	1-0	3-1
11 Lye Town	2-3	1-0	2-1	1-2	4-2	1-1	2-2	1-1	4-0	5-1		2-1	1-2	1-1	2-0	0-2	1-2	2-1	2-0	5-1	2-0	0-1
12 Malvern Town	7-1	3-2	2-2	2-1	0-0	6-0	0-2	1-1	5-2	3-4	6-0		2-0	1-2	6-0	0-0	3-1	1-2	2-0	4-1	1-2	0-0
13 Sedley White Lions	0-0	1-3	1-1	2-0	2-4	1-0	1-1	1-2	0-1	1-1	0-1	0-2		0-3	1-1	0-1	1-0	2-0	3-2	1-3	1-1	0-3
14 Shawbury United	2-1	3-0	4-2	4-2	1-2	1-1	2-1	3-4	1-0	2-1	3-3	0-3	3-2		1-2	1-3	2-1	4-0	1-2	2-1	1-1	1-1
15 Smethwick Sikh Temple	2-2	3-0	2-1	0-1	2-3	3-1	0-1	1-3	0-5	5-2	1-3	0-2	2-3	0-5		1-2	0-5	4-1	3-0	1-1	1-0	3-4
16 Tipton Town	2-2	4-2	3-0	5-2	0-0	4-1	7-0	0-1	3-0	0-2	3-2	1-2	0-1	3-2	0-0		3-3	4-2	5-2	4-0	3-0	0-1
17 Tividale	3-1	9-1	6-1	4-0	1-0	4-1	1-2	1-1	1-2	2-4	1-1	3-2	2-1	2-2	2-1	0-1		0-1	5-1	5-4	7-1	1-1
18 W'ton Casuals	0-2	2-1	2-1	1-1	2-0	3-0	0-2	4-5	3-5	2-2	2-0	4-6	5-3	0-2	4-1	3-1	0-5		1-0	0-3	3-2	1-4
19 W'ton United	0-1	0-2	1-3	0-0	3-0	2-0	2-1	1-4	3-1	3-0	2-0	0-2	3-1	1-2	2-0	0-1	3-3	1-1		4-0	4-2	0-3
20 Walsall Wood	1-4	3-0	0-3	1-1	1-0	0-2	1-1	1-5	0-2	2-7	0-1	1-1	1-2	1-1	1-1	1-3	0-3	1-2	1-1		1-1	1-1
21 Wellington	1-1	4-0	1-1	3-1	2-1	3-1	0-1	3-1	2-0	3-2	1-2	1-1	3-1	2-0	2-1	1-1	0-1	2-1	2-1	4-0		0-1
22 Westfields	2-0	6-0	4-0	7-0	4-1	2-1	6-1	1-3	1-0	3-2	3-0	0-0	2-0	4-1	1-1	2-0	0-3	3-0	7-1	6-0	2-0	

PREMIER DIVISION LEAGUE CUP 2002-03

FIRST ROUND

Kington	v	Little Drayton R'gers	3-2*
Shawbury United	v	Bromyard Town	6-2
Ledbury Town	v	Gornal Athletic	9-1
Heath Hayes	v	Brierley & Hagley All	1-4
W'ton Casuals	v	Tividale	0-6
Bustleholme	v	Wellington	4-1

*AET

SECOND ROUND

W'ton United	v	Walsall Wood	3-2
Shawbury United	v	Lye Town	1-3
Tipton Town	v	Smethwick Sikh T.	6-0
Dudley Town	v	Brierley & Hagley All	0-3
Ettingshall H T	v	Tividale	1-1* (4-2 pens)
Sedgley White Lions	v	Kington Town	0-1
Bustleholme	v	Westfields	3-1
Ledbury Town	v	Mlalvern Town	2-0

QUARTER FINALS

Ettingshall H T	v	Tipton Town	2-1
Lye Town	v	Bustleholme	2-2*(4-2p)
Ledbury Town	v	Kington Town	1-2
W'ton United	v	Brierley Hagley All	2-1

SEMI FINALS

(1st leg)

Bustleholme	v	Ettingshall H T	2-3
W'ton United	v	Kington Town	0-1

(2nd Leg)

Ettingshall H T	v	Bustleholme	1-3
Kington Town	v	W'ton United	1-0

FINAL

Bustleholme v Kington Town 0-2 at Malvern Town FC

DIVISION ONE (SOUTH) SUPPLEMENTARY CUP

PRELIMINARY ROUND

Lye Town Reserves	v	Bewdley Town	2-1
Blackheath Town	v	Wyre Forest Brintons	1-2
Ludlow Town Res.	v	Bustleholme Res.	5-2
Hinton	v	Malvern Rangers	4-0
Bridgnorth Town	v	Mahal	3-1
Leominster Town	v	Chaddesley Corbett	3-4*

QUARTER FINALS

Malvern Town Res.	v	Bridgnorth T. Res.	1-1*(3-1p)
Wyre Forest Brintons	v	Hinton	3-1
Chaddesley Corbett	v	Lye Town Reserves	1-3
Ludlow Town Res.	v	Ledbury Town Res.	3-1

SEMI FINALS

(1st Leg)

Wyre Forest Brintons	v	Malvern Town Res.	11-0
Ludlow Town Res.	v	Lye Town Reserves	1-1

(2nd Leg)

Malvern Town Res.	v	Wyre Forest Brintons	2-2
Lye Town Reserves	v	Ludlow Town Res.	1-4

FINAL

Ludlow Town Res. v Wyre Forest Brintons 0-1 at Bridgnorth Town FC

YOUTH DIVISIONS

YOUTH NORTH	P	W	D	L	F	A	Pts
Great Barr H N	16	11	2	3	45	17	35
Chasetown	16	11	2	3	33	23	35
Heath Hayes	16	10	2	4	37	19	32
Grosvenor Continental	16	9	0	7	43	26	27
Pelsall Villa Colts	16	8	3	5	27	27	27
Willenhall Town	16	5	3	8	22	32	18
Penridge Town Juniors	16	4	5	7	18	24	17
Walsall Wood	16	2	3	11	20	45	9
Rushall	16	2	0	14	15	47	6

Bilston resigned

YOUTH SOUTH	P	W	D	L	F	A	Pts
Lye Town	18	13	2	3	49	10	41
Halesowen Town Youth	18	12	3	3	39	15	39
Gornal Athletic	18	9	5	4	30	23	32
Cradley Town	18	9	2	7	38	28	29
Tividale	18	8	5	5	22	25	29
Stratford Town	18	6	3	9	33	43	21
Star	18	6	2	10	33	41	20
Tipton Town	18	6	1	11	21	33	19
Handrahan Timbers	18	3	5	10	23	35	14
Ludlow Town	18	2	4	12	16	51	10

LEAGUE CUP

SEMI FINALS

(1st Leg)

Stratford Town	v	Lye Town	2-5
Cradley Town	v	Star	3-4

(2nd Leg)

Lye Town	v	Stratford Town	1-3
Star	v	Cradley Town	5-6*(3-4p)

FINAL

Cradley Town v Lye Town 2-1 at W'ton Casual FC

BRIERLEY HILL & HAGLEY ALLIANCE

Secretary: Tony Gore, 114 Dobbins Oak Road, Pedmore, Stourbridge, W.Mids DY9 0XY
Tel: 01562 720158 (H) 07932 493128 (M)

Ground: Halesowen Harriers FC, Park Road, Halesowen, West Mids. Tel: 01384 896748
Capacity: 4,000 Seats: 350 Cover: 500 Floodlights: Yes

Directions: From M5 junction 3, follow A456 towards Kidderminster to first island. Turn right onto A459 towards Dudley. Turn left at next island onto A458 towards Stourbridge. Follow this road for 2 miles. Ground is on left-hand side.

PREVIOUS **Names**: Oldswinford F & SC 55-93, Brierley Hill Town 93-01

Founded: 1955
Nickname: Lions
Colours: Blue & white shirts & shorts, white socks
Change colours: Green & white hoops, white shorts, black socks

Programme: 20 pages, 50p
Editor: Secretary
Chairman: Lee Robson

BROMYARD TOWN

Secretary: Tony Haverfield, 16 Highwell Avenue, Bromyard, Hereford HR7 4EL
Tel & Fax: 01885 483655 (H) 07885 849948 (M)
Ground: Delahay Meadow, Stourport Road, Bromyard HR7 4NT Tel: 01885 483974

Directions: 1/4 mile outside Bromyard on the Stourport/Kidderminster road (B4203). The ground is on the right through iron gates, adjacent to O'Malleys Irish restaurant.

Honours: Smedley Cooke Mem. Cup: 2001-02, West Mid Regional Lg.: Div 1 S 99-2000, Herefordshire Cup 96-97, 99-2000
Best season: **F.A.Vase:** 2nd Rd 2001-02

Founded: 1893
Colours: Blue & black/black/blue
Change colours: Yellow/red/yellow

Chairman: Tony Watkins
Tel: 01885 483509

BUSTLEHOME

Secretary: Peter John Lewis, 19 Bernard Street, West Bromwich B71 1DJ
Tel: 0121 580 0573

Ground: Tipton Sports Academy, Wednesbury Oak Road, Tipton DY4 0BS

Directions: From M6 Junction 9, take A461, through Wednesbury Town centre to Ocker Hill Island. Follow signpost here taking a full right turn towards Bilston A4098 for half a mile, turning left at traffic lights A4037. Ground is 50 yards on left.

FACT FILE
Founded: 1975
Colours: Yellow/green/green
Change colours: All white

CLUB PERSONNEL
Chairman: Colin Hall

DUDLEY TOWN

Secretary: Margaret Turner, 3,Straits Road, Lower Gornal, Dudley, DY3 2UY Tel: 01384 214741
Ground: The Beeches, Packwood Road, Tividale W,Mids Tel : 01384 211743
Directions: M5 Jct 2 signs to Dudley (A4123). One mile past school and playing fields under walkway to lights. Left into Regent Road.,left into Elm Terrace then left again into BirchTerrace and 2nd left into Packwood Road. Ground is at end of cul-de-sac.
Capacity: 500 Cover: 1000 Seats: 100 Floodlights: Yes Club Shop: No
Clubhouse: Social club open on matchday . Food available from snackbar
HONOURS Southern Lg Midland Div 84-85, Birmingham Comb 33-34 (R-up 34-35 47-48), Midland (Worcs) Comb 31-32 (R-up 29-30 30-31), West Mids Lg Cp R-up 75-76 (Div2 Cp R-up 80-81), Birmingham Senior Cup 85-86 (R-up 64-65 83-84)Worcs SeniorCp 45-46(joint)(R-up 84-85), Camkin Cp 64-65, Worcs Junior Cp 83-84

Formed: 1893 Nickname: The Robins
Colours: Red/black/black
Change: Yellow/blackor yellow/grey or red
Midweek matchday: Tuesday 7.45pm
Programme: 28 pages 75p Editor: T.B.A.
Website: www.dtfc.net
Chairman: Nevil Jeynes
Vice Chairman: Alan Guest
President: N D Jeynes
Manager: Ian Davis Asst Man: Tony Higgins
2002-2003 Captain:& P.o.Y.: Chris Walwyn
Top Scorer: Ricki Dudley

ETTINGSHALL HOLY TRINITY

Secretary: Graham Mills, 27 Ashen Close, Sedgley, Dudley, West Mids DY3 3UZ(01902 66222)
Ground: Aldersley Stadium, Aldersley Road, Tettenhal, Wolverhampton (01902 556200)
Directions: From Wolverhampton take A41 Tettenhall Road, 1.5 miles turn right into Lower Street, then right into Aldersley Road, ground on right
HONOURS West Mids Lg Div 1 Cup R-up 85-86 (Div 2 R-up 84-85), Sporting Award 85-86,Staffs Co. Lg R-up 82-83 (Lg Shield 82-83 83-84), Ike Cooper Cup 82-84 83-84,Sporting Club Award 81-82, Wolverhampton & District Amateur Lg 80-81 (Div 1 65-66, Div 2 64-65), Div 1/2 Cup 64-65 65-66, A H Oakley Cup 80-81, J W Hunt Cup 82-83 83-84 (R-up 79-80), Wolverhampton Cup 83-84 (R-up 82-83)
PREVIOUS **League:** Wednesbury Church & Chapel (early 1900s), Bilston Youth (1950s),Wolverhampton & District Amateur (1960s), Staffs County (South)

FACT FILE
Founded: 1920 Nickname: Trins
Club Sponsors: DKB Electric/ John O'Dell
Colours: Green & white/green/green& white
Change colours: Red/white/red
Midweek matchday: Wednesday
Prog. Editor: John Edwards (01785 713458)
Chairman:John Robinson Pres: David Gadd
Manager: Graham Mills Physio: David Gads

HEATH HAYES

Secretary: John Deans, 280 Hednesford Road, Heath Hayes, Cannock, Staffs. WS12 5DS
Tel: 01543 279849 (H)
Ground: Coppice Colliery Ground, Newlands Lane, Heath Hayes, Cannock, Staffs. (07976 269280)

Directions: From Cannock, take Lichfield road. After 2.5 miles take first right past Texaco garage on right.

Colours: Blue & white stripes/blue/blue
Change Colours: Red & black/black/black

CLUB PERSONNEL
Chairman John Weldon
Manager: Paul Kent
Coach: Geraint Jones
Reserve Team Manager: Andrew Cox
Physio: John Thacker

KINGTON TOWN

Secretary: Pauline Shaw, 9 Banley Drive, Headbrook, Kington, Herefordshire HR5 3FD
Tel No: 01544 231777
Ground: Park Road Ground, Mill Street, Kington, Hereford (01544 231007)

Directions: Follow signs for Kington Town Centre, look for left turn between the Town Clock and the Burton Hotel. Carry on this road for 500 metres, ground on left as road bends

FACT FILE
Colours: Yellow /black/black
Change colours: All Red

CLUB PERSONNEL
Chairman: William Mayglothing

LEDBURY TOWN

Secretary: Mike Clueit, 55 Lawnside Road, Ledbury, Herefordshire, HR8 2AE.
Tel: 01531 633 182
Ground: New Street, Ledbury, Herefordshire Tel: 01531 631 463
Capacity: 2,500 Covered Seating: 200 Covered Standing: 100 Floodlights: Yes
Directions: Leave M50 at junction 2. Take A417 to Ledbury. At first island take first exit and at second island take fourth exit. ground is 100 yards on right.
Clubhouse Mon-Fri 7-1pm Sat & Sun: 12noon -11p.m. Hot Food on matchdays.
HONOURS: Worcs Infirmary Cup 2002-03.Div 1 South 99-00 HFA RoseBowl 99-00
PREVIOUS Leagues: Midland Combination, Banks's West Mid Div 1 South
RECORD Attendance: 500 v Malvern 2002-2003
BEST SEASON FA Vase: 4th Round 1980-81

FACT FILE
Formed: 1893
Colours: Black & white/black/black
Change colours: Red & blue/red/red
Midweek Matchday: Wednesday
Programme: Yes Price:£1.00

CLUB PERSONNEL
Chairman: Chris Stephens
Manager: Paul WilbandAsst. Man.Roly Welch
Physio:Matt Panter **2002-2003** Capt: Stuart Hall
P.o.Y.: Chris Powell Top Scorer Robert Colwell(Top Lg scorer for last 4 Seasons)

LITTLE DRAYTON RANGERS

Secretary: Brian Garratt, 4 Quarry Bank Road, Market Drayton, Shropshire TF9 1DR
Tel: 01630 654618 (H)
Ground: Greenfield Sports Club, Greenfield Lane, Market Drayton. Tel: 01630 655088

Directions: A41 to Tern Hill island, turn right for Newcastle-u-Lyme. Over 1st island and turn right at next, by Gingerbread P.H. towards town centre. After 200 yds turn right, before going over bridge, into Greenfields Lane. Ground is 150 yds down lane on right.

Colours: Royal & pale blue stripes/royal/royal
Change Colours:Red & Blue stripes/blue/red

Chairman: John Thorneycroft

LYE TOWN

Secretary: John Woodhouse, 46 Surfeit Hill, Cradley Heath, Warley, West Midlands. B64 7EB
Tel Nos: 01384 633976(H) 0121 627 6600(W) **Ground:** Sports Ground, Stourbridge Road, Lye (01384 422672) **Directions:** On A458 Birmingham-Stourbridge road about 400yds afterlights/crossroads at Lye. From M5 jct 3 take road marked Kidderminster as faras lights at bottom of Hagley Hill, right at island, 3rd turn off at nextisland,turn off left at crossroads/lights, ground about 400yds on left. Quarter mile from Lye (BR)
Capacity: 5,000 Seats: 200 Cover: 600 Floodlights: Yes **Clubhouse:** Yes (01384 822672)
HONOURS West Mids Lg R-up 76-77 78-79 79-80 80-81 (Prem. Div Cup 75-76), Midland Comb.35-36 (R-up 32-33 34-35 37-38), W.Mid Lg Winners 97-98-99
PREVIOUS **Leagues:** Midland Combination 31-39
RECORD **Gate:** 6,000 v Brierley Alliance

FACT FILE
Founded: 1930 Nickname: Flyers
Colours: Blue & white stripes/blue/blue
Change Colours: Yellow/green/yellow
Programme: 24 pages, 40p
Editor: Roy Pearson
Chairman: Roy Pearson
President: Ian Cole
Manager: Geoff Moss
Coach: John Woodhouse
Physio: Harry Hill

MALVERN TOWN

Secretary: Margaret Caldicott, 20 Nixon Court, Callow End, Worcester WR2 4UU 01905 831327
Ground: Langland Stadium, Langland Avenue, Malvern, Worcs Tel: 01684 574068
Directions: From Worcester take A449 to Malvern.Turn left at roundabout signposted B4208 to Welland. Left at traffic lights into Pickersleigh Road. Turn left at Longford Arms Pub, into Maddesfield R oad. 2nd left into Langland Ave., ground 100yds on right. 1 mile from Malvern (BR)
Capacity: 4,000 **Seats:** 140 **Cover:** 310 **Floodlights:** Yes **Shop:** No
Clubhouse: 2 bars, large dance area, teabar matchdays **Best F.A.Vase Season:** 99-00 2nd Rd
HONOURS Worcester/ Midland Comb. 55-56 Mid Comb Cup R-up 75-76, WFA Senior Urn (7), WFA Sat Junior Cup Winners (4) Banks's Brewery Premier League Cup R-up 87-88 WFA Nursing Cup Winners 97-98, Robert Biggart Cup Winners 97-98, 98-99 ,Evesham Hosp Cup 99-00
PREVIOUS League: Midland Comb. 55-79 **RECORD Gate:** 1,221 v Worcester, FA Cup

Founded:1947 Sponsors: Malvern Instruments
Colours: Claret and Sky Blue
Change:White/black/maroon
Reserves League: Banks's Brewery Div 1 S
Midweek Matchday: Tuesday
Prog: 28 pages 50p Editor: Mark Caldicott
Chairman: Geoff Brewer President: R Box
Manager: Neil Hunt
Gen Manager: Richard Anson
2002-03 Leading Goalscorer:D.Roberts/D.Cox
Captain:Dean Roberts
Player of the Year: Rik Halion

NEWPORT TOWN

Ground: Wolverhampton Casuals FC, Brinsford Lane, Coven Heath, Wolverhampton
Tel: 01902 783214

Directions: Onto M54 from M6 North, at Junc 2 turn right (A449 to Stafford).Ground half a mile, turn right into Brinsford Lane. Billbrooke (BR) 2 miles

Capacity: 2,000 Seats: 50 Cover: 50 Floodlights: No

Clubhouse: Bar & snacks, open Tues/Wed/Thurs/Sat/Sun & alternate Mondays

HONOURS: West Mids (Reg) Lge Div. 1 North 2002-03

SEDGLEY WHITE LION

Secretary: David Ferguson, 3 Earl Street, Coseley, West. Mids. WV14 8JT
Tel: 0121 520 8324 (H) 07881 856039 (M)
Ground: c/o Gornal Athletic - Garden Walk Stadium, Lower Gornal, Dudley, West Mids.
Tel: 01384 358398
Directions: From Dudley take A459 to Sedgley past the Burton Road Hospital.
1st on left at the Green Dragon public house on the B4175 (Jews Lane). Follow the road until you come to the Old Bull's Head, turn left into Rednall Road, 2nd left to Garden Walk
Capacity: 3,000 Seats: 100 Cover: 500 Floodlights: Yes Club Shop: No

Founded: 1985
Colours: White/royal blue/red
Change: All royal blue.

Chairman: Kevin Lockley
Tel: 01902 674246 (H) 07802 931346 (M)
Match Secretary: Elaine Harris
Tel: 0121 530 3257 (H)

SHAWBURY UNITED

Secretary: Dave Thomas, 183 Cordwell Park,Wem, Shropshire SY3 9JB
Tel: 01743 245457 (H)
Ground: The Butler's Sports Centre, Bowen's Field, Wem. Tel: 01939 233287

Directions: Go into Wem town centre and at the Church junction turn right.
Take the first left after pedestrian crossing, then first left with Hawkestone pub on corner. 2nd left into car park and ground.

Formed: 1992
Colours: Blue & yellow/blue/blue
Change Colours:White/yellow/yellow

Chairman: Ron Humphreys
Tel: 01939 251076

SMETHWICK SIKH TEMPLE

Secretary: Joginder Singh, 134 Sandwell Road, Handsworth, Birmingham B21 8PS
Tel: 0121 523 0259
Ground: Hadley Stadium, Wilson Road, Smethwick Tel No: 0121 434 4848

Directions: From Wolverhampton Centre, proceed along A459 to junc Parkfields Rd & Sedgley Rd. Turn left at the main Parkfield traffic lights A4039, sign Ettingshall, travel 500yds, left into Myatt Ave, 1st right into Lawn Rd. Ground on right

PREVIOUS **Name:** Smethwick Rangers

FACT FILE
Founded :1972
Colours: Red & black/black/black
Change Colours: Blue & white/blue/blue

CLUB PERSONNEL
Chairman: Mohan Singh Gill

TIPTON TOWN

Secretary: Ruth Archer, 34 Speakers Close,Oakham Park, Tividale.W.Midlands B69 1PB
Tel: 01384 242912 (H) 07876 197758 (M)
Ground: Tipton Sports Acadamy, Wednesbury Oak Road, Tipton, West Midlands
Directions: M6 Jct 9 through Wednesbury taking A461 until right at island signto Tipton. At next island - Ocker Hill - turn full right owards Bilston & Wolverhampton. After 1/3 mile turn left at traffic lights and ground is on left.**Capacity:** 1000 **Seats:** 200 **Cover:** New covered stand and dressing rooms **Floodlights**:Yes9**Clubhouse:** Open with excellent food available week-ends. 12noon - 7.00 p.m.**Club Shop:** no **Record Attendance:** Approx 1100 v Wolvesin 1.8.88
Honours: West Mid Regional League DIv One Championship and League Cup, Wednesbury Senior Charity Cup (5) Midweek Floodlit Challenge Cup
2002-2003: **Captain:** Jon Worsey **P.o.y.**:Hardip Dhanda **Top Scorer**: Ravi Sangha

FACT FILE
Founded: 1948
Sponsors: Tipton & Cseley Building Society
Colours: Black & white stripes/black/black
Change colours: White/blue/blue
Midweek Matchday: Wednesday
Reserves League:Midland Comb. Div 3
Also U18,U17,U15 and U13 teams
Programme Editor: Dave Barnfield
CLUB PERSONNEL
Chairman: Kevin Jennings Manager:John Hill
Club Captain: Mark Simms

TIVIDALE

Secretary: Leon Murray ,59 Peel Way, Tividale, Oldbury, W.Mids B69 3JZ(0121 532 6979)
Ground: The Beeches, Packwood Rd, Tividale, Warley, W. Midlands B69 1UL tel: 01384 211743
Directions: Dudley Port Station to Burnt tree, left towards Birmingham, ground1 mile on right. Or, M5 jct 2, follow Dudley signs A4123, after approx 2 miles turn left into Regent Rd & left again into Elm Terraces, 1st left into Birch Crescent. Packwood Rd is second left - ground at end of cul-de-sac
Capacity: 3,500 Seats: 200 Cover: 1,000 Floodlights: Yes Club Shop: No
Clubhouse: Mon-Fri 8-11pm, Sat 12-11pm, Sun 12-3 & 8-10.30. Cobs, rolls,sandwiches available
HONOURS West Midlands Lg Div 1 72-73 (Prem. Div Cup 76-77, Div 1 Cup 72-73), Wednesbury Charity Cup 76-77
PREVIOUS **Ground:** City Road **Leagues:** Handsworth & District 56-60; inactive 60-62; West Mids Alliance 62-66 **RECORD Attendance:** 2,400 v Telford United, FA Cup

Founded: 1954 Nickname: Dales
Sponsors: Midland & North Security Consultants
Colours: All Yellow
Change colours: All Blue
Midweek matchday: Tuesday
Programme: 40 pages, 60p Editor: c/o Club
Newsline: 0891 66 42 52
Chairman: Donald Ashton
President: Lord Peter Archer
Press Officer: T Clark
Manager: Paul Madders
Asst Manager: Ron Blackwood
Physio: John Cotton

WEDNESFIELD

Secretary: Ron Brown, 8 Hazel Grove, Wednesfield WV11 1LN Tel: 07796 975634 (M)
Ground: Cottage Ground, Amos Lane, Wednesfield, Wolverhampton Tel: 01902 735506
Directions: From Wolverhampton on the A4124 Wednesfield Rd. Stay on road right through Wednesfield until island. Leave island at 1st exit (Wood End Rd), left after 200yds into Amos Lane. Ground on right, approx. 400yds along. 3 miles Wolverhampton BR station. Bus 559 to Wood End or 560 to Red Lion.
Capacity: 1,000 Seats: 148 Cover: 250 Floodlights: Yes
Clubhouse: Evenings 7-11pm. Snacks available 1st team matchdays. **Club Shop:** No.
HONOURS West Mids Lg Div 1 76-77 (R-up 77-78).
PREVIOUS **League:** Wolverhampton & Dist. Amateur 61-76; West Midlands 77-97.
RECORDS **Attendance:** 480 v Burton Albion, FA Cup 1981.

FACT FILE
Founded: 1961 Nickname: Cottagers.
Colours: Red/black/black& white
Change : Black & White Stripes/white/white
Midweek matchday: Tuesday
Programme:£1.00
Editor: Ron Brown
CLUB PERSONNEL
Chairman: Surinda Ghattaura
Press Officer: J Massey (01902 781819).
Managers: Brian and David Saville
Physio: Mark Rowberry

WELLINGTON

Secretary: Michael Perkins, Haworth, Wellington, Hereford HR4 8AZ
Tel: 01432 830523 (H) 01432 345432 (B) 07974 447817 (M)
Ground: Wellington Playing Fields, Wellington. No telephone.

Directions: The ground is situated off the A49, 8 miles south of Leominster & 5 miles north of Hereford. At the end of the dual carriageway turn for Wellington. The ground is 1/4 mile from A49, on the left , behind Wellington School and opposite the Church.

Formed: 1968
Colours: tangerine & blue/blue/tangerine
Change colours: Blue & white/blue/blue

Chairman: Philip Smith
Tel: 01432 830096 (H)
Match Secretary: Colin Williams
Tel: 01432 830620 (H) 0374 101316 (M)

WOLVERHAMPTON CASUALS

Secretary: Michael Green, 63 St Phillips Avenue, Pennfields Wolverhampton WV67ED
Tel: 01902 333677
Ground: Brinsford Stadium, Brinsford Lane, Coven Heath, Wolverhampton (01902 783214)
Directions: Onto M54 from M6 North, at Junc 2 turn right (A449 to Stafford).Ground half a mile, turn right into Brinsford Lane. Billbrooke (BR) 2 miles
Capacity: 2,000 Seats: 50 Cover: 50 Floodlights: No
Clubhouse: Bar & snacks, open Tues/Wed/Thurs/Sat/Sun & alternate Mondays

HONOURS WMRL Div 1 94-95, R-up (3) 85-88, Div 1 Cup 85-86

PREVIOUS **Name**: Staffs Casuals (pre 81) **Ground**: Aldersley Stadium

Founded: 1899
Colours: All Green & white
Change colours: Gold/black/gold

Programme: 28pages 30p Editor: G Smith
Chairman: Barry Austin
President: Clive Hammond
Manager: Gary Walters

WOLVERHAMPTON UNITED

Secretary: John Lee, 105 Milton Road, Fallings Park, Wolverhampton WV10 0NE
Tel: 01902 723 940 (H) 07774 299 628 (M)
Ground: Wednesfield FC, Amos Lane, Wednesfield, Wolverhampton. Tel: 01902 735 506

Capacity: 1,000 Seats: 148 Cover: 250 Floodlights: Yes

Directions: From Wolverhampton, leave on B4124 Wednesfield Road. Stay on this road until you come to a traffic island. Straight over into Wood End Lane, then immediately left into Amos Lane. Ground is 400 yards on right.

Clubhouse: Evenings 7-11pm. Food (burgers, chips etc) on 1st team matchdays.

Formed: 1976
Colours: Yellow & blue/ blue/blue
Change : Black & white/black&white/black

CLUB PERSONNEL
Chairman: Clifford Dulstone
Match Secretary: Tom Ryan
Tel: 01543 422 012 (H)

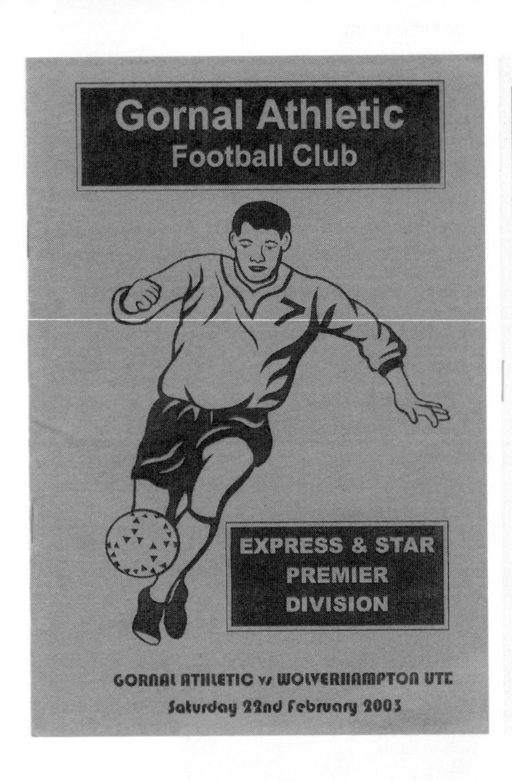

Gornal Athletic
Football Club
EXPRESS & STAR
PREMIER
DIVISION
GORNAL ATHLETIC v/ WOLVERHAMPTON UTE
Saturday 22nd February 2003

FOUNDED 1893

MATCHDAY PROGRAMME

Sponsored by:
LANSFORD ACCESS LIMITED

WEST MIDLANDS EXPRESS AND STAR
PREMIER LEAGUE

TIPTON TOWN F. C.

Express & Star League
Premier Division

Season : 2002/2003

TODAY'S MATCH SPONSOR: BILL WILLIAMS WILLIAMS & Co. Aoocountancy and Taxation Consultants

OFFICIAL MATCH
PROGRAMME

50p

EVERARDS BREWERY
LEICESTERSHIRE SENIOR FOOTBALL LEAGUE

Founded 1903

President: John M Elsom F.C.A. **Chairman:** David Jamieson
Hon Secretary: Robert J Holmes, 8 Huntsman Close, Markfield, Leics LE67 9XE
Tel/Fax: 01530 243093 Email: robertholmes@leicssenior1.freeserve.co.uk
www.leicestershireseniorfootballleague.com
Press Officer: Dave Lumley, 8 Pinewood Close, Countesthorpe, Leicester LE8 5TS
TelFax: 0116 277 8455 Email: davelumley@leicssenior.freeserve.co.uk

FINAL LEAGUE TABLES 2002-03

PREMIER DIVISION		P	W	D	L	F	A	Pts
1	Coalville Town	34	29	5	0	101	28	92
2	Barrow Town	34	25	7	2	96	33	82
3	Thurnby Rangers	34	26	3	5	92	26	81
4	Loughborough Dynamoe	34	19	3	12	75	55	60
5	Holwell Sports	34	19	2	13	61	39	59
6	St Andrews SC	34	18	4	12	68	56	58
7	Kirby Muxloe SC	34	17	6	11	63	44	57
8	Ibstock Welfare	34	17	4	13	68	47	55
9	Leicester YMCA	34	14	5	15	69	65	47
10	Ratby Sports	34	13	5	16	50	58	44
11	Highfield Rangers	34	13	3	18	53	70	42
12	Thurmaston Town	34	12	5	17	46	63	41
13	Birstall United	34	10	4	20	47	67	34
14	Blaby & Whetstone Athletic	34	8	6	20	36	68	30
15	Downes Sports	34	8	5	21	44	69	29
16	Ellistown	34	6	10	18	30	75	28
17	Friar Lane Old Boys (-3)	34	6	5	23	39	98	23
18	Anstey Nomads	34	2	6	26	24	101	12

DIVISION ONE		P	W	D	L	F	A	Pts
1	Epworth	30	27	3	0	140	21	84
2	Stapenhill	30	21	5	4	75	40	68
3	Sileby Town	30	17	6	7	80	51	57
4	Cottesmore Amateurs	30	17	2	11	62	50	53
5	Aylestone Park Old Boys	30	16	3	11	83	52	51
6	Lutterworth Town (-3)	30	16	4	10	76	47	49
7	Bardon Hill Sports	30	13	6	11	67	57	45
8	Asfordby Amateurs	30	14	2	14	54	65	44
9	Anstey Town	30	12	6	12	54	41	42
10	Earl Shilton Albion	30	10	9	11	53	53	39
11	Narborough & Littlethorpe	30	11	4	15	47	52	37
12	Leics Constabulary	30	9	6	15	46	56	33
13	North Kilworth	30	8	4	18	47	81	28
14	Saffron Dynamo	30	7	4	19	42	93	25
15	Huncote S & S (-3)	30	7	3	20	43	89	21
16	Thringstone Miners W. (-3)	30	0	3	27	15	136	0

LEAGUE CUP 2002-03

QUARTER-FINALS

Anstey Nomads	v	Stapenhill	1-0	Anstey Town	v	Barrow Town	1-5
Epworth	v	Ibstock Welfare	1-0	Thurnby Rangers	v	Leics Constabulary	6-1

SEMI-FINALS

Barrow Town	v	Anstey Nomads	3-0	Epworth	v	Thurnby Rangers	3-1

FINAL

Barrow Town v Epworth 4-2 12th May at Barrow Town

ANSTEY NOMADS

Secretary: Martin Almen, 86 Rockhill Drive, Mountsorrel, Leicester LE12 7DT (0787 651 3494)
Ground: Llimah International Park, Cropston Road, Anstey, Leicester (0116 236 4868)
Directions: Take jct 21A off M1 to Newark on A46 .Turn to Anstey after 2 miles then take third exit at village roundabout and ground is half amile on right.
Capacity: 1,500 **Seats**:100 **Cover: 100** **Floodlights**:Yes **Club shop:** No
Clubhouse: Yes (available for bookings)
HONOURS: Leics Senior Lge: (4), Leics Comb. 93-94 ,Leics Senior Cup 94-95, Leics Jun. Cup 94-95, Presidents Cup 95-96, Battle of Britain Cup (8) Rolleston Charity Cup (4)
BEST SEASON F.A.Vase: 5th Round 1994-95

Founded: 1947 Nickname: Nomads
Sponsors: Ford Signs
Colours: Red/white/white
Change colours: Blue & white/blue/blue.

Chairman: Tony Ford
Manager: Jim Johnson
Ass.Man: Robert Coileman

BARROW TOWN

Secretary: Alan Dawkins, 72 Beaumont Road, Barrow-on-Soar, Loughborough, Leics LE12 8PJ
Tel: 01509 413288 email: alan@dawkins9.freeserve.co.uk
Ground: Riverside Park, Meynell Road, Quorn, Leics Tel: 01509 620650
Directions: Access via Quorn Lodge Drive & Barrow road.
Capacity: 2,000 Seats: None Cover: 50Floodlights:Yes
Clubhouse: Yes - **Club Shop**: No - BadgesYes
HONOURS: Leics Sen Lg. 92-93 R-up 94-95 02-03; Loughboro' Charity Cup 68-69,96-97,98-99, 00-01,02-03 Leics Coimbination R-up : 2002-03 Leics Youth Lg Winners 02-03, League Cp 02-3 Leics County Sen Cup Finalists 02-03, Battle of Britain Cup Finalists 02-03
BEST SEASON FA Vase: 2nd Rd Proper. 2000-01 ,01-02

FACT FILE
Re-formed 1947 Nickname: Riversiders
Colours: Red & black/black/red
Change colours: Navy Blue
Midweek matchday: Tuesday Prog: Yes
Chairman: Michael Bland
Treasurer: Paul Carnell
Press Officer : Alan.Dawkins
Managers: Brian Cleave & Louis Carr
2002-2003
Capt: Richard GaleTop **Scorer:** Ben Brown 37
Player of the Year: Ben Brown

BIRSTALL UNITED

Secretary: Jeff Plumb, 34 Allinson Close, Leicester LE5 4ED.

Ground: Meadow Lane, Birstall Tel: 0116 267 1230

Colours: White/navy/navy

BLABY & WHETSTONE ATHLETIC

Secretary: Mrs Sandra Morris, 10 Winchester Road, Blaby, Leics LE8 3HJ Tel: 0116 277 3208

Ground: Blaby & Whetstone Boys Club, Warwick Road, Whetstone (0116 286 4852)

Colours: Navy & white/navy/navy

DOWNES SPORTS

Secretary Tony Jacques, 17 Merton Close, Broughton, Astley Leicester LE9 6QP
Tel: 01455 28402 (H) 01455 282028 (W)
Ground Leicester Rd, Hinckley Tel: 01455 615062

Directions Off northern perimeter road round Leicester

Capacity 2000 Seats: Cover: Yes Floodlights: Yes

Clubhouse Yes **Club shop:** No

HONOURS Leics. Sen. Lge. Div Two R-up 1986-87

Founded: 1968
Nickname: The Builders
Colours: Tangerine/black/tangerine
Change colours:t.b.a.
Midweek matchday: Tuesday
Programme: No
Club Personnel
Chairman: F. Down
Vice Chairman:
Manager: S. Greenhill
Asst. Man. / Coach:
Physio:

ELLISTOWN

Secretary: John Measom, 29 Standard Hill, Coalville, Leicster LE67 3HN
Tel: 01530 810941

Ground: 1 Terrace Road, Ellistown
Clubhouse: Yes

Colours: Yellow/blue shirts, yellow shorts, blue socks
Change colours: Red shirts, black shorts, red socks

FRIAR LANE OLD BOYS

Secretary: David Allen, 1 Gedge Way, Leicester LE2 6NQ

Ground: Knighton Lane East, Leicester (0116 283 3629)

Colours: Black & white stripes/black/black

HIGHFIELD RANGERS

Secretary: Maurice Christian, 18 Blanklyn Avenue, Leicester LE5 5FA Tel: 0116 273 4002

Ground: 443 Gleneagles Ave., Rushey Mead, Leicester Tel: 0116 266 0009

Colours: Yellow/blackyellow

HOLWELL SPORTS

Secretary: Chris Parkin, 15 Kennet Way, Melton Mowbray, Leics. LE13 0EX
Tel: 01664 853002 (H)
Ground: Welby Road, Asfordby Hill, Melton Mowbray, Leics Tel: 01664 812663

Colours: Green & gold/green/green & gold

IBSTOCK WELFARE

Secretary Ralph A Wilkinson, 6 Valley Rd, Ibstock, Leics. LE67 6NYTel: 01530 450243
Email: Ibstockwelfarefc@ntlworld.com **Website**www.footballnews.co.uk/clubs/22/2244/home.page
Ground The Welfare, Leicester Road, Ibstock, Leics. Tel: 01530 260656
Brief Directions: A511 towards Coalville & follow signs to Ibstock
Capacity 1500 **Seats**: 50 **Cover:** 150 **Floodlights**:Yes **Clubhouse** Evenings & matches**Shop** No
HONOURS Leics Sen Cup 93-94, R-Up 97-98; Leics Sen Lg Div 1 R-Up 90-91; Coalville Chall Cup x5, R-up x4; Loughborough Ch.Cup x4, R-up x2; Atherstone Nursing Cup (1)
PREVIOUS **Leagues:** Coalville & District, Leicester & District
BEST SEASON **FA Vase:** 2nd Round Proper
ClubSponsors for season 2003-2004: Ibstock Brick,David Wiulson Homes,Gaytonn Graham,C.W.Palletta & Son,Ravenstone Management & Marketing Services

Founded: 1962 Nickname:The Welly
Kit Sponsors: Andy Peters Racing,Vinnys Fish Bar & Shuires Traffic Management
Colours: Red/black/red
Change colours: All blue or all green
Midw'k matchday: Tuesday Prog: Yes

Club Personnel

Press Off: Craig Wheatley 0798 5242073
Man: Michael Marston Capt: Brendan Cartlidge
Ass.Mans.: Stuart Boinser & Neil Scott
Top scorer & P.o.Y.: Martin Emery .40
Manager's p.o.Y.: Royce Turville

KIRBY MUXLOE S.C.

Secretary: Philip Moloney, 16 Church Lane, Ratby, Leics LE6 0JE (0116 239 2916)

Ground: Ratby Lane, Kirby Muxloe (0116 239 3201)

Colours: Blue/black/black

LEICESTER YMCA

Secretary: Colin Chappell, 132 South Knighton Rd, Leicester, LE2 3LQ Tel: 0116 270 2721
Ground: YMCA Sports Ground, Belvoir Drive, Leicester Tel: 0116 244 0740
Directions: M1 Jct21 (M69) onto A563, Soarvalley Way, Aylestone Rd. Left at lights, to city. Belvoir Drive 2nd Right after next lights.
Capacity: 1,500 **Seats**No **Cover:** 100 **Floodlights**:Yes **Club shop:** No
Clubhouse: Yes . Sats & Suns 12.30p.m. onwards
HONOURS Leics. Sen. Lge. Div. 1 99-00;
PREVIOUS Leagues: Mid Comb. 97-9

Founded: 1910
Nickname: Beavers
Colours: Red & black/black/black
Change colours: Green/white/white
Midweek matchday: Wednesday
Programme: No

Club Personne

Chairman: Fred Smith
Manager: Tony Yeoman

LOUGHBOROUGH DYNAMO

Secretary: Max Hutchinson, 3 Wythburn Close, Loughborough, Leics LE11 3SZ
Tel: 01509 266092
Ground: Nanpanton Sport Ground, Loughborough Tel: 01509 612144
Capacity: 1,500 **Seats**: Few **Cover:**Yes **Floodlights**:No
Clubhouse: Open match days only **Club shop:** No
BEST SEASON **FA Vase:** N/A **FA Cup:** N/A
HONOURS: Leics. Sen. Lge: Div. 1 01-02, 64-65, Div 3 59-00; Cobin Trophy 62-63, 63-64, 64-65, County Medals R-up 60-61; District Lg Div 1 69-70, Three Sons Trophy 80-81; Charity Cup 87-88

Founded: 1955
First Competitive Season: 57-58
Nickname: The Moes
Colours: Gold/black/black
Change colours:All Blue
Midweek matchday: Monday
Programme: Yes
Club Personnel
Chairman: Frank Fall
Managers: Frank Fall& Kev Laundon

RATBY SPORTS

Secretary: John Rowe, 57 Danehill, Ratby, Leicester LE6 0NG Tel: 0116 238 6806

Ground: Ratby Sports Club, Desford Lane, Ratby. Tel: 0116 239 2474

Colours: All red

St ANDREWS SOCIAL CLUB

Secretary: Les Botting, 2 Neston Road, Saffron Lane, Leicester LE2 6RD Tel: 0116 224 3961

Ground: Canal Street, off Aylestone Rd, Old Aylestone,Leicester Tel: 0116 283 9298

Directions: (next to Big City Tyres)

HONOURS: Leics Sen Lg. Premier Champions: 89-90,93-94,95-96

Colours: Black & white/black/black

STAPENHILL

Ground: Maple Grove, Stapenhill, Burton-on-Trent, Staffs. Tel: 01283 562471

THURMASTON TOWN

Secretary: Reg Malloy, 96 Grange Drive, Melton Mowbray, Leics. LE13 1HA
Tel: 01664 564665 (H) 0116 222 3636 (B)

Ground: Elizabeth Park, Checklands Road, Thurmaston. Tel: 0116 260 2519

HONOURS: Dist. Lg Champs 97-99, Page & Moy Junior Cup Winners 97-98 Leics Div One Champions & Beacon Bitter Cup Winners 98-99

Colours: Black & white stripes, black,black.

THURNBY RANGERS

Secretary: Ian Henson, 13 Dudley Avenue, Thurnby Lodge, Leicester LE5 2EE
Tel: 0116 241 2741 07761 227 586 (M)

Ground: Dakyn Road, Thurnby Lodge, Leicester.
Tel: 0116 243 3698

Colours: All green
Change colours: All red

ISTHMIAN LEAGUE

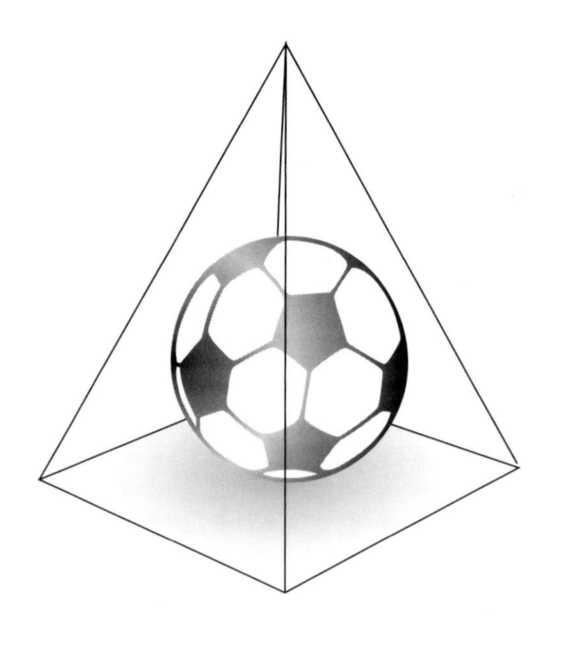

PYRAMID SECTION

Ryman
ISTHMIAN LEAGUE

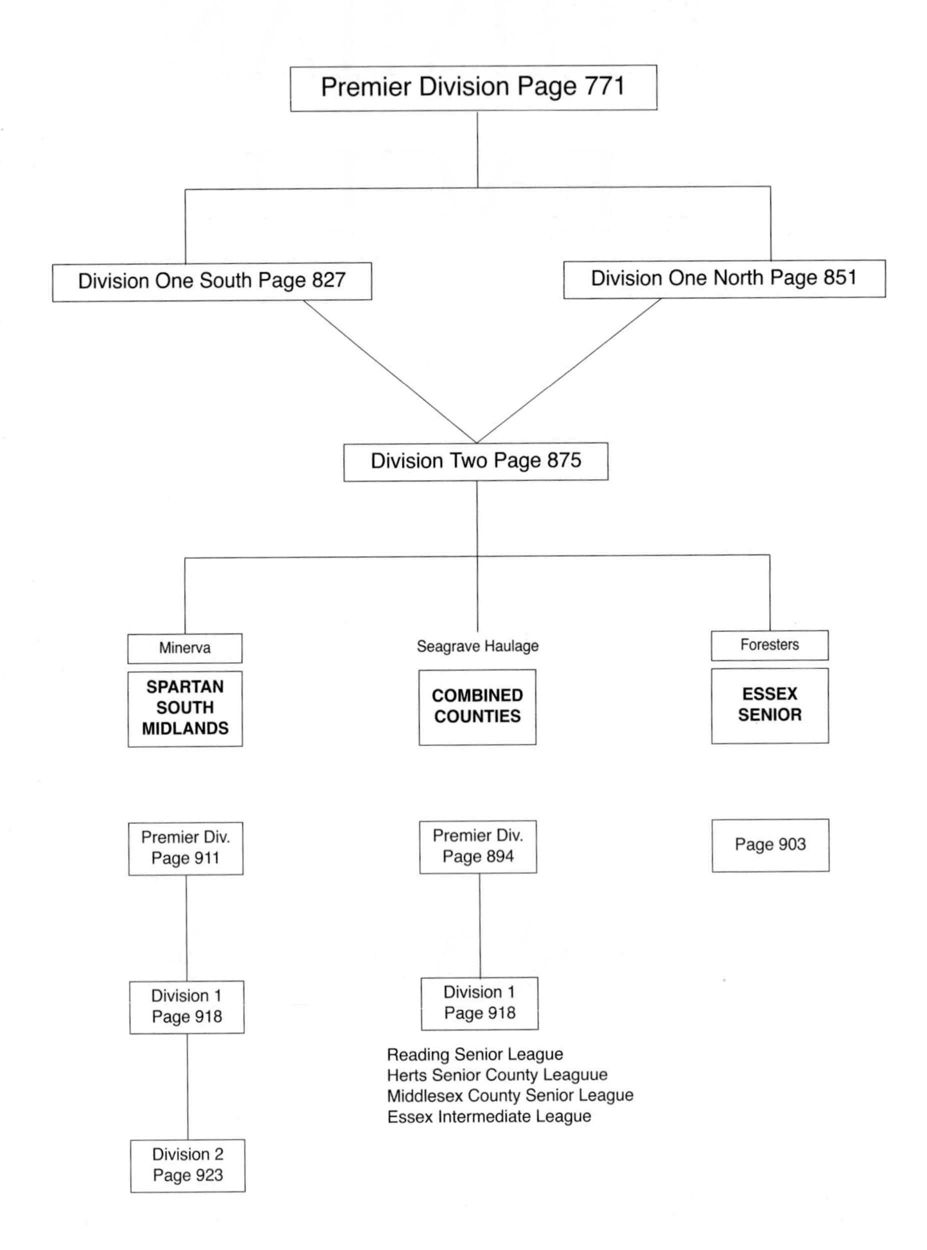

Premier Division Page 771
Division One South Page 827
Division One North Page 851
Division Two Page 875
Minerva
SPARTAN SOUTH MIDLANDS
Seagrave Haulage
COMBINED COUNTIES
Foresters
ESSEX SENIOR
Premier Div. Page 911
Premier Div. Page 894
Page 903
Division 1 Page 918
Division 1 Page 918
Division 2 Page 923
Reading Senior League
Herts Senior County Leaguue
Middlesex County Senior League
Essex Intermediate League

RYMAN LEAGUE

Chairman: A C F Turvey, MCIM, 18 Apple Way, Old Basing, Basingstoke, Hants RG24 7HA

Secretary: N R Robinson FCRArb, 226 Rye Lane, Peckham, London SE15 4NL

Tel: 020 8409 1978 (H) 020 7639 5726 (B) Fax: 020 8409 1979 (H) 020 7277 6061 (B)

Email: nickrob@clara.net secretary@isthmian.co.uk

With the race lasting to the last Saturday of the season the Ryman League Championship went to Kent for the first time in over 40 years as Gravesend & Northfleet held their nerve and finally finished four points clear of runners-up Canvey Island.

In front of over 1,700 Gravesend won 1-0 at Bedford Town and were presented with the Championship Trophy by League Administration Secretary Clive Moyse immediately after the final whistle, while Canvey, who had led the Premier Division almost continuously from October to early April, ended their campaign with a 2-1 defeat at Braintree Town.

Despite a tense closing ten minutes Ford United held on for a 2-1 home win over Uxbridge to win the First Division Championship. With Bishop's Stortford winning at Whyteleafe, Ford needed all three points to take the title. They held on and were presented with the trophy by League Secretary Nick Robinson.

In DivisionTwo Lewes ended one of their most successful seasons ever with a 3-0 win at Wivenhoe Town. Having enjoyed success in the FA Cup and FA Vase, they finished their league campaign six points clear of Horsham.

Third Division Champions Croydon Athletic beat Egham Town 3-0 in their final game of the campaign to preserve their perfect record at Mayfields this season. The side took 63 points from a possible 63 at home, scoring 83 goals in the process.

Division One Northwood lifted the Isthmian League Cup for the first time by beating Premier Division Hampton & Richmond Borough at Clarence Park. Andy Cook broke the deadlock for Northwood in the 43rd minute only for Neil Gough to equalise two minutes later. Cook scored his and Northwood's second after 74 minutes, but within another three minutes Richard O'Connor equalised for the 'Beevers' to force extra time. The winning goal came in the 92nd minute from Northwood's top scorer Lawrence Yaku.

Lewes have been awarded the presitigious Football Association Charter Standard Certificate, the National Award for Excellence in Coaching. The club is the only senior side in Sussex to have achieved the accolade which is awarded to clubs that show exceptional commitment to the development of Youth and Women's football.

Sutton United played a friendly match against the Middlesex Wanderers representative side at Gander Green Lane in May, as a memorial game for Ralph Carr, the former England amateur goalkeeper who was a player, official and director for Sutton during an association with the club which lasted over 60 years until he passed away in March 2001. He also had connections with the Wanderers dating back to the 1930's as a player, committee member and Vice President.

Dorking had their best ever FA Vase run before being knocked out in unfortunate circumstances by way of a penalty shoot out in their Fifth Round replay against Burgess Hill in a tie that attracted a total of around 1,200 fans over the two matches.

After more than 70 years at Sandy Lane, Tooting & Mitcham United played their final game at the ground in April. They marked the occasion with a 3-2 victory over Wealdstone.

PREMIER DIVISION FINAL LEAGUE TABLE 2001-02

		HOME					AWAY						
		P	W	D	L	F	A	W	D	L	F	A	Pts	GD
1.	Aldershot Town	46	17	3	3	41	16	16	3	4	40	20	105	45
2.	Canvey Island	46	14	7	2	63	27	14	1	8	49	29	92	56
3.	Hendon	46	10	5	8	29	28	12	8	3	41	28	79	14
4.	St Albans City	46	11	5	7	36	31	12	3	8	37	34	77	8
5.	Basingstoke Town	46	14	3	6	44	27	9	4	10	36	33	76	20
6.	Sutton United	46	13	6	4	44	29	9	3	11	33	33	75	15
7.	Hayes	46	13	6	4	38	19	7	7	9	29	35	73	13
8.	Purfleet	46	13	4	6	42	23	6	11	6	26	25	72	20
9.	Bedford Town	46	14	3	6	42	27	7	6	10	24	31	72	8
10.	Maidenhead United	46	8	7	8	40	37	8	10	5	35	26	65	12
11.	Kingstonian	46	10	5	8	32	29	6	12	5	39	35	65	7
12.	Billericay Town	46	10	5	8	27	21	7	6	10	19	23	62	2
13.	Bishop's Stortford	46	9	6	8	39	35	7	5	11	35	37	59	2
14.	Hitchin Town	46	7	8	8	36	32	8	5	10	33	35	58	2
15.	Ford United	46	8	7	8	42	39	7	5	11	36	45	57	-6
16.	Braintree United	46	6	4	13	28	38	8	8	7	31	33	54	-12
17.	Aylesbury United	46	9	8	6	34	33	4	7	12	28	42	54	-13
18.	Harrow Borough	46	8	4	11	31	36	7	5	11	23	39	54	-21
19.	Grays Athletic	46	9	6	8	26	24	5	5	13	27	35	53	-6
20.	Heybridge Swifts	46	8	7	8	29	38	5	7	11	23	42	53	-28
21.	Chesham United	46	8	7	8	35	39	6	3	14	21	42	52	-25
22.	Boreham Wood	46	6	8	9	24	32	5	7	11	26	26	48	-8
23.	Enfield	46	5	8	10	21	31	4	3	16	26	70	38	-54
24.	Hampton & Richmond B.	46	2	8	13	20	41	1	6	16	15	45	23	-51

PREMIER DIVISION 02-03		1	2	3	4	5	6	7	8	9	10	11	12	13	14	15	16	17	18	19	20	21	22	23	24
1	Aldershot Town		1-0	0-3	2-1	0-0	0-0	1-0	3-0	1-0	1-2	2-0	2-1	2-1	4-0	0-1	1-0	6-2	2-0	1-0	2-1	1-1	1-0	5-1	3-2
2	Aylesbury United	3-2		1-1	1-1	0-1	1-2	3-3	1-1	1-6	2-1	4-1	2-0	3-2	3-0	0-0	3-0	0-1	2-1	2-2	1-0	0-0	1-1	0-3	0-4
3	Basingstoke Town	0-1	2-2		2-1	2-0	3-1	1-1	2-1	2-1	1-2	2-3	3-0	3-1	3-1	1-2	3-1	0-2	2-2	3-0	0-1	3-2	2-1	3-1	1-0
4	Bedford Town	1-2	4-0	0-0		2-0	3-1	0-4	1-0	2-1	0-4	8-2	0-2	1-0	1-0	1-1	2-1	2-3	1-2	2-1	5-2	0-0	2-0	2-0	2-1
5	Billericay Town	0-1	1-1	1-0	4-0		1-1	0-0	1-2	2-1	1-0	0-1	1-3	4-1	0-2	1-0	1-1	0-0	2-0	1-2	0-2	2-0	1-3	1-0	2-0
6	Bishop's Stortford	1-1	2-2	3-1	1-1	1-0		1-4	1-1	1-2	2-1	1-0	0-1	1-3	2-1	4-0	2-3	4-1	2-0	2-3	2-2	3-4	2-2	0-2	1-0
7	Boreham Wood	0-1	1-2	1-5	0-1	1-3	1-1		1-2	1-3	0-0	2-1	3-2	0-2	0-0	2-2	2-0	1-1	0-0	2-2	2-1	0-3	0-0	1-0	3-0
8	Braintree Town	2-1	2-2	0-3	2-0	1-0	1-3	0-1		2-4	1-2	1-3	1-0	1-1	3-1	2-4	0-1	1-2	3-0	1-3	1-2	1-2	0-0	2-2	0-1
9	Canvey Island	0-1	2-1	4-0	1-1	3-0	0-4	1-0	1-1		4-1	10-1	3-1	2-0	4-0	2-1	2-2	4-4	4-1	3-1	1-1	3-2	2-2	6-1	1-1
10	Chesham United	1-3	1-3	3-2	1-3	0-2	3-1	3-1	1-1	2-4		2-2	2-2	2-1	1-0	1-1	2-3	1-1	3-0	2-1	0-4	0-0	1-1	1-3	2-0
11	Enfield	1-2	0-0	3-1	1-2	1-1	0-2	1-0	1-1	1-2	1-0		1-1	1-1	2-0	0-1	0-1	0-0	2-3	0-5	2-2	1-1	1-0	0-1	1-4
12	Ford United	2-3	1-2	2-3	2-0	0-2	3-2	1-1	3-0	1-3	2-0	3-1		1-0	3-0	2-0	3-3	1-3	3-3	2-2	2-2	0-3	1-1	1-1	3-4
13	Grays Athletic	0-0	3-1	1-2	0-0	1-0	1-0	2-1	1-2	1-2	1-0	3-0	1-2		1-1	4-1	1-0	0-2	0-2	1-1	1-1	1-4	2-1	0-1	0-0
14	Hampton & Richmond Borough	1-3	3-1	0-2	0-2	1-1	1-0	0-4	0-1	0-2	1-3	0-1	2-3	1-1		0-2	1-1	1-1	1-1	0-2	2-2	1-1	1-1	2-3	1-3
15	Harrow Borough	0-2	2-2	1-2	0-2	1-2	2-2	2-0	2-2	1-2	3-0	2-0	4-0	0-4	1-0		1-3	1-3	2-1	2-0	2-1	1-1	1-2	0-4	0-1
16	Hayes	1-0	1-1	1-0	2-0	0-2	2-0	0-0	1-3	2-1	1-0	4-0	2-0	1-0	2-1	6-0		0-0	2-2	2-1	2-2	0-2	1-2	3-0	2-2
17	Hendon	1-3	3-1	2-1	0-2	2-1	0-3	0-2	2-0	1-0	0-1	3-0	3-1	1-0	3-3	1-1	2-0		0-0	2-1	1-1	1-1	1-2	0-2	0-2
18	Heybridge Swifts	0-4	1-0	2-4	1-0	1-1	3-3	1-0	2-0	0-2	0-0	2-1	4-4	1-1	1-0	0-1	1-0	0-4		3-1	2-4	0-0	0-2	3-3	1-3
19	Hitchin Town	1-3	2-3	1-0	2-1	1-0	0-1	2-1	0-0	2-3	1-1	7-1	2-2	3-3	1-1	1-0	2-3	2-2	0-1		0-0	2-3	1-1	1-2	2-0
20	Kingstonian	0-2	1-0	2-1	2-2	2-0	3-1	0-0	1-4	0-4	5-1	4-2	0-2	1-0	1-1	1-3	1-1	0-1	4-0	0-0		2-0	0-1	0-2	2-1
21	Maidenhead United	1-2	2-1	2-2	3-2	1-0	2-3	2-1	2-3	1-1	5-0	3-3	0-4	0-2	1-1	2-0	1-1	0-1	2-2	1-2	4-4		1-0	0-1	4-1
22	Purfleet	1-2	1-0	1-0	3-0	0-0	2-1	0-0	1-1	3-2	6-0	5-2	2-2	3-1	5-2	4-2	1-2	1-0	1-2	0-1	0-1	1-0		1-0	0-2
23	St Albans City	2-0	3-1	1-2	1-2	1-1	3-2	2-0	2-4	2-1	1-0	0-0	3-2	1-2	2-0	1-0	1-1	1-4	2-0	0-1	2-2	1-3	2-2		2-1
24	Sutton United	1-1	3-2	1-1	0-0	1-2	2-1	3-2	3-1	0-2	3-2	2-1	4-1	2-0	1-0	3-0	2-1	2-3	2-0	3-1	1-1	2-2	1-1	2-4	

LEAGUE CUP 2002-03

FIRST ROUND
Aveley 4 Bracknell Town 0
Banstead Athletic 2 Tring Town 0
Barton Rovers 4 Croydon Athletic 1
Berkhamsted Town 4 Arlesey Town 4 (aet)
Replay - Arlesey Town 3 Berkhamsted Town 2
Chertsey Town 3 Camberley Town 2 (aet)
Cheshunt 6 Hertford Town 0
Clapton 2 Whyteleafe 2 (aet)
Replay - Whyteleafe 1 Clapton 0
Corinthian Casuals 3 Edgware Town 1
East Thurrock United 3 Wokingham Town 1
Epsom & Ewell 1 Ashford Town (Middx) 4
Great Wakering Rovers 0 Bromley 1
Hemel Hempstead Town 1 Leyton 3 (aet)
Horsham 1 Abingdon Town 1 (aet)
Replay - Abingdon Town 0 Horsham 3
Leighton Town 0 Chalfont St Peter 2
Lewes 3 Wivenhoe Town 0
Leyton Pennant 0 Flackwell Heath 1
Metropolitan Police 2 Hornchurch 6
Molesey 4 Barking & East Ham United 3
Tilbury 2 Hungerford Town 3
Ware 0 Marlow 1
Wembley 6 Kingsbury Town 0
Windsor & Eton 5 Egham Town 2
Wingate & Finchley 6 Dorking 5 (aet)
Witham Town 3 Leatherhead 0

SECOND ROUND
Ashford Town (Middx) 3 Heybridge Swifts 1
Aveley 2 Marlow 0
Barton Rovers 1 Braintree Town 3
Billericay Town 5 Enfield 0
Bromley 0 Bedford Town 1
Chalfont St Peter 1 Arlesey Town 2
Chesham United 2 Sutton United 3 (aet)
Cheshunt 1 Aldershot Town 0
Corinthian Casuals 2 Carshalton Athletic 1
Croydon 2 Banstead Athletic 0
Dulwich Hamlet 2 Chertsey Town 0
Flackwell Heath 0 Aylesbury United 3
Ford United 3 Purfleet 0
Harlow Town 1 Grays Athletic 2
Hayes 0 Canvey Island 1
Hendon 4 Staines Town 2
Horsham 1 Boreham Wood 3
Hungerford Town 0 Bishop's Stortford 0 (aet)
Replay - Bishop's Stortford 7 Hungerford Town 1
Lewes 3 Maidenhead United 3 (aet)
Replay - Maidenhead United 0 Lewes 1
Leyton 3 Wealdstone 0
Molesey 0 Hampton & Richmond Borough 1
Northwood 4 Hornchurch 2
Slough Town 1 Kingstonian 3 (aet)
St Albans City 3 Bognor Regis Town 2
Thame United 2 East Thurrock United 3 (aet)
Tooting & Mitcham United 1 Worthing 4
Uxbridge 1 Basingstoke Town 2
Walton & Hersham 0 Hitchin Town 1
Wembley 5 Oxford City 3
Whyteleafe 0 Yeading 3
Windsor & Eton 0 Harrow Borough 4
Witham Town 1 Wingate & Finchley 2 (aet)

THIRD ROUND
Ashford Town (Middx) 1 St Albans City 2
Aveley 2 Northwood 1
Aylesbury United 3 Sutton United 2
Billericay Town 3 Ford United 1
Bishop's Stortford 3 Basingstoke Town 1
Braintree Town 1 Harrow Borough 3
Cheshunt 1 Canvey Island 5
Croydon 1 Wingate & Finchley 3
East Thurrock United 0 Grays Athletic 1
Hendon 2 Arlesey Town 1
Hitchin Town 4 Boreham Wood 0
Kingstonian 3 Worthing 0
Lewes 6 Hampton & Richmond Borough 0
Leyton 3 Bedford Town 4 (aet)
Wembley 0 Dulwich Hamlet 2
Yeading 4 Corinthian Casuals 0

FOURTH ROUND
Bedford Town 1 Yeading 2
Billericay Town 1 Bishop's Stortford 1 (aet)
Bishop's Stortford 3 Billericay Town 0
Grays Athletic 1 Aylesbury United 0
Harrow Borough 2 Lewes 3
Hendon 5 Wingate & Finchley 2 (aet)
Hitchin Town 1 Canvey Island 3
Kingstonian 3 Aveley 1
St Albans City 1 Dulwich Hamlet 2

QUARTER-FINALS
Bishop's Stortford 1 Yeading 4
Canvey Island 6 Grays Athletic 0
Dulwich Hamlet 4 Lewes 1
Hendon 1 Kingstonian 0 (aet)

SEMI-FINALS
(played over two legs)
Canvey Island 4 Hendon 2
Hendon 2 Canvey Island 2
Dulwich H. 1 Yeading 3
Yeading 3 Dulwich Hamlet 3

FINAL
Canvey Island 0 Yeading 2
(5th May at Hornchurch)

AYLESBURY UNITED

CLUB OFFICIALS

Chairman: Ariel Zeckler
Vice Chairman: Les Baycroft
Secretary: Tony Graham
c/o the club.
Press Officer: Tony Graham
Email: info@aylesburyutd.co.uk

FOOTBALL MANAGEMENT TEAM

Manager: Steve Cordery
Assistant Manager: Craig Maskell
Physio: John Hay

FACT FILE

Formed: 1897 Nickname: The Ducks
Sponsors: Shanks Waste Systems
Colours: Green & w hite/white/white
Change colours: mber/black/amber
Midweek home matchday: Tuesday
Reserve Team's League: Suburban
Newsline: 0906 655 5811

2002-2003

top Scorer & P.o.Y.: Craig Marshall
Ca[tain: Greg Williams

GROUND The Stadium, Buckingham Road, Aylesbury HP20 2AQ Tel: 01296 436350
Fax: 01296 395667

Directions: On A413 to Buckingham, just off ring road opposite Horse & Jockey PH. Arriving from Buckingham ground is on left - from all other directions follow Buckingham signs and ground on right. Half hour walk from Aylesbury rail and bus stations

Capacity 4,000 Cover: 1000 Seats: 500 Floodlights: Yes

Clubhouse: Pub hours. Bar snacks available
Function room available for hire(01296 428000).

Club Shop: Sells programmes, magazines, leisurewear, badges etc.
Contact: 21 CD Club shop. c/o The Club

PROGRAMME

Pages: 36 Price: £1.50
Editor: 21st Century Ducks.

Local Press: Bucks Herald, Bucks Advertiser
Local Radio: BBC Three Counties, Mix 96

PREVIOUS **Leagues:** Bucks Contiguous 1897-1903, South Eastern 03-07, Spartan 07-51, Delphian 51-63, Athenian 63-76, Southern 76-88, GMV Conference 88-89
Grounds: Printing Works Ground 1897-1935, Sports Stadium, Wendover Rd (ground name changed to The Stadium, Turnfurlong Lane) 35-85, shared grounds 85-86 **Name:** Night School, Printing Works (merged in 1897)

CLUB RECORDS **Attendance:** 6,000 v England 1988 (at old ground: 7,500 v Watford, FA Cup 1st Rd1951)
Career goalscorer: Cliff Hercules **Career appearances:** Cliff Hercules
Transfer fee paid: £15,000 for Glenville Donegal (Northampton, 1990)
Transfer fee received: Undisclosed forJermaine Darlington (Q.P.R. 1999)

BEST SEASON **FA Trophy:** Semi-Final 2002-2003 **FA Cup:** 3rd Rd 95. League clubs defeated: Southend Utd 89-90

HONOURS Southern Lg 87-88 (Mids Div R-up 84-85, Sth Div R-up 79-80); Athenian Lg Div 2 R-up 67-68; Delphian Lg 53-54 (R-up 52-53, Lg Cup 59-60); Spartan Lg 08-09 (R-up 52-53), West Div 28-29 (R-up 45-46), Div 1 38-39 (R-up 34-35); Berks & Bucks Snr Cup 13-14 85-86 96-97; Isthmian League Cup 94-95, Isthmian Charity Shield 95-96 Isthmian League R-up 98-99

Players progressing: Ray Mabbutt (Bristol Rovers), Phil Barber (Crystal Palace 1986), Jermaine Darlington (Q.P.R. 99),Lee Cook (watford 00)

L-R - Back row: Greg Williams, Gary McCann, Scott Honeyball, Steve Cordery (Manager), Craig Maskell (Asst. player-manager), Adam Campion, Adam Wheeler, Mark Burgess.**Middle:** Peter Remnant (Reserve Team Man.), John Hay (Physio), Roni Joe, Steve McGrath, Gareth Risbridger, Phil Dicker, Chris Bangura, Tony Houghton, John Winter, Danny Grimsdell, Fiston Manuella, Ron Schmidt (Kit Man), Peter Wright (Director of Football). **Front:** Sam Sloma, Kesie Ibe, Daniel Gordon, Lewis Pritchard, Stuart Corbould, Rory Hunter, John Marsh, Danny Gray, Dwight Marshall

Date	Comp.	Opponents	Att.	Score	Goalscorers	
17/08	Rym. P	Basingstoke Town	386	2 - 2	Maskell 45, Ibe 88	
20/08	Rym. P	ST ALBANS CITY	664	0 - 3		
24/08	Rym. P	BILLERICAY TOWN	446	0 - 1		
26/08	Rym. P	Hitchin Town	474	3 - 2	Maylell 27, Ibe 65, Manuella 71	
31/08	Rym. P	ENFIELD	521	4 - 1	Maskell 21 42[p], Ibe 32 55	
03/09	Rym. P	Bishop's Stortford	439	2 - 2	Hyatt 35[p], Manuella 77	
07/09	Rym. P	CANVEY ISLAND	716	1 - 6	Gordon 6	
10/09	Rym. P	Ford United	152	2 - 1	Campion 28, Maskell 41	
14/09	Rym. P	Grays Athletic	261	1 - 3	Maskell 84	
17/09	Rym. P	BOREHAM WOOD	356	3 - 3	Campion 33, Maskell 57[p] 74	
21/09	Rym. P	Sutton United	588	2 - 3	Bangura 29, Ibe 86	
24/09	Rym. P	HAMPTON & RICHMOND B.	352	3 - 0	Baker 5, Campion 14, Maskell 41	
28/09	**F.A.C.** Q2	Aldershot Town	1815	1 - 3	Williams 69	
01/10	Rym. P	Hendon	259	1 - 3	Baker 88	
05/10	Rym. P	ALDERSHOT TOWN	905	3 - 2	Baker 53, Bangura 56, Maskell 87[p]	
12/10	Rym. P	MAIDENHEAD UNITED	518	0 - 0		
19/10	Rym. P	HARROW BOROUGH	503	0 - 0		
22/10	Rym. P	Braintree Town	260	2 - 2	Bangura 83, Maskell 86	
26/10	Rym. P	Purfleet	372	0 - 1		
02/11	**F.A.T.** 1	Burnham	201	2 - 0	Manuella 18, Baker 36	
09/11	Rym. P	BEDFORD TOWN	726	1 - 1	Ibe 89	
16/11	Rym. P	Harrow Borough	285	2 - 2	Horner 66, Baker 79	
19/11	Lge Cup 2	Flackwell Heath	n/k	3 - 0	McGrath 64, Baker 70[p], Sloma 80	
30/11	**F.A.T.** 2	Chippenham Town	580	1 - 0	McGrath 29	
07/12	Rym. P	HEYBRIDGE SWIFTS	632	2 - 1	Gordon 26, Maskell 28	
14/12	Rym. P	BASINGSTOKE TOWN	433	1 - 1	Maskell 53	
21/12	Rym. P	Hayes	294	1 - 1	Horner 82	
26/12	Rym. P	CHESHAM UNITED	802	2 - 1	Maskell 72 81[p]	
28/12	Rym. P	Billericay Town	582	1 - 1	Manuella 4	
14/01	**F.A.T.** 3	KINGSTONIAN	417	1 - 0	Baker 32	
18/01	Rym. P	Canvey Island	612	1 - 2	Maskell 75[p]	
21/01	Lge Cup 3	SUTTON UNITED	206	3 - 2	Manuella 44, Ibe 57, Maskell 71	
25/01	Rym. P	GRAYS ATHLETIC	504	3 - 2	Charles 7, Manuella 84, Smith 87[og]	
01/02	**F.A.T.** 4	Altrincham	732	1 - 0	Manuella 42	
04/02	Lge Cup 4	Grays Athletic	152	0 - 1		
08/02	Rym. P	Hampton & Richmond Bor.	302	1 - 3	Maskell 5	
15/02	Rym. P	SUTTON UNITED	421	0 - 4		
22/02	**F.A.T.** 5	WINDSOR & ETON	847	2 - 2	Williams 10, Maskell 27	
25/02	**F.A.T.** 5 rep	Windsor & Eton	577	1 - 1	Baker 73	Won 4 3 after pens.
01/03	Rym. P	HENDON	642	0 - 1		
05/03	Rym. P	St Albans City	249	1 - 3	Hunter 48	
08/03	Rym. P	BRAINTREE TOWN	402	1 - 1	McGrath 85	
15/03	**F.A.T.** QF	GLOUCESTER CITY	1435	2 - 1	Ibe 4, Hunter 15	
18/03	Rym. P	HITCHIN TOWN	332	2 - 2	Gell 40, Baker 54	
22/03	Rym. P	PURFLEET	402	1 - 1	Martin 56	
25/03	Rym. P	Bedford Town	422	0 - 4		
29/03	Rym. P	Maidenhead United	334	1 - 2	Campion 90	
01/04	Rym. P	Aldershot Town	1835	0 - 1		
05/04	**F.A.T.** SF(1)	BURSCOUGH	1546	1 - 1	Maskell 60	
12/04	**F.A.T.** SF(2)	Burscough	1773	0 - 1		
14/04	Rym. P	FORD UNITED	336	2 - 0	Harper 44, Campion 61	
16/04	Rym. P	Enfield	105	0 - 0		
19/04	Rym. P	HAYES	512	3 - 0	McGrath 11 50, Harper 82	
21/04	Rym. P	Chesham United	589	3 - 1	Campion 37, Plummer 39, Maskell 73[p]	
24/04	Rym. P	Kingstonian	324	0 - 1		
26/04	Rym. P	KINGSTONIAN	968	1 - 0	Bangura 18	
28/04	Rym. P	Boreham Wood	292	2 - 1	Maskell 14[p], Campion 58	
01/05	Rym. P	BISHOP'S STORTFORD	405	1 - 2	Stanley 68	
03/05	Rym. P	Heybridge Swifts	400	0 - 1		

PLAYING SQUAD

Goalkeepers: Jimmy Heeps (Bedford T.), Adam Wheeler (Baldock T.).

Defenders: Phil Dicker (Hampton & Richmond Bh), Danny Gordon (Youth Team), Richard Horner (Weadstone), Steve McGrath (Brook House), Peter Risley (St. Albans City), Enzo Silvestri (Barton Rovers), Greg Williams (Thame U)

Midfield: Artur Correia (Windsor & Eton), Rory Hunter (Youth Team), Ronnie Joe (Chesham Utd), **Fiston Manuella** (Hampton & Richmond B), Gareth Risbridger (Salisbury City)

Forwards: Joe Baker (Billericay T.), Chris Bangura (Totttenham Hotspur), Chris Boothe (Enfield), Adam Campion (Reading), Julian Charles (Leatherhead), Daniel Gray (Youth Team), Peter Hinks (Australia), Mitchell Murphy (Edgware T.), Dwayne Plummer (Gravesend & Northfleet)

BASINGSTOKE TOWN

CLUB OFFICIALS

Chairman: David Knight
President: Rafi Razzack
Secretary: Richard Trodd
5 Lehar Close, Brighton Hill, Basingstoke
RG22 4HT Tel: 01256 413076
Press Officer: Ian Trodd
Commercial Manager: Chris Richardson

FOOTBALL MANAGEMENT TEAM

Manager: Ernie Howe
Asst Manager: Pete Peters
Coach: Steve Richardson
Physio: Mark Randall

PROGRAMME

Pages: 24 Price: £1.50
Editor: Mike O'Neill

FACT FILE

Formed: 1896
Nickname: Stoke
Sponsors: Centerprise International
Colours: Yellow& Blue/ Blue/Yellow
Change colours: All Red
Midweek home matchday: Tuesday
Reserves' League: Suburban (Prem Div)
Website: www.btfc.co.uk

Local Press: Basingstoke Gazette (461131)
Local Radio: Radio 210 (01189 413131),
Kestrel Radio (01256 694000)

2002-03

Captain:Scott Tarr
Leading Goalscorer:Craig McAllister
Player of Year:Neville Roach

GROUND Camrose Road, Western Way, Basingstoke RG22 6EZ Tel: 01256 325063 or 01256 327575 Emai: info@btfc.co.uk
Directions: Exit 6 off M3 and follow A30 west, ground off Winchester Road. Two miles from bus and rail stations
Capacity: 6,000 Cover:2,000 Seats: 651
Clubhouse: Open every day (incl. lunchtime) Steward: Cheryl Fox (01256 464353)
Club Shop: Open daily 10-5pm, selling programmes, books, scarves, shirts, badges etc.
PREVIOUS **Leagues:** Hants 1900-40 45-71; Southern 71-87 **Ground:** Castle Field 1896-1947
CLUB RECORDS **Attendance:** 5,085 v Wycombe Wanderers, FA C 1st Rd replay 97-98
Win: 10-0 v Chichester City (H), FA Cup 1st Qualifying Rd, Sept. 1976
Defeat: 0-8 v Aylesbury United, Southern League, April 1979.
Transfer Fee Paid: £4,750 for Steve Ingham (Gosport Borough)
Transfer Fee Received: £6,750 for Steve Ingham (Bashley)
Appearances: Billy Coombs
Goalscorer: Paul Coombs 159 (Oct 91 99)
BEST SEASON **FA Trophy:** 3rd Rd 98-99, 0-2 v Yeovil T. (H)
FA Cup: 2nd Rd replay 97-98, 3-4 pens aet 0 -0 v Northampton (H) after 1-1; 2nd Rd 89-90, 2-3 v Torquay U. (H)
League clubs defeated: Wycombe Wanderers 97-98
HONOURS Southern Lge Southern Div 85-86; Isthmian League Div 1 R-up 88-89 96-97; Hants League 67-68 69-70 70-71 (R-up 65-66 66-67 68-69, North Div 11-12 19-20); HantsSenior Cup 70-71 89-90 95-96 96-97
Players progressing: Tony Godfrey (Southampton 58), John Neale (Exeter 72), Mike Doherty (Reading 82), Micky Cheetham (Ipswich 88), Matt Carmichael (Lincoln), Tony Franklin (Exeter), Steve Welsh (Peterborough 90)

Date	Comp.	Opponents	Att.	Score	Goalscorers
17/08	Rym. P	AYLESBURY UNITED	386	2 - 2	Ewin 2, McAllister 9
20/08	Rym. P	Aldershot Town	2289	3 - 0	Howes 25 57, Ewin 88
24/08	Rym. P	Grays Athletic	279	2 - 1	McAllister 49, Howells 60
26/08	Rym. P	CANVEY ISLAND	575	2 - 1	Roach 11 45
31/08	Rym. P	Ford United	142	3 - 2	Ewin 14, Roach 71, McAllister 90
03/09	Rym. P	HAMPTON & RICHMOND B.	517	3 - 1	McAllister 16, Hemmings 19, Layton 88
07/09	Rym. P	Hitchin Town	322	0 - 1	
10/09	Rym. P	BEDFORD TOWN	389	2 - 1	Roach 38, Allaway 80
14/09	Rym. P	ENFIELD	429	2 - 3	Howes 36, McAllister 90
17/09	Rym. P	Kingstonian	400	1 - 2	McAllister 33
21/09	Rym. P	HARROW BOROUGH	423	1 - 2	Stamp 25
24/09	Rym. P	Chesham United	220	2 - 3	Roach 2 19
28/09	**F.A.C.** Q2	Dover Athletic	825	0 - 2	
01/10	Rym. P	BOREHAM WOOD	252	1 - 1	McAllister 89
05/10	Rym. P	Purfleet	302	0 - 1	
19/10	Rym. P	BRAINTREE TOWN	338	2 - 1	Howes 27, McAllister 70
22/10	Rym. P	Hayes	226	0 - 1	
26/10	Rym. P	SUTTON UNITED	367	1 - 0	McAllister 70
29/10	Hants SC 2	Cowes Sports	n/k	2 - 0	
02/11	**F.A.T.** 1	Enfield	91	2 - 1	McAllister 4, Ewin 11
09/11	Rym. P	BISHOP'S STORTFORD	391	3 - 1	McAllister 32 49 68
16/11	Rym. P	Braintree Town	304	3 - 0	McAllister 17 72 78
19/11	Lge Cup 2	Uxbridge	n/k	2 - 1	McAllister 27, Roach 33
23/11	Rym. P	Heybridge Swifts	215	4 - 2	McAllister 45, Roach 76, Allaway 78, Howes 90
30/11	**F.A.T.** 2	SUTTON UNITED	529	0 - 2	
03/12	Hants SC 3	RINGWOOD TOWN	n/k	7 - 1	
07/12	Rym. P	ST ALBANS CITY	387	3 - 1	Roach 43 90, McAllister 70
14/12	Rym. P	Aylesbury United	433	1 - 1	Roach 69
17/12	Lge Cup 3	Bishop's Stortford	112	1 - 3	Roach 45
21/12	Rym. P	HENDON	355	0 - 2	
26/12	Rym. P	Maidenhead United	303	2 - 2	Rooke 27 82
28/12	Rym. P	GRAYS ATHLETIC	354	3 - 1	McAllister 44, Roach 55, Ewin 78
18/01	Rym. P	HITCHIN TOWN	319	3 - 0	Rooke 70, Own-Goal 80, Roach 84
25/01	Rym. P	Enfield	101	1 - 3	Stamp 73
28/01	Hants SC QF	Andover	359	2 - 4	
01/02	Rym. P	KINGSTONIAN	484	0 - 1	
04/02	Rym. P	Canvey Island	407	0 - 4	
08/02	Rym. P	CHESHAM UNITED	407	1 - 2	Stamp 45
15/02	Rym. P	Harrow Borough	173	2 - 1	McAllister 63, Allaway 64
22/02	Rym. P	PURFLEET	311	2 - 1	Roach 10, McAllister 25
25/02	Rym. P	Bedford Town	352	0 - 0	
01/03	Rym. P	Boreham Wood	152	5 - 1	Gibbens 4, McAllister 47 57, Roach 68 90[p]
04/03	Rym. P	Billericay Town	242	0 - 1	
08/03	Rym. P	HAYES	411	3 - 1	McAllister 49 64, Roach 80
15/03	Rym. P	Bishop's Stortford	378	1 - 3	Roach 33
22/03	Rym. P	BILLERICAY TOWN	368	2 - 0	Hemmings 15, McAllister 46
29/03	Rym. P	Sutton United	567	1 - 1	Ewin 74
05/04	Rym. P	Hampton & Richmond Bor.	210	2 - 0	N Stamp 37 88
08/04	Rym. P	ALDERSHOT TOWN	1617	0 - 1	
12/04	Rym. P	FORD UNITED	293	3 - 0	Roach 22, McAllister 32 50
19/04	Rym. P	Hendon	201	1 - 2	McAllister 66
21/04	Rym. P	MAIDENHEAD UNITED	308	3 - 2	McAllister 26, Roache 27, Gibbons 54
26/04	Rym. P	HEYBRIDGE SWIFTS	375	2 - 2	Ewin 12, Roach 59
03/05	Rym. P	St Albans City	442	2 - 1	McAllister 34 55

PLAYING SQUAD

Goalkeepers: Clive Little (Reading), Scott Tarr (Yeading)

Defenders: Ricky Allaway (Reading), Jason Bristow (Reading), Ian Dickens (Youth Team), Steve Hemmings (Youth Team), Simon Herbert (Youth Team), Tom McCormick (Hayes), Neville Stamp (Exeter City), Nathan Wallace (Staines T.)

Midfield: Tinio Christie (Bisley Sports), Alex Ewin (British Universities), Jimmy Fraser (Bath City), Stuart Girdler (Woming), Matt Hayfield (Woking), David Rae (Youth Team), Toby Sumner (Aldershot T.), Paul Wilkinson (Dorchester T.)

Forwards: Sean Gordon (Godalming & Guildford), **Craig McAllister** (Eastleigh), Richard Newbery (Carshalton Ath.), Neville Roach (Slough T.), Raymond Spence (Youth Team)

BEDFORD TOWN

CLUB OFFICIALS

Chairman: David Howell
Directors:
Dave Redman, Tony Luff, Gerry Edmunds.
Secretary: Dave Swallow c/o club
Company Secretary: Barry Stephenson

FOOTBALL MANAGEMENT TEAM

Manager: Kevin Wilson
Asst. Manager: Dave Randall
Physio: John Clare

2002-2003

Captain: Paul Covington
Player of the Year:Rob Miller
Top Scorer: Darren Lynch.

FACT FILE

Nickname: The Eagles
Founded 1908
Reformed: 1989
Sponsors: Dragons Health Cllub, Bradfordian Coaches and Charles Wells.
Colours: Blue with white trim
Change ColoursOrange & White
Midweek Matchday: Tuesday
Reserves' League: UCL Reserve Div 1
Supporters Website: www.bedfordeagles.net
Local Press:Beds Times, Beds on Sunday
Local Radio: Chiltern Radio,Three Counties

PROGRAMME

Pages: 40 Price: £1.50
Editor: Dave Swallow

GROUND: The New Eyrie, Meadow Lane, Cardington, Bedford MK44. 3SB Fax: 01234 831990 Tel: 01234 838448.
Directions: BR station Bedford Midland 3miles from ground. Bus station 5 mins walk from BR station. Service 171 & 172 stop outside ground (Canvins stop). Trains from London Thameslink run every 30 mins to Bedford. By road:**A1** going north take L. turn Bedford A603 at Sandy r'abt. Over small bridge keep on this road for 5 miles, ground on right. **M1** going North A603. Next r'abt straight over to Cambridge A1 & Bedford A603. Take 3rd turn to Bedford. At r'abt take 4th exit to Sandy A603. Ground is half a mile on left.
Capacity: 3,000 Seats: 300 Cover: 1000 Floodlights: Yes
Clubhouse: Matchdays bar snacks **Club Shop:** Good range of merchandise Gerry Edmonds (01234 381213)

PREVIOUS **Leagues:** South Midlands 91-94 (predecessors: Utd Co's 08-39; Southern 46-82)
Grounds: Allen Park, Queens Park, Bedford (park pitch) 1991-93
(predecessors: London Rd; Gasworks; Queens Pk; The Eyrie, Raleigh Street)

CLUB RECORDS **Attendance:** 3,000 v Peterborough Utd, ground opening 6/8/93.
Career scorer: Jason Reed **Career appearances:** Jason Reed
Win: 9-0 v Ickleford, and Caddington **Defeat:** 0-5 v Hendon

BEST SEASON **FA Cup:** 1st Rd proper 01-02 **FA Vase:** 5th Round 1998-99, 1-2 v Tiverton Town (H) **F.A.Trophy:** 4th Rd v Yeovil Town 99-00

HONOURS: Isthmian League: Div 1 R-up. 00-01 Div. 2 98-99; South Midlands Lg 94-95 (Div 1 92-93, F'lit Cup 94-95); Hinchingbrook Cup 94-95 94-95; Beds Sen Cup 94-95.
(Predecessors: Southern Lg 58-59 (Div 1 69-70), Utd Co's Lg 30-31 32-33 33-34 (R-up 7 Times)Vandanal Cup 97-8 Beds Prem , Beds Premier Cup 97-98 **FA Cup** 4th Rd 63-64 65-66. **FA Trophy** Semi-Final 74-75.

Players progressing: Bill Garner (Southend 69), Nicky Platnaeur (Bristol Rovers 77). Ray Bailey/Derek Bellotti/Billy Brown/Bert Carberry/PeterHall/Dave Quirke/Bobby Fold (Gillingham 56-67), Phil Driver (Wimbledon 78), Joe Dubois (Grimsby T 53), Ted Duggan (Luton T 56), Harry Duke (Noprwich C 46),John Fahy (Oxford U 64), Ken Flint (Spurs 47), Joe Hooley (Accrington 61), Joe Kirkup (Reading 55), Graham Moxon (Exeter C 75), Bela Olah (Northampton 58),Gary Sergeant (Peterborough U 77), Neil Townsend (Southend U 73)

Back row, left to right: Steven Jackman, Ian Brown, Adam Hancock, Paul Covington, Darren Lynch and Daniel French.
Front row: Eddie Lawley, Graeme Tomlinson, Josh Sozzo, Carl Williams and Rob Miller.

Date	Comp.	Opponents	Att.	Score	Goalscorers
17/08	Rym. P	Bishop's Stortford	501	1 - 1	Slinn 28
20/08	Rym. P	BRAINTREE TOWN	535	1 - 0	Jackman 38
24/08	Rym. P	SUTTON UNITED	559	2 - 1	Harrison 65 70
26/08	Rym. P	Purfleet	317	0 - 3	
31/08	Rym. P	CHESHAM UNITED	547	0 - 4	
03/09	Rym. P	Billericay Town	503	0 - 4	
07/09	Rym. P	BOREHAM WOOD	404	0 - 4	
10/09	Rym. P	Basingstoke Town	389	1 - 2	Slinn 90
14/09	Rym. P	Maidenhead United	270	2 - 3	Slinn 62, Broughton 72
17/09	Rym. P	HAMPTON & RICHMOND B.	330	1 - 0	Lawley 85
21/09	Rym. P	Ford United	194	0 - 2	
24/09	Rym. P	ALDERSHOT TOWN	693	1 - 2	Williams 13
28/09	**F.A.C.** Q2	PELSALL VILLA	461	6 - 1	Paul 30, Miller 39, Smithers 45, Morley 59, Harrison 65 85
01/10	Rym. P	Grays Athletic	197	0 - 0	
05/10	Rym. P	ST ALBANS CITY	763	2 - 0	Slinn 62, Paul 72
12/10	**F.A.C.** Q3	Wisbech Town	n/k	0 - 0	
19/10	Rym. P	Hendon	416	2 - 0	Miller 17, Slinn 40
22/10	Rym. P	HEYBRIDGE SWIFTS	446	1 - 2	Harrison 75[p]
29/10	Rym. P	CANVEY ISLAND	510	2 - 1	Howey 9, Harrison 68[p]
02/11	**F.A.T.** 1	Marlow	226	1 - 1	Slinn 22[p]
05/11	**F.A.T.** 1 rep	MARLOW	368	1 - 2	Slinn 43
09/11	Rym. P	Aylesbury United	726	1 - 1	Paul 84
16/11	Rym. P	HENDON	569	2 - 3	Howey 71, G Williams 80
23/11	Rym. P	Hayes	286	0 - 2	
03/12	Lge Cup 2	Bromley	209	1 - 0	Wilson 27
07/12	Rym. P	HARROW BOROUGH	415	1 - 1	Lawley 28[p]
10/12	Lge Cup 3	Leyton	n/k	4 - 3	Sozzo 78, Folds 84 101, Lynch 86[p]
14/12	Rym. P	BISHOP'S STORTFORD	469	3 - 1	Sozzo 57 74 85
18/12	Rym. P	Enfield	131	2 - 1	Coppard 23[og], Tomlinson 47
21/12	Rym. P	Kingstonian	562	2 - 2	Tomlinson 61 67
26/12	Rym. P	HITCHIN TOWN	951	2 - 1	Lynch 4 78
28/12	Rym. P	Sutton United	719	0 - 0	
04/01	Rym. P	PURFLEET	573	2 - 0	Lynch 16 31
18/01	Rym. P	Boreham Wood	304	1 - 0	Lynch 89
21/01	Lge Cup 4	YEADING	260	1 - 2	Covington 86
25/01	Rym. P	MAIDENHEAD UNITED	559	0 - 0	
08/02	Rym. P	Aldershot Town	2078	1 - 2	Miller 87[p]
11/02	Rym. P	Braintree Town	270	0 - 2	
15/02	Rym. P	FORD UNITED	431	0 - 2	
22/02	Rym. P	St Albans City	613	2 - 1	Lynch 41 51[p]
25/02	Rym. P	BASINGSTOKE TOWN	352	0 - 0	
01/03	Rym. P	GRAYS ATHLETIC	526	1 - 0	Covington 30
04/03	Rym. P	Hampton & Richmond Bor.	170	2 - 0	Simpson 2, Lawley 22
22/03	Rym. P	Canvey Island	613	1 - 1	Tomlinson 54
25/03	Rym. P	AYLESBURY UNITED	422	4 - 0	Lynch 35 57, Williams 47, Tomlinson 53
29/03	Rym. P	ENFIELD	493	8 - 2	French 1 53 56, Jackman 32, Tomlinson 45, Lynch 71 74, Roberts 79
05/04	Rym. P	BILLERICAY TOWN	502	2 - 0	French 49, Lynch 78[p]
12/04	Rym. P	Chesham United	333	3 - 1	Lynch 11 63[p], Tomlinson 37
19/04	Rym. P	KINGSTONIAN	605	5 - 2	French 9, Collins 25[og], Williams 26, Lynch 29 31
21/04	Rym. P	Hitchin Town	765	1 - 2	Lynch 5
26/04	Rym. P	HAYES	574	2 - 1	Lynch 42 84[p]
29/04	Rym. P	Heybridge Swifts	310	0 - 1	
03/05	Rym. P	Harrow Borough	252	2 - 0	Lynch 36[p], Tomlinson 53

PLAYING SQUAD

Goalkeepers: Duncan Roberts (Harrow Borough), Daniel Tate (Luton T.), Steve Wilson (KIngs Lynn).

Defenders: Paul Covington (Buckingham T.), Ian Edge (Emley), Liam Folds (Aston Villa), Lee Harvey (Stevenage Bor.), Lee Howey (Nuneaton Bor.), Gary Hoy (Billericay T.), Steve Jackman (Raunds T.), Eddie Lawley (Buckingham T.)

Midfield: Daniel French (Peterborough Utd), Darren Sarll (Berkhamsted T.), Josh Sozzo (Hemel Hemp[stead), Paul Turner (St Albans City).

Forwards: Ross Harrison (Bedworth Utd), Darren Lynch (Newport Pagenal), Drew Roberts (Barton Rovers), Robbie Simpson (Hemel Hempstead T.)

BILLERICAY TOWN

CLUB OFFICIALS
Chairman: Rod Moore
President: Jim Hall
Secretary: Ian Ansell c/o B.T.F.C.
Tel No: 0208 500 9778 (H)
Hon.Admin Secretary: Len Dewson
Press Officer: Rob Moore

FOOTBALL MANAGEMENT TEAM
Manager: Justin Edinburgh
Assistant Manager.: Andy Polston
Youth Developement: Tony Cross
Physio: Colin Masterson

2002-2003
Captain: Ollie Adrdeji
Top Scorer: Roy Essandoh 12
Player of the Year: Jerome John

FACT FILE
Formed: 1880
Nickname: The Town
Sponsors:Stadia Management Ltd.
Colours: Royal Blue/White/ Royal Blue
Change colours: Yellow/black/yellow
Midweek Matches: Tuesday
Local Press: Evening Echo, Billericay Gazette, Billericay Recorder
Local Radio: BBC Radio Essex, Essex Radio, Essex FM

PROGRAMME
Pages: 32 .Price: £1.50
Editor: Mark Kettlety (01277 636149)

GROUND: New Lodge, Blunts Wall Rd, Billericay CM12 9SA. 01277 652188 Club Website: www.billericaytownfc.co.uk
Directions: From Shenfield (A129) right at 1st lights then 2nd right. FromBasildon (A129) over 1st lights in town, then left at next lights and 2nd right. Half mile from Billericay (GER) (London Liverpool St. - Southend line). 5 mins walk from buses 222, 251, 357, 255, 551
Capacity: 3,500 Seats: 424 Cover: 2000 Floodlights: Yes
Clubhouse: Open every evening 8-11pm (except Monday)(1pm-11pm Sat) and weekendlunch times noon-2.30pm. Discos, live entertainment
Club Shop: Open matchdays for souvenirs, metal badges, old progs, programme swaps Andrew Turner (01277 631476)

PREVIOUS **Leagues:** Romford & Dist. 1890-1914; Mid Essex 18-47; South Essex Comb. 47-66; Essex Olympian 66-71; Essex Snr 71-77; Athenian 77-79 **Grounds**: Laindon Road (pre-1971).

CLUB RECORDS **Attendance:** 3,841 v West Ham Utd, Floodlight opener 77. Comp match: 3,193 v Farnborough Tn, FA Vase SF 1st leg 76
Win: 11-0 v Stansted (A), Essex Senior League 5/5/76
Defeat: 3-10 v Chelmsford City (A), Essex Senior Cup 4/1/93
Goalscorer: (career) F Clayden 273, (season) Leon Gutmore 51 (97-98) **Appearances:** J Pullen 418
Fees - Paid: Undisclosed **Received:** £22,500+ increments for Steve Jones (West Ham, Nov. 1992)

BEST SEASON **FA Cup:** 1st Rd Proper 97-98 **FA Vase:** Winners - 75-76, 76-77 & 78-79
FA Trophy: 5th Rd 00-01 **FA Amateur Cup:** 3rd Qual Rd 73-74

HONOURS: Essex Snr Lg 72-73 74-75 75-76, R-up 71-2 73-4, Lg Cup 71-72, Challenge Cup 72-73, 76-77 (R.up 74-75); Isthmian Lge Div 2 79-80, Div 1 R-up 80-81, 97-98; Athenian Lg 77-79 (Lg Cup 77-78); East Anglian Cup R-up 79-80 84-5; Essex Snr Cup 75-76 R-up 85-6 93-4,4-5,5-6; Essex Snr Tphy 77-78 79-80; Essex Thameside Tphy 86-87 91-92 R-up 90-1; Essex F'lit Tphy 77-78; Phillips F'lit Tphy 76-77; Rothmans Merit Award 1978

Players progressing: D Westwood (QPR) 75, A Hull, D Carter (Peterborough,Orient), D Cass (Orient) 88, D Ludden (Orient) 92, S Jones (West Ham) 92

Back Row: Dave Reddington, John Scarborough, Russell Penn (Captain), Gary Ansell, Jimmy Dormer, Danny Hockton. **Middle**: Eric Doherty (GK Coach), Gary Heywood (Reserve Team Asst.Man.), Leon Hunter, Chris Howard, Steve Jones, Jerome John, Sam Taylor, Colin Masterson (Physio), Tony Cross (Reserve Team Man.). **Front:** Jimmy Lee, Andy Jones, Justin Edinburgh (Manager), Andy Polston (Asst.Man.), Gary Henty, Dean Morris, Marlon Patterson.
Photo courtesy of the "EVENING ECHO".

Match Facts 2002-03

Date	Comp.	Opponents	Att.	Score	Goalscorers
17/08	Rym. P	HARROW BOROUGH	406	1 - 0	Fewings 19
19/08	Rym. P	Boreham Wood	222	3 - 1	Fewings 45, Brennan 48[p], Williams 71
24/08	Rym. P	Aylesbury United	446	1 - 0	McGrath 8[og]
26/08	Rym. P	HENDON	547	0 - 0	
31/08	Rym. P	Maidenhead United	317	0 - 1	
03/09	Rym. P	BEDFORD TOWN	503	4 - 0	Carthy 26 47, Essandoh 38, M Graham 88
07/09	Rym. P	SUTTON UNITED	559	2 - 0	Essandoh 4, R Graham 7
10/09	Rym. P	Braintree Town	320	0 - 1	
14/09	Rym. P	Hayes	268	2 - 0	Essandoh 6, Wallace 70
17/09	Rym. P	BISHOP'S STORTFORD	467	1 - 1	Carthy 58
21/09	Rym. P	CHESHAM UNITED	507	1 - 0	Fewings 12
24/09	Rym. P	Purfleet	362	0 - 0	
28/09	**F.A.C.** Q2	YEADING	448	3 - 1	Williams 45, Graham 65 90
05/10	Rym. P	Kingstonian	543	0 - 2	
12/10	**F.A.C.** Q3	BRAINTREE TOWN	n/k	0 - 0	
15/10	Rym. P	HEYBRIDGE SWIFTS	344	2 - 0	Essandoh 24, Campbell 51
19/10	Rym. P	St Albans City	718	1 - 1	Campbell 79
22/10	Rym. P	ENFIELD	348	0 - 1	
26/10	**F.A.C.** Q4	Havant & Waterlooville	631	1 - 3	Wallace 67
01/11	Rym. P	PURFLEET	439	1 - 3	Wallace 14
05/11	Essex SC 3	WIVENHOE TOWN	n/k	5 - 0	Graham[p], Campbell[p], Wallace, Moore, Henty
09/11	Rym. P	Aldershot Town	2288	0 - 0	
19/11	Lge Cup 2	ENFIELD	n/k	5 - 0	Wallace 3, Essandoh 17 45, Penn 60, Graham 75
23/11	Rym. P	GRAYS ATHLETIC	609	4 - 1	Essandoh 5 23, R Graham 47, Wallace 66
30/11	**F.A.T.** 2	Havant & Waterlooville	277	1 - 1	Wallace 34
03/12	**F.A.T.** 2 rep	HAVANT & WATERLOOVILLE	327	1 - 2	Penn 25
07/12	Rym. P	Hampton & Richmond Bor.	202	1 - 1	Carthy 77
10/12	Essex SC 4	HARLOW TOWN	n/k	1 - 0	
14/12	Rym. P	Harrow Borough	252	2 - 1	Essandoh 28, Campbell 59
17/12	Lge Cup 3	FORD UNITED	96	3 - 1	Carthy 45 65, Wallace 48
21/12	Rym. P	FORD UNITED	420	1 - 3	Essandoh 12
28/12	Rym. P	AYLESBURY UNITED	582	1 - 1	R Graham 18
14/01	Essex SC QF	East Thurrock United	n/k	1 - 0	
18/01	Rym. P	Sutton United	537	2 - 1	Ansell 36, Douglas 70
21/01	Lge Cup 4	BISHOP'S STORTFORD	191	1 - 1	Wallace 16
25/01	Rym. P	HAYES	438	1 - 1	Wallace 12
28/01	Rym. P	ST ALBANS CITY	287	1 - 0	Moore 20
04/02	Lge Cup 4 rep	Bishop's Stortford	161	0 - 3	
15/02	Rym. P	Chesham United	242	2 - 0	Douglas 33 89
18/02	Essex SC SF	Aveley	n/k	1 - 1	Fewings — Lost 1 3 after pens.
22/02	Rym. P	KINGSTONIAN	508	0 - 2	
25/02	Rym. P	Bishop's Stortford	265	0 - 1	
01/03	Rym. P	Heybridge Swifts	292	1 - 1	Douglas 34
04/03	Rym. P	BASINGSTOKE TOWN	242	1 - 0	Graham 20[p]
08/03	Rym. P	Enfield	107	1 - 1	Fewings 22
11/03	Rym. P	Hitchin Town	208	0 - 1	
15/03	Rym. P	ALDERSHOT TOWN	1089	0 - 1	
18/03	Rym. P	BOREHAM WOOD	170	0 - 0	
22/03	Rym. P	Basingstoke Town	368	0 - 2	
25/03	Rym. P	BRAINTREE TOWN	238	1 - 2	Wallace 23
29/03	Rym. P	HITCHIN TOWN	326	1 - 2	Adedeji 61
03/04	Rym. P	Hendon	203	1 - 2	Merritt 28
05/04	Rym. P	Bedford Town	502	0 - 2	
08/04	Rym. P	Canvey Island	327	0 - 3	
12/04	Rym. P	MAIDENHEAD UNITED	238	2 - 0	Stowe 32 62
19/04	Rym. P	Ford United	112	2 - 0	Ansell 19, Stowe 65
21/04	Rym. P	CANVEY ISLAND	540	2 - 1	Ansell 22 77
26/04	Rym. P	Grays Athletic	303	0 - 1	
03/05	Rym. P	HAMPTON & RICHMOND B.	313	0 - 2	

PLAYING SQUAD

Goalkeepers: Jerome John (Grays Ath.)

Defenders: Justin Edinburgh (Portsmouth), Kevin Jordan (Aveley), Sasha Opinel (Aldershot), Russell Penn (Enfield), Tony Polston (Ford Utd), Dave Reddington (Enfield), Nicky Savage (Ford Utd)

Midfield: Richard Graham (Chesham Utd), Gary Henty (Barking), Dean Morris (Erith & Belvedere), Pasi Pihamaa (HIFK Helsinki), Jimmy Porter (Bowers Utd), Scott Williams (Hertford T.)

Forwards: Gary Ansell (Harlow T), Luke Baulkham (Aveley), Danny Hockton (Crawley T), Jimmy Sugrue (St. Albans C), Danny Trenkel (Gt Wakering Rovers), Jamie Wallace (Ford Utd)

BISHOPS STORTFORD

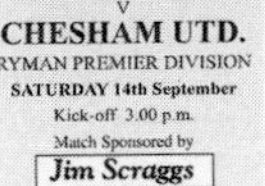

CLUB OFFICIALS

Chairman: John Goodwin
President: B W A Bayford
Secretary: Ian Kettridge,25 Cox Ley,Hatfield Heath,Bishop,s Stortford, Herts. CM22 7ER Tel No: 07904169017 (M)
Press Officer: Daniel Smart Tel No: 07736 459052 (M)

FOOTBALL MANAGEMENT TEAM

Team Manager: Martin Hayes
Assistant Månager: Tim Moylette
Physio: Peter Fox & Brian Curtis

FACT FILE

Formed: 1874 Nickname: Blues or Bishops
Colours: Blue & white stripes/blue/blue
Change colours: Yellow/yellow/yellow
Midweek matchday: Tuesday
Local Press: B.Stortford Citizen, Herts & Essex Observer, Herald
Local Radio: BBC Essex, Essex FM, Breeze AM, Mercury FM

PROGRAMME

Pages: 72 Price: £1.50
Editor: Dan Smart Tel: 07736 459052

GROUND Woodside Park, Dunmow Road, Bishop 's Stortford (01279 306456)
Directions: M11 jct 8, A1250 towards town centre, left at first roundabout. Woodside is first on right opposite Golf Club. Entrance is between industrial units on right. By rail: British Rail: W. Anglia Line (London, Liverpool Str.-Cambridge)
Capacity: 4,000 Cover: 700 Seats: 298 Floodlights: Yes
Clubhouse: Open lunchtimes,evenings and matchdays Function room(seating 250) available for hire .
Club Shop: Full stock inc. scarves, badges and other souvenirs. Massive stock of programmes and books etc. Contact Mark Pulfervia club.

PREVIOUS **Leagues:** East Herts 1896-97, 02-06, 19-21; Stansted & Dist. Lg 06-19; HertsCounty 21-25 27-29; Herts & Essex Border 25-27; Spartan 29-51; Delphian 51-63;Athenian 63-73

CLUB RECORDS **Attendance:** 6,000 v Peterborough Utd, FA Cup 2nd Rd 1972 & v Middlesbrough FACup 3rd Rd replay, 1983
Win: 11-0: Nettleswell & Butntmill, Herts Jun Cup 2nd Rd 1911
Defeat: 0-13 v Cheshunt (H), Herts Sen. Cup 1st Rd 9/1/26
Fee Paid: For Vinnie John to Grays Athletic (1999)
Fee Received: £10,000 for Carl Hoddle (Leyton O., 89)
Scorer: (Since 29) Jimmy Badcock 123
Appearances: Phil Hopkins 543

BEST SEASON **FA Amateur Cup:** Winners 73-74
FA Trophy: Winners 80-81
FA Cup: 3rd Rd rep. 82-83 (above) - League clubs beaten: Reading 82-83

HONOURS Isthmian Lg Div 1 80-1 94-5 (Lg Cup 88-9, Full Mem. Cup 90-1), Prem. Inter Lg Cup 89-90; Athenian Lg 69-70 (R-up 66-7, Div 1 65-6, Div 2 R-up 64-5); Delphian Lg 54-5; London Snr Cup 73-4; Herts Snr Cup 58-9 59-0 63-4 70-1 72-3 73-4 75-686-7; E Anglian Cup 81-2; Herts Charity Cup 62-3 65-6 73-4 81-2 82-3 84-5 87-896-7; Herts Charity Shield 54-5; Herts I'mediate Cup (res) 94-95; Eastern F'lit Cup 84-5; Essex F'lit Cup 67-8; Essex & Herts Border Comb 81-2 88-9 R-up (2) 92-4; Fred Budden Tphy R-up 78-9 90-1 92-3

Players progressing: P Phelan (Southend 61), M Hollow (Orient 62), P Phillips(Luton 69), T Baker (Colchester 86), T Sorrell (Maidstone, Colchester, Barnet 88), C Hoddle (Leyton O., Barnet 89), T English (Colchester 89), L Fortune-West (Gillingham 95), L Braithwaite (Exeter City 96)

Back row, left to right: Les Whitton (Coach), Onaldo, Colin Taylor, Ray Taylor, Alex Riches, Richard Hayward, Vinnie John, Tim Langer, Lee Mitchell, Andy Keepence, Owen Beale and Tom Moylette (Coach) **Front row:** Martin Hayes (Player/Manager), Charlie Goodwin, Glen Southam, Mark McGibboin, Jimmy Sygrue, Freddie Hyatt, Troy Braham, Carl Allison, Danny Wolf, Rob French and Trevor Paul

Match Facts 2002-03

Date	Comp.	Opponents	Att.	Score	Goalscorers
08/08	Herts CC 1	HITCHIN TOWN	n/k	3 - 0	Langer, Southam, Riches
17/08	Rym. P	BEDFORD TOWN	501	1 - 1	French 67
20/08	Rym. P	Canvey Island	559	4 - 0	Essandoh 19 29, Brown 67, John 89
24/08	Rym. P	Harrow Borough	250	2 - 2	Essandoh 10, Braham 24
26/08	Rym. P	ALDERSHOT TOWN	894	1 - 1	John 50
31/08	Rym. P	Hampton & Richmond Bor.	298	0 - 1	
03/09	Rym. P	AYLESBURY UNITED	439	2 - 2	John 25, Hyatt 67[p]
07/09	Rym. P	Purfleet	232	1 - 2	John 35
10/09	Rym. P	ENFIELD	355	1 - 0	Southam 68
14/09	Rym. P	CHESHAM UNITED	356	2 - 1	Paul 15, Hyatt 89
17/09	Rym. P	Billericay Town	467	1 - 1	Paul 81
21/09	Rym. P	Grays Athletic	295	0 - 1	
24/09	Rym. P	BRAINTREE TOWN	409	1 - 1	Braham 61
28/09	**F.A.C.** Q2	Enfield	161	5 - 1	Sugrue 22, Hyatt 38, Paul 80 83, Southam 90
05/10	Rym. P	HITCHIN TOWN	421	2 - 3	Paul 36, John 67
08/10	Herts SC 2	Cheshunt	126	0 - 1	
12/10	**F.A.C.** Q3	EASTBOURNE BOROUGH	452	1 - 0	Southam 75
14/10	Herts CC QF	Boreham Wood	138	2 - 1	Bliss, Haniff
19/10	Rym. P	Kingstonian	624	1 - 3	Paul 15
22/10	Rym. P	ST ALBANS CITY	388	0 - 2	
26/10	**F.A.C.** Q4	BOREHAM WOOD	969	1 - 1	Williamson 90
28/10	**F.A.C.** Q4 rep	Boreham Wood	903	1 - 4	John 75[p]
02/11	**F.A.T.** 1	Berkhamsted Town	191	2 - 2	Southam 11, Paul 44
05/11	**F.A.T.** 1 rep	BERKHAMSTED TOWN	221	2 - 0	Paul 43 56
09/11	Rym. P	Basingstoke Town	391	1 - 3	Southam 28
12/11	Rym. P	Heybridge Swifts	249	3 - 3	Hyatt 11, French 75, Hayes 89[p]
16/11	Rym. P	KINGSTONIAN	392	2 - 2	Paul 14, Hyatt 82
19/11	Lge Cup 2	Hungerford Town	100	0 - 0	
26/11	Rym. P	Sutton United	419	1 - 2	Paul 21
30/11	**F.A.T.** 2	MARLOW	349	2 - 2	Hyatt 89, Braham 90
03/12	**F.A.T.** 2 rep	Marlow	145	3 - 2	Paul 10, Braham 57 72 (Expelled - ineligible player)
07/12	Rym. P	HAYES	304	2 - 3	Paul 15, John 52[p]
10/12	Lge Cup 2 rep	HUNGERFORD TOWN	n/k	7 - 1	Southam 11 31, Williamson 43, Langer 55 59 69, French 86
14/12	Rym. P	Bedford Town	469	1 - 3	Hyatt 28
17/12	Lge Cup 3	BASINGSTOKE TOWN	112	3 - 1	Southam 35[p] 55, Paul 82
21/12	Rym. P	BOREHAM WOOD	318	1 - 4	Langer 81
28/12	Rym. P	HARROW BOROUGH	343	4 - 0	Williamson 4, John 27 50, Langer 71
04/01	Rym. P	Aldershot Town	1964	0 - 0	
14/01	Herts CC SF	Tring Town	75	9 - 1	Wolf 2, Paul 10 37 45 72, John 36[p] 60 84, Hayes 59
18/01	Rym. P	PURFLEET	310	2 - 2	John 45, Southam 90
21/01	Lge Cup 4	Billericay Town	191	1 - 1	Renner 69
25/01	Rym. P	Chesham United	316	1 - 3	French 58
28/01	Rym. P	CANVEY ISLAND	379	1 - 2	Paul 42
04/02	Lge Cup 4 rep	BILLERICAY TOWN	161	3 - 0	Paul 60 89, French 70
08/02	Rym. P	Braintree Town	431	3 - 1	Southam 38, Paul 43, John 78
11/02	Lge Cup QF	YEADING	154	1 - 4	John 44[p]
15/02	Rym. P	GRAYS ATHLETIC	291	1 - 3	Williamson 60
22/02	Rym. P	Hitchin Town	432	1 - 0	John 3
25/02	Rym. P	BILLERICAY TOWN	265	1 - 0	Renner 79
01/03	Rym. P	SUTTON UNITED	365	1 - 0	Renner 67
08/03	Rym. P	St Albans City	428	2 - 3	Aransibia 89, Paul 90
11/03	Rym. P	Ford United	135	2 - 3	Howell 25, French 41[p]
15/03	Rym. P	BASINGSTOKE TOWN	378	3 - 1	Gould 12, Forbes 20, Howell 78
18/03	Rym. P	Maidenhead United	189	3 - 2	Southam 43, Howell 45, Langer 59
22/03	Rym. P	Hendon	307	3 - 0	Renner 45, French 56, Wreh 79
26/03	Rym. P	Enfield	144	2 - 0	Renner 1, Southam 70[p]
29/03	Rym. P	HEYBRIDGE SWIFTS	471	2 - 0	French 17 22
12/04	Rym. P	HAMPTON & RICHMOND B.	336	2 - 1	Riches 14, Gould 59
15/04	Rym. P	HENDON	341	4 - 1	Southam 15, Gould 62, Rainford 80[p], Langer 86
19/04	Rym. P	Boreham Wood	213	1 - 1	Gould 85
21/04	Rym. P	FORD UNITED	359	0 - 1	
26/04	Rym. P	MAIDENHEAD UNITED	327	3 - 4	Haniff 75, Southam 88, Hayes 90
29/04	Herts CC F	Hemel Hempstead Town	284	3 - 1	Gould, Aransibia, Southam
01/05	Rym. P	Aylesbury United	405	2 - 1	Aransibia 14, Gould 42
03/05	Rym. P	Hayes	380	0 - 2	

PLAYING SQUAD

Goalkeepers: Micky Desborough (Grays Ath.)

Defenders: Aaronn Barnett (Gravesend & Northfleet), Grant Cooper (Chesham Utd), Danny Foot (Baldock T.), Alex Riches (Saffron Waldon T.)

Midfield: Victor Boyle-Renner (Boreham Wood), Troy Braham (Romford), Lee Double (East Thurrock Utd), Rob French (Dulwich Hamlet), Freddie Hyatt (Chelmsford City), Richard Howell (Stevenage Borough), Tim Langer (Aveley), Joel Marie-Saintt (USM Senlish (France), David Rainford (Ford Utd), Glen Southam (Enfield), Russell Williamson (Chelmsford City).

Forwards: Andy Aransibia (Harrow Borough), Roy Essendoh (Grays Ath.) , Gareth Gwilliam (Ashford Utd), Martin Hayes (Romford), Chris Wreh (St.Mirren).

BOGNOR REGIS TOWN

CLUB OFFICIALS

Chairman: Tom Martin
President: S Rowlands
Secretary: Peter Helsby, c/o The Club.
02392 291388 or 01243 822325
Press Officer: Jack Pearce

FOOTBALL MANAGEMENT TEAM

Manager: Jack Pearce
Coach:Graham Vick
Physios: S Sidaway & Heidi Simpson

2002-03

Captain: M.Birmingham
Leading Goalscorer: M.Russell
Player of the Year:

FACT FILE

Founded: 1883
Nickname: The Rocks
Sponsors: Wayne Windows
Colours: White (green trim)/green/white
Change colours: Blue/white/red
Midweek home matchday: Tuesday
Reserves ' League: None
Local Radio: Radio Sussex, Ocean Sound, Radio Solent, Southern Sound, Spirit FM
Local Press: Bognor Regis Journal & Guardian, Bognor Observer, Brighton Argus, Portsmouth News

PROGRAMME

Pages: 36 Price: £1.20
Editor: N.Folland 01243 822325

ROCKS REVIEW
THE MATCH DAY MAGAZINE OF
BOGNOR REGIS TOWN FOOTBALL CLUB
www.therocks.co.uk
19th April 2003
Kick Off
3.00pm
OUR VISITORS TODAY
TOOTING & MITCHAM UTD
Welcome to Nyewood Lane
CLUB SPONSORS: 2002/2003
WAYNE WINDOWS
Programme Price £1.20

GROUND Nyewood Lane, Bognor Regis PO21 2TY Tel: 01243 822325
Directions: West along sea front from pier, past Aldwick shopping centre then turn right into Nyewood Lane
Capacity: 6,000 Cover: 3,800 Seats: 243 Floodlights: Yes
Clubhouse: Open every night, matchdays and Sunday lunchtimes. Hot food available
Club Shop: Selling programmes and normal club items

PREVIOUS **Leagues:** W Sussex Lge 1896-1926; Brighton, Hove & District Lge 26-27; Sussex County Lge 27-72; Southern Lge 72-81

CLUB RECORDS **Attendance:** 3,642 v Swansea FA Cup 1st Rd replay, '84
Goalscorer: Kevin Clements (206) **Appearances:** Mick Pullen, 967 (20 seasons)
Transfer Fee Paid: £2,200 Guy Rutherford 95-96
Fee Received: £10,500 for John Crumplin & Geoff Cooper (Brighton & Hove Alb, 87) & Simon Rodger (C Palace 89)

BEST SEASON **FA Amateur Cup:** 1st Round 71-72 **F A Trophy:** 3rd Round 95-96
F A Cup: 2nd Rd on four occasions - League clubs beaten: Swansea 84-85, Exeter 88-89
84-85 2-6 v Reading (A), 85-86 1-6 v Gillingham (A), 88-89 0-1 v Cambridge (H), 95-96 0-4 v Peterborough (A)

HONOURS: Isthmian Lg Div 1 R-up 81-82, (Lg Cup 86-87); Southern Lg R-up 80-81 (Lg Cup R-up 80-81), Merit Cup 80-81; Sussex Lg 48-49 71-72 (R-up 38-39 51-52), Div 2 70-71, Invitation Cup 40-41 49-50 62-63 71-72; Brighton Lg R-up 26-27; W Sussex Lg (5) 20-25 (R-up 1896-97, 25-26), Jnr Lg 10-11 13-14; Southern Co's Comb 78-79; Sussex Snr Cup(9) 54-56 79-84 86-87 94-95 (R-up 51-52 58-59 84-85 00-01); Sussex Prof. Cup 73-74, Sussex RUR Cup 71-72; Sussex I'mediate Cup 52-53, Littlehampton Hosp. Cup 29-30 33-34; Bognor Charity Cup(8) 28-29 30-31 32-33 37-38 47-48 58-59 71-73; Gosport War Mem. Cup (2) 81-83 (R-up 86-87); Snr Midweek F'lit Cup R-up 74-75

Players progressing: E Randall (Chelsea 50), J Standing (Brighton 61), A Woon (Brentford 72), J Crumplin & G Cooper (Brighton 87), Simon Rodger (C Palace 89)

L-R - Back row: B.Gumbrill (Kit Man), Graham Vick (Coach), Guy Rutherford, David Wright, Kevin Murphy, Eddie Broadbent, Craig Stoner, John Tucker, Matt Russell, Jodey Rowland, Graham Bradford (mascot), Duncan Lampard (Kit Man), Shaun Sidaway (Physio).
Front: Lee Stevens, Jamie Howell, Richard Hudson, David Birmingham, Stan Rowlands (President),Tom Martin (Chairman), Michael Birmingham (Captain), Jack Pearce (Manager) Peter Helsby (Secretary), Nicky Wyatt, Steve Sargent and Miles Rutherford.

Date	Comp.	Opponents	Att.	Score	Goalscorers
17/08	Rym. 1S	Windsor & Eton	111	2 - 0	D Birmingham 20, Hall 80
20/08	Rym. 1S	CHERTSEY TOWN	203	6 - 0	Sansom 3, **Hudson 3** (8 33 45), Leigh 45, Odoye 84
24/08	Rym. 1S	MOLESEY	247	1 - 1	Leigh 3
26/08	Rym. 1S	Banstead Athletic	128	1 - 0	D Birmingham 86
31/08	**F.A.C.** P	WORTHING	706	1 - 0	
07/09	Rym. 1S	METROPOLITAN POLICE	220	4 - 0	Russell 2 6 67, Boswell 85[og]
10/09	Rym. 1S	Bracknell Town	115	1 - 3	Russell 75
14/09	**F.A.C.** Q1	WINDSOR & ETON	351	4 - 1	
21/09	Rym. 1S	Croydon Athletic	98	0 - 1	
24/09	Rym. 1S	CORINTHIAN CASUALS	197	1 - 1	Murphy 12
28/09	**F.A.C.** Q2	Hayes	311	0 - 6	
01/10	Rym. 1S	Dulwich Hamlet	154	0 - 0	
05/10	**F.A.T.** P	WIVENHOE TOWN	303	5 - 2	Russell 25 44, Wyatt 61 83, Murphy 75[p]
08/10	Rym. 1S	CROYDON	170	3 - 1	Leigh 25, Russell 42 57
12/10	Rym. 1S	Epsom & Ewell	136	1 - 1	Leigh 46
15/10	Rym. 1S	LEATHERHEAD	138	0 - 0	
19/10	Rym. 1S	BROMLEY	283	1 - 1	Russell 28
21/10	Rym. 1S	Carshalton Athletic	297	0 - 1	
26/10	Rym. 1S	STAINES TOWN	240	3 - 0	Russell 17, M Birmingham 77, Wyatt 90
02/11	**F.A.T.** 1	BOREHAM WOOD	306	2 - 0	Hudson 33, Leigh 81
09/11	Rym. 1S	Egham Town	126	6 - 1	Russell 41 48, Stevens 45, Murphy 54, Hudson 56, Wyatt 75
16/11	Rym. 1S	ASHFORD TOWN (Middx)	256	8 - 0	Stevens 5 32, Hudson 33, **Russell 4** (51 58 70[p] 72), G Rutherford 65[p]
19/11	Sussex SC 2	CRAWLEY TOWN	n/k	1 - 3	
23/11	Rym. 1S	Staines Town	177	3 - 0	Stevens 44, Russell 53, M Birmingham 57at Chertsey Town
26/11	Rym. 1S	HORSHAM	255	1 - 3	Murphy 69[p]
30/11	**F.A.T.** 2	HENDON	312	1 - 4	Russell 88
03/12	Lge Cup 2	St Albans City	134	2 - 3	Howell 22, M Birmingham 82
07/12	Rym. 1S	WALTON & HERSHAM	193	3 - 0	Stevens 12, Hudson 38, Russell 79
14/12	Rym. 1S	WINDSOR & ETON	190	2 - 1	Stevens 34 81
17/12	Rym. 1S	Whyteleafe	114	1 - 3	Stevens 74
28/12	Rym. 1S	Molesey	118	5 - 1	M Birmingham 14, Russell 20 66, Hudson 60, Tucker 82
04/01	Rym. 1S	BANSTEAD ATHLETIC	243	1 - 0	Rowland 33
18/01	Rym. 1S	EPSOM & EWELL	252	3 - 0	M Birmingham 70[p], Wyatt 78, O'Shaughnessy 85
25/01	Rym. 1S	Bromley	390	1 - 2	Harper 58
04/02	Rym. 1S	Tooting & Mitcham United	207	0 - 4	
08/02	Rym. 1S	Corinthian Casuals	100	3 - 0	Harper 26 44, Russell 54
15/02	Rym. 1S	CROYDON ATHLETIC	201	2 - 0	Stevens 26, Harper 53
18/02	Rym. 1S	Lewes	370	2 - 2	Russell 30, M Birmingham 90
22/02	Rym. 1S	Croydon	55	6 - 0	Stevens 41 45, M Birmingham 59[p] 85, Harper 61, Howell 90
01/03	Rym. 1S	DULWICH HAMLET	315	0 - 1	
04/03	Rym. 1S	Chertsey Town	125	2 - 0	D Birmingham 40, Davies 43
08/03	Rym. 1S	Ashford Town (Middx)	153	1 - 0	Russell 54
11/03	Rym. 1S	WORTHING	496	3 - 0	Russell 33 34, Stevens 39
15/03	Rym. 1S	EGHAM TOWN	301	3 - 1	M Birmingham 41[p], Thomas 68, Stevens 86
22/03	Rym. 1S	Horsham	549	2 - 1	Russell 70, Davies 88
29/03	Rym. 1S	WHYTELEAFE	367	3 - 0	Russell 15, Rowland 78, M Birmingham 87
01/04	Rym. 1S	Leatherhead	232	0 - 0	
05/04	Rym. 1S	BRACKNELL TOWN	308	0 - 1	
08/04	Rym. 1S	CARSHALTON ATHLETIC	553	1 - 0	M Birmingham 78
12/04	Rym. 1S	Metropolitan Police	220	2 - 0	Russell 37 81
19/04	Rym. 1S	TOOTING & MITCHAM UTD	408	3 - 0	Russell 2, Murphy 58, M Birmingham 68[p]
21/04	Rym. 1S	Worthing	932	1 - 1	Murphy 53
26/04	Rym. 1S	LEWES	1003	0 - 2	
03/05	Rym. 1S	Walton & Hersham	492	0 - 0	

PLAYING SQUAD

Goalkeepers: Craig Stoner (Portsmouth), Graham Bannatyne (St.Leonards).

Defenders: Tom Foster (Basingstoke T.), Chris Hall (Leatherhead), Richard Hudson (Lewes), Simon James (Worthing), Paul Jones (Reading T.), Kevin Murphy (Havant &Waterlooville), David Piper (Winchester City), Miles Rutherford (Worthing), Jon Tucker (Arundel).

Midfield: Charlie Balfe (Eastleigh), Michael Birmingham (Dorchester T.), Jamie Howell (Torquay Utd), Danny Layton (Basingstoke T.), Jodey Rowland (Arundel), Guy Rutherford (Worthing), Steve Sargent (Worthing), David Wright (Dorchester T.).

Forwards: Simon Funnell (Worthing), Jamie Laidlaw (Chichester City Utd), Matthew Russell (Horsham YMCA), Rupert Sansom (Brighton), Lee Stevens (Selsey)

BRAINTREE TOWN

CLUB OFFICIALS

Chairman: George Rosling
Vice Chairman: Ivan Kibble
President: Ron Webb
Secretary: T A Woodley, 19a Bailey Bridge Rd., Braintree, Essex CM7 5TT
Tel: 01376 326234
Press Officer: Ron Webb Tel: 01376 325338

FOOTBALL MANAGEMENT TEAM

Manager:Ben Embery
Ass Manr Steve Jackson Coach:Ken Varney
Physio: Tony Brightwell

FACT FILE

Founded: 1898
Nickname: The Iron
Sponsors: T.B.A.
Colours:Yellow with navy side panel
Change colours: White
Reserves' Lg: Essex/Herts Border Comb
Email Address:
10665.3036@ compuserve.com
Local Radio: BBC Essex (103.5 fm),
Essex Radio (102.6 fm)

GROUND Cressing Road Stadium, Clockhouse Way, Braintree, Essex (01376 345617)
Directions: From Braintree by-pass, turn into Braintree at the McDonalds r'bout, follow signs for East Braintree Ind. Est. - floodlights on left 3/4 mile into town just past. Orange Tree Pub. Entrance next left in Clockhouse Way, then left again. 1 mile from Braintree & Bocking (BR). Bus 353 from Witham or town centre Town centre 20 mins walk
Capacity: 4,000 Cover 1,500 Seats 250 Floodlights:Yes
Clubhouse: Open evenings 7-30-11, Sun 12-3, Sat matchday 12.00- 11.00 Full bar facilities
Club shop: ContactTom Marshallc/o club (75 year History of Braintree £15.99)

PROGRAMME

Pages: 40 Price: £1.50
Editor: Len Llewellyn (01277 363103 T/Fax)

PREVIOUS **Leagues:** North Essex 1898-1925; Essex & Suffolk Border 25-28 55-64; Spartan 28-35; Eastern Co's 35-37 38-39 52-55 70-91; Essex Co. 37-38; London 45-52; GtrLondon 64-66; Metropolitan 66-70; Southern 91-96
Names: Manor Works 1898-1921; Crittall Ath. 21-68; Braintree & Crittall Ath. 68-81; Braintree FC 81-82
Grounds: The Fair Field 1898-1903; Spaldings Meadow, Panfield Lane 03-23

CLUB RECORDS **Attendance:** 4,000 v Spurs, charity challenge match, May 1952
Career Goalscorer: Chris Guy 211, 63-90. **Seasonal Record Scorer:** Gary Bennett 57, 97-98
Career Appearances: Paul Young 524, 66-77 **Fee Paid:** £2,000 for Shane Bailey (Sudbury Town)
Fee Received: £10,000 Matt Metcalf (Brentford 93) & John Cheesewright(Colchester 93)
Win: 15-3 v Hopes (Birmingham Friendly 39), 12-0 v Thetford Tn (Eastern Lge 35-36)
Defeat: 0-14 v Chelmsford City A (Nth Essex Lge 23)

BEST SEASON **FA Cup:** 4th Qual. Rd 69-70 85-86 94-95 97-98

HONOURS: Isthmian Lge Div 2 R-up 97-98, Div 3 R-up 96-97; Guardian Insurance Cup R-up 96-97; Eastern Counties Lg 36-37 83-84 84-85 (R-up 86-87 87-88 88-89 90-91), Lg Cup 87-88 (R-up 35-36 74-75); Essex County Lg R-up 37-38; London Lg (East) R-up 45-46, Lg Cup 47-48(jt) 48-49 51-52 (R-up 49-50); Metropolitan Lg Cup 69-70; Essex Elizabethan Tphy R-up 68-69; E. Anglian Cup 46-47 68-69 95-96; Essex Sen.Tphy 86-87 (R-up 90-91); Essex & Suffolk Border Lg 59-60 84-85 (Lg Cup 59-60); Nth Essex Lg 05-06 10-11 11-12; Essex Sen Cup 95-96 R-up 96-97; Essex Jnr Cup R-up 04-05 05-06 22-23; RAFA Cup 56-57; Gtr Lon. Ben. Cup 65-66; Worthington Evans Cup (3) R-up (4); Eastern F'lit Cup 85-86 96-97 (R-up 94-95 97-98); Anglian F'lit Lg 69-70; Jan Havanaar Inter. Tour. 94-95 (R-up 92-93)

Players progressing: J Dick (West Ham 53), S Wright (Wrexham 83), J Cheesewright (Birmingham C. 91), G Bennett, M Metcalf (Brentford 93),R Reinelt (Gillingham 93), M de Souza (Birmingham C.), G Culling (ColchesterU 94) , S.Forbes (Southend U), S.Brown (Tottenham H) and D.Theobald (Brentford)

Back row: Andrew Potter, Paul Catley, Gavin Cowan, Tommy Noble, Adam Gillespie and Mark Jones.

Front row: Matt Hayter, Brett Girling, Neil Cousins, Dean Parratt and Nicky Hayden.

Date	Comp.	Opponents	Att.	Score	Goalscorers
17/08	Rym. P	GRAYS ATHLETIC	352	1 - 1	Parratt 86
20/08	Rym. P	Bedford Town	535	0 - 1	
24/08	Rym. P	Aldershot Town	1694	0 - 3	
26/08	Rym. P	MAIDENHEAD UNITED	255	1 - 2	Addington 7
31/08	Rym. P	Harrow Borough	193	2 - 2	Jones 50, Cousins 81
03/09	Rym. P	BOREHAM WOOD	238	0 - 1	
07/09	Rym. P	Chesham United	304	1 - 1	Noble 7
10/09	Rym. P	BILLERICAY TOWN	320	1 - 0	Noble 38
14/09	Rym. P	PURFLEET	250	0 - 0	
17/09	Rym. P	Hitchin Town	287	0 - 0	
21/09	Rym. P	HAYES	262	0 - 1	
24/09	Rym. P	Bishop's Stortford	409	1 - 1	Berquez 87
28/09	**F.A.C.** Q2	Uxbridge	130	2 - 1	Cowan 6[p], Cousins 60
01/10	Rym. P	KINGSTONIAN	267	1 - 2	Cousins 76
05/10	Rym. P	Canvey Island	754	1 - 1	Quinton 45
12/10	**F.A.C.** Q3	Billericay Town	n/k	0 - 0	
19/10	Rym. P	Basingstoke Town	338	1 - 2	Cowan 22
22/10	Rym. P	AYLESBURY UNITED	260	2 - 2	Jones 16, Noble 76
26/10	Rym. P	ENFIELD	243	1 - 3	Berquez 88
02/11	Rym. P	St Albans City	438	4 - 2	Quinton 14, Waters 47, Berquez 82, Stimpson 90
05/11	Essex SC 3	Witham Town	n/k	2 - 3	
09/11	Rym. P	Hendon	280	0 - 2	
16/11	Rym. P	BASINGSTOKE TOWN	304	0 - 3	
19/11	Lge Cup 2	Barton Rovers	n/k	3 - 1	Cousins 78, Noble 81, Berquez 84
30/11	**F.A.T.** 2	Oxford City	143	0 - 1	
07/12	Rym. P	SUTTON UNITED	252	0 - 1	
10/12	Lge Cup 3	HARROW BOROUGH	n/k	1 - 3	Simpson 79
14/12	Rym. P	Grays Athletic	217	2 - 1	Noble 22, Keevil 47
21/12	Rym. P	HAMPTON & RICHMOND B.	270	3 - 1	Noble 26 46, Simpson 66
28/12	Rym. P	ALDERSHOT TOWN	757	2 - 1	Noble 16, Quinton 88
04/01	Rym. P	Maidenhead United	232	3 - 2	Richards 35, Cobb 67, Noble 80
18/01	Rym. P	CHESHAM UNITED	290	1 - 2	Waters 12
25/01	Rym. P	Purfleet	247	1 - 1	Noble 3
04/02	Rym. P	Ford United	131	0 - 3	
08/02	Rym. P	BISHOP'S STORTFORD	431	1 - 3	Cobb 87
11/02	Rym. P	BEDFORD TOWN	270	2 - 0	Quinton 63, Richards 79
15/02	Rym. P	Hayes	203	3 - 1	Riddle 40, Richards 55 60
22/02	Rym. P	CANVEY ISLAND	575	2 - 4	Keevil 41, Blackwell 62
25/02	Rym. P	Heybridge Swifts	294	0 - 2	
04/03	Rym. P	HITCHIN TOWN	230	1 - 3	Quinton 54
08/03	Rym. P	Aylesbury United	402	1 - 1	Blackwell 23
11/03	Rym. P	Kingstonian	249	4 - 1	Cobb 19 39, Noble 25 88
15/03	Rym. P	HENDON	271	1 - 2	Cobb 50
22/03	Rym. P	Enfield	101	1 - 1	Cobb 39
25/03	Rym. P	Billericay Town	238	2 - 1	Cobb 47[p] 79
29/03	Rym. P	ST ALBANS CITY	324	2 - 2	Cobb 59, Parratt 90
05/04	Rym. P	Boreham Wood	164	2 - 1	Cobb 37, Waters 89
12/04	Rym. P	HARROW BOROUGH	257	2 - 4	Culverhouse 28, Porter 89
19/04	Rym. P	Hampton & Richmond Bor.	180	1 - 0	Quinton 80
21/04	Rym. P	HEYBRIDGE SWIFTS	501	3 - 0	Cobb 25, Riddle 57, Blackwell 65
26/04	Rym. P	FORD UNITED	294	1 - 0	Riddle 86
03/05	Rym. P	Sutton United	535	1 - 3	Cobb 51[p]

PLAYING SQUAD

Goalkeepers: Simon Morden (Wivenhoe T.)

Defenders: Dave Culverhouse (Heybridge Swifts), Brett Girling (Chelmsford City), Wayne Houghton (Tiptree Utd), Mark Jones (Romford), Louis Riddle (Stevenage Borough),

Midfield: Andy Burke (Bristol Rovers), Sam Keevil (Chelmsford City), Dave Kreyling (Heybridge Swifts), Dean Parratt (Billericay T.), Tony Porter (St. Margartesbury), Nicky Simpson (Wivenhoe T.)

Forwards: Steve Good (Romford), Bradley Quinton (Bishop's Stortford)

CANVEY ISLAND

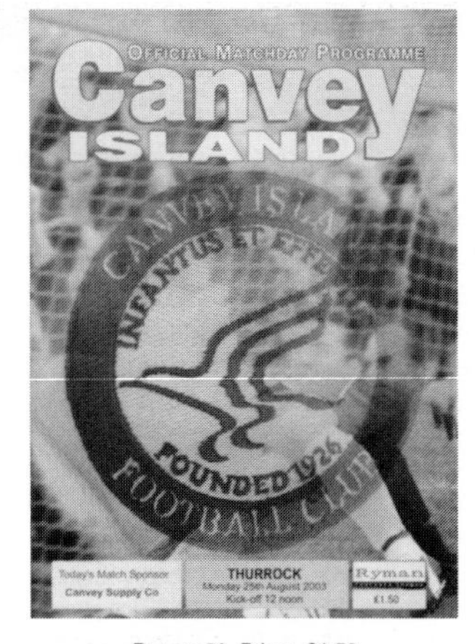

Pages: 52 Price: £1.50
Editor: Keith Johnson (07773 959125)
Local Press: Evening Echo
Local Radio: Essex FM, BBC Essex

CLUB OFFICIALS

Chairman: Ray Cross, 95 Lakeside Path, Canvey Island, Essex SS8 5PD.
Tel: 01268 684357 (H)
Secretary: Mrs Frances Roche, 56 Harvest Road, Canvey Island SS8 9RP.
Tel: 01268 698586 (H/Fax)
Press Officer: Tony Roche
Tel: 01268 698586

FOOTBALL MANAGEMENT TEAM

Manager: Jeff King. 01268 511555 (B) 07850654321 (Mobile)
Asst Manager: Glenn Pennyfather
Physio: Harry Johnson

FACT FILE

Formed: 1926
Nickname: Gulls
Sponsors: Kings Park Homes
Colours: Yellow/white/white
Change colours: Orange/navy/white
Midweek matchday: Tuesday
Reserves' League:
Essex & Herts Border Comb
Club Website: www.canveyfc.com

2002-2003

Captain: Neil Gregory
Top Scorer: Lee Boylan 47
Player of the Year: Jeff Minton

GROUND: Park Lane, Canvey Island, Essex SS8 7PXTel: 01268 682991
Directions: A130 from A13 or A127 at Sadlers Farm r/about, 1 mile through town centre, 1st right past old bus garage. Bus 3 or 151 fromBenfleet (BR) to stop after Admiral Jellicoe (PH)
Capacity: 4,100 Seats: 500 Cover: 827 Floodlights: Yes
Clubhouse: Open Tues, Thurs & Sats. Full licence. Food avaiable
Club Shop: Open matchdays. Selling programmes, badges, shirts etc.

PREVIOUS **Leagues:** Southend & Dist.; Thurrock & Thameside Comb.; Parthenon; Metropolitan;Gtr London 64-71; Essex Senior
Grounds: None **Names:** None

CLUB RECORDS **Attendance:** 3,553v Aldershot Town League 2002-2003
Win: 10-1 v Enfield **Defeat:** 7-0 v Halstead
Career Appearances: Steve Price (407) **Career Goalscorer:** Andy Jones
Fee received: £4,500 for Brian Horne from Farnborough Town.
Fee paid: £ 5,000 for Chris Duffy to Northwich Victoria

BEST SEASON **FA Cup:** 3Rd Round, 1-4 v Burnley (A) 01-02 League clubs defeated: Port Vale 2-1(A) after 1-1 (H)
FA Vase: Semi-final v Tiverton 27/3/93 **FA Trophy:** Winners 2000-01 v Forset Green Rovers 1-0

HONOURS: Ryman Lge Prem R-up 00-01,01-02,02-03 Div 1 98-99 - Div 2 95-96, 97-98,R-up 98-99 Div 3 R-up 94-95; Carlton Trophy 95-96; Essex Sen Lg 86-87 92-93 (Lg Cup 79-80 92-93),Trophy R-up 93-94; Harry Fisher Mem.Tphy 93-94; Essex Thameside Trophy 93-94; Parthenon Lge Cup 58-59; Metropolian Lge 67-68 68-69, Cup 67-68 68-69; Thameside 95-96 97-98, Essex Sen Cup 98-99,99-00,01-02

Players progressing: Peter Taylor (Spurs), Gary Heale (Luton T)

Date	Comp.	Opponents	Att.	Score	Goalscorers
17/08	Rym. P	Hayes	595	1 - 2	Parmenter 74
20/08	Rym. P	BISHOP'S STORTFORD	559	0 - 4	
24/08	Rym. P	HITCHIN TOWN	401	3 - 1	N Gregory 16 50, D Gregory 59
26/08	Rym. P	Basingstoke Town	575	1 - 2	N Gregory 61
31/08	Rym. P	SUTTON UNITED	779	1 - 1	Duffy 18
03/09	Rym. P	St Albans City	707	1 - 2	Brayley 9
07/09	Rym. P	Aylesbury United	716	6 - 1	Chenery 44, Minton 64, N Gregory 65, Brayley 78, Knight 80, Boylan 84
10/09	Rym. P	HENDON	611	4 - 4	Protheroe 31, Kennedy 32, Gregory 69 80[p]
14/09	Rym. P	HEYBRIDGE SWIFTS	619	4 - 1	Brayley 32 77, N Gregory 45, Boylan 79
17/09	Rym. P	Aldershot Town	2058	0 - 1	
21/09	Rym. P	Hampton & Richmond Bor.	405	2 - 0	Boylan 16 31[p]
24/09	Rym. P	GRAYS ATHLETIC	834	2 - 0	Boylan 43[p], N Gregory 57
28/09	**F.A.C.** Q2	FOLKESTONE INVICTA	429	2 - 1	N Gregory 41, Forbes 74
01/10	Rym. P	Ford United	265	3 - 1	N Gregory 48, Boylan 72[p], Kennedy 86
05/10	Rym. P	BRAINTREE TOWN	754	1 - 1	Johnson 17
12/10	**F.A.C.** Q3	AVELEY	423	2 - 0	
19/10	Rym. P	PURFLEET	766	2 - 2	Protheroe 30, Boylan 40
21/10	Rym. P	Boreham Wood	302	3 - 1	Forbes 65, Johnson 85, Kennedy 87
26/10	**F.A.C.** Q4	Slough Town	875	2 - 3	Forbes 4, Brayley 61
29/10	Rym. P	Bedford Town	510	1 - 2	Milton 38
09/11	Rym. P	MAIDENHEAD UNITED	509	3 - 2	Brayley 29, Duffy 75, Protheroe 83
12/11	Rym. P	HARROW BOROUGH	419	2 - 1	Jones 14, Minton 73
16/11	Rym. P	Purfleet	608	2 - 3	N Gregory 40, Boylan 41
19/11	Lge Cup 2	Hayes	n/k	1 - 0	Davidson 61
23/11	Rym. P	Enfield	119	2 - 1	Minton 16, Forbes 90
30/11	**F.A.T.** 2	CARSHALTON ATHLETIC	325	2 - 0	Parmenter 80, Minton 80
07/12	Rym. P	KINGSTONIAN	483	1 - 1	Parmenter 36
10/12	Lge Cup 3	Cheshunt	n/k	5 - 1	Minton 10, Boylan 67 78 79, Brayley 88
14/12	Rym. P	HAYES	407	2 - 2	Conan 17, Boylan 88
21/12	Rym. P	Chesham United	305	4 - 2	Minton 2, Protheroe 68, Boylan 80 83
28/12	Rym. P	Hitchin Town	488	3 - 2	Gregory 32, Boylan 36, Burke 78[og]
11/01	**F.A.T.** 3	CIRENCESTER TOWN	349	5 - 1	N Gregory 19, Boylan 25 81, Protheroe 40, Duffy 67
14/01	Lge Cup 4	Hitchin Town	119	3 - 1	N Gregory 32, Minton 62, Brayley 84
18/01	Rym. P	AYLESBURY UNITED	612	2 - 1	Boylan 65 67
25/01	Rym. P	Heybridge Swifts	406	2 - 0	Boylan 76, Berquez 90
28/01	Rym. P	Bishop's Stortford	379	2 - 1	Cowan 39, Boylan 62
31/01	**F.A.T.** 4	Northwich Victoria	708	1 - 2	Protheroe 17
04/02	Rym. P	BASINGSTOKE TOWN	407	4 - 0	Berquez 20 71, Boylan 70 78
08/02	Rym. P	Grays Athletic	586	2 - 1	Berquez 14 47
15/02	Rym. P	HAMPTON & RICHMOND B.	449	4 - 0	Minton 31 79, Boylan 47, Parmenter 83
18/02	Lge Cup QF	GRAYS ATHLETIC	337	6 - 0	Boylan 21 32, Dobinson 36 71, Ruhanen 83, N Gregory 89
22/02	Rym. P	Braintree Town	575	4 - 2	Boylan 44, Gregory 51 75, Minton 73
01/03	Rym. P	FORD UNITED	549	3 - 1	Boylan 4 18 57
08/03	Rym. P	BOREHAM WOOD	471	1 - 0	Boylan 30
15/03	Rym. P	Maidenhead United	291	1 - 1	Bennett 87
18/03	Lge Cup SF(1)	HENDON	198	4 - 2	Protheroe 36, N Gregory 58, Brayley 67, Bennett 90
22/03	Rym. P	BEDFORD TOWN	613	1 - 1	Boylan 63
25/03	Lge Cup SF(2)	Hendon	115	2 - 2	Boylan 13 24
29/03	Rym. P	Harrow Borough	316	2 - 1	N Gregory 27, Berquez 90
01/04	Rym. P	Hendon	251	0 - 1	
05/04	Rym. P	ST ALBANS CITY	703	6 - 1	Boylan 1 21 47 74, Berquez 3, Parmenter 63
08/04	Rym. P	BILLERICAY TOWN	327	3 - 0	Boylan 1, Berquez 30, Kennedy 71
12/04	Rym. P	Sutton United	643	2 - 0	Chenery 68, N Gregory 86
15/04	Rym. P	ALDERSHOT TOWN	3553	0 - 1	
19/04	Rym. P	CHESHAM UNITED	331	4 - 1	Gregory 17, Chenery 31, Boylan 49, Berquez 71
21/04	Rym. P	Billericay Town	540	1 - 2	Boylan 70[p]
26/04	Rym. P	ENFIELD	334	10 - 1	**Boylan 4** (3 10 15 61), N Gregory 31, Duffy 65, **Brayley 3** (79 81 82), Protheroe 87
03/05	Rym. P	Kingstonian	421	4 - 0	Boylan 13 52, Berquez 15, Minton 26
05/05	Lge Cup F	YEADING	701	0 - 2	(at Hornchurch)

PLAYING SQUAD

Goalkeepers: Ashley Harrison (Dover Ath.), Glen Johnson (Youth Team), Danny Potter (Weymouth).

Defenders: Micky Bennett (Brighton), Mick Bodley (Dagenham & Redbridge), Garry Britnell (Enfield), Ben Chenery (Kettering T.), Gavin Cowan (Braintree T.), Craig Davidson (Braintree T.), David Gregory (Colchester Utd), Ross Johnson (Dagenham & Redbridge), Lee Protheroe (Aldershot T.), Steve Wood (Grays Ath.).

Midfield: Mark Brennan (Billericay T.), **Chris Duffy** (Northwich V.), Scott Forbes (Southend U.), Ty Gooden (Gillingham), Kevin Johnson (Chelmsford C.), John Kennedy (Ipswich T.), Jeff Minton (Grays A.), Jukka Ruhanen (FC Haka,Finland), Adam Tanner (Colchester Utd.

Forwards: Ollie Berquez (Braintree T.), Lee Boylan (Heybridge S.), Bert Brayley (Swindon T.), Neil Gregory (Colchester U), Tony Jones (Billericay T.), Spencer Knight (Harrow B.), Steve Parmenter (Dorcherster T.), Spencer Knight (Harrow B.)

CARSHALTON ATHLETIC

CLUB OFFICIALS

Chairman: Steve Friend
President: John Carpentiere
Vice Chairman:T.B.A.
Secretary: Vic Thompson, 11 Poulton Avenue,Sutton, Surrey 0208 642 8658 (W)
Chief Executive: Barry Gartell
General Manager: Andy Abrehart
Press Officer: Roger Fear
Commercial Manager: Roger Fear

FOOTBALL MANAGEMENT TEAM

Man: Billy Smnith Ass Man:George Wakelin
Coach: Jimmy Dack
Physios: Tanya Clarke

FACT FILE

Formed: 1905
Nickname: Robins
Sponsors: CDL Exhibition Contractors
Colours: White, maroon trim/maroon/white
Change colours: Maroon/white
Midweek matchday: ~Mondays
Reserve League: Suburban
Newsline: 0930 555 877
Local Press: Sutton Comet, Sutton Herald
Local Radio: BBC Southern Counties

PROGRAMME

Pages: 20 Price: £1.50p
Editor: Roger Fear (0208 287 5880)

GROUND War Memorial Sports Ground, Colston Av, Carshalton SM5 2PW
Tel: 0208 642 8658

Directions: Turn right out of Carshalton BR Station, and Colston Avenue is first left. Entrance 150 yards on right. London Transport bus 151 from Morden to Wrythe Green Lane

Capacity: 8,000 Cover: 4,500 Seats: 240 Floodlights: Yes

Clubhouse: Open every evening and lunchtime. Licenced bar, pool, darts,machines, discos on Saturday. Separate function hall (bookings taken). Food:sandwiches, rolls, burgers, hot dogs, teas, coffees and soft drinks. (0181 642 8658)

Club Shop: Sells hats, scarves, T-shirts, badges, programmes etc

PREVIOUS **Leagues:** Southern Sub (pre-1911); Surrey Snr 22-23; London 23-46; Corinthian46-56; Athenian 56-73
Grounds: Wrythe Recreation Ground 1907-14; Culvers Park 19-20

CLUB RECORDS **Attendance:** 7,800 v Wimbledon, London Senior Cup
Career goalscorer: Jimmy Bolton(242) **Career appearances:** Jon Warden (504)
Transfer fee paid: £15,000 from Enfield for Curtis Warmington **Transfer fee paid** £30,000 for Ian Cox (Crystal Palace)
Win: 13-0 v Worthing, Loctite Cup Third Round 28/2/91

BEST SEASON **F.A.Trophy :** 3rd Rd 95-96 lodst away at Hyde United (2-3)
FA Cup: 2nd Rd 82-83, lost 1-4 at Torquay. - League clubs defeated: None

HONOURS: Isthmian League Div 2 R-up 76-77, Corinthian League 52-53 53-54, Surrey Senior League R-up 22-23, Surrey Senior Cup(3) Runners-up (5) Surrey Senior Shield 75-76 Runners-up (2)), London Challenge Cup 91-92 Isthmian Lg Cup R-up 90-91

Players progressing: Roy Lunnes (Crystal Pal. 60), Les Burns (Charlton 67), Ron Walker (Watford), Nobby Warren (Exeter),Terry Stacey (Plymouth A.), Frank GeorgelLeyton Orient) ,Tommy Williams (Colchester U), Alan Eagles (Leyton Orient), Derek Razzell (Q.PR),Muray Jones Crystal Pal.) Gus Caesar (Arsenal), Darren Annon (Brentford) 94, Ian Cox (Crystal Pal.) 94, Carl Asaba (Brentford)

L-R - Back Row: Steve Lang (coach), Graham Baker (coach), Steve Darlington, Mark Costello, Berandeh Ouefio,Tutu Henriques, Mark Pye, Stuart Searle, Peter Wood, Gary Elliott, John Hamsher, Romuald Bouadji, John(JJ)Johnson (Kit Manager)
Front Row: Matt York, Byron Glasgow, Nigel Webb, Michael Johnson, Barry Gartell (Chief Executive), Graham Roberts (Manager), Steve Friend (Chairman), Keith Dublin (Captain), Tommy Williams, Baroan Tagro, Scott Todd

Date	Comp.	Opponents	Att.	Score	Goalscorers
17/08	Rym. 1S	Lewes	257	1 - 3	Hamsher 86[p]
19/08	Rym. 1S	DULWICH HAMLET	325	2 - 0	Dublin 35, Ouefio 60
24/08	Rym. 1S	METROPOLITAN POLICE	252	2 - 0	Darlington 46, York 48
26/08	Rym. 1S	Windsor & Eton	146	1 - 1	Oueifio 68
31/08	**F.A.C.** P	Ashford Town	344	3 - 1	Todd 25, Dublin 75, Hampshire 87
07/09	Rym. 1S	WORTHING	288	2 - 1	Oueisio 19, York 69
10/09	Rym. 1S	Banstead Athletic	160	2 - 0	York 52, Webb 74
14/09	**F.A.C.** Q1	DORKING	235	4 - 0	
21/09	Rym. 1S	Bracknell Town	220	4 - 1	Darlington 5 59, Hamsher 7, Ouefio 55
23/09	Rym. 1S	EPSOM & EWELL	274	2 - 0	Darlington 42, Costello 70
28/09	**F.A.C.** Q2	CHELMSFORD CITY	577	1 - 1	Oueisio 45
02/10	**F.A.C.** Q2 rep	Chelmsford City	537	0 - 1	
12/10	Rym. 1S	WHYTELEAFE	417	2 - 1	Darlington 74, Todd 90
15/10	Rym. 1S	Ashford Town (Middx)	159	2 - 0	Falana 67, Darlington 87
19/10	Rym. 1S	Egham Town	168	1 - 1	Harvey 85
21/10	Rym. 1S	BOGNOR REGIS TOWN	297	1 - 0	Darlington 45[p]
26/10	Rym. 1S	Leatherhead	251	3 - 0	Todd 9 27, Darlington 14
28/10	Rym. 1S	STAINES TOWN	270	1 - 1	Darlington 31
02/11	**F.A.T.** 1	FOLKESTONE INVICTA	347	2 - 1	Todd 15, Johnson 22[p]
09/11	Rym. 1S	CROYDON ATHLETIC	345	2 - 1	Dublin 89 90
11/11	Rym. 1S	MOLESEY	283	1 - 1	Ouefio 50
16/11	Rym. 1S	Corinthian Casuals	181	2 - 1	Oueisio 38 59
19/11	Lge Cup 2	Corinthian Casuals	n/k	1 - 2	Costelloe 41
26/11	Rym. 1S	Walton & Hersham	155	0 - 3	
30/11	**F.A.T.** 2	Canvey Island	325	0 - 2	
07/12	Rym. 1S	HORSHAM	336	2 - 1	Green 33, Oueifio 45
14/12	Rym. 1S	LEWES	370	4 - 1	Green 15, Boateng 17, Todd 60, Ouefio 65
18/12	Rym. 1S	Croydon	160	2 - 1	Boateng 6, Green 65
21/12	Rym. 1S	Chertsey Town	153	2 - 0	Darlington 34, York 55[p]
26/12	Rym. 1S	TOOTING & MITCHAM UNITED	740	2 - 3	Hawthorne 17, Dublin 29
28/12	Rym. 1S	Metropolitan Police	205	2 - 1	Glasgow 8 58
04/01	Rym. 1S	WINDSOR & ETON	379	1 - 0	York 47
07/01	Rym. 1S	Dulwich Hamlet	218	0 - 1	
18/01	Rym. 1S	Whyteleafe	460	1 - 3	Todd 47
25/01	Rym. 1S	EGHAM TOWN	341	0 - 1	
27/01	Surrey SC 4	RAYNES PARK VALE	124	3 - 0	York, Todd, Johnson
03/02	Rym. 1S	LEATHERHEAD	248	2 - 0	Olusesi 68, Hay 78
08/02	Rym. 1S	Epsom & Ewell	228	4 - 1	Johnson 23, Hay 60 78, Elliott 88
15/02	Rym. 1S	BRACKNELL TOWN	332	2 - 2	Hannigan 61, York 72
17/02	Rym. 1S	ASHFORD TOWN (MIDDX)	291	1 - 0	Wood 35
22/02	Rym. 1S	Staines Town	1147	2 - 2	Hay 48[p], York 87
01/03	Rym. 1S	BROMLEY	469	1 - 4	Pye 57
04/03	Surrey SC QF	Sutton United	438	0 - 2	
08/03	Rym. 1S	CORINTHIAN CASUALS	295	2 - 2	Olusesi 7, Elliott 90
15/03	Rym. 1S	Croydon Athletic	240	1 - 0	Hay 41[p]
18/03	Rym. 1S	Bromley	307	3 - 0	Meah 64, York 70, Olusesi 75
22/03	Rym. 1S	WALTON & HERSHAM	313	1 - 2	Todd 90
29/03	Rym. 1S	Molesey	101	1 - 1	Oueisio 90
05/04	Rym. 1S	BANSTEAD ATHLETIC	333	1 - 0	Olusesi 80
08/04	Rym. 1S	Bognor Regis Town	553	0 - 1	
12/04	Rym. 1S	Worthing	382	0 - 2	
19/04	Rym. 1S	CHERTSEY TOWN	298	1 - 0	Dublin 23
21/04	Rym. 1S	Tooting & Mitcham United	534	2 - 0	Olusesi 50, Elliott 79[p]
26/04	Rym. 1S	CROYDON	451	1 - 0	Boateng 44
03/05	Rym. 1S	Horsham	642	1 - 0	Darlington 82

PLAYING SQUAD

Goalkeepers: Paul Borg (Youth Team), Stewart Searle (Aldershot T.)

Defenders: Mark Costello (Staines T.), Keith Dublin (Farnborough T.), Gary Elliott (Whyteleafe), Jon Hamsher (Stevenage Borough), Orlando Hollingsworth (Croydon), Bouadji Romuald (St Etienne).

Midfield: Mark Abbott (Gloucester City), Jimmy Dack (Tooting & Mitcham), Mark Hawthorne (Slough T.), Tutu Henriques (University of Luton), Michael Johnson (Croydon), Scott Kinch (Yoputh Team), Leke Odunsi (Bromley), Ngie Ouefia (Paris St Germain), David Timothy (Sutton Utd), Peter Wood (Hampton & Richmond Bh).

Forwards: Steve Darlington (Billericay T.), Darren Hay (Cheshamn Utd), Kevin Lock (Banstead Ath.), Berando Ouefio (Lee Mee Sport, France), Moses Jjunjo (Bromley), Danny Tanner (Croydon), Matt York (Banstead Ath.), Scott Todd (Ashford T. Middlesex)

FORD UNITED

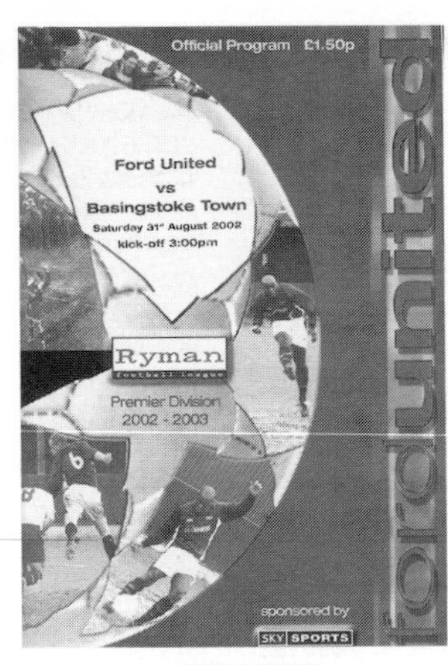

CLUB OFFICIALS

Chairman: Jimmy Chapman
President : Nick Scheeler
Secretary: Alan Wetherall, 23 Warley Avenue, Dagenham, Essex RM8 1JS
07712365424 (M)
Chief Execs: John Rowe & George Adams

FACT FILE

Founded: 1934
Nickname: Motormen
Sponsor: Sky Sports
Colours: Blue/white/red
Change: red/red/blue.
Midweek home matchday: Tuesday
Youth Section & Vets.Local Cups & Lgs

FOOTBALL MANAGEMENT TEAM

Manager: Craig Edwards
Coach: Lyndon Lynch
Assistant Coach: John Frosket
Physio.: Paul Baskin

2002-2003

Captain: John O'Sullivan
Top Scorer & P.o.Y.: Glen Poole

GROUND Oakside Stadium,Station Road, Barkingside, Ilford, Essex(0208550 3611)
Directions: From London Take A12 ,Eastern Avenue and turn left into Horns Road., Barkingside (Greengate). Right into Craven Gardens, right again into Carlton Drive and left into Station Road..Go over bridge and ground is on right next to Barkingside (Central Line). From Ilford BR station take 169 bus to Craven Gardens.
Capacity: 3,000 Seats: 316 Cover: 1000 Club Shop: Yes
Clubhouse: Large bar which is open every day 12.00 midday until 11.00 p.m.

PROGRAMME

Pages: 72 Price: £1
Editor:Mike Stephenson
Tel: 01268 402666 (W)
01268 684638 (H & Fax)
e-mail: deeps.steve@ blue yonder.co.uk

HONOURS: London Snr Cup 55-56 56-57 94-95 97-98; 00-01 Essex Snr Lge 91-92 96-97,R-up 94-95, Essex Sen. Trophy 90-91 91-92,00-01 Essex Senior Cup 39-40 49-50 50-51 51-52 85-86, R-up Spartan Lg 49-50 50-51 55-56 56-57 57-58; London Lg 36-37 38-39; Essex Elizabethan 59-60 60-61 70-71; Gtr London Lg 70-71; Sportsmanship Award 77-78 79-80 80-81; Essex Thameside Trophy: 98-=99Essex & Herts Border Comb.(res) 94-95 (Lg Cup 94-95); Isthmian League Div 3 98-99, Promoted from Div 2 99-00, Promoted to Isthmian Premier 01-02

RECORDS: **Attendance:** 58,000 Briggs Sports v Bishop Auckland, at St James Park, Newcastle, FA Amateur Cup
Appearances: Roger Bond **Goalscorer:** Jeff Wood 196
Win: Unknown **Defeat:** Unknown

PREVIOUS: **Leagues:** Spartan, Spartan, Aetolian, Metropolitan, Essex Senior
Names: Brigg Sports (1934) & Ford Sports (1934) amalgamated in 1958 **Grounds:** Ford Sports & Social Club, Rush Green Road, Romford.

BEST SEASON: **FA Vase:** 98-99, 5th Round, 1-2 v Bedlington Terriers (H)
FA Amateur Cup: Semi-Final 53-54

Players progressing: Les Allen (Spurs), Mick Flanagan (QPR, Charlton, Crystal Palace), Jim Stannard (Fulham, Southend, Millwall), Nicky Hammond (Arsenal,Swindon), Laurie Abrahams (Charlton), Doug Barton (Reading, Newport)

Date	Comp.	Opponents	Att.	Score	Goalscorers
17/08	Rym. P	St Albans City	326	2 - 3	Hackett 61, Devereux 80
20/08	Rym. P	HITCHIN TOWN	150	2 - 2	Hoddy 46, Poole 50
24/08	Rym. P	ENFIELD	98	3 - 1	Aransibia 68, Poole 70, Allen 90[p]
31/08	Rym. P	BASINGSTOKE TOWN	142	2 - 3	Bajada 26 68
03/09	Rym. P	Sutton United	463	1 - 4	Bejeda 40
07/09	Rym. P	Hendon	247	1 - 3	Cooper 87[og]
10/09	Rym. P	AYLESBURY UNITED	152	1 - 2	Marsh 80
14/09	Rym. P	ALDERSHOT TOWN	426	2 - 3	Vaughan 42, Kimble 55[p]
17/09	Rym. P	Heybridge Swifts	180	4 - 4	Rose 1, Vaughan 13, Bejada 45, Paule 84
21/09	Rym. P	BEDFORD TOWN	194	2 - 0	Buffong 1, Kimble 77[p]
23/09	Rym. P	Boreham Wood	121	2 - 3	Hackett 18 76
28/09	**F.A.C.** Q2	METROPOLITAN POLICE	61	4 - 2	Buffong 1, Poole 13, Hackett 74, Allen 83
01/10	Rym. P	CANVEY ISLAND	265	1 - 3	Aransibia 49
05/10	Rym. P	Harrow Borough	180	0 - 4	
12/10	**F.A.C.** Q3	Leatherhead	n/k	0 - 0	
19/10	Rym. P	MAIDENHEAD UNITED	86	0 - 3	
22/10	Rym. P	Chesham United	163	2 - 2	Woodards 20, Abrahams 84
26/10	**F.A.C.** Q4	Forest Green Rovers	664	1 - 2	Kimble 63
02/11	**F.A.T.** 1	Great Wakering Rovers	145	2 - 2	White 46, Fiddes 88
05/11	**F.A.T.** 1 rep	GREAT WAKERING ROVERS	88	6 - 1	Fiddes 8, O'Sullivan 93, Kimble 103[p], Bejada 105, West 109,Whyte 112
09/11	Rym. P	HAYES	131	3 - 3	Abraham 9, Poole 13, Woodards 90
16/11	Rym. P	Maidenhead United	177	4 - 0	Fiddes 35, O'Sullivan 44 74, Buffong 90
19/11	Essex SC 3	TILBURY	88	2 - 1	M Watson, Abraham
30/11	**F.A.T.** 2	Dover Athletic	804	0 - 2	
02/12	Lge Cup 2	PURFLEET	65	3 - 0	Watson 14, Collis 42, Abraham 45
07/12	Rym. P	Grays Athletic	231	2 - 1	Buffong 2, Bejada 60
10/12	London SC 3	Dulwich Hamlet	n/k	2 - 1	Abraham(2)
14/12	Rym. P	ST ALBANS CITY	155	1 - 1	Abraham 73
17/12	Lge Cup 3	Billericay Town	96	1 - 3	Poole 88
19/12	Essex SC 4	AVELEY	n/k	1 - 3	Donoghue
21/12	Rym. P	Billericay Town	420	3 - 1	Perkins 15, Poole 36, Collins 53
28/12	Rym. P	Enfield	66	1 - 1	Halle 80
07/01	Rym. P	Hampton & Richmond Bor.	144	3 - 2	Collis 17, Buffong 55, Bejada 76
18/01	Rym. P	HENDON	156	1 - 3	Poole 76
24/01	Rym. P	Aldershot Town	1848	1 - 2	Buffong 48
04/02	Rym. P	BRAINTREE TOWN	131	3 - 0	Abrahams 39, Poole 77 84
08/02	Rym. P	BOREHAM WOOD	102	1 - 1	Bejada 87
15/02	Rym. P	Bedford Town	431	2 - 0	McCloud 15, Watson 87
19/02	London SC QF	Barkingside	64	2 - 1	J Edwards, Poole
22/02	Rym. P	HARROW BOROUGH	82	2 - 0	Abraham 52, D Perkins 81
01/03	Rym. P	Canvey Island	549	1 - 3	Collis 15
08/03	Rym. P	CHESHAM UNITED	68	2 - 0	Poole 57, Fiddes 83
11/03	Rym. P	BISHOP'S STORTFORD	135	3 - 2	Abraham 19, Edwards 30, Fiddes 50
15/03	Rym. P	Hayes	219	0 - 2	
18/03	Rym. P	KINGSTONIAN	169	2 - 2	Abraham 25, Poole 34
22/03	Rym. P	HAMPTON & RICHMOND B.	92	3 - 0	Collis 29, Buffong 39, D Perkins 90
25/03	Rym. P	HEYBRIDGE SWIFTS	115	3 - 3	Edwards 71, D Perkins 82, McLeod 88
29/03	Rym. P	Purfleet	237	2 - 2	Poole 1, Cooper 27
01/04	Rym. P	Kingstonian	267	2 - 0	Abraham 56, Poole 87[p]
05/04	Rym. P	SUTTON UNITED	140	3 - 4	Poole 23[p] 30, Fiddes 45
12/04	Rym. P	Basingstoke Town	293	0 - 3	
14/04	Rym. P	Aylesbury United	336	0 - 2	
17/04	London SC SF	METROPOLITAN POLICE	136	0 - 0	Won 4 3 after pens.
19/04	Rym. P	BILLERICAY TOWN	112	0 - 2	
21/04	Rym. P	Bishop's Stortford	359	1 - 0	Poole 45
23/04	Rym. P	PURFLEET	106	1 - 1	Cooper 58
26/04	Rym. P	Braintree Town	294	0 - 1	
28/04	Rym. P	Hitchin Town	151	2 - 2	Lewis 30, Abraham 85
30/04	London SC F	Bromley	n/k	0 - 1	(at Dagenham & Redbridge)
03/05	Rym. P	GRAYS ATHLETIC	209	1 - 0	Poole 77

PLAYING SQUAD

Goalkeepers: Aleksandar Cancar (Boreham Wood), Jimmy Chapman (Barking), Paul Newell (Aveley)

Defenders: Jay Devereux (Enfield), Richard Halle (Heybridge Swifts), Ben Lewis (Grays Ath.), Alan McLoud (Grays Ath.), Chris Perkins (Canvey Island), Jeff Woolsey (Grays Ath.).

Midfield: Jonathon Buffong (Grays Ath.), Sean Cooper (Grays Ath.), Craig Edwards (Purfleet), Alex Fiddes (Grays Ath.), Greg Heighway (Grays Ath.), John O'Sullivan (Grays Ath.), Simon Livett (U.S.A.), Glenn Poole (Yeovil T.), Billy Read (Leyton Pennant), NathanThomas (Grays Ath.), Ronnie Watson (Enfield T.), Ross White (Grays Ath.), Bradley Woodards (Youth Team).

Forwards: Mervyn Abrahams (Barking & East Ham Utd), Lele Bejada (Grays Ath.), Chas Murray (Youth Team), Declan Perkins (Dulwich Hamlet)

GRAYS ATHLETIC

CLUB OFFICIALS

Chairman: Alan Barnard

Secretary & Press Officer: Phil O'Reilly
102 Luxborough Lane,Chigwell,Essex IL7 5AA Tel: 07980 643832

FOOTBALL MANAGEMENT TEAM

Manager:Mark Stimson
Asst Man.: John Polston
Physio: Christy Keane

FACT FILE

Formed: 1890
Nickname: The Blues
Sponsors: F.S.McKenzie
Colours: Blue
Change colours: White
Midweek matchday: Tuesday
Local Press: Thurrock Gazette
Local Radio: BBC Essex, Radio Essex

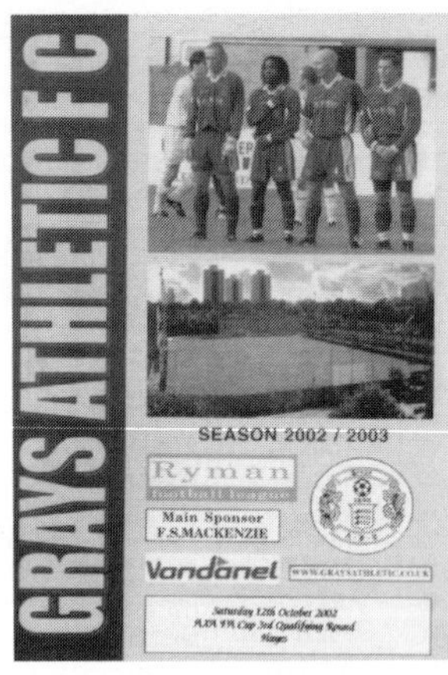

Pages: 48 Price: £1.50
Editor: Jeremy Mason (01375 400188)

GROUND Recreation Ground, Bridge Road, Grays RM17 6BZ (01375 391649)
Directions: Seven minutes walk from Grays station - turn right round one way system, right into Clarence Road, and at end into Bridge Road. Bus No. 370. By road - A13 towards Southend from London, take Grays exit and follow signs to town centre, keep left on one-way system, continue up hill for about 1/2 mile, turn right into Bridge Road, ground 1/2 mile on right
Capacity: 4,500 Cover: 1,200 Seats: 300 Floodlights: Yes
Clubhouse: Bar, pool, darts, bar snacks available. Indoor sports hall(.Steward: Chris Riley)
Club Shop: Sells `The First Hundred Years', sweaters, T-shirts, replica shirts, scarves, ties, etc. Contact Phil O'Reilly

PREVIOUS **Leagues:** Athenian 12-14, 58-83; London 14-24, 26-39; Kent 24-26; Corinthian 45-58

CLUB RECORDS **Attendance:** 9,500 v Chelmsford City, FA Cup 4th Qual. Round 1959
Win: 12-0 v Tooting (H) London Lge 24/2/23 **Defeat:** 0-12 v Enfield (A) Athenian Lge 20/4/63
Goalscorer: Harry Brand 269 (1944-52) **Appearances:** Phil Sammons, 673. 1982-97
Fee Paid: For Ian Durant (Canvey Island 85)
Fee Received: Undisclosed for Tony Witter (C. Palace), Dwight Marshall(Plymouth 1991) & Matthew Lawrence(Wycombe W)

BEST SEASON **FA Cup:** 1st Rd 51-52 88-89,00-01,01-02
FA Trophy: 4thRd 02-03, 01-02 **FA Amateur Cup:** 3rd Rd 63-64

HONOURS Isthmian Div 1 R-up 87-88 ,99-00(Div 2 Sth 84-85, Lg Cup 91-92); Athenian Lg R-up 82-83, Res. Sect. R-up 58-59 (Cup R-up 59-60); Corinthian Lg 45-46 (R-up 51-52 54-55 56-57), Lg Cup(2) 45-47, Mem. Shield(4) ; Essex Snr Cup 8(R-up 9; Essex SenTr 98-99; East Ang Cup 44-45 (R-up 43-44 54-55); Essex Thameside Tphy x 8 (R-up 7); Essex Elizabeth Tphy 76-77 (R-up 65-66); Claridge Tphy 87-88 88-89; Mithras Cup 79-80; Essex Int Cup(3) 56-57 58-60 (Jun Cup 19-20 (R-up 58-59); Essex & Herts ,Border Comb. East 87-88 (Ancillary Cup 78-79, Comb Cup 82-83); Fred Budden Tphy 86-87; Hornchurch Charity Cup 78-79 86-87; Neale Tphy 50-51; Ford Rate Tphy 83-84 85-86 87-88 (R-up 84-85 86-87); Stan Veness Mem. Tphy (8) 87-96

Players progressing: J Jordan (Spurs 47), R Kemp (Reading 49), B Silkman & TBanfield (Orient), G O'Reilly (Spurs), W Entwhistle (Bury 83), M Welch(Wimbledon 84), T Witter (C Palace 90), D Marshall (Plymouth 91), M Lawrence(Wycombe W. 96-97)

Date	Comp.	Opponents	Att.	Score	Goalscorers
17/08	Rym. P	Braintree Town	352	1 - 1	Edwards 31
20/08	Rym. P	SUTTON UNITED	329	0 - 0	
24/08	Rym. P	BASINGSTOKE TOWN	279	1 - 2	Brown 5
26/08	Rym. P	Enfield	135	1 - 1	Miller 1
31/08	Rym. P	ST ALBANS CITY	364	0 - 1	
03/09	Rym. P	Kingstonian	466	0 - 1	
07/09	Rym. P	Aldershot Town	1875	1 - 2	Browne 78
10/09	Rym. P	HEYBRIDGE SWIFTS	195	0 - 2	
14/09	Rym. P	AYLESBURY UNITED	261	3 - 1	Lock 25 69, Abbott 36
17/09	Rym. P	Hendon	175	0 - 1	
21/09	Rym. P	BISHOP'S STORTFORD	295	1 - 0	Douglas 35[p]
24/09	Rym. P	Canvey Island	834	0 - 2	
28/09	**F.A.C.** Q2	MARLOW	237	1 - 0	Hayzelden 90
01/10	Rym. P	BEDFORD TOWN	197	0 - 0	
05/10	Rym. P	Maidenhead United	248	2 - 0	Vaughan 45, McLean 71
12/10	**F.A.C.** Q3	HAYES	n/k	0 - 0	
19/10	Rym. P	HAYES	265	1 - 0	McLean 6
22/10	Rym. P	Harrow Borough	155	4 - 0	McLoud 43, Douglas 61 75 87[p]
26/10	**F.A.C.** Q4	STEVENAGE BOROUGH	760	1 - 2	Vaughan 3
05/11	Essex SC 3	DAGENHAM & REDBRIDGE	n/k	2 - 4	Vaughan 23, Woolsey 87
09/11	Rym. P	BOREHAM WOOD	255	2 - 1	Douglas 25[p], Burnett 85
12/11	Rym. P	HAMPTON & RICHMOND B.	208	1 - 1	McLean 85
16/11	Rym. P	Hayes	249	0 - 1	
20/11	Lge Cup 2	Harlow Town	n/k	2 - 1	McCleod 9, Leaburn 44
23/11	Rym. P	Billericay Town	609	1 - 4	Vaughan 90
30/11	**F.A.T.** 2	TIVERTON TOWN	334	3 - 1	Burnett 22, Douglas 52, Steele 66[og]
07/12	Rym. P	FORD UNITED	231	1 - 2	Cooper 47
10/12	Rym. P	Heybridge Swifts	78	1 - 1	Vaughan 33
14/12	Rym. P	BRAINTREE TOWN	217	1 - 2	Leaburn 40
17/12	Lge Cup 3	East Thurrock United	92	1 - 0	Broom 57
21/12	Rym. P	Hitchin Town	303	3 - 3	Leaburn 10 49, Dillon 65
26/12	Rym. P	PURFLEET	490	2 - 1	Carthy 52, Vaughan 84[p]
28/12	Rym. P	Basingstoke Town	354	1 - 3	Carthy 15
04/01	Rym. P	ENFIELD	232	3 - 0	Vaughan 13 70, Essandoh 80
14/01	**F.A.T.** 3	Purfleet	325	2 - 1	Miller 28, Leaburn 45
18/01	Rym. P	ALDERSHOT TOWN	675	0 - 0	
25/01	Rym. P	Aylesbury United	504	2 - 3	Essandoh 13, Carthy 53
01/02	**F.A.T.** 4	Halifax Town	1653	2 - 3	Vaughan 42, Fayeuwo 70
04/02	Lge Cup 4	AYLESBURY UNITED	152	1 - 0	Fayenuwo 85
08/02	Rym. P	CANVEY ISLAND	586	1 - 2	Miller 28
15/02	Rym. P	Bishop's Stortford	291	3 - 1	Carthy 42, Vaughan 51, Burnett 82
18/02	Lge Cup QF	Canvey Island	337	0 - 6	
22/02	Rym. P	MAIDENHEAD UNITED	208	1 - 4	Barnett 40
01/03	Rym. P	Bedford Town	526	0 - 1	
08/03	Rym. P	HARROW BOROUGH	237	4 - 1	Carthy 22 90, Miller 40, Nutter 85
11/03	Rym. P	Sutton United	422	0 - 2	
15/03	Rym. P	Boreham Wood	157	2 - 0	Leaburn 68, Miller 88
22/03	Rym. P	CHESHAM UNITED	225	1 - 0	Atangana 10
27/03	Rym. P	HENDON	206	0 - 2	
29/03	Rym. P	Hampton & Richmond Bor.	156	1 - 1	Essandoh 61
05/04	Rym. P	KINGSTONIAN	275	1 - 1	Carthy 5
08/04	Rym. P	Chesham United	106	1 - 2	Essandoh 71
12/04	Rym. P	St Albans City	452	2 - 1	Carthy 35, Miller 57
19/04	Rym. P	HITCHIN TOWN	233	1 - 1	Miller 2
21/04	Rym. P	Purfleet	301	1 - 3	Essandoh 73
26/04	Rym. P	BILLERICAY TOWN	303	1 - 0	Leaburn 57
03/05	Rym. P	Ford United	209	0 - 1	

PLAYING SQUAD

Goalkeepers: Melvin Capleton (Southend Utd), James Lunan (Southend Utd).

Defenders: Owen Coll (Aldershot T.), Michael Haswell (Southend Utd), Paul Hatch (Barking), Daniel Kerrigan (Billericay T.), Alan Keeper (Braintree T.), Steve Robinson (Edgware T.), Tony Sussex (Barking), Peter Smith (Canvey Island).

Midfield: Jason Broom (Dagenham & Redbridge), Wayne Bennett (Woking), Martin Carthy (Billericay T.), Danny Hazelden (Dagenham & Redbridge), Adam Miller (Canvey Island), Jamie Jarvis (Hayes), Mark Stimson (Canvey Island).

Forwards: Carl Leaburn (Q.P.R.), Tony Lock (Dagenham & Redbridge), Tony Oshitola (Narmnnet), Wayne Vaughan (Purfleet), Lee Williams (Billericay T.)

HARROW BOROUGH

CLUB OFFICIALS

Chairman: Jim Ripley **President:** T.B.A.
Secretary: Peter Rogers,
21 Ludlow Close, South Harrow, Middx HA2 8SR (0208 248 8003H)(0208 4230157W)
Commercial Manager:
Paul Carter c/o the club
Press Officer: Paul Carter (07971 848385)

FOOTBALL MANAGEMENT TEAM

Manager: Edwin Stein
Asst Manager: David Howell
Physio: Suzanne Bowen

2002-2003

Captain: Richard Clarke
Top Scorer: Robert Charles 12
Player of the Year: K evin McKenna

FACT FILE

Formed: 1933
Nickname: The Boro
Sponsors:T.B.A.
Colours: Red, white trim/red/red, white hoops
Change cols: White/navy blue trim/navy/navy
Midweek matchday: Tuesday
Website: www.harrowboro.com
Local Press: Harrow Observer and Harrorw Times

PROGRAMME

Pages: 32 Price: £2,00
Editor: Paul Carter (07971 848385)

GROUND: Earlsmead, Carlyon Avenue, South Harrow, Middx HA2 8SS Tel: 0208 422 5989 or 5221. Email: paul@harrowboro.com
Directions: Underground to Northolt (Central Line) then 140 bus to Northolt Park BR, or 282 bus, to Eastcote Arms or to South Harrow (Piccadilly Line) then 114 or H10 to Kings Rd.Junction. By road leave A40 at Macdonalds roundabout towards Northolt station (A312 north), left at lights, right at next island (Eastcote Arms pub), ground 5th turning on right.
Capacity: 3,070 Cover: 1,000 Seats: 350 Floodlights: Yes
Clubhouse: Open daily, normal pub hours. 4 bars, games room, equipped for social events. Hot and cold food available, buffets by prior request
Club Shop: Sells progs, scarves, badges, T-shirts, etc. Contact c/o club

PREVIOUS **Leagues:** Harrow & Dist 33-4; Spartan 34-40, 45-58; W Middx Comb 40-1; Middx Sen41-45; Delphian 58-63; Athenian 63-75;
Names: Roxonian 1933-8; Harrow Town 38-66 **Ground:** Northolt Road 33-4

CLUB RECORDS **Attendance:** 3,000 v Wealdstone, F.A. Cup 1st Qualifying Rd 1946 **Fee Received:** £16,000 for Lee Endersby (Enfield 97)
Scorer: Dave Pearce, 153 **Appearances:** Steve Emmanuel 522 (1st team only), Les Currell 582, Colin Payne 557
Fee Paid: Unspecified to Dagenham for George Duck & Steve Jones, Summer 81
Win: 13-0 v Handley Page (A), Middlesex Snr Lg 18/10/41. **Defeat:** 0-8 5 times: Wood Green T. (A) Middx Lge 40, Met Police (A) Spartan Lg 52, Briggs Spts (A) Spartan Lg 53, Hertford T. (A) Spartan Lge 53, Hendon (A) Middx Snr Cup 65

BEST SEASON **FA Trophy:** Semi final 82-83 **FA Cup:** 2nd Rd 83-84 (1-3 at home to Newport Co)

HONOURS: Isthmian Lg 83-84 (Div 1 R-up 78-79); Athenian Lg Div 2 R-up 63-64; Spartan Lg R-up 57-58 (Div 2 West 38-39 (R-up 37-38); Middx Senior Cup 82-83 92-93; Harrow & Dist. Lg Div 1 R-up 33-34; Middx Charity Cup 79-80 92-93 (R-up 78-79); Middx Intermediate Cup 55-56,R-up 75-76, Middx Premier Cup 81-82,R-up 82-83, Harrow Sen Cup 95 97, London Interm'te C 78-79

Players progressing: D.Russell (Arsenal), M.Lucas (L.Orient), R.Shaw (Torquay U), T.Eden (Raith R), T. Carpenter (Watford), M Bottoms (QPR 60), C Hutchings (Chelsea 80), R Holland (Crewe 85), J Kerr (Portsmouth 87), D Howell, A Pape & E Stein, (Barnet), D .Byrne (Gillingham), R.Rosario (Norwich), D Kemp (Crystal Palace), M Doherty (Reading), D Bassett (Wimbledon), G Borthwick (Bournemouth), B.Shaw, (Torquay U),T.Evans (Scunthorpe U), L.Charles (Q.P.R.), P.Barrowcliff (Brentford) M.Richardson (Camb Utd & Torquay U). **International**: K Karamoko(Mali)

Back Row L-R: Richard Goddard, Steve Dogbe, Keita Karamoko, Perry Norman, David Hook, Brian Haule, Pat Gavin.
Middle: Sue Bowen (Physio), Mark Wakeling (GK Coach), Robert Charles, Eseyas Yhdego, Abdul Yoki, Ross Fitzsimon, Godfrey Torto, Robbie Rix, Fabio Valenti, David Howell (First Team Coach).
Front: Stuart Elliott, Wayne Walters, Chris Elsegood, Kevin McKenna, Edwin Stein (Manager), Clemente Lopez, Daniel Dyer, Sean James

Date	Comp.	Opponents	Att.	Score	Goalscorers
17/08	Rym. P	Billericay Town	406	0 - 1	
20/08	Rym. P	ENFIELD	203	2 - 0	Lawford 35, Haule 84
24/08	Rym. P	BISHOP'S STORTFORD	250	2 - 2	Valenti 83, Goddard 90
26/08	Rym. P	Sutton United	491	0 - 3	
31/08	Rym. P	BRAINTREE TOWN	193	2 - 2	Goddard 35, Lawford 68
03/09	Rym. P	Chesham United	332	1 - 1	Lawford 16
07/09	Rym. P	ST ALBANS CITY	340	0 - 4	
10/09	Rym. P	Hampton & Richmond Bor.	173	2 - 0	Lawford 72, Valenti 77
14/09	Rym. P	Boreham Wood	159	2 - 2	Charles 26, Lawford 35[p]
17/09	Rym. P	MAIDENHEAD UNITED	185	1 - 1	Marney 26
21/09	Rym. P	Basingstoke Town	423	2 - 1	Goddard 43, Charles 88
24/09	Rym. P	HENDON	223	1 - 3	Lopez 81
28/09	**F.A.C.** Q2	Havant & Waterlooville	210	1 - 2	Fitzsimon 68
01/10	Rym. P	Aldershot Town	1704	1 - 0	Goddard 69
05/10	Rym. P	FORD UNITED	180	4 - 0	Charles 56 80, Lawford 73, Goddard 77
19/10	Rym. P	Aylesbury United	503	0 - 0	
22/10	Rym. P	GRAYS ATHLETIC	155	0 - 4	
26/10	Rym. P	KINGSTONIAN	301	2 - 1	Gridelet 40, Gavin 83
02/11	**F.A.T.** 1	Sutton United	332	1 - 2	Gavin 61
09/11	Rym. P	Heybridge Swifts	201	1 - 0	Yhdego 83
12/11	Rym. P	Canvey Island	419	1 - 2	Aggrey 85
16/11	Rym. P	AYLESBURY UNITED	285	2 - 2	Haule 36, Williams 76[og]
20/11	Lge Cup 2	Windsor & Eton	n/k	4 - 0	Valenti 21 68 69, Brown 88
23/11	Rym. P	HITCHIN TOWN	195	2 - 0	Charles 23 34
03/12	Middx SC 2	Hanwell Town	n/k	5 - 1	
07/12	Rym. P	Bedford Town	415	1 - 1	Charles 90
10/12	Lge Cup 3	Braintree Town	n/k	3 - 1	B Haule 9, Norman 34, D Haule 81
14/12	Rym. P	BILLERICAY TOWN	252	1 - 2	McKenna 72
21/12	Rym. P	Purfleet	235	2 - 4	D Haule 37 67
26/12	Rym. P	HAYES	360	1 - 3	Valenti 57[p]
28/12	Rym. P	Bishop's Stortford	343	0 - 4	
04/01	Rym. P	SUTTON UNITED	279	0 - 1	
18/01	Rym. P	St Albans City	452	0 - 1	
21/01	Lge Cup 4	LEWES	133	2 - 3	Aransibia 59, Lopez 61
25/01	Rym. P	BOREHAM WOOD	226	2 - 0	Valenti 20, Hackett 74
28/01	Middx SC QF	Ashford Town (Middx)	n/k	4 - 3	Dyer 23, Jones 45, McKenna 48, Goddard 75
08/02	Rym. P	Hendon	305	1 - 1	Hackett 28[p]
11/02	Rym. P	HAMPTON & RICHMOND B.	167	1 - 0	McKenna 55
15/02	Rym. P	BASINGSTOKE TOWN	173	1 - 2	Goddard 26
22/02	Rym. P	Ford United	82	0 - 2	
01/03	Rym. P	ALDERSHOT TOWN	731	0 - 2	
04/03	Middx SC SF	ENFIELD TOWN	n/k	1 - 2	Lopez
08/03	Rym. P	Grays Athletic	237	1 - 4	Fitzsimon 90[p]
12/03	Rym. P	Enfield	61	1 - 0	Everitt 26
15/03	Rym. P	HEYBRIDGE SWIFTS	177	2 - 1	Gavin 67 88
22/03	Rym. P	Kingstonian	327	3 - 1	Osborn 43 45, Gavin 89
29/03	Rym. P	CANVEY ISLAND	316	1 - 2	Valenti 39
05/04	Rym. P	CHESHAM UNITED	220	3 - 0	McKenna 73, Gavin 80, Charles 90
12/04	Rym. P	Braintree Town	257	4 - 2	Charles 36 44, Osbourne 80, Yhdego 88
19/04	Rym. P	PURFLEET	148	1 - 2	Charles 90
21/04	Rym. P	Hayes	259	0 - 6	
26/04	Rym. P	Hitchin Town	218	0 - 1	
29/04	Rym. P	Maidenhead United	191	0 - 2	
03/05	Rym. P	BEDFORD TOWN	252	0 - 2	

PLAYING SQUAD

Goalkeepers: Matthew Ferguson (Australia), Danny Gladman (Northwood), Keita Karamoko (Wembley)

Defenders: Richard Clarke (Stanway Rovers), Richard Goddard (Chesham Utd), Corey Ellis (Basildon T.), Sean James (Halesowen T.), Chris Jones (Bedford T.), Oliver Lyons (Wembley), Dean Marney (Greenwich Borough), Perry Norman (Chertsey T.), Edmond Protain (Wembley), Paul Symes (Stanway Rovers), Wayne Walters (Wembley).

Midfield: Robert Charles (Beaconsfield SYCOB), Ross Fitzsimmons (Norwich City), Phil Gridelet (Bishop's Stortford), Phil Johnson (Runcorn FC Halton), Nicolaj Lund (Gumback Utd. Singapore), Kevin McKenna (Hillingdon Bor.), Fabio Valenti (Edgware T.), Marvyn Watson (Ford Utd).

Forwards: Daniel Dyer (Wembley), Pat Gavin (Farnborough T.), Kevin Green (Local Football), Mekel Hackett (Ford Utd), David Haule (Hendon), Godfrey Torto (Arlesey T.), Gabby Williams (Hertford T), Esya Yhdego (Metropiltan Police)

HAYES

CLUB OFFICIALS

President Les Lovering
Chairman Derek Goodall
Vice Chairman Trevor Griffith
Financial Director Charles Mackintosh
Directors D Goodall, C Porter, E Stevens, T Griffith, C Mackintosh, A Bond, J Bond, N Griffith, T Gorman.
Football Secretary John Bond Jnr.
Press Officer Trevor Griffith
c/o the club Tel: 0208 573 2075

FOOTBALL MANAGEMENT TEAM

Manager: Willy Wordsworth
Player/Asst Manager: Paul Holsgrove
Physio: Carl Ballard

FACT FILE

Founded: 1909
Nickname: The Missioners
Club Sponsors: Taylor Woodrow
Club colours: Red & white shirts, black shorts, black socks
Change colours: Blue shirts, blue shorts, blue socks
Reserve team's league: Suburban Premier
Midweek home matchday: Tuesday
Local Press: Hayes Gazette
Local Radio: Capital Radio

PROGRAMME

Pages: 32 Price: £1.50
Editor: Ken Green

GROUND Townfield House, Church Road, Hayes, Middx. UB3 2LE
Tel: 0208 573 2075

Directions: M25, M4, A312 (Hayes By-Pass), A4020 (Uxbridge Road) and Church Rd. is on the left.

Capacity: 6,500 **Seated:** 450 **Terracing - Covered:** 2,000 **Uncovered:** 4,050

CLUBHOUSE: Open Sat 12 - 11pm. Sun 12 - 3pm, 7 - 11pm. Midweek 6.30 - 11pm. Hot and cold snacks are available.

CLUB SHOP: Wide range of programmes & souvenirs. Contact Lee Hermitage, c/o the club.

PREVIOUS **Leagues:** Local leagues 1909-14; Gt. Western Suburban 19-22; London 22-24; Spartan 24-30; Athenian 30-71; Isthmian 71-96; Conference 96-02. **Names:** Bokwell Mission **Ground:** Botwell Common

CLUB RECORDS **Attendance:** 15,370 v Bromley, FA Amateur Cup, 10.2.51
Win: Unknown **Defeat:** Unknown
Career Goalscorer: Unknown **Career Appearances:** Reg Leather 701
Transfer Fee Paid: £6,000 for Gary Keen (Hendon) 1990 & for Joe Francis (Enfield) 1996
Transfer Fee Received: £30,000 for Les Ferdinand (Q.P.R.) 1987

BEST SEASON **FA Cup:** 2nd Round (replay) 72-73: 0-1 v Reading (H) after 0-0; 99-00: 2-3 aet v Hull City (A) after 2-2; also 2nd Round 90-91 & 91-92 League clubs defeated: Bristol Rov.72-73, Cardiff C.90-91, Fulham 91-92
FA Trophy: Quarter Final 78-79, 1-2 v Runcorn (A); 97-98, 0-1 v Cheltenham Town (A)
FA Amateur Cup: Runners Up 1930-31 **League:** 3rd Conference 98-99

HONOURS Isthmian League 95-96; Athenian League 56-57 Spartan League 27-28; Great Western Suburban League 1920-24 (x4) Middlesex Senior Cup 19-20, 20-21, 25-26, 30-31, 35-36, 39-40, 49-50, 81-82, 95-96, 99-00; London Senior Cup 31-32, 80-81; Middlesex Charity Cup - 15 Times; London Charity Cup 60-61

Players Progressing: Cyril Bacon (Orient 46), Phil Nolan (Watford 47), Dave Groombridge (Orient 51), Jimmy Bloomfield (Brentford 52), Derek Neate & Les Champleover(Brighton 56 & 57), Gordon Phillips (Brentford 63), Robin Friday (Reading 74), Les Smith (A Villa), Cyrille Regis (WBA 1977), Les Ferdinand (QPR 87),Derek Payne (Barnet 88), Paul Hyde (Wycombe 91), Dean Hooper (Swindon95), Jason Roberts (Wolverhampton W. 97)

L-R - Back: Paul Hamer, Peter Collins, Josiah Hunt, Danny Julienne, Mark Molesey, Chris Andrews, Bertrand Bossu, Sean O'Connor, Andrew Cooper, Peter Holsgrove, Ian Addele, Glen Harris. **Middle**: Caroline Bosley (Matchday asst.), John Case, Paul Johnson, Darren Crane, John Murphy, Jamie Jarvis, James Shipperley, Rob Bixby, Yiadom Yeboah, Leeyon Phelan, Elis Kodra, John Ellis, David Warner, Sarah Phillips (reserve team physio). **Front**: Mick Harvey (chief scout), Gary Austin, Dean Clark, Matt Gray, Justin Cochrane, Willy Wordsworth (manager), Derek Goodall (chairman), Paul Holsgrove (player/asst. manager), Ryan Williams, Richard Jolly, Kevin Warner, Ian Hodges, Mick Geraghty (reserve team man.).
Photo: Ray Peploe, HFC Photography

Match Facts 2002-03

Date	Comp.	Opponents	Att.	Score	Goalscorers
17/08	Rym. P	CANVEY ISLAND	595	2 - 1	Cochrane 33 46
20/08	Rym. P	Hampton & Richmond Bor.	440	1 - 1	D Warner 10
24/08	Rym. P	Hendon	342	0 - 2	
26/08	Rym. P	BOREHAM WOOD	306	0 - 0	
31/08	Rym. P	Heybridge Swifts	170	0 - 1	
03/09	Rym. P	MAIDENHEAD UNITED	483	0 - 2	
07/09	Rym. P	Kingstonian	463	1 - 1	Jarvis 88
10/09	Rym. P	PURFLEET	174	1 - 2	Hodge 61
14/09	Rym. P	BILLERICAY TOWN	268	0 - 2	
17/09	Rym. P	Chesham United	307	3 - 2	Currie 41, Clark 44, Midson 55
21/09	Rym. P	Braintree Town	262	1 - 0	Clark 21
24/09	Rym. P	ST ALBANS CITY	269	3 - 0	Warner 6, Currie 15, Midson 78
28/09	**F.A.C.** Q2	BOGNOR REGIS TOWN	311	6 - 0	Jarvis 7, Hodge 17 58, Cochrane 60, Jolly 82, Molesey 90
02/10	Rym. P	Enfield	96	1 - 0	Clark 23[p]
05/10	Rym. P	SUTTON UNITED	394	2 - 2	Warner 9, Hodge 24
12/10	**F.A.C.** Q3	Grays Athletic	315	1 - 2	
19/10	Rym. P	Grays Athletic	265	0 - 1	
22/10	Rym. P	BASINGSTOKE TOWN	226	1 - 0	Hodges 75
26/10	Rym. P	HITCHIN TOWN	323	2 - 1	Clark 29, Cochrane 76
02/11	Rym. P	HENDON	377	0 - 0	
09/11	Rym. P	Ford United	131	3 - 3	Clark 43, Case 55, Warner 90
12/11	Rym. P	Aldershot Town	1774	0 - 1	
16/11	Rym. P	GRAYS ATHLETIC	249	1 - 0	Yeboah 9
19/11	Lge Cup 2	CANVEY ISLAND	n/k	0 - 1	
23/11	Rym. P	BEDFORD TOWN	286	2 - 0	Clark 7, D Warner 18
26/11	Middx SC 2	POTTERS BAR TOWN	n/k	4 - 1	Currie 21 43, Clark 35, Hunter 76
30/11	**F.A.T.** 2	St Albans City	468	1 - 0	Case 22
07/12	Rym. P	Bishop's Stortford	304	3 - 2	Clark 20, D Warner 46, K Warner 71
14/12	Rym. P	Canvey Island	407	2 - 2	Clark 25, Warner 44
21/12	Rym. P	AYLESBURY UNITED	294	1 - 1	K Warner 57
26/12	Rym. P	Harrow Borough	360	3 - 1	Everitt 49[og], Clark 61[p], Currie 73
04/01	Rym. P	Boreham Wood	214	0 - 2	
14/01	**F.A.T.** 3	CRAWLEY TOWN	296	2 - 1	Clark 29, K Warner 43
18/01	Rym. P	KINGSTONIAN	410	2 - 2	Hastings 31, Clark 49
25/01	Rym. P	Billericay Town	438	1 - 1	Clark 68
28/01	Middx SC QF	Hampton & Richmond Bor.	n/k	2 - 2	Lost 2 4 after pens.
08/02	Rym. P	St Albans City	457	1 - 1	Bossu 90
11/02	**F.A.T.** 4	Worksop Town	1064	3 - 2	Case 33, Hastings 40 77
15/02	Rym. P	BRAINTREE TOWN	203	1 - 3	Hastings 74
18/02	Rym. P	Purfleet	139	2 - 1	Midson 79, Cooper 83
22/02	**F.A.T.** 5	Havant & Waterlooville	456	0 - 3	
25/02	Rym. P	HAMPTON & RICHMOND B.	192	2 - 1	Jarvis 14, Molesey 47
01/03	Rym. P	ENFIELD	238	4 - 0	Cockram 26[p], Hastings 39, Molesey 57, Bixley 88
08/03	Rym. P	Basingstoke Town	411	1 - 3	Midson 44
11/03	Rym. P	CHESHAM UNITED	173	1 - 0	Currie 21
15/03	Rym. P	FORD UNITED	219	2 - 0	K Warner 17 61
22/03	Rym. P	Hitchin Town	310	3 - 2	D Warner 10, Molesey 59, K Warner 90
29/03	Rym. P	ALDERSHOT TOWN	1305	1 - 0	Currie 18
05/04	Rym. P	Maidenhead United	271	1 - 1	Cochran 90[p]
08/04	Rym. P	Sutton United	393	1 - 2	Brooker 52[og]
12/04	Rym. P	HEYBRIDGE SWIFTS	287	2 - 2	D Warner 9 45
19/04	Rym. P	Aylesbury United	512	0 - 3	
21/04	Rym. P	HARROW BOROUGH	259	6 - 0	Cochrane 29[p], Holsgrove 54 66, Molesley 64, Julliene 75, Norman 9
26/04	Rym. P	Bedford Town	574	1 - 2	Cochrane 61[p]
03/05	Rym. P	BISHOP'S STORTFORD	380	2 - 0	Case 37, Shipperley 89

PLAYING SQUAD

Goalkeepers: Bertrand Bossu (Barnet), Sean O'Connor (Berkhamsted T.), Steve Sladen (Youth Team)

Defenders: Jon Ashton (Exeter City), Mark Boyce (Watford), Jon Case (Youth Team), Brendan Gallen (Youth Team), James Spencer (Youth Team).

Midfield: Justin Cochran (Q.P.R.), Alex Dick (Q.P.R.), John Hastings (Youth), Ben Hodson (Forest Green R.), Paul Holsgrove (Slough T.), Peter Holsgrove (Wycombe W.), Mark Molesey (Youth Team), Scott Taylor (Carterton T.), Daniel Tilbury (Youth Team).

Forwards: Michael Currie (Harrow Borough), Cherif Diallo (Exeter City), Matt Gray (Dutton Utd), Jamie Richards (Braintree T.), Kevin Warner (Brook House)

HENDON

Pages: 40 Price: £1.50p
Editor: Secretary
Local Press: Hendon Times,
Willesden & Brent Chronicle
Hampstead & Highgate Express
Local Radio: Capital, GLR, LBC

CLUB OFFICIALS

Chairman: Ivor Arbiter

Secretary: Graham Etchell, c/o Hendon FC.
Tel: 020 8201 9494(Club)

Marketingl Manager:Rosa Fearria
Press Officer: David Ballheimer

FOOTBALL MANAGEMENT TEAM

Man: Dave Anderson Ass.Man: Jon Turner
Player/Coach: Warren Kelly
Physio: Michael Rayner

FACT FILE

Formed: 1908 Nickname: Dons or Greens
Sponsors: UK Packaging
Colours: Green& white /green/white
Change Colours: All Azure
Midweek matchday: Tuesday
Reserve League: Capital Football League
Club Line: 09066 555 836
Club Website: www.hendonfc.net

2002-03
Captain: Jon Barrie-Bates
Ps.o.Y: Steve Butler & Paul Towler
Top Scorer: Ricci Crace

GROUND: Claremont Road, Brent Cross, London NW2 1AE.
Tel: 020 8201 9494 Fax: 020 8905 5966
Directions: From Brent Cross station (Northern Line) to the east take first left after flyover on North Circular - Claremont Rd is then left at 4th mini-r'bout. Buses 102, 210, 226 and C11 pass ground
Capacity: 3,029 Cover: 601 Seats: 329 Floodlights: Yes
Clubhouse: (contact Sue Damary 020 8455 9185). Two banqueting suites,conference centre, room hire, restaurant & bars open licensing hours 7 days aweek. Hot & cold food, pool, darts, bingo, members club, satelite TV,entertainments
Club Shop: Contact Derek Furmedge, 020 8459 2042 (H) Sells football souvenirs

PREVIOUS **Leagues:** Finchley & Dist. 08-11, Middx 10-11, London 11-14, Athenian 14-63.
Names: Christ Church Hampstead to 08, Hampstead Town to 26, Hampstead to 33,Golders Green to 46
Grounds: Kensal Rise 08-12; Avenue Ground, Cricklewood Lane 12-26

CLUB RECORDS **Attendance:** 9,000 v Northampton, FA Cup 1st Rd 1952
Goalscorer: Freddie Evans 176 (1929-35) **Appearances:** Bill Fisher 787 (1940-
Defeat: 2-11 v Walthamstow Ave. (A), Athenian Lge 9/11/35 **Win:** 13-1 v Wingate (H), Middx Senior Cup 2/2/57
Fee Paid: Paul Whitmarsh (undisclosed) **Fee Received:** £30,000 for Iain Dowie (Luton)

BEST SEASON **F.A. Cup:** First Rd 20 times, Second Rd 5 times **F.A.Trophy:** 5th Rd 98-99

HONOURS: European Am Champions 72-3; Isthmian Lg 64-5 72-3 (R-up 63-4 65-6 73-4) Lg Cup 76-7 (R-up 86-7), Full Members Cup 94-5 97-8 98-99, Premier Inter-Lge Cup R-up 86-7; Middx Lge 12-3 13-4; Athenian Lg 52-3 55-6 60-1 (R-up 28-9 32-3 47-8 48-9 51-2); London Lg Div 1 R-up 12-13 (Amtr Div 13-4); Finchley & Dist. Lg 10-1; London Snr Cup 63-4 68-9 (R-up 35-6 50-1 54-5 58-9 71-2); Middx Snr Cup (14) (R-up 83-4), Middx Interm 64-5 66-7 72-3, Middx Charity Cup(14); London IntermCup (4) (R-up (2); Suburban Lg 92-3 (R-up 84-5 97-8)

Players progressing: Peter Shearing (WHU 60), Iain Dowie (Luton 88), PeterAnderson (Luton), Jeff Harris (Orient), Phil Gridelet (Barnsley 90), GerrySoloman (Leyton O 91), Junior Hunter & Micah Hyde (both Cambridge 94-95),Simon Clark (Peterboro' 94-95),Junior Lewis(Gillingham 99-00)

Back Row: Mike Rayner (Physio), Eugene Ofori, Steve Butler, Mark Cooper, Richard Evans, Dave King, Andy Cook, Luke Thornton, Steve Forbes, Rob Haworth, Greg Joseph, Iain Duncan.
Front Row: Ricardo Alves, Dave Hunt, Scott Cousins, Ricci Crace, Jon Turner (Asst. Manager), Dave Anderson (Manager), Warren Kelly (Coach), James Burgess, Dale Binns, Mark Burgess, Craig McIntosh.

Date	Comp.	Opponents	Att.	Score	Goalscorers
17/08	Rym. P	Enfield	159	0 - 0	
24/08	Rym. P	HAYES	342	2 - 0	Cooper 7, Randall 68
26/08	Rym. P	Billericay Town	547	0 - 0	
31/08	Rym. P	HITCHIN TOWN	280	2 - 1	Binns 68, Sappleton 76
03/09	Rym. P	Purfleet	192	0 - 1	
07/09	Rym. P	FORD UNITED	247	3 - 1	Crace 9 90, Forbes 43
10/09	Rym. P	Canvey Island	611	4 - 4	Yates 21 75, Crace 24, Randall 40
14/09	Rym. P	Hampton & Richmond Bor.	263	1 - 1	Haule 88
17/09	Rym. P	GRAYS ATHLETIC	175	1 - 0	Randall 55
21/09	Rym. P	MAIDENHEAD UNITED	292	1 - 1	Haule 90
24/09	Rym. P	Harrow Borough	223	3 - 1	Forbes 29, Ofori 50 80
28/09	**F.A.C.** Q2	TOOTING & MITCHAM UNITED	249	3 - 0	Yates 23, Haworth 29 88
01/10	Rym. P	AYLESBURY UNITED	259	3 - 1	Ofori 31 90, Yates 56
05/10	Rym. P	Heybridge Swifts	222	4 - 0	Ofori 4, Haworth 43, Forbes 47, Randall 76
12/10	**F.A.C.** Q3	Hastings United	795	1 - 2	Ford 88
15/10	Rym. P	KINGSTONIAN	233	1 - 1	Haworth 79
19/10	Rym. P	BEDFORD TOWN	416	0 - 2	
22/10	Rym. P	Sutton United	437	3 - 2	Forbes 22, Towler 45, Ofori 90
02/11	Rym. P	Hayes	377	0 - 0	
09/11	Rym. P	BRAINTREE TOWN	280	2 - 0	Crace 19, Randall 82
13/11	Rym. P	BOREHAM WOOD	194	0 - 2	
16/11	Rym. P	Bedford Town	569	3 - 2	Crace 18, G Williams 36[og], Towler 89
19/11	Lge Cup 2	STAINES TOWN	n/k	4 - 2	Haworth 2, Gallagher 28, Clarke 48, Ofori 50
30/11	**F.A.T.** 2	Bognor Regis Town	312	4 - 1	Randall 4, Towler 80, Crace 84, Ofori 85
03/12	Middx SC 2	HILLINGDON BOROUGH	n/k	5 - 1	Butler 14, Ofori 45, Yates 63, Gallagher 69, Crace 82
07/12	Rym. P	Chesham United	293	1 - 1	Randall 44
14/12	Rym. P	ENFIELD	243	3 - 0	Randall 18 27, Ofori 20
17/12	Lge Cup 3	ARLESEY TOWN	87	2 - 1	Crace 59, Towler 72
21/12	Rym. P	Basingstoke Town	355	2 - 0	Ofior 36, Hemmings 48[og]
14/01	**F.A.T.** 3	Heybridge Swifts	210	0 - 0	
18/01	Rym. P	Ford United	156	3 - 1	Ofori 14, Bourgeois 21[og], Crace 70
25/01	Rym. P	HAMPTON & RICHMOND B.	240	3 - 3	Crace 49, Endersby 78 90[p]
28/01	**F.A.T.** 3 rep	HEYBRIDGE SWIFTS	178	2 - 1	Crace 18, Gallagher 49[p]
01/02	**F.A.T.** 4	Wakefield & Emley	519	0 - 0	
04/02	**F.A.T.** 4 rep	WAKEFIELD & EMLEY	245	0 - 1	
08/02	Rym. P	HARROW BOROUGH	305	1 - 1	Haworth 64
11/02	Lge Cup 4	WINGATE & FINCHLEY	104	5 - 2	Haworth 13 75 120, Endersby 98, Yates 105
15/02	Rym. P	Maidenhead United	217	1 - 0	Haworth 24
20/02	Middx SC QF	Wealdstone	n/k	3 - 2	Binns 19, Ofori 42, Haworth 88
22/02	Rym. P	HEYBRIDGE SWIFTS	231	0 - 0	
25/02	Rym. P	ST ALBANS CITY	276	0 - 2	
01/03	Rym. P	Aylesbury United	642	1 - 0	Williams 90[og]
04/03	Lge Cup QF	KINGSTONIAN	133	1 - 0	Haworth 98
08/03	Rym. P	SUTTON UNITED	273	0 - 2	
11/03	Middx SC SF	HAMPTON & RICHMOND B.	n/k	2 - 0	
15/03	Rym. P	Braintree Town	271	2 - 1	Crace 4, Gallagher 5
18/03	Lge Cup SF(1)	Canvey Island	198	2 - 4	Crace 45, Randall 90
22/03	Rym. P	BISHOP'S STORTFORD	307	0 - 3	
25/03	Lge Cup SF(2)	CANVEY ISLAND	115	2 - 2	Crace 5, Randall 44[p]
27/03	Rym. P	Grays Athletic	206	2 - 0	Forbes 55, Ofior 58
29/03	Rym. P	Boreham Wood	238	1 - 1	Alves 18
01/04	Rym. P	CANVEY ISLAND	251	1 - 0	Crace 90
03/04	Rym. P	BILLERICAY TOWN	203	2 - 1	Alves 30, Cooper 90
05/04	Rym. P	PURFLEET	235	1 - 2	Crace 18
12/04	Rym. P	Hitchin Town	387	2 - 2	Endersby 13, Cooper 89
15/04	Rym. P	Bishop's Stortford	341	1 - 4	Midson 74
19/04	Rym. P	BASINGSTOKE TOWN	201	2 - 1	Ofori 40, Crace 78
21/04	Middx SC F	ENFIELD TOWN	n/k	2 - 0	Crace 19, Ofori 35 (at Northwood)
23/04	Rym. P	St Albans City	257	4 - 1	Butler 16, Crace 54, Binns 78[p], Randall 86
26/04	Rym. P	Aldershot Town	3419	2 - 6	Crace 45, Towler 58
29/04	Rym. P	Kingstonian	297	1 - 0	Ofori 84
01/05	Rym. P	ALDERSHOT TOWN	511	1 - 3	Crace 52
03/05	Rym. P	CHESHAM UNITED	362	0 - 1	

PLAYING SQUAD

Goalkeepers: Dave Burton (Poole Borough), Dave Hook (Hastings Utd), Dave King (Hastings Utd), Gary McCann (Slough T.)

Defenders: Mark Cooper (Windsor & Eton), Iain Duncan (Aylesbury Utd), Christian Hyslop (Harrow Bor.), Warren Kelly (St Albans City).

Midfield: Jon Barrie Bates (Harrow Bor.), Dale Binns (Youth Team), Tony Cook, Maidenhead Utd), Steve Forbes (Dagenham & Redbridge), Rob Hollingdale (Woking), Michael Woolmer (Ruislip Manor), Paul Yates (Brook House)

Forwards: Ricci Crace (Ware T.), Nathan Edwards (Youth Team), Rob Haworth (Sutton Utd), Eugene Oforo (Liberty Professionals Ghana), Ross Pickett (Walton & Hersham) , Martin Randall (Youth Team)

HEYBRIDGE SWIFTS

CLUB OFFICIALS

Chairman: Mike Springett
President: T.B.A.
Vice Chairman: Michael Gibson
Secretary: Liz Creasy c/o club
Match Secretary: Terry Stowers
74 Wood Road, Heybridge, Maldon,
Essex CM9 8JA Tel: 01621 857226
Press Offr: Tony Foster (M) 07931 330756
(H) 01376 519712
Treasurer: Chris Daines

FOOTBALL MANAGEMENT TEAM

Manager: Mark Hawkes
Coach: Dean Curtis
Physio: Glenn Churchet

FACT FILE

Formed: 1880 Nickname: Swifts
Sponsors: Towermaster.
Midweek matchday: Tuesday
Colours: Black & white stripes/black/black
Change colours: All Red or Amber/ white
Reserves' Lge: Essex & Herts Border Comb
Club Website: www.heybridgeswifts.com

PROGRAMME

Pages: 52 Price: £1.50
Editors: Tony Foster & MK Publications

2002-2003

Captain John Pollard
Top Scorer: Paul Abrahams
Players.o.Y: J. Pollard, P. Abrahams
& Danny Barber

GROUND: Scraley Road, Heybridge, Maldon, Essex CM9 8JA Tel: 01621 852978
Directions: Leave Maldon on the main road to Colchester, pass through Heybridge then turn right at the sign to Tolleshunt Major (Scraley Road). The ground on the right. Six miles from nearest station (Witham). By bus via Chelmsfordand Maldon
Capacity: 3,000 Cover: 1,200 Seats: 550 Floodlights: Yes
Clubhouse: Two bars open every night. Games room, boardroom, kitchen (on matchdays)
Club Shop: Open matchdays, sells club sweaters, shirts, scarves, baseball hats, enamel badges, old progs etc. Contact Tony Foster, c/o club.

PREVIOUS **Leagues:** Essex & Suffolk Border, North Essex, South Essex, Essex Senior 1971-84

CLUB RECORDS **Attendance:** 2,477 v Woking FA Trophy 97 and pre season v West Ham United , 3,000 +, 99-00.
Goalscorer: Julian Lamb 115 (post war), Dave Matthews 112 (Isthmian)
Appearances: Hec Askew 500+, John Pollard 455
Fee Paid: £1,000 Dave Rainford, Lee Kersey **Fee Received:** £35,000, Simon Royce (Southend Utd)

BEST SEASON **FA Trophy:** Qtr finals v Woking 22/3/97 (lost 0-1)
FA Cup: First round 0-2 v Gillingham 11/11/94, 0-3 v Bournemouth 15.11.97 **League clubs defeated:** None

HONOURS: Isthmian Lg Div 1 R-up 95-96, Div 2 North 89-90; Essex Senior Lg 81-82 82-83 83-84, Lg Cup 82-83, Trophy 81-82; JT Clarke Cup 82-83; Thorn EMI National Floodlit Competition R-up 82-83; Eastern Floodlit Cup 93-94; East Anglian Cup 93-94 94-95; Essex & Suffolk Border Lge 31-32; Essex Jun Cup 31-32; North Essex Lge 46-47 Ryman League Cup 00-01

Players progressing: Simon Royce (Southend United & Charlton Athletic), Peter Cawley & Ben Lewis (Colchester Utd), Alan Hull (Leyton Orient), Jonathan Hunt (Birmingham City), Dominic Naylor (Leyton Orient), Haken Hayrettin (Doncaster Rovers), Derek Payne & Tom Meredith (Peterborough Utd), Ben Barnett, Eddie Stein & Tim Alexander (Barnet), Ashley Vickers (Peterborough United), James Pullen (18 year old ,goal-keeper to Ipswich Town) 99-00.

Back L to R: Andy Jesney (coach), Glenn Churchett (Physio), Paul Abrahams, Lewis Baillie, Ollie Blackwell, Dave Culverhouse, Tim Bruce, Kingsley Banks, Kevin Budge, Dave Rainford, John Pollard, Dean Curtis (Assistant Manager), Ricky Clarke (coach) **Front**: Jamie Window, Chris Payne, Leon Hunter, Scott Lovett, Dave Greene (manager), Andy Tomlinson, Danny Barber, Paul Cobb, Danny Wornham.

Match Facts 2002-03

Date	Comp.	Opponents	Att.	Score	Goalscorers
20/08	Rym. P	PURFLEET	170	0 - 2	
24/08	Rym. P	CHESHAM UNITED	160	0 - 0	
26/08	Rym. P	St Albans City	401	0 - 2	
31/08	Rym. P	HAYES	170	1 - 0	Sarpong 78
03/09	Rym. P	Hitchin Town	276	1 - 0	Bailey 90
07/09	Rym. P	HAMPTON & RICHMOND B.	173	1 - 0	Budge 23
10/09	Rym. P	Grays Athletic	195	2 - 0	Budge 67, Abraham 73[p]
14/09	Rym. P	Canvey Island	619	1 - 4	Culverhouse 53
17/09	Rym. P	FORD UNITED	180	4 - 4	Windows 22 37, Abrahams 73, Budge 79
21/09	Rym. P	Aldershot Town	1813	0 - 2	
24/09	Rym. P	SUTTON UNITED	208	1 - 3	Culverhouse 45
28/09	**F.A.C.** Q2	SUTTON UNITED	310	1 - 1	Hunter 72
01/10	**F.A.C.** Q2 rep	Sutton United	385	2 - 1	Rainford 40, Abrahams 78
05/10	Rym. P	HENDON	222	0 - 4	
08/10	Rym. P	Kingstonian	449	0 - 4	
12/10	**F.A.C.** Q3	HERNE BAY	270	1 - 0	Budge 90
15/10	Rym. P	Billericay Town	344	0 - 2	
19/10	Rym. P	BOREHAM WOOD	217	1 - 0	Hunter 89
22/10	Rym. P	Bedford Town	446	2 - 1	Cobb 16 43
26/10	**F.A.C.** Q4	BIDEFORD	516	2 - 0	Cobb 28, Budge 84
02/11	**F.A.T.** 1	Bracknell Town	136	2 - 0	Budge 6, Hunter 90
05/11	Essex SC 3	CLAPTON	n/k	5 - 2	Gough 27 56, Own-Goal 43, Baillie 60, Lovett 73
09/11	Rym. P	HARROW BOROUGH	201	0 - 1	
12/11	Rym. P	BISHOP'S STORTFORD	249	3 - 3	Abrahams 42 69, Rainford 45
16/11	**F.A.C.** 1	BRISTOL CITY	2046	0 - 7	
19/11	Lge Cup 2	Ashford Town (Middx)	n/k	1 - 3	Gough 43
23/11	Rym. P	BASINGSTOKE TOWN	215	2 - 4	Wornham 60, Cobb 73
26/11	Essex SC 4	WITHAM TOWN	n/k	4 - 2	Window 26, Pollard 45, Budge 56, Lovett 86
30/11	**F.A.T.** 2	WEYMOUTH	314	2 - 1	Tilley 45[og], Sodje 85
07/12	Rym. P	Aylesbury United	632	1 - 2	Abrahams 24[p]
10/12	Rym. P	GRAYS ATHLETIC	78	1 - 1	Hunter 83
14/12	Rym. P	KINGSTONIAN	230	2 - 4	Sodje 41, Abrahams 80[p]
21/12	Rym. P	Enfield	71	3 - 2	Abrahams 74, Gillespie 82, Gould 85
28/12	Rym. P	Chesham United	278	0 - 3	
14/01	**F.A.T.** 3	HENDON	210	0 - 0	
18/01	Rym. P	Hampton & Richmond Bor.	145	1 - 1	Abrahams 2
25/01	Rym. P	CANVEY ISLAND	406	0 - 2	
28/01	**F.A.T.** 3 rep	Hendon	178	1 - 2	Abrahams 23[p]
04/02	Essex SC QF	CHELMSFORD CITY	174	0 - 2	
08/02	Rym. P	Sutton United	514	0 - 2	
15/02	Rym. P	ALDERSHOT TOWN	503	0 - 4	
22/02	Rym. P	Hendon	231	0 - 0	
25/02	Rym. P	BRAINTREE TOWN	294	2 - 0	Opara 62, Hadrava 77
01/03	Rym. P	BILLERICAY TOWN	292	1 - 1	Abrahams 88
03/03	Rym. P	Boreham Wood	143	0 - 0	
11/03	Rym. P	ST ALBANS CITY	144	3 - 3	Lowe 56, Opara 88, Budge 89
15/03	Rym. P	Harrow Borough	177	1 - 2	Budge 85
22/03	Rym. P	MAIDENHEAD UNITED	173	0 - 0	
25/03	Rym. P	Ford United	115	3 - 3	Sodje 5, Budge 50 70
29/03	Rym. P	Bishop's Stortford	471	0 - 2	
01/04	Rym. P	Maidenhead United	178	2 - 2	Hunter 14, Cousins 59
05/04	Rym. P	HITCHIN TOWN	252	3 - 1	Budge 11 85, Abrahams 18[p]
12/04	Rym. P	Hayes	287	2 - 2	Window 73, Hunter 76
15/04	Rym. P	Purfleet	156	2 - 1	Pollard 41, Window 45
19/04	Rym. P	ENFIELD	261	2 - 1	Hunter 14, Abrahams 29
21/04	Rym. P	Braintree Town	501	0 - 3	
26/04	Rym. P	Basingstoke Town	375	2 - 2	Abrahams 47, Sodje 90
29/04	Rym. P	BEDFORD TOWN	310	1 - 0	Sodje 39
03/05	Rym. P	AYLESBURY UNITED	400	1 - 0	Sodje 87

PLAYING SQUAD

Goalkeepers: Kingsley Banks (Witham T.)

Defenders: Danny Barber (Clacton T.), Ollie Blackwell (Billericay T.), Daryl Bourgeios (Cambridge Utd), Leon Hunter (Heybridge Swifts), Lee Kersey (Chelmsford City), Dan Womham (Great Wakering Rovers)

Midfield: Ronnie Bridges (Youth Team), Adam Gillespie (Braintree T.), Ronnie Gould (Purfleet), Glen Moss (Youth Team), John Pollard (St Albans City), Tommy Santer (Youth Team), Jason Shepherd (Maldon T.), Noel Staiano (New Jersey Riptide, U.S.A.), Dave Streetly (Halstead T.),,y Tomlinson (Billericay T.).

Forwards: Paul Abrahams (Wivenhoe T.), Kevin Budge (Gravesend & N'fleet), Neil Cousins (Braintree T.), Dominic Gentle (Slough T.), Kelechi Opara (Enfield), Chris Payne (Chelmsford City) Akpo Sodje (Margate), Jamie Windows (Southend Utd)

HITCHIN TOWN

The
Canary Chronicle
2002 - 03
Ryman
£1.50
Hitchin Town v Harrow Borough
Saturday April 26th 3pm
Hitchin Town v Ford United
Monday April 28th 7.30pm
Ryman League Premier Division

Pages: 24 (A4) Price: £1.50
Editor: Neil Jensen

Local Press: Hitchin Comet, Herts on Sunday
Local Radio: Chiltern, BBC Three Counties

CLUB OFFICIALS

Chairman: **Terry Barratt**
Secretary: **Roy Izzard**
2 Bedford Road, Ickleford, Hitchin, Herts
Tel: 01462 433171

Media Officer: **Neil Jensen**
Tel: 01462 454678 0207 5457921
Email: jensenneilf@aol.com

FOOTBALL MANAGEMENT TEAM

Manager: Robbie O'Keefe
Assistant Manager: Ian Donnelly
Physio: Peter Prince

FACT FILE

Formed: 1865 Reformed 1928
Nickname: The Canaries
Sponsors: Alma Engineering
Colours: Yellow/green/green
Change colours: white/black/white
Midweek matchday: Tuesday
Clubcall Line: 09066 555 817
Website: www.hitchintownfc.co.uk

2002-2003

Captain: & Top Scorer: Dean Brennan 22gls
Players of the Year: James Robinson & Dean Brennan

GROUND: Top Field, Fishponds Road, Hitchin SG5 1NU (01462434483) + 01482 459028 on match days only **Directions:** On A505 near town centre opposite large green. 1 mile from Hitchin(BR). From A1(M) Jct 8,A602 towards Bedford into Hitchin.Over two roundabouts through lights on one way system. Turn right at next roundabout for Fishponds Road.
Capacity: Cover: 1,250 Seats: 500 Floodlights: Yes
Clubhouse: (01462 434483). Members bar, Function Hall (available for hire). Open everyday. Steward: Eamonn Watson/ Nigel Collins
Club Shop: Yes, Contact - Chris Newbold on chris@bewvikd013.freeserve.co.uk

PREVIOUS **Leagues:** Spartan 28-39; Hert & Middx 39-45; Athenian 39,45-63

CLUB RECORDS **Attendance:** 7,878 v Wycombe Wanderers, FA Amateur Cup 3rd Rd 18/2/56
Win: Spartan Lge 29-30 13-0 v Cowley, 13-0 v RAF
Defeat (Isthmian Lge)**:** 0-10 v Kingstonian (A) 65-66, v Slough T. (A) 79-80
Career Appearances: Paul Giggle 769 (68-86) **Career Goals:** Paul Giggle, 214
Fee paid: £2,000 Ray Seeking Potton United, July 1989 **Fee received:** £30,000 Zema Abbey to Cambridge Utd Jan 00

BEST SEASON **FA Trophy:** 5th Rd 98-99 **FA Amateur Cup:** Semi Final 60-61, 62-63
FA Cup: 2nd Rd on four occasions -
v Swindon 1-3 (A) 76-77, v Boston Utd, 0-1 (A) 73-74, v Wycombe Wand. 0-5 (H) 94-95, v Gillingham 0-3 (A) 95-9

HONOURS: Isthmian Lge R-up 68-69Div 1 92-93 R-up 98-99, Spartan Lge 34-35; AFA Sen Cup 30-31; Herts Snr Cup (19-record); London Sen Cup 69-70 (R-up 72-73); E Anglian Cup 72-73; Herts Charity Cup(17), Herts I'mediate Cup (8); Woolwich Trophy 82-83; Televised Sport International Cup 88-89 90-91; Southern Comb. Senior Floodlit Cup 90-91

Back row: Neil Butler, Craig Rydehead, Louie Evans, Rob Simpson, Jon Barnett, Dean McElroy, Matt Childs. **Middle row:** Syd Springett (Kit Man.), Shaun Marshall, Dean Brennan, Tony Fontenelle, James Robinson, Matt Nolan, Tony Francis, Nick Sopowski (Physio)
Front row: Robbie O'Keefe, Chris McMenamin, David Bass, Terry Barnett (Chairman), Ian Scott, Jon Bone, Peter Prince (Physio)

Date	Comp.	Opponents	Att.	Score	Goalscorers
17/08	Rym. P	ALDERSHOT TOWN	974	1 - 3	Rydeheard 52
20/08	Rym. P	Ford United	150	2 - 2	Rydeheard 1, Brennan 14
24/08	Rym. P	Canvey Island	401	1 - 3	Rydeheard 1
26/08	Rym. P	AYLESBURY UNITED	474	2 - 3	Brennan 24[p] 90
31/08	Rym. P	Hendon	280	1 - 2	Brennan 7
03/09	Rym. P	HEYBRIDGE SWIFTS	276	0 - 1	
07/09	Rym. P	BASINGSTOKE TOWN	322	1 - 0	Ayres 21
09/09	Rym. P	Boreham Wood	219	2 - 2	Nolan 16, Wall 85[og]
14/09	Rym. P	St Albans City	751	1 - 0	Fontanelle 78
17/09	Rym. P	BRAINTREE TOWN	287	0 - 0	
21/09	Rym. P	KINGSTONIAN	451	0 - 0	
24/09	Rym. P	Maidenhead United	217	2 - 1	Nolan 23, Drew 32
28/09	**F.A.C.** Q2	Molesey	140	1 - 3	Fontanelle 57
01/10	Rym. P	CHESHAM UNITED	247	1 - 1	Drew 18
05/10	Rym. P	Bishop's Stortford	421	3 - 2	Grime 19, Drew 21, Nolan 61
19/10	Rym. P	SUTTON UNITED	456	2 - 0	Fontanelle 37, Ayres 48
22/10	Rym. P	Purfleet	221	1 - 0	Rydeheard 62
26/10	Rym. P	Hayes	323	1 - 2	Nolan 49
02/11	**F.A.T.** 1	CHATHAM TOWN	256	3 - 1	Brennan 10[p], Nolan 25 51
09/11	Rym. P	HAMPTON & RICHMOND B.	313	1 - 1	Brennan 68
16/11	Rym. P	Sutton United	487	1 - 3	Drew 7
19/11	Herts SC 2	London Colney	n/k	2 - 0	
23/11	Rym. P	Harrow Borough	195	0 - 2	
30/11	**F.A.T.** 2	Windsor & Eton	195	1 - 3	Nolan 11
07/12	Rym. P	ENFIELD	351	7 - 1	Brennan 1 85, Nolan 19 46 77, Drew 69 80
10/12	Lge Cup 2	Walton & Hersham	n/k	1 - 0	Barnett 89
14/12	Rym. P	Aldershot Town	1989	0 - 1	
17/12	Lge Cup 3	BOREHAM WOOD	102	4 - 0	Brennan 5, Nolan 24 43, Drew 30
21/12	Rym. P	GRAYS ATHLETIC	303	3 - 3	Drew 4 20, Ayres 17
26/12	Rym. P	Bedford Town	951	1 - 2	Drew 83
28/12	Rym. P	CANVEY ISLAND	488	2 - 3	Nolan 6, Drew 38
14/01	Lge Cup 4	CANVEY ISLAND	119	1 - 3	Rydeheard 3
18/01	Rym. P	Basingstoke Town	319	0 - 3	
25/01	Rym. P	ST ALBANS CITY	588	1 - 2	Drew 58
28/01	Herts SC QF	WATFORD	n/k	2 - 1	
08/02	Rym. P	MAIDENHEAD UNITED	334	2 - 3	Drew 19 51
15/02	Rym. P	Kingstonian	327	0 - 0	
22/02	Rym. P	BISHOP'S STORTFORD	432	0 - 1	
25/02	Herts SC SF	Berkhamsted Town	n/k	2 - 4	
01/03	Rym. P	Chesham United	272	1 - 2	Drew 4
04/03	Rym. P	Braintree Town	230	3 - 1	Rydeheard 42, Ayres 60, Brennan 85[p]
08/03	Rym. P	PURFLEET	255	1 - 1	Parker 41
11/03	Rym. P	BILLERICAY TOWN	208	1 - 0	Brennan 88
15/03	Rym. P	Hampton & Richmond Bor.	190	2 - 0	Brennan 39, Mills 76
18/03	Rym. P	Aylesbury United	332	2 - 2	Brennan 42, Dillon 74
22/03	Rym. P	HAYES	310	2 - 3	Dillon 14, Brennan 90
25/03	Rym. P	BOREHAM WOOD	202	2 - 1	Drew 64, Ayres 84
29/03	Rym. P	Billericay Town	326	2 - 1	Bone 80 84
05/04	Rym. P	Heybridge Swifts	252	1 - 3	Dillon 90
12/04	Rym. P	HENDON	387	2 - 2	Brennan 28[p], Drew 29
19/04	Rym. P	Grays Athletic	233	1 - 1	Brennan 86[p]
21/04	Rym. P	BEDFORD TOWN	765	2 - 1	Drew 59[p], Brennan 90[p]
26/04	Rym. P	HARROW BOROUGH	218	1 - 0	Parker 56
28/04	Rym. P	FORD UNITED	151	2 - 2	Evans 12, Brennan 54
03/05	Rym. P	Enfield	121	5 - 0	Brennan 5 7 72, Parker 45, Burke 90

PLAYING SQUAD

Goalkeepers: James Robinson (Inter Cardiff)

Defenders: Tim Allpress (St Albans City), James Ayres (Enfield), Mark Burke (Luton T.), Jon Bone (Bedford T.), Joe Bruce (Molesey), Matthew Childs (Hitchin Academy), Scott Cretton (Stevenage Borough), Ryan Frater (Hitchin Academy), Dean McElroy (Youth Team), Gary Williams (Wootton Blue Cross).

Midfield: David Bass (Kingstonian), Dean Brennan (Luton T.), Neil Butler (Woking), Kevin Evans (Hitchin Academy), Chris McMenamin (Boreham Wood), Stuart Maynard (Enfield), Wayne Mills (Hitchin Academy), Adam Parker (Aldershoot T.), Craig Rydeheard (Youth Team), Ian Scott (St Albans City), Carl Williams (Bedford T.).

Forwards: Mark Bridge (Arlesey T.), Jonathon Barnett (Stevenage Borough), Chris Dillon (Grays Ath.), Tony Douglas (Chesham Utd), Carl Drew (Boreham Wood), Mathew Nolan (Youth Team), James Osborn (Harrow Borough), Benn Smith (Berkhamsted T.).

HORNCHURCH

CLUB OFFICIALS

Chairman: Tony Wallace

Vice Chairman: Brian Davie

Secretary: Brian Eagling
20 Tindall Close, Harold Wood
Esssex RM3 0PB
Tel: 01708 373027

FOOTBALL MANAGEMENT TEAM

Manager: Mick Marsden
Physio: D Edkins

FACT FILE

Founded: 1923
Nickname: Urchins
Sponsors: Premier Snacks
Colours: Red & white/red/red
Change Colours: Yellow/blue
Midweek Matches: Tuesday
Reserve Lge: Essex & Herts Border Comb
Local Press: Romford Recorder
Local Radio: Essex Radio, Active FM

PROGRAMME

16-20 pages with admission
Editor: Brian Davie 01708 445107

GROUND: The Stadium, Bridge Avenue, Upminster, Essex RM14 2LX
Tel: 01708 220080 Email: enquiries@urchins.org
Website: www.urchins.org

Directions: Fenchurch Street to Upminster (BR) then 10 mins walk.
Or tube to Upminster Bridge (LT), right outside station, 2nd right into Bridge Ave. ground 150yds on right.
By road Bridge Avenue is off A124 between Hornchurch and Upminster.
Buses 248, 348, 370, 373 from Romford or Upminster BR stations

Capacity: 3,000 Seats: 300 Cover: 350 Floodlights: Yes Club Shop: Yes,

Clubhouse: Mon-Fri 7.30-11, Sat 12-11, Sun 12-3. Cafeteria open matchdays

Club Shop: Yes, selling programmes, handbooks, scarves, hats, souvenirs etc.
Contact : Ron Quantock (01708 455529)

PREVIOUS: **Leagues:** Romford 25-38; Spartan 38-52; Delphian 52-59; Athenian 59-75
Names: Founded as Upminster Wanderers in 1923 but ' Wanderers ' was dropped in1938 as Upminster F.C. had disbanded a few years earlier. When Hornchurch Council provided the Stadium at Bridge Road the club's name became Hornchurch and Upminster. Then in 1961, as the committee considered their name too unwieldy, 'Upminster' (the town of origin)was dropped.
Ground: Upminster Rec

RECORDS: **Attendance**: 3,000 v Chelmsford, FA Cup 66-67

BEST SEASON: **FA Cup:** 4th Qual Rd 66-67 **F.A. Vase:** 5th Rd 74-75

HONOURS: Athenian Lg 66-67, Romford Lg(2), Essex Snr Trophy R-up 86-87, Essex Jnr Cup, Essex Thameside Tphy 84-85, Isthmian Yth Cup, CarlsbergTrophy R-up 93-94, Ryman Lg Div3 R-up.2001-02

Players progressing to Football League: D Armstrong (Millwall), R Lee(Charlton, Newcastle U & England), Nicky Bissett (Brighton), Jesse Roast (Maidstone United), Nicky Hammond (Swindon Town)

L-R - Back Row: John Lawrence, Ken Hunt, Ollie Adedeji, Chris Moore, Kevin Jopson, Mark Risley, Steve Jones, Richard Wray, Dmitri Kharine, Paul Wood, Vincent John, Chris Sorhaindo, Steve West, Andrew Martin, Scott Gooding, Adam Locke, John Gowens, George Borg.
Front Row: Glen Dyson, Paul Suton, Gavin McGowan, Steve Carter, Bradley Kite, Craig Cripps, Keith Rowland, Jamie Southon, John Keeling, Jon Bates, Nicky Lowery, Danny Cowley, Barry Fox, Andy Findlay, Garry Kimble, Dell Edkins, Terry Glen.

Date	Comp.	Opponents	Att.	Score	Goalscorers
17/08	Rym. 1N	Slough Town	361	1 - 1	Benstock 90
20/08	Rym. 1N	WEALDSTONE	340	3 - 0	Rothan 44, Jones 70, Benstock 75
24/08	Rym. 1N	OXFORD CITY	210	3 - 1	Jones 20, Wolff 69, Bates 82
26/08	Rym. 1N	Hertford Town	139	2 - 1	Alexander 56[og], Risley 90
31/08	**F.A.C.** P	Stotfold	68	1 - 1	Elder 80
03/09	**F.A.C.** P rep	STOTFOLD	384	4 - 4	Benstock 50, Jones 79, Fox 83, Lowery 116 Lost 4 5 after pe
10/09	Rym. 1N	Barking & East Ham United	182	1 - 1	Woolf 18
14/09	Rym. 1N	Wealdstone	266	0 - 1	
21/09	Rym. 1N	YEADING	310	1 - 1	McGowan 3
24/09	Rym. 1N	Aveley	151	2 - 0	Risley 24, Jones 31
01/10	Rym. 1N	NORTHWOOD	190	1 - 0	Lowery 77
05/10	**F.A.T.** P	WALTON & HERSHAM	263	2 - 6	Fox 57, Jones 69
08/10	London SC 1	VCD ATHLETIC	n/k	4 - 2	
12/10	Rym. 1N	Uxbridge	76	1 - 0	Martin 6
15/10	Rym. 1N	HARLOW TOWN	197	1 - 2	Martin 31
19/10	Rym. 1N	TILBURY	247	2 - 0	Jones 27 72
26/10	Rym. 1N	Barton Rovers	82	1 - 0	Martin 10
29/10	Lge Cup 1	Metropolitan Police	54	6 - 2	Locke 9, Martin 19 42 62, Jones 20 75
02/11	Rym. 1N	ARLESEY TOWN	219	4 - 3	Jones 15 78, Fox 52, Martin 54
04/11	London SC 2	Ilford	n/k	2 - 3	
09/11	Rym. 1N	THAME UNITED	230	1 - 1	Jones 45
16/11	Rym. 1N	Arlesey Town	226	2 - 2	Martin 10, Theodosiou 51[og]
19/11	Essex SC 3	SOUTHEND MANOR	n/k	3 - 1	
23/11	Rym. 1N	BARTON ROVERS	204	1 - 1	Martin 40
26/11	Lge Cup 2	Northwood	n/k	2 - 4	Fox 42, Jones 60
30/11	Rym. 1N	Berkhamsted Town	80	1 - 1	Fox 82
07/12	Rym. 1N	GREAT WAKERING ROVERS	253	2 - 1	Stow 80, Locke 90
10/12	Essex SC 4	SOUTHEND UNITED	n/k	1 - 2	
14/12	Rym. 1N	SLOUGH TOWN	236	3 - 2	Locke 10, Jones 40, Cripps 80
21/12	Rym. 1N	Wembley	69	4 - 0	Martin 66, Cowley 80, Cripps 87, Locke 89[p]
26/12	Rym. 1N	WIVENHOE TOWN	542	0 - 0	
28/12	Rym. 1N	Oxford City	174	1 - 1	Cripps 68
15/01	Rym. 1N	Harlow Town	120	0 - 0	
18/01	Rym. 1N	UXBRIDGE	306	0 - 0	
25/01	Rym. 1N	Tilbury	131	2 - 1	Jones 56[p], Martin 90
28/01	Rym. 1N	HEMEL HEMPSTEAD TOWN	194	2 - 2	Benstock 15, Cripps 75
04/02	Rym. 1N	WINGATE & FINCHLEY	177	1 - 0	Benstock 40
08/02	Rym. 1N	AVELEY	417	0 - 1	
15/02	Rym. 1N	Yeading	78	2 - 1	Locke 89, Southon 90
18/02	Rym. 1N	East Thurrock United	140	3 - 4	Martin 7 78, Jones 84
22/02	Rym. 1N	MARLOW	288	0 - 3	
25/02	Rym. 1N	HERTFORD TOWN	182	2 - 1	Jopson 4, Benstock 32
01/03	Rym. 1N	Northwood	305	0 - 2	
15/03	Rym. 1N	Thame United	412	1 - 0	Avery 29[og]
18/03	Rym. 1N	LEYTON PENNANT	245	2 - 1	Jones 18 71
22/03	Rym. 1N	EAST THURROCK UNITED	269	1 - 1	Jones 54
29/03	Rym. 1N	Hemel Hempstead Town	170	3 - 1	Kimble 6, McGowan 22, Martin 55
05/04	Rym. 1N	BARKING & EAST HAM UNITED	388	5 - 1	Martin 8, Moore 32, Marsden 54, John 60 68
08/04	Rym. 1N	Leyton Pennant	103	0 - 0	
12/04	Rym. 1N	Wingate & Finchley	130	1 - 0	Jones 74
19/04	Rym. 1N	WEMBLEY	319	6 - 0	Martin 17 39, John 25 47, McGowen 28, Jones 81
21/04	Rym. 1N	Wivenhoe Town	174	5 - 1	Kimble 24, Martin 27 47 58, West 45
26/04	Rym. 1N	BERKHAMSTED TOWN	583	5 - 3	John 33 73, Marsden 41, Southon 55, Jones 80
29/04	Rym. 1N	Marlow	181	3 - 2	John 22 40, Riseley 26
03/05	Rym. 1N	Great Wakering Rovers	295	3 - 3	Martin 21, Carter 30, Lowery 44

PLAYING SQUAD

Goalkeepers: Dimitre Kharine (Glasgow Celtic).

Defenders: Ollie Adedeji (Billericay T.), Danny Banstock (Ford Utd), Craig Cripps (Youth Team), Barry Fox Romford), Scott Gooding (Whyteleafe), Garry Kimble (Ford Utd), Gavin McGowan (Bromley), Kevin Marsden (Purfleet), Chris Moore (Billericay T.), Mark Risley (Grays Ath.), Jamie Southon (Purfleet).

Midfield: Jon Bates (Youth Team), Danny Cowley (Harlow T.), Kevin Jepson (East Thurrock Utd), Nick Lowery (Youth Team), Nick McDonald (East Thurrock Utd).

Forwards: Vinnie John (Bishop's Stortford), Steve Jones (Bristol City),,rew Martin (Tooting & Mitcham), Steve West (Dagenham & Redbridge), Chris Woolf (Youth Team)

KETTERING TOWN

CLUB OFFICIALS

President Sid Chapman
Chairman Peter Mallinger
Vice Chairman Michael Leech
Directors Les Manning, David Dunham, David Tailby
Club Secretary/Press Off. Graham Starmer, c/o the club
Assistant Secretary Ann-Marie Wright

FOOTBALL MANAGEMENT

Manager: Dominic Genovese
Physio: Chris Palmer
Youth & Comunity Dev.: Dominic Genovese

2002-03

Captain, P.o.Y. & Leading Scorer: Craig Norman

FACT FILE

Founded: 1872
Nickname: Poppies
Club Sponsors: Weldon Plant Ltd.
Club colours: Red/black/red
Change colours: Blue/white/blue
Midweek home matchday: Tuesday
Local Press: Evening Telegraph; Chronicle & Echo; Herald & Post; Citizen
Local Radio: Radio Northampton; Northants 96; KCBC
Clubcall: 09068 101567

PROGRAMME

Pages: 32 Price: £2
Editor: Fox Design to Print 0116 222 8500

GROUND Rockingham Road, Kettering, Northants, NN16 9AW Tel: 01536 83028/410815 (Office) Fax: 01536 412273
email: info@ketteringtownafc.co.uk web site: http://www.ketteringtownafc.co.uk

DIRECTIONS: From south - M1 junction 15, A43 to Kettering use A14 exit Junct. 7, follow A43 to Corby/Stamford to 1st roundabout, turn right A6003, ground half a mile. **From north** - M1 or M6 use junction 19 then A14 to Kettering. Exit Junct. 7 then as above.
British Rail - Inter-City Midland - 50 mins from London (St.Pancras), 20 mins from Leicester

Capacity: 6,170 **Covered - Seating:** 1,800 **Terracing:** 2,200

Club Shop: Open before & after matches, & on request on non-match days. Situated in front of main stand. Also Alex Elmores in town centre

Clubhouse: Social Club (Poppies) 01536 410962, Vice-Presidents Bar & Sponsor's Lounge

PREVIOUS **Leagues:** Southern League??-79, 01-02; Northants League, Midland League, Birmingham League; Central Alliance, United Counties League; Conference 79-01 02-03 **Grounds:** North Park; Green Lane

CLUB RECORDS **Attendance:** 11,536, Kettering v Peterborough (pre-Taylor report)
Win: 16-0 v Higham YMCI (FA Cup 1909) **Defeat:** 0-13 v Mardy (Southern League Div. 2, 1911/12)
Transfer fee paid: £25,000 to Macclesfield for Carl Alford, 1994
Transfer fee received: £150,000 from Newcastle United for Andy Hunt
Career goalscorer: Roy Clayton 171 (1972 - 1981) **Career appearances:** Roger Ashby

BEST SEASON **FA Trophy:** Runners-up 78-79 99-00 **League:** Conference Runners-up 1980-81; 88-89; 93-94; 98-99
FA Cup: 4th Round - 88-89, 1-2 v Charlton Ath.; 91-92, 1-4 v Blackburn R. League clubs defeated: Swindon T. 61-62, Millwall 63-64, Swansea C. 74-75, Halifax T. 88-89, Bristol R. 88-89, Maidstone U. 91-92, Hull C. 00-01

HONOURS Premier Inter League Cup; FA Trophy Runners-up 78-79; Alliance Premier League (Conference) R-up x 4; Southern League Champions x 4, County Cup Winners, Daventry Charity Cup Winners x 2; Northants Senior Cup x 28; Maunsell Cup Winners x 12

Players P rogressing: Billy Kellock(Peterborough), Gary Wood (Notts Co.), Dave Longhurst (Nott'm Forest), Scott Endersby (Ipswich), Steve Fallon (Cambridge U.), Andy Rogers (Plymouth), Martyn Foster (Northampton), Cohen Griffith (Cardiff C.), Andy Hunt (Newcastle), Richard Brown (Blackburn R.) ,Ben Wright (Bristol C.),Kofi Nyamah (Stoke C.) + Adam Sollitt(North'tonT)

L-R - Back Row: Richard Graham, Wayne Diuk, Delroy Gordon, Paul Pettinger, William Gourlay, Andy Lodge, Jason Turner, Victor Asombang.
Middle: Martin Harrid (Trainer), Elliott Paschalis, Liam Carson, Brett Solkhon, Paul Fewings, Steffan Dancy, Bradley Thomas, Brian Hardie, Michael Boyle Chung, Matt Murphy, Chris Palmer (Physio).
Front: Gary Butterworth, Martin Matthews, Dominic Genovese (manager), Craig Norman, Lee Clarke

Date	Comp.	Opponents	Att.	Score	Goalscorers	
27/07	SL Shield	DORCHESTER TOWN	525	0 - 2		
17/08	Conf.	Chester City	2367	0 - 0		
20/08	Conf.	MARGATE	1602	1 - 1	Howarth 24	
24/08	Conf.	WOKING	1608	0 - 3		
26/08	Conf.	Southport	1327	0 - 0		
31/08	Conf.	YEOVIL TOWN	1670	0 - 1		
03/09	Conf.	Doncaster Rovers	3764	0 - 1		
07/09	Conf.	Scarborough	1078	1 - 4	Norman 13	
14/09	Conf.	MORECAMBE	1353	3 - 2	Inman 38, Murphy 64, Howarth 85	
17/09	Conf.	Dagenham & Redbridge	1235	1 - 3	Walsh 28	
21/09	Conf.	NORTHWICH VICTORIA	1286	2 - 2	Town 77, Murray 90[p]	
24/09	Conf.	HEREFORD UNITED	1434	2 - 3	Inman 3, Butcher 85	
28/09	Conf.	Forest Green Rovers	685	0 - 1		
05/10	Conf.	TELFORD UNITED	1481	2 - 4	Butcher 8, Inman 90[p]	
08/10	Conf.	Halifax Town	1639	0 - 4		
12/10	Conf.	Farnborough Town	794	1 - 0	Butcher 57	
19/10	Conf.	BARNET	1704	1 - 2	Murray 65	
26/10	**F.A.C.** Q4	Hastings United	1538	0 - 0		
29/10	**F.A.C.** Q4 rep	HASTINGS UNITED	1144	0 - 5		
02/11	Conf.	Leigh RMI	402	2 - 2	Butcher 24, Parker 80	
09/11	Conf.	BURTON ALBION	1743	1 - 2	Parker 25	
23/11	Conf.	Telford United	793	0 - 2		
30/11	Conf.	NUNEATON BOROUGH	1386	3 - 0	Parker 10 54, Goodwin 26	
07/12	Conf.	Gravesend & Northfleet	954	2 - 0	Inman 12, Norman 39	
14/12	Conf.	SCARBOROUGH	1372	1 - 3	Norman 40[p]	
21/12	Conf.	Morecambe	1094	0 - 1		
26/12	Conf.	STEVENAGE BOROUGH	2068	1 - 0	Murphy 2	
28/12	Conf.	Margate	1004	2 - 2	Murphy 6, Sodje 76[og]	
04/01	Conf.	CHESTER CITY	1788	0 - 1		
14/01	**F.A.T.** 3	ALTRINCHAM	1072	1 - 1	Shutt 85	
18/01	Conf.	Woking	2031	1 - 2	Norman 9[p]	
22/01	**F.A.T.** 3 rep	Altrincham	436	3 - 3	Murphy 6 41, Norman 67	Lost 4 5 after pens.
25/01	Conf.	SOUTHPORT	1200	1 - 0	Asombang 12	
08/02	Conf.	Yeovil Town	4738	0 - 4		
15/02	Conf.	DONCASTER ROVERS	1633	0 - 2		
01/03	Conf.	DAGENHAM & REDBRIDGE	1392	1 - 3	Solkhon 7	
08/03	Conf.	Hereford United	2062	0 - 2		
18/03	Conf.	Northwich Victoria	459	2 - 1	Asombang 32, Norman 81	
22/03	Conf.	Nuneaton Borough	1549	0 - 1		
25/03	Conf.	Stevenage Borough	1865	0 - 2		
29/03	Conf.	GRAVESEND & NORTHFLEET	1070	1 - 1	Revell 79	
05/04	Conf.	FARNBOROUGH TOWN	877	1 - 4	McKenzie 13	
08/04	Conf.	FOREST GREEN ROVERS	422	2 - 3	Norman 38[p], Inman 90	
12/04	Conf.	Barnet	1198	2 - 0	Langston 26[og], Clarke 69	
19/04	Conf.	HALIFAX TOWN	713	0 - 1		
21/04	Conf.	Burton Albion	1570	0 - 2		
26/04	Conf.	LEIGH RMI	768	0 - 1		

PLAYING SQUAD

Goalkeepers: Paul Pettinger (Lincoln City), Willie Gourley (Youth Team).

Defenders: Keith Colley (Sheffield Utd), Delroy Gordon (Rushden & Diamonds), Lee Howarth (Boston Utd),,y Lodge (St.Albans City), Craig Norman (Chelsea), Brett Solklon (Rushden & Diamonds).

Midfield: Gary Butterworth (Farnborough T.), Wayne Dunk (Gedling T.), Scott Goodwin (Hereford Utd), Brian Hardie (Boston Utd), Martin Mathews (Kings Lynn).

Forwards: Victor Asombang (Wealdstone), Paul Fewings (Chesham Utd), Niall Inman (Dover Ath.), Carlin Intonga (Arsenal), Jason Turner (Rothwell T.)

KINGSTONIAN

CLUB OFFICIALS

Chairman: Rajesh Khosla
Chief Executive: Anup Khosla
Directors : Rajesh Khosla,Anup Khosla, and Rishi Khosla
Club Secretary:
Graham Richards, 1 Bridge Court, Bridge Street, Leatherhead, Surrey KT22 8BWTel No: 01372 377076
Commercial Man.: Anup Khosla
Press Officer: Gary Ekins (07764 745904)

FOOTBALL MANAGEMENT TEAM

Manager: Kim Harris
Coach: Scott Steele

FACT FILE

Founded: 1885
Nickname: The Ks
Sponsors: Bass Brewers
Club Colours: Red & white hooped shirts, black shorts, black socks
Change Colours: Blue/white/blue
Midweek matchday: Tuesday

2002-2003

Captain: Peter Barnsby
Top Scorer & P.o.Y.: Tim Sills

Pages: 32 Price: £1.50
Editor: Robert Wooldridge Tel: 020 8669 3824

Local Press: Surrey Comet 020 8546 2261
Local Radio: County Sound; Southern Counties

GROUND: Kingsmeadow Stadium, Kingston Road, Kingston-upon-Thames, Surrey. KT13PB
Tel: 0208 547 3335/6 Fax: 0208 974 5713
DIRECTIONS: From town centre - Cambridge Rd on to Kingston Rd (A2043) to Malden Rd. From A3, turn off at New Malden, turn left on to A2043 - grd 1 mile on left. Half mile from Norbiton (BR)
CAPACITY: 4,262 **COVERED TERRACING:** 2,538 **SEATED:** 1,080
SOCIAL FACILITIES: Banqueting centre, open 7 days. 3 bars capacity 400.
Contact Anup Khosla (0208 647 3335)
CLUB SHOP: Sells programmes, shirts, badges etc.
Contact Sandra 7 Gary Winters 0208 747 3336

RECORDS
Win: 15-1 v Delft, friendly 5/9/51; Competitive 10-0 v Hitchin (H) Isthmian Lge 19/3/66)
Attendance: 4,582 v Chelsea (Friendly) 22.7.95
Defeat: 0-11 v Ilford (A) Isthmian Lge 13/2/37
Fee Paid: £18,000 for David Leworthy to Rushden & Diamonds '97
Goalscorer: Johnny Whing 295
Fee Received: £150,000 for Gavin Holligan from West Ham Utd. '99
Appearances: Micky Preston 555

PREVIOUS
Leagues: Kingston & Dist.; West Surrey; Southern Suburban; Athenian 1919-29; Isthmian League 29-98; Conference 98-01
Names: Kingston & Surbiton YMCA 1885-87, Saxons 87-90, Kingston Wanderers 1893-1904, Old Kingstonians 08-19
Grounds: Several to 1921; Richmond Rd 21-89

HONOURS
FA Trophy 98-99 99-00; Isthmian League 33-34, 36-37, 97-98, R-up 47-48 62-63, Div 1 R-up 84-85, League Cup 95-96; Athenian Lge 23-24 25-26, R-up 26-27; London Senior Cup 62-63 64-65 86-87, R-up x 5; Surrey Senior Cup x 9, R-up 90-91.

BEST SEASON
FA Amateur Cup: Winners 32-33 R-up 59-60
FA Trophy: Winners 98-99 99-00
FA Cup: 4th Round replay 00-01, 0-1 v Bristol City (H), after 1-1
League: 5th Conference 99-00
League clubs defeated: Brighton & H.A. 94-95, Brentford & Southend Utd. 00-01

PAST PLAYERS:
C Nastri (C Palace), H Lindsay (Southampton 65), G Still (Brighton 79), D Byrne (Gillingham 1985), J Power (Brentford 87), Jamie Ndah (Torquay), Gavin Holligan (West Ham '99)

Back Row: Jamie Street (Kit Manager) Grant Payne, Rhod Davis, Sofiane Mehdi, Trevor Jones, Lance Key, Stafford Browne, Bashiru Alimi, Helmut Dayo, Paul Ferrie (Kit Manager). **Middle Row:** Laurie Craker (Coach), Scott Smith, Liam Collins, Stephen Broad, Scott Edgar, Liam Garman, Mark Beard (Captain), Billy Mead, Greg Rowlands (Physio). **Front Row:** Phil Winfield, mark Jones, Craig Lewington, Scott Steele (Assistant Manager), Kim Harris (Manager), Chris Nurse, Max Hustwick, Greg Ball

Date	Comp.	Opponents	Att.	Score	Goalscorers
20/08	Rym. P	PURFLEET	170	0 - 2	
24/08	Rym. P	CHESHAM UNITED	160	0 - 0	
26/08	Rym. P	St Albans City	401	0 - 2	
31/08	Rym. P	HAYES	170	1 - 0	Sarpong 78
03/09	Rym. P	Hitchin Town	276	1 - 0	Bailey 90
07/09	Rym. P	HAMPTON & RICHMOND B.	173	1 - 0	Budge 23
10/09	Rym. P	Grays Athletic	195	2 - 0	Budge 67, Abraham 73[p]
14/09	Rym. P	Canvey Island	619	1 - 4	Culverhouse 53
17/09	Rym. P	FORD UNITED	180	4 - 4	Windows 22 37, Abrahams 73, Budge 79
21/09	Rym. P	Aldershot Town	1813	0 - 2	
24/09	Rym. P	SUTTON UNITED	208	1 - 3	Culverhouse 45
28/09	**F.A.C.** Q2	SUTTON UNITED	310	1 - 1	Hunter 72
01/10	**F.A.C.** Q2 rep	Sutton United	385	2 - 1	Rainford 40, Abrahams 78
05/10	Rym. P	HENDON	222	0 - 4	
08/10	Rym. P	Kingstonian	449	0 - 4	
12/10	**F.A.C.** Q3	HERNE BAY	270	1 - 0	Budge 90
15/10	Rym. P	Billericay Town	344	0 - 2	
19/10	Rym. P	BOREHAM WOOD	217	1 - 0	Hunter 89
22/10	Rym. P	Bedford Town	446	2 - 1	Cobb 16 43
26/10	**F.A.C.** Q4	BIDEFORD	516	2 - 0	Cobb 28, Budge 84
02/11	**F.A.T.** 1	Bracknell Town	136	2 - 0	Budge 6, Hunter 90
05/11	Essex SC 3	CLAPTON	n/k	5 - 2	Gough 27 56, Own-Goal 43, Baillie 60, Lovett 73
09/11	Rym. P	HARROW BOROUGH	201	0 - 1	
12/11	Rym. P	BISHOP'S STORTFORD	249	3 - 3	Abrahams 42 69, Rainford 45
16/11	**F.A.C.** 1	BRISTOL CITY	2046	0 - 7	
19/11	Lge Cup 2	Ashford Town (Middx)	n/k	1 - 3	Gough 43
23/11	Rym. P	BASINGSTOKE TOWN	215	2 - 4	Wornham 60, Cobb 73
26/11	Essex SC 4	WITHAM TOWN	n/k	4 - 2	Window 26, Pollard 45, Budge 56, Lovett 86
30/11	**F.A.T.** 2	WEYMOUTH	314	2 - 1	Tilley 45[og], Sodje 85
07/12	Rym. P	Aylesbury United	632	1 - 2	Abrahams 24[p]
10/12	Rym. P	GRAYS ATHLETIC	78	1 - 1	Hunter 83
14/12	Rym. P	KINGSTONIAN	230	2 - 4	Sodje 41, Abrahams 80[p]
21/12	Rym. P	Enfield	71	3 - 2	Abrahams 74, Gillespie 82, Gould 85
28/12	Rym. P	Chesham United	278	0 - 3	
14/01	**F.A.T.** 3	HENDON	210	0 - 0	
18/01	Rym. P	Hampton & Richmond Bor.	145	1 - 1	Abrahams 2
25/01	Rym. P	CANVEY ISLAND	406	0 - 2	
28/01	**F.A.T.** 3 rep	Hendon	178	1 - 2	Abrahams 23[p]
04/02	Essex SC QF	CHELMSFORD CITY	174	0 - 2	
08/02	Rym. P	Sutton United	514	0 - 2	
15/02	Rym. P	ALDERSHOT TOWN	503	0 - 4	
22/02	Rym. P	Hendon	231	0 - 0	
25/02	Rym. P	BRAINTREE TOWN	294	2 - 0	Opara 62, Hadrava 77
01/03	Rym. P	BILLERICAY TOWN	292	1 - 1	Abrahams 88
03/03	Rym. P	Boreham Wood	143	0 - 0	
11/03	Rym. P	ST ALBANS CITY	144	3 - 3	Lowe 56, Opara 88, Budge 89
15/03	Rym. P	Harrow Borough	177	1 - 2	Budge 85
22/03	Rym. P	MAIDENHEAD UNITED	173	0 - 0	
25/03	Rym. P	Ford United	115	3 - 3	Sodje 5, Budge 50 70
29/03	Rym. P	Bishop's Stortford	471	0 - 2	
01/04	Rym. P	Maidenhead United	178	2 - 2	Hunter 14, Cousins 59
05/04	Rym. P	HITCHIN TOWN	252	3 - 1	Budge 11 85, Abrahams 18[p]
12/04	Rym. P	Hayes	287	2 - 2	Window 73, Hunter 76
15/04	Rym. P	Purfleet	156	2 - 1	Pollard 41, Window 45
19/04	Rym. P	ENFIELD	261	2 - 1	Hunter 14, Abrahams 29
21/04	Rym. P	Braintree Town	501	0 - 3	
26/04	Rym. P	Basingstoke Town	375	2 - 2	Abrahams 47, Sodje 90
29/04	Rym. P	BEDFORD TOWN	310	1 - 0	Sodje 39
03/05	Rym. P	AYLESBURY UNITED	400	1 - 0	Sodje 87

PLAYING SQUAD

Goalkeepers: **Lance Key** (Northwich Victoria), Matthew Sargent (York City)

Defenders: Peter Barnsby (Hampton & Richmond B), Mark Beard (Southend Utd), Stephen Broad (Southend Utd), Luke Dowling (Lewes), Eddie Duah (Slough T.), Matt Elverson (Basingstoke T.), Liam Gaman (Walton & Hersham), Max Hustweek (Walton & Hersham), Mark Jones (Wimbledon), Julian Sills (Basingstoke T.).

Midfield: Basherie Alini (Millwall), David Clarke (Dover Ath.), Liam Collins (Walton & Hersham), Craig Lewington (Brentford), Scott Steele (Woking), Phil Wingfield (Sutton Utd).

Forwards: Greg Ball (Walton & Hersham), Stafford Browne (Aldershot T.), Scott Edgar (Walton & Hersham), Ronnie Green (Youth Team), Grant Payne (Woking)

MAIDENHEAD UNITED

CLUB OFFICIALS

Chairman: Jon Swan
Vice Chairman: Bob Hussey
President: Jim Parsons
Secretary: Ken Chandler
c/o Maidenhead United
Press Off .:Mike Swift (079556 494915)

FOOTBALL MANAGEMENT

Manager: John Dreyer
Asst. Manager: Phil Gray
Physio: Paul Lagerman

2002-2003

Captain: Paul Kelly
Top Scorer: Lawrence Yaku
P.o.Y.: Andy Cook

FACT FILE

Formed: 1870
Nickname: Magpies
Sponsors: C.F.Lake
Colours: Black & white stripes/black/black
Change colours: Red/white/white
Midweek matchday: Tuesday
Reserve League: Suburban
Local Press: Maidenhead Advertiser, Reading Evening Post, Slough Observer
Local Radio: 2-Ten FM, Star FM, Thames Valley FM, BBC Radio Berkshire

PROGRAMME

Pages: 36 Price: £1
Editor: S.Jinman 07909 655409

GROUND York Road, Maidenhead, Berks SL6 1SQ Tel: 01628 624739/636314

Directions: From Maidenhead BR station proceed eastwards down Bell St - 500 yds Ground is 5 miles from M4 in town centre.
Capacity: 4,500 Cover: 2,000 Seats: 400 Floodlights: Yes
Clubhouse: Open evenings & matchdays. Some hot food
Club Shop: Wide range of progs and club souvenirs. Contact Mark Smith 01753 854674

PREVIOUS **Leagues:** Southern 1894-1902; West Berks 02-04; Grt West Sub 04-22; Spartan 22-39; Grt West Comb 39-45; Corinthian 45-63; Athenian 63-73, Isthmian 1973-
Names: Maidenhead FC, Maidenhead Norfolkians. **Grounds:** Kidwells Park (Norfolkians)

CLUB RECORDS **Attendance:** 7,920 v Southall, FA Amat Cup Q/F 7/3/36 **Season's goalscorer:** Jack Palethorpe 66, 1929-30
Career appearances: Bert Randall 532, 1950-64 **Career goalscorer:** George Copas 270, 1924-35
Win: 14-1 v Buckingham Town (H), FA Amat. Cup 6/9/52 **Defeat:** 0-14 v Chesham United (A), Spartan Lge 31/3/23
Transfer fee paid: Undisclosed **Transfer fee received:** £5,000 from Norwich for Alan Cordice, 79

BEST SEASON **FA Cup:** Qtr Finals 1873-74 74-75 75-76 **F A Trophy:** 3rd Qual Rd **FA Amateur Cup:** Semi Final 35-36

HONOURS Isthmian Lg Div 2 Sth R-up 90-91,Promotion to Premier Division 99-00 Full Members Cup 96-97; Spartan Lg x3 R-upx2; Corinthian Lg 57-58 60-61 61-62 R-up 58-59 59-60, Mem. Shield 56-57 61-62,R-up x4, Neale Cup 48-49 57-58 60-61; Gt Western Suburban Lg 19-20 R-up 20-21; Berks & Bucks Snr Cup x 19, Berks & Bucks Benev. Cup x6 R-up x2; Mithras Cup R-up x4; Southern Comb. Cup R-up 81-82; Sub Lge West 97-98; Allied Counties Champ 97-98

Players progressing: A Cordice (Norwich 79), P Priddy (Brentford 72), D Kemp (Plymouth), L Sanchez (Reading),E Kelsey, J Palethorpe (Reading 30), B Laryea(Torquay), R Davies (Torquay), Mark Harris (C.Palace & Swansea C 1985),Ben Abbey (Oxford U via Crawley 99)

Back row,left to right: Paul Lagerman (Physio), Carl Levene, Nick Hart, Phil Heggie (Coach), Richard Barnard, Steve Croxford, Rickey Ibe, Lee Channell, Rob Saunders, Brian Connor, Adrian Allen, Orlando Jeffrey, Alan Devonshire (Manager) and Roger Coombs (Chairman). **Front row:** Richard Goddard (Reserve Team Manager), Adam Durrant, Andy Morley, Paul Kelly, Obinna Ulasi, Andy Rose, Chris Ferdinand, John Urry (Physio) with Dave Harrison (Coach) at the front. **Photo:** Maidenhead Advertiser

Date	Comp.	Opponents	Att.	Score	Goalscorers
03/09	Rym. P	GRAYS ATHLETIC	466	1 - 0	Clarke 50
07/09	Rym. P	HAYES	463	1 - 1	Wingfield 70
10/09	Rym. P	St Albans City	611	2 - 2	Ball 34, Collins 66
14/09	Rym. P	Sutton United	821	1 - 1	Wingfield 45
17/09	Rym. P	BASINGSTOKE TOWN	400	2 - 1	T Sills 11 53
21/09	Rym. P	Hitchin Town	451	0 - 0	
24/09	Rym. P	ENFIELD	358	4 - 2	Collins 14 90, M Jones 27, Ball 60
28/09	**F.A.C.** Q2	Clacton Town	486	3 - 2	Bailey 4[og], Clarke 43, T Sills 52
01/10	Rym. P	Braintree Town	267	2 - 1	Ball 45, Alimi 89
05/10	Rym. P	BILLERICAY TOWN	543	2 - 0	Alimi 57, Pinnock 68
08/10	Rym. P	HEYBRIDGE SWIFTS	449	4 - 0	T Sills 27, Pinnock 54, Green 82, Lampton 90
12/10	**F.A.C.** Q3	Boreham Wood	n/k	0 - 0	
15/10	Rym. P	Hendon	233	1 - 1	Hook 59[og]
19/10	Rym. P	BISHOP'S STORTFORD	624	3 - 1	Clarke 32 55, Pinnock 73
22/10	Rym. P	Maidenhead United	286	4 - 4	T Sills 50, Wingfield 64, Morley 80[og], Lampton 82
26/10	Rym. P	Harrow Borough	301	1 - 2	Wingfield 24
02/11	**F.A.T.** 1	East Thurrock United	293	3 - 1	Tomlinson 5, Jones 74, Wingfield 87
09/11	Rym. P	PURFLEET	452	0 - 1	
12/11	Rym. P	CHESHAM UNITED	373	5 - 1	T Sills 10 53 55 87, Wingfield 83
16/11	Rym. P	Bishop's Stortford	392	2 - 2	T Sills 84, Wingfield 87
19/11	Lge Cup 2	Slough Town	n/k	3 - 1	Steele 51, T Sills 95 113
26/11	Rym. P	Aldershot Town	1956	1 - 2	T Sills 74
30/11	**F.A.T.** 2	ERITH & BELVEDERE	238	5 - 1	Wingfield 6 22, Thurgood 56, Pinnock 59, T Sills 76
02/12	Rym. P	Boreham Wood	168	1 - 2	Grime 69[og]
07/12	Rym. P	Canvey Island	483	1 - 1	Jones 67
14/12	Rym. P	Heybridge Swifts	230	4 - 2	Wingfield 5 36, T Sills 11, Steele 45
17/12	Lge Cup 3	WORTHING	154	3 - 0	T Sills 49, Flitter 60, Rocastle 90
21/12	Rym. P	BEDFORD TOWN	562	2 - 2	Wingfield 41 42
26/12	Rym. P	Hampton & Richmond Bor.	567	2 - 2	Steele 45, Alimi 56
28/12	Rym. P	BOREHAM WOOD	407	0 - 0	
14/01	**F.A.T.** 3	Aylesbury United	417	0 - 1	
18/01	Rym. P	Hayes	410	2 - 2	Sills 65, Wingfield 90
25/01	Rym. P	SUTTON UNITED	902	2 - 1	Sills 9 19
28/01	Surrey SC 4	CHESSINGTON UNITED	204	2 - 0	Fontana, T Sills
01/02	Rym. P	Basingstoke Town	484	1 - 0	Barnsby 57
04/02	Lge Cup 4	AVELEY	134	3 - 1	Wingfield 36, Green 49, Sills 90
08/02	Rym. P	Enfield	158	2 - 2	Green 69, Edgar 90
15/02	Rym. P	HITCHIN TOWN	327	0 - 0	
18/02	Rym. P	ST ALBANS CITY	229	0 - 2	
22/02	Rym. P	Billericay Town	508	2 - 0	Bradford 3, Steel 90[p]
25/02	Surrey SC QF	ASH UNITED	n/k	4 - 1	
04/03	Lge Cup QF	Hendon	133	0 - 1	
08/03	Rym. P	MAIDENHEAD UNITED	323	2 - 0	T Sills 23 31
11/03	Rym. P	BRAINTREE TOWN	249	1 - 4	T Sills 76[p]
15/03	Rym. P	Purfleet	301	1 - 0	Payne 30
18/03	Rym. P	Ford United	169	2 - 2	Payne 13, Pinnock 74
22/03	Rym. P	HARROW BOROUGH	327	1 - 3	Payne 33
25/03	Surrey SC SF	Leatherhead	n/k	2 - 2	7 6
29/03	Rym. P	Chesham United	284	4 - 0	Sills 10[p] 44, Whelan 12, Edgar 78
01/04	Rym. P	FORD UNITED	267	0 - 2	
05/04	Rym. P	Grays Athletic	275	1 - 1	Steele 68
12/04	Rym. P	ALDERSHOT TOWN	1220	0 - 2	
19/04	Rym. P	Bedford Town	605	2 - 5	Payne 11, Sills 32
21/04	Rym. P	HAMPTON & RICHMOND B.	345	1 - 1	Wingfield 28
24/04	Rym. P	AYLESBURY UNITED	324	1 - 0	T Sills 30
26/04	Rym. P	Aylesbury United	968	0 - 1	
29/04	Rym. P	HENDON	297	0 - 1	
03/05	Rym. P	CANVEY ISLAND	421	0 - 4	
07/05	Surrey SC F	SUTTON UNITED	775	1 - 2	Steele 90 (at Metropolitan Police)

PLAYING SQUAD

Goalkeepers: Paul Wilson (Stevenage Borough).

Defenders: Mark Boyce (Enfield), Brian Connor (Marlow), Steve Croxford (Hampton & Richmond Bor.), John Dreyer (Stevenage Bor.), Adam Durrant (Egham T.), Chris Elsegood (Chesham Utd), Rob Paris (Aylesbury Utd), Obinna Ulasi (Hayes).

Midfield: Ryan Ashe (Northwood), Steve Brown (Feltham), Dean Coppard (Enfield), Michael Gorman (Yeading), Barry Rake (Slough T.).

Forwards: Ayodeji Abiodun (Enfield), Ibrahim Adeyoi (Leyton Orient), Adrian Allen (Leyton Pennant), Joe Narty (Barking & East Ham Utd), Lawrence Yaku (Northwood)

NORTHWOOD

CLUB OFFICIALS

Secretary: Steve Williams, 35 Evelyn Drive Hatch End, Pinner, Middx HA5 4RL
Tel: 020 8428 1533(H) 020 8421 5923 (F)

Chairman: Andy Johnson

Vice Chairman: Martin Ellis

President: Lothar Hahn

Press Off: Robin Piper (01928 840069)

FOOTBALL MANAGEMENT TEAM

Manager: Tony Choules
Coaches:Gary Farrell & John Toogood
Physio: George Price

FACT FILE

Founded: 1899 Nickname: Woods
Sponsors: Don Bruse Bookmakers
Colours: All red Change colours: All yellow
Midweek Matches: Tuesday
Reserve League: Suburban
Local Press: Ruislip & Northwood Gazette, Watford Observer
Website: www.northwoodfc.com

2002-2003

Captain: Chris Gell
Top Scorers:Chris Moore,Scott Fitzgerald 29
Players of the Year:
Dave Sargent & Danny Butler

PROGRAMME

Pages: 60 Price:£1.00
Editor: A Evans (020 8566 2880)

GROUNDNorthwood Park, Chestnut Avenue, Northwood Tel: 01923 827148 Email:alan.evansfc@btopenworld.com
Directions: A404 (Pinner-Rickmansworth) - Chestnut Ave. on left by large grey iron railway bridge. Third of a mile from Northwood Hills station (Metropolitan Line) - right out of station to r'bout, left into Pinner Rd, left into Chestnut Ave after 300yds. Buses 282 and H11 to Northwood Hills
Capacity: 3,075 Seats:307 Cover:932 Floodlights: Yes **Club Shop:** No
Clubhouse: Weekends & most eves from 6pm. Bar. Hot and cold food. Pool

HONOURS: Isthmian Lg Associate Members Cup 92-93,99-00; London Spartan Lg 91-92 (R-up 89-90), Lg Cup 89-90 91-92;Hellenic Lg Div 1 78-79 (Prem Div Cup R-up 81-82); Middx Lg 77-78 (R-up 72-73 76-77), Div 1 R-up 71-72, Challenge Cup 74-75 76-77 77-78; Middx Snr Charity Cup R-up 93-94; Middx Snr Cup SF 91-92 92-93 98-99; R-up 99-00 Jnr Cup 46-47 47-48 48-49; Harrow & Wembley Lg (9); Middlesex Premier Cup 94-95 Finallists 99-00, 01-02Isthmian League Div 1 North Champions 2002-03. Isthmian Div 2 R-up 99-00, Isthmian League Cup Winners 2001-02 Isthmia CharityShield Winners 2002

PREVIOUS: **Leagues:** Harrow & Wembley 32-69; Middlesex 69-78; Hellenic 79-84; London Spartan 84-92 **Names:** Northwood Town

CLUB RECORDS: **Attendance:** 1,642 v Chelsea Friendly July 1997
Goal Scorerin Season: Lawrence Yaku 61 (99-00) **Career Appearances:** Chris Gell (493 current total)
Win: 15-0 v Dateline (H) Middlesex Inter Cup 1973 **Defeat:** 0-8 v Bedfont (Middlesex Lg.1975)

BEST SEASON: **FA Cup:** 4th Qual Rd 00-01 **F.A.Trophy:** 3rd Rd 00-01 **FA Vase:** Quarter Final 96-97

Players progressing: Gavin Maguire, Derek Payne (Barnet), Warren Patmore (Cambridge United),Scott Fitzgerald (Watford)

Back row. left to right; Scott Fitzgerald, Wayne Carter, Lee Holman, Gary Williams, Chris Moore, Rob Bullivant, Danny Butler, Kieran Knight, Dave Sargent and George Price (Physio). **Middle row:** Craig McIntosh, Garry Farrell (Coach), John Toogood (Coach), Tony Choules (Manager), Andy Johnson (Chairman), Alan Merison (Gen-Manager), Daryl Craft and Ben Porter.
Front row: Gavin Hart, Dave Nolan, Chris Gell and Craig Totton. **Photo:** Paul Evans

Date	Comp.	Opponents	Att.	Score	Goalscorers
17/08	Rym. P	Purfleet	323	0 - 1	
20/08	Rym. P	CHESHAM UNITED	277	5 - 0	Croxford 16, Allen 55 58, Channell 83, Glynn 87
24/08	Rym. P	ST ALBANS CITY	295	0 - 1	
26/08	Rym. P	Braintree Town	255	2 - 1	Glynn 12, Nicholls 72
31/08	Rym. P	BILLERICAY TOWN	317	1 - 0	Yaku 82
03/09	Rym. P	Hayes	483	2 - 0	Glynn 62 70
07/09	Rym. P	Enfield	94	1 - 1	Ulasi 20
10/09	Rym. P	ALDERSHOT TOWN	847	1 - 2	Glynn 1
14/09	Rym. P	BEDFORD TOWN	270	3 - 2	Yaku 21 88, Nicholls 90
17/09	Rym. P	Harrow Borough	185	1 - 1	Yaku 72
21/09	Rym. P	Hendon	292	1 - 1	Asde 75
24/09	Rym. P	HITCHIN TOWN	217	1 - 2	Yaku 64
28/09	**F.A.C.** Q2	WELLING UNITED	285	1 - 2	Allen 55
01/10	Rym. P	Hampton & Richmond Bor.	149	1 - 1	Yaku 67
05/10	Rym. P	GRAYS ATHLETIC	248	0 - 2	
12/10	Rym. P	Aylesbury United	518	0 - 0	
19/10	Rym. P	Ford United	86	3 - 0	Yaku 67 82, Adeyoe 88
22/10	Rym. P	KINGSTONIAN	286	4 - 4	Morley 11 77, Kelly 31, Yaku 49
02/11	**F.A.T.** 1	Tonbridge Angels	448	2 - 3	Yaku 57, Adeyoe 88
09/11	Rym. P	Canvey Island	509	2 - 3	Adeoye 47 61
16/11	Rym. P	FORD UNITED	177	0 - 4	
26/11	Lge Cup 2	Lewes	165	3 - 3	Channell 19, Yaku 36 69
03/12	Lge Cup 2 rep	LEWES	112	0 - 1	
07/12	Rym. P	Boreham Wood	155	3 - 0	Ashe 15, Glynn 82, Allen 90
14/12	Rym. P	PURFLEET	191	1 - 0	Glynn 75
26/12	Rym. P	BASINGSTOKE TOWN	303	2 - 2	Glynn 5, Cook 67
28/12	Rym. P	St Albans City	606	3 - 1	Glynn 5, Yaku 83 90
04/01	Rym. P	BRAINTREE TOWN	232	2 - 3	Morley 71, Ashe 77
18/01	Rym. P	ENFIELD	224	3 - 3	Glynn 22[p] 87, Morley 34
25/01	Rym. P	Bedford Town	559	0 - 0	
08/02	Rym. P	Hitchin Town	334	3 - 2	Yaku 47 65, Kelly 89[p]
15/02	Rym. P	HENDON	217	0 - 1	
22/02	Rym. P	Grays Athletic	208	4 - 1	Ash 25, Yaku 28 88, Allan 75
25/02	Berks & BS QF	SLOUGH TOWN	n/k	3 - 1	Allen 48, Channell 63 74
01/03	Rym. P	HAMPTON & RICHMOND B.	232	1 - 1	Morley 5
04/03	Rym. P	Aldershot Town	2018	1 - 1	Morley 90
08/03	Rym. P	Kingstonian	323	0 - 2	
15/03	Rym. P	CANVEY ISLAND	291	1 - 1	Glynn 18
18/03	Rym. P	BISHOP'S STORTFORD	189	2 - 3	Cook 19 24
22/03	Rym. P	Heybridge Swifts	173	0 - 0	
25/03	Rym. P	Chesham United	151	0 - 0	
29/03	Rym. P	AYLESBURY UNITED	334	2 - 1	Cook 24, Nartey 28
01/04	Rym. P	HEYBRIDGE SWIFTS	178	2 - 2	Ashe 28, Webster 61
05/04	Rym. P	HAYES	271	1 - 1	Channell 10
08/04	Berks & BS SF	Windsor & Eton	n/k	5 - 0	Kelly 2, Yaku 6 48 59, Allen 78
12/04	Rym. P	Billericay Town	238	0 - 2	
15/04	Rym. P	Sutton United	446	2 - 2	O'Connor 59, Allen 61
19/04	Rym. P	SUTTON UNITED	257	4 - 1	Allen 10, Yaku 23 45, O'Connor 55
21/04	Rym. P	Basingstoke Town	308	2 - 3	Allen 13, Glynn 16
26/04	Rym. P	Bishop's Stortford	327	4 - 3	O'Connor 28, Allen 39 69, Yaku 55
29/04	Rym. P	HARROW BOROUGH	191	2 - 0	Cook 37, Yaku 61
03/05	Rym. P	BOREHAM WOOD	252	2 - 1	Kelly 45, Narty 55
05/05	Berks & BS F	Aylesbury United	n/k	4 - 1	Yaku(3), Allen (at Chesham United)

PLAYING SQUAD

Goalkeepers: Rob Bullivant (English Universities), Lee Carroll (Marlow), Daryl Pelton (Uxbridge)

Defenders: Danny Butler (British Airways), Alan Hamlet (UXbridge), Marc Leach (Boreham Wood), Craig Mc Intosh (Leighton T.), Dave (Sargent), Rene Street (Hemel Hempstead T.), Paul Watkins (Southall), Gary Williams (Uxbridge).

Midfield: Chris Gell (Wycombe Wanderers), Gavin Hart (Tring T.), Lee Holman (Southall), Kevin Knight (Enfield), Dave Nolan (Siouthall).

Forwards: Wayne Carter (Hayes), Daryl Craft (Harefield Utd), Rob Gilder (Beaconsfield SYCOB), Steve Hale (Slough T.), Martin Hook (Boreham Wood), Chris Moore (Uxbridge), Ben Porter (Kingsbury T.), Danny Yeoman (Uxbridge)

St ALBANS CITY

CLUB OFFICIALS

Chairman: John Gibson
President: Cllr Malcolm MacMillan
Vice Chairman: SteveCarroll
Secretary: Steve Eames c/o Club
Safety Officer: Rex Winn 0966 175124 (M)
Commercial Manager: Michele Sinclair

FOOTBALL MANAGEMENT TEAM

Manager: Gary Roberts & Steve Cook
Physio: Adie Blundell

FACT FILE

Formed: 1908
Nickname: The Saints
Colours: Yellow & blue
Change colours: Sky Blue
Midweek home matchday: Tuesday
Newsline: 09066 555822
Club Website:http://www.sacfc.co.uk
E-Mail: info@sacfc.co.uk

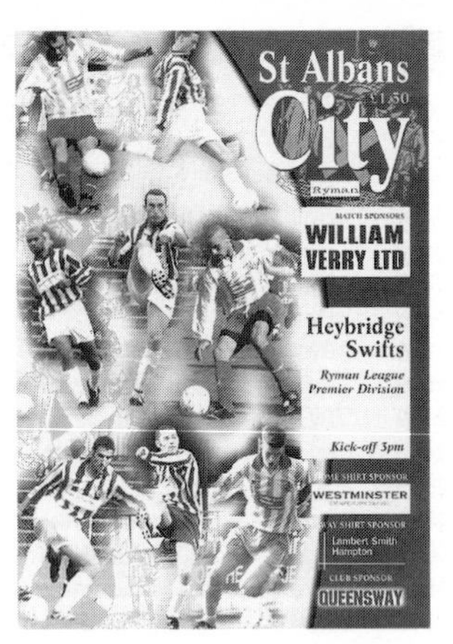

Programme: Pages: 32 Price: £1.50
Editor: T.B.A.
Local Press: St Albans & District Observer, Herts Advertiser
Local Radio: BBC Three Counties, Chiltern Radio, Oasis

GROUND: Clarence Park, York Rd, St Albans, Herts AL1 4PL Tel: 01727 864296
Directions: Left out of St Albans station - Clarence Pk 200yds ahead acrossHatfield Rd. M25, jct 21 to Noke Hotel island, straight on thru Chiswell Green towards St Albans, straight over 2 mini-r'bouts and one larger island, thru 2sets of lights and right at island at far end of city centre (St Peters St.) into Hatfield Rd, over mini-r'bout, left at 2nd lights into Clarence Rd, ground on left
Capacity: 6,000 Cover: 1,900 Seats: 904 Floodlights: Yes
Clubhouse: Open matchdays and available for functions. Manager:James Brewer
Tea bar within ground serves hot food
Club Shop: Club merchandise & League & non-League progs,magazines,videos etc
Managers:Barry Hillard c/o club

PREVIOUS **Leagues:** Herts County 08-10; Spartan 08-20; Athenian 20-23

CLUB RECORDS **Attendance:** 9,757 v Ferryhill Ath., FA Amtr Cup QF 27/2/26
Appearances: Phil Wood 900 (62-85)
Goalscorer: W H (Billy) Minter 356 (top scorer for 12 consecutive seasons 1920-32)
Win: 14-0 v Aylesbury United (H) Spartan Lge 19/10/12 **Defeat:** 0-11 v Wimbledon (H), Isthmian Lge 9/11/46.
Fee Paid: £6,000 for Paul Turner (Yeovil Town Aug 97) **Fee Received:** £92,750 for Dean Austin (Southend 90/Spurs 92)

BEST SEASON **FA Amateur Cup:** Semi final 22-23 24-25 25-26 69-70. **FA Trophy:** Semi-Final 1998-99 1-2 & 2-3 v Forest Green Rovers
FA Cup: 2nd Rd replay 68-69 (1-3 at Walsall after 1-1 draw), 80-81 (1-4 atTorquay after 1-1 draw), 96-97 (9-2 at Bristol City)

HONOURS: Isthmian Lg 23-24 26-27 27-28 (R-up 54-55 92-93), Div 1 85-86, Div 2 R-up 83-84, Lg Cup R-up 89-90, Res. Sect. R-up 48-49 60-61 61-62; Athenian Lg 20-21 21-22 (R-up 22-23); Spartan Lg 11-12 (R-up 12-13, East Div 09-10); Herts Co. Lg 09-10 (West Div 08-09, Aubrey Cup(res) 61-62); London Snr Cup 70-71 (R-up 69-70); AFA Snr Cup 33-34 (R-up 30-31 32-33 34-35); E Anglian Cup 92-93; Herts SnrCup(13) (R-up 10), Herts Snr Tphy 86-87, Herts Charity Cup(25) (R-up(18);Mithras Cup 64-65 71-72 (R-up 76-77); Wycombe F'lit Cup(2) 68-70; St AlbansHosp Cup 45-46; Hitchin Centenary Cup 70-71 (R-up 71-72); Victory Cup 25-26 27-28, Liege Cup 26-27; Billy Minter Invit. Cup (3) 90-93

Players progressing: A Grimsdell (Spurs 11), G Edmonds (Watford 14), R Burke(Man Utd 46), J Meadows (Watford 51), M Rose (Charlton 63), J Kinnear (Spurs 65), J Mitchell (Fulham 72), A Cockram (Brentford 88), D Austin (Southend 90),T Kelly (Stoke 90), M Danzey (Cambridge 92), D Williams (Brentford 93).

Back row left to right: Steve Cook (co-manager), Tom Upsher, Simon Martin, Ryan Moran, Derek Brown, Corey Campbell, Rob Smith, Richard Evans and Gary Roberts (co-manager). **Front row:** Richard Wilmot, Gary Wraight, Jon Rattle, Mike Bignall and Jimmy Sugrue.

Date	Comp.	Opponents	Att.	Score	Goalscorers
03/08	Herts CC QF	Ware	n/k	4 - 0	Martin, Gould, Townley, Crawshaw
17/08	Rym. P	FORD UNITED	326	3 - 2	Martin 16, Barr 28, De Souza 70
20/08	Rym. P	Aylesbury United	664	3 - 0	Castle 52, Martin 69, De Souza 83
24/08	Rym. P	Maidenhead United	295	1 - 0	Campbell 59
26/08	Rym. P	HEYBRIDGE SWIFTS	401	2 - 0	Challinor 41, Sippetts 83
31/08	Rym. P	Grays Athletic	364	1 - 0	Crawshaw 20
03/09	Rym. P	CANVEY ISLAND	707	2 - 1	Crawshaw 43, Smith 57
07/09	Rym. P	Harrow Borough	340	4 - 0	Crawshaw 30, Hollenbach 56, Sippetts 78, Martin 79
10/09	Rym. P	KINGSTONIAN	611	2 - 2	Martin 9 55
14/09	Rym. P	HITCHIN TOWN	751	0 - 1	
18/09	Rym. P	Enfield	208	1 - 0	Martin 82
21/09	Rym. P	BOREHAM WOOD	703	2 - 0	Martin 44, Kean 90
24/09	Rym. P	Hayes	269	0 - 3	
28/09	**F.A.C.** Q2	WINGATE & FINCHLEY	532	2 - 0	Crawshaw 31, De Souza 54
01/10	Rym. P	PURFLEET	410	2 - 2	Callinor 85, Townsley 90
05/10	Rym. P	Bedford Town	763	0 - 2	
08/10	Herts SC 1	WARE	158	6 - 0	De Souza(3), Martin, Kean, Sippetts
12/10	**F.A.C.** Q3	CHELMSFORD CITY	839	1 - 0	De Souza 82
19/10	Rym. P	BILLERICAY TOWN	718	1 - 1	De Souza 72
22/10	Rym. P	Bishop's Stortford	388	2 - 0	Browne 55 84
26/10	**F.A.C.** Q4	AFC Sudbury	780	2 - 1	Moran 83, De Souza 89
02/11	Rym. P	BRAINTREE TOWN	438	2 - 4	Challinor 65, Campbell 89
05/11	Rym. P	Sutton United	412	4 - 2	Smith 9 12 47, Challinor 82
09/11	Rym. P	CHESHAM UNITED	591	1 - 0	Browne 25
16/11	**F.A.C.** 1	Stockport County	3303	1 - 4	Brown 68
20/11	Herts SC 2	Greenacres (Hemel)	107	1 - 0	Challinor
23/11	Rym. P	HAMPTON & RICHMOND B.	458	2 - 0	De Souza 52 77
30/11	**F.A.T.** 2	HAYES	468	0 - 1	
03/12	Lge Cup 2	BOGNOR REGIS TOWN	134	3 - 2	Crawshaw 8, Martin 89, Oakes 90
07/12	Rym. P	Basingstoke Town	387	1 - 3	Brown 50
10/12	Lge Cup 3	Ashford Town (Middx)	n/k	2 - 1	Martin 7[p], Challinor 44
14/12	Rym. P	Ford United	155	1 - 1	Oakes 50
21/12	Rym. P	ALDERSHOT TOWN	1538	2 - 0	Campbell 22, Castle 27
28/12	Rym. P	MAIDENHEAD UNITED	606	1 - 3	Crawshaw 2
14/01	Herts SC QF	Berkhamsted Town	n/k	2 - 3	Campbell 56, Challinor 70
18/01	Rym. P	HARROW BOROUGH	452	1 - 0	Crawshaw 56
21/01	Lge Cup 4	DULWICH HAMLET	113	1 - 2	De Souza 40
25/01	Rym. P	Hitchin Town	588	2 - 1	Martin 60, De Souza 86
28/01	Rym. P	Billericay Town	287	0 - 1	
04/02	Rym. P	ENFIELD	215	0 - 0	
04/02	Herts CC SF	Hemel Hempstead Town	n/k	0 - 3	
08/02	Rym. P	HAYES	457	1 - 1	Lodge 44
15/02	Rym. P	Boreham Wood	268	0 - 1	
18/02	Rym. P	Kingstonian	229	2 - 0	Moran 39, Young 68
22/02	Rym. P	BEDFORD TOWN	613	1 - 2	Martin 72
25/02	Rym. P	Hendon	276	2 - 0	Martin 62, Young 90
01/03	Rym. P	Purfleet	271	0 - 1	
05/03	Rym. P	AYLESBURY UNITED	249	3 - 1	Crawshaw 9, Martin 77 80
08/03	Rym. P	BISHOP'S STORTFORD	428	3 - 2	Young 40, Kean 76, Naylor 90
11/03	Rym. P	Heybridge Swifts	144	3 - 3	Cursey 21[og], Crawshaw 35[p], De Souza 62
15/03	Rym. P	Chesham United	320	3 - 1	Martin 30 32, De Souza 40
22/03	Rym. P	SUTTON UNITED	466	2 - 1	Brown 47 84
29/03	Rym. P	Braintree Town	324	2 - 2	De Souza 61 74
05/04	Rym. P	Canvey Island	703	1 - 6	Campbell 10
12/04	Rym. P	GRAYS ATHLETIC	452	1 - 2	Brown 28
19/04	Rym. P	Aldershot Town	2883	1 - 5	Naylor 10
23/04	Rym. P	HENDON	257	1 - 4	Martin 18
26/04	Rym. P	Hampton & Richmond Bor.	210	3 - 2	Makail-Smith 32, Martin 36, Deacon 56
03/05	Rym. P	BASINGSTOKE TOWN	442	1 - 2	Martin 7

PLAYING SQUAD

Goalkeepers: Richard Wilmot (Hendon)

Defenders: Derek Brown (Bedford T.), Corey Campbell (Gravesend & Northfleet), Ryan Moran (Luton T.), Dominic Taylor (Basingstoke T.), Leon Townley (Aldershot T.).

Midfield: Steve Castle (Stevenage Borough), Jon Challinor (Kalamazoo Kingdom U.S.A.), Richard Evans (Chertsey T.), Lee Gledhill (Barnet), Matthew Glynn (Maidenhead Utd), Mark Graham (Canvey Island), Robbie Keen (Hitchin T.), Craik Mackail-Smith (Youth Team), Scott Oakes (Shelbourne), Rob Smith (Baldock T.), Martin Young (Harlow T.),

Forwards: Gary Crawshaw (Farnborough T.), Miguel de Souza (Farnborough T.), Nic McDonnell (Crawley T.), Simon Martin (Hucknall T.), Graeme Tomlinson (Bedford T.)

SUTTON UNITED

CLUB OFFICIALS
Chairman: Bruce Elliott
President: Andrew W Letts
Secretary: Dave Farebrother, Borough Sports Ground
Tel No: 07734 719936
Press Officer: Tony Dolbear
Tel: Mobile 07966 507023

FOOTBALL MANAGEMENT TEAM
Manager: John Rains
Asst.Man: Tony Rains **Coach:** Micky Cook
Physio: Jimmy Hendrie
Res Team Manager: Phil Dunne

FACT FILE
Formed: 1898 Nickname: The U's
Sponsors: Securicor
Colours:Amber & chocolate
Change colours: Green & white/black/black
Midweek matchday: Tuesday
Reserve League: Suburban League
Local Press: Sutton Advertiser, Sutton Guardian, Sutton Independent, Sutton Comet
Local Radio: Thames Radio, County Sound

2002-2003
Captain: Scott Corbett
Leading Scorers: Danny Bolt & Matt Fowler
Player 0f the Year: Ryan Palmer & Nick Bailey (Young Player)

Pages: 48 Price: £1.50
Editor: Mackrory - Lyall Reynolds
Email: sutton editor@hotmail.com

Other club publications:
'Touchliner' (Supporters' Club)

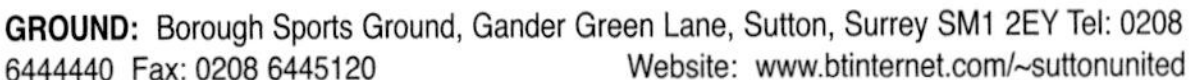

GROUND: Borough Sports Ground, Gander Green Lane, Sutton, Surrey SM1 2EY Tel: 0208 6444440 Fax: 0208 6445120 Website: www.btinternet.com/~suttonunited
Directions: Gander Green Lane runs between A232 (Cheam Road - turn by Sutton Cricket Club) and A217 (Oldfields Road - turn at`Gander' PH lights). Ground opposite `The Plough' 50 yards from West Sutton BR station. Bus 413 passes ground
Capacity: 7,032 **Seated**: 765 **Terracing - Covered:** 1,250 **Uncovered:** 5,000
Clubhouse: Open every day, food. Available for hire with five function rooms
Club Shop: Open matchdays selling a full range of souvenirs, etc, contact Tony Cove via club

PREVIOUS **Leagues:** Sutton Junior, Southern Sub 10-21, Athenian 21-63, Isthmian 63-86, 91-99, GMVC 86-91, 99-00
Names: Sutton Association, Sutton Guild Rovers **Grounds:** Western Road, Manor Lane, London Road, The Find.

CLUB RECORDS **Attendance:** 14,000 v Leeds United,FA Cup 4th Rd 24/1/70
Victory: 11-1 v Clapton 66, & leatherhead 82-83 **Defeat:** 13-0 v Barking 25-26
Scorer: Paul McKinnon (279) **Appearances:** Larry Pritchard 781 (65-84)
Fee Paid: to Malmo FF for Paul McKinnon 83 **Fee Received:** £100,000 for Efan Ekoku (Bournemouth 90)

BEST SEASON **FA Amateur Cup:** Runners-up 62-63 68-69; SF 28-29 36-37 67-68 **FA Trophy:** Runners-up 80-81; SF 92-93,99-00 **FA Cup:** 4th Rd-69-70, 0-6 v Leeds Utd (H); 88-89, 0-8 v Norwich C.(A), 3rd Rd 87-88 v Middlesbrough 1-1, 0-1, 93-94 v Notts Co(A)2-3

HONOURS Bob Lord Trophy 90-91; **Isthmian League** 66-67 84-86 98-99 R-up 67-68 70-71 81-82, Lge Cup (3) 82-84 85-86 97-98 R-up 79-80; Loctite Cup 91-92; Carlton Cup 95-96; **Athenian Lge** 27-28 45-46 57-58 R-up 46-47, Lg Cup 45-46 55-56 61-62 62-63, Res Sec 61-62 R-up 32-33; Anglo Italian Semi-Pro Cup 79 R-up 80 82; London Snr Cup 57-58 82-83; London Charity Cup 69-70 R-up 67-68 68-69 72-73; Surrey Snr Cup x15 R-up x9; Surrey Premie. Cup x5 R-up x6; Surrey Jnr Cup R-up 09-10; Surrey Snr Char. Sh. x3 R-up x6; Surrey Interm Char. Cup 31-32 R-up 34-35 38-39; Dylon Char. Sh. 84 R-up 80 82 83 85; Groningen Yth tournament 83 85 R-up 79 81 89 91; John Ullman Invit. Cup 88-89

Past Players progressing: Numerous including the following since 1980 - S Galloway (C Palace 84), P McKinnon (Blackburn 86), R Fearon (Ipswich 87), PHarding (Notts Co), E Ekoku (Bournemouth 91), M Golley (Maidstone), A Barnes (C Palace 91), P Rogers (Sheff U 92), S Massey (C Palace 92), A & R Scott (Sheff U 93), O Morah(Cambridge 94), M Watson(West Ham 95), E Hutchinson (Brentford 2000),T.Hutchinson(Dundee)

L-R - Back Row: Micky Cook (coach), Paul Honey, Ryan Palmer, Matt Hanlon, Mark Watson, Tom Dunn, John Rains (manager), Jamie Ribolla, Scott Corbett, Danny Hodges, Matt Gray, Darren Beale, Tony Rains (asst. manager).
Front: Ben Shannon, Nick Bailey, Mike Hollands, Danny Bolt, Matt Fowler, Lewis Gonsalves, Dave Timothy. **Photo**: Garry Letts

Date	Comp.	Opponents	Att.	Score	Goalscorers
17/08	Rym. P	HAMPTON & RICHMOND B.	543	1 - 0	Watson 29
20/08	Rym. P	Grays Athletic	329	0 - 0	
24/08	Rym. P	Bedford Town	559	1 - 2	Fowler 34
26/08	Rym. P	HARROW BOROUGH	491	3 - 0	Fowler 61, Hodges 70, Watson 79
31/08	Rym. P	Canvey Island	779	1 - 1	Bolt 11
03/09	Rym. P	FORD UNITED	463	4 - 1	Holt 29, Watson 52 66, Harvey 77[og]
07/09	Rym. P	Billericay Town	559	0 - 2	
10/09	Rym. P	CHESHAM UNITED	484	3 - 2	Fowler 66 81, Bolt 73[p]
14/09	Rym. P	KINGSTONIAN	821	1 - 1	Gonsalves 34
17/09	Rym. P	Purfleet	299	2 - 0	Fowler 37, Watson 82
21/09	Rym. P	AYLESBURY UNITED	588	3 - 2	Corbett 32, Bolt 43, Bailey 87
24/09	Rym. P	Heybridge Swifts	208	3 - 1	Bolt 45, Fowler 65, Bailey 89
28/09	**F.A.C.** Q2	Heybridge Swifts	310	1 - 1	Watson 21
01/10	**F.A.C.** Q2 rep	HEYBRIDGE SWIFTS	385	1 - 2	Fowler 29
05/10	Rym. P	Hayes	394	2 - 2	Bailey, Fowler
19/10	Rym. P	Hitchin Town	456	0 - 2	
22/10	Rym. P	HENDON	437	2 - 3	Bailey 8, Bolt 33
26/10	Rym. P	Basingstoke Town	367	0 - 1	
02/11	**F.A.T.** 1	HARROW BOROUGH	332	2 - 1	Corbett 34, Bolt 70
05/11	Rym. P	ST ALBANS CITY	412	2 - 4	Gonsalves 34, Watson 75
09/11	Rym. P	Enfield	101	4 - 1	Gonsalves 23, Corbett 45, Bolt 60[p], Watson 77
16/11	Rym. P	HITCHIN TOWN	487	3 - 1	Bolt 20 42, Honey 84
23/11	Rym. P	BOREHAM WOOD	506	3 - 2	Palmer 25, Bolt 33, Bailey 88
26/11	Rym. P	BISHOP'S STORTFORD	419	2 - 1	Bailey 79, Fowler 84
30/11	**F.A.T.** 2	Basingstoke Town	529	2 - 0	Fowler 32 75
07/12	Rym. P	Braintree Town	252	1 - 0	Fowler 66
14/12	Rym. P	Hampton & Richmond Bor.	292	3 - 1	Watson 18, Akuamoah 62, Gray 73
17/12	Lge Cup 2	Chesham United	71	3 - 2	Fowler 57, Corbett 108, Gray 112
26/12	Rym. P	Aldershot Town	2564	2 - 3	Fowler 56 88
28/12	Rym. P	BEDFORD TOWN	719	0 - 0	
04/01	Rym. P	Harrow Borough	279	1 - 0	Corbett 32
11/01	**F.A.T.** 3	HAVANT & WATERLOOVILLE	645	1 - 3	Watson 82
18/01	Rym. P	BILLERICAY TOWN	537	1 - 2	Bailey 84
21/01	Lge Cup 3	Aylesbury United	206	2 - 3	Watson 6, Bailey 89
25/01	Rym. P	Kingstonian	902	1 - 2	Bolt 27[p]
28/01	Surrey SC 4	Walton & Hersham	110	3 - 1	Fowler 32 69, Watson 35
08/02	Rym. P	HEYBRIDGE SWIFTS	514	2 - 0	Bolt 38[p], Fowler 88
15/02	Rym. P	Aylesbury United	421	4 - 0	Bolt 6 76, Fowler 24, Bailey 60
01/03	Rym. P	Bishop's Stortford	365	0 - 1	
04/03	Surrey SC QF	CARSHALTON ATHLETIC	438	2 - 0	Fowler, Bolt
08/03	Rym. P	Hendon	273	2 - 0	Fowler 47, Bolt 69
11/03	Rym. P	GRAYS ATHLETIC	422	2 - 0	Hodges 30, Watson 55
15/03	Rym. P	ENFIELD	533	2 - 1	Watson 49, Bolt 85
18/03	Rym. P	PURFLEET	401	1 - 1	Bolt 68[p]
22/03	Rym. P	St Albans City	466	1 - 2	Palmer 19
29/03	Rym. P	BASINGSTOKE TOWN	567	1 - 1	Watson 21
01/04	Surrey SC SF	Dulwich Hamlet	228	2 - 1	Bailey, Bolt[p]
05/04	Rym. P	Ford United	140	4 - 3	Bolt 43, Bailey 45 46, Gray 54
08/04	Rym. P	HAYES	393	2 - 1	Hanlan 43 67
12/04	Rym. P	CANVEY ISLAND	643	0 - 2	
15/04	Rym. P	MAIDENHEAD UNITED	446	2 - 2	Jeffrey 58[og], Bailey 85
19/04	Rym. P	Maidenhead United	257	1 - 4	Watson 47
21/04	Rym. P	ALDERSHOT TOWN	2002	1 - 1	Bailey 61
26/04	Rym. P	Boreham Wood	190	0 - 3	
29/04	Rym. P	Chesham United	212	0 - 2	
03/05	Rym. P	BRAINTREE TOWN	535	3 - 1	Watson 3, Bailey 80 83
07/05	Surrey SC F	Kingstonian	775	2 - 1	Jones[og], Watson (at Metropolitan Police)

PLAYING SQUAD

Goalkeepers: **Andy Pape** (Harrow Borough)

Defenders: Danny Brooker (Carshalton Ath.), Darren Beale (Youth Team), Nick Drew (Fulham), Lewis Gonzalves (Youth Team), Danny Hodges (Tooting & Mitcham Utd), MIke Hollands (Brentford), Craig Howard (Youth Team), Ryan Palmer (Brighton).

Midfield: Danny Bolt (Canvey Island), Craig Brown (Leyton Orient), Scott Corbett (Farnborough T.), Paul Honey (Youth Team), Michael Mison (St.Albans City), Graham Tydeman (Youth Team).

Forwards: Edilee Akuamoah (Bromley), Nick Bailey (Youth Team), Matt Fowler (Carshalton Ath.), Matthew Hanlon (Corinthian Casuals), Mark Watson (Aldershot T.)

THURROCK

Pages: 60 Price: £1.50
Editor: Norman Posner (01708 458301 H)
Local Press: Romford, Thurrock Recorder, Thurrock Gazette
Local Radio: Essex Radio, BBC Radio Essex

CLUB OFFICIALS

Chairman: Grant Beglan
V/Chairman/Chief Exec: Tommy Smith
Secretary: Norman Posner, 1 Chase House Gardens, Hornchurch, Essex, RM11 2PJ, Tel: 01708 458301
Match Secretary/Press Officer: Norman Posner
Comm Mger: Tony Joy (01375 392906)

FOOTBALL MANAGEMENT TEAM

Manager: Colin McBride
Asst Manager: Jimmy McFarlane
Coach: Ronnie Hanley
Physio: Michelle Sheehan

FACT FILE

Founded: 1985
Nickname: Fleet
Sponsors: Sofa Bed Shop,Shopping Centre and T&P Lead Roofing Ltd.
Colours:Yellow &green/green/yellow & green
Change colours: All white
Midweek home matchday: Tuesday
Reserve's League: None

2002-2003

Captain: Jimmy McFarland
Top Scorer: Tresor Kandol 14
Player of the Year: Mark Goodfellow

GROUND: Thurrock Hotel, Ship Lane, Grays, Essex. 01708 865492 Fax: 01708 868863
Webside: www.purfleetfootballclub.com
Directions: M25 or A13 to Dartford tunnel r'bout. Ground is fifty yards on right down Ship Lane. Nearest station is Purfleet, two miles from ground
Capacity: 4,500 Cover: 1,000 Seats: 300 Floodlights: Yes
Clubhouse: Steward: Tommy South
Club Shop: Selling programmes & magazines. Contact Tommy South (01708 868901)

PREVIOUS **League:** Essex Senior 85-89. **Names**: Purfleet 1985-2003 **Grounds:** None

CLUB RECORDS **Attendance:** 2,572 v West Ham United, friendly 1998.
Goalscorer: George Georgiou 106. **Appearances:** Jimmy McFarlane 488
Win: 10-0 v Stansted (H) 86-87, v East Ham Utd (A) 87-88 (both Essex Senior League)
Defeat: 0-6 v St Leonards Stamco(A), FA Trophy 96-97. 0-6 v Sutton United(H) Isthmian Lge 97-98

BEST SEASON **FA Cup:** Fourth Qualifying Round Replay 95-96 (lost 1-3 away to Rushden & D)
FA Trophy: Second Round Prop 95-96 (lost 1-2 away to Macclesfield Tn)

HONOURS: Isthmian Lg Div 2 91-92 Div 1 R-up 93-94, Div 2 Nth R-up 88-89, Associate Members Tphy 91-92; Essex Snr Lg 87-88 (Lg Cup (2) 86-88; Essex Snr. Cup R-up 97-98, 99-00, Stanford Charity Cup 87-88 (R-up 85-86); Essex Thames-Side Trophy 94-95; Essex Bus Houses Sen L/Cup 93-94; F Budden Trophy 94-95; Essex & HertsBorder Comb R-up 94-95; Full Members Cup R-up 99-00, 00-01.

Players progressing to Football League: Paul Cobb & Lee Williams (Leyton O.)

L-R Back Row: John Purdie, Mark Goodfellow, Tresor Kandol, Alex O'Reilly, Jimmy McFarlane, Cliff Akurang.
Front Row: Martyn Lawrence, Jon Keeling, Paul Linger, Callum Pettigrove (mascot), Kris Lee, Gary Howard.
Photo: Alan Coomes

Date	Comp.	Opponents	Att.	Score	Goalscorers
17/08	Rym. P	MAIDENHEAD UNITED	323	1 - 0	Vaughan 20
20/08	Rym. P	Heybridge Swifts	170	2 - 0	Linger 38 66
24/08	Rym. P	Hampton & Richmond Borough	183	1 - 1	Bowes 29
26/08	Rym. P	BEDFORD TOWN	317	3 - 0	Akurang 56, Lawrence 60, Jackman 63[og]
31/08	Rym. P	Boreham Wood	138	0 - 0	
03/09	Rym. P	HENDON	192	1 - 0	Vaughan 72
07/09	Rym. P	BISHOP'S STORTFORD	232	2 - 1	Linger 62, Vaughan 72
10/09	Rym. P	Hayes	174	2 - 1	Akurang 10, Bowes 30
14/09	Rym. P	Braintree Town	250	0 - 0	
17/09	Rym. P	SUTTON UNITED	299	0 - 2	
21/09	Rym. P	Enfield	87	0 - 1	
24/09	Rym. P	BILLERICAY TOWN	362	0 - 0	
28/09	FA Cup Q2	Wootton Blue Cross	121	4 - 0	Georgiou 5[p], Bowes 22, Akurang 23, Simpson 85
01/10	Rym. P	St Albans City	410	2 - 2	Georgiou 16, Simpson 84
05/10	Rym. P	BASINGSTOKE TOWN	302	1 - 0	Linger 20
12/10	FA Cup Q3	Flackwell Heath	n/k	0 - 0	
19/10	Rym. P	Canvey Island	766	2 - 2	Allen 52, Linger 62
22/10	Rym. P	HITCHIN TOWN	221	0 - 1	
26/10	Rym. P	AYLESBURY UNITED	372	1 - 0	Linger 25
01/11	Rym. P	Billericay Town	439	3 - 1	Keeling 11 46, Linger 87[p]
09/11	Rym. P	Kingstonian	452	1 - 0	Keeling 22
16/11	Rym. P	CANVEY ISLAND	608	3 - 2	Linger 11, Keeling 66 86
19/11	Essex SC 3	East Thurrock United	n/k	1 - 2	
23/11	Rym. P	CHESHAM UNITED	241	6 - 0	Lee 8 64, Bowes 77 89, Keeling 41, Edwards 50
30/11	FA Trophy 2	TONBRIDGE ANGELS	244	3 - 2	Bowes 8, Pavey 10[og], Keeling 19
02/12	Lge Cup 2	Ford United	65	0 - 3	
07/12	Rym. P	Aldershot Town	2018	0 - 1	
14/12	Rym. P	Maidenhead United	191	0 - 1	
21/12	Rym. P	HARROW BOROUGH	235	4 - 2	Keeling 40, Chandler 45[p] 52[p], Kandol 48
26/12	Rym. P	Grays Athletic	490	1 - 2	Kandol 70
28/12	Rym. P	HAMPTON & RICHMOND BOROUGH	256	5 - 2	Kandol 11 27 38 48, Bowes 77
04/01	Rym. P	Bedford Town	573	0 - 2	
14/01	FA Trophy 3	GRAYS ATHLETIC	325	1 - 2	Lee 5
18/01	Rym. P	Bishop's Stortford	310	2 - 2	Wall 20[og], Kandol 40[p]
25/01	Rym. P	BRAINTREE TOWN	247	1 - 1	Akurang 90
15/02	Rym. P	ENFIELD	241	5 - 2	Lee 37 79, Allen 46, Chandler 73, Keeling 88
18/02	Rym. P	HAYES	139	1 - 2	Kandol 21
22/02	Rym. P	Basingstoke Town	311	1 - 2	Kandor 76
01/03	Rym. P	ST ALBANS CITY	271	1 - 0	Keeling 40
08/03	Rym. P	Hitchin Town	255	1 - 1	Bowes 87
15/03	Rym. P	KINGSTONIAN	301	0 - 1	
18/03	Rym. P	Sutton United	401	1 - 1	Akurang 21[p]
22/03	Rym. P	Aylesbury United	402	1 - 1	Akurang 58
29/03	Rym. P	FORD UNITED	237	2 - 2	Linger 23, Kandol 45
05/04	Rym. P	Hendon	235	2 - 1	Lee 2, Pashley 62
12/04	Rym. P	BOREHAM WOOD	178	0 - 0	
15/04	Rym. P	HEYBRIDGE SWIFTS	156	1 - 2	Akurang 2
19/04	Rym. P	Harrow Borough	148	2 - 1	Keeling 20, Kandol 57
21/04	Rym. P	GRAYS ATHLETIC	301	3 - 1	Bowes 20, Pashley 60, Kandol 74
23/04	Rym. P	Ford United	106	1 - 1	Linger 22
26/04	Rym. P	Chesham United	223	1 - 1	Kandol 25[p]
03/05	Rym. P	ALDERSHOT TOWN	728	1 - 2	Kandol 50

PLAYING SQUAD

Goalkeepers: Paul Gothard (Dagenham & Redbridge), Chris Harvey (Ford Utd), Steve Mead (Concord Rangers), Alex O'Reilly (Bristol Rovers).

Defenders: Michael Basham (Chelmsford City), Dean Chandler (Woking), David Hadrava (Colchester Utd), Gary Howard (Boreham Wood), Jim McFarlane (Concord Rangers), Steve Pashley (East Thurrock Utd).

Midfield: Lee Allen (Enfield), Greg Barry (Millwall), Mark Cartlidge (East Thurrock Utd), Dave Collis (Ford Utd), Mark Goodfellow (Youth Team), Jon Keeling (Tilbury), Martin Ling (Leyton Orient), Paul Linger (Billericay T.), Danny Lyle (Dartford).

Forwards: Cliff Akurang (Hitchen T.), Martin Buglione (Dartford), Tresor Kandol (Chesham Utd), Martyn Lawrence (Concord Rangers), Kris Lee (Chelmsford City)

BOREHAM WOOD

Match Facts 2002-03

Date	Comp.	Opponents	Att.	Score	Goalscorers
10/08	Herts CC 1	Cheshunt	n/k	2 - 1	
17/08	Rym. P	Chesham United	283	1 - 3	Dixon 86
19/08	Rym. P	BILLERICAY TOWN	222	1 - 3	Douglas 85
26/08	Rym. P	Hayes	306	0 - 0	
31/08	Rym. P	PURFLEET	138	0 - 0	
03/09	Rym. P	Braintree Town	238	1 - 0	Dixon 18
07/09	Rym. P	Bedford Town	404	4 - 0	Meah 16, Dixon 27 57, Jones 30
09/09	Rym. P	HITCHIN TOWN	219	2 - 2	Dixon 46, Jones 71
14/09	Rym. P	HARROW BOROUGH	159	2 - 2	Dixon 48, Meah 65
17/09	Rym. P	Aylesbury United	356	3 - 3	Browne 45, Dixon 78, Meah 90
21/09	Rym. P	St Albans City	703	0 - 2	
23/09	Rym. P	FORD UNITED	121	3 - 2	Dixon 6 34 50
29/09	FA Cup Q2	Maidstone United	937	5 - 2	Meah 9 62, Dixon 18 35, Forrester 87
01/10	Rym. P	Basingstoke Town	252	1 - 1	Meah 47
05/10	Rym. P	HAMPTON & RICHMOND BOR.	170	0 - 0	
12/10	FA Cup Q3	KINGSTONIAN	n/k	0 - 0	
14/10	Herts CC QF	BISHOP'S STORTFORD	138	1 - 2	
19/10	Rym. P	Heybridge Swifts	217	0 - 1	
21/10	Rym. P	CANVEY ISLAND	302	1 - 3	Honeyball 77
26/10	FA Cup Q4	Bishop's Stortford	969	1 - 1	Boyle-Renner 31
28/10	FA Cup Q4 rep	BISHOP'S STORTFORD	903	4 - 1	Grime 8, Boyle-Renner 25, Dixon 46, Browne 90
02/11	FA Trophy 1	Bognor Regis Town	306	0 - 2	
04/11	Rym. P	ALDERSHOT TOWN	439	0 - 1	
09/11	Rym. P	Grays Athletic	255	1 - 2	Marshall 60
13/11	Rym. P	Hendon	194	2 - 0	Kodra 27, Forrester 88
16/11	FA Cup 1	Torquay United	2739	0 - 5	
19/11	Herts SC 2	Broxbourne Borough V & E	n/k	0 - 0	Lost 3 5 after pens.
23/11	Rym. P	Sutton United	506	2 - 3	Forrester 9 48
30/11	Rym. P	ENFIELD	178	2 - 1	Parker 26, Dixon 58
02/12	Rym. P	KINGSTONIAN	168	2 - 1	Dixon 80, Meah 90
07/12	Rym. P	MAIDENHEAD UNITED	155	0 - 3	
10/12	Lge Cup 2	Horsham	n/k	3 - 1	Forrester 19 42 85
14/12	Rym. P	CHESHAM UNITED	166	0 - 0	
17/12	Lge Cup 3	Hitchin Town	102	0 - 4	
21/12	Rym. P	Bishop's Stortford	318	4 - 1	Forrester 28[p] 37 58[p], Browne 87
28/12	Rym. P	Kingstonian	407	0 - 0	
04/01	Rym. P	HAYES	214	2 - 0	Dixon 17, Forrester 51
18/01	Rym. P	BEDFORD TOWN	304	0 - 1	
25/01	Rym. P	Harrow Borough	226	0 - 2	
01/02	Rym. P	Aldershot Town	1748	0 - 1	
08/02	Rym. P	Ford United	102	1 - 1	Dixon 80
15/02	Rym. P	ST ALBANS CITY	268	1 - 0	Stirling 28
22/02	Rym. P	Hampton & Richmond Borough	204	4 - 0	Ball 31, Honeyball 49, Dixon 51 76
01/03	Rym. P	BASINGSTOKE TOWN	152	1 - 5	Forrester 2
03/03	Rym. P	HEYBRIDGE SWIFTS	143	0 - 0	
08/03	Rym. P	Canvey Island	471	0 - 1	
15/03	Rym. P	GRAYS ATHLETIC	157	0 - 2	
18/03	Rym. P	Billericay Town	170	0 - 0	
25/03	Rym. P	Hitchin Town	202	1 - 2	Dixon 34
29/03	Rym. P	HENDON	238	1 - 1	Dixon 44
05/04	Rym. P	BRAINTREE TOWN	164	1 - 2	Catley 12[og]
12/04	Rym. P	Purfleet	178	0 - 0	
19/04	Rym. P	BISHOP'S STORTFORD	213	1 - 1	Imber 2
21/04	Rym. P	Enfield	117	0 - 1	
26/04	Rym. P	SUTTON UNITED	190	3 - 0	Findley 13 60
28/04	Rym. P	AYLESBURY UNITED	292	1 - 2	Nabil 36
03/05	Rym. P	Maidenhead United	252	1 - 2	Honeyball 80

CHESHAM

Match Facts 2002-03

Date	Comp.	Opponents	Att.	Score	Goalscorers
17/08	Rym. P	BOREHAM WOOD	283	3 - 1	Scarlett 11, Capone 37, Dogbe 80
20/08	Rym. P	Maidenhead United	277	0 - 5	
24/08	Rym. P	Heybridge Swifts	160	0 - 0	
26/08	Rym. P	HAMPTON & RICHMOND BOR.	251	1 - 0	Nwokeji 59
31/08	Rym. P	Bedford Town	547	4 - 0	Kandol 20 80, Scarlett 75, Hunter 82
03/09	Rym. P	HARROW BOROUGH	332	1 - 1	Hunter 75
07/09	Rym. P	BRAINTREE TOWN	304	1 - 1	Cooper 86[p]
10/09	Rym. P	Sutton United	484	2 - 3	Doghe 32, Hunter 44[p]
14/09	Rym. P	Bishop's Stortford	356	1 - 2	Hunter 16
17/09	Rym. P	HAYES	307	2 - 3	Scarlett 17, Kandol 39
21/09	Rym. P	Billericay Town	507	0 - 1	
24/09	Rym. P	BASINGSTOKE TOWN	220	3 - 2	Hay 36, Kandol 57, Hunter 79
28/09	FA Cup Q2	Walton & Hersham	228	0 - 1	
01/10	Rym. P	Hitchin Town	247	1 - 1	Dogbe 90
05/10	Rym. P	ENFIELD	354	2 - 2	Cooper 44[p], Hunter 66
19/10	Rym. P	Aldershot Town	1770	2 - 1	Capone 21, Hay 78
22/10	Rym. P	FORD UNITED	163	2 - 2	Neill 54, Hay 75
26/10	Rym. P	Hampton & Richmond Borough	185	3 - 1	Hay 3, Sinclair 24, Kandol 35
02/11	Rym. P	ALDERSHOT TOWN	671	1 - 3	Kandol 62
09/11	Rym. P	St Albans City	591	0 - 1	
12/11	Rym. P	Kingstonian	373	1 - 5	Hay 10
23/11	Rym. P	Purfleet	241	0 - 6	
30/11	FA Trophy 2	WALTON & HERSHAM	243	0 - 0	
03/12	FA Trophy 2 rep	Walton & Hersham	133	1 - 0	Hay 51
07/12	Rym. P	HENDON	293	1 - 1	Clarke 56
14/12	Rym. P	Boreham Wood	166	0 - 0	
17/12	Lge Cup 2	SUTTON UNITED	71	2 - 3	Matata 46, Fontenelle 110
21/12	Rym. P	CANVEY ISLAND	305	2 - 4	Hackett 66, Hay 73
26/12	Rym. P	Aylesbury United	802	1 - 2	Clarke 30
28/12	Rym. P	HEYBRIDGE SWIFTS	278	3 - 0	Hay 14, Bent 41, Scarlett 86
14/01	FA Trophy 3	Woking	1336	0 - 3	
18/01	Rym. P	Braintree Town	290	2 - 1	Abbott 4, Scarlett 63
25/01	Rym. P	BISHOP'S STORTFORD	316	3 - 1	Scarlett 5 42, Cooper 77[p]
08/02	Rym. P	Basingstoke Town	407	2 - 1	Bent 29, Joe 66
15/02	Rym. P	BILLERICAY TOWN	242	0 - 2	
22/02	Rym. P	Enfield	111	0 - 1	
25/02	Berks & BS QF	Burnham	60	1 - 1	Bowden-Haase 33
01/03	Rym. P	HITCHIN TOWN	272	2 - 1	Cooper 74[p], Bowdenhafe 76
04/03	Berks & BS QF rep	BURNHAM	101	2 - 2	Bowden-Hasse 30, Lewis 51[og] Lost 3 4 after pens
08/03	Rym. P	Ford United	68	0 - 2	
11/03	Rym. P	Hayes	173	0 - 1	
15/03	Rym. P	ST ALBANS CITY	320	1 - 3	Fewings 68
22/03	Rym. P	Grays Athletic	225	0 - 1	
25/03	Rym. P	MAIDENHEAD UNITED	151	0 - 0	
29/03	Rym. P	KINGSTONIAN	284	0 - 4	
05/04	Rym. P	Harrow Borough	220	0 - 3	
08/04	Rym. P	GRAYS ATHLETIC	106	2 - 1	Douglas 14 18
12/04	Rym. P	BEDFORD TOWN	333	1 - 3	Scarlett 70
19/04	Rym. P	Canvey Island	331	1 - 4	Cooper 44
21/04	Rym. P	AYLESBURY UNITED	589	1 - 3	Fewings 2
26/04	Rym. P	PURFLEET	223	1 - 1	Douglas 75
29/04	Rym. P	SUTTON UNITED	212	2 - 0	Douglas 5, Fewings 89
03/05	Rym. P	Hendon	362	1 - 0	Cooper 83[p]

ENFIELD

Match Facts 2002-03

Date	Comp.	Opponents	Att.	Score	Goalscorers
17/08	Rym. P	HENDON	159	0 - 0	
20/08	Rym. P	Harrow Borough	203	0 - 2	
24/08	Rym. P	Ford United	98	1 - 3	Armstrong 37[p]
26/08	Rym. P	GRAYS ATHLETIC	135	1 - 1	Kyriacou 75
31/08	Rym. P	Aylesbury United	521	1 - 4	Waugh 19
04/09	Rym. P	ALDERSHOT TOWN	395	1 - 2	Traori 31
07/09	Rym. P	MAIDENHEAD UNITED	94	1 - 1	Traore 53
10/09	Rym. P	Bishop's Stortford	355	0 - 1	
14/09	Rym. P	Basingstoke Town	429	3 - 2	Traore 43, Armstrong 45, Braithwaite 84
18/09	Rym. P	ST ALBANS CITY	208	0 - 1	
21/09	Rym. P	PURFLEET	87	1 - 0	Traore 43[p]
24/09	Rym. P	Kingstonian	358	2 - 4	Armstrong 66, Traore 70
28/09	FA Cup Q2	BISHOP'S STORTFORD	161	1 - 5	Coppard 44
02/10	Rym. P	HAYES	96	0 - 1	
05/10	Rym. P	Chesham United	354	2 - 2	Traore 80, Maynard 83
19/10	Rym. P	HAMPTON & RICHMOND BOR.	64	2 - 0	Traore 35, Forde 45
22/10	Rym. P	Billericay Town	348	1 - 0	Coppard 27
26/10	Rym. P	Braintree Town	243	3 - 1	Richardson 14, Forde 31, Armstrong 54
02/11	FA Trophy 1	BASINGSTOKE TOWN	91	1 - 2	Armstrong 59
05/11	Middx SC 1	Wealdstone	n/k	0 - 2	
09/11	Rym. P	SUTTON UNITED	101	1 - 4	Armstrong 25
16/11	Rym. P	Hampton & Richmond Borough	184	1 - 0	Armstrong 17
19/11	Lge Cup 2	Billericay Town	n/k	0 - 5	
23/11	Rym. P	CANVEY ISLAND	119	1 - 2	Traore 84[p]
26/11	Middx CC 2	Kingsbury Town	n/k	2 - 1	
30/11	Rym. P	Boreham Wood	178	1 - 2	Traore 56
07/12	Rym. P	Hitchin Town	351	1 - 7	Coppard 64
14/12	Rym. P	Hendon	243	0 - 3	
18/12	Rym. P	BEDFORD TOWN	131	1 - 2	Doherty 85
21/12	Rym. P	HEYBRIDGE SWIFTS	71	2 - 3	Armstrong 60, Traore 86
28/12	Rym. P	FORD UNITED	66	1 - 1	Doherty 44
04/01	Rym. P	Grays Athletic	232	0 - 3	
18/01	Rym. P	Maidenhead United	224	3 - 3	Armstrong 28, Richardson 45, Traore 79
25/01	Rym. P	BASINGSTOKE TOWN	101	3 - 1	Dickens 22[og], Armstrong 59, Traore 90[p]
04/02	Rym. P	St Albans City	215	0 - 0	
08/02	Rym. P	KINGSTONIAN	158	2 - 2	Armstrong 11, Opara 62
15/02	Rym. P	Purfleet	241	2 - 5	Braithwaite 10, Armstrong 38
22/02	Rym. P	CHESHAM UNITED	111	1 - 0	Opara 58
01/03	Rym. P	Hayes	238	0 - 4	
08/03	Rym. P	BILLERICAY TOWN	107	1 - 1	Maynard 45
12/03	Rym. P	HARROW BOROUGH	61	0 - 1	
15/03	Rym. P	Sutton United	533	1 - 2	Howell 80
22/03	Rym. P	BRAINTREE TOWN	101	1 - 1	Armstrong 54
26/03	Rym. P	BISHOP'S STORTFORD	144	0 - 2	
29/03	Rym. P	Bedford Town	493	2 - 8	Carr 27, Traore 78
05/04	Rym. P	Aldershot Town	2049	0 - 2	
16/04	Rym. P	AYLESBURY UNITED	105	0 - 0	
19/04	Rym. P	Heybridge Swifts	261	1 - 2	Traori 19
21/04	Rym. P	BOREHAM WOOD	117	1 - 0	Howe 81
26/04	Rym. P	Canvey Island	334	1 - 10	Armstrong 38
03/05	Rym. P	HITCHIN TOWN	121	0 - 5	

HAMPTON & RICHMOND

Match Facts 2002-03

Date	Comp.	Opponents	Att.	Score	Goalscorers
17/08	Rym. P	Sutton United	543	0 - 1	
20/08	Rym. P	HAYES	440	1 - 1	Stestanovic 67
24/08	Rym. P	PURFLEET	183	1 - 1	Riddell 32[p]
26/08	Rym. P	Chesham United	251	0 - 1	
31/08	Rym. P	BISHOP'S STORTFORD	298	1 - 0	Riddell 53
03/09	Rym. P	Basingstoke Town	517	1 - 3	Riddell 90
07/09	Rym. P	Heybridge Swifts	173	0 - 1	
10/09	Rym. P	HARROW BOROUGH	173	0 - 2	
14/09	Rym. P	HENDON	263	1 - 1	Mead 81
17/09	Rym. P	Bedford Town	330	0 - 1	
21/09	Rym. P	CANVEY ISLAND	405	0 - 2	
24/09	Rym. P	Aylesbury United	352	0 - 3	
28/09	FA Cup Q2	Godalming & Guildford	201	1 - 0	Sestanotch 72
01/10	Rym. P	MAIDENHEAD UNITED	149	1 - 1	McCracken 25
05/10	Rym. P	Boreham Wood	170	0 - 0	
12/10	FA Cup Q3	Slough Town	n/k	0 - 0	
19/10	Rym. P	Enfield	64	0 - 2	
22/10	Rym. P	ALDERSHOT TOWN	705	1 - 3	Riddell 66
26/10	Rym. P	CHESHAM UNITED	185	1 - 3	Sestanovich 74
02/11	FA Trophy 1	Spalding United	139	1 - 2	Cory 52
09/11	Rym. P	Hitchin Town	313	1 - 1	Cory 67[p]
12/11	Rym. P	Grays Athletic	208	1 - 1	Cross 8
16/11	Rym. P	ENFIELD	184	0 - 1	
19/11	Lge Cup2	Molesey	n/k	1 - 0	Cory 48
23/11	Rym. P	St Albans City	458	0 - 2	
03/12	Middx SC 2	Uxbridge	n/k	3 - 1	
07/12	Rym. P	BILLERICAY TOWN	202	1 - 1	Riddell 33
10/12	Lge Cup 3	Lewes	n/k	0 - 6	
14/12	Rym. P	SUTTON UNITED	292	1 - 3	Thompson 25
21/12	Rym. P	Braintree Town	270	1 - 3	Sestanovich 82
26/12	Rym. P	KINGSTONIAN	567	2 - 2	Riddell 59, Hastwick 72[og]
28/12	Rym. P	Purfleet	256	2 - 5	Cort 73, Hall 89
07/01	Rym. P	FORD UNITED	144	2 - 3	Hall 46, Gardner 73
14/01	S Comb Cup 2	Bedfont	n/k	3 - 2	
18/01	Rym. P	HEYBRIDGE SWIFTS	145	1 - 1	O'Connor 85
25/01	Rym. P	Hendon	240	3 - 3	Hall 9, Sestanovich 32, Cort 73
28/01	Middx SC QF	HAYES	n/k	2 - 2	Won 4 2 after pens.
08/02	Rym. P	AYLESBURY UNITED	302	3 - 1	O'Connor 68[p], Sestanovich 82, Cyprus 85
11/02	Rym. P	Harrow Borough	167	0 - 1	
15/02	Rym. P	Canvey Island	449	0 - 4	
22/02	Rym. P	BOREHAM WOOD	204	0 - 4	
25/02	Rym. P	Hayes	192	1 - 2	Bennett 64
01/03	Rym. P	Maidenhead United	232	1 - 1	Bennetts 27
04/03	Rym. P	BEDFORD TOWN	170	0 - 2	
08/03	Rym. P	Aldershot Town	2012	0 - 4	
11/03	Middx SC SF	Hendon	n/k	0 - 2	
15/03	Rym. P	HITCHIN TOWN	190	0 - 2	
22/03	Rym. P	Ford United	92	0 - 3	
29/03	Rym. P	GRAYS ATHLETIC	156	1 - 1	Gorman 84
05/04	Rym. P	BASINGSTOKE TOWN	210	0 - 2	
12/04	Rym. P	Bishop's Stortford	336	1 - 2	Okafor 22
19/04	Rym. P	BRAINTREE TOWN	180	0 - 1	
21/04	Rym. P	Kingstonian	345	1 - 1	Riddle 15
26/04	Rym. P	ST ALBANS CITY	210	2 - 3	Rose 6 12
03/05	Rym. P	Billericay Town	313	2 - 0	Innes 12, Deegan 38

RYMAN DIVISION ONE SOUTH

	P	HOME W	D	L	F	A	AWAY W	D	L	F	A	Pts	GD
1 Carshalton Athletic	46	15	4	4	36	21	13	4	6	37	23	92	29
2 Bognor Regis Town	46	15	4	4	52	13	11	6	6	40	21	88	58
3 Lewes	46	13	6	4	48	23	11	10	2	58	27	88	56
4 Dulwich Hamlet	46	13	7	3	41	22	10	5	8	32	27	81	24
5 Whyteleafe	46	12	6	5	45	23	9	7	7	29	28	76	23
6 Bromley	46	11	5	7	36	29	10	8	5	34	24	76	17
7 Walton & Hersham	46	9	7	7	42	34	11	6	6	45	29	73	24
8 Horsham	46	10	5	8	45	31	11	4	8	35	27	72	22
9 Epsom & Ewell	46	12	5	6	37	34	7	7	9	30	32	69	1
10 Egham Town	46	9	8	6	30	34	10	2	11	32	37	67	-9
11 Tooting & Mitcham Utd	46	5	4	14	36	45	13	5	5	47	33	63	5
12 Worthing	46	10	5	8	44	38	7	7	9	34	37	63	3
13 Windsor & Eton	46	11	5	7	39	29	7	4	12	27	36	63	1
14 Leatherhead	46	9	8	6	39	28	7	5	11	32	38	61	5
15 Staines Town	46	8	9	6	32	30	6	7	10	25	33	58	-6
16 Banstead Atheltic	46	8	5	10	35	34	6	10	7	23	25	57	-1
17 Ashford Town (Middx)	46	5	8	10	18	30	9	3	11	29	40	53	-23
18 Croydon	46	9	6	8	28	31	6	2	15	28	56	53	-31
19 Croydon Athletic	46	5	7	11	24	38	8	6	9	28	28	52	-14
20 Bracknell Town	46	6	5	12	29	44	6	11	6	28	30	52	-17
21 Corinthian Casuals	46	7	7	9	25	26	5	7	11	25	42	50	-18
22 Molesey	46	5	5	13	19	39	8	4	11	33	40	48	-27
23 Metropolitan Police	46	6	5	12	26	38	6	5	12	24	38	46	-26
24 Chertsey Town	46	2	3	18	20	64	1	4	18	23	75	16	-96

	1	2	3	4	5	6	7	8	9	10	11	12	13	14	15	16	17	18	19	20	21	22	23	24
1 Ashford		0-0	0-1	0-0	1-1	0-2	2-0	1-1	1-0	0-2	0-5	1-3	1-1	0-1	0-1	0-3	2-1	1-2	0-0	1-1	2-1	1-1	0-3	4-0
2 Banstead	2-3		0-1	0-1	3-3	0-2	3-1	4-0	2-3	0-1	4-1	3-2	4-0	1-1	1-1	1-1	1-0	2-5	0-1	2-1	0-4	1-0	1-2	0-0
3 Bognor R.	8-0	1-0		0-1	1-1	1-0	6-0	1-1	3-1	2-0	0-1	3-1	3-0	1-3	0-0	0-2	4-0	1-1	3-0	3-0	3-0	3-0	2-1	3-0
4 Bracknell	1-1	1-1	3-1		2-1	1-4	4-2	3-2	2-2	0-3	0-4	0-1	0-3	1-2	5-2	1-2	1-2	0-3	0-0	2-2	0-1	0-1	1-0	1-4
5 Bromley	2-1	2-2	2-1	2-0		0-3	4-1	2-0	3-1	0-1	1-1	1-2	1-0	1-0	1-0	3-2	2-3	0-2	2-2	2-3	3-0	1-1	0-0	1-3
6 Carshalton	1-0	1-0	1-0	2-2	1-4		1-0	2-2	1-0	2-1	2-0	0-1	2-0	2-1	2-0	4-1	2-0	1-1	1-1	2-3	1-2	2-1	1-0	2-1
7 Chertsey	0-5	1-0	0-2	1-1	1-4	0-2		0-1	4-1	1-2	1-2	1-2	0-3	1-1	2-8	1-5	1-2	2-2	0-1	0-7	1-6	1-4	1-2	0-1
8 CorinthianC	1-2	0-1	0-3	0-0	0-0	1-2	5-0		1-1	1-1	1-2	0-4	1-0	1-2	3-0	1-2	1-0	3-0	1-0	0-3	1-1	1-1	1-0	1-1
9 Croydon	2-1	0-0	0-6	1-1	1-1	1-2	3-1	0-3		1-1	1-0	3-1	0-0	0-2	1-2	1-3	1-0	1-0	3-1	0-1	2-2	2-0	0-2	4-1
10 Croydon A	0-1	1-1	1-0	0-1	1-2	0-1	2-0	0-4	3-0		0-2	2-1	1-1	0-5	1-1	2-2	1-1	1-3	1-1	1-5	2-0	2-3	2-3	0-0
11 Dulwich H	2-0	0-0	0-0	2-2	0-2	1-0	3-1	4-2	0-1	2-1		2-0	3-1	3-1	3-2	2-2	1-1	1-0	1-0	4-0	1-1	2-3	2-0	2-2
12 Egham Tn	0-3	0-0	1-6	0-3	1-0	1-1	3-3	3-1	1-0	1-1	3-0		0-3	1-0	1-1	1-5	0-0	2-1	2-1	2-0	3-3	0-1	1-1	3-0
13 Epsom & E	3-0	1-3	1-1	3-2	1-2	1-4	3-0	0-0	4-0	1-0	3-3	1-0		1-1	2-1	0-7	1-0	1-0	1-0	2-2	1-0	1-3	4-0	1-5
14 Horsham	1-0	2-0	1-2	3-3	1-1	0-1	4-0	0-1	6-1	2-2	1-0	1-2	2-1		1-2	2-2	2-0	6-2	0-2	2-3	0-1	4-2	1-0	3-3
15 Leatherhead	2-0	2-2	0-0	1-1	1-1	0-3	3-3	2-2	5-2	4-2	3-1	0-2	1-1	0-2		0-1	6-2	0-1	0-1	1-1	4-0	1-0	2-0	1-0
16 Lewes	5-2	0-2	2-2	2-0	1-0	3-1	7-0	5-0	0-2	3-2	2-0	2-0	1-0	1-0	0-0		1-1	3-2	2-2	0-1	1-1	1-1	6-2	0-2
17 Met. Police	1-1	1-3	0-2	2-2	2-2	1-2	2-1	2-1	3-2	3-0	1-1	2-3	0-1	0-1	2-1	0-3		0-2	2-2	0-2	0-2	0-1	0-2	2-1
18 Molesey	0-2	0-2	1-5	1-1	2-1	1-1	1-2	1-0	1-2	0-4	0-1	0-0	0-1	0-1	4-1	0-7	3-1		1-2	0-2	0-1	1-0	1-1	1-1
19 Staines Tn	0-2	1-1	0-3	1-0	1-2	2-2	2-2	2-0	2-1	1-0	0-0	5-0	2-2	1-1	4-1	1-1	1-2	4-1		1-2	0-7	0-0	1-0	0-0
20 Tooting & M	3-1	1-2	4-0	2-3	0-1	0-2	5-0	0-1	1-2	1-1	0-2	1-2	3-4	1-4	2-0	1-1	2-4	1-1	3-2		1-3	1-2	3-3	0-4
21 Walton & H	0-2	1-1	0-0	3-1	2-1	3-0	5-2	1-1	2-0	3-1	1-3	4-2	0-0	2-3	1-3	2-2	2-0	3-0	1-2	2-2		2-2	0-2	2-4
22 Whyteleafe	0-1	1-0	3-1	0-1	1-2	3-1	3-3	5-0	4-1	0-0	0-0	2-1	2-2	4-1	1-0	2-2	1-0	1-2	3-0	1-2	2-2		2-0	4-1
23 Windsor & E	1-1	5-0	0-2	2-0	0-1	1-1	1-0	1-1	2-3	0-1	1-0	3-2	4-3	3-1	0-2	0-0	1-1	3-1	2-1	5-2	1-4	1-2		2-0
24 Worthing	5-0	3-2	1-1	2-2	0-1	2-0	3-1	3-1	5-2	0-1	2-3	0-0	1-3	2-1	1-3	2-2	1-3	3-1	4-3	0-2	0-3	0-0	4-3	

ASHFORD TOWN (Middlesex)

CLUB OFFICIALS

Chairman: Robert Parker
Vice Chairman: Mark Vaughan
President: T.B.A.
Secretary: Alan B J Constable
3 Craigwell Close, Chertsey Lane,
Staines, Middx. TW18 3NP
Tel: 01784 440613 (H) 07956 930719 (M)
01784 451614 (Fax) Email: alanc52@aol.com
Press Secretary: Terry Ryan

FOOTBALL MANAGEMENT TEAM

Manager: Nathan Wharf

FACT FILE

Formed: 1964
Nickname: Ash Trees
Colours: Tangerine & white/white/black
Change colours:All Blue
Midweek matchday: Tuesday

2002-2003

Captain: & P.o.Y.: Ross Davidson
Top Scorer: Richard Butler 12.

PROGRAMME

Pages:40 Price: £1.50
Editor: Alan B J Constable (Secretary)

GROUND Short Lane, Stanwell, Staines, Middx Tel: 01784 245908
Club Website: www.ashfordtownmxfootballclub.co.uk
Directions: M25 jct 13, A30 towards London, 3rd left at footbridge after Ashford Hospital crossroads - ground signposted after 1/4 a mile on right down Short Lane. 2 miles from Ashford (BR) & Hatton Cross (tube) stations.
Bus route - Westlink 116 **Club Shop:** No
Capacity: 2550 Seats: 150 Cover: 300 Floodlights: Yes
Clubhouse: Open 7 days a week. Refreshments always available - hot food on matchdays

PREVIOUS **Ground:** Clockhouse Lane Rec
Leagues: Hounslow & Dist. 64-68; Surrey Intermediate 68-82; Surrey Premier 82-90 Combined Counties League 90-00

CLUB RECORDS **Appearances:** Alan Constable 650
Attendance: 750 v Brentford, friendly 29/7/8
Goalscorer: Andy Smith

BEST SEASON **FA Vase:** 4th Round 2000-2001
FA Trophy: Prelim Rd. 20002-0-2003 (Only Seaaon)
FA Cup:1st Qual. Rd. 1996-1997

HONOURS: Combined Co's Lg Champions 94-95, 95-96, 96-97, 97-8, 99-00; Chall Cup R-up 92-93 94-95, Lg Vase Cup R-up 91-92 94-95; Surrey I'mediate Lg, Surrey Prem. Cup 89-90; Middx Prem. Cup R-up 89-90; Southern Comb Cup 95-96, R-up 01-02 World Wide Carpets Prem Ch Cup 98-99 Aldershot Senior Cup: 2002-2003

Back row, left to right: Pat Munns (Physio),Mick Snowden (Coach), Steve Wilmore, Vince O'Sullivan,Anthony Egginton, Paul Burgess, Tony Wells, Lawrence Mun ns, Jamie Read, Steve Croxford, Narthan Wharf (Manager).**Front Row:** Matt Jordan, Blaize O'Brien, Chris Owen, Ross Davidson, Andy Driscoll, Baron Jolly , Andy Frost,a nd Richard Butler.

BANSTEAD ATHLETIC

CLUB OFFICIALS

Chairman: Terry Molloy
President: Gordon Taylor
Press Officer: Colin Darby
Secretary: Gordon Harrison
69 Chipstead Lane, Lower Klngswood,
Surrey KT20 6RD (01737 833817)

FOOTBALL MANAGEMENT TEAM

Manager: Bob Langford
Coach: Ray Best
Physio: John Steerwood

FACT FILE

Founded: 1944
Nickname: A's
Sponsors: PDM Marketing
Colours: Amber/black/amber
Change colours: All red
Midweek Matchday: Tuesday
Club Website: www.bansteadathletic.co.uk

2002-2003

Captain: Mark Leahy
Top Scorer: James Greenaway
Player of the Year: Aaron Day

PROGRAMME

Pages: 38 Price: £1.00
Editor: Colin Darby (0208 643 5437)

GROUND Merland Rise, Tadworth, Surrey KT20 5JG (01737 350982)

Directions: Follow signs to Tattenham Corner (Epsom racecourse), then to Banstead Sports Centre. Ground adjacent to swimming pool.
Half a mile fromTattenham Corner (BR)
Bus 420 from Sutton stops outside ground.
Also buses 406 & 727 from Epsom

Capacity: 3,500 Seats: 250 Cover: 800 Floodlights: Yes

Clubhouse: All week 11am-11pm. 2 bars, real ale, bar snacks

Club Shop Yes

PREVIOUS **Leagues:** Surrey Int., Surrey Snr 49-65, Spartan 65-75, London Spartan 75-79, Athenian 79-84

CLUB RECORDS **Attendance:** 1,400 v Leytonstone, FA Amateur 1953

Win: 11-0 **Defeat:** 0-11

Career goalscorer: Harry Clark **Career appearances:** Dennis Wall

Transfer fee received: None **Transfer fee paid:** None

BEST SEASON **FA Cup:** 3rd Qual.Rd. 86-87. 00-01 FA Vase: Semi - finals 96-97

HONOURS: Surrey Snr Lg(6) 50-54 56-57 64-65, R-up(5) 49-50 54-56 57-59, Lg Cup 57-58, Charity Cup 52-53 58-59; London Spartan Lg R-up 77-78 (Lg Cup(2) 65-67);Surrey Prem. Cup R-up 91-92, 95-96; Surrey Snr Shield 55-56; Gilbert Rice F'lit Cup 81-82 86-87 (R-up(4) 82-86); Athenian Lg Cup(2) 80-82 (R-up 82-83 (SF 79-80); Surrey Int. Lg(2) 47-49, Cup 46-47 54-55; E. Surrey Charity Cup (4) 59-6066-67 76-78, R-up 79-80, I'mediate Sect. 75-76 (R-up 76-77), Jnr Sect. 81-82;Southern Comb. Cup R-up 69-70; Suburban Lg R-up 86-87; Carlton T.V. Trophy R-Up 95-96

Players Progressing: W Chesney & B Robinson (Crystal Palace)

L-R - Back Row: Martin Beard, Mark Leahy (Capt.), Graham Knight, Steve Shaw, jamie Ribolla, Bob Langford (Manager), Aaron Smith, Stuart White, James Greenaway, Wayne Finnie. **Front Row:** Ray Best (Asst. Man.), Aaron Day, Danny Wise, Marcel Dennis, Dean Walker, Simon Mitchell, John Steerwood (Physio). Missing: Kristien Sorensen (Coach).

BRACKNELL TOWN

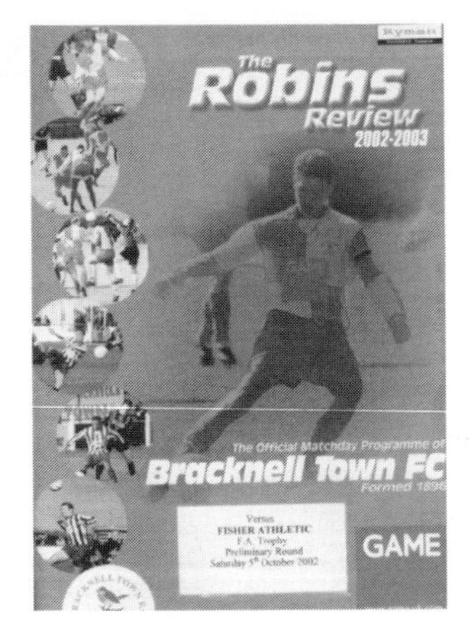

CLUB OFFICIALS

Chairman: Chris Nixon
President: Jack Quinton
Vice-Chairman & Match Secretary:
Malcolm Hutt, 3 Livingstone Gardens,
Woodley, Reading RG5 3LT
01189 694946 (H) 07977 822148 (M)

Secretary: David Mihell, 51 Upshire Gdns.,
The Warren,Bracknell, Berks RG12 9YZ
Tel: 01344 488369 (H) 07712 489415 (M)
Press Off.: Robert Scully 01344 640721

FOOTBALL MANAGEMENT TEAM

Manager: Alan Taylor
Coach: Paul Harford
Physio: Richard Lansiquot

FACT FILE

Founded: 1896
Nickname: Robins
Colours: Red & white quarters/red/red
Change colours: Blue & white stripes/blue/blue
Sponsors: GAME (www.game.uk.com)
Midweek Matchday: Tuesday
Reserve's League: Suburban (west)

GROUND Larges Lane, Bracknell RG12 9AN.
Tel: 01344 412305 (club), 01344 300933 (office- T & Fax)

Directions: Off A329 just before Met Office r'bout by Bracknell College, ground 200 yards. From Bracknell (BR)/bus station - right out of station, follow pathover bridge, left down steps and follow cycle path ahead, after 300yds follow curve over footbridge, right and follow lane to end, left and ground on leftafter bend

Capacity: 2,500 Seats: 190 Cover: 400 Floodlights: Yes
Clubhouse: Members' bar open 11am-11pm Mon-Sat, 12-3 & 7-10.30pm Sun.
Club Shop: Yes, selling metal badges, programmes, scarves, club sweaters, club ties

PROGRAMME

Pages: 48 Price: £1.00
Editor: Robert Scully 01344 640721
Local Press: Bracknell News

PREVIOUS **Leagues:** Great Western Comb.; Surrey Snr 63-70; London Spartan 70-75
Grounds: None **Names:** None

CLUB RECORDS **Attendance:** 2,500 v Newquay, FA Amateur Cup 1971
Career Goalscorer: Richard Whitty **Career Appearances:** James Woodcock

BEST SEASON **FA Cup:** 1st Round Proper, 00-01 (0-4 v Lincoln City)

HONOURS: Isthmian Lg Div 3 93-94; Berks & Bucks Snr Cup R-up; Spartan Lg 74-75, (Lg Cup 81-82 82-83); Surrey Snr Lg 68-69 (Lg Cup 68-69 69-70)

Players progressing: Willie Graham (Brentford)

Back row (from left to right): Chris Nixon (chairman), Paul Harford (player/coach), Ben Edwards, Neil Baker, Jon Underwood, Martin Hutt, Kevin Butcher, Paul Gower, Stuart Hammonds, Gavin Smith, Alan Taylor (manager), Malcolm Hutt (vice-chairman/match secretary), Jack Quinton (president).
Front row: Richard Lansiquot (physio), Gary Sargeant, Adam Crittenden, Simon Teague, Stuart Harte, James Glynn, Gavin Taylor, Giles Marchant, Jeff Dennis (fitness coach)

BROMLEY

CLUB OFFICIALS

Chairman: Jerry Dolke
Secretary: Colin Russell
124 Coombe Lane, Croydon,
Surrey CR0 5RF

FOOTBALL MANAGEMENT TEAM

Manager:Stuart McIntyre
Ass.Manager/Coach:Mark Harris

FACT FILE

Formed: 1892
Nickname: The Lilywhites
Colours: White/black/black
Change colours: All red
Midweek home matchday: Tuesday
Reserve's League: None
Youth League: Kent Youth League
Newsline: 0930 555 838

2002-2003
Captain: John Myatt
Player of the Year: Joe Vines
Top Goalscorer:Adolph Amoako

Pages: 32 Price: £1.50
Editor: Steven McCartney (07979 418 360)

Local Press: Bromley Times
Local Radio: Radio Kent,
Bromley Local Radio

GROUND Hayes Lane, Bromley, Kent BR2 9EF Tel: 0208 460 5291 or 0208 313 3992

Directions: One mile from Bromley South (BR). Buses 314, 146 and 119 pass ground.
Junction 4 off M25, then A21 towards London
Capacity: 5,000 Cover: 2,500 Seats: 1,300 Floodlights: Yes
Clubhouse: Open matchdays. Food available
Club Shop: Yes. contact Jim Brown

PREVIOUS **Leagues:** South London - 1894; Southern 94-96; London 96-98 99-1901; West Kent 01-04; Southern Suburban 04-07; Kent 1898-99, 11-14; Spartan 07-08; Isthmian 08-11; Athenian 19-52
Grounds: White Hart Field Cricket Ground, Widmore Rd & Plaistow Cricket Field (pre-1904), Hayes Lane 1904-37

RECORDS **Attendance:** 12,000 v Nigeria, 1950
Goalscorer: George Brown 570 (1938-61) **Appearances:** George Brown
Win: 13-1 v Redhill, Athenian League 1945-46 **Defeat:** 1-11 v Barking ,Athenian League 1933-34
Fee Paid: Unknown **Fee Received:** £50,000 for Jon Goodman (from Millwall 90)

BEST SEASON **FA Amateur Cup:** Winners 10-11, 37-38, 48-49
FA Trophy: Second Round 91-92 **FA Cup:** 2nd Rd replay v Scarborough 37-38, Lincoln 38-39, Watford 45-46

HONOURS: Isthmian League(4) 08-10 53-54 60-61 (R-up 52-53 55-56 87-88), Div 1 R-up 79-80 5-86 90-91, Prince Phillip 5-a-side Cup 1979; Athenian League 22-23 48-49 50-51 (R-up 35-36); London League Div 2 1896-97; Spartan League 07-08; Kent Senior Cup 49-50 76-77 91-92 96-97; Kent AmateurCup (12) 07-08 31-32 35-36 36-37 38-39 46-47 48-49 50-51 52-53 53-54 54-55 59-60; London Challenge Cup 1995-96. London Senior Cup: 09-10, 45-46, 50-51, 02-03

Players progressing: Roy Merryfield (Chelsea), Stan Charlton (Arsenal 52), RonHeckman (Orient 55), John Gregory (West Ham 51), Bill Lloyd (Millwall 56), Brian Kinsey (Charlton 56), Harold Hobbs (Charlton & England), Matt Carmichael (Lincoln 90), Leslie Locke (QPR 56), Jon Goodman (Millwall 90), Dean Wordsworth (Crystal Palace 97), Landry Zahana-ONI (Luton Town 98)

Back row, left to right: Jerome Bennett, Khalouq Ayoub, Jason McKay, Gary Drewett, John Butler,Kwabena Amaning, Mark Harris (Asst.Manager), Chuck Martini, Danny Harwood, Wade Falana, Grant Watts, Bobby George, Kirk Watts, John Wilfort, Joe Vines and Chris Cook (Physio).**Front row:** Nigel Pearce, David Smith, Billy Manuel, John Myatt (captain), Jerry Dolke (Chairman), Stuart McIntyre (Manager), Paul Greenwood (Vice-Chairman), Adolph Amoako, Michael Harney, Colin Luckett and Danny Smith.

Wembley Cup Holders/London Senior Cup Winners 2002-2003 **Official Photographer:** www.avenellphotos.com

CORINTHIAN CASUALS

CLUB OFFICIALS

Chairman: Geoff Hewitson

President: Jimmy Hill

Press Off & MatchSec Rob Cavallini (0208 4042763 & 07940 317292))

Secretary: Brian Wakefield 5 Martingales Close, Richmond, Surrey
Tel: 020 8940 9208

FOOTBALL MANAGEMENT TEAM
Manager: Mickey Stephens

FACT FILE

Founded: 1939
Sponsors: London Catering Services
Colours: Chocolate & Pink/sky/sky
Change colours: White/navy/white
Midweek Matchday: Tuesday
Reserves' League: Suburban

2002-2003

Captain: Simon Shergold
Top Goalscorer: Justin Georgiou 17
Player of the Year: Iain Waghorn

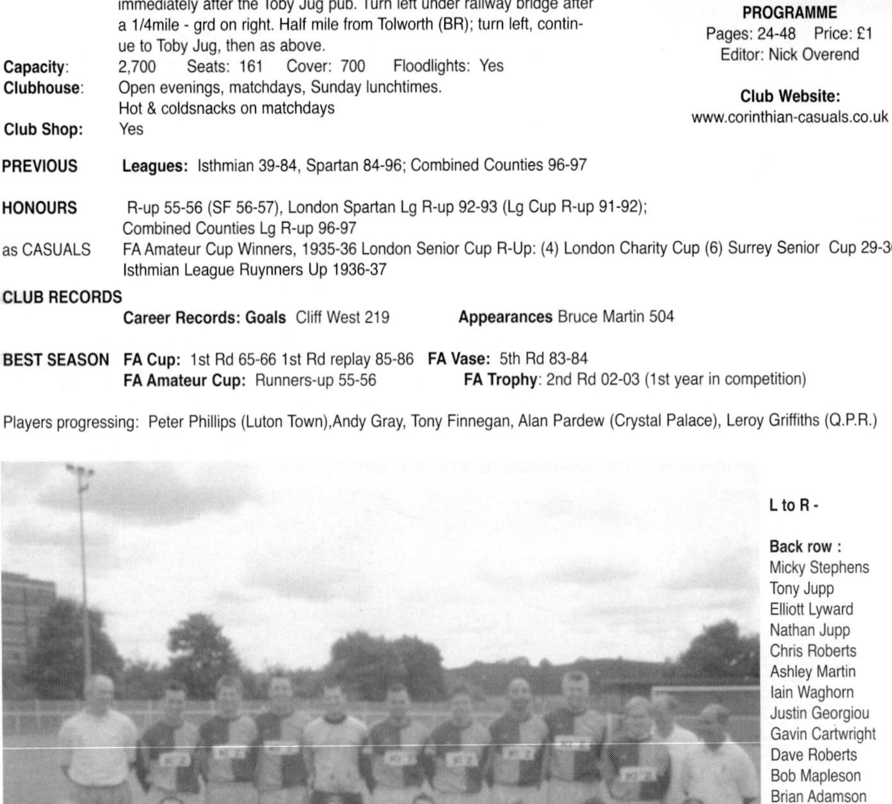

PROGRAMME
Pages: 24-48 Price: £1
Editor: Nick Overend

Club Website:
www.corinthian-casuals.co.uk

GROUND King George's Field, Hook Rise South, Tolworth, Surrey KT6 7NA
Tel: 020 8397 3368 Email Address:info@corinthian-casuals.co.uk

Directions: A3 to Tolworth r'bout (The Charrington Bowl). Hook Rise is slip road immediately after the Toby Jug pub. Turn left under railway bridge after a 1/4mile - grd on right. Half mile from Tolworth (BR); turn left, continue to Toby Jug, then as above.

Capacity: 2,700 Seats: 161 Cover: 700 Floodlights: Yes

Clubhouse: Open evenings, matchdays, Sunday lunchtimes.
Hot & coldsnacks on matchdays

Club Shop: Yes

PREVIOUS **Leagues:** Isthmian 39-84, Spartan 84-96; Combined Counties 96-97

HONOURS R-up 55-56 (SF 56-57), London Spartan Lg R-up 92-93 (Lg Cup R-up 91-92);
Combined Counties Lg R-up 96-97

as CASUALS FA Amateur Cup Winners, 1935-36 London Senior Cup R-Up: (4) London Charity Cup (6) Surrey Senior Cup 29-30
Isthmian League Ruynners Up 1936-37

CLUB RECORDS
Career Records: Goals Cliff West 219 **Appearances** Bruce Martin 504

BEST SEASON **FA Cup:** 1st Rd 65-66 1st Rd replay 85-86 **FA Vase:** 5th Rd 83-84
FA Amateur Cup: Runners-up 55-56 **FA Trophy**: 2nd Rd 02-03 (1st year in competition)

Players progressing: Peter Phillips (Luton Town),Andy Gray, Tony Finnegan, Alan Pardew (Crystal Palace), Leroy Griffiths (Q.P.R.)

L to R -

Back row :
Micky Stephens
Tony Jupp
Elliott Lyward
Nathan Jupp
Chris Roberts
Ashley Martin
Iain Waghorn
Justin Georgiou
Gavin Cartwright
Dave Roberts
Bob Mapleson
Brian Adamson

Front Row:
R Jim Taylor
Andy Gibbons
Jamie Byatt
Lyndon Buckwell
Jamie White
Tony Blunt
Simon Shergold
Paul Midwinter

CROYDON

CLUB OFFICIALS

Chairman: Jim Moody

Secretary: Gordon Tennant, 21 Sharonelle Court,Station Road, Wokingham,Berks.RG40 2AX Tel Nos: 01189891357(H) 07775 740838(M)

Press Off: Simon Hawkins (07710 459858)

FOOTBALL MANAGEMENT TEAM

Manager: Mick Read

Asst. Manager: Dave Garland

Physio: Ian Fairs

2002-2003

Captain: Danny Edwards

Top Scorer: Darren Hall. 11

P.o.Y.: Craig Dundas

FACT FILE

Formed: 1953
Nickname: The Trams
Sponsors: T.B.A.
Colours: Sky &navy
Change colours: Red & White
Midweek home matchday: Wednesday
Youth Team's League: Southern Youth
Local Press: Croydon Advertiser, Croydon Midweek Post, Times, Guardian and Whyteleaf Advertiser

PROGRAMME

Pages: 20 Price: £1.00
Editor:Vince Mitchell (01892 542671(H)

Croydon Football Club
50th Anniversary
1953 - 2003
Ryman Division One South
2003/2004 Season
Ryman

GROUNDCroydon Sports Arena, Albert Rd, S.Norwood,. SE25 4QL Tel: 0208 654 3462/8555
Directions: From Portland Rd (A@!%) turn down either Belmont Rd or Grasmere Rd. and the Stadium is off Alber5t Rd inn South Norweood.Train to East Croydon or Norwood Junction, then bus 12 to eitherBelmont or Dundee Road. Walk down either - ground at bottom. 5 mins walk fromWoodside (BR)
Capacity: 6,000 **Cover:** 1,000 **Seats**: 450 **Floodlights**: Yes
Clubhouse: Open every evening and lunchtime, snacks available. Dancing & discos, Lounge bar available for private hire **Club Shop:** Yes

PREVIOUS **Leagues:** Surrey Senior 53-63; Spartan 63-64; Athenian 64-74
Name: Croydon Amateurs 1953-74

CLUB RECORDS **Attendance:** 1,450 v Wycombe, FA Cup 4th Qualifying Rd 1975
Career appearances: Alec Jackson (1977-88) 452 + 111goals and Tony Luckett(1962-73) 411 appearances
Transfer fee paid: Steve Brown **Transfer fee received:** Peter Evans (to Sutton Utd)

BEST SEASON **FA Cup:** 2nd Round replay 79-80, 2-3 v Millwall after 1-1 **F.A.Vase:** 4th Round 1994-95
FA Trophy: 2nd Round 81-82, 82-83 **FA Amateur Cup:** 3rd round 71-72 **F.A.Youth Cup**: 4th Round 1976-77

HONOURS Isthmian Lg Div. 1 99-2000, R-up 75-76 Div 2 95-96, Lg Cup: R-up 74-75, 00-01 FM Cup 99-2000; Surrey Snr Cup 81-82 (R-up 76-77 99-00), Surrey Prem Cup 86-87, Spartan Lg 63-64, Athenian Lg R-up 71-72 Div 2 65-66 (R-up 70-71)), Surrey Snr Lg R-up 56-57 60-61 62-63 (Lg Cup 60-61), Charity Cup 53-54 62-63, Res Section 57-58), London Senior Cup Winners 2001-02 R-up 77-78, Suburban Lg South 86-87(Lg Cup(2), Southern Yth Lg 85-86 (Lg Cup 85-86 87-88), Berger Yth Cup 78-79, Southern Youth Lg Cup 96-97. Womens F.A.Cup 95-6,99-00 R-up 97-98 Premier Lg 99-00
Players progressing: Alan Barnett (Plymouth 1955), Peter Bonetti (Chelsea), Leroy Ambrose (Charlton 1979), Steve Milton (Fulham - via Whyteleafe), Murray Jones (Crystal Pal. - via Carshalton and)John Bailey (Bournemouth via Enfield and Dagenham)

L-R - Back: John Finch (coach), Ian Fairs (Physio), Chris Walsh, Mark Tompkins, Jamie White, Oliver Hunt, Danny Moody, Matt Martin, Stuart Read, Craig Dundas, Roy Newman, Roger Hoyte (Reserve Team Man.), Mick Read (Manager). **Front:** Trevor Reddick, James Cecil, Shane Sutherland, Michael Ebanks, Danny Edwards, Jiim Moody (Chairman), Kris Hollidge, Darren Hall, Rob Fraser.

CROYDON ATHLETIC

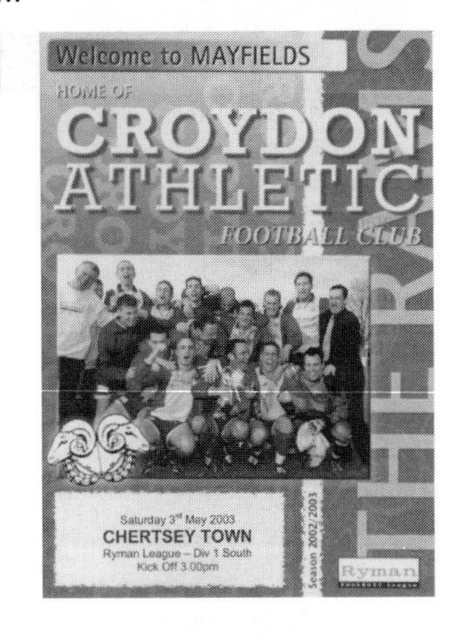

Welcome to MAYFIELDS
HOME OF
CROYDON
ATHLETIC
FOOTBALL CLUB
Saturday 3rd May 2003
CHERTSEY TOWN
Ryman League - Div 1 South
Kick Off 3.00pm
Season 2002/2003
Ryman

CLUB OFFICIALS

Chairman: Keith Tuckey
V Chairman/ Press Officer:
Clive Thompson
Chief Executive: Dean Fisher
153 Chipstead Valley Road,
Coulsdon, Surrey CR5 3BQ
Tel: 020 8407 3296 (H & Fax)
020 7556 6092

FOOTBALL MANAGEMENT TEAM

Manager: Hayden Bird
Asst Man.: Peter Thomas
1st Team Coach: Simon Liddle
Chief Scout: Chris Roots
Physio: Mick Reed

FACT FILE

Founded: 1990 Sponsors: T.C.S. Media

Colours: Maroon & white/maroon/maroon

Change colours: Yellow/royal/royal/royal

Midweek matches: Tuesday

Reserve League: Suburban (S)

2002-2003

Captain: Dean Davenport

Top Goallscorer: Billy Jackson

Player of the Year: Jon Waite

GROUND Mayfields, off Mayfield Road, Thornton Heath, Surrey, CR7 6DN.
Tel: 0208 6648343: Email: dfisher@croydonathletic.co.uk

Directions: Follow A23 from London & continue on A23 into Thornton Road.
After roundabout take !st on right into Silverleigh Road, left fork into Trafford Road which continues into Mayfield Road. To end and turn left and follow narrow road to ground. 1 mile from Norbury (BR).
Buses 109, 60

Capacity: 3,000 Seats: 163 Cover: 660 Floodlights: Yes
Clubhouse: Open every evening & weekends **Club Shop:** Yes

PROGRAMME

Pages: 52 Price: £1
Editor: Steve O'Brien
Club Website:
www.croydonathletic.co.uk

PREVIOUS **Leagues:** None

RECORDS **Attendance:** 550
Goalscorer: John Fowler
Appearances: Graham Edginton/ Paul Gall/Leon Maxwell

BEST SEASON **FA Vase:** 4th Rd 00-01 FA Trophy:
FA Cup: 2nd Qual. Rd 94-95

HONOURS: London Spartan Lg 94-95, R-up 88-89 93-94, (Reserve Div 88-89, R-up 88-89); London Snr Cup R-up 91-92; Southern Youth Lg 92-93; Bearman Harber MemTrophy 87-88; Wirral Prog 86-87 96-97; Umbro Fair Play 97-98; Isthmian League Div 3 2001-02

Players progressing to Football League: Jamie Ndah (Torquay Utd)

Back row, left to right: Simon Liddle, Jamie Gibson, Danny Cecil, John Fowler, Tony Quinton and Gavin Harrison. **Middle row:** Mick Reed (Physio), Tyrone Myton, Billy Jackson, Rob Frank;land, Leon Raishbrook, Leon Johnson and Peter Thomas (Assistant Manager) **Front row:** Jon Waite, Justin Brauer-Jones, Dean Davenport, Hayden Bird (Manager), Danny Stassinos, Adrian Moses and James Evans.

DULWICH HAMLET

CLUB OFFICIALS
Chairman: Martin Eede
President: Tommy Jover
Vice Chairman: Brian Shears
Secretary:: John Leahy, 58 Newquay House, Black Prince Road, Kennington, London S.E.11 6HL Tel: 0207 582 9296
Press Officer: John Lawrence Tel: 020 8761 2091

FOOTBALL MANAGEMENT TEAM
Manager: Martin Eede
Physio: Danny Keenan

FACT FILE
Formed: 1893
Nickname: The Hamlet
Sponsors: M R Jennings for Insurance
Colours: Navy blue & pink/navy/navy
Change: All white with pink trim
Midweek matchday: Tuesday
Reserve League: Suburban
Local Press: South London Press, Southwark News

PROGRAMME
Pages: 48 Price: £1.30
Editor: John Lawrence

2002-03
Captain and P.o.Y: Lee Akers
Top Scorer: Omari Coleman - 25

GROUND: Champion Hill Stadium, Edgar Kail Way, East Dulwich, London SE22 8BD Tel: 020 7274 8707
Directions: East Dulwich station, 200yds. Denmark Hill station, 10 mins walk. Herne Hill station then bus 37 stops near grd. Buses 40 & 176 from Elephant & Castle, 185 from Victoria
Capacity: 3,000 Cover: 1,000 Seats: 500 Floodlights: Yes
Clubhouse: Open 7 days a week. Function rooms & meeting room available for hire Health Club,Gymnasium,Squash courts (020 7274 8707)
Club Shop: Sells programmes, pennants, badges, scarves, baseball caps, replica shirts (by order only).

PREVIOUS **Leagues:** Camberwell 1894-97; S/thern Sub 1897-1900 01-07; Dulwich 00-01; Spartan 07-08
Grounds: Woodwarde Rd 1893-95; College Farm 95-96; Sunray Avenue 96-1902; Freeman's Ground, Champion Hill 02-12; Champion Hill (old ground) 1912-92; Sandy Lane (groundshare with Tooting & Mitcham F.C.) 91-92

CLUB RECORDS **Attendance:** 20,744, Kingstonian v Stockton, FA Am Cup Final 1933 (at refurbished ground): 1,835 v Southport FAC 98-99
Career Goalscorer: Edgar Kail 427 (1919-33)
Career Appearances: Reg Merritt 576 (50-66)
Fee Paid: T Eames (Wimbledon), G Allen (Carshalton Ath 80)
Fee Received: E Nwajiobi (Luton 83)
Win: 13-0 v Walton-on-Thames, 37-38
Defeat: 1-10 v Hendon, 63-64

BEST SEASON **FA Amateur Cup:** Winners 19-20 31-2 33-4 36-7
FA Trophy: Quarter Final 79-80
FA Cup: 1st Rd replay 30-31 33-34. 1st Rd on 14 occasions

HONOURS: Isthmian League 19-20 25-26 32-33 48-49, (R-up(7) Div 1 77-78; London Senior Cup 24-25 38-39 49-50 83-84 (R-up 05-06 07-08 20-21 27-28, 01-02); Surrey Senior Cup 14 (R-up -6); London Chal. Cup 98-9 R-up 91-92; 99-00 London Charity Cup(12); Surrey Senior Shield 72-73; Surrey Centen. Shld 77-78; Sth of the Thames Cup (4) 56-60; Southern Comb Cup 73-74

Players progressing: W Bellamy (Spurs), A Solly (Arsenal), L Fishlock/A Gray/APardew (C Palace), J Moseley & E Toser (Millwall), R Dicks (Middlesborough), GJago/J Ryan (Charlton Ath 51/63), G Pearce (Plymouth), R Crisp (Watford 61), ENwajiobi (Luton 83), C Richards & J Glass (Bournemouth), P Coleman (Millwall86), A Perry (Portsmouth 86), N Kelly (Stoke City), C Emberson (Rotherham), CAsaba (Brentford)S.Watts (Leyton O), M.King (Barnet),J Darlington (Q.P.R.), D.McEwen (Spurs)

EGHAM TOWN

CLUB OFFICIALS

Chairman: Peter Atkins
Vice Chairmen:
Peter Barnes & Brian Askew
President: Peter Barnes
Press Officer: Secretary
Club Administrator:
Alison Thompson, 138A Thorpe Lea Rd,
Egham, Surrey. TW20 8BL
Tel: 01784 463562

FOOTBALL MANAGEMENT TEAM

Manager:Byron Walton
Coaches: Alf Coulton Physio: Ken Weaver

FACT FILE

Founded: 1877
Nickname: Sarnies/Town
Colours: Yellow & Green/green/yellow
Change colours: All blue
Midweek Matches: Tuesday
Reserves' League: Suburban

Local Press: Herald & News
Local Radio: County Sound

The Sarnies
Egham Town Football Club
SPONSORED BY
COURAGE
RYMAN DIVISION 1 SOUTH
Ryman football league
PROGRAMME SPONSOR
A
Arena Mechanical Handling Group Ltd
OFFICIAL PROGRAMME SEASON 2002-2003

GROUND: Runnymeade Stadium, Tempest Road, Egham, Surrey TW20 8HX
Tel: 01784 435226 Club email: eghamtownfc.co.uk

Directions: M25 jct 13, follow signs to Egham, under M25 at r'bout, left to end, left at mini r'bout, over railway crossing, left to end (Pooley Green Rd), right, Tempest Rd. 2nd right. Bus 41 43 441 from Staines to Pooley Green Rd. 30 mins from Egham or Staines (BR)
Capacity: 5,635 Seats: 335 Cover: 1,120 Floodlights: Yes Club Shop: No
Clubhouse: (01784 435226) 7-11pm daily & weekend lunchtimes. Function hall

PROGRAMME

Pages: 40 Price: £1
Editor: A lisonThompson
Tel: 01784 463562 (H)

PREVIOUS **Leagues:** Hounslow & District 1896-1914; Surrey Intermediate 19-22; Surrey Senior 22-28 65-67; Spartan 29-33 67-74; Parthenon 64-65; Athenian 74-77
Names: Runnymede Rovers 1877-1905; Egham FC 05-63
Grounds: Anglers Rest 1877-1914; Manorcroft Rd 19-26; Vicarage Rd 26-27 28-39;Green Lane 27-28

RECORD **Attendance:** 1,400 v Wycombe Wanderers, FA Cup 2ndQual Rd 72
Scorer: Mark Butler 50 (91-92) Career record scorer as well **Appearances:** Dave Jones 850+
Win: 10-1 v Camberley, 81-82 **Defeat:** 0-10 v Fisher Ath. (A), Parthenon League 64-65
Transfer Fee Paid: £3,000 for Mark Butler, 1990
Transfer Fee Received: £4,000 for Mark Butler (Wycombe Wanderers, 1988)

BEST SEASON **FA Cup:** 4th Qual Rd 90-91, 0-2 v Telford Utd (A)

HONOURS Isthmian Lg Assoc Members Tphy R-up 91-92; Spartan Lg 71-72 (Lg Cup R-up 67-68); Athenian Lg R-up 75-76 (Div 2 74-75); Surrey Snr Cup R-up 91-92, Surrey Snr Lg 22-23, Lg Charity Cup 22-23 (R-up 26-27 34-35); Surrey Intermediate Lg 20-21, Charity Cup 19-20 20-21 (R-up 26-27); North West Surrey Charity Cup 20-21;
Egham Twinning Tournament 67-68 71-72 74-75 75-76 76-77 80-81; S.Comb. F'lit Cup 77-78 (R-up 83-84).
Promotion to Div 1.

Left to right

Back row:
Gary Duffy
Alan Jordan,
Paul de Luca,
Michael Bolger,
Andy Bugdale and
Jack McKinlay

Front row:
Andy Durbin,
Paul Reed,
Reece White and
Matt Edwards

Grant Eaton is missing

Photo:
Alan Coomes.

EPSOM & EWELL

CLUB OFFICIALS
President: Stella Lamont
Chairman: Peter Lumm
Vice Chairman: Derick Hayles
Secretary: D Wilson, 33 Delaporte Close,
Epsom, Surrey KT17 4AF
Tel: 01372 729817
email: d.wilson@nbad.co.uk

FOOTBALL MANAGEMENT TEAM
Manager: Barry Barnes
Coaches: Mick Stratford
Physio: Kevin Taylor

FACT FILE
Founded: 1917
Nickname: E's
Colours: Royal & white
Change: All yellow
Midweek Matches: Tuesday
Reserves' League: Suburban
2002-2003
Captain: Graham Morris
Leading Goalscorer: James Hall
Player of the Year: Barry Stevens

GROUND:GROUND: Groundshare with Banstead Athletic FC.
Merland Rise, Tadworth, Surrey KT20 5JG Tel: 01737 350982
Directions: Follow signs to Tattenham Corner (Epsom racecourse), then to Banstead Sports Centre. Ground adjacent to swimming pool.
Half a mile fromTattenham Corner (BR)
Bus 422 from Sutton stops outside ground.
Also buses 460 & 727 from Epsom
Capacity: 3,500 Seats: 250 Cover: 800 Floodlights: Yes
Clubhouse: Normal licensinghourd, food available **Club Shop:** No

PROGRAMME
Pages: 28/32 Price: £1.00
Editor: Stella Lamont (01737 356245)

Club Website www.eefc.net

PREVIOUS
Leagues: Surrey Snr 24-27 73-75; London 27-49; Corinthian 49-63; Athenian 63-73 75-77
Grounds: Horton Lane, Epsom 1925-26 and West Atreet, Ewell 1926-93
Names: Epsom Town (previously Epsom FC) merged with Ewell & Stoneleigh in 1960

CLUB RECORDS
Attendance: 5,000 v Kingstonian, F.A. Cup 2nd Qual. Rd, 15/10/49
Record Goalscorer: Tommy Tuite

BEST SEASON
FA Cup: 1st Round 33-34 **FA Trophy:** 2nd Roundd 81-82
FA Vase: Runners-up 74-75

HONOURS
FA Vase R-up 74-75; London Lg 27-28, R-up (5); Corinthian Lg Memorial Shield 59-60 (R-up 51-52 56-57); Athenian Lg Div 2 R-up 75-76 (Lg Cup R-up 76-77, Div2 Cup R-up 67-68); Isthmian Lg Div 2 77-78 (Div 1 R-up 83-84), Div 2 S . Promotion 01-02 Vandanel Ass Members Trophy R-up 97-98; Surrey Snr Lg 25-26 26-27 74-75 (R-up 73-74), Lg Cup 73-74 74-75, Charity Cup 26-27 (R-up 73-74), Surrey Snr Cup 80-81 (R-up 3); Surrey Snr Shield 32-33 54-55; Surrey Interm'te Cup 29-30,Charity Cup 57-58; S Comb. Cup 79-80 (R-up 82-83 92-93)

Players progressing: Matt Elliott (Leicester), Chris Powell(Derby), Paul Harding (Notts County, Birmingham), Murray Jones (Grimsby), Alan Pardew (Charlton), Mick Leonard (Chesterfield)

Back row, left to right: Kevin Espinosa, Matt Sinclair, Adrian Toppin, James Hall, Graham Morris, Kevin Webb, Simon Huckle and Jamie Buckley.
Front row: Richard Ingham, Marcus Kempster, Joel Rogers, Barry Stevens, Nigel Bennett and Mark Freeborough.

Photo: Alan Coomes

HAMPTON & RICHMOND BOROUGH

CLUB OFFICIALS
Chairman: Graham Wood
President: Alan Simpson OBE
Vice Chairman: Michael Holland
Press Officer: Les Rance
Football Secretary: Stephen Hosmer,27 St. Georges Road, Hanworth, Feltham, Midd'sex.(020 8894 1244)

FOOTBALL MANAGEMENT TEAM
Manager: Alan Devonshire
Coach: T.B.A.

FACT FILE
Formed: 1921
Nickname: Beavers/Borough
Sponsors: M.M Cox.Properties Ltd.
Colours: Red & blue/white/blue
Change Colours: White/blue/white
Midweek Matchday: Tuesday
Website: http://www.hamptonfc.co.uk
Local Press: Middx Chronicle, Surrey Comet, Richmond & Twickenham Times, The Informer

PROGRAMME
Pages: 28 Price: £1.50p
Editor: Stefan Rance

2002-2003
Captain: Dudley Gardner
Top Scorer: Lee Riddell
Player of the Year: Andy Iga

GROUND: Beveree Stadium, Beaver Close, off Station Rd, Hampton TW12 2BX
Tel: Office 020 89412838 (matchdays only) Club: 020 8979 2456 Boardroom: 020 8941 2838
Directions: A3 out of London, fork left (signed Staines/Esher/Sandown Pk) onto A243, A309 Staines exit to Hampton Ct at `Scilly Isles' r'bout, left at r'bout after Hampton Court Bridge onto A308, after 1 mile right into Church St (A311), left after White Hart after 200yds into High St, Station Rd on right just before junction with A308
Capacity: 3,000 Seats: 300 Cover: 800 Floodlights: Yes
Clubhouse: (020 8979 2456). Lounge bar and hall, open on matchdays and training nights. Hall available for hire.
Club Shop: Sells various souvenirs & prog. Contact: Adrian Mann (020 8773 0858)

PREVIOUS **Leagues:** Kingston & District 21-33; South West Middx 33-59; Surrey Snr 59-64; Spartan 64-71; Athenian 71-73
Grounds: Hatherop Rec (until 1959)
CLUB RECORDS **Win:** 11-1 v Eastbourne Utd, Isthmian Lge Div 2 (S), 90-91 **Defeat:** 0-13 v Hounslow Town, Middlesex Senior Cup 62-63
Goalscorer: Peter Allen (176) 1964-73 **Appearances:** Tim Hollands (700) 1977-95
Fees - Paid: £3,000 for Matt Flitter (Chesham United) June 2000
Fees - Received: £40,000 for Leroy Griffiths from Q.P.R.May 2001
BEST SEASON **FA Cup:** 1st Rd Proper 00-01 (1-2 v Barnet) **FA Amateur Cup:** 1st Rd Prop 73-74 (2-4 v Leytonstone)
FA Trophy: 4th Rd 01-02 .1-4 v Hereford United (A)
FA Vase: 3rd Rd 91-92 (0-1 v Newport IOW), 95-96 (0-1 v Colllier Row)
HONOURS: London Snr Cup(2) 86-88; Spartan Lg(4) 64-67 69-70, (R-up 67-68), Lg Cup(4) 64-68 (R-up 2); Surrey Snr Lg 63-64 (Lg Cup R-up 60-61); Middx Charity Cup 69-70 95-96 97-98,98-99 (R-up 68-69 71-72 89-90 94-95); Middx Snr Cup R-up 71-72 76-77 95-96; Athenian Lg Div 2 R-up 72-73; Southern Comb. Cup 68-69 71-72 76-77 81-82 83-84 85-86 96-97 (R-up 77-78 79-80 97-98); Isthmian Lge promotion from Div 1 97-98, Div 2 95-96, Div 3 91-92. Isthmian Lg.Cup Finalists 01-02

Players progressing: Andy Rogers (Southampton), Dwight Marshall (Plymouth), Paul Rogers (Sheffield Utd via Sutton Utd), Derek Bryan Brentford 97), Darren Powell (Brentford 98), Julian Charles (Brentford 99.), Leroy Griffiths (Q.P.R. 01)

Back row. left to right: Gareth Workman (Physio), Jeff Dadswell (Asst.Physio), Enrico Grimm, Victor Fayenuwo, Tony Houghton, Lee Riddell, Andy Iga, Alan Imms, Sam Okafor, Stuart Harte, Brian Cottingham (Caretaker Manager) Malcolm Taylor (Asst. Caretaker Manager)
Front row: Aaron Downes, Mourad Boudjemaa, Yemi Abiodum, Dudley Gardner, Chris Rose, Darren Deegan and Scott Bennetts.
Photo: Stephan Rance.

HORSHAM

CLUB OFFICIALS

Chairman: Frank King
Vice Chairman: Tim Hewlett
President: Geoff Holtom
Press Officer: Jeff Barrett (01403 267730)
Secretary: Jef Barrett, 3Bunting Close, Horsham, West Sussex RH13 5PA.
Tel: 01403 267730
Email : jeff.barrett@btinternet.com

FOOTBALL MANAGEMENT TEAM

Manager: John Maggs
Asst Mgr/Coach:Ali Rennie
Physio: Geoff Brittain

FACT FILE

Founded: 1885
Nickname: Hornets
Club Sponsors: Sunley Homes
Colours: Amber & Green
Change colours: Maroon & Lincoln Green
Midweek Matches: Tuesday
Local Press: West Sussex County Times: Market Square, Horsham (01403 253371

2002-2003

Captain & Player of the Year: Eddie French
Top Scorer: Gavin Geddes

PROGRAMME

Pages: 40 Price: £1.20
Editor:Adam Hammond (01403 217316)

GROUND: Queen St, Horsham RH13 5AD Tel: 01403 252310 E mail address : c/o Sec

Directions: From the station turn left into North Street. Pass the Arts Centre to lights and turn left. At next set of lights (200 yards) turn left again into East Street. East St. becomes Queen Street after the Iron Bridge and the ground lies opposite Queens Head pub.

Capacity: 3,000 Seats: 300 Cover:1,400 Floodlights: Yes

Clubhouse: Matchdays only. Hot and cold snacks. Dancehall **Club Shop:** Yes

PREVIOUS
Leagues: W Sussex Sen; Sussex County 26-51; Metropolitan 51-57; Corinthian 57-63; Athenian 63-73
Grounds: Horsham Park, Hurst Park, Springfield Park

CLUB RECORDS
Attendance: 8,000 v Swindon, FA Cup 1st Rd, November 1966
Victory: 16-1 v Southwick Susussex Co Lg 1945-46
Defeat: 1-11 v Worthing Sussex Sen Cup 1913-14

BEST SEASON
FA Cup: 1st Rd 47-48 (lost 1-9 at Notts County), 66-67 (lost 0-3 v Swindon)
F.A. Trophy: 1st Rd Proper Replay 76-77 **F.A.Vase:** 4th Rd Replay 85-86

HONOURS
Sussex Snr Cup 33-34 38-39 49-50 53-54 71-72 73-74 75-76; Sussex RUR Cup (13); Sussex Floodlight Cup 77-78;01-02 Sussex County Lg (7), R-up (4), Lg Cup 45-46 46-47; Metropolitan Lg 51-52; Ryman League Div 2 R-up 2001-02 Athenian Lg Div 1 72-73, Div 2 69-70 72-73; West Sussex Sen Lge (4); ICIS Div 3 95-96

Players progressing: Jamie Ndah (Barnet), Darren Freeman (Fulham)

Back row, left to right: Jeff Barrett (Secretary), Geoff Brittain (Physio), Eddie French (Captain), Ian Chatfield, Gavin Geddes, John Kirby, Steffan Ball, Lee Butcher, Matt Ottley, David Flemming, Scott Kenward, Stuart Hardy, John Maggs (Manager) and Frank King (Chairman).
Front row: Barrie Westgate, Gary Charman, James Grant, Ali Rennie (Asst. Manager),Lee Carney, Carlo Castrechino and Andy Salako.

LEATHERHEAD

CLUB OFFICIALS

Chairman: Tim Edwards
Secretary: Gerald Darby
Ranmore, 31 Harriots Lane, Ashtead, Surrey, KT21 2QG
Press Office/Comm. Director: Tim Edwards

FOOTBALL MANAGEMENT TEAM

Manager: Alex Inglethorpe
Asst. Manager:Paul Harford
Youth Team Manager:Martin Bullen
Physio: Sarah Watson

FACT FILE

Founded: 1946
Nickname: Tanners
Sponsors: The Beer Seller
Colours: Green and White/green/green
Change colours: Blue & white
Midweek Matchday: Tuesday

2002-2003

Captain: Danny Lavender
Top Scorer: Phil Ruggles
PLayer of the Year: Justin Gray

LEATHERHEAD F.C.
RYMAN FOOTBALL LEAGUE DIVISION 1 SOUTH
THE tanners Vs
SEASON 2002 - 2003
TOOTING & MITCHAM UTD
Tuesday 11th March 2003 : 7.45pm
RYMAN LEAGUE DIVISION ONE SOUTH
OFFICIAL PROGRAMME
PRICE £1.50p
Egham Town vs Leatherhead - 22 February 2003
Ryman
football league
KIT SPONSOR
MILNER CARPETS

Pages: 40 Price: £1.40
Edito: Tony Hodson
Local Press: Leatherhead Advertiser, Surrey Advertiser
Local Radio: County Sound

GROUND Fetcham Grove, Guildford Rd, Leatherhead, Surrey KT22 9AS
Tel: 01372 360151, Fax: 01372 362705

Directions: M25 jct 9 to Leatherhead; follow signs to Leisure Centre, ground adjacent.
Half mile from Leatherhead (BR)
London Country Buses 479 and 408 - ground opposite bus garage

Capacity: 3,400 Seats: 200 Cover: 445 Floodlights: Yes

Clubhouse: Bar open 12-11pm matchdays. Full catering. Tel: 01372 360151

Club Shop: Yes. Tel: 01372 362705

PREVIOUS **Leagues:** Surrey Snr 46-50; Metropolitan 50-51; Delphian 51-58; Corinthian 58-63; Athenian 63-72

CLUB RECORDS **Attendance:** 5,500 v Wimbledon, 1976
Win: 13-1 v Leyland Motors 46-47 Surrey Sen Lge
Defeat: 1-11 v Sutton United
Career goalscorer: Steve Lunn 96-97 (46)
Career appearances: P Caswell 200
Fee paid: £1,500 to Croydon (B Salkeld)
Fee received: £1,500 from Croydon (B Salkeld)

BEST SEASON **FA Amateur Cup:** Semi finalists 70-71 73-74
FA Trophy: Runners-up 77-78
F A Cup: 4th Round 74-75, 2-3 v Leicester C.(A). Also 2nd Rd 75-76 76-77 78-79,1st Rd 77-78 80-81
League clubs defeated: Colchester, Brighton 74-75, Cambridge Utd 75-76,Northampton 76-77

HONOURS FA Trophy R-up 77-78; Isthmian Lg Cup 77-78; Corinthian Lg 62-63; Athenian Lg Div 1 63-64; Surrey Snr Cup 68-69 (R-up 64-65 66-67 74-75 78-79); Surrey Snr Lg 46-47 47-48 48-49 49-50(Lg Cup 49-50), Snr Shield 68-69, Charity Cup 46-47 49-50); E. Surrey Charity Cup 68-69 (R-up 67-68); London Snr Cup R-up 74-75 77-78; Surrey Inter Cup 89-90; Southern Comb. Cup 89-90

Players progressing: Chris Kelly (Millwall), B Friend (Fulham), L Harwood (Port Vale), John Humphrey (Millwall), Ali Chaaban (Farnborough T)

L-R - Back Row: Barry Wilde (Asst. Man.), Paul Harford (Jt Player/Manager), Wes Harrison, Iain Hendry, Marc CCharles-Smith, Justin Gray, Michael Webb, Phil Ruggles, Jeremy Jones, Alex Inglethorpe (Jt Player/Manager). **Front Row:** Sarah Watson (Physio), Paul McKay, Jon Lloyd, Victor Tavares, Danny Oliver, Julian Thompson, Adam Gray.

LEWES

CLUB OFFICIALS

President: T. Carr

Chairman: T. Parris

Secretary: Laurie Pilbeam
Lewes F.C.,Westgate Street,Lewes.
East Sussex BN7 1YR
Tel: 01273 474518

FOOTBALL MANAGEMENT

Manager: Jimmy Quinn

FACT FILE

Founded: 1885
Nickname: Rooks
Colours: Red & Black /black/black
Change colours: All white
Midweek matches: Tuesday
Reserves' League: Sussex Co. Res. Sect
Local Press: Evening Argus, Sussex Express
Local Radio:
Southern F.M.,B.B.C. Southern Counties

PROGRAMME

Pages: 32 pages Price: £1
Editor: Laurie Pilbeam

SEASON 2002/2003
Official Programme & Matchday Magazine
LEWES FOOTBALL CLUB
LEWES
Ryman
£1.00

GROUND: The Dripping Pan, Mountfield Road, Lewes BN7 1XN Tel: 01273 472100

Directions: Two minute walk from Lewes (BR) - turn left out of station and left into Mountfield Road. Ground 100 yards on right

Capacity: 2,600 Cover: 400 Seats: 400 Floodlights: Yes

Club Shop: Yes

Clubhouse: (01273 472100). Bar, tea bar

PREVIOUS: **Leagues:** Mid Sussex 1886-1920; Sussex Co 20-65; Athenian 65-77

RECORDS: **Attendance:** 2,500 v Newhaven, Sussex County Lg 26/12/47
Goalscorer: Mark Stafford 192 **Appearances:** Terry Parris 662
Transfer Fee Paid: None **Transfer Fee Received:** £2,500 for Grant Horscroft (Brighton)

BEST SEASON: **FA Cup:** 1st Rd Proper 2001-02 v Stoke City 0-2
FA Trophy: 1st Rd 82-83 **FA Amateur Cup:** 2nd Rd 67-68
FA Vase: Quarter Final 2001-02

HONOURS Isthmian Lg Div 2 Champions 01-02, R-up 79-80 91-92; Div 3 R-up 00-01. Ath'n Lg Div 1 69-70 (Div 2 67-68); Sussex Co. Lg 64-65 (R-up 24-25 33-34 58-59 63-64, Lg Cup 39-40); Mid Sussex Lg 10-11 13-14; Sussex Snr Cup 64-65 70-71 84-85 00-01(R-up 79-80 82-83 87-88); Sussex Royal Ulster Rifles Charity Cup(3) 61-63 64-65; Gilbert Rice F'lit Cup 82-83 88-89; Neale Tphy 68-69; Sussex F'lit Cup 76-77 (SF 83-84); Southern Counties Comb Div 1 80-81

Players progressing: (to Brighton unless stated) Don Bates(1950), Peter Knight (1964), Terry Stanley (1969), Colin Woffuden (1970), G Elphick & Steve Ford (Stoke 1981), Glen Geard, Grant Horscroft (1987), J Hammond (Fulham), S Funnell, L Allen (Wimbledon), M Rice (Watford)

DIVISION ONE SOUTH ACTION

Tooting's James Mordey (stripes) slides in to dispossess Carshalton's Scott Todd. **Photo**: Alan Coomes

MARLOW

CLUB OFFICIALS

Chairman: Terry Staines

Secretary: Paul Burdell,
69 Wycombe Rd., Marlow.
Tel: 01628 890540

Press Off./Comm. Man.: Terry Staines

FACT FILE

Formed: 1870
Nickname: The Blues
Sponsors: North West Estates
Colours: Royal, white trim/royal/royal
Change colours: White & black
Midweek matchday: Tuesday
Reserves' League: Suburban Premier

FOOTBALL MANAGEMENT TEAM

Manager: Derek Sweetman
Coach:Tim Cook
Physio: Mark Skoyles

2002-2003

Captain: Tim Cook
Top Scorer: Nicky Ryder
Player of the Year:Nicky Ryder

PROGRAMME

Pages: 40 Price: £1
Editor: Terry Staines
Local Press: Bucks Free Press, Maidenhead Advertiser, Evening Post
Local Radio: Eleven 70, Radio 210, Thames Valley Radio

GROUND: Alfred Davis Memorial Ground, Oak Tree Road, Marlow SL7 3ED
Tel: 01628 483970 Information Line (normal call rates): 01932 710215

Directions: A404 to Marlow (from M4 or M40), then A4155 towards town centre. Turn right into Maple Rise (by ESSO garage), ground in road opposite (Oak Tree Rd).
1/2 mile from Marlow (BR). 1/4 mile from Chapel Street bus stops

Capacity: 3,000 Cover: 600 Seats: 250 Floodlights: Yes

Clubhouse: Open matchdays & most evenings. Snack bar open matchdays

PREVIOUS: **Leagues:** Reading & Dist.; Spartan 1908-10 28-65; Great Western Suburban;Athenian 65-84
Name: Great Marlow **Grounds:** Crown Ground 1870-1919); Star Meadow 19-24

CLUB RECORDS: **Attendance:** 3,000 v Oxford United, FA Cup 1st Rd 1994.
(Ground - 8,000 SloughT. v Wycombe W., Berks & Bucks Snr Cup Final, 1972)
Goalscorer: Kevin Stone 31
Appearances: Mick McKeown 500+
Fees - Paid: £5,000 for Richard Evans (Sutton Utd. 94)
Received: £8,000 for David Lay from Slought Town 94

BEST SEASON: **FA Cup:** Semi-Finals 1882; 3rd Rd 94-95 (0-2 v Swindon), 92-93 (1-5 v Tottenham);
1st Rd - 19 times -1871-85 86-88 92-93 1991-92 94-95
FA Trophy: 3rdRd 2002-2003
FA Vase: 5th Rd replay 74-75, 5th Rd 00-01

HONOURS: Isthmian Lg Div 1 87-88, Div 2 South R-up 86-87, Lg Cup 92-93, Associate Members Trophy: 2000-01; SpartanLg Div 1 37-38 (Div 2 West 29-30); Berks & Bucks Sen Cup (11)

Players progressing: Leo Markham (Watford 1972), NaseemBashir (Reading)

L-R - Back row: Reuben Howell, Olly Lewingdon, Karl Croft, John Beale, Kieran Drake, Tim Cook, John Isaac, Micky Floyd, Daniel Pedley and Mark Skoyles (Physio)
Front row: Shane Small, Alex Rodrigues, Paul Freeman, Derek Sweetman (Manager), Bobby Wilkinson, Jeff Lamb, Gavin Mernagh.

METROPOLITAN POLICE

CLUB OFFICIALS

Chairman: Des Flanders QPM
Vice Chairman: Ian Carter
President: Sir John Stevens QPM
Secretary: Tony Brooking
15 Westmoreland Ave,
Hornchurch, Essex. RM112EJ.
Tel: (01708 450715)

FOOTBALL MANAGEMENT TEAM

Manager: T.B.A.
Physio: Dick Pierce

FACT FILE

Founded: 1919 Nickname: Blues
Club Sponsors: Hatch Associates
& News of the World Newspaper
Colours: All blue
Change colours:White
Midweek Matches: Tuesday
Reserves' League: Suburban

2002-2003

Top Scorer: Eric Tomlinson
Capt: Ian Batten
P.O.Y.Stuart Mackenzie

Pages: 10 Price: Free
Editor/ Press Officer:
Cliff Travis (01932 782215)

Local Press: Surrey Comet, Surrey Herald
Local Radio: County Sounds

GROUND: Metropolitan Police Sports Ground, Imber Court, East Molesey Tel: 0208 398 7358)

Directions: From London: A3 then A309 to Scilly Isles r'bout, right into Hampton Court Way, left at 1st r'bout into Ember Court Rd - ground faces in 300yds. From M25 jct 10: A3 towards London for 1 mile, A307 through Cobham, left immd. after Sandown Park into Station Rd - ground 1 mile on left.
Half mile from either Thames Ditton or Esher BR stations

Capacity: 3,000 Seats: 297 Cover: 1,800 Floodlights: Yes **Club Shop:** No
Clubhouse: (0181 398 1267). Four bars, dancehall, cafeteria open 9am-11pm. Hot & cold food

REVIOUS: **Leagues:** Spartan 28-60; Metropolitan 60-71; Southern 71-78
Grounds: None **Name:** None

CLUB RECORDS: **Attendance:** 4,500 v Kingstonian, FA Cup 1934
Goal Scorer: Mario Russo
Appearances: Pat Robert
Win: 10-1 v Tilbury 1995
Defeat: 1-11 v Wimbledon, 1956

BEST SEASON **FA Cup:** 1st Rd - 32-33, 0-9 v Northampton T. (A); 84-85, 0-3 v Dartford (H); 94-95, 0-3 v Crawley T. (H)

HONOURS: Isthmian Lg Div 2 R-up 77-78 87-88; Spartan Lg 28-29 29-30 36-37 38-39 45-46 53-54 54-55, (R-up 47-48), Lg Cup 59-60 (R-up 57-58); Middx Snr Cup 27-28;Surrey Snr Cup 32-33, Charity Shield 38-39; Metropolitan Lg Cup 68-69 (Amtr Cup 68-69 69-70); London Snr Cup R-up 34-35 40-41; Herts & Middx Comb. 39-40;Diadora Lg Carlsberg Trophy 94-95

L-R - Back: Geoff Foreman, Kori Davis, Dave Newman, Stuart MacKenzie, Mark Harper (Coach), Mickey Palmer, Scott Bennetts, Stuart Harte.
Front: Darren Lonergan, Symon James, Ian Batten (Captain), Nick Sowden, Matt Jones, Carl Naylor, Paul Barrowcliff

MOLESEY

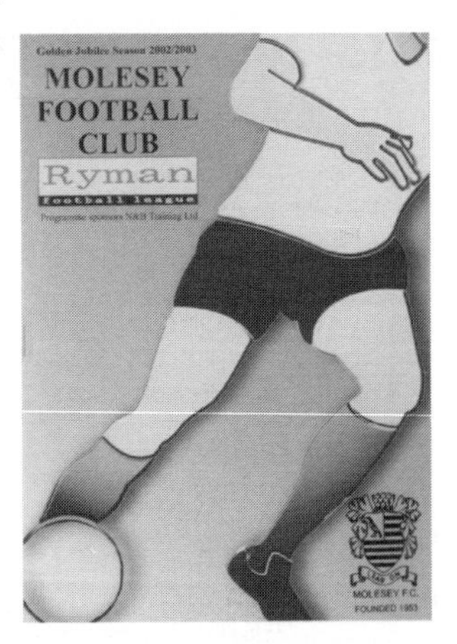

CLUB OFFICIALS

Chairman: Norman Clark

President: T.B.A.

Pres Officer: Peter Bowers

Secretary : Fiona Bowers
(c/o the club)

FOOTBALL MANAGEMENT TEAM

Manager: Ian Hazel
Asst Man/Coach: Jimmy Dack
Reserve Team Manager:T.B.A.
Youth Team Manager: John Lampard

2002-2003

Captain: Lee Doherty
Top Scorer: Richard Brady 12
Player of the Year: Gus Hurdle

FACT FILE

Formed: 1952 (as senior club)
Nickname: The Moles
Colours: White/black/black
Change colours: All Yellow
Midweek home matchday: Tuesday
Reserve Team's League: Suburban
Youth Team: Southern Yth Lge
Local Press: Surrey Comet,
Surrey Herald, Molesey News
Local Radio: Thames 107.8 FM
Hospital Radio, County Sound,
Three Counties, Star FM.

PROGRAMME

Pages:24 Price: £1
Editor: Pete Bowers c/o the club

GROUND **Address:** 412 Walton Road, West Molesey, Surrey KT8 0JG Tel: 0181 941 7989 (Boardroom) 0181 979 4823 (Clubhouse)
Directions A3 from London to Hook, thenA309 to Marquis of Granby pub, right to Hampton Court station, turn left forWest Molesey, ground one mile on left
Capacity 4,000 Cover: 600 Seats: 400 Floodlights: Yes
Clubhouse Open every evening and weekend lunchtimes 2 bars, discos, live artists, darts, bingo, pool. Steward: John Chambers
Club Shop: Contact John Chambers

PREVIOUS **Leagues:** Surrey Intermediate 53-56; Surrey Snr 56-59; Spartan 59-72; Athenian72-77
Name: Molesey St Pauls 1950-53. **Grounds:** None

CLUB RECORDS **Attendance:** 1,255 v Sutton United, Surrey Senior Cup Semi-Final 1966
CareerGoalscorer: Michael Rose, 139
Career Appearances: Frank Hanley, 453
Transfer fee paid: £500 for Chris Vidal (Leatherhead 88)
Transfer fee received: £5,000 for Chris Vidal (Hythe Town 89)

BEST SEASON **FA Vase:** 6th Rd 81-82. **FA Trophy:** 1st Rd replay 90-91
FA Cup: First Round Proper 94-95, 0-4 v Bath City (H)

HONOURS Isthmian Lg Div 1 R-up 92-93, Div 2 South R-up 89-90, Lg Cup R-up 92-93, Surrey Senior Lg 57-58, Lg Charity Cup 56-57, Spartan Lg R-up 59-60. Lg Cup 61-62 R-up 63-64, Surrey Senior Shield R-up 74-75, Southern Combination Cup 90-91 94-95

Players progressing: John Finch (Fulham), Cyrille Regis (WBA, Coventry &England)

Back row, left to right: L.Philips, R.Hughes, M Azzapardi, A.Sayer, A.Rose.,S.Lampard and W. Cain. **Front row:** G.Schmidt, I.Hazel, C.Kane., L.Doherty, M. Royal, E.Ibrahim, B.Harris, C.Morrison, G.Hurdle, A.Sweet and L.Craker .**Photo: Dave West**

SLOUGH TOWN

CLUB OFFICIALS

Chairman: Martin Deaner
Secretary / Press Off.: Roy Merryweather
Tel: 01753 554833 (Ground)
01735 534033(W)
01189 722871(H)
01753 533949 (Fax)

FOOTBALL MANAGEMENT TEAM

Manager: T.B.A.
Coach: T.B.A.
Physio: Kevin McGoldrick

FACT FILE

Formed: 1890
Nickname: The Rebels
Sponsor:Lakes Video-HiFi of Slough
Colours: Amber/navy blue/amber
Change colours: All white
Midweek home matchday: Tuesdays
Website: www.sloughtownfc.net

2002-2003

Captain: Steve Daly
Top scorer: Tony Boot 31
Player of the Year: Tony Boot

Pages: 36 Price: £1.50
Editor: John Tebbit

Local Press: Slough Observer Slough Express
Local Radio: Thames Valley FM, Star FM
Radio Berkshire

GROUND: Wexham Park Stadium, Wexham Road, Slough, Berkshire. SL2 5QR.
Tel: 01753 554833 Fax: 01753 539201

Directions: From North : M25 J16 East London M40 J1 - South A412 through Iver Heath to George Green. 2nd set lights turn right by George PH, George Green.Church Lane 1 mile to end, then small roundabout, turn left, ground 1/4 mile onright

Capacity: 5,000 Cover: 1,890 Seats: 450 Floodlights: Yes

Clubhouse: Lounge bar open weekdays 7pm-11pm, weekends, lunchtimes, evenings. Banqueting hall for all types of function) email: shop@sloughtownfc.net

Club Shop: Contact: Graham Thomas (07989 434371 *M)

PREVIOUS **Leagues:** Southern Alliance 1892-93; Berks & Bucks 1901-05; Gt Western Suburban1906-19; Spartan 1920-39; Herts & Middx 1940-45; Corinthian 1946-63; Athenian1963-73; Isthmian 1973-90, 94-95; Alliance Prem. (GMVC) 90-94
Grounds: Dolphin Playing Fields & Stadium, Chalvey Rd Sports Grd, YorkRd Maidenhead 1920, Centre Sports Ground 36-42

CLUB RECORDS **Attendance:** 8,000 - Schoolboys u15 Final Slough v Liverpool - 1976
Win: 17-0 v Railway Clearing House - 1921-22
Defeat: 1-11 v Chesham Town 1909/10
Fee Paid: £18,000 for Colin Fielder from Farnborough - 1991
Career appearances: Terry Reardon 458 - 64/81
Fee Received: £22,000 from Wycombe W. for Steve Thompson
Career goalscorer: E.J.C. Tory Norris 84 - 25/26

BEST SEASON **FA Cup:** 2nd Round Proper, 79-80 (Yeovil T), 82-83 (Bishop's Stortford), 85-86 (Leyton O.), 86-87 (Swansea C.).
League clubs defeated: Millwall, 1-0 (H) Jan. 1983
FA Trophy: Semi-Final 1976-77, 2-6(agg) v Dagenham; 97-98, 1-2(agg) v Southport

HONOURS: FA Amateur Cup R-up 72-73; Great Western Suburban League R-up 19-20: Spartan League R-up 20-21 21-22 31-32 32-33 38-39; Herts & Middx League R-up 43-44; Corinthian League 50-51 (R-up 45-46 46-47 57-58); Athenian League 67-68 71-72 72-73 (R-up 68-69),LgCup 71-2 72-3 Div 1 64-65, Memorial Shield 64-65 71-72 72-73); Isthmian League 80-81 89-90 R-up 94-95, (Div 2 R-up 73-74),Lg Cup 75-76 80-81 R-up 94-95 Lge Shield 89-90 ; Berks & Bucks Sen Cup (10) 02-03 19-20 23-24 26-27 35-36 54-55 70-72 76-77 80-81

L-R - Back Row: Clement James, Ricky Browne, Dean Palmer, Nicky Gyoury, Dominique Jean-Zepherin, Adrian Blake, Anthony Howard, Adrian Brown, Tony Boot, Ryan Williams.
Front: Ian Hodges, Byron Bubb, Steve Daly (capt), Christian Metcalfe, Darron Wilkinson, Ryan Spencer, Sammy Winston, Rav Braich

STAINES TOWN

Welcome to Wheatsheaf Park
home of the 'Swans'
Ryman
Division One South

CLUB OFFICIALS

Chairman: Alan Boon
Vice Chairman: Ken Williams
Secretary: Steve Parsons
3 Birch Green, Staines, Middx TW18 4HA
Tel: 01784 450420
General Manager: Chris Wainwright
Commercial Manager: Ken Williams
Press Officer: Stuart Moore (01784 421118)

FOOTBALL MANAGEMENT

Manager: Steve Cordery
Asst Man: Craig Maskell
Physios: Gareth Workman & Geoff Dadswell

PROGRAMME

Pages: 44 Price: £1.50
Editor: Sec. & Stuart Moore (01784 421118)

FACT FILE

Formed: 1892
Nickname: The Swans
Sponsors: The Exchange Nightclub
Colours: Old gold (blue trim)/royal/royal
Change colours: All white
Midweek matchday: Tuesday
Reserve league: Sutton & District Vets Lg.
Local Press: Staines & Ashford News, Middx Chronicle, Informer,Staines Gaurdian
Local Radio: County Sound, GLR, Capital, Star FM, Radio Wey.

2002-03

Leading Scorer: Neil Selby - 14
P.o.Y.: Steve battams

GROUNDWheatsheaf Park, Wheatsheaf Lane,Staines,Middlesex TW18 2PD(01784 455988)
Directions: M25 Jct13 to A30 Staines by-pass to Crooked Billet roundabout.Take town centre exit(A308) and left into South St., at iron bridge. Pass bus staion and bear left into Laleham Rd. Wheatsheafe Lane is 1km on right Buses 481, 570,and 573 pass Wheatsheaf Lane.
Capacity: 3,000 **Cover:** 850 **Seats:** 300 **Floodlights**:Yes **Food:** Rolls and snacks available
Club HQ & Clubhouse: Staines Town FC, Wheatsheaf Lane, Staines Modern sports bar.
Club Shop: Souvenirs available from Ray Moore c/o STFC.

PREVIOUS **Leagues:** W London All (pre-1900), W London, W Middx (pre-1905), Gt WesternSuburban 05-13 20-24, Gt Western Comb, Munitions Lg (World War 1), London Works(World War 1), Hounslow & Dist 19-20, Spartan 24-35 58-71, Middx Sen 43-52; Parthenon 52-53, Hellenic 53-58, Athenian 71-73
Names: Staines Albany and St Peters Institute (merged) in 1895, Staines 05-18,Staines Lagonda 18-25, Staines Vale (2nd World War)
Grounds: Edgell Rd (St Peters Inst); The Lammas, Shortwood Common, Mill Mead(Hammonds/Wicks/Pursers Farm); Shepperton Road (to 51); Wheatsheaf Lane - From 51-except g/share Chertsey Town (1996-8), Walton & Hersham (2001-02) & Egham Town (2002-Feb 03)

CLUB RECORDS **Attendance:** 2,750 v Banco di Roma (Barassi Cup) 1975 (70,000 saw 1st leg in Rome)
Goalscorer: Alan Gregory 122 **Appearances:** Dickie Watmore 840
Win: 14-0 v Croydon (A), Isthmian League Div. 1 19/3/94 **Defeat:** 1-18 v Wycombe Wands. (A), G West Sub Lge 27.12.09
Fee Paid: For R Teale (Slough 81) **Fee Received:** For Scott Taylor (Millwall 95-96)

BEST SEASON **FA Amateur Cup:** 3rd Rd 23-24 **FA Trophy:** 2nd Rd 2nd Replay 76-77l (Last 32)
FA Cup: 1st Rd 84-85, 0-2 v Burton Alb (A) & 1879-80 & 80-81 (as St Peters Institute)

HONOURS Isthmian Lg Div 1 74-75 88-89 (Div 2 74-75); Athenian Lg Div 2 71-72 (Div 1 R-up 72-73); Spartan Lg 59-60 (R-up 70-71), Lg Cup 68-69 (R-up 60-61 70-71); Hellenic Lg R-up 55-56 (Lg Cup R-up 53-54 55-56); Gt Western Suburban Lg Div 1R-up 11-12 22-24 (Div 2 (Middx) 20-21); W London All Div 1 1899-1900; W LondonLg Div 1 00-01; W Middx Lg 04-05 (R-up 03-04); London Snr Cup R-up 76-77 80-81; Middx Snr Cup(7), (R-up 09-10 32-33 79-80), Snr Charity Cup 94-95; Barassi Cup76; Southern Comb. Chall. Cup 64-65 66-67 68-69 94-95 96-97,(R-up 67-68 94-95,99-00);W Middx Cup 23-24; Staines Cottage Hosp Cup 24-25; Merthyr Middx Charity Shield 90-91,(R-up 94-95); El Canuelo Trophy 92-93 94-95 94-95; Carlsberg Cup 94-95; Melksham Middx Charity Shield 96-97 Jim Lawford Memorial Cup 99-00, Midd'x Bowl 2001-2 (shared)

Players progressing: R Bennett (Southend 72), J Love (C Palace 75), P Shaw(Charlton 77), E Young (Wolves), G Hill (Millwall), W Stemp (Brighton), MFerney (Fulham), S Taylor (Millwall & Bolton W)

Back row left to right: Danny Pipe (Assistant Manager), Paul McCarthy, Danny Hayward, Andrew Sullivan, Mark Parker, Matthew Lovett, Richard Taylor, Damien Smith, Paul Johnson, Paul Greaves, Ken Ballard (Manager) and Chris Witcher (Physio).
Front row: Kohei Lio, Steve Battams, Joe O'Shea, Nick Hooper and Neil Selby. **Photo:** Mick Gaughan.

TOOTING & MITCHAM UTD

TOOTING &
MITCHAM
UNITED FOOTBALL CLUB
SEASON
2002-3
Ryman
football league

CLUB OFFICIALS

Chairman: John Buffoni
President: Cliff Bilham
Vice Chairman: Alan Simpson

Secretary: Les Roberts, 91 Fernlea Road, Mitcham, Surrey CR4 2HG (01816 465275)

Commercial Manager: John Pollard
Press Officer: Steve Taylor c/o club

FOOTBALL MANAGEMENT TEAM
Manager: Ian Hazell
Coach: Peter Shaw
Physio: Danny Keenan

FACT FILE

Formed: 1932
Nickname: Terrors
Sponsors: Claremont Coaches
Colours: Black & white stripes/black/white
Change colours: All red
Midweek matchday: Tuesday
Reserve League: Suburban
Local Press: Mitcham News, South London Press, South London Guardian
Local Radio: Capital

PROGRAMME
Pages: 24 Price: 80p
Editor: Steve Taylor

GROUND: Imperial Fields, Bishopsford Road, Morden, Surrey SM4 6BF
Tel Nos: 020 8648 3248 (ground) 020 8685 9229 (board room)
Directions: Phone club please.
Capacity: 8,000 Cover: 1,990 Seats: 1,990 Floodlights: Yes
Clubhouse: Open every evening and weekend lunchtimes. Wide variety of food available
Club Shop: Sells souvenirs & confectionary

PREVIOUS: **Leagues:** London 32-37, Athenian 37-56 **Ground:** None **Name:** None

CLUB RECORDS: **Attendance:** 17,500 v QPR, FA Cup 2nd Rd 56-57
Goalscorer: Alan Ives 92 (1972-78) **Appearances:** Danny Godwin 470
Win: 11-0 v Welton Rovers, FA Amateur Cup 62-63
Defeat: 1-8 v Kingstonian, Surrey Snr Cup 66-67 v Redbridge Forest (H), LoctiteCup 3rd Rd 19/2/91
Fee Paid: £9,000 for Dave Flint (Enfield) **Fee Received:** £10,000 for Herbie Smith (Luton)

BEST SEASON: **FA Trophy:** 2nd Qualifying Rd Replay 71-72 81-82
FA Amateur Cup: 1st Rd replay 22-23 **FA Vase:**
FA Cup: 4th Rd 75-76, 1-3 v Bradford C. (A) 3rd Rd 58-59; 2nd Rd 56-57 76-77;1st Rd 5 other occasions
League clubs defeated: Bournemouth & Boscombe Ath, Northampton 58-59, Swindon 75-76

HONOURS: Isthmian League 57-58 59-60 (Full Members Cup 92-93); Athenian League 49-50 54-55; London Challenge Cup R-up 59-60; Surrey Senior Cup 37-38 43-44 44-45 52-53 59-60 75-76 76-77 77-78; Surrey Senior Shield 51-52 60-61 61-62 65-66 London Senior Cup 42-43 48-49 58-59 59-60 (R-up 43-44 44-45); South Thames Cup 69-70;

Players progressing: Trevor Owen (Orient 58), Dave Bumpstead (Millwall 58), Paddy Hasty (Aldersot 58), Walter Pearson(Aldershot), Richie Ward & Alex Stepney (Millwall 62 & 63), Vic Akers(Watford 75), Paul Priddy (Wimbledon 78), Carlton Fairweather & Brian Gayle(Wimbledon 84)

Lee Doherty, (3rd from left) scores with this header against Croydon Athletic to give Tooting & Mitcham their first competitive goal at the new ground.
Photo: Francis Short

WALTON & HERSHAM

CLUB OFFICIALS

Chairman: Alan Smith
President: Allen Batsford
Secretary: Michael Groom,15 Windsor Walk, Weybridge, Surrey KT13 9AP
Tel No: 01932 842982
Press Officer: Mervyn Rees
Tel: 01932 245756

FOOTBALL MANAGEMENT TEAM

Manager: Laurence Batty
Physio: Stuart Smith

FACT FILE

Formed: 18960 Nickname: Swans
Sponsors: Beales
Colours: All red
Change colours: Yellow/Green/yellow
Midweek home matchday: Tuesday
Reserve Team's League: Suburban
Club Website: waltonandhershamfc.org.uk
2002-2003
Captain:& P.o.Y.: Francis Dean
Top Scorer: Scott Edgar

Official Match Day Programme
Walton Hersham F.C.
The Ryman Football League
£1.50

Pages: 36 Price: £1.50
Editor: Mark Massingham Tel: 01932 885814

Local Press: Surrey Herald, Surrey Comet
Local Radio: County Sound, BBC Southern Counties

GROUND: Sports Ground, Stompond Lane, Walton-on-Thames Tel: 01932 245263 (club)
Directions: From North: Over Walton Bridge & along New Zealand Ave., down 1-way street and up A244 Hersham Rd - grd 2nd right. From Esher: Down Lammas Lane then Esher Rd, straight over 1st r'bout, 4th exit at next r'bout (WestGrove) 2nd left at end of Hersham Rd and Stompond Lane 1/2 mile on left.Ten min walk Walton-on-Thames (BR). Bus 218 passes grd
Capacity: 6,500 Cover: 2,500 Seats: 500 Floodlights: Yes
Clubhouse: (01932 245263). Open every night. TV, darts, pool, refreshments on matchdays
Club Shop: Open matchdays. Contact Richard Olds c/o the club

PREVIOUS **Leagues:** Surrey Senior; Corinthian 45-50; Athenian 50-71

CLUB RECORDS **Attendance:** 10,000 v Crook Town, FA Amateur Cup Quarter Final 1951-52
Scorer: Reg Sentance 220 in 11 seasons **Appearances:** Terry Keen 449 in 11 seasons
Win: 10-0 v Clevedon, FA Amateur Cup 1960 **Defeat:** 11-3 v Kingstonian Surrey Sen Shield 58
Transfer fee paid: £6,000 **Transfer fee received:** £150,000 for Nathan Ellington 99

BEST SEASON **FA Trophy:** 4th Round 99-00 **FA Amateur Cup:** Winners 72-73, (SF 51-52, 52-53)
FA Cup: 2nd Rd 72-73 (v Margate), 73-74 (v Hereford). League clubs defeated: Exeter 72-73, Brighton 73-74

HONOURS: Isthmian Lg R-up 72-73, Barassi Cup 73-74; Athenian Lg 68-69 (R-up 50-51 69-70 70-71, Lg Cup 69-70); Corinthian Lg 46-49 (R-up 49-50), Premier Midweek F'litLg 67-69 70-71 (R-up 71-72); Surrey Snr Cup 47-48 50-51 60-61 61-62 70-71 72-73 R-up (6); London Snr Cup R-up 73-74; SouthernComb. Cup 82-83 88-89 91-92; 99-00 00-01Surrey Comb.Cup 49-50 91-92.

Players progressing: Dennis Pacey (Leyton O 1952), Keith Amos (Arsenal1952),Mike Whitear (Crystal Palacr), Andy McCulloch (QPR 1970), Mick Heath (Brentford 1971),Paul Priddy (Brentford 1972), Richard Teale (Q.P.R. 1973), SteveParsons (Wimbledon 1977), Stuart Massey (Crystal Palace), Ross Davidson(Sheffield Utd), Nathan Ellington (Bristol Rovers), Paul Smith (Brentford),Tommy Williams (West Ham United) and Basir Savage (Reading)

Back row, left to right: Stuart Smith (physio), Luke Gerrard, Lee O'Donnell, Chris Whelan, Nicky Andrews, Scott Edgar, Alan Dowson, Tristan Frontin and Jamie Laister **Front row:** Adam Thompson, Marcus Rose, Adam Fennell, Paul Harkness, Ben Loney, Francis Dolan, Wes Goggin and mascot Ali Crawford

WHYTELEAFE

CLUB OFFICIALS
Chairman: Mark Coote
Sec: Graham Douce c/o Whyteleafe F.C.
Press Sec:: Brian Davis,Tel: 020 8651 2999
Commercial Manager: T Douce
Tel: 01883 343450
Match Secretary: Edward Lucas:
Braeside,Johns Road,Tatsfield,Westerham,
Kent TN16 2AP.Tel No: 01959 577361 (H)
Director of Football: C.Turner

FACT FILE
Formed: 1946 Nickname: Leafe
Sponsors: Custom cables
Colours: Green & white hoops/green
Change colours: Yellow /green/green
Midweek matchday: Tuesday
Reserve Team's League: Suburban
2002-03
Captain: Danny Rose
Top scporer: Paul Scott
P.o.Y.:Ali Reeve

FOOTBALL MANAGEMENT TEAM
Manager: Lee Richardson   Assistant Man.: Bernie Donnelly
Coach: Billy Patterson   Physio: John Knapton   Chief Scout: M.Taylor

GROUND 15 Church Road, Whyteleafe, Surrey CR3 0AR
Tel: 020 8660 5491 (Ground) 020 8645 0422 (Boardroom)
Directions: Five minutes walk from Whyteleafe (BR) - turn right from station, and left into Church Road
Capacity: 5,000   Cover: 600   Seats:400   Floodlights: Yes

Clubhouse: Every evening & lunches at w/e. Hot & cold food, pool, darts, gaming machines
Clubshop: Yes

Programme
Pages: 36 Price: £1.00
Editor: Chris Layton (01883 381169)
Local Press: Croydon Advertiser
Local Radio: Mercury

PREVIOUS **Leagues**: Caterham & Edenbridge, Croydon, Thornton Heath & Dist., SurreyIntermediate (East) 54-58, Surrey Senior 58-75, Spartan 75-81, Athenian 81-84
Names: None   **Grounds:** None

CLUB RECORDS **Attendance:** 2,210 v Chester City F.A.Cup 1st Rd 99-00.
Transfer fee paid: £1,000 for Gary Bowyer (Carshalton)**Transfer fee received:** £25,000 for Steve Milton

BEST SEASON **FA Vase:** 5th Rd 80-81 85-86
FA Trophy: 4th Rd 98-99 v Kingstonian   **FA Cup:** First Round proper, 99-00 v Chester City (H)

HONOURS Isthmian Lge Div 2 South R-up 88-89; Surrey Senior Lge 68-69 (Lge Cup R-up 68-69, Lge Charity Cup 71-72, Res Sect 62-63 (Chall. Cup 62-63 (R-up 59-60); Surrey Sen. Cup 68-69 (R-up 87-88); Surrey Prem. Cup R-up 84-85; E. Surrey Charity Cup 79-80 (R-up 76-77 77-78); Thornton Heath & Dist Lge 51-52(Lge Cup 51-52) Div 4 R-up 51-52; Edenbridge Charity Cup 51-52; Caterham & Purley Hospital Cup 51-52; Surrey County Interm Lge East Sect 1 55-56; Surrey Jun. Cup R-up 51-52; Caterham & Edenbridge Lge Div 3 51-52; Borough of Croydon Charity Cup 56-57; Southern Yth Lge 89-90 (R-up 88-89), Lge Cup 88-89 89-90; Southern Counties M'week F'lit Cup 95-96
Players progressing: Steve Milton (Fulham), Ian Cox and Alan Pardew (Crystal Palace)

Back row, left to right: Bernie Donnelly, Kevin Smith, Mark Dickinson, Paul Scott, Lee Richardson (Manager), Danny Rose, Mark Coote (Chairman), Nigel Golley, Ian Peddle, Pater Garland, Stuart Massey, John Knapton (Physio) and Colin Turner (Director of Football)
Front row: Andre Robinson, Ryan Gray, Kenny Lowhing, Luke Basford, Ali Reeve, Graham Brett, Danny Bowere and Tim Strong (Kit Manager).

WINDSOR & ETON

CLUB OFFICIALS

Chairman: Peter Simpson
President: T.B.A.
Secretary: Steve Rowland, c/o Football Club
Tel: 07887 770630 (M)
Press Officer: Secretary

FOOTBALL MANAGEMENT TEAM

Manager: Dennis Greene
Asst Manager:Colin Ferguson

FACT FILE

Founded: 1892
Nickname: Royalists
Colours: All red with green trim
Change colours: Blue
Midweek matches: Tuesday
Reserves' League: Suburban (South)
Local Press: Windsor & Eton Express, Windsor & East Berks Observer, Evening Post
Local Radio: BBC Radio Berkshire,Star FM

PROGRAMME

28 pages Price: £!.00
Editor: Malcolm Williams

GROUND Stag Meadow, St Leonards Road, Windsor, Berkshire SL4 3DR (01753 860656)
Directions: A332 from M4 junct 6. Third left at r'bout , left into St Leonards Rd at lights on T-junction, ground 500 yards on right on B3022 opposite Stag &Hounds PH. 1 mile from town centre -
BR to Windsor Central station (from) Slough or Windsor Riverside (change at Staines from Waterloo)
Capacity: 4,500 Cover: 650 Seats: 400 Floodlights: Yes
Clubhouse: Yes **Club Shop:** Yes

PREVIOUS **Leagues:** Southern 1895-96; West Berks; Great Western Suburban 1907-22; Athenian 22-29 63-81; Spartan 29-32; Great Western Comb; Corinthian 45-50; Metropolitan 50-60; Delphian 60-63 **Ground:** Ballon Meadow 1892-1912

CLUB RECORDS **Attendance:** 8,500 (Charity match) **Appearances:** Kevin Mitchell
Fee Paid: £9,000 for Keith White (Slough Town)
Fee Received: £45,000 for Michael Banton & Michael Barnes (Barnet)

BEST SEASON **FA Amateur Cup:** 4th Rd 21-22 **FA Vase:** Semi-Final 80-81 (QF 79-80) **FA Trophy:** 3rd Rd 88-89
FA Cup: 2nd Rd replay 83-84. 1st Rd 7 times 25-26 80-81 82-86 91-92. League clubs defeated: None

HONOURS Isthmian Lg Div 1 83-84 Div 2 R-up 82-83 2000-01,
Athenian Lg 79-80 80-81 Lg Cup 79-80 R-up 78-79 80-81, Div 2 Cup 63-64 R-up 68-69, Spartan Lg R-up 36-37 37-38 Div 1 30-31,
Metropolitan Lg R-up 53-54 Lg Amtr Cup 51-52 52-53, Lg Cup 52-53 R-up 53-54 54-55, Gt Western Suburban Lg R-up 21-22,
Berks & Bucks Snr Cup (11) 10-11 36-38 40-45 61-62 87-89 R-up 07-08 24-25 26-27 38-39 46-47 62-63,
Berks & Bucks Benev. Cup 35-36 37-38 46-47 62-63 R-up 38-39 47-48 49-50

Players progressing: Reg Dare (Southampton 1949), Steve Adams (Charlton 1979), Dave Barnett (Colchester 1988), Vic Woodley (Chelsea & England), Billy Coward (QPR, Walsall), Ken Groves (Preston), Dave Regis (Notts County), Damian Spencer (1998)

BOGNOR CELEBRATE PROMOTION Photo: Francis Short

WORTHING

PROGRAMME
Pages: 48 Price: £1.2
Editor: Ian Fowler

CLUB OFFICIALS

Chairman: Beau Reynolds
President: Morty Hollis
Vice Chairman: Ray Smith

Secretary/Press Off.: Paul Damper
19 Fletcher Road, Worthing,
West Sussex BN14 8EX
Tel: 01903 210290

FOOTBALL MANAGEMENT TEAM
Manager: Barry Lloyd
Assistant Manager:Keith Rowley
Physio: Alan Robertson

FACT FILE
Formed: 1886 Nickname: The Rebels
Colours: Red, with white trim/red/red
Change : White withbluetrim/ white/white
Midweek matches: Tuesday
Local Press: Evening Argus, Worthing Herald,Worthing Guardian
Local Radio: Southern FM,Splash F.M. Southern Counties Radio

2002-2003
Captain; Gary Young
Top Scorer: Mark Knee
Player of the Year: Ben Carrington

GROUND Woodside Road, Worthing, West Sussex BN14 7HQ (01903 239575)
Directions: Follow A24 to town, at end of Broadwater Rd having gone over railway bridge, 1st right into Teville Rd, right into South Farm RD, 2nd left into Pavilion Rd, Woodside Rd is first right. Half a mile fromWorthing (BR)
Capacity: 4,500 Seats: 450 Cover: 1,500 Floodlights: Yes
Clubhouse: Open 2 hrs before kick-off & closes 11pm. Hot & cold food available
Club Shop: Yes

PREVIOUS **Leagues:** West Sussex Sen 1896-04, 05-14, 19-20; Brighton, Hove & Dist 19-20; Sussex County 20-40, 45-48; Corinthian 48-63; Athenian 63-77 **Names:** Worthing Association pre 1899 **Grounds:** Homefield Park, Beach House Park

CLUB RECORDS **Attendance:** Claimed to be 4,500 v Depot Battalion Royal Engineers, FA Amtr Cup 07-08
Transfer fee paid: Undisclosed fee forMarc Rice (Havant & Waterlooville1998)
Transfer fee received: £7,500 for Tim Read (Woking, 1990)
Win: 25-0 v Littlehampton (H) West Sussex Lge 1911-12 **Defeat:** 0-14 v Southwick (A), Sussex County Lge 1946-47
Career Goalscorer: Mick Edmonds 276 **Career Appearances:** David Bloom 397

BEST SEASON **FA Vase:** 5th Rd 78-79**FA Trophy:** 3rd Rd Replay 85-86 **FA Amateur Cup:** Quarter-Final replay 07-08
FA Cup: 2nd Rd 82-83, 0-4 v Oxford Utd; 1st Rd 36-37, 94-95 (1-3 v AFC Bournem'th), 99-00 (0-3 v Rotherham United)

HONOURS Isth.Lg R-up (2) 83-85 (Div 1 82-83, Div 2 81-82 92-93);Isth Full members Cup r-up98-99, Athenian Lg Div 1 R-up 63-64, Div 2 R-up 71-72, Lg Cup R-up 72-73, Mem. Shield R-up 63-64; SussexSnr Cup (21); Sussex RUR Char. Cup (13); Sussex Co. Lg(8)W Sussex Lg (7); Brighton Char. Cup(10) Worthing Char. Cup (11); AFA Invit. Cup 63-64 68-69 73-74 75-76 (Snr Cup R-up 36-37 46-47 48-49); Corinth. Lg Mem. Shield R-up 49-50 (NealeTphy 58-59); Roy Hayden Mem. Tphy 75(jt), 77 78,99. Don Morecraft Tphy 72 73 76 8182; Sussex F'lit Cup(3) 88-90 97-98; Sussex I'mediate Cup 34-35 64-65; BrightonChal. Shield 29-30 31-32

Players progressing: Ken Suttle (Chelsea 48), Alan Arnell & Fred Perry (Liverpool 54), Craig Whitington (Scarborough, via Crawley Town) 93, Darren Freeman (Gillingham), Paul Musselwhite (Scunthorpe), Trevor Wood (Port Vale), Richard Tiltman (Brighton), David Cameron (Lincoln C), Charlie Webb (Brighton 1908),Vince Taylor (Arsenal), Eric Parsons (West Ham U & Chelsea), E.G.D.Wright (Hull City)

Back row, left to right: Keith Rowley (Asst.Manager), Alan Robertson (physio), Peter Brackley, Wesley Lopez, Tom Graves, Ben Carrington, Andrew Beech, Luke Burton, Danny Stevens, Chris Hibberd, Gavin Jones, Peter Knee (coach), John Lock (coach) and Gareth Nicholas (kit man).**Front row:** Andy Alexander, Jordan Rhodes, Paul Brown, Mark Knee, Gary Young, Shane Moses, Richard Lewis and Andy Walker.
Photo: Stephen Goodger of Worthing Herald

RYMAN DIVISION ONE NORTH

		P	HOME W	D	L	F	A	AWAY W	D	L	F	A	Pts	GD
1	Northwood	46	17	2	4	66	26	11	5	7	43	30	91	53
2	Hornchurch	46	13	7	3	46	25	12	8	3	39	23	90	37
3	Hemel Hempstead Town	46	15	2	6	41	31	11	5	7	29	24	85	15
4	Slough Town	46	14	6	3	48	20	8	8	7	38	39	80	27
5	Uxbridge	46	13	6	4	35	18	10	4	9	27	23	79	21
6	Aveley	46	10	6	7	27	24	11	8	4	39	24	77	18
7	Berkhamsted Town	46	13	3	7	54	37	8	10	5	38	31	76	24
8	Thame United	46	13	5	5	50	17	7	7	9	34	34	72	33
9	Wealdstone	46	14	4	5	51	30	7	5	11	34	39	72	16
10	Harlow Town	46	11	6	6	28	21	9	6	8	38	32	72	13
11	Marlow	46	11	4	8	39	31	8	6	9	35	32	67	11
12	Barking & East Ham Utd	46	9	3	11	32	38	10	6	7	41	38	66	-3
13	Yeading	46	11	6	6	37	28	7	5	11	40	41	65	8
14	Great Wakering Rovers	46	9	8	6	36	31	8	6	9	28	39	65	-6
15	Oxford City	46	10	8	5	39	25	7	5	11	16	26	64	4
16	Arlesey Town	46	8	10	5	33	27	9	2	12	36	44	63	-2
17	East Thurrock United	46	11	6	6	48	35	6	4	13	27	44	61	-4
18	Wingate & Finchley	46	8	5	10	38	41	7	6	10	32	33	56	-4
19	Barton Rovers	46	9	4	10	23	27	6	3	14	30	38	52	-12
20	Tilbury	46	8	5	10	30	43	6	2	15	25	53	49	-41
21	Wivenhoe Town	46	5	5	13	30	43	4	6	13	26	51	38	-38
22	Leyton Pennant	46	4	4	15	18	35	5	3	15	20	46	34	-43
23	Wembley	46	4	7	12	33	53	3	4	16	24	58	32	-54
24	Hertford Town	46	3	4	16	25	54	3	2	18	21	65	24	-73

	1	2	3	4	5	6	7	8	9	10	11	12	13	14	15	16	17	18	19	20	21	22	23	24
1 Arlesey T.		0-0	0-0	1-0	2-2	2-0	0-4	1-2	0-0	6-0	2-2	3-1	0-0	2-3	1-0	1-0	3-3	0-2	0-1	3-3	3-2	0-0	1-1	2-1
2 Aveley	3-3		1-2	2-1	0-3	1-0	1-1	1-0	1-1	1-0	0-2	0-1	1-0	1-2	0-0	1-1	1-2	2-0	2-1	1-2	2-0	1-0	3-1	1-1
3 Barking&EH	3-1	1-3		0-3	3-5	4-0	0-4	3-1	0-1	1-0	1-1	2-0	1-2	0-0	0-0	2-1	2-1	1-0	0-1	2-0	1-5	0-2	3-4	2-3
4 Barton R.	1-0	1-1	1-2		0-0	0-4	0-0	1-0	2-0	2-1	0-1	0-1	1-2	3-2	1-2	2-2	1-0	2-3	1-0	0-1	1-2	0-3	1-0	2-0
5 Berkhamsted	1-2	1-2	2-2	3-1		3-0	4-2	2-2	1-0	4-0	1-1	2-0	1-4	3-4	4-2	3-1	2-3	3-0	0-1	1-5	3-1	1-0	6-2	3-2
6 E Thurrock	2-1	0-1	0-4	2-5	1-1		5-0	0-0	2-0	5-1	4-3	0-1	3-3	2-3	2-1	0-2	1-1	3-1	1-0	2-2	5-0	2-0	3-3	3-2
7 G Wakering	2-3	1-1	4-3	2-1	1-1	0-4		1-1	0-1	2-0	3-3	2-0	0-0	2-0	0-1	2-2	0-0	0-1	0-3	2-1	5-0	1-1	3-2	3-2
8 Harlow T.	3-1	2-1	3-2	0-0	1-1	1-0	2-0		0-2	0-2	0-0	0-0	2-1	1-3	0-0	2-2	2-0	2-0	0-1	0-1	2-1	0-2	3-1	2-0
9 Hemel Hem.	1-1	0-1	2-1	2-1	2-3	4-1	2-3	0-2		3-1	1-3	2-1	1-0	3-2	1-0	2-2	3-1	3-2	1-3	2-1	2-1	1-0	1-0	2-1
10 Hertford Tn	2-4	0-3	1-3	0-4	2-2	0-1	1-1	1-2	0-2		1-2	2-2	2-6	0-5	0-1	1-3	1-3	0-1	1-3	3-2	2-0	3-3	0-1	2-0
11 Hornchurch	4-3	0-1	5-1	1-1	5-3	1-1	2-1	1-2	2-2	2-1		2-1	0-3	1-0	3-1	3-2	1-1	2-0	0-0	3-0	6-0	1-0	0-0	1-1
12 Leyton Pen.	0-1	0-2	1-2	1-0	1-1	0-2	1-2	0-1	0-2	2-3	0-0		1-1	1-3	0-1	0-2	0-1	2-3	2-4	1-2	2-1	1-0	0-0	2-1
13 Marlow	1-0	4-3	1-2	3-1	0-0	1-4	0-0	4-1	0-2	4-1	2-3	4-0		1-0	1-2	2-3	2-1	2-0	0-0	2-0	0-1	2-2	2-1	1-4
14 Northwood	6-0	1-1	1-2	2-1	2-0	4-2	4-0	1-4	2-1	5-1	2-0	5-1	1-3		2-1	5-1	2-0	5-1	0-1	2-1	6-1	4-1	1-0	3-3
15 Oxford City	0-1	0-0	4-1	2-1	0-2	2-0	1-2	3-2	1-1	3-0	1-1	2-1	2-0	0-3		1-1	1-1	5-0	1-0	0-3	1-1	2-2	5-0	2-2
16 Slough Tn	3-0	1-1	3-1	1-0	3-2	2-0	4-0	1-1	0-1	2-2	1-1	5-1	2-0	2-1	3-0		2-0	5-1	1-1	0-1	2-1	0-3	4-0	0-2
17 Thame Utd	2-1	1-1	2-1	1-0	1-1	1-3	2-0	0-0	8-2	0-0	0-1	3-1	4-0	0-1	1-0	1-1		3-0	4-0	4-2	5-0	0-1	7-0	0-1
18 Tilbury	1-4	1-1	0-1	3-1	2-1	1-1	1-1	3-2	1-0	2-1	1-2	1-1	0-2	0-3	0-0	3-0	1-6		1-4	2-0	2-1	1-3	0-3	3-5
19 Uxbridge	2-0	2-0	1-1	5-0	1-2	1-1	0-0	3-1	1-0	4-1	0-1	3-2	0-0	0-0	1-0	0-1	2-1	1-4		1-0	2-1	1-1	1-0	3-1
20 Wealdstone	1-3	0-2	2-2	2-3	3-0	3-0	4-2	1-1	0-2	4-0	1-0	1-0	2-0	4-4	4-0	3-2	1-2	4-1	2-1		1-1	3-2	3-2	2-0
21 Wembley	0-3	2-6	2-2	2-3	0-2	1-1	2-3	1-5	1-1	3-1	0-4	0-1	1-1	2-2	0-2	2-2	2-4	4-2	2-1	0-0		4-1	2-3	0-3
22 Wingate & F.	1-2	1-2	0-3	1-0	0-4	3-0	3-0	1-4	1-4	2-3	0-1	4-1	4-3	1-2	1-1	2-3	1-0	2-1	1-1	5-2	1-1		1-1	2-2
23 Wivenhoe T	3-1	2-1	1-2	1-2	1-1	4-1	0-1	1-3	0-2	3-1	1-5	1-2	1-3	0-0	0-1	1-2	2-2	1-1	2-0	1-4	2-2	2-3		0-3
24 Yeading	2-1	3-5	1-1	1-1	0-1	5-1	0-1	2-1	1-2	5-1	1-2	2-1	2-1	1-0	1-0	0-2	1-1	1-1	1-0	1-1	2-1	3-2	1-1	

ARLESEY TOWN

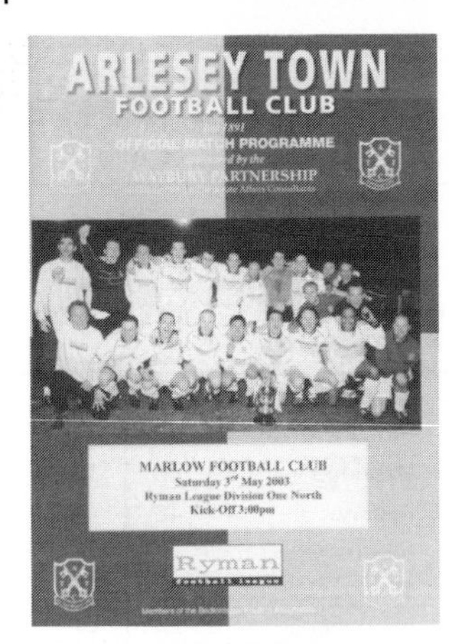

PROGRAMME

Price: £1.00

Editor: Pete Brennan (01462 834455)

CLUB OFFICIALS

Chairman: Bryan Ellis (01462 682612)

Vice-Chairman: Chris Albon (01462 628565)

President: Maurice Crouch

Secretary: Keitgh Broughton

9 davis Row,Arlesey , Beds. SG15 6RB

Email: secretary@arleseytown.co.uk

FOOTBALL MANAGEMENT TEAM

Manager: Nicky Ironton

Asst Man:Keith Barrett Coach:Andy Theodosiou Physio: Eric Turner

FACT FILE

Founded: 1891

Nickname: Blues

Colours: Sky & navy quarters/navy/navy

Change Colours: All white.

Midweek matchday: Tuesday

Reserves' Lge: S. Midlands Lge Res Div 1

Club Website: www.arleseyfc.co.uk

2002-2003

Captain: Stuart Beevor

P.o.Ys.: Steve Magona,Dean Harding & Martyn Patching

Top Scorers:

Marvin Samuel & Wayne Cort

GROUND: Hitchin Rd, Arlesey, Beds SG15 6RS
Tel: 01462 734504 and www.arleseyfc.co.uk

Directions: A1 take A507 to Shefford, at 3rd roundabout turn left, 1st left follow road through village, ground 1.5 miles on left

Capacity: 2,920 Seats: 150 Cover: 600 Floodlights: Yes

Club Shop: Yes Old programmes, leisure wear,replica hits andd various souvenirs

Clubhouse: Open daily 7- 11.00, Sat 12p.m.-11.30, Sun 12-2.30 7-11.30
Members bar ,wide screen for Sky TV, function suite and hot food available.

PREVIOUS: **Leagues:** Biggleswade & Dist.; Beds. Co. (S. Mids) 22-26 ,27-28; Parthenon; London 58-60; Utd Co's 33-36 82-92. Spartan South Midlands 92-99

RECORDS: **Attendance:** 2,000 v Luton Town Reserves, Beds Senior Cup 1906
Appearances: Gary Marshall

BEST SEASON: **FA Vase:** Winners 94-95 **FA Cup:** 4th Qual.Round 2002-2003 v Hererford United (0-1)

HONOURS: FA Vase Winners 1994-5; Isthmian League (Ryman) Div 3 Champions 00-01, Beds Sen Cup 65-66 78-79 96-97, Prem Cup 83-84, 01-02, Interm Cup 57-58; S Mids Lge Prem Div 51-52 52-53 94-95 95-96.99-00, Div 2 29-30 31-32 35-36, Chall Trophy 79-80, Prem Shield 64-65, O'Brien Prem Cup 93-94, F'litCup 90-91; Utd Co Lge Prem Div 84-85, KO Cup 87-88; Hinchingbrooke Cup 77-78 79-80 81-82 96-97; Biggleswade KO Cup 77-78 80-81

Players Progressing: Roland Legate (Luton), Pat Kruse (Brentford, Leicester) & Dave Kitson (Camb U)

L-R - Back row: James Dillnutt, Shaun Marshall, Matt Corbould, Steve Magona, Tony Fontenelle, Keith B arrett (Asst Manager), Andy Theodosiou (player coach), Martyn Patching, Craig Reynolds, Dave Hatchett, Eric Turner, (Physio), Margaret Brabrook (physio) and Nicky Ironton (Manager). **Front row:** Stuart Beevor, Mitch Barrett, Jamie Lever, Harry Ironton (Mascot), Dean Harding, Simeon Bird (mascot), Matt Turnbull, George Ironton, Barry Dellar, Bradley Poole, Lee Tekell, Sam Parratt and Karl Spring.

AVELEY

CLUB OFFICIALS

Chairman: David Patient
President: Ken Clay
Press Officer: Terry King
Secretary: Craig Johnston
10 San Juan Drive, Chafford Hundred,
Grays, Essex RM16 6LQ.
Tel: 01375 650220 (H) 07946 438540 (M)

FOOTBALL MANAGEMENT TEAM

Manager : Brian Horne
Assistant Manager : David Guiver
Physio : Paul Wilson

FACT FILE

Founded: 1927
Sponsors: Freightmaster
Colours: All Royal blue
Change: All Red
Midweek matches: Tuesday
Reserves' Lge: Essex Business House

2002 - 03

Captain : Wesley Faulkner
POY : Ernie Bentley
Top Scorer : Danny Curran 18

Pages: 48 Price: £1
Editor: Terry King
Local Press: Thurrock Gazette
Romford Recorder
Local Radio: Radio Essex, Essex Radio

GROUND: `Mill Field', Mill Road, Aveley, Essex RM15 4TR
Tel: 01708 865940

Directions: London - Southend A1306, turn into Sandy Lane at Aveley.
Rainham or Purfleet BR stations then bus No. 723 to the ground. Bus from Rainham No 324

Capacity: 4,000 Cover: 400 Seats: 400 Floodlights: Yes

Clubhouse: Normal pub hours. Bar snacks and hot food available

Club Shop: No

PREVIOUS **Leagues:** Thurrock Com 46-49; London 49-57; Delphian 57-63; Athenian 63-73

RECORDS **Attendance:** 3,741 v Slough T., FA Amateur Cup 27.2.71
Goalscorer: Jotty Wilks, 214 **Appearances:** Ken Riley, 422
Win: 11-1 v Histon, 24/8/63
Defeat: 0-8 v Orient, Essex Thameside Trophy, 11/4/85

BEST SEASON **FA Cup:** 1st Rd 70-71, 0-1 v Yeovil League clubs defeated: None
FA Amateur Cup QF 70-71 **FA Trophy** 3rd Qual Rd replay 74-75 **F.A.Vase** 3rd Rd 89-90

HONOURS: Isthmian Lg Div 2 (North) R-up 89-90, Lg (AC Delco) Cup 89-90; London Lg 51-5254-55 (R-up 55-56, Lg Cup 53-54); Delphian Lg R-up 57-58 (Lg Cup 61-62);Athenian Lg 70-71 (Div 2 R-up 68-69); Essex Junior Cup 47-48 48-49; Essex Thameside Trophy 79-80 R-up 97-98; Hornchurch Charity Cup 81-82 (R-up 83-84); East Anglian Cup 88-89, R-up 97-98 Essex Senior Cup Finalists 2002/03

Players progressing: David Case & Alan Hull (Orient), Alan Parkinson (Orient 1967), Yilmaz Orhan (W Ham 1972), Keith Day (Colchester 1984), Paul Williams (Charlton, Sheff Wed & C.Palace) Paul Wilson (Barnet), David Morrison (Peterborough U), Tony Sorrell (Maidstone Utd), Steve Crane (Gillingham), David Matthews (Walsall, Southend United)

L-R - Back Row: Brian Horne (Manager), Craig Etherington, Danny Greaves, Adam Furness, Terry Scotchmer, Marc Palmer, Nicky Wilson, Karl Shuttlewood, Ernie Bentley, David Guiver (Asst. Manager), Kevin Hoody. **Front Row:** Arron Wright, Lee Guiver, Steve Pashley, Anthony Savage, Steve Dickinson (Captain), Paul Sammons, Michael Hart, Tolo Mas, Paul Wilson (Physio).

BARKING & EAST HAM UNITED

CLUB OFFICIALS

Chairman: John Edgeworth
Vice-Chairman: Paul Lovell
President: Terry Lovell
Secretary: Roger Chilvers
50 Harrow Rd, Barking, Essex IG11 7RA Tel: 020 8591 5313
Press Officer: Derek Pedder
Tel: 020 85292 483

FOOTBALL MANAGEMENT TEAM

Manager: Richard Thomas
Asst Manager: Mark Lord
Reserves' Manager:Dorian West
Goalkeeping Coach: Marc Baker
Physio: Shuc Davis

FACT FILE

Founded: 1880 Nickname: The Blues
Main Sponsors: Capital Coin and Peter Webster Property M & S
.Other Sponsors: Global Games, New Spice & Docklands Coachworks
Colours: Blue & white Change Cols: White
Midweek matchday: Tuesday
Reserves' Lge: Essex & Herts Border Div 1
Ladies Lg: F.A. Prem Div 1 (South)
Youth League: Eastern Junior Alliance
Club Website: www.barkingfc.co.uk
2002-2003 Captain: Paul Salmon
P.o.Y.: Jamie Dormer
Top Scorers: Jay Murray & Billy Read

GROUND Mayesbrook Park, Lodge Avenue, Dagenham RM8 2JR Tel: 020 8595 6900/6511
Email Address: john@capitalcair.co.uk

Directions: Off A13 on A1153 (Lodge Ave), and ground 1 mile on left.
Bus 162 from Barking station or Nos 5 or 87 to Robin Hood. Nearest tube Becontree.

Capacity: 2,500 Cover: 600 Seats: 200 Floodlights: Yes
Clubhouse: 2 large bars, open daily 11am-11pm (Sundays Noon-11pm).
Hot & cold food and drinks.
Club Shop: Yes. Manager: Brad Robinson

PROGRAMME

Pages: 16 Price: £1.00
Editor: Roger Chilvers
Local Press: B arking & Dagenham Post
B & D Recorder.
Local Radio: Active FM

PREVIOUS
Grounds: Eastbury Field, Kennedy Estate,Movers Lane,Barking Recreation Ground Merry Fiddlers,Vicarage Field (until 1973)
Names: Barking Rovers,Barking Woodville, Barking Institute,Barking Town and Barking
Leagues: London 1896-98 09-23, South Essex 1898-21, Leyton & Dist 1899-1900,Athenian 12-13 + 23-52 S.E.Combination 39-40

CLUB RECORDS
Attendance: (At Mayesbrook) 1,972 v Aldershot FA Cup 2nd Rd 78
Win: 14-0 v Sheppey Utd Mithras Cup 69-70 **Defeat:** 0-8 v Marlow.
Fee received: £6,000 for Alan Hull (Orient) **Fee paid:** None over £1,000
Goal scorer: Neville Fox 241 (65-73) **Appearances:** Bob Makin 566

BEST SEASON
FA Vase: 96-97 5th Rd **FA Amateur Cup:** Runners-up 26-27 **F.A.Trophy:** 2nd Rd 79-80
FA Cup: 2nd Rd rep. 81-82 1-3v Gillingham (A) after 1-1. Also 2nd Rd 78-79 79-80 83-84, and 1st Rd 26-27 28-29 78-80.
League clubs defeated: Oxford Utd 79-80.

HONOURS FA Amateur Cup R-up 26-27; Isthmian Lg 78-79 (Lg Cup R-up 76-77); Athenian Lg 34-35 (R-up 24-25); London Lg 20-21 (Div 1 (A) 09-10); South Essex Lg Div 1 (2),R-up (3), Div 2 (4); London Senior Cup (4), R-up (3); Essex Senior Cup (7), R-up (8); Dylon Shield 79-80; Eastern Floodlit R-up (3); Essex Elizabethian 66-67, R-up (2); Essex Thameside (4), R-up (4); London Charity Cup 61-62 R-up 21-22; London Intermediate Cup (3) ,R-up(1); East Anglian Cup 37-38 53-54;Mithras Cup (3), R-up (2); Premier Midweek (2). Vandanel Trophy R-up 99-00

Players progressing:39 players to date including: - 1956; Peter Carey (Orient 57), Lawrie Abrahams (Charlton 77), Kevin Hitchcock (Nottm Forest83 & Chelsea), Dennis Bailey (Fulham 86), Alan Hull (Orient 87) Joe Sibley1939, Hedley Sheppard 1932, Paul Wilson (Barnet) John Still (Ex-Manager Barnet), Mark Lazarus (Leyton O),J.Tresarden 1922 (West Ham U & England) and H.j.Holse,1908 (Manchester U & England)

BARTON ROVERS

CLUB OFFICIALS

Chairman: Trevor Capon
President: Pat Howarth
Vice Chairman: Richard Carey
Football Secretary: Owen Clark,
c/o Barton Rovers F.C.
Tel: 01582 882398
Press Officer: Nick Rhodes
Tel: 01582 881865

FOOTBALL MANAGEMENT TEAM

Manager: Ian Allinson
Assistant Manager: Geoff Livingstone
Physio: Mark Boulding

FACT FILE

Formed: 1898
Nickname: Rovers
Sponsors: Hillson Builders
Colours: All royal blue with white trim
Change colours: All yellow
Midweek Matchday: Tuesday
Reserves' League: None
Local Press: Luton News, Herald,
Beds on Sunday
Local Radio: Radio Chiltern, Radio Beds
Three Counties Radio

PROGRAMME
Pages: 64 Price: £1.20
Editor: Sec & Nick Rhodes (01582 881865)

GROUND Sharpenhoe Road, Barton-le-Clay, Bedford MK45 4SD
Tel: 01582 707772

Directions: M1 Jct 12, from London exit turn right, take 2nd right through Harlington and Sharpenhoe. Entrance to ground 44 yds on right down concrete drive entering village. 41/2 miles from Harlington (BR), 6 miles from Luton (BR), good bus or taxis service from Luton
Capacity: 4,000 Seats: 160 Cover: 1,120 Floodlights: Yes

Clubhouse: Noon-3pm weekends (no football), noon-11pm (matchdays), 7-11pm weekdays. Real ale, hot & cold snacks, pool, darts, gaming machines
Club Shop: Yes (contact 01582 751013)

PREVIOUS
Leagues: Luton & Dist. 47-54; Sth Midlands 54-79
Grounds: Church Pitch 1898-1912; Barton Cutting 1912; Sharpenhoe Rd 12-33; Faldo Rd 33-38; Barton Rec. 46-75

CLUB RECORDS
Attendance: 1,900 v Nuneaton, FA Cup 4th Qual. Rd 1976
Win: 17-1 v Flitwick Athletic (H), S Midlands Lge Div 1 55-56
Defeat: 1-11 v Leighton United (H), S Midlands Lge Prem Div 62-63
Scorer: Richard Camp 152, 1989-98 **Appearances:** Tony McNally 514 (1988-2000)
Fees - Paid: £1,000 for B Baldry (Hitchin Town, 1980) **Received:** £1,000 for B Baldry (Bishop's Stortford, 1981)

BEST SEASON
FA Cup: 1st Round 1980-81, 0-2 v Torquay United (A)
FA Vase: Runners-up 77-78 (SF 76-77 81-82, QF 75-76 78-79)
FA Trophy: 2nd Rd 98-99, 99-00

HONOURS: Sth Mids Lg(8) 70-73 74-79 (R-up 67-68), Div 1 64-65 (R-up 55-56), Div 2 54-55, Lg Shield 57-58 60-61 68-69, Chal. Tphy 71-72 74-75 77-78 78-79; Beds Snr Cup (7), R-up (5); Beds Premier Cup 95-96, R-up 81-82 83-84 88-89, 99-00 01-02 Beds Intermediate Cup 53-54; Luton & Dist. Lg Div 3 47-48; North Beds Charity Cup 72-73 74-75 76-77 77-78 79-80 80-81 (R-up 70-71); Isthmian Lge Div 2 R-Up 94-95, Assoc. Members Trophy R-up 92-93; South Midlands Floodlight Cup 98-99. Hinchingbroke Cup 2001-02 R-up: 98-99,99-00

Players progressing: Kevin Blackwell (Huddersfield T.)

L-R - Back Row: Kevin Thoburn (u18 Manager), Paul Donnelly, Mark Boulding (Physio), Steve Turner, Keiran Carey, Dave Cook, Leon Cashman, Brad Gillham, Brett Donnelly, Chris Payne, Danny Kennoy, Robert Messina, Matt Endersby, Owen Clark (secretary) Front: Dave Brown, Jermaine Daley, Keith Coughlin, Ian Allinson (Manager), Stuart Lochhead (Cpatain), Geoff Livingstone (Asst. Manager), Drew Roberts, Paul Ayling, Richard Fisher

BERKHAMSTED TOWN

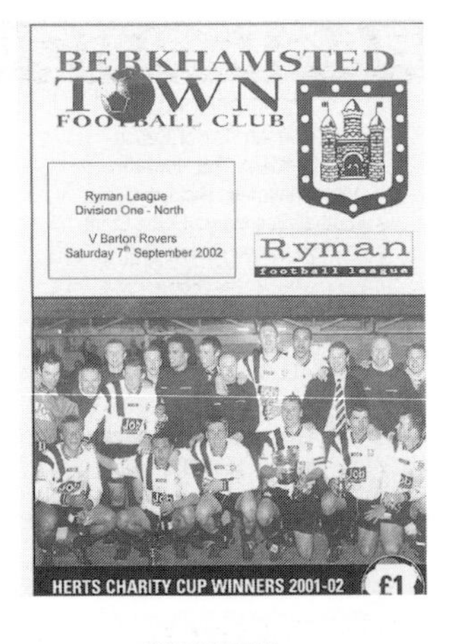

CLUB OFFICIALS

Chairman: Danny Jennings

Secretary: David Stanley
17 Old Vicarage Gardens, Markyate,
St Albans, Herts. AL3 8PW.
Tel: 01582 840707

Press Officer: Bob Sear
Tel: 01442 864547 (H & B)

FOOTBALL MANAGEMENT TEAM
Manager: Steve Bateman
Coach: Mark Pearson
Physio: Bryan Hardy

FACT FILE
Formed: 1895
Nickname: Lilywhites
Sponsors: T.B.A.
Colours: White/black/black
Change Colours: Yellow/blue/blue
Midweek Matchday: Tuesday
Reserves' Lge: Suburban League Prem Div
Local Press: Berkhamsted Herald, Berkhamsted Gazette
Local Radio: Chiltern Radio, Mix '96', Three Counties Radio
Website: www.berkhamstedfc.co.uk

PROGRAMME
Pages: 64 Price: £1
Editor: David Stanley

GROUND Broadwater, Lower Kings Road, Berkhamsted, Herts HP4 2AA
Tel: 01442 862815

Directions: Adjacent to Berkhamsted station (Euston-Birmingham line). A41 toBerkhamsted town centre traffic lights, left into Lower Kings Road

Capacity: 2,500 Seats: 170 Cover: 350 Floodlights: Yes

Clubhouse: Open 7 days a week. Pool & darts - Big screen

Club Shop: Contact Doug Pearcey

PREVIOUS
Leagues: Herts Co. 1895-1922; Herts Co: 1921,Spartan 22-51, 66-75; Delphian 51-63; Athenian 63-66, 83-84; London Spartan 75-83
Grounds: Sunnyside Enclosure 1895-1919, Sports Ground 1919-83
Name: Bekhamsted Comrades 1919-22

CLUB RECORDS
Attendance: 1,732 v Bedlington Terriers F.A.Vase Semi Final 2nd Leg 2001
Career appearances: Ray Jeffrey (612)
Victory: 14-0 **Defeat:** 2-12

BEST SEASON
FA Cup: 3rd Qual Rd v Barnet 87-88, v Slough 91-92, v Chesham U. 92-93, v Burton Albion 2001-02
FA Vase: Finalists 2000-01
FA Trophy: 1st Rd v Kidderminster Harriers 97-98

HONOURS
Herts Senior Cup 52-53; London Spartan Lge 79-80 (Div 2 26-27);Herts Charity Cup: 2001-02
Herts Charity Shield 50-51(jt) 73-74 79-80 84-85 90-91; Herts Senior County Lge Aubrey Cup 52-53; St Marys Cup(13); Apsley Senior Charity Cup (9); Southern Comb 84-85(F/lit Cup 84-85)

Players progressing: Frank Broome(Aston Villa & England), Maurice Cook (Fulham), Keith Ryan(Wycombe), Maurice Telling (Millwall)

BOREHAM WOOD

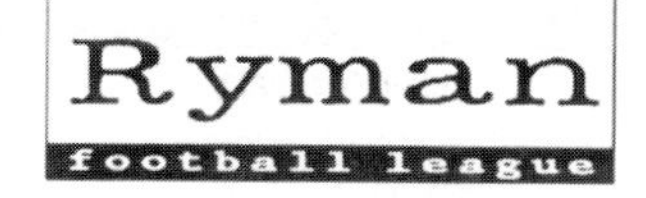

CLUB OFFICIALS

Chairman: Danny Hunter

President: W F O'Neill

Secretary: Peter Smith, 26 Briarwood Road, Stoneleigh, Epsom, Surrey KT19 2LY
Tel: 020 8393 2902(H) 0771 1745987(W)

Press Officer: John D Gill (020 8723 6407)

FOOTBALL MANAGEMENT TEAM

Manager: Micky Engwell
Asst Manager: Roger Goodhind
Physio: Dave Dickens

FACT FILE

Formed: 1948
Nickname: The Wood
Sponsors: One 2 One
Colours: White/black/black
Change : Alll yellow
Midweek matchday: Tuesday
Local Radio: Chiltern Radio
Local Press: Boreham Wood Times, Watford Observer, Herts Advertiser

PROGRAMME

Pages: 44 Price: £1.50
Editor: John Gill (020 8723 6407)

GROUND: Meadow Park, Broughinge Rd, Boreham Wood,Herts WD6 5AL (020 8953 5097)
Directions: A1 towards London from M25, 1st turn for Boreham Wood, head for town centre, into Brook Rd at r'bout before town centre, Broughinge Rd is 1st right. 1 mile from Elstree & Boreham Wood station (Thameslink),or bus 292 or107 to McDonalds (5 minutes walk)
Capacity: 4,502 Cover: 1,568 Seats: 600 Floodlights: Yes
Clubhouse: (020 8953 5097). Open during normal licensing hours. Snacks available. Function room (250) available for hire
Club Shop: Sells good selection of souvenirs & programmes. Contact: Dell Ward (020 8363 7345)

PREVIOUS **Leagues:** Mid Herts 48-52, Parthenon 52-57, Spartan 56-66, Athenian 66-74
Ground: Eldon Avenue 1948-63 **Names:** Boreham Wood Rovers and Royal Retournez, amalgamated in 1948

CLUB RECORDS **Attendance:** 3,892 v Arsenal , 9 July 99 (friendly)
Goalscorer: Micky Jackson, 208 **Appearances:** Dave Hatchett, 714

BEST SEASON **FA Amateur Cup:** 3rd Rd. replay 70-71 **FA Trophy:** 3rd Rd 1995-96. Replay at Chorley 3-4, 3rd Rd replay 97-98
FA Cup: 2nd Round v Luton Town 1996-97. v Cheltenham Town 97-98

HONOURS: Isthmian Lg.Prem Div R-Up 97-98 Div I 94-95, 00-01 Isthmian Lg Div 2 76-77 (Yth Cup R-up 80-81), Isthmian Lge. Cup 96-97; R-Up 94-95,95-96 ,98-99 Athenian Lg 73-74 (Div 2 68-69, Div 1 R-up 69-70), Spartan Lg R-up 65-66, Herts Senior Cup 71-72 ,98-99 (R-up 66-67 74-75 79-80 87-88,96-97,97-98), Herts Junior Cup 51-52, Parthenon Lg 55-56 (R-up(2) 53-55 56-57, Herts Charity Shield 64-65, Herts Interm Cup 69-70, Herts Charity Cup (5) 80-81 83-84 85-86 88-90 (R-up 71-72 84-85 86-87 90-91 91-92 92-93), London Senior Cup R-up89-90, London Intermediate Cup 70-71, Neale Trophy 69-70, Essex & Herts BorderComb 72-73 (Lg Cup 72-73, Western Div R-up 82-83 89-90), Mithras Cup 76-77, Middx Border Lg 81-82 (Lg Cup 79-80), Wallspan Floodlit 86-87, London Challenge Cup 97-98

Players progressing: Colin Franks (Watford & Sheff Utd), Charles Ntamark (Walsall), Dean Samuels (Barnet 96),Justin gentle (Colchester U),Kenny Veyse (Plymouth Argyle), Matthew Brady (Wycombe Wanderers)

Back row left to right: Jeran Meah, Chima Eberendu, Chris Harvey, David Kirby, Gary Wotton, Noel Imber, Gary Dixon, Paul Lamb, Brian Jones, Daniel Hewitt, Paul Davies and Corey Browne.
Front row: Steve Gracie (Physio), Steve Sinclair, Dean Parratt, Lee Harvey (Assistant Manager), Micky Engwell (Manager), Dominic Grime, Dave McDonald, Sam McCarthy and Dave Dickens (Kit Manager)

CHESHAM UNITED

CLUB OFFICIALS

President: Bill Wells
Chairman: Tony O'Driscoll
Secretary: T.B.A.
c/o Chesham United FC.
Tel: 01494 775490 (H) 0181327 4016(B)
Commercial Manager: T.B.A.
Press Officer: Phil Morgan

FACT FILE

Formed: 1886 Nickname: The Generals
Sponsors: T.B.A.
Colours: Claret & blue quarters/claret/claret
Change colours: White & blue/blue/white
Midweek home matchday: Tuesday
Reserve Team's League: Suburban North
Match information: 09068 335505

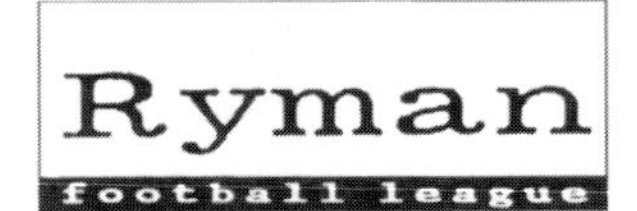

FOOTBALL MANAGEMENT TEAM
Manager: Colin Lippiatt
Physio: Kevin Campbell

GROUND: The Meadow, Amy Lane, Amersham Road, Chesham, Bucks. HP5 1NE
Tel: 01494 783964 (ground clubhouse) Fax: 01494 794244 Club Website: www.cheshamunit-edfc.co.uk Email Address: jimchamberschesham@talk21.com

Directions: M25 junction 18, A404 to Amersham, A416 to Chesham - go down to r-about at foot of Amersham Hill, then sharp left. 10 mins walk from Chesham station (Metropolitan Line)
Capacity: 5,000 Cover: 2,500 Seats: 284 Floodlights: Yes

Clubhouse: Open every evening & matchdays. Bar snacks. Available for hire(business training meetings, weddings etc)
Club Shop: Open matchdays Metal Badges: Yes

Pages: 52 Price: £1.50
Editors: Alan Calder
(01442 230420 [H])

Local Radio: Three Counties
Local Press: Bucks Examiner, Bucks Advertiser, Bucks Free Press

PREVIOUS **Leagues:** Spartan 17-47; Corinthian 47-63; Athenian 63-73

CLUB RECORDS **Attendance:** 5,000 v Cambridge Utd, FA 3rd Rd 5/12/79
Goalscorer: John Willis **Appearances:** Martin Baguley (600+)
Record Fees - Paid & Received: Undisclosed (club policy)

BEST SEASON **FA Cup:** 3rd Rd 79-80. 1st Rd 66-67 68-69 76-77 82-83
FA Amtr Cup: R-up 67-68 **FA Trophy:** 3rd Rd 92-93 (1-3 v Sutton United [H])

HONOURS: FA Amtr Cup R-up 67-68, Isthmian Lg 92-93 (Div 1 90-91 96-97), Div 2 Nth 86-87, Associate Members Cup R-up 90-91, Charity Shield 94-95; Athenian Lg Div 1 Cup 63-64 68-69; Corinthian Lg R-up (2) 60-62 (Lg Cup 60-61); Spartan Lg(4) 21-23 24-25 32-33 (R-up 26-27 29-30 33-34); Berks & Bucks Snr Cup 21-22 25-26 28-29 33-34 47-48 50-51 64-65 66-67 75-76 92-93. 00-01 (R-up 94-95, 01-02)

Players progressing: Bill Shipwright & Jimmy Strain (Watford 53 & 55), StewartScullion (Charlton 65), John Pyatt (L'pool 67), Brian Carter (Brentford 68),Kerry Dixon (Spurs 78), Tony Currie (Torquay 84), Dwayne Plummer (Bristol Rovers)

Left to right

Back row:
Steve Dogbe
Grant Cooper,
Delroy Preddie,
Mark Kleboe,
Daniel Braithwaite and
Paul Fewings

Front row:
James Bent,
Andre Scarlett,
Steve Sinclair,
Andy Douglas and
John Morgan

Photo Arthur Evans

CHESHUNT

Cheshunt Football Club
Sponsored by
Temptations
Season 2002/03
Chalfont St Peter
ISTHMIAN LEAGUE ASSOCIATE MEMBERS TROPHY
Quarter-final
Ryman
£1.50

CLUB PERSONNEL
Chairman: Vince Satori
Vice Chairman: Georgios Savva
President: Paul Philips
Secretary & Press Officer:
Robert Brassett
32 Firbank Close, Windmill Chase, Enfield,
Middl'x EN2 7ER Tel: 0208 364 4058 (H)
email: cheshunt@brassett.net

FOOTBALL MANAGEMENT
Manager: Andy Leese
Coach: Kevin Mudd
Asst Manager: John Meakes
Physio: Gill Miller

FACT FILE
Founded: 1946
Nickname: Ambers
Sponsors: Temptations
Colours: Gold & black/Black/Black
Change colours: Sky & Navy Blue
Midweek matchday: Tuesday
Reserves' Lge:Herts Co.Senior Reserve
Website:http://www.cheshuntfc.net

Programme
Pages: 40 Price: £1.50
Editor: Robert Brassart 07761 374357 (M)
Local Press: Herts Mercury, Enfield Gazette,
Herald (Free paper)

GROUND **Address:** The Stadium, Theobalds Lane, Cheshunt, Herts. Tel: 01992 626752
Directions: M25 J 25, A10 north towards Hertford, next r'about 3rd exit to next r'about, turn left proceed under railway bridge, turn left, ground approx 400 yards on right. 400yds from Theobalds Grove BR station, Buses 310, 242, & 311 to station
Capacity: 2,500 Seats: 285 Standing Cover: 350 Floodlights: Yes
Clubhouse: 120 Bar + 170 Function Hall **Club Shop:** No **Parking**: 150

PREVIOUS **Name:** Cheshunt Sports 46-47
Leagues: Athenian 19-20 21-31 64-77; London 46-51 55-59; Delphian 52-55; Aetolian 59-62; Spartan 62-64; Isthmian 77-87
Grounds: Gothic Sports , Theobalds Lane 1946, College Rd. 46-49 Cheshunt Stadium 49-50, Brookfield Lane 50-58

RECORDS **Attendance:** 5,000 v Bromley, F.A. Amateur Cup 2nd Rd 28.01.50
Victory: 11-0 v Royal Ordinance Factories (a) 1946-47 London Lg. Div.1
Defeat: 0-10 v Eton Manor London League 17.04.56
Record All Time Goalscorer: Eddie Sedgwick 128 **Most all time Appearances:** John Poole 526

BEST SEASON **FA Vase:** Quarter Final 81-82 **FA Cup:** 4th Qual. Rd (4) **F.A.Amateur Cup** 3rd Rd 49-50, 69-70

HONOURS Athenian Lg 75-76 R-up 73-74, Div 1 67-68, Div 2 R-up 65-66, Lg Cup 74-75 75-76; Spartan Lg 62-63, Lg Cup 63-64 92-93, R-up 89-90; London Lg 49-50 R-up 56-57, Div 1 47-48 48-49 R-up 46-47, Div 1 Cup 46-47, Lg Cup R-up 58-59, Park Royal Cup 46-47; Isthmian Lg Div 2 Champions 2002-03, R-up 81-82 Div 3 R-up 94-95; Herts Snr Cup 23-24 R-up 48-49 49-50 68-69 69-70 71-72 73-74; Herts Charity Cup 00-01 05-06 R-up 70-71 74-75 80-81; Herts Charity Shield 46-47 65-66 R-up 52-53 53-54 54-55 63-64 64-65; Herts Snr Centenary Tphy 91-92; E. Anglian Cup 74-75 R-up 75-76; Mithras F'lit Cup 69-70 R-up 75-76; London Charity Cup 73-74; Roy Bailey Tphy 90-91 94-95 97-98 98-99 99-00

Players progressing: Ian Dowie, Ruben Abgula, SteveSedgeley, Lee Hodges, Paul Marquis, Steve Terry, Neil Prosser, Mario Walsh

A jubilant Cheshunt having clinched the Ryman Division 2 title with their 4-1 win against Ware. **Photo**: Gordon Whittington

DUNSTABLE TOWN

CLUB PERSONNEL

Chairman: Ian Tompkins

Secretary: Malcolm Aubrey,
25 Copperfields Close, Houghton Regis,
Dunstable, Beds. LU5 5TE
Tel: 01582 667555 (H) 0771 8580625 (M)
email: malcolmaubrey@btopenworld.com

GROUND

Address: Creasey Park, Brewers Hill Rd, Dunstable LU6 1DN
Tel: 01582 667555

Directions: Travel north on A5, Through centre Dunstable, left at 1st r/about into Brewers Hill Rd, str over mini r/about, grd on right

FACT FILE

Colours:
Blue & white stripes/blue/blue & white

Change Colours:
Red & black hoops/black/red & black

Programme Editor:
Paul Reeves: 0961 951103

PREVIOUS League: Spartan South Midlands

HONOURS: S.S.M. Champions 2002-03

EAST THURROCK UNITED

East Thurrock United
FOOTBALL CLUB
www.eastthurrockunited.com
season 2003-2004
Ryman
football league

CLUB OFFICIALS

Chairman: Gary Snell

Secretary: Peter Lambert

30 Thames Cres., Corringham,
Essex, SS17 9DU
Tel: 01375 643418

Press Officer: Malcolm Harris

FOOTBALL MANAGEMENT TEAM

Manager: Andy McDonald
Assistant Manager.: Kevin Rolls
Physio: Richard Mainwaring

FACT FILE

Founded: 1969
Nickname: Rocks
Colours: Amber/black/black
Change: All Blue
Midweek Matchday: Tuesday
Reserves' Lge: Essex/Herts Border Comb.

GROUND: Rookery Hill, Corringham, Essex
Tel: 01375 644166-club

Directions: A13 London-Southend, take 1014 at Stanford-le-Hope for two and a half miles - ground on left. Two miles from Stanford-le-Hope and Basildon BR stations

Capacity: 3,000 Seats: 160 Cover: 500 Floodlights: Yes

Clubhouse: Open all day seven days a week. Hot and cold snacks

Club Shop: No

PROGRAMME

36 pages £1.00
Editor: Tony Smith (01375 892855)
Local Press:
Thurrock Gazette/ Thurrock Recorder
Local Radio: BBC Essex

PREVIOUS
Leagues: Sth Essex Comb.; Gtr London; Metropolitan 72-75; London Spartan 75-79; Essex Snr 79-92
Grounds: Billet, Stanford-le-Hope 70-73 74-76; Grays Athletic 73-74; Tilbury FC 77-82; New Thames Club 82-84
Name: Corringham Social (pre-1969 Sunday side)

CLUB RECORDS
Attendance: 947 v Trevor Brooking XI, May 1987. Competitive: 845 v Bashley, FA Vase 1989
Goalscorer: Graham Stewart 102 **Appearances:** Glen Case 600+
Win: 7-0 v Coggeshall (H) 1984
Defeat: 0-9 v Eton Manor (A) 1982, both Essex Snr League
Transfer Fee Paid: £22,000 for Greg Berry (Leyton Orient)

BEST SEASON
FA Cup: 3rd Qual 93-94 **FA Vase:** 5th Rd 84-85

HONOURS:
Metropolitan Lg Div 2 72-73, Essex Snr Lg R-up 88-89 (Lg Cup 88-89 91-92, Harry Fisher Mem. Tphy 83-84 90-91, Sportsmanship Award 81-82 86-87 89-89), Essex SnrTphy R-up 91-92 95-96, Fred Budden Tphy R-up 89-90, Essex & Herts Border Comb.89-90,01-02 (Lg Cup 89-90) , Isthmian League Div. Three 99-00

Players progressing to Football League: Greg Berry (Leyton Orient & Wimbledon)

Back row,left to right: Chris Marshall, Steve Carter, Tim Bird, Neil Cullis, Mick Dickson, Danny Dafter and Jamie Bowler.
Front row: Wayne Tomkins, Marc Wingrove, James Dwyer, Keith Wilson, Lee Carter, Eliot Caton and Paul Hume.**Photo**: Alan Coomes

ENFIELD

CLUB OFFICIALS
Chairman: A Lazarou
President: R.Prosser
Secretary & Match Sec: Derek Bird,
17 Fishers Close, Waltham Cross,Herts.
Tel: 01992 301741 07765 837246 (M)
07992 066605 (Fax)

FOOTBALL MANAGEMENT
Manager: Terry Back

2002-2003
Captain: Stuart Maynard
Top Scorer & P.o.Y.: Paul Armstrong 15

FACT FILE
Formed: 1893
Nickname: The E's
Sponsors: T.B.A.
Colours: White/blue/white
Change colours: All Yellow
Midweek matchday: Monday
Reserves' League: Middlesex Co.
Local Press: Enfield Gazette,
Enfield Advertiser, Enfield Independent
Website: www.enfieldfc.com

PROGRAMME
Pages: 48 Price: £1.50
Editor: Derek Bird

ENFIELD
FOOTBALL CLUB
Sponsored by
ACRE HOMES
PROPERTY DEVELOPERS
Ryman
HITCHIN TOWN FC
Saturday 3rd May 2003 Kick off 3pm
£1.50

GROUND: Meadow Park, Broughinge Rd, Boreham Wood, Herts WD6 5AL. Tel: 0208 9535097 Email: efcltd@lineone.net
Directions: A1 towards London from M25, 1st turn for Boreham Wood, head for town centre, into Brook Rd at r'bout before town centre, Broughinge Rd is 1st right. 1 mile from Elstree & Boreham Wood station (Thameslink), or bus 292 or 107 to McDonalds (5 minutes walk)
Capacity: 4,502 Cover: 1,568 Seats: 500 Floodlights: Yes
Club Shop: Alan Farmer (0208366 6066)

PREVIOUS **Leagues**: Tottenham & Dist 1894-95; Nth Middx 96-1903; London 03-13 20-21; Middx 08-12, 19-20; Athenian 12-14 21-39 45-63; Herts & Middx Comb 39-42; Isthmian 63-81; GMV Conference 81-90
Name: Enfield Spartans 1893-1900 **Grounds:** Baileys Field 1893-96; Tuckers Field 96-1900; Cherry Orchard Lane1900-36

CLUB RECORDS **Attendance:** 10,000 (10/10/62) v Spurs, floodlight opener Southbury Road 1936-1999
Win: 18-0 v Stevenage FA Cup 2nd Qual 22/10/27 (H) **Defeat:** 0-12 v Woolwich Polytechnic, London Lge Div 2 27/4/04
Fee Paid: for Gary Abbott (Barnet) **Fee Received:** for Paul Furlong (Coventry City)
Scorer: Tommy Lawrence, 191 1959-1964. **Appearances:** Steve King 617 (77-89)

BEST SEASON **FA Amateur Cup:** Winners 66-7 69-70 R-up 63-4 71-2 **FA Trophy:** Winners 81-2 87-8
FA Cup: 4th Rd replay 80-81, 0-3 v Barnsley (at Spurs), Att 35,244, after 1-1.
League clubs beaten: Wimbledon, Northampton 77-78, Hereford, Port Vale 80-81, Wimbledon 81-82, Exeter 84-85, Orient 88-89, Aldershot 91-92, Cardiff City 94-95, Torquay Utd 94-95, Chesterfield 99-00

HONOURS: Alliance Premier Lge 82-83 85-86 (R-up 81-82), Lg Cup R-up 81-82; IsthmianLg(8) 67-70 75-78 79-80 94-95 (R-up 64-65 71-72 74-75 80-81 90-92 95-96), LgCup(2) 78-80 (R-up 91-92 94-95); Athenian Lg(2) 61-63 (R-up 34-35); London LgDiv 1 11-12 (R-up 04-05 06-07); Middx Snr Cup 13-14 46-47 61-62 65-66 68-71 77-81 88-89 90-91 97-98, (R-up 10-11 20-21 47-48 51-52 57-60 62-63 66-67 72-73 75-76 84-85); London Snr Cup 34-35 60-61 66-67 71-73 75-76 (R-up 63-64 67-68 70-71); Middx Lg (West) 09-10 (R-up 10-11); European Amtr Cup Winners Cup 69-70

Players progressing: Terry McQuade (Millwall 61), Roger Day (Watford 61), Jeff Harris (Orient 64), Peter Feely (Chelsea 70), Carl Richards & Jon Bailey (B'mouth 80 & 95), Paul Furlong (Coventry 91), Andy Pape (Barnet 91), GregHeald (Peterborough 94), Lee Marshall (Norwich City 97)

The Enfield line-up before their final game last season against Hitchin Town.

GREAT WAKERING ROVERS

CLUB OFFICIALS

Chairman: Roy Kettridge
Vice-Chairman: Barry Beadle
President: Eddie Ellis
Secretary: Roger Sampson
37 Lee Lotts, Gt. Wakering,
Southend SS3 0HA
Tel: 01702 217812
Press Officer: Nobby Johnson
Tel: 01702 468243

FOOTBALL MANAGEMENT TEAM

Manager: Alan Hull
Physio: Clive Taylor

FACT FILE

Founded: 1919
Nickname: Rovers
Sponsors:I.M.S.
Colours:Green & white /white/green
Change Coours: All Red
Midweek Matchday: Tuesday
Reserves' Lge: Essex & Herts Border Comb

2002-2003

Top Scorer: Dan Trenkel 21
Player of the Year: DanTrenkel

PROGRAMME

Pages: 24-32 Price: £1.00
Editor: Nobby Johnson (01702 468243)
Website: great wakeringroversfc.co.uk

GROUND: Borroughs Park, Little Wakering Hall Lane, Gt. Wakering, Southend SS3 OHQ
Tel: 01702 217812

Directions: 4a bus from Shoeburyness (BR), 4a or 4b from Southend - alight at British Legion in Gt Wakering alongside which runs Little Wakering Hall Lane. A127 past Southend signed Gt Wakering. In Gt Wakering, .5 mile past large Total garage along High Street is Little Wakering Hall Lane, ground 250 yds along on left

Capacity: 2,500 Cover: 300 Seats: 150 Floodlights: Yes
Clubhouse: Open every eve., Sat 11-11, Sun 12-3 & 7.30-10.30.
Hot meals, snacks etc matchdays only **Club Shop:** No

PREVIOUS **Leagues:** Southend & Dist. 19-81, Southend All. 81-89, Essex I'mediate 89-92
Ground: Gt Wakering Rec

RECORDS **Attendance:** 659 v Potters Bar FA Vase 5th Rd 7-2-98
Win (in Senior Football): 9-0 v Eton Manor 27/12/93
Defeat (in Senior Football): 1-7 v Bowers Utd, Essex Snr Lge 1-4-98

BEST SEASON **FA Cup:** 2nd Qual 98-99
FA Vase: 5th Round 97-98, 01-02

HONOURS Isthmian League div. 3 R-iup 99-00; Essex I'mediate Cup 91-92, Essex I'mediate Lg Div 2 91-92, Div 3 90-91, Lg Cup 91-92, Southend Charity Shld 90-91 91-92, Essex Snr Lg. 94-95, Lg Res. Sect. 94-95
(Wirral Programme Essex Sen. Lg. Award 92-93 94-95)

Players progressing: Les Stubbs (Southend, Chelsea) 1947, Jackie Bridge(Southend Utd) 1948, Kevin Maddocks (Maidstone Utd)

HARLOW TOWN

CLUB OFFICIALS

Chairman: **Jeff Bothwell**

President: **Ron Bruce**

Press Officer: **T.B.A.**

Secretary: **Graeme Auger**
58 Braziers Quay, South Street,Bishop's Stortford, Herts (01279 465998)

FOOTBALL MANAGEMENT TEAM

Manager: John Kendall
Coach: Jeff Wood
Physio: T.B.A.

FACT FILE

Founded: 1879
Nickname: Hawks
Sponsors: BritSec Int. Ltd
Colours: Red & white/white/white
Change: White / Black/ Black
Midweek Matchday: Wednesday
Reserves' Lg: Essex & Herts Border Comb.
Website:www.harlowtown.co.uk
Local Press: Harlow Citizen, Harlow Star, Harlow Herald & Post
Local Radio: Essex Radio, BBC Essex, Ten 17

PROGRAMME

36 pages £1.00
Editor: Phil Tuson (01279 416743)

GROUND Harlow Sports Centre, Hammarskjold Rd, Harlow CM20 2JF Tel: 01279 445319 Email: jeff.bothwell@ britsec.co.uk

Directions: Near town centre, 10 mins walk from Harlow Town (BR) station

Capacity: 10,000 Cover: 500 Seats: 400 Floodlights: Yes

Club Shop: Yes **Clubhouse:** Open daily 11-11 (10.30 Sundays). Hot & cold food available

PREVIOUS **Leagues:** East Herts (pre-1932); Spartan 32-39 46-54; London 54-61; Delphian 61-63; Athenian 63-73; Isthmian 73-92; Inactive 92-93
Grounds: Marigolds 1919-22; Green Man Field 22-60

CLUB RECORDS **A ttendance:** 9,723 v Leicester, FA Cup 3rd Rd replay 8/1/80
Goalscorer: Jeff Wood (45 in 88-89) **Appearances:** Norman Gladwin 646 (1949-70)
Win: 12-0 v Hertford Ath. (H), E. Herts Lge 5/10/29 **Defeat:** 0-11 v Ware (A), Spartan Lge Div. One (East) 6/3/48

BEST SEASON **FA Amateur Cup:** 2nd Rd 72-73 **FA Trophy:** 2nd Rd(2) 80-82 **FA Vase:** 3rd Rd 88-89
FA Cup: 4th Rd 79-80 (lost 3-4 at Watford). Also 1st Rd 80-81 81-82 League clubs defeated: Southend, Leicester 79-80

HONOURS Isthmian Lg Div 1 78-79 (R-up 82-83, Div 2 Nth 88-89, Yth Cup 77-78), Ath'n LgDiv 1 71-72, E Angl. Cup 89-90, 01-02Knight F'lit Cup R-up 87-88, Essex Snr Cup 78-79, Essex F'lit Competition R-up 71-72, London Lg Chal. Cup 59-60, Spartan LgCup 52-53, Epping Hosp. Cup (3) 46-49, Essex & Herts Border Comb Cup 75-76, Fred Budden Trophy 88-89 89-90, Chelmsford Yth Lg 86-87 (Lg Cup 86-87 87-88)

Players progressing: Jeff Wood (Charlton 75), Neil Prosser (B'mouth 80)

Back row left to right: Nigel Tester (coach), Neil Moore, Marvin Samuel, Tony McNally, James Hasell, Glenn Southgate, Danny Cowley, Steve Blaney, Dave Cook, and John Kendall (Manager) **Front Row:** Micky Stevens (Physio), Marc Salmon, Justin Gentle, Chris Wilson, Liam Tremayne (Mascot), Martin Young, Soner Zumrutel, Nick Cowley and Ian Green (Coach)

HEMEL HEMPSTEAD TOWN

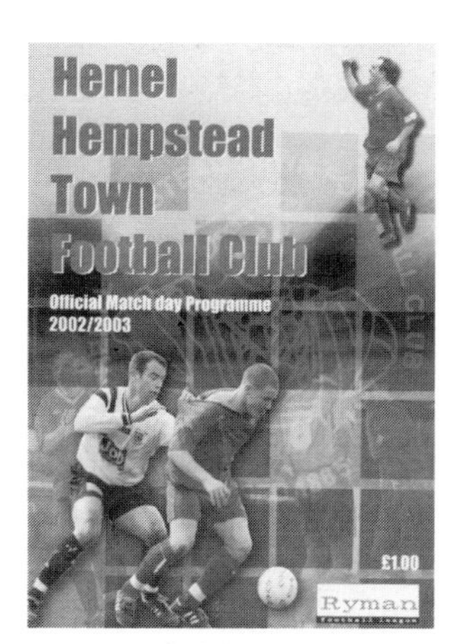

CLUB OFFICIALS

Chairman: David Boggins

President: Brendan Glynn

Vice President: Dave Lloyd

Secretary: Bob Jackson

Press Officer: Harry Kelly

FOOTBALL MANAGEMENT TEAM

Manager: Tony Kelly
Asst Manager: Chris Walton
Coach: Ninny Ryan Physio:John Burt

FACT FILE

Founded: 1885
Nickname: Tudors
Sponsors: Haven
Colours: All red with white trim
Change colours: Yellow & Blue
Midweek Matches: Tuesday
Local Press: Hemel Gazette, Herald
Local Radio: Sports Talk, Chiltern, Three Counties Radio

GROUND: Vauxhall Ground, Adeyfield Rd, Hemel Hempstead HP2 4HW
Tel: 01442 259777 e-mail: info@hemeltownfc.com

Directions: Euston to Hemel Hempstead Station.
H2 or H3 bus to Windmill Rd., Longlands

Capacity: 3,152 Seats: 250 Covered Standing : Yes Floodlights: Yes

Clubhouse: Open 7-11pm weekdays, 12-11pm weekends & Bank Hols.
Tea bar with hot snacks open matchdays. Tel: 01442 259777.

Club Shop: None

PROGRAMME

Pages: 48 Price: 80p
Editor/Press Off.: Paul Bullen
Website: www.hemeltownfc.com

PREVIOUS **Leagues:** Spartan 22-52; Delphian 52-63; Athenian 63-77
Names: Apsley 1885-1947; Hemel Hempstead Town (merged with Hemel Hempstead Utd in1947)
Grounds: Crabtree Lane (til '71)

CLUB RECORDS **Attendance:** 2,000 v Watford 1985 (at Crabtree Lane: 3,500 v Tooting, FA AmtrCup 1st Rd 1962)
Goalscorer: Dai Price **Appearances:** John Wallace, 1012

BEST SEASON **FA Cup:** Never past Qualifying Rounds
FA Vase: 4th Rd 98-99 v Taunton Town

HONOURS Ryman Lge Div 3 98-99; Herts Snr Cup 05-06 07-08 08-09 25-26 61-62 65-66 91-92,
Herts Charity Cup/Shield 25-26 34-35 51-52 63-64 76-77 83-84 (R-up 90-91), Spartan Lg 33-34,
Herts Intermediate Cup 54-55 65-66 83-84, West Herts St Mary Cup 70-71 75-76 82-83 85-86 90-91 91-92 93-94,
Athenian Lg Div 1 R-up 64-65 (Res Cup 65-66), Delphian Lg (res) 54-55 (Res Cup 54-55 61-62)

L-R - Back Row: Chris Walton (coach), Lee Graves, Rene Street, Darren Grieves, Robbie Simpson, Danny Turner, Mat Rawdon, Fergus Moore, Paul Lamb, Darren Bonfield, James Hannington, Daniel West, Gary Fitzgerald, Steve Baker, Marvyn Watson, John Simon White. **Front Row**: Joe Narty, Marcelle Bruce, Nick Jackson, Bobby Highton, Danny Adams, Vinnie Ryan (coach), Tony Kelly (manager), Bryan Hammett, Vinnie Somers, Chris Watters, Richard McDonagh

LEYTON

CLUB PERSONNEL
Chairman: Costa Sophocleous
Hon. Life President: Doug Digby
President: Laurie Aldridge

Secretary / Press Officer / Match Sec.
Tony Hampford
282 Lea Bridge Rd, Leyton,
London E10 7LD
Tel: 0208 539 5405 (B)
07904 012402 (M)

FOOTBALL MANAGEMENT
Manager: Costa Sophocleous
Assistant Manager: Stuart Hibberd
Coach: Alan Payne
Physio: Simon Purton

FACT FILE
Founded: 1868
Nickname: Lilywhites
Colours: White/ blue/ white
Change colours: Blue/ white/ blue
Midweek Matches: Tuesday
Reserves' Lge: Essex & Herts Border Comb

Programme
36 pages Price £1.00
Editor: Tony Hampford

2002-03
Leading Goalscorer: Manny Williams
Captain: Ben Wood
Players of the Year:
Jeff Wood & Manny Williams

GROUND

Address: Leyton Stadium, 282 Lea Bridge Road, Leyton, London E10 7LD Tel: 0208 539 5405 email: enquiries@leytonfc.co.uk
Directions: Lea Bridge Rd. is the A104, ground next to Hare & Hounds PH.
Leyton (Central Line) thence bus 58 or 158 to Lea Bridge Road.
Clapton (BR) Walk 100 yds to Lea Bridge Rd. roundabout, buses 48, 55, 56 to ground.
Bus 48 runs direct to ground from London Bridge (BR) station

Capacity: 2,500 Seats: Yes Cover: Yes Floodlights: Yes
Clubhouse: Lounge Bar open week days and Saturdays 11am-11pm Sunday 11pn-10.30 pm
Club Shop Contact Tony Hampford 020 8539 5405

PREVIOUS

Leagues: Ryman Div 2, Essex Senior 02; Essex Intermediate; London Spartan

RECORDS

Attendance: 100,000 for 1952 F.A.Amateur Cup Final v Walthamstowe A. at Wembley

BEST SEASONS

FA Cup: 1st Rd Proper 84-85 v Swanseaa City (A)
FA Amateur Cup: Winners 1926-27,1927-28, R-up 1951-52

HONOURS FA Amateur Cup 26-27 27-28

L-R - Back row: Stuart Hibberd (asst. manager) Jeff Wood Jordan Kelly Mark Sophocleous Simon Peddie Martin Peat James Hassel Alan Fenn Ian Bass Scott Curley George Gregoriou Costa Sophocleous (manager) Alan Payne (head coach)
Front row: Alan Hyde (match day Physio) Frank Fuschillo (asst. coach) Manny Williams Des Thomas Vas Soteriou Ben Wood (captain) Roy Parkyn Sal Abdullah Paul Golby

OXFORD CITY

CLUB OFFICIALS

Chairman:T.B.A.
President: T.B.A.
Vice Chairman: B.Cox
Press Officer/Secretary: John Shepperd
20 Howe Close, Wheatley, Oxford OX33 1SS
Tel: 01865 872181 (& Fax)

FOOTBALL MANAGEMENT TEAM

Manager: Paul Lee
Asst Manager:
Physio: C. Perkins

FACT FILE

Formed: 1882
Nickname: City
Sponsors: S.M.C.
Colours: Blue & white hoops/white/white
Change colours: yellow,black,black
Midweek Matchday: Tuesday
Reserves Lge: Suburban
Website: oxfordcityfc.co.uk

2002-2003

Captain: Julian Dark
Top Gopalscorer: Danny Wise 14
Players of the Year:
Martin Brown & Justin Lee

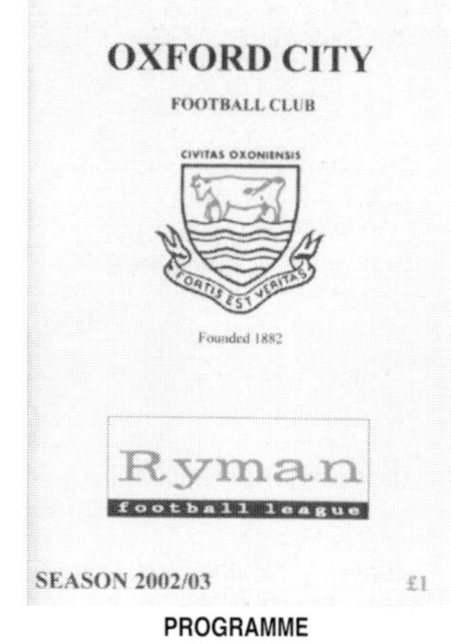

OXFORD CITY
FOOTBALL CLUB
CIVITAS OXONIENSIS
FORTIS EST VERITAS
Founded 1882
Ryman
football league
SEASON 2002/03
£1

PROGRAMME

Pages: 60 Price: £1
Editor: Colin Taylor
Local Press: Oxford Mail
Local Radio: Radio Oxford FM, Fox FM

GROUND Court Place Farm, Marsh Lane, Marston, Oxford. OX3 0NQ. Tel: 01865 744493.**Directions:** From London M40/A40, ring-road to North, take 1st slip road, follow signs to John Radcliffe hospital and Court Place Farm Stadium, ground on left after leaving flyover. From the north same ring-road.
Capacity: 3,000 Seats: 300 Cover: 400 Floodlights: Yes
Clubhouse: Open matchdays, most refreshments available
Club Shop: Yes, open matchdays, selling souvenirs. Contact Paul Cotterell

PREVIOUS
Leagues: Isthmian 07-88; South Midlands 90-93
Grounds: The White House 1882-1988; Cuttleslowe Pk 90-91; Pressed Steel,Romanway 91-93

CLUB RECORDS
Attendance: 9,500 v Leytonstone, FA Amateur Cup 50
Win: 9-0 v Harlow Town, Isthmian League 9/10/76
Defeat: 0-8 v Wycombe Wanderers, Isthmian League - date unknown
Scorer: John Woodley **Appearances:** John Woodley
Fee Paid: £3,000 for S Adams (Woking) **Fee Received:** £17,500 for Howard Forinton (Yeovil T. 1.97)

BEST SEASON
FA Amateur Cup: Winners 05-06 Runners-up 02-03 12-13 **FA Vase:** Runners-up 94-95
FA Cup: Second Round 69-70, 1-5 v Swansea City (H) **FA Trophy:** 1st Rd Prop 96 v Merthyr Tydfil

HONOURS
FA Amateur Cup 05-06 (R-up 02-03 12-13); F.A.Vase R-Up 94-95; Isthmian Lg R-up 34-35 45-46, Div 1 95-96 R-up 77-78 South MidlandsLg 92-93; Oxon Senior Cup - 28 times

Players progressing: A Blakeman (Brentford 46), C Holton (Arsenal 50), K Savin(Derby 50), R Adams (Blackpool 48), A Jeffries (Brentford 49), P James (Luton 49), D Gordon/E Wilcox (WBA 47/48), V Mobley (Sheffield Wed 63), J Varney (Hull 50), P Lee (Hereford 73), H Poole (Port Vale 55), G Parker (Luton 81), M Keown(Arsenal 84), D Meeson (Wolves 52) S.Nelson (Doncaster Rovers)

L-R - Back Row: Chris Perkins (Physio), Steve Kenny (Res. Physio), Jermaine Ferreira, Jamie Charles, Lewis Craker, Martin Brown, Steven Benbow, Matt Hayward, Matty Whitehead, Shaun Wimble, Mark Simms, Kelvin Alexis (Res. Manager), Paul Lee (Manager).
Front Row: Micky Lewis (Coach), Julian Dark (Capt.), Danny Wise, Justin Lee, Robert Cruse, Craig Farley, Andrew Ballard.

THAME UNITED

Pages: 24 Price: £1
Editor: T.B.A.
Local Press: Oxford Mail, Thame Gazette, Bucks Free Press
Local Radio: Radio Oxford, Fox FM, Mix 96

CLUB OFFICIALS

Chairman: Jim Tite

Vice Chairman: Bernard Wakelin

Secretary: Fred Saulsbury, 86 Station Road, Chinnor,Oxon.

FOOTBALL MANAGEMENT TEAM

Manager: Andy Sinott
Assistant Manager: Mark West

FACT FILE

Founded: 1883
Sponsors:T.B.A.
Nickname: United
Colours: Red & blacks/black/red & black.
Change colours: Green & white
Midweek Matchday: Tuesday
Reserves' League: Suburban

2002-2003

Captain: James Saulsbury
Top Scorer: Mark West
Player of the Year: Tony Joyce

GROUND: Windmill Road, Thame, Oxon OX9 2DR (01844 213017)
Club Website: www.thameunitedfc.co.uk

Directions: Into Nelson Street from Market Square. 3 miles from Haddenham &Thame Parkway (BR). Nearest bus stop at Town Hall (half mile away)

Capacity: 3,600 Seats: 284 Cover: 850 Floodlights: Yes

Clubhouse: Open every evening and weekend lunch times **Club Shop:** No -
Banqueting facilities for 200 (weddings, dinners, dances etc)

PREVIOUS **Leagues:** Oxon Senior; Hellenic 1959-87; South Midlands 1987-91
Name: Thame FC **Ground:** None

CLUB RECORDS **Attendance:** 1,035 v Aldershot, Isthmian Div 2 4/4/94
Win:11-3 v Barton Rovers 16/09/01 **Defeat:** 2-11 v Hungerford, FA Cup Prelim. Rd 1984
Career Goalscorer: Not known **Career Appearances:** Steve Mayhew

BEST SEASON **FA Cup:** Third Qualifying Round 91-92, 0-4 v Salisbury
FA Vase: Semi Final 1998/99

HONOURS Isthmian Lg Div 2 94-95, Div 2 R-up 98-99 Div 3 R-up 92-93; Hellenic Lg 61-62 69-70, Premier Div Cup (4); Sth Mids Lg 90-91; Oxon Snr Cup 1894-95 05-06 08-09 09-10 75-76 80-81 92-93;00-01,01-02. Oxon Interm Cup 76-77 78-79 91-92,99-00 02-03; Oxon Charity Cup

Players progressing to the Football League: None

TILBURY

CLUB OFFICIALS

Chairman: Robin Nash

Vice Chairman: Daniel Nash

President: T.B.A.

Secretary / Press Officer: Lloyd Brown
52 Lionel Oxley House,New Road,
Grays, Essex RM176PP
Tel: 01375 409938 (H)
0776 232 6519 (M)

FOOTBALL MANAGEMENT TEAM

Manager: Bill McMeekin
Physio: Steve Bell

FACT FILE

Founded: 1900
Nickname: Dockers
Colours: Black& white stripes,black,black
Change: Red & white stripes,white,red
Midweek Matches: Tuesday

2002-2003

Captain: John Scarboroough
Top scorer: Jean Marie Okita
Playerof the Year.: Kevin Mully

PROGRAMME
36 Pages   Price: £1.00
Editor: Lloyd Brown

Local Press: Thurrock Gazette, Thurrock Recorder
Local Radio: Essex Radio, BBC Essex

GROUND: Chadfields, St Chad's Rd, Tilbury, Essex RM18 8NL
Tel: 01375 843093

Directions: BR from Fenchurch Street to Tilbury Town then one mile walk.
By road: M25 (jct 30 or 31) - A13 Southend bound, Tilbury Docks turn off after 4 miles, Chadwell St Mary turn off (left) after another 1.5 miles, right after 400 metres, rt at r'bout (signed Tilbury), right into St Chad's Rd after .5 mile, 1st rt into Chadfields for ground.

Capacity: 4,000   Seats: 350   Cover: 1,000   Floodlights: Yes   **Club Shop**: No

Clubhouse: Open evening, all day Fri. & Sat. and Sun. lunchtimes. Hot &cold food

PREVIOUS
Leagues: Grays & Dist.& Sth Essex (simultaneously); Kent 27-31; London 31-39 46-50 57-62; Sth Essex Comb. (war-time); Corinthian 50-57; Delphian 62-63; Athenian 63-73
Grounds: Green & Silley Weir Ground 1900-11; Orient Field 19-38   **Names:** None

RECORDS
Attendance: 5,500 v Gorleston, FA Cup 4th Q Rd 19/11/49
Goalscorer: Ross Livermore 282 (in 305 games, 1958-66)   **Appearances:** Nicky Smith 424 (1975-85)
Fee received: £2,000, Tony Macklin to Grays A. 1990 & for Steve Conner to Dartford, 1985
Win: 17-0 v No.9 Coy Royal Artillery (H), South Essex Lg 4/10/02.
In Senior Football; 13-2 v Chalfont National (A), London Lg 28/4/92
Defeat: 1-10 - v Maidstone U. (A), Corinthian Lge 4.9.62 & v Met. Police (A), Isthmian Lg. 6.5.95

BEST SEASON
FA Cup: 3rd Rd 77-78, 0-4 v Stoke City (A)
FA Amateur Cup: Quarter Final v Wimbledon 46-7
FA Vase: Round 4 v Cowes Sports (a) 99-00

HONOURS: Isthmian Lg Div 1 75-76, (Div 1 Cup 74-75), Div 3 Prom.: 91-92, 99-00; Athenian Lg 68-69 (Div 2 62-63); London Lg 58-59 59-60 60-61 61-62, Lg Cup 58-59 60-61 61-62, R-up (3); DelphianLg 67-68 (Div 2 62-63); Essex Snr Cup 60-61 63-64 72-73 74-75 (R-up 46-47 47-48 69-70 71-72 78-79);

Players progressing to Football League: L Le May, T Scannell, T Oakley, JEvans

Other HONOURS: Essex Professional Cup 75-76; Mithras Cup 72-73 75-76 76-7778-79 (R-up 71-72 74-75); Essex Elizabethan Tphy 63-64 68-69 (R-up 55-56 59-60 64-65 67-68 70-71); Essex F'lit Comp. 68-69, Anglo-Italian Barassi Cup R-up 75-76; Essex Jnr Cup 08-09 24-25 (R-up 03-04); Stanford Charity Cup 62-63 92-93;Grays & Dist. Lg(numerous); Neale Trophy 65-66; Memorial Shield R-up 87-88

L-R - Back Row: Lloyd Brown (Sec.), Kevin Stubbs. John Ray, Mark Hardingham, Jean-Marie Okita, Scott Larkin, Kevin Mully.
Centre: Bill McMeekin (manager), Kitman, Lee Mpensah, Danny Whybrow.
Front: Ricky Downs, Paul Talbot, Jason White, Steve Jones.

UXBRIDGE

CLUB OFFICIALS

Chairman: Alan Holloway
President: Alan Odell
Secretary: Roger Stevens, 9 Bourne Avenue, Hillingdon, Middlessex UB8 3AR
Tell No: 01895 236879
Match Sec: Mick Burrell Tel: 01895 443094
Match Sec Res:PeterGranville 01595 233208
Commercial Manager: Derek Marshall
Press Officer: Richard Russell
Youth Team Sec: David Gill 0208 581 6517

FACT FILE

Formed: 1871
Nickname: The Reds
Sponsor:
Colours: Red/white/red
Change: All blue.
Midweek matchday: Tuesday
Reserves' League: Suburban (North Div)

2002--2003

Captain: Gavin Bamford
Top Scorer: Mark Nicholls
PLayer of the Year: Stuart Bamford

FOOTBALL MANAGEMENT TEAM

Manager: George Talbot Ass. Manager: Sean Dawson
Coach: Mark Gill Physios: Ian Doubleday & Paul Donnell
Res Manager: Phil Granville Youth Manager: Robert Frape

GROUND Honeycroft, Horton Road, West Drayton, Middx UB7 8HX Tel: 01895 443557
Directions: From West Drayton (BR) turn right then 1st right (Horton Road).Ground 1 mile on left. From Uxbridge (LT) take 222 or U3 bus to West Draytonstation, then follow as above. By road, ground 1 mile north of M4 jct 4 takingroad to Uxbridge and leaving by first junction and turning left into Horton Rd- ground 500yds on right
Capacity: 3,770 Cover: 760 Seats: 339 Floodlights: Yes
Clubhouse: Open every evening and weekend/bank holiday lunchtimes. (01895 443557)
Hot & cold snacks available on matchdays Large clubhouse with bar and function room availablefor hire.

Pages: 44 Price: £1.00
Editor: Richard Russell

Local Press: Uxbridge Gazette & Leader, Uxbridge Recorder
Local Radio: Capital, G L R, Star FM

PREVIOUS **Leagues:** Southern 1894-99; Gt Western Suburban 1906-19, 20-23; Athenian 1919-20, 24-37, 63-82; Spartan 37-38; London 38-46; Gt Western Comb. 39-45;Corinthian 46-63
Name: Uxbridge Town 23-45 **Grounds:** RAF Stadium 23-48, Cleveland Rd 48-78

CLUB RECORDS **Attendance:** 1,000 v Arsenal, opening of floodlights 1981
Career Scorer: Phil Duff, 153 **Career Appearances:** Roger Nicholls, 1054

BEST SEASON **FA Trophy:** 2nd Rd.1998-99, 99-00, 00-01 **FA Vase:** 4th Rd 83-84
FA Cup: 2nd Rd 1873-74. Also 1st Rd 1883-84 84-85 85-86 **FA Amateur Cup:** Runners-up 1897-98

HONOURS FA Amateur Cup R-up 1897-98; London Chall. Cup 93-94 96-97 98-99, R-up 97-98; IsthLge Div 2 S. R-up 84-85; Athenian Lge Cup R-up 81-82, Res. Sect. 69-70, Res. Cup R-up 68-69; Corinthian Lge 59-60 (R-up 48-49), Lge Mem. Shield 50-51 52-53; Middx Sen.Cup 1893-94 95-96 1950-51, 2000-01 R-up 97-98; Middx Sen. Charity Cup 07-08 12-13 35-36 81-82 (R-up 69-70 82-83 85-86); Middx PremCup 95-96 (R-up 2000-01; Allied Counties Yth Lge [East] 92-93 (Lge Cup R-up 86-87), Lge Shield 88-89 92-93, R-up 97-98; AC Delco Cup R-up 85-86; Suburban Lge North Div 95-96 97-98, R-up 96-97; Middx Sen Yth Cup 96-97

Players progressing: William Hill (QPR 51), Lee Stapleton (Fulham 52), Gary Churchouse (Charlton A.), Tony Witter (QPR), Guy Butters (Spurs), Michael Meaker (QPR)

Back row, left to right: Mark Gill (Coach), Troy Bantleman, Gavin Bamford, Harry Howell, Daryl Pelton, John Swift, Mark Nicholls, Kevin Swift, Chris O'Leary, Sean Dawson (Assistant Manager)
Front row: George Talbot (Manager), Lee Tunnell, Steve Walters, Wayne Morriss, Ben Swift, Ian Jones, Glen Donnelly, Ian Doubleday (Physio)

WALTHAM FOREST

CLUB OFFICIALS

Chairman: Harry Ramis

Vice-Chairman: Altann Kemal

President: George Cross

Secretary / Press Officer: Andy Perkins
4 Chestnut Drive,Wanstead, London E11 2TA
Tel: 02085304551

FOOTBALL MANAGEMENT TEAM

Team Manager Hakan Ramis Heyrattin

Asst.Man : Warren Hackett Physio: Lee Elliot

FACT FILE

Formed: 1995
Nickname: Lilywhites
Sponsors:T.B.A.
Colours: White/black/white
Change colours: Yellow & Blue
Midweek home matchday: Tuesday
Reserves' Lge: Suburban & Capital
2002-2003
Captain: Ian Barnes
Top Scorers: Dwight Marshall & Chris Stevens

Season 2003 - 2004

WALTHAMFOREST FOOTBALL CLUB

Ryman football league

Pages: 32 Price: £1
Editor: Tony Hampford

Local Press: Waltham Forest Guardian,
Local Radio: LBC
Website: www.waltham forestfc.com

GROUND: Wadham Lodge Sports Ground,Kitchener Road, Walthamstowe,London E17
Tel: 020 8527 2444 **Email:** andyperkins@btinternet.com

Directions: Take the North Circular Road to The Crooked Billet,then turn right into Chingford Road and into Brookscroft Road , ground is in Kitchener Road first on left .Walthamstowe Central (Victoria Line tube) is one mile away then buses W21 or 256

Capacity: 2,000 Cover: 600 Seats: 200 Floodlights: Yes

Clubhouse: Open 11-11 Mon-Sat 12-3 & 7-10-30 Sun. Tel: 0208 527 2444
No hot food but snacks available on match days from tea bar.

Club Shop: Sells progs, pennants, scarves, badges etc. Contact Ian Ansell c/o club

PREVIOUS **Name:** Walthamstow Pennant (64-95), Leyton Pannant (1995-2003)

CLUB RECORDS **Attendance:** 676 v Aldershot, Isthmian Lge 10/2/96
100,000, Leyton v Walth'stow Ave., FA Am Cup final, Wembley, April 26th 1952)

Win: 10-2 v Horsham 1982
Career goalscorer: Steve Lane 118
Defeat: 1-11 v Barnet 1946
Career appearances: Steve Hamberger 387
Transfer Fee Paid: £200 for Dwight Marshall (Hampton) **Received:** £6,000 for T Williams (Redbridge Forest)

BEST SEASON **FA Amateur Cup:** Winners 26-27 27-28, R-up x6 **FA Vase:** Sixth Rd 83-84
FA Trophy: 3rd Rd 86-87 **FA Cup:** 3rd Rd 09-10 League clubs defeated: None

HONOURS London Challenge Cup Runners-Up 1995-96, 1996-97

Left to right -

Back row:
Martin Neufville,
Liam Baptiste,
David Field,
Danny Bailey,
Wesley Jackman and
Danny Moore.

Front row:
Warren Hackett,
Dwight Marshall,
Pail Adolphe,
Rene Regis and
Ian Barnes.

Photo: Alan Coomes

WEALDSTONE

Pages: 36-40 Price: £1.50
Editor: Steve Paull & Tim Parks

Local Press:
Harrow Observer, Harrow Times
Local Radio: None give reports
Stones Soccerline: 09003 800 160

CLUB OFFICIALS

Chairman: **Nick Symmpons**
Vice Chairman: **Nick Dugard**
Secretary: **Roger Slater,** c/o 31 Jersey Avenue,Stanmore,Middlesex HA7 2JG
Tel: 0208 552 3595
Commercial Director: **Howard Krais**
Press Officer: **Roger Slater**
Company Secretary: **Graham Clark**

FOOTBALL MANAGEMENT TEAM

Manager: Gordon Bartlett
Asst Mgr: Leo Morris
Coaches: Fred Cummings & Toni Kelly
Physio: Richard price

FACT FILE

Formed: 1899
Nickname: The Stones
Sponsors:Fleetline
Colours: Blue & white quarters
Change colours: Navy & Yellow Quarters
Midweek matches: Tuesday
Reserves' League: Suburban
Club Website: http://come.to/wealdstonefc

2002-2003
Captain: Robin Tucker
Tp scorer:Mick Swaysland 29
Players of the Year: Mick Swaysland & Marvin Morgan

GROUND: (Sharing with Edgware FC) White Lion Ground, High Street,Edgware,Middlesex (Ground Tel No: 020 8952 6799) Email Address: roge@ dircon.co.uk
Directions: Left out of Edgware station(Northern Line), left again at crossroads and ground is on right , 300 yards down Edgware High Street opposite Warwick Wright behind Premier Lodge Hotel

Clubhouse: Open nightly and Friday, Saturday and Sunday lunch time. Hot and cold food on matchdays.

PREVIOUS Leagues: Willesden & Dist. 1899-1906 08-13; London 1911-22; Middx 13-22; Spartan 22-28; Athenian 28-64; Isthmian 64-71; Southern 71-79 81-82,88-95; GMVConference 79-81 82-88
Grounds: College Farm 03-10; Belmont Rd 10-22; Lower Mead Stad 22-91; Vicarage Rd (Watford FC) 91-93; The Warren (Yeading F.C.) 93-95

CLUB RECORDS Attendance: 13,504 v Leytonstone FA Amateur Cup Fourth Round replay 5/3/49
Goalscorer: George Duck, 251 **Appearances:** Charlie Townsend, 514
Win: 22-0 v The 12th London Regiment (The Rangers)(H), FA Amateur Cup 13/10/23
Defeat: 0-14 v Edgware Town (A), London Senior Cup 9/12/44
Fees Paid: £15,000 for David Gipp (Barnet, 90) **Received:** £25,000 for Stuart Pearce (Coventry City 83); for Sean Norman (Chesham, 1989)

BEST SEASON FA Amateur Cup: Winners 1965-66 **FA Trophy:** Winners 1984-85
FA Cup: Third Round 77-78, 0-4 v Q.P.R. (A). 1st Rd on 13 occasions. League clubs defeated: Hereford Utd and Reading, 77-78

HONOURS: FA Trophy 84-85; FA Amateur Cup 65-66; GMV Conference 84-85; Isthmian Lge - Div3 96-97; Southern Lg Southern Div 81-82, Div 1 South 73-74, Lg Cup 81-82; Athenian Lg 51-52 (R-up 52-53 58-59 60-61); Spartan Lg R-up 22-23; London LgDiv 2 12-13 (R-up 11-12); London Snr Cup 61-62 (jt) (R-up 39-40 51-52 60-61); Middx Snr Cup (11); Middx Senior Charity Cup (11); Capital League 84-85 86-87

Players progressing: Stuart Pearce (Coventry City 83), Vinnie Jones(Wimbledon 86), Danny Bailey (Exeter 89), Phil White (Orient 53), Tom McGhee & John Ashworth (Portsmouth 54 & 62), Charlie Sells (Exeter City 62), Eddie Dilsworth (LincolnCity 67), Colin Franks (Watford 69)

Back row, left to right: Gordon Bartlett (Manager), Rob Courtnage, Marvin Morgan, Matt Carvell, Dave Ryan, David Godfrey, Andy Carter, Jermaine Beckford, Mick Swaysland, Billy Amarteifo,James Fisherand and Leo Morris (Asst.Manager) **Front row:** Toni Kelly, Danny White, Tyronne Hercules, Jason Shaw, Robin Tucker (Captain),Charlie Mapes, Martin Carter and Richard Price (Physio) **Photo:** Graham Smith

WINGATE & FINCHLEY

CLUB OFFICIALS

Chairman: Peter Rebak

Presidents: Peter Rebak& Harvey Ackerman

Press Off.:Adam Rynhold
Tel: 020 8888 7530 (H) 079561 43291(M)

Secretary: Maurice Hanover,c/o Club.
Tel : Club - as below.
020 8501 0607(H) 07976 265588(M)

FOOTBALL MANAGEMENT TEAM

Manager: Adam Lee
Coach: AdamJeff Bookman

FACT FILE

Founded: 1991
Nickname: Blues
Colours: SkyBlue & white stripes/white/white
Change Colours: All yellow
Midweek matches: Tuesday
Reserve's Lge: Sub Lge U18

PROGRAMME

32 pages Price: £1.50
Editor: Peter Rebak (0208 8371 6001)

GROUND: The Abrahams Stadium, Summers Lane, Finchley, London N12 0PD
Tel: 0208 446 2217 Fax: 020 8343 8194

Directions: North Circular (A406) to junction with High Road Finchley (A1000).
Go north and Summers Lane is 200 yds on right - parking for 80 cars.
Tube to East Finchley (Northern Line) and then 263 bus to Summers Lane towards North Finchley

Capacity: 8,500 **Seats:** 500 **Cover:** 500 **Floodlights:** Yes **Club Shop:** No

Clubhouse: Open during matches. Also tea-bar selling most refreshments

PREVIOUS: **Names:** Wingate (founded 46), Finchley (founded late 1800s) merged in 91
Leagues: (as Wingate & Finchley) South Mids 89-95
Finchley: London 02-12 14-15 23-25 30-39; Athenian 12-14 29-30 45-73; Isthmian73-91
Wingate: Middx 46-52; London 52-62; Delphian 62-63; Athenian 63-75; Barnet Yth,Hendon & Dist. Sunday 75-84; Herts 84-89

CLUB RECORDS: **Attendance:** 9,555 - Finchley v Bishop Auckland, F.A. Amat Cup QF 49-50
Career Goalscorer: Marc Morris 578 **Career Appearances:** Marc Morris 587(1975-93)
Win: 9-0, Wingate v Sarratt, Herts Co. Lge Div. 1, 20/4/85
Defeat: 0-9 v Edgware,Ryman League Division Two. 15.1.2000

BEST SEASON **FA Vase:** 74-75 Quarter Final (Wingate)
FA Amateur Cup: Semi-Final (Finchley)

HONOURS: Isthmian League Div. 3 R-up 98-99, Promoted (7th) 2001-02, London Senior Cup winners 94-95

Previous Honours Finchley: London Snr Cup, London Charity Cup, FA Amtr Cup SF, Athenian Lg 53-54(R-up 63-64 65-66), London Lg 36-37 (R-up 35-36, Div 2 06-07(jt with Enfield),Lg Cup 34-35, Park Royal Cup 37-38)
Wingate: Middx Lg(2)(R-up(1), Lg Cup), London Lg R-up(2)(Lg Cup(1)), Middx SnrCup SF, Athenian Lg Div 2 69-70, Herts Co. Lg Div 1 84-85 (Aubrey Cup 85-86),Herts I'mediate Cup 84-85, Herts Snr Tphy 86-87, Sth Mids Lg Div 1 R-up 89-90(Lg Cup SF 89-90), Barnet Yth Lg 75-76, Pete Morrison Cup 82-83 83-84 (R-up 79-80 84-85), Hendon & Dist. Int. Div 79-80. Win & Fin: London Sen Cup 79-80

Back row, left to right: Adam Lee, Marcus Davis, A Newman, Andy Walker, Daniel Boateng, Steve Forwell and Robert Donn
Front row: Daniel Nielson, Daniel Fitzpatrick, John Butterfield, Dean Williams, Paul Wood, Daniel Berg, Clive Wilson and Guy Morris.
Photo: Arthur Evans

CLUB OFFICIALS

Chairman: Maz Brook

Secretary / Press Officer: Mike Boyle,
15 Daniell Drive, Colchester, Essex
Tel: 01206 573223

FOOTBALL MANAGEMENT TEAM

Manager: Steve Pitt

FACT FILE

Formed: 1925
Nickname: The Dragons
Colours: Royal blue/white
Change colours: Red/black
Reserves' League: Essex & Suffolk Border
Midweek matchday: Tuesday

Official Matchday Programme Season 02/03
WIVENHOE TOWN FOOTBALL CLUB
Sponsored by Jones & Whymark
Ryman football league
Saturday 31st August 2002
The Dragons V Yeading
FA Cup Preliminary Round
Official Website: www.wivenhoetown.com

48 Pages Price: £1.00
Editor: J. Gooding

Local Press: East Anglian Daily Times, Colchester Evening Gazette
Local Radio: BBC Radio Essex, S.G.R.

GROUND: Broad Lane Ground, Elmstead Road, Wivenhoe CO7 7HA
Tel: 01206 825380

Directions: Coming out of Colchester towards Clacton take first turning (right) towards Wivenhoe, then 1st left and the ground is clearly visible on the right at the cross-roads. 1 mile from Wivenhoe (BR)

Capacity: 3,000 Cover: 1,300 Seats: 250 Floodlights: Yes

Clubhouse: Open normal pub hours. Tel: 01206 825380

Club Shop: A full range of souvenirs etc

PREVIOUS: **Leagues:** Brighlingsea & District 1927-50; Colchester & East Essex 50-71; Essex & Suffolk Border 71-79; Essex Senior 79-86
Name: Wivenhoe Rangers
Grounds: Spion Kop; Broomfield (twice); Claude Watcham's Meadow; Vine Farm; King George V Playing Fields; Essex University

CLUB RECORD **Attendance:** 1,912 v Runcorn, FA Trophy 1st Rd, Feb 1990
Transfer fee received: £5,875 for Bobby Mayes (Redbridge Forest)
Win: 18-0 v Nayland. **Defeat:** 0-8 v Carshalton A. (H), Isthmian Lg 28/8/93
Career goalscorer: Paul Harrison, 258 in 350 games **Career appearances:** Keith Bain, 536

BEST SEASON **FA Cup:** 4th Qual Rd 89-90 2-3 v Halesowen Tn (A), 94-95 1-2 v Enfield (H)
FA Trophy: 2nd Rd replay 89-90 **FA Vase:** 5th Rd 82-83;

HONOURS Isthmian Lg Div 1 89-90 (Div 2 Nth 87-88); Essex Snr Lg R-up 79-80 81-82 85-86(Harry Fisher Tphy 83-84 85-86); Essex & Suffolk Border Lg 78-79, Div 1 72-73,Div 2 71-72, Lg Cup R-up(2); Colchester & East Essex Lg 52-53 55-56 (R-up 70-71), Div 1 59-60 69-70, Div 2 R-up 68-69, Lg KO Cup 51-52 52-53 54-55 55-56 (R-up 59-60), Challenge Cup 52-53); Brighlingsea & Dist Lg Div 1 35-36 36-37 47-48(R-up 37-38), Lg KO Cup 36-37 37-38 47-48, Challenge Cup 36-37; Essex Snr Tphy87-88 Essex Jnr Cup R-up 55-56 78-79; Amos Charity Cup(7) (R-up 72-73); StokesCup(3); Wivenhoe Charity Cup (4), (R-up [4]); Cristal Monopole Cup (5), (R-up 2); Sidney James Mem. Tphy 69-70 (R-up 72-73), Tolleshunt D'Arcy Mem. Cup(3)(R-up 2); Walton & District Charity Cup 73-74 78-79; Coggeshall Brotherhood Cup80-81; Brantham Charity Cup R-up 82-83; Worthington Evans Cup 81-82 (R-up 80-8185-86); Harwich Snr Cup R-up 84-85; Woodbridge Chal. Cup 91-92; Mat FowlerShield 92-93 94-95

Players progressing: Robert Reinelt (Gillingham) 1993

CLUB OFFICIALS

Chairman: Philip Spurden

Secretary: Joanne Powell,
42 Roberts Ride, Hazlemere, Bucks. HP15 7AF
Tel: 01494 712442
Email: yeading@yeadingfc.co.uk

Commercial Manager: Bill Perryman
Tel: 020 8756 1200

Press Officer: Tim Fuell (0778 2284164)

FOOTBALL MANAGEMENT TEAM

Managers: Johnson Hippolyte
Asst. Manager: Dereck Brown
Coaches: Erskine Smart & Jason Tucker

FACT FILE

Formed: 1965
Nickname: The Ding
Colours: Red & black stripes/black/black
Change colours: All white
Midweek matchday: Tuesday
Reserves League: Capital
Website: www.yeadingfc.co.uk
Local Newspapers: Hayes Gazette, Hillingdon Times

2002-2003

Captains: Steve Ashley & Nevin Saroya
Top Scorer: Matt Miller 30
Players of the Year: Keith Newby & Emond Protain

Programme - Pages: 36 Price: £1.50
Editor: Tim Fuell

GROUND The Warren, Beaconsfield Rd.Hayes, MiddlesexUB4 0SL
Tel: 020 8848 7362 Fax: 020 8756 1200 email: yeading@yeadingfc.co.uk
Directions: 2 miles from Hayes (BR) - take Uxbridge Road and turn right towards Southall, right into Springfield Rd and then left into Beaconsfield Rd. Bus 207 stops 1/2 mile from ground
Capacity: 3,500 Cover: 1,000 Seats: 250 Floodlights: Yes
Clubhouse: Open normal pub hours.' The Warren' Conference & Banquetting suite available for hire.
Club Shop: No Metal Badges: Yes

PREVIOUS **Leagues:** Uxbridge & Dist. 65-67; W. Middx. Comb. 67-68; S W Middx 68-74; Middx 74-84; Spartan 84-87

CLUB RECORDS **Attendance:** 3,000; v Hythe Town, FA Vase SF 1990; v Tottenham Hotspur, friendly
Career Goalscorer: Dave Burt 327 **Career Appearances:** Norman Frape 457
Fee Paid: £3,000 for Matt Edwards to Hucknall Town **Fee Received:** £45,000 for Andrew Impey (QPR)

BEST SEASON **FA Cup:** First Round Proper 93-94 & 94-95
FA Vase: Winners 89-90 **FA Trophy:** 2nd Round 97-98, 98-99, 00-01

HONOURS FA Vase 89-90; Isthmian League Div 2 Sth 89-90 (Div 1 R-up 91-92) League Cup 2002-03;Spartan League 86-87 (R-up 85-86, Senior Div R-up 84-85, League Cup 85-86 86-87); Middlesex Snr League (6) 71-73 74-76 81-82 83-84 (R-up 73-74 74-75 78-79, LeagueCup (6) 72-73 75-76 79-83); South West Middlesex League (2) 69-71; Middlesex Snr Cup 89-90 91-92, Middlesex Prem. Cup 80-81, Middlesex I'mediate Cup (5) 70-7274-76 77-78, Middlesex Jnr Cup (4) 68-69 70-72 74-75; Uxbridge League 66-67; Middlesex Border League Cup 86-87 (AJA Cup 86-87); Suburban League Nth 87-88; Allied Counties Yth League 89-90 (Lge Cup 89-90)
Players progressing: Andrew Impey (Leicester City ,West Ham United , QPR and England U 21) and Lee Charles (Q.P.R.via Chertsey Town) Charlie Oatway(Cardiff C)

Yeading FC 2002/03 (left to right, back row first)
Johnson Hippolyte (Manager), Danny Jordan, Simon Chang (no longer with the club), Kevin Randall, Steve Ashley,
Dereck Brown (Asst Manager), Nevin Saroya, Emond Protain, Nick Leach, Otis Hutchings
Erskine Smart (Coach), Matt Miller, Keith Newby, Carl Levene, Ryan McIntosh, Errol Telemaque, Leon Woodruffe, Jonathan Hippolyte (Mascot)
Inset: Bobby Behzadi, Darti Brown, DJ Campbell, Daniel Hawkesworth, Matt Hodson, Dwane Lee, Jonathan Mills

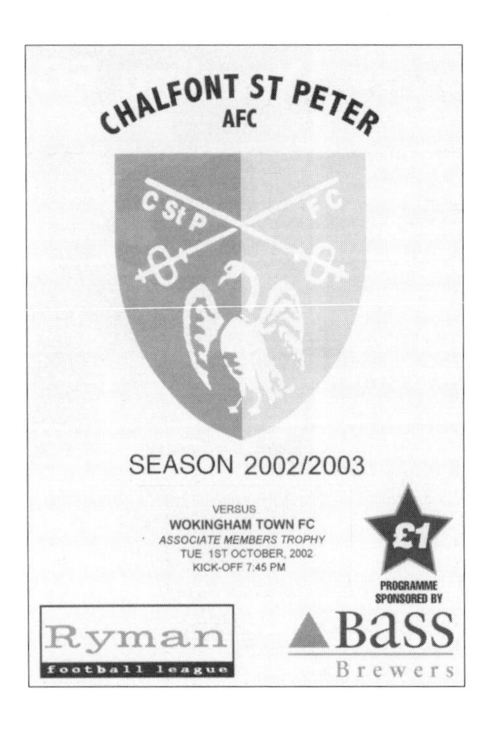

RYMAN DIVISION TWO PROGRAMMES

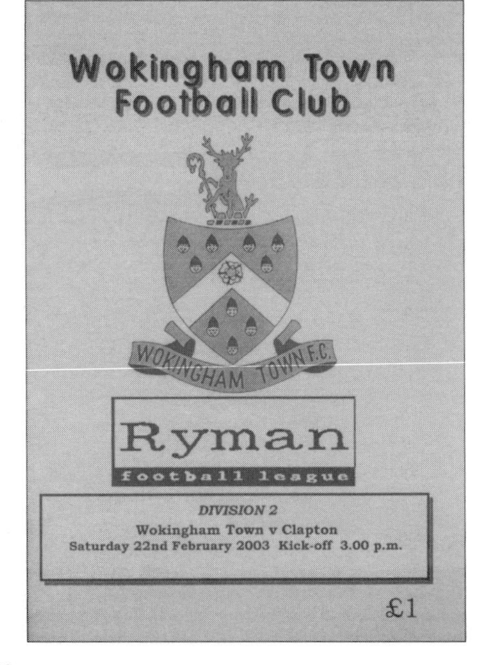

RYMAN DIVISION TWO

			HOME					AWAY						
		P	W	D	L	F	A	W	D	L	F	A	Pts	GD
1	Cheshunt	30	13	2	0	44	11	12	1	2	47	18	78	62
2	Leyton	30	13	1	1	46	8	8	4	3	31	14	68	55
3	Flackwell Heath	30	9	0	6	22	21	8	3	4	30	23	54	8
4	Abingdon Town	30	8	5	2	33	14	6	6	3	32	28	53	23
5	Hungerford Town	30	6	6	3	25	18	6	6	3	24	18	48	13
6	Leighton Town	30	7	2	6	34	24	7	1	7	27	19	45	18
7	Witham Town	30	8	4	3	26	19	4	4	7	14	24	44	-3
8	Ware	30	7	4	4	29	28	5	1	9	18	25	41	-6
9	Clapton	30	6	4	5	23	27	6	1	8	17	20	41	-7
10	Tring Town	30	7	2	6	29	29	4	3	8	20	29	38	-9
11	Kingsbury Town	30	5	7	3	17	13	4	4	7	21	35	38	-10
12	Edgware Town	30	6	0	9	28	32	4	3	8	21	33	33	-16
13	Wokingham Town	30	3	3	9	15	42	4	4	7	19	39	28	-47
14	Dorking	30	4	4	7	25	28	2	2	11	24	35	24	-14
15	Chalfont St Peter	30	4	2	9	18	31	2	3	10	16	32	23	-29
16	Camberley Town	30	2	2	11	11	28	2	2	11	12	33	16	-38

		1	2	3	4	5	6	7	8	9	10	11	12	13	14	15	16
1	Abingdon Town		4-0	3-1	1-2	2-2	2-1	1-1	2-3	0-0	1-1	3-1	5-1	6-1	1-0	0-0	2-0
2	Camberley Town	0-3		1-4	2-3	1-2	2-0	0-0	0-2	1-3	0-1	0-2	1-1	0-3	2-0	0-1	1-3
3	Chalfont St Peter	1-2	0-1		0-4	0-3	1-0	1-3	1-4	1-2	3-0	5-3	1-3	2-1	0-3	0-0	2-2
4	Cheshunt	4-1	2-1	3-0		3-0	1-0	6-1	3-1	0-0	7-0	2-1	1-1	3-2	2-1	3-1	4-1
5	Clapton	2-2	2-1	2-0	0-5		3-3	0-5	2-4	2-0	0-1	0-2	1-1	3-1	3-0	1-1	2-1
6	Dorking	2-2	2-0	2-2	3-6	0-1		1-2	1-2	1-1	1-1	2-1	0-7	0-1	1-2	4-0	5-0
7	Edgware Town	0-3	0-1	0-4	1-3	0-1	3-6		3-0	0-1	1-6	1-0	3-1	2-3	2-1	3-1	9-1
8	Flackwell Heath	0-4	3-2	1-0	0-2	2-1	3-0	3-1		1-3	2-0	1-0	0-2	3-2	2-1	1-2	0-1
9	Hungerford Town	1-1	1-0	5-1	1-3	3-0	2-0	3-2	1-2		2-2	1-0	0-2	1-1	1-1	1-1	2-2
10	Kingsbury Town	1-1	1-1	2-2	2-0	2-1	0-0	1-0	2-2	0-0		1-1	0-2	3-1	0-1	2-0	0-1
11	Leighton Town	3-3	2-1	2-0	0-5	0-1	3-0	8-0	3-3	2-3	5-2		0-1	0-1	2-1	2-0	2-3
12	Leyton	8-0	3-0	4-0	5-2	1-0	4-0	3-1	3-0	3-2	0-0	1-3		1-0	2-0	3-0	5-0
13	Tring Town	2-0	3-0	1-1	1-6	0-2	3-1	2-1	0-2	3-1	7-1	2-7	0-2		2-3	2-1	1-1
14	Ware	3-5	0-0	2-1	1-4	3-2	4-2	3-1	2-1	1-1	3-2	0-3	0-0	3-1		1-2	3-3
15	Witham Town	0-4	7-2	2-0	0-0	1-0	3-2	1-3	0-0	1-1	2-1	0-1	2-1	2-2	4-2		1-0
16	Wokingham Town	1-1	3-2	2-0	1-2	2-1	1-9	0-0	0-4	2-6	1-3	0-2	0-6	0-0	1-2	1-4	

ABINGDON TOWN

GROUND

Address: Culham Road, Abingdon OX14 3HP (01235 521684)

Directions: On A415 road to Dorchester-on-Thames half a mile south of town centre. Nearest rail station is Culham. Main line: Didcot Parkway or Oxford. Bus service from Didcot & London

Capacity: 3,000 Cover: 1,771 Seats: 271 Floodlights: Yes

Clubhouse: (01235 521684). 7.30-11pm. 6pm matchdays. 12.30-2.30, 4-11 Sat. Hot food on matchdays. Pool, darts, jukebox, canteen

Club Shop: Selling programmes, magazines, scarves. Metal Badges: £2

HONOURS

Berks & Bucks Sen Cup 58-59 (R-up 88-89 92-93); Isthmian League Div 2 (Sth) 90-91 (Assoc. Mem. Tphy R-up 90-91); London Spartan Lg 88-89 Hellenic Lge(4) 56-57 58-60 86-87, R-up(3) 70-72 87-88,Lg Cup 57-58 70-71 81-82 (R-up 83-84 86-87), Div 1 75-76, Div 1 Cup 75-76,Res. Div(3) 69-71 86-87, Res. Div Cup 70-71 85-86, Res. Div Suppl. Cup 74-75;Oxford & Dist. Lg (3) 1898-1901; Reading & Dist. Lg 47-48; Berks & Bucks Jnr Cup 06-07; Abingdon Centenary Cup 58-59; Joan Lee Mem. Cup 69-70 70-71 86-87

PREVIOUS

Leagues: Oxford & Dist.; West Berks; Reading Temperance; North Berks; Reading & Dist. 1927-50; Spartan 50-53; Hellenic 53-88; London Spartan 88-89

Name: Abingdon FC (merged with St Michaels in 1899).

CLUB RECORDS

Attendance: 1,400 v Oxford City, FA Cup September 1960

Career appearances: John Harvey-Lynch

BEST SEASON

FA Vase: Fifth Round, replay, 1989-90.

FA Cup: 4th Qualifying Round

60-61 0-2 v Hitchin, 89-90 1-3 v Slough(H), 92-93 1-2 v Merthyr T.(A) after 0-0

Players progressing: Maurice Owen (Swindon Town), George Buck (Stockport County& Reading), Sammy Chung (Reading, Norwich City, Watford & WolverhamptonWanderers), Jermaine McSporran (Wycombe Wanderers via Oxford City), Howard Forinton (Birmingham City,Plymouth Argyle via Oxford City and Yeovil Town)

FACT FILE

Formed: 1870
Nickname: The Abbotts
Sponsors: Wootton Trucks
Colours: Yellow & green/green/yellow
Change colours: Black & white

Programme: Pages: 40 Price:£1.00
Editor: Kevin Rowland(01235 522115)

Midweek Matchday: Tuesday
Reserves ' League: Suburban (North)

Local Press: Oxford Mail, Oxford Times, Abingdon Herald, South Oxon Guardian

CLUB PERSONNEL

Chairman: Phil Evans
President: Dr Tim Reynolds
Secretary: Ted Quail,
107 Park Lane, Thatcham,
Newbury, Berks RG18 3BZ
Tel: 01635868967
Press Off : Roger Nicholl
Tel: 07768 427268 (M)

Manager: Alan Thorne
Asst Manager: Peter Lamont
Physio: Anton Titcombe
Coach: T.B.A.

CAMBERLEY TOWN

GROUND

Address: Krooner Park, Krooner Road, off Frimley Rd, Camberley, Surrey, GU15 2QP. Tel: 01276 65392

Directions: M3 Jct 4, follow signs to Frimley, then B3411 towards Camberley, ground on left opposite `The Standard' pub

Capacity: 3,000 Seats: 195 Cover: 280 Floodlights: Yes Club Shop: Yes **Clubhouse**: Open matchdays & 2 evenings. Food available from burger bar matchdays

HONOURS:

Isthmian Lg Div 2 R-up 78-79; Surrey Snr Lg 30-31 31-32 32-33 (R-up 46-47 61-62), Lg Charity Cup 37-38 51-52 (R-up 31-32 36-37 54-55 72-73); Surrey Snr Cup 78-79 (R-up 35-36); W. Surrey Lg 13-14 (R-up 12-13); Ascot & Dist Lg 03-04; Surrey Jnr Charity Cup R-up 08-09; Surrey Jnr Cup 1897-98 1909-10 (R-up 07-08); Aldershot Snr Lg 12-13 (Lg Charity Cup R-up 21-22); Southern Comb. Cup 80-81 (R-up 78-79 85-86 87-88); Aldershot Sen Cup 96-97 97-98

PREVIOUS **Leagues:** Ascot & District; West Surrey; Aldershot Snr; Surrey Snr 22-73 Spartan 73-75; Athenian 75-77 82-84; Isthmian 77-82
Names: Camberley & Yorktown 1896-1946; Camberley FC 46-67
Grounds: London Rd Rec 1898-1905 12-18/ Southwell Park Rd 05-09/ Martins Meadow 09-12

CLUB RECORDS: **Attendance:** 3,500 v Crystal Pal. friendly 14.10.74
Competitive: 2,066 v Aldershot Town, Isthmian Lge Div. 3, 10.11.92
Appearances: Brian Ives
Win: 15-0 v Royal Engineers, friendly, 20/9/19
Defeat: 0-11 v Abingdon Town (A), Isthmian Lge Div. 2 (South) 25/8/90

BEST SEASON: **FA Vase:** Quarter Final 85-86, 98-99 v Woodbridge
FA Cup:1st Rd Prop 98-99 v Brentford 4th Qual. 32-33 33-34 97-98

FACT FILE

Founded: 1896
Nickname: Krooners, Reds or Town
Colours: Red & white stripes/red/red
Change :Green & white hoops'black/black
Midweek Matches: Tuesday
Reserve's League: Suburban

Programme: 24 pages, £1
Local Press: Camberley News
Bracknell News

CLUB PERSONNEL

Chairman: Ian Waldren
Press Office & Prog.Ed,: Andy Vaughan
Secretary: David Clifford
63 Inglewood Ave, Camberley,
Surrey. GU15 1RS
Tel & Fax: 01276 516613
Website: www.cambrleytownfc .co.uk

Manager: Les Rider
Asst.Mans: Eric Howard & Richard Brown
Physio: T.B.A.

2002-03

Top Scorer: Jamie Shannon
Captain:Ricky McNamara
P.o.Y.:Mark Robertson

CHALFONT ST. PETER

GROUND

Address: Mill Meadow, Amersham Road, Chalfont St Peter SL9 7BQ
Tel: 01753 885797

Directions: A413 from Uxbridge (London) to Chalfont. Turn left 100 yds after 2nd major roundabout (between Ambulance station and Community Centre.
Just under two miles from Gerrards Cross (BR)
Regular buses from Slough & Uxbridge

Capacity: 4,500 Cover: 120 Seats: 220 Floodlights: Yes Club Shop: No

Clubhouse: Open every evening, Saturday afternoons and Sunday lunchtimes

PREVIOUS **Leagues:** Great Western Combination 1948-58; Parthenon 58-59; London 60-62; Spartan 62-75; London Spartan 75-76; Athenian 76-84

BEST SEASON **FA Trophy:** 3rd Qual Rd 89-90 91-92
FA Vase: 4th Rd 87-88
FA Cup: 3rd Qual Rd85-86 (wins over Banbury, King's Lynn and Barking)

HONOURS Isthmian Lg Div 2 87-88; Athenian Lg R-up 83-84 (Lg Cup 76-77 82-83); London Spartan Lg Div 2 75-76; Berks & Bucks Intermediate Cup 52-53; Berks & Bucks Benevolent Cup 64-65

CLUB RECORDS **Attendance:** 2,550 v Watford, benefit match 1985
Career Goalscorer: Unknown **Career Appearances:** Colin Davies
Transfer Fee Paid: £750 to Chertsey (Steve Church, March 1989)

Players progressing to Football League: Paul Barrowcliff (Brentford), Dean Hooper (Swindon)

FACT FILE

Founded: 1926
Nickname: Saints
Colours: Red, green,red.
Change colours:All Blue
Midweek matchday: Tuesday
Reserves' League:
Programme: Pages: 30 Price: £1.00
Editor: Nigel Orr
Local Press: Bucks Advertiser, Bucks Examiner, Bucks Free Press, Wycombe Midweek
Local Radio: Chiltern Radio

CLUB PERSONNEL

Chairman:Denis Mair
Press Officer: Nick Simon (0776 5963184)
Secretary: Migel Orr,Trio Nicol Road,Chalfont St Peter, Bucks Sl9 9NF
Tel No: 01753 887209
Manager: Martin Dean

2002-2003

Captain: Kevin Powell
Players of the Year: Mark Needham & Peter Weirich Top Scorer: Barry Brosnan.

CHERTSEY TOWN

GROUND

Address: Alwyns Lane, Chertsey, Surrey KT16 9DW
Tel: 01932 561774 Email: ctfc.freeserve.co.uk
Directions: Alwyns Lane is off Windsor Street at north end of shopping centre. 10 mins walk from Chertsey (BR). London Country bus
Capacity: 3,000 Seats: 250 Cover: 1000 Floodlights: Yes
Clubhouse: Open weekday evenings and weekend lunchtimes
Club Shop: Open matchdays, selling club & football souvenirs. Contact Daniel Dullaway

PREVIOUS

Leagues: West Surrey (pre-1899); Surrey Jnr 1899-1920; Surrey Intermediate 20-46; Surrey Snr 46-63; Metropolitan 63-66; Gtr London 66-67; Spartan 67-75; London Spartan 75-76; Athenian 76-84; Isthmian 84-85; Combined Counties 85-86.
Grounds: The Grange (pre-World War 1), The Hollows (pre-1929)

CLUB RECORDS

Attendance: 2,150 v Aldershot, Isthmian Lge Div. 2 4/12/93
Goalscorer: Alan Brown 54, 1962-63
Win: 10-1 v Clapton (H), Isthmian Lge Div. 3, 91-92
Defeat: 1-12 v Bromley (H), FA Cup Preliminary Rd, 82-83
Transfer fee received: £67,500.

BEST SEASON

FA Vase: Quarter Final 87-88 91-92
FA Cup: 3rd Qual. Rd 92-93, 1-3 v Kingstonian (H)
FA Trophy: 2nd Qual Rd 95-96
FA Amateur Cup: 3rd Qual Rd 61-62

HONOURS

Isthmian Lge Cup 94-95 (Assoc. Members Trophy 94-95), Div 2 R-up 94-95, Div 3 R-up 91-92; Surrey Snr Lge 59-60 61-62 62-63 (Lge Cup 59-60 61-62); Combined Co's Lge R-up 85-86 (Concours Tphy 85-86); Surrey Snr Cup R-up 85-86; Spartan Lge & Lge Cup R-up 74-75
Players progressing:
Rachid Harkouk (Crystal Palace), Peter Cawley (Wimbledon 87), Lee Charles (Q.P.R. 95)

FACT FILE

Formed: 1890
Nickname: Curfews
Sponsors: Holly Tree
Colours: Blue & white stripes/white/blue
Change colours: Yellow & Black
Midweek Matchday: Tuesday
Club Website: www.curfews.com

Programme

Pages: 36 Price: £1
Editor: Chris Gay (01276 20745)
Local Press: Surrey Herald
Local Radio: BBC Southern Counties, County Sound

CLUB OFFICIALS

Chairman: Steve Powes
President: Cllr Chris Norman
Vice Chairman: Nick Keel

Press Officer / Secretary:

Ben O'Conner
2 Monaveen Gardens, West Molesey, Surrey KT8 1SB Tel: 0208 224 1387

FOOTBALL MANAGEMENT TEAM

Manager: Steve Johnson
Asst Manager: Tom Maloney
Coach: Ian Barrado
Physio: Peter Chessman

CLAPTON

GROUND
Address: The Old Spotted Dog, Upton Lane, Forest Gate, London E7 9NP
Tel: 0208 4720822
Directions: BR to Forest Gate.Tube to Plaistow (District Line).
Official entrance in Upton Lane.
Docklands Light Railway to Prince Regent then 325 bus to ground
Capacity: 2,000 Seats: 100 Cover: 180 Floodlights: Yes
Club Shop: No
Clubhouse: Match days. Light snacks available. To hire please contact club

HONOURS: FA Amateur Cup: 06-07 08-09 14-15 23-24 24-25 (R-up 04-05); Isthmian Lg 10-11 22-23 (R-up 05-06 07-08 09-10 24-25), Div 2 82-83; Essex Thames-side Tphy(2); A.F.A.Invitation Cup (2); London Snr Cup (2); London Charity Cup; Essex Snr Cup (4); Middlesex Snr Cup; Essex Sen Trophy; First English team to play on the continent, beating a Belgian Select XI over Easter 1890.

PREVIOUS **Leagues:** Southern 1894-96 (founder members); London 1896-97
Grounds: None

CLUB RECORDS **Attendance:** 12,000 v Tottenham Hotspur, FA Cup 1898-99
Defeat: 0-14 v Nottingham Forest (H), FA Cup 1st Rd 1890-91

BEST SEASON **FA Cup:** 3rd Rd Proper 25-26 (lost 2-3 to Swindon at Upton Park)
League clubs defeated Norwich City 25-26.
FA Amateur Cup: 06-07 08-09 14-15 23-24 24-25 (R-up 04-05);

Players progressing to Football Lge: Numerous over past 116 years. Currently:, Gary Charles (West Ham)

FACT FILE
Founded: 1878
Nickname: Tons
Sponsors: Knights
Colours: Red & white stripes/black/black
Change colours: Blue & White
Midweek Matchday: Tuesday

Programme: up to 30 pages £1.00
Editor: Linda C Ambrose

CLUB PERSONNEL
Chairman: Dickson Gill
Chief Executive: Vince McBean

Secretary: Linda Ambrose,
8 Sylvan Hill, Crystal Palace, SQ19 2QF
Tel: 0208 6538000

Manager:Dickson Gill
Physios:Lucelta Eugene
& Caroline Touruas

2002-03
Leading Goalscorer: Gary Thomas
Captain:Orlando Hollingsworth
Player of the Year: Aaron Nicholls

DORKING

GROIUND
Address: Meadowbank, Mill Lane, Dorking, Surrey RH4 1DX
Tel: 01306 884112

Directions: Mill Lane is off Dorking High St. next to Woolworths and Marks &Spencers, & opposite the White Horse pub. Fork right in Mill Lane past the Malthouse pub. 1/2 mile from both Dorking and Deepdene (BR) stations

Capacity: 3,600 Cover: 800 Seats: 200 Floodlights: Yes
Club Shop: Yes
Clubhouse: All week &Sun. 4-11 p.m. Sats 12-11pm Hot & cold food on matchdays

HONOURS Isthmian Lge Div 2 Sth 88-89, (Full Members Cup R-up 92-93); Surrey Sen Cup R-up 1885-86 1989-90; Surrey Senior Shield (2), R-up (3); Surrey Sen Lge (4), R-up (2), Lge Cup (3); Lge Charity Cup (4), R-up (5); Gilbert Rice F'lit Cup 87-88 (R-up 89-90); Surrey I'mediate Cup 56-57 (R-up 54-55); Southern Comb.Challenge Cup 92-93

PREVIOUS **Ground:** Prixham Lane (until 1953)
Leagues: Surrey Senior 22-56 77-78; Corinthian 56-63; Athenian 63-74 78-80; Southern 74-77
Names: Dorking Town 77-82; Guildford & Dorking United (when club merged with Guildford in1974)/

CLUB RECORDS **Attendance:** 4,500 v Folkestone Town, FA Cup 1st Qual. Rd 1955 and v Plymouth Argyle 1st Rd F.A.Cup 92-93
Goalscorer: Andy Bushnell **Appearances**: Steve Lunn
Win: 7-0 v Barking, Isthmian Lge Div. One, 31/10/92

BEST SEASON **FA Cup:** 1st Round Proper 92-93, 2-3 v Plymouth A. (H)
FA Vase: 5th Round 2001-2002 **FA Trophy:** 2nd Rd 91-92

Players progressing to Football League:
Steve Scrivens & John Finch (Fulham), Andy Ansah (Brentford 1989)

FACT FILE
Formed: 1880
Nickname: The Chicks
Colours: Green & white hoops/green/green
Change colours: All navy blue
Midweek matches: Tuesday
Reserve League: Suburban
Programme
48 pages £1 Editor: Bryan Bletso
Local Press: Dorking Advertiser, Surrey Mirror, Surrey Advertiser
Local Radio: County Sound, BBC Southern Counties, Radio Mercury

CLUB PERSONNEL
Chairman: Jack Collins
President: Ingram Whittingham
Vice-Chairman: Ray Collins
Co. Sec.: Martin Collins
Secretary: Ray Collins
11 Richmond Way, Fetcham,
Surrey KT22 9NP
Tel: 01372 453867
Press Officer: Bryan Bletso

Managers: Steve Lunn & Nick Torpey
Physio: Bennie Fishlock

2002-03
Leading Goalscorer:
Captain:
Player of the Year:

EDGWARE TOWN

GROUND
Address: White Lion Ground, High Street, Edgware HA8 5AQ. Tel: 0181 9526799

Directions: Left out of Edgware tube station (Northern Line), left again at crossroads and ground is 300yds on right in Edgware High St. . Buses 32, 288 142

Capacity: 5,000 Seats: 220 Cover: 1,500 Floodlights: Yes
Club Shop: No
Clubhouse: Open nightly and Fri, Sat, Sun lunchtimes.
Hot & cold food matchdays, cold food lunchtimes

HONOURS: Isthmian Lg Div 3 91-92; London Spartan Lg 87-88 89-90 (Lg Cup 87-88); Corinthian Lg R-up 53-54, Memorial Shield 52-53 61-62; Athenian Lge R-up 81-82; Middx Snr Lg 40-41 41-42 42-43 43-44 44-45, Cup 47- 48 (R-up 73-74 94-95); London Snr Cup R-up 47-48; Middx Border Lg Cup 79-80; Suburban Lg Div R-up 89-90

PREVIOUS **Leagues:** Corinthian 46-63; Athenian 64-84; London Spartan 84-90
Names: Edgware F.C. **Grounds:** None

CLUB RECORDS **Attendance:** 8,500 v Wealdstone, FA Cup 1948
Career Appearances: John Mangan
Career Goalscorer: Steve Newing

BEST SEASON **FA Vase:** 5th Round, 1991-92

Players progressing: Brian Stein (Luton), Dave Beasant (Wimbledon), Scott McGleish (Charlton 94)

FACT FILE

Founded: 1939
Nickname: Wares
Colours: Green & white quarters/green/green
Change colours: All yellow
Midweek Matchday: Tuesday
Reserve League: Suburban
Sponsor: Philiam Construction

Programme:
Pages: 16 Price: 50p
Editor: Paul Gregory (0181 959 2535)
Website: www.edgwaretownfc.com

CLUB PERSONNEL

Chairman: Paul Karaiskos
President: Mr V Deritis
Patron: Russell Grant

Secretary: Peter Evans,
5 Windmill Ct., Windmill Lane, Bushey,
Herts WD23 1NG
Tel: 0208 420 4750
Fax: 0208 950 8924

Manager: John Harding
Asst Manager: Noel Blackwell
Physio: Sarah Gow

2002-03
Leading Goalscorer:
Captain:
Player of the Year:

FLACKWELL HEATH

GROUND:
Address: Wilks Park, Heath End Rd, Flackwell Heath, High Wycombe. HP10 9EA
Tel: 01628 523892

Directions: M40 jct 3 Wycombe East, follow signs for F/Heath left up Treadway Hill & right at top of hill at roundabout. Wilks park 800yds on right, grd at rear of Magpie (PH). Bus 301 either from bus station or High Street near bottom of Crendon Street which comes from BR station. Ask for Oakland Way

Capacity: 2,000 Seats: 150 Cover: Yes Floodlights: Yes

Club Shop: No
Clubhouse: Open every night 6.30-11pm & before & after matches. Hot food in tea bar

HONOURS: Gt Western Combination 57-58 62-63; Hellenic Lg Div 1 R-up 76-77; Berks & Bucks Snr Cup SF 85-86

PREVIOUS: **Leagues:** Wycombe & District; Gt Western Comb.; Hellenic 76-82; Athenian 82-84

RECORDS: **Attendance:** 4,500 v Oxford U., charity game 1986
(competitive: 700 v Aldershot Town, 27/10/92)
Goalscorer: Tony Wood **Appearamces:** Lee Elliott
Win: 6-0 v Clapton & v Petersfield (both away)
Defeat: 0-7 v Aveley (H)

BEST SEASON: **FA Cup:** 4th Qual. Rd 1-4 v Crawley Town 2002-2003

FACT FILE

Founded: 1907
Colours: Red/red/white & black
Change colours: Yellow/black/black
Midweek Matches: Tuesday
Programme: 18 pages £1
Editor:

CLUB PERSONNEL

Chairman: T Glynn
Vice Chairman: G.Turner
President: Ken Crook

Secretary: Mrs Christine Hobbs
23 Southfield Rd., Flackwell Heath,
Bucks. HP10 9BT
Tel: 01628 521051

2002-03
Leading Goalscorer: Gavin Mernagh
Captain:Matt Flint
Player of the Year: Lee Knott (GK)

HERTFORD TOWN

GROUND
Address: Hertingfordbury Park, West Street, Hertford Tel: 01992 583716

Directions: Rail to Hertford Nth (from Moorgate) or Hertford East (LiverpoolStr.); both 15 mins walk. Green Line bus to town centre then 10 mins walk.
By road; off bypass heading east, turn off at Ford garage
Capacity: 6,500 Seats: 200 Cover: 1,500 Floodlights: Yes
Club Shop: Souvenirs
Clubhouse: Yes

PREVIOUS
Leagues: Herts Co.; Spartan 21-47 48-59; Delphian 59-63; Athenian 63-72; Eastern Co's 72-73
Names: None
Grounds: None

BEST SEASON
FA Cup: 4th Qual. Rd. 73-74 (lost 1-2 at Hillingdon Borough)

CLUB RECORDS
Gate: 5,000 v Kingstonian, F.A. Amateur Cup 2nd Rd 55-56
Appearances: Robbie Burns

HONOURS
Herts Char. Cup 72-73, 89-90, Herts Snr Cup 66-67, Hertford Char.Shd 19-20 20-21 35-36 49-50 55-56 59-60, Eastern Co's Lg Cup 72-73, East Anglian Cup 62-63 69-70, Southern Co's Comb. F-lit Cup 94-95, Mithras Cup SF 85-86, Ryman Div 3 R-up 97-98

Players progressing to Football League: G Mazzon (Aldershot), J.Hooker (Brentford)

FACT FILE
Founded: 1908
Nickname: The Blues
Sponsors: T.B.A.
Colours: Blue & yellow stripes/blue/blue
Change colours: Red
Midweek Matches: Tuesday
Reserves' Lge: Essex & Herts Border Comb
Website: www..hertfordtownfc.co.uk

PROGRAMME
Pages: 24 Price:£1.00
Editor: Elaine Waumsley (01992 302110)
Local Newspapers: Hertfordshire Mercury

CLUB OFFICIALS
President: John Hedley
Chairman: Ray Hill

Secretary & Press Officer:
Stephen Hedley
29 Upper Field Road, Wewyn Garden City,
Herts AL7 3LP
Tel: 01707 333712

FOOTBALL MANAGEMENT
Manager: Brian Owen
Physio: Ian Priest

2002-2003
Captain: Glenn Draper
Top Scorer & P.o.Y.: Johnny Moore

KINGSBURY TOWN

GROUND:
Address: Silver Jubilee Park, Townsend Lane, Kingsbury, London NW9 7NE
Tel: 0208 2051645 Website:www.madasafish.com/~kingsbury-town
Directions: Underground to Kingsbury, cross road and take bus 183 to TownsendLane (2 miles) - ground in far left-hand corner of Silver Jubilee Park
Capacity: 2,500 Seats: 165 Cover: 400 Floodlights: Yes
Club Shop: Sells club ties, pennants, metal badges
Contact Allan Davies (01895 443761)
Clubhouse Mon-Fri 7-11, Sat 12-11, Sun 12-2.30 & 7-10.30. Food on matchdays

HONOURS: Isthmian Lg Div 2 Nth R-up 85-86; Spartan Lg Cup R-up 59-60 64-65; Parthenon Lg 51-52 (Prem Charity Cup 52-53 53-54; Snr Charity Cup 53-54); Middx Snr Cup R-up 88-89; Middx Charity Cup 85-86 (R-up 88-89); Middx Lg Charity Cup (3) 44-47; Willesden & Dist. Lg R-up 30-31 (Div 2 34-35)

PREVIOUS: **Leagues:** Hellenic 27-30 (as Davis Sports); Willesden & District 30-43; MiddxSnr 44-47; Parthenon 47-59; Spartan 59-76 78-81; Athenian 76-78 81-84
Grounds: None **Name**: Davis Sports

RECORDS: **Attendance:** 1 ,300 v Wealdstone, FA Amateur Cup 1971
Appearances: Mick Coffey (goalkeeper)
Win: 8-0 v Eastbourne United, 91-92. Defeat: ?????
Record Fees - Paid: £500 **Received**: £600

BEST SEASON: **FA Vase:** 4th Rd 74-75
FA Cup: 3rd Qual. Rd. 87-88, 0-1 v Leytonstone-Ilford (H)

Players progressing to Football League: Billy Dare (Brentford & West Ham), JohnMeadows, Dave Underwood, Dwight Marshall (Plymouth (via Grays Ath.), Ashley Bayes (Leyton Orient)

FACT FILE
Founded: 1927
Nickname: Kings
Sponsors:
VPA Entertainment Technology
Colours: Royal blue & White/white/royal
Change colours: Yellow/navy/yellow
Midweek Matches: Tuesday
Reserves' League: Suburban

Programme
16-20 pages 50p
Editor: Dave Thomas
Local Press: Harrow Observer, Willesden Chronicle, Allsport Weekly, Edgware & Finchley Times

CLUB PERSONNEL
Chairman: Mark Harrt
Press Officer: Dave Thoomas
Secretary: David Thomas,
9 Hillview Gardens, Kingsbury, NW9 0DE

Manager: Toni Kelly
Physio: Ann Bryan

2002-03
Leading Goalscorer:
Captain:
Player of the Year:

LEIGHTON TOWN

GROUND:

Address: Bell Close, Lake Street, Leighton Buzzard, Beds
Tel: 01525 373311

Directions: From bypass (A505) take A4146 (Billington Rd) towards Leighton Buzzard, straight overfirst roundabout then straight over mini-r'bout & 1st left into car park - ground behind Camden Motors just before town centre.
Half mile from Leighton Buzzard (BR) station.
Buses from Luton, Aylesbury and Milton Keynes

Capacity: 2,800 Seats: 155 Cover: 300 Floodlights: Yes

Club Shop: No

Clubhouse: Normal licensing hours.
Snack bar on matchdays - full range of hot snacks & drinks

HONOURS Isthmian Lge Div 3 R-up 95-96; Sth Midlands Lg 66-67 91-92, Lg Cup 90-91, O'Brien Tphy 90-91, Reserve Div 1 87-88 91-92 94-95, Res Div 2 76-77, Res Challenge Cup 93-94 94-95; Beds Snr Cup 26-27 67-68 68-69 69-70 92-93; Bucks Charity Cup 94-95;98-99 Spartan Lg Div 2 23-24 27-28; Leighton & District Lg, Beds Intermediate Cup (res) 90-91; Beds Yth Cup 91-92 92-93,94-95 94-95; Chiltern Youth Lg 94-95, Lg Cup 93-94; East Anglian Yth. Cup 94-95; Assoc Mem. Cup 96-97.98-99, S.E. Co.Youth F'lit Lge (Corinthian Div.) 99-00, 01-02

BEST SEASON **FA Cup:** Third Qual. Round 70-71, 1-2 v St Albans City (A)
FA Vase: 2nd Round 1980-81, 94-95, 95-96, 00-01

PREVIOUS **Leagues:** Leighton & Dist; South Midlands 22-24 26-29 46-54 55-56 76-92; Spartan 22-53 67-74; United Counties 74-76
Name: Leighton United 1922-63 **Ground:** Wayside

CLUB RECORDS **Attendance:** 1,522 v Aldershot T., Isthmian Lg Div 3, 30/1/93
As Leighton Utd. **Win:13-0** v Met. Railway 1925/6 (H) Spartan League
Defeat: 0-12 v Headington Utd (A) 18.10.47 Spartan League
As Leighton Town **Win:10-1** v Skefko(H) 31.12.66
Defeat: 0-8 v Electrolux(A) 16.10.65 & **0-8** v Harpenden 1965/66 4.11.65

FACT FILE
Founded: 1885
Nickname: Reds
Colours: Red & white
Change colours: Orange & black
Midweek Matchday: Tuesday
Reserves' League: Suburban

Programme: £1.00
Editor: James Ullyett
Local Press:
Leighton Buzzard Observer, The Citizen
Local Radio: Three Counties Radio, Radio Chiltern, Mix 96
Website: www.leightontownfc.co.uk

CLUB PERSONNEL
Secretary: James Green
c.o L.T.F.C.
Chairman: Iain S McGregor
President: M.Hide
Press Officer: Iain McGregor
Manager: Paul Burgess
Physio: Geoge Lathwell & Roy Parker

2002-03
Leading Goalscorer: Matt Rawdon
Captain: Steve Gallen
Player of the Year: James Kidd

TRING TOWN

GROUND:

Address: Pendley Sports Centre, Cow Lane, Tring, Herts HP23 5NS
Tel: 01442 824018

Directions: One mile from Tring centre on A41
- direct connection to M25 (jct20) via new A41 bypass.
One and a half miles from Tring (BR).
Numerous busesfrom station and Watford-Aylesbury routes serve ground

Capacity: 2,500 Seats: 150 Cover: 250 Floodlights: Yes

Club Shop: No

Clubhouse: All licensing hours. Dancehall, pool, darts, kitchen.

HONOURS: Spartan Lg 67-68, R-up 68-69. Herts Charity Shield winners 4, R-up 2. Athenian Lg Div 2 R-up 76-77, Herts Snr Cup R-up 77-78

PREVIOUS: **Leagues:** Gt Western Combination; Spartan 53-75; Athenian 75-77
Names: None Ground: Tring Cricket Ground (40 yrs)

RECORD: **Attendance:** 2,500 v West Ham, friendly
Competitive: 2,000 - Aylesbury U. v Slough T., FA Cup 1st Rd replay, 86
Goalscorer & Appearances: Gary Harthill
Win: 8-1 v Willesdon Isthmian Lge 77
Defeat: 1-11 v Epsom & Ewell Isthmian Lge 96

BEST SEASON: **FA Cup:** 3rd Qual. Rd replay 84-85, 0-5 v Fisher(A) after 1-1
FA Vase: 5th Rd 76-77, 0-2 v Farnborough Town (H)

Players progressing: Peter Gibbs (Watford)

FACT FILE

Founded: 1904
Nickname: T's
Colours: Red & white /red/red
Change: Yellow & blue stripes/blue/yellow
Midweek Matchday: Tuesday
Reserves' Lge: Suburban Lge
Programme: 24 pages £1
Editor/Press Officer:
Alan Lee (01702 216063)

Local Radio: Chiltern, Mix 96
BBC Three Counties Radio

CLUB PERSONNEL

Chairman: Harry Bowden

Secretary: Laurie McParland,
125 Bennetts End Rd,
Hemel Hempstead, Herts HP3 8DX
Tel: 01442 263902 (H) 07836 265105 (M)

Manager: Howard Cowley
Physio: Keith Hardy

2002-03
Leading Goalscorer:
Captain:
Player of the Year:

WARE

GROUND:

Address: Wodson Park, Wadesmill Road, Ware Herts SG12 0HZ
Tel: 01920 463247

Directions: A10 off at junction A602 & B1001 (Ware North), turn right at roundabout 300yds, and follow Ware sign, past Rank factory, turn left at main round about onto A1170 (Wadesmill Rd). After 3/4 mile stadium on right

Capacity: 3,300 Seats: 312 Cover: 500 Floodlights: Yes
Club Shop: Yes
Clubhouse: Licensed bar open matchdays. Light snacks at refreshment bar

HONOURS: Herts Snr Cup 1898-99 03-04 06-07 21-22 53-54, Herts Char. Shield 26-27 56-57 58-59 62-63 85-86, Herts Char. Cup R-up 64-65 65-66 78-79 89-90, Spartan Lg 52-53 (Div 1 Sect.B 51-52, Div 2 Sect.A 26-27), Athenian Lg Div 2 Cup 65-66 72-73,East Anglian Cup 73-74, Herts Co. Lg 08-09 21-22, East Herts Lg 04-05 06-07 (LgCup 06-07), Perry Cup 26-27 28-29 37-38 51-52 52-53 53-54 55-56, Dunkels Cup 52-53, Rolleston Cup 39-40 51-52

PREVIOUS: **Leagues:** East Herts; North Middx 07-08; Herts County 08-25; Spartan 25-55;Delphian 55-63; Athenian 63-75
Grounds: Highfields; Canons Park; London Rd, Presdales Lower Park 1921-26

RECORDS **Attendance:** 3,800 v Hendon Amt Cup 56-57
Career Goalscorer: M Hibbert 229.
Goalscorer (season): George Dearman 98(1926-27)
Career Appearances: Gary Riddle 654
Win: 10-1 v Wood Green Town **Defeat**: 0-11 v Barnet

BEST SEASON: FA Cup: First Round Proper 68-69, 1-6 v Luton Town.

Players progressing: Derek Saunders (Chelsea), Ken Humphrey (QPR)

FACT FILE
Founded: 1892
Nickname: Blues
Sponsors: Charvill Bros Ltd
Colours: Blue & white stripes/blue/blue
Change colours: Amber/black
Midweek Matchday: Tuesday
Reserves' Lge:
Essex & Herts Border Comb

Programme: 24 pages, 50p
Editor : K.Mynott (01992 551605
Local Press: Herts Mercury, Herts Star, Herald & Post

CLUB PERSONNEL
Chairman: W ally Luck
Press Officer: Secretary

Secretary: Ian Bush,
42 Burnett Square, Hertford SG14 2HD
Tel: 01992 587334

Manager: Grah am Norcott
Coach: Dermot Drummy
Physio: Frank Roberts

2002-03
Leading Goalscorer:
Captain:
Player of the Year:

WEMBLEY

GROUND
Address: Vale Farm, Watford Road, Sudbury, Wembley HA0 4UR Tel: 0181 908 8169

Directions: Sudbury Town station (Underground) 400 yds, or 10 mins walk from North Wembley (BR) station. Buses 18, 92, 245 & 182
Capacity: 2,000 Cover: 350 Seats: 350 Floodlights: Yes

Clubhouse: Open every night & weekend lunchtimes. Hot food on matchdays (0181 904 8169)
Club Shop: No
PREVIOUS
Leagues: Middx 46-49; Spartan 49-51; Delphian 51-56; Corinthian 56-63; Athenian 63-75

CLUB RECORDS
Attendance: 2,654 v Wealdstone, FA Amateur Cup 52-53
Career goalscorer: Bill Handrahan 105 (1946-52)
Career appearances: Spud Murphy 505 (78-88)
Win: 11-1 v Hermes, London Senior Cup 1963
Defeat: 0-16 v Chelsea, London Challenge Cup 59-60
Fee received: £10,000 for Gary Roberts (Brentford, 1981) **Transfer Fee paid:** Nil

BEST SEASON
FA Trophy: 1st Round proper 91-92 **FA Amateur Cup:** 2nd Round 66-67, 68-69
FA Cup: 1st Round Proper 1980-81, 0-3 v Enfield (A)

HONOURS
Middx Sen Cup 83-84 86-87 (R-up 55-56 68-69 78-79 87-88 91-92 92-93 98-99); Middx Lge 47-48 (Lge Cup 46-47), Middx Charity Cup 67-68 (jnt) 80-81(jnt) 82-83 86-87 94-95,(R-up 83-84 87-88 96-97); Middx Invitation Cup 56-57; Athenian Lge R-up 74-75 (Div 1 R-up 67-68); Corinthian Lge Mem Shield R-up 58-59; Delphian Lge R-up 55-56; Spartan Lge Div 1 West 50-51 (Dunkel Trophy 50-51 jnt); London Sen Cup R-up 55-56; Hitachi Cup SF 83-84; Suburban Lge North 85-86, Lge Cup 84-85 (R-up 83-84)
Players progressing
Keith Cassells (Watford 1977), MikeO'Donague (Southampton 1979), A McGonigle (Olympiakos), Gary Roberts (Brentford1980), Richard Cadette (Orient 1984)

FACT FILE
Formed: 1946
Nickname: The Lions
Sponsors: G & B Builders
Colours: Red & white/red/red
Change colours: All gold
Midweek matchday: Tuesday
Reserves' League: Suburban

Programme
Pages: 28 Price: £1
Editor: Richard Markiewicz
(0208 902 0541 - before 9pm)
Local Press: Wembley & Harrow Observer
Local Radio: Capital, G.L.R

CLUB OFFICIALS
Chairman: Brian Gumm
President: Eric Stringer
Commercial Manager: Nick Bennett

Secretary: Mrs Jean Gumm
14 Woodfield Avenue, North Wembley, Middx. HA0 3NR Tel: 0208 908 3353
Press Officer: Richard Markiewicz
Tel: 0208 902 0541 before 9pm

FOOTBALL MANAGEMENT
Manager: Scott Cousins
Asst. Manager: Roger Linton

WITHAM TOWN

Ground: Spa Road, Witham, Essex CM8 1UN
Tel: 01376 511198 (lounge) 500146 (reception) 520996 (boardroom)

Directions: From Witham BR (network S.E.) station; through pub car park and follow road to Faulkbourne, at main r'bout turn left and ground is on the right.
By road: Off A12 at Witham sign, left at 1st lights (Spinks Lane), right at end of road, follow road under railway bridge - ground 100yds on left

Capacity: 2,500 Seats: 150 Cover: 300 Floodlights: Yes

Clubhouse: Open every night and weekend lunctimes.Hot bar snacks.

Club Shop: No

HONOURS: Essex Snr Lg 70-71 85-86 (R-up 84-85 86-87), Tphy 85-86 (R-up 88-89); Essex Thameside Trophy R-up 95-96; Loctite Tphy SF 90-91

PREVIOUS: **Leagues:** Mid Essex; Essex & Suffolk Border; Essex Senior 71-87
Ground: Spa Road **Names:** None

CLUB RECORDS **Attendance:** 800 v Billericay Town, Essex Senior League, May 1976
Win: 7-0 v Banstead 27/9/94 **Defeat:** 0-9 v Collier Row 21/10/95
Goalscorer: Colin Mitchell **Appearances:** Keith Dent (16 years)
Fee received: for Steve Tilson (Southend)

BEST SEASON: **FA Vase:** 5th Round, 85-86
FA Cup: 2nd Qual. Rd 87-88 (v Gravesend), 88-89 (v B. Stortford), 89-90 (v Dartford)

Players progressing to Football League: Steve Tilson (Southend)

FACT FILE
Founded: 1947
Nickname: Town
Colours: Red & black stripes/black/black
Change colours: Blue & white
Midweek Matchday: Tuesday
Reserves' Lge: Essex & Herts Border Comb

Programme: 24 pages, 60p
Editor: Nigel Dudley
Local Press: Witham & Braintree Times, Essex Chronicle, East Anglian DailyTimes, Evening Gazette
Local Radio: BBC Essex, Essex Radio, Chelmer Radio

CLUB PERSONNEL
Acting Chairman: Dave Puttock
President: B Olley
Press Officer: G Vale (01376 513861)

Secretary: Jim Claydon,
58 Silver Street, Silver End, Witham, Essex CM8 3QG
Tel: 01376 584086 (H)
01376 583241 x 426 (B)

Manager: Tony Last
Assistant Manager: & Physio: Stuart Bevis

WOKINGHAM TOWN

GROUND
Address: c/o Egham Town F.C..
Directions: As Egham Town F.C.
Club Shop: No
Clubhouse: As Egham Town F.C.

HONOURS Isthmian Lg R-up 89-90 (Div 1 81-82, Full Members Cup R-up 94-95), Berks & Bucks Snr Cup 68-69 82-83 84-85 95-96, Berks & Bucks I'mediate Cup 52-53

PREVIOUS **Leagues:** Reading & Dist.; Great Western Comb 07-54; Metropolitan 54-57; Delphian 57-59; Corinthian 59-63; Athenian 63-73.
Grounds: Oxford Road 1875-1883; Wellington Road 83-96; Langborough Rd 96-1906, Finchampstead Road 06-99

BEST SEASONS **FA Trophy:** Semi finals 87-88 **FA Amateur Cup:** 4th Rd 57-58
F.A Cup: 1st Rd replay 82-83, 0-3 v Cardiff (A) after 1-1

CLUB RECORDS **Career Appearances:** Dave Cox, 533
Fee received: £25,000 for Mark Harris (C Palace 88)
Fee paid: £5,000 for Fred Hyatt (Burnham, 1990)

Players progressing: Ian Kirkwood (Reading 53), John Harley (Hartlepool 76), Kirk Corbin (Cambridge 78), Phil Alexander (Norwich 81), DougHatcher (Aldershot 83), Steven Butler & George Torrance (Brentford 84), MarkHarris (C Palace 88), Gary Smart (Oxford 88), Darren Barnard (Chelsea 90), PaulHolsgrove (Luton Town 91), Darron Wilkinson (Brighton) 92

FACT FILE
Formed: 1875
Nickname: The Town
Sponsors: Trademark Windows
Colours: Amber & black/black/black
Change colours: All w hite
Midweek matchday: Tuesday

Programme: Pages: 36 Price: £1
Editor: John Allsberry
Local Press: Wokingham Times, Wokingham News, Reading Evening Post
Local Radio: 210 FM, Reading 107

CLUB PERSONNEL
Chairman: Mark Ashwell
President: T.B.A.

Secretary: John Aulsberry,
8 Paice Green, Wokingham RG40 1YN
Tel: 01189 790441

Manager: Paul Colley
Assistant Manager: Stev Morris
Physio: Stev Viney

2002-03
Captain: Alan Beeton
P.o.Y.: Nick Rowe
Top scorers: John Finnieston & Stuart Tanfield 15

WEMBLEY F.C

Left to Right

Back Row:
Gareth Paxton
Tobi Jinadu
Mariusz Tryc
Deji Davies
Michael Barima
Steve Griffiths

Front Row:
Mark Harewood
Avi Schwarz
Ian Bates
Kris Zidi
Howard Newton

Photo:
Alan Coomes

Leon Archer scores Cheshunt's 4th goal against Ware in the match that clinched the Division 2 title.

Photo: Gordon Whittington

SEAGRAVE HAULAGE COMBINED COUNTIES LEAGUE

President: Ron Monkley **Chairman:** John Bennett
General Secretary: Clive Tidey, 22 Silo Road, Farncombe, Godalming, Surrey GU7 3PA
Tel: 01483 428453 Fax: 01483 426117

The arrival of AFC Wimbledon along with the generous sponsorship agreement secured with Greenford based Seagrave Haulage, ensured that season 2002-03 would become the most momentous in the league's history.

The league was quick to spot the potential of AFC Wimbledon and within one hour of the Ryman League's refusal to accept them, the possibility of making an application to the Combined Counties was put to them and a week later they were duly accepted into the constitution, along with Frimley Green, promoted from the Surrey Senior League, and North Greenford United, kindly released by the Middlesex County League.

With the average 'gate' in the league being substantially less than 100, it was always going to be a gamble taking AFC Wimbledon on board, given their huge following. Sandhurst Town were chosen to be the first club to host Wimbledon and they coped superbly with the crowd of almost 2500 people, inspiring just about every other club in the league to do likewise and the gamble turned into a magnificent success, with the visit of AFC Wimbledon breaking every single club's home attendance record and putting much needed revenue into every club's coffers. Recognition must be given to Wimbledon's officers for their truly professional assistance with the organisation required and indeed to their supporters, who generally brought great credit upon their newly formed club.

In the meantime, the league were putting the final touches to their three year sponsorship agreement with Greenford based Seagrave Haulage, with an option on a further three years, and the league would very much like to formally record its thanks to Andy Lonsdale of Seagrave Haulage and his colleagues for their generosity.

The league, with 24 clubs for the first time, started predictably with the likes of Ash United, Withdean 2000 and champions AFC Wallingford all dictating the early pace. AFC Wimbledon made a tenuous start, taking a little time to achieve a settled team, and indeed it was those early games that ultimately cost the club promotion in their first season, as they finished just outside the top two.

By Christmas, inexplicably, Ash United had fallen away, and the league always then looked to be between AFC Wallingford and Withdean. The latter though, following a successful FA Vase run that took them to the 4th round that only ended with a midweek replay at Diss Town, found themselves with the mother of all fixture backlogs, not helped by the fact that they were competing not only with their landlords Worthing but also with Brighton & Hove Albion's reserve team on occasions, for use of the ground.

It was a major surprise to see former champions Chipstead having an awful season by their standards, although conversely they set a new league scoring record with their 14-1 home thrashing of bottom club Viking Greenford.

AFC Wimbledon, meanwhile had found their feet and led the chasing pack consisting of Feltham, Godalming and Guildford, who themselves went on an unbeaten 20 game sequence during the season, whilst Bedfont kept close to the chasing pack.

Newcomers North Greenford United also took the eye with some notable performances, whilst at the bottom, both Viking Greenford and Cove became the league's whipping boys, mustering up just eight wins between them by the end of the season.

As the season drew to a conclusion, Withdean earned the admiration of all by overcoming a fixture backlog extending to 12 games at times, by not losing a single one, despite playing three times a week near the end and with Wallingford finally experiencing a poor patch at just the wrong time, it was the Sussex club who eventually carried off the championship by nine clear points, scoring 143 goals in the process. Indeed it was a high scoring season all round, with no less than seven other clubs notching more than 100 league goals.

In the Premier Challenge Cup, the management committee had dared to hope, without undue bias, that AFC Wimbledon might reach the final so as to boost the crowd figure to untold heights. However, it was not to be as they were soundly beaten 1-5 at home to Southall in the second round.

AFC Wallingford came through the first two rounds with ease, scoring ten goals in the process but were then knocked out on penalties in the quarter finals, after a 1-1 draw with North Greenford, who found themselves in the semi-final, along with Ash United, trying to salvage something from the season, and Withdean and Westfield. Holders Cobham were eliminated in the first round, losing to Chessington & Hook.

The semi-final draw saw Ash United at home to North Greenford, and saving their best form for the Cup, were easy 3-0 winners. Westfield had to travel down to Withdean where the result was never in doubt despite the narrow scoreline of 1-0 to Withdean. A good crowd attended the final at Woking, who were excellent hosts as usual, and again the score was 1-0 in Withdean's favour, the goal coming in the first few minutes. Once again the scoreline did not demonstrate Withdean's overall superiority on the evening but it was enough to secure a well deserved cup double for the club.

In outside competitions, as mentioned, Withdean reached the fourth round of the Vase whilst in the FA Cup both AFC Wallingford and Godalming & Guildford reached the second qualifying round. Although drawn at home, both were facing strong opposition in the shape of Eastbourne Borough and Hampton & Richmond Borough and both succumbed but only by 0-1 in each case.

In County Cups, Ash did well to reach the fifth round of the Surrey Senior Cup, whilst Raynes Park Vale got as far as the fourth round. Feltham, though, progressed to the final of the Middlesex Charity Cup and went on to beat Ryman League Hendon to win the trophy for the first time in their history.

At reserve level, with just 15 clubs competing, all the honours were mopped up by Raynes Park Vale and Westfield, finishing first and second respectively. Westfield also won the Division Challenge Cup whilst Raynes Park Vale won the shield competition, both beating each other in the respective finals. The two matches were played within days of each other and the league paid tribute to the sportsmanship showed by both clubs in both finals.

The prestigious sportsmanship trophy was won by Chipstead, with Raynes Park Vale in second place. AFC Wimbledon won the 'Programme of the Season' award with Merstham second. Thanks to the sponsorship, there were two new awards at the end of the season. Bedfont won the 'Most Hospitable Club' award, based on referees' marks through the season, with Ash in second. Whilst the 'Best Kept Ground' award went to Chipstead, with Sandhurst taking the runners-up spot.

As these notes are being written, news has come of the sad demise of Viking Greenford FC, who back in the 1950s were pioneers of foreign tours to such places as Russia and Czechoslovakia, when such visits were unheard of. Withdean in the meantime have appealed to the Football Association over the Ryman League's refusal to allow them promotion whilst ground sharing at Worthing.

One exciting development for season 2003-04 is the formation of a further division, with the merger between the league and the Surrey Senior league. The merger, in line with the FA's stated preference for level three leagues, will create a stronger competition, with 18 clubs in the newly formed division one, several of whom are already preparing to improve their facilities to allow them to progress to the premier division in the fullness of time.

Alan Constable - Fixture Secretary.

FINAL LEAGUE TABLE 2002-03

PREMIER DIVISION		P	W	D	L	F	A	Pts
1	Withdean	46	40	4	2	143	32	124
2	AFC Wallingford	46	37	4	5	129	33	115
3	AFC Wimbledon	46	36	3	7	125	46	111
4	Feltham	46	25	10	11	101	48	85
5	Bedfont	46	25	5	16	106	73	80
6	Sandhurst Town	46	23	9	14	86	57	78
7	Godalming & Guildford	46	25	3	18	95	75	78
8	Raynes Park Vale	46	24	5	17	101	79	77
9	Ash United	46	23	5	18	110	83	74
10	North Greenford Utd	46	22	7	17	104	87	73
11	Hartley Wintney	46	23	4	19	88	84	73
12	Southall	46	19	11	16	91	77	68
13	Westfield	46	19	9	18	75	86	66
14	Chessington & Hook	46	18	9	19	96	80	63
15	Reading Town	46	18	6	22	67	79	60
16	Chipstead	46	16	10	20	92	87	58
17	Merstham	46	16	10	20	61	80	58
18	Walton Casuals	46	12	10	24	60	95	46
19	Chessington United	46	13	6	27	54	84	45
20	Frimley Green	46	13	5	28	65	98	44
21	Cobham (-3)	46	11	10	25	61	108	40
22	Farnham Town	46	5	9	32	45	130	24
23	Cove	46	5	6	35	46	160	21
24	Viking Greenford (+3)	46	3	2	41	35	175	14

LEADING GOALSCORERS 2002-03

PREMIER DIVISION

47	S Francis	Withdean 2000
37	J Hill	North Greenford
32	K Cooper	AFC Wimbledon
31	D Lovett	Feltham
28	M Anderson	Sandhurst Town
27	S Holman	Hartley Wintney

DIVISION ONE

16	T Finlayson	Ash United
14	S Shepherd	Ash United
12	A Jordan	Raynes Park Vale
11	J Ryder	North Greenford
11	R Emeterio	Sandhurst Town
10	D Lyllo	Frimley Green
10	S Obe	Sandhurst Town

PREM.	1	2	3	4	5	6	7	8	9	10	11	12	13	14	15	16	17	18	19	20	21	22	23	24
1 AFC Wallingf'		3-0	2-0	6-2	8-0	4-1	4-2	3-0	5-0	3-0	2-0	4-0	3-0	4-1	3-0	2-2	0-1	4-0	7-1	2-0	7-0	0-3	6-0	1-0
2 AFC Wimble'	3-2		5-3	5-1	4-3	2-1	1-2	4-0	3-2	0-0	0-1	1-0	2-1	3-1	1-0	4-3	5-1	2-0	2-1	2-2	5-0	3-0	5-0	0-2
3 Ash United	2-3	3-2		1-2	1-0	3-5	2-2	1-0	6-1	7-0	3-2	5-0	0-2	3-1	2-2	3-5	0-3	3-1	3-0	2-1	2-0	1-0	2-3	1-2
4 Bedfont	0-1	1-2	2-4		1-0	2-2	3-0	4-0	6-1	2-0	3-2	2-1	0-4	5-1	3-1	2-0	1-2	2-0	1-2	3-5	6-0	4-1	1-1	1-3
5 ChessingtonU	0-2	1-3	1-0	0-2		0-1	1-0	0-1	9-0	1-1	1-4	1-2	3-1	2-1	0-0	0-1	0-1	2-0	0-0	2-3	5-0	1-2	1-1	0-4
6 Chess'ton&H.	0-1	0-3	2-2	1-3	2-1		2-2	2-1	7-0	1-1	0-2	2-1	4-1	1-0	0-1	0-3	1-1	1-2	1-0	3-3	5-1	3-0	1-2	2-1
7 Chipstead	0-3	2-3	2-1	1-0	2-1	4-4		0-0	3-2	3-1	0-2	5-2	0-0	4-3	2-2	1-0	1-1	6-1	0-2	3-1	14-1	7-0	2-3	0-1
8 Cobham	1-1	0-5	1-5	1-5	0-2	0-5	3-3		4-0	6-1	1-1	0-0	2-3	0-4	2-4	1-2	0-5	2-0	1-2	1-3	7-1	2-2	0-3	0-6
9 Cove	0-1	1-4	1-4	0-12	1-2	0-4	4-2	1-1		1-1	0-2	4-1	1-3	2-5	0-2	1-1	0-5	2-2	1-1	0-2	0-4	1-3	1-2	1-6
10 Farnham T.	0-5	0-1	3-3	1-3	1-4	1-4	3-2	0-3	3-0		1-4	1-6	2-2	3-0	0-3	0-4	1-2	3-2	1-3	1-4	2-5	2-2	1-1	0-4
11 Feltham	0-1	1-2	1-2	5-0	4-0	2-2	6-1	4-1	5-1	4-1		3-2	5-1	0-2	1-1	1-1	4-0	0-0	0-3	2-1	5-1	4-1	2-3	1-1
12 Frimley Gr.	0-1	0-5	4-0	1-3	2-3	2-3	1-1	1-1	3-2	2-1	1-0		1-0	4-6	1-4	0-5	2-1	1-2	2-1	1-2	1-0	1-1	2-0	0-1
13 Godalming&G	1-2	1-3	3-1	4-2	2-0	3-1	3-1	2-1	5-1	3-0	3-0	2-1		3-2	1-2	0-2	3-1	3-0	1-2	2-2	4-1	3-1	0-2	0-4
14 Hartley Wint.	1-1	2-0	1-8	3-1	4-1	1-0	4-0	1-1	1-3	3-0	0-2	1-0	3-5		1-3	2-1	3-2	1-0	0-3	1-1	1-0	1-0	3-1	2-4
15 Merstham	0-4	0-2	0-4	0-1	0-1	3-0	1-0	1-2	2-1	1-1	1-3	3-2	2-1	1-3		0-2	1-4	2-2	2-1	0-0	1-0	2-2	1-2	3-5
16 Nth Greenford	4-2	2-6	1-2	1-1	2-0	4-2	4-2	5-0	5-2	4-2	0-3	3-2	0-3	2-4	5-1		1-3	1-1	3-3	2-0	5-1	3-2	5-4	2-4
17 Raynes Park V	1-3	0-5	3-4	1-1	0-1	3-2	0-3	1-4	1-2	3-0	0-0	3-1	3-2	5-2	2-2	4-0		2-1	3-0	4-2	3-1	3-1	5-0	0-1
18 Reading Town	0-0	0-2	2-0	0-1	2-0	5-2	2-1	0-2	2-0	4-0	1-2	1-0	3-1	0-3	2-0	3-0	4-1		0-2	1-3	5-1	1-2	2-1	1-4
19 Sandhurst T.	1-2	1-2	2-2	3-1	7-0	1-0	0-1	2-2	3-0	2-0	1-1	3-2	0-1	2-1	2-0	3-1	4-0	0-0		4-2	7-0	2-0	5-2	0-3
20 Southall	1-3	0-0	2-1	2-3	3-0	3-2	2-2	5-0	5-2	2-1	0-3	3-1	1-0	2-0	1-2	1-1	1-3	2-3	0-1		2-1	6-1	2-2	1-3
21 Viking Greenf.	1-3	0-4	1-4	1-2	3-2	0-8	0-2	0-3	1-2	1-3	1-5	1-2	2-3	0-5	1-3	0-4	1-7	0-3	1-1	1-4		0-4	0-1	1-3
22 Walton Cas.	1-2	0-5	2-3	1-1	1-1	0-3	1-0	2-0	1-1	1-0	1-2	2-4	2-6	0-1	1-1	3-1	3-0	2-4	2-1	1-1	0-0		0-1	1-2
23 Westfield	0-2	0-4	1-0	0-4	1-1	3-1	4-1	1-2	6-0	2-0	0-0	2-2	1-2	1-2	2-0	2-0	1-4	5-2	1-1	2-2	1-0	2-3		2-5
24 Withdean	3-1	2-0	4-1	2-0	3-0	2-2	2-0	5-1	4-0	7-1	0-0	3-0	3-1	0-0	4-0	4-1	4-3	5-0	2-0	2-0	9-0	3-1	1-0	

PREMIER CHALLENGE CUP 2002-03

SEMI-FINALS

Ash United	v	North Green United	3-0	Withdean 2000	v	Westfield	1-0

FINAL

Ash United	v	Withdean 2000	0-1	At Woking FC

DIVISION ONE CHALLENGE CUP 2002-03

SEMI-FINALS

Westfield	v	Sandhurst Town	2-0	Raynes Park Vale	v	Ash United	1-0

FINAL

Raynes Park Vale	v	Westfield	0-1	At Ashford Town (Middx) FC

DIVISION ONE CHALLENGE SHIELD 2002-03

SEMI-FINALS

Feltham	v	Raynes Park Vale	1-3	Westfield	v	Merstham	4-0

FINAL

Raynes Park Vale	v	Westfield	2-1 (aet)	at Sandhurst Town FC

HONOURS 2002-03

Premier Division Champions	Withdean 2000
Premier Division Runners up	AFC Wallingford
Premier Challenge Cup Winners	Withdean 2000
Premier Challenge Cup R/U	Ash United
Division One Champions	Raynes Park Vale
Division One Runners up	Westfield
Div One Challenge Cup Winners	Westfield
Div One Challenge Cup R/U	Raynes Park Vale
Div One Challenge Shield Winners	Raynes Park Vale
Div One Challenge Shield R/U	Westfield
Prem Div Fair Play Champions	Chipstead
Prem Div Fair Play Runners up	Chessington & H.
Div One Fair Play Champions	Westfield
Div One Fair Play Runners up	Ash United
Programme of the Season Winners	AFC Wimbledon
Programme of the Season R/U	Merstham
Best kept Ground Winners	Chipstead
Best kept Ground R/U	Sandhurst Town
Most hospitable Club (based on referee marks)	Bedfont
Most hospitable Club R/U	Ash United

President's Monthly Award:

Aug:	AFC Wallingford
Sept:	Withdean 2000
Oct:	Godalming & G.
Nov:	Withdean 2000
Dec:	Feltham
Jan:	Not awarded
Feb:	North Greenford
Mar:	Withdean 2000
Apr:	Feltham

AFC WALLINGFORD

Secretary: Richard may, 27 Chiltern Crescent, Wallingford, Oxon OX100PG
Tel Nos: 01491 837391 (H) 01491 823612 (W) 07748 828574(M)
Ground: Wallingford Sports Park, Hithercroft Road,Wallingford,Oxon.(Tel:01491 835044
Directions : Nearest Railway station: Cholsey & Moulsford. Bus - Thames Transit.
Capacity: 1,500 Cover: 100 Seats: 40 Floodlights: Yes
Clubhouse: Open evenings 7.30-11.00, Sat & Sun Tea & snacks available 01491 835044
HONOURS: Chiltonian Prem Lge 97-98; Bon Accord Trophy 95-96 Combined Counties League Premier Division Champions 01-02,Runners Up 2000-01, Berks & Bucks Senior Trophy : Winners 01-02 Finalists 2000-01, North Bucks Nairne Paul Cup Winners 2000-01
RECORDS: **Attendance:** 280 v Reading Town **Goalscorer:** Carl Henry 62, 97-98
In Career: Steve Wood 130 92-98 **Appearances**: Anthony Hill 243
PREVIOUS: **Leagues:** Chiltonian Lge 95-98

FACT FILE
Founded: 1995
Colours: Red & black hoops/black/red & black
Change colours: Blue & white
Midweek matchday: Tuesday
Programme: 20 pages; price 50p
Editor: Andy Ham (01491 837608)

CLUB PERSONNEL
President: Ken Lester
Chairman: Lindsay Townsend
Tel: 01491 839103 (H)
Match Secretary: G Lee
21 Orchard Close, Brightwell, Wallingford, Oxon. Tel: 01491 836921 (H)
Manager: Dave Crowdy

AFC WIMBLEDON

Secretary: Trevor Williams, 110B Cavendish Road, Colliers Wood, London SW19 2EZ
Tel: 0208 401 1702 or 0208 540 0771 (H) 0208 540 7396 (B)
email: clubsec@afcwimbledon.co.uk

Ground: Kingsmeadow Stadium, Jack Goodchild Way, 422a Kingston Rd., Kingston-upon-Thames, Surey KT1 3PB
Tel: 0208 547 3335/6 0208 974 5713 (Fax)
Website: www.afcwimbledon.co.uk
Directions: From town centre - Cambridge Rd on to Kingston Rd (A2043) to Malden Rd.
From A3, turn off at New Malden, turn left on to A2043 - grd 1 mile on left.
Half mile from Norbiton (BR)
Capacity: 9,000 **Covered - Terracing:** 3,500 **Seating:** 690

FACT FILE
Founded: 2002 Nickname: The Dons
Colours: All blue
Change Colours:
Midweek Matchday:
Programme: Price: Pages:
Editor:

CLUB PERSONNEL
President: Alan Batsford
Chairman: Kris Stewart
0208 540 7396 (B) 07970 702798 (M)
Press Secretary: Ivor Heller
0208 946 4664 (H) 0208 542 9535 (B)
07973 322409 (M)
Manager:

ASH UNITED

Secretary: James Avenell, 82 Ewins Close,Ash,Aldershot, Hants. GU12 6SB
Tel/FAX No: 01252 321528
Email: garethwatmore@hotmail.com
Ground: Youngs Drive, off Shawfield Rd, Ash, Nr Aldershot Tel: 01252 745757
Directions: A323 towards Ash, left into Shawfield Rd, left into Youngs Drive
1 mile from both Ash and Ash Vale BR stations. Bus - Stagecoach 20A, 550
Capacity: 1,500 Seats: None Cover: Yes Floodlights: Yes
HONOURS: Prem Chall Cup 97-98; Comb Co Lge 81-2, 86-7, 98-99; Aldershot Sen Cup 98-99,01-02
CLUB RECORDS **Attendance;**914 v AFC Wimbledon .League 2002-2003
Goalscorer: Shaun Mitchell 44 **Appearances:** Tommy Burton 540
BEST SEASON **FA Cup:** 2nd Qual Rd v Walton & Hersham 98-99
FA Vase: 4th Rd v Tiverton Town 98-99 & v Tow Law 2001-02
PREVIOUS **Ground:** Ash Common Rec. 70-71 **Leagues:** Surrey Snr, Aldershot Snr.

FACT FILE
Founded: 1911
Colours: Green with red trim/green/red
Change colours: All blue
Midweek Matchday: Tuesday
Prog: 36 pages, £1.00 Editor: Secretary

CLUB PERSONNEL
President; Paul Murray
Chairman: Robert J Atkins V-Chair: Geoff Hills
Press Off: Gareth Watmore (07739 657994)
Manager: Tony Calvert
2002-2003
Captain: Stuart Woodhouse
Top Scorer: Scott Joyce 26
Player of the Year: Matthew Short

BEDFONT

Secretar Les King, 14 Harlequin Close, Isleworth, Middlesex. TW7 7LA
Tel No: 0208 894 5525 (H) 0208 392 3021 (W)
Ground: The Orchard, Hatton Rd, Bedfont, Middx. Tel: 0208 8907264
Directions: Turn down Faggs Rd opposite Hatton Cross (Picadilly Line) station on Great South Western Rd (A30), then sharp right into Hatton Rd. Ground opposite Duke of Wellington pub. Bus - Westlink 203
Capacity:2,000 Seats: 100 Cover: 50Floodlights: Yes Clubhouse: Yes
HONOURS Comb. Co's Chal. Vase 92-93 (Res. Div R-up 88-89, Res. Cup R-up 89-90, Grant McClennan Yth Cup 91-92), Middx Lg 73-74 76-77 (Div 1 (Res) & Div 1 Cup 71-72 78-79 79-80, Surrey Prem. Lg 84-85 86-87, Middx I'mediate Cup 69-70 76-77, Inter. Contois Tour. 1992, Liege Euromann Tour. 89, Harold Clayton Cup 90-91, Hounslow & Dist. Div 1 (Res) 86-87
PREVIOUS Names: Bedfont Inst.(1900), Bedfont Rangers(1950) & Fairholme Utd(1953) merged 1968. Club later merged with Interharvester(1973) & Bedfont Eagles(1988). **Ground:** Bedfont Rec.

FACT FILE
Founded: 1968
Colours: Yellow & blue stripes/blue/blue
Change colours: All red or White/navy/navy
Midweek matches: Tuesday
Programme: 20 pages, 50p. Editors: Les King (020 8891 1985)

CLUB PERSONNEL
President: Roger Cooper
Chairman: Mick Carroll
Manager: John Morris
Coach: Ron Griffin
Asst. Man.: Mark Wilson

CHESSINGTON & HOOK UNITED

Secretary: Alan Warwick, 38 Hartfield Road, Chessington, Surrey. KT9 2PW
Tel:020 8397 1843(H)

Ground: Chalky Lane, Chessington, Surrey. Tel: 01372 729892

Directions: Turn off A243 into Chalky Lane opposite Chessington World of Adventure Theme Park Railway - Chessington South. Bus - London Transport 71.

Floodlights: Yes

HONOURS: Combined Counties Lge Prem Cup R-up 97-98, Surrey County Lge Prem Div R-up 96-97, Div 1 70-71, Combination Cup 2001-02

PREVIOUS **Leagues:** Middx Lge 68-69, Surrey County 69-72, Home Counties 72-78 Comb Co 78-81, Surrey Prem, Surrey Comb, Surrey Prem.

FACT FILE
Founded: 1968
Colours: All blue
Change colours: Yellow/black/yellow
Midweek Matchday:
Programme: Yes Price:

CLUB PERSONNEL
President: Ray Hall
Chairman: Graham Ellis
63 Stormont Way, Chessington,
Surrey. KT9 2QW
Tel: 020 8391 4829(H)
Manager: Paul Ellis 020 8397 8499 (H)

CHESSINGTON UNITED

Secretary: John Carleton, 22 Dawson Road, Kingston upon Thames, Syurrey KT1 3AT
Tel No: 0208546 8266 & 0208241 8461 FAx: 0208241 8461 Mombilr: 07785 986943
Email: carleton-john@ hotmail.com

Ground: Fetcham Park Utd., Riverlane, Leatherhead, Surrey. Tel: 01372 363995
Directions: .
Nearest : Railway Station: Leatherhead
Buses: London Country 465 & 479

FACT FILE
Formed:
Colours: Gren & white hoops/white/green
Change Colours:
Midweek Matchday:
Programme: Price: Pages:
Editor:

CLUB PERSONNEL
President:R.Jaramillo
Chairman:Terry Parmenter
Match Secretary: Mike Smith: 07763 984867

CHIPSTEAD

Secretary: Geoff Corner, 20 Sunnymede Avenue, Carshalton Beeches, Surrey SM54JF
Tel: 0181 642 0827 (H)

Ground: High Road, Chipstead, Surrey. Tel: 01737 553250

Directions: Brighton Road northbound, left into Church Lane, left into HogcrossLane, right High Road. 1 1/2/ miles from Chipstead (BR). Bus -London County 405, 407

Capacity: 2,000 Seats: 30 Cover: 100 Floodlights: Yes

HONOURS Surrey Premier Lg R-up 82-83 83-84 85-86 (Lg Cup 82-83 84-85 85-86), Combined Co's Lg 89-90 (R-up 90-91 92-93, Lg Cup 86-87 90-91 92-93, Elite Class Cup R-up 89-90, Reserve Section Cup 92-93)

BEST SEASON **FA Cup:** 1998-99 **FA Vase:** 1998-99

CLUB RECORDS Attendance:1,770
Goalscorer: Appearances:

PREVIOUS **Leagues:** Surrey Intermediate 62-82; Surrey Premier 82-86

FACT FILE
Founded: 1906 Nickname: Chips
Colours: Green & white/black/black
Change colours: Purple/yellow/yellow
Midweek matchday: Tuesday
Programme: 36 pages Price: 50p
Editor:Terry Antell

CLUB PERSONNEL
President: Dave Argent
Chairman: Don.Faircloth,156 St Andrews Rd, Coulsdon,Surrey CR5 3HF(0208 668 8348)
Manager: Jim Cannon Coach: T.B.A.

2002-2003
Captain: Steve Eggleton
Top Scorer: Stev Jenns

COBHAM

Secretary: Ken Reed, 29 Waterer Gardens,Tadworth, Surrey KT20 5PS (01737 352641)

Ground: Leg O'Mutton Field, Anvil Lane, Downside Bridge Rd, Cobham, Surrey
Tel: 01932 865959

Directions: A3 turnoff A245, A307 (Portsmouth) towards Leatherhead, right intoBetween Streets, rt into Downside Rd then rt opposite car park. Cobham & StokeD'Abernon (BR) 2 miles. Bus - Green Line 715, London Country 501, 513

Capacity: 2,000 Seats: None Cover: Yes Floodlights: Yes Club Shop: No
Clubhouse: Yes

HONOURS Combined Co's Lge Cup 01-02, League R-Up: 98-99 Reserves Lge (3)

BEST SEASON **FA Cup: 1st Q 02-03** **FA Vase:** 1998-99 3rd Rd.

CLUB RECORDS **Attendance:** 2,000 v Showbiz XI, charity game 1975

PREVIOUS **League:** Surrey Senior **Grounds:** Cobham Rec

2002-2003 **Captain:** Chris Osbourne **P.o.Y.**: Mick Petruzziello**Top Scorer:** Steve Mesyer

FACT FILE
Founded: 1892
Nickname: Hammers
Sponsor:Prestege Couriers
Colours: Red & Black Hoops /black/black
Change colours:All white
Midweek matchday: Tuesday
Programme: Yes

CLUB PERSONNEL
Chairman: Chris Woolston
President: Davvid Robinson
Manager: Matt Alexander
Coach: Ian Savage
Physio: C Bird

COVE

Secretary: Graham Brown, 6 Longfield Close,Haley Estate, Farnborough. GU14 8HQ
Tel: 01252 650920 - Club Email: covefc1897@aol.com
Ground: Oak farm Fields,7 Squirrels Lane, Farnborough, Hants GU14 8PB. Tel.: 01252 543615
Directions: Farnborough (BR) 2 miles; right into Union Street, right at lights into Prospect Rd, left into West Heath Rd, right into Romayne Close and follow signs to Cove FC. Or, M3 jct 4, follow A325 signed Aldershot & Farnham, right into Prospect Rd. (signed Cove FC & Farnborough Town FC), then as above
Capacity: 3,500 Seats: 75 Cover: 475 Floodlights: Yes Club Shop: No
Clubhouse: Mon-Fri 7-11, Sat 12-11, Sunday 12-3 & 7-11. Hot food on matchdays
HONOURS: Surrey I'mediate Lg; Surrey Prem. Lg x5, R-up x3, Lg Cup x3, Res.Section x4 ,R-up x4, Res. Cup x2; Combined Co's Lg Cup 81-82; Hants Lg Div 3, Div 4, Div 2 R-up; Aldershot - Snr Cup x5, R-up, Snr Shield x4, Snr Lg, Div 2x3, Div 2 Cup, Div 4 Cup
PREVIOUS Leagues: Aldershot Jnr; Aldershot I'mediate 45-48; Surrey I'mediate 48-71; Surrey Snr 71-73; Hants 74-81; Combined Counties 81-90 &95-01; Isthmian 90-95;
CLUB RECORDS **Attendance:** 1,798 v Aldershot, Isthmian Lg Div 3, 1/5/93
BEST SEASON **FA Cup**: 2nd Rd 2000-01 **FA Vase:** 5th Rd 00-01 2-3 v Chippenham Tn. (H)

FACT FILE
Founded: 1897
Sponsors: Sunnyside Removals
Colours: Yellow & black stripes/yellow/yellow
Change colours: Red & white stripes/red/red
Midweek Matches: Tuesday
Reserves' League: Comb. Cos. 1st Div
Programme: 30 pages, 50p
Editor: Graham Brown (01252 650920)

CLUB PERSONNEL
Chairman: P.Wentworth
President: Ron Brown

FARNHAM TOWN

Secretary: CharlieWhite,37 Upper Way, Farnham, Surrey GU9 8RL Tel No: 01252 726303 (H)
Ground: Memorial Ground, West Street, Farnham, Surrey (01252 715305)

Directions: From A31, direction Winchester, take 2nd turning into town at Coxbridge roundabout. Follow West Street until you come to new mini roundabout - the Memorial Ground is on the right.

Capacity: 2,000 Seats: 30 Cover: 150 Floodlights: Yes
Clubhouse: Open every evening and match daysClub Shop: No

HONOURS Combined Counties Lg 90-91 91-92, Challenge Cup Prem Div 95-96, Challenge Tphy 91-92 (R-up 89-90).
CLUB RECORDS **Attendance:** 1,138 v A.F.C.Wimbledon, League 2002-2003
PREVIOUS **Leagues:** Surrey Intermediate; Surrey Snr 47-71: Spartan 71-75: London Spartan 75-80: Combined Counties 80-92.
BEST SEASON **FA Cup:** Never past Qualifying Rounds

FACT FILE
Founded: 1921 Nickname: The Town
Sponsors:T.B.A.
Colours: Claret & blue stripes/white/sky blue
Change: All Yellow
Midweek Matchday: Tuesday
Reserve League: Comb Counties Res Div
Programme: 32 pages 50p
Editor: T,B,A,
CLUB PERSONNEL
Chairman: Keith Haskell
President; Paul Cooper
Press Officer: Charlie White
Manager: Andy Nunn
Asst Manager: Dave Ward
Coach: Simon Musslewhite

FELTHAM

Secretary: John Cronk,Flat 8 Wyvern Court, 24 Gordon Rd, Ashford, Middsx TW15 3EZ
Tel: 01784 243122 (H) 0208 839 2104 (B) Website: http://www.felthamfc.freeserve.co.uk/
Ground: Feltham Arena(All weather surface), Shakespeare Ave., Feltham, Middx.Tel: 0208 890 6164 (club), 0208 890 6905 (ground)**Directions:** BR to Feltham & 5 mins walk thro' Glebelands Park. Buses 90, 285,117, 237, H24 or H25 to Feltham station, or 116 to top of Shakespeare Ave. By car: M3, M4, A312 Staines road towards Bedfont, 2nd left is Shakespeare Ave
Capacity: 10,000 Seats: 650 Cover: 1,500 Floodlights: Yes
Clubhouse: Open 7 days a week. 2 bars, dancehall available for hire Club Shop: No
HONOURS Surrey Snr Lg R-up 65-66 (Lg Cup 65-66, Charity Cup 63-64 65-66),Southern Comb. Cup(2)(R-up(2)), Middx Summer Cup, Isthmian Div 2 80-81, Comb.Cos. Lge Co. 96-97
PREVIOUS **Leagues:** Feltham: West Middx Sunday; Staines & Dist.; Hounslow & Dist.; Surrey Snr 63-68; Spartan 68-73; Athenian 74-77; Isthmian 78-95
CLUB RECORDS **Attendance:** 1,9 38 v Hampton,Middlesex Senior Cup 1968
Goalscorer: Paul Clarke 130**Appearances:** Paul Clarke 326
BEST SEASON **FA Cup:** 3rd Qual.Rd.77-78, 1-4 v Tilbury; 82-83, 0-1 v Chesham U

FACT FILE
Founded: 1946 Sponsors: Feltham first
Colours: Royal blue & white halves/blue/blue
Change colours: Red /White or Blue/White
Midweek Matches: Wednesday
Programme: 20 pages, 50p
Editor:Chris Thompso
Email: cjthompson-uk@yahoo.co.uk
CLUB PERSONNEL
Chairman: Brian Barry
Prsident/Patron: Andy Lonsdale
Press Officer: Secretary
Managers: Sammy Boyd & Dave Patience
Players progressing:Rachid Harkouk,Tony Witter(CrystalP) Andy Pape (QPR), Pat Gavin (Gillingham) Bobby Wilson (Brentford)

FRIMLEY GREEN

Secretary: Mark O'Grady, 8 Rokers Place, Yateley, Hants. GU46 6FF
Tel: 01252 879883 (H) 01923 234300 (B) 07812 026390 (M)
email: mogradyuk@yahoo.co.uk

Ground: Frimley Green Recretarion Ground, Frimley Green Road, Frimley Green, Camberley, Surrey GU16 Tel: 01252 835089

Travel: Nearest railway station: Frimley or Farnborough (North)
Bus: Stagecoach, Hants & Surrey 49, 50 & 530

FACT FILE
Founded: 1919
Colours: Blue & white halves/blue/blueChange

CLUB PERSONNEL
President: Paul Grace
Chairman: Craig Fennell
Tel: 01252 317325 (H) 07831 248260 (M)

GODALMING & GUILDFORD

Secretary: Eddie Russell, 31 Harts Gardens, Guildford, Surrey GU2 9QB. 01483 535287 (H & B)

Ground: Weycourt, Meadrow, Godalming, Surrey (01483 417520)
Directions: A3100 from Guildford - past Out & About Hotel on left, then 'Save' petrol station on right, then 1st right 50 yards on. From Godalming on A3100, grd on left by Leathern Bottle pub. Three quarters of a mile from Farncombe BR station

Capacity: 3,000 Seats: 200 Cover: 200 Floodlights: Yes Club Shop: No
Clubhouse: Open Tues, Thurs eves, matchdays. Hot & cold snacks available
HONOURS Combined Co's Lg 83-84, Lge Chall. Trophy 82-83, Res Lge 95-96 96-97, Res Chall Cup 92-93 97-98, Chall Shield 96-97: Southern Comb Chall Cup 97-98
PREVIOUS **Leagues:** Guildford & Dist 50-71; Surrey Intermediate 71-78; Surrey Co. Senior 78-79
RECORDS **Attendance:** 1,305 v A.F.C. Wimbledon 5.10.02
Goalscorer: Sean Gorman 127 **Appearances:** Paul Monger 356
BEST SEASON FA Cup: 2nd Q.Rd. **FA Vase:** 2nd Rd.
Players progressing: John Humphreys (MIllwall)

FACT FILE
Founded: 1950 Nickname: The Gees
Colours: Yellow/green/green
Change colours: Blue & white/white/blue.
Midweek matchday: Tuesday Prog Yes
CLUB PERSONNEL
Chairperson: Jane Phillips
Life President: Bill Kyte
Press Officer: Secretary
Manager: Roger Steer
Asst Managers: Mick Wollen
Coach: Dave Ward Physio: Jan Eaton
2002-2003
Captain: Vic Flynn
Top Scorer: Shaun Lydon
Player of the Year: James Mariner

HARTLEY WINTNEY

Secretary: Alan Watson,17 Victoria Drive, Blackwater,Camberley, GU17 0PL
Tel No: 01276 508807 (H) 07932 739228 (M)
Tel No: 01252 844421 (H) 01252 844402 (W) 07703 193689 (M)
Ground: Memorial Playing Fields, Green Lane, Hartley Wintney, Hants
Tel: 01252 843586
Directions: A30 west through Camberley, left at parade of shops at beginning of village then sharp right - ground on right. Two miles from Winchfield (BR)
Buses: Stagecoach 200, Bee Line 111, 112
Capacity: 4,000 Seats: None Cover: Yes Floodlights: Yes
HONOURS: Aldershot Senior League winners: 73-74,74-75,75-76. Alderhot Senior Cup Winners 76-77,80-81 CoCo.League Winners 82-83,R-up 80-81
BEST SEASON **FA Cup:** Do not compete **FA Vase:** Do not compete
PREVIOUS **Leagues:** Basingstoke/ Aldershot

ACT FILE
Founded: 1897
Nickname: The Row
Colours: Orange & black/black/orange
Change colours: All white or Red/black/black
Midweek matchday: Tuesday
Programme: Yes
CLUB PERSONNEL
Chairman: Ron HigginsPresident: W A Mitchell
Treasurer: D.Willoughby
Press Officer: Luke Mullen (07860 729608 (M)

HORLEY TOWN

Secretary:
Ground: The New Defence, Court Lodge Road, Horley, Surrey.

PREVIOUS Leagues: Surrey County Lge >2003

MERSTHAM

Secretary: Richard Baxter, 2 Wood Street, Merstham, Surrey. RH1 3PF
Tel: 01737 645748 (H) 01293 450809 (B) Email: the.baxters@virgin.net
Ground: Merstham Rec., Weldon Way, Merstham, Redhill, Surrey RH1 3QB (01737 644046)
Directions: Leave Merstham village (A23) by School Hill, take 5th right (WeldonWay), clubhouse and car park 100m on right. 10 mins walk from Merstham (BR);down School Hill, under railway bridge, then 5th turning on right into WeldonWay. Bu98-99s - London Country 430, 432 & 435
Capacity: 2,000 Seats: 100 Cover: 100 Floodlights: Yes Club Shop: No
Clubhouse: Across adjacent footpath. Open daily (am & pm). Snacks available
HONOURS Combined Co's Lg R-up 87-88 89-90 (Elite Class Cup 89-90 (R-up 90-91), Res. Sect. 90-91), Spartan Lg 79-89 (Lg Cup 79-80), Surrey Snr Lg 71-72, Surrey Snr Char. Cup 79-80, E. Surrey Char. Cup 80-8 98-99, Surrey I'mediate Lg 52-3.Fair Play & Prog Awards 01-02
CLUB RECORDS **Attendance:** 1,587 v AFC Wimbledon 9.11.02
BEST SEASON **FA Cup:** 3rd Q Rd **FA Vase:** 4th Rd.
PREVIOUS **Leagues:** Redhill & Dist.; Surrey Co.S.E. I'mediate; Surrey Snr 64-78; London Spartan 78-85 **Grounds:**None

FACT FILE
Founded: 1892
Club Sponsors: Brewers
Colours: Amber & black stripes/black/amber
Change colours:White,navy, red.
Midweek matches: Tuesday/Thursday
Programme: Yes Editor:Mrs S Fish
CLUB PERSONNEL
Chairman:Ted Hickman President: Bill Lawton
Press Officer: Roger Peerless
Manager: Mick Sullivan
Paul O'GormanPeter Gibson
2002-2003
Captain: Shayne Trayner P.o.Y.: Chris Boulter
Top Scorer: Chris Watts

Ash United. Back Row (L-R): Shaun Mitchell, James Blason, Matthew Short, Andy Hunt, Alan Hanning, Jez Jukes, Ricky Jones, Richard Bryant, Ian Jopling, Terry Wilson.
Front Row: Jamie Horton, Scott Joyce, Matthew Everard (with Aldershot Cup), Benn Wilson, Paul Bonner.
Kneeling: Tony Calvert (Now New manager), David Johnston.

Photo: Eric Marsh.

Sandhurst Town at the end of a sixty game season!
Standing: Mark Anderson, Kevin Brown, Peter Browning (Manager), Colin Bland, Errol Hutchings, Darren Wilson, Danny Wilde, Peter Mulvaney, Grant Nesbitt, James Smith.
Kneeling: Colin Hutchins, Steve Stairs, Roy Atkin.

NORTH GREENFORD UNITED

Secretary: Mrs B Bivens, 1 The Green, sarratt, Hertfordshire WD3 6AY
Tel: 01923 270057 (H & Fax)

Ground: Berkeley Fields, Berkeley Avenue, Greenford, Middlesex UB6
Tel: 0208 422 8923

Travel: Nearest railway station: Greenford (Central Line) & Sudbury Hill (Piccadilly)
Bus: Metro Link 92

FACT FILE
Founded: 1944
Colours: Blue & white/blue/blue

CLUB PERSONNEL
President: John Bignell
Chairman: Mick Hardwick
Tel: 0208 423 0702 (H)
Press Secretary: Secretary

RAYNES PARK VALE

Secretary: Paul Armour, 9 Banstead Road, East Ewell, Surrey KT17 3EP
Tel:07980 914211 (M) Fax: 0207 492 1132
e-mail: paul.armour2bt.com

Ground: Prince George's Playing Field, Raynes Park. SW20 9NB Tel: 07714 339747
Capacity: 2,000 Covered Seating: 200 Covered Standing: 100 Floodlights: Yes

Directions: Bus - London Transport 163 & 152
Nearest railway station - Raynes Park.

HONOURS: Div 1 Champions 2002-03 Combined Counties Lg: Div 1 Cup R-up 02-03,
Div 1 Challenge Shield 02-03

Club Records Attendance: 1,871 v AFC Wimbledon (played at Carshalton Ath F.C.)

FACT FILE
Formed 1995 Nickname: The Vale
Sponsors:Korea Foods Company Ltd.
Colours: Red & blue/red/blue
Change cols: Yellow/blue/yellow
Midweek Matchday:Tuesday
Programme: Pages: 32 Price:£1.00
Website: http://raynesparkvalefc.tripod.com.

CLUB PERSONNEL
President: Robert Hallett
Chairman: Syd Toulson
Vice Chairman:Nigel Thorn
Director of Football: Steve Smith
Managers:Lee Dobinson & Brian Imms
Coach: Gary Clark

READING TOWN

Secretary & Fixture Sec: Richard Grey, 6 Milestone View Court, Lowfield Road, Caversham Park, Reading RG4 6ND Tel: 0118 948 4920 Email:richardigrey@aol.com

Ground: Reading Town Spts Ground, Scours Lane, Tilehurst, Reading, Berks (0118 945 3555)

Directions: Out of Reading on Oxford road (A329), past Battle Hosp. Scours Lane 1st right after roundabout ,Nearest station - Tilehurst or Reading (General). Bus -Reading Bus 17(Tilehurst)

Capacity: 2,000 Seats: No Cover: Yes Floodlights: Yes Clubhouse: Yes

PREVIOUS Leagues: Chiltonian 89-95, Reading 66-89 **Ground**:Adwest Spts Grd,Kings Meadow
Names: Lower Burghfield, XL United, Vincents Utd, Reading Garage, ITS Reading Town

CLUB RECORDS **Attendance:** 1,067 v AFC Wimbledon 2002-03
Defeat: 0-10 v Feltham(A) 96-97
Win: 7-0 v Cranleigh/Viking Spts/AFC Wallingford all Home 97-98

BEST SEASON **FA Cup:** 1st Qual. Rd. 00-01 **FA Vase:** 4th Rd 96-97

HONOURS Comb. Counties Lge R-up 97-98; Chiltonian Lge Champions 94-95,
Berks &Bucks Sen. Trophy 95-96, R-up 96-97

FACT FILE
Founded: 1968
Colours: Red & black stripes/black/black
Change colours: Navy/navy/red
Midweek Matchday: Tuesday
Programme: 20 pages 50p
Editor: Richard Grey

CLUB PERSONNEL
Chairman: Roland Ford, 103 Little Heath Road, Tilehurst, Berkshire RG31 5TG
Tel: 0118 941 2270
Manager:Colin Millard

2002-2003
Captain: & P.o.Y.: Andy Sharrett
Top Scporer: Ashaine Murray 21

SANDHURST TOWN

Secretary & Match Sec): Tony Ford, Pennings Cottage, Aldershot Road, Guildford, Surrey GU3 3AA Tel Nos: 01483 567284 (H) 07778 628547(M)

Ground: Bottom Meadow, Memorial Ground, Yorktown Rd, Sandhurst (07831 366140)

Directions: M3 Jn4- A331 -A321 or M4 Jn10 -A329 -A321. Park in main council offices car park off A321. Walk down tarmac path to ground. Nearest station: Sandhurst. Buses: 174,193 & 194

Capacity: 2,500 Seats: Eight Cover: Yes Floodlights: Yes Clubhouse: after matches only

PREVIOUS **Leagues:** Reading & Dist.; East Berks; Aldershot Snr 79-84; Chiltonian84-90

CLUB RECORDS **Attendance:** 2,449 v AFC Wimbledon 187.08.02 League
Win: 9-1 v Cranleigh (08.01.2000) **Defeat:** 0-8 v Cobham 26.10.1991)
Goalscorer: Glenn Price **Appearances:** John Parker

BEST SEASON **FA Vase:** 2nd Rd 01-02,02-03 **FA Cup:** 1st Rd Qualifying

HONOURS Combined Co's Lge Chal. Vase R-up 92-93 (Reserve Chal. Cup R-up 91-92), Chiltonian Lg R-up 86-87, Aldershot Snr Lg R-up 83-84; Berks & Bucks Sen.Trophy R-up 92-93 Aldershot Senior Cup: 00-01 , Co.Co. Res Cup 00-01, 01-02

FACT FILE
Founded: 1910
Nickname: Fizzers
Colours: Red/black/black
Change colours: Yellow,blue,yellow
Midweek matchday: Tuesday
Programme: Yes Editor:Tony Ford

CLUB PERSONNEL
Chairman:Phil Sigley (01276 32742)
President: Malcolm Watts
Manager:Peter Browning

2002-2003
Top Scorers: : Mark Anderson & Peter Mulvaney 31Captain: Aaron Roberts
Player of the Year: Colin Bland

SOUTHALL

Secretary: Geoff Harrison, 241 High Street South,Dunstasbnle, Beds. LU6 3HY
Tel Nos: 01582 658603 (W) 07879 4035&2 (M)
Ground: Ground share with Chesham United F.C. Tel No: 01494 783964
Directions: A413 from Uxbridge (London) to Chalfont. Turn left 100 yds after2nd major roundabout (between Ambulance station and Community Centre. 2 miles from Gerrards Cross (BR), regular buses from Slough & Uxbridge
Capacity: 4,500 Cover: 120 Seats: 220 Floodlights: Yes
PREVIOUS: **Leagues**: Southern 1896-1905; Gt Western Suburban; Herts & Middx; Athenian 19-73, Ryman 73-00
BEST SEASON: **FA Cup:** 3rd Round 35-36, 1-4 v Watford (H)
FA Vase: Runners-up 85-86 **FA Amateur Cup:** Runners-up 24-25
HONOURS: FA Amtr Cup R-up 24-25, FA Vase R-up 85-86, Isthmian Lg Div 2 R-up 74-75, Gt Western Suburban Lg 12-13, Athenian Lg 26-27 R-up 54-55, Middx Snr Cup x12, Middx Charity Cup x9

FACT FILE
Founded: 1871 Nickname: Fowlers
Colours: Red & white /black/red
Change: Yellow & black
Midweek Matchday: Wednesday
Res' Lge: Middx County
Prog: 6 pages, 50p Ed: Steve Hawkins

CLUB PERSONNEL
Chairman: B.S.Gill Prersident: S.S.Dhami
Manager: Keith Chamberlin
Physio: Keith Chamberlin
Club Website: www.southallfootballclub.co.uk
Club Email: geoff@southallfootballclub..co.uk

WALTON CASUALS

Secretary: Stuart Roberts, 47 Foxholes, Weybridge, Surrey. KT13 0BN. Tel: 01932845923
Email: sroberts@cattronuk.com

Ground: Franklyn Road Sports Ground, Waterside Drive, Walton-on-Thames, Surrey KT12 2JG
Tel No: 01932 787749 Website: http://www.waltoncasualsfc.co.uk
Directions: Next to Elmbridge Leisure Centre, left off Terrace Rd at first roundabout out of Walton centre. Hersham (BR), then bus 564 to Elmbridge Leisure Centre.
Capacity: 1,500 Seats: None Cover: 80Floodlights: Yes
Clubhouse: Matchdays only. Hot food available from Tea Bar Club Shop: No

HONOURS Suburban Lge (South) 82-83, (R-up 83-84); Surrey Prem Lge R-up 94-95, S.P.L. Chall Cup 93-94, (R-up 94-95); Surrey Premier Cup R-up 86-87,CoCo Lg Cup 99-00 R-up 00-01
BEST SEASON **FA Vase:** 1Rd Proper 00-01 **FA Cup:** PrelimRd 2000-01,01-02
PREVIOUS **Leagues:** Surrey Premier, Surrey Senior, Surrey Intermediate, Suburban.
CLUB RECORDS **Attendance:** 178 v Pagham FA Vase 96/97

FACT FILE
Founded: 1948
Nickname: The Stags
Sponsors: Browns Building Centre
Colours: Tangerine/black/tangerine
Change colours: All Blue
Midweek Matchday: Tuesday
Programme: 28 pages70p
Editor/Press Officer: Stuart Roberts

CLUB PERSONNEL
Chairman:Graham James (01932 227921)
General Manager: David Symonds
President: Grahan James
Manager: Ray Noad

WESTFIELD

Secretary: Mrs Helen Gauton,1 Geffers Ride,Ascot, Berks. SL5 7JY
Tel `No: 01344 627858
GROUND Woking Park, Kingfield, Woking, Surrey Tel: 01483 771106

Directions: (Adjacent to Woking FC.)
M25 J10 or 11, signposted from outskirts of Town.Ground 1 mile.
Woking B.R.Station & buses from Woking
Capacity: 1,000 Seats: None Cover: Yes Floodlights: Yes
Clubhouse Yes - open matchdays when snacks are available.
Club Shop No
HONOURS
PREVIOUS **League:** Surrey County Senior League

FACT FILE
Founded: 1953
Colours:Yellow/black/yellowChange colours:Yellow/Black/Yellow
Midweek Matchday:Tuesday
Programme: No

CLUB PERSONNEL
President: Richard Hill
Chairman: Steven Perkins
Tel: 01252 547900 (B)
Press Officer: Pat Kel;ly (07710 305200 (M)
Manager: John Cassidy
Asst. Managers:
Alan Morton & Brian Hennessy

WITHDEAN 2000

Secretary: Brian Davies, 119 Church Road, Hove BN3 2AF
Tel: 01272 272776 (H) 01273 764874 (B)
Email: briand@bdinsurance.demon.co.uk
Ground: **Worthing F.C.,**Withdean Stadium, Tongdean Lane, Brighton BN3 2AF
Tel: 01273 542100
Capacity: 10,000 **Seats:** 6,000 **Cover:** 1,000 **Floodlights**: No
Directions: Off main London - Brighton road
Nearest Station: Buses: ?
Clubhouse: Pub on ground **Club Shop:** No
HONOURS Sussex Co. Lg Div 3 92-93 (Div 3 Cup 91-92)
PREVIOUS **Leagues:** Brighton Hove & District
Ground: Council pitch
CLUB RECORDS **Attendance:**

FACT FILE
Founded: 1984
Colours:White/black/white
Change Colours:
Midweek Matchday:
Programme Editor: Gary Arnold
Local Newspaper: Brighton Evening Argus

CLUB PERSONNEL
Chairman: Desmond Ralfe
President: Stan Hunt
Manager: Dave Cole

EASTWAY
ESSEX SENIOR LEAGUE

President: Arthur Dimond **Chairman & Publicity:** Robert Errington

Secretary: David Walls, 2 Hillsfield Cottage, Layer, Breton, Essex CO2 0PS

Tel & Fax: 01206 330146 Email: EssexSenior@wallsd.freeserve.co.uk

Enfield Town, in only their second season as a club, won the League championship after a thrilling battle with four other clubs, one of which, Concord Rangers did not drop a point after Christmas. In addition to this they won the Gordon Brasted Memorial Trophy at Burnham On Crouch in a close encounter with Saffron Walden Town and then achieved something quite unique for an Essex Senior League club, reaching their own Senior County Cup final against mighty Hendon at Northwood.

The Cup final, held at Barkingside was a triumph for Ilford who are emerging as a club with intentions to be added to the now growing list of Essex Senior Clubs that have gained promotion through the Isthmian League side of the National Game. Promotion was not to be for any club this past season but the carrot can now clearly be seen with Dunstable Town having being promoted from the same level in the Spartan South Midlands League to Division One North of the Ryman. Again, the only goal of the match, in front of over 400, from O'Reilly so far over on the right wing that he might have caught a Central Line tube to London was enough to beat Sawbridgeworth Town who, at least had the consolation of previously knocking Enfield Town out of the competition.

A three year sponsorship with the Foresters Friendly Society came to an end but with fond memories of a very amicable partnership. The League are deeply indebted to Mr Costas Sophocleous, Chairman and owner of Leyton FC, the last successful ESL club to be promoted, for stepping in with his company Eastway Construction to sponsor us this coming season.

Brentwood won the Sportsmanship Award for the third year in a row and Bill Robertson of Ilford FC was the Secretary of the Year.

Sadly, past League champions, Saffron Walden Town, have decided to take a year out of football before moving over to pastures new, leaving with many happy memories not least some of the greatest hospitality encountered at an ESL club. Woodford Town after many struggles at the wrong end of the table were not re-elected but we welcome London APSA (London All Peoples Sports Association) to the fray, ground sharing at Aveley FC and keen to add a new dimension to football in Essex.

With 16 member clubs, the League continues to be party to the on-going talks with the FA on the future of level 3 football and are most anxious to follow the governing bodies lead with a National common ground criteria.

The League still continue to look forward and have made it clear that they intend to bring back their Reserve Division in 2004 as a Division One, the constitution of which will be decided in the coming months.

Robert Errington, Chairman

ILford FC celebrate after their Essex Senior League Cup victory. Photo: Robert Errington.

FINAL LEAGUE TABLE 2002-03

		P	W	D	L	F	A	Pts
1	Enfield Town	32	23	6	3	77	28	75
2	Concord Rangers	32	23	2	7	83	46	71
3	Ilford	32	21	4	7	87	40	67
4	Southend Manor	32	20	7	5	73	43	67
5	Romford	32	21	4	7	63	34	67
6	Sawbridgeworth Town	32	18	7	7	57	30	61
7	Bowers United	32	16	6	10	58	49	54
8	Burnham Ramblers	32	14	4	14	45	43	46
9	Barkingside	32	14	3	15	66	55	45
10	Waltham Abbey	32	12	6	14	45	41	42
11	Brentwood	32	12	5	15	44	62	41
12	Saffron Walden Town	32	10	4	18	49	57	34
13	Basildon United	32	9	4	19	54	71	31
14	Stansted	32	8	4	20	36	64	28
15	Hullbridge Sports	32	5	3	24	35	90	18
16	Eton Manor	32	3	8	21	44	98	17
17	Woodford Town	32	3	3	26	22	87	12

		1	2	3	4	5	6	7	8	9	10	11	12	13	14	15	16	17
1	Barkingside		6-2	2-0	2-1	3-0	1-2	0-2	2-0	2-0	3-5	0-1	0-0	2-0	3-4	3-1	1-1	7-0
2	Basildon United	3-1		2-3	0-0	2-3	1-3	1-3	2-2	3-1	1-3	1-2	3-2	1-4	1-2	3-0	0-1	2-4
3	Bowers United	2-1	0-4		2-1	0-0	1-3	0-1	1-1	3-0	1-3	1-2	3-0	3-2	5-4	3-1	1-2	4-3
4	Brentwood	3-2	2-0	1-3		1-0	0-3	0-3	1-1	5-2	0-3	0-2	3-1	0-2	1-1	2-0	0-4	3-1
5	Burnham Ramblers	2-0	1-2	1-2	1-2		0-4	0-3	4-2	2-2	0-1	1-2	1-0	0-1	4-0	3-0	2-1	2-0
6	Concord Rangers	5-2	3-1	3-1	1-1	4-1		2-0	6-3	4-1	2-2	5-0	3-2	3-0	2-3	2-1	3-2	2-1
7	Enfield Town	4-4	0-1	2-1	7-2	1-0	1-2		3-0	2-0	2-1	1-1	4-1	1-1	2-0	1-0	1-1	3-1
8	Eton Manor	1-5	4-2	2-2	1-5	0-4	0-1	1-4		5-2	2-2	3-3	2-4	0-3	1-6	1-1	0-1	3-0
9	Hullbridge Sports	4-1	1-3	1-2	1-1	1-3	0-4	3-4	5-2		0-5	0-4	1-1	0-3	0-4	0-3	0-2	3-1
10	Ilford	3-2	7-1	0-1	5-1	2-0	1-3	0-7	4-0	4-0		0-1	2-1	2-2	2-2	5-1	5-1	3-0
11	Romford	3-0	1-0	1-1	4-0	0-1	4-0	0-2	5-2	4-1	1-2		5-1	1-3	1-2	3-2	1-0	1-0
12	Saffron Walden Town	1-2	2-2	0-1	3-1	2-4	4-1	2-3	3-0	4-0	1-2	1-2		0-2	1-2	2-1	1-0	4-0
13	Sawbridgeworth Town	0-1	2-0	1-1	3-0	1-1	2-1	0-1	7-3	3-0	1-0	1-3	3-0		1-3	1-1	2-0	0-0
14	Southend Manor	1-0	4-2	1-1	1-0	2-0	4-1	1-1	2-0	2-3	3-2	1-1	4-1	1-1		3-1	1-1	5-1
15	Stansted	2-6	2-1	2-0	1-3	1-2	3-2	1-1	3-1	2-1	0-2	1-3	0-2	0-2	0-1		1-0	1-0
16	Waltham Abbey	1-2	2-2	2-3	2-3	1-1	0-1	0-1	4-0	1-0	0-4	1-0	0-0	1-2	3-1	3-1		5-0
17	Woodford Town	1-0	0-5	0-6	0-1	0-1	3-2	1-6	1-1	1-2	0-5	0-1	0-2	0-1	0-2	2-2	1-2	

LEAGUE CUP 2002-03

FIRST ROUND							
Saffron Walden Town	v	5 Brentwood	5-1	Brentwood	v	Saffron Walden Town	0-3
SECOND ROUND							
Barkingside	v	Southend Manor	3-0	Southend Manor	v	Barkingside	3-3
Basildon United	v	Concord Rangers	0-1	Concord Rangers	v	Basildon	6-2
Enfield Town	v	Sawbridgeworth Town	1-1	Sawbridgeworth Tn	v	Enfield Town	1-0
Eton Manor	v	Saffron Walden Town	1-1	Saffron Walden Tn	v	Eton Manor	2-3 (aet)
Ilford	v	Hullbridge Sports	0-0	Hullbridge Sports	v	Ilford	2-4
Romford	v	Burnham Ramblers	3-1	Burnham Ramblers	v	Romford	3-2
Stansted	v	Woodford Town	4-1	Woodford Town	v	Stansted	2-5
Waltham Abbey	v	Bowers	0-2	Bowers	v	Waltham Abbey	2-0
QUARTER-FINALS							
Barkingside	v	Stansted	5-1	Stansted	v	Barkingside	1-3
Concord Rangers	v	Romford	2-0	Romford	v	Concord Rangers	1-1
Ilford	v	Bowers United	0-1	Bowers United	v	Ilford	1-2 (aet) 2-4p
Sawbridgeworth Town	v	Eton Manor	2-1	Eton Manor	v	Sawbridgeworth Tn	1-1
SEMI-FINALS							
Concord Rangers	v	Ilford	2-2	Ilford	v	Concord Rangers	4-3 (aet)
Sawbridgeworth Town	v	Barkingside	1-1	Barkingside	v	Sawbridgeworth Tn	1-2
FINAL							
Ilford	v	SawbridgeworthTown	1-0	5th May at Barkingside			

BARKINGSIDE

Secretary: John Taylor, 2 Courage Close.Hornchurch, Essex RM11 2BJ (01708 456373)
Ground: Oakside, Station Road, Barkingside, Ilford, Essex Tel: 020 8550 3611
Directions: From London A12 Eastern Ave to Green Gate, left into Hurns Rd to Barkingside, right into Craven Gardens, right Carlton Drive to Station Rd, under bridge and grd on right. Next to Barkingside station (Central Line). From Ilford station (BR) take 169 Bus to Craven Gardens
Capacity: 2,500 Seats: 140 Cover: 240 Floodlights: Yes Club Shop: No
Clubhouse: Saturdays 1pm-12. midweeek matchnights 6.30-11pm. Rolls, hotdogs,hamburgers
HONOURS: Spartan Lge. Prem. Div. 96-97, R-up 90-91 (Harry Sunderland Shld 83-84 (R-up 84-85); London Sen. Cup 96-97; S. Essex Lge R-up 46-47, L'don Lg R-up 49-50 (Lg Cup 55-56 (R-up 52-53 62-63)), Gtr L'don Lg 64-65,S.S.Mids Premier 98-99.Harry Fisher Mem Trophy 00-1
PREVIOUS: Leagues: Ilford & Dist. 1898-1925 44-47; Ilford Minor 25-44; Sth Essex 47-48; Walthamstow 48-50; London 50-64; Gtr London 64-71; Metropolitan-London 71-75; Spartan 76-South Midlands 1996-99 **Grounds:** Fulwell Cross PF 1898-1921; Clayhall Rec 21-29; Hainault PF 29-33; Barkingside Rec 33-57 **RECORDS: Gate:** 957 v Arsenal Res., London Lg 1957

FACT FILE
Founded: 1898
Colours: All Sky Blue
Change colours: All Red
Midweek matchday: Monday
Programme: Yes
Editor: John Taylor

CLUB PERSONNEL
Chairman: John Taylor
Manager: Tony Myers
Physio:

BASILDON UNITED

Secretary: Frank Ford, 23 Oldwycki,Basildon, Essex SS16 4NU
Tel Nos: :01268 552994(H) 07789 534164(M)
Ground: Gardiners Close, Gardiners Lane, Basildon, Essex SS14 3AW Tel: 01268 520268

Directions: A176 off Southend arterial (A127), left at r'bout into Cranes FarmRoad, proceed to end of duel carriageway, left at lights, Gardiners Close is 1st left (Football Club signed). Two and a half miles from Basildon BR station
Capacity: 2,000 Seats: 400 Cover: 1,000 Floodlights: Yes
Clubhouse: Open lunchtimes, evenings, weekends. Hot food sold Club Shop: No

HONOURS Isthmian Lge Div 2 83-83; Essex Senior Lge (5) 76-80 93-94, Lg Cup 77-78 93-94 97-98, Res. Cup 92-93; Essex Senior Trophy 78-79; Res. Lge &Shield 94-95
PREVIOUS **Leagues:** Grays & Thurrock; Gtr London 68-70; Essex Snr 70-80; Athenian 80-81; Isthmian 81-91 **Name:** Armada Sports **Ground:** Grosvenor Park 63-69
CLUB RECORDS **Attendance:** 4,000 v West Ham, ground opening 11/8/70

FACT FILE
Founded: 1963
Sponsors: T.B.A.
Colours: Amber & black stripes/black/black
Change:Green & white hoops/white/g&w
Midweek Matches: Wednesday
Programme: 16 pages, 50p
Editor:John Moran (07801 461605)

CLUB PERSONNEL
President: J Oakes
Chairman: Jim Gooding
Press Officer: Frank Ford (07789 534174)
Manager: Mark Jenkins
Asst. Manager/Coach:
Physio:

BOWERS UNITED

Secretary: Lee Stevens, 59 Cross Green, Lee Chapel South, Basildon, Essex SS16 5Q
Tel No: 01268 548 493 (H)
Ground: Len Salmon Stadium, Crown Avenue, off Kenneth Rd,Pitsea, Basildon (01268 452068)
Directions: Turn into Rectory Rd from Old London Rd (B1464) at Pitsea Broadway into Kenneth Rd, right at top Crown Ave. 1.25 miles Pitsea (BR). Bus 5& 42 toRectory Rd, Bowers Gifford
Capacity: 2,000 Seats: 200 Stand: Yes Floodlights: Yes
Clubhouse: Open every night Club Shop: No
PREVIOUSLeagues: Thurrock & Thameside Comb.; Olympian**Ground:** Gun Meadow, Pitsea
HONOURS Thurrock & Thameside Comb. 58-59; Essex Snr Lg 80-81,98-99 R-up 83-84 Div 1 Cup 90-91,Lg Cup Winners 81-82,98-99 R-up (3) Harry FisherMem Trophy 91-92 R-up (4)
E.S.L. Charity Cup 99-00
BEST SEASON **FA Cup:** 1st Rd Q 98-99 **FA Vase:** 4th Rd 98-99
CLUB RECORDS **Attendance:** 1,800 v Billericay F.A.Vase
Players progressing: Steve Tilson (Southend Utd)

FACT FILE
Founded: 1946
Colours: Red & white stripes/black/black
Change colours:All Yellow
Midweek Matches:Wednesday7.30
Res League; Essex & Herts Border Comb
Programme: 30pages 50p
Editor:Lee Stevens

CLUB PERSONNEL
Chairman:Barry Hubbard
Vice Chairman: Denis Osborne
Manager: Tony Fenn

BRENTWOOD

Secretary: Colin Harris, 56 Viking Way, Pilgrims Hatch, Brentwood, Essex CM15 9HY
Tel: 01277 219564 (H) Email Address: khobbs1057@aol.com
Ground: Brentwood Centre, Doddinghurst Rd, Brentwood, Essex. 01277 215151 Ext.713
Directions: From east end High St (Wilsons Corner) turn north into Ongar Rd. 3rd mini-round-about ,Right into Doddinghurst Rd, Centre half mile on right after A12 Bridge, ground far right.
Capacity: !,000 Cover: 100 Seats: Floodlights: Yes
Clubhouse: Open Tues & Thur evening & matchdays Club Shop: No
PREVIOUS **Names:** Manor Ath. 55-70, Brentwood Ath. 70-72
Grounds: King George, Hartswood, `Larkins', Ongar (pre-92), East Thurrock 92/93
Leagues: Romford & Dist., Sth Essex Comb., London & Essex Border,Olympian
HONOURS Olympian Lg Cup 67-68, Essex Inter. Cup 76-77, Essex Lg Cup 75-76 78-79 90-91; Harry Fisher Mem. Trophy 95-96 ,Essex Senior League 2000-01, League Sportsmanship Award 00-01,01-02
BEST SEASON **FA Vase:** 3rd Rd Prop 95-96

FACT FILE
Founded: 1955
Nickname: Blues
Sponsor: CLC Construction
Colours: Sky blue/navy blue/sky blue
Change colours: All Yellow
Midweek Matches: Tuesday
Programme: 50p
ED:K.Hobbs(kenhobbs@brentwoodfc.co.uk)
Club Website:www.brentwoodfc.co.uk

CLUB PERSONNEL
Chairman: Terry Smith
Manager: Paul Delea (H) 01708 550630
2002-2003
Capt: Dave Stittle Top Scorer: Liam Bright 17

BURNHAM RAMBLERS

Secretary: Mrs Christine Revell c/o Club
Ground: Leslie Fields Stadium, Springfield Rd, Burnham-on-Crouch CM0 8TE (01621 784383)
Club Website: www.burnhamramblersfc.co.uk
Directions: On B1010 from South Woodham Ferrers, trt,1/2 mile before town.
10 mins -Burnham on Crouch railway station
Capacity: 2,000 Seats:156 Stand: Yes Floodlights: Yes Club Shop: No
Clubhouse: Mon-Fri 7-11pm, Sat 12noon -11pm, Sun 12-3 & 7-9.30pm. Hot meals & snacks available

HONOURS Olympian Lg 65-66; Essex I'mediate Cup R-up 81-82; Essex Snr Lg Cup R-up 86-87 89-90 97-98, (Reserve Cup 89-90 (R-up 92-93), Reserve Shield R-up 90-91; Harry Fisher Mem. Trophy 96-97, R-up 97-98 99-00; Sportsmanship Award 96-97
PREVIOUS **Leagues:** N Essex, Mid-Essex, Olympian, S.E. Essex
Grounds: Wick Rd ,Millfields and Saltcourts
BEST SEASON **FA Vase:** 5th Rd 88-89
CLUB RECORDS **Gate:** 1,500 v Arsenal at opening of new stand

FACT FILE
Founded: 1900 Nickname: Ramblers
Colours: Blue/black/blue
Change colours: Yellow/black/yellow
Midweek matches: Tuesday
Reserves' Lge: Essex & Herts Comb.
Prog: 32 pages, £1.00 Editor: Chris Dobson
CLUB PERSONNEL
Chairman:William Hannan
Vice Chairman: Shaun Pugh
President: R J Cole, Esq
Press Officer: Nigel Radcliffe, 016217774
Manager: Mike Everett Physio:T.B.A.
2002-03
Capt: Matt Dowse Top Scorer: Kristian Down

CONCORD RANGERS

Secretary: Eddie Crace, 71 Tilburg Road, Canvey Island, Essex, SS8 9ER. Tel: 01268 681868H
07889 904109M 01268 2950288W
Ground: Thames Road, Canvey Island, Essex. SS8 0HP 01268 691780 / 515750
Website: www.concordrangersfc.co.uk Email: ecrace@newholland.com
Directions: Follow A130 onto Canvey Island and turn right into Thorney Bay Road, then right again into Thames Road.
Capacity: 1,500 Cover: Yes Seats: No Floodlights: Yes
HONOURS Southend & Dist. Lge - Lge & Cup 84-85; Southend Alliance - Lge & Cup 87-88;
Essex Intermediate Lg Div 2 90-91; Essex Sen Lge 97-98, Cup 96-97;
Wirral Programme Award 93-94, Harry Fisher Trophy 99-00 ESL Charity Cup 00-01
PREVIOUS **Leagues:** Southend & Dist. All., Essex I'mediate (pre-1991) **Ground:** Waterside
CLUB RECORDS **Gate:** 1,500 v Lee Chapel North, FA Sunday Cup 89-90
Win: 12-1 v Woodford, Essex Snr Lge 00-01

FACT FILE
Founded: 1967
Colours:Yellow & Blue/blue/yellow
Change colours: white/black/black
Midweek Matches: Tuesday
Clubhouse: Evenings & weekends
Programme: 20 pages, 50p
Editor: Mike Stephenson
CLUB PERSONNEL
President: Albert Lant
Chairman: Antony Smith
Manager: Ben Embery

ENFIELD TOWN

Secretary: Roger Reed, 16 College Gardens, Enfield, Middlesex.EN2 0QF(0208 3504064)
Press Officer: Peter Coath, 33 Ashford Crescent.,Enfield Middx EN3 7HX
Tel.Nos: 020 8292 4495 (H) 07949 378931 (M) **Website:** www.enfieldtownfootballclub.co.uk
Fixture Sec.: Keith Wortley, Greenways, Appleby Street, Cheshunt, Herts EN7 6QZ
Tel nos: 01992 201690 (H) 07732 319897 (M)
Ground: Brimsdown Sports & Social Club, Goldsdown Road, Enfield Tel: 020 8804 5491
Capacity: 2000 Covered Seats: 150 Covered Standing: 300 Floodlights: Yes
Clubhouse: Yes
Directions: BR from Liverpool Street to Brimsdown (half mile away) or Southbury Road.
By road off Green Street, itself off Hertford Road (A1010). Buses 191 or 307
Honours: Essex League Champions 02-03 R-up: 01-02 Lg Cup Winners 01-02, Cherry Red Books Trophy 01-02, Gordon Brasted Mem Trophy 02-03 Middlesex SenCup R-up 02-03
Records: 521 v AFC Wimbledon 12.08.02 **Apps & Goals**: Daniel Clarke: 100apps 68 goals
Best Victory: 7-0 v Ilford (away) 28.04.03

FACT FILE
Founded: June 2001
Nickname ETs or Towners
Sponsor: Direct Boot & Embroidery
Colours: White/blue/white Change:All yellow
Midweek Matchday: Variable
Programme: Price: £1.50 Pages:32
Editor:Peter Coath
CLUB PERSONNEL
Chairman: David Bryant
Fixture Sec: Keith Wortley (07732 319897)
Manager: Jim Chandler
2002-2003
Captain: John Ridout
Top Scorer: Daniel Clarke 22
Player of the Year: Andy Hall

ETON MANOR

Secretary: Larry mcDonald, 20 Heynes Rd, Dagenham, Essex RM8 2SX Tel No: 0208 5902863
Ground: Waltham Lodge Sports Ground,Kitchener Rd.,Walthamstowe London E17 4JP(020 8527 2444)
Directions: Sharing with Potters Bar Town F.C.
Capacity: 1,000 Seats: 60 Cover: 60Floodlights: Yes Clubhouse: Yes
HONOURS Essex Snr Cup R-up 37-38, London Lg 33-34 37-38 52-53 53-54 (R-up 48-49 57-58, Lg Cup 55-56 (R-up 46-47 54-55)), Greater London Lg 64-65, Essex Intermediate Cup 64-65, London Intermediate Cup R-up 33-34 66-67, Essex Snr Lg Sportsmanship Award 75-76 (Div 1 Cup 90-91, Res. Div 76-77, Res. Div Cup 91-92).
PREVIOUS **Leagues:** London 33-59; Aetolian 59-64; Greater London 64-69; Metropolitan 69-75.
Grounds: Wildness, Hackney; GUS Sports Ground, Clapton; Walthamstow Ave. FC; Norwegian Ground, Barking; Roding Lane, Buckhurst Hill, ThurrockHotel **Name:** Wilderness Leyton.
CLUB RECORDS **Gate:** 600 v Leyton Orient, opening of floodlights at Roding Lane.
Goalscorer: Dave Sams

FACT FILE
Founded: 1901
Nickname: The Manor
Colours: Sky/navy/navy
Change: Yellow/dark blue/light blue
Midweek Matches: Tuesday
Prog: 12 pages with entry
.CLUB PERSONNEL
Chairman & Prog Ed.: Reg Curtis
Manager:Kirk Whitelock
General Manager: Alex Lee
Coach: Matt Tallon. Physio: Alf Jones
2002-2003
Captain& P.o.Y:Noel Duff.
Player of the Year:Bradlet Knapman.

HULLBRIDGE SPORTS

Secretary: Mrs.Beryl Petre, 58 Grasmere Ave., Hullbridge, Essex SS5 6LF
Tel: 01702 230630 (H) 01702 552211 (B)
Ground: Lower Road, Hullbridge, Hockley, Essex SS5 6BJ Tel: 01702 230420
Directions: Turn into Rawreth Lane from A130 (left if arriving fromChelmsford), down to mini-r'bout, left, across next mini-r'bout, up hill, ground signed on right just past garage
Capacity: 1,500 Seats: No Cover: Yes Floodlights: Yes Club Shop: No
Clubhouse: Lounge bar, function hall with bar & changing rooms - set in 16 acres

HONOURS Essex Intermediate Snr Div Cup 87-88, Southend & District Lg Div 1 65-66 (Div 2 51-52, Div 3 56-57), French Cup 51-52, Essex Snr Lg Sportsmanship Award 91-92 92-93 93-94

PREVIOUS **Leagues:** Southend & Dist., Alliance, Essex I'mediate
Grounds: Pooles Lane Rec

RECORD ATTENDANCE: 800 v Blackburn Rovers F.A.Youth Cup 99-00

FACT FILE
Founded: 1945
Sponsor: Thermo Shield
Colours: Royal Blue & white/blue/white
Change colours: Red & white/black/black
Midweek matches: Tues/Thursday
Programme Editor: T.B.A.
Website: www.sportsworldwide.co.uk

CLUB PERSONNEL
Chairman: Terry Scourfield
Manager: Jayson Stephens

ILFORD

Secretary: Bill Robertson, 2 Humphrey Close, Clayhall, Ilford, Essex JG5 0RW
Tel: 0208 550 6680 (H) 07930 104076 (W)
All club correspondance to Ilford F.C. to the pavillion, Cricklefield Stadium as below
Ground: Cricklefield Stadium, High Road, Ilford, Essex. IG1 1UB Tel: 0181 514 0019
Directions: 5 min walk from Seven Kings Station. Opposite 'TheCauliflower' publ, Or 86 Bus
Capacity: 5,000 Seats: 216 Cover: Yes Floodlights: Yes
Clubhouse: Open matchdays. Snacks available **PREVIOUS League:** Spartan 87-95
HONOURS: FA Amateur Cup: 28-29 29-30, R-up 35-36 57-58 1973-74 Isthmian Lge Champ. 06-07 20-21 21-22 R-up 11-12 26-27 31-32 37-38 38-39 Essex Senior Cup x14 (record nos. of wins), R-up x5; London Sen. Cup: x7 R-up x 5; London Charity Cup: x 6 R-up x 7: Essex I'mediate Cup R-up x1; London I'mediate Cup R-up x1; Eastern F'lit Comp. Group Winners 96-97
BEST SEASON **FA Cup:** 73-74 2nd Rd, 0-2 v Southend Utd. (H)
FA Vase: 99-00 2nd Rd 1-2 v Watton United (a)
CLUB RECORDS **Attendance:** 17,000 Ilford Boys v Swansea Boys (Schools Trophy Final)

FACT FILE
Founded: 1881
Re-Formed: 1987
Sponsor: Kelvin Hughes
Colours: Blue & white hoops/blue/blue & white
Change colours: Red & white hoops/red/r+w
Midweek matches: Wednesday
Prog Editor: Len Llewellyn(01277 363103)

CLUB PERSONNEL
Chairman: George Hogarth
Vice Chairman: Melvin Attwell
President: Lord John Taylor of Warwick
Manager: Stewart Margolis (07739 741917)

LONDON APSA

Secretary:

Ground: Aveley FC, `Mill Field', Mill Road, Aveley, Essex RM15 4TR
Tel: 01708 865940. Fax: 01708 680995

Directions: London - Southend A1306, turn into Sandy Lane at Aveley. Rainham or Purfleet BR stations then bus No. 723 to the ground. Bus from Rainham No 324

Capacity: 4,000 Cover: 400 Seats: 400 Floodlights: Yes

Clubhouse: Normal pub hours. Bar snacks and hot food available

PREVIOUS League: London Intermediate Lge >2003

ROMFORD(2002)

Secretary: Colin Ewenson,71 Riversdale Rd.,Romford, RM52NR (07973 717075)
Ground: Ford Sports & Social Club,Rush greeen Road, Romford RM5 2NR (01708 745678)
Club Call: 09066 555 841 Website: www.romfordfc.co.uk
Directions: Take the A12 from London as far as the Moby Dick junction.
Turn left and then right at the 1st r'about into Collier Row Rd. The ground entrance is signposted 200 yards on the right. Nearest station is Romford (BR). From directly outside the station the London bus 247 passes the ground.
Capacity: 2,500 Cover: 300 Seats: 175 Floodlights: Yes
Previous **Leagues:** Essex Senior 92-96, Isthmian 96-02
Grounds: Hornchurch 92-95, Ford Utd 95-96
Club Records - Attendance: 820 v Leatherhead (IL2) 15/4/97; **Career Goalscorer:** Micky Ross 57; **Season goalscorer:** Vinny John 45 (97-98); **Career Appearances:** Danny Benstock 197
Best Season: FA Vase: 5th Rd 96-97 v Bedlington Terriers 2-1
HONOURS Essex Senior Lge 95-96, Lge Cup 95-96;
Isthmian Div 2 96-97; East Anglian Cup 97-98

FACT FILE
Reformed: 1992 Nickname: The Boro
Colours: Blue & old gold quarters/blue/blue
Change colours: All white
Midweek home matchday: Tuesday (7.45)
Reserves' Lge: Essex & Herts Border Prem
Programme: Pages: 40 Price: £1.20
Editor: Derek RobinsonTel: 01708 507803
Local Press: Romford Recorder
Local Radio:Active FM

CLUB OFFICIALS
Chairman:Steve Gardener
Press Officer: Steve Gardener
Manager:Mark Reed
Physio: Colin Maherson

Ilford line up before their FA Cup victory over Kempston Rovers. Photo: Franics Short.

Southend Manors' Kyle Reeves and Gary Smith are outjumped by Buckingham Town's Stuart Blaik in this season's (03-04) FA Cup Extra Preliminary Round. Photo: Alan Coomes.

SAWBRIDGEWORTH TOWN

Secretary: Mrs Leslie Atkins,41 The Orchards,, Sawbridgeworth.CM21 9BB (01279 725665)
Ground: Crofters End, West Road, Sawbridgeworth, Herts. CM21 0DE (01279 722039)

Directions: Three quarters of a mile from the station; up Station Road then into West Road.

Capacity: 1,500 Seats: None Cover: 250 Floodlights: Yes Club Shop: No

HONOURS Essex Olympian Lg 71-72; Essex Snr Lg R-up 92-93 94-95; Harry FisherMem. Cup 87-88; Lg Cup 94-95 R-up 92-93 93-94, Res. Div 91-92 92-93 (R-up 93-94), Res. Shield R-up 92-93); Herts Snr Tphy 90-91 93-94 (R-up 92-93);Herts Charity Shield 92-93 94-95 95-96; Uttlesford Charity Cup 92-93; Herts Intermediate Cup R-up 93-93(res); S. Midlands F'lit Cup R.up 94-95; Res. Sect S.M Lge & Lg.Cup R-Up 94-95
PREVIOUS **Leagues:** Essex Olympian, Spartan 36-53
CLUB RECORDS **Attendance:** 610 v Bishop's Stortford.
PREVIOUS GROUNDS: Hyde Hall, Pishiobury, Hand & Crown.

FACT FILE
Founded: 1890
Nickname: Robins
Colours: Red & black stripes/black/black
Change colours: Sky Blue & White
Midweek Matchday;
Prog Editor: T.B.A

CLUB PERSONNEL
Chairman: Barry Hodges
President: Ron Alder
Manager:Don Watters
Physio: T.B.A.

SOUTHEND MANOR

Secretary: Steve Durrant, 11 Clayton Rd.,Southend on Seas, Essex SS25DL (01702 301572)
Ground: Southchurch Park Arena, Lifstan Way, Southend-on-Sea. Tel: 01702 615577
Directions: A127 then A1159 for 1 mile turn right at second roundabout by Invisible Man PH, then due south for 1 mile, ground on right near sea front
Capacity: 2,000 Seats: 500 Cover: Yes Floodlights: Yes
Clubhouse: Open every evening Club Shop: No
HONOURS Essex Sen Trophy 92-93; Essex Interm'te Cup 78-79; Essex Sen League 90-91, R-Up: 99-00 Essex Sen League Cup 87-88, R-Up:99-00,00-01 Challenge Cup 89-90;Harry Fisher Mem Trophy 90-91 92-93 (R-up 91-92) Essex Sen Cup 2001-02 , ESL Charity Cup 2001-02
PREVIOUS **Leagues:** Southend Borough Combination, Southend Alliance
Grounds: Victory Spts/ Oakwood Rec
RECORDS **Attendance:** 1,521 v Southend Utd, 22/7/91, floodlight opener
BEST SEASON **FA Vase:** 1996-97

FACT FILE
Founded: 1955 Nickname: The Manor
Sponsors: Info-Line
Colours: Yellow/black/yellow
Change colours: All white
Midweek Matchday: Tuesday
Reserves Lge: Essex & Herts Border Comb
Programme: 10 pages, 50p
Editor/Press Off: Chris Hunt 01702 615897
Website: www.southendmanor.co.uk

CLUB PERSONNEL
Chairman: Robert Westley
Vice-Chairman: Geoff Gorham
Manager::Steve Sinnett
Coach: Andy Dixon

STANSTED

Secretary: Terry Shoebridge ,2 Dawson Close,Saffron Walden ,Essex Home Telephone Number: 01799 -527937 (H)
Ground: Hargrave Park, Cambridge Road, Stansted, Essex. (01279 812897)
Directions: B1383 north of Bishops Stortford on west side of Cambridge Rd. Stansted (BR) - 1/2 mile
Capacity: 2,000 Seats: 200 Cover: Yes Floodlights: Yes
Clubhouse: Matchdays till 11pm. Sandwiches available. Club Shop: No

HONOURS FA Vase Winners 83-84; Essex Snr Lg R-up 82-83; Essex Snr Lg Cup 83-84, (R-up 72-73 94-95); Harry Fisher Mem Cup 82-83 84-85 (R-up 92-93 93-94); E. AnglianCup 83-84; Eastern F/lit Cup 83-84 R-up 01-02; Uttlesford Char. Cup 93-84 86-87 88-89 94-95 97-98 01-02
PREVIOUS **Leagues:** Spartan; London; Herts Co. **Grounds:** Greens Meadow; ChapelHill
RECORDS **Attendance:** 828 v Whickham (FA Vase 83-84)
BEST SEASON **FA Cup:** 97-98 **FA Vase:** Winners 83-84

FACT FILE
Founded: 1902 Nickname: The Blues
Sponsor: Leyton Orient Community Sports Programme
Colours: Blue /Blue/White
Change: Yellow & Black/Black/Black
Midweek matches: Tuesday
Reserves League:Esex & Herts Border Comb.
Under 18's : Eastern Junior Alliance

CLUB PERSONNEL
Chairman: Terry Shoebridge
President: Percy Heal
Manager: Tony Mercer

WALTHAM ABBEY

Secretary: Dave Hodges, 13 Rosebank,Waltham Abbey, Essex EN9 3DE
Tel Nos: 07956 570408 (M) 01992 651594(H) 01992 719333(W)
FAX: 019902 768111

Ground: Capershotts, Sewardstone Road, Waltham Abbey, Essex. Tel: 01992 711287
Directions Nearest Bus: Waltham Abbey Nearest Station: Waltham Cross

Previous League: Essex & Herts Border Comb.

FACT FILE
Formed:
Colours:A;ll Green & White

Change Colours: All Red & Black

CLUB OFFICIALS
Chairman: Joe Collins (01992 467375)

SPARTAN SOUTH MIDLANDS FOOTBALL LEAGUE

President: B F Smith **Chairman:** Pat Burns

Hon. Gen. Secretary: M Mitchell, 26 Leighton Court, Dunstable, Beds. LU6 1EW

Tel: 01582 667291

Dunstable Town, in only their second season in the Premier Division, were League Champions. For Dunstable, who were formed at the beginning of the 1998-99 season to play in Division Two and have now been accepted for a place in the Ryman League, it has been a real success story both on and off the pitch. They finished five points clear of Beaconsfield SYCOB, and were the only Premier team to score 100 league goals. Playing on the former Dunstable Southern League ground they have completely renovated the condemned and dilapidated stand, fitting it with 200 seats obtained from Wembley Stadium, plus making improvements to obtain a Ryman grading.

The early season pacemakers were Potters Bar Town, who finished third, and promoted Greenacres, who won their first four games but fell away and finished 14th. For the other promoted side, Harefield United, it was an excellent season. They finished in fourth position, and also won the SSML trophy by beating Dunstable 4-1 in the two-legged final. St Margaretsbury finished fifth, the same position as last season. Last season's champion's, London Colney, who lost several key players gained only two points from their first six matches. They recovered, and finished sixth. Holmer Green finished in bottom place. Hanwell's Keith Rowlands was the leading goalscorer in the Division with a total of 37. Second was Dunstable's Alan Arthur who netted 27 times. Hanwell Town won the Premier Division Cup, beating Harefield United 2-0 in the final.

Division One winners were Pitstone & Ivinghoe in their second season since being promoted from Division Two. Pitsonte lost two of their first four league matches but this was followed by a run of 20 games without defeat, stretching from September to March 22nd. They moved top of the 16th April and a run of four wins in seven days saw them several points clear. They lost only four games and scored 107 goals, finishing ten points clear of second placed Harpenden Town, who had been top of the Division for most of the season. Harpenden were top goalscorers in the Division with a total of 122. Tring Athletic maintained their record of consistency in the Division by finishing in third place, one point behind Harpenden. Leverstock Green were fourth and Colney Heath, who were third last season, finished fifth. Risborough Rangers finished bottom with only four wins. The promoted clubs, Haywood United and Shillington both finished mid-table. Top goalscorer was Phil Chanel of Pitstone with 39. Team mate Danny Jones and Ian Cooper of Cockfosters shared second place with 27 each. Tring won the Division One Cup, defeating Stony Stratford 21 in the final.

Division Two winners were former Premier side Buckingham Athletic, finishing two points above Old Dunstablians, who topped the table for most of the season. Both sides scored 113 goals. Kent Athletic were 3rd, with Crawley Green fourth. Bottom team was Padbury United, Top goalscorer was Glen Hawkins of Buckingham (36) followed by Dunstablians' Ikeme Ojulah (34). Crawley Green won the Division One Cup, beating Buckingham 2-0 in the final.

Stan Eaton.

FINAL LEAGUE TABLE 2002-03

PREMIER	DIVISION	P	W	D	L	F	A	Pts
1	Dunstable Town	36	26	6	4	104	32	84
2	Beaconsfield SYCOB	36	24	7	5	66	30	79
3	Potters Bar Town	36	23	6	7	80	42	75
4	Harefield Town	36	21	7	8	79	45	70
5	St Margaretsbury	36	18	6	12	79	60	60
6	London Colney	36	15	10	11	65	57	55
7	Ruislip Manor	36	15	8	13	47	56	53
8	Hanwell Town	36	16	4	16	94	82	52
9	Milton Keynes City	36	15	7	14	58	57	52
10	Hoddesdon Town	36	14	9	13	54	48	51
11	Biggleswade Town	36	13	6	17	59	67	45
12	Hillingdon Borough	36	12	6	18	44	57	42
13	Broxbourne B. V&E (-3)	36	13	5	18	49	64	41
14	Greenacres (Hemel)	36	11	6	19	66	77	39
15	Haringey Borough	36	10	8	18	50	70	38
16	Royston Town	36	10	7	19	46	63	37
17	Brook House (-3)	36	10	9	17	36	67	36
18	Bedford United & Valerio	36	7	8	21	40	74	29
19	Holmer Green	36	5	3	28	40	108	18

Letchworth record expunged.

	PREMIER	1	2	3	4	5	6	7	8	9	10	11	12	13	14	15	16	17	18	19	20
1	Beaconsfield SYCOB	2-1	1-1	1-1	2-0	2-5	3-1	5-1	0-0	5-0	2-1	2-1	2-1	-	1-0	2-0	2-1	2-0	4-1	0-0	
2	Bedford UNited & Valerio	0-2		1-4	0-2	0-1	2-2	4-1	0-2	2-2	0-4	1-1	1-2	3-1	3-2	0-2	1-3	1-1	0-3	1-2	3-2
3	Biggleswade Town	1-2	1-2		3-0	0-1	4-5	1-0	1-4	3-4	3-3	1-0	1-2	3-0	-	0-1	3-1	2-1	3-1	1-1	3-1
4	Brook House	0-2	2-0	2-1		1-1	1-3	1-4	1-6	0-1	1-2	1-0	1-1	1-1	1-3	2-2	2-1	1-2	2-2	1-0	1-0
5	Broxbourne Borough V&E	0-3	0-3	0-1	2-0		0-4	2-6	3-2	1-1	4-1	0-1	2-1	4-0	3-3	1-1	0-3	0-1	0-1	3-0	0-0
6	Dunstable Town	0-1	2-1	11-0	4-0	3-2		0-0	3-4	2-0	2-0	1-1	2-0	3-1	-	2-0	8-2	2-0	2-2	6-0	1-2
7	Greenacres (Hemel)	1-1	3-0	3-3	5-0	1-3	0-4		6-2	0-3	3-1	3-0	0-2	4-1	-	3-4	1-3	0-0	4-1	1-2	3-2
8	Hanwell Town	1-5	6-1	4-1	3-1	2-4	0-2	4-0		2-2	4-2	3-2	1-2	6-3	-	1-4	1-0	3-0	4-1	0-2	4-0
9	Harefield United	1-0	2-2	2-1	5-2	6-0	0-1	4-1	3-2		3-1	2-0	3-2	3-0	-	6-1	3-0	5-1	2-3	2-0	2-1
10	Haringey Borough	2-0	1-0	1-2	1-1	2-3	0-6	2-1	3-3	0-1		0-1	3-0	2-1	-	3-2	3-1	0-2	4-0	2-4	1-1
11	Hillingdon Borough	1-1	1-1	1-0	1-2	1-0	0-2	3-1	3-1	4-1	1-0		4-1	4-1	-	0-3	2-3	2-3	2-4	0-1	0-4
12	Hoddesdon Town	0-1	4-1	2-0	4-0	1-0	0-0	1-0	2-2	3-0	1-1	4-1		1-1	-	1-1	0-0	0-2	3-0	0-2	3-1
13	Holmer Green	1-3	0-1	0-4	1-2	2-3	0-6	1-2	4-2	1-4	3-2	2-1	1-1		-	0-6	0-1	0-6	2-1	1-2	2-6
14	Letchworth	3-3	-	3-4	-	-	-	-	-	2-2	-	-	-	-		-	3-2	-	-	-	-
15	London Colney	0-1	3-3	0-0	2-0	2-2	2-2	3-0	0-7	1-1	3-1	2-0	2-1	2-1	-		2-1	0-2	1-2	1-1	1-3
16	Milton Keynes City	2-0	4-1	0-1	1-1	1-0	0-2	4-4	4-2	2-0	2-2	0-1	1-2	4-1	-	3-2		1-1	1-0	1-1	2-2
17	Potters Bar Town	1-1	3-0	2-2	2-1	4-3	0-1	4-0	5-2	2-0	2-0	4-1	2-1	3-1	-	3-1	1-3		2-0	4-0	4-3
18	Royston Town	0-1	1-1	3-2	2-0	0-3	0-1	1-1	3-1	1-3	0-0	1-2	4-1	2-3	-	0-0	2-1	1-1		1-2	1-2
19	Ruislip Manor	2-1	0-1	2-1	0-0	5-0	1-2	2-1	1-1	1-0	0-0	0-0	2-2	4-2	-	1-3	0-1	1-6	2-1		1-3
20	St Margaretsbury	2-3	2-1	3-1	1-2	2-1	4-2	5-2	3-1	2-2	4-0	1-1	3-2	4-0	-	2-5	3-1	1-2	2-1	2-1	

Letchworth withdrew from the league.

FINAL LEAGUE TABLE 2002-03

	DIVISION ONE	P	W	D	L	F	A	Pts
1	Pitstone & Ivinghoe	36	30	2	4	107	33	92
2	Harpenden Town	36	26	4	6	122	35	82
3	Tring Athletic	36	24	9	3	89	31	81
4	Leverstock Green	36	21	8	7	82	37	71
5	Colney Heath	36	23	1	12	85	42	70
6	Welwyn Garden City	36	18	7	11	76	46	61
7	Cockfosters	36	19	3	14	89	66	60
8	Biggleswade United	36	17	6	13	68	55	57
9	Haywood United	36	16	6	14	78	68	54
10	Brache Sparta	36	17	3	16	67	61	54
11	Brimsdown Rovers	36	14	7	15	51	58	49
12	Stony Stratford Town	36	11	10	15	51	66	43
13	Langford	36	9	6	21	62	90	33
14	Kings Langley	36	8	9	19	50	89	33
15	The 61 FC	36	9	5	22	37	79	32
16	Shillington	36	9	4	23	45	94	31
17	New Bradwell St Peter	36	6	11	19	47	88	29
18	Ampthill Town	36	8	1	27	38	102	25
19	Risborough Rangers	36	4	4	28	35	139	16

CHALLENGE TROPHY

QUARTER-FINALS

Harefield United	2-1(aet)	London Colney
Dunstable Town	3-1	Tring Athletic
Beaconsfield SYCOB	3-2	Cockfosters
Greenacres	0-2	Milton Keynes City

SEMI-FINALS

Milton Keynes City	1-3	Dunstable Town
Harefield United	3-1	Beaconsfield SYCOB

FINAL

Dunstable Town	1-2	Harefield United
Harefield United	2-0	Dunstable Town

PREMIER DIVISION CUP

SEMI-FINALS

Biggleswade Town	2-4	Hanwell Town
Ruislip Manor	0-1	Harefield United

FINAL

Harefield United	0-2	Hanwell Town

DIVISION ONE CUP

SEMI-FINALS

Stony Stratford Town	2-1	Harpenden Town
Tring Athletic	6-3	Pitstone & Ivinghoe

FINAL

Stony Stratford Town	1-2	Tring Athletic

BEACONSFIELD SYCOB

Secretary: Ken Barrett, 31 Stockey End, Abingdon, Oxon OX14 2NF. Tel: 01235202058 (H), 01235 537080 (B) Email: kj17ox@aol.com

GROUND: Holloway Park, Slough Road, Beaconsfield, Bucks (01494 676868).
Directions: M40 (Jct 2), 1st exit to A355. Club 100yds on right. 1.5 miles from Beaconsfield BR Bus 441Slough/ High Wyc'be**PREVIOUS NAMES:** SloughYCOB & Beaconsfield U merged 1994
Capacity: 3,000 Cover: 400 Seats:: 250 Floodlights: Yes C lub Shop: Clu
Clubbhouse: Open eves & matchdays. Bar, Committee Room, Hall, Kitchen, Changing Room l
HONOURS: As Slough : Chilt.Lg R-up: 93-4,Lg Cup 92-3 Slough T Cup R-up 91-2
Champios Spartan South Midlands 2000-01
Leagues: Beaconsfield Utd: Wycombe & District; Maidenhead. Slough YCOB: Windsor, Slough & District; East Berks; Chiltonian (pre 1994) **Previous Grounds:** As Slough: Haymill Community Centre,Burnham Lane,slough (pre 1944)
Record Gate: 300 Beaconsfield Utd v Chesham Utd, Berks & Bucks Sen Cup 1985
BEST SEASONS: **FA Cup:** 3rd Q Rd 98-998 **FA Vase:** Beaconsfield: 1st Rd 83-84 85-86 87-88

FACT FILE
Founded: 1994 Nickname: The Rams
Colours:Red & white quarters/black/red & white
Change colours: Navy Blue
Midweek Matches: Monday or Tuesday
Reserves' League: Suburban
Programme: Yes, £1
Editor: Andy Jackson, 7 Boundary Lane, Chipperfield Rd., Bovingdon, Herts.HP3 0JT
Tel: 01442 834203

CLUB PERSONNEL
President: D Piercy Chairman: Fred Deanus
Manager: Colin Barnes

2002-2003
Captain: Robert Paris P.o.Y.: Adrian Sear
Top Scorer: DamionMarkman

BEDFORD UNITED & VALERIO

Secretary: Jim McMullen,7 Buttermere Close, Kempston, Bedford MK42 8JU(01234 300765)
GROUND: McMullen Park, Meadow Lane, Cardington, Bedford MK45 3SB (01234 831024)

Directions: M1 jct 13, A421 to Bedford by-pass. Third exit, A603 ground 500 yards on left
Capacity: 5,000 Seats: 25 Cover: 100 Floodlights: Yes
Clubhouse: Open matchdays. Hot & cold snacks and drinks available

HONOURS: Bedford & Dist Lg Premier Division & Division One, County Junior Cup, Biggleswade KO Cup, Butchers Cup(2), Britania Cup, Bedford Charity Cup
PREVIOUS: **Leagues**: Bedford & Dist. Lge (57-70 & 80-89); United Cos. Lge 70-80
Name: Printers Diemer-Reynolds (pre'72)
Grounds: Allen Park (57-80); Fairhill, Clapham Road (80-93); Hillgrounds, Kempston 93-96)

RECORD: Attendance: (at Fairhill) 1500 v Bedford Town, South Midlands Lge Div. 1 26/12/92
Scorer: Neil Tysoe 220 **Appearances:** Simon Fordham 418

Founded: 1957 Nickname: United
Club Sponsors: JDP Finance
Colours: Blue & White/blue/blue
Change colours: Red & black/red/red
Midweek matches: Wednesday
Reserves' League: S. Mids Lge Res. sect
Programme: 24 pages, £1
Editor: Graham Williams (01234 312 982)

Chairman: John Cleverley
Vice Chairman/Press Off Jim McMullen
President: D Rostron
Manager: Cliff Canavan -Smith
Asst. Man.: M Ackroyd
Coach/Physio: Dave Petrie

BIGGLESWADE TOWN

Secretary: Graham Arkwright, 47Honeysuckle Close Biggleswade, Beds SG188ST
Tel: 01767 318370
GROUND: `Fairfield', Fairfield Road, Biggleswade, Beds (01767 312374).
Directions: A1 North r'bout, first left after bridge to car park.10 mins walk from Biggleswade(BR).
Capacity: 2,400 Seats: 50 Cover: 100 Floodlights: Yes Club Shop: No.
RECORD: **Attendance:** 2,000 **Clubhouse:** Open all matchdays. , teas, coffees, snacks.
HONOURS:S Mids Lge: Res Div 2 87-88, Res Chall Trophy 88-89,S.M. Floodlit Cup 95-96,02-03; Beds Snr Cup 02-03 07-08 46-47 51-52 61-62 62-63 66-67 73-74; Beds Premr Cup 22-23 27-28; N. Beds Charity Cup x13; Utd Co's Lg Cup 73-74; Hinchingbrooke Cup 03-04 12-13 92-93 Hunts Prem Cup (6); Jess Piggott Trophy 87-88 89-90 91-92 92-93 N.Beds Charity Cup: (13)
PREVIOUS: Leagues: Biggleswade & Dist. 02-20; Bedford & Dist. 09-12; Utd Co's (prev. Northants Lg) 20-39 51-55 63-80; Spartan 46-51; Eastern Co's 55-63 **Name:** Biggleswade F.C.
2002-2003: Captain: Mark Winwood **Top Scorer**: Mark Phillips **P.o.Y.**: Adrian Mapletoft.
Players progressing: Darren Hay (Cambridge Utd) 1994

FACT FILE
Founded: 1874 Nickname: Waders
Club Sponsors: Mantles Ford & Letchworth Couriers
Colours:green/black/green
Change: All red
Midweek Matchday: Tuesday
Programme: 32 pages, admission
Editor: Brian Doggett (01767 318307 (H).

CLUB PERSONNEL
Chairman:M.Dorrington V. Chair:M Jarvis
President: R Dorrington
Man: David Northfield Coach: Mark Smith
Physio: Lucy Burton

BROOK HOUSE

Secretary: Barry Crump, 19 Bradenham Road, Hayes, Middlesex UB4 8LP.
Fax & Tel: 0208 841 3959 (H), 07966 468029(B)

Ground: Farm Park, Kingshill Avenue, Hayes, Middlesex (0208 842 1448)
Directions: From North Circular road: A40 Western Ave. to Target r'about, left towards Hayes (A312), over White Hart r'about towards Yeading/Hayes, right at traffic lights in to Kingshill Ave, ground 1 mile on right. Nearest BR stationis Hayes & Harlington, then bus 90 or 195 to Brook House pub. Nearest tube is Northolt (central line), then bus to ground
Capacity: 2,000 Cover: 100 Seats: 120 Floodlights: Yes Club Shop: No
Clubhouse: Open weekdays 7-11pm, Sat noon-11pm, Sun noon-11.00pm

HONOURS: SSM Prem South 97-98, Prem Div R-Up 99-00, Lge Cup 99-00 ,91-92.
BEST SEASON: **FA Vase:** 3rd Round Proper 97-98 **FA Cup:** 1st Qual Rd 93-94
Players progressing: Neil Shipperley (Crystal Palace), MarkHyde (Orient), Mark Perry (QPR) David Warner (To Watford for £10,000) and Anthony Charles (To Crewe Alexandrafor £6,000)

FACT FILE
Founded: 1974
Colours: Blue & white stripes/blue/blue
Change colours: Red & Black
Midweek matchday: Tuesday
Reserve League: Suburban League
Programme: 28 pages, £3 with entry
Editor: Dave Swann

CLUB PERSONNEL
President: Victor Kirby
Chairman: Mick Ralph
Vice-Chairman: JohnHandell
Press Officer: Lawrie Watts
Manager: Bob Strutton Ass Man: Joe Mitchell

BROXBOURNE BOROUGHV & E

Secretary: Peter Harris, 30 Lordship Road, Cheshunt, Herts. EN7 5DP
Tel : 01992 429297 (H) 0208 345 1274(W) **Email address:** savefc@fcmail.com

Ground: V & E Club, Goffs lane, Cheshunt, Herts. Tel: 01992 624281

Capacity: 500 Seats: 20 Cover: Yes Floodlights: Yes Club Shop: No

Directions: M25 junct. 25, A10 towards Cheshunt. Take the first left at the first roundabout onto the B198 (Cuffley & Goffs Oak). At the end of the road turn right off roundabout into Goffs lane. Clubhouse on immediate right. Open 11 a.m. 11 p.m. every day.

Previous League: Herts County

Club Website www.savefc.thesportcity.com

FACT FILE
Founded: 1959
Colours: White & blue/blue/blue
Change Colours: Orange/white/orange
Midweek Matchday: Tuesday
Reserves League; Essex ,Herts Border
Programme Editor: Peter Harris
01992 429297 (H) 0208 1274 (B)

CLUB PERSONNEL
Chairman:Dave Bidwell
Tel: 01992 428187 (H)
Vice Chairman:Mario Persico
President: Doug Bacon
Manager:David Craig
Assistant manager: Mark Standen

GREENACRES (Hemel Hempstead)

Secretary: Hayley Smith, 437 Barnacres, Hemel Hempstead, Herts. HP3 8JS
Tel No: 01442 214739 (H) 01442 264300 (W)

Ground: Hemel Hempstead FC, Vauxhall Rd., Adeyfield, Hemel Hempstead.
Tel: 01442 259777

Directions: M1 J8; over two roundabouts, then first right off dual carriageway.
First left and then right at roundabout

Capacity: 3,000 **Seats:** 100 **Cover:** Yes **Floodlight:** Yes **Club Shop:** No

Clubhouse: as for Hemel Hempstead F.C.

Colours:
Green & white hoops/white/green & white
Change Colours: All red & white
Midweek Matchday: Wednesday
Programme: £1.00
Editor: William Cain

Chairman: David Boggins
01442 264300 (H)
Match Sec. David Lloyd
01442 259721 (H)

Manager: Paul Burgess
Physio:

HANWELL TOWN

Secretary: John Wake, 38 Warwick Ave., S Harrow, Middx. HA2 8RD. Tel/Fax: 0208 4221048(H)
GROUND: Reynolds Field, Perivale Lane, Perivale, Greenford, Middx (0208 998 1701)
Directions: A40(M) west from London, leave opp Hoover building (B456 for Ealing), turn left into Argyle Rd, left into Perivale Lane. Grd on left. 500 yards from Perivale tube station (Central line)
Capacity: 2,000 Seats: 90 Cover: 200 Floodlights: Yes Club Shop: No
Clubhouse: Saturday matchdays 2-11pm, Tuesdays 6-11pm, Non-matchdays 7.30-11pm

HONOURS: Spartan Sen Lg R-up 98-99 83-84 (Lg Cup R-up 93-94, London Snr Cup 91-92 92-93 (R-up 93-94), Middx Charity Cup R-up 92-93, 99-00

PREVIOUS: **Leagues:** Dauntless Lge, Harrow, Wembley & District and Middlesex County

RECORDS: **Attendance:** 600 v Spurs, Floodlight opening October 1989
Scorer: Keith Rowlands **Appearances:** Phil Player, 20 seasons, 617 games

BEST SEASON: **FA Cup:** 3rd Rd Qual 97-98

FACT FILE
Founded: 1948 Nickname: The Town
Colours: Black & white stripes/black/black & white
Change colours: White with red trim
Midweek matchday: Tuesday
Reserves' League: S.S.M.Res Lg
Programme: 16 pages, with entry
Editor: Bob Fisher as below

CLUB PERSONNEL
Chairman/Press Officer: Bob Fisher
Tel: 0208 952 4142 (H) 0207 510 4954 (B)
President: Dave Iddiols
Patron: Stephen Pound MP
Manager: Ray Duffy

HAREFIELD UNITED

Secretary: Robin Holloway, 88 Ash Grove,Harefield, Midd'sex UB96NZ (01895 824722)
GROUND: Preston Park, Breakespeare Rd North, Harefield, Middx UB9 6DG (01895 823474)
Directions: M25 jct 16 to M40 East, left at 1st roundabout, then 2nd left into Harvill Rd. Follow road up the Church Hill into village, right at mini roundabout, ground on right. Denham (BR)
Capacity: 2,000 Seats: 100 Cover: Yes Floodlights: Yes Club Shop: No
Clubhouse: (01895 823474) 4-11pm w/days. Noon -11pm Fri-Sun. Hot & Cold snacks

HONOURS: Middx Premier Cup 85-86, Athenian Lg R-up 83-84, Parthenon Lg 64-65 (Div 1 Cup 65-66), Middx Lg 66-67 68-71 (Lg Cup 66-67 68-69)
Spartan South Mids Div. 1 R-up 01-02 Cup Winners 2003

BEST SEASON: **FA Cup:** 2nd Qual. Rd replay 80-81, 86-87,02-03 **F.A.Vase:** 6th Rd 1989-90

RECORD: **Gate:** 430 v Bashley, FA Vase

PREVIOUS **Leagues:** Uxbridge & Dist.; Gt Western Comb. 46-64; Parthenon 64-68; Middx 68-75; Athenian 75-84, Isthmian 85-9

2002-03 **Leading Goalscorer**:Robert Ursell & Ricky Pither **Captain:**Jose Pena
Player of the Year: Colin Day

Founded: 1868
Nickname: Hares
Colours: Red & white stripes/black/red
Change: Blue & ye llow,blue/blue.
Midweek Matches: Tuesday
Reserves' League: Suburban Div 2 North
Programme: 12-40 pages, 30p
Editor: Keith Ronald

Chairman: Keith Ronald. Tel: 01895 824287
President: Dave West
Manager: Stuart Leavy
Assistant Manager:Jeff Fanner
Physio: Chas Cox

Bedford United & Valerio. Back Row (L-R): Lui La Mura (Manager), Stuart Paul, Paul McKeaveney, Neil Beddeau, Paul Campbell, Paul Nigro, Edu Danghi, Trevor Porter-Harris (Coach). Front Row: Deep Banguard, Paul George, Jules Furtes, Louis Hunt, Aaron Coker, Andy Smith, Oliver Porter-Harris, Steve Armstrong.

Photo: Gordon Whittingham.

Hanwell Town line up before their FA Vase victory over Dereham. Photo: Francis Short.

Holmer Green F.C. *Photo: Gordon Whittington.*

HARINGEY BOROUGH

Secretary: John Bacon, 7 Everett Close, West Cheshunt, Herts., EN7 6XD Tel: 01707 873187
GROUND: Coles Park, White Hart Lane, Tottenham N17 (020 88891415) Clubhouse: Yes
Directions: M25 to J.25 turn south on A10 approx 6 miles, over jnct with N. Circular Rd (A406) Turn R. at T.lght 1 mile into White Hart Lne grd approx 500yds on L. Bus W3 from Finsbury Park. Mainline & Under-grd stn to Northumberland Park mainline station passes grd can be boarded at Alexandra Palace or White Hart Ln. Mainline stations or Wood Green Underground station.
Capacity: 2,500 Seats: 280 Cover: Yes Floodlights: Yes
Best Seasons: F.A.Vase: 6th Rd 77-78 **F.A. Cup:** 3rd Qualifying Round 86-87
HONOURS: FA Am Cup R-up 19-20; London Sen Cup 12-13, 90-91; Athenian Lge 13-14; Div 2 Cup winners 67-68, 68-69; Spartan Lg Cup r-up 90-91 Spartan S. Mids Prem Div cup r-up 97-98
PREVIOUS: **Leagues:** London 07-14; Isthmian 19-52 84-88; Spartan 52-54; Delphian 54-63; Athenian 63-84 **Names:** Edmonton; Tufnell Park; Tufnell Park (Edmonton); Edmonton & Haringey (merged with Wood Green Town in early seventies)

FACT FILE
Formed:1907
Colours: Yellow/green/yellow
Change colours: Green/black/green
Midweek Matchday: Tuesday
Reserves League - Middlesex County
Programme Editor: As Secretary

CLUB PERSONNEL
Chairman: Peter Lawlor Tel: 020 8889 2726
Match Secretary : As Secretary
Manager: Julian Hudson

2002-2003
Capt: Martin Ryan Top Scorer: Junior Fung 10
Player of the Year: Isaac Rukundoo

HARPENDEN TOWN

Secretary: Neil Ludlow, 93 RussellSt.,Luton,Beds LU1 5EB 01582 486802(H) 01582 424233(W)
GROUND: Rothamsted Park, Amenbury Lane, Harpenden (01582 715724)
Directions: A1081 to Harpenden. Turn left/right at George public housel into Leyton Rd.Turn left into Amenbury Rd, then left again (50yds) into `Pay and Display' carpark - entrance is signposted thru car park to opposite corner next to swimming pool.
Capacity: 1,500 Seats: 25 Cover: 100 Floodlights: Yes Club Shop: No
Clubhouse: Open matchdays
PREVIOUS: **Leagues:** Mid-Herts; Herts County **Name:** Harpenden FC 1891-1908
BEST SEASON: F.A.Cup: 1st Rd Qual. **F.A.Vase:** 2nd Rd
HONOURS: Sth Mids Lg 61-62 64-65, Championship Shield 67-68, Lg Cup 70-71, Div 1 89-90, Prem Div Tphy 89-90, Res Div 89-90; Herts Co. Lg 11-12 49-50 51-52 53-54(Aubrey Cup 20-21 28-29 50-51 51-52); Mid-Herts Lg 09-10 20-21, Div 1 99-00; Pratt Cup 06-07 08-09 10-11; Herts Jnr Cup 01-02 09-10 11-12 20-21 25-26; Herts I'mediate Cup 52-53; Herts Charity Shield 07-08; Bingham Cox Cup 1896-97 1902-03 09-10 20-21.

FACT FILE
Founded: 1891
Nickname: The Town
Colours: Yellow/blue/blue
Change: Red & black hoops/black/black
Midweek matches: Tuesday
Programme: 50p Editor: Chairman

CLUB PERSONNEL
Chairman: Mick Archer (07802 81 843)
Managers: Graham Golds & Gordon Guile

2002-03
Captain: Nathan Dawes
Top Scorer: Adam Price
P.o.Y.: Paul Barnes

HILLINGDON BOROUGH

Secretary: Garry Grant, 19 Leveret Close,Leavesden, Watford, herts WD2 7AX
Tel Nos: 01923 463602 (H) 0958 409678 (W)
GROUND: Middlesex Stadium, Breakspear Road, Ruislip, Middx HA4 7SB (01895 639544)
Website: www.hillingdonboroughfc.uk.co **E-mail:** alanhbfc@hotmail.com
Directions: From A40 take B467 (signed Ickenham), left at 2nd r'bout into Breakspear Rd South, right after 1 mile by Breakspear pub - ground half mile on left. Nearest station is Ruislip. Bus U1 passes ground
Capacity: 1,500 Seats: 150 Cover: 150 Floodlights: Yes Club Shop: No
Clubhouse: Mon-Fri 7.30-11pm, Sat & Sun lunchtime & 7.30-11.00pm

RECORDS: **Win:** 12-0 v Hanwell T. (H), S.S.M. Prem 97/98
Defeat: 1-11 v St. Albans City (A), FA Cup 2nd Qual. Rd. 24.9.94
Transfer Fee Received: ¨1,000 for Craig Johnson (Wealdstone)

FACT FILE
Founded: 1990 Nickname: Boro
Sponsors: Airport Motor Radiator Co
Colours: White/blue/blue
Change colours: All red
Midweek Matches: Tuesday
Reserves' League: Suburban
Programme: 20 pages Editor/Press Off: Alan Taylor (0181 581 0981)

CLUB PERSONNEL
Chairman: Dhally Dhaliwall
Commercial Mgr: Garry grant
Manager: Steve Hawkins
Asst Man.: Ian Lancaster
Physio: Dave Pook

HODDESDON TOWN

Secretary: Brenda Timpson, 82 Tolmers Rd,Cuffley, Herts EN6 4JY (01707 874028)
GROUND: `Lowfield', Park View, Hoddesdon, Herts (01992 463133)
Directions: A10, A1170 into Hoddesdon, over 1st r'about, right at 2nd r'aboutand follow signs to Broxbourne, keeping to the left. Turn right at 1st mini r-about into Cock Lane and 1st right is Park View. Ground 200yds on the left,entrance opposite Park Rd. BR station is Broxbourne
Capacity: 3,000 Seats: 100 Cover: 250 Floodlights: Yes Club Shop: Scarves,badges,hats &pens
Clubhouse: Bar and well-stocked Tea Bar with hot food. Open at every home game
HONOURS: FA Vase 74-75 (1st winners); S.S.M. Lg Prem Div Plate 97-98 (R-up 96-97, SthMids Lge Lg Cup 85-86 86-87 91-92 (Prem Div Tphy R-up 92-93); Spartan Lg 70-71(R-up(3) 71-74), Div 1 35-36, Div 2 `B' 27-28, Lg Cup(2) 70-72; S.Mids Floodlit Cup 01-02
PREVIOUS: **Lges:** East Herts 1896-1908, 11-21; Herts Co. 08-25; N Middx Dist 10-22; Spartan 25-75; London Spartan 75-77; Athenian 77-84; South Midlands 84-97
RECORDS: **Attendance:** 3,500 v West Ham, (Floodlight opening friendly), 1975
BEST SEASON: **FA Vase:** Winners 74-75

FACT FILE
Founded: 1879 Nickname: Lilywhites
Colours: White/black/black
Change Colours: navy blue/jellow/navy
Midweek matchday: Tuesday
Reserves' Lge: Herts
Programme: 100 + pages £1.00
Editor: Mrs Jane Sinden Tel: 01767 631297

CLUB PERSONNEL
Pres: Peter Haynes Chairman: Roger Merton
Gen Man: Jim Briggs
Man : Bill O'Driscoll Ass.Man: Darren White
Coach : Danny Buck
2002-03: Capts: Paul Evett & Paul Mann P.o.Y.: D.Stuber Top Scorer: Ryan Redford

HOLMER GREEN

Secretary: Jim Dale
GROUND: Watchet Lane, Holmer Green, High Wycombe (01494 711485)
Directions: From Amersham on A404 High Wycombe Road, after approx 2 miles turn right into Sheepcote Dell Road. Continue until end of road by Bat & Ball PH.Turn right then immediate left, continue approx 1/2 mile until 2 mini roundabouts, turn left in front of the Mandarin Duck into Watchet Lane. The ground is 150 yards on the right
Capacity: 1,000 Seats: 25 Cover:Yes Floodlights:Yes Club Shop:No
Clubhouse: Saturdays 12pm -11 pm midweek 7pm 11pm Badges: Yes (£3)
HONOURS: Berks & Bucks Sen Tr.Finalists 98-99, BB Jun Cup Winners 52-53, 63-64 B&B Inter'iate Cup Winners 76-77; S.Mid Sen Div Winners (2), S.Mid Sen Cup Winners 96-97 Additional Honours: Cheshm Charity Cup Winners (6),Wycombe Sen Cup Winners: (5),Wycombe Lg Winners (4) and Lg Cup Winners 80-8181 Chiltonian League Winners: (3) Lg Cup Winners 94-95, Spartan South Midlands Sen Div Cup Winners: 97-98
PREVIOUS Leagues: 1908--34 Chesham. 34-84 Wyc Comb. 84-95 Chiltonian 95-98 S Mids

FACT FILE
Founded: 1908
Colours: Green & White/ Green/Green
Change colours: All blue
Midweek Matchday: Tuesday (7.45)
Prog: Yes - Inc.Admission
Editor: Mal Keeman
Club Website: www.hgfc1908@freeserve.co.uk
CLUB PERSONNEL
President: John Anderson
Chairman: Bill Scholes 01494 713867 (H)
Match Secretary: Bill Scholes
Manager JezHodges
Manager: Ross Parrett
Leading Goalscorer (2002-03): Daniel Stone
Captain (2003-04): Daniel moakes

LEVERSTOCK GREEN

Secretary: Brian Barter, 11 Curlew Close, Berkhamsted, Herts HP4 2HZ (01442 862322)
GROUND: Pancake Lane, Leverstock Green, Hemel Hempstead. Tel: 01442 246280.
Directions: From M1 leave at A4147 to 2nd r-about. 1st exit to LeverstockGreen, Pancake Lane is on left 300 yrds past the `Leather Bottle' pub
Capacity: Seats: 25 Cover: 100 Floodlights: Yes
Clubhouse: Opens one hour before kick-off, hot food available
Club Shop: Yes

HONOURS: South Midlands Lge - Sen. Div 96-97, Sen Div Cup R-up 93-94, Herts CentenaryTphy R-up 91-92, Herts Charity Shield R-up 91-92, Frank Major Tphy 1991
PREVIOUS: **Leagues:** West Herts (pre-1950); Herts County 50-91
Players progressing to Football League: Dean Austin (Tottenham Hotspur)

FACT FILE
Founded: 1895
Nickname: The Green
Sponsor: M J L Prestige Cars
Colours: White/green trim
Change Colours: Yellow/blue/blue
Midweek Matchday: Tuesday
Programme
40/44 pages, £1 Editor: Brian Barter
Chairman: Bill Dawes 01442 395748 (H)
Match Sec: Brian Pollard 01442 256720 (H)
Press Officer: Tony Smart
Manager: Mick Vipond
Coach: Danny Johnson
2002-03
Leading Goalscorer: Matt Wardle
Captain: Neal Bartlett
Player of the Year: Andy Phillips

LONDON COLNEY

Secretary: Dave Brock, 50 Seymour Rd., St Albans, Herts. AL3 5HW. Tel: 01727 761644 (H)
Ground: Cotslandswick, London Colney (01727 822132)
Directions: From London Colney r'bout (junction of A414/A1081) take A414 towards Watford, after layby (300yds) turn left (hidden turning marked `SportsGround') and follow around to gates.
Capacity: 1,000 Cover: 100 Seats: 30 Floodlights: Yes Club Shop:
Clubhouse: Open after games. Hot food available
HONOURS Sth Mids Lg Sen Div 94-95 R-up 93-94 (Chall. Tphy 93-94, Div 1 R-up 92-93, Res.Div 1 92-93), Herts Co. Lg 56-57 59-60 86-87 88-89 (R-up 57-58 58-59). Aubrey Cup 21-22 22-23 56-57 58-59 81-82, Res. Div 1 87-88 88-89 89-90 91-92, Res. Cup 62-63 89-90 91-92 (R-up 70-71)
PREVIOUS **Leagues:** Mid Herts 1907-54; Herts Co. 07-92
Ground: Whitehorse Lane 07-75
Record Attendance: 300 v St Albans City. Herts Senior Cup 98-99

FACT FILE
Founded: 1907 Nickname: Blueboys
Sponsors: City Glass
Colours: All Royal blue
Change Colours: Yellow/ & black/black/yellow
Midweek Matchday: Tuesday
Programme: £1 with entry
Editor: Bill Gash (01727 767556)
CLUB PERSONNEL
Chairman: Bill Gash
Vice Chairman: P Light
President: K.Parsons
Manager: Mick Wright
Physio: J Burt

MILTON KEYNES CITY

Secretary: Peter Baldwin,1 Wantage Close, Hackleton,Nirthants NN7 2AG (01604 870457 (H) 01908 245408 (W) FAX 01908 245088 (Fax at Work)
Ground: Wolverton Park,Old Wolverton Rd.,Wolverton,Milton Keynes MK12 5QH(01908 318317)
Directions: From A5 trunk road exit at Milton Keynes North onto Great Monks Way (V5). Continue over two oundabouts onto Old Wolverton Road. Ground is 1 milwe on right, between two railway arches and next to Wolverton BR station.p
Capacity: 3000 Cover: Yes Seats: 150 Floodlights: Yes Club Shop: No
Clubhouse: On ground and open normal opening hours.Closed Mondays
HONOURS: North Bucks Lge - Div 1 90-91, Prem. Div Cup 92-93, I'mediate Tphy 91-92; Daimler-Benz Austrian International Tournament R-up 1990
S.S.M.Lg Trophy Winners 99-00 **Previous Name:** Mercedes - Benz F.C.
PREVIOUS: **Leagues:** Milton Keynes Sunday/ North Bucks & District (pre'93)
RECORD **Scorer:** Stuart Collard 132 **Appearances:** Stuart Collard 206
Win: 24-2 v Milton Keynes Saints, Berks & Bucks Jun Cup 1st Rd 16/10/93
Defeat: 1-8 v Greenleys, Milton Keynes Sun Lge Cup 1st Rd 22/11/87

FACT FILE
Founded: 1967 Nickname: Blues or City
Sponsors: Wright Tile Centre
Colours: All Royal Blue
Change Colours: Old Gold/Black/Old Gold
Midweek matches: Tuesday
Reserves' league: S.S.M. Reserve Div
Programme: 25 pages,£1.00
Editor: Stuart Collard, 01908 505042 (H), 01908 600394 (B)
CLUB PERSONNEL
Chairman: Bob Flight. President: T.B.A.
Manager & Assistant T.B.A.
Physio: Andy Nicholls

POTTERS BAR TOWN

Secretary: Kevin Wilmot,83 Mandeville Court, Lower Hall Lane, Chingford, London E4 8JD
Tel No: 020 8529 9475 (H) 07905 378789 (M) pottersbarto@aol.com
GROUND: Parkfield, The Walk, Potters Bar, Herts EN6 1QN, 01707 654833
Directions: M25 jct 24, enter Potters Bar along Southgate Rd (A111), at 1st lights right into the High St (A1000), half mile left into The Walk, grd 200yds on right (opp. Potters Bar Cricket Club)
Capacity: 2,000 Seats: 150 Cover: 100 Floodlights: Yes Club Shop: No Contact Jeff Barnesfor details of pennants,badges, car stickers and hangers etc.
Clubhouse: Sat 12.30-11pm, Sun noon-5pm, Tues & Thurs 7.30-11pm, midweek matchnights
HONOURS: South Midlands Lge. - Prem. Div. 96-97, Plate 96-97; Herts. Sen. Co. Lge. -Prem. Div. 90-91, Div. 1 73-74, 81-82, Div. 2 68-69; North London Comb. - Prem.Div. 67-68, Div. 1 67-68, Div. 2 R-up 65-66;SSMLg R-up 98-99 Prem Div North R-up 97-98 ,SML Floodlight Cup 99-00
PREVIOUS: **Leagues:** Barnet & Dist. 60-65/ N London Comb. 65-68/ Herts Snr Co. 68-91
RECORD: **Attendance:** 4000 v Eastenders XI, 20.4.97. 306 v Barnet, f/light open93
Competitive: 268 v Wealdstone ,F.A.Cup 1998
BEST SEASON: **FA Vase:** 6th Rd 97-98

FACT FILE
Founded: 1960
Nickname: The Grace or The Scholars
Colours: Red & royal stripes/royal/royal
Blue & Yellow stripes/ryellow/yellow
Midweek matchday: Tuesday or Wednesday
Prog Ed: Kevin Wright(07905 378789)
Programme: 40pages, £1 and Website- www.pottersbartown.co.uk
CLUB PERSONNEL
Chairman: Peter Waller V Chair:John Robinson
President: B Wright General Mger: L Eason
Manager: Steve Smart
Coach: Paul Mohan Physio: Brian Simpson
2002-03: Capt: Jeff Cross P.o.Y.: Gary Doolan
Top Scorer: Lee Talbot

ROYSTON TOWN

Secretary/Press Officer: Elaine Phillips, 14 Roan walk, Royston, Herts SG8 9HT
Tel No: 01763 241041 (H)
GROUND: Garden Walk, Royston, Herts SG8 7HP (01763 241204).
Directions: FromBaldock, A505 to Royston bypass, right at 2nd island onto A10 towards London, 2nd left is Garden Walk; ground 100 yds on left.
Capacity: 4,000 Seats: 300 Cover: 300 Floodlights: Yes Club Shop: Yes
Clubhouse: Mon-Thurs 7-11, Fri 11-3 & 7-11, Sat 11-3 & 4-11, Sun 12-3.
HONOURS Herts Co. Lg 76-77 (Div 1 69-70 76-77); Sth Mids Lg R-up 79-80 (Div 1 78-79,Chall. Cup R-up 78-79;
PREVIOUS **Leagues:** Buntingford & Dist. 18-28; Cambs 28-50; Herts Co. 50-59 62-77; SthMids 59-62 77-84; Isthmian 84-94
RECORDS **Attendance:** 876 v Aldershot, 13/2/93
Scorer: Trevor Glasscock 289 (1968-82) **Appearances:** Fred Bradley 713
BEST SEASON **FA Cup:** 2nd Qual. Rnd 59-60, 0-9 v Barnet (A), 89-90, 0-3 V Bromley (A)

FACT FILE
Founded: 1875 Nickname: Crows
Res League: Essex & Herts Border Comb
Sponsors: ABA Consultants
Colours: White/black/black
Change colours: Red/white/white
Midweek Matches: Tuesday
Programme: 16 pages, 30p
Editor: Secretary
CLUB PERSONNEL
Chairman: Graham Phillips
Vice-Chairman: Bernard Brown
President: Alan Barlow
Manager: Gavin Head
Asst Mgr: S Salomone Physio: C Mardell

RUISLIP MANOR

Secretary: John Price, 1 Filey Way, Ruislip,Middlesex (01895 631933)
Ground: Grosvenor Vale, off West End Rd, Ruislip, Middx 01895 637487-office,676168-boardroom
Directions: A40 to Ruislip, turn off on A4180, right at r'bout into West EndRd, right into Grosvenor Vale after a 1 1/2 miles - ground at end. From RuislipManor station (Metropolitan Line) turn left out of station, then 1st right intoShenley Ave, 3rd left into Cranley Dr - ground 150 yds on left
Capacity: 3,000 Seats: 250 Cover: 600 Floodlights: Yes Club Shop: Yes
Clubhouse: Mon-Fri 12-3.30 & 5.30-11pm, Sat & Sun 12-3 & 7.30-10.30
HONOURS London Lg R-up 51-52 (Div 1 R-up 47-48), Isthmian Lg Div 2 R-up 92-93 (Associate Members Tphy 90-91), Athenian Lg Div 2 72-73, Middx Snr Cup SF (6), Middx Charity Cup R-up 90-91 95-96
PREVIOUS **Leagues:** Uxbridge 38-39; Middx Snr 39-46; London 46-58; Spartan 58-65; Athenian65-84; Isthmian 84-96
RECORDS **Attendance:** 2,000 v Tooting & Mitcham United, F.A. Amateur Cup 1962
Appearances: Chris Balls, 350 **Goalscorer:** Kevin Quinn, 76
BEST SEASON **FA Cup:** 4th Q Rd 90-91, 2-5 v Halesowen T (A) **F.A.Am.Cup:** 1st Rd 73-74

FACT FILE
Founded: 1938 Nickname: The Manor
Sponsors: Light Years
Colours: Black & White/black/black
Change colours: Blue & yellow/blue/blue.
Midweek Matches: Monday
Reserve League: Suburban Lge (North)
Programme: 24 Price: 50p
Editor/ Press Off.: Chris Thomas
01895 636930

CLUB PERSONNEL
Chairman: Tom O'Shea
Vice Chairman: Keith Cham berlain
Manager:Paul Pitfield
Physio: Gary Strudwick

St MARGARETSBURY

Secretary: Ashley Ward, 1 Village Close, Hoddesdon, Herts. EN11 0GJ (01992 410386)
GROUND: Station Road, Stanstead St Margarets, Nr Ware, Herts (01920 870473)

Directions: Harlow/Chelmsford exit from A10 to A414, take B181 at Amwell roundabout after 300yds towards Stanstead Abotts, ground quarter mile on right. 300yds from St Margaretsbury BR station (Liverpool Str.-Hertford East line)
Capacity: 1,000 Seats: 60 Cover: 60 Floodlights: Yes Club Shop: No

Clubhouse: Bar open every evening 7.30-11, plus Sat 12-2, Sun 12-3. Bar snacks available
HONOURS: Herts Snr Cent Tphy 92-93; Herts Co. Lg Div 2 48-49, Div 3 78-79; Aubrey Cup 48-49 71-72; Res. Div 1 82-83 86-87; Res. Cup 84-85 86-87 87-88); Waltham &Dist Lg 46-47; Spartan Lge 95-96; Roy Bailey Mem Trophy 95-96, Herts Charity Shield 97-98.
PREVIOUS: Lges: East Herts; Hertford & Dist.; Waltham & District 47-48; Herts Co. 48-92
RECORD: Attendance: 327 v Wisbech Town, FA Vase 3rd Round 14/12/85
BEST SEASON **FA Vase:** 3 Rd 1985

FACT FILE
Founded: 1894 Nickname: The Bury
Sponsors: Lawfords Building Supplies
Colours: Red & black/white/white
White/Black/Black
Midweek matchday: Tuesday
Reserve Lg: Essex & Herts Border Comb.
Programme: £3.00 with entry
Editor/Match Sec.: Jon Gooding
Tel:07931 191026
CLUB PERSONNEL
Chairman: Dave Stock
President: R L Groucott
Manager:Martin Gutteridge
Physio: John Elliott

Colney Heath *Photo: Gordon Whittingham.*

The 61 FC (Luton) *Photo: gordon Whittington.*

Tring Athletic Back Row (L-R): Steve Johnson, Jamie McBeath, trevor Gibbs, Grant Mosley, Tom Vincent, Jamie Robbins, david Foskett, Keith Eldridge, John Perry, Stuart Stedman, Ray Brimson (Joint Manager). Front Row: Tony Mendicino, Andy Humphreys, Adie Skyers, Mark Boniface (Capt), Julian James, Paul Lewis.
Photo: Gordon Whittingham.

AMPTHILL TOWN

Secretary: Eric Turner, 34 Dunstable Street, Ampthill, Beds MK45 2JT.
Tel:01525 403128 (H & B)

Ground: Ampthill Park, Woburn Road, Ampthill, Beds. Tel: 01525 404440

Directions: From Ampthill Town Centre follow signs to Woburn then take the first right into Ampthill Park

Chairman: Peter Foxall
Tel: 01525 755041
Manager: Nicholas Burton
Programme Editor: As Secretary
Colours: Yellow & navy blue/navy/navy
Change Colours: Green/black/black

2000-01

Leading goalscorer: Danny Giggs 14
Captain: Carl Page
P.o.Y.: James Slack

BIGGLESWADE UNITED

Secretary: Tracey James, 17 Havelock Road, Biggleswade, Beds SG18 0DB.
Tel: 01767 316270 (H), 020 7270 6045(B), 0771 466 1827(M)
GROUND: Second Meadow, Fairfield Road, Biggleswade, Beds. (01767 600408)
Directions: From A1 Sainsbury's roundabout, cross over iron bridge and take 2nd left into Sun Street.(before Peugot Garage) Take first left into Fairfield Road ground at bottom of road in lane
Capacity: 2,000 Seats: 30 Cover: 130 Floodlights: Yes Club Shop: No
Clubhouse: Open all matchdays, rolls available. Also refreshment hut with hot snacks
HONOURS: Hunts F.A. Prem Cup : 98-99,S.Mids Lg Div 1 96-97 Cup Winners 96-97Beds & District Prtem Div.94-95, 95-96, Div 1. 91-92, Div2 90-91,Div3 88-89 Beds F.A. Inter Cup (2)
Record Crowd: 250 v Biggleswade Town 28.12.98 **Previous Name:**Biggleswade F.C.
Best Season in F.A.Vase: 1st Rd Proper 95-96

Founded: 1959 (original club 1935)
Colours: Red & navy/navy/red
Change : Yellow & Black/black/yellow
Midweek Matchday: Tuesday /Thursday
Prog-With admission Editor: Secretary
Chairman: David McCormick.(01767 316018)
Match Sec.: Mick Brown, (01767 221512)
Manager: 'Snowy' Wright
Physio: Phil Lunceford

BRACHE SPARTA

Secretary: Roy Standring, 37 Taunton Avenue, Luton, Beds. LU2 0LN. Tel: 01582 736574
GROUND: Foxdell Sports Ground, Dallow Rd, Luton LU1 1UP (01582 720751).
Directions: From M1 jct11, take A505 towards Luton. Right at Chaul End roundabout. Across A505 keep B&Q on left, into Dallow Rd. Ground 50 yds on right by Foxdell junior school.
Capacity: 400 Cover: 100 Seats: 25 Floodlights: Yes Club Shop: No
Clubhouse: Open daily 12-3 & 7.30-11. Light snacks & refreshments etc available
HONOURS: South Mids Lg R-up 92-93, 96-97 (Div 1 R-up 83-84 87-88), Lg Cup R-up 75-76 80-81 92-93 97-98, Premier Div Cup Winners 97-98 R-up 91-92, Res Div 2 R-up 75-76, Res Cup R-up 87-88; Luton & Dist. Lg 67-68 69-70 70-71 71-72; William Pease Trophy 66-67 67-68 70-71 71-72; Beds Interm Cup 71-72 (R-up 68-69 70-71), BedsJnr Cup 82-83; Leighton Challenge Cup R-up 69-70 South Mids Lg Prem Div 1 North Champions 97-98, Beds Premier Cup R-up. 97-98

FACT FILE
Founded: 1960 Nickname: The Foxes
Colours: White/navy/white
Change Colours: All royal
Midweek matches: Tuesday
Prog: 32 pages, £2.50 (incl. admission)
Career Record Goalscorer: Keith Denness

CLUB PERSONNEL
Chairman: Roy Standring
President: Doug Smith
Manager: Steve Brinkman
Physio: Chris Garner

BRIMSDOWN ROVERS

Secretary: Mrs Lorraine Winter,,141 Kinwood Crescent,Enfield, Midd'x EN1 4US (Tel & Fax: 020 8366 1075 , Fax: 0208 8045491 and Mobile: 07747 681044) Email: lw@bssc.freeserve.co.uk
GROUND: Brimsdown Sports & Social Club, Goldsdown Road, Enfield, Middlesex EN3 7RR
Tel: 0208 804 5491 **Directions:** BR from Liverpool Street to Brimsdown (half mile away) or Southbury Road. By road off Green Street, itself off Hertford Road (A1010). Buses 191 or307
Capacity: 1,000 Seats: 25Cover: 50Floodlights: Yes Club Shop:
Clubhouse: Large lounge & clubroom, games room & stage. 3 bars (300 capacity)
HONOURS: Spartan Lg 92-93. Spartan Lg Cup 95-96
RECORD: **Gate:** 412 v Chesham Utd, FA Cup 3rd Qual. Rd 12/10/91
BEST SEASON: **FA Vase:** 3rd Rd 93-94 **FA Cup:** 3rd Qual. replay 91-92
PREVIOUS: **Leagues:** Northern Suburban **Names:** Durham Rovers; Brimsdown FC

FACT FILE
Founded: 1947
Colours: Black & white stripes/black/black
Change colours: Yellow/Blue/Yellow
Midweek Matchday: Tuesday
Programme: With admission
Editor: Peter Wade
Chairman: Gary Simpson
Match Secretary: Peter Wade.
5 Goldsdown Close, Enfield Middlesex EN3 7RR Tel: 0208 804 7053
Manager:Dave Farenden

BUCKINGHAM ATHLETIC

Secretary: Neil Holman, 3 Chandos Close, Buckingham, Bucks. MK18 1AW
Tel: 01280 815539

Ground: Stratford Fields, Stratford Rd, Buckingham
Tel: 01280 816945

Directions: From Milton Keynes take the A422 Stony Stratford-Buckingham road -ground on left just before town centre. From Oxford, Aylesbury or Bletchley, take the ring road to the A422 Stony Stratford roundabout, turn left, the ground is situated at the bottom of the hill on the left

COCKFOSTERS

Secretary: Graham Bint, 15 Chigwell Park, Chigwell, Essex IG7 5BE (0208 500 7369)
GROUND: Cockfosters Sports Ground, Chalk Lane, Cockfosters, Barnet (0208 449 5833)
Directions: M25 Jct 24 (Potters Bar), take A111 signed Cockfosters - ground 2 miles on right. Adjacent to Cockfosters underground station (Picadilly Line). Bus 298 to Cockfosters station
Capacity: 1,000 Seats: None Cover: 50 Floodlights: Yes Club Shop: No
Clubhouse: 7-11pm Tues & Thurs, 4-11pm Sat, 12-3pm Sun. Hot & cold food onmatchdays
HONOURS: London Interm Cup 70-71 89-90, Herts Snr Co. Lg 78-79 80-81 83-84 R-up 82-83 84-85, Aubrey Cup 78-79 84-85 R-up 70-71 77-78, Herts Interm Cup 78-79 R-up x3
Previous Leagues: Wood Green & Dist. 21-46/ Northern Suburban 46-66/ Herts Snr Co.66-91
BEST SEASON: **FA Vase:** 2nd Round 91-92
RECORDS: **Gate:** 408 v Saffron Walden, Herts Senior County Lg 68-69

Founded: 1921 Nickname: Fosters
Colours: All Red Change colours: All White
Midweek matches: Tuesday
Sponsors: T.S.I.Design
Programme: 12 pages with entry
Editor: A Simmons (0208 440 7998)
Chairman/Press Off.: Frank Brownlie (0208 500 5930)
President: Les Langdale Manager: Dean Cole
Physio: John Walsh

COLNEY HEATH

Secretary: Karen Whitehead, 15 Cutmore Drive, Colney Heath, St. Albans, Herts. AL4 0PH

Ground: The Pavillion Recreaton Ground, High St., Colney Heath, St. Albans, Herts.
Tel: 01727 826188

Directions: Turn off the A414 (was A405) into Colney Heath village and the ground is behind the school on the left.

Formed:
Colours:
Change Colours:
Midweek Matchday:
Programme- Price Pages
Editor

Chairman:
Other Club Officer(s):
Manager:
Physio:

HAYWOOD UNITED

Secretary: Lynne Nappin, 6 Evesham Green, Aylesbury, Bucks. HP19 9RX
Tel: 01296 486924

Ground: Stocklake Sports & Social Club, Haywards Way, Aylesbury, Bucks. Tel: 01296 423324

Directions: Follow signs to Bicester from Aylesbury ring road.
At fifth road island, with Aylesbury Duck P.H. on right, turn right into Jackson Road and then second left into Haywood Way. Club is at bottom of the road.

Previous Leagues: Chiltonian

KINGS LANGLEY

Secretary: Andy Mackness, 79 Weymouth Street, Apsley, Hemel Hempstead, Herts HP3 9SJ
Tel: 01442 398186 (H) 020 7587 4153 (B) 07976 692801 (M)

Ground: Gaywood Park, Hempstead Road, Kings Langley. Tel: 01923 264489

Directions: From M25 leave at Junction 20. Take A4251 to Kings Langley.
The ground is approx. 1 mile on the right.

Colours: Black & white stripes/black/black
Change colours: All white
Programme: Yes
Editor: Adrian Marston Tel: 01923 893320 (H)

Chairman: Derry Edgar
Tel: 01923 268301 (H)

Manager: Colin Jones
Tel: 01442 394986 (H)

LANGFORD

Secretary: Frank Woodward, 4 West View, Langford, Biggleswade. Beds. SG18 9RT
Tel: 01462 701015 (H) Club Email: langfordfc@talk21.com
GROUND: Forde Park, Langford Road, Henlow SG16 6AF Tel: 01462 816106
Directions: Halfway between Langford and Henlow on A6001 Hitchin to Biggleswade road. Bus 177 on main Hitchin-Biggleswade route stops right outside ground
Capacity: 4,000 Seats: 50 Cover: 250 Floodlights: Yes Club Shop: Yes
Clubhouse: Weekday evenings, matchdays 11am-11pm, Sun 12-3pm. Hot food on matchdays
HONOURS: S Mids Lg 88-89 (Lg Cup 73-74 75-76, Prem. Div Tphy 88-89,94-95.O'Brien Div 1 Tphy 84-85), N Beds Charity Cup 27-28 30-31 69-70 75-76 86-87 92-93 94-95 98-99 01-02Bedford & Dist. Lg 30-31 31-32 32-33, Bedfs I'mediate Cup 68-69, Hinchingbrooke Cup 72-73
RECORD: **Gate:** 450 v Q.P.R., 75th Anniversary and clubhouse opening, 22/8/85

Founded: 1908 Nickname: Reds
Sponsors:Armitage Asphalt
Colours: All red with white trim
Change Colours: Blue & white
Midweek matches: Tuesday
Programme: With admission.
Editors: Bob Davies (01438 238066)
Chairman: Mick Quinlan President: Ted Rutt
Com. Man: Diane Woodward Man: Roy Ryall
2002-2003 Captain: Barry Laurence
P.o.Y.: Robert Groves Top Scorers: Darren Mortimore & Joe West

NEW BRADWELL St PETER

Secretary: Les Smith, 25 Bishopstone,Bradville, Milton Keynes. MK13 7DQ (01908 315736)
Ground: Recreation Ground, Bradwell Rd, New Bradwell, Milton Keynes MK13 7AT
Tel.: 01908 313835
Directions: From M1 Jnt 14 go towards Newport Pagnell, left at 1st r-about into H3 (A422 Monks Way). Over 5 r-abouts, right at 6th island into V6 (GraftonSt.), At 1st roundabout go right the way round (back on yourself) then take 1st left at mini-r'about turn left into Bradwell Rd. Go straight over next mini r'about. Ground immediately on left.
Capacity: Seats: 30 Cover: 100 Floodlights: Yes
Clubhouse: Members only (member can sign in 2 guests). Evenings & w/e mid day. No food.
HONOURS: Sth Mids Lg Div 1 76-77 83-84 Sen Div Champs 97-98, (Res Div 2 R-up 76-7), Berks& Bucks Senior Trophy 1999-2000

FACT FILE
Founded: 1902 Nickname: Peters
Colours: All Maroon
Change: Amber/black/black.
Midweek matches: Tuesday
Programme: 32 pages, £3 with entry
Editor: Paul Smith 01908 550211 (H)
CLUB PERSONNEL
Chairman John Haynes President: J P Booden
Vice-Chairman: R.Creasey
Press Officer: P Smith
Managers:J. Gunn & E.Byrne

PITSTONE & IVINGHOE

Secretary: Jay Adlem, 22 Maud Janes Close, Ivinghoe, Leighton Buzzard. LU7 9ED.
Tel: 01296 668663 (H)

Ground: Pitstone Recreation Ground, Vicarage Road, Pitstone, Bucks Tel: 01296 661271

Directions: Tring Rd (B489) from Dunstable, turn right for Ivinghoe, and continue through to Pitstone r-about; ground left then right. From Aylesbury -left at `Rising Sun' in Aston Clinton, keep on that road to Pitstone r'bout; ground right then right.
Bus 61 from Luton or Aylesbury. Nearest BR stations are Tring or Cheddington.

Colours: Red & black/black/black
Change Colours:
Sky & navy stripes/navy/sky & navy hoops
Programme: Yes
Editor: Rob Adlem Tel: 01296 668663 (H)

Chairman: David Hawkins
Tel: 01296 661456
Manager: Sean Downey
Tel: 01525 634019

SHILLINGTON

Secretary: Aubrey Cole, 32 Greenfields, Shillington, Hitchin, Herts. SG5 3NX
Tel: 01462 711322

Ground: Playing Field, Greenfields, Shillington
Tel: 01462 711757

Directions: From Luton on A6 after bypassing Barton, turn right at large roundabout.
Through Gobian to Shillington.
From Bedfford or Hitchin, A600 to RAF Henlow. At Bird in Hand roundabout take exit to Upper Stondon.

STONY STRATFORD TOWN

Secretary: Maurice J Barber, 26 Boundary Cres., Stony Stratford, Milton Keynes MK11 1DF
Tel: 01908 567930 (H)
GROUND: Sports Ground, Ostlers Lane, Stony Stratford (01908 562267).
Directions: From Dunstable use old A5, Watling Street. Approaching Bletchley continue on A5 loop road (Hinkley) to end of dual c'way to A422/A508 r'bout. First exit, thru lights, 2nd right into Ostlers Lane.
Capacity: 600 Seats: 30 Cover: 120 Floodlights: Yes Club Shop: No
Clubhouse: Open evenings & weekends
HONOURS: Sth Mids Lg R-up 70-71 71-72 (Div 1 93-94, Div 1 Cup 93-94)
PREVIOUS: **Leagues:** North Bucks & Dist.; Northampton Combination
RECORD: **Attendance:** 476 v Aston Villa U21, floodlight opening 12.11.96

Reformed: 1898
Sponsor:Amity Mortgages Ltd.
Colours:Sky blue/navy/navy
Change Colours:All yellow
Midweek matches: Tuesday
Reserves' League: SSM Res. Div. One
Programme: 28 pages, £3.00 (Incl. entrance)
Editor: Paul Grimsley Chairman: Mike Judd
Mtch Sec.:Mrs. E. Sartain Man:Chris Johnson
2001-02 Leading goalscorer: Paul Sloley 55
Captain: Brendan Quill
P.o.Y.: 'Joe' Major

SUN SPORTS

Secretary:
Ground: Bellmount Wood Avenue, Watford, Herts. Tel: 01923 227453
Directions:
PREVIOUS Names: Sun Postal Sports >2003 **Leagues:** Herts Senior County Lge. >2003

THE 61 FC

Secretary: Richard Everitt, 44 Somersby Close, Luton LU1 3XB. Tel: 01582 485095 (H)

Ground: Kingsway, Beverley Road, Luton, Beds. 01582 495417

Directions: M1 jct 11, A505 to Luton centre, right at 1st island, 1st left, Beverley Rd is 3rd left, entrance in Beverley Rd, exactly 1 mile junction 11.All Luton to Dunstable buses pass ground - alight at Beech Hill Bowling Club. 1mile from both Leagrave & Luton BR stations

Colours: Sky blue/royal blue/royal
Change Colours: Red & white/black/red
Programme: Yes
Editor: Richard Everitt Tel: 01582 485095

Chairman: Mark Davie
Tel: 01582 416011
Manager: Richard Everitt
Tel: 01582 485095 (H)

TRING ATHLETIC

Secretary: Ralph Griffiths, 42 Bedgrove, Aylesbury, Bucks HP21 7BD.Tel: 01296 426425 (H), email: ralph.griffiths@ntworld.com
Ground: Miswell Lane, Tring, Herts. HP23 4DR(01442 828331) Website: www.tafc.co.uk
Directions: Through Tring on main rd to Aylesbury, rt after Anchor PH into Miswell Lane, grd 500yds on rt opp Beaconsfield Rd. Tring station is several miles outside town, grd by bus ortaxi
Capacity: Seats: 25+ Cover: 100+ Floodlights: No Club Shop: No
Clubhouse: Bar, open matchdays, training nights & Sunday lunchtimes
HONOURS: West Herts Div 1 (3), Lg R-up 72-73 ,Lg Cup 65-66. SSMlds: Senior Div 99-00,Lg Cup 89-90,Herts Charity Shield 99-00,01-02 Cherry Red Trophy (2) Herts Centenary Trophy (2). SSMDivision One Cup 02-03
PREVIOUS: **League:** West Herts 58-88
RECORD **Scorer:** Ian Butler **Appearances:** Mark Boniface

Founded: 1958 Nickname: Athletic
Sponsors: R.O.Allum & Sons(Contractors)
Colours: Red & black/black/black
Change colours: yellow/green/yellow
Midweek matchday: Wednesnay
Programme: 36 pages, £1.50 Editor: Sec
President: T.B.A.
Chairman: Barry Johnson
Manager: Mick Eldridge
Asst Manager: Ray Brimson
Coach &Physio: Richard Vincent

WELWYN GARDEN CITY

Secretary: James Bruce, 6 Autumn Grove, Welwyn G.C., Herts AL7 4DB. Tel: 01707331048 (H)
GROUND: Herns Lane, Welwyn Garden City (01707 328470)
Directions: From A1 follow signs for industrial area. Take one-way systemopposite Avdel Ltd (signed Hertford B195), take 2nd exit off one-way system.Ground 400 yards on left. One and a half miles from Welwyn GC (BR)
Capacity: 1,500 Seats: 40 Cover: 120 Floodlights: Yes Club Shop: Yes
Clubhouse: Open every night and weekend lunchtimes. Members Bar, Hall.Steward:Gary Bevan
HONOURS: Herts Snr Centenary Tphy 84-85 (R-up 88-89), Herts Charity Shield 27-28 86-8787-88 94-95 (R-up 48-49), Sth Mids Lg 73-74 (R-up 85-86, Div 1 69-70 81-82, LgCup R-up 74-75 81-82 88-89, Reserve Cup 85-86)
PREVIOUS: **Leagues:** Spartan; Metropolitan; Gtr London. **Ground:** Springfields

Founded: 1921 Nickname: Citzens
Colours: Maroon & blue/blue/maroon
Change Colours: All white
Midweek Matches: Tuesday
Programme: 24 pages, 50p
Editor: Dave Fallon 01438 235701
Local Press: Welwyn & Hatfield Times, Welwyn & Hatfield Herald & Post
Chairman: Terry Hazel
Manager: David Steedman
Assistant Manager: Ray Greenhall
Physio: Danny Milliken

Caddington F.C. *Photo: Gordon Whittingham.*

Rory Bray opens the scoring for Buckingham Athletic against Caddington in this Division Two encounter which saw Buckingham add a further seven goals to their tally to win the match 8-1.

Photo: Gordon Whittingham.

DIVISION TWO CLUBS

ABBEY NATIONAL (Loughton.)
Secretary: Clare O'Connor, 18 Cranwell Close,Shenley Brook End, Milton Keynes MK5 7BU (01908 520370)
Ground: Loughton Sports & Social Club, Lincesdale Grove, Loughton, Milton Keynes. Tel: 01908 690668 **Directions:** From M1 Jct 14 follow H6, Childs Way for 5 miles until V4 Watling Way (Knowlhill r-about), right to Loughton r-about, right along H5 Portway 1st right Linceslade Grove

AMERSHAM TOWN
Secretary: Michael Gahagan, 7 Ely Close, Lincoln Pk,Amersham,Bucks.HP7 9HS (01494 24798)
Ground: Spratley's Meadow, School Lane, Old Amersham, Bucks. (01494 727428) **Directions:** From London A413 to Amersham Old town, in front of market hall, right into Church St., first left into School Lane, ground on left past Mill Lane. 1 mile from Amersham Station - BR & underground Metropolitan Line

CADDINGTON
Secretary: Dave Mark, 7 Heathfield Close, Caddington, Luton, Beds. LU1 4HD Tel: 01582 421404 (H) 01797 147968 (B)
Ground: Caddington Recreation Club, Manor Road, Caddington (01582 450151) **Directions:** On entering village turn into Manor Road (adjacent to shops andvillage green), proceed 500 metres: Clubhouse and ground on left side next to Catholic Church

CRANFIELD UNITED
Secretary: Ed Frost, 9 Pollys Yard, Newport Pagnell MK16 8YU (01908 210877)
Ground: Crawley Road, Cranfield (01234 751444)
Directions: Take north Crawley/Newport Pagnell road from Cranfield village and ground is on left before leaving speed limit signs.

CRAWLEY GREEN
Secretary: Alan Burgess, 23 Higham Drive, Luton LU2 9SP (01582 483172)
Ground: Crawley Green Recreation Ground, Crawley Green Road, Luton, Beds. 01582 451058 **Directions:** From M1 jct 10 , to r'about at end of motorway slip road into Airport Way. At 4th r'about turn right into Crawley Green Rd. Ground is 1/2 mile on left past Ashcroft High School.

FLAMSTEAD
Secretary: Mark McGreevy, 3 White Hill, Flamstead, Herts. AL3 8DN (01582 841 481)
Ground: Flamstead Sports Assoc., Friendless Lane, Flamstead, St Albans, Herts (0582 841307)
Directions: From Dunstable Town Centre travel south on A5 Trunk Roadtowards the M1. Follow for approximately 3 miles then turn right oppositeHertfordshire Moat House Hotel. Ground and parking approximately half a mile onthe corner of the first right turn

KENT ATHLETIC
Secretary: Irene Oodian, 9 Gafield Court, Handcross Road,Luton, Beds. LU2 8JZ (01582 483090)
Ground: Kent Social Club, Tenby Drive, Leagrave, Luton Tel: 01582 582723 **Directions:** M1 J11 take A505 towards Luton. Take the first turning on the left (Stoneygate Road), straight over at r'about and turn right at lights into Beechwood Road. Take the first road on the left and then the first right into Tenby Drive. Ground and car park 100 yards on left

MURSLEY UNITED
Secretary: Geoff Curtis, 26 Berwick Drive, Bletchley, Milton Keynes MK3 7NB (01908 377196)
Ground: Station Road, Mursley, Milton Keynes
Directions: A421 Bletchley to Buckingham Road, first right in village

OLD BRADWELL UNITED
Secretary: Paul Mills, 36 Craddocks Close, Bradwell, Milton Keynes MK13 9DX (01908 227520)
Ground: Abbey Road, Bradwell, Milton Keynes (01908 312355)
Directions: M1 junction 14 go towards Newport Pagnell. Turn left at firstroundabout into H3 Honks Way. Go six r'abouts then left onto V6 Grafton Street.Take 1st right at mini-r'about into Rawlins Road and then 2nd left intoLoughton Road. Take 1st right into Primrose Road and at the 'T' junction turnright into Abbey Road

OLD DUNSTABLIANS
Secretary: Craig Renfrew, 75B Princes Street. Dunstable. LU6 3AS. Tel: 01582471794 (H), 01234 265444 (B)
Ground: Lancot Park. Dunstable Road, Totternhoe (01582 663735)
Directions: From Dunstable Town Centre take the B489 Tring Road. At the 4throundabout turn right, signposted Totternhoe. The pitch is located withionDunstable Town Cricket Club which is on the right just before entering thevillage of Totternhoe

PADBURY UNITED
Secretary: James Clarke, 41 Moorhen Way, Buckingham, Bucks. MK18 1GN (01280 824513
Ground: Springfields,Playing Fields, Padbury **Directions:** From Buckingham follow ring road with signs,to Aylesbury (A413), then towards Buckingham and Padbury is two miles south of the town A413 and three miles north west of Winslow on A413. Turn off opposite bus shelter on Springfields Estate and follow road forward.

RISBOROUGH RANGERS
Secretary: Derrick J Wallace, 42 Ash Road, Princes Risborough, Bucks, HP27 0BQ Tel: 01844 345179 (H), 01844 345435 (B)
Ground: `Windsor', Horsenden Lane, Princes Risborough. (01844 274176) **Directions:** Rear of Princes Risborough BR Station (Chiltern Line). A4010 fromAylesbury thru Princes Risborough, fork right onto A4009, left by thatched cottage, over railway bridge, immediate right ground 150 yds on right

SCOT
Secretary: William Land, 18 Coleridge Close, Bletchley, Milton Keynes MK3 5AF (01908 372228)
Ground: Selbourne Avenue, Bletchley, Milton Keynes (01908 368881)
Directions: Main roads to Bletchley then A421 Buckingham road, at Glen Garageright into Newton Rd, 2nd left into Selbourne Ave., through railway bridge to bottom of road

TOTTERNHOE
Secretary: Jim Basterfield, 41 Park Avenue, Totternhoe, Dunstable, Beds LU6 1QF. Tel: 01582 667941 (H)
Ground: Totternhoe Recreation Ground, Dunstable (01582 606738)
Directions: Turn off the main Dunstable to Tring Road B489. Ground on right as you enter Totternhoe. Five miles from Leighton Buzzard (BR), 7 miles from Luton. Bus 61 Luton-Aylesbury

WINSLOW UNITED
Secretary: David F Ward, 28 Park Road, Winslow, Buckingham MK18 3DL. Tel: 01296713202 (H), 01865 781210 (B)
Ground: Recreation Ground, Elmfields Gate, Winslow, Bucks.
Tel: 01296 713057
Directions: A413 from Aylesbury to Winslow, in High Street turn right into Elmfields Gate, ground on left opp. car park.A421 from Milton Keynes to Buck'ham then thro 'Gt Horwood

Sun Postal Sports - Runners-up in the Herts Senior County League.

Photo: Gordon Whittington.

HERTS SENIOR COUNTY LEAGUE

President: Eric Dear **Chairman:** Cecil T Husdon

General Secretary: Kevin Folds, 6 Lanthony Court,
High Street, Arlesey, Beds SG15 6TU
Tel: 01462 734102 Email: KFoldsHSCL@aol.com

Website: www.football.mitoo.co.uk/News.cfm?LeagueCode=HSCL

FINAL LEAGUE TABLES 2002-03

PREMIER DIVISION		P	W	D	L	F	A	Pts
1	Oxhey Jets	30	24	1	5	91	26	73
2	Sun Postal Sports	30	21	5	4	79	33	68
3	Elliott Star	30	16	7	7	73	50	55
4	Bovingdon	30	14	7	9	53	37	49
5	Sandridge Rovers	30	14	5	11	62	50	47
6	London Lions	30	14	5	11	54	44	47
7	Chipperfield Corinthians	30	12	5	13	39	49	41
8	Hadley	30	12	4	14	50	60	40
9	Cuffley	30	11	6	13	42	64	39
10	Wormley Rovers	30	10	8	12	53	50	38
11	Bushey Rangers	30	10	6	14	47	50	36
12	Bedmond Sports & Social	30	10	6	14	38	52	36
13	Met. Police Bushey	30	10	4	16	52	66	34
14	Old Parmiterians	30	8	8	14	35	57	32
15	St Peters	30	7	8	15	44	52	29
16	Croxley Guild	30	3	3	24	24	96	12

DIVISION ONE		P	W	D	L	F	A	Pts
1	Hatfield Town	26	17	3	6	66	40	54
2	Hinton	26	14	10	2	78	22	52
3	Mill End S&S Athletic	26	15	5	6	61	27	50
4	Codicote	26	14	7	5	63	25	49
5	Evergreen	26	13	9	4	55	23	48
6	Lemsford	26	14	5	7	59	38	47
7	Whitewebbs	26	14	4	8	64	40	46
8	Standon Puckeridge	26	11	5	10	46	44	38
9	Allenburys Sports	26	12	2	12	50	59	38
10	Cheshunt Club	26	10	4	12	58	73	34
11	Kimpton Rovers	26	5	4	17	47	89	19
12	Buntingford Town	26	4	4	18	28	68	16
13	North Mymms	26	3	5	18	32	85	14
14	Sarratt	26	2	1	23	24	98	7

AUBREY CUP 2002-03

FIRST ROUND

Bovingdon	v	Bedmond S&S	0-0 (aet) 5-6p
Chipperfield Corinthians	v	North Mymms	5-3
Elliott Star	v	London Lions	2-1 (aet)
Kimpton Rovers	v	Sandridge Rovers	1-3
Mill End S&S Ath.	v	Met. Police Bushey	2-0
St Peters	v	Cuffley	3-1
The Cheshunt Club	v	Hinton	2-6
Bushey Rangers	v	Codicote	3-3 (aet) 4-3p
Croxley Guild	v	Hatfield Town	2-5 (aet)
Hadley	v	Buntingford Town	1-0
Lemsford	v	Wormley Rovers	3-1
Sarratt	v	Allenburys Sports	0-3
Standon & Puckeridge	v	Old Parmiterians	4-0
Whitewebbs	v	Evergreen	0-3

SECOND ROUND

Bedmond S&S	v	Elliott Star	0-0 (aet) 4-3p
Hinton	v	Oxhey Jets	1-3
Mill End S&S Ath.	v	Chipperfield Corinthians	3-1
Standon & Puckeridge	v	Hatfield Town	1-3
Evergreen	v	Lemsford	2-1
Hadley	v	Bushey Rangers	4-6
Sandridge	v	Allenburys	3-0
Sun Postal Sports	v	St Peters	2-0

QUARTER-FINALS

Bushey	v	Sandridge Rovers	2-3
Mill End S&S Ath.	v	Oxhey Jets	1-2
Evergreen	v	Bedmond	1-0
Sun Postal	v	Hatfield Town	1-3

SEMI-FINALS

Evergreen	v	Sandridge Rovers	0-1 (aet)
Oxhey Jets	v	Hatfield Town	1-0

FINAL

Oxhey Jets	v	Sandridge	1-0	5th May at Ware

CHAIRMAN'S CUP 2002-03

SEMI-FINALS

Allenburys Sports	v	The Cheshunt Club	2-1
Whitewebbs	v	Hinton	3-1

FINAL

Whitewebbs	v	Allenburys Sports	2-2 (aet) 5-3p	30th April at Oxhey Jets

PREMIER DIVISION CONSTITUTION FOR 2002-03

Bedmond Sports & Social
Toms Lane Recreation Ground, Toms Lane, Bedmont, Herts. Tel: 01923 267991

Bovingdon
Green Lane, Bovingdon, Hemel Hempstead, Herts. Tel: 01442 832628

Bushey Rangers
Moatfield, Bournehall Lane, Bushey, Herts. Tel: 020 8386 1875

Chipperfield Corinthians
Queens Street, Chipperfield, Herts. Tel: 01923 269554

Cuffley
King George's Playing Fields, Northaw Road East, Cuffley, Herts. Tel: 07815 174434

Elliott Star
Pursley Football Ground, London Road, Shenley, Herts. Tel: 020 8953 5087

Hadley
Hadley Sports Ground, Brickfield Lane, Arkley, Barnet, Herts. Tel: 020 8449 1144

Hatfield Town
Birchwood Leisure Centre, Longmead, Birchwood, Herts Tel: 01707 270772

Hinton
Holtwhites Sports & Social, Kirkland Drive, Enfield, Middlesex. Tel: 020 8363 4449

London Lions
Laing Sports, Rowley Lane, Barnet, Hertfordshire Tel: 020 8441 6051

Metropolitan Police Bushey
Met Police SC, Aldenham Rd, Bushey, Watford. Tel: 01923 243947

Mill End Sports & Social
King George V Playing Fields, Penn Road, Mill End, Hertfordshire. Tel: 01923 776892

Old Parmiterians
Parmiters School, High Elms Lane, Garston, Watford, Herts. Tel: 01923 682805

Oxhey Jets
Altham Centre, Little Oxhey Lane, South Oxhey, Herts. Tel: 020 8421 4965

Sandridge Rovers
Spencer Recreation Ground, Sandridge, St Albans, Herts. Tel: 01727 855159/835506

Wormley Rovers
Wormley Sports Club, Church Lane, Wormley, Herts. Tel: 01992 460650

Chipperfield Corinthians. *Photo: Gordon Whittington.*

Allenburys Sports *Photo: Gordon Whittington.*

Buntingford Town *Photo: Gordon Whittington.*

MIDDLESEX COUNTY FOOTBALL LEAGUE

Founded 1984

President: Peter Rogers **Chairman:** Reg Johnson

Secretary: Stephen C. Hosmer, 27 St Georges Road, Hanworth, Middx. TW13 6RD
Tel: (H) 020 8894 1244 (Fax) 020 8894 0499 (M) 07831 393559
Email: stephen@hosmer.freeserve.co.uk

FINAL LEAGUE TABLES 2002-03

PREMIER DIVISION	P	W	D	L	F	A	Pts
Hanworth Villa	20	16	2	2	61	13	50
Willesden Constantine	20	15	2	3	50	18	47
CB Hounslow United	20	13	3	4	51	28	42
Spelthorne Sports (-4)	20	9	4	7	40	29	27
Wraysbury (-3)	20	9	2	9	51	38	26
Stonewall	20	8	2	10	36	61	26
FC Deportivo Galicia	20	6	3	11	26	35	21
Brentford New Inn	20	6	1	13	34	50	19
Broadfields United (-4)	20	6	4	10	40	43	18
Neasden	20	6	0	14	25	45	18
Technicolor CAV	20	4	1	15	20	74	13

DIVISION ONE	P	W	D	L	F	A	Pts
Southall Town Reserves	18	13	3	2	47	20	42
Marsh Rangers	18	11	5	2	55	24	38
Actual Soccer	18	7	6	5	40	28	27
Spelthorne Spts Res.	18	8	3	7	25	23	27
Hounslow Wanderers	18	6	8	4	46	34	26
Signcraft	18	8	2	8	33	33	26
Ealing Assyrians (-3)	18	8	4	6	36	29	25
Neasden Res. (-3)	18	5	2	11	27	42	14
Hanworth Villa Reserves	18	3	4	11	31	51	13
Southall Reserves	18	2	1	15	16	72	7

A QUOTE INSURANCE READING FOOTBALL LEAGUE

President: Leon Summers **Chairman:** John Dell

Secretary: David Jeanes, 6 Hawkesbury Drive, Fords Farm, Calcot, Reading RG31 5ZP

Tel: 01734 413926 (H)

http://www.rdgleague.mcmail.com

FINAL LEAGUE TABLES 2002-03

	SENIOR DIVISION	P	W	D	L	F	A	Pts
1	Forest Old Boys	24	20	2	2	80	29	62
2	Royal Mail	24	15	3	6	53	29	48
3	Cookham Dean	24	12	5	7	39	31	41
4	Highmoor/IBIS	24	11	5	8	58	38	38
5	Westwood United	24	10	6	8	36	30	36
6	Ascot United	24	10	5	9	47	47	35
7	Marlow United	24	10	4	10	58	51	34
8	Mortimer	24	8	6	10	31	36	30
9	Checkendon Spts	24	7	9	8	32	41	30
10	West Reading	24	8	4	12	28	43	28
11	Midgham	24	6	4	14	29	61	22
12	Woodley Town	24	4	6	14	23	39	18
13	Unity	24	3	5	16	21	60	14

	PREMIER DIVISION	P	W	D	L	F	A	Pts
1	Reading YMCA	22	15	3	4	68	36	48
2	Hurst	22	15	3	4	55	25	48
3	Berks County Sports	22	15	2	5	54	25	47
4	Emmbrook Sports	22	11	7	4	46	22	40
5	Shinfield	22	12	2	8	49	42	38
6	Roundhead United	22	9	2	11	42	49	29
7	Sonning Common	22	8	3	11	33	42	27
8	Forest Old Boys Res.	22	8	3	11	43	58	27
9	Newtown Henley	22	7	3	12	43	51	24
10	Goring United (-1)	22	5	5	12	28	52	19
11	REME Arborfield	22	4	3	15	34	60	15
12	Westwood United Res.	22	4	2	16	40	73	14

	DIVISION ONE	P	W	D	L	F	A	Pts
1	Reading Old Blues	20	16	2	2	58	21	50
2	Spencers Wood	20	13	3	4	44	25	42
3	Woodcote/Stoke Row	20	11	3	6	43	36	36
4	Frilsham/Yattendon	20	10	2	8	39	32	32
5	Rides United	20	9	3	8	53	45	30
6	Emmbrook Sp. Res.	20	7	7	6	30	30	28
7	Cookham Dean Res.	20	8	2	10	37	45	26
8	Finchampstead 'A'	20	6	3	11	38	50	21
9	Highmoor/IBIS Res.	20	6	2	12	35	41	20
10	Woodley Town Res.	20	5	3	12	23	44	18
11	AFC Maidenhead	20	3	2	15	25	56	11

R.S.R. TYRES SURREY COUNTY SENIOR LEAGUE

Chairman: Tony Osborn
General Secretary: Les Pharo, 17 Nigel Fisher Way, Chessington, Surrey KT9 2SN
Tel: 020 8391 0297

FINAL LEAGUE TABLES 2002-03

	PREMIER DIVISION	P	W	D	L	F	A	Pts
1	Hersham RBL	32	21	6	5	71	36	69
2	Colliers Wood United	32	19	8	5	84	39	65
3	Horley Town	32	16	7	9	56	31	55
4	Bookham	32	15	9	8	56	40	54
5	Worcester Park	32	15	8	9	57	43	53
6	Crescent Rovers	32	15	7	10	75	54	52
7	Ditton	32	14	7	11	60	53	49
8	Netherne Village	32	13	9	10	49	38	48
9	AFC Guildford	32	14	6	12	50	43	48
10	Farleigh Rovers	32	14	6	12	61	55	48
11	Staines Lammas	32	14	5	13	85	59	47
12	Sheerwater	32	11	10	11	62	65	43
13	Seelec Delta	32	9	10	13	50	49	37
14	Chobham & Ottershaw	32	9	8	15	60	83	35
15	Croydon M. O.	32	3	8	21	38	99	17
16	Cranleigh (-6)	32	5	7	20	42	106	16
17	Shottermill & Haslemere	32	3	3	26	29	92	12

LEAGUE CUP 2002-03

FIRST ROUND

Seelec Delta	v	2 Sheerwater	2-2 (aet)	Replay - Sheerwater	v	Seelec Delta	3-2

SECOND ROUND

Chobham & Ottershaw	v	Bookham	0-0 (aet)	Replay - Bookham	v	Chobham	3-1 (aet)
Colliers Wood United	v	Sheerwater	1-4	Cranleigh	v	AFC Guildford	1-4
Crescent Rovers	v	Shottermill & H.	8-1	Ditton	v	Staines Lammas	0-1
Farleigh Rovers	v	Worcester Park	5-2	Hersham RBL	v	Croydon MO	5-1
Netherne Village	v	Horley Town	1-2	(ineligible player – Horley Town expelled)			

QUARTER-FINALS

AFC Guildford	v	Crescent Rovers	3-1 (aet)	Netherne Village	v	Hersham RBL	2-1
Sheerwater	v	Farleigh Rovers	2-3	Staines Lammas	v	Bookham	6-4

SEMI-FINALS

Farleigh Rovers	v	0 AFC Guildford	0-0 (aet)	Replay - AFC Guildford	v	Farleigh R.	3-3(aet) 4-5p
Netherne Village	v	Staines Lammas	3-1				

FINAL

Netherne Village	v	Farleigh Rovers	2-3	13th May at Chipstead

SUBURBAN FOOTBALL LEAGUE

Chairman: David Stanley

Chief Executive: Michael Bidmead

55 Grange Road, Chessington, Surrey KT9 1EZ

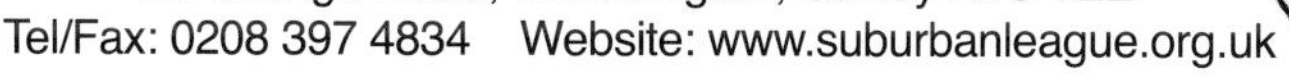
Tel/Fax: 0208 397 4834 Website: www.suburbanleague.org.uk

FINAL LEAGUE TABLES 2002-03

	PREMIER DIVISION	P	W	D	L	F	A	Pts
1	Hayes Reserves	34	22	2	10	90	51	68
2	Maidenhead United Reserves	34	20	3	11	80	67	63
3	Carshalton Athletic Reserves	34	18	4	12	67	49	58
4	Crawley Town Reserves	34	17	7	10	56	44	58
5	Sutton United Reserves	34	17	5	12	64	54	56
6	Marlow Reserves	34	16	6	12	63	57	54
7	Basingstoke Town Reserves	34	15	7	12	67	62	52
8	Northwood Reserves	34	13	10	11	66	56	49
9	Berkhamsted Reserves	34	14	7	13	64	61	49
10	Met. Police Reserves	34	13	9	12	50	51	48
11	Kingstonian Reserves	34	13	7	14	61	58	46
12	Wingate & Finchley Reserves	34	13	6	15	49	61	45
13	Dulwich Ham. Reserves	34	13	4	17	60	55	43
14	Brook House Reserves	34	13	4	17	42	57	43
15	Thame United Reserves	34	11	9	14	52	67	42
16	Walton & Hersham Reserves	34	11	5	18	49	63	38
17	Corinthian Casuals Reserves	34	7	7	20	42	75	28
18	Hendon Reserves	34	7	4	23	49	83	25

	NORTH DIVISION	P	W	D	L	F	A	Pts
1	Oxford City Reserves	34	25	3	6	92	31	78
2	Aylesbury United Reserves	34	23	6	5	82	41	75
3	Boreham Wood Reserves	34	19	8	7	77	48	65
4	Leighton Town Reserves	34	19	7	8	74	39	64
5	Uxbridge Reserves	34	16	10	8	69	46	58
6	Thatcham Town Reserves	34	15	8	11	75	66	53
7	Chesham United Reserves	34	15	7	12	73	49	52
8	Hanwell Town Reserves	34	15	5	14	55	50	50
9	Beaconsfield SYCOB Reserves	34	15	5	14	55	59	50
10	Wembley Reserves	34	13	8	13	59	65	47
11	Hillingdon Borough Reserves	34	11	9	14	62	80	42
12	Abingdon Town Reserves	34	12	3	19	45	71	39
13	Ruislip Manor Reserves	34	10	6	18	48	63	36
14	Abingdon United Reserves	34	10	6	18	51	72	36
15	Hungerford Town Reserves	34	7	10	17	56	79	31
16	Burnham Reserves	34	9	4	21	53	80	31
17	Reading Town Reserves	34	9	3	22	39	99	30
18	AFC Wallingford Reserves	34	8	2	24	52	79	26

	SOUTH DIVISION	P	W	D	L	F	A	Pts
1	Whyteleafe Reserves	34	25	5	4	96	30	80
2	Ashford (Mx) Reserves	34	22	5	7	83	40	71
3	Wealdstone Reserves	34	20	8	6	91	41	68
4	Tooting & Mitcham Reserves	34	20	4	10	118	46	64
5	Fisher Athletic Reserves	34	20	4	10	83	64	64
6	Croydon Athletic Reserves	34	19	4	11	76	49	61
7	Epsom & Ewell Reserves	34	17	8	9	73	61	59
8	Tonbridge Angels Reserves	34	16	7	11	67	54	55
9	Windsor & Eton Reserves	34	15	7	12	75	64	52
10	Bracknell Town Reserves	34	13	8	13	53	53	47
11	Croydon Reserves	34	12	4	18	57	63	40
12	Molesey Reserves	34	11	5	18	50	71	38
13	Camberley Town Reserves	34	10	5	19	49	66	35
14	Chipstead Reserves	34	9	5	20	45	94	32
15	Walton Cas. Reserves	34	7	8	19	38	76	29
16	Godalming & Guildford Reserves	34	7	6	21	32	69	27
17	Chertsey Town Reserves	34	7	3	24	37	102	24
18	Fleet Town Reserves	34	6	4	24	44	124	2

ESSEX, & HERTS
BORDERING COUNTIES COMBINATION

Hon Secretary: Fred Hawthorn, PO Box 115,
Upminster, Essex RM14 3AQ Tel: 01708 225451

FINAL LEAGUE TABLES 2002-03

PREMIER DIVISION

		Home			Away			Totals						
	P	W	D	L	W	D	L	W	D	L	F	A	GD	Pts
Canvey Island	30	13	0	2	10	3	2	23	3	4	101	28	73	72
Hornchurch	30	12	2	1	10	2	3	22	4	4	91	22	69	70
Great Wakering Rovers	30	10	4	1	8	3	4	18	7	5	81	34	47	61
Braintree Town	30	12	1	2	6	3	6	18	4	8	65	34	31	58
Leyton	30	8	4	3	9	1	5	17	5	8	77	32	45	56
East Thurrock United (-2)	30	9	6	0	6	5	4	15	11	4	60	26	34	54
Ilford	30	9	1	5	6	3	6	15	4	11	60	54	6	49
Witham Town	30	7	2	6	8	1	6	15	3	12	62	61	1	48
Heybridge Swifts	30	9	1	5	2	7	6	11	8	11	69	57	12	41
Ware	30	5	5	5	6	3	6	11	8	11	48	68	-20	41
Brentwood	30	5	4	6	3	1	11	8	5	17	48	73	-25	29
Tilbury	30	5	2	8	3	3	9	8	5	17	38	64	-26	29
Cheshunt	30	4	2	9	2	1	12	6	3	21	40	80	-40	21
Broxbourne Borough	30	3	2	10	1	3	11	4	5	21	39	99	-60	17
Waltham Abbey	30	3	4	8	1	0	14	4	4	22	30	97	-67	16
Burnham Ramblers	30	3	0	12	2	1	12	5	1	24	34	114	-80	16

DIVISION ONE

	P	W	D	L	W	D	L	W	D	L	F	A	GD	Pts
Purfleet	26	11	1	1	8	5	0	19	6	1	80	20	60	63
Barking & east Ham United	26	10	2	1	7	3	3	17	5	4	72	29	43	56
St Albans City	26	9	2	2	8	2	3	17	4	5	74	31	43	55
Romford	26	6	1	6	7	2	4	13	3	10	52	48	4	42
Bowers United	26	5	6	2	3	5	5	8	11	7	32	41	-9	35
Concord Rangers	26	5	2	6	4	5	4	9	7	10	42	49	-7	34
Basildon United	26	7	2	4	3	2	8	10	4	12	35	49	-14	34
Sawbridgeworth Town	26	3	3	7	7	1	5	10	4	12	34	58	-24	34
Maldon Town (-3)	26	6	3	4	3	3	7	9	6	11	43	46	-3	30
Southend Manor	26	4	4	5	4	2	7	8	6	12	37	45	-8	30
Hertford Town	26	3	4	6	4	4	5	7	8	11	37	41	-4	29
Harlow Town	26	3	6	4	3	3	7	6	9	11	35	47	-12	27
Stansted	26	4	4	5	0	4	9	4	8	14	27	55	-28	20
Hoddesdon Town	26	2	3	8	0	2	11	2	5	19	28	69	-41	11

Bishop's Stortford withdrew - record expinged.

COMBINATION CUP 2002-03

THIRD ROUND

St Albans City	v	Heybridge	3-1
Hornchurch	v	Leyton	4-0
Romford	v	Gt. Wakering Rovers	0-4
Barking & East Ham	v	Purfleet	1-2

SEMI-FINALS

Gt. Wakering Rovers	v	St Albans City1-1 (aet) 5-4p	
Hornchurch	v	Purfleet	1-4

FINAL

Gt. Wakering Rovers	v	Purfleet	4-0

FRED BUDDEN TROPHY 2002-03

THIRD ROUND

Canvey Island	v	Hornchurch	1-0
St Albans City	v	Leyton	0-1
Bowers United	v	Sawbridgeworth Tn	1-0
Concord Rangers	v	Purfleet	0-3

SEMI-FINALS

Bowers United	v	Canvey Island	0-1
Leyton	v	Purfleet	3-0

FINAL

Canvey Island	v	Leyton	0-0 (aet) 5-4p

CAPITAL FOOTBALL LEAGUE

Chairman & Treasurer: David Free **Secretary:** Adrian Cook
41 Amis Avenue, New Haw, Addlestone, Surrey KT15 3ET
Tel 01932 888474 Fax: 01932 345604

FINAL LEAGUE TABLE 2002-03

		Home					Away						
	P	W	D	L	F	A	W	D	L	F	A	GD	Pts
SOUTH WEST DIVISION													
Yeading	12	4	1	1	14	6	5	0	1	19	8	19	28
Woking	12	5	1	0	11	5	3	1	2	13	9	10	26
Aldershot Town	12	2	1	3	15	13	3	1	2	17	13	6	17
Farnborough Town	12	3	1	2	13	10	2	0	4	8	15	-4	16
Havant & Waterlooville	12	2	2	2	13	14	2	1	3	13	16	-4	15
Slough Town	12	2	0	4	10	14	1	3	2	7	8	-5	12
Harrow Borough	12	1	1	4	8	18	0	1	5	3	15	-22	5
NORTH EAST DIVISION													
Stevenage Borough	16	5	1	2	20	18	6	1	1	16	4	14	35
Purfleet	16	7	1	0	26	4	3	2	3	16	17	21	33
Dagenham & Redbridge	16	3	4	1	21	10	5	1	2	15	6	20	29
Hitchin Town	16	5	1	2	22	11	4	1	3	27	22	16	29
Gravesend & Northfleet	16	4	1	3	25	13	4	2	2	27	11	28	27
Grays Athletic	16	3	2	3	11	12	2	0	6	8	21	-14	17
Bishop's Stortford	16	3	2	3	14	18	1	1	6	10	28	-22	15
Bedford Town	16	1	1	6	14	21	1	2	5	8	25	-24	9
Billericay Town	16	1	1	6	4	26	0	4	4	6	23	-39	8

We got there - just!

I think you will agree it was not the easiest of seasons but with the new two league structure it did manage to finish. Special thanks to Adrian Cook and Alan Couch whose perseverance ensured that all fixtures were scheduled and played. The Capital League is always going to rank behind first team fixtures so there will never be a perfect solution to this problem but on behalf of the league I would also like to thank the fixtures secretaries at each club.We bid farewell to Havant and Bedford and wish them well. We will be welcoming new clubs at our AGM and will see the continuing growth of our league. Amazingly we now enter season number 19 and for Peter Cork, Peter Braxton and myself, this means 19 years of loyal service.

Congratulations to Yeading and Stevenage for winning their respective divisions and to Stevenage and Slough for reaching the final of the Doxhill President's Challenge Cup.

A special mention too for our sponsors - Sygnus Office Partnership and Doxhill, who have yet again supported our league financially and enable us to offer prize money. They are both committed to next season.

Enjoy your well-earned break. **David Free - Chairman.**

SOUTH WEST	**1**	**2**	**3**	**4**	**5**	**6**	**7**
1 Aldershot		4-2	2-2	6-1	1-2	0-1	2-5
2 Farnborough	1-2		5-0	2-0	1-1	3-1	1-6
3 Harrow Borough	4-3	1-4		1-5	0-0	2-4	0-2
4 Havant & Waterlooville	4-4	1-2	1-0		3-2	2-2	2-4
5 Slough Town	0-4	3-0	4-1	2-3		0-4	1-2
6 Woking	2-1	1-0	1-0	3-2	2-2		2-0
7 Yeading	2-3	5-0	2-0	2-2	1-0	2-1	

NORTH EAST	**1**	**2**	**3**	**4**	**5**	**6**	**7**	**8**	**9**
1 Bedford Town		3-3	1-2	0-3	1-4	1-2	3-4	5-1	0-2
2 Billericay T.	0-3		1-0	1-5	1-6	1-4	0-4	0-4	0-0
3 Bishop's S.	1-0	3-1		1-4	2-2	3-1	1-5	3-3	0-2
4 Dagenham & R	3-3	0-0	2-2		3-1	4-0	7-1	2-2	0-1
5 Gravesned & N	3-0	4-0	9-1	0-2		4-0	4-4	1-2	0-4
6 Grays Ath.	4-1	1-1	4-1	0-0	1-6		1-0	0-1	0-2
7 Hitchin Town	1-1	5-0	6-1	0-1	3-2	4-1		2-1	1-4
8 Purfleet	6-0	6-0	2-1	3-0	0-0	1-0	5-2		3-1
9 Stevenage B.	7-0	1-1	3-2	1-0	0-6	3-0	1-7	4-2	

2003 -04 CONSTITUTION

SOUTH WEST	NORTH EAST
Chesham United	Billericay Town
Farnborough Town	Bishop's Stortford
Harrow Borough	Dagenham & Red.
Hendon	Ford United
Slough Town	Gravesned & Nflt.
Staines Town	Hitchin Town
Woking	Hornchurch
Yeading	Stevenage Boro'
	Thurrock
	Waltham Forest

DOXHILL PRESIDENT'S CUP 2002-03

Harrow B	3					
Bedford T.	2					
Grays Ath	AT					
Aldershot		Harrow Boro.	0			
Billericay	2	Slough Town	3			
Stevenage	4			Slough Town	5	
Purfleet	3	Bishop's Stort.	2	Purfleet	2	Slough Town
Woking	2	Grays Ath.	0			Stevenage
Gravesend	6					To be played early
Havant & W	1	Stevenage	5			03-04 season
Yeading	1	Yeading	3	Bishop's Stort.	1	
Dagenham	0			Stevenage	2	
Farnborough	*3	Gravesend	0			
Bishop's S.	4	Purfleet	4			
Slough	4					
Hitchin	0					

AT - Awarded Tie. *AET 2-2 @ 90mins

COUNTY FOOTBALL ASSOCIATIONS

BEDFORDSHIRE F.A.

Tel: 01582 565111 (B) Fax: 01582 565222 Email: info@bedfordshirefa.com
Century House, Skimpot Road, Dunstable LU5 4JU

Secretary: Peter D Brown

Executives (Responsibility)	Century House for Coaching Exams/Courses, Referees, Womens Football
Number of Affiliated Clubs	Senior: 507
Number of Affiliated Leagues:	Senior: 9 Junior: 5
County Representative Teams:	Senior, U18, U16, Intermediate, Womens
Inter County Competitions:	East Anglia Counties Intermediate, U18, U16 & Womens, FA County Youth Cup

President: R Berridge

BEDFORDSHIRE SENIOR TROPHY - FOUNDED 2002-03

(12entries)

FIRST ROUND

Crawley Green v Old Dunstablians	1-2
Kent Athletic v Langford	2-3
Brache Sparta v Cranfield United	3-0
Ampthill Town v Shillington	0-2

SECOND ROUND 19th October

Totternhoe v Old Dunstablians	0-6
Langford v Potton United	1-3
(Result Void Winners disqualified - Club re-instated)	
Brache Sparta v 61 FC Luton	*4-3
Caddington v Shillington	3-2

SEMI-FINALS

Brache Sparta v Old Dunstablians	*4-2
Potton United v Caddington	5-0

FINAL Tuesday 29th April 2003

Brache Sparta v Langford	*2-1
at Stotfold FC	

BEDFORDSHIRE SENIOR CUP

(12 entries)

LAST SEASON'S FINAL

Barton Rovers 2 Stotfold 3

FIRST ROUND w/c 23rd September

Barton Rovers v Dunstable Town	1-2
Biggleswade United v Stotfold	0-2
Kempston Rovers v Wootton Blue Cross	0-1
Leighton Town v Biggleswade Town	*1-3

SECOND ROUND w/c 11th November

Bedford United v Dunstable Town	0-4
Stotfold v Bedford Town	0-3
Wootton Blue Cross v Luton Town	3-4pens *0-0
Biggleswade Town v Arlesey Town	1-2

SEMI-FINALS 4th & 5th March

1 Arlesey Town v Dunstable Town	0-1
2 Bedford Town v Luton Town	BT W-O

FINAL Tuesday 6th May

Bedford Town v Dunstable Town	0-1
at Arlesey Town FC	

BERKS & BUCKS F.A. LIMITED

Tel: 01367 242099 Fax: 01367 242158
15a London Street, Faringdon, Oxon SN7 7HD
email: info@berks-bucksfa.com www.berksandbucksfa.com

Chief Executive: Brian Moore **Press Officer:** Brian Moore

Responsibilities Richard Lipscombe (Cup Comps)
P R Hill (Referees)

Number of Affiliated Leagues: Senior: 18 Junior: 10

County Representative Teams: U18, Women

Inter County Competitions: South/South West Counties Championship Youth

President: W J Gosling
Chairman: J Atkins

BERKS & BUCKS SENIOR CUP - FOUNDED 1878 - 79

(14 entries)

LAST SEASON'S FINAL

Maidenhead United 3 Slough Town 2

MOST WINS

Wycombe 24 Maidenhead united 18 Marlow 13

FIRST ROUND

Slough Town v Wycombe Wanderers	1-0
Aylesbury United v Wokingham Town	4-0
Burnham v Hungerford Town	3-1
Flackwell Heath v Chalfont St Peter	*1-1 2-1
Marlow v Bracknell Town	5-1
Windsor & Eton v Abingdon Town	3-1
Chesham United	bye
Maidenhead United	bye

QUARTER-FINALS

Flackwell Heath v Aylesbury United	2-2 0-4
Maidenhead United v Slough Town	3-1
Windsor & Eton v Marlow	1-0
Burnham v Chesham United	1-1 *2-2 4-3pens

SEMI-FINALS

Aylesbury United v Burnham	5-0
2Windsor & Eton v Maidenhead United	0-5

FINAL Monday 5th May 3pm

Aylesbury United v Maidenhead United	1-4

at Chesham United FC

BERKS & BUCKS SENIOR TROPHY

(13 entries)

LAST SEASON'S FINAL

Milton Keynes City 3 Thatcham Town 1

FIRST ROUND by Friday 29th November

Reading Town v Wantage Town	4-2
Sandhurst Town v Beaconsfield SYCOB	*3-0
Thatcham Town v Buckingham Town	2-1
Holmer Green v Didcot Town	1-3
Newport Pagnell Town v Newbury	1-3
Abingdon United	bye
Wallingford	bye
Milton Keynes City	bye

QUARTER-FINALS

Milton Keynes City v Newbury	2-1
Wallingford v Didcot Town 1-2	
Reading Town v Abingdon United	1-1 0-4
Sandhurst Town v Thatcham Town	0-1

SEMI-FINALS by Friday 21st March

1 Milton Keynes City v Thatcham Town	1-0
2 Didcot Town v Abingdon United	3-0

FINAL Saturday 26th April 3pm

Didcot Town v Milton Keynes City	2-0

at Didcot Town FC

Didcot Town celebrate their 2-0 Berks & Bucks Senior Trophy win over Milton Keynes City.

BIRMINGHAM COUNTY F.A.

Tel: 0121 357 4278 Fax: 0121 358 1661 Email: secretary@bcfa.co.uk or info@birminghamfa.com

Ray Hall Lane, Great Barr, Birmingham B43 6JF

Company Secretary: M Pennick F.F.A.

Secretary: D Selton **PR Officer:** A Lacey

Executives (Responsibility) T Stack (Coaching Exams/Courses) D Sheltonl (Referees)
Natalie Justice (Football Development Officer)
Rachael Dunlop (Womens Football)

President: K H Goodfellow

Number of Affiliated Clubs Senior: 1,663 U.18: 484

Number of Affiliated Leagues: Senior: 55 Junior: 14

County Representative Teams: U18, U17, Womens Open, U18, U16

Inter County Competitions: FA County Youth, Midland County Youth (Men & Women)

County Publications: "The Centre Circle" bi-monthly newsletter

BIRMINGHAM SENIOR CUP - FOUNDED 1875-76

(31 entries)

LAST SEASON'S FINAL

West Bromwich Albion 1 Wednesfield 0

MOSTS WINS

Aston Villa 19 Birmingham City 10 Kidderminster Harriers 7 Wolverhampton Wanderers 7

FIRST ROUND on or before 26th October

Atherstone United v Bromsgrove Rovers	1-3
Stratford Town v Rushall Olympic	*2-3
Racing Club Warwick v Willenhall Town	*4-4 3-4pens

SECOND ROUND on or before 23rd November

Bromsgrove Rovers v Moor Green	0-3
Hednesford Town v Rugby United	7-2
Grosvenor Park v Tamworth	2-5
Rushall Olympic v Nuneaton Borough	1-5
Bedworth United v Cradley Town	4-0
Sutton Coldfield Town v Willenhall Town	1-0
Boldmere St Michaels v Stourbridge	*2-2 0-4
Halesowen Town v Studley	3-0
Solihull Borough v Halesowen Harriers	2-0
Wednesfield v Oldbury United	2-6
Burton Albion v Redditch United	2-1
Banbury United v Causeway United	4-2

THIRD ROUND by 11th January 2003

Tamworth v West Bromwich Albion	*1-1 4-3pens
Halesowen Town v Birmingham City	1-3
Solihull Borough v Walsall 0-4	
Hednesford Town v Oldbury United	0-3
(Oldbury United fielded an ineligible player and are removed from the competition Hednesford T reinstated)	
Banbury United v Stourbridge	2-1
Nuneaton Borough v Bedworth United	6-0
Moor Green v Sutton Coldfield Town	2-1
Burton Albion v Wolverhampton Wanderers	0-5

QUARTER-FINALS

Nuneaton Borough v Walsall	0-5
Hednesford Town v Wolverhampton Wanderers	1-3
Moor Green v Tamworth	1-3
(Moor Green re-instated, Tamworth ineligible player)	
4 Banbury United v Birmingham City	2-4

SEMI FINALS

Moor Green v Wolverhampton Wanderers	2-1
Walsall v Birmingham City	0-2

FINAL Monday 28th April

Birmingham City v Moor Green	2-0
at Solihull Borough FC	

CAMBRIDGESHIRE F.A. LTD

Tel: 01223 576770 Fax: 01223 576780 Email: info@cambridgeshirefa.com
City Ground, Milton Road, Cambridge CB4 1FA

Secretary: Roger Pawley

Executives (Responsibility) Richard Nichols (Asst Gen Sec, County Referees Sec)
Jim Hill (Football Development Officer)
Phil Mitcham (Competitions Secretary)
Kirsty Prior (Girls/Womens Development Officer)

Number of Affiliated Clubs Senior: 350 U.18: 50

Number of Affiliated Leagues: Senior: 1 Junior: 6

County Representative Teams: U18, U16, Womens

Inter County Competitions: East Anglian Counties

President: W W Ashton
Chairman: J W Coad

CAMBRIDGESHIRE INVITATION CUP - FOUNDED 1950-51

(11 entries)

LAST SEASON'S FINAL

Ely City 2 Cambridge City 0

MOST WINS

Cambridge City 10 Wisbech Town 9 Chatteris Town 7

Preliminary Round Tuesday 22nd October 2002

Histon v Whittlesey United	8-0
Newmarket Town v Mildenhall Town	3-1
March Town United v Sawston United	0-2

FIRST ROUND Tuesday 7th January 2003

1 Cambridge City v Fordham		5-0
2 Soham Town Rangers v Histon	116	1-5
3 Newmarket Town v Ely City	66	7-1
4 Wisbech Town v Sawston United	123	0-1

SEMI-FINALS

Newmarket Town v Histon	0-1
Sawston United v Cambridge City	0-2

FINAL Monday 14th April

Cambridge City v Histon	*2-2 8-7pens
at Cambridge United FC	att: 535

CHESHIRE F.A.

Tel: 01606 871166 Fax: 01606 871292 Football Development: 01606 871155
The Cottage, Moss Farm Recreation Centre, Winnington, Northwich CW8 4BG

Secretary & Press Officer: Maureen J Dunford

Executives (Responsibility) John Ackerley (Coaching Exams/Courses & Development Officer)
Bob Cooper (Referees), Jacci Cooper (Women's Football)

President: Alan Burbidge

Number of Affiliated Clubs Senior: 816 U.18: 325

Number of Affiliated Leagues: Senior: 27 Junior: 13

County Representative Teams: Senior, U18s, Womens, U16 Girls teams

Inter County Competitions: FA County Youth, Northern Counties Youth Cup, Ladies Cup and Senior Cup

CHESHIRE SENIOR CUP - FOUNDED 1879-80

(18 entries)

LAST SEASON'S FINAL

Stalybridge Celtic 2 Crewe Alexandra 7

MOST WINS

Macclesfield Town 20 Northwich Victoria 16 Crewe Alexandra 14 Runcorn 12

PRELIMINARY ROUND

Witton Albion v Congleton Town	*5-4
Hyde United v Northwich Victoria	1-3

FIRST ROUND

Cheadle Town v Chester City	1-4
Northwich Victoria v Stalybridge Celtic	2-1
Woodley Sports v Alsager Town	*5-5 3-2
Nantwich Town v Stockport County	1-1 1-2
Macclesfield Town v Tranmere Rovers	1-2
Crewe Alexandra v Altrincham	3-1
Winsford United v Warrington Town	2-1
Vauxhall Motors v Witton Albion	3-2

SECOND ROUND

Stockport County v Chester City	*1-3
(Tie awarded to Stockport County)	
Winsford United v Northwich Victoria	0-3
Tranmere Rovers v Woodley Sports	7-1
Crewe Alexandra v Vauxhall Motors	2-1
(played at Vauxhall Motors)	

SEMI-FINALS

Crewe Alexandra v Tranmere Rovers	5-2
Stockport County v Northwich Victoria	1-2

FINAL

Crewe Alexandra v Northwich Victoria	2-1
at Altrincham FC	

CORNWALL F.A.

Tel: 01726 74080 Fax: 01726 76174 E-mail: cornwallcfa@aol.com
1 High Cross Street, St Austell, Cornwall PL25 4AB

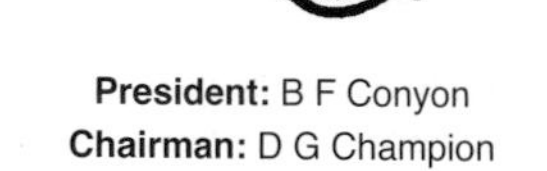

Secretary: Barry Cudmore

Executives (Responsibility) David Bray (Youth Secretary)
Ian Anear (Referees)
Phil Cardew (Football Development Officer)

Number of Affiliated Clubs Senior: 311 U.18: 84

Number of Affiliated Leagues: Senior: 20 Youth: 2

County Representative Teams: Senior, Youth U18

Inter County Competitions: South West Counties Senior, Youth & Womens, FA County Youth Cup

President: B F Conyon
Chairman: D G Champion

CORNWALL SENIOR CUP - FOUNDED 1892-93

(41 entries)

LAST SEASON'S FINAL

Liskeard Athletic 0 St. Blazey 2

MOST WINS

Truro City 12 St Blazey 12 St Austell 11 Penzance 10 Torpoint Athletic 10

FIRST ROUND

Dobwalls v Bude Town	4-2
Goonhavern Athletic v Illogan RBL	3-1
Hayle v Camelford	6-3
Marazion Blues v Mousehole	1-2
Nanpean Rovers v Padstow United	2-2 4-1
Perranwell v St Just	1-2
Sticker v St Cleer	1-8
St agnes v st Dennis	2-1
St Ives Town v RNAS Culdrose	2-0

(7 Byes & 16 (SWL) Exemptions to Second Round)

SECOND ROUND

Bodmin Town v Helston Athletic	3-1
Callington Town v Nanpean Rovers	3-1
Falmouth Town v Mousehole	7-0
Foxhole Stars v Saltash United	4-1
Goonhavern Athletic v Penryn Athletic	1-2
Hayle v Ludgvan	7-1
Liskeard Athletic v St Austell	3-0
Millbrook v Dobwalls	3-2
Mullion v Launceston	1-3
Penzance v Wendron	4-0
St Agnes v St Cleer	2-2 3-2
St Blazey v Roche	8-1
St Ives Town v Newquay	2-4
Torpoint Athletic v Probus	5-1
Truro City v Porthleven	0-7
Wadebridge Town v St Just	3-2

QUARTER-FINALS

Launceston v Liskeard Athletic	0-3
Millbrook v Penzance	2-1
St Blazey v Bodmin Town	3-0
Torpoint Athletic v Wadebridge Town 2-2 *1-1	7-8pens

SEMI-FINALS

1 Liskeard Athletic v Torpoint Athletic 3-2
2 Millbrook v St Blazey0-3

FINAL Monday 21st April 2003
Liskeard Athletic v St Blazey 1-1
at Penzance FC

FINAL (replay) Wednesday 30th April
St Blazey v Liskeard Athletic *1-1 2-4pens
at Millbrook FC

CUMBERLAND F.A.

Tel: 01900 872310 Fax: 01900 872310
17 Oxford Street, Workington, Cumbria CA14 2AL

Secretary & Press Officer:	Geoff Turrell			
Development Officer:	R Patterson			
Executives (Responsibility)	Paul Devlin (Coaching Exams/Courses)			
	Harry Upton & Thomas Jackson (Referees)			
Number of Affiliated Clubs	Senior: 170		U.18:	211
Number of Affiliated Leagues:	Senior: 6		Junior:	3
County Representative Teams:	Senior, Youth, Womens			
Inter County Competitions:	FA County Youth, Northern Counties			

President: Brian Taylor
Chairman: R J Turner

CUMBERLAND SENIOR CUP - FOUNDED 1960-61
(33 entries)

LAST SEASON'S FINAL
Carlisle City 0 Carlisle United 2

MOST WINS
Penrith 11 Gretna 9 Haig Colliery 3

FIRST ROUND
Northbank Carlisle v Greystoke 6-0

SECOND ROUND Saturday 2nd November
1 Silloth v Mirehouse Community 0-4
2 Hearts of Liddlesdale v Whitehaven 1-6
3 Wetheriggs United v Braithewaite 8-1
4 Salterbeck v St Bees 3-5
5 British Steel v Penrith Rangers 3-0
6 Abbeytown v Longtown 2-0
7 Pirelli v Workington *2-1
8 Harraby Catholic v Windscales 1-2
9 Whitehaven Miners v Egremont St Mary's 5-0
10 Cleator Moor Celtic v (Thornhill) Netherall 1-3
11 Frizington White Star v Penrith *2-4
12 Carlisle City v Keswick 5-0
13 Carleton Rovers v Northbank 1-6
14 Aspatria v Carlisle United Res 2-5
15 Wigton Harriers v Cockermouth 4-2
16 New Harraby v Kirkoswald 1-4

THIRD ROUND Saturday 7th December
Kirkoswald v Mirehouse 0-1
Wetheriggs v Windscale *2-2 6-5pens
Whitehaven Miners v Penrith 0-8
British Steel v Abbeytown 2-0
Carlisle United Res v Pirelli 5-0
St Bees v Whitehaven 2-3
Netherall v Northbank *0-0 1-3pens
Carlisle City v Wigton Harriers 3-0

FOURTH ROUND 8th March
British Steel Workington v Varlisle United Res 1-4
Mirehouse v Penrith 1-3
Wetheriggs v Whitehaven *3-3 2-3pens
Carlisle City v Northbank 2-3

SEMI-FINALS 12th April
Carlisle United Res v Whitehaven 2-1
Penrith v Northbank 0-2

FINAL 5th May
Carlisle United Res v Northbank 0-4
at Brunton Park, Carlisle United FC

DERBYSHIRE F.A.

Tel: 01332 361422 Fax: 01332 360130
Nos 8-9 Stadium Business Court, Millennium Way, Pride Park, Derby DE24 8HZ

Secretary & Press Officer: K Compton
Executives (Responsibility) County Secretary (Referees)
Craig Lee & Debbie Wood
(Football Development & Womens Football)
No. Affiliated Clubs & Leagues 800
County Representative Teams: U16, U18
Inter County Competitions: Midlands Youth Football Championships

Chairman: R F Johnson

DERBYSHIRE SENIOR CUP - FOUNDED 1883-84
(23 entries)

LAST SEASON'S FINAL
Gresley Rovers 4 Alfreton Town 5 on aggregate

MOST WINS
Derby County 15 Ilkeston Town 13 Buxton 8 Chesterfield 8 Heanor Town 8

FIRST ROUND on or before 5th October

Blackwell M W v Khalsa Sports GAD	4-1
Holbrook v Sandiacre Town	5-1
South Normanton Athletic v Graham St Prims	3-2
Stapenhill v Ripley Town	1-5

SECOND ROUND Saturday 2nd November
Heanor Town v South Normanton Athletic*2-2 7-8pens
Holbrook v Blackwell M W 1*2
New Mills v Ripley Town 3-5

THIRD ROUND by Saturday 23rd November

Alfreton Town v Ripley Town	3-0
Belper Town v Glapwell	*1-1 5-4pens
Long Eaton United v Ilkeston Town	2-3
Matlock Town v Shirebrook Town	5-3
Glossop North End v Blackwell M W	2-1
Gresley Rovers v Buxton	4-0
Mickleover Sports v Borrowash Victoria	3-0
Staveley M W v South Normanton Athletic	1-2

FOURTH ROUND

Alfreton Town v Glossop North End	3-0
Belper Town v Matlock Town	4-0
Ilkeston Town v Mickleover Sports	0-2
South Normanton Athletic v Gresley Rovers	2-3

SEMI-FINALS Tuesday 18th February

Belper Town v Alfreton Town	0-1
Gresley Rovers v Mickleover Sports	0-4

FINAL First Leg Tuesday 15th April
Mickleover Sports v Alfreton Town 0-5
at Station Road, Mickleover Sports FC

FINAL Second Leg Tuesday 29th April
Alfreton Town v Mickleover Sports 2-1
at The North Street Ground, Alfreton Town FC

Alfreton won 7-1 on aggregate.

DEVON F.A.

Tel: 01626 332077 Fax: 01626 336814
County Headquarters, Coach Road, Newton Abbot, Devon TQ12 1EJ

Secretary & Press Officer:	Chris J Davidson
Executives (Responsibility)	R Soper (Coaching Exams) C Cox (Referees)
	M Lawrence (Womens Football) C Davey (Coaching Courses)
Number of Affiliated Clubs	Senior: 161 U.18: 252
Number of Affiliated Leagues:	Senior: 50 Junior: 10
County Representative Teams:	Senior, U18, Womens
Inter County Competitions:	South West Counties Championship
County Publications:	"Kick Off" - bi-monthly Newsletter

Chairman: Brian Williams

Westinsure DEVON PREMIER CUP
(68 entries)

LAST SEASON'S FINAL

Tavistock 1 Vospers Oak Villa 0

FIRST ROUND by 14th September 2002

Combined 89 v St Martins	1-3
Teignmouth v Chelston	3-1
Calmpton United v East Allington	3-2
Buckfastleigh Rangers v Plymouth Command	4-1
High Bickington v Exeter St Thomas	3-1
Chudleigh Athletic v Combe Martin	0-4
Elmore Res v Hatherleigh Town	5-0
Tap & Barrel v Pinhoe	6-1
Dolton Rangers v Mainstone Sports	DR W-O
Roborough v Sidmouth Town	5-1
Torrington Admirals v Northam Lions	1-4
Putford v Totnes Town	1-5
Witheridge v Prince Rock	4-2
Barnstaple AAC v Seaton Town	0-1
Manstow v Kingsteignton Athletic	3-2
Plympton United v Mount Gould B P	0-2
Okehampton Argyle v South Molton	8-1
Willand Rovers v Liverton United	4-0
Kingskerswell v Civil Service Sport & Leisure	1-2
Wessex Rangers RM v Shamwickshire Rovers	1-3

6 Byes Upton Athletic; Bradworthy United; Braunton; Hele Rovers; Georgeham Croyde; Victoria Rangers.

SECOND ROUND on or by 5th October

Stoke Gabriel v Elmore	1-0
Okehampton Argyle v Shamwickshire Rovers	0-3
Braunton v Manstow	1-0
Bradworthy United v St Martins	5-1
Appledore v Georgeham & Croyde	3-0
Crediton v Teignmouth	1-7
Tap & Barrel v Dolton Rangers	13-1
Witheridge v Plymstock United	1-2
Victoria Rangers v Hele Rovers	1-4
Willand Rovers v High Bickington	8-0
Buckfastleigh Rangers v Civil service S & L	0-1
Seaton Town v Dartington Sports Club	1-2
Totnes Town v Upton Athletic	0-6
Northam Lions v Mount Gold B P	0-2
Roborough v Combe Martin	1-2
Gampton United v Tavistock	0-5

THIRD ROUND on or by 26th October

Mount Gold Black Prince v Tavistock	0-2
Plymstock v Hele Rovers	*0-0 3-0pens
Newton Abbot v Exeter Civil Service	4-0
Teignmouth v Alphington	0*2
Upton Athletic v Appledore	3-1
Civil service S&L v Budleigh Salterton	5*3
Newton abbot Spurs v Ivybridge Town	1-7
Topsham Town v Elburton Villa	2-1
Dartmouth v Dartington SC	1-0
Vospers Oak Villa v Cullompton Rangers	2-0
Bradworthy United v Plymouth Parkway	2-3
Buckland athletic v Tap & Barrel	4-0
Shamwickshire v HeaviTree United	1-2
Stoke Gabriel v Willand Rovers	1-2
Combe Martin v Holsworthy	1-2
Braunton v Ottery St Mary	0-1

FOURTH ROUND

Plymouth Parkway v Vospers Oak Villa	4-1
Civil Service S & L v Topsham Town	3-0
Heavitree United v Ottery St Mary	5-1
Ivybridge Town v Tavistock 1-2	
Buckland Athletic v Plymstock United	1-2
Holsworthy v Alphington	1-0
Upton Athletic v Willand Rovers	9-1
Dartmouth v Newton Abbot 3-0	

QUARTER-FINALS

Holsworthy v Dartmouth	0-3
Tavistock v Plymouth Parkway	1-2
Upton Athletic v Heavitree United	3-1
Plymstock United v Civil Service Sport & Leisure	3-0

SEMI-FINALS 15th February

Plymstock United v Dartmouth	2-1
Upton Athletic v Plymouth Parkway	*1-1 4-2pens

FINAL Monday 31/3

Plymstock United v Upton Athletic	2-0

at Plainmoor, Torquay United FC

DEVON ST LUKES BOWL 2002-03

(13 entries)

LAST YEAR'S FINAL

Exeter City 3 Torquay United 1

FIRST ROUND

Elmore v Torquay United	1-4
Exmouth Town v Tiverton Town	*3-3 4-5pens
Barnstaple Town v Plymouth Argyle	2-5
Clyst Rovers v Torrington	2-1
Bideford v Exeter City	B W-O

Byes Dawlish Town, Ilfracombe, Willand Rovers

SECOND ROUND

Willand Rovers v Dawlish Town	2-0
Ilfracombe Town v Torquay United	0-1
Tiverton Town v Plymouth Argyle	3-2
Clyst Rovers v Bideford	1-4

SEMI-FINALS

Willand Rovers v Torquay United	0-2
Tiverton Town v Bideford	2-0

FINAL Pre-season

Torquay United v Tiverton Town	0-1

at Plainmoor, Torquay United FC

DORSET F.A.

Tel: 01202 682375 Fax: 01202 666577
County Ground, Blandford Close, Hamworthy, Poole BH15 4BF

Chief Executive: Peter Hough
Cup & Competitions Manager: Colin Chainey
Press Officer: Ian Hallett
Executives (Responsibility) Sue Hough (Football Development Manager)
Gary Knight (Football Development Officer)
S N Whittle (Referees)
County Representative Teams: Senior, U18, Womens
Inter County Competitions: South West Championship for all the above

President: Spencer Miles
Chairman: Doug Smurthwaite

DORSET SENIOR CUP - FOUNDED 1887-88

(43 entries)

LAST SEASON'S FINAL

Dorchester Town 1 Weymouth 1 (aet)

Weymouth won 3-1 after penalties

MOST WINS

Weymouth 27 Poole Town 10 Portland United 10 Bridport 9

FIRST ROUND by 5th October

St Mary's RC v Bournemouth Sports	0-6
Royal Oak Cougars v Poole Town	0-1
Wareham Rangers v Poole Borough	4-3
Sturmister Newton United v Weymouth United	*3-2
West Moors v Holt United	*3-6
Okeford United v Piddletrenthide United	3-6
Cranborne v Stourpaine	3-1
Chickerell United v Shaftsbury	1-3
Cobham Sports v Sherborne Town	2-1
Dorchester Sports v Trinidad New Star	1-2
Barwick & Stoford v Allendale	0-3
Weymouth Post Office v Dorset Knob	0-1
Verwood Town v Weymouth Sports	4-0
St Pauls Jersey v Gillingham Town	2-3
Dorchester United v Witchampton United	3-0
Sturminster Marshall v Moreton	2-3
Crossways v Marina Sports	1-2
(Tie awarded to Crossways)	

SECOND ROUND on or by 2nd November

Cranbourne v Verwood Town	*0-0 1-3
Dorset Knob v Dorchester United	3-4
Holt United v Hamworthy Recreation	3-1
Crossways v Bournemouth Sports	2-4
Blandford United v Gillingham Town	2-5
Piddletrenthide United v Allendale	1-3
Poole Town v Sturminster Newton United	W-O
(Walkover for Poole Town)	
Wareham Rangers v Trinidad New Star	3-1
Cobham Sports v Shaftsbury	2-1
Hamworhy United v Moreton	5-1

THIRD ROUND Saturday 7th December

Allendale v Wimborne Town	2-5
Weymouth v Wareham Rangers	4-0
Hamworthy United v Holt United	2-0
Cobham Sports v Portland United	1-5
Gillingham Town v Bridport	0-1
Dorchester United v Swanage Town & Herston	*2-4
Poole Town v Dorchester Town	0-2
Bournemouth Sports v Cranborne	1-2

FOURTH ROUND

Bridport v Swanage Town & Herston	8-0
Dorchester Town v Hamworthy United	7-0
Portland United v Wimborne Town	*2-1
Weymouth v Cranborne	3-0

SEMI-FINALS

Portland United v Dorchester Town	0-2
Weymouth v Bridport	2-1

FINAL 15th April

Dorchester Town v Weymouth	2-0
at The Avenue, Dorchester Town FC att; 708	

DURHAM F.A.

Tel: 0191 384 8653 Fax: 0191 384 3234
"Codeslaw', Ferens Park, Durham DH1 1JZ

Secretary: John Topping

Executives (Responsibility)	A Philliskirk (Coaching Exams/Courses)				
	J C Topping (Referees)				
Number of Affiliated Clubs	Senior: 1100	Junior:	900		**President:** F D Pattison
Number of Affiliated Leagues:	Senior: 50	Junior:	26		**Chairman:** F D Pattison
County Representative Teams:	U18				
Inter County Competitions:	Association of Northern Counties, FA County Youth				

Albany DURHAM CHALLENGE CUP - FOUNDED 1883-84

(48 entries)

LAST SEASON'S FINAL

Bishop Auckland 1 Billingham Town 0

MOST WINS

Sunderland 21 Spennymoor United 15 Bishop Auckland 15

PRELIMINARY ROUND 5th October

West Auckland Town v Sunderland Res	0-1
Whickham v Washington Nissan	2-1
Washington v Shotton Comrades	4-1
Ryton v Wolviston	2-3
Spennymooor United v Norton & Stockton	6-4
South Shields Cleadon SC v Tow Law Town	1-5
Billingham Synthonia v Shildon	*3-2(Golden Goal)
Stanley United v Eppleton CW	1-4
Boldon C A v Sunderland Kennek Ryhope CA	3-1
Barnard Castle Glaxo v Birtley Town	0-2
Consett v South Shields Harton & Westoe	2-0
Seaham Red Star v Durham City	0-4
Annfield Plain v Murton	2-3
Esh Winning v Darlington Railway Athletic	7-0
Darlington Res v Hebburn Town	*3-2 (GG)
Sunderland Ryhope CW v Jarrow	3-1

FIRST ROUND Saturday 26th October 2002

Wolviston v Birtley	5-1
Whickham v South Shields	2-1
Gateshead v Consett	4-1
Peterlee Newtown v Tow Law Town	2-4
Murton v Chester Le Street Town	5-4
Horden v Crook Town	5-1
Hartlepool United Res v Birtley Town (played at Seaham)	0-2
Willington v Sunderland Ryhope CW	5-0
Bishop Auckland v Evenwood Town	1-0
Spennymoor United v Durham City	3-2
Esh Winning v Billingham Synthonia	*1-1 6-7pens
Eppleton CW v Boldon CA	0-1
Jarrow Roofing & BCA v Easington Colliery	6-1
Sunderland Res v Brandon United (played at Durham City FC)	5-2
Dunston Federation Brewery v Billingham Town	2-1
Washington v Darlington	3-2

SECOND ROUND by Saturday 16th November

1 Sunderland Res v Spennymoor United	1-2
2 Boldon C A v Billingham Synthonia	0-1
3 Wolviston v Whickham	3-1
4 Jarrow Roofing BCA v Dunston FB	1-3
5 Birtley Town v Bishop Auckland	1-0
6 Willington v Horden	0-5
7 Washington v Gateshead	1-3
8 Murton v Tow Law Town	2-0

THIRD ROUND

Dunston Federation v Spennymoor United	3-0
Birtley Town v Wolviston	4-1
Horden v Murton	5-0
Billingham Synthonia v Gateshead	*4-4 6-5pens

SEMI-FINALS

Billingham Synthonia v Dunston Federation	1-0
Horden v Birtley Town	2-0

FINAL Monday 21st April 11am

Billingham Synthonia v Horden at Durham City FC	0-1

EAST RIDING F.A. LTD

Tel: 01482 221158 Fax: 01482 221159 E.Mail: info@eastridingfa.com
50 Boulevard, Hull HU3 2TB

Secretary & Press Officer: Dennis R Johnson
Football Development Officer: Jonathan Day
Executives (Responsibility) T Mason (Child Protection) P Summerbell (Referees)
D Furniss (Youth) M Edge (Womens Football) P Thomas (Drug Education)
Number of Affiliated Clubs Senior: 400 Youth: 200
Number of Affiliated Leagues: Senior: 7 Junior: 3
County Representative Teams: Senior, U18, Womens
Inter County Competitions: Association of Northern Counties, FA County Youth, Midlands Youth

President: Chris Bodsworth
Chairman: M Rawding

EAST RIDING SENIOR CUP - FOUNDED 1902

(23 entries)

LAST SEASON'S FINAL: Bridlington Town 0 North Ferriby 2

MOST WINS: Hull City 25 Bridlington Town 12 North Ferriby United 9

FIRST ROUND 12th October

St Andrews Sutton v Withernsea	2-1
Hedon United v Charleston	5-2
Bridlington SC v Sculcoates Amateurs	1-2
Keyingham v Bransholme Athletic	4-2
Westella & Willerby v Pocklington Town	4-0
Easington United v Driffield	2-0
East Hull Amateurs v Automatrix	W-O
(Walkover for East Hill Am.)	

SECOND ROUND

Bridlington Town v Hull City	2-1
East Hull Amateurs v Keyingham	0-3
St Andrews Sutton v Discount Carpets	5-1
(St Andrews ineligible player DC reinstated)	
Easington United v Hedon United	4-0
Hider Foods v Reckitts	3-2
Beverley Town v Sculcoates Amateurs	3-5
Hutton Cranswick United v Hall Road Rangers	3-0
North Ferriby United v Westella & Willerby	

THIRD ROUND Quarter-Finals 8th February

Sculcoates Amateurs v Hider Foods	2-3
Easington United v Discount Carpets	3-1
Hutton Cranswick United v North Ferriby Utd	2-4
Bridlington Town v Keyingham AFC	7-0

SEMI-FINALS

Easington United v Bridlington Town	0-2
Hider Foods v North Ferriby United	*2-3

FINAL Thursday 24th April 7.30pm

Bridlington Town v North Ferriby United	1-3
at Boothferry Park, Hull.	Att: 450

EAST RIDING COUNTRY CUP

(18 entries)

LAST SEASON'S FINAL: Filey Town 1 Pocklington Town 2

FIRST ROUND Saturday 19th October

Filey Town v Hornsea Town	5-1
Riccall v Malton Bacon Factory	1-10

SECOND ROUND Saturday 16th November

Long Riston v Malton BF	4-5
North Cave v Pocklington Town Res	0-5
Thorngumbald v Nags Head Bridlington	2-1
Holme Rovers v Hunmanby United	1-2
Filey Town v Brandesburton	6-3
South Cave United v Beverley Town Res	3-4
Walkington Wanderers v Dunnington	1-4
Hutton Cranswick United Res v Ward	1-4

THIRD ROUND Quarter-Finals 15th February

Pocklington Town Res v Beverley Town Res	4-0
Malton Bacon Factory v Ward	3-2
Hunmanby United v Thorngumbald	5-1
Dunnington v Filey Town	1-4

SEMI-FINALS

Hunmanby United v Filey Town	5-2
at Rudston Tuesday 15th April 6pm	
Malton Bacon Factory v Pocklington Town Res	1-4
at Dunnington Thursday 17th April 6pm	

FINAL Saturday 10th May 3.00pm (Golden Goal)

Hunmanby United v Pocklington Town Res	*1-2 (GG)
at Queensgate Bridlington Town FC	

ESSEX F.A.

Tel: 01245 357727 Fax: 01245 344430 Email: info@EssexFA.com
31 Mildmay Road, Chelmsford CM2 0DN

Chief Executive: Philip Sammons

Number of Affiliated Clubs Senior: 1153 U.18: 434

Number of Affiliated Leagues: Senior: 38 U18: 10

County Representative Teams: Senior, Intermediate, U18, U16, Womens

Inter County Competitions: East Anglian, Southern Counties

Chairman: R Brooks
Vice -Chairman: E Fairchild

ESSEX SENIOR CUP - FOUNDED 1883-84

(42 entries)

LAST SEASON'S FINAL

Canvey Island 6 Dagenham & Redbridge 1

MOST WINS

Ilford 13 Walthamstow Avenue 12 Grays Athletic 8 Leyton 8

FIRST ROUND on or by 21st September

Waltham Abbey v Saffron Walden Town	4-1
Hullbridge Sports v Brentwood	0-2
Barkingside v Woodford Town	*0-0 4-3pens
Southend Manor v Stansted	3-1
Concord Rangers v Burnham Ramblers	2-1
Bowers United v Romford	*3-2

SECOND ROUND on or by 19th October

Waltham Abbey v Basildon United	3-2
Southend Manor v Bowers United	*3-2
Ilford v Brentwood	3-0
Concord Rangers v Barkingside	*2-5

THIRD ROUND by 16th November

Witham Town v Braintree Town	3-2
Tiptree United v Stanway Rovers	4-0
Ilford v Aveley	2-3
Barkingside v Waltham Abbey	0-2
Heybridge Swifts v Clapton 5-2	
Harwich & Parkeston v Harlow Town	1-4
Billericay Town vWivenhoe Town	5-0
Barking & East Ham United v Maldon Town	3-4
Leyton Pennant v Clacton Town	1-2
East Thurrock United v Purfleet	2-1
Halstead Town v Chelmsford City	0-5
Ford United v Tilbury	2-1
Great Wakering Rovers v Southend United	1-2
Grays Athletic v Dagenham & Redbridge	*2-4
Hornchurch v Southend Manor	3-1
Canvey Island v Brightlingsea United	W-O
(Walkover for Canvey ISland)	

FOURTH ROUND by 14th December 2002

Clacton Town v East Thurrock United	0-1
Hornchurch v Southend United	1-2
Ford United v Aveley	1-3
Billericay Town v Harlow Town	1-0
Canvey Island v Chelmsford City	1-4
Maldon Town v Dagenham & Redbridge	1-2
Waltham Abbey v Tiptree United	1-4
(Played at Tiptree)	
Heybridge Swifts v Witham Town	4-2

FIFTH ROUND Quarter-Finals

East Thurrock United v Billericay Town	0-1
Dagenham & Redbridge v Southend United	1-4
Heybridge Swifts v Chelmsford City	0-2
Tiptree United v Aveley	1-6

SEMI-FINALS

Aveley v Billericay Town	*1-1 3-1pens
Chelmsford City v Southend United	2-0

FINAL Monday 24th March 2003

Aveley v Chelmsford City	0-5
at Roots Hall, Southend United FC	

ESSEX THAMES-SIDE TROPHY - FOUNDED 1945-46

(22 entries)

LAST SEASON'S FINAL

Tilbury 1 Grays Athletic 3

MOST WINS

Ilford 13 Walthamstow Avenue 12 Grays Athletic 8 Leyton 8

FIRST ROUND by 15th November 2002

Hullbridge Sports v Maldon Town	0-3
Burnham Ramblers v Great Wakering Rovers	0-4
Brentwood v Leyton Pennant	1-0
Barking & East Ham United v Bowers United	2-0
Concord Rangers v Hornchurch	1-2
Aveley v Ilford	6-0

SECOND ROUND

Hornchurch v Brentwood	4-0
Basildon United v Great Wakering Rovers	*2-4
Maldon Town v Barking & East Ham United	*3-2
Southend Manor v East Thurrock United	*2-2 6-5pens
Woodford Town v Canvey Island @CI	0-4
Romford v Ford United	*2-4
Clapton v Tilbury	1-0
Grays Athletic v Aveley	3-1

THIRD ROUND

Southend Manor v Canvey Island	0-5
Ford United v Clapton	3-0
Hornchurch v Great Wakering Rovers	1-0
Maldon Town v Grays Athletic	3-0

SEMI-FINALS Pre-season

Ford United v Canvey Island

Hornchurch v Maldon Town

FINAL Pre-season 1 v 2

GLOUCESTERSHIRE F.A. LIMITED

Tel: 01454 615888 Fax: 01454 618088
Oaklands Park, Almondsbury, Bristol BS32 4AG

Company Sec. & Press Officer: Paul Britton
Executives (Responsibility) Paul Britton (Coaching Exams/Courses, Womens Football)
K E Fry (Referees)
Number of Affiliated Clubs Senior: 849 U.18: 193
Number of Affiliated Leagues: Senior: 23 Junior: 10
County Representative Teams: Senior, U18, Womens, Womens U18
Inter County Competitions: South & South West Counties Championship, FA County Youth Cup

President: A C D Barrett
Chairman: R F Burden

GLOUCESTERSHIRE SENIOR CUP - FOUNDED 1936-37

(8 entries)

LAST SEASON'S FINAL: Bristol City v Cirencester Town - Bristol City won

MOST WINS: Cheltenham Town 32 Gloucester City 18 Forest Green Rovers 3

FIRST ROUND

Gloucester City v Bristol City 1-2
Bristol Rovers v Cinderford Town 3-2
Mangotsfield United v Cirencester Town 2-0
Forest Green Rovers v Cheltenham Town 1-5

SEMI-FINALS

Mangotsfield United v Bristol Rovers 2A1 1-0
Bristol City v Cheltenham Town 6-0

FINAL Monday 28th April
Bristol City v Mangotsfield United 0-1
at Mangotsfield United FC. Att: 446

GLOUCESTERSHIRE SENIOR TROPHY - FOUNDED 1978-79

(36 entries)

LAST SEASON'S FINAL: Cirencester Academy 1 Gloucester United 0

MOST WINS: Mangotsfield United 6 Moreton Town 3 Shortwood United 2

PRELIMINARY ROUND Saturday 21st September

Cadbury Heath v Shortwood United 1-3
Tuffley Rovers v Wotton Rovers *1-1 9-10pens
DRG Stapleton v Hallen 0-2
Taverners v Whitminster *1-1 7-6pens

FIRST ROUND Saturday 19th October

Axa v Bitton 0-4
Slimbridge v Bristol Manor Farm 3*1
Cheltenham Saracens v Old Georgians *1-1 5-3pens
Ellwood v Mangotsfield United Res *1-1 2-4pens
Highridge United v Fairford Town 0-1
Almondsbury v Totterdown POB *4-2
Viney St Swithens v Roman Glass St George 0-1
Pucklechurch v Thornbury Town 0-2
Wotton Rovers v Bishops Cleeve 0-2
Taverners v Shortwood United 2-3
Henbury O B v Hardwicke 4-1
Hallen v Yate Town 2-3
Winterbourne United v Cirencester United W-O
(Walkover for Winterbourne)
Patchway Town v Cirencester Academy W-O
(Walkover for Patchway Town)
Harrow Hill v Gloucester United 3-2
Almondsbury Town v Tytherington Rocks 3-4

SECOND ROUND Saturday 7th December 1,45pm

1 Almondsbury v Shortwood United 3-1
2 Bitton v Mangotsfield United Res 3-1
3 Roman Glass St George v Thornbury Town 4-3
4 Slimbridge v Patchway Town 1-4
5 Yate Town v Tytherington Rocks 1-0
6 Winterbourne United v Harrow Hill 1-2
7 Fairford Town v Bishops Cleeve 2-1
8 Cheltenham Saracens v Henbury Old Boys 0-6

QUARTER-FINALS

1 Roman Glass St George v Fairford Town 1-2
2 Harrow Hill v Almondsbury 1-0
3 Patchway Town v Bitton 2-3
4 Yate Town v Henbury Old Boys 2-1

SEMI-FINALS

1 Bitton v Fairford Town *1-3
2 Yate Town v Harrow Hill 5-1

FINAL Tuesday 6th May
Fairford Town v Yate Town 2-0
at Oaklands Park, Almondsbury, Glos Co FA Grd

HAMPSHIRE F.A.

Tel: 02380 791110 Fax: 02380 788340 Email: info@HampshireFA.co.uk www.HampshireFA.com
William Pickford House, 8 Ashwood Gardens, off Winchester Road, Southampton SO16 7PW

Chief Executive: L C Jones
Managers: N A Cassar (Football Operations)
S Nicholas (Football Development)
Number of Affiliated Clubs: Senior: 2000 U.18: 450
County Representative Teams: Womens, U21, Girls U16, Boys U18, Girls U18
Inter County Competitions: South West Counties, FA County Youth Cup

President: M E Turner
Chairman: E J Ward

HAMPSHIRE SENIOR CUP - FOUNDED 1887-88

(44 entries)

LAST SEASON'S FINAL

Bashley 1 Aldershot Town 2
Att: 4092

MOST WINS

Southampton 13 Newport 7 Cowes 6

FIRST ROUND by 5th October

Vosper Thornycroft v Lymington & New Milton	3-2
Andover v R S Basingstoke	8-0
Petersfield Town v Lymington Town	1-4
Winchester City v Liss Athletic	4-0
Hamble AASC v Fareham Town	2-1
Blackfield & Langley v Bournemouth	0-1
Stockbridge v Horndean	4-0
B A T Sports v Hartley Wintney	*6-2
Hythe & Dibden v Locksheath	3-0
East Cowes Victoria Athletic v Fawley FC	10-0
Cowes Sports v Portsmouth Royal Navy	4-2
Brockenhurst v Bishops Waltham Town	1-0
Andover New Street v Christchurch	4-5

SECOND ROUND by 2nd November

Hamble ASSC v Gosport Borough	0-3
Brockenhurst v Andover	2-6
Pirelli General v BAT Sports	1-4
Havant & Waterlooville v Whitchurch United	6-0
Alton Town v Brading Town	16-2
Aldershot Town v Farnborough Town	2-1
Bournemouth v East Cowes Victoria Athletic	2-1
Bashley v Vosper Thorneycroft	3-2
St Peters Jersey v Winchester City	0-7
Stockbridge v Ringwood Town	1-6
Cove v Christchurch	0-4
Fleet Town v Bournemouth AFC (Walkover for Fleet Town)	W-O
Eastleigh v Newport (IOW)	3-0
Cowes Sports v Basingstoke Town	0-2
Totton AFC v Lymington Town	4-5
Moneyfields v Hythe & Dibden	1-0

THIRD ROUND Saturday 7th December

Andover v Alton Town	3-0
Basingstoke Town v Ringwood Town	7-1
Winchester City v Gosport Borough	3-2
Bournemouth v Aldershot Town	2-3
Eastleigh v Moneyfields	5-0
Lymington Town v Havant & Waterlooville	1-4
Fleet Town v Bashley	1-2
Christchurch v BAT Sports	3-1

FOURTH ROUND Quarter-Finals

Bashley v Winchester City	*2-1
Aldershot Town v Eastleigh 0A1	2-1
Andover v Basingstoke Town	4-2
Christchurch v Havant & Waterlooville	0-4

SEMI-FINALS Two Legs

Bashley v Havant & Waterlooville	2-0 2-1 = 4-1
Aldershot Town v Andover	2-0 2-2 = 4-2

FINAL THURSDAY 8th May 2003 kick off 7.45pm

Aldershot Town v Bashley	2-1

at at St Mary's Stadium, Southampton FC

Hampshire Senior Cup Action

Aldershot Town 2 - 1 Bashley
at St Mary's Stadium
Southampton FC

HEREFORDSHIRE F.A.

Tel: 01432 342179 Fax: 01432 279265 Email: val.lambert@herefordshirefa.com
County Ground Offices, Widemarsh Common, Hereford HR4 9NA

Secretary & Press Officer:	Jim Lambert			
Assistant Secretary;	Val Lambert			
Executives (Responsibility)	Paul Carpenter (Football Development Officer)			
	Neil Jenkins (Referees) G Stevens (County Coach)			
	Jim Lambert (Womens Football)			
Number of Affiliated Clubs	Senior: 125	U.18: 114		
Number of Affiliated Leagues:	Senior: 1	Junior: 1		
County Representative Teams:	Under 18, Under 16			
Inter County Competitions:	Midland Counties U18, East Midland U16			

President: Sir Colin Shepherd
Chairman: W E Shorten

HEREFORDSHIRE CHALLENGE CUP - FOUNDED 1973-74

(16 entries)

LAST SEASON'S FINAL

Kington Town 1 Westfields 3

FIRST ROUND Saturday 12th October

Pegasus Juniors v Hereford Civil Service	W-O
(Walkover for Pegasus Juniors)	
Ewyas Harold v Sutton United	4-3
Fownhope v Kington Town	0-5
Woofferton v Wellington	1-0
Ross United Services v Ross Town	2-1
Ledbury Town v Leominster Town	3-0
Hinton v Westfields	0-5
Bromyard Town v Weston Under Penyard	5-1

SECOND ROUND Saturday 16th December

Westfields v Bromyard Town	5-1
Woofferton v Kington Town	1-3
Ross United Services v Pegasus Juniors	W-O
(Walkover for Ross United)	
Ewyas Harold v Ledbury Town	1-5

SEMI-FINALS

Kington Town v Ross United Services	5-0
Ledbury Town v Westfields	0-1

FINAL 21st April 11am

Kington Town v Westfields	0-2
at Edgar Street, Hereford United FC	

HERTFORDSHIRE F.A.

Tel: 01462 677622 Fax: 01462 677624 E.Mail: competitions@hertsfa.demon.co.uk
County Ground, Baldock Road, Letchworth, Herts S96 2EN

Secretary: E W J King **Press Officer:** County HQ
Company Secretary: Mrs D Button
Executives (Responsibility) D Gorringe (Executive Officer)
A Ackrell (Football Development Officer)
R G Dowden (Referees) M Spacey (Womens Football)
Number of Affiliated Clubs Senior: 860 U.18: 190
Number of Affiliated Leagues: Senior: 24 Junior: 11
County Representative Teams: Senior, U18, U16
Inter County Competitions: East Anglian, EMYFC

President: R G Kibble
Chairman: W H Dance

ICIS CLUBWEAR HERTFORDSHIRE SENIOR CUP - FOUNDED 1886-87

(22 entries)

LAST SEASON'S FINAL

Boreham Wood 3 London Colney 2

MOST WINS

Hitchin Town 21 Barnet 16 Watford 14

FIRST ROUND W/c 7th October

Royston Town v Broxbourne Borough V & E	1-2
Hoddesdon Town v Hertford Town	1-4
Berkhamsted Town v Letchworth	W-O
(Walkover for Berkhamstead)	
Hemel Hempstead Tn v Sawbridgeworth Tn	*2-2 2-3p
Greenacres Hemel v St Margaretsbury	3-2
St Albans City v Ware6-0	

SECOND ROUND W/c 18th November

Greenacres v St Albans City	0-1
London Colney v Hitchin Town	0-2
Cheshunt v Bishops Stortford	1*0
Potters Bar Town v Barnet	2-0
Tring Town v Watford	0-1
Hertford Town v Berkhamsted Town	1-4
Broxbourne Borough V&E v Boreham Wood	*0-0 5-3p
Stevenage Borough v Sawbridgeworth Town	7-0

THIRD ROUND Tuesday 7th January 2003

Cheshunt v Potters Bar Town	2-0
Broxbourne Borough V&E v Stevenage Borough	2-4
Berkhamsted Town v St Albans City	3-2
Watford v Hitchin Town	1-2
(Played at Hitchin Town)	

SEMI-FINALS

1 Cheshunt v Stevenage Borough	4-2
2 Berkhamsted Town v Hitchin Town	4-2

FINAL 15th April

Berkhamsted Town v Cheshunt	2-0

at Hemel Hempstead Town FC

GREEN KING HERTFORDSHIRE SENIOR TROPHY

(22 entries)

LAST SEASON'S FINAL

Elliott Star 3 Oxhey Jets 4

FIRST ROUND Saturday 2nd November

Chipperfield Corinthians v Met Police Bushey	6-0
Tring Athletic v Croxley Guild	11-0
Leverstock Green v Harpenden Town	1-2
Bovingdon v Bushey Rangers	4-1
Hadley v Kings Langley	0-3
St Peters v London Lions	*2-3

SECOND ROUND Saturday 7th December

Sun Postal Sports v London Lions	3-0
Harpenden Town v Chipperfield Corinthians	1-3
Wormley Rovers v Kings Langley	*7-4
Welwyn Garden City v Old Parmiterians	2-0
Bovingdon v Elliott Star	*3-1
Sandridge Rovers v Oxhey Jets	1-4
Colney Heath v Cuffley	5-1
Tring Athletic v Bedmond Sports	3-0

QUARTER FINALS

Chipperfield Corinthians v Welwyn Garden City	1-0
Wormley Rovers v v Oxhey Jets	1-0
Tring Athletic v Sun Postal Sports	2-1
Colney Heath v Bovingdon(5/2)	3A3 *4-2

SEMI-FINALS Saturday 8th March

Tring Athletic v Wormley Rovers	4-1
Colney Heath v Chipperfield Corinthians	9-0

FINAL Tuesday 8th April 2003

Colney Heath v Tring Athletic	0-1
at County FA Ground, Letchworth	

HUNTINGDONSHIRE F.A.

Tel: 01480414422 Fax: 01480 412691 Email: info@hunts-fa.org
Cromwell Chambers, 8 St Johns Street, Huntingdon, Cambs. PE29 3DD

Secretary & Press Officer: Maurice Armstrong
Executives (Responsibility) M A Hair (Referees)
S Batchelor (Football Development Officer)
Number of Affiliated Clubs Senior: 130 U.18: 30
Number of Affiliated Leagues: Senior: 1 Junior: 1
County Representative Teams: Senior, Under 18, Under 16, Colts
Inter County Competitions: U18 & U16, Midlands Youth Football Championships

President: D A Roberts
Chairman: E K Heads

HUNTINGDONSHIRE SENIOR CUP - FOUNDED 1888-89

(20 entries)

LAST SEASON'S FINAL

St Neots Town 0 Ely City 4

MOST WINS

St Neots 34 Eynesbury Rovers 14 Huntingdon Town 12

FIRST ROUND Saturday 26th October 2.30pm

Somersham Town v Great Paxton	*3*3 1-3pens
St Neots Town v Warboys Town	4-0
Ortonians v Eynesbury Rangers	1-3
Hotpoint v Yaxley	1-0

SECOND ROUND Saturday 30th November 1.30pm

Hotpoint v Hemingford United	2-0
Great Paxton v Stilton United	*5-5 2-4pens
Bluntisham Rangers v Ramsey Town	2-0
Brampton v Godmanchester Rovers	*0-0 3-4pens
Alconbury v Eynesbury Rovers	2-9
Eaton Socon v Woodlands 7-1	
St Ives Town v Huntingdon United 2000	5-0
St Neots Town v Huntingdon Town	3-0

QUARTER-FINALS Saturday 8th February

Bluntisham Rangers v Hotpoint	
Eynesbury Rovers v Eaton Socon	6-1
Godmanchester Rovers v St Neots Town	0-1
St Ives Town v Stilton United	6-1

SEMI-FINALS

Eynesbury Rovers v Hotpoint	0-2
St Ives Town v St Neots Town	0-3

FINAL Monday 5th May 3.00pm

Hotpoint v St Neots Town	*3-3 5-4pens

at Warboys Town FC

Bengeo Trinity Football Club
Hertfordshire Junior Cup Winners

Bengeo Trinity celebrate after tbeating Hertford Heath 1-0 in the final.
Photo: Gordon Whittingham.

KENT F.A. Limited

Tel: 01634 843824 Fax: 01634 815369 E.Mail: enquiries@kent-fa.org
69 Maidstone Road, Chatham, Kent ME4 6DT

KCFA LIMITED

Chief Executive: K T Masters
Press Officer: Tony Hudd
Executives (Responsibility) Alan Walker (Coaching) John Newson (Referees)
Nici Rice (County Development)
Liz Symons (Girls & Womens Football)
Number of Affiliated Clubs Adult: 954 U.18: 183
Number of Affiliated Leagues: Senior: 2 Junior:41 Youth: 10
County Representative Teams: U18, U16, Womens, Girls

President: N Chatfield
Chairman: B W Bright

KENT FACIT SENIOR CUP - FOUNDED 1888-89

(14 entries)

LAST SEASON'S FINAL: Margate 0 Gravesend & Northflett 5
MOST WINS: Maidstone United 15 Dartford 9 Northfleet United 9

FIRST ROUND by 30th November 2002

Folkestone Invicta v Dartford	*1-0
Welling United v Thamesmead Town	*2-2 3-1pens
Chatham Town v Fisher Athletic London	4-1
Ashford Town v Erith & Belvedere	0-2
Dover Athletic v Sittingbourne	2-3
Tonbridge Angels v Bromley	0-3
Gravesend & Northfleet	bye
Margate	bye

SECOND ROUND on or by 31st January

Folkestone Invicta v Welling United	1-6
Gravesend & Northfleet v Erith & Belvedere	2-3
Chatham Town v Bromley	3-4
Margate v Sittingbourne	3-1

SEMI-FINALS

Erith & Belvedere v Margate	*0-3
(Played at Margate)	
Welling United v Bromley	2-0

FINAL Wednesday 30th April

Welling United v Margate	*1-2
at Welling United FC	Att: 704

KENT PLAAYA SENIOR TROPHY - FOUNDED 1874-75

(21 entries)

LAST SEASON'S FINAL: Cray Wanderers 0 Thamesmead Town 2
MOST WINS: Ramsgate 3 Alma Swanley 2 Corinthian 2 Faversham Town 2 Fisher Athletic 2

FIRST ROUND

West Wickham v Milton United	*2-2 *2-1
Cray Wanderers v Slade Green	*3-2
Erith Town v Faversham Town	2-0
Bearsted v Lordswood	2-4
Greenwich Borough v Stansfeld O&B	*1-1 2-0

SECOND ROUND

Whitstable Town v Erith Town	*4-1
Maidstone United v Crockenhill	6-0
West Wickham v VCD Athletic	1-2
Beckenham Town v Ramsgate	*2-2 0-2pens
Deal Town v Hythe Town	2-0
Greenwich Borough v Lordswood	2-1
Cray Wanderers v Tunbridge Wells	*3-3 1-0
Sevenoaks v Herne Bay	0-2

THIRD ROUND 14th January

Maidstone United v Deal Town	3-0
Greenwich Borough v VCD Athletic	0-2
Cray Wanderers v Herne Bay	*3-0
Ramsgate v Whitstable Town	1-3

SEMI-FINALS 8th March 2003

Cray Wanderers v Whitstable Town	4-1
Maidstone United v VCD Athletic	2-1

FINAL Saturday 19th April.

Cray Wanderers v Maidstone United	0-3
at Chatham Town FC	Att: 576

LANCASHIRE F.A.

Tel: 01772 624000 Fax: 01772 624700
The County Ground, Thurston Road, Leyland PR25 2LF

Company Secretary:	J Kenyon, ACIS
Assistant Secretary:	D P Burgess
Press Officer:	J Bullen 01942 874719
Executives (Responsibility)	D Egan (Development Officer) Tel: 01772 490440
	E J Parker (Referees & Discipline)
Number of Affiliated Clubs	Senior: 1600 U.18: 300
County Representative Teams:	Senior, U18, Womens
Inter County Competitions:	FA County Youth, Northern Counties Senior, U18 & Womens

President: D J Lewin

MARSDEN LANCASHIRE TROPHY - FOUNDED 1885-86

(29 entries)

LAST SEASON'S FINAL

Accrington Stanley 2 Barrow 0

FIRST ROUND 16th November

Bamber Bridge v Marine	2-3
Nelson v Bacup Borough	2-0
Squires Gate v Flixton	*1-1 2-4pens
Kendal Town v Atherton Collieries	3-0
Fleetwood Town v Skelmersdale United	1-0
Leigh R M I v Radcliffe Borough	1-0
Great Harwood Town v Southport	1-4
(Played at Southport)	
Darwen v Lancaster City	1-4
Rossendale United v Colne	4-1
Atherton L R v Holker Old Boys	1-3
Blackpool Mechanics v Burscough	1-0
(Played at Burscough)	
Morecambe v Ramsbottom United	2-1
Castleton Gabriels v Chorley	0-2
Accrington Stanley	bye
Barrow	bye
Clitheroe	bye

SECOND ROUND 11th January 2003

Clitheroe v Holker Old Boys	5-1
Flixton v Leigh R M I	0-7
Blackpool Mechanics v Nelson	2-1
Fleetwood Town v Lancaster City	0-1
Rossendale United v Marine	*2-1
Morecambe v Chorley	1-3
Barrow v Kendal Town	0-1
Accrington Stanley v Southport	2-0

THIRD ROUND

Kendal Town v Clitheroe	1-0
Accrington Stanley v Lancaster City	3-1
Rossendale United v Leigh RMI	2-4
Chorley v Blackpool Mechanics	5-1

SEMI-FINALS

Leigh RMI v Chorley	1-0
Accrington Stanley v Kendal Town	1-2

FINAL Wednesday 16th April

Kendal Town v Leigh RMI	0-2

at Accrington Stanley FC

LEICESTERSHIRE & RUTLAND F.A.

Tel: 0116 286 7828 Fax: 0116 286 4858 Email: leicscfa@aol.com
Holmes Park, Dog & Gun Lane, Whetstone LE8 6FA

Secretary & Press Officer: Paul Morrison
Executives (Responsibility) J Ward (Referees)
Mrs G F Wait (Womens Football)

Number of Affiliated Clubs Senior: 500 U.18: 180
Number of Affiliated Leagues: Senior: 12 Junior: 7
County Representative Teams: Under 18, Under 16, Under 16 Girls
Inter County Competitions: Midlands Youth Combination U18 & U16 and U16 Girls

President: G E Cooper
Chairman: D J Jamieson

LEICESTERSHIRE 'JELSON HOMES' SENIOR CUP - FOUNDED 1887-88

(34 entries)

LAST SEASON'S FINAL: Coalville Town 3 Thurnby Rangers 4

MOST WINS: Leicester City 27 Enderby Town 6 Shepshed Dynamo 6

FIRST ROUND 5th October

Thurmaston Town v Loughborough Dynamo	1-4
Friar Lane OB v Kirby Muxloe	3-2

SECOND ROUND

Downes Sports v Coalville Town	1-4
Birstall United v Blaby & Whetstone	0-4
Asfordby Amateurs v Saffron Dynamo	1-4
Lutterworth Town v Bardon Hill Sports	5-1
Anstey Town v Barrow Town	1-6
St Andrews SC v Huncote S&S	6-1
Epworth v Leicester YMCA	4-2
Anstey Nomads v Thurnby Rangers	0-8
Friar Lane OB v Loughborough Dynamo	0-4
Aylestone Park v Earl Shilton Albion	2-0
Cottesmore Amateurs v Holwell Sports	2-3
Ratby Sports v Leivester Constabulary	4-0
Sileby Town v Ibstock Welfare	1-2
Ellistown v Thringstone MW	13-0
Narborough & Littlethorpe v Highfield Rangers	5-2
North Kilworth v Loughborough	2-4

THIRD ROUND

Loughborough Dynamo v Lutterworth Town	4-1
Saffron Dynamo v Blaby & Whetstone Athletic	1-4
Ratby Sports v Narborough & Littlethorpe	5-2
Barrow Town v Thurnby Rangers	2-0
Holwell Sports v Epworth	2-5
Ellistown v Aylestone Park	1-0
St Andrews SC v Ibstock Welfare	1-3
Coalville Town v Loughborough	4-0

QUARTER-FINALS

Coalville Town v Ratby Sports	4-1
Blaby & Whetstone v Ibstock Welfare	1-0
Loughborough Dynamo v Epworth	5-3
Ellistown v Barrow Town	0-6

SEMI-FINALS

Loughborough Dynamo v Blaby & Whetstone	2-1
at Heather St Johns FC	
Coalville Town v Barrow Town	0-2
at Shepshed Dynamo FC	

FINAL Tuesday 15th April 7pm

Barrow Town v Loughborough Dynamo	0-1
at Holmes Park, Leicestershire & Rutland FA	

LEICESTERSHIRE WESTERBY CHALLENGE CUP

(12 entries)

LAST SEASON'S FINAL: Hinckley United 3 Oadby Town 1

FIRST ROUND

Kirby Muxloe v Leicester City	1-3
Friar Lane v Shepshed Dynamo	1-5
Thurnby Rangers v Coalville Town	3-1
Barwell v Quorn	3-0

SECOND ROUND

Leicester City v Downes Sports @DS	6-3
Oadby Town v St Andrews 0A0 *5-3	
Barwell v Hinckley United	1-7
Thurnby Rangers v Shepshed Dynamo	0-1

SEMI-FINALS

Hinckley United v Leicester City	0-7
at Holmes Park, Leicestershire & Rutland FA	
Oadby Town v Shepshed Dynamo	1-2
at Holmes Park, Leicestershire & Rutland FA	

FINAL Tuesday 29th April

Leicester City v Shepshed Dynamo	1-0
at Walkers Stadium, Leicester City FC	Att: 650

LINCOLNSHIRE F.A.

Tel: 01522 524917 Fax: 01522 528859
PO Box 26, 12 Dean Road, Lincoln LN2 4DP

President: N A Saywell
Chairman: R D Teanby

Secretary:	J Griffin			
Executives (Responsibility)	Board of Directors			
Number of Affiliated Clubs	Senior: 875		U.18:	283
Number of Affiliated Leagues:	Senior: 19		Junior:	13
County Representative Teams:	U18			
Inter County Competitions:	Midlands Counties Youth Combination			

LINCOLNSHIRE SENIOR CUP - FOUNDED 1935-36

(8 entries)

LAST SEASON'S FINAL: Grantham Town v Scunthorpe United - Scunthorpe won.

MOST WINS: Grimsby Town 14 Lincoln City 12 Boston United 5 Lincoln Moorlands 2

FIRST ROUND
Lincoln United v Grimsby Town *2-2 3-2pens
Lincoln City v Grantham Town 1-3
Stamford v Boston United 2-1
Gainsborough Trinity v Scunthorpe United 2-1

SEMI-FINALS
Stamford v Grantham Town 0-1
Gainsborough Trinity v Lincoln United 2-1

FINAL Tuesday 29th April
Gainsborough Trinity v Grantham Town 4-0
at Gainsborough Trinity FC

LINCOLNSHIRE SENIOR 'A' CUP
FOUNDED 1949-50

(13 entries)

LAST SEASON'S FINAL

Holbeach United 0 Lincoln Moorlands 1

MOST WINS

Boston Town 6 Holbeach United 4
Skegness Town 4

FIRST ROUND
Blackstone v Barton Town OB 5-0
Brigg Town v Spalding United 2-0
Bottesford Town v Holbeach United 0-1
Nettleham v Winterton Rangers *3-3 5-4pens
Boston Town v Deeping Rangers 3-2
Lincoln Moorlands bye
Bourne Town bye
Louth United bye

SECOND ROUND Quarter-Finals
Lincoln Moorlands v Nettleham 0-1
Bourne Town v Holbeach United 1-3
Blackstone v Boston Town 1-2
Louth United v Brigg Town 1-4

SEMI-FINALS
Nettleham v Brigg Town 0-1
Holbeach United v Boston Town *2-0

FINAL Wednesday 14th May
Brigg Town v Holbeach United 1-3
at Boston Town FC

LINCOLNSHIRE SENIOR 'B' CUP
FOUNDED 1949-50

(10 entries)

LAST SEASON'S FINAL

Harrowby United 2 Sleaford Town 3

MOST WINS

Brigg Tn 5 Appleby Frodingham Ath 4
Lincoln Moorlands 3

PRELIMINARY ROUND Saturday 28th September
Limestone Rangers v Horncastle Town 5-1
Harrowby United v Appleby Frodingham 4-1

FIRST ROUND Saturday 26th October 2.30pm
Harrowby United v Limestone Rangers *4-3
Wyberton v Skegness Town *2-2 4-3pens
Grimsby Amateurs v Sleaford Town 1-3
Alstom Sports v Hykeham Town *5-5 5-4pens

SEMI-FINALS
Wyberton v Harrowby United 1-2
Sleaford Town v Alstom Sports 4-0

FINAL Wednesday 30th April 2003
Harrowby United v Sleaford Town 0-1
at Boston United FC

Cray Wanderers (above) and Maidstone United (below) line up before their Kent Senior Trophy final, which Maidstone won 3-0, played at Chatham Town FC.

LIVERPOOL F.A.

Tel: 0151 523 4488 Fax: 0151 523 4477 Email: info@liverpoolfa.com www,liverpoolcfa.com
Liverpool Soccer Centre, Walton Hall Park, Walton Hall Avenue, Liverpool L4 9XP

Secretary: F L Hunter **Press Officer:** Tim Johnson
Executives (Responsibility) S A Catterall (Asst. Secretary), M McGlynn (Co. Dev Manager) D J Quine (Finance Director), C Smith (Football Dev. Officer, Mrs M Marley (Womens Football), Miss N O'Donnell (Women's Football Dev. Officer), D Cleveland (Referees' Secretary)

Number of Affiliated Clubs	Senior:	500	U.18:	600	**President:** N Dainty
Number of Affiliated Leagues:	Senior:	19	Junior:	28	
Inter County Competitions:	All FA Competitions				

Nat West LIVERPOOL SENIOR CUP - FOUNDED 1977-78

(11 entries)

LAST SEASON'S FINAL
Liverpool v Everton - Everton won.

MOST WINS: Marine 5 Liverpool 3 South Liverpool 3

FIRST ROUND

Prescot Cables v Southport	1-3
Skelmersdale v Warrington Town	0-1
	Att: 62
Burscough v St Helens Town	*3-2
	Att: 157

SECOND ROUND

Runcorn FC Halton v Tranmere Rovers	1*4
Southport v Everton	14th Aug 03
Burscough v Liverpool	0-5
Marine v Warrington Town	1-0

SEMI-FINALS

Liverpool v Tranmere Rovers	*3-3 6-7pens
Marine v Southport/Everton	tba Pre Season

FINAL

Tranmere Rovers v Marine/Southport/Everton	TBA

LONDON F.A.

Tel: 020 8690 9626 Fax: 020 8690 9471 Email: enquiries@londonfa.fsnet.co.uk
6 Aldworth Grove, Lewisham, London SE13 6HY

Cheif Exeecutive:	D G Fowkes			
Executives (Responsibility)	J Drabwell (Coaching Exams) A Porter (Referees)			
	C Arundale (Womens Football) Miss A Arli (Coaching Courses)			
Number of Affiliated Clubs	Adult: 3247	U18: 500		**President:** F J Lock MBE
Number of Affiliated Leagues:	Adult: 85	U18: 18		**Chairman:** N R J Moss
County Representative Teams:	Senior, Womens, U16			
Inter County Competitions:	Southern Counties Cup (men), Southern Counties Cup (women), FA County Youth Cup			

LONDON SENIOR CUP - FOUNDED 1882
(34 entries)

LAST SEASON'S FINAL: Croydon 2 Dulwich Hamlet 1

PRELIMINARY ROUND 9-14 September
Civil Service v Barkingside 1-2
Wimbledon AFC v Brimsdown Rovers *3-3 5-4pens

FIRST ROUND 14-19 October
Cockfosters v Bedfont 1-2
Hornchurch v VCD Athletic 4-2
Clapton v Thames Poly 3-1
Wimbledon v Woodford Town 4-0
Crown & Manor v Haringey Borough 1-4
Romford v Thamesmead Town *2-1
Barkingside v Erith Town 2-0
Hoddesdon Town v Leyton *2-3

SECOND ROUND 11-16 November
Barkingside v Haringey Borough
Wingate & Finchley v Cray Wanderers 1-2
Leyton v Barking & East Ham United
Wimbledon v Bedfont
Romford v Clapton
Ilford v Hornchurch *3-2
Erith & Belvedere v Bromley *2-2 3-4pens
Tooting & Mitcham Utd v Corinthian Casuals 2-0

THIRD ROUND 9-14 December
Barking & East Ham United v Tooting &Mitcham 2-1
Hanwell Town v Welling United 2-1
Croydon Athletic v Romford 0-1
Metropolitan Police v Fisher Athletic London *4-3
Wimbledon v Barkingside 0-3
Ilford v Bromley 1-2
Cray Wanderers v Uxbridge *1-2
Dulwich Hamlet v Ford United 1-2

FOURTH ROUND 13-18 January 2003
Romford v Uxbridge 1-2
Barkingside v Ford United 1-2
Barking-East Ham Utd v Met. Police *2-2 3-4pens
Hanwell Town v Bromley 0-1

SEMI-FINALS
Ford United v Metropolitan Police *0-0 5-3pens
Uxbridge v Bromley 0-1

FINAL Wednesday 30th April
Bromley v Ford United 1-0
at Dagenham & Redbridge FC a

MANCHESTER F.A.

Tel: 0161 881 0299 Fax: 0161 881 6833 E-mail: info@manchesterfa.com
Brantingham Road, Chorlton, Manchester M21 0TT

Secretary & Press Officer:	Jon Dutton
Executives (Responsibility)	Anita Blair (Education)
	Phil Morris (Referees)
	Stephen Brown (Development Manager)
Number of Affiliated Clubs	Senior: 542 U.18: 154
Number of Affiliated Leagues:	Senior: 29 Junior: 13
County Representative Teams:	U18
Inter County Competitions:	FA County Youth, Association of Northern Counties Youth Competition

President: Frank Hannah

MANCHESTER PREMIER CUP - FOUNDED 1979-80
sponsored by SPARTA SPORTSWEAR

(12 entries)

LAST SEASON'S FINAL: Ashton United 3 Salford City 1

MOST WINS: Curzon Ashton 5 Ashton United 4 Hyde United 3 Droylsden 3 Mossley 2

FIRST ROUND

Curzon Ashton v Maine Road	2-4
Ashton United v Trafford	*3-2
Stand Athletic v Flixton	W-O
(Walkover for Flixton)	
Abbey Hey v Mossley	1-0
Chadderton	bye
Droylsden	bye
Oldham Town	bye
Salford City	bye

SECOND ROUND 8th to 15th January 2003

Maine Road v ashton United	0-4
Flixton v Chadderton	2-1
Droylsden v Abbey Hey	1-0
Oldham Town v Salford City	0-4

SEMI-FINALS

Ashton United v Flixton	6-1
Droylsden v Salford City	W-O
(Walkover for Droylsden)	

FINAL Wednesday 16th April 2003

Ashton United v Droylsden	2-0
at Oldham Athletic FC	

MIDDLESEX COUNTY F.A.

Tel: 0208 424 8524 Fax: 0181 863 0627 E.Mail: peter.clayton@middlesexfa.com
39 Roxborough Road, Harrow, Middlesex HA1 1NS

Secretary: Peter Clayton — Executive Officer: Mark Frost
Executives (Responsibility) — P Clayton (Coaching Exams/Courses, Womens Football, Referees)
Number of Affiliated Clubs — Snr: 32; Inter: 12; U18 232; Jnr 583; Wmn 19; Other 337 — **President:** John Wake
Number of Affiliated Leagues: Adult: 30 Youth: 8 — **Chairman:** Derek Mennell
County Representative Teams: Senior, Intermediate, U18, U16, Womens, U16, Womens U16
Inter County Competitions: FA County Yth, Home Counties Yth, Southern Counties (Intermediate, Women)

MIDDLESEX SENIOR CUP - FOUNDED 1888-89

(25 entries)

LAST SEASON'S FINAL

Hendon 4 Northwood 2 (aet)

MOST WINS

Enfield 14 Hendon 12 Southall 12 Wealdstone 11 Hayes 10

FIRST ROUND w/c 4th November

Harefield United v Hanwell Town	0-6
Potters Bar Town v Bedfont	7-3
Viking Greenford v Hillingdon Borough	0-6
Wembley v Kingsbury Town	*2-1
North Greenford United v Ashford Town	2-4
Wealdstone v Enfield	2-0
Brook House v Feltham	*3-3 1-4pens
Southall Town v Staines Town	5-2
Yeading v Ruislip Manor	0-1

SECOND ROUND w/c 2nd December

Wealdstone v Northwood	3-0
Hanwell Town v Harrow Borough	1-5
Feltham v Enfield Town	0-1
Ruislip Manor v Wembley	*2-1
Ashford Town v Southall Town	3-1
Hendon v Hillingdon Borough	5-1
Uxbridge v Hampton & Richmond Borough	1-3
Hayes v Potters Bar Town	4-1

THIRD ROUND w/c 27th January

Wealdstone v Hendon	2-3
Ashford Town v Harrow Borough	3-4
Enfield Town v Ruislip Manor	*0-0 5-3pens
Hampton & Richmond Borough v Hayes	*2-2 4-2pens

SEMI-FINALS w/c 3rd March

Harrow Borough v Enfield Town	1-2
Hendon v Hampton & Richmond Borough	2-0

FINAL Easter Monday 21st April 7.30pm

Enfield Town v Hendon	0-2

at Northwood FC

NORFOLK F.A.

Tel: 01603 717177 Fax: 01603 717187
Plantation Park, Blofield, Norwich NR13 4PL

Chief Executive:	Roger J Howlett			
Executives (Responsibility)	Through County Office (Coaching Exams/Courses, Referees, Womens Football)			
Number of Affiliated Clubs	Senior: 423	U.18: 183		**President:** R W Kiddell
Number of Affiliated Leagues:	Senior: 17	Junior: 8		**Chairman:** B Woodhouse
County Representative Teams:	U18, Womens			
Inter County Competitions:	FA County Youth, East Anglian Counties			

NORFOLK SENIOR CUP - FOUNDED 1881-82
(33 entries)

LAST SEASON'S FINAL
Great Yarmouth Town 1 Wroxham 2

MOST WINS
King's Lynn 19 Great Yarmouth Town 14 Gorleston 13

PRELIMINARY ROUND
Norwich Anglian Windows v Norwich Union 2-4
Hindringham v Hempnall 1-0
Stalham Town v Watton United 1-2
Wymondham Town v Mattishall 1-3

FIRST ROUND
Halvergate United v Thorpe Village 4-1
Loddon United v Hindringham 2-0
Sprowston Wanderers v Norwich Union *1-4
Watton United v Mattishall 3-0

SECOND ROUND 21st October 2002
Acle United v Loddon United 6-0
Blofield United v North Walsham Town 3-0
Downham Town v Cromer United 0-5
Halvergate United v Thetford Town *1-1 *0-0 7-8pens
Norwich Union v Wells Town *1-1 4-1
Scole United v Mulbarton United 7-1
Sprowston Athletic v St Andrews 4-1
Swaffham Town v Kings Lynn Res 2-3
Watton United v Attleborough Town 2-4

THIRD ROUND Saturday 23rd November
Sprowston Athletic v Cromer United 0-2
Blofield United v Attleborough Town 3-1
Gorleston v Thetford Town 9-0
Dereham Town v Diss Town *1-1 1-5
Wroxham v Great Yarmouth Town 0-1
Kings Lynn Res v Acle United 2-1
Fakenham Town v Norwich Union 6-1
Scole United v Norwich United 0-3

QUARTER-FINALS
Cromer United v Gorleston 0-1
Fakenham Town v Diss Town *1-2
Kings Lynn Res v Norwich United *4-3
Great Yarmouth Town v Blofield United *0-0 5-0
Att: 138

SEMI-FINALS Saturday 1st February
Diss Town v Gorleston4-1
King's Lynn Res v Great Yarmouth Town 1-3

FINAL Tuesday 22nd April
Diss Town v Great Yarmouth Town 4-1
at Carrow Road, Norwich City FC

NORTHAMPTONSHIRE F.A.

Tel: 01604 670741 Fax: 01604 670742
2 Duncan Close, Moulton Park, Northampton

Chief Executive:	D Payne			
Executives (Responsibility)	N Levett (County Development Manager)			
	Jim Wilkinson (Referees)			
	Mrs J Jeffrey (Womens Football)			
Number of Affiliated Clubs	Senior: 373		U.18:	177
Number of Affiliated Leagues:	Senior: 10		Junior:	6
County Representative Teams:	U18 & Women's U16			
Inter County Competitions:	Midland Youth Combination			

President: D Vernum
Chairman: D Joyce

NORTHAMPTONSHIRE 'HILLIER' SENIOR CUP - FOUNDED 1883-84

(14 entries)

LAST SEASON'S FINAL

Rothwell Town 2 Peterborough United 1

MOST WINS

Kettering Town 31 Northampton Town 11 Peterborough United 11

FIRST ROUND w/k commencing 7th October

Ford Sports Daventry v Stewart & Lloyds Corby	3-2
Daventry Town v Corby Town	1-3
Raunds Town v Woodford United	1-0
Northampton Spencer v Brackley Town	0-1
Desborough Town v Long Buckby	4-1
Rothwell Town v Cogenhoe United	3-1
Northampton Town	exempt Rd 2
Peterborough United	exempt Rd 2

SECOND ROUND

Desborough Town v Northampton Town	*0-1
Raunds Town v Peterborough United	0-6
Corby Town v Brackley Town	0-4
Ford Sports Daventry v Rothwell Town	1-2

SEMI-FINALS

Peterborough United v Northampton Town	1-0
Rothwell Town v Brackley Town	5-0

FINAL Monday 28th April

Rothwell Town v Peterborough United	2-1
at Rothwell Town FC.	Att: 171

NORTH RIDING F.A.

Tel: 01642 717770 Fax: 01642 717776 Email: enquiries@northridingfa.com
Broughton Road, Stokesley, Middlesbrough TS9 5NY

Chief Executive: Mark Jarvis
Executives (Responsibility) Andy Clay (Football Development Officer/Womens Football)
Contact County Office for Exams/Courses, Referees
Number of Affiliated Clubs Senior: 500 U.18: 120
Number of Affiliated Leagues: Senior: 20 Junior: 10
County Representative Teams: Senior, U18, Ladies
Inter County Competitions: Northern Counties Competitions, FA Youth Competition

President: K Boyer

NORTH RIDING SENIOR CUP - FOUNDED 1881-82

(15 entries)

LAST SEASON'S FINAL
Whitby Town 3 Middlesbrough 3 (aet)
(Middlesbrough won 4-2 after penalties)

MOST WINS
Middlesbrough 47 Scarborough 17 South Bank 8 Stockton 8 York City 8

1st Preliminary ROUND by 31st October

Nunthorpe Athletic v Grangetown BC	3-2
Fishburn Park v Carlin How	2*4

2nd Preliminary ROUND by 30th November

Carlin How v Marske United	2-3
Edgehill v Whitby Town	0-4
Nunthorpe Athletic v Northallerton Town	3-0
Thornaby v Guisborough Town	*2-5
Pickering Town v Bedale	0-1

FIRST ROUND PROPER by 31st January 2003

Whitby Town v York City	3-0
Nunthorpe Athletic v Middlesbrough	0-3
(Played at Billingham Synthonia)	
Marske United v Scarborough	0-3
Guisborough Town v Bedale	4-2

SEMI-FINALS by 28th February 2003

Scarborough v Whitby Town	3-2
Middlesbrough v Guisborough Town	4-1

FINAL Wednesday 23rd July

Middlesbrough v Scarborough	2-1
(Played at Scarborough)	

NORTHUMBERLAND F.A.

Tel: 0191 2 700 700
Whitley Park, Whitley Road, Newcastle upon Tyne NE12 9FA

Chief Executive: Rowland E Maughan **Press Officer:** Bill Gardner

Executives (Responsibility) Stuart W Leason (County Development Manager)
Mark Woodhall (Football Development Officer)
Bill Darby (Referees Development Officer)

President: E A Wright

Number of Affiliated Clubs Senior: 432 U.18: 492
Number of Affiliated Leagues: Senior: 18 Junior: 4
County Representative Teams: Senior, U18
Inter County Competitions: Northern Counties Senior & Youth Cups, FA County Youth Cup
County Publications: "The Far Corner" - Bi-monthly Newsletter

NORTHUMBERLAND SENIOR CUP - FOUNDED 1883-84

Sponsored by "Absolut"

(16 entries)

LAST SEASON'S FINAL: Bedlington Terriers 2 West Allotment Celtic 1
MOST WINS: Blyth Spartans 21 Newcastle United 21 North Shields 12

FIRST ROUND 16-26 October

Newcastle Blue Star v Amble United	0-1
Walker Central v Ashington	0-2
Bedlington Terriers v Newcastle United Res	0-3
West Allotment Celtic v Blyth Spartans	1-2
Newcastle Benfield Saints v Whitley Bay	2-5
Morpeth Town v Prudhoe Town	3-1
Alnwick Town v Ponteland United	0-3
North Shields v Shankhouse	1-2

SECOND ROUND

Blyth Spartans v Ashington	2-1
Shankhouse v Morpeth Town	2-1
Ponteland United v Newcastle United	1-4
Amble United v Whitley Bay	0-2

SEMI-FINALS

Shankhouse v Whitley Bay	0-3
Blyth Spartans v Newcastle United Rs	1-3

FINAL Wednesday 7th May

Newcastle United Res v Whitley Bay	2-0

at St James' Park, Newcastle United FC

NORTHUMBERLAND BENEVOLENT BOWL - FOUNDED 1975-76

Sponsored by "Brother"

(12 entries)

LAST SEASON'S FINAL: Heaton Stannington 0 Newcastle Benfield Sts. 3
MOST WINS: Morpeth Town 2 Stobswood Welfare 2

FIRST ROUND 12th October 2002

Seaton Delaval Amateurs v Heaton Stannington	1-2
P & G Sports Heddon v Wark	3-1
Bedlington Terriers 'A' v Newbiggin Central W	3-0
Cullercoats v Haydon Bridge United	1-5

SECOND ROUND Saturday 8th February

Heaton Stannington v Percy Main Amateurs	2-1
University Northumbria v Bedlington Terriers A	*3-4
Spittal Rovers v Haydon Bridge United	4-2
P & G Heddon v Wallington	3-4

SEMI-FINALS

1 Wallington v Spitall Rovers	1-2
2 Bedlington Terriers 'A' v Percy Main Amateurs	1-2

FINAL Thursday 8th May 7pm

Percy Main Amateurs v Spittal Rovers	0-1

at Whitley Park, Northumberland FA County Ground

Damon Miles gives Bishops Stortford Swifts the lead during the final of the Hertfordshire Intermediate Cup final against Leverstock Green Reserves. Photo: Gordon Whittington.

Bishops Stortford Swifts celebrate after their 4-2 win over Leverstock Green Reserves in the final of the Hertfordshire Intermediate Cup.

Photo: Gordon Whittington.

NOTTINGHAMSHIRE F.A. LIMITED

Tel: 0115 941 8954 Fax: 0115 941 5254 Email: info@nottinghamshirefa.com
7 Clarendon Street, Nottingham NG1 5HS

Secretary: Mike Kilbee

Executives (Responsibility)	Elaine Oram (Office Manager)			
	Helen Bennett (Discipline Secretary)			
Number of Affiliated Clubs	Senior: 561	U.18: 198		**President:** John Waterall
Number of Affiliated Leagues:	Senior: 8	Junior: 4		**Chairman:** David Woolrich
County Representative Teams:	U18			
Inter County Competitions:	FA County Youth Cup, East Midlands Youth Combination			

NOTTINGHAMSHIRE SENIOR CUP - FOUNDED 1883-84

(34 entries)

LAST SEASON'S FINAL

Southwell City 0 Gedling Town 1

MOST WINS

Nottingham Forest 17 Sutton Town 17 Notts County 11

FIRST ROUND Saturday 5th October

Clifton All Whites v Cotgrave CW United	3-2
Pelican v Kimberley Town	4-1
Blidworth Welfare v Dunkirk	4-3
Clipstone Welfare v Gedling M W	4-1
Nottinghamshire Police v Radcliffe Olympic	1-4
Ruddington United v Kimberley M W	3-0
Forest Town v Radford	4-0
Greenwood Meadows v Selston	2-0
Keyworth United v Rainworth M W	2-3
Retford United v Wollaton	1-5
Ollerton Town v Thoresby C W	2-0
Sutton Town v Newark Flowserve	2-0

SECOND ROUND Saturday 7th December

Clifton All Whites v Clipstone Welfare	1-2
Forest Town v Blidworth Welfare	0-5
Wollaton v Greenwood Meadows	4-2
Rainworth MW v Ollerton Town	2-0
Sutton Town v Pelican	3-1
Radcliffe Olympic v Ruddington United	3-0

THIRD ROUND

Southwell City v Gedling Town	0-2
Eastwood Town v Teversal	3-4
Arnold Town v Sutton Town	1-2
Blidworth Welfare v Carlton Town	2-3
Rolls Royce Hucknall v Radcliffe Olympic	0-1
Welbeck Welfare v Clipstone Welfare	1-5
Boots Athletic v Hucknall Town	2-3
Rainworth MW v Wollaton	*3-3 5-3pens

QUARTER-FINALS by 1st March

Rainworth MW v Radcliffe Olympic	2-4
Gedling Town v Clipstone Welfare	2-1
Hucknall Town v Sutton Town	1-0
Teversal v Carlton Town	*3-3 5-4pens

SEMI-FINALS

Radcliffe Olympic v Hucknall Town	3-4
Gedling Town v Teversal	0-1

FINAL Thursday 24th April

Hucknall Town v Teversal	2-0

at Meadow Lane, Notts County FC

OXFORDSHIRE F.A.

Tel: 01993 778586 Fax: 01993 772191 Email: Ian.Mason@oxfordshirefa.com
PO Box 62, Witney, Oxon OX28 1HA

Secretary: Ian Mason
Executives (Responsibility) Ted Mitchell (Football Development/Coaching)
Paul Faulkner (Referees) Liz Verrall (Womens Football
)
Number of Affiliated Clubs 320
Number of Affiliated Leagues: 12
County Representative Teams: Under 18, Under 16 Boys & Girls
Inter County Competitions: Under 18, Under 16 Boys & Girls

President: J Webb
Chairman: T Williams

OXFORDSHIRE SENIOR CUP - FOUNDED 1884-85

(34 entries)

LAST SEASON'S FINAL

North Leigh 3 Thame United 4

MOST WINS

Oxford City 31 Witney Town 9 Oxford United 8

FIRST ROUND Saturday 16th November

Worcester & Bletchingdon v Marston Saints	2-1
Eynsham v Chipping Norton Town	2-4
Old Woodstock Town	bye
Yarnton v Garsington	1-6
Headington Amateurs v Quarry Nomads	3-1
Ardley United v Adderbury Park	2-0
Sonning Common v Carterton Town	0-4
Watlington Town v Broughton-North Newington	3-1
Clanfield v Witney United	1-2
Easington Sports v Hook Norton	0-2
Checkendon Sports v Kidlington Old Boys	1-3
Henley Town v Middle Barton	4-1
Launton sports v Charlton United	3-1
Highfield Old Boys	bye
Bicester Town v Kidlington	2-1
Chinnor v Goring United	2-1

SECOND ROUND Saturday 14th December

Carterton Town v Highfield OB	3-1
Hook Norton v Launton Sports	2-1
Chinnor v Bicester Town	2-5
Worcester & Bletchingdon v Old Woodstock Tn	1-3
Witney United v Kidlington O B	2-1
Chipping Norton Town v Watlington Town	4-0
Ardley United v Headington Amateurs	4-0
Garsington v Henley Town	0-12

THIRD ROUND

Old Woodstock Town v Chipping Norton Town	1-2
Henley Town v Bicester Town	3-1
Ardley United v Carterton Town	2-3
Hook Norton v Witney United	2-1

QUARTER-FINALS

Hook Norton v Carterton Town	2-0
Henley Town v North Leigh	*1-1 6-5pens
Chipping Norton Town v Oxford City	1-3
Banbury United v Thame United	1-2

SEMI-FINALS

Thame United v Hook Norton	0-1
Henley Town v Oxford City 3-4	

FINAL Tuesday 29th April (Golden Goal)

Hook Norton v Oxford City	*2-3 (GG)

at The Kassam Stadium, Oxford United FC

SHEFFIELD & HALLAMSHIRE F.A.

Tel: 0114 241 4999 Fax: 0114 241 4990
Clegg House, 69 Cornish Place, Cornish Street, Shalesmoor, Sheffield S6 3AF

Secretary & Press Officer: J P Hope-Gill
Executives (Responsibility) John Warnock (Coaching Exams/Courses)
Peter Jackson (Referees) Julie Callaghan (Womens Football)
Brian Peck (Development Officer)
Number of Affiliated Clubs Senior: 888 U.18: 243 **President:** C L Milner
Number of Affiliated Leagues: Senior: 17 Junior: 7 **Chairman:** M Matthews
County Representative Teams: Under 18, Under 16 Girls
Inter County Competitions: Midlands Youth Combination, FA County Youth Cup

SHEFFIELD & HALLAMSHIRE SENIOR CUP - FOUNDED 1876-77

(20 entries)

LAST SEASON'S FINAL

Doncaster Rovers 3 Emley 0

FIRST ROUND Saturday 12th October

Worsbrough Bridge MWA v Hallam	*0-0 3-4
Frickley Athletic v Harworth Colliery Institute	3-1
Frecheville C A v Penistone Church	1-3
Rossington Main v Stocksbridge Park Steels	3-7

SECOND ROUND Saturday 9th November

Frickley Athletic v Stocksbridge Park Steels	1-2
Grimethorpe MW v Worksop Town	*1-4
Parkgate v Hallam	3-1
Penistone Church v Maltby Main	3-2
(Played at Malby Main)	
South Kirkby Colliery v Sheffield	3-0
Yorkshire Main v Doncaster Rovers	0-10
(Played at Doncaster Rovers)	
Swinton athletic v Wakefield & Emley	1-2
(Played at Emley)	
Mexborough Main Street v Brodsworth Welfare	3-1

THIRD ROUND

1 Parkgate v Stocksbridge Park Steels	2-5
2 Maltby Main v Wakefield & Emley	*5-3
3 Doncaster Rovers v Mexborough Main Street	7-0
4 South Kirkby Colliery v Worksop Town	1-5

SEMI-FINALS

1 Doncaster Rovers v Malty Main	2-1
2 Stocksbridge Park Steels v Worksop Town	0-4

FINAL Tuesday 6th May 7pm

Doncaster Rovers v Worksop Town 1-2
at Sheffield Wednesday FC

SHROPSHIRE F.A.

Tel: 01743 362769 Fax: 01743 240474
Gay Meadow, Abbey Foregate, Shrewsbury, Shropshire SY2 6AB

Secretary: David Rowe **Press Officer:** Neil Sambrook (Office Manager)
Football Development Officer: Mick Murphy
Eric Adams (Referees)

Number of Affiliated Clubs	Senior:	320	U.18:	90
Number of Affiliated Leagues:	Senior:	9	Junior:	5

County Representative Teams: U18, Womens
Inter County Competitions: FA County Youth, Midland County Youth, Gilbert Trophy

FLOREAT SALOPIA

President: A W Brett
Chairman: S T Farmer

SHROPSHIRE COUNTY CUP

(21 entries)

LAST SEASON'S FINAL
Little Drayton Rangers 5 Newport Town 1

FIRST ROUND 12th October

Ludlow Town Res v Wellington Amateurs	1-2
Hanwood United v Craven arms Town	0-1
Oakengates Town v Morda United	0-1
Ludlow Town Res v Wellington Amateurs	2-5
Wem Town v Bridgnorth Town Res	0-1

SECOND ROUND 9th November

Star v Bridgnorth Town Res	1-2
Meole Brace v Tiberton United	2-4
Church Stretton Town v Newport Town	*2-4
Whitchurch Alport v Morda United	2-3
Wrockwardine Wood v Broseley Juniors	0-2
Wellington Amateurs v Shawbury United	2-4
Craven Arms Town v Little Drayton Rangers	0-6
Haughmond v Belle Vue	4-1

THIRD ROUND

Bridgnorth Town Res v Tibberton United	3-0
Newport Town v Haughmond	5-0
Broseley Juniors v Morda United	*2-5
Little Drayton Rangers v Shawbury United	3-5

SEMI-FINALS

Morda United v Newport Town 1-4
Wem Town FC Saturday 22nd February
Shawbury United v Bridgnorth Town Res 2-1
at Newport Town FC Saturday 22nd February

FINAL Wednesday 23rd April

Newport Town v Shawbury United 1-2
at Gay Meadow, Shrewsbury Town FC

SOMERSET F.A.

Tel: 01761 410280 / 01761 410287 Fax: 01761 410477 (Coaching and Development)
30 North Road, Midsomer Norton, Radstock, Somerset BA3 2QD

Secretary: Mrs H Marchment

Executives (Responsibility) I Tincknell (Coaching Representative)
J H Day (Referees), K Hodges (Football Development)

Number of Affiliated Clubs	Senior:	89	Junior:	326	Youth:	153	**President:** F P Hillier
Number of Affiliated Leagues:	Senior:	1	Junior:	13	Youth:	6	**Chairman:** A J Hobbs

County Representative Teams: Youth U18s, Womens U18s

Inter County Competitions: FA County Youth, South West Counties Championship (Youth & Womens U18)

SOMERSET PREMIER CUP- FOUNDED 1948-49

(24 entries)

LAST SEASON'S FINAL

Team Bath 1 Clevedon Town 2

MOST WINS

Bath City 17 Yeovil Town 15 Bristol City 6

FIRST ROUND Tuesday 8th October (unless stated)

Brislington v Weston super Mare	*1-1 3-5pens
Street v Bishop Sutton	*1-1 2-0pens
(Played at Bishop Sutton)	
Team Bath v Keynsham Town	1-0
Backwell United v Minehead Town	2-1
Wellington v Taunton Town	0-3
Clevedon Town v Frome Town	3-2
Bitton v Bridgwater Town	4-2
Paulton Rovers v Bristol Manor Farm	4-0

SECOND ROUND Tuesday 19th November

Welton Rovers v Paulton Rovers	1-2
Odd Down(Bath) v Bath City	4-3
Taunton Town v Chard Town	*4-4 5-4pens
Weston super Mare v Bitton	4-1
Bristol City v Team Bath	2-0
Yeovil Town v Mangotsfield United	*2-1
Shepton Mallet v Clevedon Town	*2-3
Backwell United v Street	2-0

QUARTER-FINALS W/c 17th February 2003

Yeovil Town v Odd Down Bath	2-0
Backwell United v Clevedon Town	0-1
Bristol City v Weston super Mare @W	4-1
(Played at Weston)	
Taunton Town v Paulton Rovers	5-1

SEMI-FINALS

Clevedon Town v Yeovil Town	0-4
Bristol City v Taunton Town	1-2

FINAL Tuesday 29th April

Taunton Town v Yeovil Town	2-1
at The Hand Stadium, Clevedon Town FC.	Att: 914

SOMERSET SENIOR CUP - FOUNDED 1895-96

(56 entries)

LAST SEASON'S FINAL

Watchet Town 3 Wells City 1 (aet)

MOST WINS

Paulton Rovers 12 Radstock Town 12 Welton Rovers 9

FIRST ROUND

Radstock Town v Worle	6-2
St George Easton in Gordano v Glastonbury	1-0
Shepton Mallet Res v Langford Rovers	7-3
First Tower United v Dundry Athletic	6-2
Saltford v Blackbrook	5-2
SC Somerton v Teyfant Athletic	W-O
(Walkover for SC Somerton)	
Castle Cary v Robinsons	3-1
Ashton United v Bristol Spartak	2-1
Combe St Nicholas v Fry Club	2-1
Clevedon United v Portishead	1-5
Yatton Athletic v Weston super Mare Res	0-1
Keynsham Town Res v Burnham United	*5-3
Larkhall Athletic v Congresbury	3-1
Ilminster Town v Westland United	0-6
Nailsea United v Bridgwater Town Res	2-3
Broad Plain House v Winscome	4-1
Peasedown Athletic v Brislington Res	2-3
Backwell United Res v Wells City	2-1
Wrington Redhill v Weston St Johns	0-4
Tunley Athletic v Hengrove Athletic	*2-3
Welton Rovers Res v Crewkerne	4-2
Watchet Town v Clutton	1-0
Cutters Friday Bristol v Clandown	3-4
Hartcliffe OB v Stockwood Green	0-2

SECOND ROUND Saturday 7th December

1 Clandown v Watchet Town	0-3
2 Hengrove Athletic v Keynsham Town Res	2-3
3 Paulton Rovers res v Team Bath Res	2-3
4 Broad Plain House v Larkhall Athletic	1-2
5 Backwell United Res v Bishop Sutton Res	2-0
6 Timsbury Athletic v Ashton United	3-0
7 Weston St Johns v Welton Rovers Res	2-0
8 Odd Down Bath Res v Cheddar	4p3 5*5
9 Saltford v Cleeve West Town	0-4
10 St George Easton in Gordano v First Tower Utd	0-2
11 Portishead v Frome Collegians	7-0
12 Westland United v Combe St Nicholas	*1-0
13 Shepton Mallet Res v Brislington Res	1-2
14 Stockwood Green v Bridgwater Town Res	2-1
15 Castle Cary v Sporting Club Somerton	1-0
16 Weston super Mare Res v Radstock Town	1-0

THIRD ROUND

Backwell United Res v Keynsham Town Res	1-5
Portishead v Weston super Mare Res	1-0
Odd Down Res v Westland United	1-2
Watchet Town v Weston St John	1-2
Castle Cary v Larkhall Athletic	0-4
Stockwood Green v Paulton Rovers	0-1
Cleeve West Town v Brislington	0-1
Timsbury Athletic v First Tower United	*1-0

FOURTH ROUND Quarter-Finals

Portishead v Timsbury Athletic	3-0
Westland United v Brislington Res	1-0
Keynsham Town Res v Larkhall Athletic	5-1
Paulton Rovers v Weston St Johns	3-2

SEMI-FINALS

Westland united v Paulton Rovers	*1-1 4-3pens
Keynsham Town Res v Portishead	*3-3 3-1pens

FINAL Monday 5th May 3pm

Keynsham Town Res v Westland United 4-0
at The Hand Stadium, Clevedon Town/United FC

STAFFORDSHIRE F.A.

Tel: 01785 256994 Fax: 01785 224334
County Showground, Weston Road, Stafford ST18 0BD

Secretary: Brian Adshead

Executives (Responsibility) Andy Weston (Football Development Officer)
Nick Broad (Referees)
Adam Evans (Competitions)

Number of Affiliated Clubs Senior: 567 U18: 553

Number of Affiliated Leagues: Senior: 15 U18: 14

County Representative Teams: U 18 Boys, U 16 Boys, Ladies, U 16 Girls

Inter County Competitions: FA County Youth Challenge Cup, Midland Counties Youth Championship

President: P Savage

Chairman: P Hodgkinson

STAFFORDSHIRE SENIOR CHALLENGE CUP - FOUNDED 1891-92

(17 entries)

LAST SEASON'S FINAL

Newcastle Town 1 Tamworth 3 (on aggregate)

MOST WINS

Stoke City 18 Aston Villa 16 West Bromwich Albion 13

FIRST ROUND Week / comencing 7th October

Biddulph Victoria v Pelsall Villa	0-1

SECOND ROUND W/c 18th November

Stafford Rangers v Pelsall Villa	7-0
Leek Town v Stoke City	0-2
Newcastle Town v Rocester	2-1
Shifnal Town v Kidsgrove Athletic	3-2
Port Vale v Alsager Town	W-O
(Walkover for Port Vale)	
Hednesford Town v Chasetown	7-0
Tamworth v Rushall Olympic	1-1 1-3
Burton Albion v Stafford Town	5-1

QUARTER-FINALS

Burton Albion v Hednesford Town	1-2
Stoke City v Rushall Olympic	*2-2 4-2pens
(Played at Rushall Olympic)	
Stafford Rangers v Newcastle Town	4-0
Port Vale v Shifnal Town	2-1
(Played at Shifnal Town)	

SEMI-FINALS

Hednesford Town v Stoke City	2-6
Port Vale v Stafford Rangers	1-2

FINAL Wednesday 30th April 7.45pm

Stafford Rangers v Stoke City	5-1
at Vale Park, Port Vale FC.	Att: 881

SUFFOLK F.A.

Tel: 01449 616606 Fax: 01449 616607 email: info@suffolkfa.com
The Buntings, Ledars Park, Stowmarket, Suffolk IP14 5GZ

Secretary:	Martin Head				
Executives (Responsibility)	Will Cook (Development Officer)				
	Barry Felgate (Referees)				
Number of Affiliated Clubs	Senior:	450	U.18:	200	**President:** Gordon Blake
Number of Affiliated Leagues:	Senior:	13	Junior:	7	**Chairman:** George Whight
County Representative Teams:	U18, U16, Womens				
Inter County Competitions:	All in East Anglian Counties Championships				

SUFFOLK PREMIER CUP - FOUNDED 1958-59

(9 entries)

LAST SEASON'S FINAL: Felixstowe & Walton United 1 Sudbury 3

MOST WINS: Sudbury Town 13 Bury Town 10 Lowestoft Town 6

PRELIMINARY ROUND

Mildenhall Town v Woodbridge Town	4-0

FIRST ROUND 22nd or 23rd October

Sudbury v Stowmarket Town	3-1
Lowestoft Town v Ipswich Wanderers	7-0
Bury Town v Mildenhall Town	1-2
Newmarket Town v Felixstowe & Walton United	4-1

SEMI-FINALS

Lowestoft Town v Mildenhall Town	*3-3 3-4pens
at Lowestoft Town FC 7.45pm	
Newmarket Town v Sudbury	*1-2
at Newmarket Town FC 7.45pm	

FINAL Monday 5th May

Mildenhall Town v Sudbury	0-1
at Bury Town FC.	Att: 420

SUFFOLK SENIOR CUP - FOUNDED 1885-86

(31 entries)

LAST SEASON'S FINAL: Haverhill Rovers 3 Kirkley 4

MOST WINS: Ipswich Town 16 Lowestoft Town 10 Stowmarket Town 8

FIRST ROUND Saturday 12th October

Achilles v Leiston St Margarets	1-0
Felixstowe & Walton United Rs v Haughley Utd	2-3
Beccles Town v Cornard United	0-2
Westerfield United v Stowmarket Town Res	0-7
East Bergholt United v Ipswich Athletic	1-4
Crane Sports v Sudbury Res	2-0
Bramford United v Brandon Town	*3-3 5-3pens
Capel Plough v Tuddenham Rovers	0-2
Woodbridge Athletic v Stanton	0-4
Leiston v Needham Market	3-0
Hadleigh United v Kirkley	0-4
Whitton United v Grundisburgh	1-0
Long Melford v Lowestoft Town Res	2-1
Stonham Aspal v Haverhill Rovers	*3-3 3-4pens
Old Newton United v Melton St Audrys	3-0
Walsham Le Willows bye	

SECOND ROUND 23rd November

Stanton v Haughley United 3p2 1*1	
Long Melford v Haverhill Rovers	1-0
Ipswich Athletic v Walsham Le Willows	1-8
Cornard United v Whitton United	*2-2 6-5pens
Leiston v Kirkley	*0-1
Achilles v Tuddenham Rovers	2-0
Bramford United v Old Newton United	2-1
Stowmarket Town Res v Crane Sports	*3-1

QUARTER-FINALS

Kirkley v Corbard United	0-1
Stowmarket Town Res v Bramford United	3-1
Achilles v Stanton	0-2
Walsham le Willows v Long Melford	1-2

SEMI-FINALS

Stanton v Cornard United 3-1	
at Needham Market FC 2.30pm	
Long Melford v Stowmarket Town Res	3-2
at Hadleigh United FC 3pm	

FINAL Tuesday 1st April 7.30pm

Long Melford v Stanton	5-0
at Portman Road, Ipswich Town FC	

SURREY F.A.

Tel: 01372 373543 Fax: 01372 361310
Website: www.surreyfa.co.uk Email: info@surreyfa.com
321 Kingston Road, Leatherhead, Surrey KT22 7TU

Secretary: Ray Ward

Executives (Responsibility) Larry May (Football Development Officer)
Phil Whatling (Referees) Peter Adams (Womens Football)
Michelle Jeffcoate (Women's Football Development Officer)

President: A P Adams
Chairman: R S Lewis

Number of Affiliated Clubs Senior: 37
Number of Affiliated Leagues: Senior: 2 Junior: 20
County Representative Teams: Under 18
Inter County Competitions: Home Counties Womens U16 & U18 Competition, FA County Youth Cup

SURREY SENIOR CUP - FOUNDED 1882-83

(34 entries)

LAST SEASON'S FINAL

Crystal Palace 3 Woking 0

FIRST ROUND 14-28/9/02

Chipstead v Chessington & Hook United	4-3
Ashford Town v Egham Town	*3-2
Molesey v Frimley Green	3-0
Raynes Park Vale v Cobham	3-0
Epsom & Ewell v Westfield	4-2
Chessington United v Redhill	2-1

SECOND ROUND 19/10 to 2/11/02

Farnham Town v Raynes Park Vale	1-7
Metropolitan Police v Chipstead	3-0
Molesey v Camberley Town	2-3
Godalming & Guildford v Ash United	3-4
Banstead Athletic v Chessington United	0-1
Ashford Town v Dorking	2-1
Epsom & Ewell v Walton Casuals	0-1
Corinthian Casuals v Merstham	4-3

THIRD ROUND 16 to 30th November

Ashford Town v Metropolitan Police	2-3
Corinthian Casuals v Raynes Park Vale	2-3
Chessington United v Walton Casuals	W-O
(Walkover for Chessington United)	
Camberley Town v Ash United	2-3

FOURTH ROUND 18/1 to 1/2/2003

Leatherhead v Croydon	4-1
Woking v Dulwich Hamlet	0-1
Ash United v Tooting & Mitcham United	2-1
Walton & Hersham v Sutton United	1-3
Kingstonian v Chessington United	2-0
Whyteleafe v Chertsey Town	1-0
Metropolitan Police v Crystal Palace	1-4
Carshalton Athletic v Raynes Park Vale	3-0

FIFTH ROUND 15/2 to 1/3/03

Leatherhead v Crystal Palace	*0-0 5-4pens
Kingstonian v Ash United	4-1
Whyteleafe v Dulwich Hamlet	1-2
Sutton United v Carshalton Athletic	2-0

SEMI-FINALS 22nd to 29th March 2003

Leatherhead v Kingstonian	*2-2 6-7pens
Dulwich Hamlet v Sutton United	1-2

FINAL Wednesday 7th May

Kingstonian v Sutton United	1-2
at Metropolitan Police FC	

SUSSEX F.A.

Tel: 01903 753547 Fax: 01903 761608
Website: sussex-fa.org E-mail: info@sussexfa.com
Culver Road, Lancing, West Sussex BN15 9AX

Chief Executive	Ken Benham			
Executives (Responsibility)	L Thompson (Coaching Admin)			
	M Bodenham (Head of Refereeing)			
	H Millington (County Development Officer)			
Number of Affiliated Clubs	Senior: 951	Youth: 246		
Number of Affiliated Leagues:	Senior: 18	Junior: 10		
County Representative Teams:	Senior, Inter, U18, U16, Womens, U18			
Inter County Competitions:	FA County Youth, Home Counties Youth U16's, U18's			
	South West Counties Senior, Womens U18's, Southern Counties Intermediate			

President: John Davey
Chairman: Ron Pavey

Yellow Jersey SUSSEX SENIOR CUP - FOUNDED 1882-83

(46 entries)

LAST SEASON'S FINAL

Eastbourne Borough 2 Lewes 1

MOST WINS

Worthing 20 Eastbourne Town 12 Southwick 10

FIRST ROUND October

1	Worthing United v Westfield	2-1
2	Wick v Lancing	3-0
3	Sidlesham v Seaford	3-1
4	Wealden v East Preston	2-3
5	Southwick v Shoreham	0-2
6	Crawley Down v Rye & Iden United	*3-4
7	Oakwood v Broadbridge Heath	1-2
8	Mile Oak v Horsham YMCA	1-5
9	Eastbourne United v Peacehaven & Tels	*1-1 5-2
10	Whitehawk v East Grinstead Town	2-0
11	Hassocks v Shinewater Association	6-1
12	Oving v Pease Pottage Village	1-0
13	Eastbourne Town v Saltdean United	*2-1
14	Littlehampton Town v Steyning Town	*0-0 1-2

SECOND ROUND 19th November (unless Stated)

1	Bognor Regis Town v Crawley Town	1-3
2	St Leonards v Sidlesham	5-1
3	Brighton & Hove Albion v Hastings United	1-0
4	Horsham v Hassocks	1-0
5	Horsham YMCA v Eastboune United	5-1
6	Lewes v Worthing	0-2
7	Worthing United v Arundel	1-2
8	Pagham v Steyning Town	*2-1
9	Whitehawk v Ringmer	3-0
10	Eastbourne Borough v Shoreham	5-0
11	Wick v Selsey	2-1
12	East Preston v Broadbridge Heath	6-0
13	Oving v Rye & Iden United	2-4
14	Eastbourne Town v Sidley United	4-1
15	Burgess Hill Town v Three Bridges	1-0
16	Chichester City United v Hailsham Town	5-1

THIRD ROUND

1	Worthing v Horsham YMCA	*0-0 3-1
2	Horsham v Crawley Town	1-3
3	Pagham v Chichester City United	2-1
4	Brighton & Hove Albion v East Preston	2-1
	(Played at East Preston)	Att: 343
5	Burgess Hill Town v St Leonards	2-0
6	Whitehawk v Eastbourne Town	*6-6 1-2
7	Rye & Iden United v Arundel	2-1
8	Wick v Eastbourne Borough	1-3

QUARTER-FINALS

1	Pagham v Worthing1*0	
2	Eastbourne Borough v Eastbourne Town	3-1
3	Rye & Iden United v Burgess Hill Town	*0-0 2-1
4	Brighton & Hove v Crawley Town @CT	0-1

SEMI-FINALS

1	Rye & Iden United v Crawley Town	*0-3
2	Pagham v Eastbourne Borough	0-1

FINAL Monday 5th May 3pm
Eastbourne Borough v Crawley Town *0-0 5-6pens
at Priory Lane, Eastbourne Borough FC

Melksham Town Football Club
Wiltshire Senior Cup Winners 2002-03

Back Row (L-R): Dave Phillips (Secretary), Gary Sanks, Dean Ranger, Robbie Lardner, Nigel Tripp, Andrew Snadell, Darren Chitty, Simon Price, Dave Clayton, Adrian Stagg.
Front Row (L-R): Steve Casey, Gordon Smith, Kevin Banks, Justin Messenger (Capt), Daniel Lardner, Matthew Bown, Russell Fishlock, Sam Fielding (Mascot)
Photo: David Phillips - Wiltshire Publications Ltd.

MELKSHAM TOWN
FOOTBALL CLUB
SEASON 2002/2003
Founded 1876
M T F C
LEAGUE
SCREWFIX
THE CONIGRE REVIEW
50p
Sponsored By
AVON
TYRES

WESTMORLAND F.A.

Tel: 01539 730946 Fax: 01539 730946 E-mail: info@westmorlandfa.com
Unit 1, Angel Court, 21 Highgate, Kendal, Cumbria LA9 4DA

Executive Officer: P G Ducksbury
Executives (Responsibility) J Ashworth (football Development/Coach Education)
J R Cother (Referees Training
Number of Affiliated Clubs Senior: 55 U.18: 30
Number of Affiliated Leagues: Senior: 3 Junior: 1
Chairman: G Aplin
County Representative Teams: Senior, U18, U16
Inter County Competitions: FA County Youth, Association of Northern Counties Senior & Youth Competitions

WESTMORLAND CAR SALES SENIOR CUP - FOUNDED 1896-97

(26 entries)

LAST SEASON'S FINAL
Kendal Town 1 Milnthorpe Corinthians 3

MOST WINS
Corinthians 14 Netherfield 12 Burneside 7 Windermere 7

FIRST ROUND

Ambleside United v Staveley United	0-7
Appleby v Burton Thistle	4-2
Burneside v Keswick	3-2
Carlton Rovers v Dent	7-1
Carvetii United v Endmoor KGR	4-3
Esthwaite Vale United v Windermere SC	2-5
Kendal Celtic v Lunesdale United	4-5
Kendal County v Arnside	3-0
Victoria SC v Shap United	5-0
Wetheriggs United v Greystoke	5-1

SECOND ROUND Saturday 9th November

Appleby v Windermere SC	5-2
Burneside v IBIS	0-3
Carleton Rovers v Carvetii United	1-2
(Carleton awarded tie after Carveti played ineligible player)	
Kendal Town Res v Coniston	5-3
Kirkby Lonsdale v Corinthians	*2-0
(Corinthians awarded tie after Kirkby played ineligible player)	
Lunesdale v Sedburgh Wanderers	2-0
Victoria S C v Kendal County	5-3
Wetheriggs United v Staveley United	*2-2 5-3pens

(v= ineligible players Clubs re-instated)

THIRD ROUND Saturday 7th December 2002

Appleby v Wetheriggs United	5-3
IBIS v Kendal Town Res	2-3
Milnthorpe Corinthians v Carlton Rovers	3-4
Lunesdale United v Victoria SC	1-0

SEMI-FINALS 1st March

Appleby v Lunesdale	6-0
Kendal v Carlton Rovers	2-0

FINAL Saturday 5th April 2003

Kendal Town v Appleby	*3-3 4-2pens

at Kendal Town FC

WEST RIDING F.A.

Tel: 01132 821222 Fax: 01132 821525 Email: info@wrcfa.com
Fleet Lane, Woodlesford, Leeds LS26 8NX www.wrcfa.com

Secretary: G R Carter

Executives (Responsibility) Danny Philpott (Football Development Officer)
Julie Chipchase (Womens/Girls Football)

Number of Affiliated Clubs Senior: 950 U.18: 300

Number of Affiliated Leagues: Senior: 40 Junior: 12

County Representative Teams: Senior, Junior U18, Womens, Junior U16

Inter County Competitions: Association of Northern Counties Senior, Junior U18 & Womens, FA County Youth

President: A C Taylor
Chairman: P Marsden

WEST RIDING COUNTY CUP - FOUNDED 1924-25

(20 entries)

LAST SEASON'S FINAL
Farsley Celtic 0 Harrogate Town 4

MOST WINS
Goole Town 11 Farsley Celtic 9 Guiseley 5

FIRST ROUND

Halifax Town v Ossett Albion	3-0
Guiseley v Pontefract Collieries	2-1
Armthorpe Welfare v Tadcaster Albion	1-0
Liversedge v Glasshoughton Welfare	4-3

SECOND ROUND Tuesday 10th December

Liversedge v Selby Town	4-1
Harrogate Town v Harrogate Railway Athletic	3-1
Yorkshire Amateur v Bradford Park Avenue	1-4
Hatfield Main v Thackley	0-3
Garforth Town v Eccleshill United	1-2
Farsley Celtic v Guiseley	3-0
Goole v Armthorpe Welfare	*1-0
Ossett Town v Halifax Town	1-2

QUARTER-FINALS

Liversedge v Goole	0-2
Halifax Town v Harrogate Town	1-2
Bradford Park Avenue v Eccleshill United	1-0
Thackley v Farsley Celtic	0-1

SEMI-FINALS

Harrogate Town v Bradford Park Avenue	2-0
Goole v Farsley Celtic	0-1

FINAL Wednesday 16th April

Farsley Celtic v Harrogate Town	*1-3

at West Riding Co FA Ground, Woodlesford, Leeds

WILTSHIRE F.A.

Tel: 01793 486047 or 525245 Fax: 01793 692699 Email: info@wiltshirefa.com
18 Covingham Square, Covingham, Swindon, Wilts SN3 5AA

Secretary: Michael Benson
Executives (Responsibility) Ian Whitehouse (Referees)
B J Stephens (Development Officer)
Number of Affiliated Clubs: 456
Number of Affiliated Leagues: 17
County Representative Teams: Senior, U21, U18, Womens Senior & U18
Inter County Competitions: All levels

President: K J Mulraney
Chairman: R Gardiner

WILTSHIRE PREMIER SHIELD - FOUNDED 1926-27

(4 entries)

LAST SEASON'S FINAL: Chippenham Town 4 Swindon Town 0
MOST WINS: Swindon Town 26 Salisbury City 11 Trowbridge Town 9

SEMI-FINALS Two Legs

Chippenham Town v Salisbury City	0-2
Salisbury City v Chippenham Town	3-3
Swindon Supermarine v Swindon Town	2-1
Swindon Town v Swindon Supermarine	0-0

FINAL Monday 5th May 3pm

Salisbury City v Swindon Supermarine	3-1

at The Ray McEnhill Stadium, Salisbury City FC

WILTSHIRE SENIOR CUP - FOUNDED 1886-87

(24 entries)

LAST SEASON'S FINAL: Malmesbury Victoria 1 Pwesey Vale 0
MOST WINS: Devizes Town 14 Swindon Town 10 Chippenham Town 8

FIRST ROUND

Bemerton Heath Harlequins v Westbury United	2-1
Bradford Town v Highworth Town	0-3
Calne Town v Chiseldon Castrol	3-0
Downton v Purton	0-1
Malmesbury Victoria v Malborough Town	*2-2 1-0
Shrewton United v Devizes Town	1-3
Stratton Crosslink v Wroughton	0-2
Warminster Town v Biddestone	1-4

SECOND ROUND Sat 18th Jan

Aldbourne FC v Devizes Town	0-2
Calne Town v Amesbury Town	2-0
Bemerton Heath Harlequins v Trowbridge Town	0-3
Corsham Town v Purton	5-1
Biddestone v Pewsey Vale	1-5
Wootton Bassett Town v Cricklade Town	3-0
Wroughton v Melksham Town	1-2
Highworth Town v Malmesbury Victoria	6-0

THIRD ROUND Saturday 15th February 3pm

Melksham Town v Corsham Town	2-0
Highworth Town v Pewsey Vale	3-0
Devizes Town v Trowbridge Town	1-0
Trowbridge awarded tie	
Wootton Bassett Town v Calne Town	0-1

SEMI-FINALS

Melksham Town v Highworth Town	4-0
Trowbridge Town v Calne Town	3-1

FINAL Wednesday 23rd April 7.30pm

Melksham Town v Trowbridge Town	2*1

at Chippenham Town FCat Kendal Town FC

WORCESTERSHIRE F.A.

Tel: 01905 827137 Fax:01905 798963 Email: info@worcestershirefa.com
Craftsman House, De Salis Drive, Hampton Lovett Ind. Estate, Droitwich, Worcs WR9 0QE

Company Secretary: Mervyn Leggett **Treasurer:** Mick Thomson
Executives (Responsibility) John Lovegrove (Disciplinary Secretary)
Andy Norman (Football Development Officer)
Julie Leroux (Girls' & Womens' FDO)
Bill Allsopp (Referees Co-ordinator)
Number of Affiliated Clubs Senior: 19 Junior: 239 Youth: 103
Womens & Girls: 23 Small-Sided: 74
Number of Affiliated Leagues: Senior: 7 Junior: 3
County Representative Teams: U18 Youth, U16 Girls'
Inter County Competitions: FA County Youth Cup, Midland Youth Football Championships

President: Percy Rushton
Chairman: Ken Clifford

WORCESTERSHIRE SENIOR CUP - FOUNDED 1893-94
(10 entries)

FIRST ROUND
Stourport Swifts v Halesowen Town 0-3
Sutton Coldfield Town v Redditch United 1A0 3-1

SECOND ROUND
Solihull Borough v Moor Green 2-3
Evesham United v Sutton Coldfield Town 2-1
Halesowen Town v Worcester City 2-1
Kidderminster Harriers v Bromsgrove Rovers 1-2

SEMI-FINALS
Bromsgrove Rovers v Halesowen Town 1-3
Evesham United v Moor Green 1-0

FINAL FIRST LEG Tuesday 8th April
Halesowen Town v Evesham United 2-0
at Halesowen Town FC

SECOND LEG Wednesday 23rd April 7.45pm
Evesham United v Halesowen Town 0-1
at Evesham United FC

WORCESTERSHIRE SENIOR URN 2002-03
(9 entries)

FIRST ROUND
Pegasus Juniors v Malvern Town *2-2 4-5pens

SECOND ROUND
Studley v Malvern Town(20/11) 3-1
Kings Heath v Pershore Town(26/11) * 2-2 5-4pens
Fernhill County Sports v Lye Town(3/12) 1-3
Feckenham v Alvechurch(27/11) 2-5

SEMI-FINALS
Alvechurch v Studley 1-5
Lye Town v Castle Vale Kings Heath *2-1

FINAL Thursday 24th April 7.30pm
Lye Town v Studley 0-3
at Aggborough, Kidderminster Harriers FC

Halesowen Town - Winners of the Worcestershire Senior Cup 2002-03

Back Row (L-R) Geoff Jones (Trainer), Michael Blackwood, Les Hines, Jason Burnham, Neil Gibson, Phil Trainor, Andy Spencer, Gary Hateley, Richard Leadbeater, Stuart Skidmore, Ryan Robinson Little (Kit Man), Neil Smith.
Front Row (L-R): Mark Danks, Tim Clarke (G/K), Gavin Stone, Jason Ashby, Kirk Master, Lee Collins, Richard Colwell.
Photo: Mark Wood.

SOUTH WEST COUNTIES CHAMPIONSHIP

YOUTH GROUP A

		1	2	3	4	5	6
1	Army		1-4	2-1	3-2	3-2	4-2
2	Cornwall	4-1		6-1	0-1	1-1	0-1
3	Gloucester	1-2	1-6		6-2	2-2	1-3
4	Gwent	2-3	1-0	2-6		0-3	3-3
5	Hampshire	2-3	1-1	2-2	3-0		6-3
6	Oxford	2-4	1-0	3-0	3-3	3-6	

	P	W	D	L	F	A	Pts
1 Army	5	4	0	1	13	11	12
2 Hampshire	5	2	2	1	14	9	8
3 Cornwall	5	2	1	2	11	5	7
4 Oxford	5	2	1	2	12	14	7
5 Gloucester	5	1	1	3	11	15	4
6 Gwent	5	1	1	3	8	15	4

Winners: Army   Runners up: Hampshire

YOUTH GROUP B

		1	2	3	4	5	6
1	Berks/Buck		0-2	2-1	1-0	1-1	3-2
2	Devon	2-0		2-1	2-3	0-2	1-2
3	Dorset	1-2	1-2		1-0	1-2	1-2
4	Guernsey	0-1	3-2	0-1		2-3	1-5
5	Somerset	1-1	2-0	2-1	3-2		2-1
6	Wiltshire	2-3	2-1	2-1	5-1	1-2	

	P	W	D	L	F	A	Pts
1 Somerset	5	4	1	0	10	5	13
2 Berks/Bucks	5	3	1	1	7	6	10
3 Wiltshire	5	3	0	2	12	8	9
4 Dorset	5	2	0	3	6	7	6
5 Devon	5	1	0	4	6	9	3
6 Guernsey	5	1	0	4	6	12	3

Winners: Somerset   Runners up: Berks/Bucks

Final

Army 2 - 4 Somerset

WIRRAL PROGRAMME CLUB

The non-profit making Club formed in March 1967

Secretary: I.R.W. Runham

3 Tansley Close, Newton, West Kirby, Wirral CH48 9XH Tel: 0151 625 9554

28th NON-LEAGUE FOOTBALL PROGRAMME OF THE YEAR SURVEY 2002-2003

This season's survey saw 1039 clubs represented, one up on last season, with reserve and youth programmes there were 1099 places, four down on last season.

Again there were many superb programmes with many clubs showing an improvement on last season. It is again pleasing to see clubs issue for the first time or returning after a gap of many seasons. All clubs that issue a programme are to be congratulated, a single sheet is better than nothing. There would be no programmes without the hard work of the editors, plus any helpers they can find, put in to get them out. I'm sure that most supporters and many committee members have no idea of the time and effort needed to produce a programme, so our special thanks go to all these people. Our thanks are also due to all those who sent in programmes for the survey and to those who helped spread the word, the clubs themselves, their supporters, our members, other collectors, the Football Association, the County Associations, the League Secretaries, the Non League Directory, the Non League Paper, the Non League Magazine, the Football Traveller, Welsh Football, Programme Monthly, and those who lent programmes for the survey. Sincere apologies to anyone inadvertently omitted.

Some clubs only issue for a Saturday game, some for just cup games, some change the style, content, price, editor, etc, during the season; some have special connections with printers, etc., often we are not aware of these circumstances. Obviously we can only survey the programmes we receive. Some are from early in the season, others from just before the closing date, most from in between. The results always create a lot of interest with varying comments being expressed; some of these we hear, often second or third hand, but most miss our ears, if you have any comments on the survey please let us know. I am sure the day will never come when there is complete agreement over the results, however the more discussion there is over the survey the better, it will keep programmes to the forefront and hopefully encourage clubs at least to maintain or even improve the standards, better still it may encourage more clubs to issue next season.

The club with the overall winning programme will receive a framed certificate, the winners of each league will also receive a certificate. Please note the programmes have been surveyed, not as many assume voted upon. Marks were awarded to each programme as follows (the maximum marks in each section are given):

Cover 15 (design 10, match details 5), **Page size** 10, **Team layout and position within the programme** 10, **Results** 10, **League tables** 10, **Price** 15, **Pictures** 15, **Printing and paper quality** 20, **Frequency of issue** 20, **Value for money** 20 (this takes into account the ratio of adverts to content, the club's league etc),

Contents 245 (other than those listed) taking into account the relevance to the club, its league, environs etc, the size of the print used, the spacing between the lines, the size of the margins, and if all the contents are original or reproduced (from League Bulletins, newspapers, magazines etc).

To gain full marks in the Frequency of issue section we needed to receive programmes from six different current season matches for each team entered (allowances were made if six home games were not played by the closing date and we were informed of this). The minimum entry was one programme.

As many programmes varied from issue to issue all programmes were surveyed, the marks in each section totalled and divided by the number of issues to get the final mark for each section, the marks from each section were then totalled to get the final score.

A new standard of marks is set each season so this season's total should not be compared with those of earlier seasons, as the comparison will almost certainly be inaccurate; a programme identical to last season's will almost certainly have gained a different points total.

The results of this season's survey are as follows:

1st	Redhill	268 points	**11**	Weymouth	188	**22**	Horsham	172
2nd	Hoddesdon Town	223 points	**12**	Hayes	187	**23**	Hastings United	171
3rd	Northwood	206 points	**13**	Nuneaton Borough	179	**24=**	Easington United	
			14=	Potters Bar Town			Worthing	170
4	Bath City	205		Prestwich Heys	177	**26=**	Curzon Ashton	
5	Arlesey Town	203	**16=**	Aldershot T			Ludlow Town	169
6	Eastbourne Borough	200		Lancing		**28**	AFC Sudbury	168
7	Broxbourne B V&E	194		Woking	176	**29=**	Blackwell MW	
8	Atherton LR	193	**19**	Doncaster Rovers	175		Buckland A	
9	Sutton United	192	**20=**	Bedford Town			Colden Common	
10	Morecambe	189		Dorchester Town	173		Falmouth Town	167

INDIVIDUAL LEAGUE RESULTS The first number after the club's name is the number of programmes received - 6 shows six or more different programmes were surveyed or every programme if less than six matches were played and all programmes received, the second number is the total points gained. The leagues are in no particular order.

LEAGUE + No of entries			FIRST		SECOND		THIRD	
Nationwide Conference		21	Morecambe	1-189	Nuneaton Borough	1-179	Woking	1-176
Dr Martens	Overall	64	Bath City	5-205	Eastbourne Borough	6-200	Weymouth	6-188
	Prem Div	22	Bath City	5-205	Weymouth	6-188	Hastings United	6-171
	West Div	22	Rugby United	6-164	Gloucester City	1-156	Swindon Supermarine	6-156
	East Div	20	Eastbourne Borough	6-200	Dorchester Town	6-173	Fleet Town/Sittingbourne	6-161
Ryman	Overall	72	Northwood	6-206	Arlesey Town	6-203	Sutton United	6-192
	Prem Div	23	Sutton United	6-192	Hayes	6-187	Aldershot Town	6-176
	Div 1 N.	21	Northwood	6-206	Arlesey Town	6-203	Wealdstone	6-157
	Div 1 S.	20	Horsham	6-172	Worthing	6-170	Carshalton Athletic	6-159
	Div 2	8	Witham Town	6-147	Cheshunt	6-137	Leyton	1-135
Unibond	Overall	41	Alfreton Town	1-160	Altrincham	6-159	Leek Town	6-155
							Vauxhall Motors	1-155
	Prem Div	22	Altrincham	6-159	Vauxhall Motors	1-155	Stalybridge Celtic	6-154
	Div 1	19	Alfreton Town	1-160	Leek Town	6-155	Rossendale United	1-145
Minerva	Overall	41	Hoddesdon Town	6-223	Broxbourne Borough V&E	6-194	Potters Bar Town	4-177
Spartan	Prem Div	19	Hoddesdon Town	6-223	Broxbourne Borough V&E	6-194	Potters Bar Town	4-177
South Mids	Div 1	17	Kings Langley	6-147	Leverstock Green	6-130	Haywood United	6-125
							Tring Athletic	1-125
	Div 2	5	Old Dunstablians	1-90	Kent Athletic	1-87	Padbury United	1-85
Seagrave Haulage Comb.		17	AFC Wimbledon	1-164	Sandhurst Town	6-147	Ash United	6-138
Go Travel Kent Lge		14	Crays Wanderers	6-150	Herne Bay	1-133	Slade Celtic	6-129
Foresters Essex Senior		5	Romford	6-166	Enfield Town	6-155	Saffron Walden Town	6-105
Jewson Wessex		14	Eastleigh	1-148	Christchurch	1-136	Blackfield & Langley	6-133
Matthew	Overall	20	Redhill	6-268	Lancing	6-176	Eastbourne United	6-155
Clark	Div. 1.	11	Redhill	6-268	Burgess Hill Town	1-135	Horsham YMCA	6-117
Sussex	Div. 2.	4	Lancing	6-176	Eastbourne United	6-155	East grinstead Town	6-123
County Lge	Div. 3.	5	Ifield	6-140	St Francis Rangers	1-79	Bexhill United	1-71
Screwfix	Overall	13	Frome Town	6-146			Corsham Town	6-136
Direct			Minehead Town	6-146				
Western	Prem.	7	Frome Town	6-146	Bridgwater Town	6-131	Keynsham Town	6-123
	Div.1.	6	Minehead Town	6-146	Corsham Town	6-136	Street	1-111
Jewson	Overall	30	AFC Sudbury	6-168	Felixstowe & Walton Utd	6-156	Long Melford	1-151
Eastern	Prem.	18	AFC Sudbury	6-168	Lowestoft Town	6-150	Clacton Town	1-148
Counties	Div.1.	12	Felixstowe & W U	6-156	Long Melford	1-151	Godmanchester Rovers	1-114
Eagel Bitter	Overall	21	Eynesbury Rovers	6-150	St Neots Town	1-142	Yaxley	3-137
United	Prem.	15	St Neots Town	1-142	Yaxley	3-137	Daventry Town	6-132
Counties	Div.1.	6	Eynesbury Rovers	6-150	Potton United	1-109	Harrowby United	1-90
Cherry Red	Overall	37	Didcot Town	6-163	Abingdon United	1-138	Wotton Bassett Town	1-132
Records	Prem.	16	Didcot Town	6-163	Abingdon United	1-138	Wotton Bassett Town	1-132
Hellenic	Div.1.W	13	Purton	6-119	Witney United	1-114	Cirencester United	1-112
	Div.1.E	8	Quarry Nomads	1-87	Milton United	1-82	Penn & Tylers Green	1-78
							Prestwood	1-78
Midland Alliance		20	Ludlow Town	6-169	Stourbridge	6-166	Willenhall Town	6-160
North West	Overall	19	Atherton L R	6-193	Curzon Ashton	6-169	Ashton Town	6-157
Counties	Div.1.	14	Atherton L R	6-193	Curzon Ashton	6-169	Clitheroe	1-153
	Div.2.	5	Ashton Town	6-157	Maine Road	1-107	Darwen	1-106
Northern	Overall	31	Arnold Town	6-157	Ossett Albion	6-152	Pontefract Collieries	6-149
Counties	Prem	18	Arnold Town	6-157	Ossett Albion	6-152	Sheffield	6-143
East	Div.1.	13	Pontefract Coll.	6-149	Maltby Main	6-144	Mickleover Sports	1-142
Albany	Overall	27	Newcastle Blue Star	6-160	Durham City	6-142	Consett	6-140
Northern	Div.1.	18	Newcastle Blue Star	6-160	Durham City	6-142	Consett	6-140
	Div.2.	9	Murton	6-129	Evenwood Town	6-122	Thornaby	1-121
Select App Middlesex		10	Harworth Villa	1-97	Stonewall	1-93	Marsh Rangers	1-86
Surrey Senior		13	Staines Lammas	1-106	Sheerwatre	1-95	Colliers Wood United	1-93
Carling Essex		7	Bishop Stortford S.	6-121	Shell Club Corringham	4-93	Manford Way	4-85
Intermediate							Sandon Royals Reserves	1-85
British Energy Kent Co		8	Seveonoaks Town	1-107	Crockenhill	6-98	Aylesford Paper Mills	1-97
Hampshire	Overall	12	Coldon Common	6-167	Poole Town	6-162	Amesbury Town	6-138
	Prem.	6	Poole Town	6-162	Amesbury Town	6-138	Winchester City	6-130
	Div.1.	3	Coldon Common	6-167	Alresford Town	6-126	Verwood Town	1-102
	Div.2.	3	QK Southampton	6-117	Laverstock & Ford	6-112	M & T Awbridge	2-98
Elite Teamwear Dorset		9	Poole Borough	6-135	Gillingham Town	1-133	Bournemouth Sports	1-78
Firewatch Devon		9	Buckland Athletic	6-167	Cullompton Rangers	1-103	Alphington	1-101
							Exeter Civil Service	1-101
Carlsberg South Western		12	Falmouth Town	6-167	Penzance	6-154	Saltash United	6-146
Gloucestershire County		3	Highridge United	6-154	Thornbury Town	6-127	Roman Glass St George	1-76
Devon & Exeter		3	Buckland Ath. Res.	1-134	Tap and Barrel	1-104	Okehampton Argyle	1-97
Longwell	Overall	12	Beccles Town	1-104	Blofield United	4-102	Attleborough	1-99
Blake	Prem	7	Beccles Town	1-104	Blofield United	4-102	Attleborough	1-99
Anglian C.	Other Divs.	5	Watton United	1-86	Aylsham Wanderers	1-71	Sheringham	1-70
Metaltec Suffolk & IPS		4	WalshamLe Willows	1-123	Tuddenham Rovers	1-88	Crane Sports	1-68
World Class	Overall	17	Oxhley Jets	2-120	Chipperfield Corinth.	2-103	London Lions	2-101
Homes	Prem	14	Oxhley Jets	2-120	Chipperfield Corinth.	2-103	London Lions	2-101
Herts	Div.1.	3	Buntingford Town	1-83	Allenbury Sports	1-70	Hinton	1-70

Express & St Overall	32	Bilston Town	6-129	Walsall Wood	6-121	Tipton Town	6-116
West Prem	15	Walsall Wood	6-121	Tipton Town	6-116	Malvern Town	6-115
Midlands Div.1.N.	8	Bilston Town	6-129	Shenstone Pathfinder	6-106	Walsall Wood Res.	1-104
Div.1.S.	6	Chaddesley Corbet	5-94	Malvern Town Res	1-92	Blackheath Town	5-83
Youth	3	Cradley Town	3-96	Walsall Wood	1-89	Halesowen Town	1-89
ICIS Midland Overall	38	West Midlands Police	6-138	Alvechurch	6-133	Coleshill Town	6-120
Combination Prem	22	West Midlands Police	6-138	Alvechurch	6-133	Coleshill Town	6-120
Div.1.	10	Kenilworth Town	6-117	Bloxwich Town	4-108	Oldhill Town	5-104
Div.2.	3	Earlswood Town	3-77	Barnt Green Spartak	3-69	Littleton	1-61
Div.3.	3	Kenilworth Town Res.	2-119	Newhall United	6-113	Inkberrow	1-56
Kitclub Overall	18	Blackwell Miners W.	6-167	Teversal	1-135	Retford United	1-123
Central Supremel	14	Blackwell Miners W.	6-167	Teversal	1-135	Retford United	1-123
Midlands Prem	4	Forest Town	1-111	Thoresby Coll Welfare	1-104	Pelican	1-91
Everards Brew Leics Senior	7	Loughborough Dyn.	6-132	Ibstock Welfare	6-123	Ratby Sports	1-103
Notts Alliance	4	Rainworth Minres W.	6-139	Cotgrave Coll. Welfare	6-131	Cotgrave Coll Wel Res	1-113
Carlsberg West Cheshire	4	New Brighton	6-146	New Brighton Res	6-117	Manweb	1-71
Coor/WPRC Mid Cheshire	3	Whitchurch Alport	1-99	Cheadle Heath Nomads	1-80	Crewe	1-59
ASDA Logic Overall	8	Charnock Richard	6-159	Hesketh Bank	1-111	Euxton Villa	1-108
West Lancs Prem	4	Charnock Richard	6-159	Fulwood Amateur	1-80	Dalton United	1-76
Other Divs.	4	Hesketh Bank	1-111	Euxton Villa	1-108	Furness Cavaliers	6-92
Air Miles Manchester	7	Prestwich Heys	6-177	New Mills	6-160	Willows	1-126
West Yorkshire	3	Boston Spartans	1-71	Boston Spartans Res	1-59		
				Pontefract Sp & Social	1-59		
Humber Premier	7	Easington United	6-170	Hutton Cranswick United	1-108	Westalla & Willerby	4-94
Wade Assoc Northern All.	5	Walker Fosse	1-123	West Allotment Celtic	6-107	Percy Main Amateur	1-82
Other Leagues	27	Hemsworth Miners W.	6-147	Rivington	6-144	Lakenheath	6-142
Youth Clubs/Schools	6	Colchester Girls	6-142	Warmley Rangers	5-102	Sandhurst T Boys/Girls	6-96
Club Youth XIs	6	New Brighton	6-94	Pontefract Coll U19	6-92	Walsall Wood	1-89
FA Youth Cup	20	Chester Le Street Town	1-144	Burscough	1-123	Alfreton Town	1-109
Reserves	30	Coldon Common	6-159	Ifield	6-139	Buckland Athletic	1-134
Isle of Man	4	Rushen United	1-130	Ramsey	1-107	Ramsey Reserves	1-102
Ireland	8	Linfield	1-127	Portadown	1-118	Cork City	1-115
Wales Overall	68	Gresford Athletic	6-166	Caersws	6-158	Aberystwyth Town	1-156
JT Hughes Welsh Premier	17	Caersws	6-158	Aberystwyth Town	1-156	Barry Town	1-150
H Grays Fitlock All.	10	Gresford Athletic	6-166	Holywell Town	1-139	Porthmadog	1-125
Welsh Lge Overall	17	Tillery	6-144	Ely Rangers	4-115	Cardiff Corinthians	6-104
Div.1.	4	Ely Rangers	4-115	Cardiff Corinthians	6-104	Pontardawe Town	1-92
Div.2.	6	Treharris Athletic	1-88	Aberaman	4-86	Newport YMCA	1-82
Div.3.	7	Tillery	6-144	Bryntirion Athletic	1-89	Risca & Gelli United	1-81
Tyn Lon Volvo Welsh All.	6	Rhyl Reserves	6-120	Llandudno Junction	1-118	Penmaenmawr	6-94
Spar Mid Wales	3	Waterloo Rovers	1-119	Penrhyncoch	1-79	Llanfyllin Town	1-77
Regal Travel Overall	9	Cwmaman Institute	6-140	FC Abercwmboi	1-89	Osborne Athletic	1-85
South Wales Div.1.	4	Cwmaman Institute	6-140	Corus Steel	1-72	Ynysddu Welfare	1-66
Amateur Div.2.	5	FC Abercwmboi	1-89	Osborne Athletic	1-85	Tonyrefail Welfare	1-71
George Ford Gwent Co	4	Abertillery B'birds	1-133	Tillery United	6-131	Goytre	1-56
Welsh Nat Wrexham	2	Chirk AA	6-148	Mynydd Isa	1-100		
Scotland Overall	39	Dunbar United	1-145	Tayport	6-141	Forres Thistle	6-134
Scot Ads Highland	6	Buckie Thistle	1-119	Rothes	1-110	Forres Mechanics	1-105
East of Scotland	5	Edinburgh City	6-122	Craigroyston	6-104	Lothian Thistle	1-100
West Region Overall	15	Kilbirnie Ladeside	1-122	Maryhill	6-121	Kilwinning Rangers	6-111
Prem	9	Kilbirnie Ladeside	1-122	Maryhill	6-121	Kilwinning Rangers	6-111
Div.1.	3	Renfrew	1-79	Petershill	1-68	Troon	1-62
Cent. Divs.	3	East Kilbride Thistle	1-92	Vale of Clyde	1-77	Ashfield	1-54
East Region	7	Dunbar United	1-145	Tayport	6-141	Thornton Hibs	1-119
North Region	4	Forres Thistle	6-134	Duffton	1-118	Buckie Rovers	1-82
Other Leagues	2	Girvan	1-102	Crosshouse Waverley	1-80		
Ladies Overall	70	Stockport County	6-151	Tranmere Rovers	6-147	Stockport Celtic	6-144
National Lge Overall	17	Tranmere Rovers	6-147	Garswood Saints	4-131		
				Lincoln City	5-131		
Nat.Div.	6	Tranmere Rovers	6-147	Arsenal	1-111	Birmingham City	1-98
Nth.Div.	8	Garswood Saints	4-131			Oldham Curzon	1-120
		LincolnCity	5-131				
Sth.Div.	3	Barking	6-123	Bristol City	1-101		
				Merthyr Tydfil	1-101		
Northern Combination	3	Stockport County	6-151	Chester City	6-109	Newcastle	1-59
Other Leagues	11	Stockprot Celtic	6-144	Rushden & Diamonds	6-129	Cardiff City	1-111
FA Womens Cup	39	Stockport Celtic	1-134			Rushden & Diamonds	1-125
		Stockport County	1-134				
Sunday Overall	10	Turnergraphic	6-141	Palace Court	6-119	Palce court Reserves	6-112
Blackmore Vale	3	Palace Court	6-119	Palace Court Reserves	6-112	Sherborne West End	1-67
Kidderminster	3	Brintons Social Club	1-89	Grange Athletic	1-68	Hainge Rovers	1-67
Other Leagues	4	Turnergraphic	6-141	New Brighton Youth	6-94	Whitenap	2-86
FA Sunday Cup	49	Biggleswade Sunday	1-90	Little Paxton	1-80	Casino Cars	1-75
						Hartlepool Lion Hill	1-75
Springbank Vending Mid	3	Eccleshall	6-138	Brocton	6-127	Norton AG	1-81

SKIP IT"

Soaking up the rays at Shoreham

1901
THREE BRIDGES FC

MATTHEW CLARK
SUSSEX COUNTY LEAGUE
REDHILL
v
THREE BRIDGES
Monday 21st April 2003
Kick Off 11.00 am

Redhill took the honours again in the Wirral Programme Survey by a clear forty five points, ahead of Hoddesdon Town.

Again in A4 format, programme editor, Michael Stewart, has not changed his policy of filling the 80 pages with, not only Redhill information and news but with articles from around the non-League world, and all for only 50p.

Congratulations again to Michael for a superb publication.

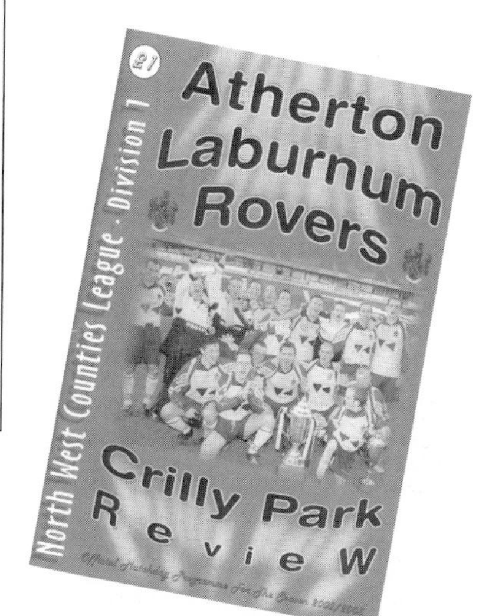

Atherton Laburnum Rovers improved on last year's 19th position to earn themselves a place in the top ten, at number eight. Their colourful and well designed front cover no doubt gained them some extra points.

LEAGUE OF WALES

President: D W Shanklin

Secretary: D G Collins **Chief Executive:** D G Collins
Plymouth Chambers, 3 Westgate Street, Cardiff CF10 1DP
Tel: 029 2037 2325 Fax: 029 2034 3961

FINAL LEAGUE TABLE 2002-03

			HOME					AWAY					TOTAL					
		P	W	D	L	F	A	W	D	L	F	A	W	D	L	F	A	Pts
1	Barry Town	34	14	2	1	45	12	12	3	2	39	14	26	5	3	84	26	83
2	Total Net. Solutions	34	13	2	2	33	11	11	6	0	35	10	24	8	2	68	21	80
3	Bangor City	34	12	2	3	39	15	10	3	4	36	19	22	5	7	75	34	71
4	Aberystwyth Town	34	9	6	2	30	14	8	3	6	24	24	17	9	8	54	38	60
5	Connah's Quay N.	34	10	3	4	31	20	8	2	7	24	26	18	5	11	55	46	59
6	Rhyl	34	8	4	5	21	12	9	3	5	31	21	17	7	10	52	33	58
7	Afan Lido	34	5	5	7	17	21	9	5	3	27	13	14	10	10	44	34	52
8	Caersws	34	8	5	4	30	22	7	1	9	27	30	15	6	13	57	52	51
9	Cwmbran Town	34	9	5	3	27	15	5	3	9	24	25	14	8	12	51	40	50
10	Newtown	34	5	2	10	25	32	7	4	6	23	22	12	6	16	48	54	42
11	Port Talbot Town	34	6	3	8	16	24	5	3	9	20	27	11	6	17	36	51	39
12	Flexsys Cefn Druids	34	6	2	9	16	17	5	3	9	21	34	11	5	18	37	51	38
13	Haverfordwest Co.	34	4	2	11	23	43	6	3	8	17	25	10	5	19	40	68	35
14	Caernarfon Town	34	4	7	6	21	26	4	3	10	22	27	8	10	16	43	53	34
15	Carmarthen Town	34	4	3	10	17	37	5	2	10	16	29	9	5	20	33	66	32
16	Oswestry Town	34	2	4	11	14	32	4	6	7	22	35	6	10	18	36	67	28
17	Welshpool Town	34	4	3	10	20	33	3	4	10	10	29	7	7	20	30	62	28
18	Llanelli	34	3	1	13	28	46	1	4	12	14	43	4	5	25	42	89	17

		1	2	3	4	5	6	7	8	9	10	11	12	13	14	15	16	17	18
1	Aberystwyth Town		0-0	0-1	3-1	1-1	1-3	2-0	3-1	1-1	3-0	2-1	2-0	3-1	5-1	1-0	1-1	2-2	0-0
2	Afan Lido	1-1		1-2	0-1	0-1	1-0	2-0	3-0	1-2	0-3	0-0	2-2	1-2	0-0	2-0	1-1	0-6	2-0
3	Bangor City	0-1	2-1		1-1	3-1	5-0	3-2	2-1	2-1	2-0	2-1	8-0	0-1	2-2	3-0	1-0	0-2	3-1
4	Barry Town	5-1	1-0	3-0		3-2	3-2	3-0	3-1	2-1	6-0	3-0	1-0	2-2	4-0	0-1	4-1	0-0	2-1
5	Caernarfon Town	0-3	1-1	2-2	1-4		1-2	2-1	2-0	3-1	3-3	0-1	1-1	1-2	1-1	2-1	0-2	1-1	0-0
6	Caersws	2-2	1-2	1-1	0-1	2-1		4-1	1-0	1-1	2-1	1-1	4-0	1-0	2-3	3-1	2-2	0-4	3-1
7	Carmarthen Town	0-2	0-2	0-6	2-2	0-3	3-1		1-1	0-4	0-1	0-2	2-1	1-4	2-1	0-2	0-3	1-1	5-1
8	Connah's Quay Nomads	2-1	2-1	2-1	0-2	1-1	1-3	1-0		1-1	4-1	3-1	3-0	1-0	2-4	2-2	2-1	0-1	4-0
9	Cwmbran Town	2-1	0-2	0-0	2-3	1-0	3-2	4-0	0-2		0-0	3-1	3-2	2-1	0-0	1-1	2-0	0-0	4-0
10	Flexsys Cefn Druids	3-0	0-1	0-2	0-3	2-1	0-1	0-1	0-0	1-0		0-1	4-0	3-0	0-0	3-2	0-2	0-1	0-2
11	Haverfordwest County	0-3	1-4	0-4	2-4	3-1	3-2	0-2	1-3	4-0	2-4		2-3	2-2	0-2	2-1	1-5	0-3	0-0
12	Llanelli	2-3	1-3	2-5	2-3	3-3	3-2	1-2	3-5	0-3	3-1	1-3		2-3	3-1	0-2	0-3	2-3	0-1
13	Newtown	3-1	1-2	2-1	0-0	0-3	0-2	2-2	1-2	4-1	1-2	4-0	2-1		1-3	2-4	0-2	2-4	0-2
14	Oswestry Town	0-1	0-3	1-2	0-4	3-0	0-2	1-2	2-3	0-5	0-1	1-1	3-1	0-0		0-0	2-3	0-3	1-1
15	Port Talbot Town	0-1	0-2	0-2	0-5	3-2	0-0	0-2	0-1	1-0	2-1	3-0	1-1	0-2	4-1		0-3	1-1	1-0
16	Rhyl	0-0	2-2	0-1	0-1	1-0	4-0	1-0	1-2	2-1	1-0	1-0	1-1	1-2	1-1	3-0		0-1	2-0
17	Total Network Solutions	3-0	1-1	4-2	1-0	0-2	2-1	2-0	2-0	1-0	2-0	1-2	3-1	1-1	2-1	1-0	5-0		2-0
18	Welshpool Town	1-3	0-0	1-4	0-4	1-0	0-4	1-1	1-2	1-2	3-3	0-2	1-0	1-0	6-1	2-3	0-2	1-2	

WELSH LEAGUE FINAL LEAGUE TABLE 2002-03

DIVISION ONE		P	W	D	L	F	A	Pts
1	Bettws	34	24	5	5	89	30	77
2	Neath	34	24	5	5	70	29	77
3	UWIC Inter Cardiff	34	23	7	4	67	33	76
4	Ton Pentre	34	22	3	9	86	35	69
5	Goytre United	34	19	3	12	56	39	60
6	Garw Athletic	34	16	5	13	61	56	53
7	Briton Ferry Athletic	34	14	4	16	49	53	46
8	Cardiff Civil Service	34	12	9	13	45	52	45
9	Maesteg Park Athletic	34	13	6	15	44	57	45
10	Pontardawe Town	34	12	7	15	51	49	43
11	Cardiff Corinthians	34	12	6	16	40	58	42
12	Caerleon	34	10	10	14	48	48	40
13	Llanwern	34	11	5	18	44	64	38
14	Gwynfi United	34	10	7	17	56	57	37
15	Ely Rangers	34	10	6	18	46	51	36
16	Garden Village	34	9	7	18	39	65	34
17	Penrhiwceiber Rangers	34	9	7	18	47	80	34
18	Milford United	34	1	8	25	26	108	11

CYMRU ALLIANCE FINAL LEAGUE TABLE 2002-03

		P	W	D	L	F	A	Pts
1	Porthmadog	32	28	2	2	106	19	86
2	Llandudno Town	32	20	7	5	81	41	67
3	Buckley Town	32	19	7	6	85	34	64
4	Llangefni Town	32	21	1	10	78	39	64
5	Airbus UK	32	17	5	10	70	50	56
6	Ruthin Town	32	17	3	12	79	45	54
7	Halkyn United	32	14	9	9	56	57	51
8	Lex XI	32	13	5	14	83	72	44
9	Amlwch Town	32	11	9	12	45	55	42
10	Holyhead Hotspurs	32	11	8	13	60	62	41
11	Flint Town United	32	11	7	14	50	61	40
12	Mold Alexandra	32	8	7	17	35	56	31
13	Gresford Athletic	32	8	6	18	52	64	30
14	Llanfairpwll	32	8	5	19	35	66	29
15	Guilsfield	32	7	7	18	43	86	28
16	Cemaes Bay	32	7	3	22	41	129	24
17	Holywell Town (-9)	32	4	5	23	33	96	8

WELSH FOOTBALL LEAGUE DIVISION TWO

	P	W	D	L	F	A	Pts
Dinas Powys	34	24	7	3	97	31	79
Grange Harlequins	34	22	6	6	95	46	72
Bridgend Town	34	21	9	4	73	33	72
AFC Llwydcoed	34	18	11	5	67	33	65
Taffs Well	34	15	7	12	65	54	52
Newport YMCA	34	15	7	12	50	46	52
Pontypridd Town	34	12	15	7	62	41	51
Aberaman Athletic	34	14	8	12	69	65	50
Tredegar Town	34	14	6	14	70	63	48
Ammanford	34	14	5	15	65	63	47
Blaenrhondda	34	13	4	17	45	70	43
Treharris Athletic	34	10	10	14	55	55	40
Morriston Town	34	11	6	17	55	76	39
Merthyr Saints	34	11	5	18	50	69	38
Porthcawl Town	34	10	4	20	55	98	34
Porth Tywyn Suburbs	34	9	5	20	52	79	32
AFC Rhondda	34	8	7	19	48	73	31
Fields Park Pontllanfraith	34	3	2	29	36	114	11

DIVISION THREE

	P	W	D	L	F	A	Pts
Pontyclun	34	21	7	6	73	39	70
Skewen Athletic	34	22	4	8	78	45	70
Caldicot Town	34	19	8	7	69	43	65
Caerau Ely	34	19	7	8	77	46	64
Bryntirion Athletic	34	19	4	11	70	41	61
Seven Sisters	34	15	7	12	59	53	52
Troedyrhiw	34	15	5	14	53	52	50
Pontlottyn Blast Furnace	34	14	8	12	70	72	50
Treowen Stars	34	13	7	14	50	48	46
Tillery	34	11	10	13	64	72	43
Albion Rovers	34	11	7	16	54	64	40
Risca & Gelli United	34	10	9	15	53	65	39
Cwmamman United	34	11	5	18	57	70	38
Chepstow Town	34	10	8	16	67	84	38
Pentwyn Dynamo	34	9	8	17	59	70	35
Newcastle Emlyn	34	10	5	19	51	75	35
RTB Ebbw Vale	34	10	3	21	52	82	33
Caerau United	34	8	6	20	58	93	30

WELSH NATIONAL LEAGUE WREXHAM AREA PREMIER

	P	W	D	L	F	A	Pts
Castell Alun Colts	30	21	2	7	97	41	65
Penycae	30	19	5	6	74	47	62
Mynydd Isa	30	18	5	7	71	43	59
Ruthin Town Res.	30	18	4	8	74	48	58
Brymbo Broughton	30	16	7	7	78	41	55
Rhos Aelwyd	30	18	1	11	70	52	55
Cefn United	30	16	5	9	75	41	53
Llangollen Town	30	15	6	9	70	46	51
Brickfield Rangers	30	13	3	14	63	64	42
Bala Town (-3)	30	10	4	16	43	66	31
Chirk AAA	30	8	7	15	45	71	31
Llay Welfare	30	9	3	18	50	74	30
Borras Park Albion	30	7	4	19	57	97	25
Penley	30	6	5	19	35	77	23
Llanuwchllyn	30	5	6	19	42	94	21
Corwen Amateurs	30	5	5	20	34	76	20

DIVISION ONE

	P	W	D	L	F	A	Pts
Queens Park (-3)	24	21	1	2	79	27	61
Rhostyllen United	24	18	0	6	90	40	54
Acrefair Youth	24	16	3	5	69	29	51
Airbus UK Reserves	24	15	1	8	75	32	46
Bradley Villa	24	12	3	9	64	59	39
Summerhill Utd	24	11	2	11	57	57	35
Gresford Ath. Reserves	24	10	2	12	63	59	32
Glyn Ceiriog	24	10	1	13	52	64	31
Brymbo Broughton Res.	24	8	5	11	47	44	29
Penycae Reserves	24	8	3	13	38	57	27
Ruthin Town Colts	24	8	2	14	35	70	26
Rhos Aelwyd Reserves	24	4	3	17	35	72	15
Corwen Ams Reserves	24	1	2	21	22	116	5

Wales Semi Professional Team line-up before their game with Ireland in the Four Nations Tournament, hosted by Wales. Photo: Roger Turner.

ABERYSTWYTH TOWN

Secretary: Rhun Owens, 31 Maesgogerddan, Aberystwyth.
Tel: 01970 623520 (H) 0777 323 0894 (M)
Ground: Park Avenue, Aberystwyth, Ceredigion. Tel: 01970 612122
Club Email: atfc@btopenworld.com
Directions: From south: A487, 1st right at Trefachan Bridge to r'bout, 1st right with Park Ave. being 3rd right. From north: A487 and follow one-way system to railway station, at r'bout 1st left with Park Avenue being 3rd right. 5 mins walk from Aberystwyth (BR) - follow as above

Capacity: 4,500 Seats: 650 Cover: 1,200 Floodlights: Yes
Clubhouse: Open daily noon-3 & 7-12pm. Snacks available **Club Shop:** Yes

HONOURS Welsh Cup 1899-1900; Welsh I'mediate Cup 85-86 87-88; Mid Wales Lg (11) (Lg Cup(7); Welsh Amtr Cup (3); Welsh Lg Div 2 Sth 51-52; Cambrian Coast Lg (8) Central Wales Chal. Cup(6)

PREVIOUS **League:** Welsh 1896-97; Nth Wales Comb. 99-1900; Montgomeryshire & Dist. 04-20; Central Wales 21-25 81-87; Mid-Wales 26-32 51-81; Cambrian Coast 32-51; Welsh Lg South 51-63; Abacus 87-92

RECORD **Attendance:** 4,500 v Hereford, Welsh Cup 1971
Goalscorer: David Williams 476, 66-83

FACT FILE
Founded: 1884
Nickname: Seasiders
Sponsors: Continental Cambria Tyres
Colours: Black & green/white/black
Change colours: Yellow/navy/white
Midweek Matchday: Tuesdays
Reserves League: Mid-Wales
Programme: 64 pages, £1.00
Editor: D.Roberts Young (01970 617705)
Website:www.atfcnews.co.uk

CLUB PERSONNEL
Chairman: Donald Kane
President: D Jones
Press Officer: Rhun Owens
Manager: Gary Finley

2002-2003
Captain: David Burrows P.o.Y.: Bari Morgan
Top Scorers: Anthony Wright 13

AFAN LIDO

Secretary: P.Robinson.56 Abbeyville Avenue,Sandfields Estate, Port Talbot SA12 6PY
Tel Nos: 01639 885638 (H) 07812 142 833(M)

Ground: Runtech Stadium, Princess Margaret Way, Aberavon Beach, Port Talbot.
Tel: 01639 892960 (Club) 01639 881432 (Office)

Honours: League of Wales R-up 94-95, League of Wales Cup 92-93 93-94

FACT FILE

Colours: All red
Change colours: All yellow
Midweek Rixtures: Tuesday

CLUB PERSONNEL
Chairman: David Dale
Tel: 01639 891579

Manager: Mark Robinson
Tel:01639 822026

Head of Youth Academy:
P.Robinson

BANGOR CITY

Secretary: Alun Griffiths, 12 Lon-Y-Bryn, Menai Bridge, Anglesey, Gwynedd LL575NM
Tel: 01248 712820
Ground: The Stadium, Farrar Road, Bangor, Gwynedd (01248 355852)
Directions: Old A5 into Bangor, 1st left before railway station, ground on leftby garage
Capacity 2,000 Seats: 700 Cover: 1,200 Floodlights: Yes
Clubhouse: Not on ground **Club Shop:** Yes
HONOURS FA Tphy R-up 83-84; Northern Prem. Lg 81-82 (R-up 86-87, Lg Cup 68-69, Presidents Cup 88-89, Chal. Shield 87-88), Cheshire Co. Lg R-up 53-54 58-59,Lancs Comb. R-up 30-31, League of Wales 94-95 (Lg Cup R-up 94-95), WelshNational Lg 27-28 (R-up 26-27), Nth Wales Coast Lg 1895-96, Welsh Cup 1888-89 95-96 1961-62 (R-up 27-28 60-61 63-64 72-73 77-78 84-85), Nth Wales Chal. Cup 26-27 35-36 36-37 37-38 46-47 51-52 57-58 64-65 67-68, Welsh Amtr Cup 1894-9596-96 97-98 98-99 1900-01 02-03 04-05 05-06 11-12, Welsh Jnr Cup 1995-96 97-981919-20, Welsh All. Alves Cup 49-50 59-60 (Cookson Cup 61-62 68-69 84-85 86-87)
RECORD **Attendance:** 10,000 v Wrexham, Welsh Cup final 78-79
PREVIOUS **Leagues:** N Wales Coast 1893-98 1911-12; The Comb 1898-1910; N Wales Comb 30-33; WMids 32-38; Lancs Comb 38-39 46-50; Ches Co 50-68; NPL 68-79 81-82 84-92; AlliancePrem 79-81 82-84, Welsh Cup 97-98,North Wales Challenge Cup 1998-99

FACT FILE
Founded: 1876 Nickname: Citizens
Sponsors: Pentraeth Group
Colours: All blue
Change colours: All red
Midweek Matchedays: Tuesday
Reserve League: Welsh Alliance
Programme: 32 pages, £1.00
Editor: Sam Vilaski

CLUB PERSONNEL
President: Gwyn Pierce Owen
Marketing Manager: Hayle Meek
Chairman: Ken Jones
Vice Chairman: David Gareth Jones
Press Officer: Alun Griffiths
Manager: Peter Davenport
Assistant Manager: Marc Lloyd Williams
Coach:Stephen Owen Physio: Arwel Jones
Head of Youth Acadeny: M.Jones

BARRY TOWN

Secretary: Craig Griffiths, 15 Thistle Close, Barry, South Glam. 01446 733576
Ground: Jenner Park, Barry CF62 9BG Tel: 01446 735858 Fax: 01446 701884
Website: www.barrytown.cjb.net
Directions: M4 jct 33 via Wenvoe (A4050) to Barry. Left at 1st 2 r'bouts to Jenner Park.
Nearest rail station is Cadoxton
Capacity: 3,000 Seats: 3,000 Cover: Yes Floodlights: Yes
Clubhouse: Open normal licensing hours, 11.00-11.00 daily
HONOURS Welsh Cup (3); Welsh Trophy 94-95; Southern Lg R-up 20-21;
Western Lg R-up 11-12, Welsh Lg (7), Lg Cup (4); South Wales Senior Cup (13);
SA Brain Cup (3); League of Wales 95-96 96-97 97-98 98-99 01-02, R-up 99-00;
UEFA Cup 2 Qual Rds 96-97, Prel Rd 97-98 Champs . 2nd . Prelim Rd 01-02

PREVIOUS **Leagues:** Western 08-13; Southern 13-82 89-93; Welsh 82-89 94-95

BEST SEASON **FA Cup**: 2nd Rd 29-30 **FA Trophy** 3rd Qualifying Rd replay 90-91

RECORD **Attendance:** 7,400 v Queens Park Rangers, FA Cup 1st Rd 1961
Goalscorer: Clive Ayres **Appearances:** Basil Bright

Players progressing Chris Simmonds (Millwall) 47, Derek Tapscott/Dai Ward(Arsenal) 53/54, Laurie Sheffield/Gordon Fazer/Phil Green (Newport) 62/66/84,Chris Pike (Fulham) 85, Ian Love (Swansea) 86, Tony Bird/Dave O'Gorman (SwanseaCity) 97, Mark Ovendale (Bournemouth) 98 Eifion Williams (Torquay United) 99

FACT FILE

Founded: 1923
Nickname: Dragons
Sponsors: Tango
Colours: Yellow & blue/yellow/blue
Change: Maroon & white trim
Midweek Matchdays: Tuesday
Programme: Yes

CLUB PERSONNEL

Chairman: Craig Griffiths
Player Manager: Kenny Brown
Head of Youth Academy: A.York

CAERNARFON TOWN

Secretary: T.B.A.
Ground: The Oval, Marcus Street, Caernarfon, Gwynedd Tel: 01286 675002
Directions: A55 coast road to A487 bypass to Caernarfon. At inner relief road r'bout follow Beddlegert sign, then 2nd right - ground opposite.
Nearest BR station is 9 miles distant at Bangor. Local buses to Hendre estate
Capacity: 3,678 Seats: 178 Cover: 1,500 Floodlights: Yes
Clubhouse: 2 snooker tables, darts, pool, fruit machines & live entertainment **Club Shop:** Yes
HONOURS N West Co's Lg R-up 84-85 (Div 2 R-up 82-83); Lancs Comb 81-82 (Lg Cup 80-81); Welsh Lg (North)(4) 46-47 65-66 77-79, R-up (4) 56-58 72-73 79-80; Alves Cup(4) 38-39 74-75 77-79; Cookson 56-57 77-78; N Wales Combination 32-33; Welsh National Lg 26-27 29-30 (R-up 28-29); N Wales Coast Lg 11-12
PREVIOUS **Leagues:** North Wales Coast 06-21; Welsh National 26-30; North Wales Comb. 32-33; Welsh Lg (North) 37-76 77-80; Lancs Comb. 80-82; North West Counties 82-85; Northern Premier
BEST SEASON **FA Trophy:** 1st Round replay 87-88
FA Cup : 3rd Rd replay 86-87, 0-1 v Barnsley (A). Also 2nd Rd 29-30
RECORD **Attendance:** 6,002 v Bournemouth, FA Cup 2nd Rd 1929
Goalscorer: W Jones 255 (1906-26) **Appearances:** Walter Jones 306

FACT FILE
Founded: 1876
Nickname: Canaries
Sponsors: T.J. Fixit
Colours: Yellow & green/green/yellow
Change colours: Sky & claret/claret/claret
Midweek Matchday: Wednesday
Reserve Team: Yes
Programme: 48pgs 70p
Editor: Marc Roberts

CLUB PERSONNEL
President: Jack F Thomas
Chairman: G.Lloyd Owen
Vice-Chairmen: Eilian Angel
Press Officer: Geraint Lloyd Owen
Tel: 01286 830307
Manager: Adrian Jones
Coach: Alan McDonald
Head of Youth Academy: R.Holroyd
Physio: Ian Humphreys

CAERSWS

Secretary: G.D.Lewis,1 Dolwnog,Main Street,Caersws, Pows SY 17 5EN
Tel Nos: 01686 688586 (H), 01686 627476 (W) 07989 318003 (M).
Ground: The Recreation Ground, Caersws, Powys. Tel: 01686 688753
Directions: Entering Caersws, which lies between Newtown & Llanidloes on the A470, the ground entrance is on the left by bridge
Capacity: 3,250 Seats: 250 Cover: 300 Floodlights: Yes **Club Shop:** No
Clubhouse: Not on ground, but in village centre. Normal licensing hours. Food available
HONOURS Welsh Amtr Cup 60-61, I'mediate Cup 88-89 (R-up 91-92); Mid-Wales Lg (9) 59-61 62-63 77-78 82-83 85-86 88-90 96-97 (Lg Cup 79-80 82-83 87-88 89-90); Cent. Wales Chall.Cup 77-78 82-83 87-88 89-90 (Yth Cup 69-70 72-73 Lg01-02); Montgomeryshire Chall. Cup (18) 52-53 59-60 62-63 69-72 74-75 76-78 83-89 90-91 94-95 94-95 96-97 97-98 98-99;01-02,02-03 Montgomeryshire Lg 77-78
U.E.F.A. Inter Toto Cup 01-02, 02-03.

PREVIOUS **Leagues:** Mid-Wales (pre-1989)/Cymru Alliance 90-92

RECORD **Attendance:** 2,795 v Swansea City, Welsh Cup 1990
Goalscorer: Gareth Davies

Players progressing: P Woosnam (Leyton O.), M Evans (Wolverhampton W.), KLloyd (Hereford U) Graham Evans (Aston Villa), R Stephens (Shrewsbury Town)

FACT FILE
Founded: 1877
Nickname: Bluebirds
Sponsor: Dave Smith
Colours: Blue & white/white/blue
Change colours: Orange/black/black
Midweek Matchday: Tuesday
Reserve League: Mid-Wales
Programme: 44 pages, £1.00
Editor: Ian Baker

CLUB PERSONNEL
Chairman:Garth Williams V-Chair: Joff Rogers
Pres: Dilwyn Lewis
Press Officer: Ivor Williams
Manager: Mickey Evans
Asst Manager: Barry Harding
Physio: Wynne Jones

2002-2003
Captain: Antony Griffiths
P.o.Y. & Top Scorer: Garth Williams

CARMARTHEN TOWN

Secretary: G.O.Jones,Glaslyn,3 Nant Y Felin,Caerfyrddin SA 31 3DT
Tel Nos: 01267 233359 (H) 01267 221838 (W) 01267 222851 (Fax)

Ground: Richmond Park, Priory Street, Carmarthen Dyfed
Tel: 01267 232101 Fax: 01267 222851

Directions: Proceed into Carmarthen on A48, pick up A40 to Llandilo at the 1st rounabout and follow town centre signs for 800 meters.Ground on left in Priory Street

Capacity: 2,500 Seats: 500 Cover: 500 Floodlights: Yes

Clubhouse: Yes **Club Shop:** Yes

HONOURS Welsh Lge Div 2 59-60, Div 1 95-96, Cup Winners 95-96

RECORD **Attendance:** 3,000

PREVIOUS **Leagues:** Welsh League

FACT FILE
Founded: 1948
Nickname: The Town
Sponsors: R.S.J. Windows
Colours: Old gold/black/black
Change colours:White with blue trim
Midweek Matchday:Wednesday
Reserve League: C C Sports Welsh Lge
Programme: £1.00
Editor: Alun Charles

CLUB PERSONNEL
Chairman: Jeff Thomas
President: Anthony Jenkins
Manager : Tommi Morgan
Head of Youth Academy:C.Staples
Physio: Nigel Davies
2002-2003
Captain: David Barnhouse
Top Scorer: Jon Keaveny
Player of the Year: Dale Price

CONNAH'S QUAY NOMADS

Secretary/Press Officer
Robert Hunter, 40 Brookdale Ave., Connah's Quay, Deeside, Clywd CH5 4LU
Tel: 01244 831212 (H)

Ground: Deeside Stadium Connah's Quay

Directions: On main coast road (A548) from Chester to Rhyl west end of Connah's Quay Deeside College.

Capacity: 3,500 Seats: 500 Cover: 500 Floodlights: Yes

Clubhouse: Yes, in college. **Club Shop:** No

HONOURS Welsh Amtr Cup 52-53 54-55, Nth Wales FA Amtr Cup 52-53 54-55, North Wales Coast Challenge Cup, Welsh Intermediate Cup 80-81, Welsh Alliance CooksonCup 87-88, Welsh Youth Cup 47-48

PREVIOUS **Leagues:** Clywd; Welsh Alliance; Cymru Alliance 90-92

RECORD **Attendance:** 1,500 v Rhyl, Welsh Cup SF 29/3/93

FACT FILE
Founded: 1946
Nickname:Westenders
Sponsors: T.B.A.
Colours: White/black/black&white
Change colours: Maroon/white/maroon
Midweek Matchday: Tuesday
Reserve League: Clwyd Premier
Programme: 26 pages, £1.00
Editor: D.Rapson

CLUB PERSONNEL
Chairman: Mr R Morris
President: Mr R Jones
Manager: Neville Powell
Asst Manager: S.Gelder
Physio: M Latter
2002-03
Captain: Stephen Hopkins
P.o.Y.: Gary McCosh
Top Scorer: Tommy Mutton 23

CYMBRAN TOWN

Secretary: R L Langley, 77 Hampton Crescent East, Cyncoed, Cardiff CF23 6RG, Tel: 029 20764381 (H/Fax) 0771 892 3142 (M)

Ground: Cwmbran Stadium, Henllys Way, Cwmbran, Gwent
Tel: 01633627100 Fax 01633627103

Directions: M4 jct 26, follow signs for Cwmbran. At 1st r/about (approx 1.5miles) take 1st exit & proceed along Cwmbran Drive umtil passing Stadium onright. At r/about take 1st exit, then immediately at next r/about take 3rdexit.
Ground entrance 150 yardson right.
One and a half miles from Cwmbran(BR)

Capacity: 8,201 **Seats**: 2,200 **Cover:** 2,200 **Floodlights:** Yes **Club Shop:** Yes

Clubhouse: And clubhouse at 5/7 Commercial Street, Old Cwmbran (01633 483282

HONOURS Lg of W. 92-93; Welsh Lg Div 2 67-67, Welsh Lg Cup 90-91, Welsh Cup Finalists 96-97,99-00 02-03 UEFA Champions Cup 93-4 ,UEFA CUP WInners `CUP 97-8 ,UEFA Cup 99-00,01-01, 03-04 UEFA Inter Toto Cup 00-01

PREVIOUS **Leagues:** Monmouthshire Snr 51-59/ Welsh 60-92

RECORD **Attendance:** 8,148 v Manchester Utd Aug 1994
Goalscorer : Graham Reynolds **Appearances:** Mostyn Lewis

Players progressing: Simon King (Newport 1984), Mark Waite (Bristol Rovers1984), Nathan Wigg (Cardiff 1993), Chris Watkins (Swansea 1993), Daniel Gabbidon(W.B.A.,Cardiff)C)

FACT FILE
Founded: 1951 Nickname: The Town
Sponsors:Colley Hyunda1
Colours: Dark blue.
Change colours: Black & white/black/black
Midweek Matches: Wednesday
Programme: 40 pages, £1.00
Programme Editor/Press Off: Terry Daley

CLUB PERSONNEL
President &Chairman: John Colley
Vice Chairman: Clive Edwrads
General Secretary: Roy Langley
Press Officer: Terry Daley
Manager: Brian Coyne
Coach: Sean Wharton Physio: Tommy Cosh
Youth Academy: Delwyn Cheedy
Fitness Coach: Richard Hughes
2002-03
Captain: Adam Moore
P.o.Y.: Gareth Wharton
Top Scorer: Chris Summers

HAVERFORDWEST COUNTY

Secretary: Barry Vaughan Tel: 01437 731779 (H) 01437 769048 (B)
Woodbine Cottage,Clarbeston Road, Haverfordwest, Pembs. SA63 4QS

Ground: Bridge Meadow Stadium, Haverfordwest, Pembs.SA61 2EX
Tel: 01437 769048 Fax: 01437 769048

Directions: Off the Safeway roundabout near town centre

Capacity: 4,000 Covered Seats: 500 Floodlights: Yes **Club Shop:** Yes

HONOURS West Wales Sen Cup 81-82 88-89 91-92 92-93 97-98 98-99, R-up 37-38 49-50 56-57 60-61 80-81; Welsh Lge 56-57, R-up 67-70 70-71, Prem Div 80-81, National Div 89-90, Div 1 96-97, R-up 94-95 95-96; SA Brains Cup 88-89 R-up 84-85

2002-2003 Captain: Eston Chiverton **Top Scorer and Player of the Year**: Rhys Griffiths

FACT FILE

Nickname: Bluebirds
Sponsor: Preseli Taxis
Colours: All Blue
Change cols: Orange & black/black/orange & black
Midweek Matchday: Tuesday
Programme: 28 Pages £1.00
Editor: JohnHughes

CLUB PERSONNEL

Chairman: W. Griffiths
Directors: J.Daniels, D Shanklin, B.Vaughan
Chief Executive: B.Vasughan
Press Officer: Robert Nesbitt
Manager: Deryn Brace Asst Man:Mike Lewis
Head of Youth Academy: Mike Ellis
Coaches: Dereck Roberts, Ron Beynon, Derek Carnegie and George Barrah
Physio: John Robertts

NEWI CEFN DRUIDS

Secretary: Mr I.Williams,Hillview,Overton Road, St Martins, Oswestry. SY11 3DG
Tel Nos: 01691 777937 07779 433618 (M)

Ground: Plas Kynaston lane, Plas Kynaston, Cefn Mawr, Wrexham
Tel Nos: 01978 824279(Club) 01978 824332 (Office)

Website: www.cefndruids@ wrexham.gov.uk

FACT FILE

Colours: Black & white/black/black
Change colours: All Yellow

Midweek Fixtures: Tuesday

CLUB PERSONNEL

Chairman: Mr M Pritchard
Tel: 01978 812100 (H)

Manager: Steve O'Shaugnessy
Tel: 01978 855357 (H)
07787 805 075(M)

Head of Youth Academy: J.Hunter

NEWTOWN

Team Secretary: Howard Ellis, 30Court Close, Abermull, Montgomery, Powys (01686 630372 (H) 01686 626121 (W))

Ground: Latham Park, Newtown, Powys Tel: 01686 622666/623120, Fax: 623813
Directions: A43 to Newtown, right at 1st lights into Back Lane & town centre -400yds left into Park St., 500yds right (at Library) into Park Lane - ground at end
Capacity: 5,000 Seats:1,100 Cover: 850 Floodlights: Yes
Clubhouse: Open every evening & matchday afternoons. Hot/cold snacks, pool,darts
Club Shop: Yes

HONOURS League of Wales R-up 95-96 97-98; Welsh Cup 1878-79 94-95 (R-up 85-65 87-88 96-97), Welsh Amtr Cup 1954-55, Central Wales Lg 75-76 78-79 81-82 86-87 87-88 (R-up 51-52 52-53 55-56 56-57 74-75 82-83, Lg Cup 54-55 56-57 74-75 75-76 81-82 83-84), Arthur Barritt Cup 86-87, Central Wales Cup 74-75 80-81 92-93, Emrys Morgan Cup 80-81

PREVIOUS **Leagues:** The Combination/ Central Wales/ Northern Premier

RECORD **Attendance:** 5,002 v Swansea City, Welsh Cup 1954

BEST SEASON **FA Trophy:** 3rd Qual. 89-90
FA Cup: 2nd Rd 1884-85. Also 1st Rd 1885-86

FACT FILE

Founded: 1875Nickname: Robins
Sponsors: ControlTechniques & Elliott Presco
Colours: Red/white/red
Change : Yellow/blue/blue
Midweek Matchdays: Tuesday
Reserves League:Spar Mid Wales
Programme: 36 pages, £1
Editors: Keith Harding/ Nigel Bevan & Barry Gardiner

CLUB PERSONNEL

President: Richard Edwards
Chairman:Phil Trenbath
Exec Co-Ordinator: Mrs Lyn Barnett
Match Sec/Press Officer: John Annereau
Man : Brian Coyne Asst Man : Richard Pike
Physio:T.B.A.
Res.Team Manager: Jack Watkins
2001-02
Captain: Colin Reynolds P.o.Y,ChrisAdamson
Top Scorer: Steve McCormick 19

PORT TALBOT TOWN

Secretary: Mr P. Fisher, 87 Village Gardens, Baglan Moors, Port Talbot SA12 7LP
Tel: 01639 793689 (H) 07974 446720 (M) 01639 778886 (W)
Fax: 01639 778 884. Email: p.fisher@ntlworld.com

Ground: Victoria Road, Port Talbot, SA12 6AD
Tel: 01639 882465
Fax: 01639 886991

FACT FILE

Colours: Blue & white/blue/blue
Change colours: White/black/black

Midweek Fixtures: Tuesday

Website: www.porttalbotfc.co.uk

CLUB PERSONNEL

Chairman: Andrew Edwards
Tel: 01639 888515 (H)

Manager: M.Jones
Tel: 07885 118 115(H)

Head of Youth Academy: B.Wells
c/o Club

PORTHMADOG

Secretary: P.G.Owen, 56 Mials Gerddi, Portmmadog, (01766 512991)

Ground: Y Traeth, Porthmadog, Gwynedd Tel: 01766 514687
Directions: At towncentre crossroads (by Woolworths) into Snowdon Str., pass RBL/Craft Centre onto unmade track, over railway line - ground on right
Capacity: 4,000 Seats: 100 Cover: 400 Floodlights: Yes
Club Shop: Yes
Clubhouse: Station Buffet usded after matches.
HONOURS Welsh Amtr Cup(3) 55-58, N. Wales Amtr Cup 37-38 56-57 58-59 62-63, Lge of Wales Cup R-up 92-93, N. Wales Coast Chal. Cup(5) 55-56 73-75 76-78, WelshAll.(8) 02-03 37-38 66-69 74-76 89-90 (Cookson Cup 75-76 89-90, Barritt Cup 77-78, Alves Cup 65-66 73-74 76-77) ,Cymru Alliance Lg Cup 98-99
PREVIOUS **Leagues:** N Wales; Gwynedd; Bangor & Dist.; Lleyn & Dist.; Cambrian Coast; Welsh Alliance; Cymru Alliance
RECORD **Attendance:** 3,500 v Swansea, Welsh Cup 64-65

FACT FILE

Founded: 1884
Nickname: Porth
Colours: Red & black/black/black
Change: Yellow/red/red
Midweek Matchday: Wednesday
Reserve League: Caernarfon District
Programme: 28 pages, &1.00
Editor:P.G.Owen

CLUB PERSONNEL

Chairman: R.J.Havelock
President: William Pike
Manager: Colin Hawkins
Physio: Ifor Roberts

RHYL

Secretary: Dennis McNamee, 3 Maes Rhosyn, Rhuddlan. Tel: 01745 591287 (H)
Ground: Belle Vue, Grange Road, Rhyl, Clwyd Tel: 01745 338327
Directions: Leave A55 at the St Asaph/Rhyl turn off and take A525 to Rhuddlan.At roundabout take 2nd turn for Rhyl, then left at next roundabout and over next two roundabouts .After 1mile urn right into Pendyffryn Rd, then left at junction and ground is 300yds on left.
Capacity: 3,800 Cover: 1,200 Seats: 500 Floodlights: Yes
Club Shop: Yes Clubhouse: No

HONOURS Welsh Cup 51-52 52-53 (R-up 29-30 36-37 92-93), Welsh Amateur Cup 72-73, Northern Premier Lg Presidents Cup 84-85, North West Counties Lg R-up 82-83,North Wales Coast Challenge Cup, Cheshire County Lg 47-48 50-51 71-72 (R-up 48-49 49-50 51-52 55-56, Div 2 R-up 81-82, Lg Cup 48-49 51-52 70-71, Div 2 Shield 81-82), Cyrmu Alliance 93-94 (R-up 92-93, Lg Cup 92-93)

PREVIOUS LEAGUES: **North Wales Coast League,** Cheshire County; North West Counties; Northern Premier; Cymru Alliance 92-94
BEST SEASON **FA Cup :** 4th Rd Proper 56-57 (lost 0-3 at Bristol City)
RECORD **Attendance:** 10,000 v Cardiff City, Welsh Cup 1953
Goalscorer: Don Spendlove **Appearances:** Not known
Players progressing:
Ian Edwards, Grenville Millington, Brian Lloyd, Andy Holden, Barry Horne, Andy Jones

FACT FILE

Founded: 1870 (as Rhyl Skull & Crossbones)
Nickname: Lilywhites
Sponsors: Rhyl Tyre & Battery
Colours: White/black/black
Change: Blue & maroon/ blue/blue
Midweek matches: Tuesday
Programme: 40 pages £1
Editor: Ian Johnson 01745 353976 (H)
or 07960 071197 (M)

CLUB PERSONNEL

Managing Director; Doug Mortimer
Chairman: Dave Simmons
Vice Chairmen; Dave Milner
President: R B G Webster
Company Secretary : David Milner
Press Officer: David .Williams
Manager: J.Hulse
Tel No: 0151 653 9874
Head of Youth Academy: J.Smith

TOTAL NETWORK SOLUTIONS

Secretary: Gwynfor Hughes, Birch Lea, Porthywaen, Oswestry, Shrops SY10 8LY
Tel: 01691 828645 (H) Fax: 01691 828645

Ground: Recreation Park, Treflan, Llansantffraid Tel: 01691 828112 & Fax 01691 828862

Directions: **From North**A483 between Oswestry and Welshpool, right at Llynclys (A495) to village Right opposite Mill towards Llynclys Community Centre. Ground is behind housing estate.**From south** A483 turn left at FGourCrosses B4393 to village and once again right opposite Mill.

Capacity: 2,000 Seats: 500 Standing: 1,500 Floodlights: Yes Shop: no

Clubhouse: Open every evening except Sunday, plus weekend afternoons.

HONOURS League of Wales Champions 99-00 R-up 01-02,02-03 Welsh Cup 95-96; R-up: 00-01 Welsh Intermediate Cup 92-93; League of Wales Cup 94-95;Cymru Alliance Lge 92-93, R-up 91-92; Central Wales Sen Cup 98-99,R-up 92-93 97-98;Central Wales Lg R-up 90-91 94-95 95-96, Lge Cup 95-96; Montgomeryshire Amtr Lg (7), Village Cup (17); UEFA Champions League 00-01, European Cup Winners Cup Preliminary Rd 96-97 U.E.F.A. Cup: 2001-02,02-03

PREVIOUS **League:** Mid-Wales; Cymru Alliance (pre-1993)

RECORD **Attendance:** 2,100 v KS Ruch Chorzow Euro Cup Winners 96(at Wrexham F.C.)
Goalscorer: Adrian Jones **Appearances:** Andy Mulliner

FACT FILE

Founded: 1959
Nickname: The Saints
Sponsors: Total Network Solutions
Colours: Green and white/white/white
Change: All Blue
Midweek Matchdays: Tuesday
Programme: 40 pages, £1
Editor:Tony Williams

CLUB PERSONNEL

Chairman: Edgar Jones
President: Mike Hughes
Manager:Ken McKenna
Assistant Manager: John Carroll
Physio: Gordon Evans& Tony McHugh

2002-03

Captain:Gary Brabin
Top Scorer:Michael Wilde
P.o.Y.:Steven Evans

WELSHPOOL

Secretary: Mr C McNamee, Paradise Cottage, Hope, Leighton, Welshpool, Powys SY21 8JD
Tel: 01938 552 270 (H) 01938 553311 (B) 07989 429290 (M)
Fax:: 01938 555885 email: clivemcnamee@lineone.net

Chairman: Mr B Jones, Park View, Forden, Nr. Welshpool, Powys.
Tel: 01938 580529 (H) 01938 552260 (B)

Ground: Maes y Dre Recreation Ground, Welshpool, Powys
Tel: 01938 553027

Capacity: Cover: 100 Seating:

Honours: Cymru Alliance 01-02

FACT FILE

Founded: 1878
Nickname: Seasiders
Colours: White/black/white
Change colours: Purple/white/purple
Midweek Matchday: Wednesday

Manager
Russ Cadwallader
Tel: 01686 668608

Wales' Steve Evans gets up well to meet the ball before any of the Ireland players, during the Four Nations Tournament.

Wales and Barry Town defender, Lee Jarman, keeps his eye on the ball under pressure from an Ireland player.

Hereford and Wales international Paul Parry fires in a shot against Ireland during the home country's 0-2 defeat at Haverfordwest.

Photos: Roger Turner.

SCOTTISH NON-LEAGUE FOOTBALL

Compiled by Bill Mitchell with thanks to Stewart Davidson

OVD SCOTTISH JUNIOR CUP 2002-03

FIFTH ROUND

Bellshill Athletic 0 Linlithgow Rose 1
Bo'ness United 2 Fauldhouse United 0
Bonnyrigg Rose 1 Arthurlie 4
Cumnock Juniors 3 Renfrew 2
Kirkintilloch Rob Roy 2 Kilbirnie Ladeside 2
Maryhill 1 Petershill 0
Shettleston 0 Beith Juniors 1
Tayport 2 Irvine Meadow 0

Replay

Kilbirnie Ladeside 0 Kirkintilloch Rob Roy 0
(aet - Kilbirnie Ladeside won 4-2 on penalties)

SIXTH ROUND

Arthurlie 0 Bo'ness United 1
Cumnock Junior 1 Tayport 1
(Left: Cumnock's Aidan McVeigh (stripes) battles with Tayport's goalscorer Scott Peters. Photo: John B. Vass.)
Linlithgow Rose 6 Beith Juniors 1
Maryhill 0 Kilbirnie Ladeside 0

Replays

Kilbirnie Ladeside 0 Maryhill 2
Tayport 3 Cumnock Juniors 1

SEMI-FINALS

(Friday, 4th April 2003. At Broadwood Stadium, Cumbernauld)

MARYHILL 0-1 TAYPORT
Craik

(Friday, 11th April 2003. At The City Stadium, Livingston)

BO'NESS UNITED 0-2 LINLITHGOW ROSE
Beaton, Flynn

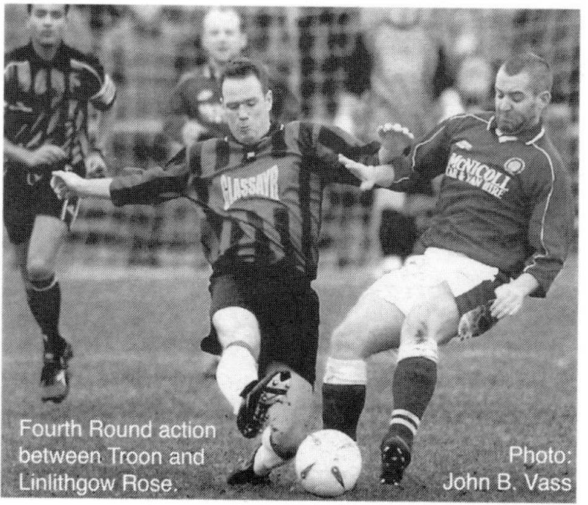

Fourth Round action between Troon and Linlithgow Rose. Photo: John B. Vass

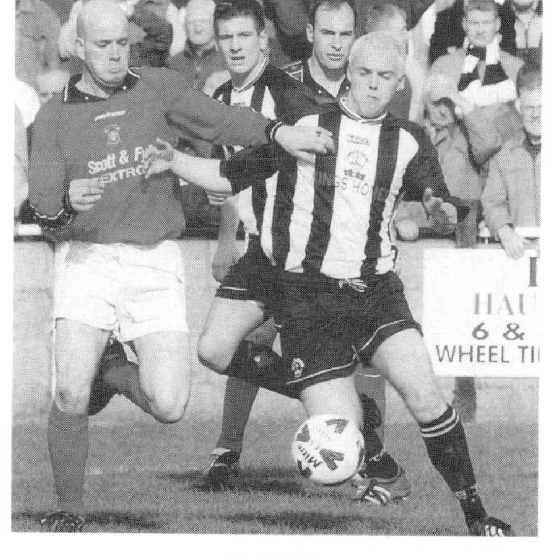

THE FINAL

(Sunday, 1st June 2003. At Partick Thistle FC, Firhill Park, Glasgow)

LINLITHGOW ROSE 0-1 TAYPORT
Craik
(aet - half-time and 90 minutes 0-0 - 0-1 at 105 minutes)
Attendance: 4,613

Man of the Match: John Ward (Tayport).

LINLITHGOW ROSE: G Logan; S Swift, R Gibb, G Landels, D Beaton, D Smith (captain), M Whyte, I McLaughlin, D Flynn, B Moffat, M Corcoran. Substitutes: S Dickov for Moffat 73 minutes, G Higgins for Flynn 90 minutes, D Sinclair for Gibb 96 minutes; H Kennedy and K McKeown (goalkeeper) did not play.
Booked: Landels, Gibb, Corcoran, Gibb.

TAYPORT: F Fitzpatrick; S Peters, G Paterson (captain), J Ward, R Morris, B Craik, B McNaughton, S Stewart, G Dailly, R Gunnion, J Mitchell. Substitutes: D Evans for Dailly 65 minutes, A Ramsay for Craik 105 minutes, D Scott for Fraser 116 minutes. R Hunter and G Buist did not play. Booked: Gunnion, Mitchell, Ward. Sent-off: Gunnion 79 minutes (second yellow card).

Referee: M Tumilty.
Assistant referees: W Gilfillan, C Brown.
Fourth Official: C Marshall.

JUNIOR CUP FINAL REVIEW

FOR a club that was only founded in 1990 Tayport has come a long way and could now claim to be the best Junior side in Scotland as in this latest campaign they have not only won the game's top honour - the OVD Scottish Junior Cup - but have also won the W & M East Super League in its initial season along with several local knock-out events and in the process have lost only two matches in all their various fixtures with seven draws and only seventeen goals conceded at the last count.

This success by an effectively community supported outfit has been based on a sound defence, which has been well organised by Scott Peters and John Ward and inspired by the superb Grant Paterson, who is a traditional left-back and stallwart of the side since its recent foundation, while to that can be added the opportunism of Brian Craik and the persistence up front of Barry McNaughton, Steven Stewart, Gareth Dailly, Ross Gunnion and Jonathan Mitchell plus a thruster in David Evans. One must also remember the shrewd management skills of Dave Baikie and his coaching staff of Graeme Irons, Derek Carr and David Nicoll with physio Norrie Marshall keeping the lads fit.

With all this behind them it was no surprise that they went into the final as favourites and the only surprise was that a mainly outplayed Linlithgow Rose side managed to keep their goal intack until the fourth minute of extra-time and then it took a scrambled effort by Brian Craik after a defensive mix-up to bring victory to the Fifers, although the television experts did claim that a first half 'goal' by Ward should have been allowed and not chalked off because the referee, but not the linesman, thought that the ball had gone out of play.

The match never reached great heights and it started with Tayport looking by far the superior outfit in terms of skill and drive with Rose giving away too many free kicks from late tackles, which saw Graeme Landels booked as early as the ninth minute, but otherwise the East club enjoyed numerous moments of luck and some goalbound shots were cleared either by a brave goalkeeper in Greg Logan and last ditch interventions by the veterans Gibb and Beaton, the former being one of the yellow carded men for a silly piece of dissent.

Linlithgow's best attacker was Mark Corcoran, a bustling outside left, but his crosses were either well cleared by the Tayport defence or wasted on the few occasions opportunities to shoot presented themselves. Corcoran was another man to be booked, again for dissent in the opening half - as was skipper Daniel Smith later in the game.

Rose did improve after the half-time break thanks to Corcoran, whose efforts did lead to bookings for Gunnion, Mitchell and Ward (the eventual Man of the Match), but gradually this threat fizzled out through lack of support, so it was a shock when Gunnion fouled him again and had to take the long walk leaving his colleagues to face the final ten minutes of normal time and - as it happened - extra-time a man short, but the continued superiority in attack of 'Port' made the 'handicap' difficult to notice.

Once Craik had scrambled his goal there was never any likelihood that Linlithgow would come back and once again defending holders had to surrender the cup to a better team as was generally acknowledged by their superb supporters, who never stopped trying to lift them.

It was a beautiful afternoon in Glasgow and the occasion was still one to savour despite the fact that only one goal was scored and as usual Partick Thistle presented the match very well, although it is not the kind of occasion when hooliganism raises its ugly head. Junior fans are just not like that, as they are basically townsfolk who are proud of their civic duties and the brave men who represent them, while the players - many of them former seniors - always give one hundred percent, which does nothing but good for the game.

WEST, CENTRAL & EAST LEAGUES

WEST REGION

SUPERLEAGUE CALEDONIAN PAPER

PREMIER DIVISION

	P	W	D	L	F	A	Pts
Pollok	22	11	10	1	50	27	43
Neilston	22	12	7	3	42	31	43
Glenafton Athletic	22	11	7	4	39	20	40
Kilwinning Rangers	22	10	5	7	38	24	35
Johnstone Burgh	22	9	8	5	27	28	32
Kilbirnie Ladeside	22	8	7	7	31	31	31
Larkhall Thistle	22	7	8	7	34	30	29
Maryhill	22	8	5	9	31	32	29
Cumnock	22	8	4	10	28	40	28
Auchinleck Talbot	22	7	6	9	40	36	27
Irvine Meadow	22	5	4	13	29	45	19
Benburb	22	1	2	19	18	63	5

FIRST DIVISION

	P	W	D	L	F	A	Pts
Arthurlie	22	13	5	4	41	19	44
Troon	22	14	2	6	45	33	41
Bellshill Athletic	22	12	5	5	38	30	41
Beith	22	11	4	7	48	34	37
Shettleston	22	9	5	8	29	23	32
Petershill	22	9	5	8	36	33	32
Shotts Bon Accord	22	7	5	10	31	38	26
Renfrew	22	6	6	10	32	47	24
Hurlford United	22	4	11	7	28	42	23
Cumbernauld United	22	5	8	9	26	27	20
Cambuslang Rangers	22	4	8	10	23	34	20
Largs Thistle	22	3	6	13	20	37	15

WEST OF SCOTLAND CUP

THIRD ROUND

Arthurlie 0 Troon 2
Bellshill Athletic 5 Rutherglen Glencairn 3
Glenafton Athletic 1 Kilwinning Rangers 1 (Glenafton Athletic won 4-2 on penalties)
Johnstone Borough 2 Blantyre Victoria 3
Petershill 1 Kilbirnie Ladeside 3
Shettleston 0 Beith 2
Thorniewood 1 Auchinleck Talbot 3
Vale of Leven 3 Shotts Bon Accord 1

FOURTH ROUND

Bellshill Athletic 1 Beith 1 (Bellshill Athletic won 5-4 on penalties)
Glenafton Athletic 2 Auchinleck Talbot 0
Kilbirnie Ladeside 3 Blantyre Victoria 1
Troon 6 Vale of Leven 1

SEMI-FINALS

Bellshill Athletic 1 Troon 1
(Bellshill Athletic won 3-1 on penalties)
Kilbirnie Ladeside 3 Glenafton Athletic 4

FINAL

(Saturday, 24th May 2003. At Irvine Meadow FC)

GLENAFTON ATHLETIC 4-2	BELLSHILL ATHLETIC
Johnstone, Caruth, Agnew, Callaghan (pen)	Muir (2)

ROCKWARE GLASS AYRSHIRE LEAGUE

	P	W	D	L	F	A	Pts
Lugar Boswell Thistle	24	20	2	2	88	28	62
Maybole	24	18	3	3	67	27	57
Muirkirk	24	15	1	8	57	39	46
Kello Rovers	24	13	4	7	68	46	43
Dalry Thistle	24	11	6	7	45	45	39
Irvine Victoria	24	11	5	8	46	38	38
Saltcoats Victoria	24	11	3	10	45	55	36
Craigmark Burntonians	24	10	5	9	46	50	35
Ardrossan Winton Rovers	24	8	2	14	38	49	26
Annbank United	24	7	4	13	48	56	25
Ardeer Thistle	24	5	1	18	42	81	16
Whitletts Victoria	24	5	0	19	38	78	15
Darvel	24	3	2	19	30	68	11

KERR & SMITH LEAGUE CUP

QUARTER-FINALS

Beith 1 Irvine Meadow 1 (Irvine Meadow - playing at home - won 4-3 on penalties)
Glenafton Athletic 4 Maybole 0
Hurlford United 0 Auchinleck Talbot 2
Kilwinning Rangers 2 Kilbirnie Ladeside 1

SEMI-FINALS

Glenafton Athletic 0 Auchinleck Talbot 2
Irvine Meadow 3 Kilwinning Rangers 2

FINAL

(Monday, 21st October 2002. At Somerset Park, Ayr. Att: 1,036)

AUCHINLECK TALBOT 3-1	IRVINE MEADOW
Friels, O'Neill, Wallace	Roberston

Auchinleck Talbot celebrate after their 3-1 win over Irvine Meadow in final of the Kerr and Smith League Cup.
Photo: John B. Vass.

Cumnock's John Dempster, scorer of his sides winning goal, holds off an Irvine Meadow player during the final of the Ayeshire District Cup. Photo: John B. Vass.

IRVINE TIMES
AYRSHIRE DISTRICT CUP

THIRD ROUND

Cumnock 2 Glenafton Athletic 1
Irvine Victoria 1 Irvine Meadow 1
(Irvine Meadow won 54 on penalties)
Kilbirnie Ladeside 0 Beith 0
(Kilbirnie Ladeside won 3-2 on penalties)
Kilwinning Rangers 2 Hurlford United 2
(Kilwinning Rangers won 5-4 on penalties)

SEMI-FINALS

Irvine Meadow 2 Kilbirnie Ladeside 1
Kilwinning Rangers 2 Cumnock 2 (Cumnock won 5-3 on penalties)

FINAL

(Monday, 2nd June 2003. at Lugar Boswell Thistle FC, Attendance: 340)

CUMNOCK	1-0	IRVINE MEADOW
Dempster		

'ARDROSSAN & SALTCOATS HERALD' AYRSHIRE CUP

THIRD ROUND

Hurlford United 0 Beith 1
Kilbirnie Ladeside 0 Glenafton Athletic 2
Kilwinning 3 Irvine Meadow 0
Troon 2 Cumnock 1

SEMI-FINALS

Glenafton Athletic 1 Beith 2
Kilwinning Rangers 3 Troon 1

FINAL

(Friday, 6th June 2003. At Irvine Meadow FC)

BEITH	3-1	KILWINNING RGES
Criag (3)		Mason

EAST AYRSHIRE CUP

SEMI-FINALS

Darvel 0 Hurlford United 2
Muirkirk 1 Glenafton Athletic 2

FINAL

(Thursday, 19th June 2003. At Auchinleck Talbot FC)

GLENAFTON ATHLETIC	1-1	HURLFORD UNITED
Miller		MacGregor

(Glenafton Athletic won 4-3 on penalties)

NORTH AYRSHIRE CUP

SEMI-FINALS

Irvine Victoria 1 Beith 1 (Irvine Meadow won 3-2 on penalties)

Saltcoats Victoria 1 Kilbirnie Ladeside 3

FINAL

(Sunday, 15th June 2003. At Kilwinning Rangers FC)

KILBIRNIE LADESIDE	2-2	IRVINE MEADOW
Muir, Eades		Lennox, Myler

SOUTH AYRSHIRE CUP

SEMI-FINALS

Annbank United 2 Maybole 4

Whitletts Victoria 0 Troon 4

FINAL

(Tuesday, 10th June 2003. At Troon FC)

TROON	1-1	MAYBOLE
Nolan		Porte (pen)

(Troon won 3-1 on penalties)

CENTRAL LEAGUE - 2002-03

First Division	P	W	D	L	F	A	Pts
Kilsyth Rangers	22	15	4	3	61	31	49
Rutherglen Glenc'n	22	13	4	5	48	27	43
Greenock	22	12	4	6	34	21	40
Vale of Leven	22	10	7	5	38	27	37
Lanark United	22	10	5	7	40	38	35
East Kilbride Thist	22	8	8	6	37	29	32
Kirkintilloch RRoy	22	7	5	10	32	44	26
Glasgow Perthshire	22	7	4	11	39	47	25
Vale of Clyde	22	6	7	9	34	47	25
St Rochs	22	6	4	12	34	43	22
Lesmahagow	22	5	5	12	28	49	20
Blantyre Victoria	22	2	5	15	33	55	11

Second Division	P	W	D	L	F	A	Pts
St Anthony's	24	16	7	1	66	26	55
Port Glasgow	24	15	6	3	65	36	51
Dunipace	24	13	8	3	59	27	47
Ashfield	24	14	1	9	58	43	43
Baillieston	24	9	7	8	52	49	34
Forth Wanderers	24	10	4	10	43	47	34
Wishaw	24	8	9	7	45	40	33
Yoker Athletic	24	9	3	12	42	55	30
Thorniewood United	24	8	4	12	43	50	28
Stonehouse Violet	24	8	3	13	45	61	37
Coltness United	24	5	6	13	29	58	21
Carluke Rovers	24	5	5	14	40	59	20
Royal Albert	24	2	5	17	34	70	11

EVENING TIMES CUP WINNERS CUP

SECOND ROUND

Auchinleck Talbot 0 Beith 3

Larkhall Thistle 1 Glenafton Ath. 1 (Larkhall won 3-1 on pens)

Pollok 1 Kilsyth Rangers 2

St Anthonys 1 Arthurlie 0

SEMI-FINALS

Kilsyth Rangers 2 Beith 0

Larkhall Thistle 2 St Anthonys 2 (Larkhall won 4-1 on pens)

FINAL

(Saturday, 14th June 2003 at Petershill FC)

KILSYTH RANGERS	1-0	LARKHALL THISTLE
Earlie		

Above: Lugar Boswell Thistle's Paul Ferguson (left) tries to get in front of Troon's John Nolan, during their Ayeshire Cup second round tie.

Right: Victorious Troon after the final of the South Ayrshire Cup.

Photo: John B. Vass.

'BEATONS COACHES' SECTIONAL CUP

PLAY-OFFS

Benburb 1 Shettleston 0
Larkhall Thistle 2 Bellshill Athletic 3

QUARTER-FINALS

Bellshill Athletic 2 Benburb 0
East Kilbride Thistle 2 Cumbernauld United 2 (East Kilbride Thistle won 4-3 on penalties)
Neilston 1 Vale of Leven 1 (Neilston won 3-0 on penalties)
Glasgow Perthshire 4 Shotts Bon Accord 1

SEMI-FINALS

Bellshill Athletic 2 Neilston 1
Glasgow Perthshire 1 East Kilbride Thistle 4

FINAL

(Tuesday, 6ht November 2002. At Firhill Park, Glasgow. Attendance 1,000)

BELLSHILL ATHLETIC	0-2	EAST KILBRIDE TH.
		McVey, Brogan

CENTRAL DISTRICT CUP

QUARTER-FINALS

Baillieston 1 Larkhall Thistle 5 1
Johnstone Borough 1 Cambuslang Rangers 3
Kirkintilloch Rob Roy 1 Arthurlie 5
Shotts Bon Accord 1 Renfrew 2

SEMI-FINALS

Cambuslang Rangers 0 Arthurlie 1
Renfrew 0 Larkhall Thistle 0 (Larkhall Thistle won 4-2 on penalties)

FINAL

(Friday, 31st May 2003. At Petershill FC)

ARTHURLIE	2-1	LARKHALL THISTLE
McKeown, Watret		Downs

CLYDESDALE CUP

SEMI-FINALS

Lanark United 4 Forth Wanderers 0
Lesmehagow 2 Carluke Rovers 0

FINAL

(Monday, 5th August 2002 at Lesmehagow FC)

LESMAHAGOW	1-4	LANARK UNITED
Ferguson		Wilkinson (3), Miller
Carr		

(NB: Lanark United won this competition for the sixth successive season)

EAST REGION - 2002-03

EAST SUPERLEAGUE

	P	W	D	L	F	A	Pts
Tayport	22	17	3	2	47	9	54
Hill of Beath Hawthorn	22	16	2	4	50	24	50
Bathgate Thistle	22	13	5	4	43	30	44
Arniston Rangers	22	13	4	5	41	32	43
Linlithgow Rose	22	8	7	7	36	34	31
Bonyrigg Rose	22	8	4	10	31	35	28
Oakley United	22	7	6	9	27	34	27
Glenrothes	22	7	5	10	25	26	26
North End	22	6	8	8	30	32	26
Carnoustie Panmure	22	7	5	10	31	38	26
Edinburgh United	22	1	4	17	17	46	7
Dundee Violet	22	2	1	19	27	65	7

LOTHIANS DIVISION ONE

	P	W	D	L	F	A	Pts
Bo'ness United	18	10	5	3	45	29	35
Whitburn	18	11	2	5	30	26	35
Sauchie	18	9	5	4	49	30	32
Fauldhouse United	18	10	0	8	38	35	30
Musselburgh Ath'tic	18	8	2	8	31	34	26
Newtongrange Star	18	7	4	7	33	24	25
Camelon	18	6	5	7	39	37	23
Armadale Thistle	18	7	1	10	29	39	22
Pumpherston	18	4	3	11	24	36	15
Bonnybridge	18	3	3	12	25	54	12

LOTHIANS DIVISION TWO

	P	W	D	L	F	A	Pts
Harthill Royal	20	13	5	2	46	23	44
Dunbar United	20	11	4	5	48	28	37
Peniciuk Athletic	20	10	7	3	30	16	37
Broxburn Athletic	20	10	4	6	39	26	34
Blackburn United	20	9	7	4	37	29	34
West Calder United	20	8	4	8	38	37	28
Dalkeith Thistle	20	8	3	9	29	33	27
Tranent	20	6	5	9	34	38	23
Haddington United	20	5	4	11	40	54	19
Livingston United	20	2	5	13	26	48	11
Stoneyburn	20	3	2	15	20	55	11

CARLSBERG EAST LEAGUE CUP

THIRD ROUND

Bathgate Thistle 3 Stoneyburn 2
Bo'ness United 1 Fauldhouse United 1 (Bo'ness United won 3-1 on penalties)
Musselburgh Athletic 2 Haddington Athletic 0
Sauchie 3 Whitburn 1

SEMI-FINALS

Fauldhouse United 2 Sauchie 1 (at Bathgate)
Musselburgh Athletic 0 Bathgate Thistle 1 (at Newtongrange)

FINAL

(Wednesday, 18th Sept 2002 at Linlithgow Rose FC)

FAULDHOUSE UNITED	3-2	BATHGATE THISTLE
Allison (2), McMurney		Hayton, Ritchie

Above: Action from the Second Round tie between Auchinleck Talbot and Cruden in which home side Talbot progressed through to the next round of the OVD Junior Cup thanks to a 4-2 win.

Below left: Maybole take on Fraserburgh in their OVD Junior Cup second round replay. Once again it was the home side, Maybole, that booked their place in the third round with a 4-1 victory.

Below right: Cumnock (stripes) in action against Renfrew during their 3-2 OVD Junior Cup second round win.

Photos: John B. Vass.

CALDERS EAST CUP

THIRD ROUND

Fauldhouse United 1 Linlithgow Rose 1 (Linlithgow Rose won 5-4 on penalties)
Musselburgh Athletic 2 Armadale Thistle 1
Pumpherston 1 Bonnyrigg Rose 1 (Bonnyrigg Rose won 3-0 on penalties)
Sauchie 2 Arniston Rangers 0

SEMI-FINALS

Linlithgow Rose 1 Musselburgh Athletic 1 (Musselburgh Athletic won 3-1 on penalties)
Sauchie 1 Bonnyrigg Rose 1 (Bonnyrigg Rose won 3-1 on penalties)

FINAL

(Monday, June 2003 at Arniston Rangers FC. Attendance: 500)

MUSSELBURGH ATH.	3-5	BONNYRIGG ROSE
Brigain, Hall, Morrice		Bailey (2), Watt, Hall og, Sutherland (1)

After extra-time - score at 90 minutes 3-3.

'DOUG M'AL CUP' BROWN CUP

QUARTER-FINALS

Arniston Rangers 2 Dalkeith Thistle 0
Bathgate Thistle 0 Harthill Rovers 1
Bo'ness United 0 Camelon 1
Haddington United 4 Dunbar United 0

SEMI-FINALS

Arniston Rangers 2 Camelon 0
Harthill Rovers 3 Haddington United 0

FINAL

(Monday, 16th June 2003 at Armadale)

HARTHILL ROVERS	2-0	ARNISTON RANGERS
Pettigrew, Fulton		

STREAMLINE TAXIS ST MICHAELS CUP

QUARTER-FINALS

Fauldhouse United 5 Bo'ness United 3 Camelon 1 (aet)
Linlithgow Rose 2 Edinburgh United 1
Livingston United 0 Bathgate Thistle 3
Whitburn 2 Sauchie 2 (Whitburn won 4-3 on penalties)

SEMI-FINALS

Fauldhouse United 0 Bathgate Thistle 2
Linlithgow Rose 2 Whitburn 2 (Linlithgow Rose won 4-1 on penalties)

FINAL

(Monday, 9th June 2003 at Camelon FC))

LINLITHGOW ROSE	5-0	BATHGATE THISTLE
Flynn (3), Sinclair, McLaughlin		

Cumnock v Pollok in the Caledonian Super Premier League. Pollok's 3-1 victory over Cumnock ensured the away club won the inaugural Super Premier League title.
Photo: John B. Vass.

HEINEKEN FIFE & LOTHIANS CUP

FOURTH ROUND:

Armadale Thistle 4 Dalkeith Thistle 0
Bo'ness United 0 Glenrothes 1
Hill of Beath Hawthorn 1 Newtongrange Star 1
(Hill of Beath Hawthorn won 4-2 on penalties)
Sauchie 1 Arniston Rangers 1
(Sauchie won 4-2 on penalties)

SEMI-FINALS:

Glenrothes 2 Hill of Beath Hawthorn 0
Sauchie 3 Armadale Thistle 1

FINAL:

(Saturday, 24th May 2003 at Camelon FC)

GLENROTHES	3-5	SAUCHIE
Caithness, Gray (2)		Woods (2 pens), Irvine Barr, Hutcheon

FIFE REGION - 2002-03

FIFE DIVISION

	P	W	D	L	F	A	Pts
Kelty Hearts	22	18	3	1	65	18	57
Thornton Hibs	22	17	3	2	59	12	54
Dundonald Bluebell	22	12	5	5	61	27	41
Lochore Welfare	22	11	5	6	44	32	38
St Andrews United	22	9	5	8	51	45	32
Crossgates Primrose	22	8	5	9	33	36	29
Kirkcaldy YM	22	8	5	9	40	47	29
Steelend Victoria	22	7	4	11	24	44	25
Rosyth Recreation	22	7	3	12	33	47	24
Newburgh	22	5	4	13	38	52	19
Lochgelly Albert	22	5	3	14	28	60	18
Tulliallan Thistle	22	2	1	19	25	81	7

PEDDIE SMITH MALOCCO CUP

SECOND ROUND

Glenrothes 2 Newburgh 0
Hill of Beath Hawthorn 2 Thornton Hibs 0
Kirkcaldy YM 1 Rosyth Recreation 1 (Kircaldy YM won 5-4 on penalties)
Oakley United 0 Kelty Hearts 2

SEMI-FINALS

Hill of Beath Hawthorn 8 Kirkcaldy YM 0
Kelty Hearts 1 Glenrothes 0

FINAL

(Wednesday, 4th June 2003. At Rosyth Recreation FC)

HILL OF BEATH HAW.	3-1	KELTY HEARTS
Wright, Haddow, Adam (pen)		Noble

STELLA ARTOIS KINGDOM KEGS CUP

SECOND ROUND

Dundonald Bluebell 1 Kelty Hearts 2
Hill of Beath Hawthorn 4 Thornton Hibs 1
Kirkcaldy YM 1 St Andrews United 2
Lochore Welfare 3 Lochgelly Albert 2

SEMI-FINALS

Hill of Beath Hawthorn 1 Lochore Welfare 3
St Andrews United 0 Kelty Hearts 1

FINAL

(Wednesday, 18th June 2003. At Glenrothes)

KELTY HEARTS	1-2	LOCHORE WELFARE
Coutts		Sinclair (2)

INTERBREW CUP

SECOND ROUND

Crossgates Primrose 0 Oakley United 2
Hill of Beath Hawthorn 5 Kirkcaldy YM 0
Kelty Hearts 1 Newburgh 4
St Andrews United 1 Thornton Hibs 4

SEMI-FINALS

Newburgh 1 Thornton Hibs 2
Oakley United 2 Hill of Beath Hawthorn 4

FINAL

(Tuesday, 10th June 2003. At Lochore Welfare FC)

THORNTON HIBS	0-3	HILL OF BEATH HAW.
		McIntosh, Noble, Dair

'REDWOOD LEISURE' FIFE/TAYSIDE CUP

THIRD ROUND:

Lochee United 2 St Andrews United 2 (Lochee United won 4-3 on penalties)
Lochore Welfare 2 Carnoustie Panmure 1
Oakley United 0 Tayport 0 (Oakley United won 4-3 on penalties)
Dundee Violet 0 Hill of Beath Hawthorn 4

SEMI-FINALS:

Lochee United 2 Lochore Welfare 0
Oakley United 1 Hill of Beath Hawthorn 2

FINAL:

(Saturday, 14th June 2003. At North End FC)

HILL OF BEATH HAW.	5-0	OAKLEY UNITED
Smart (3), Thomson, McIntosh		

NORTH REGION - 2002-03

East Section

Printagraph Premier Division

	P	W	D	L	F	A	Pts
Sunnybank	26	19	3	4	58	25	60
Culter	26	16	4	6	61	34	52
Longside	26	15	6	5	53	30	51
East End United	26	14	4	8	51	38	46
FC Stoneywood	26	14	1	11	45	40	43
Formartine United	26	12	6	8	49	48	42
Stonehaven	26	11	6	9	50	43	39
Banks o'Dee	26	9	7	10	50	40	34
Lads Club	26	10	3	13	41	52	33
Glentanar	26	10	2	14	47	44	32
Cruden Bay	26	8	5	13	46	55	29
Hermes	26	9	2	15	47	56	29
Wilsons XI	26	7	5	14	33	48	26
Deveronside	26	0	2	24	22	100	2

Camstruction Division One East

	P	W	D	L	F	A	Pts
Turriff United	24	17	3	4	65	34	54
Fraserburgh United	24	12	8	4	45	31	44
Lewis United	24	12	2	10	46	40	38
Ellon United	24	10	7	7	48	43	37
Banchory St Ternan	24	10	6	9	51	47	36

Other positions: Dyce Juniors (32 points), Hall Russell United (29), Buchanhaven Hearts (20), Parkvale (18).

GRILL BAR LEAGUE CUP

QUARTER-FINALS

Banks o'Dee 5 Lewis United 2
East End 2 Culter 1
Lossiemouth United 3 Islavale 5
Strathspey Thistle 5 Sunnybank 1

SEMI-FINALS

Banks o'Dee 5 Islavale 1
East End 1 Strathspey Thistle 2

FINAL

(Sunday, 1st December 2002. At Keith Park, Aberdeen)

STRATHSPEY THISTLE	2-2	BANKS O'DEE
Hendry (2)		Garrett, Singer

(aet - Strathspey Thistle won 4-3 on penalties)

ROLLSTUD REGIONAL CUP

QUARTER-FINALS

Banks o'Dee 3 Turriff United 2
Cruden Bay 0 Islavale 2
FC Stoneywood 3 Burghead Thistle 3 (FC Stoneywood won 5-4 on penalties)
Strathspey Thistle 5 Buchanhaven Hearts 1

SEMI-FINALS

Banks o'Dee 2 FC Stoneywood 0
STrathspey Thistle 0 Islavale 1 (after extra-time)

FINAL

(Thursday, 17th April 2003 at Pittodrie, Aberdeen)

BANKS O'DEE	2-3	ISLAVALE
Craib, Smith		Jaffray (2), Sharp

ACORN HEATING CUP

QUARTER-FINALS:

Banks o'Dee 1 Cruden Bay 2
Longside 2 Hermes 0
Stonehaven 1 Culter 3
Sunnybank 1 FC Stoneywood 1

SEMI-FINALS:

Cruden Bay 2 Culter 4
Longside 1 Sunnybank 1
(Longside won 5-4 on penalties)

FINAL:

(Friday, 30th May 2003. At Sunnybank)

CULTER	1-0	LONGSIDE
A Thain		Attendance: 230.

Annbank United player Craig Main curls the ball over the wall and into the net during the 1-1 draw against home side Craigmark Burntonians in a Ayrshire District League game.

Photo: John B. Vass.

MORRISON TROPHY

QUARTER-FINALS:
Buchanhaven Hearts 1 Parkvale 2
Dyce Juniors 1 Lewis United 2
Fraserburgh United 4 Ellon United 1
Hall Russell United 1 Turriff United 20

SEMI-FINALS:
Lewis United 3 Fraserburgh United 1
Parkvale 2 Turriff United 1

FINAL:
(Tuesday. 13th May 2002. At Dyce Juniors FC)

LEWIS UNITED	2-1	PARKVALE
Campbell, Stenner		D Keith

NCR NORTH/TAYSIDE CUP

(for Tayside and North clubs)

FOURTH ROUND
Carnoustie Panmure 0 North End 3
Forfar West End 2 Turriff United 5
Scone Thistle 0 Glentanar 3
Tayport 4 Lochee United 0 0

SEMI-FINALS
Tayport 1 Glentanar 0
Turriff United 0 North End 3

FINAL
(Saturday, 17th May 2003. At Glenesk Park, Dundee)

TAYPORT	3-0	NORTH END
McNaughton (2), Ward (pen)		

WEST SECTION
SCOTSCOUP DIVISION ONE WEST

	P	W	D	L	F	A	Pts
Forres Thistle	26	23	1	2	86	26	70
Strathspey Thistle	26	17	7	2	84	19	58
Islavale	26	17	7	2	75	27	58
Buckie Rovers	26	16	4	6	65	31	52
Dufftown	26	16	3	7	86	45	51
New Elgin	26	15	4	7	65	33	49
Lossiemouth United	26	10	5	11	49	59	35

Other positions: Whitehills (32 points), Bishopmill United (26), Burghead Thistle (25), Fochabers (17), Kinloss (14), Nairn St Ninian (13), RAF Lossiemouth (8).

GORDON WILLIAMSON CUP

SECOND ROUND
Fochabers 5 Burghead Thistle 2
Forres Thistle 1 Nairn St Ninian 0
Islavale 3 Strathspey Thistle 1
Whitehills 3 Bishopmill United 0

SEMI-FINALS
Forres Thistle 1 Fochabers 0
Islavale 3 Whitehills 1

FINAL
(Saturday, 24th May 2003. At Buckie Rovers FC)

FORRES THISTLE	1-0	ISLAVALE
Minty		(after extra-time)

TAYSIDE REGION - 2002-03

Division One

	P	W	D	L	F	A	Pts
Lochee United	18	14	3	1	61	23	45
Arbroath SC	18	11	2	5	39	31	35
Broughty Athletic	18	10	4	4	38	29	34
Montrose Roselea	18	9	5	4	44	28	32
Forfar West End	18	6	6	6	29	31	24
Downfield	18	6	3	9	40	42	21
Elmwood	18	6	3	9	26	32	21
Kirrie Thistle	18	5	8	9	26	43	23
East Craigie	18	2	5	11	27	50	11
Arbroath Victoria	18	2	4	12	22	48	10

Division Two

	P	W	D	L	F	A	Pts
Scone Thistle	18	14	1	3	50	21	43
Kinnoull	18	13	3	2	68	17	42
Forfar Albion	18	12	2	4	40	26	38
Blairgowrie	18	9	3	6	42	24	30
Coupar Angus	18	8	6	4	41	24	30
Lochee Harp	18	6	5	7	40	46	24
Luncarty	18	6	5	7	31	34	23
Jeanfield Swifts	18	5	1	12	23	49	16
Brechin Victoria	18	1	3	14	19	69	5
Bankfoot Athletic	18	0	4	14	16	60	4

DJ LAING CUP

QUARTER-FINALS
Downfield 3 Kinnoull 1 (after extra-time)
Kirrie Thistle 3 Forfar West End 4 (after extra-time)
Lochee United 0 Montrose Roselea 2
Scone Thistle 4 Arbroath Victoria 0

SEMI-FINALS
Downfield 1 Forfar West End 2
Montrose Roselea 1 Scone Thistle 0

FINAL
(Sunday, 30th March 2003. At Carnoustie Panmure FC. Attendance: 300)

MONTROSE ROSELEA	4-2	FORFAR WEST END
Watson 3 (1 pen), Atagan,		Black, Paige

HERSCHEL TROPHY

(Wednesday, 7th August 2002. At Tayport FC)

MONTROSE ROSELEA	1-1	TAYPORT
Paige		Evans

(after extra-time - Tayport won 7-6 on penalties)

'REDWOOD LEISURE' FIFE & TAYSIDE CUP

THIRD ROUND

Lochee United 2 Andrews United 2
(Lochee United won 4-3 on penalties)
Lochore Welfare 2 Carnoustie Panmure 1
Oakley United 0 Tayport 0
(Oakley United won 4-3 on penalties)
Dundee Violet 0 Hill of Beath Hawthorn 4

SEMI-FINALS

Lochee United 2 Lochore Welfare 0
Oakley United 1 Hill of Beath Hawthorn 2

FINAL

(Saturday, 14th June 2003. At North End FC)

HILL OF BEATH HAW.	5-0	LOCHEE UNITED
Smart (3), Thomson, McIntosh		

NORTH END CHALLENGE CUP

THIRD ROUND

Dundee Violet 2 Coupar Angus 1
Elmwood 2 Tayport 3
Forfar West End 2 Lochee Harp 3
Kinnoull 0 Blairgowrie 3

SEMI-FINALS

Dundee Violet 1 Blairgowrie 0
Lochee Harp 0 Tayport 4 (attendance: 261)

FINAL

(Tuesday, 117h June 2003. At Dundee North End FC)

TAYPORT	2-1	DUNDEE VIOLET
Mitchell, Holden		Jones

(after extra-time)

FINDLAY & COMPANY TROPHY

THIRD ROUND

Downfield 1 Broughty Athletic 3
Jeanfield Swifts 3 Scone Thistle 5 (after extra-time)
Lochee United 1 Carnoustie Panmure 2
North End 0 Coupar Angus 2

SEMI-FINALS

Broughty Athletic 4 Scone Thistle 1
Carnoustie Panmure 4 Coupar Angus 1

FINAL

(Tuesday. 10th June 2003. At Lochee United FC)

CARNOUSTIE PAN.	3-2	BROUGHTY ATH
Kenneth, McAllister Kelly		Mulligan, Ward

TAY LANDROVER CUP

SECOND ROUND

Blairgowrie 4 Scone Thistle 0
Forfar Albion 6 Brechin Victoria 2
Lochee Harp 3 Kinnoull 5 (after extra-time)
Luncarty 3 Coupar Angus 1

SEMI-FINALS

Blairgowrie 2 Kinnoull 0
Luncarty 2 Forfar Albion 3

FINAL

(Wednesday, 11th June 2003. At Kirriemuir)

BLAIRGOWRIE	2-2	FORFAR ALBION
McLaughlan, Reid,		Haldane, Coyle

(After extra-time - Blairgowrie won 3-1 on penalties)

DOWNFIELD SC CUP

SECOND ROUND

Arbroath Victoria 1 East Craigie 2
Brechin Victoria 1 Montrose Roselea 2 (after extra-time)
Jeanfield Swifts 3 Kinnoull 2
Lochee harp 3 Blairgowrie 2

SEMI-FINALS

East Craigie 1 Montrose Roselea 4
Jeanfield Swifts 1 Lochee harp 0

FINAL

(Monday, 10th June 2002 at Downfield)

JEANFIELD SWIFTS	4-3	MONTROSE R. (aet)
Hamilton, D Mitchell, Simpson, own goal		Ferri, S Mitchell, Christie

SUMMARY

THE outstanding Junior club in Scotland was without doubt Tayport in a season, when the new Superleagues were introduced with two divisions (Premier and First) in the West of Scotland) and another in the East, and the final outcomes could not have been more different with Pollok finishing top of the Caledonian Paper Division, made up of former Central and Ayrshire League clubs, although only (albeit comfortably) on goals difference from Neilston, whereas in the East Superleague of a single division Tayport, the oustanding Scottish Junior team of the campaign, lost only two matches and conceded a mere nine goals in beating off the brave challenge of Hill of Beath Hawthorn, Fife's best side.

Tayport also won the Scottish Junior Cup in a dour final against holders Linlithgow Rose by the game's only goal in extra-time, even though by then they were down to ten men in a match that they had dominated throughout, and they were without doubt superior to all comers in the junior game with an inability to score more goals to support a superb defence their main weakness, but to add to their claims they also won three parochial cup competitions.

Other clubs to have cause for celebration were Arthurlie and Troon, both promoted to the Superleague's Caledonian Paper Division and Glenafton Athletic (winners of the West of Scotland Cup and Ayrshire's top outfit) in the West, with Bo'ness United, Kelty Hearts (the Fife League Champions), Lochee United (Tayside League's yop side) and Sunnybank in the North, which until now is providing no clubs for competition in the East's Superleague.

The only problem with superleagues, which may sooner rather than later be combined into one national elite competition for junior clubs, is that it might - Old Firm-like - draw support away from the small town teams, which are after all the lifeblood of the whole show, but we must wait and see.

Anyone, who saw Tayport and others play, must wonder why the country's semi-professional selectors do not look at the junior sides, because it would be an insult to the intelligence for anyone to claim that there are not enough players there to strengthen the overall challenge to the possible superiority of other countries in comparison to Scotland.

Do we want to win competitions or would we prefer parochial interests to hold sway? It should be a rhetorical question, but at the moment is it one?

SCOTTISH SENIOR NON-LEAGUE FOOTBALL 2002-03

SCOT-ADS HIGHLAND LEAGUE TABLE

	P	W	D	L	F	A	Pts
Deveronvale	28	21	6	1	90	24	69
Keith	28	17	1	10	66	35	53
Cove Rangers	28	14	7	7	69	46	49
Buckie Thistle	28	14	7	7	59	37	49
Nairn County	28	13	7	8	67	47	46
Fraserburgh	28	14	4	10	61	45	46
Clachnacuddin	28	13	4	11	46	50	43
Huntly	28	12	5	11	53	42	41
Inverurie Locos	28	11	7	10	50	50	40
Lossiemouth	28	12	4	12	41	53	40
Forres Mechanics	28	12	2	14	59	61	38
Rothes	28	8	6	14	27	46	30
Wick Academy	28	8	2	18	33	68	26
Brora Rangers	28	3	6	19	30	77	15
Fort William	28	2	4	22	20	90	10

Leading Highland League goalscorers:

47 Murray (Deveronvale)
27 McKenzie (Deveronvale)
26 Beatttie (Cove Rangers)
20 Polworth (Clachnacuddin), K Coull (Cove Rgers) Chisholm (Deveronvale), Nicol (Keith)

QUALIFYING CUP NORTH

1ST ROUND

(Saturday, 31st August 2002)
Brora Rangers 0 Clachnacuddin 5
Forres Mechanics 0 Cove Rangers 4
Golspie Sutherland 1 Inverurie Loco Works 4
Keith 0 Fort William 0
Nairn County 2 Deveronvale 3
Rothes 1 Buckie Thistle 1
Wick Academy 2 Huntly 3
Lossiemouth v Fraserburgh postponed
(match played on Saturday, 7th September 2002)
Lossiemouth 1 Fraserburgh 3

Replays

(Saturday, 7th September 2002)
Buckie Thistle 1 Rothes 1
(Buckie Thistle won 4-3 on penalties)
(Saturday, 14th September 2002)
Fort William 0 Keith 3

QUARTER-FINALS:

(Saturday, 21st September 2002)
Clachnacuddin 2 Cove Rangers 3
Deveronvale 2 Buckie Thistle 1
Fraserburgh 2 Keith 2
Huntly 5 Inverurie Loco Works 1
Replay (Saturday, 28th September 2002)
Keith 2 Fraserburgh 1

SEMI-FINALS

(Saturday, 5th October 2002)
Huntly 0 Cove Rangers 2
Deveronvale 0 Keith 2

FINAL

(Saturday, 2nd November 2002. At Harlaw Stadium, Imverurie.
Attendance: 895)
COVE RANGERS 2-2 KEITH (aet)
Yeats, Beattie — Reid, McKenzie
(Keith won 3-1 on penalties) Attendance: 850.
Man of the Match: Craig Yeats (Cove Rangers)

COVE RANGERS: M Coull; McGinlay, Cheyne, Allan, Murphy, McCraw, Coutts, Yeats, K Coull, Beattie (captain), Brown. Substitutes: Clark for Coutts 58 minutes, Mullen for McGinlay 88 minutes, Smith for Yeats 99 minutes. Charles (GK) and Adam did not play. Booked: Yeats 34 minutes, McGinlay 70 minutes.
Beattie scores with one penalty shoot-out attempt.

KEITH: Pirie; Brown, King, Calder, McKenzie, Morrison, Still (captain), Smith, Cadger, Nicol, Donaldson. Substitutes: Robertson for Calder 65 minutes, Reid for Donaldson 69 minutes, Park for Still 118 minutes. Penalty shoot-out scorers: Cadger, McKenzie, Robertson.

Referee: D McDonald. Assistant referees: J Hasson, M Northcroft, S MacDonald (Fourth official)

BY all that is just and logical any match that is played in dreadful conditions - gale force winds or heavy rain or both - should have been a farce, but instead these two sides of modestly paid part-timers gave their all and it was sad that there had to be a loser, particularly as an anti-climatic series of penalties eventually decided the destiny of the cup.

Players did their best to play skilled football, but were frustrated some of the time by the swirl, which helped Cove Rangers to take the lead on twelve minutes, when a Brown in-singing corner was just too much for the Keith defence and Yeats, later booked for a foul and then voted Man of the Match, had a simple tap-in to perform.

Keith tried hard for the rest of the half to draw level and nearly did when a shot hit a post and when Nicol failed just on the break to convert a sitter - a wind-assisted error.

With the elements slightly in their favour Keith spent a large proportion of the second period on the offensive, but Cove still managed to double their lead when Beattie beat Pirie with a fine effort on 59 minutes.

Substitute Reid then reduced the deficit with 70 minutes on the clock when what looked suspiciously like an intended cross was caught by the wind to leave poor Marc Coull flat on his back and beaten badly, but Beattie then headed a ball against a post to deny the Aberdeen side a decisive advantage.

With five minutes remaining the Cove defence for once failed properly to clear a loose ball and Kenny McKenzie from fully 35 yards drove the ball through a crowd of players to beat the unsughted opposition keeper.

Extra-time saw plenty of effort with Marc Coull the busier keeper, but in the end it had to be penalties and victory for Keith was just about right after an epic encounter which was watched by Herr Berti Vogts among others, none of whom could escape something of a drenching, the match officials, ground staff and everyone all deserving the highest praise for endurance. A good show all round.

'HUTCHEON SERVICES' ABERDEENSHIRE CUP

FIRST ROUND:

Wednesday, 31st July 2002
Fraserburgh 0 Buckie Thistle 2

SECOND ROUND:

Wednesday, 7th August 2002
Buckie Thistle 1 Huntly 2
Cove Rangers 2 Deveronvale 6
Inverurie Locos 1 Aberdeen 'A' 6
Keith 3 Peterhead 'A' 1

SEMI-FINALS:

Deveronvale 5 Huntly 0
Keith 1 Aberdeen 'A' 3

FINAL

(Tuesday, 20th August 2002. At Harlaw Park, Inverurie. Attendance: 844)

DEVERONVALE	0-3	ABERDEEN 'A'
		Michie, O'Donoghue, McHattie

DEVERONVALE: Speirs; Dolan, Kinghorn, Chisholm, Dlugonski, Anderson, McAllister, Stephen, Murray, McKenzie, Brown. Substitutes: McRonald for Chisholm 69 minutes, Pressley for Brown 77 minutes.

ABERDEEN 'A': Preece; Payne, Morrison, O'Donoghue, Hedderman, Jones, Carella, McKenzie, Milne, Michie, Duncan.

Referee: S Duff

ABERDEENSHIRE SHIELD

FIRST ROUND:

(Wednesday, 9th October 2002)
Buckie Thistle 1 Inverurie Loco Works 2
Deveronvale 5 Huntly 1
Keith 2 Cove Rangers 1

SEMI-FINALS:

Fraserburgh 3 Deveronvale 3 (after extra-time - 2-2 at 90 minutes - Deveronvale won 4-3 on penalties)
Keith 1 Inverurie Loco Works 2

FINAL:

(Wednesday, 30th October 2002. At Kynoch Park, Keith. Attendance: 800)

DEVERONVALE	3-2	INVERURIE LOCO W.
Murray (2, 1 pen), McKenzie		McKay, Davidson

Half-tme: 2-0.

DEVERONVALE: Speirs; Dolan, Kinghorn, Chisholm, Glugonski, Anderson, Urquhart, L Stephen, McKenzie, Murray, Brown. Substitutes: Pressley for Chisholm 71 minutes, McAllister for Stephen 85 minutes.

INVERURIE LOCO WORKS: Christie; Young, Bisset, Baxter, Anderson, Park, Fraser, Walker, Reid, McKay, McWilliam. Substitutes: Ross for Baxter 70 minutes, Davidson for McWilliam 84 minutes.

Referee: A Freeland.

A PULSATING match between the Highland League's two front runners saw the competition's newest team go two goals behind in the first half to splendid efforts by Ian Murray on eighteen minutes and McKenzie ten minutes later, but Locos fought back bravely after the break and in the 55th minute a Stephen mistake in defence gave Young the chance to set up a goal for McKay.

With only a few minutes to go the match was left precariously poised as substitute Davidson struck a superb equaliser for the Garioch club, but immediately Steven Park brought down Ian Murray, who made no mistake with the resulting penalty to bring his goals total for the season to 25 of the best.

It was a cruel end to a fine match played on a chilly evening in Keith.

INVERNESS CUP

FIRST ROUND

Wednesday, 31st July 2002
Fort William 5 Brora Rangers 3 (after extra-time)
Wednesday, 7th August 2002
Clachnaccuddin 2 Ross County 'A' 4
Nairn County 3 Elgin City 'A' 1
Inverness Caledonian Thistle 'A' w/o Forres Mechanics (scratched)

SEMI-FINALS

(Tuesday, 13th August 2002)
Fort William 1 Ross County 'A' 6
Nairn County 0 Inverness Caledonian 'A' 2 (after extra-time)

FINAL

(Tuesday, 3rd September 2002. At Grant Street Park, Inverness)

INVERNESS CAL. T.. 'A' 0-1 ROSS COUNTY 'A'

NORTH OF SCOTLAND CUP

FIRST ROUND

Golspie Sutherland 1-1 Clachnacuddin 1 (after extra-time - Golpsie Sutherland won 5-4 on penalties)
Nairn County 3 Forres Mechanics 1

QUARTER-FINALS

Elgin City w/o Brora Rangers
Golspie Sutherland 0 Rothes 1
Lossiemouth 3 Fort William 1
Nairn County 3 Wick Academy 2 (after extra-time)

SEMI-FINALS

(Saturday, 29th March 2003)
Lossiemouth 4 Brora Rangers 2
Nairn County 0 Rothes 1

FINAL:

(Saturday, 19th April 2003. At Mosset Park, Forres. Attendance: 600)

LOSSIEMOUTH	3-1	ROTHES	
Scott, Mathieson, Green		Grant	Half-time: 1-0

LOSSIEMOUTH: Main; Dixon, Youngson, Sim, Morrison, Maguire, McMullan, Mathieson, Scott, McHardy, Cameron, Substitutes: Green for Dixon 47 minutes, Witkowski for Mathieson 84 minutes, Forde for Scott 86 minutes.

ROTHES: Strong; Main, MacRae, Esson, Grant, C Smith, R Smith, Shortreed, Ord, Mathieson, Hamilton. Substitute: Miller for Shortreed 61 minutes.

Referee: G Cheyne, Aberdeen.

TWO of the Highland League's less vaunted clubs gave an excellent show at Forres in the Final of the McEwan's North of Scotland Cup, which was in the end won by Lossiemouth for a fifth time in nine years against brave fellow Morayshire rivals Rothes.

The latter actually had the better of the first half, and still fell behind to a 24th minute goal by the unmarked Shawn Scott from a superb pass by ex-Ranger Scott Mathieson, the ultimate Man of the Match, but soon after half-time Rothes were level when a powerful Michael Grant header from a Mark Hamilton free kick was too much for Kevin Main.

Hereabaouts Mathieson came into his own and in the 76th minute Pete Maguire threaded the ball into his path and his high shot was too much for Darren Strong, who was again beaten in stoppage time by Mike Green, when he fired home into the roof of the net a pass from fellow substitute Ryan Witkowski.

The match was well handled by Gary Cheyne, who was a late replacement for originally appointed Scott MacDonald and did not find it necessary to use a card during the match.

HIGHLAND LEAGUE CUP

1ST ROUND

(Saturday, 5th April 2003)

Buckie Thistle 1 Cove Rangers 3
Clachnacuddin 2 Fraserburgh 1
Fort William 0 Keith 2
Inverurie Loco Works 2 Brora Rangers 0
Lossiemouth 1 Deveronvale 8
Nairn County 4 Forres Mechanics 1
Rothes 0 Huntly 1
Wick Academy bye

QUARTER-FINALS

(Saturday, 13th April 2003)

Deveronvale 3 Cove Rangers 0
Huntly 2 Inverurie Loco Works 5 (after extra-time)
Nairn County 1 Keith 2
Wick Academy 0 Clachnacuddin 3 (after-extra-time)
Lossiemouth 2 Huntly 1 (after extra-time)

SEMI-FINALS:

(Saturday, 26th April 2003)

Inverurie Loco Works 1 Deveronvale 2
Keith 1 Clachnacuddin 0

FINAL:

(Saturday, 10th May 2003. At Harlaw Park, Inverurie)

DEVERONVALE	2-3	KEITH	
Murray (2),		Robertson, Niddrie	
		Still	Att: 1,069.

DEVERONVALE: Speirs; Dolan, Kinghorn, Chisholm, Dlugonski, Anderson, McAllister, Brown, McKenzie, Murray, L Stephen. Substitutes: Taylor for McAllister 63 minutes, B Stephen for Chisholm 68 minutes. Sent off: Brown 90 minutes (second yellow card).

KEITH: Shearer; Brown, King, Robertson, McKenzie, Niddrie, Still, Calder, Cadger, Nicol, Stephen. Substitute: Reid for Cadger 79 minutes.

THE final important competitive match of the 2002-03 season was a superb advertisement for Highland League football and the outcome of the game was in the balance right until the final whistle after Keith had seen their three goal lead cut to a single counter after goals before half-time by Neil Robertson - the result of poor defending - and a great effort 120 seconds later by Darren Still at a time when only 23 minutes had elapsed, while on the one hour mark Kris Niddrie landed his first goal for Keith - another result of poor defensive work.

It looked as if the champions were in for a thrashing, but a free-kick by Murray with twelve minutes left followed by another neatly taken effort in 85 minutes brought a nail biting ending, which was enhanced when the same player had a chance for his hat-trick and a 50th goal during the campaign from a very harshly awarded penalty only to see Andy Shearer make a marvellous save and the only remaining incident was the result of frustration and a second yellow card for Vale's Robbie Brown, who departed seconds ahead of the others.

This kind of game does wonders for the reputation of the competition, which has struggled to make up for the loss of five clubs to the Scottish League itself.

QUALIFYING CUP SOUTH

PRELIMINARY ROUND:

Edinburgh City 2 Spartans 1
Edinburgh University 1 Annan Athletic 4
Glasgow University 1 Preston Athletic 2
Newton Stewart 0 Hawick Royal Albert 2
Vale of Leithen 4 Tarff Rovers 1

FIRST ROUND:

Annan Athletic 2 Dalbeattie Star 1
Civil Service Strollers 1 Threave Rovers 1
Coldstream 2 Edinburgh City 5
Gala Fairydean 1 Vale of Leithen 1
Girvan 5 Wigtown & Badenoch 0
St Cuthbert wanderers 0 Preston Athletic 3
Selkirk 4 Burntisland Shipyard 0
Whitehill Welfare 2 Hawick Royal Albert 1

Replays:

Threave Rovers 3 Civil Service Strollers 0
Vale of Leithen 1 Gala Fairydean 2

SEMI-FINALS:

(Saturday, 5th October 2002)

Preston Athletic 1 Threave Rovers 1
Selkirk 1 Whitehill Welfare 3

Replay:

(Saturday, 12th October 2002)

Threave Rovers 1 Preston Athletic 1
(After extra-time - 1-1 at 90 minutes - Threave Rovers won 4-3 on penalties)

FINAL:

(Saturday, 2nd November 2002. At Stirling Albion FC,
THREAVE ROVERS 0-3 WHITEHILL WELFARE
Ronaldson (2), O'Donnel.

EAST OF SCOTLAND LEAGUE

PREMIER DIVISION	P	W	D	L	F	A	Pts
Whitehill Welfare	22	14	6	2	55	18	48
Annan Athletic	22	14	2	6	59	32	44
Spartans	22	13	4	5	71	38	43
Gala Fairydean	22	12	5	5	55	42	41
Threave Rovers	22	11	4	7	51	37	37
Craigroyston	22	10	3	9	47	49	33
Lothian Thistle	22	8	5	9	32	41	29
Edinburgh City	22	8	4	10	36	40	28
Preston Athletic	22	8	3	11	37	46	27
Vale of Leithen	22	5	4	13	38	57	24
Coldstream	22	5	4	13	36	65	19
Peebles Rovers	22	1	2	19	23	75	5

DIVISION ONE	P	W	D	L	F	A	Pts
Edinburgh Univ'ty	22	17	0	5	56	27	51
Civil Service Strl	22	13	3	6	52	26	42
Dalbeattie Star	22	11	7	4	53	32	40
Kelso United	22	11	5	6	48	33	38
Edinburgh Athletic	22	10	7	5	37	23	37
Heriot-Watt Univ	22	10	5	7	46	42	35
Pencaitland/Ormist	22	7	5	10	27	33	26
Selkirk	22	7	5	10	44	52	26
Hawick R Albert	22	6	7	9	36	40	25
Easthouses	22	5	7	10	32	44	22
Tollcross United	22	4	5	13	28	46	17
Eyemouth United	22	1	4	17	22	83	7

Cup Competitions - East of Scotland

IMAGE PRINTERS EAST OF SCOTLAND CUP

1ST ROUND

Edinburgh University 1 Peebles Rovers 0
Hawick Royal Albert 0 Edinburgh Athletic 1
Heriot Watt University 2 Selkirk 1
Lothian Thistle 1 Tollcross United 0
Vale of Leithen 1 Spartans 4

2ND ROUND

Civil Service Strollers 0 Heriot-Watt University 1
Coldstream 0 Lothian Thistle 1 3
Craigroyston 1 Preston Athletic 0
Easthouses 0 Whitehill Welfare 4
Edinburgh Athletic 0 Spartans 1
Eyemouth United 2 Edinburgh City 10
Kelso United 4 Gala Fairydean 2
Pencaitland-Ormiston 1 Edinburgh University 2

3RD ROUND

Craigroyston 1 Whitehill Welfare 0ity 0
Edinburgh City 2 Kelso United 1
Edinburgh University 1 Heriot-Watt University 0
Spartans 1 Lothian Thistle 2

SEMI-FINALS

Craigroyston 0 Edinburgh City 1
Edinburgh University 2 Lothian Thistle 1

FINAL

(Sunday, 23rd March 2003. At Preston Athletic FC)

EDINBURGH CITY 2-1 EDINBURGH UNIVERSITY
Foster, Hartley Crawford

KING CUP

1ST ROUND:

Easthouses 1 Peebles Rovers 4
Edinburgh University 0 Spartans 1
Gala Fairydean 3 Preston Athletic 1
Heriot-Watt University 2 Selkirk 0
Whitehill Welfare 3 Craigroyston 2

2ND ROUND:

Coldstream 4 Peebles Rovers 4
(Coldstream won 4-2 on penalties)
Edinburgh Athletic 3 Vale of Leithen 5
Eyemouth United 1 Tollcross United 2
Gala Fairydean 3 Edinburgh City 1
Lothian Thistle 0 Civil Service Strollers 2
Pencaitland-Ormiston 3 Heriot-Watt University 0
Spartans 4 Kelso United 1
Whitehill Welfare 1 Hawick Royal Albert 2

3RD ROUND:

Civil Service Strollers 4 Tollcross United 1
Coldstream 3 Vale of Leithen 4
Hawick Royal Albert 1 Pencaitland-Ormiston 1
(Pencaitland-Ormiston won 3-2 on penalties)
Spartans 7 Gala Fairydean 2

SEMI-FINALS:

Pencaitland-Ormiston 2 Civil Service Strollers 1
Vale of Leithen 0 Spartans 5

FINAL:

(Saturday, 17th May 2003. At Whitehill Welfare FC)

SPARTANS 2-0 PENCAITLAND ORMISTON
Hobbins, Manson

ALEX JACK CUP

1ST ROUND

Easthouses 2 Peebles Rovers 2
(Easthouses won 8-7 on penalties)
Pencaitland-Ormiston 0 Edinburgh Athletic 2

SECOND ROUND

Easthouses 0 Lothian Thistle 3
Edinburgh Athletic 3 Craigroyston 2d 2
Eyemouth United 4 Heriot-Watt University 7
Kelso United 3 Tollcross United 2

SEMI-FINALS

Heriot-Watt University 0 Edinburgh Athletic 2
Lothian Thistle 2 Kelso United 0

FINAL

(Sunday, 10th November 2002. At Whitehill Welfare FC)

EDINBURGH ATHLETIC 2-1 LOTHIAN THISTLE
Thomas , Brownlie Anderson

EAST LEAGUE CUP

1ST ROUND

Annan Athletic 5 Peebles Rovers 1
Edinburgh Athletic 1 Dalbeattie Star 2
Eyemouth United 0 Spartans 5
Gala Fairydean 4 Edinburgh University 1
Lothian Thistle 3 Selkirk 0
Preston Athletic 0 Whitehill Welfare 2
Tollcross United 1 Coldstream 0
Vale of Leithen 0 Easthouse 4

2ND ROUND

Civil Service Strollers 0 Dalbeattie Star 3
Easthouses 2 Craigroyston 3
Heriot-Watt University 0 Annan Athletic 2
Pencaitland-Ormiston 2 Kelso United 5
Spartans 2 Edinburgh University 1
Threave Rovers 0 Spartans 1
Tollcross United 0 Lothian Thistle 1
Whitehill Welfare 1 Gala Fairydean 0

THIRD ROUND

Annan Athletic 0 Craigroyston 1
Dalbeattie Star 2 Lothian Thistle 1
Threave Rovers 0 Spartans 1 Craigroyston 0
Whitehill Welfare 1 Kelso United 0

SEMI-FINALS

Craigroyston 2 Spartans 1
Dalbeattie Star 2 Whitehill Welfare 6

FINAL

(Sunday, 11th May 2003. At Saughton)

CRAIGROYSTON 0-2 WHITEHILL WELFARE
Cocker, Ronaldson

CITY CUP

(2001-02 Season)

SEMI-FINALS

Berwick Rangers 2 Whitehill Welfare 0
Spartans 4 Livingston 1

FINAL

(Sunday, 28th July 2002. At Whitehill Welfare FC)

BERWICK RANGERS 2-1 SPARTANS
Neil , Wood Jardine

NB: Livingstone are no longer members of the East of Scotland FA, so future City Cup Finals will involve Berwick Rangers and the winners of the Image Printers Cup.

SOUTH OF SCOTLAND LEAGUE

	P	W	D	L	F	A	Pts
Stranraer Athletic	28	22	2	4	93	42	68
Tarff Rovers	28	18	3	7	66	43	67
Gretna 'A'	28	16	5	7	86	50	53
Girvan	28	15	6	7	81	43	51
St Cuthbert Wands	28	14	8	6	66	48	50
Abbeyvale	28	13	4	11	76	58	43
Crichton Royal	28	13	4	11	64	70	43
Dumfries FC	28	12	6	10	80	66	42
Nithsdale Wanderers	28	11	4	13	73	85	37
Wigtown & Badenoch	28	9	5	14	55	66	32
Creetown	28	7	7	14	59	66	28
Threave Rovers A	28	10	1	17	46	75	28
Annan Athletic 'A'	28	8	2	18	64	79	26
Dalbeattie Star 'A'	28	5	4	19	32	76	13
Newton Stewart	28	4	2	22	35	101	8

Note Points deducted:
Dalbeattie Star 'A' - 8 pts
Newton Stewart- 6 pts
Threave Rovers 'A' 3 pts

Cup competitions in South of Scotland 2002-03

POTTS CUP

1ST ROUND

Creetown 0 Gretna 'A' 3
Crichton Royal 2 Wigtown & Badenoch 4
Dumfries FC 4 Dalbeattie Star 'A' 4
(after extra-time - Dumfries FC won 4-2 on penalties)
Tarff Rovers 5 Nithsdale Wanderers 4
Threave Rovers 'A' 3 St Cuthbert Wanderers 4

2ND ROUND

Abbeyvale 2 Dumfries FC 1
St Cuthbert Wanderers 1 Gretna 'A' 6
Stranrear Athletic 2 Annan Athletic 'a' 5
Wigtown & Badenoch 0 Tarff Rovers 1 (after extra-time)

SEMI-FINALS

Annan Athletic 'A' 7 Abbeyvale 0
Tarff Rovers w/o Gretna 'A'2

FINAL

(Monday, 28th April 2003. At Annan Athletic FC)

ANNAN ATHLETIC 'A' 3-0 TARFF ROVERS
Pratt (3)

HAIG GORDON CUP

1ST ROUND

Creetown 3 Stranraer Athletic 4
Crichton Royal 5 Newton Stewart 1
Dumfries FC 3 Abbeyvale 4
St Cuthbert Wanderers 2 Annan Athletic 'A' 1
Tarff Rovers 5 Nithsdale Wanderers 4
Wigtown & Badenoch 1 Dalbeattie Star 'A' 2

2ND ROUND

Crichton Royal 3 Stranraer Athletic 5 (after extra-time)
Dumfries FC 5 Dalbeattie Star 'A' 2
St Cuthbert Wanderers 0 Gretna 'A' 8
Threave Rovers lost to Tarff Rovers

SEMI-FINALS

Dumfries FC 1 Gretna 'A' 2
Tarff Rovers 1 Stranraer Athletic 0

FINAL

(Monday, 5th May 2003. At Tarff Rovers FC, Kirkcowan)

TARFF ROVERS 3-5 GRETNA 'A'
Telfer, Bel og, Skinner (3), Errington
C Tennent Gordon

CREE LODGE CUP

1ST ROUND

Abbeyvale 4 Creetown 2
Annan Athletic 'A' 5 Newton Stewart 1
Dalbeattie Star 'A' 1 Nithsdale Wanderers 1 (Dalbeattie Star 'A' won 7-6 on penalties)
Dumfries FC 1 Wigtown & Badenoch 7
Girvan 1 Stranraer Athletic 1 (After extra-time - Stranrear Athletic won 4-3 on penalties)
Gretna 'A' 5 Tarff Rovers
Threave Rovers 'A' lost to St Cuthbert Wanderers

2ND ROUND

Annan Athletic 'A' 10 Dalbeattie Star 'A' 0
Crichton Royal 0 Wigtown & Badenoch 5
Gretna 'A' 6 Abbeyvale 0
Stranraer Athletic 2 St Cuthbert Wanderers 1

SEMI-FINALS

Stranraer Athletic 3 Gretna 'A' 2
Wigtown & Badenoch 0 Annan Athletic 'A' 0 (after extra-time - Annan Athletic 'A' won 4-3 on penalties)

FINAL

Saturday, 3rd May 2003. At Annan Athletic FC)

ANNAN ATHLETIC 'A' 3-2 STRANRAER ATHLETIC
Moffat (2), Pratt Doyle, Walker

TWEEDIE CUP

1ST ROUND

Abbeyvale 4 Gretna 'A' 2
Creetown 1 Crichton Royal 2
Dumfries FC 7 Nithsdale Wanderers 4
Newton Stewart 2 Wigtown & Badenoch 3
St Cuthbert Wanderers 1 Girvan 2 (after extra-time)
Tarff Rovers 0 Stranrear Athletic 1

2ND ROUND

Abbeyvale 0 Creetown 2
Stranraer Athletic 2 Dumfries FC 3
Threave Rovers 'A' lost to Anna Athletic 'A'
Wigtown & Badenoch 2 Girvan 5

SEMI-FINALS

Annan Athletic 'A' 0 Creetown 4
Girvan 5 Dumfries FC 1

FINAL

(Wednesday. 7th May 2003. At Creetown FC)

CREETOWN 4-0 GIRVAN
G McClymont (3),
Davidson

SOUTH OF SCOTLAND LEAGUE CUP

1ST ROUND

Abbeyvale 5 Dunfries FC 3
Annan Athletic 3 Stranrear 2
Newton Stewart 1 Creetown 9
Nithsdale Wanderers 5 St Cuthbert Wanderers 3
Tarff Rovers 4 Dalbeattie Star 'A' 1
Threave Rovers 'A' beat Gretna 'A'
Wigtown & Badenoch 1 Girvan 4

2ND ROUND

Annan Athletic 'A' 0 Nithsdale Wanderers 1
Creetown 2 Gretna 'A' 0
Crichton Royal 2 Girvan 1
Tarff Rovers 2 Abbeyvale 6

SEMI-FINALS

Crichton Royal 5 Abbeyvale 2
Nithsdale Wanderers 2 Creetown 1

FINAL

(Saturday, 26th October 2002. At Crichton Royal FC)

CRICHTON ROYAL 4-1 NITHSDALE WANDERERS
D Johnstone (3), Bell
Crosbie

SOUTH OF SCOTLAND CHALLENGE CUP

1ST ROUND

Abbeyvale 1 Creetown 2
Dalbeattie Star 'A' 3 Dumfries FC 1
Gretna 'A' 2 Crichton Royal 1
Newton Stewart 1 Nithsdale Wanderers 7
Stranraer 'A' 3 St Cuthbert Wanderers 0
Stranrear Athletic 2 Annan Athletic 'A' 0
Threave Rovers 'A' 0 Queen of the South 'A' 2
Wigtown & Badenoch 1 Tarff Rovers 2

2ND ROUND

Dalbeattie Star 'A' 2 Creetown 2
Nithsdale Wanderers 1 Tarff Rovers 3
Queen of the South 'A' 6 Gretna 'A' 3
Stranrear Athletic w/o Stranraer 'A'

SEMI-FINALS

Stranraer Athletic 3 Creetown 2 (after extra-time)
Tarff Rovers 0 Queen of the South 'A' 1

FINAL

(Wednesday, 23rd April 2003. At Stranrear Athletic FC)

STRANRAER ATH. 0-2 QUEEN OF THE SOUTH 'A'
Ferrie, Gibson (pen)

DETROIT TROPHY TOP SIX FINAL POSITIONS:

Stranrear Athletic	78 points
Tarff Rovers	67 points
Gretna 'A'	65 points
Girvan	55 points
Abbeyvale	52 points
St Cuthbert Wanderers	50 points

NB: For financial reasons Tarff Rovers have withdrawn from all competition apart from the South Qualifying Cup and the Souhern Counties Challange Cup, but the league has been expanded to include Mid-Annandale, Queen of the South Reserves and Stranrear Reserves.

NORTH CALEDONIAN LEAGUE

	P	W	D	L	F	A	Pts
Thurso	18	14	3	1	63	14	45
Alness United	18	14	0	4	42	21	42
Golspie Sutherland	18	12	3	3	46	23	39
Balintore	18	8	4	6	46	27	28
Dornoch	18	8	1	9	40	55	25
Bonar Bridge	18	7	3	8	37	53	24
Halkirk	18	6	4	8	45	37	22
Invergordon	18	5	2	11	41	56	17
Tain	18	2	2	14	28	78	8
Bunilidh	18	1	4	13	19	43	7

Cup competitions in North Caledonian area 'POST SERVICES' CHIC ALLAN CUP

1ST ROUND

Balintore 1 Bonar Bridge 1
(Balintore won 5-4 on penalties)
Invergordon 1 Alness United 3

2ND ROUND

Alness United 5 Bunilidh 2
Halkirk 5 Dornoch 43
Tain 2 Balintore 6
Thurso 2 Golspie Sutherland 0

SEMI-FINALS

Alness United 2 Halkirk 0
Balintore 1 Thurso 0

FINAL (Saturday, 28th October 2002. At Tain FC)
ALNESS 2-0 BALINTORE

PCT CUP

1ST ROUND

Tain 5 Bonar Bridge 3
Thurso 2 Balintore 1 (after extra-time)

2ND ROUND

Alness United 2 Thurso 3
Dornoch 4 Tain 2
Golspie Sutherland 1 Bunilidh 0
Halkirk 2 Invergordon 3 (after extra-time)

SEMI-FINALS

Dornoch 2 Thurso 1
Invergordon 1 Golspie Sutherland 2

FINAL

(Saturday, 8th February 2003. At Brora Rangers FC)
GOLSPIE SUTHERLAND 3-1 DORNOCH

MORRIS NEWTON CUP

1ST ROUND

Halkirk 6 Invergordon 3
Tain 4 Dornoch 7

2ND ROUND

Balintore 0 Alness United 2
Bonar Bridge 4 Dornoch 2 (after extra-time)
Bunilidh 1 Golspie Sutherland 1
(Bunilidh won 4-3 on penalties)
Thurso 3 Halkirk 1

SEMI-FINALS

Bonar Bridge 3 Alness United 2
Thurso 6 Bunilidh 0

FINAL

(Saturday, 6th April 2003. At Ross County FC, Dingwall)

BONAR BRIDGE 0-5 THURSO

FOOTBALL TIMES CUP

FIRST ROUND

Balintore 2 Thurso 3
Bunilidh 4 Bonar Bridge 3

2ND ROUND

Dornoch 1 Alness United 7
Invergordon 3 Golspie Sutherland 5 (after extra-time)
Tain 2 Halkirk 6
Thurso w/o Bunilidh (scratched)

SEMI-FINALS

Golspie Sutherland 2 Thurso 3 (after extra-time)
Halkirk 2 Alness United 1 (after extra-time)

FINAL

(Saturday, 12th April 2003. At Thurso)

THURSO 1-0 HALKIRK

NON-LEAGUE CLUBS IN THE SCOTTISH CUP

FIRST ROUND:

Saturday, 7th December 2002
East Stirling 1 Threave Rovers 1
Forfar Athletic 3 Huntly 1
Preston Athletic 0 Hamilton Academical 1
Selkirk 1 Cowdenbeath 4
Stranraer 1 Whitehill Welfare 1

Replays:

Saturday, 21st December 2003
Threave Rovers 2 East Stirling 1
Whitehill Welfare 2 Stranraer 3

SECOND ROUND:

Saturday, 4th January 2003
Gretna 3 Cove Rangers 0
Keith 1 Cowdenbeath 3
Monday, 13th January 2003
Morton 4 Deveronvale 3
Tuesady, 14th January 2003
Airdrie United 1 Threave Rovers 0

SENIOR NON-LEAGUE SUMMARY

THE four senior non-League competitions in Scotland in the new season will contain 61 teams (including all the reserve sides in the South of Scotland League), and there were two outstanding teams in Deveronvale, who won the Highland League for the first time and also took the Aberdeenshire Shield, and Whitehill Welfare, who accomplished the double of the local title and the South Qualifying Cup with the East League Cup to add to their lustre, but the almost complete lack of success of non-League outfits against Scottish League opposition - Threave Rovers's defeat of struggling East Stirling in a replay was the only triumph - emphasised the gap that has become larger since five clubs were admitted to the big time in recent seasons.

There was a case before that happened for suggesting that any Scotland Semi-Professional selection could be selected from the two main senior non-League competitions (i.e the Highland and East of Scotland Leagues), but, as they now consist of only 39 clubs in total, those who choose the squad to represent Scotland at that level have a duty to their fellow country fans to widen the net and consider all players who are eligible to take part in the annual Semi-Professional tournament, which was recently revived with our men only having so far won once in six outings with one draw.

This becomes particularly important now that the next tournament is due to be played in the Aberdeen and North East area in 2004, and the selectors will earn themselves no thanks if they choose to place parochial considerations above the national best interests, which means that part-timers in the Scottish League itself along with the best Junior players must come into the reckoning and, if the present selection committee refuses to bend to the nation's needs, a decision should be forced on them by the Scottish Football Association, although that should not be necessary as common sense will probably prevail.

Meanwhile, Deveronvale won the Highland League by a massive margin of fifteen points over runners-up Keith, whose consolations came in terms of victories in the North Qualifying Cup after an epic contest in dreadful conditions against Cove Rangers, which went to penalties, and in the Highland League Cup itself, while it was good to see frequent strugglers Lossiemouth and Rothes contest a good North of Scotland Cup Final with the former taking the honours for the fifth time in nine years.

Meanwhile, up near the Arctic Circle Thurso had an oustanding campaign, winning the North Caledonian League after a fine tussle with Alness United, who won one of the local cups but had to watch as the champions won the two others, but geography probably prevents any of the teams in that competition from having further ambitions.

Whitehill Welfare's main competiiton came from Annan Athletic and defending champions Spartans, but it is an irony that the South of Scotland League itself has struggled bravely for survival and most of its leading outfits now see the East of Scotland League as its main chance of making an impression with reserve sides likely to win most of the honours in coming years.

It remains a struggle for too many clubs to survive, and the virtual demise of Tarff Rovers in the South emphasises just how tough the problem is, but thanks to enough brave and loyal supporters most will manage, provided that they do not spend more money than they have and also can continue to benefit from local generous sponsors.

SCOTTISH AMATEUR REGIONAL CHAMPIONS

Central Scottish League Premier Division: Harestanes
Border Amateur League Division A: Earlston Rhymers
Ayrshire Premier: Knockentiber
Caithness Division One: Wick Thistle
Lanarkshire Premier: Wishaw HS
Midlands Premier: Riverside
Fife Premier: Inverkeithing HS
Aberdeenshire Premier: Kincorth

AMATEUR FOOTBALL ALLIANCE

President: F J Banner
Company Secretary: Mike Brown, 55 Islington Park Street, London N1 1QB
Tel: 020 7359 3493 Fax: 020 7359 5027
Website: www.amateur-fa.org Email: A.F.A.@dial.Pipex.com

A F A SENIOR CUP

Sponsored by Ladbrokes

1ST ROUND PROPER
South Bank Cuaco 5 Old Cholmeleians 1
Old Finchleians 1* Old Salopians 0*
Polytechnic 0 Honourable Artillery Company 1
Brentham 1 Winchmore Hill 8
BB Eagles 3 The Rugby Clubs 1
Civil Service 4 Carshalton 3
Weirside Rangers 2 Glyn Old Boys 3
Mill Hilll Village 3 Old Danes 4
Alleyn Old Boys 7 Old Minchendenians 1
Old Esthameians 5 University of Hertfordshire 0
Old Stationers 0 Old Latymerians 1
Crouch End Vampires 1*:4p Old Parmiterians 1*:5p
Latymer Old Boys 2 Old Wilsonians 0
Hale End Athletic 1 Parkfield 0
Cardnal Manning O B 2 HSBC 7
Old Manorians 3 Old Sedcopians 1
Old Owens 7 Old Westminister Citizens 0
Old Salesians 3 Old Foresters 0
Old Challoners 0 Bromleians Sports 2
Nottsborough 11 William Fitt 1
Old Reptonians 2 Bank of England 4
UCL Academicals 4 Old Salvatorians 2
Old Hamptonians 7 Old Ignatians 1
Pegasus 0 Old Grammarians 3
Old Fairlopians 0 Old Meadonians 2
St Mary's College 0*:3p Old Aloysians 0*:4p
Hale End Athletic 3 Southgate County 2
Southgate Olympic 4 Ibis 1
Old Tenisonians 2*:2p E. Barnet O. Gramm'ns 2*:3p
Enfield Old Grammarians 2:2* Kew Association 2:5*
West Wickham 2 Albanian 0
Old Witleians 2 Old Actonians Association 4

2ND ROUND PROPER
South Bank Cuaco 2 Old Finchleians 0
Honourable Artillery Company 1 Winchmore Hill 4
Old Tiffinians 4 BB Eagles 2
Civil Service 5 Glyn Old Boys 0
Old Danes 1 Alleyn Old Boys 3
Old Esthameians 4* Old Latymerians 3*
Old Parmiterians 0* Latymer Old Boys 2*
HSBC 3 Old Manorians 2
Old Owens 2* Old Salesians 1*
Bromleians Sports 2 Nottsborough 0
Bank of England 4 UCL Academicals 0
Old Hamptonians 0 Old Grammarians 0
Old Meadonians 5 St Mary's College 0
Hale End Athletic 3 Southgate Olympic 0
E. Barnet O. Gramm's 4 Enfield O. Gramm'ns 0
West Wickham 0*:2p Old Actonians Assn 0*:3p

3RD ROUND PROPER
South Bank Cuaco 2 Winchmore Hill 3
Old Tiffinians 0 Civil Service 6
Alleyn Old Boys 2*:4p Old Esthameians 2*:2p
Latymer Old Boys 6 HSBC 1
Old Owens 2* Bromleians Sports 3*
Bank of England 2 Old Hamptonians 0
Old Meadonians 1 Hale End Athletic 2
E. Barnet O.Gramm'ns 3 Old Actonians Ass'n 5

4TH ROUND PROPER
Winchmore Hill 1 Civil Service 0
Alleyn Old Boys 1 Latymer Old Boys 2
Bromleians Sports 1*:5p Bank of England 1*:4p
Hale End Athletic 1 Old Actonians Ass'n 3

Semi-Finals
Winchmore Hill 0*:4 Latymer Old Boys 0*:0
O. Bromleians Sports 1*:3p O. Actonians Ass'n 1*:2p

FINAL
Winchmore Hill 1 Bromleians Sports 0

OTHER CUP FINALS

Essex Senior
Hale End Athletic 2 Old Parkonians 0
Middlesex Senior
Old Meadonians 2 Winchmore Hill 0
Surrey Senior
Old Wokingians 3:3* Nottsborough 3:5*
Intermediate
Old Camdenians 1st 3 UCL Academicals Res 2
Junior
Old Aloysians 3rd 2* UCL Academicals 3rd 1*
Minor
Old Magdalenians 1st 1 Nottsborough 4th 2
Veterans
William Fitt 2 Old Parmiterians "A" 3
Open Veterans
Awarded to Nalgo - opponents defaulted

Greenland
Old Owens 3 UCL Academicals 0
Essex Intermediate
Mount Pleasant P O 1st 1 Old Buckwellians Res 2
Kent Intermediate
Granby Sports 1st 0:1*:3p W. Wickham Res 0:1*:5p
Middlesex Intermediate
Civil Service Res 1:3* E. Barnet O. Gramm'ns Res 1:3*
Surrey Intermediate
Old Tiffinians Res 1 Nottsborough Res 3
Senior Novets
Winchmore Hill 5th 2 Civil Service 5th 0
Intermediate Novets
Parkfield 6th 3 UCL Academicals 6th 0
Junior Novets
Marsh 4th 1*:4p Old Kolsassians 1*:2p

YOUTH

Saturday
U-18
Norsemen 6 Battersea Park Rangers 2
U-17
Devas 2 Shoreditch 5
U-16
Norsemen 4 Rockingham United 2
U-15
Bec United 2 Providence House 7
U-14
Pro Hawks 0 Santley United 2
U-13
Bethwin Boys "A" 2 Future Stars 5
U-12
Norseen 5 Accra 2000 2
U-11
Minchenden Youth "B" 1 Bec United 2

Sunday
U-18
Alexandra Park 3 Young Parmiterians "A" 1
U-16
Sheen Tigers 3*:2p Percival Youth 3*:3p
U-15
Young Parmiterians "A" 3 Potters Bar United "A" 1
U-14
Alexandra Park "B" 4 Alexandra Park "A" 2
U-13
Alexandra Park "A" 2 Young Parmiterians 1
U-12 Invitation
Alexandra Park 6 Young Parmiterans 4
U-12
Minchenden 3 Alexandra Park "A" 0
U-11
Norsemen 1*:4p Alexandra Park "B" 1*:3p

AMATEUR FOOTBALL COMBINATION

(A merger of the former Old Boys' and Southern Olympian Leagues)

PREMIER DIVISION	P	W	D	L	F	A	Pts
Old Meadonians	19	15	3	1	51	19	48
Old Hamptonians	20	12	2	6	37	22	38
Hale End Athletic	20	8	6	6	45	36	30
Albanian	20	8	5	7	35	35	29
Old Aloysians	19	9	2	8	35	37	29
Old Wilsonians	20	8	4	8	39	39	28
UCL Academicals	20	7	6	7	40	36	27
Old Danes	20	5	5	10	33	49	20
Old Ignatians	20	6	2	12	27	46	20
Parkfield	20	4	7	9	34	45	19
Honourable Artillery Company	20	4	4	12	30	42	16

SENIOR DIVISION 1	P	W	D	L	F	A	Pts
Old Salvatorians	20	16	1	3	58	24	49
Latymer Old Boys	20	15	2	3	50	19	47
Old Bealonians	20	13	1	6	61	24	40
Southgate County	20	10	3	7	49	38	33
Old Vaughanians	20	8	7	5	39	34	31
Old Tiffinians	20	8	3	9	44	41	27
Phoenix Old Boys	20	7	3	10	35	43	24
Cardinal Manning Old Boys	20	7	0	13	41	61	21
Mill Hill Village	20	5	2	13	41	55	17
Shene Old Grammarians	20	3	3	13	28	61	12
Ulysses	20	3	3	13	32	78	9

SENIOR DIVISION 2	P	W	D	L	F	A	Pts
Old Tenisonians	22	15	2	5	47	20	47
Old Wokingians	22	13	7	2	55	32	46
Glyn Old Boys	22	12	3	7	39	37	39
Old Isleworthians	22	11	2	9	49	44	35
Enfield Old Grammarians	22	9	6	7	41	37	33
Old Dorkinians	22	8	8	6	34	33	32
Old Manorians	22	8	7	7	46	46	31
Old Grammarians	22	8	2	12	34	41	26
Old Suttonians	22	8	2	12	37	45	26
St Mary's College	22	5	4	13	35	50	19
Old Woodhouseians	22	4	6	12	35	49	18
King's Old Boys	22	4	5	13	38	56	17

SENIOR DIVISION 3	P	W	D	L	F	A	Pts
Economicals	20	15	1	4	75	29	46
Old Buckwellians	20	12	4	4	62	41	40
Queen Mary College Old Boys	20	10	5	5	50	30	35
University of Hertford	20	10	3	7	61	38	33
Wood Green Old Boys	20	9	4	6	51	43	31
Pegasus	20	9	4	7	42	40	31
Old Reigatians	20	7	4	9	31	38	25
Old Minchendenians	20	6	4	10	39	55	22
Brent	20	5	5	10	31	43	20
The Rugby Clubs	20	2	7	11	29	56	13
BBC	20	3	1	15	26	84	10

SENIOR DIVISION 4	P	W	D	L	F	A	Pts
Old Vaughanians Res	18	11	5	2	40	27	38
John Fisher Old Boys	18	11	3	4	56	33	36
Clapham Old Xavierians	18	10	4	4	53	33	34
City of London	18	10	2	6	51	45	32
Latymer Old Boys Res	18	6	6	6	40	34	24
Old Sedcopians	18	7	3	8	46	49	24
Centymca	18	6	2	10	41	46	20
Old Aloysians Res	18	3	7	8	38	37	16
Old Woodhouseians Res	18	4	3	11	32	61	15
Old Tenisonians Res	18	3	3	12	24	56	9

SENIOR DIVISION 5 North	P	W	D	L	F	A	Pts
Parkfield Res	22	15	5	2	68	25	50
Old Challoners	22	12	8	2	58	21	44
UCL Academicals Res	22	13	3	6	65	26	42
Albanians Res	22	13	3	6	57	56	42
Old Tollingtonians	22	10	7	5	49	35	37
Hale End Athletic Res	22	9	2	11	54	53	29
Old Salvatorians Res	22	7	8	7	36	40	29
Pegasus Res	22	7	3	12	47	57	24
Egbertian	22	5	5	12	41	61	20
Mill Hill Village Res	22	4	6	12	33	60	18
Old Manorians Res	22	5	3	14	28	78	15
Old Edmontonians	22	3	5	14	47	71	14

SENIOR DIVISION 5 South	P	W	D	L	F	A	Pts
Chertsey Old Salesians	21	16	3	2	69	33	51
Old Hamptonians Res	22	17	0	5	58	37	51
Old Wilsonians Res	20	14	1	5	45	17	43
Sinjuns	22	12	4	6	68	42	40
London Welsh	22	12	3	7	61	60	39
Witan	22	9	3	10	48	50	30
Honourable Artillery Co Res	22	8	3	11	48	54	27
Mickleham Old Boxhillians	22	7	5	10	54	54	26
St Mary's College Res	21	6	5	10	46	58	23
Old Meadonians Res	21	4	3	14	34	61	15
Old St Marys	21	3	3	15	24	54	12
Old Grammarians Res	22	2	5	15	45	80	11

* - Pts deducted - breach of Rule

OTHER DIVISIONS

	Teams	Won by:
Intermediate Div. North	11	Old Aloysians 3rd
Intermediate Div. South	11	Old Thorntonians
Intermediate Div. West	11	Hampstead Heathens
Northern:		
Division 1	11	Old Camdenians
Division 2	9	Old Edmontonians 3rd
Division 3	10	UCL Academicals 4th
Division 4	11	Old Ignatians 4th
Division 5	9	Ravenscroft Old Boys Res
Division 6	10	Leyton County Old Boys Res
Division 7	10	Southgate County 5th
Division 8	10	Wood Green Old Boys 5th
Southern:		
Division 1	10	Wandsworth Borough
Division 2	9	Old Guildfordians
Division 3	10	Centymca Res
Division 4	11	Clapham Old Xaverians 3rd
Division 5	11	Old Tiffinians 3rd
Division 6	11	Sinjuns 3rd
Division 7	11	Old Meadonians 8th
Division 8	11	John Fisher Old Boys 5th
Division 9	10	Old Guildfordians 3rd
Division 10	10	FulhamCompton Old Boys 3rd
Western:		
Division 1	10	Old Salvatorins 3rd
Division 2	10	Hampstead Heathens Res
Division 3	10	Old Salvatorians 5th
Division 4	10	Parkfield 5th
Division 5	9	Old Kolsassians
Division 6	10	Ealing Association Res

ARTHUR DUNN CUP
Old Salopians 2 Old Carthusians 1

ARTHURIAN LEAGUE

PREMIER DIVISION	P	W	D	L	F	A	Pts
Old Foresters	18	13	3	2	48	19	42
Old Brentwoods	18	9	2	7	44	36	29
Lancing Old Boys	18	9	2	7	32	35	29
Old Salopians	18	8	4	6	27	28	28
Old Carthusians	18	8	2	8	32	31	26
Old Harrovians	18	8	1	9	54	48	25
Old Westminsters	18	7	3	8	20	22	24
Old Etonians	18	7	3	8	32	43	24
Old Reptonians	18	3	8	7	30	34	17
Old Chigwellians	18	2	4	12	19	42	10

DIVISION 1	P	W	D	L	F	A	Pts
Old Cholmeleians	14	12	1	1	44	18	37
Old Bradfieldian	14	11	2	1	51	12	35
Old Witleians	14	7	3	4	26	23	24
Old Haberdashers	14	6	4	4	28	28	22
Old Aldenhamians	14	4	2	8	24	34	14
Old Malvernians	14	3	2	9	27	45	11
Old Wykehamists	14	2	2	10	19	37	8
Old Wellingburians***	14	2	2	10	22	44	5

DIVISION 2	P	W	D	L	F	A	Pts
Old Chigwellians Res	14	9	3	2	37	20	30
Old Salopians Res	14	7	2	5	38	30	23
Old Cholmeleians Res	14	7	2	5	36	28	23
Old Carthusians Res	14	6	4	4	31	24	22
Old Etonians Res	14	5	3	6	24	29	18
Old Carthusians 3rd	14	4	4	6	24	32	16
Old Etonians 3rd	14	3	4	7	21	28	13
Old Brentwoods Res	14	4	0	10	25	45	12

DIVISION 3	P	W	D	L	F	A	Pts
Lancing Old Boys Res	12	9	1	2	40	17	28
Old Foresters Res	12	8	1	3	27	22	25
Old Haileyburians	12	6	2	4	32	30	20
Old Bradfieldians Res	12	5	3	4	26	18	18
Old Cholmeleians 3rd	12	4	2	6	25	32	14
Old Foresters 3rd	12	3	1	8	25	31	10
Old Aldenhamians Res	12	2	0	10	15	40	6

* -Point deducted - breach of Rule

DIVISION 4 - 7 Teams - Won by:Old Westminsters Res
DIVISION 5 - 6 Teams Won by:Old Bradfieldian 3rd

JUNIOR LEAGUE CUP
Old Chigwellians Res 4 Old Carthusians 3rd 1
DERRIK MOORE VETERANS' CUP
Old Carthusians 6 Old Aldenhamians 1
JIM DIXSON SIX-A-SIDE CUP
Won by Old Bradfieldian

LONDON FINANCIAL FOOTBALL ASSOCIATION

DIVISION ONE	P	W	D	L	F	A	Pts
Dresdner Kleinwort Wasserstein	16	13	2	1	54	21	41
Mount Pleasant Post Office	16	11	2	3	47	19	35
Zurich Eagle Star*	16	7	4	5	43	25	24
Granby Sports Club	16	5	5	6	27	25	20
Bank of America	16	5	5	6	31	38	20
National Westminster Bank	16	4	6	6	27	40	18
Royal Sun Alliance	16	4	5	7	31	44	17
Churchill Insurance	16	3	3	10	21	43	12
J P Morgan	16	3	2	11	24	50	11

Coutts & Co. Record expunged - insufficient games

DIVISION TWO	P	W	D	L	F	A	Pts
Marsh	16	11	2	3	55	27	35
Royal Sun Alliance Res	16	9	3	4	53	30	30
Citigroup	16	7	5	4	42	24	26
Citigroup Res	16	7	3	6	36	37	24
Granby Sports Club Res	16	6	4	6	34	33	22
NatWest Bank Res	16	7	1	8	28	45	22
Marsh Res	16	6	2	8	36	38	20
Citigroup CIB	16	4	1	11	21	55	13
Royal Bank of Scotland	16	3	3	10	31	47	12

DIVISION THREE	P	W	D	L	F	A	Pts
Marsh 3rd	16	11	3	2	58	30	36
Coutts & Co. Res	16	10	0	6	40	31	30
Royal Sun Alliance 3rd	16	7	6	3	49	25	27
National Westminster Bank 3rd	16	8	3	5	41	34	27
Credit Suisse First Boston	16	8	3	5	36	34	27
National Westminster Bank 4th	16	6	4	6	34	25	22
Granby 3rd	16	4	3	9	28	40	15
Temple Bar	16	3	3	10	27	46	12
Foreign & Commonwealth Office*	16	2	1	13	20	68	6

DIVISION FOUR	P	W	D	L	F	A	Pts
NatWest Bank 5th	14	10	2	2	55	29	32
Zurich Eagle Star Res	14	10	0	4	59	22	30
Marsh 4th	14	9	3	2	48	19	30
Granby 4th	14	6	3	5	36	34	21
South Bank Cuaco 6th	14	5	3	6	31	43	18
Bank of Ireland*	14	4	1	9	20	53	12
Royal Bank of Scotland Res	14	3	2	9	23	38	11
Temple Bar Res	14	1	2	11	22	56	5

G E FC Record expunged - insufficient games
* -Point deducted - breachof Rule

CHALLENGE CUP
Zurich Eagle Star 3*:7p Weirside Rangers 3*:6p
SENIOR CUP
Coutts & Co. 5 Bank of America 0
JUNIOR CUP
Natwest Bank 5th 2 Natwest Bank 4th 1

LONDON LEGAL LEAGUE

DIVISION I	P	W	D	L	F	A	
Pts Slaughter & May			18	11	4	3	44
30	37	KPMG ICE		18	9	4	5
45	27	31	Denton Wilde Sapte (A)18				
8	6	4	38	34	30		
Gray's Inn	18	8	5	5	37	32	29
Linklaters & Alliance	18	7	4	7	40	39	25
Watson Farley & Williams	18	7	3	8	28	31	24
Clifford Chance	18	7	3	8	35	39	24
Eversheds	18	5	6	7	28	34	21
CMS Cameron McKenna	18	6	1	11	26	30	19
Lovells	18	2	4	12	21	46	10

DIVISION II	P	W	D	L	F	A	Pts
Baker & McKenzie	18	12	2	4	58	37	38
Simmons & Simmons	18	10	6	2	39	27	36
Freshfields Bruckhaus Deringer	18	7	6	5	39	32	27
Titmuss Sainer Dechert	18	6	8	4	39	33	26
Norton Rose	18	7	3	8	41	42	24
Allen & Overy	18	7	1	10	39	43	22
Barlow Lyde & Gilbert	18	6	3	9	35	53	21
Nicholson Graham & Jones	18	5	4	9	41	42	19
Richards Butler	18	5	4	9	38	47	19
Herbert Smith	18	5	3	10	31	44	18

DIVISION III	P	W	D	L	F	A	Pts
Macfarlanes	18	13	3	2	63	26	42
Ashurst Morris Crisp	18	12	4	2	52	23	40
Financial Services A	18	12	3	3	44	29	39
Denton Wilde Sapte (B)	18	12	2	4	32	18	24
Stephenson Harwood	18	8	2	8	44	35	26
Pegasus (Inner Temple)	18	7	1	10	20	47	22
Mishcon de Reya*	18	5	2	11	34	33	16
Hammonds Suddards Edge	18	5	1	12	30	48	16
S J Berwin & Co	18	3	1	14	28	57	10
Taylor Joynson & Garrett	18	3	1	14	19	50	10

*Point deducted - breach of Rule

LEAGUE CHALLENGE CUP

Gray's Inn 4 Slaughter & May 1

WEAVERS ARMS CUP

Cameron McKenna 2 Simons & Simmons 3

INVITATION CUP

Lovells 2 Baker & McKenzie 3

REPRESENTATIVE MATCHES

v Amateur Football Combination Won 2 - 1

LONDON OLD BOYS CUP

Senior

Old Ignatians	2*	Old Meadonians	4*

Intermediate

Old Camdenians	1*	Old Uxonians	0*

Junior

Old Actonians Assn. 3rd	1	Mill Hill Village 3rd	0

Minor

Old Actonians Assn. 5th	0*:4p	Old Salvatorians 4th	0*:5p

Drummond

Old Chigwellians 4th	3	Old Parmiterians 9th	2

Nemean

Old Danes 4th	4	Phoenix Old Boys 5th	1

Olympian

Old St Mary's 3rd	3	Mickleham O. Boxhillians Res	0

Veterans

Old Vaughanians	0	Old Finchleians	2

* - after extra time :: p - kicks from the penalty mark

OLD BOYS' INVITATION CUPS

Senior

Old Esthameians 4 Old Finchleians 0

Junior

Old Owens Res 2 Old Parkonians Res 1

Minor

Old Finchleians 0* Old Wilsonians 1*

4th XIs

Old Finchleians 4th 1 Old Tenisonian 4th 0

5th XIs

Old Tenisonians 5th 2 Alleyn Old Boys 5th 1

6th XIs

Old Owens 6th 1 Old Stationers 6th 0

7th XIs

Old Tenisonians 7th 3 Old Finchleians 7th 2

Veterans'

E. Barnet O Grammarians 5 Old Lyonians 2

MIDLAND AMATEUR ALLIANCE

Premier Division	P	W	D	L	F	A	Pts
Caribbean Cavaliers	22	18	3	1	107	32	57
Bracken Park	22	16	1	5	75	35	49
Ashland Rovers	22	15	3	4	67	34	48
Wollaton 3rd	22	13	3	6	57	41	42
Nottingham Trent University	22	12	3	7	67	62	39
Magdala Amateurs Res	22	10	3	9	77	73	33
Squareform Stealers	22	9	2	11	64	63	29
Nottinghamshire	22	7	4	11	42	41	25
Lady Bay	22	7	2	13	52	77	23
Old Elizabethans	22	6	2	14	76	76	20
Bassingfield	22	3	2	17	34	83	11
Woodborough United	22	1	2	19	27	128	5

Division 1	P	W	D	L	F	A	Pts
Derbyshire Amateurs Res	24	20	1	3	86	31	61
Kirkby Autocentre	24	18	4	2	88	25	58
(fmly FLL Aerospace)							
Old Bemrosians	24	16	2	6	63	36	50
Sherwood Forest	24	13	2	9	63	47	41
Nottinghamshire Res	24	13	1	10	54	47	40
Beeston Old Boys Assn	24	11	6	7	57	35	39
County NALGO	24	11	4	9	78	65	37
Racing Athletic	24	10	6	8	48	49	36
Wollaton 4th	24	6	3	15	44	88	21
Southwell Arms	24	3	7	14	40	73	16
ASC Dayncourt Res	24	4	3	17	41	76	15
Bassingfield Res	24	3	6	15	33	69	15
Clinphone	24	4	3	17	28	82	15

Division 2	P	W	D	L	F	A	Pts
Brunts Old Boys	28	20	3	5	99	41	63
Old Elizabethans Res	28	19	5	4	113	47	62
Kirkby Autocentre Res	28	18	3	7	81	46	57
Nottinghamshire 3rd	28	15	6	7	73	53	51
West Bridgford United	28	14	5	9	85	53	47
Caribbean Cavaliers Res	28	14	5	9	77	51	47
Keyworth United Res	28	14	4	10	58	43	46
Wollaton 5th	28	13	2	13	64	68	41
Jigsaw	28	11	7	10	98	65	40
Magdala Arms 3rd	28	11	5	12	90	113	38
Beeston O B Association Res	28	11	3	14	47	69	36
Dynamo	28	5	9	14	39	60	24
Old Bemrosians Res	28	4	8	16	51	89	20
Derbyshire Amateurs 3rd	28	4	1	23	37	125	13
Tibshelf Old Boys	28	3	2	23	42	131	11

LEAGUE SENIOR CUP

Nottinghamshire 3 Caribbean Cavaliers 2

LEAGUE INTERMEDIATE CUP

Derbyshire Amateurs Res 5 Beeston OB Ass'n 1

LEAGUE MINOR CUP

Old Elizabethans Res 1 Caribbean Cavaliers 0

SOUTHERN AMATEUR LEAGUE

SENIOR SECTION DIV 1	P	W	D	L	F	A	Pts
Old Salesians	22	14	6	2	45	15	48
Old Esthameians	22	10	7	5	38	22	37
Norsemen	22	8	7	7	36	26	31
Old Owens	22	9	4	9	35	34	31
Alleyn Old Boys***	22	9	5	8	28	32	29
Broomfield	22	8	5	9	26	42	29
Polytechnic	22	7	7	8	33	35	28
Old Actonians Association	22	8	4	10	25	31	28
HSBC	22	7	6	9	26	27	27
Civil Service	22	5	10	7	27	31	25
East Barnet Old Grammarians	22	6	5	11	29	34	23
BB Eagles (fmly BarclaysBank)	22	6	4	12	22	41	22

3 Points deducted - breach of Rule

DIVISION 2	P	W	D	L	F	A	Pts
Winchmore Hill	22	17	2	3	56	18	53
West Wickham	22	16	4	2	45	14	52
Nottsborough	22	12	8	2	56	22	44
Old Finchleians	22	9	7	6	46	37	34
Old Parkonians	22	10	1	11	25	39	31
South Bank Cuaco (Merged)	22	8	5	9	41	43	29
Old Stationers	22	7	5	10	34	40	26
Old Lyonians	22	7	3	12	45	44	24
Carshalton	22	7	3	12	36	47	24
Weirside Rangers (fmly Lensbury)	22	5	7	10	36	41	22
Lloyds TSB Bank	22	4	5	13	27	54	17
Crouch End Vampires	22	3	4	15	30	78	13

DIVISION 3	P	W	D	L	F	A	Pts
Bank of England	22	14	2	2	50	12	44
Old Parmiterians	22	12	3	3	60	22	39
Old Westminster Citizens	22	10	2	6	41	34	32
Kew Association	22	9	4	5	50	35	31
Alexandra Park	22	8	5	5	46	30	29
Old Latymerians	22	7	2	9	39	40	23
Merton	22	7	2	9	36	41	23
Ibis	22	4	2	12	22	47	14
Southgate Olympic	22	4	1	13	31	60	13
Brentham	22	3	1	14	23	77	10

Reserve Team Section:	Teams:	Won by:
Division 1	12	Polytechnic Res
Division 2	12	Nottsborough Res
Division 3	10	Ibis Res
Third Team Section:		
Division 1	12	Old Actonians Association 3rd
Division 2	12	Nottsborough 3rd
Division 3	10	Old Westminster Citizens 3rd
Fourth Team Section:		
Division 1	12	Old Actonians Association 4th
Division 2	10	Old Owens 4th
Division 3	10	South Bank Cuaco 4th
Fifth Team Section:		
Division 1	10	Winchmore Hill 5th
Division 2	10	Old Esthameians 5th
Division 3	8	Broomfield 5th
Sixth Team Section:		
Division 1	11	Kew Association 6th
Division 2	10	East Barnet Old Grammarians 6th
Minor Section:		
Division 1	10	Old Parmiterians 7th
Division 2	10	Old Finchleians 8th
Division 3	10	Old Finchleians 9th

Challenge Cups:

JuniorWinchmore Hill 3rd	2	Ibis 3rd	1
MinorCarshalton 4th	4	Winchmore Hill 4th	1
Senior NovetsNorsemen 5th	1	Winchmore Hill 5th	0
Intermediate NovetsCarshalton 6th	2	Norsemen 6th	1
Junior NovetsOld Finchleians 9th	5	Norsemen 7th	3

LONDON UNIVERSITY REPRESENTATIVE XI

v Royal Navy XI	Drawn	1 - 1
v Oxford University	Drawn	0 - 0
v Amateur Football Combination	Won	4 - 3
v Oxford University	Lost	0 - 3
v Amateur Football Alliance	Lost	0 - 1
v Deloitte Touche	Won	6 - 0
v United Hospitals	Lost	0 - 1
v Arthurian League	Lost	0 - 3
v Southern Amateur League	Lost	1 - 4
v Portobello College Dublin	Drawn	0 - 0
v University of Oslo	Drawn	0 - 0
v ASE Bucharest	Drawn	0 - 0

UNIVERSITY OF LONDON UNION
MEN'S COMPETITIONS
(Limited to one game against each member)

Premier Division One	P	W	D	L	F	A	Pts
King's College	12	10	2	0	41	7	32
Royal Holloway College	12	10	1	1	24	9	31
University College	12	10	0	2	35	9	30
Imperial College	12	8	2	2	41	13	26
London School of Economics	12	4	4	4	28	22	16
Imperial Coll. School of Medicine	12	5	1	6	20	26	16
R Free, UC & Middx Hospitals M S	12	5	1	6	25	22	16
Sch. Oriental & African Studies	12	3	4	5	26	36	13
Guy's, King's & St. Thomas's M S	12	3	3	6	11	19	12
Queen Mary Westfield College	12	4	0	8	21	31	12
St Barts & R. London Hospitals M C	12	2	2	8	13	29	8
St George's Hospital M S	11	2	1	8	7	29	7
Goldsmiths' College	11	0	1	10	7	47	1

Premier Division Two	P	W	D	L	F	A	Pts
Imperial College Res	11	9	1	1	38	4	28
London School of Eco. Res	11	9	0	2	40	13	27
University College Res	11	8	0	3	30	14	24
University College 3rd	11	6	1	4	30	26	19
Birkbeck College Students	11	5	2	4	34	31	17
Q. Mary Westfeld College Res	11	5	1	5	21	16	16
St George's Hospital M S Res	11	5	1	5	14	23	16
King's College 3rd	11	4	2	5	19	28	14
King' College Res	11	4	0	7	17	32	12
Imperial College Sch Med Res	11	3	1	7	25	40	10
Imperial College 3rd	11	3	0	8	16	27	9
St Barts & R. London Hosps M C Res	11	0	1	10	12	42	1

(Played as conventional Leagues)

Division 1	P	W	D	L	F	A	Pts
London School of Eco. 3rd	22	19	2	1	72	28	59
Royal Holloway College Res	21	15	2	4	73	29	47
University College 4th	22	13	2	7	61	38	41
Royal Holloway College 3rd	22	12	5	5	48	25	41
Royal Holloway College 4th	22	11	6	5	34	25	39
London School of Eco. 4th	22	11	2	9	39	35	35
Guy's, King's, St. T M S Res	22	9	2	11	41	49	29
Imperial College 4th	22	7	4	11	32	62	25
R Free, UC & Middx Hosp M S Res	21	7	5	9	31	32	26
Goldsmiths' College Res	20	7	3	10	35	45	24
King's College 4th	22	1	1	20	15	69	4
Imperial C Sch Med Res 3rd	22	1	0	21	16	60	3

Division 2	P	W	D	L	F	A	Pts
Guy's, King's, St. T MS 3rd	22	18	1	3	65	28	55
R Free, UC & Middx Hosp M S 3rd	22	16	4	2	81	17	52
Imperial College (R. School of Mines)	22	16	1	5	69	30	49
Royal Holloway College 5th	19	10	2	7	44	37	32
Imperial College Sch Med 4th	21	10	1	10	34	50	31
London School of Eco. 5th	16	8	2	6	31	18	26
R Free, UC & Middx Hosp M S 4th	15	6	1	8	19	35	19
St Barts & R. L. Hosps M C 3rd	20	6	0	14	27	54	18
Guy's, King's, St. T. M S 4th	22	6	0	16	35	84	18
Q. Mary Westfield College 3rd	15	4	0	11	28	48	12
Wye College	17	4	2	11	13	23	14
Goldsmiths' College 3rd	15	2	0	13	13	35	6

Division 3	P	W	D	L	F	A	Pts
Royal Veterinary College	20	17	2	1	71	24	53
Imperial College 6th	22	13	6	3	72	52	45
University College 6th	21	12	4	5	66	27	40
Imperial College 5th	22	11	1	10	60	51	34
University College 7th	21	10	3	8	58	47	33
R College of Science (I C)	22	9	3	10	48	49	30
Q. Mary Westfield College 4th	21	7	3	11	44	51	24
King's College 6th	20	7	2	11	44	57	23
Q. Mary Westfield College 5th	20	7	1	12	32	54	22
University College 5th	19	6	2	11	47	50	20
King's College 5th	19	5	3	11	26	60	18
London School of Eco. 6th	21	5	0	16	30	76	15

Division 4	P	W	D	L	F	A	Pts
London School of Eco. 7th	16	10	1	5	39	28	31
King's College 7th	15	10	1	4	45	36	31
Sch. of Oriental & African Studies Res	14	9	3	2	68	21	30
Royal Veterinary College Res	16	6	5	5	35	35	23
Guy's, King's, St. T. M S 5th	16	5	4	7	31	46	19
School of Pharmacy	14	7	1	6	30	14	22
Imperial College 7th	15	5	3	7	29	36	18
St George's Hospital M S 3rd	16	5	2	9	31	44	17
R. School of Mines Res	16	2	0	14	19	67	6

* - Point deducted - breach of rule

Challenge Cup
University College 4 R Free, UC & Mx Hosps MS 1
Reserves' Challenge Cup
Imperial College Res 0*:0 Imperial College 3rd 0*:1
Reserves' Plate
R Holloway 4th 2*:5p R Free UC & Mx HMS 4th 2*:2p
VaseKing's College 5th 1*:2 Lon Sch Economis 5th 1*:1

WOMEN'S LEAGUES

Premier Division	P	W	D	L	F	A	Pts
Guy's, King's & St. T. M S	10	9	1	0	81	8	28
Queen Mary Westfield College	10	8	1	1	69	11	25
University College	9	4	0	5	35	35	12
London School of Economics	10	4	0	6	29	40	12
Imperial College	9	2	0	7	10	58	6
School of Oriental & African Studies	8	0	0	8	5	77	0

Division 1	P	W	D	L	F	A	Pts
Royal Holloway College	10	8	1	1	64	15	25
King's College	10	6	3	1	41	9	21
R Free, UC & Middx Hosp M S	10	3	1	6	8	19	10
Royal Veterinary College	9	2	3	4	10	17	9
Goldsmiths' College	9	3	0	6	2	65	9
St George's Hospital M S	10	2	2	6	19	19	8

Division 2	P	W	D	L	F	A	Pts
Guy's, King's, St. T. MS Res	8	7	0	1	30	7	21
R Free, UC & Middx Hosp M S Res	8	5	0	3	18	15	15
University College Res	8	5	0	3	17	17	15
Wye College	8	3	0	5	10	26	9
Royal Holloway College Res	8	0	0	8	8	18	0

U-16 GIRLS CENTRE OF EXCELLENCE LEAGUE

Pts	P	W	D	L	F	A	
Arsenal	20	20	0	0	106	11	60
Southampton	20	15	2	3	117	23	47
Fulham	20	11	5	4	41	20	38
Reading	20	10	4	6	43	30	34
Charlton Athletic	19	9	3	7	38	30	30
Leyton Orient	20	9	3	8	34	47	30
Chelsea	20	6	3	11	21	43	21
Colchester United	19	6	2	11	30	43	20
Wimbledon	20	4	2	14	15	52	14
Brighton & Hove Albion	20	3	1	16	28	129	10
Millwall	20	2	3	15	15	61	9

HUMAN
KINETICS

HUMAN
KINETICS

SERVICES FOOTBALL

THE KENTISH CUP

	UK Armed Forces v Netherlands AF	UK AF v Belgian AF	Belgium v Netherlands	Wiinners
1987	1-0	0-0	3-2	Belgian
1988	2-2	2-0	1-3	Netherlands
1989	1-0	4-1	1-1	UK
1990	4-2	1-1	4-0	Belgian
1991	1-3	0-1	3-1	Belgian
1992	2-2	0-0	2-1	Belgian
1993	1-3	1-1	2-1	Belgian
1994	0-2	4-2	2-1	Netherlands
1995	2-5	2-0	1-1	Netherlands
1996	1-1	1-2	0-4	UK
1997	0-3	3-3	1-1	Netherlands
1998	4-0	4-1	0-3	UK
1999	0-0	0-3	2-0	Belgian
2000	1-1	1-1	3-2	Netherlands
2001	1-2	0-0	1-5	Netherlands
2002	1-1	2-1	0-2	Netherlands
2003	2-2	3-0	1-3	UK

INTER SERVICES CUP

The men's Army team won the Inter Services Cup outright for the first time since 1993, when they defeated the RAF 4-2 in the final game of the competition. With the RAF winning against the Navy the week before, the Army, having only drawn with the Navy, had to make sure of the win to secure the championship. Last year's winners, The Navy, had to settle for the 'wooden spoon'.

The Women's team made it a double success for the Army in the Inter Services Championship, when they defeated the Navy 1-0. Having previously defeated the RAF 3-0, the title once again came down to the last game, with the Navy also looking for a one hundred percent record.

CHAMPIONSHIP DECIDING GAMES

INTER SERVICE (MEN)

Army 4 v 2 RAF

Inter Service Champions 2002/03: Army

INTER SERVICE (WOMEN)

Royal Navy 0 v 1 Army

Inter Sevice Champions 2002/03: Army

CHANNEL ISLANDS FOOTBALL

Guernsey Football Season 2002-2003

by Matt Fallaize of The Guernsey Press

Vale Rec won the Priaulx League for the first time in a decade. Ray Blondel the island's most successful club manager of all time, returned to the Corbet Field hot seat to maintain his amazing record of never having failed to win the championship during each of his five seasons in charge in three different spells.

In winning the title, Vale stopped Sylvans landing a record breaking 10th successive championship. Sylvans were forced to settle for second place having, the season before last, equalled St Martin's record of nine successive title wins.

Vale started slowly, drawing three of their first four league games and winning just one of their opening six matches in all competitions. But they lost just twice in the league all season and put together a superb post-christmas run of seven wins out of nine, during which they conceded only three goals, to wrap up their fifteenth championship since 1973.

The real turning point in the title race was Vale's surprise 1-0 victory over stuttering Sylvans at the end of February. Sylvans were at full strength and Vale were missing no less than seven regulars, but a heroic defensive display and a break away goal by reserve defender Tony Manning set Vale on their way to victory in that match and the title . Northerners finished third again having thrown away a glorious chance to win the championship for the first time since 1992. North had led the table for much of the season, but a series of four consecutive home draws at the tail end of the season ultimately cost them.

In the main knock out competitions, Sylvans beat Vale Rec on penalties in the final of the Stranger Cup, and Jersey Scottish, also on penalties, to win the Wheway Cup. In the Jeremie Cup, Trinity won an all Jersey final and in the Under 18 F.A.County Youth Cup, the Guernsey team reached a creditable last eight.

Guernsey's senior Island team endured another disappointing campaign in the South West Counties Championship, drawing one and losing three of their matches. However the season ended on a high note when Guernsey beat the Isle of Man to retain the Island Games gold medal.

On a political note, Dave Dorey, the very well respected Guernsey chief executive suddenly resigned at the end of the season.Mr Dorey had lifted Guernsey football into the modern era during ten successful years at the G.F.A.. The association now faces a massive challenge to continue progression without their inspiration at the helm.

League Winners:
Priaulx: Vale Recreation
Jackson League: Northerners
Railway League: St Martins
Youth Division One: Northerners
Youth Division Two: Rangers.

CUP FINALS

MURATTI				
	Guernsey	3 - 3	Jersey (aet)
Replay				
	Jersey	1 - 0	Guernsey
UNDER 21 MURATTI				
	Jersey	4 - 1	Guernsey
UNDER 18 MURATTI				
	Jersey	1 - 0	Guernsey
UNDER 15 STAR TROPHY				
	Guernsey	0 - 1	Jersey (aet)
LADIES MURATTI				
	Guernsey	2 - 3	Jersey
UPTON PARK				
	Trinity	1 - 0	Vale Rec.
JUNIOR UNDER 18 UPTON PARK				
	Guernsey Northerners	1 - 3	First Tower

PRIAULX LEAGUE

		P	W	D	L	F	A	Pts
1	Vale Recreation	18	11	5	2	45	16	38
2	Sylvans	18	12	1	5	56	22	37
3	North	18	9	7	2	30	14	34
4	St Martin	18	8	4	6	33	23	28
5	Belgraves	18	5	6	7	21	33	21
6	Rovers	18	3	3	12	13	51	12
7	Rangers	18	0	4	14	9	48	4

JERSEY
FLYBE FOOTBALL COMBINATION
DIVISION ONE

		P	W	D	L	F	A	Pts
1	Trinity	18	13	5	0	45	13	44
2	Jersey Scottish	18	12	4	2	59	18	40
3	St. Pauls	18	7	4	7	29	32	25
4	St. Peters	18	7	3	8	30	28	24
5	First Tower United	18	8	0	10	36	40	24
6	Magpies	18	6	5	7	22	30	23
7	Portuguese Club	18	6	4	8	35	49	22
8	Jersey Wanderers	18	5	5	8	33	41	20
9	Grouville	18	5	3	10	26	35	18
10	St. Clement	18	3	3	12	19	48	12

DIVISION TWO

		P	W	D	L	F	A	Pts
1	Sporting Accies	16	13	1	2	59	22	40
2	Rozel Rovers*	16	11	0	5	46	21	33
3	St. John	16	10	3	3	43	18	33
4	St. Martin	16	9	0	7	49	50	27
5	St. Ouen	16	8	2	6	34	26	26
6	St. Brelade	16	6	2	8	46	41	20
7	Beeches	16	6	1	9	35	46	19
8	St. Lawrence	16	2	1	13	14	62	7
9	S.C.F.	16	1	2	13	8	48	5

*Gained promotion via 3-1 play-off win over St. John.

THE ISLAND GAMES FOOTBALL TOURNEMENT

GROUP A

	P	W	D	L	F	A	Pts
1 Isle of Man	2	2	0	0	6	1	6
2 Ynys Mon	2	1	0	1	3	2	3
3 Saaremaa	2	0	0	2	0	6	0

Results:
Saaremaa 0 Ynys Mon 2
Isle of Man 4 Saaremaa 0
Ynys Mon 1 Isle of Man 2.

GROUP B

	P	W	D	L	F	A	Pts
1 Jersey	3	2	1	0	10	1	7
2 Shetland Islands	3	1	1	1	3	6	4
3 Gotland	3	0	3	0	2	2	3
4 Froya	3	0	1	2	4	10	1

Results:
Froya 1 Jersey 5
Shetland Islands 0 Gotland 0
Gotland 2 Froya 2
Jersey 5 Shetland Islands 0
Shetland Islands 3 Froya 1
Jersey 0 Gotland 0.

GROUP C

	P	W	D	L	F	A	Pts
1 Guernsey	2	2	0	0	17	1	6
2 Orkney	2	1	0	1	3	11	3
3 Alderney	2	0	0	2	2	10	0

Results:
Guernsey 7 Alderney 1
Guersney 10 Orkney 0
Orkney 3 Alderney 1

GROUP D

	P	W	D	L	F	A	Pts
1 Isle of Wight	3	2	0	1	23	3	6
2 Gibraltar	3	2	0	1	22	2	6
3 Greenland	3	2	0	1	18	3	6
4 Sark	3	0	0	3	0	55	0

Results:
Gilbraltar 19 Sark 0
Isle of Wight 1 Greenland 2
Isle of Wight 20 Sark 0
Gibraltar 2 Greenland 0
Isle of Wight 2 Gibraltar 1
Greenland 16 Sark 0

9th - 12th Play off
Alderney 0 - 3 Greenland
Saaremaa 0 - 3 Gotland

5th - 8th Play off
Ynys Mon 2 - 1 Shetland Islands
Orkney 1 - 7 Gibraltar

Semi Finals
Guernsey 3 - 1 Isle of Wight
Isle of Man 2 - 1 Jersey

13th/14th Play off
Froya 15 - 0 Sark

11th/12th Play off
Saaremaa 0 - 1 Alderney

9th/10th Play off
Gotland 2 - 1 Greenland

7th/8th Play off
Orkney 0 - 6 Shetlands Islands

5th/6th Play off
Gibraltar 0 - 2 Ynys Mon

Bronze Medal Play off
Jersey 3 - 0 Isle of Wight

THE FINAL

Isle of Man 0 - 3 Guernsey
Warren 11, 20, 83 (pen)

THE TEAMS

Isle of Man			Guernsey
Christopher Bass			Jody Bisson
Mark Blair	SO83		Steven Brehauf
Lee Dixon	S83		Chris Chamberlain
Anthony Halsall		S22	Neil Clegg
Paul Jones			Jonathan Eley
Peter Langridge			John Nobes
John Myers		S83	Paul Nobes
Andrew Perry	S28		Stuart Polson
Martin Reilly		S83	Anthony Vance
Nigel Shimmin			Matthew Warren
Robert Sorby	S61		Michael Wilson

SUBS

Robin Bates		S22	Daniel Bisson
Robert Cottier			Kevin Gilligan
Alan Cowley	S83	S83	Matthew Le Cras
Johnny Cowley	S61	S83	Gavin Le Page
Chris Fenney			Darren Martin
Mark Gorman			Nathan Patimore
Julian Ringham	S28		Ian Potter

SO - Sent off. S - Substituted

BRITISH UNIVERSITIES SPORTS ASSOCIATION

THE 22ND WORLD UNIVERSITY GAMES
DAEGU, SOUTH KOREA AUGUST 21ST – 31ST 2003

As we put this year's Directory 'to bed' the British Universities Football team are taking part in the 22nd World University games in South Korea. The squad taking part in the compeitition included four players from the 2001 squad that were beaten in the quarter finals in Beijing, Andy Murfin, Phil Denney, Kevin Langan and Ellis Wilmot. Joining these players are a host of some of the best young talent from the Nationwide Conference and its feeder leagues, as well as the professional leagues in the USA.

Northwich Victoria's Richard Norris, capped last season for the England National Game Team, will earn his first cap at GB level following an outstanding season in the Conference which culminated in also being capped for the England National Game Futsal Team.

Having won FA Trophy winners medals with Burscough last season, highly rated centre half Joe Taylor, now at Tamworth, and striker Kris McHale are rewarded for their substantial progress at non-league level by being named in Dell's high profile squad.

Danny Jackson who graduated from the University of North Carolina at Chapel Hill last year and became the first English player to be signed in the MLS Draft in the United States is also included.

Commenting on his final selection Dell said:

"Anyone who knows the semi-professional game will recognise that this is an extremely talented but young squad with great potential. I am excited by what it offers me in terms of flexibility in playing styles and adaptability, all of which are essential in international football where the opposition remain somewhat unknown. All of these players are not only proper athletes, which was a major factor in my selection process for the final group, but they are also hungry for this chance to improve themselves and move into the professional game. Many of these lads have been involved in our programme for two years or more and their improvement over that time justifies our investment whilst sending a clear message of what the BUSA programme offers back to the National Game.

"We are at the end of a four-year development cycle and the technical ability of this final group demonstrates the efforts that we have put in to assembling and improving a squad that can compete at Olympic level. The fact that we have been able to identify the overseas-based players and include them in this squad is testament to our thoroughness and a major step in ensuring that our talent identification covers all of the British players available to us. It is rewarding to know that all of these players have decided that this international opportunity will benefit their football development in the long run."

"It's appropriate at this time to place on record our gratitude on behalf of the players, to the clubs who have agreed to release them without conflict, having recognised what an opportunity this represents and how the club will also benefit after they return.

"The focus now for this very fortunate group is on the task of 'achieving' in Korea against what will be some very tough opposition. That won't only be limited to the other teams but also the climate and the general environment of a Games Village and the excitement that goes with such a massive tournament. I have a very tight schedule in which to work with the group and in which to prepare them technically but, they are all bright and willing to learn which will make the education part of my job that bit easier."

The Great Britain team were seeded fifth for the draw which matched them up with the Ukraine (2001 runners up), Mexico and Morocco. The full draw was as follows:

POOL A

KOREA
ITALY
IRELAND
THAILAND

POOL B

JAPAN
CZECH REPUBLIC
SOUTH AFRICA
ALGERIA

POOL C

UKRAINE
GREAT BRITAIN
MEXICO
MOROCCO

POOL D

CHINA
URUGUAY
IRAN
CANADA

GOALKEEPERS

TIM MULLOCK age 23 d.o.b 04/10/79 Loughborough University

Stoke on Trent

Graduated in 2002 and qualifies as a year downer. A 6'2" goalkeeper who has attracted the attentions of a number of professional clubs recently, having been at Man City as a non-contract player before attending university. Played at Kidsgrove Athletic in the Unibond last season and was also capped at British and England Universities over the past two seasons. Played for England Schoolboys U18 before going to university.

PAUL ROGERS age 25 d.o.b 09/05/78 University of Indianapolis USA

Brighton

A 6'4" goalkeeper who initially moved to the USA on a football scholarship in 1997. Currently signed as professional for Indiana Blast in the 'A' League. Played at QPR as a youngster before taking up his scholarship and will be training with Premiership Fulham before the squad departs for Korea.

DEFENDERS

ANDREW MURFIN age 25 d.o.b. 26/11/77 Roehampton Institute

Doncaster

Graduated from Loughborough in 2001 having been a member of the GBR teams in 1999 and 2001. Former pro at Scunthorpe before entering university where he played for Burton Albion and Kettering. A utility left sided player with exceptional pace. Ran this years London marathon on 3hrs 13mins.

ELLIS WILMOT age 23 d.o.b. 02/11/79 University of Bath

Bristol

A member of the GBR team in 2001 that went to China. Recently transferred from Mangotsfield United to Chippenham Town in the Dr Martens Premier. Also capped at British and England universities level in the past three seasons. Previous clubs include Bristol City, Yeovil & Bath City. A versatile right sided player who is also comfortable in midfield. A strong and athletic player who has demonstrated his ability with better players around him.

MARK SPOONER age 19 d.o.b. 08/08/83 Niagara University USA

Derby

A former Crewe schoolboy who then moved to Northampton as a YTS. Offered a scholarship at Niagara in 2002 after a successful PFA Exit Trial. A left footed defender who is equally comfortable on the right. Selected in last seasons US regional Conference & State all-star teams. He has shown massive improvement in the last 12 months since being at Niagara.

JOE TAYLOR age 23 d.o.b 06/04/80 Nottingham University

Parbold, Wigan

A remarkable success for his first season in men's football having won an FA Trophy winners medal for Burscough. Highly rated as one of the brightest non-league prospects to shine last season. Just returned from a pre-season tour to Belgium with Yeovil, now being out of contract at Burscough. Capped at England and British Universities level over the past three seasons, his ability having been identified early on. Captained the Development Squad in an international tournament in Libya in 2002. Returning to University upon his return to do a Law conversion.

GREG YOUNG age 19 d.o.b 25/07/83 Berry College USA

Newcastle

Offered a scholarship in the USA at Berry College, following his brother to the same college in 2000. A 6'3" central defender who is comfortable with both feet. Played for Wallsend Boys Club and Cramlington Juniors, following the footsteps of Alan Shearer. Studying PE and will graduate in 2005.

DANNY JACKSON age 23 d.o.b 20/10/79 University of North Carolina

Leeds

The first ever British player to sign for the MLS through the NCAA college Draft having graduated last year from Chapel Hill. A former Leeds United youth team player who was offered a scholarship in the USA. Signed for Colorado Rapids in the draft to playing alongside former Arsenal midfielder Gilles Grimaldi as well as Columbian Carlos Valderama. Moved at the end of last season to Seattle Sounders in the A League where he has been an ever present. A skillful central defender who uses his 6'1" height with great effect.

SIMON GREGORY age 22 d.o.b 17/09/80 University of Wales, Swansea

Fairford, Gloucestershire

Triallled at Swansea City at the end of last season following an impressive run of performances in the Swansea BUSA championship winning side and will trial again following his return from Korea. Just finished an BSc in Economics.

RICHARD FOLLETT age 23 d.o.b 29/08/79 Coventry University

Leamington Spa

A regular in Tamworth's first team last season earning promotion to the Conference and a runners up medal in last seasons FA Trophy final. Tamworth players' player of the year 2002/2003. A former professional at Notts Forest under Frank Clark and then Dave Bassett. Studying to be a physiotherapist. Selected for the England National Game Futsal Team this season but withdrew for a minor cartilage operation to prepare for these Games. Has made a full recovery.

KEVIN LANGAN age 25 d.o.b.07/04/78 University of Bath

Jersey

Currently under contract at Forest Green in the Football Conference where he has just completed his second full season having been a regular first teamer. Capped for GBR in 2001 for the Beijing Games, which he describes as one of the highlights of his career to date. Played a handful of games for Bristol City in the first division as a professional and also capped at British and England universities level. An exceptionally bright player with a thorough understanding of the game at all levels.

MIDFIELD

RICHARD NORRIS age 25 d.o.b. 05/01/78 University of Salford

Wirral

Just signed a renewal of his contract at Northwich Victoria, having been capped for the England National Game X1 this year and the England National Game Futsal team at the KL World 5s. Former professional at Crewe under Dario Gradi, Crewe having paid Marine a record fee for him at that time. A versatile midfielder who shows tremendous potential to play much higher. Qualified as a physiotherapist this year.

TOM RUTTER **age** **d.o.b** **GEORGIA SOUTHERN USA**
Gloucester
Capped for GBR in the 2001 Beijing Games after being selected onto the original Development Programme in 1999. Returned to the US A to graduate from Coastal Carolina's football programme under the tutelage of Shaun Docking and is now doing a masters at Georgia. A dynamic midfield player who was at Swindon until he was 18. Played for FC Fram in Iceland last year for a short period.

MAX ROOKE **age** **d.o.b** **MERCER COLLEGE USA**
Swindon
Former youth team captain at Reading, graduated as a teacher last year from Mercer and qualifies as a year downer. Came back to England at the start of last season and played for Basingstoke in the Ryman Premier. Returned to sign with West Palm Beach Pumas in the Professional Development League (PDL). A versatile player with two good feet who can play anywhere in midfield.

FORWARDS

ALEX EWIN **age 22** **d.o.b 09/05/81** **University of Nottingham**
Aldershot
Just finished his first full season under Ernie Howe at Basingstoke in the Ryman Premier having scored 8 goals from the right hand side of midfield. Capped at England Students in 2001 and 2002, graduated in 2002 with a 2:1 in Management Studies. Previous clubs include Reading and Aldershot.

LEE PAUL **age 24** **d.o.b 18/09/78** **JUDSON COLLEGE, USA**
Portsmouth
Currently playing professional in the USA at Charlotte Eagles in the A League. Former YTS at Portsmouth from where he went to the US on scholarship and has played for Chicago Shockers and Chicago Fire in the PDL. A proven goalscorer at the higher level despite only limited appearances this season. Named in the NCAA Collegiate All-Star team in 2002 having reached the National finals with Judson in that same year.

NEIL BLACK **age 21** **d.o.b 14/012/81** **Edge Hill College**
Liverpool
Just about to start his fourth season at Marine, a sharp and lively forward despite spending most of last season in midfield. Graduated this year after studying Sports Studies. Capped for England and British Universities last season having demonstrated his ability to score goals at a higher level. Former schoolboy at Tranmere.

PHIL DENNEY **age 23** **d.o.b 14/12/79** **Crewe & Alsager**
Bury
Currently at Ashton United in the Unibond Premier where he ended the season as one the clubs leading scorers. A much improved 6'3" striker since being part of the GBR team in 2001, who started his career at Bury FC and transferred from Bradford Park Avenue to Ashton in 2001. Capped for the England National Game Futsal Team this season in the KL World 5s.

MICHAEL LENNON **age 21** **d.o.b. 25/07/81** **Crewe & Alsager**
Spennymoor
Leading goalscorer for Newcastle Town in the North West Counties until he broke his fibula in December 2002, scoring 20 goals in 25 appearances until the injury. Having been put under a full rehab programme with the BOA's physiotherapists he has made a full recovery and has come back stronger and ready to start what will hopefully be a full season. Capped at England universities over the past two seasons. Graduated this year as a PE Teacher.

KRIS McHALE **age 23** **d.o.b. 28/08/79** **Liverpool John Moores**
Liverpool
FA Trophy winner last season with Burscough under Shaun Teale. A 6'2" powerful left footed forward having formerly played at Marine, Leigh RMI and Tranmere. Has a knack of scoring important goals having started 20 games for Burscough despite suffering a hamstring injury at Christmas. Studying molecular biology at LJMU and wants to be a dentist.

PREMIER LEAGUE CONFERENCE

MEN'S NORTH

		P	W	D	L	F	A	Pts
1	Loughborough 1st	10	7	1	2	30	8	22
2	Crewe & Alsager 1st	10	5	3	2	15	6	18
3	Nottingham 1st	10	5	3	2	16	12	18
4	Leeds Metropolitan	10	4	2	4	8	20	14
5	Northumbria 1st	10	2	4	4	7	11	10
6	Newcastle 1st	10	0	1	9	2	21	1

MEN'S SOUTH

		P	W	D	L	F	A	Pts
1	Bath 1st	10	6	3	1	37	12	21
2	Exeter 1st	10	5	2	3	28	16	17
3	Bristol 1st	10	4	2	4	25	21	14
4	Greenwich 1st	10	3	3	4	18	33	12
5	Brunel WL 1st	10	3	1	6	19	21	10
6	Chichester 1st	10	3	1	6	10	34	10

MEN'S 1ST TEAM FOOTBALL CHAMPIONSHIP

QUARTER- FINALS

Bath 1st 4 - 0 Leeds Metropolitan 1st
Edge Hill 1st 2 - 1 Brunel WL 1st
Edinburgh 1st 2 - 2 Northumbria 1st
(Northumbria won 3-2 on pens)
UW Swansea 1st 4 - 2 Oxford 1st (aet)

SEMI-FINALS

UW Swansea 1st 1 - 1 Bath 1st
(Swansea won 4-3 on pens)
Edge Hill 1st 2 - 4 Northumbria 1st

FINAL

UW Swansea 1st 1 - 0 Northumbria 1st

MEN'S 1ST TEAM FOOTBALL PLATE

Coventry 1st 0 - 2 Robert Gordon 1st

MEN'S 1ST TEAM FOOTBALL SHIELD

Brighton 1st 1 - 1 Wolverhampton 1st
(Wolverhampton won 5-4 on pens)

ENGLISH SCHOOLS' FOOTBALL ASSOCIATION

Publicity: Mike Simmonds, 19 The Spinney, Bulcote, Burton Joyce, Nottingham NG14 5GX
Tel: 0115 931 3299 Fax: 0115 931 2758

THE E.S.F.A. UNDER 18 SQUAD

Following two seasons during which tours to the Far East and the United States took place, teh England Schools' Under 18 programme in 2002-03 was restricted solely to matches in teh BRitish Isles in the Centenary Shield. It was also one of the least successful in recent years with only a single victory and three defeats.

A thorough selection process which started at Keele University in August and finished at Lilleshall in early February included matches against an RAF Under-25 side (3-0), Loughborough University (2-1) and Independent Schools (2-0) but once the international season began in earnest, the selected squad could not produce similar success.

After the postponement of their first match, due to a waterlogged pitch, the squad travelled to the Republic of Ireland and although they dominated the first half, found themselves 1-0 down at the break. The Republic went further ahead immediately after the restart and although John Cunliffe pulled a goal back, England could not break down a well drilled team who were eventually to win the Centenary Shield.

It was a similar story in Scotland at Banff when the home side went two ahead before James Riley's header gave England hope of a draw, which did not materialise. The first home match, the re-arranged match against Northern IReland at Conference club Forest Green Rovers, produced a third successive 2-1 defeat, Riley again heading England's only goal.

England's solitary victory came against Wales at Lowestoft Town's ground as part of the annual Under-19 English Schools' Festival at Pakefield. Poor finishing, a feature throughout the season, meant that it was not until the 18st minute of a game dominated by England that midfielder Matthew Stares scored the only goal of the game.

INTERNATIONAL CAPS
Awarded to the ESFA Under 18 Schoolboys Season 2001-02

	A	B	C	D
Chris Barnett (Lincolnshire)	1s	1s	1s	1
John Cunliffe (Lancashire)	1	1	1s	1s
Ben Elkington (Buckinghamshire)	1s	1s	1s	1
Kieran Hall (Lancashire)	1	1	1	1
Dale Johnson (Greater Manchester)	1s	1	1	1
Scott MacDonald (Northumberland)	1	1	1	1s
Joe Manning (Leicestershire)	1	1	1	-
Andrew Neilson (Leicestershire)	1	1	1	1s
Steven Orchard (Devon)	1	1s	1	1
Dean Pilcher (Surrey)	1s	1	-	1
James Riley (West Yorkshire)	1s	1	1	1
Neil Stacey (Warwickshire)	1	1s	1s	1s
Matthew Stares (Humberside)	-	-	1	1
Lee Stevens (Gloucestershire)	1	1c	1	1
Lee Summerscales (Norfolk)	1c	-	1c	1c
Chris Wales (Surrey)	1	1	1s	1s
David Yale (Cleveland)	1	1	1	1

Key: S = Substitute appearance. C = Captain

GAME A v. Republic of Ireland L 1-2
GAME B v. Scotland L 1-2
GAME C v. Northern Ireland L 1-2
GAME D v. Wales W 1-0

The ESFA U18 Squad - Back Row (l-r): Steven Orchard, Lee Stevens, Ben Elkington, Joe Manning, Dale Johnson, James Riley, Neil Stacey. **Middle:** Peter Chisholm, Ian Shead, Keiran Hall, John Cunliffe, Andrew Neilson, Chris Barnett, David Yale, Chris wales, Alan Gallafant, Dr. Arthur Tabor, Vic Bragg. **Front:** Lee Summerscales, John read, Dennis Fulton, Nigel Brown, Scott MacDonald.

THE INTER-ASSOCIATION COMPETITIONS
ENGLISH SCHOOLS' F.A. WIZARDS TROPHY FINAL

1st Leg

Cambridge & District 2 v 2 Plymouth (at the Abbey Stadium)

2nd Leg

Plymouth 3 v 2 Cambridge & District (at Home Park)

Plymouth won 5-4 on aggregate

Two of the most thrilling matches in the history of the E.S.F.A. Inter-Association Trophy saw Plymouth take the national title for the first time, appropriately enough in their centenary year. It is interesting to reflect that in the first year of the competition, back in 1904, Plymouth were excluded because organisers considered it was too far to travel!

Plymouth's narrow victory was certainly achieved the hard way as in the first leg at the Abbey Stadium, Cambridge, they found themselves 2-0 behind after only five minutes, whilst in the second leg they led 2-0 only for the visitors to draw level, before Chris Wright's hat-trick goal won the trophy for the Devon side.

The first leg started in dramatic fashion when Cambridge took the lead from the penalty spot. Plymouth's David Harding fouled Anthony Blandford in the area and Jamie Thurlbourne hammered the penalty past Mike Fowler. Two minutes later Thurlbourne's corner was misjudged by Fowler and sailed into the back of the net. The goalkeeper made amends with a magnificent save from Blandford who then hit the post just before half-time.

Plymouth got back into the game seven minutes after the break when Danny McAdam linked well with Matt Green whose cross was flicked on by Wright for Lee Summerfield to poke the ball in at the far post. Fowler made another excellent save from Sam Reed and this seemed to inspire Plymouth who equalised after 66 minutes. Summerfield's free-kick rebounded off a defender to Danny Brook who volleyed in from the edge of the penalty area but Cambridge almost took a lead into the second leg when Harry O'Connor's header, from a corner, hit the top of the bar in the last minute.

Chris Wright gave Plymouth the lead with a close range header in the 10th minute of the second leg at Home Park and although Fowler was forced to deny O'Connor and Blandford, the home side went two ahead just before half-time, when Wright tucked in a defence splitting pass from Mark Robotham.

It was Cambridge's turn to launch a fight back and Fowler did well to save from Matt Green but had no chance from the resulting corner as Sam Reed drove in to make it 2-1 at half-time. They were level early in the second half when the accomplished Blandford scored a superb individual goal.

The visitors' joy was short-lived as Wright completed his hat-trick with a coolly taken close range shot following good work from Green and Summerfield. Cambridge fought hard to the end but Plymouth held out for an historic victory.

PLYMOUTH: Mike Fowler, David Harding, Lee James, Matthew Green, Ryan Gibbons, Seve Catindig-Stagg, Luke Summerfield, Danny Brook, Chris Wright, Danny McAdam, Mark Robotham, Lewis Seely, Guy Stroud, Shaun Manley, James Donnelon, Craig Errington, John Heveran, Michael Landricombe.

CAMBRIDGE & DISTRICT: Lewis Fordham, Robert Tyler, Sam Reed, Jamie

Back Row l to r: Brian Howard (Manager), James Donnellon, danny McAdam, Seve Catindig-Stagg, Guy Stroud, Lee James, Shaun Manley, Luke Summerfield, danny Brook, Chris Wright. **Front Row:** John Heveran, Matthew Green, Michael Fowler, Lewis Seeley, Craig Errington, Michael Landricombe, Mark Robotham. **Inset:** David Harding (capt), Ryan Gibbons

ROUTES TO THE FINAL

Plymouth			
1st Rnd	v West Cornwall	(A)	3-1
2nd Rnd	v Torbay	(H)	4-0
3rd Rnd	v Exeter	(H)	8-0
4th Rnd	v Mid Wiltshire	(H)	4-0
5th Rnd	v Mid Oxfordshire	(A)	4-0
6th Rnd	v Southampton	(H)	3-2
SF	v Sefton	(H)	2-1

Cambridge & District			
1st Rnd	v West Suffolk	(H)	6-0
2nd Rnd	v West Norfolk	(A)	4-1
3rd Rnd	v Waltham Forest	(H)	5-0
4th Rnd	v Newham	(H)	6-0
5th Rnd	v North Kent	(A)	2-1
6th Rnd	v Wolverhampton	(A)	2-1
SF	v Salford	(H)	4-2

E.S.F.A./F.A. PREMIER LEAGUE UNDER 19 COUNTY CHAMPIONSHIP

FINAL

SHROPSHIRE 0 - 1 SUFFOLK

at Maine Road - Manchester City FC

Suffolk Schools had to wait 50 years for their first national title but only two to repeat the feat when they defeated Shropshire 1-0 to take the UNder 19 County Championship for the second time in three seasons. In one of the last matches to be played at the famous Maine Road ground, Suffolk captain Lee Sim received the Premier League Trophy after himself netting the only goal of the game.

Shropshire started brightly and it needed a fine early save from Paul Cudworth turning a shot from Danny Edwards on to the bar to deny them the lead. Suffolk, whose squad consisted mainly of players from West Suffolk College, gradually gained in confidence and a set piece on the left after 25 minutes paved the way for the winning goal. Substitute Craig Parker's free-kick found Tommy Smith and he set up Sim to fire home a 30 yard shot over Dave Littleford in Shropshire's goal.

The Suffolk Schools' Under 19 squad celebrate their County Championship success at Manchester City's Maine Road stadium.

E.S.F.A. PREMIER LEAGUE UNDER 16 COUNTY CHAMPIONSHIP

FINAL

SUSSEX 3 - 0 SHROPSHIRE

at Leyton Orient FC

Sussex capped an impressive season in which they conceded only one goal in seven games with a comfortable 3-0 win over Shropshire. Dean Cox gave them a first-half lead with Ryan McMillan and Darren Turner adding further goals after the break.

The Sussex Route to the Final

v Kent	Regional League	1-1
v Surrey	Regional League	3-0
v Buckinghamshire	Regional League	1-0
v Inner London	Regional Semi-final	3-0
v Somerset	National Quarter-final	1-0
v Berkshire	National Semi-final	3-0

E.S.F.A. UNDER 16 GIRLS' COUNTY CHAMPIONSHIP

FINAL

CHESHIRE 5 - 2 HAMPSHIRE

at Witton Albion

Hampshire had won this title twice and been runners-up once in the previous five years but, not helped by their late arrival, stood no chance against a rampant Cheshire side who raced into a 4-0 interval lead. A Runcorn sister act set Cheshire on their way when Vicky Jones crossed for identical twin Kelly to volley in after only three minutes, goals from Laura Robins, Kerry Baker and Alison Hindley soon followed to put them firmly in control at the break. With this in mind Cheshire introduced all five permitted substitutes for the second half, and scored only minutes after the restart thanks to Kerry Baker's second of the match. Hampshire managed to save face by scoring two late goals to win the half but from early in the match there was never any doubt about the destination of the trophy.

THE INDIVIDUAL SCHOOLS' COMPETITIONS

E.S.F.A. UNDER 19 SCHOOLS AND COLLEGES CHAMPIONSHIP

FINAL

SHREWSBURY COLLEGE 1 - 1 EAST BERKSHIRE COLLEGE

at Gay Meadow - Shrewsbury Town FC

The Trophy was shared after a game dominated by defences although East Berkshire will have been disappointed not to win, having been the better side before half-time. They looked likely winners when they took the lead midway through the first half but with four minutes left, Shrewsbury produced a dramatic equaliser. Richard Jones released Andrew Snyder and the midfielder showed great composure to round the goalkeeper and find teh net from a tight angle.

Extra time saw East Berkshire again most of the early running and Shrewsbury were indebted to four top class saves from busy goalkeeper Dave Littleford. As the game oped up both Rob Taylor and Ryan Garbett broke through for the home side but were unable to find the finishing touch.

East Berkshire College 'keeper, Liam Shurvill punches clear from Shrewsbury's Ryan Garbett.

E.S.F.A. UNDER 19 INDIVIDUAL SCHOOLS' CHAMPIONSHIP

SEMI-FINALS

HIGHFIELD SCHOOL (Hertfordshire) 5 - 2 HARTBRIDGE HIGH SCHOOL (Gwent)

GROBY COMMUNITY COLLEGE (Leics) 2 - 3 WICKERLSEY SCHOOL (S.Yorkshire)

FINAL

HIGHFIELD SCHOOL 1 - 6 WICKERSLEY SCHOOL

at Leyton Orient FC

E.S.F.A. UNDER 16 SCHOOLSNET CUP

FINAL

STOKE HIGH SCHOOL (Ipswich) 2 - 0 CODSALL SCHOOL (Wolverhampton)

at Highbury

Stoke High School Under 16's capped a wonderful five years in which they lost only two games with this victory in the national Under 16 competition. They have been Suffolk champions for the past three years and won five matches to qualify for the national stages. Another five rounds in the national competition, four of them involving extra time and one penalties took them through to the final where a goal in each half from Lee Smith and Craig Byam brought the title.

The Stoke High School squad celebrate their victory with the English Schools' F.A. Chairman Dennis Fulton.

Abraham Darby School, winners of the E.S.F.A. Under 16 Girls' Cup.
Back (L-R): Samantha Love, Jessica Munt, Leanne Fisher, Kim Kitson, Megan Edwards, Sarah Parton, Stacey Ward, Tara McCaffrey. Front: Zoe Butler, Carly Patterson, Carly Dunn, Katrina Ravai, Clare Payton, Toni Evans, Natasha Cooper.

E.S.F.A. UNDER 16 GIRLS' INDIVIDUAL SCHOOLS' CUP

FINAL

ABRAHAM DARBY SCHOOL (Telford, Shropshire) 6 - 0 LITTLE HEATH SCHOOL (Reading, Berkshire)
at Telford United FC

Abraham Darby School became the third winners of this competition from Shropshire in the eight years since its inception. Five of their squad had already won a national title as they had been members of the school's Under 12 squad which won the E.S.F.A. Wagon Wheel indoor 5-a-side Cup in 1999. In a one-sided final, Sarah Parton set Abraham Darby on their way with a first half hat-trick and Katrina Ravai with two and Toni Evans netted in the second half.

Abraham Darby qualified for the national competition by taking the Shropshire title before Christmas and then went on to score 32 goals and concede only eight in the national rounds. The strike duo of Parton and Ravai shared a remarkable 28 of those goals.

E.S.F.A. UNDER 14 INDIVIDUAL SCHOOLS' CUP

FINAL

DOROTHY STRINGER SCHOOL (Brighton) 1 - 3 ST. FRANCIS XAVIER SCHOOL (Liverpool)
at Blackburn Rovers FC

E.S.F.A. COCA COLA UNDER 13 INDIVIDUAL SCHOOLS' CUP

After some 'pilot' competitions in the previous two seasons, the English Schools' F.A. was delighted when Coca Cola decided to sponsor national competitions for both boys and girls. Those teams which qualified for the later stages had the opportunity of playing at Premiership grounds such as The Riverside, St. Mary's Stadium, Stamford Bridge and Villa Park while the finals were played at Anfield but as Chris Masterton of Coca Cola Enterprises said, "It's not just the 100 youngsters who played the finals' day, it's about the collective effort of all 2,000 schools and around 30,000 young players who participated from September to May."

BOYS NATIONAL CUP FINAL

SANDERS DRAPER SCHOOL (Essex) 5 - 1 AYLESTONE SCHOOL (Herefordshire)

3rd/4th place play-off

EGGBUCKLAND SCHOOL (Devon) 2 - 2 HOUGHTON KEPIER (Durham)

An even first half saw Sanders Draper and Aylestone, with the latter taking the lead and going in level at the break but a much better second half from the Hornchurch school saw Freddie Sears put them ahead soon after the restart. He added a second later in the game while Ryan Mason added to his first half goal and John Oakley netted the fifth although the score perhaps flattered Sanders Draper. The winners received the Coca Cola Cup from Rt. Hon. Richard Caborn, the Sports Minister and Chairman of the E.S.F.A. Dennis Fulton.

GIRLS NATIONAL COCA COLA CUP FINAL

THOMAS TELFORD SCHOOL	6	-	1	LORD WILLIAM'S SCHOOL (Thame, Oxfordshire)

3rd/4th place play-off

AYLSHAM SCHOOL (North Norfolk)	2	-	0	WRIGHT ROBINSON SCHOOL (Manchester)

Charlotte Corbett wrote her name in the history books by vecoming one of the few visiting players (and possibly the first female) to score a hat-trick at Anfield as Thomas Telford School recovered from an early own goal to defeat a gallant Lord william's team 6-1 in the final. Jodie Goodall got an important touch on a loose ball to equalise before Corbett netted two goals before half-time, the second of which was a wonderful individual effort. After the interval, Abi Mears made it 4-1 before Corbett completed her hat-trick and Chamaigne Bailey added the sixth.

Thomas Telford School girls celebrate their Coca Cola Cup success.

THE SMALL-SIDED COMPETITIONS

E.S.F.A. WAGON WHEELS UNDER 12 INDOOR 5-A-SIDE CUPS

BOYS' FINAL

LAURENCE JACKSON SCHOOL (Cleveland)	3	-	2	MILTON CROSS SCHOOL (Portsmouth)

(after extra time - golden goal)

GIRLS' FINAL

CHURCH STRETTON SCHOOL (Shropshire)	2	-	0	ST. JOHN FISHER SCHOOL (N.Yorkshire)

E.S.F.A. UNDER 11 INDIVIDUAL SCHOOLS' 6-A-SIDE CHAMPIONSHIP

SEMI-FINALS

WANSDYKE SCHOOL (Gloucestershire)	1	-	0	DUNSTAN HILL SCHOOL (Durham)
EASTLANDS SCHOOL (Nottinghamshire)	0	-	1	FARNHAM COMMON SCHOOL (Bucks)

3rd/4th PLACE PLAY-OFF

WANSDYKE SCHOOL	0	-	1	EASTLANDS SCHOOL

FINAL

FARNHAM COMMON SCHOOL	2	-	0	DUNSTAN HILL SCHOOL

E.S.F.A. SMALL PRIMARY SCHOOLS' SOCCER SIXES

SEMI-FINALS

CAWSTON SCHOOL (Norfolk)	1	-	0	SPRINGWELL SCHOOL (Durham)
OUR LADY & ST. TERESA'S SCHOOL (Warks)	2	-	0	CROFT SCHOOL (Gloucestershire)

3rd/4th PLACE PLAY-OFF

CROFT SCHOOL	1	-	0	SPRINGWELL SCHOOL

FINAL

OUR LADY & ST. TERESA'S SCHOOL	1	-	0	CAWSTON SCHOOL

E.S.F.A. UNDER 11 INTER-ASSOCIATION 7-A-SIDE CHAMPIONSHIP

3rd/4th PLACE PLAY-OFF

HILLINGDON	3	-	2	SWINDON	(aet - penalties)

FINAL

LIVERPOOL	1	-	0	HULL

F.A. YOUTH CUP 2002-03

FIRST QUALIFYING ROUND

Home		Away	Score	Att
Garforth Town	v	Curzon Ashton	0-1	86
Prudhoe Town	v	Yorkshire Amateur	4-1	37
Scarborough	v	Whitley Bay	6-2	16
Selby Town	v	Ossett Town	2-4*	29
Leigh RMI	v	Wakefield & Emley	5-1	54
Consett	v	Witton Albion	2-3	76
Guiseley	v	Chadderton	1-5	46
Lancaster City	v	Morecambe	0-1	106
Altrincham	v	Frickley Athletic	5-0	62
Farsley Celtic	v	Pontefract Collieries	2-3	36
Chester City	v	Northwich Victoria	1-2*	96
New Mills	v	Bradford (Park Avenue)	3-1	90
Barrow	v	Warrington Town	1-2*	44
Workington	v	Doncaster Rovers	2-7	54
Chester-Le-St. Town	v	Southport	6-1	73
Halifax Town	v	Marine	1-1*	160
(Halifax won 5-4 on pens)				
Harrogate Railway	v	Thackley	0-7	68
Burscough	v	Gretna		
(walkover for Burscough after Gretna withdrawn)				
Gornal Athletic	v	Congleton Town	5-0	59
Malvern Town	v	Holbeach United		
(walkover for Malvern after Holbeach withdrawn)				
Rugby United	v	Belper Town	3-1	26
Lincoln United	v	Sutton Coldfield Town	1-3	43
Boldmere St Michaels	v	Kettering Town	1-2	73
Hucknall Town	v	Wisbech Town	1-0	73
Cradley Town	v	Arnold Town	3-2	67
Louth United	v	Mickleover Sports	1-2	65
Grantham Town	v	Lincoln Moorlands	5-2*	49
Quorn	v	Stone Dominoes	2-1	65
Hednesford Town	v	Oadby Town	1-3	80
Racing Club Warwick	v	Matlock Town	4-2	51
Coventry Sphinx	v	Gresley Rovers	3-3*	60
(Gresley Rovers won 5-4 on pens)				
Nantwich Town	v	Lye Town	0-4	98
Chasetown	v	Bedworth United	1-5	35
Atherstone United	v	Long Buckby	2-0	13
Alfreton Town	v	Corby Town	3-0	66
Concord Rangers	v	Edgware Town	1-0	43
Histon	v	Uxbridge	3-1	49
Ruislip Manor	v	AFC Wallingford	4-2*	45
(Tie awarded to Wallingford after Ruislip played an ineligible player)				
Clapton	v	Barton Rovers	2-9	60
Marlow	v	Hampton & Richmond	0-3	82
Cogenhoe United	v	Southend Manor	0-4	45
Canvey Island	v	Royston Town	6-0	55
Hayes	v	Cambridge City	1-4	98
Heybridge Swifts	v	Sawbridgeworth Town	3-0	43
Leighton Town	v	Ilford	1-2	81
Hoddesdon Town	v	Henley Town	5-2	57
Cheshunt	v	Chesham United	0-2	42
Soham Town Rangers	v	Chelmsford City	2-3	52
Bedford Town	v	Bugbrooke St Michaels	2-4	48
Northampton Spencer	v	Haringey Borough	1-1*	58
(Haringey Borough won 3-1 on pens)				
Stevenage Borough	v	Biggleswade United	7-0	92
Hullbridge Sports	v	Hornchurch	0-5	70
Tilbury	v	Welwyn Garden City	1-0	50
(Played at Welwyn Garden City FC)				
Wembley	v	Leyton	2-2*	54
(Leyton won 4-3 on pens)				
St Ives Town	v	Diss Town	2-1	10
Beaconsfield SYCOB	v	Banbury United	1-0	54
Brentwood	v	Witham Town	2-0	43
Woodbridge Town	v	Dereham Town	4-1	52
Newmarket Town	v	Hemel Hempstead	0-4	49
Wingate & Finchley	v	Great Wakering Rovers	1-3	62
Purfleet	v	Bishop's Stortford	3-1	79
Great Yarmouth Town	v	Aylesbury United	0-5	77
Wealdstone	v	Ipswich Wanderers	0-3	61
(Tie awarded to Wealdstone after Ipswich played an ineligible player)				
Burnham Ramblers	v	Arlesey Town	0-1	39
Ware	v	Bowers United	8-1	75
Lowestoft Town	v	Bury Town	1-3	83
Northwood	v	Milton Keynes City	2-4	35
Hitchin Town	v	Potters Bar Town	0-2	56
Halstead Town	v	Romford	1-4	29
Wokingham Town	v	Thame United		
(walkover for Thame after Wokingham withdrawn)				
Molesey	v	Fleet Town	7-1	25
Leatherhead	v	Horsham	5-1	70
Dartford	v	Gravesend & Northfleet	2-4	94
Farnborough Town	v	Aldershot Town	1-4	103
Walton & Hersham	v	Wick	1-3	48
Eastbourne Town	v	Moneyfields	3-1	30
Eastleigh	v	Banstead Athletic	4-2	61
St Albans City	v	Berkhamsted Town	5-0	52
Dover Athletic	v	Burgess Hill Town	6-2	125
North Leigh	v	Bracknell Town		
(walkover for Bracknell after North Leigh withdrawn)				
Chessington United	v	Chertsey Town	5-1*	46
Sandhurst Town	v	Thatcham Town	3-4	56
Milton United	v	Tonbridge Angels	1-2	65
Littlehampton Town	v	Hillingdon Borough	0-3	41
Alton Town	v	Horndean	4-5*	56
Gosport Borough	v	Croydon	1-2	61
Crowborough Athletic	v	Thamesmead Town	0-6	102
Merstham	v	Ashford Town (Middx)	1-3	30
Reading Town	v	Dulwich Hamlet	2-3	43
Abingdon United	v	Cobham	2-1	55
Hailsham Town	v	Three Bridges	0-6	50
Sittingbourne	v	Croydon Athletic	0-2	39
Saltdean United	v	Farnham Town	1-2	47
Eastbourne United	v	Havant & Waterlooville	2-10	32
Lewes	v	Pagham	2-0	95
Winchester City	v	Ramsgate	0-2	86
Chipstead	v	Tooting & Mitcham Utd	1-6	65
Carshalton Athletic	v	Basingstoke Town	4-2*	75
Erith Town	v	AFC Newbury	2-1	72
Chatham Town	v	Kingstonian	0-3	98
Walton Casuals	v	Chichester City Utd	2-2*	68
(Chichester won 5-4 on pens)				
Bashley	v	Westfield		
(walkover for Westfield after Bashley withdrawn)				
Swindon Supermarine	v	Cinderford Town	4-0	60
Worcester City	v	Newport County	4-0	71
Bitton	v	Cirencester Town	1-4	66
Yeovil Town	v	Chippenham Town	3-1	104
Gloucester City	v	Hereford United	6-2	69
Salisbury City	v	Evesham United	5-3	40
Forest Green Rovers	v	Bath City	1-5	68
Pershore Town	v	Mangotsfield United	0-4	61
Brislington	v	Clevedon Town	3-2*	37
Paulton Rovers	v	Bournemouth	2-3	63
Frome Town	v	Corsham Town	1-0	36

SECOND QUALIFYING ROUND

Morecambe	v	Leigh RMI	3-1	48
Ossett Town	v	Pontefract Collieries	0-3	45
Scarborough	v	Chadderton	4-0	52
New Mills	v	Chester-Le-St. Town	0-2	120
Witton Albion	v	Halifax Town	1-9	97
Doncaster Rovers	v	Prudhoe Town	5-1	86
Curzon Ashton	v	Northwich Victoria	0-3	92
Burscough	v	Altrincham	2-1*	87
Stocksbridge Park	v	Warrington Town	2-0	47
Pickering Town	v	Thackley	1-3	46
Mickleover Sports	v	Racing Club Warwick	2-3*	72
Worksop Town	v	Grantham Town	2-1	105
Tamworth	v	Sutton Coldfield Town	2-3	46
Hucknall Town	v	Kettering Town	0-2	84
Quorn	v	Malvern Town	1-2	49
Cradley Town	v	Gornal Athletic	2-1	69
Nuneaton Borough	v	Deeping Rangers	5-4*	54
Bedworth United	v	Marconi	1-3	58

(Tie awarded to Bedworth after Marconi played an ineligible player)

Oadby Town	v	Atherstone United	2-1	62
Burton Albion	v	Hinckley United	1-1*	52

(Burton Albion won 3-1 on pens)

Gresley Rovers	v	Alfreton Town	0-1	77
Lye Town	v	Rugby United	2-1	62
Ilford	v	Arlesey Town	4-1	63
Cambridge Cityv		Hampton & Richmond	5-0	97
Purfleet	v	St Albans City	0-4	53
Aylesbury United	v	Brentwood	0-1	58
Concord Rangers	v	Heybridge Swifts	1-2	78
Romford	v	Ware	0-3	43
Saffron Walden Tn	v	Milton Keynes City	1-3	45
Tilbury	v	Hemel Hempstead Tn	3-5*	55

(played at Hemel Hempstead)

Haringey Borough	v	Leyton	1-0	36
Beaconsf'd SYCOB	v	Canvey Island	0-5	45
Hitchin Town	v	Bugbrooke St Michaels	2-0	51
AFC Wallingford	v	Stevenage Borough	0-7	60
Woodbridge Town	v	Chelmsford City	1-4	65
Bury Town	v	St Ives Town	8-0	79
Hoddesdon Town	v	Wealdstone	6-3*	60
Gt Wakering Rovers	v	Histon	1-3	78
Southend Manor	v	Chesham United	0-2	42
Barton Rovers		Hornchurch	1-1*	60

(Barton won 4-2 on pens)

Bracknell Town	v	Erith Town	1-1*	55

(Bracknell won 20 on pens)

Eastleigh	v	Aldershot Town	2-2*	72

(Aldershot won 4-1 on pens)

Ramsgate	v	Lordswood	4-0	79
Tooting & Mitcham	v	Croydon Athletic	3-1	106
Thame United	v	Dover Athletic	0-4	32
Camberley Town	v	Kingstonian	1-4	76
Whyteleafe	v	Westfield	0-1	54
Ashford Town (Middx)	v	Havant & Waterlooville	0-5	41
Horndean	v	Dulwich Hamlet	1-3	76
Three Bridges	v	Eastbourne Town	5-3*	44
Woking	v	Hillingdon Borough	3-2	64
Leatherhead	v	Croydon	2-4	45
Farnham Town	v	Tonbridge Angels	1-5	28
Chichester City	v	Abingdon United	2-2*	48

(Abingdon won 6-5 on pens)

Chessington United	v	Carshalton Athletic	2-1	48
Lewes	v	Molesey	5-2	69
Wick	v	Thatcham Town	2-3	65
Gravesend & Northfleet	v	Thamesmead Town	2-1	92
Salisbury City	v	Gloucester City	2-1	33
Yeovil Town	v	Cirencester Town	1-1*	83

(Cirencester won 9-8 on pens) - At Cirencester Town

Worcester City	v	Devizes Town	9-2	51
Frome Town	v	Mangotsfield United	1-3	25
Bournemouth	v	Brislington	1-0	59
Swindon Supermarine	v	Bath City	0-5	45

THIRD QUALIFYING ROUND

Heybridge Swifts	v	Barton Rovers	0-3	104
Cirencester Town	v	Worcester City	4-3	77
Stocksbridge PS	v	Morecambe	0-3	55
Burton Albion	v	Oadby Town	1-2	78
Tooting & Mitcham	v	Chessington United	7-1	95
Dover Athletic	v	Gravesend & Northfleet	3-1	203
Thatcham Town	v	Croydon	1-5	60
Bath City	v	Salisbury City	3-3*	77

(Salisbury won 3-2 on pens)

Mangotsfield United	v	Bournemouth	4-4*	80

(Bournemouth won 5-4 on pens)

Halifax Town	v	Doncaster Rovers	0-2	174
Scarborough	v	Burscough	2-3	48
Haringey Borough	v	Milton Keynes City	2-1	24
Cradley Town	v	Malvern Town	3-0	56
Kettering Town	v	Sutton Coldfield Town	2-3	122
Alfreton Town	v	Bedworth United	5-5*	101

(Bedworth won 7-6 on pens)

Racing Club Warwick	v	Nuneaton Borough	0-5	73
Chesham United	v	Stevenage Borough	3-4	96
Bury Town	v	St Albans City	0-2	55
Abingdon United	v	Ramsgate	1-2	35
Bury Town	v	St. Albans City	0-2	65
Bracknell Town	v	Three Bridges	1-4	74
Aldershot Town	v	Lewes	4-0	220
Dulwich Hamlet	v	Westfield	9-0	59
Tonbridge Angelsv		Havant & Waterlooville	2-0	100
Chester-Le-St. Town	v	Thackley	3-0	118
Worksop Town	v	Lye Town	2-1	96
Brentwood	v	Hoddesdon Town	0-1	42
Kingstonian	v	Woking	2-1	99
Pontefract Collieries	v	Northwich Victoria	2-5	72
Ware	v	Hitchin Town	2-3	58
Chelmsford City	v	Hemel Hempstead Tn	1-0	126
Ilford	v	Canvey Island	3-0	64
Cambridge City	v	Histon	4-0	131

FIRST ROUND

Macclesfield Town	v	York City	0-1	93
Stockport County	v	Doncaster Rovers	1-1*	263

(Doncaster won 3-1 on pens)

Scunthorpe United	v	Morecambe	5-2	80
Wigan Athletic	v	Wrexham	0-1	214
Mansfield Town	v	Rushden & Diamonds	2-1	329
AFC Bournemouth	v	Southend United	5-3*	489
Port Vale	v	Chesterfield	5-2	158
Tooting & Mitcham	v	Tonbridge Angels	3-0	69
Exeter City	v	Plymouth Argyle	2-1	216
Burscough	v	Rochdale	2-1	147
Nuneaton Borough	v	Cambridge United	1-5	91
Oadby Town	v	Kidderminster Harriers	3-1	117
Sutton Coldfield Tn	v	Worksop Town	3-2	75
Croydon	v	Hoddesdon Town	1-3	60
Aldershot Townv		Colchester United	1-4	190
Chester-Le-St Town	v	Hartlepool United	1-2*	200
Bristol City	v	Swansea City	5-3	158
Huddersfield Town	v	Carlisle United	3-0	271
Crewe Alexandrav		Barnsley	0-1	603
Darlington	v	Blackpool	2-3	87
Shrewsbury Town	v	Northampton Town	0-2	134
Peterborough United	v	Cradley Town	8-1	278
Bedworth United	v	Notts County	0-1	87
Brentford	v	Luton Town	0-3	403
Three Bridges	v	Hitchin Town	5-2	75
Ilford	v	Wycombe Wanderers	1-4	31
Cambridge City	v	Sutton United	2-0	164
Swindon Town	v	Salisbury City	4-0	204
Northwich Victoria	v	Tranmere Rovers	0-6	211
Dulwich Hamlet	v	Stevenage Borough	3-1	84
Haringey Borough	v	St Albans City	1-6	57
Kingstonian	v	Barton Rovers	2-3	108
Bournemouth	v	Cheltenham Town	0-4	159

Ramsgate	v	Leyton Orient	3-4*	210
Oldham Athletic	v	Hull City	2-3	210
Bury	v	Lincoln City	2-1	163
Dover Athletic	v	Chelmsford City	3-4	124
Queens Park Rangers	v	Oxford United	1-0	446
Cirencester Town	v	Bristol Rovers	2-1	103
Torquay United	v	Cardiff City	0-3	152

SECOND ROUND

Port Vale	v	Hartlepool United	4-3*	209
Wrexham	v	Sutton Coldfield	1-0	110
Tranmere Rovers	v	York City	2-0	247
Mansfield Town	v	Barnsley	1-2	230
Burscough	v	Blackpool	1-2	211
Hull City	v	Huddersfield Town	1-1	231
(Huddersfield won 8-7 on pens)				
Oadby Town	v	Northampton Town	1-0	211
Notts County	v	Scunthorpe United	4-0	119
Bury	v	Doncaster Rovers	5-3	186
Exeter City	v	AFC Bournemouth	3-2	180
Dulwich Hamlet	v	Cambridge City	3-2	111
Cardiff City	v	Three Bridges	3-1	148
Barton Rovers	v	Cheltenham Town	1-3	154
Chelmsford City	v	Swindon Town	2-9	268
Wycombe Wanderers	v	Cirencester Town	2-0	158
Colchester United	v	St Albans City	4-2	194
Hoddesdon Town	v	Queens Park Rangers	1-0*	191
Peterborough United	v	Leyton Orient	2-1	378
Cambridge United	v	Bristol City	1-0*	391
Tooting & Mitcham Utd	v	Luton Town	1-3	225

THIRD ROUND

Walsall	v	Wolverhampton W.	0-4	310
Fulham	v	Dulwich Hamlet	1-1*	182
(Fulham won 3-2 on pens) - played at Woking FC				
Portsmouth	v	Tottenham Hotspur	1-3	1780
Grimsby Town	v	Chelsea	0-1	629
Bolton Wanderers	v	Cambridge United	0-1	1038
Liverpool	v	Barnsley	1-2	770
Peterborough United	v	Nottingham Forest	1-0*	565
Derby County	v	Southampton	0-2	721
Reading	v	Sheffield Wednesday	1-2*	520
Ipswich Town	v	Notts County	1-2*	556
Luton Town	v	Stoke City	1-0	401
Burnley	v	Crystal Palace	0-2	500
Sheffield United	v	Birmingham City	4-3*	282
Manchester City	v	Wrexham	3-0	255
Hoddesdon Town	v	Swindon Town	1-4	224
Wycombe Wanderers	v	Tranmere Rovers	2-3	251
Brighton & Hove Albion	v	Wimbledon	1-0	177
Everton	v	Port Vale	0-1	1018
West Ham United	v	Oadby Town	4-1	330
Blackburn Rovers	v	Blackpool	5-1	377
Coventry City	v	Leicester City	2-1	422
Arsenal	v	Colchester United	2-0	667
Cardiff City	v	Charlton Athletic	1-3	223
Leeds United	v	Gillingham	4-0	726
Watford	v	Exeter City	0-2	308
Middlesbrough	v	Bury	3-1	823
Rotherham United	v	Cheltenham Town	2-3*	180
Millwall	v	West Bromwich Albion	2-0	247
Bradford City	v	Preston North End	2-0	315
Newcastle United	v	Manchester United	1-3	847
Norwich City	v	Aston Villa	2-1	1584
Huddersfield Town	v	Sunderland	1-2	227

FOUTH ROUND

Tranmer Rovers	v	Cheltenham Town	3-0	260
Tottenham Hotspur	v	Swindon Town	1-0	2970
Millwall	v	Arsenal	2-1	1221
Cambridge United	v	Leeds United	2-4*	2281
West Ham United	v	Fulham	6-1	528
Luton Town	v	Bradford City	1-0	446
Charlton Athletic	v	Wolverhampton W.	1-0	513
Southampton	v	Sunderland	0-1*	540
Wimbledon	v	Norwich City	0-2	206
Crystal Palace	v	Notts County	3-1	564
Barnsley	v	Middlesborough	0-1	506
Sheffield United	v	Coventry City	1-0	234
Port Vale	v	Chelsea	2-1	1958
Blackburn Rovers	v	Exeter City	6-0	649
Manchester United	v	Sheffield Wednesday	2-0	428
Peterborough United	v	Manchester City	0-1	1468

FIFTH ROUND

Crystal Palace	v	Tottenham Hotspur	0-1	688
Luton Town	v	Middlesborough	1-1*	635
(Middlesbrough won 4-3 on pens)				
West Ham United	v	Norwich City	2-1	1234
Manchester Utd*	v	Sheffield Utd	1-1*	460
(Manchester United won 4-3 on pens)				
Leeds Utd	v	Blackburn Rovers	3-2	2410
Tranmere Rovers	v	Port Vale	4-1	1304
Sunderland	v	Charlton Athletic	2-2*	414
(Charlton won 4-3 on pens)				
Millwall	v	Manchester City	0-1	762

QUARTER FINALS

Middlesborough	v	Tottenham Hotspur	1-0	929
Manchester United	v	Tranmere	3-1	930
(At Altrincham FC)				
Leeds United	v	Charlton Athletic	0-1	2422
Manchester City	v	West Ham United	2-0	1645
(At Hyde United FC)				

SEMI-FINALS

Manchester City	v	Middlesborough	1-2	5729
Middlesborough	v	Manchester City	1-1	1635
Middlesbrough won	3-2	on aggregate.		

Charlton Athletic	v	Manchester United	1-1	9074
Manchester United	v	Charlton Athletic	2-0	4427
Manchester Utd won	3-1	on aggregate.		

THE FINAL

Middlesborough	v	Manchester United	0-2	8310
Manchester United	v	Middlesborough	1-1	14849
Manchester Utd won	3-1	on aggregate.		

F.A. SUNDAY CUP 2002-03

FIRST ROUND

Dickie Lewis	v	East Levenshulme	3-1
Clubmoor Nalgo	v	Fairweather Green	1-2
East Bowling Unity	v	Ford Motors	3-2
Lobster	v	Bolton Woods	1-3
Taxi Club	v	Sandon	1-1*
(Taxi Club won on pens)			
Hetton Lyons Cricket Club	v	Oakenshaw	2-0
Norcoast	v	Prestige Brighams	2-1
Seymour	v	Redcar Workingmens	2-3
Hessle Rangers	v	Nicosia	0-3
Travellers	v	Three Horse Shoes	9-1
Linfield Yenton	v	Sporting Khalsa	5-0
St Gerards	v	St Josephs (Luton)	0-2
Gossoms End	v	Hammer	1-4
Walsall Wood Royal Ex.	v	Slade Celtic	6-3
FC Houghton Centre	v	London Colney BCH	2-2*
(London Colney BCH won on pens)			
Schofields	v	Readflex Rangers	2-0
Brache Green Man	v	Capel Plough	
(walkover for Capel Plough)			
Standens Barn	v	Mackadown Lane S&S	1-2
Celtic SC (Luton)	v	Duke Of York	0-3
St Margarets	v	St Joseph's (South Oxhey)	4-1
Theale (Sunday)	v	Quested	1-4
Ouzavich	v	Percival	2-3
Hexton	v	Lea Bridge Rangers	1-2
Lebeq Tavern Courage	v	Mayfair United	2-1
Southcote Video	v	Pioneer	3-8
General Panel Sports	v	Palmerston WMC	5-1

SECOND ROUND

Albion Sports	v	Dickie Lewis	3-2
Garston Woodcutter's	v	St Aloysius 'E	1-4
Clifton	v	Fairweather Green	0-3
Hartlepool Lion Hillcarter	v	Smith & Nephew	3-0
A3 (Canada)	v	Britannia	3-2
East Bowling Unity	v	Shankhouse United	2-0
Bolton Woods	v	Canon	0-2
Orchard Park	v	Western Approaches	4-1
Burradon & New Fordley	v	Nicosia	4-3
Fantail Manfast	v	Hetton Lyons Cricket Club	4-3
Taxi Club	v	Redcar Workingmens	1-2
Allerton	v	Norcoast	5-1
Queens Park	v	Queensbury	4-0
Jolly Farmers	v	Linfield Yenton	1-0
Little Paxton	v	Travellers	2-4
Marden	v	St Josephs (Luton)	0-3
Toll End	v	Trooper	7-2
Crawley Green (Sunday)	v	Hammer	0-1
Queensmen	v	Walsall Wood Royal Exchange	3-2
Casino Cars	v	London Colney BCH	1-0
Moat	v	Schofields	3-2
Belstone	v	Capel Plough	1-0
Lewsey Social	v	Mackadown Lane S&S	2-3
Biggleswade (Sunday)	v	Duke Of York	1-5
Lodge Cottrell	v	St Margarets	3-4
Creekmore Lions	v	Percival5-5*	
(Percival won on pens)			
General Panel Sports	v	Heybridge Social	4-2
Quested		Pioneer	5-4
Cavaliers (Reading)	v	Lea Bridge Rangers	0-2
Old Oak	v	Toby	1-1*
(Old Oak won on pens)			
Bournemouth Electric	v	Lebeq Tavern Courage	3-1
Rainham Sports	v	Reading Irish	0-4

THIRD ROUND

Burradon & New Fordley	v	Albion Sports	1-4
Hartlepool Lion Hillcarter	v	Fantail Manfast	1-0
Canon	v	Jolly Farmers	0-3
Fairweather Green WMC	v	Redcar Workingmens	1-0
St Aloysius 'E	v	Queens Park	5-1
Allerton	v	Orchard Park	3-1
A3 (Canada)	v	East Bowling Unity	3-2
Travellers	v	General Panel Sports	7-0
Duke of York	v	Lea Bridge Rangers	3-0
Reading Irish	v	Mackadown Lane S&S	5-0
Belstone	v	Hammer	2-3
St Josephs (Luton)	v	Moat	7-0
Toll End	v	Casino Cars	0-1
Queensmen	v	Bournemouth Electric	3-1
St Margarets	v	Percival	5-1
Quested	v	Old Oak	7-0

FOURTH ROUND

Fairweather Green WMC	v	A3 (Canada)	1-3
Hartlepool Lion Hillcarter	v	St Aloysius 'E	4-2
Allerton	v	Jolly Farmers	4-0
Albion Sports	v	St Margarets	3-3*
(St Margarets won on pens)			
St Josephs (Luton)	v	Queensmen	4-0
Reading Irish	v	Hammer	4-0
Casino Cars	v	Travellers	0-4
Duke of York	v	Quested	6-1

QUARTER FINALS

St Margarets	v	Hartlepool Lion Hillcarter	1-2
Allerton	v	A3 (Canada)	1-1
(Allerton won on pens)			
Duke of York	v	Reading Irish	3-0
Travellers	v	St Josephs (Luton)	1-3
(Tie awarded to Travellers)			

SEMI FINALS

Travellers	v	Duke of York	3-5	339
Hartlepool Lion Hillcarter	v	Allerton	1-3	787

THE FINAL

Allerton	v	Duke of York	1-3	2203

At Anfield.

F.A. COUNTY YOUTH CUP 2002-03

FIRST ROUND

Isle of Man*	v	Manchester	1-1*
(Isle of Man won on pens)			
Shropshire	v	Westmoreland	2-0
Cheshire	v	Leics & Rutland	1-0
North Riding	v	Derbyshire	7-0
Staffordshire	v	Northumberland	1-5
Sheffield & Hallam.	v	Lincolnshire	2-1
(Tie awarded to Lincolnshire)			
Herefordshire	v	Gloucestershire	2-0
Oxfordshire	v	Hampshire	6-4
Devon	v	Wiltshire	0-2
Surrey	v	Huntingdonshire	2-0
Worcestershire	v	Essex	3-1
London	v	Hertfordshire	3-2
Sussex	v	Dorset	3-6
Cambridgeshire	v	Army	2-2*
(Cambridgshire won on pens)			
Northamptonshire	v	Berks & Bucks	1-0

SECOND ROUND

Cumberland	v	North Riding	0-3
East Riding	v	West Riding	1-4
Birmingham	v	Shropshire	3-0
Durham	v	Nottinghamshire	2-1
Cheshire	v	Lincolnshire	0-1
Lancashire	v	Northumberland	2-2*
(Northumberland won on pens)			
Liverpool	v	Isle of Man	3-2
Cornwall	v	Somerset	6-3
Dorset	v	Cambridgeshire	0-2
Suffolk	v	Bedfordshire	4-3
Norfolk	v	Surrey	2-0
London	v	Jersey	4-2
Kent	v	Northamptonshire	1-0
Guernsey	v	Oxfordshire	6-2
Herefordshire	v	Wiltshire	0-1
Worcestershire	v	Middlesex	1-2

THIRD ROUND

Birmingham	v	Durham	4-3
Suffolk	v	Northumberland	0-2
Lincolnshire	v	Middlesex	0-1
East Riding	v	Kent	1-5
Liverpool	v	Norfolk	1-0
Cambridgeshire	v	London	2-0
North Riding	v	Wiltshire	3-4
Guernsey	v	Cornwall	1-1*
(Guernsey won on pens)			

QUARTER FINALS

Wiltshire	v	Liverpool	1-2
Birmingham	v	Northumberland	0-1
Cambridgeshire	v	Middlesex	1-2
Kent	v	Guernsey	2-1

SEMI FINALS

Liverpool	v	Kent	3-0
Northumberland	v	Middlesex	3-1

THE FINAL

Liverpool	v	Northumberland	0-1

Played at Southport FC

Congratulations to Champions Yeovil Town...

So much has been written about Yeovil Town's promotion but the style with which they won the championship represented one of the most outstanding achievements in the history of the Alliance/Conference.

A number of famous non-league sides have recorded memorable season's achievements such as; Altrincham, Enfield, Runcorn, Telford United, Kidderminster Harriers, Wycombe Wanderers and Rushden & Diamonds. All these clubs had very special squads with some great individuals, and their trophies and special results will always be remembered.But most of these clubs fielded mature sides with an average age around the thirty mark. Yeovil Town were young and still are. They have plenty to learn and may come unstuck while developing, but to achieve the championship in such style at such a low average age put Gary Johnson's boys in a class of their own.

Most successful senior non-league clubs have built their success on an acumulation of points from a strong defence, hitting long passes forward and pushing up to close down and squeeze the opposition before taking advantage of their mistakes . All this played at a hectic rate with little thinking or original movement. Results were ground out by power play.

Yeovil Town were a breath of fresh air, as their smooth quick passes out of defence swept across the turf through midfield, switching from wing to wing with defenders and midfield players quite happy to interchange with their forwards at any time. The Somerset supporters also learnt to be patient in the knowledge that their lads' football usually wore down the sternest of defences, and once on top, there were usually all sorts of goalmouth entertainment to enjoy.

Nine internationals in the squad is surely confirmation of a superb club being recognised for their football inspired by Gary Johnson and coach Steve Thompson and the unanimous praise from all who watched them underlined the respect given to this very special set of 'Glovers'

Congratulations to them all and good luck in the future. Tony Williams

...and to play-off winners Doncaster Rovers

Doncaster Rovers had been an established Football League name for many years so their relegation into the Conference amidst horrendous financial and legal headlines was extremely hurtful to their supporters.

A gradual rebuilding within non-league football's senior competition not only gave them their pride back but many of their more mature supporters actually grew to enjoy the spirit of the game throughout the country at this level. The young supporters who had behaved badly in the League, started off with an unpleasant attitude in their first months of Conference football but soon the atmosphere at Belle Vue improved, and although the sad element turned up again at the play offs, the club will surely sort them out.

Dave Penny built a thoroughly competent squad who stood out last season, as they reached their peak at exactly the right time. He has already added more players of Football League quality so the future looks good. The character and determination shown in the play offs has given everyone confidence and, if needed, they can always call on their owner in the last few minutes to come on and help close the game down when protecting a lead.!

The system has proved successful once again. When relegated, Rovers were in no state to look after themselves at a high level, but after five years of tender loving care in the Conference, they are returning to claim their rightful place with confidence restored on and off the field.

Tony Williams.

DONCASTER ROVERS

The number shown directly below the player's name is his squad number.
Where a number is shown instead of an'x' in the columns this represents a substitute appearance and the number indicates the player replaced.

Comp.	Date	Opponents	Venue.	Score	Goalscorers	Att.
						SQUAD NUMBER
Lg 1	Aug-17	Barnet	H	W 2-1	Green Morley	3023
Lg 2	Aug-20	Leigh RMI	A	W 2-0	Barnes(p) Jackson	867
Lg 3	Aug-24	Telford U	A	D 4-4	Tierney(2) Morley Barrick	1170
Lg 4	Aug-26	Farnborough T	H	W 1-0	Tierney	3436
Lg 5	Aug-31	Northwich V	A	W 2-1	Watson Jackson	1160
Lg 6	Sep-03	Kettering T	H	W 1-0	Owen	3764
Lg 7	Sep-07	Dagenham & R	H	W 5-1	Watson Gill Paterson(p) Barnes Vickers(og)	4294
Lg 8	Sep-10	Halifax T	A	L 1-2	Barnes	3082
Lg 9	Sep-17	Southport	H	D 0-0		3975
Lg 10	Sep-21	Margate	A	L 1-2	Green	1002
Lg 11	Sep-24	Gravesend & N	A	D 2-2	Paterson Barnes	1326
Lg 12	Sep-28	Chester C	H	D 0-0		4867
Lg 13	Oct-05	Nuneaton B	A	W 3-0	Barnes(2,1p) Watson	1759
Lg 14	Oct-08	Stevenage B	H	D 0-0		3477
Lg 15	Oct-11	Forest Green R	H	W 1-0	Barnes	3508
Lg 16	Oct-19	Yeovil T	A	D 1-1	Hudson	6674
LDV 1	Oct-22	Scarborough	A	W 2-1	Hudson(2)	1206
FAC 4q	Oct-27	Telford U	A	W 2-0	Barnes(2,1p)	1012
Lg 17	Nov-02	Hereford U	H	W 2-0	Albrighton Barnes(p)	3486
Lg 18	Nov-09	Morecambe	A	L 0-3		1971
LDV 2	Nov-12	Wigan Athletic	A	W 1-0	Albrighton	2030
FAC 1	Nov-16	Bournemouth	A	L 1-2	Gill	5371
Lg 19	Nov-23	Nuneaton B	H	D 1-1	Barnes(p)	2913
Lg 20	Dec-01	Woking	H	W 3-1	Morley Gill Paterson	3051
Lg 21	Dec-06	Burton A	A	W 2-1	Barnes Gill	2341
LDV 3	Dec-10	Crewe Alexandra	A	L 0-8		2188
Lg 22	Dec-14	Dagenham & R	A	D 3-3	Barnes(2) Gill	1739
Lg 23	Dec-20	Halifax T	H	D 0-0		3201
Lg 24	Dec-26	Scarborough	A	W 5-2	Gill(2) Paterson(2) Barnes	3435
Lg 25	Dec-28	Leigh RMI	H	W 1-0	Paterson	3719
Lg 26	Jan-04	Barnet	A	W 2-1	Paterson Gill	1859
FAT 3	Jan-14	Halifax T	A	L 1-4	Green	1770
Lg 27	Jan-18	Telford U	H	L 1-3	Barnes	3333
Lg 28	Feb-08	Northwich V	H	L 1-2	Barnes	2941
Lg 29	Feb-15	Kettering T	A	W 2-0	Barnes(2)	1633
Lg 30	Feb-22	Burton A	H	W 1-0	Jackson	3026
Lg 31	Feb-25	Farnborough T	A	D 0-0		947
Lg 32	Mar-01	Southport	A	W 4-0	Green(2) Gill Barnes	1265
Lg 33	Mar-08	Gravesend & N	H	W 4-1	Blunt(2) Morley Barnes	3156
Lg 34	Mar-17	Chester C	A	L 0-1		2928
Lg 35	Mar-22	Woking	A	D 2-2	Foster Campbell(og)	2007
Lg 36	Mar-25	Margate	H	W 3-1	Barnes(2) Blunt	2888
Lg 37	Apr-01	Scarborough	H	L 0-1		4155
Lg 38	Apr-05	Forest Green R	A	W 2-1	Morley Barnes	986
Lg 39	Apr-12	Yeovil T	H	L 0-4		5344
Lg 40	Apr-19	Stevenage B	A	W 3-2	Tierney Whitman Barnes	2424
Lg 41	Apr-21	Morecambe	H	D 1-1	Burton	2783
Lg 42	Apr-26	Hereford U	A	W 4-2	Watson Whitman Barnes Blundell	2449
PSF 1	May-01	Chester C	H	D 1-1	Whitman	6857
PSF 2	May-05	Chester C	A	D 1-1	Barnes *Agg: 2-2, won 4-3 after pens.*	5702
PF	May-10	Dagenham & R	N	W 3-2	Green Morley Tierney *@ Stoke City FC*	13092

Andy WARRINGTON	Simon MARPLES	Tim RYAN	David MORLEY	Dean BARRICK	John DOOLAN	Mark ALBRIGHTON	Francis TIERNEY	Gareth OWEN	Paul BARNES	Justin JACKSON	Jamie PATERSON	Stuart NELSON	Andy WATSON	Robert GILL	Tristram WHITMAN	Kevin SANDWITH	Chris BEECH	Jamie PRICE	Ricky RAVENHILL	Paul GREEN	Danny BENT	Tyrone THOMPSON	Alan MORGAN	Keith FOY	Steve FOSTER	Brian QUAILEY	Tarkan MUSTAFA	Don GOODMAN	Dene SHIELDS	Steve BURTON	Erdem ARTUN	Jon McCARTHY	Gregg BLUNDELL	Ben MUIRHEAD	Danny HUDSON	John RYAN	Warren PEYTON	Jason BLUNT
1	2	3	4	5	5	6	7	8	9	10	11	13	14	15	16	17	17	18	19	20	21	21	22	22	23	24	24	24	25	25	26	26	26	27	28	28	29	30
x	x	x	x	x			x	x	x	14			x	x					22	15			x															
x	x	x	x	x			x	x	x	x						x			17	x						7												
x	x	x	x	x			x	x	x	x			x	14					8	x					7													
x	x	x	x	x			x	x	x	x			x						20	x					8	9												
x	x	x		x			x	x	x	x			x						x	7			19		x				9									
x	x	x		x				x	x	x	x		x						x	11					x				10									
x	x	x		x		23		x	x		x		x	x	11				x	14					x													
x	x	x		x		x		x	x		x		x	x	15				x	19																		
x	x	x		x		x		x	x		x		x	x						x									15									
x	x	x		x		x		x	x		x		x	25						22			x						x		14							
x	26	x	x	x		x		x	x		x			x	15	11				x											x							
x	x	x	x	x		x		x	x	x	x		x							8																		
x	x	x	x	x		x		x	x	x			x	10	20			8		x																		
x	x	x	x	x		x			x	x			x	10	26			x		18												x						
x	x	x	x	x		x			x	x			x	14	5			x		4														x				
x	x	x	x	x		x			x	x	27		x					14																x	x			
x		x	20	23		x		x			x			x	x			x		x	15				x										x			
x	x	x	x	x		x		28	x	x	x		x	10																					x			
x	x	x	x	x		x		x	x	x	x		x																					14				
x	x	x	x	x		x		x	x	x	x			11						8														x				
x	x	x	x			x		x	x	x	x							x	11	27														x				
x	x	x	x	6		x		x	x	x	x		8	11				x																	x			
x	x	x		x		x			x	x	x		x							28					x									14	x			
x	x		x	x				15	x		x		x	x					x						x									14	x			
x	x	x	x	x					x		x		x	x	14				x																x			
x	x	x	x	x		9			x					x	x		x		x	5					3										x			
x	x	x	x	x		x			x	15	x			x			x		2																x		11	
x		x		x		x		x	x	15	x			x	17		x										x								x		8	
x		x	11	x		x		x	x	9	x			x			x		28								x								x			
x		x	17	x		x		x	x	15	x			x			x		28								x								x			
x		x	11	x		x		x	x	15	x			x			x		28								x								x			
x			x	x		x		x		x	x		11	x	10		x			28							x								x			
x			x	x		x		x	x	24	x		x	x	15				8	x							x											
x	x	x		x		x		6	x	x	x		x	10	14				x						x													
x	x	x					19		x	x							x		x	x					x												x	x
x	x	x	19						x	x				20	29		x		x	x					x												x	x
x	x	x	2				x		x				16	x	x		x								x												x	x
x		x	x			20	x		x				7	x	9		x		x	x					x													x
x		x	x				x		x				7	x	15		x		x	x					x													x
x	15		x			x	x	7	x					x			x		x	x					x			19										x
x			x		x	x	x		x						7		x		x	30					x			x										x
x		x	x		x		x		x					x	20		x		7	x					x			15										x
x	23	x	x		x		x		x					x	30		x			x					x			15										x
x		x	x		x	17	x		x					x			x		x	7					x			15										x
x	x	x	x		x		30		x					24	5				x	x					x			x										x
	x	17			x	x	x		x			x	30		x		x			5					x												x	x
	x	x	x				11				x	x	x	x	15					x		x		x						x								
x	x	x			x		x		x				x		x		x		x						x								7			9		5
x	x	x	23		x				x		x		x		x		x		x	14					x								5					
x		x	x				x		x		x		9		x		x		x	x					x								7					17
x	x	x	x				x		x		x				x				x	x					x								16					11

YEOVIL TOWN

Match Facts 2002-03

The number shown directly below the player's name is his squad number.
Where a number is shown instead of an'x' in the columns this represents a substitute appearance and the number indicates the player replaced.

Comp.	Date	Opponents	Venue.	Score	Goalscorers	Att.
						SQUAD NUMBER
Conf 1	Aug-17	Gravesend & N	H	D 2-2	Crittenden Skiverton	2948
Conf 2	Aug-20	Barnet	A	L 1-2	Johnson	1668
Conf 3	Aug-24	Morecambe	A	W 2-1	Alford Forinton	1343
Conf 4	Aug-26	Nuneaton B	H	W 3-2	McIndoe Williams Lockwood	2504
Conf 5	Aug-31	Kettering T	A	W 1-0	Skiverton	1670
Conf 6	Sep-03	Farnborough T	H	W 2-0	Crittenden Johnson	2231
Conf 7	Sep-07	Northwich V	H	W 2-1	Skiverton Grant	2154
Conf 8	Sep-14	Stevenage B	A	D 2-2	Skiverton Demba	1879
Conf 9	Sep-17	Hereford U	A	D 0-0		2282
Conf 10	Sep-21	Halifax T	H	W 3-0	Crittenden(2p) Williams	2126
Conf 11	Sep-24	Woking	H	W 4-0	Demba McIndoe Skiverton Forinton	4003
Conf 12	Sep-28	Leigh RMI	A	W 4-2	Skiverton McIndoe Crittenden Alford	415
Conf 13	Oct-05	Southport	H	W 6-0	Demba(3) Williams Crittenden Elkholti	4727
Conf 14	Oct-08	Burton A	A	D 1-1	Demba	1989
Conf 15	Oct-13	Telford U	A	W 5-0	Crittenden(p) Lockwood Lindegaard Forinton Williams	1509
Conf 16	Oct-19	Doncaster R	H	D 1-1	Williams	6674
LDV 1	Oct-23	Boston United	A	L 2-4	Lockwood Alford	1323
FAC 4q	Oct-27	Bath City	A	D 1-1	Lockwood	3470
FAC 4qr	Oct-29	Bath City	H	W 3-1	Demba(2) McIndoe	4393
Conf 17	Nov-02	Chester C	A	D 2-2	Crittenden Forinton	3821
Conf 18	Nov-09	Dagenham & R	H	D 2-2	McIndoe Smith(og)	4289
FAC 1	Nov-16	Cheltenham Town	H	L 0-2		6455
Conf 19	Nov-23	Southport	A	W 1-0	McIndoe	1602
Conf 20	Nov-30	Margate	H	W 2-1	Elkholti Crittenden(p)	4147
Conf 21	Dec-07	Scarborough	A	L 1-2	Elkholti	1470
Conf 22	Dec-14	Northwich V	A	W 2-1	McIndoe Jackson	691
Conf 23	Dec-21	Stevenage B	H	W 2-1	Jackson Pluck	4940
Conf 24	Dec-26	Forest Green R	A	L 1-2	Skiverton	1836
Conf 25	Dec-28	Barnet	H	D 0-0		4850
Conf 26	Jan-01	Forest Green R	H	W 1-0	Jackson	4692
Conf 27	Jan-04	Gravesend & N	A	W 4-2	Lindegaard(3) Jackson	1404
FAT 3	Jan-14	Hereford U	A	W 2-1	Pluck Lockwood	2425
Conf 28	Jan-18	Morecambe	H	W 2-0	Lindegaard Jackson	4353
Conf 29	Jan-25	Nuneaton B	A	D 1-1	Lindegaard	1717
FAT 4	Feb-01	Morecambe	H	W 2-1	Jackson Skiverton	3984
Conf 30	Feb-08	Kettering T	H	W 4-0	Pluck Gall Jackson McIndoe	4738
Conf 31	Feb-15	Farnborough T	A	W 4-2	Jackson(2) Johnson McIndoe(p)	2114
FAT 5	Feb-22	Northwich V	H	W 2-1	Lockwood Gall	4469
Conf 32	Mar-01	Hereford U	H	W 4-0	Lockwood Gall Jackson McIndoe(p)	6487
Conf 33	Mar-04	Halifax T	A	W 3-2	Gall(3)	2222
Conf 34	Mar-08	Woking	A	D 1-1	Jackson	3332
Conf 35	Mar-11	Leigh RMI	H	W 3-1	Jackson(2) Gall	5330
FAT 6	Mar-15	Burscough	H	L 0-2		4934
Conf 36	Mar-22	Margate	A	W 2-1	Jackson(2)	1083
Conf 37	Mar-28	Scarborough	H	W 1-0	Jackson	7008
Conf 38	Apr-05	Telford U	H	W 3-0	McIndoe(2) Jackson	7558
Conf 39	Apr-12	Doncaster R	A	W 4-0	Way McIndoe(p) Johnson Gall	5344
Conf 40	Apr-19	Burton A	H	W 6-1	Gall(4) Williams Giles	5691
Conf 41	Apr-21	Dagenham & R	A	W 4-0	Jackson(3) Gall	2588
Conf 42	Apr-26	Chester C	H	D 1-1	Gall	8111

Chris WEALE 1	Adam LOCKWOOD 2	Anthony TONKIN 3	Jason BLUNT 3	Terry SKIVERTON 4	Colin PLUCK 5	Darren WAY 6	Adam STANSFIELD 7	Lee JOHNSON 8	Carl ALFORD 9	Kevin GALL 9	Nick CRITTENDEN 10	Michael McINDOE 11	Chris GILES 12	Jon SHEFFIELD 13	Roy O'BRIEN 14	Stephen REED 15	Andy LINDEGAARD 16	Tom WHITE 17	Kim GRANT 18	Abdoulai DEMBA 19	Gavin WILLIAMS 20	Steve COLLIS 22	Howard FORINTON 23	Neil MUSTOE 23	Abdelhalim EL KHOLTI 24	Kirk JACKSON 25	Jimmy AGGREY 26
x	x	x		x		x	x	x	2		x	x						x		7	x						
x	x	x		x		x		x	17		x	x	19				10	x		x	x						
x	x	x		x	19	x		x	x		x	x			8					x	x		9				
x	x	x		x	8	x		x	x		x	x			19					x	x		9				
x	x	x		x	10	x		x	x		x	x							9	x	x		19				
x	x			x	x	x		x			x	x			10		18		x	23	x		x				
x	x			x	x	x		x			x	x		18	8				x	23	x		x				
x	x	x		x	x	x		x	23		x	x								3	x		x				
x	x	x		x	x	x		x	19		x						3			x	x		x				
	x			x	x	x		x			x	x		x	23					x	x		x				
	x			x	x	x		x	19		x	x		x	23		5			x	x		x				
	x			x	x	x		x	23		x	x		x			6		x		x		x		18		
	x				x	x		x	18		x	x		x	x		6		x	x	x				19		
	x				x	x		x	18		x	x		x	x				x	x	x						
	x				x	x		x	23		x	x	2	x	x		x				x		x		6		
	x			5	x	x		x	16		x	x		x	x		x			23	x		x				
	x			x		x		x	14		x	x		x	x		x		19	x	x				16		
x	x			x		x		x	19		x	x	8		x				x	x	x		18				
x	x			x		x		x	23		x	x			x		19			x	x		x				
x	x			x		x		x			x	x			x		19		23	x	x		x				
x	x			x	x	x					x	x			x		18		x	23	x		x				
x				x	x	x			23		x	x	x		x		x		5	16			x		x		
x	x			x	x	x		x	12		x	x	19						24	x	x				x		
x	x			x	x	x		x			x	x			24						x				x	x	
x	x					x		x			x	x			x				24		x				x	x	x
x	x			x	x	x		x			x	x			x		24								x	x	
x	x			x	x	x		x			x	x			x						x				14	x	4
x	x			x	x	x		x			x	x			x				25		x				14	x	
x	x			x	x	x		x			x	x					20		25		x				x	x	2
x	x			x	x	x		x			x	x			5		x				x				20	x	4
x	x				x	x		x			x	x			25		x				x				5	x	x
x	x				x	x		x			x	x			x		x		16		x				10	x	
x	x			5	x	x		x				x			x		x				x				x	x	24
x	x			2	x	x		x			x	x			x		x				x				10	x	
x	x			x	x	x		x				x					x		16		x				x	x	
x	x		20	x	x	x		x		16		x			5		x				x				x	x	
x	x			x		x		x		16		x			x		x				x			6	x	x	14
x	x			x	x	x		x		x		x			5						x				x	x	
x	x			x	x			x		x		x			23		20		25		x			x	x	x	
x	x			x	x	x		x		x		x			5						x				x	x	
x	x			x	x	x		x		x		x					20				x				x	x	
x	x			x	x	x		x		x	25	x			2		20				x				x	x	
x	x			x	x	x		x		x	2	x					8		25		x				x	x	
x				x	x			x		x	23	x	24		x		x							x	x	x	4
x	8			x	x	x		x		x	24	x	25		x		x								x	x	
x	14			x	x	x		x		x	16	x			x		x				x				20	x	
x	14			x	x	x		x		x	9	x			x		x				x				16	x	
x	20			x	x	x		x		x		x	5		x		x				x				25	x	
	x			x	14	x		x		x	x	x	10		x	24						x			x	x	
x	x			x	2	x		x		x	x	x			x		20				x				10	x	

THE FOOTBALL ASSOCIATION

FIXTURE LIST 2003-04

JULY 2003	Sat 5	Intertoto Cup 2 (1)
	Sat 12	Intertoto Cup 2 (2)
	Wed 16	UEFA Champions League 1Q (1)
	Sat 19	Intertoto Cup 3 (1)
	Wed 23	UEFA Champions League 1Q (2)
	Sat 26	Intertoto Cup 3 (2)
	Wed 30	UEFA Champions League 2Q (1)
		Intertoto Cup SF (1)
AUGUST 2003	Wed 6	UEFA Champions League 2Q (2)
		Intertoto Cup SF (2)
	Sat 9	Start of Football League
		Start of Football Conference
	Sun 10	FA Community Shield
	Tue 12	Intertoto Cup Final (1)
	Wed 13	UEFA Champions League 3Q (1)
		UEFA Cup Q (1)
		Football League Cup 1
	Sat 16	Start of FA Premier League
	Sun 17	Start of FA Women's Premier League
	Wed 20	International (Friendly)
	Sat 23	FA Cup EP
	Tue 26	Intertoto Cup Final (2)
	Wed 27	UEFA Champions League 3Q (2)
		UEFA Cup Q (2)
	Fri 29	UEFA Super Cup
	Sat 30	FA Cup P
	Sun 31	FA Women's Premier League Cup P
SEPTEMBER 2003	Sat 6	Macedonia v England (EC Qualifier)
		FA Vase 1Q
		FA Youth Cup 1Q
	Sun 7	FA Women's Cup 1Q
	Tue 9	U21 England v Portugal
	Wed 10	England v Liechtenstein (EC Qualifier)
	Thu 11	Women's Friendly Internationl v Germany
	Sat 13	FA Cup 1Q
	Sun 14	FA Women's Premier League Cup 1
	Tue 16	UEFA Champions League Match Day 1
	Wed 17	UEFA Champions League Match Day 1
	Sat 20	FA Vase 2Q
		FA Youth Cup 2Q
	Wed 24	UEFA Cup 1 (1)
		Football League Cup 2
	Sat 27	FA Cup 2Q
	Sun 28	FA Women's Cup 2Q
	Tue 30	UEFA Champions League Match Day 2
OCTOBER 2003	Wed 1	UEFA Champions League Match Day 2
	Sat 4	FA Trophy P
		FA Youth Cup 3Q
		FA County Youth Cup 1
	Sun 5	FA Sunday Cup 1
	Fri 10	U21 Turkey v England
	Sat 11	FA Cup 3Q
		Turkey v England (EC Qualifier)
	Sun 12	FA Women's Premier League Cup 2
	Wed 15	UEFA Cup 1 (2)
		LDV Vans Trophy (1)
	Sat 18	FA Vase 1P
	Tue 21	UEFA Champions League Match Day 3
	Wed 22	UEFA Champions League Match Day 3
	Sat 25	FA Cup 4Q
		FA Youth Cup 1P
	Sun 26	FA Women's Cup 1P
	Wed 29	Football League Cup 3
NOVEMBER 2003	Sat 1	FA Trophy 1
	Sun 2	FA Sunday Cup 2
		FA Women's Premier League Cup 3
	Tue 4	UEFA Champions League Match Day 4
	Wed 5	UEFA Champions League Match Day 4
		LDV Vans Trophy 2
	Thu 6	UEFA Cup 2 (1)
	Sat 8	FA Cup 1P
		FA Youth Cup 2P
		FA County Youth Cup 2
	Sun 9	FA Women's Cup 2P
	Sat 15	Euro 2004 Play-off
	Wed 19	Euro 2004 Play-off
		FA Cup 1P Replay
	Sat 22	FA Vase 2P
	Tue 25	UEFA Champions League Match Day 5
	Wed 26	UEFA Champions League Match Day 5
	Thu 27	UEFA Cup 2 (2)
	Sat 29	FA Trophy 2
	Sun 30	UEFA 2004 Draw for Finals
		FA Sunday Cup 3
DECEMBER 2003	Tue 2	Inter-Continental Cup
	Wed 3	Football League Cup 4
	Sat 6	FA Cup 2P
		FA Youth Cup 3P
	Sun 7	FA Women's Cup 3P
	Tue 9	UEFA Champions League Match Day 6
	Wed 10	UEFA Champions League Match Day 6
		LDV Vans Trophy QF
	Sat 13	FA Vase 3P
		FA County Youth 3
	Sun 14	FA Women's Premier League Cup SF
	Wed 17	FA Cup 2P Replay
		Football League Cup 5
JANUARY 2004	**Sat 3**	**FA Cup 3P**
	Sun 4	FA Women's Cup 4P
	Sat 10	FA Trophy 3
	Sun 11	FA Sunday Cup 4
	Wed 14	FA Cup 3P Replay
	Sat 17	FA Vase 4P
	Wed 21	Football League Cup SF (1)
		LDV Vans Trophy Area SF
	Sat 24	FA Cup 4P
	Sun 25	FA Women's Cup 5P
	Wed 28	Football League Cup SF (2)
	Sat 31	FA Trophy 4
		FA Youth Cup 4P
		FA County Youth Cup 4
FEBRUARY 2004	Sun 1	FA Sunday Cup 5
	Wed 4	FA Cup 4P Replay
	Sat 7	FA Vase 5P
	Sun 8	FA Women's Cup 6P
	Wed 11	LDV Vans Trophy Area Final (1)
	Sat 14	FA Cup 5P
		FA Trophy 5
	Wed 18	International (Friendly)
	Sat 21	FA Vase 6P
		FA Youth Cup 5P
	Tue 24	UEFA Champions League 1/8 (1)
	Wed 25	UEFA Champions League 1/8 (1)
		FA Cup 5P Replay
		LDV Vans Trophy Area Final (2)
	Thu 26	UEFA Cup 3 (1)
	Sat 28	FA Trophy 6
	Sun 29	Football League Cup Final
MARCH 2004	Wed 3	UEFA Cup 3 (2)
	Sat 6	FA Cup 6P
		FA County Youth Cup SF
	Tue 9	UEFA Champions League 1/8 (2)
	Wed 10	UEFA Champions League 1/8 (2)
	Thu 11	UEFA Cup 1/8 (1)
	Sat 13	FA Vase SF (1)
		FA Youth Cup 6P
	Sun 14	FA Women's Cup SF
	Wed 17	FA Cup 6P Replay
	Sat 20	FA Vase SF (2)
	Sun 21	FA Sunday Cup SF
	Tue 23	UEFA Champions League QF (1)
	Wed 24	UEFA Champions League QF (1)
	Thu 25	UEFA Cup 1/8 (2)
	Sat 27	FA Trophy SF (1)
	Sun 28	LDV Vans Trophy Final
		FA Women's Premier League Cup Final
	Wed 31	International (Friendly)
APRIL 2004	Sat 3	FA Trophy SF (2)
		FA Youth Cup SF (1)
	Sun 4	FA Cup SF
	Tue 6	UEFA Champions League Qf (2)
	Wed 7	UEFA Champions League QF (2)
	Thu 8	UEFA Cup Qf (1)
	Wed 14	UEFA Cup Qf (2)
	Sat 17	FA Youth Cup SF (2)
	Tue 20	UEFA Champions League SF (1)
	Wed 21	UEFA Champions League SF (1)
	Thu 22	UEFA Cup SF (1)
	Sat 24	FA County Youth Cup Final
		End of Football Conference
	Sun 25	FA Sunday Cup Final
		End of FA Women's Premier League
	Wed 28	International (Friendly)
MAY 2004	Mon 3	FA Women's Cup Final (Prov)
	Tue 4	UEFA Champions League SF (2)
	Wed 5	UEFA Champions League SF (2)
	Thu 6	UEFA Cup SF (2)
	Sat 8	End of Football League
	Sat 15	FA Vase Final
		End of FA Premier League
	Wed 19	UEFA Cup Final
	Sat 22	FA Cup Final
	Sun 23	FA Trophy Final
	Wed 26	UEFA Champions League Final
	Fri 28	Start of UEFA U21 Championship Finals
	Sat 29	Football League Division 1 Play off final
	Sun 30	Football League Division 2 Play off final
	Mon 31	Football League Division 3 Play off final
JUNE 2004	Sun 6	UEFA U21 Championship Final - Antas Stadium, Porto
	Sat 12	Start of UEFA Championship Finals
	Wed 23	UEFA Championship Finals - end of group stage
	Thu 24	UEFA Championship Finals - QF 1
	Fri 25	UEFA Championship Finals - QF 2
	Sat 26	UEFA Championship Finals - QF 3
	Sun 27	UEFA Championship Finals - QF 4
	Wed 30	UEFA Championship Finals - SF 1
07/04	Thu 1	UEFA Championship Finals - SF 2
	Sun 4	UEFA Championship Final - Luz Stadium, Lisbon

WOMEN'S FOOTBALL

NATIONAL DIVISION TABLE 2002-03

		P	W	D	L	F	A	Pts	GD
1	Fulham Ladies	18	16	2	0	63	13	49	50
2	Doncaster Belles	18	13	2	3	34	19	41	15
3	Arsenal Ladies	18	13	1	4	53	21	40	32
4	Charlton Women	18	10	4	4	44	20	34	24
5	Birmingham City Ladies	18	6	3	9	26	31	21	-5
6	Tranmere Rovers Ladies	18	6	3	9	25	48	21	-23
7	Leeds United Ladies	18	5	4	9	33	42	19	-9
8	Everton Ladies	18	5	1	12	18	38	16	-20
9	Southampton Saints	18	2	5	11	10	30	11	-20
10	Brighton & Hove Women	18	1	1	16	18	62	4	-44

Fulham deducted 1pt for fielding an ineligible player.

NORTHERN DIVISION TABLE 2002-03

		P	W	D	L	F	A	Pts	GD
1	Aston Villa Ladies	22	16	4	2	59	18	52	41
2	Sunderland AFC Women	22	15	4	3	48	25	49	23
3	Oldham Curzon	22	14	2	6	48	29	44	19
4	Bangor City Ladies	22	11	4	7	46	37	37	9
5	Wolves Women	22	9	5	8	28	26	32	2
6	Liverpool Ladies	22	7	8	7	37	32	29	5
7	Lincoln City Ladies	22	6	7	9	38	46	25	-8
8	Manchester City Ladies	22	5	6	11	31	37	21	-6
9	Middlesbrough FC Ladies	22	6	2	14	25	44	20	-19
10	Sheffield Wed. Ladies	22	5	5	12	15	36	20	-21
11	Ilkeston Town Women	22	5	4	13	24	44	19	-20
12	Garswood Saints	22	4	7	11	26	51	19	-25

SOUTHERN DIVISION TABLE 2002-03

		P	W	D	L	F	A	Pts	GD
1	Bristol Rovers Women	20	17	1	2	76	19	52	57
2	Ipswich Town Women	20	11	2	7	49	36	35	13
3	Bristol City Women	20	10	5	5	47	34	35	13
4	Millwall Lionesses	20	10	4	6	41	33	34	8
5	Barnet Ladies	20	10	4	6	29	24	34	5
6	Chelsea Ladies	20	10	2	8	33	31	32	2
7	Merthyr Tydfil Women	20	9	3	8	30	34	30	-4
8	Langford Ladies	20	8	5	7	38	35	29	3
9	Wimbledon Women	20	5	1	13	27	48	16	-21
10	Enfield Ladies	20	3	2	15	32	59	11	-27
11	Barking Town Ladies	20	2	1	17	22	71	7	-49

Premier League Review

This was the year that money dominated domestic women's football. Fulham, in their last season as full time professionals and their first year in the top flight, swept the board in all competitions. They remained unbeaten throughout the entire campaign, whilst Arsenal (who incidentally turned semi-pro) experienced their first silverware drought in over a decade.

Well funded and well supported, Bristol Rovers capitalised on the demise of Barry Town who folded following their relegation from the National Division. They signed a number of their experienced players and cruised to the Southern Division title. There was a bigger battle for the promotion spot in the Northern, where Aston Villa pipped Sunderland by winning their games in hand.

Combination League Final Tables

South East Combination

	P	W	D	L	F	A	Pts
WATFORD	20	16	1	3	86	18	49
QPR	20	12	2	6	45	28	38
BEDFORD TOWN BELLS	20	12	1	7	43	27	37
WEST HAM UTD	20	9	4	7	31	18	31
COLCHESTER UTD*	20	10	2	8	52	43	28
NORWICH CITY RACERS	20	8	3	9	39	52	27
STOWMARKET*	20	8	5	7	37	45	36
GILLINGHAM	20	8	2	10	50	66	26
BROOK HOUSE	20	7	2	11	35	41	23
DENHAM UTD	20	3	6	11	33	64	15
CAMBRIDGE UNI*	20	2	2	26	43	91	0

*pts deducted

South West Combination

	P	W	D	L	F	A	Pts
PORTSMOUTH	21	20	1	0	85	6	61
READING ROYALS	22	17	3	2	95	19	54
CARDIFF CITY	22	17	3	2	87	18	54
PLYMOUTH ARGYLE	22	12	1	9	57	56	37
SWINDON TOWN	22	11	3	8	57	55	36
CLEVEDON TOWN SBW	21	9	3	9	56	37	30
CHESHAM UTD	22	9	2	11	58	39	29
YEOVIL TOWN	22	7	2	13	31	42	23
NEWTON ABBOT	22	6	2	14	50	99	20
EXETER CITY	22	5	4	13	40	53	19
READING	22	5	2	15	35	74	17
AYLESBURY UTD	22	0	0	22	12	165	0

Northern Combination

	P	W	D	L	F	A	Pts
STOCKPORT COUNTY	22	19	3	0	97	19	60
NEWCASTLE	22	15	4	3	56	14	49
MANCHESTER UTD	22	14	6	2	71	23	48
BLACKBURN ROVERS	22	14	5	3	63	24	47
LEEDS CITY VIXENS	22	7	6	9	42	74	27
BLACKPOOL WREN RVRS	22	7	5	10	29	48	26
CHESTER CITY	22	7	4	11	40	36	25
SCUNTHORPE UTD	22	7	4	11	47	60	25
BARNSLEY	22	7	3	12	47	52	24
GRETNA	22	5	2	15	34	72	17
LIVERPOOL FEDS	22	3	3	16	21	66	12
HUDDERSFIELD	22	3	3	16	26	85	12

Midland Combination

	P	W	D	L	F	A	PS
CHESTERFIELD	22	18	1	3	65	24	55
PARKGATE LADIES	22	18	0	4	91	40	54
BRIDGNORTH SPARTANS	22	12	3	7	42	37	39
COVENTRY CITY	22	12	2	8	47	37	38
LICHFIELD DIAMONDS	22	11	4	7	79	54	37
SHREWSBURY TOWN	22	10	5	7	66	41	35
STAFFORD RANGERS	22	10	2	10	39	45	32
LOUGHBORO STUDENTS	22	8	4	10	47	42	28
ILKESTON LADIES	22	7	5	10	35	48	26
HIGHFIELD RANGERS	22	7	2	13	44	54	23
PETERBOROUGH UTD	22	4	2	16	29	67	14
TELFORD UTD	22	0	0	22	18	114	0

WOMEN'S PYRAMID OF FOOTBALL

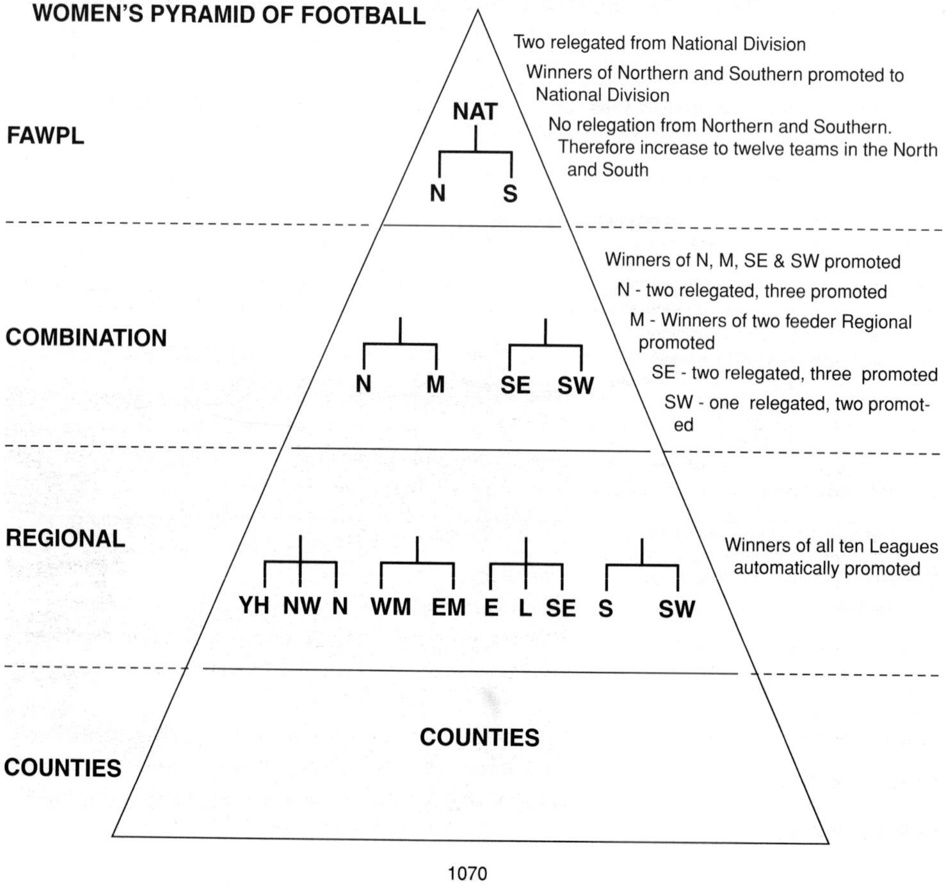

FAWPL

NAT
N S

Two relegated from National Division

Winners of Northern and Southern promoted to National Division

No relegation from Northern and Southern. Therefore increase to twelve teams in the North and South

COMBINATION

N M SE SW

Winners of N, M, SE & SW promoted

N - two relegated, three promoted

M - Winners of two feeder Regional promoted

SE - two relegated, three promoted

SW - one relegated, two promoted

REGIONAL

YH NW N WM EM E L SE S SW

Winners of all ten Leagues automatically promoted

COUNTIES

COUNTIES

Fifth Annual FA Women's Football Awards

Nationwide Players' Player of the Year: .... Jayne Ludlow (Arsenal)

Sky Sports International Player: .... Karen Walker (Doncaster Rovers Belles)

Umbro Young Player of the Year: .... Eniola Aluko (Birmingham City)

Nationwide Manager of the Year: .... Marcus Bignot (Birmingham City)

Umbro Top Goal Scorer Awards
National Division : .... Amanda Barr (Charlton Athletic, 17 goals)
Southern Division: T .... Rudy Williams (Bristol Rovers, 37 goals)
Northern Division: .... Mel Reay (Sunderland AFC Women, 17 goals)
.... Kelly Dean (Oldham Curzon, 17 goals)

Special Achievement Award: .... Mary Hull, Chairperson of Aston Villa, for 40 years of
.... service developing women's football in the West
.... Midlands.

Team of the Year: .... Fulham (Treble winners)

FA Women's Cup in partnership with Nationwide

Charlton Athletic 0 – 3 Fulham

at Selhurst Park - Monday 5th May 2003
Attendance: 10,389

Fulham completed an historic treble with this comfortable win, their last before losing their professional status. An early goal from centre forward Kristy Moore set Fulham on their way before two Charlton own goals made the game safe.

Charlton did start brightly but the full-timers gradually took control and broke the deadlock when a Margunn Haugenes corner from the left was completely missed by Pauline Cope and fell invitingly for Rachel Unitt at the far post. Her right foot volley flew back across the face of goal, caught the Charlton defence napping and when Haugenes crossed again, striker Kristy Moore made no mistake, sliding in to convert at the far post.

Their second goal came from a hopeful Rachel Unitt forward ball that drifted into the penalty area, where Kristy Moore, goalkeeper Pauline Cope and defender Hills challenged each other for possession. Bizarrely the ball missed all of the players and, brushing off the outstretched leg of Hills, bounced agonisingly into the Charlton goal.

Fulham's third goal, which effectively killed the match as a spectacle, came just after the hour mark. Unitt took a yet another Fulham corner from the left, which swung towards the head of substitute Fara Williams. Williams, with her very first touch of the ball, couldn't get enough on the ball to clear to safety and instead the ball cannoned off her head and into the goal.

Charlton Athletic: Cope; Stoney, Pond, Hills, Loizou; Broadhurst (Smith), Hunn (Williams), Barr, Lorton (Whitter 71), Walker, Rea
Subs not used: Kierans, Abbott

Fulham: Johannessen; Jerray-Silver, McArthur, Unitt, Phillip; Petersen, Haugenes, Duncan; Moore (Gibbons 85), Yankey (Therkelsen 88), Nwajei (Spacey 77)
Subs not used: Smith, Wright

Player of the Match: Rachel Yankey

Referee: George Cain

Rachel Yankey evades another Chalrton challenge.

LEAGUE INDEX

Leagues are listed alphabetically below with their relevant page numbers.
Where a league entry runs to more than one page, the number indicated is that of the first page of the section.

As in previous years, sponsors' names have been omitted to ease reference.

League sponsors, however, get their deserved recognition in the appropriate sections

Vase & Trophy CLUB INDEX

INDEX

Barrow FC	284	Northern Prem. P	Lancashire FA
Barrow Town FC	766-67	Leicestershire Senior P	Leics. & Rutland FA
Barton Rovers FC	859	Isthmian 1N	Bedfordshire FA
Barwell FC	737-745	Midland Alliance	Leics. & Rutland FA
Bashley FC	548	Southern E	Hampshire FA
Basingstoke Town FC	778	Isthmian P	Hampshire FA
BAT Sports FC	678-686	Wessex 1	Hampshire FA
Bath City FC	474	Southern P	Somerset FA
Beaconsfield SYCOB FC	911-917	Spartan South Mids. P	Berks & Bucks FA
Beckenham Town FC	616-624	Kent	Kent FA
Bedfont FC	894-900	Combined Counties P	Middlesex FA
Bedford Town FC	780	Isthmian P	Bedfordshire FA
Bedford United & Valerio FC	911-917	Spartan South Mids. P	Bedfordshire FA
Bedlington Terriers FC	429-437	Northern 1	Northumberland FA
Bedworth United FC	524	Southern W	Birmingham FA
Belper Town FC	329	Northern Prem. 1	Derbyshire FA
Bemerton Heath Harlequins FC	678-686	Wessex 1	Wiltshire FA
Berkhamsted Town FC	860	Isthmian 1N	Hertfordshire FA
Bicester Town FC	593-603	Hellenic P	Oxfordshire FA
Biddulph Victoria FC	737-745	Midland Alliance	Staffordshire FA
Bideford FC	699-707	Western P	Devon FA
Biggleswade Town FC	911-917	Spartan South Mids. P	Bedfordshire FA
Biggleswade United FC	918-924	Spartan South Mids. 1	Bedfordshire FA
Billericay Town FC	782	Isthmian P	Essex FA
Billingham Synthonia FC	429-437	Northern 1	Durham FA
Billingham Town FC	429-437	Northern 1	Durham FA
Birstall United FC	766-67	Leicestershire Senior P	Leics. & Rutland FA
Bishop Auckland FC	330	Northern Prem. 1	Durham FA
Bishop Sutton FC	699-707	Western P	Somerset FA
Bishop's Cleeve	593-601	Hellenic P	Gloucestershire FA
Bishop's Stortford FC	784	Isthmian P	Hertfordshire FA
Bitton AFC	708-713	Western 1	Gloucestershire FA
Blaby & Whetstone Athletic FC	766-67	Leicestershire Senior P	Leics. & Rutland FA
Blackfield & Langley FC	678-686	Wessex 1	Hampshire FA
Blackpool Mechanics FC	365-370	North West Counties 2	Lancashire FA
Blackstones FC	658-666	United Counties P	Lincolnshire FA
Blackwell MW FC	412-416	Central Midlands S.D.	Derbyshire FA
Blidworth Welfare	417-418	Central Midlands P D	Nottinghamshire FA
Blyth Spartans AFC	286	Northern Prem. P	Northumberland FA
Bodmin Town	717-724	South Western	Cornish FA
Bognor Regis Town FC	786	Isthmian P	Sussex FA
Boldmere St Michaels FC	737-745	Midland Alliance	Birmingham FA
Bolehall Swifts FC	749-753	Midland Combination P	Birmingham FA
Boreham Wood FC	861	Isthmian 1N	Hertfordshire FA
Borrowash Victoria FC	395-402	Northern Counties East P	Derbyshire FA
Boston Town FC	658-666	United Counties P	Lincolnshire FA

Chalfont St Peter FC	883	Isthmian 2	Berks & Bucks FA
Chard Town FC	708-713	Western 1	Somerset FA
Chasetown FC	737-745	Midland Alliance	Staffordshire FA
Chatham Town FC	551	Southern E	Kent FA
Cheadle Town FC	365-370	North West Counties 2	Cheshire FA
Chelmsford City FC	478	Southern P	Essex FA
Chertsey Town FC	883	Isthmian 2	Surrey FA
Chesham United FC	862	Isthmian 1N	Berks & Bucks FA
Cheshunt FC	863	Isthmian 1N	Hertfordshire FA
Chessington & Hook United FC	894-900	Combined Counties P	Surrey FA
Chessington United FC	894-900	Combined Counties P	Surrey FA
Chester City FC	163	Conference	Cheshire FA
Chester-Le-Street Town FC	429-437	Northern 1	Durham FA
Chichester City United FC	636-645	Sussex 1	Sussex FA
Chippenham Town FC	480	Southern P	Wiltshire FA
Chipping Norton Town FC	593-601	Hellenic P	Oxfordshire FA
Chipstead FC	894-900	Combined Counties P	Surrey FA
Chorley FC	332	Northern Prem. 1	Lancashire FA
Christchurch FC	678-686	Wessex 1	Hampshire FA
Cinderford Town FC	526	Southern W	Gloucestershire FA
Cirencester Town FC	527	Southern W	Gloucestershire FA
Clacton Town FC	572-582	Eastern Counties P	Essex FA
Clapton FC	884	Isthmian 2	London FA
Clevedon Town FC	528	Southern W	Somerset FA
Clevedon United FC	707-712	Western 1	Somerset FA
Clitheroe FC	355-364	North West Counties 1	Lancashire FA
Coalville Town FC	737-746	Midland Alliance	Leics. & Rutland FA
Cobham FC	894-900	Combined Counties P	Surrey FA
Cockfosters FC	918-924	Spartan South Mids. 1	London FA
Cogenhoe United FC	658-666	United Counties P	Northants. FA
Colne FC	365-370	North West Counties 2	Lancashire FA
Colney Heath FC	918-924	Spartan South Mids. 1	Hertfordshire FA
Colwyn Bay FC	333	Northern Prem. 1	Wales
Concord Rangers FC	901-907	Essex Senior P	Essex FA
Congleton Town FC	355-364	North West Counties 1	Cheshire FA
Consett FC	438-443	Northern 2	Durham FA
Corby Town FC	552	Southern E	Northants. FA
Corinthian Casuals FC	834	Isthmian 1S	London FA
Cornard United FC	583-587	Eastern Counties 1	Suffolk FA
Corsham Town FC	708-713	Western 1	Wiltshire FA
Cove FC	894-900	Combined Counties P	Hampshire FA
Coventry Sphinx FC	749-753	Midland Combination P	Birmingham FA
Cowes Sports FC	678-686	Wessex 1	Hampshire FA
Cradley Town FC	737-745	Midland Alliance	Birmingham FA
Crawley Town FC	482	Southern P	Sussex FA
Cray Wanderers FC	616-624	Kent	Kent FA

Enfield Town FC	901-907	Essex Senior P	Middlesex FA
Epsom & Ewell FC	839	Isthmian 1S	Surrey FA
Erith & Belvedere FC	555	Southern E	Kent FA
Erith Town FC	616-624	Kent	London FA
Esh Winning FC	429-437	Northern 1	Durham FA
Eton Manor FC	901-907	Essex Senior P	Essex FA
Evenwood Town FC	438-443	Northern 2	Durham FA
Evesham United FC	529	Southern W	Worcesters. FA
Exeter City	175	Conference	Devon FA
Exmouth Town FC	699-706	Western P	Devon FA
Eynesbury Rovers FC	667-673	United Counties 1	Huntingdonshire FA
Fairford Town FC	593-603	Hellenic P	Gloucestershire FA
Fakenham Town FC	572-582	Eastern Counties P	Norfolk FA
Falmouth Town AFC	717-722	South Western	Cornwall FA
Fareham Town FC	678-686	Wessex 1	Hampshire FA
Farnborough Town FC	179	Conference	Hampshire FA
Farnham Town FC	894-900	Combined Counties P	Surrey FA
Farsley Celtic FC	334	Northern Prem. 1	W. Riding FA
Felixstowe & Walton United FC	583-587	Eastern Counties 1	Suffolk FA
Fisher Athletic FC	556	Southern E	London FA
Flackwell Heath FC	885	Isthmian 2	Berks & Bucks FA
Fleet Town FC	557	Southern E	Hampshire FA
Fleetwood Town FC	355-364	North West Counties 1	Lancashire FA
Flixton FC	365-370	North West Counties 2	Manchester FA
Folkestone Invicta FC	558	Southern E	Kent FA
Ford Sports Daventry FC	658-666	United Counties P	Northants. FA
Ford United FC	794	Isthmian P	London FA
Forest Green Rovers FC	185	Conference	Gloucestershire FA
Friar Lane OB FC	766-67	Leicestershire Senior P	Leics. & Rutland FA
Frickley Athletic FC	294	Northern Prem. P	Sheff. & Hallams. FA
Frimley Green	894-900	Combined Counties	Surrey FA
Frome Town FC	699-707	Western P	Somerset FA
Gainsborough Trinity FC	296	Northern Prem. P	Lincolnshire FA
Garforth Town FC	404-408	Northern Counties East 1	W. Riding FA
Gateshead FC	335	Northern Prem. 1	Durham FA
Gedling Town FC	404-408	Northern Counties East 1	Nottinghamshire FA
Glapwell FC	395-402	Northern Counties East P	Derbyshire FA
Glasshoughton Welfare FC	395-402	Northern Counties East P	W. Riding FA
Glossop North End FC	355-364	North West Counties 1	Derbyshire FA
Gloucester City FC	530	Southern W	Gloucestershire FA
Godalming & Guildford FC	894-900	Combined Counties P	Surrey FA
Godmanchester Rovers	583-588	Eastern Counties 1	Huntingdonshire FA
Goole AFC	395-402	Northern Counties East P	W. Riding FA
Gorleston FC	572-582	Eastern Counties P	Norfolk FA
Gornal Athletic FC	759-763	West Midlands P	Birmingham FA
Gosport Borough FC	678-686	Wessex 1	Hampshire FA

Henley Town FC	593-603	Hellenic P	Oxfordshire FA
Hereford United FC	203	Conference	Herefordshire FA
Herne Bay FC	616-624	Kent	Kent FA
Hertford Town FC	886	Isthmian 2	Hertfordshire FA
Heybridge Swifts FC	804	Isthmian P	Essex FA
Highfield Rangers FC	766-67	Leicestershire Senior P	Leics. & Rutland FA
Highgate United FC	749-754	Midland Combination P	Birmingham FA
Highworth Town FC	593-603	Hellenic P	Wiltshire FA
Hillingdon Borough FC	911-917	Spartan South Mids. P	Middlesex FA
Hinckley United FC	496	Southern P	Leics. & Rutland FA
Histon FC	560	Southern E	Cambridgeshire FA
Hitchin Town FC	806	Isthmian P	Hertfordshire FA
Hoddesdon Town FC	911-917	Spartan South Mids. P	Hertfordshire FA
Holbeach United FC	658-666	United Counties P	Lincolnshire FA
Holker Old Boys FC	365-370	North West Counties 2	Lancashire FA
Holmer Green FC	911-917	Spartan South Mids. P	Berks & Bucks FA
Horden CW FC	429-437	Northern 1	Durham FA
Hornchurch FC	808	Isthmian P	Essex FA
Horndean FC	689-690	Hampshire P	Hampshire FA
Horsham FC	841	Isthmian 1S	Sussex FA
Horsham YMCA FC	636-645	Sussex 1	Sussex FA
Hucknall Town FC	300	Northern Prem. P	Nottinghamshire FA
Hullbridge Sports FC	901-907	Essex Senior P	Essex FA
Hungerford Town FC	593-601	Hellenic P	Berks & Bucks FA
Hyde United FC	307	Northern Prem. 1	Cheshire FA
Hythe Town FC	616-624	Kent	Kent FA
Ibstock Welfare FC	766-67	Leicestershire Senior P	Leics. & Rutland FA
Ilford FC	901-907	Essex Senior P	Essex FA
Ilfracombe Town FC	708-713	Western 1	Devon FA
Ilkeston Town FC	533	Southern W	Derbyshire FA
Ipswich Wanderers FC	583-588	Eastern Counties 1	Suffolk FA
Jarrow Roofing Boldon CA FC	429-437	Northern 1	Durham FA
Kempston Rovers FC	667-673	United Counties 1	Bedfordshire FA
Kendal Town FC	338	Northern Prem. 1	Westmorland FA
Kennek Ryhope CA FC	438-443	Northern 2	Durham FA
Kettering Town FC	810	Isthmian P	Northants. FA
Keynsham Town FC	699-707	Western P	Somerset FA
Kidsgrove Athletic FC	339	Northern Prem. 1	Staffordshire FA
Kimberley Town FC	417-418	Central Midlands P	Nottinghamshire FA
Kings Lynn FC	561	Southern E	Norfolk FA
Kingsbury Town FC	886	Isthmian 2	Middlesex FA
Kingstonian FC	812	Isthmian P	Surrey FA
Kirby Muxloe FC	766-67	Leicestershire Senior P	Leics. & Rutland FA
Lancaster City FC	302	Northern Prem. P	Lancashire FA
Lancing FC	646-651	Sussex 2	Sussex FA
Langford FC	918-924	Spartan South Mids. 1	Bedfordshire FA

Metropolitan Police FC	845	Isthmian 1S	London FA
Mickleover Sports FC	404-408	Northern Counties East 1	Derbyshire FA
Mildenhall Town FC	572-582	Eastern Counties P	Suffolk FA
Mile Oak	645-651	Sussex 2	Sussex FA
Milton Keynes City FC	911-917	Spartan South Mids. P	Berks & Bucks FA
Milton United FC	608-611	Hellenic 1E	Berks & Bucks FA
Minehead Town FC	708-713	Western 1	Somerset FA
Molesey FC	846	Isthmian 1S	Surrey FA
Moneyfields FC	678-686	Wessex 1	Hampshire FA
Moor Green FC	500	Southern P	Birmingham FA
Morecambe FC	221	Conference	Lancashire FA
Morpeth Town FC	429-437	Northern 1	Northumberland FA
Mossley AFC	355-364	North West Counties 1	Manchester FA
Murton FC	438-443	Northern 2	Durham FA
Nantwich Town FC	355-364	North West Counties 1	Cheshire FA
Needham Market FC	583-587	Eastern Counties 1	Suffolk FA
Nelson FC	365-370	North West Counties 2	Lancashire FA
Nettleham FC	412-416	Central Midlands S.D.	Lincolnshire FA
New Mills FC	387-388	Manchester P	Derbyshire FA
Newcastle Benfield Saints FC	438-443	Northern 2	Northumberland FA
Newcastle Blue Star FC	438-443	Northern 2	Northumberland FA
Newcastle Town FC	355-364	North West Counties 1	Staffordshire FA
Newmarket Town FC	572-582	Eastern Counties P	Suffolk FA
Newport County FC	502	Southern P	Wales
Newport(IW) FC	561	Southern E	Hampshire FA
Newport Pagnell Town FC	658-666	United Counties P	Berks & Bucks FA
Newton Abbot FC	725-726	Devon	Devon FA
Newquay FC	717-724	South Western	Cornish FA
North Ferriby United FC	343	Northern Prem. 1	E. Riding FA
North Greenford United FC	894-900	Combined Counties P	Middlesex FA
North Leigh FC	593-603	Hellenic P	Oxfordshire FA
North Shields FC	447-449	Wearside	Northumberland FA
Northallerton Town FC	438-443	Northern 2	N. Riding FA
Northampton Spencer FC	658-666	United Counties P	Northants. FA
Northwich Victoria FC	227	Conference	Cheshire FA
Northwood FC	816	Isthmian P	Middlesex FA
Norton & Stockton Ancients FC	438-443	Northern 2	Durham FA
Norton United FC	365-370	North West Counties 2	Staffordshire FA
Norwich United FC	572-582	Eastern Counties P	Norfolk FA
Nuneaton Borough FC	504	Southern P	Birmingham FA
Nuneaton Griff FC	749-753	Midland Combination P	Birmingham FA
Oadby Town FC	737-745	Midland Alliance	Leics. & Rutland FA
Oakwood FC	646-651	Sussex 2	Sussex FA
Odd Down FC	699-707	Western P	Somerset FA
Oldbury United FC	737-745	Midland Alliance	Birmingham FA
Oldham Town FC	365-370	North West Counties 2	Manchester FA

Rugby Town FC	749-753	Midland Combination P	Birmingham FA
Rugby United FC	536	Southern W	Birmingham FA
Ruislip Manor FC	911-917	Spartan South Mids. P	Middlesex FA
Runcorn FC Halton	308	Northern Prem. P	Liverpool FA
Rushall Olympic FC	737-745	Midland Alliance	Staffordshire FA
Rye & Iden United FC	635-644	Sussex 1	Sussex FA
Ryton FC	421-424	Notts Alliance P	Durham FA
Salford City FC	355-364	North West Counties 1	Manchester FA
Salisbury City FC	564	Southern E	Wiltshire FA
Saltash United FC	717-724	South Western	Cornwall FA
Saltdean United FC	646-651	Sussex 2	Sussex FA
Sandhurst Town FC	894-900	Combined Counties P	Berks & Bucks FA
Sandiacre Town FC	412-416	Central Midlands S P	Derbyshire FA
Sawbridgeworth Town FC	901-907	Essex Senior P	Hertfordshire FA
Scarborough FC	233	Conference	N. Riding FA
Seaham Red Star FC	438-443	Northern 2	Durham FA
Selby Town FC	395-402	Northern Counties East P	W. Riding FA
Selsey FC	636-645	Sussex 1	Sussex FA
Shawbury United FC	759-763	West Midlands P	Shropshire FA
Sheffield FC	395-402	Northern Counties East P	Sheff. & Hallams. FA
Shepshed Dynamo FC	537	Southern W	Leics. & Rutland FA
Shepton Mallet AFC	708-713	Western 1	Somerset FA
Shifnal Town FC	749-754	Midland Combination P	Shropshire FA
Shildon FC	429-437	Northern 1	Durham FA
Shirebrook Town FC	404-408	Northern Counties East 1	Derbyshire FA
Shortwood United FC	593-603	Hellenic P	Gloucestershire FA
Shotton Comrades FC	438-443	Northern 2	Durham FA
Shrewsbury Town FC	239	Conference	Shropshire FA
Sidlesham FC	636-645	Sussex 1	Sussex FA
Sidley United FC	636-645	Sussex 1	Sussex FA
Silsden FC	461	West Riding County	West Riding FA
Sittingbourne FC	565	Southern E	Kent FA
Skelmersdale United FC	355-364	North West Counties 1	Liverpool FA
Slade Green FC	616-624	Kent	Kent FA
Slough Town FC	847	Isthmian 1S	Berks & Bucks FA
Soham Town Rangers FC	572-582	Eastern Counties P	Cambridgeshire FA
Solihull Borough FC	538	Southern W	Birmingham FA
Somersham Town FC	583-587	Eastern Counties 1	Huntingdonshire FA
South Shields FC	438-443	Northern 2	Durham FA
Southall Town FC	593-603	Hellenic P	Middlesex FA
Southend Manor FC	901-907	Essex Senior P	Essex FA
Southport FC	310	Northern Prem. P	Lancashire FA
Southwick FC	636-645	Sussex 1	Sussex FA
Spalding United FC	658-666	United Counties P	Lincolnshire FA
Spennymoor United FC	312	Northern Prem. P	Durham FA
[illegible]ires Gate FC	355-364	North West Counties 1	Lancashire FA

Thurrock FC	822	Isthmian P	Essex FA
Tilbury FC	873	Isthmian 1N	Essex FA
Tipton Town FC	759-763	West Midlands P	Birmingham FA
Tiptree United FC	572-582	Eastern Counties P	Essex FA
Tiverton Town FC	508	Southern P	Devon FA
Tividale FC	759-763	West Midlands P	Birmingham FA
Tonbridge Angels FC	567	Southern E	Kent FA
Tooting & Mitcham United FC	849	Isthmian 1S	Surrey FA
Torrington FC	699-706	Western P	Devon FA
Tow Law Town FC	429-437	Northern 1	Durham FA
Trafford FC	355-364	North West Counties 1	Manchester FA
Tring Town FC	887	Isthmian 2	Hertfordshire FA
Tuffley Rovers FC	593-603	Hellenic P	Gloucestershire FA
Tunbridge Wells FC	616-624	Kent	Kent FA
Uxbridge FC	874	Isthmian 1N	Middlesex FA
Vauxhall Motors FC	316	Northern Prem. P	Cheshire FA
VCD Athletic FC	616-624	Kent	Kent FA
Wakefield & Emley FC	318	Northern Prem. P	Sheff. & Hallams. FA
Waltham Forest FC	875	Isthmian 1N	Essex FA
Walton & Hersham FC	850	Isthmian 1S	Surrey FA
Walton Casuals FC	894-900	Combined Counties P	Surrey FA
Wantage Town FC	608-612	Hellenic 1E	Berks & Bucks FA
Warboys Town FC	583-587	Eastern Counties 1	Huntingdonshire FA
Ware FC	888	Isthmian 2	Hertfordshire FA
Warrington Town FC	355-364	North West Counties 1	Cheshire FA
Washington FC	429-437	Northern 1	Durham FA
Washington Nissan FC	438-443	Northern 2	Durham FA
Wealdstone FC	876	Isthmian 1N	Middlesex FA
Wednesfield FC	759-763	West Midlands P	Birmingham FA
Welling United FC	510	Southern P	London FA
Wellington FC	759-763	West Midlands P	Herefordshire FA
Wellington Town FC	708-713	Western 1	Somerset FA
Welton Rovers FC	699-707	Western P	Somerset FA
Wembley FC	888	Isthmian 2	Middlesex FA
West Allotment Celtic FC	453-454	Northern Alliance P	Northumberland FA
West Auckland Town FC	429-437	Northern 1	Durham FA
West Midlands Police FC	749-753	Midland Combination P	Birmingham FA
Westbury United FC	708-713	Western 1	Wiltshire FA
Westfield FC	894-900	Combined Counties P	Surrey FA
Westfields FC	737-746	Midland Alliance	Herefordshire FA
Weston Super Mare FC	512	Southern P	Somerset FA
Weymouth FC	514	Southern P	Dorset FA
Whickham FC	438-443	Northern 2	Durham FA
Whitby Town FC	320	Northern Prem. P	N. Riding FA
Whitchurch United FC	678-686	Wessex 1	Hampshire FA
[illegible]tehawk FC	636-645	Sussex 1	Sussex FA

Whitley Bay FC	429-437	Northern 1	Northumberland FA
Whitstable Town FC	616-624	Kent	Kent FA
Whitton United FC	583-587	Eastern Counties 1	Suffolk FA
Whyteleafe FC	851	Isthmian 1S	Surrey FA
Wick FC	645-651	Sussex 2	Sussex FA
Willand Rovers FC	708-713	Western 1	Devon FA
Willenhall Town FC	737-745	Midland Alliance	Birmingham FA
Willington FC	438-443	Northern 2	Durham FA
Wimborne Town FC	678-686	Wessex 1	Dorset FA
Winchester City FC	678-686	Wessex 1	Hampshire FA
Windsor & Eton FC	852	Isthmian 1S	Berks & Bucks FA
Wingate & Finchley FC	877	Isthmian 1N	London FA
Winsford United FC	365-370	North West Counties 2	Cheshire FA
Winterton Rangers FC	404-408	Northern Counties East 1	Lincolnshire FA
Wisbech Town FC	572-582	Eastern Counties P	Cambridgeshire FA
Witham Town FC	889	Isthmian 2	Essex FA
Withdean 2000 FC	894-900	Combined Counties P	Sussex FA
Witton Albion FC	348	Northern Prem. 1	Cheshire FA
Wivenhoe Town FC	878	Isthmian 1N	Essex FA
Woking FC	261	Conference	Surrey FA
Wokingham Town FC	889	Isthmian 2	Berks & Bucks FA
Woodbridge Town FC	572-582	Eastern Counties P	Suffolk FA
Woodford United	658-666	United Counties P	Northamptonshire FA
Woodley Sports FC	355-364	North West Counties 1	Cheshire FA
Wootton Bassett Town FC	593-603	Hellenic P	Wiltshire FA
Wootton Blue Cross FC	658-666	United Counties P	Bedfordshire FA
Worcester City FC	516	Southern P	Worcesters. FA
Workington FC	349	Northern Prem. 1	Cumberland FA
Worksop Town FC	322	Northern Prem. P	Sheff. & Hallams. FA
Worsbrough Bridge MW FC	404-408	Northern Counties East 1	Sheff. & Hallams. FA
Worthing FC	853	Isthmian 1S	Sussex FA
Wroxham FC	572-582	Eastern Counties P	Norfolk FA
Yate Town FC	544	Southern W	Gloucestershire FA
Yaxley FC	658-666	United Counties P	Huntingdonshire FA
Yeading FC	879	Isthmian 1N	Middlesex FA
Yorkshire Amateur FC	404-408	Northern Counties East 1	W. Riding FA